McCoy's RCRA Reference

2010 Edition

McCoy and Associates, Inc.
Lakewood, Colorado
www.mccoyseminars.com

ISBN: 978-0-930469-55-9

Publisher

McCoy and Associates, Inc.
Lakewood, Colorado
(303) 526-2674
www.mccoyseminars.com

Technical Editors

Paul V. Gallagher, P.E., President
Rodger A. Goffredi, P.E., Vice President and Director of Publishing
Eric J. Weber, Vice President and Director of Product Development
W. Carl Severn, Senior Environmental Scientist

Production Director and Cover Design

Robyn C. Weber, Director of Marketing and Strategy

Interior Book Design and Layout

Barbara J. Wilson

January 2010
Manufactured in the United States of America

McCOY

Waiting for normal

It would be profoundly reassuring to view the current economic situation as simply a rough patch in the road that will smooth out over time. Unfortunately, the stakes have never been higher and today's mix of uncertainty and urgency will likely continue as the norm for awhile. Most organizations cannot erect a firewall against intense competition, increased pressure on workers, and bi-polar views on environmental management.

The task of leading during sustained times of difficulty takes the utmost patience and endurance. Environmental managers, who routinely are placed squarely in the center of controversial decision-making, must embrace both.

Regarding compliance within plant operations, there are often two distinct phases to navigate. The first is an emergency phase, where your task is to stabilize the situation and buy time. The second is the adaptive phase, when you diagnose underlying causes and build a more proactive approach for handling tough operational issues. The adaptive phase is especially tricky: supervisors can put enormous pressure on you to respond to their anxieties with authoritative certainty—even if doing so means overselling what you know and discounting what you don't.

That's where we can help. The primary responsibility of McCoy technical experts is to focus on, study, and understand the regulations and guidance, and then transform the massive amounts of data into compliance publications you can trust.

We believe *McCoy's RCRA Unraveled* is the clearest discussion of the regs available. *RCRA Reference* isn't merely the full text of the regulations, it actually alerts you to practical guidance in *RCRA Unraveled*. Our *RCRA Compliance CD* includes both books, over 40,000 hyperlinks, and powerful search capabilities. And we've applied this engineered approach to the behemoth Clean Air Act in *McCoy's CAA Unraveled, First Edition*.

We can't remove all the potholes, but we're good company to have along for the ride. And that's quite reassuring. Visit us at understandrcra.com.

Preface

This publication contains the complete text of the federal hazardous waste regulations that implement Subtitle C of the Resource Conservation and Recovery Act (RCRA). The regulations contained in this book consist of 40 *CFR* Parts 260–280 and 148; they are current as of November 20, 2009.

One of the key features of this book of regulations is that it contains hundreds of cross-references to all of the current EPA guidance we could find for many regulatory topics. The cross-references (indicated by little book (📖) symbols) refer to section numbers in its companion publication, *McCoy's RCRA Unraveled.* Using both books together, the reader can quickly find specific guidance (in the form of either narrative text that we wrote or detailed examples from EPA) that explains or clarifies the meaning of the federal RCRA regulations. For example, as cited in this book, §261.4(a)(1) provides the important domestic sewage exclusion in the RCRA regulations, but it consists of just 37 words total. The cross-referenced guidance in *McCoy's RCRA Unraveled* consists of six, plain-English pages of text explaining how the exclusion applies and provides numerous references to specific guidance documents on this topic.

Both of these publications are included in our electronic offering: *McCoy's RCRA Compliance CD.* Our goal is to provide an electronic product that is powerful and easy to use. We reformatted the content with large type so on-screen reading is comfortable. We've included over 40,000 hyperlinks, 1,300 RCRA Online documents, and 275 *Federal Register* notices (1995 and later) to lighten your research load. And there are three ways to find the specific information you need: hyperlinked table of contents, knowledge-based indexes, and Find and Search capability. Take a look at a few sample pages at www.mccoyseminars.com.

The material presented in this book is used extensively in McCoy's RCRA seminars—call (303) 526-2674 for information. However, this publication is designed for standalone use by readers of all experience levels.

Significant Rule Changes in Last Three Years

Final rules issued by EPA that have significantly changed the RCRA regulatory program in the past three years (2007–2009) are summarized in the table on the following page and are discussed briefly below. Please note that many of these rules made the federal regulations less stringent and are not applicable in RCRA-authorized states until they are adopted by the state.

Revisions to the comparable fuels exclusion—Section 261.38 of the RCRA regulations notes that hazardous spent materials, sludges, and by-products that are comparable to commercial fuels are not solid waste if burned. To prove that such secondary materials are comparable to commercial fuels, the generator must show that the materials meet heating value, viscosity,

Rule	Issue date	*Federal Register* reference	Federal effective date
Revisions to comparable fuels exclusion	December 19, 2008	73 *FR* 77954	January 20, 2009
Streamlining hazardous waste management in academic laboratories	December 1, 2008	73 *FR* 72912	December 31, 2008
Changes to the definition of solid waste for hazardous secondary materials sent for reclamation	October 30, 2008	73 *FR* 64668	December 29, 2008
Revision of F019 listing to exclude sludges from auto manufacturing	June 4, 2008	73 *FR* 31756	July 7, 2008

and contaminant concentration specifications. However, one of the primary impediments to claiming this exclusion is the stringency of the existing contaminant concentration specifications. The low contaminant limits (e.g., 39 ppm for methyl ethyl ketone) create a significant barrier and result in many high-Btu secondary materials being manifested offsite as hazardous wastes. Yet, many of these "contaminants" burn quite cleanly.

To encourage additional use of the comparable fuels exclusion, EPA finalized revisions to §261.38, creating a new type of RCRA-excluded material called "emission-comparable fuel" (ECF). When burned in an industrial or utility boiler, an ECF must generate emissions comparable to those from burning fuel oil (for which it would substitute). In other words, rather than meeting physical/chemical specs, ECFs must be comparable to fuel oil from an emissions standpoint. EPA believes that hazardous secondary materials that meet the revised comparable fuels exclusion are, as generated, more commodity-like than waste-like and will be treated as such from the point of generation through all phases of management. To qualify for the new ECF exclusion from the definition of solid waste, management conditions include:

- All otherwise applicable provisions for comparable fuels in §261.38 must be met; however, the contaminant concentration specifications for 37 specific hydrocarbons and oxygenates (e.g., isobutyl alcohol and methyl ethyl ketone) are waived. The heating value of the ECF must be 8,000 Btu/lb or greater as-generated.
- Storage is allowed in containers and aboveground tanks only, and significant regulatory requirements apply to such storage (e.g., secondary containment, organic emission controls, etc.).
- If shipping ECF to offsite, unaffiliated burners, generators must make "reasonable efforts" to ensure that the burner will manage the ECF under the conditions of the exclusion.
- Only an industrial or utility boiler or a hazardous waste combustor may be used to burn ECF, and carbon monoxide emissions and, under certain conditions, combustion gas temperature must meet specified limits.
- Co-burning with at least 50% fossil fuels is required (although there are some exceptions to this requirement) and maximum allowable feed rates for the 37 ECF constituents are specified.
- Substantial burner design standards and operating conditions apply.
- Additional notification, reporting, and recordkeeping are required.

Streamlining hazardous waste management in academic laboratories—Academic institutions often find it difficult to make hazardous waste determinations per §262.11 at the point wastes are generated in their laboratories. This is largely because most of the individuals in laboratories generating wastes are students, who are usually untrained to make hazardous waste determinations. To address this issue, EPA has added a new, optional Subpart K to the hazardous waste generator standards in Part 262 that allows non-RCRA management of unwanted lab materials until a hazardous waste determination is made.

To be eligible to operate under Subpart K, a facility must be a 1) college or university, 2) nonprofit research institute that is owned by or has a formal written affiliation with a college or university, or 3) teaching hospital that is owned by or affiliated with a college or university. However, "government facilities with laboratories that are operated by colleges and universities (such as many of the Department of Energy's laboratories) would not be eligible to opt into Subpart K, because the government facility is not an eligible academic entity and the laboratories are not owned by an eligible academic entity." [73 *FR* 72924]

A laboratory is defined as "an area owned by an eligible academic entity where relatively small quantities of chemicals and other substances are used on a nonproduction basis for teaching or research (or diagnostic purposes at a teaching hospital) and are stored and used in containers that are easily manipulated by one person. Photo laboratories, art studios, and field laboratories are considered laboratories. Areas such as chemical stockrooms and preparatory laboratories that provide a support function to teaching or research laboratories (or diagnostic laboratories at teaching hospitals) are also considered laboratories." [§262.200]

Basically, Subpart K allows unused or used chemicals, solvents, and analytical residues that are no longer needed in a lab to be managed outside of the formal hazardous waste program until RCRA-trained personnel determine whether the materials are wastes and, if they are, whether they are hazardous wastes. These "unwanted materials" are defined as follows: "any chemical, mixtures of chemicals, products of experiments or other material from a laboratory that is no longer needed, wanted or usable in the laboratory and that is destined for hazardous waste determination by a trained professional." [§262.200] This definition allows some unwanted material to still be usable in another lab setting, thereby not meeting the definition of solid waste. Thus, unwanted materials are not subject to RCRA hazardous waste regulations but to performance-based standards while the unwanted materials remain in the lab. EPA establishes a framework for the performance-based standards in Subpart K, and the academic facility has to flesh out these standards by preparing a formal, enforceable laboratory management plan. [§262.214] For example, eligible facilities have up to six months to remove unwanted materials from labs; however, if the volume of these materials exceeds 55 gallons, then all unwanted materials have to be removed from the lab within 10 calendar days. [§262.208]

Finally, the new Subpart K regs provide an incentive for eligible academic facilities to conduct periodic laboratory cleanouts of old, unneeded chemicals. Once a year, each laboratory will have 30 days to conduct a cleanout and move unwanted materials to an onsite central accumulation or permitted area. And, significantly, the facility will not have to count any listed or characteristic hazardous wastes (that are unused chemicals) generated during those 30 days towards the facility's generator status.

Definition of solid waste (DSW) rule—EPA finalized two self-implementing exclusions from the definition of solid waste for spent materials (that are hazardous by either listing or characteristic), listed sludges, and listed by-products that are reclaimed in compliance with specified provisions. The first exclusion is for these materials that are generated and reclaimed "under the control of the generator." The DSW rule requires that these materials, when managed in either non-land-based units (e.g., tanks, containers, and containment buildings) [§261.2(a)(2)(ii)] or land-based units (e.g., piles and surface impoundments) [§261.4(a)(23)], be "contained" in such units (basically, this means that the material is not released into the environment) before recycling. "Under the control of the generator" means:

1. The material is generated and reclaimed at the generating facility (located in the U.S. or its territories); or
2. The material is generated and reclaimed at different facilities (both of which are located in the U.S. or its territories), both facilities are controlled by the same "person," and the controlling "person" must certify responsibility for safe management of the recycled material; or
3. The material is generated pursuant to a written contract between a tolling contractor and a toll manufacturer (both of which are located in the U.S. or its territories) and is reclaimed by the tolling contractor (who certifies ownership and responsibility for the secondary materials, even while they are managed at the toll manufacturer's facility).

The second exclusion is for materials that are transferred to another person or company for reclamation, but only if the following conditions are met [§261.4(a)(24)]:

- The material is not handled by any person or facility other than the generator, the transporter, an intermediate facility, and one or more reclaimers. An intermediate facility is allowed to store the material for more than 10 days, but the generator/intermediate facility must ensure that the material is sent to the generator-designated reclamation facility.

- The generator must make "reasonable efforts," repeated, documented, and certified every three years, to ensure that each reclaimer will legitimately recycle the material and that any intermediate facility and reclaimer will manage the material in a manner protective of human health and the environment (e.g., the generator could audit these facilities). "Reasonable efforts" are only required for reclaimers and any intermediate facilities where management of the material is not addressed under a RCRA permit or interim status standards.
- The generator, any intermediate facility, and each reclaimer must keep records of each shipment of hazardous secondary material for at least three years. Additionally, generators must receive confirmations of receipt from each intermediate facility and reclaimer and maintain them for at least three years.
- The reclaimer and any intermediate facility must manage the material in a manner that is at least as protective as that employed for the analogous raw material and the secondary material must be contained.
- Any residues generated from the reclamation process must be managed in a manner that is protective of human health and the environment (e.g., any hazardous wastes must be managed in accordance with RCRA Subtitle C).
- The reclaimer and any intermediate facility must obtain financial assurance (similar to that required for permitted TSD facilities) per new Subpart H of Part 261, thereby demonstrating that they will not abandon the secondary material.

As an option under the second exclusion, EPA also excluded materials that are exported for reclamation from the definition of solid waste, subject to conditions in §261.4(a)(25).

There are numerous materials to which the exclusions will *not* apply: 1) K171/K172 spent catalyst from petroleum refineries, 2) spent lead-acid batteries, 3) materials that are otherwise subject to material-specific management conditions under §261.4(a) when reclaimed [e.g., used, broken CRTs at §261.4(a)(22)(iii)], 4) materials that are speculatively accumulated, 5) materials that are reclaimed and then used to produce products that are applied to the land, and 6) materials that are reclaimed and then used to produce fuels.

The DSW rule also codifies factors for determining whether materials are being legitimately recycled under the newly added exclusions. Section 260.43 codifies four factors for determining if hazardous secondary materials are being legitimately recycled. Previously, such legitimacy determinations were made on a case-by-case basis by regulators using EPA's "sham" recycling guidance (see January 4, 1985; 50 *FR* 638).

Finally, generators, reclaimers, and any intermediate facilities, tolling contractors, and/or toll manufacturers that manage hazardous secondary materials that have previously been subject to regulation as hazardous waste, but which are excluded from regulation under the DSW rule, must send notification to EPA or the state. The notification must be sent prior to managing the material under one of the new exclusions and by March 1st of each even-numbered year thereafter. [§260.42]

As of November 2009, these new exclusions from the definition of solid waste were in effect in only four states: Alaska and Iowa, where EPA administers RCRA, and New Jersey and Pennsylvania, which have adopted the rule.

Revision to F019 listing—EPA amended the F019 listing at §261.31, exempting wastewater treatment sludges generated from zinc phosphating used in the automotive assembly process. Until this rule was issued, the zinc phosphating (conversion coating) step in the manufacture of motor vehicles containing aluminum parts resulted in generation of F019 sludge from the wastewater treatment systems at auto plants. To qualify for this exemption, which applies at the point of generation, generators must satisfy the following conditions:

- The waste must be generated from manufacture of automobiles and light-duty trucks/vehicles (NAICS codes 336111 and 336112, respectively).
- Prior to offsite shipment, the waste must not be placed outside on the land.
- The waste must be disposed in a landfill that is either 1) a state-permitted or authorized Subtitle D (municipal or industrial) unit that is equipped with at least a single clay liner, or 2) subject to, or otherwise meeting, the requirements in §258.40, 264.301, or 265.301.
- Generators must maintain documentation onsite proving that they meet the above conditions exempting their wastewater treatment sludges from the F019 listing.

Features

One of the most useful features of this publication is the complete keyword index to the federal hazardous waste regulations that we have included at the end of the regulations. This index was generated by our seminar instructors using their detailed knowledge of the subject matter—it was not generated by search-engine software. For example, the derived-from rule is one of the fundamental concepts of the RCRA regulatory program, but you won't find that term actually used in the text of the regulations. You will find that our index references the various elements of the derived-from rule in §§261.3(c–d) and 261.3(g)(2)(ii).

For the convenience of the readers of this publication, a light gray shading has been placed over regulatory text that has changed or been added in the past year since our previous edition of this book. Please note that table headers and some EPA forms contain darker gray shading that is part of the formatting and does not indicate a change.

The format of this publication is somewhat similar to the RCRA regulations available in the *Code of Federal Regulations* (*CFR*). We used a two-column layout to keep the book manageable in size, but (unlike the *CFR*) we have indented the different levels of paragraphs and subparagraphs so you can tell where you are within a section. The beginning and ending section numbers included on each page are noted at the top left- and right-hand corner, respectively. Tabs are included on each page to help you quickly thumb through the book to find a part or subpart within the regulations.

Whenever we found that EPA or the Office of Federal Register has made an error in updating the RCRA regulations (an error that we found in the *CFR*), we have added a Publisher's Note explaining the problem and what we did to fix it.

Comments

If you have any comments or questions regarding this publication, please don't hesitate to call us at (303) 526-2674 or e-mail us at info@mccoyseminars.com. For up-to-date information regarding our seminars and publications, visit our website at www.mccoyseminars.com.

PART 260—HAZARDOUS WASTE MANAGEMENT SYSTEM: GENERAL

Authority: 42 U.S.C. 6905, 6912(a), 6921–6927, 6930, 6934, 6935, 6937, 6938, 6939, and 6974.

Source: 45 FR 33073, May 19, 1980, unless otherwise noted.

Effective Date Note: The reporting or recordkeeping provisions included in the final rule published at 47 FR 32274, July 26, 1982, will be submitted for approval to the Office of Management and Budget (OMB), and will not become effective until OMB approval has been obtained. EPA will publish a notice of the effective date of the reporting and recordkeeping provisions of this rule after it obtains OMB approval.

Subpart A—General

§260.1 Purpose, scope, and applicability.

(a) This part provides definitions of terms, general standards, and overview information applicable to parts 260 through 265 and 268 of this chapter.

(b) In this part: (1) Section 260.2 sets forth the rules that EPA will use in making information it receives available to the public and sets forth the requirements that generators, transporters, or owners or operators of treatment, storage, or disposal facilities must follow to assert claims of business confidentiality with respect to information that is submitted to EPA under parts 260 through 265 and 268 of this chapter.

(2) Section 260.3 establishes rules of grammatical construction for parts 260 through 265 and 268 of this chapter.

(3) Section 260.10 defines terms which are used in parts 260 through 265 and 268 of this chapter.

(4) Section 260.20 establishes procedures for petitioning EPA to amend, modify, or revoke any provision of parts 260 through 265 and 268 of this chapter and establishes procedures governing EPA's action on such petitions.

(5) Section 260.21 establishes procedures for petitioning EPA to approve testing methods as equivalent to those prescribed in parts 261, 264, or 265 of this chapter.

(6) Section 260.22 establishes procedures for petitioning EPA to amend subpart D of part 261 to exclude a waste from a particular facility.

[45 FR 33073, May 19, 1980, as amended at 51 FR 40636, Nov. 7, 1986]

§260.2 Availability of information; confidentiality of information.

(a) Any information provided to EPA under parts 260 through 265 and 268 of this chapter will be made available to the public to the extent and in the manner authorized by the Freedom of Information Act, 5 U.S.C. section 552, section 3007(b) of RCRA and EPA regulations implementing the Freedom of Information Act and section 3007(b), part 2 of this chapter, as applicable.

(b) Any person who submits information to EPA in accordance with parts 260 through 266 and 268 of this chapter may assert a claim of business confidentiality covering part or all of that information by following the procedures set forth in §2.203(b) of this chapter. Information covered by such a claim will be disclosed by EPA only to the extent, and by means of the procedures, set forth in part 2, subpart B, of this chapter except that information required by §262.53(a) and §262.83 that is submitted in a notification of intent to export a hazardous waste will be provided to the U.S. Department of State and the appropriate authorities in the transit and receiving or importing countries regardless of any claims of confidentiality. However, if no such claim accompanies the information when it is received by EPA, it may be made available to the public without further notice to the person submitting it.

[45 FR 33073, May 19, 1980, as amended at 51 FR 28682, Aug. 8, 1986; 51 FR 40636, Nov. 7, 1986; 61 FR 16309, Apr. 12, 1996]

§260.3 Use of number and gender.

As used in parts 260 through 265 and 268 of this chapter:

(a) Words in the masculine gender also include the feminine and neuter genders; and

(b) Words in the singular include the plural; and

(c) Words in the plural include the singular.

[45 FR 33073, May 19, 1980, as amended at 51 FR 40636, Nov. 7, 1986]

Subpart B—Definitions

§260.10 Definitions.

When used in parts 260 through 273 of this chapter, the following terms have the meanings given below:

Above ground tank means a device meeting the definition of "tank" in §260.10 and that is situated in such a way that the entire surface area of the tank is completely above the plane of the adjacent surrounding surface and the entire surface area of the tank (including the tank bottom) is able to be visually inspected.

Act or *RCRA* means the Solid Waste Disposal Act, as amended by the Resource Conservation and Recovery Act of 1976, as amended, 42 U.S.C. section 6901 et seq.

Active life of a facility means the period from the initial receipt of hazardous waste at the facility until the Regional Administrator receives certification of final closure.

Active portion means that portion of a facility where treatment, storage, or disposal operations are being or have been conducted after the effective date of part 261 of this chapter and which is not a closed portion. (See also "closed portion" and "inactive portion".)

Administrator means the Administrator of the Environmental Protection Agency, or his designee.

Ancillary equipment means any device including, but not limited to, such devices as piping, fittings, flanges, valves, and pumps, that is used to distribute, meter, or control the flow of hazardous waste from its point of generation to a storage or treatment tank(s), between hazardous waste storage and treatment tanks to a point of disposal onsite, or to a point of shipment for disposal off-site.

📖 9.1.2.3, 10.1.4

Aquifer means a geologic formation, group of formations, or part of a formation capable of yielding a significant amount of ground water to wells or springs.

Authorized representative means the person responsible for the overall operation of a facility or an operational unit (*i.e.*, part of a facility), *e.g.*, the plant manager, superintendent or person of equivalent responsibility.

Battery means a device consisting of one or more electrically connected electrochemical cells which is designed to receive, store, and deliver electric energy. An electrochemical cell is a system consisting of an anode, cathode, and an electrolyte, plus such connections (electrical and mechanical) as may be needed to allow the cell to deliver or receive electrical energy. The term battery also includes an intact, unbroken battery from which the electrolyte has been removed.

📖 8.1

Boiler means an enclosed device using controlled flame combustion and having the following characteristics:

(1)(i) The unit must have physical provisions for recovering and exporting thermal energy in the form of steam, heated fluids, or heated gases; and

(ii) The unit's combustion chamber and primary energy recovery sections(s) must be of integral design. To be of integral design, the combustion chamber and the primary energy recovery section(s) (such as waterwalls and superheaters) must be physically formed into one manufactured or assembled unit. A unit in which the combustion chamber and the primary energy recovery section(s) are joined only by ducts or connections carrying flue gas is not integrally designed; however, secondary energy recovery equipment (such as economizers or air preheaters) need not be physically formed into the same unit as the combustion chamber and the primary energy recovery section. The following units are not precluded from being boilers solely because they are not of integral design: process heaters (units that transfer energy directly to a process stream), and fluidized bed combustion units; and

(iii) While in operation, the unit must maintain a thermal energy recovery efficiency of at least 60 percent, calculated in terms of the recovered energy compared with the thermal value of the fuel; and

(iv) The unit must export and utilize at least 75 percent of the recovered energy, calculated on an annual basis. In this calculation, no credit shall be given for recovered heat used internally in the same unit. (Examples of internal use are the preheating of fuel or combustion air, and the driving of induced or forced draft fans or feedwater pumps); or

(2) The unit is one which the Regional Administrator has determined, on a case-by-case basis, to be a boiler, after considering the standards in §260.32.

Carbon regeneration unit means any enclosed thermal treatment device used to regenerate spent activated carbon.

Cathode ray tube or CRT means a vacuum tube, composed primarily of glass, which is the visual or video display component of an electronic device. A used, intact CRT means a CRT whose vacuum has not been released. A used, broken CRT means glass removed from its housing or casing whose vacuum has been released.

Certification means a statement of professional opinion based upon knowledge and belief.

Closed portion means that portion of a facility which an owner or operator has closed in accordance with the approved facility closure plan and all applicable closure requirements. (See also "active portion" and "inactive portion".)

Component means either the tank or ancillary equipment of a tank system.

Confined aquifer means an aquifer bounded above and below by impermeable beds or by beds of distinctly lower permeability than that of the aquifer itself; an aquifer containing confined ground water.

Container means any portable device in which a material is stored, transported, treated, disposed of, or otherwise handled. **6.3.4.2, 9.1**

Containment building means a hazardous waste management unit that is used to store or treat hazardous waste under the provisions of subpart DD of parts 264 or 265 of this chapter. **6.3.4.4, 13.8.4.1**

Contingency plan means a document setting out an organized, planned, and coordinated course of action to be followed in case of a fire, explosion, or release of hazardous waste or hazardous waste constituents which could threaten human health or the environment. **6.3.8**

Corrosion expert means a person who, by reason of his knowledge of the physical sciences and the principles of engineering and mathematics, acquired by a professional education and related practical experience, is qualified to engage in the practice of corrosion control on buried or submerged metal piping systems and metal tanks. Such a person must be certified as being qualified by the National Association of Corrosion Engineers (NACE) or be a registered professional engineer who has certification or licensing that includes education and experience in corrosion control on buried or submerged metal piping systems and metal tanks.

CRT collector means a person who receives used, intact CRTs for recycling, repair, resale, or donation.

CRT glass manufacturer means an operation or part of an operation that uses a furnace to manufacture CRT glass.

CRT processing means conducting all of the following activities:

(1) Receiving broken or intact CRTs; and

(2) Intentionally breaking intact CRTs or further breaking or separating broken CRTs; and

(3) Sorting or otherwise managing glass removed from CRT monitors.

Designated facility means: **6.6.3.4, 7.2.2.6**

(1) A hazardous waste treatment, storage, or disposal facility which:

(i) Has received a permit (or interim status) in accordance with the requirements of parts 270 and 124 of this chapter;

(ii) Has received a permit (or interim status) from a State authorized in accordance with part 271 of this chapter; or

(iii) Is regulated under §261.6(c)(2) or subpart F of part 266 of this chapter; and

(iv) That has been designated on the manifest by the generator pursuant to §262.20.

(2) *Designated facility* also means a generator site designated on the manifest to receive its waste as a return shipment from a facility that has rejected the waste in accordance with §264.72(f) or §265.72(f) of this chapter.

(3) If a waste is destined to a facility in an authorized State which has not yet obtained authorization to regulate that particular waste as hazardous, then the designated facility must be a facility allowed by the receiving State to accept such waste.

Destination facility means a facility that treats, disposes of, or recycles a particular category of universal waste, except those management activities described in paragraphs (a) and (c) of §§273.13 and 273.33 of this chapter. A facility at which a particular category of universal waste is only accumulated, is not a destination facility for purposes of managing that category of universal waste. **8.4.2**

Dike means an embankment or ridge of either natural or man-made materials used to prevent the movement of liquids, sludges, solids, or other materials.

Dioxins and furans (D/F) means tetra, penta, hexa, hepta, and octa-chlorinated dibenzo dioxins and furans.

Discharge or *hazardous waste discharge* means the accidental or intentional spilling, leaking, pumping, pouring, emitting, emptying, or dumping of hazardous waste into or on any land or water.

Disposal means the discharge, deposit, injection, dumping, spilling, leaking, or placing of any solid waste or hazardous waste into or on any land or water so that such solid waste or hazardous waste or any constituent thereof may enter the environment or be emitted into the air or discharged into any waters, including ground waters.

Disposal facility means a facility or part of a facility at which hazardous waste is intentionally placed into or on any land or water, and at which waste will remain after closure. The term disposal facility does not include a corrective action management unit into which remediation wastes are placed.

Drip pad is an engineered structure consisting of a curbed, free-draining base, constructed of non-earthen materials and designed to convey preservative kick-back or drippage from treated wood, precipitation, and surface water run-on to an associated collection system at wood preserving plants. 📖 6.3.4.3, 10.1.3.4

Elementary neutralization unit means a device which: 📖 7.5.1

(1) Is used for neutralizing wastes that are hazardous only because they exhibit the corrosivity characteristic defined in §261.22 of this chapter, or they are listed in subpart D of part 261 of the chapter only for this reason; and 📖 10.1.1

(2) Meets the definition of tank, tank system, container, transport vehicle, or vessel in §260.10 of this chapter. 📖 7.5.1.1.2

EPA hazardous waste number means the number assigned by EPA to each hazardous waste listed in part 261, subpart D, of this chapter and to each characteristic identified in part 261, subpart C, of this chapter.

EPA identification number means the number assigned by EPA to each generator, transporter, and treatment, storage, or disposal facility.

EPA region means the states and territories found in any one of the following ten regions:

Region I—Maine, Vermont, New Hampshire, Massachusetts, Connecticut, and Rhode Island.

Region II—New York, New Jersey, Commonwealth of Puerto Rico, and the U.S. Virgin Islands.

Region III—Pennsylvania, Delaware, Maryland, West Virginia, Virginia, and the District of Columbia.

Region IV—Kentucky, Tennessee, North Carolina, Mississippi, Alabama, Georgia, South Carolina, and Florida.

Region V—Minnesota, Wisconsin, Illinois, Michigan, Indiana and Ohio.

Region VI—New Mexico, Oklahoma, Arkansas, Louisiana, and Texas.

Region VII—Nebraska, Kansas, Missouri, and Iowa.

Region VIII—Montana, Wyoming, North Dakota, South Dakota, Utah, and Colorado.

Region IX—California, Nevada, Arizona, Hawaii, Guam, American Samoa, Commonwealth of the Northern Mariana Islands.

Region X—Washington, Oregon, Idaho, and Alaska.

Equivalent method means any testing or analytical method approved by the Administrator under §§260.20 and 260.21.

Existing hazardous waste management (HWM) facility or *existing facility* means a facility which was in operation or for which construction commenced on or before November 19, 1980. A facility has commenced construction if: 📖 17.6.1

(1) The owner or operator has obtained the Federal, State and local approvals or permits necessary to begin physical construction; and either

(2)(i) A continuous on-site, physical construction program has begun; or

(ii) The owner or operator has entered into contractual obligations—which cannot be cancelled or modified without substantial loss—for physical construction of the facility to be completed within a reasonable time.

Existing portion means that land surface area of an existing waste management unit, included in the original Part A permit application, on which wastes have been placed prior to the issuance of a permit.

Existing tank system or *existing component* means a tank system or component that is used for the storage or treatment of hazardous waste and that is in operation, or for which installation has commenced on or prior to July 14, 1986. Installation will be considered to have commenced if the owner or operator has obtained all Federal, State, and local approvals or permits necessary to begin physical construction of the site or installation of the tank system and if either (1) a continuous on-site physical construction or installation program has begun, or (2) the owner or operator has entered into contractual obligations—which cannot be canceled or modified without substantial loss—for physical construction of the site or installation of the tank system to be completed within a reasonable time. 📖 10.1.5.1

Explosives or *munitions emergency* means a situation involving the suspected or detected presence of unexploded ordnance (UXO), damaged or deteriorated explosives or munitions, an improvised explosive device (IED), other potentially explosive material or device, or other potentially harmful military chemical munitions or device, that creates an actual or potential imminent threat to human health, including safety, or the environment, including property, as determined by an explosives or munitions emergency response specialist. Such situations may require immediate and expeditious action by an explosives or munitions emergency response specialist to control, mitigate, or eliminate the threat.

Explosives or *munitions emergency response* means all immediate response activities by an explosives and munitions emergency response specialist to control, mitigate, or eliminate the actual or potential threat encountered during an explosives or munitions emergency. An explosives or munitions emergency response may include in-place render-safe procedures, treatment or destruction of the explosives or munitions and/or transporting those items to another location to be rendered safe, treated, or destroyed. Any reasonable delay in the completion of an explosives or munitions emergency response caused by a necessary, unforeseen, or uncontrollable circumstance will not terminate the explosives or munitions emergency. Explosives and munitions emergency responses can occur on either public or private lands and are not limited to responses at RCRA facilities.

Explosives or *munitions emergency response specialist* means an individual trained in chemical or conventional munitions or explosives handling, transportation, render-safe procedures, or destruction techniques. Explosives or munitions emergency response specialists include Department of Defense (DOD) emergency explosive ordnance disposal (EOD), technical escort unit (TEU), and DOD- certified civilian or contractor personnel; and other Federal, State, or local government, or civilian personnel similarly trained in explosives or munitions emergency responses.

Facility means:

(1) All contiguous land, and structures, other appurtenances, and improvements on the land, used for treating, storing, or disposing of hazardous waste, or for managing hazardous secondary materials prior to reclamation. A facility may consist of several treatment, storage, or disposal operational units (e.g., one or more landfills, surface impoundments, or combinations of them).

(2) For the purpose of implementing corrective action under 40 CFR 264.101 or 267.101, all contiguous property under the control of the owner or operator seeking a permit under Subtitle C of RCRA. This definition also applies to facilities implementing corrective action under RCRA Section 3008(h). 📖 17.5

(3) Notwithstanding paragraph (2) of this definition, a remediation waste management site is not a facility that is subject to 40 CFR 264.101, but is subject to corrective action requirements if the site is located within such a facility.

Federal agency means any department, agency, or other instrumentality of the Federal Government, any independent agency or establishment of the Federal Government including any Government corporation, and the Government Printing Office.

Federal, State and local approvals or permits necessary to begin physical construction means permits and approvals required under Federal, State or local hazardous waste control statutes, regulations or ordinances.

Final closure means the closure of all hazardous waste management units at the facility in accordance with all applicable closure requirements so that hazardous waste management activities under parts 264 and 265 of this chapter are no longer conducted at the facility unless subject to the provisions in §262.34.

Food-chain crops means tobacco, crops grown for human consumption, and crops grown for feed for animals whose products are consumed by humans.

Free liquids means liquids which readily separate from the solid portion of a waste under ambient temperature and pressure. 📖 2.2.1.1

Freeboard means the vertical distance between the top of a tank or surface impoundment dike, and the surface of the waste contained therein.

Gasification. For the purpose of complying with 40 CFR 261.4(a)(12)(i), gasification is a process, conducted in an enclosed device or system, designed and operated to process petroleum feedstock, including oil-bearing hazardous secondary materials through a series of highly controlled steps utilizing thermal decomposition, limited oxidation, and gas cleaning to yield a synthesis gas composed primarily of hydrogen and carbon monoxide gas.

Generator means any person, by site, whose act or process produces hazardous waste identified or listed in part 261 of this chapter or whose act first causes a hazardous waste to become subject to regulation. 📖 6.5

Ground water means water below the land surface in a zone of saturation.

Hazardous secondary material means a secondary material (e.g., spent material, by-product, or sludge) that, when discarded, would be identified as hazardous waste under part 261 of this chapter. 📖 1.2, 1.2.6.3.1, 11.1.1

Hazardous secondary material generated and reclaimed under the control of the generator means: 📖 1.2.6.3.1, 11.2.3.1

(1) That such material is generated and reclaimed at the generating facility (for purposes of this definition, generating facility means all contiguous property owned, leased, or otherwise controlled by the hazardous secondary material generator); or 📖 11.2.3.1.1

(2) That such material is generated and reclaimed at different facilities, if the reclaiming facility is controlled by the generator or if both the generating facility and the reclaiming facility are controlled by a person as defined in §260.10, and if the generator provides one of the following certifications: "on behalf of [insert generator facility name], I certify that this facility will send the indicated hazardous secondary material to [insert reclaimer facility name], which is controlled by [insert generator facility name] and that [insert the name of either facility] has acknowledged full responsibility for the safe management of the hazardous secondary material," or "on behalf of [insert generator facility name] I certify that this facility will send the indicated hazardous secondary material to [insert reclaimer facility name], that both facilities are under common control, and that [insert name of either facility] has acknowledged full responsibility for the safe management of the hazardous secondary material." For purposes of this paragraph, "control" means the power to direct the policies of the facility, whether by the ownership of stock, voting rights, or otherwise, except that contractors who operate facilities on behalf of a different person as defined in §260.10 shall not be deemed to "control" such facilities, or 11.2.3.1.2

(3) That such material is generated pursuant to a written contract between a tolling contractor and a toll manufacturer and is reclaimed by the tolling contractor, if the tolling contractor certifies the following: "On behalf of [insert tolling contractor name], I certify that [insert tolling contractor name], has a written contract with [insert toll manufacturer name] to manufacture [insert name of product or intermediate] which is made from specified unused materials, and that [insert tolling contractor name] will reclaim the hazardous secondary materials generated during this manufacture. On behalf of [insert tolling contractor name], I also certify that [insert tolling contractor name] retains ownership of, and responsibility for, the hazardous secondary materials that are generated during the course of the manufacture, including any releases of hazardous secondary materials that occur during the manufacturing process. For purposes of this paragraph, tolling contractor means a person who arranges for the production of a product or intermediate made from specified unused materials through a written contract with a toll manufacturer. Toll manufacturer means a person who produces a product or intermediate made from specified unused materials pursuant to a written contract with a tolling contractor. 11.2.3.1.3

Hazardous secondary material generator means any person whose act or process produces hazardous secondary materials at the generating facility. For purposes of this paragraph, "generating facility" means all contiguous property owned, leased, or otherwise controlled by the hazardous secondary material generator. For the purposes of §261.2(a)(2)(ii) and §261.4(a)(23), a facility that collects hazardous secondary materials from other persons is not the hazardous secondary material generator.

Hazardous waste means a hazardous waste as defined in §261.3 of this chapter.

Hazardous waste constituent means a constituent that caused the Administrator to list the hazardous waste in part 261, subpart D, of this chapter, or a constituent listed in table 1 of §261.24 of this chapter.

Hazardous waste management unit is a contiguous area of land on or in which hazardous waste is placed, or the largest area in which there is significant likelihood of mixing hazardous waste constituents in the same area. Examples of hazardous waste management units include a surface impoundment, a waste pile, a land treatment area, a landfill cell, an incinerator, a tank and its associated piping and underlying containment system and a container storage area. A container alone does not constitute a unit; the unit includes containers and the land or pad upon which they are placed.

In operation refers to a facility which is treating, storing, or disposing of hazardous waste.

Inactive portion means that portion of a facility which is not operated after the effective date of part 261 of this chapter. (See also "active portion" and "closed portion".)

Incinerator means any enclosed device that:

(1) Uses controlled flame combustion and neither meets the criteria for classification as a boiler, sludge dryer, or carbon regeneration unit, nor is listed as an industrial furnace; or

(2) Meets the definition of infrared incinerator or plasma arc incinerator.

Incompatible waste means a hazardous waste which is unsuitable for:

(1) Placement in a particular device or facility because it may cause corrosion or decay of containment materials (*e.g.*, container inner liners or tank walls); or

(2) Commingling with another waste or material under uncontrolled conditions because the commingling might produce heat or pressure, fire or explosion, violent reaction, toxic dusts, mists, fumes, or gases, or flammable fumes or gases.

(See appendix V of parts 264 and 265 of this chapter for examples.)

Individual generation site means the contiguous site at or on which one or more hazardous wastes are generated. An individual generation site, such as a large manufacturing plant, may have one or more sources of hazardous waste but is considered a single or individual generation site if the site or property is contiguous.

Industrial furnace means any of the following enclosed devices that are integral components of manufacturing processes and that use thermal treatment to accomplish recovery of materials or energy:

(1) Cement kilns

(2) Lime kilns

(3) Aggregate kilns

(4) Phosphate kilns

(5) Coke ovens

(6) Blast furnaces

(7) Smelting, melting and refining furnaces (including pyrometallurgical devices such as cupolas, reverberator furnaces, sintering machine, roasters, and foundry furnaces)

(8) Titanium dioxide chloride process oxidation reactors

(9) Methane reforming furnaces

(10) Pulping liquor recovery furnaces

(11) Combustion devices used in the recovery of sulfur values from spent sulfuric acid

(12) Halogen acid furnaces (HAFs) for the production of acid from halogenated hazardous waste generated by chemical production facilities where the furnace is located on the site of a chemical production facility, the acid product has a halogen acid content of at least 3%, the acid product is used in a manufacturing process, and, except for hazardous waste burned as fuel, hazardous waste fed to the furnace has a minimum halogen content of 20% as-generated.

(13) Such other devices as the Administrator may, after notice and comment, add to this list on the basis of one or more of the following factors:

(i) The design and use of the device primarily to accomplish recovery of material products;

(ii) The use of the device to burn or reduce raw materials to make a material product;

(iii) The use of the device to burn or reduce secondary materials as effective substitutes for raw materials, in processes using raw materials as principal feedstocks;

(iv) The use of the device to burn or reduce secondary materials as ingredients in an industrial process to make a material product;

(v) The use of the device in common industrial practice to produce a material product; and

(vi) Other factors, as appropriate.

Infrared incinerator means any enclosed device that uses electric powered resistance heaters as a source of radiant heat followed by an afterburner using controlled flame combustion and which is not listed as an industrial furnace.

Inground tank means a device meeting the definition of "tank" in §260.10 whereby a portion of the tank wall is situated to any degree within the ground, thereby preventing visual inspection of that external surface area of the tank that is in the ground. 📖 10.2

Injection well means a well into which fluids are injected. (See also "underground injection".)

Inner liner means a continuous layer of material placed inside a tank or container which protects the construction materials of the tank or container from the contained waste or reagents used to treat the waste.

Installation inspector means a person who, by reason of his knowledge of the physical sciences and the principles of engineering, acquired by a professional education and related practical experience, is qualified to supervise the installation of tank systems.

Intermediate facility means any facility that stores hazardous secondary materials for more than 10 days, other than a hazardous secondary material generator or reclaimer of such material.

International shipment means the transportation of hazardous waste into or out of the jurisdiction of the United States.

Lamp, also referred to as "universal waste lamp", is defined as the bulb or tube portion of an electric lighting device. A lamp is specifically designed to produce radiant energy, most often in the ultraviolet, visible, and infra-red regions of the electromagnetic spectrum. Examples of common universal waste electric lamps include, but are not limited to, fluorescent, high intensity discharge, neon, mercury vapor, high pressure sodium, and metal halide lamps. 📖 8.1

Land-based unit means an area where hazardous secondary materials are placed in or on the land before recycling. This definition does not include land-based production units.

Landfill means a disposal facility or part of a facility where hazardous waste is placed in or on land and which is not a pile, a land treatment facility, a surface impoundment, an underground injection well, a salt dome formation, a salt bed formation, an underground mine, a cave, or a corrective action management unit.

Landfill cell means a discrete volume of a hazardous waste landfill which uses a liner to provide isolation of wastes from adjacent cells or wastes. Examples of landfill cells are trenches and pits.

Land treatment facility means a facility or part of a facility at which hazardous waste is applied onto or incorporated into the soil surface; such facilities are disposal facilities if the waste will remain after closure.

Leachate means any liquid, including any suspended components in the liquid, that has percolated through or drained from hazardous waste. 📖 **5.1.6.1, 5.2.6.1, 14.2.1.2**

Leak-detection system means a system capable of detecting the failure of either the primary or secondary containment structure or the presence of a release of hazardous waste or accumulated liquid in the secondary containment structure. Such a system must employ operational controls (*e.g.*, daily visual inspections for releases into the secondary containment system of aboveground tanks) or consist of an interstitial monitoring device designed to detect continuously and automatically the failure of the primary or secondary containment structure or the presence of a release of hazardous waste into the secondary containment structure. 📖 **10.3.3**

Liner means a continuous layer of natural or man-made materials, beneath or on the sides of a surface impoundment, landfill, or landfill cell, which restricts the downward or lateral escape of hazardous waste, hazardous waste constituents, or leachate.

Management or *hazardous waste management* means the systematic control of the collection, source separation, storage, transportation, processing, treatment, recovery, and disposal of hazardous waste.

Manifest means: The shipping document EPA Form 8700–22 (including, if necessary, EPA Form 8700–22A), originated and signed by the generator or offeror in accordance with the instructions in the appendix to 40 CFR part 262 and the applicable requirements of 40 CFR parts 262 through 265. 📖 **6.6**

Manifest tracking number means: The alphanumeric identification number (*i.e.*, a unique three letter suffix preceded by nine numerical digits), which is pre-printed in Item 4 of the Manifest by a registered source.

Mercury-containing equipment means a device or part of a device (including thermostats, but excluding batteries and lamps) that contains elemental mercury integral to its function. 📖 **8.1**

Military munitions means all ammunition products and components produced or used by or for the U.S. Department of Defense or the U.S. Armed Services for national defense and security, including military munitions under the control of the Department of Defense, the U.S. Coast Guard, the U.S. Department of Energy (DOE), and National Guard personnel. The term military munitions includes: confined gaseous, liquid, and solid propellants, explosives, pyrotechnics, chemical and riot control agents, smokes, and incendiaries used by DOD components, including bulk explosives and chemical warfare agents, chemical munitions, rockets, guided and ballistic missiles, bombs, warheads, mortar rounds, artillery ammunition, small arms ammunition, grenades, mines, torpedoes, depth charges, cluster munitions and dispensers, demolition charges, and devices and components thereof. Military munitions do not include wholly inert items, improvised explosive devices, and nuclear weapons, nuclear devices, and nuclear components thereof. However, the term does include non-nuclear components of nuclear devices, managed under DOE's nuclear weapons program after all required sanitization operations under the Atomic Energy Act of 1954, as amended, have been completed. 📖 **14.6.1**

Mining overburden returned to the mine site means any material overlying an economic mineral deposit which is removed to gain access to that deposit and is then used for reclamation of a surface mine. 📖 **4.12**

Miscellaneous unit means a hazardous waste management unit where hazardous waste is treated, stored, or disposed of and that is not a container, tank, surface impoundment, pile, land treatment unit, landfill, incinerator, boiler, industrial furnace, underground injection well with appropriate technical standards under part 146 of this chapter, containment building, corrective action management unit, unit eligible for a research, development, and demonstration permit under 40 CFR 270.65, or staging pile.

Movement means that hazardous waste transported to a facility in an individual vehicle.

New hazardous waste management facility or *new facility* means a facility which began operation, or for which construction commenced after October 21, 1976. (See also "Existing hazardous waste management facility".)

New tank system or *new tank component* means a tank system or component that will be used for the storage or treatment of hazardous waste and for which installation has commenced after July 14, 1986; except, however, for purposes of §264.193(g)(2) and §265.193(g)(2), a new tank system is one for which construction commences after July 14, 1986. (See also "existing tank system.") 📖 10.1.5.1

On ground tank means a device meeting the definition of "tank" in §260.10 and that is situated in such a way that the bottom of the tank is on the same level as the adjacent surrounding surface so that the external tank bottom cannot be visually inspected.

On-site means the same or geographically contiguous property which may be divided by public or private right-of-way, provided the entrance and exit between the properties is at a cross-roads intersection, and access is by crossing as opposed to going along, the right- of-way. Non-contiguous properties owned by the same person but connected by a right-of-way which he controls and to which the public does not have access, is also considered on-site property. 📖 6.6.2.2

Open burning means the combustion of any material without the following characteristics: 📖 6.3.5.2, 7.5.4.2

(1) Control of combustion air to maintain adequate temperature for efficient combustion,

(2) Containment of the combustion-reaction in an enclosed device to provide sufficient residence time and mixing for complete combustion, and

(3) Control of emission of the gaseous combustion products.

(See also "incineration" and "thermal treatment".)

Operator means the person responsible for the overall operation of a facility.

Owner means the person who owns a facility or part of a facility.

Partial closure means the closure of a hazardous waste management unit in accordance with the applicable closure requirements of parts 264 and 265 of this chapter at a facility that contains other active hazardous waste management units. For example, partial closure may include the closure of a tank (including its associated piping and underlying containment systems), landfill cell, surface impoundment, waste pile, or other hazardous waste management unit, while other units of the same facility continue to operate.

Performance Track member facility means a facility that has been accepted by EPA for membership in the National Environmental Performance Track Program and is still a member of the Program. The National Environmental Performance Track Program is a voluntary, facility based, program for top environmental performers. Facility members must demonstrate a good record of compliance, past success in achieving environmental goals, and commit to future specific quantified environmental goals, environmental management systems, local community outreach, and annual reporting of measurable results.

Person means an individual, trust, firm, joint stock company, Federal Agency, corporation (including a government corporation), partnership, association, State, municipality, commission, political subdivision of a State, or any interstate body.

Personnel or *facility personnel* means all persons who work at, or oversee the operations of, a hazardous waste facility, and whose actions or failure to act may result in noncompliance with the requirements of part 264 or 265 of this chapter. 📖 6.4.1.1

Pesticide means any substance or mixture of substances intended for preventing, destroying, repelling, or mitigating any pest, or intended for use as a plant regulator, defoliant, or desiccant, other than any article that: 📖 8.1

(1) Is a new animal drug under FFDCA section 201(w), or

(2) Is an animal drug that has been determined by regulation of the Secretary of Health and Human Services not to be a new animal drug, or

(3) Is an animal feed under FFDCA section 201(x) that bears or contains any substances described by paragraph (1) or (2) of this definition.

Pile means any non-containerized accumulation of solid, nonflowing hazardous waste that is used for treatment or storage and that is not a containment building. 📖 10.1.3.1

Plasma arc incinerator means any enclosed device using a high intensity electrical discharge or arc as a source of heat followed by an afterburner using controlled flame combustion and which is not listed as an industrial furnace.

Point source means any discernible, confined, and discrete conveyance, including, but not limited to any pipe, ditch, channel, tunnel, conduit, well, discrete fissure, container, rolling stock, concentrated animal feeding operation, or vessel or other floating craft, from which pollutants are or may be discharged. This term does not include return flows from irrigated agriculture. 📖 4.2.2

Publicly owned treatment works or *POTW* means any device or system used in the treatment (including recycling and reclamation) of municipal sewage or industrial wastes of a liquid nature which is owned by a "State" or "municipality" (as defined by section 502(4) of the CWA). This definition includes sewers, pipes, or other conveyances only if they convey wastewater to a POTW providing treatment. 📖 4.1.2.2

Qualified Ground-Water Scientist means a scientist or engineer who has received a baccalaureate or post-graduate degree in the natural sciences or engineering, and has sufficient training and experience in ground-water hydrology and related fields as may be demonstrated by state registration, professional certifications, or completion of accredited university courses that enable that individual to make sound professional judgements regarding ground-water monitoring and contaminant fate and transport.

Regional Administrator means the Regional Administrator for the EPA Region in which the facility is located, or his designee.

Remediation waste means all solid and hazardous wastes, and all media (including ground water, surface water, soils, and sediments) and debris, that are managed for implementing cleanup. 📖 13.1.3.1, 14.1.5, 17.15

Remediation waste management site means a facility where an owner or operator is or will be treating, storing or disposing of hazardous remediation wastes. A remediation waste management site is not a facility that is subject to corrective action under 40 CFR 264.101, but is subject to corrective action requirements if the site is located in such a facility. 📖 17.15

Replacement unit means a landfill, surface impoundment, or waste pile unit (1) from which all or substantially all of the waste is removed, and (2) that is subsequently reused to treat, store, or dispose of hazardous waste. "Replacement unit" does not apply to a unit from which waste is removed during closure, if the subsequent reuse solely involves the disposal of waste from that unit and other closing units or corrective action areas at the facility, in accordance with an approved closure plan or EPA or State approved corrective action.

Representative sample means a sample of a universe or whole (*e.g.*, waste pile, lagoon, ground water) which can be expected to exhibit the average properties of the universe or whole. 📖 2.8.3, 18.5.1-2

Run-off means any rainwater, leachate, or other liquid that drains over land from any part of a facility. 📖 5.1.6.1, 5.2.6.2

Run-on means any rainwater, leachate, or other liquid that drains over land onto any part of a facility.

Saturated zone or *zone of saturation* means that part of the earth's crust in which all voids are filled with water.

Sludge means any solid, semi-solid, or liquid waste generated from a municipal, commercial, or industrial wastewater treatment plant, water supply treatment plant, or air pollution control facility exclusive of the treated effluent from a wastewater treatment plant. 📖 1.2.5.2, 11.2.1

Sludge dryer means any enclosed thermal treatment device that is used to dehydrate sludge and that has a maximum total thermal input, excluding the heating value of the sludge itself, of 2,500 Btu/lb of sludge treated on a wet-weight basis. 📖 7.2.1.3.1

Small Quantity Generator means a generator who generates less than 1000 kg of hazardous waste in a calendar month. 📖 6.1.1, 6.3.1

Solid waste means a solid waste as defined in §261.2 of this chapter. 📖 1.0

Sorbent means a material that is used to soak up free liquids by either adsorption or absorption, or both.

Sorb means to either adsorb or absorb, or both.

Staging pile means an accumulation of solid, non-flowing remediation waste (as defined in this section) that is not a containment building and that is used only during remedial operations for temporary storage at a facility. Staging piles must be designated by the Director according to the requirements of 40 CFR 264.554. 📖 17.13

State means any of the several States, the District of Columbia, the Commonwealth of Puerto Rico, the Virgin Islands, Guam, American Samoa, and the Commonwealth of the Northern Mariana Islands.

Storage means the holding of hazardous waste for a temporary period, at the end of which the hazardous waste is treated, disposed of, or stored elsewhere.

Sump means any pit or reservoir that meets the definition of tank and those troughs/trenches connected to it that serve to collect hazardous waste for transport to hazardous waste storage, treatment, or disposal facilities; except that as used in the landfill, surface impoundment, and waste pile rules, "sump" means any lined pit or reservoir that serves to collect liquids drained from a leachate collection and removal system or leak detection system for subsequent removal from the system. 📖 7.5.4.1.1, 10.2

Surface impoundment or *impoundment* means a facility or part of a facility which is a natural topographic depression, man-made excavation, or diked area formed primarily of earthen materials (although it may be lined with man-made materials), which is designed to hold an accumulation of liquid wastes or wastes containing free liquids, and which is not an injection well. Examples of surface impoundments are holding, storage, settling, and aeration pits, ponds, and lagoons. 📖 **10.1.3.2, 13.1.3**

Tank means a stationary device, designed to contain an accumulation of hazardous waste which is constructed primarily of non-earthen materials (*e.g.*, wood, concrete, steel, plastic) which provide structural support. 📖 **6.3.4.1, 7.2.1.3, 7.2.2.7, 10.1**

Tank system means a hazardous waste storage or treatment tank and its associated ancillary equipment and containment system. 📖 **10.1.4**

TEQ means toxicity equivalence, the international method of relating the toxicity of various dioxin/furan congeners to the toxicity of 2,3,7,8-tetrachlorodibenzo-p-dioxin.

Thermal treatment means the treatment of hazardous waste in a device which uses elevated temperatures as the primary means to change the chemical, physical, or biological character or composition of the hazardous waste. Examples of thermal treatment processes are incineration, molten salt, pyrolysis, calcination, wet air oxidation, and microwave discharge. (See also "incinerator" and "open burning".)

Thermostat means a temperature control device that contains metallic mercury in an ampule attached to a bimetal sensing element, and mercury-containing ampules that have been removed from these temperature control devices in compliance with the requirements of 40 CFR 273.13(c)(2) or 273.33(c)(2).

Totally enclosed treatment facility means a facility for the treatment of hazardous waste which is directly connected to an industrial production process and which is constructed and operated in a manner which prevents the release of any hazardous waste or any constituent thereof into the environment during treatment. An example is a pipe in which waste acid is neutralized. 📖 **7.5.2**

Transfer facility means any transportation-related facility, including loading docks, parking areas, storage areas and other similar areas where shipments of hazardous waste or hazardous secondary materials are held during the normal course of transportation. 📖 **6.3.3, 6.6.3.3.1**

Transport vehicle means a motor vehicle or rail car used for the transportation of cargo by any mode. Each cargo-carrying body (trailer, railroad freight car, etc.) is a separate transport vehicle. 📖 **4.17.2.3**

Transportation means the movement of hazardous waste by air, rail, highway, or water.

Transporter means a person engaged in the offsite transportation of hazardous waste by air, rail, highway, or water. 📖 **6.6.3.3**

Treatability Study means a study in which a hazardous waste is subjected to a treatment process to determine: (1) Whether the waste is amenable to the treatment process, (2) what pretreatment (if any) is required, (3) the optimal process conditions needed to achieve the desired treatment, (4) the efficiency of a treatment process for a specific waste or wastes, or (5) the characteristics and volumes of residuals from a particular treatment process. Also included in this definition for the purpose of the §261.4 (e) and (f) exemptions are liner compatibility, corrosion, and other material compatibility studies and toxicological and health effects studies. A "treatability study" is not a means to commercially treat or dispose of hazardous waste. 📖 **4.18.2.1**

Treatment means any method, technique, or process, including neutralization, designed to change the physical, chemical, or biological character or composition of any hazardous waste so as to neutralize such waste, or so as to recover energy or material resources from the waste, or so as to render such waste non-hazardous, or less hazardous; safer to transport, store, or dispose of; or amenable for recovery, amenable for storage, or reduced in volume. 📖 **5.1.4, 7.1**

Treatment zone means a soil area of the unsaturated zone of a land treatment unit within which hazardous constituents are degraded, transformed, or immobilized.

Underground injection means the subsurface emplacement of fluids through a bored, drilled or driven well; or through a dug well, where the depth of the dug well is greater than the largest surface dimension. (See also "injection well".)

Underground tank means a device meeting the definition of "tank" in §260.10 whose entire surface area is totally below the surface of and covered by the ground.

Unfit-for use tank system means a tank system that has been determined through an integrity assessment or other inspection to be no longer capable of storing or treating hazardous waste without posing a threat of release of hazardous waste to the environment.

Unsaturated zone or *zone of aeration* means the zone between the land surface and the water table.

United States means the 50 States, the District of Columbia, the Commonwealth of Puerto Rico, the U.S. Virgin Islands, Guam, American Samoa, and the Commonwealth of the Northern Mariana Islands.

Universal Waste means any of the following hazardous wastes that are managed under the universal waste requirements of part 273 of this chapter: 📖 **8.0, 8.1**

(1) Batteries as described in §273.2 of this chapter;

(2) Pesticides as described in §273.3 of this chapter;

(3) Mercury-containing equipment as described in §273.4 of this chapter; and

(4) Lamps as described in §273.5 of this chapter.

Universal Waste Handler: 📖 8.2–3

(1) Means:

(i) A generator (as defined in this section) of universal waste; or

(ii) The owner or operator of a facility, including all contiguous property, that receives universal waste from other universal waste handlers, accumulates universal waste, and sends universal waste to another universal waste handler, to a destination facility, or to a foreign destination.

(2) Does not mean:

(i) A person who treats (except under the provisions of 40 CFR 273.13 (a) or (c), or 273.33 (a) or (c)), disposes of, or recycles universal waste; or

(ii) A person engaged in the off-site transportation of universal waste by air, rail, highway, or water, including a universal waste transfer facility.

Universal Waste Transporter means a person engaged in the off-site transportation of universal waste by air, rail, highway, or water. 📖 8.4.1

Uppermost aquifer means the geologic formation nearest the natural ground surface that is an aquifer, as well as lower aquifers that are hydraulically interconnected with this aquifer within the facility's property boundary.

Used oil means any oil that has been refined from crude oil, or any synthetic oil, that has been used and as a result of such use is contaminated by physical or chemical impurities. 📖 12.0

Vessel includes every description of watercraft, used or capable of being used as a means of transportation on the water.

Wastewater treatment unit means a device which: 📖 7.2, 9.1.2.3

(1) Is part of a wastewater treatment facility that is subject to regulation under either section 402 or 307(b) of the Clean Water Act; and 📖 7.2.1.1

(2) Receives and treats or stores an influent wastewater that is a hazardous waste as defined in §261.3 of this chapter, or that generates and accumulates a wastewater treatment sludge that is a hazardous waste as defined in §261.3 of this chapter, or treats or stores a wastewater treatment sludge which is a hazardous waste as defined in §261.3 of this Chapter; and 📖 7.2.1.2

(3) Meets the definition of tank or tank system in §260.10 of this chapter. 📖 7.2.1.3

Water (bulk shipment) means the bulk transportation of hazardous waste which is loaded or carried on board a vessel without containers or labels.

Well means any shaft or pit dug or bored into the earth, generally of a cylindrical form, and often walled with bricks or tubing to prevent the earth from caving in.

Well injection: (See "underground injection".)

Zone of engineering control means an area under the control of the owner/operator that, upon detection of a hazardous waste release, can be readily cleaned up prior to the release of hazardous waste or hazardous constituents to ground water or surface water.

[45 FR 33073, May 19, 1980, as amended at 45 FR 72028, Oct. 30, 1980; 45 FR 76075, Nov. 17, 1980; 45 FR 76630, Nov. 19, 1980; 45 FR 86968, Dec. 31, 1980; 46 FR 2348, Jan. 9, 1981; 46 FR 27476, May 20, 1981; 47 FR 32349, July 26, 1982; 48 FR 2511, Jan. 16, 1983; 48 FR 14293, Apr. 1, 1983; 49 FR 10500, Mar. 20, 1984; 50 FR 661, Jan. 4, 1985; 51 FR 10174, Mar. 24, 1986; 51 FR 16443, May 2, 1986; 51 FR 25471, July 14, 1986; 51 FR 40636, Nov. 7, 1986; 52 FR 46963, Dec. 10, 1987; 53 FR 27301, July 19, 1988; 53 FR 34086, Sept. 2, 1988; 55 FR 2353, Jan. 23, 1990; 55 FR 50482, Dec. 6, 1990; 56 FR 7206, Feb. 21, 1991; 56 FR 66368, Dec. 23, 1991; 57 FR 3486, Jan. 29, 1992; 57 FR 37263, Aug. 18, 1992; 57 FR 38564, Aug. 25, 1992; 57 FR 41611, Sept. 10, 1992; 57 FR 54460, Nov. 18, 1992; 58 FR 8682, Feb. 16, 1993; 60 FR 25540, May 11, 1995; 62 FR 6650, Feb. 12, 1997; 63 65937, Nov. 30, 1998; 64 FR 36487, July 6, 1999; 64 FR 53070, Sept. 30, 1999; 67 FR 3024, Jan. 22, 2002; 70 FR 10814, Mar. 4, 2005; 70 FR 45520, Aug. 5, 2005; 70 FR 53453, Sept. 8, 2005; 71 FR 16902, Apr. 4, 2006; 71 FR 40258, July 14, 2006; 71 FR 42947, July 28, 2006; 73 FR 72, Jan. 2, 2008; 73 FR 64757, Oct. 30, 2008]

§260.11 References.

(a) When used in parts 260 through 268 and 278 of this chapter, the following publications are incorporated by reference. These incorporations by reference were approved by the Director of the Federal Register pursuant to 5 U.S.C. 552(a) and 1 CFR part 51. These materials are incorporated as they exist on the date of approval and a notice of any change in these materials will be published in the *Federal Register*. Copies may be inspected at the Library, U.S. Environmental Protection Agency, 1200 Pennsylvania Ave., NW. (3403T), Washington, DC 20460, libraryhq@epa.gov; or at the National Archives and Records Administration (NARA). For information on the availability of this material at NARA, call 202–741–6030, or go to: http://www.archives.gov/federal_register/code_of_federal_regulations/ibr_locations.html.

(b) The following materials are available for purchase from the American Society for Testing and Materials, 100 Barr Harbor Drive, P.O. Box C700, West Conshohocken, PA 19428–2959.

(1) ASTM D–93–79 or D–93–80, "Standard Test Methods for Flash Point by Pensky-Martens Closed Cup Tester," IBR approved for §261.21.

(2) ASTM D–1946–82, "Standard Method for Analysis of Reformed Gas by Gas Chromatography," IBR approved for §§264.1033, 265.1033.

(3) ASTM D 2267–88, "Standard Test Method for Aromatics in Light Naphthas and Aviation Gasolines by Gas Chromatography," IBR approved for §264.1063.

(4) ASTM D 2382–83, "Standard Test Method for Heat of Combustion of Hydrocarbon Fuels by Bomb Calorimeter (High-Precision Method)," IBR approved for §§264.1033, 265.1033.

(5) ASTM D 2879–92, "Standard Test Method for Vapor Pressure—Temperature Relationship and Initial Decomposition Temperature of Liquids by Isoteniscope," IBR approved for §265.1084.

(6) ASTM D–3278–78, "Standard Test Methods for Flash Point for Liquids by Setaflash Closed Tester," IBR approved for §261.21(a).

(7) ASTM E 168–88, "Standard Practices for General Techniques of Infrared Quantitative Analysis," IBR approved for §264.1063.

(8) ASTM E 169–87, "Standard Practices for General Techniques of Ultraviolet-Visible Quantitative Analysis," IBR approved for §264.1063.

(9) ASTM E 260–85, "Standard Practice for Packed Column Gas Chromatography," IBR approved for §264.1063.

(10) ASTM E 926–88, "Standard Test Methods for Preparing Refuse-Derived Fuel (RDF) Samples for Analyses of Metals," Test Method C—Bomb, Acid Digestion Method.

(c) The following materials are available for purchase from the National Technical Information Service, 5285 Port Royal Road, Springfield, VA 22161; or for purchase from the Superintendent of Documents, U.S. Government Printing Office, Washington, DC 20402, (202) 512–1800.

(1) "APTI Course 415: Control of Gaseous Emissions," EPA Publication EPA–450/2–81–005, December 1981, IBR approved for §§264.1035 and 265.1035.

(2) Method 1664, Revision A, n-Hexane Extractable Material (HEM; Oil and Grease) and Silica Gel Treated n-Hexane Extractable Material (SGT–HEM; Non-polar Material) by Extraction and Gravimetry, PB99–121949, IBR approved for part 261, appendix IX.

(3) The following methods as published in the test methods compendium known as "Test Methods for Evaluating Solid Waste, Physical/Chemical Methods," EPA Publication SW–846, Third Edition. A suffix of "A" in the method number indicates revision one (the method has been revised once). A suffix of "B" in the method number indicates revision two (the method has been revised twice). A suffix of "C" in the method number indicates revision three (the method has been revised three times). A suffix of "D" in the method number indicates revision four (the method has been revised four times).

(i) Method 0010, dated September 1986 and in the Basic Manual, IBR approved for part 261, appendix IX.

(ii) Method 0020, dated September 1986 and in the Basic Manual, IBR approved for part 261, appendix IX.

(iii) Method 0030, dated September 1986 and in the Basic Manual, IBR approved for part 261, appendix IX.

(iv) Method 1320, dated September 1986 and in the Basic Manual, IBR approved for part 261, appendix IX.

(v) Method 1311, dated September 1992 and in Update I, IBR approved for part 261, appendix IX, and §§261.24, 268.7, 268.40.

(vi) Method 1330A, dated September 1992 and in Update I, IBR approved for part 261, appendix IX.

(vii) Method 1312 dated September 1994 and in Update III, IBR approved for part 261, appendix IX and §278.3(b)(1).

(viii) Method 0011, dated December 1996 and in Update III, IBR approved for part 261, appendix IX, and part 266, appendix IX.

(ix) Method 0023A, dated December 1996 and in Update III, IBR approved for part 261, appendix IX, part 266, appendix IX, and §266.104.

(x) Method 0031, dated December 1996 and in Update III, IBR approved for part 261, appendix IX.

(xi) Method 0040, dated December 1996 and in Update III, IBR approved for part 261, appendix IX.

(xii) Method 0050, dated December 1996 and in Update III, IBR approved for part 261, appendix IX, part 266, appendix IX, and §266.107.

(xiii) Method 0051, dated December 1996 and in Update III, IBR approved for part 261, appendix IX, part 266, appendix IX, and §266.107.

(xiv) Method 0060, dated December 1996 and in Update III, IBR approved for part 261, appendix IX, §266.106, and part 266, appendix IX.

(xv) Method 0061, dated December 1996 and in Update III, IBR approved for part 261, appendix IX, §266.106, and part 266, appendix IX.

(xvi) Method 9071B, dated April 1998 and in Update IIIA, IBR approved for part 261, appendix IX.

(xvii) Method 1010A, dated November 2004 and in Update IIIB, IBR approved for part 261, appendix IX.

(xviii) Method 1020B, dated November 2004 and in Update IIIB, IBR approved for part 261, appendix IX.

(xix) Method 1110A, dated November 2004 and in Update IIIB, IBR approved for §261.22 and part 261, appendix IX.

(xx) Method 1310B, dated November 2004 and in Update IIIB, IBR approved for part 261, appendix IX.

(xxi) Method 9010C, dated November 2004 and in Update IIIB, IBR approved for part 261, appendix IX and §§268.40, 268.44, 268.48.

(xxii) Method 9012B, dated November 2004 and in Update IIIB, IBR approved for part 261, appendix IX and §§268.40, 268.44, 268.48.

(xxiii) Method 9040C, dated November 2004 and in Update IIIB, IBR approved for part 261, appendix IX and §261.22.

(xxiv) Method 9045D, dated November 2004 and in Update IIIB, IBR approved for part 261, appendix IX.

(xxv) Method 9060A, dated November 2004 and in Update IIIB, IBR approved for part 261, appendix IX, and §§264.1034, 264.1063, 265.1034, 265.1063.

(xxvi) Method 9070A, dated November 2004 and in Update IIIB, IBR approved for part 261, appendix IX.

(xxvii) Method 9095B, dated November 2004 and in Update IIIB, IBR approved, part 261, appendix IX, and §§264.190, 264.314, 265.190, 265.314, 265.1081, 267.190(a), 268.32.

(d) The following materials are available for purchase from the National Fire Protection Association, 1 Batterymarch Park, P.O. Box 9101, Quincy, MA 02269–9101.

(1) "Flammable and Combustible Liquids Code" (1977 or 1981), IBR approved for §§264.198, 265.198, 267.202(b).

(2) [Reserved]

(e) The following materials are available for purchase from the American Petroleum Institute, 1220 L Street, Northwest, Washington, DC 20005.

(1) API Publication 2517, Third Edition, February 1989, "Evaporative Loss from External Floating-Roof Tanks," IBR approved for §265.1084.

(2) [Reserved]

(f) The following materials are available for purchase from the Environmental Protection Agency, Research Triangle Park, NC.

(1) "Screening Procedures for Estimating the Air Quality Impact of Stationary Sources, Revised", October 1992, EPA Publication No. EPA–450/R–92–019, IBR approved for part 266, appendix IX.

(2) [Reserved]

(g) The following materials are available for purchase from the Organisation for Economic Co-operation and Development, Environment Direcorate, 2 rue Andre Pascal, 75775 Paris Cedex 16, France.

(1) OECD Green List of Wastes (revised May 1994), Amber List of Wastes and Red List of Wastes (both revised May 1993) as set forth in Appendix 3, Appendix 4 and Appendix 5, respectively, to the OECD Council Decision C(92)39/FINAL (Concerning the Control of Transfrontier Movements of Wastes Destined for Recovery Operations), IBR approved for 262.89 of this chapter.

(2) [Reserved]

[46 FR 35247, July 7, 1981, as amended at 50 FR 18374, Apr. 30, 1985; 52 FR 8073, Mar. 16, 1987; 52 FR 41295, Oct. 27, 1987; 54 FR 40266, Sept. 29, 1989; 55 FR 8949, Mar. 9, 1990; 55 FR 25493, June 21, 1990; 56 FR 7206, Feb. 21, 1991; 58 FR 38883, July 20, 1993; 58 FR 46049, Aug. 31, 1993; 59 FR 468, Jan. 4, 1994; 59 FR 28484, June 2, 1994; 59 FR 62926, Dec. 6, 1994; 60 FR 17004, Apr. 4, 1995; 62 FR 32462, June 13, 1997; 64 FR 26327, May 11, 1999; 66 FR 34376, June 28, 2001; 70 FR 34560, June 14, 2005; 70 FR 53453, Sept. 8, 2005; 70 FR 59575, Oct. 12, 2005; 72 FR 39352, July 18, 2007]

Subpart C—Rulemaking Petitions

§260.20 General.

(a) Any person may petition the Administrator to modify or revoke any provision in parts 260 through 266, 268 and 273 of this chapter. This section sets forth general requirements which apply to all such petitions. Section 260.21 sets forth additional requirements for petitions to add a testing or analytical method to part 261, 264 or 265 of this chapter. Section 260.22 sets forth additional requirements for petitions to exclude a waste or waste-derived material at a particular facility from §261.3 of this chapter or the lists of hazardous wastes in subpart D of part 261 of this chapter. Section 260.23 sets forth additional requirements for petitions to amend part 273 of this chapter to include additional hazardous wastes or categories of hazardous waste as universal waste.

(b) Each petition must be submitted to the Administrator by certified mail and must include:

(1) The petitioner's name and address;

(2) A statement of the petitioner's interest in the proposed action;

(3) A description of the proposed action, including (where appropriate) suggested regulatory language; and

(4) A statement of the need and justification for the proposed action, including any supporting tests, studies, or other information.

(c) The Administrator will make a tentative decision to grant or deny a petition and will publish notice of such tentative decision, either in the form of an advanced notice of proposed rulemaking, a proposed rule, or a tentative determination to deny the petition, in the *Federal Register* for written public comment.

(d) Upon the written request of any interested person, the Administrator may, at his discretion, hold an informal public hearing to consider oral comments on the tentative decision. A person requesting a hearing must state the issues to be raised and explain why written comments would not suffice to communicate the person's views. The Administrator may in any case decide on his own motion to hold an informal public hearing.

(e) After evaluating all public comments the Administrator will make a final decision by publishing in the *Federal Register* a regulatory amendment or a denial of the petition.

[45 FR 33073, May 19, 1980, as amended at 51 FR 40636, Nov. 7, 1986; 57 FR 38564, Aug. 25, 1992; 60 FR 25540, May 11, 1995]

§260.21 Petitions for equivalent testing or analytical methods.

(a) Any person seeking to add a testing or analytical method to part 261, 264, or 265 of this chapter may petition for a regulatory amendment under this section and §260.20. To be successful, the person must demonstrate to the satisfaction of the Administrator that the proposed method is equal to or superior to the corresponding method prescribed in part 261, 264, or 265 of this chapter, in terms of its sensitivity, accuracy, and precision (*i.e.*, reproducibility).

(b) Each petition must include, in addition to the information required by §260.20(b):

(1) A full description of the proposed method, including all procedural steps and equipment used in the method;

(2) A description of the types of wastes or waste matrices for which the proposed method may be used;

(3) Comparative results obtained from using the proposed method with those obtained from using the relevant or corresponding methods prescribed in part 261, 264, or 265 of this chapter;

(4) An assessment of any factors which may interfere with, or limit the use of, the proposed method; and

(5) A description of the quality control procedures necessary to ensure the sensitivity, accuracy and precision of the proposed method.

(c) After receiving a petition for an equivalent method, the Administrator may request any additional information on the proposed method which he may reasonably require to evaluate the method.

(d) If the Administrator amends the regulations to permit use of a new testing method, the method will be incorporated by reference in §260.11 and added to "Test Methods for Evaluating Solid Waste, Physical/Chemical Methods," EPA Publication SW–846, U.S. Environmental Protection Agency, Office of Resource Conservation and Recovery, Washington, DC 20460.

[45 FR 33073, May 19, 1980, as amended at 49 FR 47391, Dec. 4, 1984; 70 FR 34561, June 14, 2005; 74 FR 30230, June 25, 2009]

§260.22 Petitions to amend part 261 to exclude a waste produced at a particular facility.

(a) Any person seeking to exclude a waste at a particular generating facility from the lists in subpart D of part 261 may petition for a regulatory amendment under this section and §260.20. To be successful:

(1) The petitioner must demonstrate to the satisfaction of the Administrator that the waste produced by a particular generating facility does not meet any of the criteria under which the waste was listed as a hazardous or an acutely hazardous waste; and

(2) Based on a complete application, the Administrator must determine, where he has a reasonable basis to believe that factors (including additional constituents) other than those for which the waste was listed could cause the waste to be a hazardous waste, that such factors do not warrant retaining the waste as a hazardous waste. A waste which is so excluded, however, still may be a hazardous waste by operation of subpart C of part 261.

(b) The procedures in this Section and §260.20 may also be used to petition the Administrator for a regulatory amendment to exclude from §261.3(a)(2)(ii) or (c), a waste which is described in these Sections and is either a waste listed in subpart D, or is derived from a waste listed in subpart D. This exclusion may only be issued for a particular generating, storage, treatment, or disposal facility. The petitioner must make the same demonstration as required by paragraph (a) of this section. Where the waste is a mixture of solid waste and one or more listed hazardous wastes or is derived from one or more hazardous wastes, his demonstration must be made with respect to the waste mixture as a whole; analyses must be conducted for not only those constituents for which the listed waste contained in the mixture was listed as hazardous, but also for factors (including additional constituents) that could cause the waste mixture to be a hazardous waste. A waste which is so excluded may still be a hazardous waste by operation of subpart C of part 261.

(c) If the waste is listed with codes "I", "C", "R", or "E", in subpart D,

(1) The petitioner must show that the waste does not exhibit the relevant characteristic for which the waste was listed as defined in §261.21, §261.22, §261.23, or §261.24 using any applicable methods prescribed therein. The petitioner also must show that the waste does not exhibit any of the other characteristics defined in §261.21, §261.22, §261.23, or §261.24 using any applicable methods prescribed therein;

(2) Based on a complete application, the Administrator must determine, where he has a reasonable basis to believe that factors (including additional constituents) other than those for which the waste was listed could cause the waste to be hazardous waste, that such factors do not warrant retaining the waste as a hazardous waste. A waste which is so excluded, however, still may be a hazardous waste by operation of subpart C of part 261.

(d) If the waste is listed with code "T" in subpart D,

(1) The petitioner must demonstrate that the waste:

(i) Does not contain the constituent or constituents (as defined in Appendix VII of part 261 of this chapter) that caused the Administrator to list the waste; or

(ii) Although containing one or more of the hazardous constituents (as defined in appendix VII of part 261) that caused the Administrator to list the waste, does not meet the criterion of §261.11(a)(3) when considering the factors used by the Administrator in §261.11(a)(3) (i) through (xi) under which the waste was listed as hazardous; and

(2) Based on a complete application, the Administrator must determine, where he has a reasonable basis to believe that factors (including additional constituents) other than those for which the waste was listed could cause the waste to be a hazardous waste, that such factors do not warrant retaining the waste as a hazardous waste; and

(3) The petitioner must demonstrate that the waste does not exhibit any of the characteristics defined in §261.21, §261.22, §261.23, and §261.24 using any applicable methods prescribed therein;

(4) A waste which is so excluded, however, still may be a hazardous waste by operation of subpart C of part 261.

(e) If the waste is listed with the code "H" in subpart D,

(1) The petitioner must demonstrate that the waste does not meet the criterion of §261.11(a)(2); and

(2) Based on a complete application, the Administrator must determine, where he has a reasonable basis to believe that additional factors (including additional constituents) other than those for which the waste was listed could cause the waste to be a hazardous waste, that such factors do not warrant retaining the waste as a hazardous waste; and

(3) The petitioner must demonstrate that the waste does not exhibit any of the characteristics defined in §261.21, §261.22, §261.23, and §261.24 using any applicable methods prescribed therein;

(4) A waste which is so excluded, however, still may be a hazardous waste by operation of subpart C of part 261.

(f) [Reserved for listing radioactive wastes.]

(g) [Reserved for listing infectious wastes.]

(h) Demonstration samples must consist of enough representative samples, but in no case less than four samples, taken over a period of time sufficient to represent the variability or the uniformity of the waste.

(i) Each petition must include, in addition to the information required by §260.20(b):

(1) The name and address of the laboratory facility performing the sampling or tests of the waste;

(2) The names and qualifications of the persons sampling and testing the waste;

(3) The dates of sampling and testing;

(4) The location of the generating facility;

(5) A description of the manufacturing processes or other operations and feed materials producing the waste and an assessment of whether such processes, operations, or feed materials can or might produce a waste that is not covered by the demonstration;

(6) A description of the waste and an estimate of the average and maximum monthly and annual quantities of waste covered by the demonstration;

(7) Pertinent data on and discussion of the factors delineated in the respective criterion for listing a hazardous waste, where the demonstration is based on the factors in §261.11(a)(3);

(8) A description of the methodologies and equipment used to obtain the representative samples;

(9) A description of the sample handling and preparation techniques, including techniques used for extraction, containerization and preservation of the samples;

(10) A description of the tests performed (including results);

(11) The names and model numbers of the instruments used in performing the tests; and

(12) The following statement signed by the generator of the waste or his authorized representative:

I certify under penalty of law that I have personally examined and am familiar with the information submitted in this demonstration and all attached documents, and that, based on my inquiry of those individuals immediately responsible for obtaining the information, I believe that the submitted information is true, accurate, and complete. I am aware that there are significant penalties for submitting false information, including the possibility of fine and imprisonment.

(j) After receiving a petition for an exclusion, the Administrator may request any additional information which he may reasonably require to evaluate the petition.

(k) An exclusion will only apply to the waste generated at the individual facility covered by the demonstration and will not apply to waste from any other facility.

(l) The Administrator may exclude only part of the waste for which the demonstration is submitted where he has reason to believe that variability of the waste justifies a partial exclusion.

[45 FR 33073, May 19, 1980, as amended at 50 FR 28742, July 15, 1985; 54 FR 27116, June 27, 1989; 58 FR 46049, Aug. 31, 1994; 70 FR 34561, June 14, 2005; 71 FR 40258, July 14, 2006]

Editorial Note: For information on the availability of a guidance manual for petitions to delist hazardous wastes, see 50 FR 21607, May 28, 1985.

§260.23 Petitions to amend 40 CFR part 273 to include additional hazardous wastes.

(a) Any person seeking to add a hazardous waste or a category of hazardous waste to the universal waste regulations of part 273 of this chapter may petition for a regulatory amendment under this section, 40 CFR 260.20, and subpart G of 40 CFR part 273.

(b) To be successful, the petitioner must demonstrate to the satisfaction of the Administrator that regulation under the universal waste regulations of 40 CFR part 273: Is appropriate for the waste or category of waste; will improve management practices for the waste or category of waste; and will improve implementation of the hazardous waste program. The petition must include the information required by 40 CFR 260.20(b). The petition should also address as many of the factors listed in 40 CFR 273.81 as are appropriate for the waste or category of waste addressed in the petition.

(c) The Administrator will grant or deny a petition using the factors listed in 40 CFR 273.81. The decision will be based on the weight of evidence showing that regulation under 40 CFR part 273 is appropriate for the waste or category of waste, will improve management practices for the waste or category of waste, and will improve implementation of the hazardous waste program.

(d) The Administrator may request additional information needed to evaluate the merits of the petition.

[60 FR 25540, May 11, 1995]

§260.30 Non-waste determinations and variances from classification as a solid waste.

In accordance with the standards and criteria in §260.31 and §260.34 and the procedures in §260.33, the Administrator may determine on a case-by-case basis that the following recycled materials are not solid wastes:

(a) Materials that are accumulated speculatively without sufficient amounts being recycled (as defined in §261.1(c)(8) of this chapter);

(b) Materials that are reclaimed and then reused within the original production process in which they were generated;

(c) Materials that have been reclaimed but must be reclaimed further before the materials are completely recovered.

(d) Hazardous secondary materials that are reclaimed in a continuous industrial process; and

(e) Hazardous secondary materials that are indistinguishable in all relevant aspects from a product or intermediate.

[50 FR 661, Jan. 4, 1985; 50 FR 14219, Apr. 11, 1985, as amended at 59 FR 48041, Sept. 19, 1994; 73 FR 64758, Oct. 30, 2008]

§260.31 Standards and criteria for variances from classification as a solid waste.

(a) The Administrator may grant requests for a variance from classifying as a solid waste those materials that are accumulated speculatively without sufficient amounts being recycled if the applicant demonstrates that sufficient amounts of the material will be recycled or transferred for recycling in the following year. If a variance is granted, it is valid only for the following year, but can be renewed, on an annual basis, by filing a new application. The Administrator's decision will be based on the following criteria:

(1) The manner in which the material is expected to be recycled, when the material is expected to be recycled, and whether this expected disposition is likely to occur (for example, because of past practice, market factors, the nature of the material, or contractual arrangements for recycling);

(2) The reason that the applicant has accumulated the material for one or more years without recycling 75 percent of the volume accumulated at the beginning of the year;

(3) The quantity of material already accumulated and the quantity expected to be generated and accumulated before the material is recycled;

(4) The extent to which the material is handled to minimize loss;

(5) Other relevant factors.

(b) The Administrator may grant requests for a variance from classifying as a solid waste those materials that are reclaimed and then reused as feedstock within the original production process in which the materials were generated if the reclamation operation is an essential part of the production process. This determination will be based on the following criteria:

(1) How economically viable the production process would be if it were to use virgin materials, rather than reclaimed materials;

(2) The extent to which the material is handled before reclamation to minimize loss;

(3) The time periods between generating the material and its reclamation, and between reclamation and return to the original primary production process;

(4) The location of the reclamation operation in relation to the production process;

(5) Whether the reclaimed material is used for the purpose for which it was originally produced when it is returned to the original process, and whether it is returned to the process in substantially its original form;

(6) Whether the person who generates the material also reclaims it;

(7) Other relevant factors.

(c) The Regional Administrator may grant requests for a variance from classifying as a solid waste those materials that have been reclaimed but must be reclaimed further before recovery is completed if, after initial reclamation, the resulting material is commodity-like (even though it is not yet a commercial product, and has to be reclaimed further). This determination will be based on the following factors:

(1) The degree of processing the material has undergone and the degree of further processing that is required;

(2) The value of the material after it has been reclaimed;

(3) The degree to which the reclaimed material is like an analogous raw material;

(4) The extent to which an end market for the reclaimed material is guaranteed;

(5) The extent to which the reclaimed material is handled to minimize loss;

(6) Other relevant factors.

[50 FR 662, Jan. 4, 1985, as amended at 59 FR 48041, Sept. 19, 1994; 71 FR 16902, Apr. 4, 2006]

§260.32 Variances to be classified as a boiler.

In accordance with the standards and criteria in §260.10 (definition of "boiler"), and the procedures in §260.33, the Administrator may determine on a case-by-case basis that certain enclosed devices using controlled flame combustion are boilers, even though they do not otherwise meet the definition of boiler contained in §260.10, after considering the following criteria:

(a) The extent to which the unit has provisions for recovering and exporting thermal energy in the form of steam, heated fluids, or heated gases; and

(b) The extent to which the combustion chamber and energy recovery equipment are of integral design; and

(c) The efficiency of energy recovery, calculated in terms of the recovered energy compared with the thermal value of the fuel; and

(d) The extent to which exported energy is utilized; and

(e) The extent to which the device is in common and customary use as a "boiler" functioning primarily to produce steam, heated fluids, or heated gases; and

(f) Other factors, as appropriate.

[50 FR 662, Jan. 4, 1985, as amended at 59 FR 48041, Sept. 19, 1994]

§260.33 Procedures for variances from classification as a solid waste, for variances to be classified as a boiler, or for non-waste determinations.

The Administrator will use the following procedures in evaluating applications for variances from classification as a solid waste, applications to classify particular enclosed controlled flame combustion devices as boilers, or applications for non-waste determinations.

(a) The applicant must apply to the Administrator for the variance or non-waste determination. The application must address the relevant criteria contained in §260.31, §260.32, or §260.34, as applicable.

(b) The Administrator will evaluate the application and issue a draft notice tentatively granting or denying the application. Notification of this tentative decision will be provided by newspaper advertisement or radio broadcast in the locality where the recycler is located. The Administrator will accept comment on the tentative decision for 30 days, and may also hold a public hearing upon request or at his discretion. The Administrator will issue a final decision after receipt of comments and after the hearing (if any).

(c) For non-waste determinations, in the event of a change in circumstances that affect how a hazardous secondary material meets the relevant criteria contained in §260.34 upon which a non-waste determination has been based, the applicant must re-apply to the Administrator for a formal determination that the hazardous secondary material continues to meet the relevant criteria and therefore is not a solid waste.

[59 FR 48041, Sept. 19, 1994; 73 FR 64758, Oct. 30, 2008]

§260.34 Standards and criteria for non-waste determinations.

(a) An applicant may apply to the Administrator for a formal determination that a hazardous secondary material is not discarded and therefore not a solid waste. The determinations will be based on the criteria contained in paragraphs (b) or (c) of this section, as applicable. If an application is denied, the hazardous secondary material might still be eligible for a solid waste variance or exclusion (for example, one of the solid waste variances under §260.31). Determinations may also be granted by the State if the State is either authorized for this provision or if the following conditions are met:

(1) The State determines the hazardous secondary material meets the criteria in paragraphs (b) or (c) of this section, as applicable;

(2) The State requests that EPA review its determination; and

(3) EPA approves the State determination.

(b) The Administrator may grant a non-waste determination for hazardous secondary material which is reclaimed in a continuous industrial process if the applicant demonstrates that the hazardous secondary material is a part of the production process and is not discarded. The determination will be based on whether the hazardous secondary material is legitimately recycled as specified in §260.43 and on the following criteria:

(1) The extent that the management of the hazardous secondary material is part of the continuous primary production process and is not waste treatment;

(2) Whether the capacity of the production process would use the hazardous secondary material in a reasonable time frame and ensure that the hazardous secondary material will not be abandoned (for example, based on past practices, market factors, the nature of the hazardous secondary material, or any contractual arrangements);

(3) Whether the hazardous constituents in the hazardous secondary material are reclaimed rather than released to the air, water or land at significantly higher levels from either a statistical or from a health and environmental risk perspective than would otherwise be released by the production process; and

(4) Other relevant factors that demonstrate the hazardous secondary material is not discarded.

(c) The Administrator may grant a non-waste determination for hazardous secondary material which is indistinguishable in all relevant aspects from a product or intermediate if the applicant demonstrates that the hazardous secondary material is comparable to a product or intermediate and is not discarded. The determination will be based on whether the hazardous secondary material is legitimately recycled as specified in §260.43 and on the following criteria:

(1) Whether market participants treat the hazardous secondary material as a product or intermediate rather than a waste (for example, based on the current positive value of the hazardous secondary material, stability of demand, or any contractual arrangements);

(2) Whether the chemical and physical identity of the hazardous secondary material is comparable to commercial products or intermediates;

(3) Whether the capacity of the market would use the hazardous secondary material in a reasonable time frame and ensure that the hazardous secondary material will not be abandoned (for example, based on past practices, market factors, the nature of the hazardous secondary material, or any contractual arrangements);

(4) Whether the hazardous constituents in the hazardous secondary material are reclaimed rather than released to the air, water or land at significantly higher levels from either a statistical or from a health and environmental risk perspective than would otherwise be released by the production process; and

(5) Other relevant factors that demonstrate the hazardous secondary material is not discarded.

[73 FR 64758, Oct. 30, 2008]

§260.40 Additional regulation of certain hazardous waste recycling activities on a case-by-case basis.

(a) The Regional Administrator may decide on a case-by-case basis that persons accumulating or storing the recyclable materials described in §261.6(a)(2)(iii) of this chapter should be regulated under §261.6 (b) and (c) of this chapter. The basis for this decision is that the materials are being accumulated or stored in a manner that does not protect human health and the environment because the materials or their toxic constituents have not been adequately contained, or because the materials being accumulated or stored together are incompatible. In making this decision, the Regional Administrator will consider the following factors:

(1) The types of materials accumulated or stored and the amounts accumulated or stored;

(2) The method of accumulation or storage;

(3) The length of time the materials have been accumulated or stored before being reclaimed;

(4) Whether any contaminants are being released into the environment, or are likely to be so released; and

(5) Other relevant factors.

(b) [Reserved]

The procedures for this decision are set forth in §260.41 of this chapter.

[50 FR 662, Jan. 4, 1985, as amended at 71 FR 40258, July 14, 2006]

§260.41 Procedures for case-by-case regulation of hazardous waste recycling activities.

The Regional Administrator will use the following procedures when determining whether to regulate hazardous waste recycling activities described in §261.6(a)(2)(iii) under the provisions of §261.6 (b) and (c), rather than under the provisions of subpart F of part 266 of this chapter.

(a) If a generator is accumulating the waste, the Regional Administrator will issue a notice setting forth the factual basis for the decision and stating that the person must comply with the applicable requirements of subparts A, C, D, and E of part 262 of this chapter. The notice will become final within 30 days, unless the person served requests a public hearing to challenge the decision. Upon receiving such a request, the Regional Administrator will hold a public hearing. The Regional Administrator will provide notice of the hearing to the public and allow public participation at the hearing. The Regional Administrator will issue a final order after the hearing stating whether or not compliance with part 262 is required. The order becomes effective 30 days after service of the decision unless the Regional Administrator specifies a later date or unless review by the Administrator is requested. The order may be appealed to the Administrator by any person who participated in the public hearing. The Administrator may choose to grant or to deny the appeal. Final Agency action occurs when a final order is issued and Agency review procedures are exhausted.

(b) If the person is accumulating the recyclable material as a storage facility, the notice will state that the person must obtain a permit in accordance with all applicable provisions of parts 270 and 124 of this chapter. The owner or operator of the facility must apply for a permit within no less than 60 days and no more than six months of notice, as specified in the notice. If the owner or operator of the facility wishes to challenge the Regional Administrator's decision, he may do so in his permit application, in a public hearing held on the draft permit, or in comments filed on the draft permit or on the notice of intent to deny the permit. The fact sheet accompanying the permit will specify the reasons for the Agency's determination. The question of whether the Regional Administrator's decision was proper will remain open for consideration during the public comment period discussed under §124.11 of this chapter and in any subsequent hearing.

[50 FR 663, Jan. 4, 1985, as amended at 71 FR 40258, July 14, 2006]

§260.42 Notification requirement for hazardous secondary materials.

📖 11.2.3.1.4, 11.2.3.2.2

(a) Hazardous secondary material generators, tolling contractors, toll manufacturers, reclaimers, and intermediate facilities managing hazardous secondary materials which are excluded from regulation under §261.2(a)(2)(ii), §261.4(a)(23), (24), or (25) must send a notification prior to operating under the exclusion(s) and by March 1 of each even numbered year thereafter to the Regional Administrator using EPA Form 8700-12 that includes the following information:

(1) The name, address, and EPA ID number (if applicable) of the facility;

(2) The name and telephone number of a contact person;

(3) The NAICS code of the facility;

(4) The exclusion under which the hazardous secondary materials will be managed (e.g., §261.2(a)(2)(ii), §261.4(a)(23), (24), and/or (25));

(5) For reclaimers and intermediate facilities managing hazardous secondary materials in accordance with §261.4(a)(24) or (25), whether the reclaimer or intermediate facility has financial assurance (not applicable for persons managing hazardous secondary materials generated and reclaimed under the control of the generator);

(6) When the facility expects to begin managing the hazardous secondary materials in accordance with the exclusion;

(7) A list of hazardous secondary materials that will be managed according to the exclusion (reported as the EPA hazardous waste numbers that would apply if the hazardous secondary materials were managed as hazardous wastes);

(8) For each hazardous secondary material, whether the hazardous secondary material, or any portion thereof, will be managed in a land-based unit;

(9) The quantity of each hazardous secondary material to be managed annually; and

(10) The certification (included in EPA Form 8700-12) signed and dated by an authorized representative of the facility.

(b) If a hazardous secondary material generator, tolling contractor, toll manufacturer, reclaimer or intermediate facility has submitted a notification, but then subsequently stops managing hazardous secondary materials in accordance with the exclusion(s), the facility must notify the Regional Administrator within thirty (30) days using EPA Form 8700-12. For purposes of this section, a facility has stopped managing hazardous secondary materials if the facility no longer generates, manages and/or reclaims hazardous secondary materials under the exclusion(s) and does not expect to manage any amount of hazardous secondary materials for at least one year.

[73 FR 64759, Oct. 30, 2008]

§260.43 Legitimate recycling of hazardous secondary materials regulated under §260.34, §261.2(a)(2)(ii), and §261.4(a)(23), (24), or (25).

11.5

(a) Persons regulated under §260.34 or claiming to be excluded from hazardous waste regulation under §261.2(a)(2)(ii), §261.4(a)(23), (24), or (25) because they are engaged in reclamation must be able to demonstrate that the recycling is legitimate. Hazardous secondary material that is not legitimately recycled is discarded material and is a solid waste. In determining if their recycling is legitimate, persons must address the requirements of §260.43(b) and must consider the requirements of §260.43(c) below.

(b) Legitimate recycling must involve a hazardous secondary material that provides a useful contribution to the recycling process or to a product or intermediate of the recycling process, and the recycling process must produce a valuable product or intermediate.

(1) The hazardous secondary material provides a useful contribution if it

(i) Contributes valuable ingredients to a product or intermediate; or

(ii) Replaces a catalyst or carrier in the recycling process; or

(iii) Is the source of a valuable constituent recovered in the recycling process; or

(iv) Is recovered or regenerated by the recycling process; or

(v) Is used as an effective substitute for a commercial product.

(2) The product or intermediate is valuable if it is

(i) Sold to a third party; or

(ii) Used by the recycler or the generator as an effective substitute for a commercial product or as an ingredient or intermediate in an industrial process.

(c) The following factors must be considered in making a determination as to the overall legitimacy of a specific recycling activity.

(1) The generator and the recycler should manage the hazardous secondary material as a valuable commodity. Where there is an analogous raw material, the hazardous secondary material should be managed, at a minimum, in a manner consistent with the management of the raw material. Where there is no analogous raw material, the hazardous secondary material should be contained. Hazardous secondary materials that are released to the environment and are not recovered immediately are discarded.

(2) The product of the recycling process does not

(i) Contain significant concentrations of any hazardous constituents found in Appendix VIII of part 261 that are not found in analogous products; or

(ii) Contain concentrations of any hazardous constituents found in Appendix VIII of part 261 at levels that are significantly elevated from those found in analogous products; or

(iii) Exhibit a hazardous characteristic (as defined in part 261 subpart C) that analogous products do not exhibit.

(3) In making a determination that a hazardous secondary material is legitimately recycled, persons must evaluate all factors and consider legitimacy as a whole. If, after careful evaluation of these other considerations, one or both of the factors are not met, then this fact may be an indication that the material is not legitimately recycled. However, the factors in this paragraph do not have to be met for the recycling to be considered legitimate. In evaluating the extent to which these factors are met and in determining whether a process that does not meet one or both of these factors

is still legitimate, persons can consider the protectiveness of the storage methods, exposure from toxics in the product, the bioavailability of the toxics in the product, and other relevant considerations.

[73 FR 64759, Oct. 30, 2008]

Appendix

Appendix I to Part 260—Overview of Subtitle C Regulations

The Agency believes that there are many people who suspect, but are not sure, that their activities are subject to control under the RCRA Subtitle C rules. This appendix is written for these people. It is designed to help those who are unfamiliar with the hazardous waste control program to determine with which, if any, of the regulations they should comply.

Definition of Solid Waste

The first question which such a person should ask himself is: "Is the material I handle a solid waste?" If the answer to this question is "No", then the material is not subject to control under RCRA and, therefore, the person need not worry about whether he should comply with the Subtitle C rules.

Section 261.2 of this chapter provides a definition of "solid waste" which expands the statutory definition of that term given in section 1004(27) of RCRA. This definition is diagrammed in Figure 1 below.

Figure 1 explains that all materials are either: (1) Garbage refuse, or sludge; (2) solid, liquid, semi-solid or contained gaseous material; or (3) something else. No materials in the third category are solid waste. All materials in the first category are solid waste. Materials in the second category are solid waste unless they are one of the five exclusions specified in §261.4(a).

Definition of Hazardous Waste

If a person has determined that his material is a "solid waste", the next question he should ask is: "Is the solid waste I handle a hazardous waste?"

Hazardous waste is defined in §261.3 of this chapter. Section 261.3 provides that, in general, a solid waste is a hazardous waste if: (1) It is, or contains, a hazardous waste listed in subpart D of part 261 of this chapter, or (2) the waste exhibits any of the characteristics defined in subpart C of part 261. However, parts 260 and 261 also contain provisions which exclude (§§261.4(b), 260.20, and 260.22) certain solid wastes from the definition of "hazardous waste", even though they are listed in subpart D or exhibit one or more of the characteristics defined in subpart C. Figure 2 depicts the interplay of these special provisions with the definition of "hazardous waste". It presents a series of questions which a person should ask himself concerning his waste. After doing so, the person should be able to determine if the solid waste he handles is a hazardous waste.

Hazardous Waste Regulations

If this is the case, the person should look at Figure 3. Figure 3 depicts the special provisions specified in the final part 261 rules for hazardous waste which:

1. Is generated by a small quantity generator
2. Is or is intended to be legitimately and beneficially used, reused, recycled, or reclaimed
3. Is a sludge; is listed in part 261, subpart D; or is a mixture containing a waste listed in part 261, subpart D.

For each of these Groups, Figure 3 indicates with which subtitle C regulations (if any) the person handling these wastes must comply. Figure 3 also explains that, if a person handles hazardous waste which is not included in any one of the above three categories, his waste is subject to the subtitle C regulations diagrammed in Figure 4.

Figure 4 is a flowchart which identifies the three categories of activities regulated under the subtitle C rules, and the corresponding set of rules with which people in each of these categories must comply. It points out that all people who handle hazardous waste are either: (1) Generators of hazardous waste, (2) transporters of hazardous waste, (3) owners or operators of hazardous waste treatment, storage, or disposal facilities, or (4) a combination of the above. Figure 4 indicates that all of these people must notify EPA of their hazardous waste activities in accordance with the Section 3010 Notification Procedures (see 45 FR 12746 et seq.), and obtain an EPA identification number.

It should be noted that people handling wastes listed in subpart D of part 261 who have filed, or who intend to file an application to exempt their waste from regulation under the subtitle C rules, must also comply with the notification requirements of section 3010.

If a person generates hazardous waste, Figure 4 indicates that he must comply with the part 262 rules. If he transports it, he must comply with the part 263 rules. The standards in both these parts are designed to ensure, among other things, proper recordkeeping and reporting, the use of a manifest system to track shipments of hazardous waste, the use of proper labels and containers, and the delivery of the waste to a permitted treatment, storage, or disposal facility.

If a person owns or operates a facility which treats, stores, or disposes of hazardous waste, the standards with which he must comply depend on a number of factors. First of all, if the owner or operator of a storage facility is also the person who generates the waste, and the waste is stored at the facility for less than 90 days for subsequent shipment off-site, then the person must comply with §262.34 of the part 262 rules.

All other owners or operators of treatment, storage, or disposal facilities must comply with either the part 264 or the part 265 rules. To determine with which of these sets of rules an owner or operator must comply, he must find out whether his facility qualifies for interim status. To qualify, the owner or operator must: (1) Have been treating, storing, or disposing of the hazardous waste, or commenced facility construction on or before October 21, 1976, (2) comply with the section 3010 notification requirements, and (3) apply for a permit under part 270 of this chapter.

If the owner or operator has done all of the above, he qualifies for interim status, and he must comply with the part 265 rules. These rules contain administrative requirements, monitoring and closure standards, and an abbreviated set of technical and closure and post-closure cost estimate requirements. The owner or operator must comply with these standards until final administrative disposition of his permit application is made. If a permit is issued to the owner or operator, he must then comply with the permit which will be based on the part 264 rules.

If the owner or operator has not carried out the above three requirements, he does not qualify for interim status. Until he is issued a permit for his facility, the owner or operator must stop waste management operations (if any) at the facility, and send his hazardous waste (if any) to a facility whose owner or operator has interim status or to a storage facility following the part 262 rules.

In order to apply for a permit, the owner or operator must comply with the procedures specified in part 270 of this chapter.

It should be noted that the Agency will be periodically revising the rules depicted in Figures 3 and 4. All persons are encouraged to write to EPA to verify that the regulations which they are reading are up-to-date. To obtain this verification, contact: Solid Waste Information, U.S. Environmental Protection Agency, 26 West St. Clair Street, Cincinnati, Ohio 45268 (513) 684-5362.

Figure 1
Definition of a Solid Waste

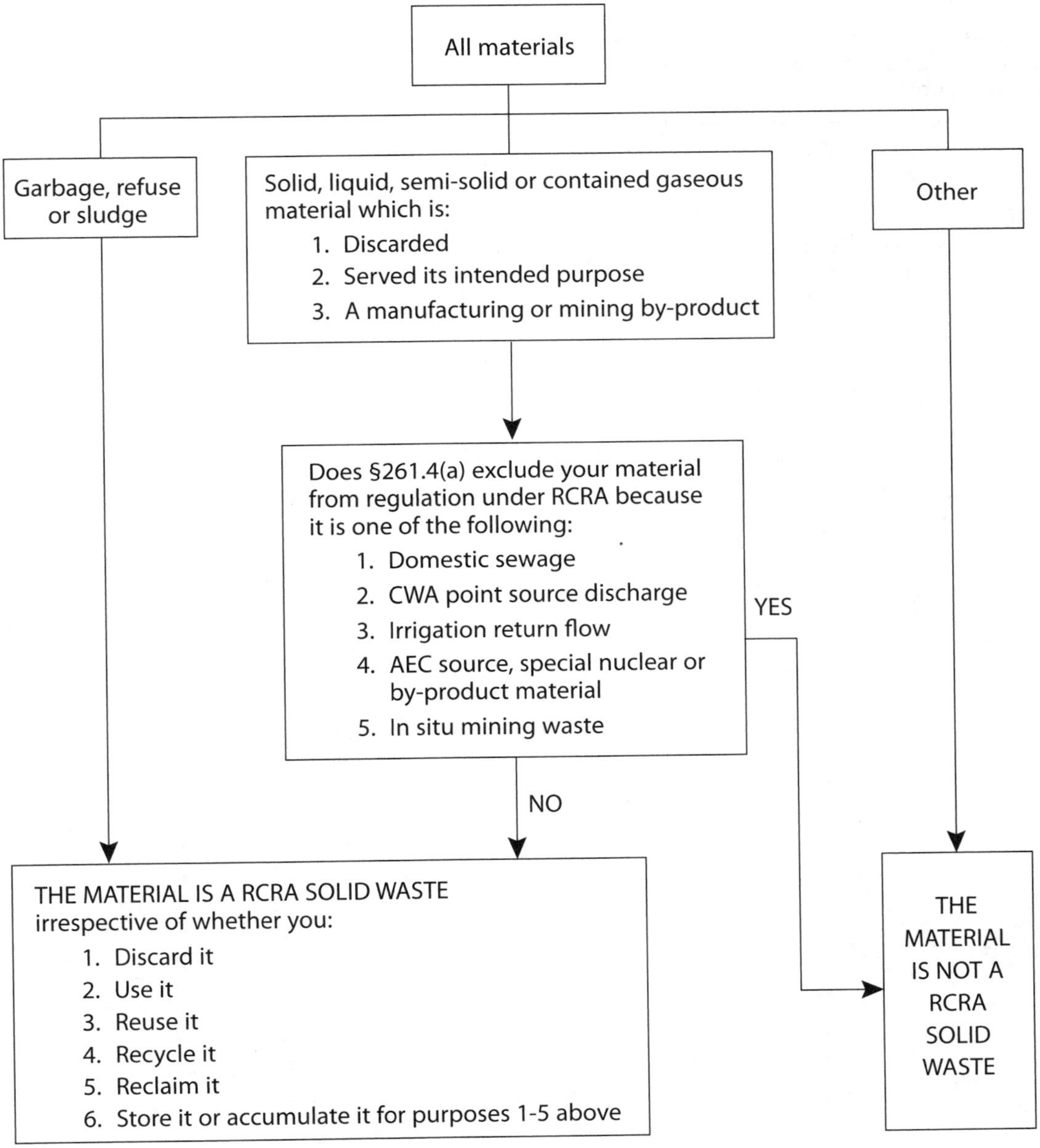

Publisher's Note: This figure hasn't been updated to reflect changes to Part 261 of the federal RCRA regulations. Therefore, it should be used with caution.

Figure 2
Definition of a Hazardous Waste

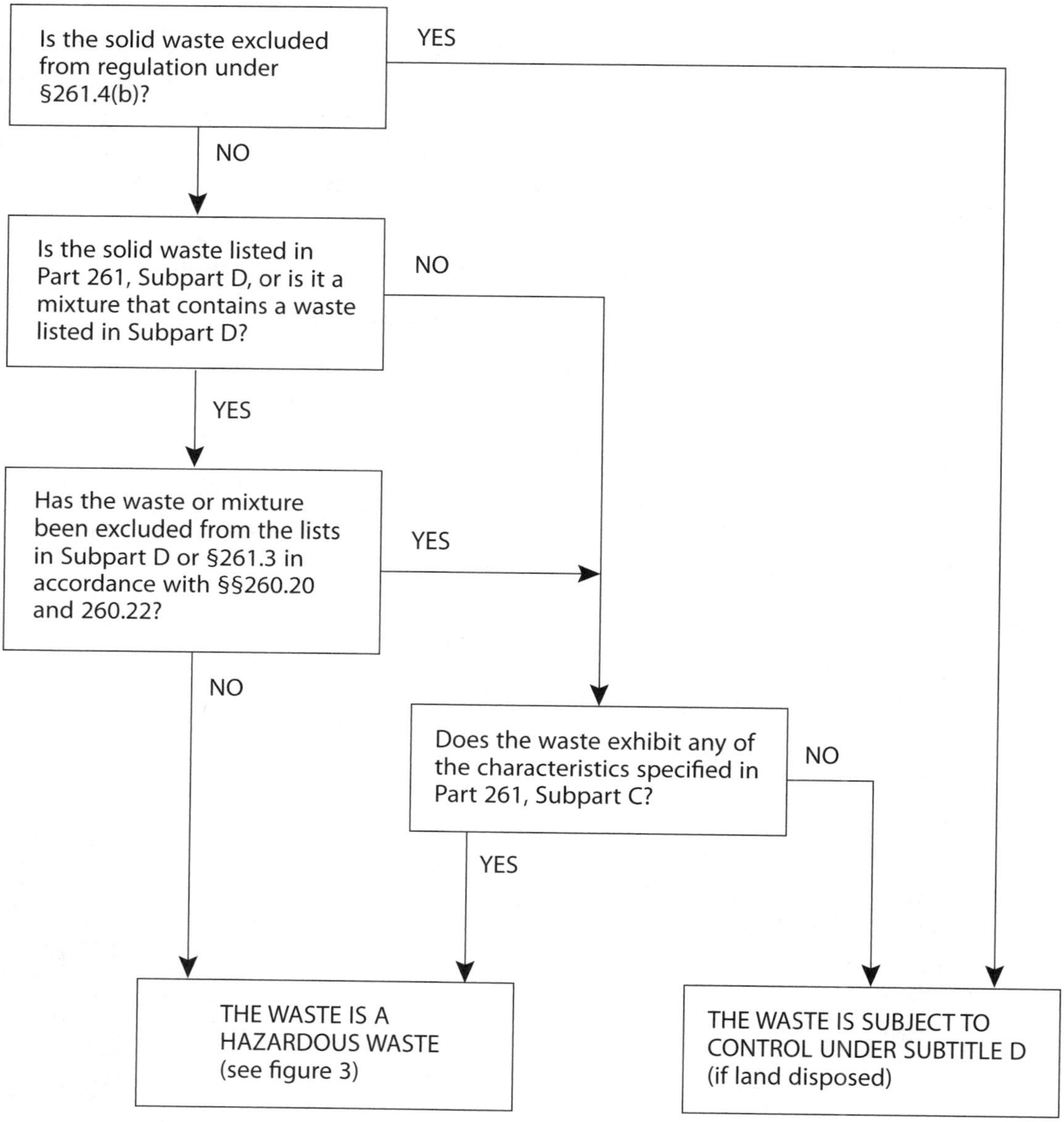

Figure 3
Special Provisions for Certain Hazardous Waste

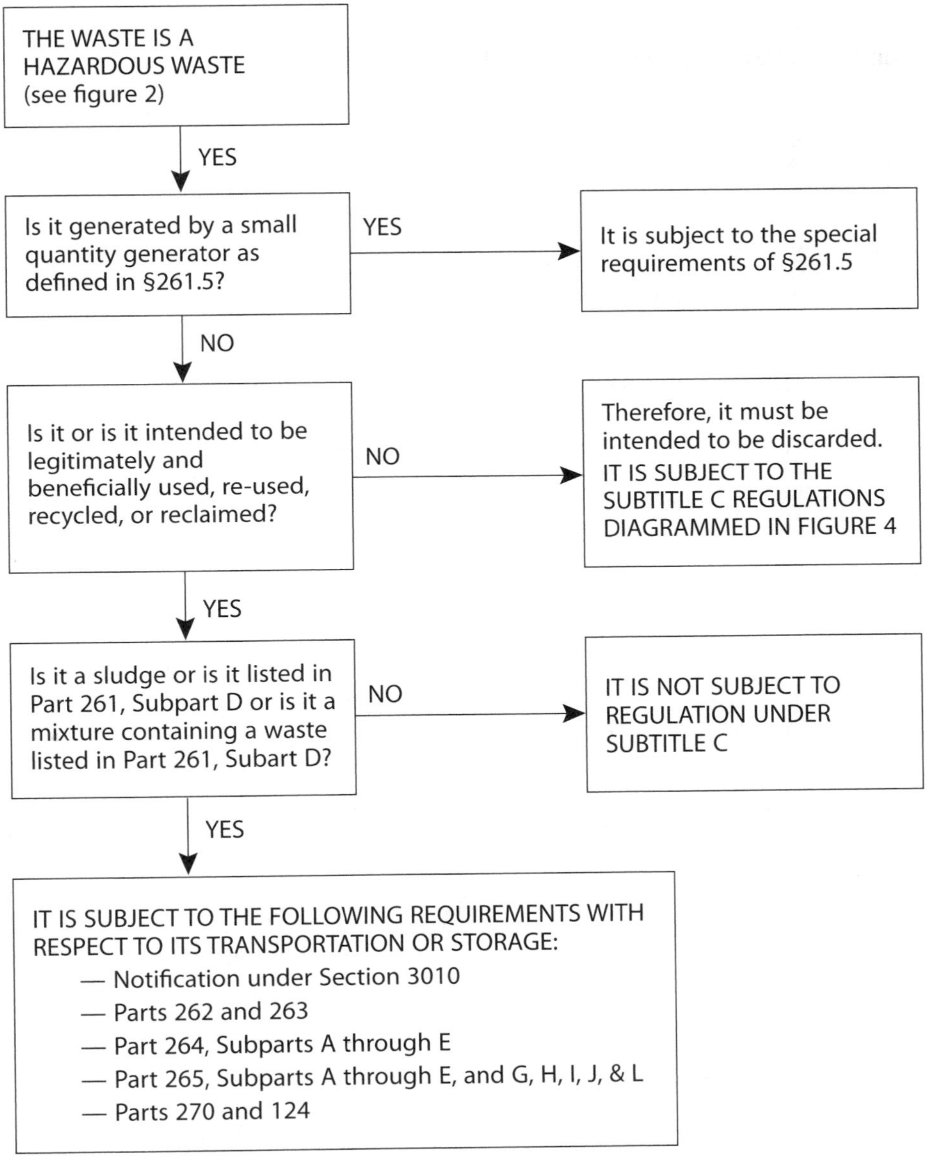

Publisher's Note: This figure hasn't been updated to reflect changes to Part 261 of the federal RCRA regulations. Therefore, it should be used with caution.

Figure 4
Regulations for Hazardous Waste Not Covered in Diagram 3

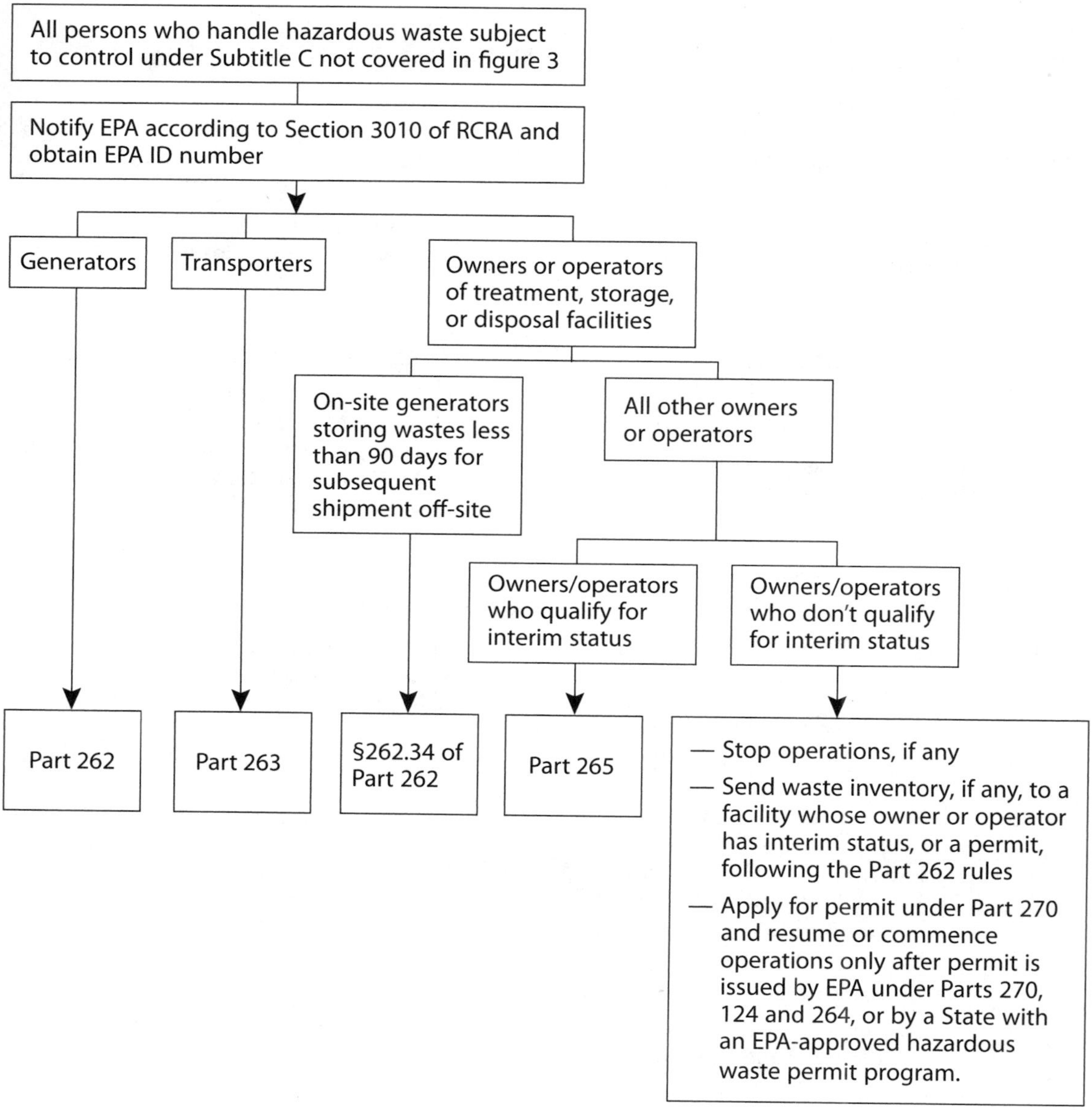

[45 FR 33073, May 19, 1980, as amended at 48 FR 14293, Apr. 1, 1983]

PART 261—IDENTIFICATION AND LISTING OF HAZARDOUS WASTE

Authority: 42 U.S.C. 6905, 6912(a), 6921, 6922, 6924(y), and 6938.

Source: 45 FR 33119, May 19, 1980, unless otherwise noted.

Subpart A—General

§261.1 Purpose and scope.

(a) This part identifies those solid wastes which are subject to regulation as hazardous wastes under parts 262 through 265, 268, and parts 270, 271, and 124 of this chapter and which are subject to the notification requirements of section 3010 of RCRA. In this part:

(1) Subpart A defines the terms "solid waste" and "hazardous waste", identifies those wastes which are excluded from regulation under parts 262 through 266, 268 and 270 and establishes special management requirements for hazardous waste produced by conditionally exempt small quantity generators and hazardous waste which is recycled.

(2) Subpart B sets forth the criteria used by EPA to identify characteristics of hazardous waste and to list particular hazardous wastes.

(3) Subpart C identifies characteristics of hazardous waste.

(4) Subpart D lists particular hazardous wastes.

(b)(1) The definition of solid waste contained in this part applies only to wastes that also are hazardous for purposes of the regulations implementing subtitle C of RCRA. For example, it does not apply to materials (such as non-hazardous scrap, paper, textiles, or rubber) that are not otherwise hazardous wastes and that are recycled.

(2) This part identifies only some of the materials which are solid wastes and hazardous wastes under sections 3007, 3013, and 7003 of RCRA. A material which is not defined as a solid waste in this part, or is not a hazardous waste identified or listed in this part, is still a solid waste and a hazardous waste for purposes of these sections if:

(i) In the case of sections 3007 and 3013, EPA has reason to believe that the material may be a solid waste within the meaning of section 1004(27) of RCRA and a hazardous waste within the meaning of section 1004(5) of RCRA; or

(ii) In the case of section 7003, the statutory elements are established.

(c) For the purposes of §§261.2 and 261.6:

(1) A "spent material" is any material that has been used and as a result of contamination can no longer serve the purpose for which it was produced without processing; 📖 1.2.5.1

(2) "Sludge" has the same meaning used in §260.10 of this chapter; 📖 1.2.5.2

(3) A "by-product" is a material that is not one of the primary products of a production process and is not solely or separately produced by the production process. Examples are process residues such as slags or distillation column bottoms. The term does not include a co-product that is produced for the general public's use and is ordinarily used in the form it is produced by the process. 📖 1.2.5.3

(4) A material is "reclaimed" if it is processed to recover a usable product, or if it is regenerated. Examples are recovery of lead values from spent batteries and regeneration of spent solvents. In addition, for purposes of §§261.2(a)(2)(ii), 261.4(a)(23), and 261.4(a)(24) smelting, melting and refining furnaces are considered to be solely engaged in metals reclamation if the metal recovery from the hazardous secondary materials meets the same requirements as those specified for metals recovery from hazardous waste found in §266.100(d)(1)–(3) of this chapter, and if the residuals meet the requirements specified in §266.112 of this chapter. 📖 1.2.6.3, 11.2.3, 11.3.1.2

(5) A material is "used or reused" if it is either: 📖 11.3

(i) Employed as an ingredient (including use as an intermediate) in an industrial process to make a product (for example, distillation bottoms from one process used as feedstock in another process). However, a material will not satisfy this condition if distinct components of the material are recovered as separate end products (as when metals are recovered from metal-containing secondary materials); or

(ii) Employed in a particular function or application as an effective substitute for a commercial product (for example, spent pickle liquor used as phosphorous precipitant and sludge conditioner in wastewater treatment).

(6) "Scrap metal" is bits and pieces of metal parts (*e.g.*, bars, turnings, rods, sheets, wire) or metal pieces that may be combined together with bolts or soldering (*e.g.*, radiators, scrap automobiles, railroad box cars), which when worn or superfluous can be recycled. 📖 1.2.5.5, 4.21

(7) A material is "recycled" if it is used, reused, or reclaimed. 📖 11.1

(8) A material is "accumulated speculatively" if it is accumulated before being recycled. A material is not accumulated speculatively, however, if the person accumulating it can show that the material is potentially recyclable and has a feasible means of being recycled; and that—during the calendar year (commencing on January 1)—the amount of material that is recycled, or transferred to a different site for recycling, equals at least 75 percent by weight or volume of the amount of that material accumulated at the beginning of the period. In calculating the percentage of turnover, the 75 percent requirement is to be applied to each material of the same type (*e.g.*, slags from a single smelting process) that is recycled in the same way (*i.e.*, from which the same material is recovered or that is used in the same way). Materials accumulating in units that would be exempt from regulation under §261.4(c) are not to be included in making the calculation. (Materials that are already defined as solid wastes also are not to be included in making the calculation.) Materials are no longer in this category once they are removed from accumulation for recycling, however. 📖 1.2.6.4

(9) "Excluded scrap metal" is processed scrap metal, unprocessed home scrap metal, and unprocessed prompt scrap metal. 📖 1.2.5.5.1, 4.21.2

(10) "Processed scrap metal" is scrap metal which has been manually or physically altered to either separate it into distinct materials to enhance economic value or to improve the handling of materials. Processed scrap metal includes, but is not limited to scrap metal which has been baled, shredded, sheared, chopped, crushed, flattened, cut, melted, or separated by metal type (*i.e.*, sorted), and, fines, drosses and related materials which have been agglomerated. (*Note:* shredded circuit boards

being sent for recycling are not considered processed scrap metal. They are covered under the exclusion from the definition of solid waste for shredded circuit boards being recycled (§261.4(a)(13)).

Publisher's Note: The above reference to §261.4(a)(13) is incorrect and should refer to §261.4(a)(14).

(11) "Home scrap metal" is scrap metal as generated by steel mills, foundries, and refineries such as turnings, cuttings, punchings, and borings.

(12) "Prompt scrap metal" is scrap metal as generated by the metal working/fabrication industries and includes such scrap metal as turnings, cuttings, punchings, and borings. Prompt scrap is also known as industrial or new scrap metal.

[45 FR 33119, May 19, 1980, as amended at 48 FR 14293, Apr. 1, 1983; 50 FR 663, Jan. 4, 1985; 51 FR 10174, Mar. 24, 1986; 51 FR 40636, Nov. 7, 1986; 62 FR 26018, May 12, 1997; 73 FR 64760, Oct. 30, 2008]

§261.2 Definition of solid waste.

(a)(1) A *solid waste* is any discarded material that is not excluded under §261.4(a) or that is not excluded by a variance granted under §§260.30 and 260.31 or that is not excluded by a non-waste determination under §§260.30 and 260.34. 📖 1.0

(2)(i) A *discarded material* is any material which is: 📖 1.1.1

(A) Abandoned, as explained in paragraph (b) of this section; or

(B) Recycled, as explained in paragraph (c) of this section; or

(C) Considered inherently waste-like, as explained in paragraph (d) of this section; or

(D) A military munition identified as a solid waste in §266.202. 📖 14.6

(ii) A hazardous secondary material is not discarded if it is generated and reclaimed under the control of the generator as defined in §260.10, it is not speculatively accumulated as defined in §261.1(c)(8), it is handled only in non-land-based units and is contained in such units, it is generated and reclaimed within the United States and its territories, it is not otherwise subject to material-specific management conditions under §261.4(a) when reclaimed, it is not a spent lead acid battery (see §266.80 and §273.2), it does not meet the listing description for K171 or K172 in §261.32, and the reclamation of the material is legitimate, as specified under §260.43. (See also the notification requirements of §260.42). (For hazardous secondary materials managed in land-based units, see §261.4(a)(23)). 📖 1.2.6.3.1, 11.2.3.1, 11.4.2

(iii) Considered *inherently waste-like*, as explained in paragraph (d) of this section; or

(iv) A *military munition* identified as a solid waste in 40 CFR 266.202.

(b) Materials are solid waste if they are *abandoned* by being: 📖 1.1.4.1, 14.4.1

(1) Disposed of; or

(2) Burned or incinerated; or

(3) Accumulated, stored, or treated (but not recycled) before or in lieu of being abandoned by being disposed of, burned, or incinerated. 📖 1.1.4.1.3

(c) Materials are solid wastes if they are *recycled*—or accumulated, stored, or treated before recycling—as specified in paragraphs (c)(1) through (4) of this section. 📖 1.2, 11.2

(1) *Used in a manner constituting disposal.* (i) Materials noted with a "*" in Column 1 of Table 1 are solid wastes when they are: 📖 1.2.6.1

(A) Applied to or placed on the land in a manner that constitutes disposal; or

(B) Used to produce products that are applied to or placed on the land or are otherwise contained in products that are applied to or placed on the land (in which cases the product itself remains a solid waste).

(ii) However, commercial chemical products listed in §261.33 are not solid wastes if they are applied to the land and that is their ordinary manner of use. 📖 1.2.5.4.2, 1.2.6.1.3, 14.3.1.1

(2) *Burning for energy recovery.* (i) Materials noted with a "*" in column 2 of Table 1 are solid wastes when they are: 📖 1.2.6.2

(A) Burned to recover energy;

(B) Used to produce a fuel or are otherwise contained in fuels (in which cases the fuel itself remains a solid waste).

(ii) However, commercial chemical products listed in §261.33 are not solid wastes if they are themselves fuels. 📖 1.2.5.4.3, 1.2.6.2, 2.5.3.1

(3) *Reclaimed.* Materials noted with a "–" in column 3 of Table 1 are not solid wastes when reclaimed. Materials noted with an "*" in column 3 of Table 1 are solid wastes when reclaimed unless they meet the requirements of §§261.2(a)(2)(ii), or 261.4(a)(17), or 261.4(a)(23), or 261.4(a)(24) or 261.4(a)(25). 📖 1.2.6.3, 11.2.3, 11.3.1.2.2, 14.4.7

Table 1

📖 1.2.4

		Use constituting disposal (§261.2(c)(1)) (1)	Energy recovery/fuel (§261.2(c)(2)) (2)	Reclamation (§261.2(c)(3)), except as provided in §§261.2(a)(2)(ii), 261.4(a)(17), 261.4(a)(23), 261.4(a)(24), or 261.4(a)(25) (3)	Speculative accumulation (§261.2(c)(4)) (4)
Spent Materials	📖 1.2.5.1	(*)	(*)	(*)	(*)
Sludges (listed in 40 CFR Part 261.31 or 261.32)	📖 1.2.5.2	(*)	(*)	(*)	(*)
Sludges exhibiting a characteristic of hazardous waste	📖 1.2.5.2	(*)	(*)	—	(*)
By-products (listed in 40 CFR 261.31 or 261.32)	📖 1.2.5.3	(*)	(*)	(*)	(*)
By-products exhibiting a characteristic of hazardous waste	📖 1.2.5.3	(*)	(*)	—	(*)
Commercial chemical products listed in 40 CFR 261.33	📖 1.2.5.4, 3.5.3	(*)	(*)	—	—
Scrap metal other than excluded scrap metal (see 261.1(c)(9))	📖 1.2.5.5	(*)	(*)	(*)	(*)

Note: The terms "spent materials," "sludges," "by-products," and "scrap metal" and "processed scrap metal" are defined in §261.1.

(4) *Accumulated speculatively.* Materials noted with a "*" in column 4 of Table 1 are solid wastes when accumulated speculatively. 📖 1.2.6.4

(d) *Inherently waste-like materials.* The following materials are solid wastes when they are recycled in any manner: 📖 1.1.4.2

(1) Hazardous Waste Nos. F020, F021 (unless used as an ingredient to make a product at the site of generation), F022, F023, F026, and F028.

(2) Secondary materials fed to a halogen acid furnace that exhibit a characteristic of a hazardous waste or are listed as a hazardous waste as defined in subparts C or D of this part, except for brominated material that meets the following criteria:

(i) The material must contain a bromine concentration of at least 45%; and

(ii) The material must contain less than a total of 1% of toxic organic compounds listed in appendix VIII; and

(iii) The material is processed continually on-site in the halogen acid furnace via direct conveyance (hard piping).

(3) The Administrator will use the following criteria to add wastes to that list:

(i)(A) The materials are ordinarily disposed of, burned, or incinerated; or

(B) The materials contain toxic constituents listed in appendix VIII of part 261 and these constituents are not ordinarily found in raw materials or products for which the materials substitute (or are found in raw materials or products in smaller concentrations) and are not used or reused during the recycling process; and

(ii) The material may pose a substantial hazard to human health and the environment when recycled.

(e) *Materials that are not solid waste when recycled.* (1) Materials are not solid wastes when they can be shown to be recycled by being: 📖 1.2, 11.3

(i) Used or reused as ingredients in an industrial process to make a product, provided the materials are not being reclaimed; or 📖 11.3.1

(ii) Used or reused as effective substitutes for commercial products; or 📖 11.3.2

(iii) Returned to the original process from which they are generated, without first being reclaimed or land disposed. The material must be returned as a substitute for feedstock materials. In cases where the original process to which the material is returned is a secondary process, the materials must be managed such that there is no placement on the land. In cases where the materials are generated and reclaimed within the primary mineral processing industry, the conditions of the exclusion found at §261.4(a)(17) apply rather than this paragraph. 📖 11.3.3

(2) The following materials are solid wastes, even if the recycling involves use, reuse, or return to the original process (described in paragraphs (e)(1)(i) through (iii) of this section): 📖 11.4.1

(i) Materials used in a manner constituting disposal, or used to produce products that are applied to the land; or 📖 11.4.1.1

(ii) Materials burned for energy recovery, used to produce a fuel, or contained in fuels; or 📖 11.4.1.2

(iii) Materials accumulated speculatively; or

(iv) Materials listed in paragraphs (d)(1) and (d)(2) of this section.

(f) *Documentation of claims that materials are not solid wastes or are conditionally exempt from regulation.* Respondents in actions to enforce regulations implementing subtitle C of RCRA who raise a claim that a certain material is not a solid waste, or is conditionally exempt from regulation, must demonstrate that there is a known market or disposition for the material, and that they meet the terms of the exclusion or exemption. In doing so, they must provide appropriate documentation (such as contracts showing that a second person uses the material as an ingredient in a production process) to demonstrate that the material is not a waste, or is exempt from regulation. In addition, owners or operators of facilities claiming that they actually are recycling materials must show that they have the necessary equipment to do so. 📖 11.6

[50 FR 664, Jan. 4, 1985, as amended at 50 FR 33542, Aug. 20, 1985; 56 FR 7206, Feb. 21, 1991; 56 FR 32688, July 17, 1991; 56 FR 42512, Aug. 27, 1991; 57 FR 38564, Aug. 25, 1992; 59 FR 48042, Sept. 19, 1994; 62 FR 6651, Feb. 12, 1997; 62 FR 26019, May 12, 1997; 63 FR 28636, May 26, 1998; 64 FR 24513, May 11, 1999; 67 FR 11253, Mar. 13, 2002; 71 FR 40258, July 14, 2006; 73 FR 64760, Oct. 30, 2008]

§261.3 Definition of hazardous waste.

(a) A solid waste, as defined in §261.2, is a hazardous waste if: 📖 1.1.3

(1) It is not excluded from regulation as a hazardous waste under §261.4(b); and

(2) It meets any of the following criteria:

(i) It exhibits any of the characteristics of hazardous waste identified in subpart C of this part. However, any mixture of a waste from the extraction, beneficiation, and processing of ores and minerals excluded under §261.4(b)(7) and any other solid waste exhibiting a characteristic of hazardous waste under subpart C is a hazardous waste only if it exhibits a characteristic that would not have been exhibited by the excluded waste alone if such mixture had not occurred, or if it continues to exhibit any of the characteristics exhibited by the non-excluded wastes prior to mixture. Further, for the purposes of applying the Toxicity Characteristic to such mixtures, the mixture is also a hazardous waste if it exceeds the maximum concentration for any contaminant listed in Table 1 to §261.24 that would not have been exceeded by the excluded waste alone if the mixture had not occurred or if it continues to exceed the maximum concentration for any contaminant exceeded by the nonexempt waste prior to mixture. 📖 2.0, 5.1.2, 7.1.2.2

(ii) It is listed in subpart D of this part and has not been excluded from the lists in subpart D of this part under §§260.20 and 260.22 of this chapter. 📖 3.0

(iii) [Reserved]

(iv) It is a mixture of solid waste and one or more hazardous wastes listed in subpart D of this part and has not been excluded from paragraph (a)(2) of this section under §§260.20 and 260.22, paragraph (g) of this section, or paragraph (h) of this section; however, the following mixtures of solid wastes and hazardous wastes listed in subpart D of this part are not hazardous wastes (except by application of paragraph (a)(2)(i) or (ii) of this section) if the generator can demonstrate that the mixture consists of wastewater the discharge of which is subject to regulation under either section 402 or section 307(b) of the Clean Water Act (including wastewater at facilities which have eliminated the discharge of wastewater) and; 📖 4.16, 5.1.2, 7.1.2.2

(A) One or more of the following spent solvents listed in §261.31—benzene, carbon tetrachloride, tetrachloroethylene, trichloroethylene or the scrubber waters derived-from the combustion of these spent solvents—*Provided*, That the maximum total weekly usage of these solvents (other than the amounts that can be demonstrated not to be discharged to wastewater) divided by the average weekly flow of wastewater into the headworks of the facility's wastewater treatment or pretreatment system does not exceed 1 part per million, OR the total measured concentration of these solvents entering the headworks of the facility's wastewater treatment system (at facilities subject to regulation under the Clean Air Act, as amended, at 40 CFR parts 60, 61, or 63, or at facilities subject to an enforceable limit in a federal operating permit that minimizes fugitive emissions), does not exceed 1 part per million on an average weekly basis. Any facility that uses benzene as a solvent and claims this exemption must use an aerated biological wastewater treatment system and must use only lined surface impoundments or tanks prior to secondary clarification in the wastewater treatment system. Facilities that choose to measure concentration levels must file a copy of their sampling and analysis plan with the Regional Administrator, or State Director, as the context requires, or an authorized representative ("Director" as defined in 40 CFR 270.2). A facility must file a copy of a revised sampling and analysis plan only if the initial plan is rendered inaccurate by changes in the facility's operations. The sampling and analysis plan must include the monitoring point location (headworks), the sampling frequency and methodology, and a list of constituents to be monitored. A facility is eligible for the direct monitoring option once they receive confirmation that the sampling and analysis plan has been received by the Director. The Director may reject the sampling and analysis plan if he/she finds that, the sampling and analysis plan fails to include the above information; or the plan parameters would not enable the facility to calculate the weekly average concentration of these chemicals accurately. If the Director rejects the sampling and analysis plan or if the Director finds that the facility is not following the sampling and analysis plan, the Director shall notify the facility to cease the use of the direct monitoring option until such time as the bases for rejection are corrected; or 📖 4.16.1

(B) One or more of the following spent solvents listed in §261.31—methylene chloride, 1,1,1-trichloroethane, chlorobenzene, o-dichlorobenzene, cresols, cresylic acid, nitrobenzene, toluene, methyl ethyl ketone, carbon disulfide, isobutanol, pyridine, spent chlorofluorocarbon solvents, 2-ethoxyethanol, or the scrubber waters derived-from the combustion of these spent solvents—*Provided* That the maximum total weekly usage of these solvents (other than the amounts that can be demonstrated not to be discharged to wastewater) divided by the average weekly flow of wastewater into the headworks of the facility's wastewater treatment or pretreatment system does not exceed 25 parts per million, OR the total measured concentration of these solvents entering the headworks of the facility's wastewater treatment system (at facilities subject to regulation under the Clean Air Act as amended, at 40 CFR parts 60, 61, or 63, or at facilities subject to an enforceable limit in a federal operating permit that minimizes fugitive emissions), does not exceed 25 parts per million on an average weekly basis. Facilities that choose to measure concentration levels must file a copy of their sampling and analysis plan with the Regional Administrator, or State Director, as the context requires, or an authorized representative ("Director" as defined in 40 CFR 270.2). A facility must file a copy of a revised sampling and analysis plan only if the initial plan is rendered inaccurate by changes in the facility's operations. The sampling and analysis plan must include the monitoring point location (headworks), the sampling frequency and methodology, and a list of constituents to be monitored. A facility is eligible for the direct monitoring option once they receive confirmation that the sampling and analysis plan has been received by the Director. The Director may reject the sampling and analysis plan if he/she finds that, the sampling and analysis plan fails to include the above information; or the plan parameters would not enable the facility to calculate the weekly average concentration of these chemicals accurately. If the Director rejects the sampling and analysis plan or if the Director finds that the facility is not following the sampling and analysis plan, the Director shall notify the facility to cease the use of the direct monitoring option until such time as the bases for rejection are corrected; or 📖 4.16.1

(C) One of the following wastes listed in §261.32, provided that the wastes are discharged to the refinery oil recovery sewer before primary oil/water/solids separation—heat exchanger bundle cleaning sludge from the petroleum refining industry (EPA Hazardous Waste No. K050), crude oil storage tank sediment from petroleum refining operations (EPA Hazardous Waste No. K169), clarified slurry oil tank sediment and/or in-line filter/separation solids from petroleum refining operations (EPA Hazardous Waste No. K170), spent hydrotreating catalyst (EPA Hazardous Waste No. K171), and spent hydrorefining catalyst (EPA Hazardous Waste No. K172); or 📖 4.16.2

(D) A discarded hazardous waste, commercial chemical product, or chemical intermediate listed in §§261.31 through 261.33, arising from *de minimis* losses of these materials. For purposes of this paragraph (a)(2)(iv)(D), *de minimis* losses are inadvertent releases to a wastewater treatment system, including those from normal material handling operations (*e.g.*, spills from the unloading or transfer of materials from bins or other containers, leaks from pipes, valves or other devices used to transfer materials); minor leaks of process equipment, storage tanks or containers; leaks from well maintained pump packings and seals; sample purgings; relief device discharges; discharges from safety showers and rinsing and cleaning of personal safety equipment; and rinsate from empty containers or from containers that are rendered empty by that rinsing. Any manufacturing facility that claims an exemption for *de minimis* quantities of wastes listed in §§261.31 through 261.32, or any nonmanufacturing facility that claims an exemption for *de minimis* quantities of wastes listed in subpart D of this part must either have eliminated the discharge of wastewaters or have included in its Clean Water Act permit application or submission to its pretreatment control authority the constituents for which each waste was listed (in 40 CFR 261 appendix VII) of this part; and the constituents in the table "'Treatment Standards for Hazardous Wastes'" in 40 CFR 268.40 for which each waste has a treatment standard (*i.e.*, Land Disposal Restriction constituents). A facility is eligible to claim the exemption once the permit writer or control authority has been notified of possible *de minimis* releases via the Clean Water Act permit application or the pretreatment control authority submission. A copy of the Clean Water permit application or the submission to the pretreatment control authority must be placed in the facility's on-site files; or 📖 **4.16.3, 9.5.5.1**

(E) Wastewater resulting from laboratory operations containing toxic (T) wastes listed in subpart D of this part, *Provided*, That the annualized average flow of laboratory wastewater does not exceed one percent of total wastewater flow into the headworks of the facility's wastewater treatment or pre-treatment system or provided the wastes, combined annualized average concentration does not exceed one part per million in the headworks of the facility's wastewater treatment or pre-treatment facility. Toxic (T) wastes used in laboratories that are demonstrated not to be discharged to wastewater are not to be included in this calculation; or 📖 **4.16.4**

(F) One or more of the following wastes listed in §261.32—wastewaters from the production of carbamates and carbamoyl oximes (EPA Hazardous Waste No. K157)—*Provided* that the maximum weekly usage of formaldehyde, methyl chloride, methylene chloride, and triethylamine (including all amounts that cannot be demonstrated to be reacted in the process, destroyed through treatment, or is recovered, *i.e.*, what is discharged or volatilized) divided by the average weekly flow of process wastewater prior to any dilution into the headworks of the facility's wastewater treatment system does not exceed a total of 5 parts per million by weight OR the total measured concentration of these chemicals entering the headworks of the facility's wastewater treatment system (at facilities subject to regulation under the Clean Air Act as amended, at 40 CFR parts 60, 61, or 63, or at facilities subject to an enforceable limit in a federal operating permit that minimizes fugitive emissions), does not exceed 5 parts per million on an average weekly basis. Facilities that choose to measure concentration levels must file copy of their sampling and analysis plan with the Regional Administrator, or State Director, as the context requires, or an authorized representative ("Director" as defined in 40 CFR 270.2). A facility must file a copy of a revised sampling and analysis plan only if the initial plan is rendered inaccurate by changes in the facility's operations. The sampling and analysis plan must include the monitoring point location (headworks), the sampling frequency and methodology, and a list of constituents to be monitored. A facility is eligible for the direct monitoring option once they receive confirmation that the sampling and analysis plan has been received by the Director. The Director may reject the sampling and analysis plan if he/she finds that, the sampling and analysis plan fails to include the above information; or the plan parameters would not enable the facility to calculate the weekly average concentration of these chemicals accurately. If the Director rejects the sampling and analysis plan or if the Director finds that the facility is not following the sampling and analysis plan, the Director shall notify the facility to cease the use of the direct monitoring option until such time as the bases for rejection are corrected; or 📖 **4.16.5**

(G) Wastewaters derived-from the treatment of one or more of the following wastes listed in §261.32—organic waste (including heavy ends, still bottoms, light ends, spent solvents, filtrates, and decantates) from the production of carbamates and carbamoyl oximes (EPA Hazardous Waste No. K156).—*Provided*, that the maximum concentration of formaldehyde, methyl chloride, methylene chloride, and triethylamine prior to any dilutions into the headworks of the facility's wastewater treatment system does not exceed a total of 5 milligrams per liter OR the total measured concentration of these chemicals entering the headworks of the facility's wastewater treatment system (at facilities subject to regulation under the Clean Air Act as amended, at 40 CFR parts 60, 61, or 63, or at facilities subject to an enforceable limit in a federal operating permit that minimizes fugitive emissions), does not exceed 5 milligrams per liter on an average weekly basis. Facilities that choose to measure concentration levels must file copy of their sampling and analysis plan with the Regional Administrator, or State Director, as the context requires, or an authorized representative ("Director" as defined in 40 CFR 270.2). A facility must file a copy of a revised sampling and analysis plan only if the initial plan is rendered inaccurate by changes in the facility's operations. The sampling and analysis plan must include the monitoring point location (headworks), the sampling frequency and methodology, and a list of constituents to be monitored. A facility is eligible for the direct monitoring option once they receive confirmation that the sampling and analysis plan has been received by the Director. The Director may reject the sampling and analysis plan if he/she finds that, the sampling and analysis plan fails to include the above information; or the plan parameters would not enable the facility to calculate the weekly average concentration of these chemicals accurately. If the Director rejects the sampling and analysis plan or if the Director finds that the facility is not following the sampling and analysis plan, the Director shall notify the facility to cease the use of the direct monitoring option until such time as the bases for rejection are corrected. 📖 4.16.5

(v) *Rebuttable presumption for used oil.* Used oil containing more than 1000 ppm total halogens is presumed to be a hazardous waste because it has been mixed with halogenated hazardous waste listed in subpart D of part 261 of this chapter. Persons may rebut this presumption by demonstrating that the used oil does not contain hazardous waste (for example, to show that the used oil does not contain significant concentrations of halogenated hazardous constituents listed in appendix VIII of part 261 of this chapter). 📖 12.1.4

Publisher's Note: Subparagraphs (A) and (B) below were inadvertently deleted from the *CFR* when EPA changed the introductory text of §261.3(a)(2)(v) on June 14, 2005 [70 *FR* 34561].

(A) The rebuttable presumption does not apply to metalworking oils/fluids containing chlorinated paraffins, if they are processed, through a tolling agreement, to reclaim metalworking oils/fluids. The presumption does apply to metalworking oils/fluids if such oils/fluids are recycled in any other manner, or disposed.

(B) The rebuttable presumption does not apply to used oils contaminated with chlorofluorocarbons (CFCs) removed from refrigeration units where the CFCs are destined for reclamation. The rebuttable presumption does apply to used oils contaminated with CFCs that have been mixed with used oil from sources other than refrigeration units.

(b) A solid waste which is not excluded from regulation under paragraph (a)(1) of this section becomes a hazardous waste when any of the following events occur:

(1) In the case of a waste listed in subpart D of this part, when the waste first meets the listing description set forth in subpart D of this part. 📖 14.1.1.1

(2) In the case of a mixture of solid waste and one or more listed hazardous wastes, when a hazardous waste listed in subpart D is first added to the solid waste. 📖 5.1.2, 5.1.5, 14.1.1.1

(3) In the case of any other waste (including a waste mixture), when the waste exhibits any of the characteristics identified in subpart C of this part. 📖 5.1.2, 14.1.1.1

(c) Unless and until it meets the criteria of paragraph (d) of this section: 📖 5.2

(1) A hazardous waste will remain a hazardous waste.

(2)(i) Except as otherwise provided in paragraph (c)(2)(ii), (g) or (h) of this section, any solid waste generated from the treatment, storage, or disposal of a hazardous waste, including any sludge, spill residue, ash, emission control dust, or leachate (but not including precipitation run-off) is a hazardous waste. (However, materials that are reclaimed from solid wastes and that are used beneficially are not solid wastes and hence are not hazardous wastes under this provision unless the reclaimed material is burned for energy recovery or used in a manner constituting disposal.) 📖 3.2.5, 5.1.6.1, 5.2.2, 5.2.4, 11.3.1.2.1

(ii) The following solid wastes are not hazardous even though they are generated from the treatment, storage, or disposal of a hazardous waste, unless they exhibit one or more of the characteristics of hazardous waste: 📖 5.2.3.4

(A) Waste pickle liquor sludge generated by lime stabilization of spent pickle liquor from the iron and steel industry (SIC Codes 331 and 332).

(B) Waste from burning any of the materials exempted from regulation by §261.6(a)(3)(iii) and (iv).

(C)(*1*) Nonwastewater residues, such as slag, resulting from high temperature metals recovery (HTMR) processing of K061, K062 or F006 waste, in units identified as rotary kilns, flame reactors, electric furnaces, plasma arc furnaces, slag reactors, rotary hearth furnace/electric furnace combinations or industrial furnaces (as defined in paragraphs (6),

(7), and (13) of the definition for "Industrial furnace" in 40 CFR 260.10), that are disposed in subtitle D units, provided that these residues meet the generic exclusion levels identified in the tables in this paragraph for all constituents, and exhibit no characteristics of hazardous waste. Testing requirements must be incorporated in a facility's waste analysis plan or a generator's self-implementing waste analysis plan; at a minimum, composite samples of residues must be collected and analyzed quarterly and/or when the process or operation generating the waste changes. Persons claiming this exclusion in an enforcement action will have the burden of proving by clear and convincing evidence that the material meets all of the exclusion requirements. 📖 3.4.2.7.1

Constituent	Maximum for any single composite sample–TCLP (mg/l)
Generic exclusion levels for K061 and K062 nonwastewater HTMR residues	
Antimony	0.10
Arsenic	0.50
Barium	7.6
Beryllium	0.010
Cadmium	0.050
Chromium (total)	0.33
Lead	0.15
Mercury	0.009
Nickel	1.0
Selenium	0.16
Silver	0.30
Thallium	0.020
Zinc	70
Generic exclusion levels for F006 nonwastewater HTMR residues	
Antimony	0.10
Arsenic	0.50
Barium	7.6
Beryllium	0.010
Cadmium	0.050
Chromium (total)	0.33
Cyanide (total) (mg/kg)	1.8
Lead	0.15
Mercury	0.009
Nickel	1.0
Selenium	0.16
Silver	0.30
Thallium	0.020
Zinc	70

(*2*) A one-time notification and certification must be placed in the facility's files and sent to the EPA region or authorized state for K061, K062 or F006 HTMR residues that meet the generic exclusion levels for all constituents and do not exhibit any characteristics that are sent to subtitle D units. The notification and certification that is placed in the generators or treaters files must be updated if the process or operation generating the waste changes and/or if the subtitle D unit receiving the waste changes. However, the generator or treater need only notify the EPA region or an authorized state on an annual basis if such changes occur. Such notification and certification should be sent to the EPA region or authorized state by the end of the calendar year, but no later than December 31. The notification must include the following information: The name and address of the subtitle D unit receiving the waste shipments; the EPA Hazardous Waste Number(s) and treatability group(s) at the initial point of generation; and, the treatment standards applicable to the waste at the initial point of generation. The certification must be signed by an authorized representative and must state as follows: "I certify under penalty of law that the generic exclusion levels for all constituents have been met without impermissible dilution and that no characteristic of hazardous waste is exhibited. I am aware that there are significant penalties for submitting a false certification, including the possibility of fine and imprisonment."

(D) Biological treatment sludge from the treatment of one of the following wastes listed in §261.32—organic waste (including heavy ends, still bottoms, light ends, spent solvents, filtrates, and decantates) from the production of carbamates and carbamoyl oximes (EPA Hazardous Waste No. K156), and wastewaters from the production of carbamates and carbamoyl oximes (EPA Hazardous Waste No. K157).

(E) Catalyst inert support media separated from one of the following wastes listed in §261.32—Spent hydrotreating catalyst (EPA Hazardous Waste No. K171), and Spent hydrorefining catalyst (EPA Hazardous Waste No. K172).

(d) Any solid waste described in paragraph (c) of this section is not a hazardous waste if it meets the following criteria:

(1) In the case of any solid waste, it does not exhibit any of the characteristics of hazardous waste identified

in subpart C of this part. (However, wastes that exhibit a characteristic at the point of generation may still be subject to the requirements of part 268, even if they no longer exhibit a characteristic at the point of land disposal.) **5.2.2**

(2) In the case of a waste which is a listed waste under subpart D of this part, contains a waste listed under subpart D of this part or is derived from a waste listed in subpart D of this part, it also has been excluded from paragraph (c) of this section under §§260.20 and 260.22 of this chapter. **5.2.3, 5.3**

(e) [Reserved]

(f) Notwithstanding paragraphs (a) through (d) of this section and provided the debris as defined in part 268 of this chapter does not exhibit a characteristic identified at subpart C of this part, the following materials are not subject to regulation under 40 CFR parts 260, 261 to 266, 268, or 270: **5.2.3.6**

(1) Hazardous debris as defined in part 268 of this chapter that has been treated using one of the required extraction or destruction technologies specified in Table 1 of §268.45 of this chapter; persons claiming this exclusion in an enforcement action will have the burden of proving by clear and convincing evidence that the material meets all of the exclusion requirements; or **5.3.2, 13.8.1**

(2) Debris as defined in part 268 of this chapter that the Regional Administrator, considering the extent of contamination, has determined is no longer contaminated with hazardous waste. **5.3.2, 13.8.1**

(g)(1) A hazardous waste that is listed in subpart D of this part solely because it exhibits one or more characteristics of ignitability as defined under §261.21, corrosivity as defined under §261.22, or reactivity as defined under §261.23 is not a hazardous waste, if the waste no longer exhibits any characteristic of hazardous waste identified in subpart C of this part. **3.1.2, 3.2.1.5, 5.3.1.1**

(2) The exclusion described in paragraph (g)(1) of this section also pertains to:

(i) Any mixture of a solid waste and a hazardous waste listed in subpart D of this part solely because it exhibits the characteristics of ignitability, corrosivity, or reactivity as regulated under paragraph (a)(2)(iv) of this section; and **5.1.2.2**

(ii) Any solid waste generated from treating, storing, or disposing of a hazardous waste listed in subpart D of this part solely because it exhibits the characteristics of ignitability, corrosivity, or reactivity as regulated under paragraph (c)(2)(i) of this section. **5.2.2.2**

(3) Wastes excluded under this section are subject to part 268 of this chapter (as applicable), even if they no longer exhibit a characteristic at the point of land disposal. **5.1.3, 5.2.5, 13.2, 13.5**

(4) Any mixture of a solid waste excluded from regulation under §261.4(b)(7) and a hazardous waste listed in subpart D of this part solely because it exhibits one or more of the characteristics of ignitability, corrosivity, or reactivity as regulated under paragraph (a)(2)(iv) of this section is not a hazardous waste, if the mixture no longer exhibits any characteristic of hazardous waste identified in subpart C of this part for which the hazardous waste listed in subpart D of this part was listed. **5.1.2.4**

(h)(1) Hazardous waste containing radioactive waste is no longer a hazardous waste when it meets the eligibility criteria and conditions of 40 CFR part 266, Subpart N ("eligible radioactive mixed waste") **4.4.5**

(2) The exemption described in paragraph (h)(1) of this section also pertains to:

(i) Any mixture of a solid waste and an eligible radioactive mixed waste; and

(ii) Any solid waste generated from treating, storing, or disposing of an eligible radioactive mixed waste.

(3) Waste exempted under this section must meet the eligibility criteria and specified conditions in 40 CFR 266.225 and 40 CFR 266.230 (for storage and treatment) and in 40 CFR 266.310 and 40 CFR 266.315 (for transportation and disposal). Waste that fails to satisfy these eligibility criteria and conditions is regulated as hazardous waste.

[57 FR 7632, Mar. 3, 1992; 57 FR 23063, June 1, 1992, as amended at 57 FR 37263, Aug. 18, 1992; 57 FR 41611, Sept. 10, 1992; 57 FR 49279, Oct. 30, 1992; 59 FR 38545, July 28, 1994; 60 FR 7848, Feb. 9, 1995; 63 FR 28637, May 26, 1998; 63 FR 42184, Aug. 6, 1998; 66 FR 27297, May 16, 2001; 66 FR 50333, Oct. 3, 2001; 70 FR 34561, June 14, 2005; 70 FR 57784, Oct. 4, 2005; 71 FR 40258, July 14, 2006]

§261.4 Exclusions.

(a) *Materials which are not solid wastes.* The following materials are not solid wastes for the purpose of this part:

(1)(i) Domestic sewage; and **4.1, 13.1.3.1**

(ii) Any mixture of domestic sewage and other wastes that passes through a sewer system to a publicly-owned treatment works for treatment. "Domestic sewage" means untreated sanitary wastes that pass through a sewer system.

(2) Industrial wastewater discharges that are point source discharges subject to regulation under section 402 of the Clean Water Act, as amended. 📖 4.2, 13.1.3.1

[*Comment:* This exclusion applies only to the actual point source discharge. It does not exclude industrial wastewaters while they are being collected, stored or treated before discharge, nor does it exclude sludges that are generated by industrial wastewater treatment.]

(3) Irrigation return flows. 📖 4.3

(4) Source, special nuclear or by-product material as defined by the Atomic Energy Act of 1954, as amended, 42 U.S.C. 2011 *et seq.* 📖 4.4

(5) Materials subjected to in-situ mining techniques which are not removed from the ground as part of the extraction process. 📖 4.5

(6) Pulping liquors (*i.e.*, black liquor) that are reclaimed in a pulping liquor recovery furnace and then reused in the pulping process, unless it is accumulated speculatively as defined in §261.1(c) of this chapter. 📖 4.6

(7) Spent sulfuric acid used to produce virgin sulfuric acid, unless it is accumulated speculatively as defined in §261.1(c) of this chapter. 📖 11.3.1.5

(8) Secondary materials that are reclaimed and returned to the original process or processes in which they were generated where they are reused in the production process provided: 📖 10.1.2.5, 11.3.4

(i) Only tank storage is involved, and the entire process through completion of reclamation is closed by being entirely connected with pipes or other comparable enclosed means of conveyance; 📖 11.3.4.2

(ii) Reclamation does not involve controlled flame combustion (such as occurs in boilers, industrial furnaces, or incinerators); 📖 11.3.4.3

(iii) The secondary materials are never accumulated in such tanks for over twelve months without being reclaimed; and 📖 11.3.4.2

(iv) The reclaimed material is not used to produce a fuel, or used to produce products that are used in a manner constituting disposal. 📖 11.3.4.4

(9)(i) Spent wood preserving solutions that have been reclaimed and are reused for their original intended purpose; and

(ii) Wastewaters from the wood preserving process that have been reclaimed and are reused to treat wood.

(iii) Prior to reuse, the wood preserving wastewaters and spent wood preserving solutions described in paragraphs (a)(9)(i) and (a)(9)(ii) of this section, so long as they meet all of the following conditions:

(A) The wood preserving wastewaters and spent wood preserving solutions are reused on-site at water borne plants in the production process for their original intended purpose;

(B) Prior to reuse, the wastewaters and spent wood preserving solutions are managed to prevent release to either land or groundwater or both;

(C) Any unit used to manage wastewaters and/or spent wood preserving solutions prior to reuse can be visually or otherwise determined to prevent such releases;

(D) Any drip pad used to manage the wastewaters and/or spent wood preserving solutions prior to reuse complies with the standards in part 265, subpart W of this chapter, regardless of whether the plant generates a total of less than 100 kg/month of hazardous waste; and

(E) Prior to operating pursuant to this exclusion, the plant owner or operator prepares a one-time notification stating that the plant intends to claim the exclusion, giving the date on which the plant intends to begin operating under the exclusion, and containing the following language: "I have read the applicable regulation establishing an exclusion for wood preserving wastewaters and spent wood preserving solutions and understand it requires me to comply at all times with the conditions set out in the regulation." The plant must maintain a copy of that document in its on-site records until closure of the facility. The exclusion applies so long as the plant meets all of the conditions. If the plant goes out of compliance with any condition, it may apply to the appropriate Regional Administrator or state Director for reinstatement. The Regional Administrator or state Director may reinstate the exclusion upon finding that the plant has returned to compliance with all conditions and that the violations are not likely to recur.

(10) EPA Hazardous Waste Nos. K060, K087, K141, K142, K143, K144, K145, K147, and K148, and any wastes from the coke by-products processes that are hazardous only because they exhibit the Toxicity Characteristic (TC) specified in section 261.24 of this part when, subsequent to generation, these materials are recycled to coke ovens, to the tar recovery process as a feedstock to produce coal tar, or mixed with coal tar prior to the tar's sale or refining. This exclusion is conditioned on there being no land disposal of the wastes from the point they are generated to the point

they are recycled to coke ovens or tar recovery or refining processes, or mixed with coal tar.

(11) Nonwastewater splash condenser dross residue from the treatment of K061 in high temperature metals recovery units, provided it is shipped in drums (if shipped) and not land disposed before recovery.

(12)(i) Oil-bearing hazardous secondary materials (*i.e.*, sludges, byproducts, or spent materials) that are generated at a petroleum refinery (SIC code 2911) and are inserted into the petroleum refining process (SIC code 2911—including, but not limited to, distillation, catalytic cracking, fractionation, gasification (as defined in 40 CFR 260.10) or thermal cracking units (i.e., cokers)) unless the material is placed on the land, or speculatively accumulated before being so recycled. Materials inserted into thermal cracking units are excluded under this paragraph, provided that the coke product also does not exhibit a characteristic of hazardous waste. Oil-bearing hazardous secondary materials may be inserted into the same petroleum refinery where they are generated, or sent directly to another petroleum refinery and still be excluded under this provision. Except as provided in paragraph (a)(12)(ii) of this section, oil-bearing hazardous secondary materials generated elsewhere in the petroleum industry (i.e., from sources other than petroleum refineries) are not excluded under this section. Residuals generated from processing or recycling materials excluded under this paragraph (a)(12)(i), where such materials as generated would have otherwise met a listing under subpart D of this part, are designated as F037 listed wastes when disposed of or intended for disposal. 📖 4.7.1

(ii) Recovered oil that is recycled in the same manner and with the same conditions as described in paragraph (a)(12)(i) of this section. Recovered oil is oil that has been reclaimed from secondary materials (including wastewater) generated from normal petroleum industry practices, including refining, exploration and production, bulk storage, and transportation incident thereto (SIC codes 1311, 1321, 1381, 1382, 1389, 2911, 4612, 4613, 4922, 4923, 4789, 5171, and 5172.) Recovered oil does not include oil-bearing hazardous wastes listed in subpart D of this part; however, oil recovered from such wastes may be considered recovered oil. Recovered oil does not include used oil as defined in 40 CFR 279.1. 📖 4.7.2.1

(13) Excluded scrap metal (processed scrap metal, unprocessed home scrap metal, and unprocessed prompt scrap metal) being recycled. 📖 1.2.5.5.1, 4.21.2

(14) Shredded circuit boards being recycled provided that they are: 📖 4.21.5.2

(i) Stored in containers sufficient to prevent a release to the environment prior to recovery; and

(ii) Free of mercury switches, mercury relays and nickel-cadmium batteries and lithium batteries.

(15) Condensates derived from the overhead gases from kraft mill steam strippers that are used to comply with 40 CFR 63.446(e). The exemption applies only to combustion at the mill generating the condensates.

(16) Comparable fuels, emission-comparable fuels, or comparable syngas fuels that meet the requirements of §261.38. 📖 4.8, 14.5.3.4

(17) Spent materials (as defined in §261.1) (other than hazardous wastes listed in subpart D of this part) generated within the primary mineral processing industry from which minerals, acids, cyanide, water, or other values are recovered by mineral processing or by beneficiation, provided that: 📖 1.2.6.3.2, 4.15.2

(i) The spent material is legitimately recycled to recover minerals, acids, cyanide, water or other values;

(ii) The spent material is not accumulated speculatively;

(iii) Except as provided in paragraph (a)(17)(iv) of this section, the spent material is stored in tanks, containers, or buildings meeting the following minimum integrity standards: a building must be an engineered structure with a floor, walls, and a roof all of which are made of non-earthen materials providing structural support (except smelter buildings may have partially earthen floors provided the secondary material is stored on the non-earthen portion), and have a roof suitable for diverting rainwater away from the foundation; a tank must be free standing, not be a surface impoundment (as defined in 40 CFR 260.10), and be manufactured of a material suitable for containment of its contents; a container must be free standing and be manufactured of a material suitable for containment of its contents. If tanks or containers contain any particulate which may be subject to wind dispersal, the owner/operator must operate these units in a manner which controls fugitive dust. Tanks, containers, and buildings must be designed, constructed and operated to prevent significant releases to the environment of these materials.

(iv) The Regional Administrator or State Director may make a site-specific determination, after public review and comment, that only solid mineral processing spent material may be placed on pads rather than tanks containers, or buildings. Solid mineral processing spent materials do not contain any free liquid. The decision-maker must affirm that pads are designed, constructed and operated to prevent significant releases of the secondary material into the environment. Pads must provide the same degree of containment afforded by the non-RCRA tanks, containers and buildings eligible for exclusion.

(A) The decision-maker must also consider if storage on pads poses the potential for significant releases via groundwater, surface water, and air exposure pathways. Factors to be considered for assessing the groundwater, surface water, air exposure pathways are: The volume and physical and chemical properties of the secondary material, including its potential for migration off the pad; the potential for human or environmental exposure to hazardous constituents migrating from the pad via each exposure pathway, and the possibility and extent of harm to human and environmental receptors via each exposure pathway.

(B) Pads must meet the following minimum standards: Be designed of non-earthen material that is compatible with the chemical nature of the mineral processing spent material, capable of withstanding physical stresses associated with placement and removal, have run on/runoff controls, be operated in a manner which controls fugitive dust, and have integrity assurance through inspections and maintenance programs.

(C) Before making a determination under this paragraph, the Regional Administrator or State Director must provide notice and the opportunity for comment to all persons potentially interested in the determination. This can be accomplished by placing notice of this action in major local newspapers, or broadcasting notice over local radio stations.

(v) The owner or operator provides notice to the Regional Administrator or State Director providing the following information: The types of materials to be recycled; the type and location of the storage units and recycling processes; and the annual quantities expected to be placed in land-based units. This notification must be updated when there is a change in the type of materials recycled or the location of the recycling process.

(vi) For purposes of paragraph (a)(7) of this section, mineral processing spent materials must be the result of mineral processing and may not include any listed hazardous wastes. Listed hazardous wastes and characteristic hazardous wastes generated by non-mineral processing industries are not eligible for the conditional exclusion from the definition of solid waste.

Publisher's Note: The above reference to "paragraph (a)(7)" was incorrectly revised in 67 FR 11254 and should refer to paragraph (b)(7).

(18) Petrochemical recovered oil from an associated organic chemical manufacturing facility, where the oil is to be inserted into the petroleum refining process (SIC code 2911) along with normal petroleum refinery process streams, provided: 📖 4.7.2.2

(i) The oil is hazardous only because it exhibits the characteristic of ignitability (as defined in §261.21) and/or toxicity for benzene (§261.24, waste code D018); and

(ii) The oil generated by the organic chemical manufacturing facility is not placed on the land, or speculatively accumulated before being recycled into the petroleum refining process. An "associated organic chemical manufacturing facility" is a facility where the primary SIC code is 2869, but where operations may also include SIC codes 2821, 2822, and 2865; and is physically co-located with a petroleum refinery; and where the petroleum refinery to which the oil being recycled is returned also provides hydrocarbon feedstocks to the organic chemical manufacturing facility. "Petrochemical recovered oil" is oil that has been reclaimed from secondary materials (*i.e.*, sludges, byproducts, or spent materials, including wastewater) from normal organic chemical manufacturing operations, as well as oil recovered from organic chemical manufacturing processes.

(19) Spent caustic solutions from petroleum refining liquid treating processes used as a feedstock to produce cresylic or naphthenic acid unless the material is placed on the land, or accumulated speculatively as defined in §261.1(c). 📖 4.9

(20) Hazardous secondary materials used to make zinc fertilizers, provided that the following conditions specified are satisfied: 📖 1.2.6.1.1, 11.4.1.1

(i) Hazardous secondary materials used to make zinc micronutrient fertilizers must not be accumulated speculatively, as defined in §261.1(c)(8).

(ii) Generators and intermediate handlers of zinc-bearing hazardous secondary materials that are to be incorporated into zinc fertilizers must:

(A) Submit a one-time notice to the Regional Administrator or State Director in whose jurisdiction the exclusion is being claimed, which contains the name, address and EPA ID number of the generator or intermediate handler facility, provides a brief description of the secondary material that will be subject to the exclusion, and identifies when the manufacturer intends to begin managing excluded, zinc-bearing hazardous secondary materials under the conditions specified in this paragraph (a)(20).

(B) Store the excluded secondary material in tanks, containers, or buildings that are constructed and maintained in a way that prevents releases of the secondary materials into the environment. At a minimum, any building used for this purpose must be an engineered structure made of non-earthen materials that provide structural support, and must have a floor, walls and a roof that prevent wind dispersal and contact with rainwater. Tanks used for this purpose must be structurally sound and, if outdoors, must have roofs or covers that prevent contact with wind and rain. Containers used for this purpose must be kept closed except when it is necessary to add or remove material, and must be in sound condition. Containers that are stored outdoors must be managed within storage areas that:

(*1*) have containment structures or systems sufficiently impervious to contain leaks, spills and accumulated precipitation; and

(*2*) provide for effective drainage and removal of leaks, spills and accumulated precipitation; and

(*3*) prevent run-on into the containment system.

(C) With each off-site shipment of excluded hazardous secondary materials, provide written notice to the receiving facility that the material is subject to the conditions of this paragraph (a)(20).

(D) Maintain at the generator's or intermediate handlers's facility for no less than three years records of all shipments of excluded hazardous secondary materials. For each shipment these records must at a minimum contain the following information:

(*1*) Name of the transporter and date of the shipment;

(*2*) Name and address of the facility that received the excluded material, and documentation confirming receipt of the shipment; and

(*3*) Type and quantity of excluded secondary material in each shipment.

(iii) Manufacturers of zinc fertilizers or zinc fertilizer ingredients made from excluded hazardous secondary materials must:

(A) Store excluded hazardous secondary materials in accordance with the storage requirements for generators and intermediate handlers, as specified in paragraph (a)(20)(ii)(B) of this section.

(B) Submit a one-time notification to the Regional Administrator or State Director that, at a minimum, specifies the name, address and EPA ID number of the manufacturing facility, and identifies when the manufacturer intends to begin managing excluded, zinc-bearing hazardous secondary materials under the conditions specified in this paragraph (a)(20).

(C) Maintain for a minimum of three years records of all shipments of excluded hazardous secondary materials received by the manufacturer, which must at a minimum identify for each shipment the name and address of the generating facility, name of transporter and date the materials were received, the quantity received, and a brief description of the industrial process that generated the material.

(D) Submit to the Regional Administrator or State Director an annual report that identifies the total quantities of all excluded hazardous secondary materials that were used to manufacture zinc fertilizers or zinc fertilizer ingredients in the previous year, the name and address of each generating facility, and the industrial process(s) from which they were generated.

(iv) Nothing in this section preempts, overrides or otherwise negates the provision in §262.11 of this chapter, which requires any person who generates a solid waste to determine if that waste is a hazardous waste.

(v) Interim status and permitted storage units that have been used to store only zinc-bearing hazardous wastes prior to the submission of the one-time notice described in paragraph (a)(20)(ii)(A) of this section, and that afterward will be used only to store hazardous secondary materials excluded under this paragraph, are not subject to the closure requirements of 40 CFR Parts 264 and 265.

(21) Zinc fertilizers made from hazardous wastes, or hazardous secondary materials that are excluded under paragraph (a)(20) of this section, provided that:

📖 1.2.6.1.1, 11.4.1.1

(i) The fertilizers meet the following contaminant limits:

(A) For metal contaminants:

Constituent	Maximum Allowable Total Concentration in Fertilizer, per Unit (1%) of Zinc (ppm)
Arsenic	0.3
Cadmium	1.4
Chromium	0.6
Lead	2.8
Mercury	0.3

(B) For dioxin contaminants the fertilizer must contain no more than eight (8) parts per trillion of dioxin, measured as toxic equivalent (TEQ).

(ii) The manufacturer performs sampling and analysis of the fertilizer product to determine compliance with the contaminant limits for metals no less than every six months, and for dioxins no less than every twelve months. Testing must also be performed whenever changes occur to manufacturing processes or ingredients that could significantly affect the amounts of contaminants in the fertilizer product. The manufacturer may use any reliable analytical method to demonstrate that no constituent of concern is present in the product at concentrations above the applicable limits. It is the responsibility of the manufacturer to ensure that the sampling and analysis are unbiased, precise, and representative of the product(s) introduced into commerce.

(iii) The manufacturer maintains for no less than three years records of all sampling and analyses performed for purposes of determining compliance with the requirements of paragraph (a)(21)(ii) of this section. Such records must at a minimum include:

(A) The dates and times product samples were taken, and the dates the samples were analyzed;

(B) The names and qualifications of the person(s) taking the samples;

(C) A description of the methods and equipment used to take the samples;

(D) The name and address of the laboratory facility at which analyses of the samples were performed;

(E) A description of the analytical methods used, including any cleanup and sample preparation methods; and

(F) All laboratory analytical results used to determine compliance with the contaminant limits specified in this paragraph (a)(21).

(22) Used cathode ray tubes (CRTs) 📖 2.7.3.1

(i) Used, intact CRTs as defined in §260.10 of this chapter are not solid wastes within the United States unless they are disposed, or unless they are speculatively accumulated as defined in §261.1(c)(8) by CRT collectors or glass processors. 📖 2.7.3.1

(ii) Used, intact CRTs as defined in §260.10 of this chapter are not solid wastes when exported for recycling provided that they meet the requirements of §261.40. 📖 2.7.3.2

(iii) Used, broken CRTs as defined in §260.10 of this chapter are not solid wastes provided that they meet the requirements of §261.39. 📖 2.7.3.1

(iv) Glass removed from CRTs is not a solid waste provided that it meets the requirements of §261.39(c).

(23) Hazardous secondary material generated and reclaimed within the United States or its territories and managed in land-based units as defined in §260.10 of this chapter is not a solid waste provided that: 📖 1.2.6.3.1, 11.2.3.1, 11.4.2

(i) The material is contained;

(ii) The material is a hazardous secondary material generated and reclaimed under the control of the generator, as defined in §260.10;

(iii) The material is not speculatively accumulated, as defined in §261.1(c)(8);

(iv) The material is not otherwise subject to material-specific management conditions under paragraph (a) of this section when reclaimed, it is not a spent lead acid battery (see §266.80 and §273.2 of this chapter), and it does not meet the listing description for K171 or K172 in §261.32;

(v) The reclamation of the material is legitimate, as specified under §260.43 of this chapter, and

(vi) In addition, persons claiming the exclusion under this paragraph (a)(23) must provide notification as required by §260.42 of this chapter. (For hazardous secondary material managed in a non-land-based unit, see §261.2(a)(2)(ii)).

(24) Hazardous secondary material that is generated and then transferred to another person for the purpose of reclamation is not a solid waste, provided that: 📖 1.2.6.3.1, 11.2.3.2

(i) The material is not speculatively accumulated, as defined in §261.1(c)(8);

(ii) The material is not handled by any person or facility other than the hazardous secondary material generator, the transporter, an intermediate facility or a reclaimer, and, while in transport, is not stored for more than 10 days at a transfer facility, as defined in §260.10 of this chapter, and is packaged according to applicable Department of Transportation regulations at 49 CFR Parts 173, 178, and 179 while in transport;

(iii) The material is not otherwise subject to material-specific management conditions under paragraph (a) of this section when reclaimed, it is not a spent lead-acid battery (see §266.80 and §273.2 of this chapter), and it does not meet the listing description for K171 or K172 in §261.32;

(iv) The reclamation of the material is legitimate, as specified under §260.43 of this chapter;

(v) The hazardous secondary material generator satisfies all of the following conditions:

(A) The material must be contained.

(B) Prior to arranging for transport of hazardous secondary materials to a reclamation facility (or facilities) where the management of the hazardous secondary materials is not addressed under a RCRA Part B permit or interim status standards, the hazardous secondary material generator must make reasonable efforts to ensure that each reclaimer intends to properly and legitimately reclaim the hazardous secondary material and not discard it, and that each reclaimer will manage the hazardous secondary material in a manner that is protective of human health and the environment. If the hazardous secondary material will be passing through an intermediate facility where the management of the hazardous secondary materials is not addressed under a RCRA Part B permit or interim status standards, the hazardous secondary material generator must make contractual arrangements with the intermediate facility to ensure that the hazardous secondary material is sent to the reclamation facility identified by the hazardous secondary material generator, and the hazardous secondary material generator must perform reasonable efforts to ensure that the intermediate facility will manage the hazardous secondary material in a manner that is protective of human health and the environment. Reasonable efforts must be repeated at a minimum of every three years for the hazardous secondary material generator to claim the exclusion and to send the hazardous secondary materials to each reclaimer and any intermediate facility. In making these reasonable efforts, the generator may use any credible evidence available, including information gathered by the hazardous secondary material generator, provided by the reclaimer or intermediate facility, and/or provided by a third party. The hazardous secondary material generator must affirmatively answer all of the following questions for each reclamation facility and any intermediate facility:

(*1*) Does the available information indicate that the reclamation process is legitimate pursuant to §260.43 of this chapter? In answering this question, the hazardous secondary material generator can rely on their existing knowledge of the physical and chemical properties of the hazardous secondary material, as well as information from other sources (e.g., the reclamation facility, audit reports, etc.) about the reclamation process. (By responding to this question, the hazardous secondary material generator has also satisfied its requirement in §260.43(a) of this chapter to be able to demonstrate that the recycling is legitimate).

(*2*) Does the publicly available information indicate that the reclamation facility and any intermediate facility that is used by the hazardous secondary material generator notified the appropriate authorities of hazardous secondary materials reclamation activities pursuant to §260.42 of this chapter and have they notified the appropriate authorities that the financial assurance condition is satisfied per paragraph (a)(24)(vi)(F) of this section? In answering these questions, the hazardous secondary material generator can rely on the available information documenting the reclamation facility's and any intermediate facility's compliance with the notification requirements per §260.42 of this chapter, including the requirement in §260.42(a)(5) to notify EPA whether the reclaimer or intermediate facility has financial assurance.

(*3*) Does publicly available information indicate that the reclamation facility or any intermediate facility that is used by the hazardous secondary material generator has not had any formal enforcement actions taken against the facility in the previous three years for violations of the RCRA hazardous waste regulations and has not be classified as a significant non-complier with RCRA Subtitle C? In answering this question, the hazardous secondary material generator can rely on the publicly available information from EPA or the state. If the reclamation facility or any intermediate facility that is used by the hazardous secondary material generator has had a formal enforcement action taken against the facility in the previous three years for violations of the RCRA hazardous waste regulations and has been classified as a significant non-complier with RCRA Subtitle C, does the hazardous secondary material generator have credible evidence that the facilities will manage the hazardous secondary materials properly? In answering this question, the hazardous secondary material generator can obtain additional information from EPA, the state, or the facility itself that the facility has addressed the violations, taken remedial steps to address the violations and prevent future violations, or that the violations are not relevant to the proper management of the hazardous secondary materials.

(*4*) Does the available information indicate that the reclamation facility and any intermediate facility that is used by the hazardous secondary material generator have the equipment and trained personnel to safely recycle the hazardous secondary material? In answering this question, the generator may rely on a description by the reclamation facility or by an independent third party of the equipment and trained personnel to be used to recycle the generator's hazardous secondary material.

(*5*) If residuals are generated from the reclamation of the excluded hazardous secondary materials, does the reclamation facility have the permits required (if any) to manage the residuals? If not, does the reclamation facility have a contract with an appropriately permitted facility to dispose of the residuals? If not, does the hazardous secondary material generator have credible evidence that the residuals will be managed in a manner that is protective of human health and the environment? In answering these questions, the hazardous secondary material generator can rely on publicly available information from EPA or the state, or information provided by the facility itself.

(C) The hazardous secondary material generator must maintain for a minimum of three years documentation and certification that reasonable efforts were made for each reclamation facility and, if applicable, intermediate facility where the management of the hazardous secondary materials is not addressed under a RCRA Part B permit or interim status standards prior to transferring hazardous secondary material. Documentation and certification must be made available upon request by a regulatory authority within 72 hours, or within a longer period of time as specified by the regulatory authority. The certification statement must:

(*1*) Include the printed name and official title of an authorized representative of the hazardous secondary material generator company, the authorized representative's signature, and the date signed;

(*2*) Incorporate the following language: "I hereby certify in good faith and to the best of my knowledge that, prior to arranging for transport of excluded hazardous secondary materials to [insert name(s) of reclamation facility and any intermediate facility], reasonable efforts were made in accordance with §261.4(a)(24)(v)(B) to ensure that the hazardous secondary materials would be recycled legitimately, and otherwise managed in a manner that is protective of human health and the environment, and that such efforts were based on current and accurate information."

(D) The hazardous secondary material generator must maintain at the generating facility for no less than three (3) years records of all off-site shipments of hazardous secondary materials. For each shipment, these records must, at a minimum, contain the following information:

(*1*) Name of the transporter and date of the shipment;

(*2*) Name and address of each reclaimer and, if applicable, the name and address of each intermediate facility to which the hazardous secondary material was sent;

(*3*) The type and quantity of hazardous secondary material in the shipment.

(E) The hazardous secondary material generator must maintain at the generating facility for no less than three (3) years confirmations of receipt from each reclaimer and, if applicable, each intermediate facility for all off-site shipments of hazardous secondary materials. Confirmations of receipt must include the name and address of the reclaimer (or intermediate facility), the type and quantity of the hazardous secondary materials received and the date which the hazardous secondary materials were received. This requirement may be satisfied by routine business records (e.g., financial records, bills of lading, copies of DOT shipping papers, or electronic confirmations of receipt); and

(vi) Reclaimers of hazardous secondary material excluded from regulation under this exclusion and intermediate facilities as defined in §260.10 of this chapter satisfy all of the following conditions:

(A) The reclaimer and intermediate facility must maintain at its facility for no less than three (3) years records of all shipments of hazardous secondary material that were received at the facility and, if applicable, for all shipments of hazardous secondary materials that were received and subsequently sent off-site from the facility for further reclamation. For each shipment, these records must at a minimum contain the following information:

(*1*) Name of the transporter and date of the shipment;

(*2*) Name and address of the hazardous secondary material generator and, if applicable, the name and address of the reclaimer or intermediate facility which the hazardous secondary materials were received from;

(*3*) The type and quantity of hazardous secondary material in the shipment; and

(*4*) For hazardous secondary materials that, after being received by the reclaimer or intermediate facility, were subsequently transferred off-site for further reclamation, the name and address of the (subsequent) reclaimer and, if applicable, the name and address of each intermediate facility to which the hazardous secondary material was sent.

(B) The intermediate facility must send the hazardous secondary material to the reclaimer(s) designated by the hazardous secondary materials generator.

(C) The reclaimer and intermediate facility must send to the hazardous secondary material generator confirmations of receipt for all off-site shipments of hazardous secondary materials. Confirmations of receipt must include the name and address of the reclaimer (or intermediate facility), the type and quantity of the hazardous secondary materials received and the date which the hazardous secondary materials were received. This requirement may be satisfied by routine business records (e.g., financial records, bills of lading, copies of DOT shipping papers, or electronic confirmations of receipt).

(D) The reclaimer and intermediate facility must manage the hazardous secondary material in a manner that is at least as protective as that employed for analogous raw material and must be contained. An "analogous raw material" is a raw material for which a hazardous secondary material is a substitute and serves the same function and has similar physical and chemical properties as the hazardous secondary material.

(E) Any residuals that are generated from reclamation processes will be managed in a manner that is protective of human health and the environment. If any residuals exhibit a hazardous characteristic according to subpart C of 40 CFR part 261, or if they themselves are specifically listed in subpart D of 40 CFR part 261, such residuals are hazardous wastes and must be managed in accordance with the applicable requirements of 40 CFR parts 260 through 272.

(F) The reclaimer and intermediate facility has financial assurance as required under subpart H of 40 CFR part 261.

(vii) In addition, all persons claiming the exclusion under this paragraph (a)(24) of this section must provide notification as required under §260.42 of this chapter.

(25) Hazardous secondary material that is exported from the United States and reclaimed at a reclamation facility located in a foreign country is not a solid waste, provided that the hazardous secondary material generator complies with the applicable requirements of paragraph (a)(24)(i)–(v) of this section (excepting paragraph (a)(v)(B)(*2*) of this section for foreign reclaimers and foreign intermediate facilities), and that the hazardous secondary material generator also complies with the following requirements: 📖 11.2.3.2.1

(i) Notify EPA of an intended export before the hazardous secondary material is scheduled to leave the United States. A complete notification must be submitted at least sixty (60) days before the initial shipment is intended to be shipped off-site. This notification may cover export activities extending over a twelve (12) month or lesser period. The notification must be in writing, signed by the hazardous secondary material generator, and include the following information:

(A) Name, mailing address, telephone number and EPA ID number (if applicable) of the hazardous secondary material generator;

(B) A description of the hazardous secondary material and the EPA hazardous waste number that would apply if the hazardous secondary material was managed as hazardous waste and the U.S. DOT proper shipping name, hazard class and ID number (UN/NA) for each hazardous secondary material as identified in 49 CFR parts 171 through 177;

(C) The estimated frequency or rate at which the hazardous secondary material is to be exported and the period of time over which the hazardous secondary material is to be exported;

(D) The estimated total quantity of hazardous secondary material;

(E) All points of entry to and departure from each foreign country through which the hazardous secondary material will pass;

(F) A description of the means by which each shipment of the hazardous secondary material will be transported (e.g., mode of transportation vehicle (air, highway, rail, water, etc.), type(s) of container (drums, boxes, tanks, etc.));

(G) A description of the manner in which the hazardous secondary material will be reclaimed in the receiving country;

(H) The name and address of the reclaimer, any intermediate facility and any alternate reclaimer and intermediate facilities; and

(I) The name of any transit countries through which the hazardous secondary material will be sent and a description of the approximate length of time it will remain in such countries and the nature of its handling while there (for purposes of this section, the terms "Acknowledgement of Consent", "receiving country" and "transit country" are used as defined in 40 CFR 262.51 with the exception that the terms in this section refer to hazardous secondary materials, rather than hazardous waste):

(ii) Notifications submitted by mail should be sent to the following mailing address: Office of Enforcement and Compliance Assurance, Office of Federal Activities, International Compliance Assurance Division, (Mail Code 2254A), Environmental Protection Agency, 1200 Pennsylvania Ave., N.W., Washington, DC 20460. Hand-delivered notifications should be delivered to: Office of Enforcement and Compliance Assurance, Office of Federal Activities, International Compliance Assurance Division, Environmental Protection Agency, Ariel Rios Bldg., Room 6144, 12th St. and Pennsylvania Ave., N.W., Washington, DC 20004. In both cases, the following shall be prominently displayed on the front of the envelope: "Attention: Notification of Intent to Export."

(iii) Except for changes to the telephone number in paragraph (a)(25)(i)(A) of this section and decreases in the quantity of hazardous secondary material indicated pursuant to paragraph (a)(25)(i)(D) of this section, when the conditions specified on the original notification change (including any exceedance of the estimate of the quantity of hazardous secondary material specified in the original notification), the hazardous secondary material generator must provide EPA with a written renotification of the change. The shipment cannot take place until consent of the receiving country to the changes (except for changes to paragraph (a)(25)(i)(I) of this section and in the ports of entry to and departure from transit countries pursuant to paragraphs (a)(25)(i)(E) of this section) has been obtained and the hazardous secondary material generator receives from EPA an Acknowledgment of Consent reflecting the receiving country's consent to the changes.

(iv) Upon request by EPA, the hazardous secondary material generator shall furnish to EPA any additional information which a receiving country requests in order to respond to a notification.

(v) EPA will provide a complete notification to the receiving country and any transit countries. A notification is complete when EPA receives a notification which EPA determines satisfies the requirements of paragraph (a)(25)(i) of this section. Where a claim of confidentiality is asserted with respect to any notification information required by paragraph (a)(25)(i) of this section, EPA may find the notification not complete until any such claim is resolved in accordance with 40 CFR 260.2.

(vi) The export of hazardous secondary material under this paragraph (a)(25) is prohibited unless the receiving country consents to the intended export. When the receiving country consents in writing to the receipt of the hazardous secondary material, EPA will send an Acknowledgment of Consent to the hazardous secondary material generator. Where the receiving country objects to receipt of the hazardous secondary material or withdraws a prior consent, EPA will notify the hazardous secondary material generator in writing. EPA will also notify the hazardous secondary material generator of any responses from transit countries.

(vii) For exports to OECD Member countries, the receiving country may respond to the notification using tacit consent. If no objection has been lodged by any receiving country or transit countries to a notification provided pursuant to paragraph (a)(25)(i) of this section within thirty (30) days after the date of issuance of the acknowledgement of receipt of notification by the competent authority of the receiving country, the transboundary movement may commence. In such cases, EPA will send an Acknowledgment of Consent to inform the hazardous secondary material generator that the receiving country and any relevant transit countries have not objected to the shipment, and are thus presumed to have consented tacitly. Tacit consent expires one (1) calendar year after the close of the thirty (30) day period; renotification and renewal of all consents is required for exports after that date.

(viii) A copy of the Acknowledgment of Consent must accompany the shipment. The shipment must conform to the terms of the Acknowledgment of Consent.

(ix) If a shipment cannot be delivered for any reason to the reclaimer, intermediate facility or the alternate reclaimer or alternate intermediate facility, the hazardous secondary material generator must re-notify EPA of a change in the conditions of the original notification to allow shipment to a new reclaimer in accordance with paragraph (iii) of this section and obtain another Acknowledgment of Consent.

(x) Hazardous secondary material generators must keep a copy of each notification of intent to export and each Acknowledgment of Consent for a period of three years following receipt of the Acknowledgment of Consent.

(xi) Hazardous secondary material generators must file with the Administrator no later than March 1 of each year, a report summarizing the types, quantities, frequency and ultimate destination of all hazardous secondary materials exported during the previous calendar year. Annual reports submitted by mail should be sent to the following address: Office of Enforcement and Compliance Assurance, Office of Federal Activities, International Compliance Assurance Division (Mail Code 2254A), Environmental Protection Agency, 1200 Pennsylvania Ave., NW., Washington, DC 20460. Hand-delivered reports should be delivered to: Office of Enforcement and Compliance Assurance, Office of Federal Activities, International Compliance Assurance Division, Environmental Protection Agency, Ariel Rios Bldg., Room 6144, 12th St. and Pennsylvania Ave., NW., Washington, D.C. 20004. Such reports must include the following information:

(A) Name, mailing and site address, and EPA ID number (if applicable) of the hazardous secondary material generator;

(B) The calendar year covered by the report;

(C) The name and site address of each reclaimer and intermediate facility;

(D) By reclaimer and intermediate facility, for each hazardous secondary material exported, a description of the hazardous secondary material and the EPA hazardous waste number that would apply if the hazardous secondary material was managed as hazardous waste, DOT hazard class, the name and US EPA ID number (where applicable) for each transporter used, the total amount of hazardous secondary material shipped and the number of shipments pursuant to each notification;

(E) A certification signed by the hazardous secondary material generator which states: "I certify under penalty of law that I have personally examined and am familiar with the information submitted in this and all attached documents, and that based on my inquiry of those individuals immediately responsible for obtaining the information, I believe that the submitted information is true, accurate, and complete. I am aware that there are significant penalties for submitting false information including the possibility of fine and imprisonment."

(xii) All persons claiming an exclusion under this paragraph (a)(25) must provide notification as required by §260.42 of this chapter.

(b) *Solid wastes which are not hazardous wastes.* The following solid wastes are not hazardous wastes:

(1) Household waste, including household waste that has been collected, transported, stored, treated, disposed, recovered (*e.g.*, refuse-derived fuel) or reused. "Household waste" means any material (including garbage, trash and sanitary wastes in septic tanks) derived from households (including single and multiple residences, hotels and motels, bunkhouses, ranger stations, crew quarters, campgrounds, picnic grounds and day-use recreation areas). A resource recovery facility managing municipal solid waste shall not be deemed to be treating, storing, disposing of, or otherwise managing hazardous wastes for the purposes of regulation under this subtitle, if such facility: 📖 **4.10, 5.1.6.4, 6.5.6.3**

(i) Receives and burns only

(A) Household waste (from single and multiple dwellings, hotels, motels, and other residential sources) and

(B) Solid waste from commercial or industrial sources that does not contain hazardous waste; and

(ii) Such facility does not accept hazardous wastes and the owner or operator of such facility has established contractual requirements or other appropriate notification or inspection procedures to assure that hazardous wastes are not received at or burned in such facility.

(2) Solid wastes generated by any of the following and which are returned to the soils as fertilizers: 📖 4.11

(i) The growing and harvesting of agricultural crops.

(ii) The raising of animals, including animal manures.

(3) Mining overburden returned to the mine site. 📖 4.12

(4) Fly ash waste, bottom ash waste, slag waste, and flue gas emission control waste, generated primarily from the combustion of coal or other fossil fuels, except as provided by §266.112 of this chapter for facilities that burn or process hazardous waste. 📖 4.13, 5.2.3.1

(5) Drilling fluids, produced waters, and other wastes associated with the exploration, development, or production of crude oil, natural gas or geothermal energy. 📖 4.14, 5.1.2.5, 5.2.3.1

(6)(i) Wastes which fail the test for the Toxicity Characteristic because chromium is present or are listed in subpart D due to the presence of chromium, which do not fail the test for the Toxicity Characteristic for any other constituent or are not listed due to the presence of any other constituent, and which do not fail the test for any other characteristic, if it is shown by a waste generator or by waste generators that: 📖 2.6.4

(A) The chromium in the waste is exclusively (or nearly exclusively) trivalent chromium; and

(B) The waste is generated from an industrial process which uses trivalent chromium exclusively (or nearly exclusively) and the process does not generate hexavalent chromium; and

(C) The waste is typically and frequently managed in non-oxidizing environments.

(ii) Specific wastes which meet the standard in paragraphs (b)(6)(i) (A), (B), and (C) (so long as they do not fail the test for the toxicity characteristic for any other constituent, and do not exhibit any other characteristic) are:

(A) Chrome (blue) trimmings generated by the following subcategories of the leather tanning and finishing industry; hair pulp/chrome tan/retan/wet finish; hair save/chrome tan/retan/wet finish; retan/wet finish; no beamhouse; through-the-blue; and shearling.

(B) Chrome (blue) shavings generated by the following subcategories of the leather tanning and finishing industry: Hair pulp/chrome tan/retan/wet finish; hair save/chrome tan/retan/wet finish; retan/wet finish; no beamhouse; through-the-blue; and shearling.

(C) Buffing dust generated by the following subcategories of the leather tanning and finishing industry; hair pulp/chrome tan/retan/wet finish; hair save/chrome tan/retan/wet finish; retan/wet finish; no beamhouse; through-the-blue.

(D) Sewer screenings generated by the following subcategories of the leather tanning and finishing industry: Hair pulp/chrome tan/retan/wet finish; hair save/chrome tan/retan/wet finish; retan/wet finish; no beamhouse; through-the-blue; and shearling.

(E) Wastewater treatment sludges generated by the following subcategories of the leather tanning and finishing industry: Hair pulp/chrome tan/retan/wet finish; hair save/chrome tan/retan/wet finish; retan/wet finish; no beamhouse; through-the-blue; and shearling.

(F) Wastewater treatment sludges generated by the following subcategories of the leather tanning and finishing industry: Hair pulp/chrome tan/retan/wet finish; hair save/chrome tan/retan/wet finish; and through-the-blue.

(G) Waste scrap leather from the leather tanning industry, the shoe manufacturing industry, and other leather product manufacturing industries.

(H) Wastewater treatment sludges from the production of TiO_2 pigment using chromium-bearing ores by the chloride process.

(7) Solid waste from the extraction, beneficiation, and processing of ores and minerals (including coal, phosphate rock, and overburden from the mining of uranium ore), except as provided by §266.112 of this chapter for facilities that burn or process hazardous waste. 📖 4.15, 5.1.2.4, 5.2.3.1

(i) For purposes of §261.4(b)(7) beneficiation of ores and minerals is restricted to the following activities; crushing; grinding; washing; dissolution; crystallization; filtration; sorting; sizing; drying; sintering; pelletizing; briquetting; calcining to remove water and/or carbon dioxide; roasting, autoclaving, and/or chlorination in preparation for leaching (except where the roasting (and/or autoclaving and/or chlorination)/leaching sequence produces a final or intermediate product that does not undergo further beneficiation or processing); gravity concentration; magnetic separation; electrostatic separation; flotation; ion exchange; solvent extraction; electrowinning; precipitation; amalgamation; and heap, dump, vat, tank, and in situ leaching. 📖 4.15.1.2

(ii) For the purposes of §261.4(b)(7), solid waste from the processing of ores and minerals includes only the following wastes as generated: 📖 4.15.2

(A) Slag from primary copper processing;

(B) Slag from primary lead processing;

(C) Red and brown muds from bauxite refining;

(D) Phosphogypsum from phosphoric acid production;

(E) Slag from elemental phosphorus production;

(F) Gasifier ash from coal gasification;

(G) Process wastewater from coal gasification;

(H) Calcium sulfate wastewater treatment plant sludge from primary copper processing;

(I) Slag tailings from primary copper processing;

(J) Fluorogypsum from hydrofluoric acid production;

(K) Process wastewater from hydrofluoric acid production;

(L) Air pollution control dust/sludge from iron blast furnaces;

(M) Iron blast furnace slag;

(N) Treated residue from roasting/leaching of chrome ore;

(O) Process wastewater from primary magnesium processing by the anhydrous process;

(P) Process wastewater from phosphoric acid production;

(Q) Basic oxygen furnace and open hearth furnace air pollution control dust/sludge from carbon steel production;

(R) Basic oxygen furnace and open hearth furnace slag from carbon steel production;

(S) Chloride process waste solids from titanium tetrachloride production;

(T) Slag from primary zinc processing.

(iii) A residue derived from co-processing mineral processing secondary materials with normal beneficiation raw materials or with normal mineral processing raw materials remains excluded under paragraph (b) of this section if the owner or operator: 📖 4.15.2.1

(A) Processes at least 50 percent by weight normal beneficiation raw materials or normal mineral processing raw materials; and,

(B) Legitimately reclaims the secondary mineral processing materials.

(8) Cement kiln dust waste, except as provided by §266.112 of this chapter for facilities that burn or process hazardous waste.

(9) Solid waste which consists of discarded arsenical-treated wood or wood products which fails the test for the Toxicity Characteristic for Hazardous Waste Codes D004 through D017 and which is not a hazardous waste for any other reason if the waste is generated by persons who utilize the arsenical-treated wood and wood products for these materials' intended end use.

(10) Petroleum-contaminated media and debris that fail the test for the Toxicity Characteristic of §261.24 (Hazardous Waste Codes D018 through D043 only) and are subject to the corrective action regulations under part 280 of this chapter. 📖 2.6.4, 13.8

(11) Injected groundwater that is hazardous only because it exhibits the Toxicity Characteristic (Hazardous Waste Codes D018 through D043 only) in §261.24 of this part that is reinjected through an underground injection well pursuant to free phase hydrocarbon recovery operations undertaken at petroleum refineries, petroleum marketing terminals, petroleum bulk plants, petroleum pipelines, and petroleum transportation spill sites until January 25, 1993. This extension applies to recovery operations in existence, or for which contracts have been issued, on or before March 25, 1991. For groundwater returned through infiltration galleries from such operations at petroleum refineries, marketing terminals, and bulk plants, until [insert date six months after publication]. New operations involving injection wells (beginning after March 25, 1991) will qualify for this compliance date extension (until January 25, 1993) only if:

(i) Operations are performed pursuant to a written state agreement that includes a provision to assess the groundwater and the need for further remediation once the free phase recovery is completed; and

(ii) A copy of the written agreement has been submitted to: Waste Identification Branch (5304), U.S. Environmental Protection Agency, 1200 Pennsylvania Ave., NW., Washington, DC 20460.

(12) Used chlorofluorocarbon refrigerants from totally enclosed heat transfer equipment, including mobile air conditioning systems, mobile refrigeration, and commercial and industrial air conditioning and refrigeration systems that use chlorofluorocarbons as the heat transfer fluid in a refrigeration cycle, provided the refrigerant is reclaimed for further use. 📖 2.6.4

(13) Non-terne plated used oil filters that are not mixed with wastes listed in subpart D of this part if these oil filters have been gravity hot-drained using one of the following methods: 📖 4.21.6, 12.1.5

(i) Puncturing the filter anti-drain back valve or the filter dome end and hot-draining;

(ii) Hot-draining and crushing;

(iii) Dismantling and hot-draining; or

(iv) Any other equivalent hot-draining method that will remove used oil.

(14) Used oil re-refining distillation bottoms that are used as feedstock to manufacture asphalt products. 12.1.1.2

(15) Leachate or gas condensate collected from landfills where certain solid wastes have been disposed, provided that: 14.2.1.2

(i) The solid wastes disposed would meet one or more of the listing descriptions for Hazardous Waste Codes K169, K170, K171, K172, K174, K175, K176, K177, K178 and K181 if these wastes had been generated after the effective date of the listing;

(ii) The solid wastes described in paragraph (b)(15)(i) of this section were disposed prior to the effective date of the listing;

(iii) The leachate or gas condensate do not exhibit any characteristic of hazardous waste nor are derived from any other listed hazardous waste;

(iv) Discharge of the leachate or gas condensate, including leachate or gas condensate transferred from the landfill to a POTW by truck, rail, or dedicated pipe, is subject to regulation under sections 307(b) or 402 of the Clean Water Act.

(v) As of February 13, 2001, leachate or gas condensate derived from K169–K172 is no longer exempt if it is stored or managed in a surface impoundment prior to discharge. As of November 21, 2003, leachate or gas condensate derived from K176, K177, and K178 is no longer exempt if it is stored or managed in a surface impoundment prior to discharge. After February 26, 2007, leachate or gas condensate derived from K181 will no longer be exempt if it is stored or managed in a surface impoundment prior to discharge. There is one exception: if the surface impoundment is used to temporarily store leachate or gas condensate in response to an emergency situation (*e.g.*, shutdown of wastewater treatment system), provided the impoundment has a double liner, and provided the leachate or gas condensate is removed from the impoundment and continues to be managed in compliance with the conditions of this paragraph (b)(15)(v) after the emergency ends.

(16) Reserved.

(17) Solid waste that would otherwise meet the definition of low-level mixed wastes (LLMW) pursuant to §266.210 of this chapter that is generated at the Ortho-McNeil Pharmaceutical, Inc. (OMP Spring House) research and development facility in Spring House, Pennsylvania and treated on-site using a bench-scale high temperature catalytic oxidation unit is not a hazardous waste provided that:

(i) The total volume of LLMW generated and treated is no greater than 50 liters/year,

(ii) OMP Spring House submits a written report to the EPA Region III office once every six months beginning six months after June 27, 2005, that must contain the following:

(A) Analysis demonstrating the destruction and removal efficiency of the treatment technology for all organic components of the wastestream,

(B) Analysis demonstrating the capture efficiencies of the treatment technology for all radioactive components of the wastestream and an estimate of the amount of radioactivity released during the reporting period,

(C) Analysis (including concentrations of constituents, including inorganic constituents, present and radioactivity) of the wastestream prior to and after treatment,

(D) Volume of the wastestream being treated per batch, as well as a total for the duration of the reporting period, and

(E) Final disposition of the radioactive residuals from the treatment of the wastestream.

(iii) OMP Spring House makes no significant changes to the design or operation of the high temperature catalytic oxidation unit or the wastestream.

(iv) This exclusion will remain in affect for 5 years from June 27, 2005.

(c) Hazardous wastes which are exempted from certain regulations. A hazardous waste which is generated in a product or raw material storage tank, a product or raw material transport vehicle or vessel, a product or raw material pipeline, or in a manufacturing process unit or an associated non-waste-treatment-manufacturing unit, is not subject to regulation under parts 262 through 265, 268, 270, 271 and 124 of this chapter or to the notification requirements of section 3010 of RCRA until it exits the unit in which it was generated, unless the unit is a surface impoundment, or unless the hazardous waste remains in the unit more than 90 days after the unit ceases to be operated for manufacturing, or for storage or transportation of product or raw materials. 4.17, 7.1.1.1, 10.1.2.2, 14.1.1.2, 17.2.2

(d) *Samples.* (1) Except as provided in paragraph (d)(2) of this section, a sample of solid waste or a sample of water, soil, or air, which is collected for the sole purpose of testing to determine its characteristics or composition, is not subject to any requirements of this part or parts 262 through 268 or part 270 or part 124 of this chapter or to the notification requirements of section 3010 of RCRA, when: 4.18.1

(i) The sample is being transported to a laboratory for the purpose of testing; or

(ii) The sample is being transported back to the sample collector after testing; or

(iii) The sample is being stored by the sample collector before transport to a laboratory for testing; or

(iv) The sample is being stored in a laboratory before testing; or 4.18.1.4.1

(v) The sample is being stored in a laboratory after testing but before it is returned to the sample collector; or

(vi) The sample is being stored temporarily in the laboratory after testing for a specific purpose (for example, until conclusion of a court case or enforcement action where further testing of the sample may be necessary).

(2) In order to qualify for the exemption in paragraphs (d)(1) (i) and (ii) of this section, a sample collector shipping samples to a laboratory and a laboratory returning samples to a sample collector must:

(i) Comply with U.S. Department of Transportation (DOT), U.S. Postal Service (USPS), or any other applicable shipping requirements; or

(ii) Comply with the following requirements if the sample collector determines that DOT, USPS, or other shipping requirements do not apply to the shipment of the sample:

(A) Assure that the following information accompanies the sample:

(*1*) The sample collector's name, mailing address, and telephone number;

(*2*) The laboratory's name, mailing address, and telephone number;

(*3*) The quantity of the sample;

(*4*) The date of shipment; and

(*5*) A description of the sample.

(B) Package the sample so that it does not leak, spill, or vaporize from its packaging.

(3) This exemption does not apply if the laboratory determines that the waste is hazardous but the laboratory is no longer meeting any of the conditions stated in paragraph (d)(1) of this section.

(e) *Treatability Study Samples.* (1) Except as provided in paragraph (e)(2) of this section, persons who generate or collect samples for the purpose of conducting treatability studies as defined in section 260.10, are not subject to any requirement of parts 261 through 263 of this chapter or to the notification requirements of Section 3010 of RCRA, nor are such samples included in the quantity determinations of §261.5 and §262.34(d) when: 4.18.2

(i) The sample is being collected and prepared for transportation by the generator or sample collector; or

(ii) The sample is being accumulated or stored by the generator or sample collector prior to transportation to a laboratory or testing facility; or

(iii) The sample is being transported to the laboratory or testing facility for the purpose of conducting a treatability study.

(2) The exemption in paragraph (e)(1) of this section is applicable to samples of hazardous waste being collected and shipped for the purpose of conducting treatability studies provided that:

(i) The generator or sample collector uses (in "treatability studies") no more than 10,000 kg of media contaminated with non-acute hazardous waste, 1000 kg of non-acute hazardous waste other than contaminated media, 1 kg of acute hazardous waste, 2500 kg of media contaminated with acute hazardous waste for each process being evaluated for each generated waste stream; and 4.18.2.3

(ii) The mass of each sample shipment does not exceed 10,000 kg; the 10,000 kg quantity may be all media contaminated with non-acute hazardous waste, or may include 2500 kg of media contaminated with acute hazardous waste, 1000 kg of hazardous waste, and 1 kg of acute hazardous waste; and 4.18.2.3

(iii) The sample must be packaged so that it will not leak, spill, or vaporize from its packaging during shipment and the requirements of paragraph A or B of this subparagraph are met.

(A) The transportation of each sample shipment complies with U.S. Department of Transportation (DOT), U.S. Postal Service (USPS), or any other applicable shipping requirements; or

(B) If the DOT, USPS, or other shipping requirements do not apply to the shipment of the sample, the following information must accompany the sample:

(*1*) The name, mailing address, and telephone number of the originator of the sample;

(*2*) The name, address, and telephone number of the facility that will perform the treatability study;

(*3*) The quantity of the sample;

(*4*) The date of shipment; and

(*5*) A description of the sample, including its EPA Hazardous Waste Number.

(iv) The sample is shipped to a laboratory or testing facility which is exempt under §261.4(f) or has an appropriate RCRA permit or interim status.

(v) The generator or sample collector maintains the following records for a period ending 3 years after completion of the treatability study:

(A) Copies of the shipping documents;

(B) A copy of the contract with the facility conducting the treatability study;

(C) Documentation showing:

(*1*) The amount of waste shipped under this exemption;

(*2*) The name, address, and EPA identification number of the laboratory or testing facility that received the waste;

(*3*) The date the shipment was made; and

(*4*) Whether or not unused samples and residues were returned to the generator.

(vi) The generator reports the information required under paragraph (e)(2)(v)(C) of this section in its biennial report.

(3) The Regional Administrator may grant requests on a case-by-case basis for up to an additional two years for treatability studies involving bioremediation. The Regional Administrator may grant requests on a case-by-case basis for quantity limits in excess of those specified in paragraphs (e)(2) (i) and (ii) and (f)(4) of this section, for up to an additional 5000 kg of media contaminated with non-acute hazardous waste, 500 kg of non-acute hazardous waste, 2500 kg of media contaminated with acute hazardous waste and 1 kg of acute hazardous waste:

(i) In response to requests for authorization to ship, store and conduct treatability studies on additional quantities in advance of commencing treatability studies. Factors to be considered in reviewing such requests include the nature of the technology, the type of process (*e.g.*, batch versus continuous), size of the unit undergoing testing (particularly in relation to scale-up considerations), the time/quantity of material required to reach steady state operating conditions, or test design considerations such as mass balance calculations.

(ii) In response to requests for authorization to ship, store and conduct treatability studies on additional quantities after initiation or completion of initial treatability studies, when: There has been an equipment or mechanical failure during the conduct of a treatability study; there is a need to verify the results of a previously conducted treatability study; there is a need to study and analyze alternative techniques within a previously evaluated treatment process; or there is a need to do further evaluation of an ongoing treatability study to determine final specifications for treatment.

(iii) The additional quantities and timeframes allowed in paragraph (e)(3) (i) and (ii) of this section are subject to all the provisions in paragraphs (e) (1) and (e)(2) (iii) through (vi) of this section. The generator or sample collector must apply to the Regional Administrator in the Region where the sample is collected and provide in writing the following information:

(A) The reason why the generator or sample collector requires additional time or quantity of sample for treatability study evaluation and the additional time or quantity needed;

(B) Documentation accounting for all samples of hazardous waste from the waste stream which have been sent for or undergone treatability studies including the date each previous sample from the waste stream was shipped, the quantity of each previous shipment, the laboratory or testing facility to which it was shipped, what treatability study processes were conducted on each sample shipped, and the available results on each treatability study;

(C) A description of the technical modifications or change in specifications which will be evaluated and the expected results;

(D) If such further study is being required due to equipment or mechanical failure, the applicant must include information regarding the reason for the failure or breakdown and also include what procedures or equipment improvements have been made to protect against further breakdowns; and

(E) Such other information that the Regional Administrator considers necessary.

(f) *Samples Undergoing Treatability Studies at Laboratories and Testing Facilities.* Samples undergoing treatability studies and the laboratory or testing facility conducting such treatability studies (to the extent such facilities are not otherwise subject to RCRA requirements) are not subject to any requirement of this part, part 124, parts 262-266, 268, and 270, or to the notification requirements of Section 3010 of RCRA provided that the conditions of paragraphs (f) (1) through (11) of this section are met. A mobile treatment unit (MTU) may qualify as a testing facility subject to paragraphs (f) (1) through (11) of this section. Where a group of MTUs are located at the same site, the limitations specified in (f) (1) through (11) of this section apply to the entire group of MTUs collectively as if the group were one MTU. 4.18.2

(1) No less than 45 days before conducting treatability studies, the facility notifies the Regional Administrator, or State Director (if located in an authorized State), in writing that it intends to conduct treatability studies under this paragraph.

(2) The laboratory or testing facility conducting the treatability study has an EPA identification number.

(3) No more than a total of 10,000 kg of "as received" media contaminated with non-acute hazardous waste, 2500 kg of media contaminated with acute hazardous waste or 250 kg of other "as received" hazardous waste is subject to initiation of treatment in all treatability studies in any single day. "As received" waste refers to the waste as received in the shipment from the generator or sample collector.

(4) The quantity of "as received" hazardous waste stored at the facility for the purpose of evaluation in treatability studies does not exceed 10,000 kg, the total of which can include 10,000 kg of media contaminated with non-acute hazardous waste, 2500 kg of media contaminated with acute hazardous waste, 1000 kg of non-acute hazardous wastes other than contaminated media, and 1 kg of acute hazardous waste. This quantity limitation does not include treatment materials (including nonhazardous solid waste) added to "as received" hazardous waste.

(5) No more than 90 days have elapsed since the treatability study for the sample was completed, or no more than one year (two years for treatability studies involving bioremediation) have elapsed since the generator or sample collector shipped the sample to the laboratory or testing facility, whichever date first occurs. Up to 500 kg of treated material from a particular waste stream from treatability studies may be archived for future evaluation up to five years from the date of initial receipt. Quantities of materials archived are counted against the total storage limit for the facility.

(6) The treatability study does not involve the placement of hazardous waste on the land or open burning of hazardous waste.

(7) The facility maintains records for 3 years following completion of each study that show compliance with the treatment rate limits and the storage time and quantity limits. The following specific information must be included for each treatability study conducted:

(i) The name, address, and EPA identification number of the generator or sample collector of each waste sample;

(ii) The date the shipment was received;

(iii) The quantity of waste accepted;

(iv) The quantity of "as received" waste in storage each day;

(v) The date the treatment study was initiated and the amount of "as received" waste introduced to treatment each day;

(vi) The date the treatability study was concluded;

(vii) The date any unused sample or residues generated from the treatability study were returned to the generator or sample collector or, if sent to a designated facility, the name of the facility and the EPA identification number.

(8) The facility keeps, on-site, a copy of the treatability study contract and all shipping papers associated with the transport of treatability study samples to and from the facility for a period ending 3 years from the completion date of each treatability study.

(9) The facility prepares and submits a report to the Regional Administrator, or state Director (if located in an authorized state), by March 15 of each year, that includes the following information for the previous calendar year:

(i) The name, address, and EPA identification number of the facility conducting the treatability studies;

(ii) The types (by process) of treatability studies conducted;

(iii) The names and addresses of persons for whom studies have been conducted (including their EPA identification numbers);

(iv) The total quantity of waste in storage each day;

(v) The quantity and types of waste subjected to treatability studies;

(vi) When each treatability study was conducted;

(vii) The final disposition of residues and unused sample from each treatability study.

(10) The facility determines whether any unused sample or residues generated by the treatability study are hazardous waste under §261.3 and, if so, are subject to parts 261 through 268, and part 270 of this chapter, unless the residues and unused samples are returned to the sample originator under the §261.4(e) exemption.

(11) The facility notifies the Regional Administrator, or State Director (if located in an authorized State), by letter when the facility is no longer planning to conduct any treatability studies at the site.

(g) *Dredged material that is not a hazardous waste.* Dredged material that is subject to the requirements of a permit that has been issued under 404 of the Federal Water Pollution Control Act (33 U.S.C.1344) or section 103 of the Marine Protection, Research, and Sanctuaries Act of 1972 (33 U.S.C. 1413) is not a hazardous waste. For this paragraph (g), the following definitions apply: 📖 **4.2.4, 5.3.1.2**

(1) The term dredged material has the same meaning as defined in 40 CFR 232.2;

(2) The term permit means:

(i) A permit issued by the U.S. Army Corps of Engineers (Corps) or an approved State under section 404 of the Federal Water Pollution Control Act (33 U.S.C. 1344);

(ii) A permit issued by the Corps under section 103 of the Marine Protection, Research, and Sanctuaries Act of 1972 (33 U.S.C. 1413); or

(iii) In the case of Corps civil works projects, the administrative equivalent of the permits referred to in paragraphs (g)(2)(i) and (ii) of this section, as provided for in Corps regulations (for example, see 33 CFR 336.1, 336.2, and 337.6).

[45 FR 33119, May 19, 1980, as amended at 45 FR 72037, Oct. 30, 1980; 45 FR 76620, Nov. 19, 1980; 45 FR 78531, Nov. 25, 1980; 45 FR 80287, Dec. 4, 1980; 46 FR 27476, May 20, 1981; 46 FR 47429, Sept. 25, 1981; 48 FR 14293, Apr. 1, 1983; 48 FR 30115, June 30, 1983; 50 FR 665, Jan. 4, 1985; 50 FR 14219, Apr. 11, 1985; 50 FR 28743, July 15, 1985; 51 FR 25471, July 14, 1986; 51 FR 40636, Nov. 7, 1986; 53 FR 27301, July 19, 1988; 53 FR 35420, Sept. 13, 1988; 54 FR 36641, Sept. 1, 1989; 55 FR 2353, Jan. 23, 1990; 55 FR 11862, Mar. 29, 1990; 55 FR 26987, June 29, 1990; 55 FR 40837, Oct. 5, 1990; 55 FR 50482, Dec. 6, 1990; 56 FR 3978, Feb. 1, 1991; 56 FR 5915, Feb. 13, 1991; 56 FR 7206, Feb. 21, 1991; 56 FR 13411, Apr. 2, 1991; 56 FR 27318, June 13, 1991; 56 FR 30195, July 1, 1991; 56 FR 41177, Aug. 19, 1991; 57 FR 21534, May 20, 1992; 57 FR 27888, June 22, 1992; 57 FR 29220, July 1, 1992; 57 FR 30658, July 10, 1992; 57 FR 37305, Aug 18, 1992; 58 FR 26424, May 3, 1993; 59 FR 8365, Feb. 18, 1994; 59 FR 38545, July 28, 1994; 61 FR 13106, Mar. 26, 1996; 62 FR 26019, May 12, 1997; 63 FR 18635, Apr. 15, 1998; 63 FR 28637, May 26, 1998; 63 FR 33823, June 19, 1998; 63 FR 42184, Aug. 6, 1998; 63 FR 54356, Oct. 9, 1998; 63 FR 65937, Nov. 30, 1998; 64 FR 6814, Feb. 11, 1999; 64 FR 25414, May 11, 1999; 65 FR 47325, Aug. 2, 2000; 65 FR 54965, Sep. 12, 2000; 66 FR 23624, May 9, 2001; 66 FR 58297, Nov. 20, 2001; 67 FR 11253, Mar. 13, 2002; 67 FR 48414, July 24, 2002; 70 FR 9175, Feb. 24, 2005; 70 FR 36857, June 27, 2005; 71 FR 16902, Apr. 4, 2006; 71 FR 40258, July 14, 2006; 71 FR 42948, July 28, 2006; 73 FR 72, Jan. 2, 2008; 73 FR 35946, June 25, 2008; 73 FR 64760, Oct. 30, 2008; 73 FR 77997, Dec. 19, 2008; 74 FR 38109, July 31, 2009]

§261.5 Special requirements for hazardous waste generated by conditionally exempt small quantity generators.

(a) A generator is a conditionally exempt small quantity generator in a calendar month if he generates no more than 100 kilograms of hazardous waste in that month. 📖 **6.1.1**

(b) Except for those wastes identified in paragraphs (e), (f), (g), and (j) of this section, a conditionally exempt small quantity generator's hazardous wastes are not subject to regulation under parts 262 through 266, 268, and parts 270 and 124 of this chapter, and the notification requirements of section 3010 of RCRA, provided the generator complies with the requirements of paragraphs (f), (g), and (j) of this section. 📖 **6.7**

(c) When making the quantity determinations of this part and 40 CFR part 262, the generator must include all hazardous waste that it generates, except hazardous waste that: 📖 **6.1.3–5, 6.5.3, 9.1.2.2**

(1) Is exempt from regulation under 40 CFR 261.4(c) through (f), 261.6(a)(3), 261.7(a)(1), or 261.8; or

(2) Is managed immediately upon generation only in on-site elementary neutralization units, wastewater treatment units, or totally enclosed treatment facilities as defined in 40 CFR 260.10; or

(3) Is recycled, without prior storage or accumulation, only in an on-site process subject to regulation under 40 CFR 261.6(c)(2); or

(4) Is used oil managed under the requirements of 40 CFR 261.6(a)(4) and 40 CFR part 279; or

(5) Is spent lead-acid batteries managed under the requirements of 40 CFR part 266, subpart G; or

(6) Is universal waste managed under 40 CFR 261.9 and 40 CFR part 273; 📖 **8.1–3**

(7) Is a hazardous waste that is an unused commercial chemical product (listed in 40 CFR part 261, subpart D or exhibiting one or more characteristics in 40 CFR part 261, subpart C) that is generated solely as a result of a laboratory clean-out conducted at an eligible academic entity pursuant to §262.213. For purposes of

this provision, the term eligible academic entity shall have the meaning as defined in §262.200 of Part 262.

(d) In determining the quantity of hazardous waste generated, a generator need not include: 6.1.6

(1) Hazardous waste when it is removed from on-site storage; or

(2) Hazardous waste produced by on-site treatment (including reclamation) of his hazardous waste, so long as the hazardous waste that is treated was counted once; or 14.1.3

(3) Spent materials that are generated, reclaimed, and subsequently reused on-site, so long as such spent materials have been counted once.

(e) If a generator generates acute hazardous waste in a calendar month in quantities greater than set forth below, all quantities of that acute hazardous waste are subject to full regulation under parts 262 through 266, 268, and parts 270 and 124 of this chapter, and the notification requirements of section 3010 of RCRA: 6.1.7

(1) A total of one kilogram of acute hazardous wastes listed in §§261.31, 261.32, or 261.33(e).

(2) A total of 100 kilograms of any residue or contaminated soil, waste, or other debris resulting from the clean-up of a spill, into or on any land or water, of any acute hazardous wastes listed in §§261.31, 261.32, or 261.33(e).

[*Comment:* "Full regulation" means those regulations applicable to generators of greater than 1,000 kg of non-acutely hazardous waste in a calendar month.]

(f) In order for acute hazardous wastes generated by a generator of acute hazardous wastes in quantities equal to or less than those set forth in paragraph (e)(1) or (2) of this section to be excluded from full regulation under this section, the generator must comply with the following requirements:

(1) Section 262.11 of this chapter;

(2) The generator may accumulate acute hazardous waste on-site. If he accumulates at any time acute hazardous wastes in quantities greater than those set forth in paragraph (e)(1) or (e)(2) of this section, all of those accumulated wastes are subject to regulation under parts 262 through 266, 268, and parts 270 and 124 of this chapter, and the applicable notification requirements of section 3010 of RCRA. The time period of §262.34(a) of this chapter, for accumulation of wastes on-site, begins when the accumulated wastes exceed the applicable exclusion limit;

(3) A conditionally exempt small quantity generator may either treat or dispose of his acute hazardous waste in an on-site facility or ensure delivery to an off-site treatment, storage, or disposal facility, either of which, if located in the U.S., is:

(i) Permitted under part 270 of this chapter;

(ii) In interim status under parts 270 and 265 of this chapter;

(iii) Authorized to manage hazardous waste by a State with a hazardous waste management program approved under part 271 of this chapter;

(iv) Permitted, licensed, or registered by a State to manage municipal solid waste and, if managed in a municipal solid waste landfill is subject to Part 258 of this chapter;

(v) Permitted, licensed, or registered by a State to manage non-municipal non-hazardous waste and, if managed in a non-municipal non-hazardous waste disposal unit after January 1, 1998, is subject to the requirements in §§257.5 through 257.30 of this chapter; or

(vi) A facility which:

(A) Beneficially uses or reuses, or legitimately recycles or reclaims its waste; or

(B) Treats its waste prior to beneficial use or reuse, or legitimate recycling or reclamation; or

(vii) For universal waste managed under part 273 of this chapter, a universal waste handler or destination facility subject to the requirements of part 273 of this chapter.

(g) In order for hazardous waste generated by a conditionally exempt small quantity generator in quantities of less than 100 kilograms of hazardous waste during a calendar month to be excluded from full regulation under this section, the generator must comply with the following requirements:

(1) Section 262.11 of this chapter;

(2) The conditionally exempt small quantity generator may accumulate hazardous waste on-site. If he accumulates at any time more than a total of 1000 kilograms of his hazardous wastes, all of those accumulated wastes are subject to regulation under the special provisions of part 262 applicable to generators of between 100 kg and 1000 kg of hazardous waste in a calendar month as well as the requirements of parts 263 through 266, 268, and parts 270 and 124 of this chapter, and the applicable notification requirements of section 3010 of RCRA. The time period of §262.34(d) for accumulation of wastes on-site begins for a conditionally exempt small quantity generator when the accumulated wastes exceed 1000 kilograms;

(3) A conditionally exempt small quantity generator may either treat or dispose of his hazardous waste in an on-site facility or ensure delivery to an off-site treatment, storage or disposal facility, either of which, if located in the U.S., is:

(i) Permitted under part 270 of this chapter;

(ii) In interim status under parts 270 and 265 of this chapter;

(iii) Authorized to manage hazardous waste by a State with a hazardous waste management program approved under part 271 of this chapter;

(iv) Permitted, licensed, or registered by a State to manage municipal solid waste and, if managed in a municipal solid waste landfill is subject to Part 258 of this chapter;

(v) Permitted, licensed, or registered by a State to manage non-municipal non-hazardous waste and, if managed in a non-municipal non-hazardous waste disposal unit after January 1, 1998, is subject to the requirements in §§257.5 through 257.30 of this chapter; or

(vi) A facility which:

(A) Beneficially uses or reuses, or legitimately recycles or reclaims its waste; or

(B) Treats its waste prior to beneficial use or reuse, or legitimate recycling or reclamation; or

(vii) For universal waste managed under part 273 of this chapter, a universal waste handler or destination facility subject to the requirements of part 273 of this chapter.

(h) Hazardous waste subject to the reduced requirements of this section may be mixed with non-hazardous waste and remain subject to these reduced requirements even though the resultant mixture exceeds the quantity limitations identified in this section, unless the mixture meets any of the characteristics of hazardous waste identified in subpart C. 📖 6.1.3.6

(i) If any person mixes a solid waste with a hazardous waste that exceeds a quantity exclusion level of this section, the mixture is subject to full regulation.

(j) If a conditionally exempt small quantity generator's wastes are mixed with used oil, the mixture is subject to part 279 of this chapter. Any material produced from such a mixture by processing, blending, or other treatment is also so regulated.

[51 FR 10174, Mar. 24, 1986, as amended at 51 FR 28682, Aug. 8, 1986; 51 FR 40637, Nov. 7, 1986; 53 FR 27163, July 19, 1988; 58 FR 26424, May 3, 1993; 60 FR 25541, May 11, 1995; 61 FR 34278, July 1, 1996; 63 FR 24968, May 6, 1998; 63 FR 37782, July 14, 1998; 68 FR 44665, July 30, 2003; 73 FR 72954, Dec. 1, 2008]

§261.6 Requirements for recyclable materials.

(a)(1) Hazardous wastes that are recycled are subject to the requirements for generators, transporters, and storage facilities of paragraphs (b) and (c) of this section, except for the materials listed in paragraphs (a)(2) and (a)(3) of this section. Hazardous wastes that are recycled will be known as "recyclable materials."

(2) The following recyclable materials are not subject to the requirements of this section but are regulated under subparts C through N of part 266 of this chapter and all applicable provisions in parts 270 and 124 of this chapter:

(i) Recyclable materials used in a manner constituting disposal (40 CFR part 266, subpart C);

(ii) Hazardous wastes burned for energy recovery in boilers and industrial furnaces that are not regulated under subpart O of part 264 or 265 of this chapter (40 CFR part 266, subpart H);

(iii) Recyclable materials from which precious metals are reclaimed (40 CFR part 266, subpart F); 📖 4.19, 7.4.2.1, 13.1.2

(iv) Spent lead-acid batteries that are being reclaimed (40 CFR part 266, subpart G). 📖 4.20

(3) The following recyclable materials are not subject to regulation under parts 262 through parts 266 or parts 268, 270 or 124 of this chapter, and are not subject to the notification requirements of section 3010 of RCRA:

(i) Industrial ethyl alcohol that is reclaimed except that, unless provided otherwise in an international agreement as specified in §262.58:

(A) A person initiating a shipment for reclamation in a foreign country, and any intermediary arranging for the shipment, must comply with the requirements applicable to a primary exporter in §§262.53, 262.56 (a)(1)-(4), (6), and (b), and 262.57, export such materials only upon consent of the receiving country and in conformance with the EPA Acknowledgment of Consent as defined in subpart E of part 262, and provide a copy of the EPA Acknowledgment of Consent to the shipment to the transporter transporting the shipment for export;

(B) Transporters transporting a shipment for export may not accept a shipment if he knows the shipment does not conform to the EPA Acknowledgment of Consent, must ensure that a copy of the EPA Acknowledgment of Consent accompanies the shipment and must ensure that it is delivered to the facility designated by the person initiating the shipment.

(ii) Scrap metal that is not excluded under §261.4(a)(13); 📖 1.2.5.5, 4.21

(iii) Fuels produced from the refining of oil-bearing hazardous waste along with normal process streams at a petroleum refining facility if such wastes result from normal petroleum refining, production, and transportation practices (this exemption does not apply to fuels produced from oil recovered from oil-bearing hazardous waste, where such recovered oil is already excluded under §261.4(a)(12); 📖 5.2.3.4

(iv)(A) Hazardous waste fuel produced from oil-bearing hazardous wastes from petroleum refining, production, or transportation practices, or produced from oil reclaimed from such hazardous wastes, where such hazardous wastes are reintroduced into a process that does not use distillation or does not produce products from crude oil so long as the resulting fuel meets the used oil specification under §279.11 of this chapter and so long as no other hazardous wastes are used to produce the hazardous waste fuel; 📖 5.2.3.4

(B) Hazardous waste fuel produced from oil-bearing hazardous waste from petroleum refining production, and transportation practices, where such hazardous wastes are reintroduced into a refining process after a point at which contaminants are removed, so long as the fuel meets the used oil fuel specification under §279.11 of this chapter; and

(C) Oil reclaimed from oil-bearing hazardous wastes from petroleum refining, production, and transportation practices, which reclaimed oil is burned as a fuel without reintroduction to a refining process, so long as the reclaimed oil meets the used oil fuel specification under §279.11 of this chapter.

(4) Used oil that is recycled and is also a hazardous waste solely because it exhibits a hazardous characteristic is not subject to the requirements of parts 260 through 268 of this chapter, but is regulated under part 279 of this chapter. Used oil that is recycled includes any used oil which is reused, following its original use, for any purpose (including the purpose for which the oil was originally used). Such term includes, but is not limited to, oil which is re-refined, reclaimed, burned for energy recovery, or reprocessed. 📖 12.1

(5) Hazardous waste that is exported to or imported from designated member countries of the Organization for Economic Cooperation and Development (OECD) (as defined in §262.58(a)(1)) for purpose of recovery is subject to the requirements of 40 CFR part 262, subpart H, if it is subject to either the Federal manifesting requirements of 40 CFR Part 262, to the universal waste management standards of 40 CFR Part 273, or to State requirements analogous to 40 CFR Part 273.

(b) Generators and transporters of recyclable materials are subject to the applicable requirements of parts 262 and 263 of this chapter and the notification requirements under section 3010 of RCRA, except as provided in paragraph (a) of this section.

(c)(1) Owners and operators of facilities that store recyclable materials before they are recycled are regulated under all applicable provisions of subparts A though L, AA, BB, and CC of parts 264 and 265, and under parts 124, 266, 268, and 270 of this chapter and the notification requirements under section 3010 of RCRA, except as provided in paragraph (a) of this section. (The recycling process itself is exempt from regulation except as provided in §261.6(d).) 📖 7.4.1

(2) Owners or operators of facilities that recycle recyclable materials without storing them before they are recycled are subject to the following requirements, except as provided in paragraph (a) of this section: 📖 7.4.1.2

(i) Notification requirements under section 3010 of RCRA;

(ii) Sections 265.71 and 265.72 (dealing with the use of the manifest and manifest discrepancies) of this chapter.

(iii) Section 261.6(d) of this chapter.

(d) Owners or operators of facilities subject to RCRA permitting requirements with hazardous waste management units that recycle hazardous wastes are subject to the requirements of subparts AA and BB of part 264 or 265 of this chapter. 📖 7.4.1.3, 15.1.1.4, 15.2.1.5

[50 FR 49203, Nov. 29, 1985, as amended at 51 FR 28682, Aug. 8, 1986; 51 FR 40637, Nov. 7, 1986; 52 FR 11821, Apr. 13, 1987; 55 FR 25493, June 21, 1990; 56 FR 7207, Feb. 21, 1991; 56 FR 32692, July 17, 1991; 57 FR 41612, Sept. 10, 1992; 59 FR 38545, July 28, 1994; 60 FR 25541, May 11, 1995; 61 FR 16309, Apr. 12, 1996; 61 FR 59950, Nov. 25, 1996; 62 FR 26019, May 12, 1997; 63 FR 24968, May 6, 1998; 63 FR 42185, Aug. 6, 1998; 66 FR 28085, May 22, 2001; 71 FR 40259, July 14, 2006; 73 FR 37860, July 2, 2008]

§261.7 Residues of hazardous waste in empty containers. 📖 9.5

(a)(1) Any hazardous waste remaining in either: (i) an empty container; or (ii) an inner liner removed from an empty container, as defined in paragraph (b) of this section, is not subject to regulation under parts 261 through 265, 267, 268, 270, or 124 of this chapter or to the notification requirements of section 3010 of RCRA. 📖 9.5.5

(2) Any hazardous waste in either (i) a container that is not empty or (ii) an inner liner removed from a container that is not empty, as defined in paragraph (b) of this section, is subject to regulation under parts 261 through 265, and parts 268, 270 and 124 of this chapter and to the notification requirements of section 3010 of RCRA. 📖 9.5

(b)(1) A container or an inner liner removed from a container that has held any hazardous waste, except a waste that is a compressed gas or that is identified as an acute hazardous waste listed in §§261.31, 261.32, or 261.33(e) of this chapter is empty if: 📖 9.5.1

(i) All wastes have been removed that can be removed using the practices commonly employed to remove materials from that type of container, *e.g.*, pouring, pumping, and aspirating, *and*

(ii) No more than 2.5 centimeters (one inch) of residue remain on the bottom of the container or inner liner, or

(iii)(A) No more than 3 percent by weight of the total capacity of the container remains in the container or inner liner if the container is less than or equal to 119 gallons in size; or

(B) No more than 0.3 percent by weight of the total capacity of the container remains in the container or inner liner if the container is greater than 119 gallons in size.

(2) A container that has held a hazardous waste that is a compressed gas is empty when the pressure in the container approaches atmospheric. 📖 9.5.3, 14.5.2.1

(3) A container or an inner liner removed from a container that has held an acute hazardous waste listed in §§261.31, 261.32, or 261.33(e) is empty if: 📖 9.5.2

(i) The container or inner liner has been triple rinsed using a solvent capable of removing the commercial chemical product or manufacturing chemical intermediate;

(ii) The container or inner liner has been cleaned by another method that has been shown in the scientific literature, or by tests conducted by the generator, to achieve equivalent removal; or 📖 9.5.2.2

(iii) In the case of a container, the inner liner that prevented contact of the commercial chemical product or manufacturing chemical intermediate with the container, has been removed.

[45 FR 78529, Nov. 25, 1980, as amended at 47 FR 36097, Aug. 18, 1982; 48 FR 14294, Apr. 1, 1983; 50 FR 1999, Jan. 14, 1985; 51 FR 40637, Nov. 7, 1986; 70 FR 10815, Mar. 4, 2005; 70 FR 53453, Sept. 8, 2005]

§261.8 PCB wastes regulated under Toxic Substance Control Act.

The disposal of PCB-containing dielectric fluid and electric equipment containing such fluid authorized for use and regulated under part 761 of this chapter and that are hazardous only because they fail the test for the Toxicity Characteristic (Hazardous Waste Codes D018 through D043 only) are exempt from regulation under parts 261 through 265, and parts 268, 270, and 124 of this chapter, and the notification requirements of section 3010 of RCRA. 📖 2.6.4

[55 FR 11862, Mar. 29, 1990]

§261.9 Requirements for Universal Waste.

The wastes listed in this section are exempt from regulation under parts 262 through 270 of this chapter except as specified in part 273 of this chapter and, therefore are not fully regulated as hazardous waste. The wastes listed in this section are subject to regulation under 40 CFR part 273: 📖 8.1, 8.2, 13.13.3

(a) Batteries as described in 40 CFR 273.2;

(b) Pesticides as described in §273.3 of this chapter;

(c) Mercury-containing equipment as described in §273.4 of this chapter; and

(d) Lamps as described in §273.5 of this chapter.

[60 FR 25541, May 11, 1995, as amended at 64 FR 36487, July 6, 1999; 70 FR 45520, Aug. 5, 2005]

Subpart B—Criteria for Identifying the Characteristics of Hazardous Waste and for Listing Hazardous Waste

§261.10 Criteria for identifying the characteristics of hazardous waste.

(a) The Administrator shall identify and define a characteristic of hazardous waste in subpart C only upon determining that:

(1) A solid waste that exhibits the characteristic may:

(i) Cause, or significantly contribute to, an increase in mortality or an increase in serious irreversible, or incapacitating reversible, illness; or

(ii) Pose a substantial present or potential hazard to human health or the environment when it is improperly treated, stored, transported, disposed of or otherwise managed; and

(2) The characteristic can be:

(i) Measured by an available standardized test method which is reasonably within the capability of generators of solid waste or private sector laboratories that are available to serve generators of solid waste; or

(ii) Reasonably detected by generators of solid waste through their knowledge of their waste.

(b) [Reserved]

§261.11 Criteria for listing hazardous waste.

(a) The Administrator shall list a solid waste as a hazardous waste only upon determining that the solid waste meets one of the following criteria:

(1) It exhibits any of the characteristics of hazardous waste identified in subpart C.

(2) It has been found to be fatal to humans in low doses or, in the absence of data on human toxicity, it has been shown in studies to have an oral LD 50 toxicity (rat) of less than 50 milligrams per kilogram, an inhalation LC 50 toxicity (rat) of less than 2 milligrams per liter, or a dermal LD 50 toxicity (rabbit) of less than 200 milligrams per kilogram or is otherwise capable of causing or significantly contributing to an increase in serious irreversible, or incapacitating reversible, illness. (Waste listed in accordance with these criteria will be designated Acute Hazardous Waste.)

(3) It contains any of the toxic constituents listed in appendix VIII and, after considering the following factors, the Administrator concludes that the waste is capable of posing a substantial present or potential hazard to human health or the environment when improperly treated, stored, transported or disposed of, or otherwise managed: 18.2

(i) The nature of the toxicity presented by the constituent.

(ii) The concentration of the constituent in the waste.

(iii) The potential of the constituent or any toxic degradation product of the constituent to migrate from the waste into the environment under the types of improper management considered in paragraph (a)(3)(vii) of this section.

(iv) The persistence of the constituent or any toxic degradation product of the constituent.

(v) The potential for the constituent or any toxic degradation product of the constituent to degrade into non-harmful constituents and the rate of degradation.

(vi) The degree to which the constituent or any degradation product of the constituent bioaccumulates in ecosystems.

(vii) The plausible types of improper management to which the waste could be subjected.

(viii) The quantities of the waste generated at individual generation sites or on a regional or national basis.

(ix) The nature and severity of the human health and environmental damage that has occurred as a result of the improper management of wastes containing the constituent.

(x) Action taken by other governmental agencies or regulatory programs based on the health or environmental hazard posed by the waste or waste constituent.

(xi) Such other factors as may be appropriate.

Substances will be listed on appendix VIII only if they have been shown in scientific studies to have toxic, carcinogenic, mutagenic or teratogenic effects on humans or other life forms. (Wastes listed in accordance with these criteria will be designated Toxic wastes.)

(b) The Administrator may list classes or types of solid waste as hazardous waste if he has reason to believe that individual wastes, within the class or type of waste, typically or frequently are hazardous under the definition of hazardous waste found in section 1004(5) of the Act.

(c) The Administrator will use the criteria for listing specified in this section to establish the exclusion limits referred to in §261.5(c).

[45 FR 33119, May 19, 1980, as amended at 55 FR 18726, May 4, 1990; 57 FR 14, Jan. 2, 1992]

Subpart C—Characteristics of Hazardous Waste

§261.20 General. 2.1, 14.4.3

(a) A solid waste, as defined in §261.2, which is not excluded from regulation as a hazardous waste under §261.4(b), is a hazardous waste if it exhibits any of the characteristics identified in this subpart.

[*Comment:* §262.11 of this chapter sets forth the generator's responsibility to determine whether his waste exhibits one or more of the characteristics identified in this subpart]

(b) A hazardous waste which is identified by a characteristic in this subpart is assigned every EPA Hazardous Waste Number that is applicable as set forth in this subpart. This number must be used in complying with the notification requirements of section 3010 of the Act and all applicable recordkeeping and reporting requirements under parts 262 through 265, 268, and 270 of this chapter.

(c) For purposes of this subpart, the Administrator will consider a sample obtained using any of the applicable sampling methods specified in appendix I to be a representative sample within the meaning of part 260 of this chapter. 18.5.1

[*Comment:* Since the appendix I sampling methods are not being formally adopted by the Administrator, a person who desires to employ an alternative sampling method is not required to demonstrate the equivalency of his method under the procedures set forth in §§260.20 and 260.21.]

[45 FR 33119, May 19, 1980, as amended at 51 FR 40636, Nov. 7, 1986; 55 FR 22684, June 1, 1990; 56 FR 3876, Jan. 31, 1991]

§261.21 Characteristic of ignitability. 2.2

(a) A solid waste exhibits the characteristic of ignitability if a representative sample of the waste has any of the following properties:

(1) It is a liquid, other than an aqueous solution containing less than 24 percent alcohol by volume and has flash point less than 60°C (140°F), as determined by a Pensky-Martens Closed Cup Tester, using the test method specified in ASTM Standard D 93–79 or D 93–80 (incorporated by reference, see §260.11), or a Setaflash Closed Cup Tester, using the test method specified in ASTM Standard D 3278–78 (incorporated by reference, see §260.11). 2.2.1, 18.2.2.1, 18.3.3.1

(2) It is not a liquid and is capable, under standard temperature and pressure, of causing fire through friction, absorption of moisture or spontaneous chemical changes and, when ignited, burns so vigorously and persistently that it creates a hazard. 2.2.2

(3) It is an ignitable compressed gas. 2.2.3, 14.5.2.1

(i) The term "compressed gas" shall designate any material or mixture having in the container an absolute pressure exceeding 40 p.s.i. at 70°F or, regardless of the pressure at 70°F, having an absolute pressure exceeding 104 p.s.i. at 130°F; or any liquid flammable material having a vapor pressure exceeding 40 p.s.i. absolute at 100°F as determined by ASTM Test D–323.

(ii) A compressed gas shall be characterized as ignitable if any one of the following occurs:

(A) Either a mixture of 13 percent or less (by volume) with air forms a flammable mixture or the flammable range with air is wider than 12 percent regardless of the lower limit. These limits shall be determined at atmospheric temperature and pressure. The method of sampling and test procedure shall be acceptable to the Bureau of Explosives and approved by the director, Pipeline and Hazardous Materials Technology, U.S. Department of Transportation (see Note 2).

(B) Using the Bureau of Explosives' Flame Projection Apparatus (see Note 1), the flame projects more than 18 inches beyond the ignition source with valve opened fully, or, the flame flashes back and burns at the valve with any degree of valve opening.

(C) Using the Bureau of Explosives' Open Drum Apparatus (see Note 1), there is any significant propagation of flame away from the ignition source.

(D) Using the Bureau of Explosives' Closed Drum Apparatus (see Note 1), there is any explosion of the vapor-air mixture in the drum.

(4) It is an oxidizer. An oxidizer for the purpose of this subchapter is a substance such as a chlorate, permanganate, inorganic peroxide, or a nitrate, that yields oxygen readily to stimulate the combustion of organic matter (see Note 4). 2.2.4

(i) An organic compound containing the bivalent -O-O- structure and which may be considered a derivative of hydrogen peroxide where one or more of the hydrogen atoms have been replaced by organic radicals must be classed as an organic peroxide unless:

(A) The material meets the definition of a Class A explosive or a Class B explosive, as defined in §261.23(a)(8), in which case it must be classed as an explosive,

(B) The material is forbidden to be offered for transportation according to 49 CFR 172.101 and 49 CFR 173.21,

(C) It is determined that the predominant hazard of the material containing an organic peroxide is other than that of an organic peroxide, or

(D) According to data on file with the Pipeline and Hazardous Materials Safety Administration in the U.S. Department of Transportation (see Note 3), it has been determined that the material does not present a hazard in transportation.

(b) A solid waste that exhibits the characteristic of ignitability has the EPA Hazardous Waste Number of D001.

Note 1: A description of the Bureau of Explosives' Flame Projection Apparatus, Open Drum Apparatus, Closed Drum Apparatus, and method of tests may be procured from the Bureau of Explosives.

Note 2: As part of a U.S. Department of Transportation (DOT) reorganization, the Office of Hazardous Materials Technology (OHMT), which was the office listed in the 1980 publication of 49 CFR 173.300 for the purposes of approving sampling and test procedures for a flammable gas, ceased operations on February 20, 2005. OHMT programs have moved to the Pipeline and Hazardous Materials Safety Administration (PHMSA) in the DOT.

Note 3: As part of a U.S. Department of Transportation (DOT) reorganization, the Research and Special Programs Administration (RSPA), which was the office listed in the 1980 publication of 49 CFR 173.151a for the purposes of determining that a material does not present a hazard in transport, ceased operations on February 20, 2005. RSPA programs have moved to the Pipeline and Hazardous Materials Safety Administration (PHMSA) in the DOT.

Note 4: The DOT regulatory definition of an oxidizer was contained in §173.151 of 49 CFR, and the definition of an organic peroxide was contained in paragraph 173.151a. An organic peroxide is a type of oxidizer.

[45 FR 33119, May 19, 1980, as amended at 46 FR 35247, July 7, 1981; 55 FR 22684, June 1, 1990; 70 FR 34561, June 14, 2005; 71 FR 40259, July 14, 2006]

§261.22 Characteristic of corrosivity. 📖 2.3, 18.2.2.2, 18.3.3.2

(a) A solid waste exhibits the characteristic of corrosivity if a representative sample of the waste has either of the following properties:

(1) It is aqueous and has a pH less than or equal to 2 or greater than or equal to 12.5, as determined by a pH meter using Method 9040C in "Test Methods for Evaluating Solid Waste, Physical/Chemical Methods," EPA Publication SW–846, as incorporated by reference in §260.11 of this chapter. 📖 2.3.1–2

(2) It is a liquid and corrodes steel (SAE 1020) at a rate greater than 6.35 mm (0.250 inch) per year at a test temperature of 55°C (130°F) as determined by Method 1110A in "Test Methods for Evaluating Solid Waste, Physical/Chemical Methods," EPA Publication SW–846, and as incorporated by reference in §260.11 of this chapter. 📖 2.3.3

(b) A solid waste that exhibits the characteristic of corrosivity has the EPA Hazardous Waste Number of D002.

[45 FR 33119, May 19, 1980, as amended at 46 FR 35247, July 7, 1981; 55 FR 22684, June 1, 1990; 58 FR 46049, Aug. 31, 1993; 70 FR 34561, June 14, 2005]

§261.23 Characteristic of reactivity. 📖 2.4, 18.2.2.3, 18.3.3.3

(a) A solid waste exhibits the characteristic of reactivity if a representative sample of the waste has any of the following properties:

(1) It is normally unstable and readily undergoes violent change without detonating.

(2) It reacts violently with water.

(3) It forms potentially explosive mixtures with water.

(4) When mixed with water, it generates toxic gases, vapors or fumes in a quantity sufficient to present a danger to human health or the environment.

(5) It is a cyanide or sulfide bearing waste which, when exposed to pH conditions between 2 and 12.5, can generate toxic gases, vapors or fumes in a quantity sufficient to present a danger to human health or the environment. 📖 2.4.2

(6) It is capable of detonation or explosive reaction if it is subjected to a strong initiating source or if heated under confinement. 📖 2.5.1

(7) It is readily capable of detonation or explosive decomposition or reaction at standard temperature and pressure.

(8) It is a forbidden explosive as defined in 49 CFR 173.51, or a Class A explosive as defined in 49 CFR 173.53 or a Class B explosive as defined in 49 CFR 173.88. 📖 2.4.3.4

Publisher's Note: DOT's definitions for forbidden, Class A, and Class B explosives have changed. Nevertheless, generators must use the 1980 definitions of forbidden, Class A, and Class B explosives to determine §261.23(a)(8) reactivity. DOT includes a table in their current regs showing the relationships between the old and the new definitions for these explosives (see 49 *CFR* 173.53 and 173.54).

(b) A solid waste that exhibits the characteristic of reactivity has the EPA Hazardous Waste Number of D003.

[45 FR 33119, May 19, 1980, as amended at 55 FR 22684, June 1, 1990]

§261.24 Toxicity characteristic. 📖 2.6, 18.2.2.4, 18.3.3.4

(a) A solid waste (except manufactured gas plant waste) exhibits the characteristic of toxicity if, using the Toxicity Characteristic Leaching Procedure, test Method 1311 in "Test Methods for Evaluating Solid Waste, Physical/Chemical Methods," EPA Publication SW–846, as incorporated by reference in §260.11 of this chapter, the extract from a representative sample of the waste contains any of the contaminants listed in Table 1 at the concentration equal to or greater than the respective value given in that table. Where the waste contains less than 0.5 percent filterable solids, the waste itself, after filtering using the methodology outlined in Method 1311, is considered to be the extract for the purpose of this section. 📖 2.6.2–3

(b) A solid waste that exhibits the characteristic of toxicity has the EPA Hazardous Waste Number specified in Table 1 which corresponds to the toxic contaminant causing it to be hazardous.

Table 1—Maximum Concentration of Contaminants for the Toxicity Characteristic

EPA HW No. [1]	Contaminant	CAS No. [2]	Regulatory Level (mg/L)
D004	Arsenic	7440-38-2	5.0
D005	Barium	7440-39-3	100.0
D018	Benzene	71-43-2	0.5
D006	Cadmium	7440-43-9	1.0
D019	Carbon tetrachloride	56-23-5	0.5
D020	Chlordane	57-74-9	0.03
D021	Chlorobenzene	108-90-7	100.0
D022	Chloroform	67-66-3	6.0
D007	Chromium	7440-47-3	5.0
D023	o-Cresol	95-48-7	[4] 200.0
D024	m-Cresol	108-39-4	[4] 200.0
D025	p-Cresol	106-44-5	[4] 200.0
D026	Cresol		[4] 200.0
D016	2,4-D	94-75-7	10.0
D027	1,4-Dichlorobenzene	106-46-7	7.5

Table 1—Maximum Concentration of Contaminants for the Toxicity Characteristic

EPA HW No. [1]	Contaminant	CAS No. [2]	Regulatory Level (mg/L)
D028	1,2-Dichloroethane	107-06-2	0.5
D029	1,1-Dichloroethylene	75-35-4	0.7
D030	2,4-Dinitrotoluene	121-14-2	[3] 0.13
D012	Endrin	72-20-8	0.02
D031	Heptachlor (and its epoxide)	76-44-8	0.008
D032	Hexachlorobenzene	118-74-1	[3] 0.13
D033	Hexachlorobutadiene	87-68-3	0.5
D034	Hexachloroethane	67-72-1	3.0
D008	Lead	7439-92-1	5.0
D013	Lindane	58-89-9	0.4
D009	Mercury	7439-97-6	0.2
D014	Methoxychlor	72-43-5	10.0
D035	Methyl ethyl ketone	78-93-3	200.0
D036	Nitrobenzene	98-95-3	2.0
D037	Pentachlorophenol	87-86-5	100.0
D038	Pyridine	110-86-1	[3] 5.0
D010	Selenium	7782-49-2	1.0
D011	Silver	7440-22-4	5.0
D039	Tetrachloroethylene	127-18-4	0.7
D015	Toxaphene	8001-35-2	0.5
D040	Trichloroethylene	79-01-6	0.5
D041	2,4,5-Trichlorophenol	95-95-4	400.0
D042	2,4,6-Trichlorophenol	88-06-2	2.0
D017	2,4,5-TP (Silvex)	93-72-1	1.0
D043	Vinyl chloride	75-01-4	0.2

[1] Hazardous waste number.

[2] Chemical abstracts service number.

[3] Quantitation limit is greater than the calculated regulatory level. The quantitation limit therefore becomes the regulatory level. 📖 2.6.1.2

[4] If o-, m-, and p-Cresol concentrations cannot be differentiated, the total cresol (D026) concentration is used. The regulatory level of total cresol is 200 mg/l.

[55 FR 11862, Mar. 29, 1990, as amended at 55 FR 22684, June 1, 1990; 55 FR 26987, June 29, 1990; 58 FR 46049, Aug. 31, 1993; 67 FR 11254, Mar. 13, 2002; 71 FR 40259, July 14, 2006]

Subpart D—Lists of Hazardous Wastes

§261.30 General. 📖 3.1, 14.2, 14.4.4

(a) A solid waste is a hazardous waste if it is listed in this subpart, unless it has been excluded from this list under §§260.20 and 260.22.

(b) The Administrator will indicate his basis for listing the classes or types of wastes listed in this subpart by employing one or more of the following Hazard Codes:

Ignitable Waste . . . . (I)
Corrosive Waste . . . . (C)
Reactive Waste . . . . (R)
Toxicity Characteristic Waste . . . (E)
Acute Hazardous Waste . . . . (H)
Toxic Waste . . . . (T)

Appendix VII identifies the constituent which caused the Administrator to list the waste as a Toxicity Characteristic Waste (E) or Toxic Waste (T) in §§261.31 and 261.32.

(c) Each hazardous waste listed in this subpart is assigned an EPA Hazardous Waste Number which precedes the name of the waste. This number must be used in complying with the notification requirements of Section 3010 of the Act and certain recordkeeping and reporting requirements under parts 262 through 265, 268, and part 270 of this chapter.

(d) The following hazardous wastes listed in §261.31 or §261.32 are subject to the exclusion limits for acutely hazardous wastes established in §261.5: EPA Hazardous Wastes Nos. F020, F021, F022, F023, F026, and F027.

[45 FR 33119, May 19, 1980, as amended at 48 FR 14294, Apr. 1, 1983; 50 FR 2000, Jan. 14, 1985; 51 FR 40636, Nov. 7, 1986; 55 FR 11863, Mar. 29, 1990]

§261.31 Hazardous wastes from non-specific sources. 📖 3.1.1

(a) The following solid wastes are listed hazardous wastes from non-specific sources unless they are excluded under §§260.20 and 260.22 and listed in appendix IX.

Industry and EPA hazardous waste No.	Hazardous waste	Hazard code
Generic:		
F001	The following spent halogenated solvents used in degreasing: Tetrachloroethylene, trichloroethylene, methylene chloride, 1,1,1-trichloroethane, carbon tetrachloride, and chlorinated fluorocarbons; all spent solvent mixtures/blends used in degreasing containing, before use, a total of ten percent or more (by volume) of one or more of the above halogenated solvents or those solvents listed in F002, F004, and F005; and still bottoms from the recovery of these spent solvents and spent solvent mixtures. 📖 3.2-3, 13.5	(T)
F002	The following spent halogenated solvents: Tetrachloroethylene, methylene chloride, trichloroethylene, 1,1,1-trichloroethane, chlorobenzene, 1,1,2-trichloro-1,2,2-trifluoroethane, ortho-dichlorobenzene, trichlorofluoromethane, and 1,1,2-trichloroethane; all spent solvent mixtures/ blends containing, before use, a total of ten percent or more (by volume) of one or more of the above halogenated solvents or those listed in F001, F004, or F005; and still bottoms from the recovery of these spent solvents and spent solvent mixtures. 📖 3.2-3, 13.5	(T)

Industry and EPA hazardous waste No.	Hazardous waste	Hazard code
F003	The following spent non-halogenated solvents: Xylene, acetone, ethyl acetate, ethyl benzene, ethyl ether, methyl isobutyl ketone, n-butyl alcohol, cyclohexanone, and methanol; all spent solvent mixtures/blends containing, before use, only the above spent non-halogenated solvents; and all spent solvent mixtures/blends containing, before use, one or more of the above non-halogenated solvents, and, a total of ten percent or more (by volume) of one or more of those solvents listed in F001, F002, F004, and F005; and still bottoms from the recovery of these spent solvents and spent solvent mixtures. 📖 **3.2-3, 13.5**	(I)*
F004	The following spent non-halogenated solvents: Cresols and cresylic acid, and nitrobenzene; all spent solvent mixtures/blends containing, before use, a total of ten percent or more (by volume) of one or more of the above non-halogenated solvents or those solvents listed in F001, F002, and F005; and still bottoms from the recovery of these spent solvents and spent solvent mixtures. 📖 **3.2-3, 13.5**	(T)
F005	The following spent non-halogenated solvents: Toluene, methyl ethyl ketone, carbon disulfide, isobutanol, pyridine, benzene, 2-ethoxyethanol, and 2-nitropropane; all spent solvent mixtures/blends containing, before use, a total of ten percent or more (by volume) of one or more of the above non-halogenated solvents or those solvents listed in F001, F002, or F004; and still bottoms from the recovery of these spent solvents and spent solvent mixtures. 📖 **3.2-3, 13.5**	(I,T)
F006	Wastewater treatment sludges from electroplating operations except from the following processes: (1) Sulfuric acid anodizing of aluminum; (2) tin plating on carbon steel; (3) zinc plating (segregated basis) on carbon steel; (4) aluminum or zinc-aluminum plating on carbon steel; (5) cleaning/stripping associated with tin, zinc and aluminum plating on carbon steel; and (6) chemical etching and milling of aluminum. 📖 **3.4.2, 5.2.3.3**	(T)
F007	Spent cyanide plating bath solutions from electroplating operations. 📖 **3.4.3**	(R, T)
F008	Plating bath residues from the bottom of plating baths from electroplating operations where cyanides are used in the process. 📖 **3.4.4**	(R, T)
F009	Spent stripping and cleaning bath solutions from electroplating operations where cyanides are used in the process. 📖 **3.4.5**	(R, T)
F010	Quenching bath residues from oil baths from metal heat treating operations where cyanides are used in the process.	(R, T)
F011	Spent cyanide solutions from salt bath pot cleaning from metal heat treating operations.	(R, T)
F012	Quenching waste water treatment sludges from metal heat treating operations where cyanides are used in the process.	(T)
F019	Wastewater treatment sludges from the chemical conversion coating of aluminum except from zirconium phosphating in aluminum can washing when such phosphating is an exclusive conversion coating process. Wastewater treatment sludges from the manufacturing of motor vehicles using a zinc phosphating process will not be subject to this listing at the point of generation if the wastes are not placed outside on the land prior to shipment to a landfill for disposal and are either: disposed in a Subtitle D municipal or industrial landfill unit that is equipped with a single clay liner and is permitted, licensed or otherwise authorized by the state; or disposed in a landfill unit subject to, or otherwise meeting, the landfill requirements in §258.40, §264.301 or §265.301. For the purposes of this listing, motor vehicle manufacturing is defined in paragraph (b)(4)(i) of this section and (b)(4)(ii) of this section describes the recordkeeping requirements for motor vehicle manufacturing facilities. 📖 **3.4.6, 5.2.3.3**	(T)
F020	Wastes (except wastewater and spent carbon from hydrogen chloride purification) from the production or manufacturing use (as a reactant, chemical intermediate, or component in a formulating process) of tri- or tetrachlorophenol, or of intermediates used to produce their pesticide derivatives. (This listing does not include wastes from the production of Hexachlorophene from highly purified 2,4,5-trichlorophenol.)	(H)
F021	Wastes (except wastewater and spent carbon from hydrogen chloride purification) from the production or manufacturing use (as a reactant, chemical intermediate, or component in a formulating process) of pentachlorophenol, or of intermediates used to produce its derivatives.	(H)
F022	Wastes (except wastewater and spent carbon from hydrogen chloride purification) from the manufacturing use (as a reactant, chemical intermediate, or component in a formulating process) of tetra-, penta-, or hexachlorobenzenes under alkaline conditions.	(H)
F023	Wastes (except wastewater and spent carbon from hydrogen chloride purification) from the production of materials on equipment previously used for the production or manufacturing use (as a reactant, chemical intermediate, or component in a formulating process) of tri- and tetrachlorophenols. (This listing does not include wastes from equipment used only for the production or use of Hexachlorophene from highly purified 2,4,5-trichlorophenol.)	(H)
F024	Process wastes, including but not limited to, distillation residues, heavy ends, tars, and reactor clean-out wastes, from the production of certain chlorinated aliphatic hydrocarbons by free radical catalyzed processes. These chlorinated aliphatic hydrocarbons are those having carbon chain lengths ranging from one to and including five, with varying amounts and positions of chlorine substitution. (This listing does not include wastewaters, wastewater treatment sludges, spent catalysts, and wastes listed in §261.31 or §261.32.)	(T)

PART 261—Subpart D

Industry and EPA hazardous waste No.	Hazardous waste	Hazard code
F025	Condensed light ends, spent filters and filter aids, and spent desiccant wastes from the production of certain chlorinated aliphatic hydrocarbons, by free radical catalyzed processes. These chlorinated aliphatic hydrocarbons are those having carbon chain lengths ranging from one to and including five, with varying amounts and positions of chlorine substitution.	(T)
F026	Wastes (except wastewater and spent carbon from hydrogen chloride purification) from the production of materials on equipment previously used for the manufacturing use (as a reactant, chemical intermediate, or component in a formulating process) of tetra-, penta-, or hexachlorobenzene under alkaline conditions.	(H)
F027	Discarded unused formulations containing tri-, tetra-, or pentachlorophenol or discarded unused formulations containing compounds derived from these chlorophenols. (This listing does not include formulations containing Hexachlorophene sythesized from prepurified 2,4,5-trichlorophenol as the sole component.)	(H)
F028	Residues resulting from the incineration or thermal treatment of soil contaminated with EPA Hazardous Waste Nos. F020, F021, F022, F023, F026, and F027.	(T)
F032	Wastewaters (except those that have not come into contact with process contaminants), process residuals, preservative drippage, and spent formulations from wood preserving processes generated at plants that currently use or have previously used chlorophenolic formulations (except potentially cross-contaminated wastes that have had the F032 waste code deleted in accordance with §261.35 of this chapter or potentially cross-contaminated wastes that are otherwise currently regulated as hazardous wastes (*i.e.*, F034 or F035), and where the generator does not resume or initiate use of chlorophenolic formulations). This listing does not include K001 bottom sediment sludge from the treatment of wastewater from wood preserving processes that use creosote and/or pentachlorophenol.	(T)
F034	Wastewaters (except those that have not come into contact with process contaminants), process residuals, preservative drippage, and spent formulations from wood preserving processes generated at plants that use creosote formulations. This listing does not include K001 bottom sediment sludge from the treatment of wastewater from wood preserving processes that use creosote and/or pentachlorophenol.	(T)
F035	Wastewaters (except those that have not come into contact with process contaminants), process residuals, preservative drippage, and spent formulations from wood preserving processes generated at plants that use inorganic preservatives containing arsenic or chromium. This listing does not include K001 bottom sediment sludge from the treatment of wastewater from wood preserving processes that use creosote and/or pentachlorophenol.	(T)
F037	Petroleum refinery primary oil/water/solids separation sludge—Any sludge generated from the gravitational separation of oil/water/solids during the storage or treatment of process wastewaters and oil cooling wastewaters from petroleum refineries. Such sludges include, but are not limited to, those generated in oil/water/ solids separators; tanks and impoundments; ditches and other conveyances; sumps; and stormwater units receiving dry weather flow. Sludge generated in stormwater units that do not receive dry weather flow, sludges generated from non-contact once-through cooling waters segregated for treatment from other process or oily cooling waters, sludges generated in aggressive biological treatment units as defined in §261.31(b)(2) (including sludges generated in one or more additional units after wastewaters have been treated in aggressive biological treatment units) and K051 wastes are not included in this listing. This listing does include residuals generated from processing or recycling oil-bearing hazardous secondary materials excluded under §261.4(a)(12)(i) , if those residuals are to be disposed of.	(T)
F038	Petroleum refinery secondary (emulsified) oil/water/solids separation sludge—Any sludge and/or float generated from the physical and/or chemical separation of oil/water/solids in process wastewaters and oily cooling wastewaters from petroleum refineries. Such wastes include, but are not limited to, all sludges and floats generated in: induced air flotation (IAF) units, tanks and impoundments, and all sludges generated in DAF units. Sludges generated in stormwater units that do not receive dry weather flow, sludges generated from non-contact once-through cooling waters segregated for treatment from other process or oily cooling waters, sludges and floats generated in aggressive biological treatment units as defined in §261.31(b)(2) (including sludges and floats generated in one or more additional units after wastewaters have been treated in aggressive biological treatment units) and F037, K048, and K051 wastes are not included in this listing.	(T)
F039	Leachate (liquids that have percolated through land disposed wastes) resulting from the disposal of more than one restricted waste classified as hazardous under subpart D of this part. (Leachate resulting from the disposal of one or more of the following EPA Hazardous Wastes and no other Hazardous Wastes retains its EPA Hazardous Waste Number(s): F020, F021, F022, F026, F027, and/or F028.) 📖 **5.2.6.1, 14.2.1.2**	(T)

*(I, T) should be used to specify mixtures that are ignitable and contain toxic constituents.

(b) Listing Specific Definitions: (1) For the purposes of the F037 and F038 listings, oil/water/solids is defined as oil and/or water and/or solids.

(2)(i) For the purposes of the F037 and F038 listings, aggressive biological treatment units are defined as units which employ one of the following four treatment methods: activated sludge; trickling filter; rotating biological contactor for the continuous accelerated biological oxidation of the wastewaters; or high-rate aeration. High-rate aeration is a system of surface impoundments or tanks, in which intense mechanical aeration is used to completely mix the wastes, enhance biological activity, and (A) the units employ a minimum of 6 hp per million gallons of treatment volume; and either (B) the hydraulic retention time of the unit is no longer than 5 days; or (C) the hydraulic retention time is no longer than 30 days and the unit does not generate a sludge that is a hazardous waste by the Toxicity Characteristic.

(ii) Generators and treatment, storage and disposal facilities have the burden of proving that their sludges are exempt from listing as F037 and F038 wastes under this definition. Generators and treatment, storage and disposal facilities must maintain, in their operating or other onsite records, documents and data sufficient to prove that: (A) the unit is an aggressive biological treatment unit as defined in this subsection; and (B) the sludges sought to be exempted from the definitions of F037 and/or F038 were actually generated in the aggressive biological treatment unit.

(3)(i) For the purposes of the F037 listing, sludges are considered to be generated at the moment of deposition in the unit, where deposition is defined as at least a temporary cessation of lateral particle movement.

(ii) For the purposes of the F038 listing,

(A) sludges are considered to be generated at the moment of deposition in the unit, where deposition is defined as at least a temporary cessation of lateral particle movement and

(B) floats are considered to be generated at the moment they are formed in the top of the unit.

(4) For the purposes of the F019 listing, the following apply to wastewater treatment sludges from the manufacturing of motor vehicles using a zinc phosphating process.

(i) Motor vehicle manufacturing is defined to include the manufacture of automobiles and light trucks/utility vehicles (including light duty vans, pick-up trucks, minivans, and sport utility vehicles). Facilities must be engaged in manufacturing complete vehicles (body and chassis or unibody) or chassis only.

(ii) Generators must maintain in their on-site records documentation and information sufficient to prove that the wastewater treatment sludges to be exempted from the F019 listing meet the conditions of the listing. These records must include: the volume of waste generated and disposed of off site; documentation showing when the waste volumes were generated and sent off site; the name and address of the receiving facility; and documentation confirming receipt of the waste by the receiving facility. Generators must maintain these documents on site for no less than three years. The retention period for the documentation is automatically extended during the course of any enforcement action or as requested by the Regional Administrator or the state regulatory authority.

[46 FR 4617, Jan. 16, 1981, as amended at 46 FR 27477, May 20, 1981; 49 FR 5312, Feb. 10, 1984; 49 FR 37070, Sept. 21, 1984; 50 FR 665, Jan. 4, 1985; 50 FR 2000, Jan. 14, 1985; 50 FR 53319, Dec. 31, 1985; 51 FR 2702, Jan. 21, 1986; 51 FR 6541, Feb. 25, 1986; 54 FR 50977, Dec. 11, 1989; 55 FR 5342, Feb. 14, 1990; 55 FR 22684, June 1, 1990; 55 FR 46396, Nov. 2, 1990; 55 FR 50482, Dec. 6, 1990; 55 FR 51707, Dec. 17, 1990; 56 FR 3877, Jan. 31, 1991; 56 FR 21958, May 13, 1991; 56 FR 27336, June 13, 1991; 57 FR 61502, Dec. 24, 1992; 60 FR 33913, June 29, 1995; 63 FR 42185, Aug. 6, 1998; 65 FR 36366, June 8, 2000; 71 FR 40259, July 14, 2006; 73 FR 31768, June 4, 2008]

§261.32 Hazardous wastes from specific sources.

📖 3.1.1

(a) The following solid wastes are listed hazardous wastes from specific sources unless they are excluded under §§260.20 and 260.22 and listed in appendix IX.

Industry and EPA hazardous waste No.	Hazardous waste	Hazard code
Wood preservation:		
K001	Bottom sediment sludge from the treatment of wastewaters from wood preserving processes that use creosote and/or pentachlorophenol.	(T)
Inorganic pigments:		
K002	Wastewater treatment sludge from the production of chrome yellow and orange pigments.	(T)
K003	Wastewater treatment sludge from the production of molybdate orange pigments.	(T)
K004	Wastewater treatment sludge from the production of zinc yellow pigments.	(T)
K005	Wastewater treatment sludge from the production of chrome green pigments.	(T)
K006	Wastewater treatment sludge from the production of chrome oxide green pigments (anhydrous and hydrated).	(T)
K007	Wastewater treatment sludge from the production of iron blue pigments.	(T)
K008	Oven residue from the production of chrome oxide green pigments.	(T)
Organic chemicals:		
K009	Distillation bottoms from the production of acetaldehyde from ethylene.	(T)
K010	Distillation side cuts from the production of acetaldehyde from ethylene.	(T)
K011	Bottom stream from the wastewater stripper in the production of acrylonitrile.	(R, T)

Industry and EPA hazardous waste No.	Hazardous waste	Hazard code
K013	Bottom stream from the acetonitrile column in the production of acrylonitrile.	(R, T)
K014	Bottoms from the acetonitrile purification column in the production of acrylonitrile.	(T)
K015	Still bottoms from the distillation of benzyl chloride.	(T)
K016	Heavy ends or distillation residues from the production of carbon tetrachloride.	(T)
K017	Heavy ends (still bottoms) from the purification column in the production of epichlorohydrin.	(T)
K018	Heavy ends from the fractionation column in ethyl chloride production.	(T)
K019	Heavy ends from the distillation of ethylene dichloride in ethylene dichloride production.	(T)
K020	Heavy ends from the distillation of vinyl chloride in vinyl chloride monomer production.	(T)
K021	Aqueous spent antimony catalyst waste from fluoromethanes production.	(T)
K022	Distillation bottom tars from the production of phenol/acetone from cumene.	(T)
K023	Distillation light ends from the production of phthalic anhydride from naphthalene.	(T)
K024	Distillation bottoms from the production of phthalic anhydride from naphthalene.	(T)
K025	Distillation bottoms from the production of nitrobenzene by the nitration of benzene.	(T)
K026	Stripping still tails from the production of methyl ethyl pyridines.	(T)
K027	Centrifuge and distillation residues from toluene diisocyanate production.	(R, T)
K028	Spent catalyst from the hydrochlorinator reactor in the production of 1,1,1-trichloroethane.	(T)
K029	Waste from the product steam stripper in the production of 1,1,1-trichloroethane.	(T)
K030	Column bottoms or heavy ends from the combined production of trichloroethylene and perchloroethylene.	(T)
K083	Distillation bottoms from aniline production.	(T)
K085	Distillation or fractionation column bottoms from the production of chlorobenzenes.	(T)
K093	Distillation light ends from the production of phthalic anhydride from ortho-xylene.	(T)
K094	Distillation bottoms from the production of phthalic anhydride from ortho-xylene.	(T)
K095	Distillation bottoms from the production of 1,1,1-trichloroethane.	(T)
K096	Heavy ends from the heavy ends column from the production of 1,1,1-trichloroethane.	(T)
K103	Process residues from aniline extraction from the production of aniline.	(T)
K104	Combined wastewater streams generated from nitrobenzene/aniline production.	(T)
K105	Separated aqueous stream from the reactor product washing step in the production of chlorobenzenes.	(T)
K107	Column bottoms from product separation from the production of 1,1-dimethylhydrazine (UDMH) from carboxylic acid hydrazines.	(C, T)

Industry and EPA hazardous waste No.	Hazardous waste	Hazard code
K108	Condensed column overheads from product separation and condensed reactor vent gases from the production of 1,1-dimethylhydrazine (UDMH) from carboxylic acid hydrazides.	(I, T)
K109	Spent filter cartridges from product purification from the production of 1,1-dimethylhydrazine (UDMH) from carboxylic acid hydrazides.	(T)
K110	Condensed column overheads from intermediate separation from the production of 1,1-dimethylhydrazine (UDMH) from carboxylic acid hydrazides.	(T)
K111	Product washwaters from the production of dinitrotoluene via nitration of toluene.	(C, T)
K112	Reaction by-product water from the drying column in the production of toluenediamine via hydrogenation of dinitrotoluene.	(T)
K113	Condensed liquid light ends from the purification of toluenediamine in the production of toluenediamine via hydrogenation of dinitrotoluene.	(T)
K114	Vicinals from the purification of toluenediamine in the production of toluenediamine via hydrogenation of dinitrotoluene.	(T)
K115	Heavy ends from the purification of toluenediamine in the production of toluenediamine via hydrogenation of dinitrotoluene.	(T)
K116	Organic condensate from the solvent recovery column in the production of toluene diisocyanate via phosgenation of toluenediamine.	(T)
K117	Wastewater from the reactor vent gas scrubber in the production of ethylene dibromide via bromination of ethene.	(T)
K118	Spent adsorbent solids from purification of ethylene dibromide in the production of ethylene dibromide via bromination of ethene.	(T)
K136	Still bottoms from the purification of ethylene dibromide in the production of ethylene dibromide via bromination of ethene.	(T)
K149	Distillation bottoms from the production of alpha- (or methyl-) chlorinated toluenes, ring-chlorinated toluenes, benzoyl chlorides, and compounds with mixtures of these functional groups, (This waste does not include still bottoms from the distillation of benzyl chloride.).	(T)
K150	Organic residuals, excluding spent carbon adsorbent, from the spent chlorine gas and hydrochloric acid recovery processes associated with the production of alpha- (or methyl-) chlorinated toluenes, ring-chlorinated toluenes, benzoyl chlorides, and compounds with mixtures of these functional groups.	(T)
K151	Wastewater treatment sludges, excluding neutralization and biological sludges, generated during the treatment of wastewaters from the production of alpha- (or methyl-) chlorinated toluenes, ring-chlorinated toluenes, benzoyl chlorides, and compounds with mixtures of these functional groups.	(T)

Industry and EPA hazardous waste No.	Hazardous waste	Hazard code
K156	Organic waste (including heavy ends, still bottoms, light ends, spent solvents, filtrates, and decantates) from the production of carbamates and carbamoyl oximes. (This listing does not apply to wastes generated from the manufacture of 3-iodo-2-propynyl n-butylcarbamate.).	(T)
K157	Wastewaters (including scrubber waters, condenser waters, washwaters, and separation waters) from the production of carbamates and carbamoyl oximes. (This listing does not apply to wastes generated from the manufacture of 3-iodo-2-propynyl n-butylcarbamate.).	(T)
K158	Bag house dusts and filter/separation solids from the production of carbamates and carbamoyl oximes. (This listing does not apply to wastes generated from the manufacture of 3-iodo-2-propynyl n-butylcarbamate.).	(T)
K159	Organics from the treatment of thiocarbamate wastes.	(T)
K161	Purification solids (including filtration, evaporation, and centrifugation solids), bag house dust and floor sweepings from the production of dithiocarbamate acids and their salts. (This listing does not include K125 or K126.).	(R, T)
K174	Wastewater treatment sludges from the production of ethylene dichloride or vinyl chloride monomer (including sludges that result from commingled ethylene dichloride or vinyl chloride monomer wastewater and other wastewater), unless the sludges meet the following conditions: (i) they are disposed of in a subtitle C or non-hazardous landfill licensed or permitted by the state or federal government; (ii) they are not otherwise placed on the land prior to final disposal; and (iii) the generator maintains documentation demonstrating that the waste was either disposed of in an on-site landfill or consigned to a transporter or disposal facility that provided a written commitment to dispose of the waste in an off- site landfill. Respondents in any action brought to enforce the requirements of subtitle C must, upon a showing by the government that the respondent managed wastewater treatment sludges from the production of vinyl chloride monomer or ethylene dichloride, demonstrate that they meet the terms of the exclusion set forth above. In doing so, they must provide appropriate documentation (*e.g.*, contracts between the generator and the landfill owner/operator, invoices documenting delivery of waste to landfill, etc.) that the terms of the exclusion were met.	(T)
K175	Wastewater treatment sludges from the production of vinyl chloride monomer using mercuric chloride catalyst in an acetylene-based process.	(T)
K181	Nonwastewaters from the production of dyes and/or pigments (including nonwastewaters commingled at the point of generation with nonwastewaters from other processes) that, at the point of generation, contain mass loadings of any of the constituents identified in paragraph (c) of this section that are equal to or greater than the corresponding paragraph (c) levels, as determined on a calendar year basis. These wastes will not be hazardous if the nonwastewaters are: (i) disposed in a Subtitle D landfill unit subject to the design criteria in §258.40, (ii) disposed in a Subtitle C landfill unit subject to either §264.301 or §265.301, (iii) disposed in other Subtitle D landfill units that meet the design criteria in §258.40, §264.301, or §265.301, or (iv) treated in a combustion unit that is permitted under Subtitle C, or an on-site combustion unit that is permitted under the Clean Air Act. For the purposes of this listing, dyes and/or pigments production is defined in paragraph (b)(1) of this section. Paragraph (d) of this section describes the process for demonstrating that a facility's nonwastewaters are not K181. This listing does not apply to wastes that are otherwise identified as hazardous under §§261.21–261.24 and 261.31–261.33 at the point of generation. Also, the listing does not apply to wastes generated before any annual mass loading limit is met.	(T)
Inorganic chemicals:		
K071	Brine purification muds from the mercury cell process in chlorine production, where separately prepurified brine is not used.	(T)
K073	Chlorinated hydrocarbon waste from the purification step of the diaphragm cell process using graphite anodes in chlorine production.	(T)
K106	Wastewater treatment sludge from the mercury cell process in chlorine production.	(T)
K176	Baghouse filters from the production of antimony oxide, including filters from the production of intermediates (e.g., antimony metal or crude antimony oxide).	(E)
K177	Slag from the production of antimony oxide that is speculatively accumulated or disposed, including slag from the production of intermediates (e.g., antimony metal or crude antimony oxide).	(T)
K178	Residues from manufacturing and manufacturing-site storage of ferric chloride from acids formed during the production of titanium dioxide using the chloride-ilmenite process.	(T)
Pesticides:		
K031	By-product salts generated in the production of MSMA and cacodylic acid.	(T)
K032	Wastewater treatment sludge from the production of chlordane.	(T)
K033	Wastewater and scrub water from the chlorination of cyclopentadiene in the production of chlordane.	(T)

Industry and EPA hazardous waste No.	Hazardous waste	Hazard code
K034	Filter solids from the filtration of hexachlorocyclopentadiene in the production of chlordane.	(T)
K035	Wastewater treatment sludges generated in the production of creosote.	(T)
K036	Still bottoms from toluene reclamation distillation in the production of disulfoton.	(T)
K037	Wastewater treatment sludges from the production of disulfoton.	(T)
K038	Wastewater from the washing and stripping of phorate production.	(T)
K039	Filter cake from the filtration of diethylphosphorodithioic acid in the production of phorate.	(T)
K040	Wastewater treatment sludge from the production of phorate.	(T)
K041	Wastewater treatment sludge from the production of toxaphene.	(T)
K042	Heavy ends or distillation residues from the distillation of tetrachlorobenzene in the production of 2,4,5-T.	(T)
K043	2,6-Dichlorophenol waste from the production of 2,4-D.	(T)
K097	Vacuum stripper discharge from the chlordane chlorinator in the production of chlordane.	(T)
K098	Untreated process wastewater from the production of toxaphene.	(T)
K099	Untreated wastewater from the production of 2,4-D.	(T)
K123	Process wastewater (including supernates, filtrates, and washwaters) from the production of ethylenebisdithiocarbamic acid and its salt.	(T)
K124	Reactor vent scrubber water from the production of ethylenebisdithiocarbamic acid and its salts.	(C, T)
K125	Filtration, evaporation, and centrifugation solids from the production of ethylenebisdithiocarbamic acid and its salts.	(T)
K126	Baghouse dust and floor sweepings in milling and packaging operations from the production or formulation of ethylenebisdithiocarbamic acid and its salts.	(T)
K131	Wastewater from the reactor and spent sulfuric acid from the acid dryer from the production of methyl bromide.	(C, T)
K132	Spent absorbent and wastewater separator solids from the production of methyl bromide.	(T)
Explosives:		
K044	Wastewater treatment sludges from the manufacturing and processing of explosives.	(R)
K045	Spent carbon from the treatment of wastewater containing explosives.	(R)
K046	Wastewater treatment sludges from the manufacturing, formulation and loading of lead-based initiating compounds.	(T)
K047	Pink/red water from TNT operations.	(R)
Petroleum refining:	📖 **4.16.2, 5.2.3.2**	
K048	Dissolved air flotation (DAF) float from the petroleum refining industry.	(T)
K049	Slop oil emulsion solids from the petroleum refining industry.	(T)
K050	Heat exchanger bundle cleaning sludge from the petroleum refining industry.	(T)
K051	API separator sludge from the petroleum refining industry.	(T)
K052	Tank bottoms (leaded) from the petroleum refining industry.	(T)
K169	Crude oil storage tank sediment from petroleum refining operations.	(T)
K170	Clarified slurry oil tank sediment and/or in-line filter/separation solids from petroleum refining operations.	(T)
K171	Spent Hydrotreating catalyst from petroleum refining operations, including guard beds used to desulfurize feeds to other catalytic reactors (this listing does not include inert support media).	(I, T)
K172	Spent Hydrorefining catalyst from petroleum refining operations, including guard beds used to desulfurize feeds to other catalytic reactors (this listing does not include inert support media).	(I, T)
Iron and steel:		
K061	Emission control dust/sludge from the primary production of steel in electric furnaces. 📖 **11.3.1.4**	(T)
K062	Spent pickle liquor generated by steel finishing operations of facilities within the iron and steel industry (SIC Codes 331 and 332).	(C, T)
Primary copper:		
Primary lead:		
Primary zinc:		
Primary aluminum:		
K088	Spent potliners from primary aluminum reduction.	(T)
Ferroalloys:		
Secondary lead:		
K069	Emission control dust/sludge from secondary lead smelting. (*Note:* This listing is stayed administratively for sludge generated from secondary acid scrubber systems. The stay will remain in effect until further administrative action is taken. If EPA takes further action effecting this stay, EPA will publish a notice of the action in the *Federal Register*).	(T)
K100	Waste leaching solution from acid leaching of emission control dust/ sludge from secondary lead smelting.	(T)
Veterinary pharmaceuticals:		
K084	Wastewater treatment sludges generated during the production of veterinary pharmaceuticals from arsenic or organo-arsenic compounds.	(T)
K101	Distillation tar residues from the distillation of aniline-based compounds in the production of veterinary pharmaceuticals from arsenic or organo-arsenic compounds.	(T)

Industry and EPA hazardous waste No.	Hazardous waste	Hazard code
K102	Residue from the use of activated carbon for decolorization in the production of veterinary pharmaceuticals from arsenic or organo-arsenic compounds.	(T)
Ink formulation:		
K086	Solvent washes and sludges, caustic washes and sludges, or water washes and sludges from cleaning tubs and equipment used in the formulation of ink from pigments, driers, soaps, and stabilizers containing chromium and lead.	(T)
Coking:		
K060	Ammonia still lime sludge from coking operations.	(T)
K087	Decanter tank tar sludge from coking operations.	(T)
K141	Process residues from the recovery of coal tar, including, but not limited to, collecting sump residues from the production of coke from coal or the recovery of coke by-products produced from coal. This listing does not include K087 (decanter tank tar sludges from coking operations).	(T)
K142	Tar storage tank residues from the production of coke from coal or from the recovery of coke by-products produced from coal.	(T)
K143	Process residues from the recovery of light oil, including, but not limited to, those generated in stills, decanters, and wash oil recovery units from the recovery of coke by-products produced from coal.	(T)
K144	Wastewater sump residues from light oil refining, including, but not limited to, intercepting or contamination sump sludges from the recovery of coke by-products produced from coal.	(T)
K145	Residues from naphthalene collection and recovery operations from the recovery of coke by-products produced from coal.	(T)
K147	Tar storage tank residues from coal tar refining.	(T)
K148	Residues from coal tar distillation, including but not limited to, still bottoms.	(T)

(b) *Listing Specific Definitions:* (1) For the purposes of the K181 listing, dyes and/or pigments production is defined to include manufacture of the following product classes: dyes, pigments, or FDA certified colors that are classified as azo, triarylmethane, perylene or anthraquinone classes. Azo products include azo, monoazo, diazo, triazo, polyazo, azoic, benzidine, and pyrazolone products. Triarylmethane products include both triarylmethane and triphenylmethane products. Wastes that are not generated at a dyes and/or pigments manufacturing site, such as wastes from the offsite use, formulation, and packaging of dyes and/or pigments, are not included in the K181 listing.

(c) *K181 Listing Levels.* Nonwastewaters containing constituents in amounts equal to or exceeding the following levels during any calendar year are subject to the K181 listing, unless the conditions in the K181 listing are met.

Constituent	Chemical abstracts No.	Mass levels (kg/yr)
Aniline	62–53–3	9,300
o-Anisidine	90–04–0	110
4-Chloroaniline	106–47–8	4,800
p-Cresidine	120–71–8	660
2,4-Dimethylaniline	95–68–1	100
1,2-Phenylenediamine	95–54–5	710
1,3-Phenylenediamine	108–45–2	1,200

(d) *Procedures for demonstrating that dyes and/or pigment nonwastewaters are not K181.* The procedures described in paragraphs (d)(1)–(d)(3) and (d)(5) of this section establish when nonwastewaters from the production of dyes/pigments would not be hazardous (these procedures apply to wastes that are not disposed in landfill units or treated in combustion units as specified in paragraph (a) of this section). If the nonwastewaters are disposed in landfill units or treated in combustion units as described in paragraph (a) of this section, then the nonwastewaters are not hazardous. In order to demonstrate that it is meeting the landfill disposal or combustion conditions contained in the K181 listing description, the generator must maintain documentation as described in paragraph (d)(4) of this section.

(1) *Determination based on no K181 constituents.* Generators that have knowledge (*e.g.,* knowledge of constituents in wastes based on prior sampling and analysis data and/or information about raw materials used, production processes used, and reaction and degradation products formed) that their wastes contain none of the K181 constituents (*see* paragraph (c) of this section) can use their knowledge to determine that their waste is not K181. The generator must document the basis for all such determinations on an annual basis and keep each annual documentation for three years.

(2) *Determination for generated quantities of 1,000 MT/yr or less for wastes that contain K181 constituents.* If the total annual quantity of dyes and/or pigment nonwastewaters generated is 1,000 metric tons or less, the generator can use knowledge of the wastes (*e.g.,* knowledge of constituents in wastes based on prior analytical data and/or information about raw materials used, production processes used, and reaction and degradation products formed) to conclude that annual mass loadings for the K181 constituents are below the listing levels of paragraph (c) of this section. To make this determination, the generator must:

(i) Each year document the basis for determining that the annual quantity of nonwastewaters expected to be generated will be less than 1,000 metric tons.

(ii) Track the actual quantity of nonwastewaters generated from January 1 through December 31 of each year. If, at any time within the year, the actual waste quantity exceeds 1,000 metric tons, the generator must comply with the requirements of paragraph (d)(3) of this section for the remainder of the year.

(iii) Keep a running total of the K181 constituent mass loadings over the course of the calendar year.

(iv) Keep the following records on site for the three most recent calendar years in which the hazardous waste determinations are made:

(A) The quantity of dyes and/or pigment nonwastewaters generated.

(B) The relevant process information used.

(C) The calculations performed to determine annual total mass loadings for each K181 constituent in the nonwastewaters during the year.

(3) *Determination for generated quantities greater than 1,000 MT/yr for wastes that contain K181 constituents.* If the total annual quantity of dyes and/or pigment nonwastewaters generated is greater than 1,000 metric tons, the generator must perform all of the steps described in paragraphs ((d)(3)(i)–(d)(3)(xi) of this section) in order to make a determination that its waste is not K181.

(i) Determine which K181 constituents (see paragraph (c) of this section) are reasonably expected to be present in the wastes based on knowledge of the wastes (*e.g.*, based on prior sampling and analysis data and/or information about raw materials used, production processes used, and reaction and degradation products formed).

(ii) If 1,2-phenylenediamine is present in the wastes, the generator can use either knowledge or sampling and analysis procedures to determine the level of this constituent in the wastes. For determinations based on use of knowledge, the generator must comply with the procedures for using knowledge described in paragraph (d)(2) of this section and keep the records described in paragraph (d)(2)(iv) of this section. For determinations based on sampling and analysis, the generator must comply with the sampling and analysis and recordkeeping requirements described below in this section.

(iii) Develop a waste sampling and analysis plan (or modify an existing plan) to collect and analyze representative waste samples for the K181 constituents reasonably expected to be present in the wastes. At a minimum, the plan must include:

(A) A discussion of the number of samples needed to characterize the wastes fully;

(B) The planned sample collection method to obtain representative waste samples;

(C) A discussion of how the sampling plan accounts for potential temporal and spatial variability of the wastes.

(D) A detailed description of the test methods to be used, including sample preparation, clean up (if necessary), and determinative methods.

(iv) Collect and analyze samples in accordance with the waste sampling and analysis plan.

(A) The sampling and analysis must be unbiased, precise, and representative of the wastes.

(B) The analytical measurements must be sufficiently sensitive, accurate and precise to support any claim that the constituent mass loadings are below the listing levels of paragraph (c) of this section.

(v) Record the analytical results.

(vi) Record the waste quantity represented by the sampling and analysis results.

(vii) Calculate constituent-specific mass loadings (product of concentrations and waste quantity).

(viii) Keep a running total of the K181 constituent mass loadings over the course of the calendar year.

(ix) Determine whether the mass of any of the K181 constituents listed in paragraph (c) of this section generated between January 1 and December 31 of any year is below the K181 listing levels.

(x) Keep the following records on site for the three most recent calendar years in which the hazardous waste determinations are made:

(A) The sampling and analysis plan.

(B) The sampling and analysis results (including QA/QC data)

(C) The quantity of dyes and/or pigment nonwastewaters generated.

(D) The calculations performed to determine annual mass loadings.

(xi) Nonhazardous waste determinations must be conducted annually to verify that the wastes remain nonhazardous.

(A) The annual testing requirements are suspended after three consecutive successful annual demonstrations that the wastes are nonhazardous. The generator can then use knowledge of the wastes to support subsequent annual determinations.

(B) The annual testing requirements are reinstated if the manufacturing or waste treatment processes generating the wastes are significantly altered, resulting in an increase of the potential for the wastes to exceed the listing levels.

(C) If the annual testing requirements are suspended, the generator must keep records of the process knowledge information used to support a nonhazardous determination. If testing is reinstated, a description of the process change must be retained.

(4) *Recordkeeping for the landfill disposal and combustion exemptions.* For the purposes of meeting the landfill disposal and combustion condition set out in the K181 listing description, the generator must maintain on site for three years documentation demonstrating that each shipment of waste was received by a landfill unit that is subject to or meets the landfill design standards set out in the listing description, or was treated in combustion units as specified in the listing description.

(5) *Waste holding and handling.* During the interim period, from the point of generation to completion of the hazardous waste determination, the generator is responsible for storing the wastes appropriately. If the wastes are determined to be hazardous and the generator has not complied with the subtitle C requirements during the interim period, the generator could be subject to an enforcement action for improper management.

[46 FR 4618, Jan. 16, 1981, as amended at 46 FR 27476-27477, May 20, 1981; 49 FR 37070, Sept. 21, 1984; 50 FR 42942, Oct. 23, 1985; 51 FR 5330, Feb. 13, 1986; 51 FR 19322, May 28, 1986; 51 FR 33612, Sept. 22, 1986; 51 FR 37729, Oct. 24, 1986; 52 FR 28698, Aug. 3, 1987; 53 FR 35420, Sept. 13, 1988; 54 FR 41407, Oct. 6, 1989; 55 FR 18505, May 2, 1990; 56 FR 19952, May 1, 1991; 57 FR 37305, Aug. 18, 1992; 57 FR 47385, Oct. 15, 1992; 60 FR 7849, Feb. 9, 1995; 62 FR 32977, June 17, 1997; 63 FR 24625, May 4, 1998; 63 FR 42185, Aug. 6, 1998; 64 FR 56470, Oct. 20, 1999; 65 FR 14474, Mar. 17, 2000; 65 FR 67126, Nov. 8, 2000; 66 FR 58297, Nov. 20, 2001; 70 FR 9175, Feb. 24, 2005; 70 FR 35033, June 16, 2005; 71 FR 40259, July 14, 2006]

§261.33 Discarded commercial chemical products, off-specification species, container residues, and spill residues thereof.

📖 3.5, 14.5.2.2.1

The following materials or items are hazardous wastes if and when they are discarded or intended to be discarded as described in §261.2(a)(2)(i), when they are mixed with waste oil or used oil or other material and applied to the land for dust suppression or road treatment, when they are otherwise applied to the land in lieu of their original intended use or when they are contained in products that are applied to the land in lieu of their original intended use, or when, in lieu of their original intended use, they are produced for use as (or as a component of) a fuel, distributed for use as a fuel, or burned as a fuel. 📖 3.5.6.1

(a) Any commercial chemical product, or manufacturing chemical intermediate having the generic name listed in paragraph (e) or (f) of this section. 📖 3.5.3.1–2

(b) Any off-specification commercial chemical product or manufacturing chemical intermediate which, if it met specifications, would have the generic name listed in paragraph (e) or (f) of this section. 📖 3.5.3.3

(c) Any residue remaining in a container or in an inner liner removed from a container that has held any commercial chemical product or manufacturing chemical intermediate having the generic name listed in paragraphs (e) or (f) of this section, unless the container is empty as defined in §261.7(b) of this chapter. 📖 3.5.3.4

[*Comment:* Unless the residue is being beneficially used or reused, or legitimately recycled or reclaimed; or being accumulated, stored, transported or treated prior to such use, re-use, recycling or reclamation, EPA considers the residue to be intended for discard, and thus, a hazardous waste. An example of a legitimate re-use of the residue would be where the residue remains in the container and the container is used to hold the same commercial chemical product or manufacturing chemical intermediate it previously held. An example of the discard of the residue would be where the drum is sent to a drum reconditioner who reconditions the drum but discards the residue.] 📖 9.5.4

(d) Any residue or contaminated soil, water or other debris resulting from the cleanup of a spill into or on any land or water of any commercial chemical product or manufacturing chemical intermediate having the generic name listed in paragraph (e) or (f) of this section, or any residue or contaminated soil, water or other debris resulting from the cleanup of a spill, into or on any land or water, of any off-specification chemical product and manufacturing chemical intermediate which, if it met specifications, would have the generic name listed in paragraph (e) or (f) of this section. 📖 3.5.3.5, 14.4.4.2

[*Comment:* The phrase "commercial chemical product or manufacturing chemical intermediate having the generic name listed in . . ." refers to a chemical substance which is manufactured or formulated for commercial or manufacturing use which consists of the commercially pure grade of the chemical, any technical grades of the chemical that are produced or marketed, and all formulations in which the chemical is the sole active ingredient. It does not refer to a material, such as a manufacturing process waste, that contains any of the substances listed in paragraph (e) or (f). Where a manufacturing process waste is deemed to be a hazardous waste because it contains a substance listed in paragraph (e) or (f), such waste will be listed in either §261.31 or §261.32 or will be identified as a hazardous waste by the characteristics set forth in subpart C of this part.] 📖 3.5.3.6–8

(e) The commercial chemical products, manufacturing chemical intermediates or off-specification commercial chemical products or manufacturing chemical intermediates referred to in paragraphs (a) through (d) of this section, are identified as acute hazardous wastes (H) and are subject to the small quantity exclusion defined in §261.5(e). 1.2.5.4, 3.5

[*Comment:* For the convenience of the regulated community the primary hazardous properties of these materials have been indicated by the letters T (Toxicity), and R (Reactivity). Absence of a letter indicates that the compound only is listed for acute toxicity. Wastes are first listed in alphabetical order by substance and then listed again in numerical order by Hazardous Waste Number.]

Publisher's Note: For the convenience of our readers, we have separated the alphabetical list and the numerical list into two tables.

These wastes and their corresponding EPA Hazardous Waste Numbers are:

Alphabetical List

Hazardous waste No.	Chemical abstracts No.	Substance
P023	107-20-0	Acetaldehyde, chloro-
P002	591-08-2	Acetamide, N-(aminothioxomethyl)-
P057	640-19-7	Acetamide, 2-fluoro-
P058	62-74-8	Acetic acid, fluoro-, sodium salt
P002	591-08-2	1-Acetyl-2-thiourea
P003	107-02-8	Acrolein
P070	116-06-3	Aldicarb
P203	1646-88-4	Aldicarb sulfone.
P004	309-00-2	Aldrin
P005	107-18-6	Allyl alcohol
P006	20859-73-8	Aluminum phosphide (R,T)
P007	2763-96-4	5-(Aminomethyl)-3-isoxazolol
P008	504-24-5	4-Aminopyridine
P009	131-74-8	Ammonium picrate (R)
P119	7803-55-6	Ammonium vanadate
P099	506-61-6	Argentate(1-), bis(cyano-C)-, potassium
P010	7778-39-4	Arsenic acid H_3AsO_4
P012	1327-53-3	Arsenic oxide As_2O_3
P011	1303-28-2	Arsenic oxide As_2O_5
P011	1303-28-2	Arsenic pentoxide
P012	1327-53-3	Arsenic trioxide
P038	692-42-2	Arsine, diethyl-
P036	696-28-6	Arsonous dichloride, phenyl-
P054	151-56-4	Aziridine
P067	75-55-8	Aziridine, 2-methyl-
P013	542-62-1	Barium cyanide
P024	106-47-8	Benzenamine, 4-chloro-
P077	100-01-6	Benzenamine, 4-nitro-
P028	100-44-7	Benzene, (chloromethyl)-
P042	51-43-4	1,2-Benzenediol, 4-[1-hydroxy-2-(methylamino)ethyl]-, (R)-
P046	122-09-8	Benzeneethanamine, alpha,alpha-dimethyl-
P014	108-98-5	Benzenethiol
P127	1563-66-2	7-Benzofuranol, 2,3-dihydro- 2,2-dimethyl-, methylcarbamate.

Alphabetical List

Hazardous waste No.	Chemical abstracts No.	Substance
P188	57-64-7	Benzoic acid, 2-hydroxy-, compd. with (3aS-cis)-1,2,3,3a,8,8a-hexahydro-1,3a,8-trimethylpyrrolo[2,3-b]indol-5-yl methylcarbamate ester (1:1).
P001	[1]81-81-2	2H-1-Benzopyran-2-one, 4-hydroxy-3-(3-oxo-1-phenylbutyl)-, & salts, when present at concentrations greater than 0.3%
P028	100-44-7	Benzyl chloride
P015	7440-41-7	Beryllium powder
P017	598-31-2	Bromoacetone
P018	357-57-3	Brucine
P045	39196-18-4	2-Butanone, 3,3-dimethyl-1-(methylthio)-, O-[(methylamino)carbonyl] oxime
P021	592-01-8	Calcium cyanide
P021	592-01-8	Calcium cyanide $Ca(CN)_2$
P189	55285-14-8	Carbamic acid, [(dibutylamino)-thio]methyl-, 2,3-dihydro-2,2-dimethyl-7-benzofuranyl ester
P191	644-64-4	Carbamic acid, dimethyl-, 1-[(dimethyl-amino)carbonyl]- 5-methyl-1H- pyrazol-3-yl ester
P192	119-38-0	Carbamic acid, dimethyl-, 3-methyl-1-(1-methylethyl)-1H- pyrazol-5-yl ester
P190	1129-41-5	Carbamic acid, methyl-, 3-methylphenyl ester
P127	1563-66-2	Carbofuran
P022	75-15-0	Carbon disulfide
P095	75-44-5	Carbonic dichloride
P189	55285-14-8	Carbosulfan
P023	107-20-0	Chloroacetaldehyde
P024	106-47-8	p-Chloroaniline
P026	5344-82-1	1-(o-Chlorophenyl)thiourea
P027	542-76-7	3-Chloropropionitrile
P029	544-92-3	Copper cyanide
P029	544-92-3	Copper cyanide Cu(CN)
P202	64-00-6	m-Cumenyl methylcarbamate.
P030		Cyanides (soluble cyanide salts), not otherwise specified
P031	460-19-5	Cyanogen
P033	506-77-4	Cyanogen chloride
P033	506-77-4	Cyanogen chloride (CN)Cl
P034	131-89-5	2-Cyclohexyl-4,6-dinitrophenol
P016	542-88-1	Dichloromethyl ether
P036	696-28-6	Dichlorophenylarsine
P037	60-57-1	Dieldrin
P038	692-42-2	Diethylarsine
P041	311-45-5	Diethyl-p-nitrophenyl phosphate
P040	297-97-2	O,O-Diethyl O-pyrazinyl phosphorothioate
P043	55-91-4	Diisopropylfluorophosphate (DFP)
P004	309-00-2	1,4,5,8-Dimethanonaphthalene, 1,2,3,4,10,10-hexa- chloro-1,4,4a, 5,8,8a,-hexahydro-, (1alpha,4alpha, 4abeta, 5alpha,8alpha,8 abeta)-

Alphabetical List

Hazardous waste No.	Chemical abstracts No.	Substance
P060	465-73-6	1,4,5,8-Dimethanonaphthalene, 1,2,3,4,10,10-hexa- chloro-1,4,4a,5,8,8a-hexahydro-, (1alpha,4alpha,4abeta, 5beta,8beta,8abeta)-
P037	60-57-1	2,7:3,6-Dimethanonaphth[2,3-b]oxirene, 3,4,5,6,9,9-hexachloro-1a,2,2a,3,6,6a,7,7a-octahydro-, (1aalpha,2beta,2aalpha,3beta,6beta,6a alpha,7beta, 7aalpha)-
P051	[1]72-20-8	2,7:3,6-Dimethanonaphth [2,3-b] oxirene, 3,4,5,6,9,9-hexachloro-1a,2,2a,3,6,6a,7,7a-octahydro-, (1aalpha,2beta,2abeta,3alpha,6alpha, 6abeta,7beta, 7aalpha)-, & metabolites
P044	60-51-5	Dimethoate
P046	122-09-8	alpha,alpha-Dimethylphenethylamine
P191	644-64-4	Dimetilan
P047	[1]534-52-1	4,6-Dinitro-o-cresol, & salts
P048	51-28-5	2,4-Dinitrophenol
P020	88-85-7	Dinoseb
P085	152-16-9	Diphosphoramide, octamethyl-
P111	107-49-3	Diphosphoric acid, tetraethyl ester
P039	298-04-4	Disulfoton
P049	541-53-7	Dithiobiuret
P185	26419-73-8	1,3-Dithiolane-2-carboxaldehyde, 2,4-dimethyl-, O- [(methylamino)-carbonyl] oxime.
P050	115-29-7	Endosulfan
P088	145-73-3	Endothall
P051	72-20-8	Endrin
P051	72-20-8	Endrin, & metabolites
P042	51-43-4	Epinephrine
P031	460-19-5	Ethanedinitrile
P194	23135-22-0	Ethanimidothioic acid, 2-(dimethylamino)-N-[[(methylamino) carbonyl]oxy]-2-oxo-, methyl ester
P066	16752-77-5	Ethanimidothioic acid, N-[[(methylamino)carbonyl]oxy]-, methyl ester
P101	107-12-0	Ethyl cyanide
P054	151-56-4	Ethyleneimine
P097	52-85-7	Famphur
P056	7782-41-4	Fluorine
P057	640-19-7	Fluoroacetamide
P058	62-74-8	Fluoroacetic acid, sodium salt
P198	23422-53-9	Formetanate hydrochloride.
P197	17702-57-7	Formparanate
P065	628-86-4	Fulminic acid, mercury(2+) salt (R,T)
P059	76-44-8	Heptachlor
P062	757-58-4	Hexaethyl tetraphosphate
P116	79-19-6	Hydrazinecarbothioamide
P068	60-34-4	Hydrazine, methyl-
P063	74-90-8	Hydrocyanic acid
P063	74-90-8	Hydrogen cyanide
P096	7803-51-2	Hydrogen phosphide
P060	465-73-6	Isodrin

Alphabetical List

Hazardous waste No.	Chemical abstracts No.	Substance
P192	119-38-0	Isolan
P202	64-00-6	3-Isopropylphenyl N-methylcarbamate
P007	2763-96-4	3(2H)-Isoxazolone, 5-(aminomethyl)-
P196	15339-36-3	Manganese, bis(dimethylcarbamodithioato-S,S')-,
P196	15339-36-3	Manganese dimethyldithiocarbamate
P092	62-38-4	Mercury, (acetato-O)phenyl-
P065	628-86-4	Mercury fulminate (R,T)
P082	62-75-9	Methanamine, N-methyl-N-nitroso-
P064	624-83-9	Methane, isocyanato-
P016	542-88-1	Methane, oxybis[chloro-
P112	509-14-8	Methane, tetranitro- (R)
P118	75-70-7	Methanethiol, trichloro-
P198	23422-53-9	Methanimidamide, N,N-dimethyl-N'-[3-[[(methylamino)-carbonyl]oxy]phenyl]-, monohydrochloride
P197	17702-57-7	Methanimidamide, N,N-dimethyl-N'-[2-methyl-4-[[(methylamino)carbonyl] oxy]phenyl]-
P050	115-29-7	6,9-Methano-2,4,3-benzodioxathiepin, 6,7,8,9,10,10- hexachloro-1,5,5a,6,9,9a-hexahydro-, 3-oxide
P059	76-44-8	4,7-Methano-1H-indene, 1,4,5,6,7,8,8-heptachloro- 3a,4,7,7a-tetrahydro-
P199	2032-65-7	Methiocarb
P066	16752-77-5	Methomyl
P068	60-34-4	Methyl hydrazine
P064	624-83-9	Methyl isocyanate
P069	75-86-5	2-Methyllactonitrile
P071	298-00-0	Methyl parathion
P190	1129-41-5	Metolcarb
P128	315-8-4	Mexacarbate.
P072	86-88-4	alpha-Naphthylthiourea
P073	13463-39-3	Nickel carbonyl
P073	13463-39-3	Nickel carbonyl $Ni(CO)_4$, (T-4)-
P074	557-19-7	Nickel cyanide
P074	557-19-7	Nickel cyanide $Ni(CN)_2$
P075	[1]54-11-5	Nicotine, & salts
P076	10102-43-9	Nitric oxide
P077	100-01-6	p-Nitroaniline
P078	10102-44-0	Nitrogen dioxide
P076	10102-43-9	Nitrogen oxide NO
P078	10102-44-0	Nitrogen oxide NO_2
P081	55-63-0	Nitroglycerine (R)
P082	62-75-9	N-Nitrosodimethylamine
P084	4549-40-0	N-Nitrosomethylvinylamine
P085	152-16-9	Octamethylpyrophosphoramide
P087	20816-12-0	Osmium oxide OsO_4, (T-4)-
P087	20816-12-0	Osmium tetroxide
P088	145-73-3	7-Oxabicyclo[2.2.1]heptane- 2,3-dicar-boxylic acid
P194	23135-22-0	Oxamyl
P089	56-38-2	Parathion
P034	131-89-5	Phenol, 2-cyclohexyl-4,6-dinitro-
P048	51-28-5	Phenol, 2,4-dinitro-

Alphabetical List

Hazardous waste No.	Chemical abstracts No.	Substance
P047	[1]534-52-1	Phenol, 2-methyl-4,6-dinitro-, & salts
P020	88-85-7	Phenol, 2-(1-methylpropyl)-4,6-dinitro-
P009	131-74-8	Phenol, 2,4,6-trinitro-, ammonium salt (R)
P128	315-18-4	Phenol, 4-(dimethylamino)-3,5-dimethyl-, methylcarbamate (ester)
P199	2032-65-7	Phenol, (3,5-dimethyl-4-(methylthio)-, methylcarbamate
P202	64-00-6	Phenol, 3-(1-methylethyl)-, methyl carbamate
P201	2631-37-0	Phenol, 3-methyl-5-(1-methylethyl)-, methyl carbamate
P092	62-38-4	Phenylmercury acetate
P093	103-85-5	Phenylthiourea
P094	298-02-2	Phorate
P095	75-44-5	Phosgene
P096	7803-51-2	Phosphine
P041	311-45-5	Phosphoric acid, diethyl 4-nitrophenyl ester
P039	298-04-4	Phosphorodithioic acid, O,O-diethyl S-[2-(ethylthio)ethyl] ester
P094	298-02-2	Phosphorodithioic acid, O,O-diethyl S-[(ethylthio)methyl] ester
P044	60-51-5	Phosphorodithioic acid, O,O-dimethyl S-[2-(methylamino)-2-oxoethyl] ester
P043	55-91-4	Phosphorofluoridic acid, bis(1-methylethyl) ester
P089	56-38-2	Phosphorothioic acid, O,O-diethyl O-(4-nitrophenyl) ester
P040	297-97-2	Phosphorothioic acid, O,O-diethyl O-pyrazinyl ester
P097	52-85-7	Phosphorothioic acid, O-[4-[(dimethylamino)sulfonyl]phenyl] O,O-dimethyl ester
P071	298-00-0	Phosphorothioic acid, O,O,-dimethyl O-(4-nitrophenyl) ester
P204	57-47-6	Physostigmine
P188	57-64-7	Physostigmine salicylate.
P110	78-00-2	Plumbane, tetraethyl-
P098	151-50-8	Potassium cyanide
P098	151-50-8	Potassium cyanide K(CN)
P099	506-61-6	Potassium silver cyanide
P201	2631-37-0	Promecarb
P070	116-06-3	Propanal, 2-methyl-2-(methylthio)-, O-[(methylamino)carbonyl]oxime
P203	1646-88-4	Propanal, 2-methyl-2-(methyl-sulfonyl)-, O-[(methylamino)carbonyl] oxime
P101	107-12-0	Propanenitrile
P027	542-76-7	Propanenitrile, 3-chloro-
P069	75-86-5	Propanenitrile, 2-hydroxy-2-methyl-
P081	55-63-0	1,2,3-Propanetriol, trinitrate (R)
P017	598-31-2	2-Propanone, 1-bromo-
P102	107-19-7	Propargyl alcohol
P003	107-02-8	2-Propenal
P005	107-18-6	2-Propen-1-ol
P067	75-55-8	1,2-Propylenimine

Alphabetical List

Hazardous waste No.	Chemical abstracts No.	Substance
P102	107-19-7	2-Propyn-1-ol
P008	504-24-5	4-Pyridinamine
P075	[1]54-11-5	Pyridine, 3-(1-methyl-2-pyrrolidinyl)-, (S)-, & salts
P204	57-47-6	Pyrrolo[2,3-b]indol-5-ol, 1,2,3,3a,8,8a-hexahydro-1,3a,8-trimethyl-, methylcarbamate (ester), (3aS-cis)-
P114	12039-52-0	Selenious acid, dithallium(1+) salt
P103	630-10-4	Selenourea
P104	506-64-9	Silver cyanide
P104	506-64-9	Silver cyanide Ag(CN)
P105	26628-22-8	Sodium azide
P106	143-33-9	Sodium cyanide
P106	143-33-9	Sodium cyanide Na(CN)
P108	[1]57-24-9	Strychnidin-10-one, & salts
P018	357-57-3	Strychnidin-10-one, 2,3-dimethoxy-
P108	[1]57-24-9	Strychnine, & salts
P115	7446-18-6	Sulfuric acid, dithallium(1+) salt
P109	3689-24-5	Tetraethyldithiopyrophosphate
P110	78-00-2	Tetraethyl lead
P111	107-49-3	Tetraethyl pyrophosphate
P112	509-14-8	Tetranitromethane (R)
P062	757-58-4	Tetraphosphoric acid, hexaethyl ester
P113	1314-32-5	Thallic oxide
P113	1314-32-5	Thallium oxide $Tl_2 O_3$
P114	12039-52-0	Thallium(I) selenite
P115	7446-18-6	Thallium(I) sulfate
P109	3689-24-5	Thiodiphosphoric acid, tetraethyl ester
P045	39196-18-4	Thiofanox
P049	541-53-7	Thioimidodicarbonic diamide $[(H_2 N)C(S)]_2 NH$
P014	108-98-5	Thiophenol
P116	79-19-6	Thiosemicarbazide
P026	5344-82-1	Thiourea, (2-chlorophenyl)-
P072	86-88-4	Thiourea, 1-naphthalenyl-
P093	103-85-5	Thiourea, phenyl-
P185	26419-73-8	Tirpate
P123	8001-35-2	Toxaphene
P118	75-70-7	Trichloromethanethiol
P119	7803-55-6	Vanadic acid, ammonium salt
P120	1314-62-1	Vanadium oxide $V_2 O_5$
P120	1314-62-1	Vanadium pentoxide
P084	4549-40-0	Vinylamine, N-methyl-N-nitroso-
P001	[1]81-81-2	Warfarin, & salts, when present at concentrations greater than 0.3%
P205	137-30-4	Zinc, bis(dimethylcarbamodithioato-S,S')-,
P121	557-21-1	Zinc cyanide
P121	557-21-1	Zinc cyanide $Zn(CN)_2$
P122	1314-84-7	Zinc phosphide $Zn_3 P_2$, when present at concentrations greater than 10% (R,T)
P205	137-30-4	Ziram

[1]CAS Number given for parent compound only.

PART 261—Subpart D

Numerical List

Hazardous waste No.	Chemical abstracts No.	Substance
P001	[1] 81–81–2	2H-1-Benzopyran-2-one, 4-hydroxy-3-(3-oxo-1-phenylbutyl)-, & salts, when present at concentrations greater than 0.3%
P001	[1] 81–81–2	Warfarin, & salts, when present at concentrations greater than 0.3%
P002	591–08–2	Acetamide, -(aminothioxomethyl)-
P002	591–08–2	1-Acetyl-2-thiourea
P003	107–02–8	Acrolein
P003	107–02–8	2-Propenal
P004	309–00–2	Aldrin
P004	309–00–2	1,4,5,8-Dimethanonaphthalene, 1,2,3,4,10,10-hexa-chloro-1,4,4a,5,8,8a,-hexahydro-, (1alpha,4alpha,4abeta, 5alpha,8alpha,8abeta)-
P005	107–18–6	Allyl alcohol
P005	107–18–6	2-Propen-1-ol
P006	20859–73–8	Aluminum phosphide (R,T)
P007	2763–96–4	5-(Aminomethyl)-3-isoxazolol
P007	2763–96–4	3(2H)-Isoxazolone, 5-(aminomethyl)-
P008	504–24–5	4-Aminopyridine
P008	504–24–5	4-Pyridinamine
P009	131–74–8	Ammonium picrate (R)
P009	131–74–8	Phenol, 2,4,6-trinitro-, ammonium salt (R)
P010	7778–39–4	Arsenic acid $H_3 AsO_4$
P011	1303–28–2	Arsenic oxide $As_2 O_5$
P011	1303–28–2	Arsenic pentoxide
P012	1327–53–3	Arsenic oxide $As_2 O_3$
P012	1327–53–3	Arsenic trioxide
P013	542–62–1	Barium cyanide
P014	108–98–5	Benzenethiol
P014	108–98–5	Thiophenol
P015	7440–41–7	Beryllium powder
P016	542–88–1	Dichloromethyl ether
P016	542–88–1	Methane, oxybis[chloro-
P017	598–31–2	Bromoacetone
P017	598–31–2	2-Propanone, 1-bromo-
P018	357–57–3	Brucine
P018	357–57–3	Strychnidin-10-one, 2,3-dimethoxy-
P020	88–85–7	Dinoseb
P020	88–85–7	Phenol, 2-(1-methylpropyl)-4,6-dinitro-
P021	592–01–8	Calcium cyanide
P021	592–01–8	Calcium cyanide $Ca(CN)_2$
P022	75–15–0	Carbon disulfide
P023	107–20–0	Acetaldehyde, chloro-
P023	107–20–0	Chloroacetaldehyde
P024	106–47–8	Benzenamine, 4-chloro-
P024	106–47–8	p-Chloroaniline
P026	5344–82–1	1-(o-Chlorophenyl)thiourea
P026	5344–82–1	Thiourea, (2-chlorophenyl)-
P027	542–76–7	3-Chloropropionitrile

Numerical List

Hazardous waste No.	Chemical abstracts No.	Substance
P027	542–76–7	Propanenitrile, 3-chloro-
P028	100–44–7	Benzene, (chloromethyl)-
P028	100–44–7	Benzyl chloride
P029	544–92–3	Copper cyanide
P029	544–92–3	Copper cyanide Cu(CN)
P030		Cyanides (soluble cyanide salts), not otherwise specified
P031	460–19–5	Cyanogen
P031	460–19–5	Ethanedinitrile
P033	506–77–4	Cyanogen chloride
P033	506–77–4	Cyanogen chloride (CN)Cl
P034	131–89–5	2-Cyclohexyl-4,6-dinitrophenol
P034	131–89–5	Phenol, 2-cyclohexyl-4,6-dinitro-
P036	696–28–6	Arsonous dichloride, phenyl-
P036	696–28–6	Dichlorophenylarsine
P037	60–57–1	Dieldrin
P037	60–57–1	2,7:3,6-Dimethanonaphth[2,3-b]oxirene, 3,4,5,6,9,9-hexachloro-1a,2,2a,3,6,6a, 7,7a-octahydro-, (1aalpha,2beta, 2aalpha,3beta,6beta,6aalpha,7beta, 7aalpha)-
P038	692–42–2	Arsine, diethyl-
P038	692–42–2	Diethylarsine
P039	298–04–4	Disulfoton
P039	298–04–4	Phosphorodithioic acid, O,O-diethyl S-[2-(ethylthio)ethyl] ester
P040	297–97–2	O,O-Diethyl O-pyrazinyl phosphorothioate
P040	297–97–2	Phosphorothioic acid, O,O-diethyl O-pyrazinyl ester
P041	311–45–5	Diethyl-p-nitrophenyl phosphate
P041	311–45–5	Phosphoric acid, diethyl 4-nitrophenyl ester
P042	51–43–4	1,2-Benzenediol, 4-[1-hydroxy-2-(methylamino)ethyl]-, (R)-
P042	51–43–4	Epinephrine
P043	55–91–4	Diisopropylfluorophosphate (DFP)
P043	55–91–4	Phosphorofluoridic acid, bis(1-methylethyl) ester
P044	60–51–5	Dimethoate
P044	60–51–5	Phosphorodithioic acid, O,O-dimethyl S-[2-(methyl amino)-2-oxoethyl] ester
P045	39196–18–4	2-Butanone, 3,3-dimethyl-1-(methylthio)-, O-[(methylamino)carbonyl] oxime
P045	39196–18–4	Thiofanox
P046	122–09–8	Benzeneethanamine, alpha,alpha-dimethyl-
P046	122–09–8	alpha,alpha-Dimethylphenethylamine
P047	[1] 534–52–1	4,6-Dinitro-o-cresol, & salts
P047	[1] 534–52–1	Phenol, 2-methyl-4,6-dinitro-, & salts
P048	51–28–5	2,4-Dinitrophenol
P048	51–28–5	Phenol, 2,4-dinitro-

Numerical List

Hazardous waste No.	Chemical abstracts No.	Substance
P049	541–53–7	Dithiobiuret
P049	541–53–7	Thioimidodicarbonic diamide [(H$_2$ N)C(S)]$_2$ NH
P050	115–29–7	Endosulfan
P050	115–29–7	6,9-Methano-2,4,3-benzodioxathiepin, 6,7,8,9,10,10-hexachloro-1,5,5a,6,9,9a-hexahydro-, 3-oxide
P051	[1] 72–20–8	2,7:3,6-Dimethanonaphth [2,3-b]oxirene, 3,4,5,6,9,9-hexachloro-1a,2,2a,3,6,6a,7,7a-octahydro-, (1aalpha,2beta,2abeta,3alpha,6alpha,6a beta,7beta, 7aalpha)-, & metabolites
P051	72–20–8	Endrin
P051	72–20–8	Endrin, & metabolites
P054	151–56–4	Aziridine
P054	151–56–4	Ethyleneimine
P056	7782–41–4	Fluorine
P057	640–19–7	Acetamide, 2-fluoro-
P057	640–19–7	Fluoroacetamide
P058	62–74–8	Acetic acid, fluoro-, sodium salt
P058	62–74–8	Fluoroacetic acid, sodium salt
P059	76–44–8	Heptachlor
P059	76–44–8	4,7-Methano-1H-indene, 1,4,5,6,7,8,8-heptachloro-3a,4,7,7a-tetrahydro-
P060	465–73–6	1,4,5,8-Dimethanonaphthalene, 1,2,3,4,10,10-hexa-chloro-1,4,4a,5,8,8a-hexahydro-, (1alpha,4alpha,4abeta, 5beta,8beta,8abeta)-
P060	465–73–6	Isodrin
P062	757–58–4	Hexaethyl tetraphosphate
P062	757–58–4	Tetraphosphoric acid, hexaethyl ester
P063	74–90–8	Hydrocyanic acid
P063	74–90–8	Hydrogen cyanide
P064	624–83–9	Methane, isocyanato-
P064	624–83–9	Methyl isocyanate
P065	628–86–4	Fulminic acid, mercury(2+) salt (R,T)
P065	628–86–4	Mercury fulminate (R,T)
P066	16752–77–5	Ethanimidothioic acid, N-[[(methylamino)carbonyl]oxy]-, methyl ester
P066	16752–77–5	Methomyl
P067	75–55–8	Aziridine, 2-methyl-
P067	75–55–8	1,2-Propylenimine
P068	60–34–4	Hydrazine, methyl-
P068	60–34–4	Methyl hydrazine
P069	75–86–5	2-Methyllactonitrile
P069	75–86–5	Propanenitrile, 2-hydroxy-2-methyl-
P070	116–06–3	Aldicarb
P070	116–06–3	Propanal, 2-methyl-2-(methylthio)-, O-[(methylamino)carbonyl]oxime
P071	298–00–0	Methyl parathion
P071	298–00–0	Phosphorothioic acid, O,O,-dimethyl O-(4-nitrophenyl) ester

Numerical List

Hazardous waste No.	Chemical abstracts No.	Substance
P072	86–88–4	alpha-Naphthylthiourea
P072	86–88–4	Thiourea, 1-naphthalenyl-
P073	13463–39–3	Nickel carbonyl
P073	13463–39–3	Nickel carbonyl Ni(CO)$_4$, (T-4)-
P074	557–19–7	Nickel cyanide
P074	557–19–7	Nickel cyanide Ni(CN)$_2$
P075	[1] 54–11–5	Nicotine, & salts
P075	[1] 54–11–5	Pyridine, 3-(1-methyl-2-pyrrolidinyl)-, (S)-, & salts
P076	10102–43–9	Nitric oxide
P076	10102–43–9	Nitrogen oxide NO
P077	100–01–6	Benzenamine, 4-nitro-
P077	100–01–6	p-Nitroaniline
P078	10102–44–0	Nitrogen dioxide
P078	10102–44–0	Nitrogen oxide NO$_2$
P081	55–63–0	Nitroglycerine (R)
P081	55–63–0	1,2,3-Propanetriol, trinitrate (R)
P082	62–75–9	Methanamine, -methyl-N-nitroso-
P082	62–75–9	N-Nitrosodimethylamine
P084	4549–40–0	N-Nitrosomethylvinylamine
P084	4549–40–0	Vinylamine, -methyl-N-nitroso-
P085	152–16–9	Diphosphoramide, octamethyl-
P085	152–16–9	Octamethylpyrophosphoramide
P087	20816–12–0	Osmium oxide OsO$_4$, (T-4)-
P087	20816–12–0	Osmium tetroxide
P088	145–73–3	Endothall
P088	145–73–3	7-Oxabicyclo[2.2.1]heptane-2,3-dicarboxylic acid
P089	56–38–2	Parathion
P089	56–38–2	Phosphorothioic acid, O,O-diethyl O-(4-nitrophenyl) ester
P092	62–38–4	Mercury, (acetato-O)phenyl-
P092	62–38–4	Phenylmercury acetate
P093	103–85–5	Phenylthiourea
P093	103–85–5	Thiourea, phenyl-
P094	298–02–2	Phorate
P094	298–02–2	Phosphorodithioic acid, O,O-diethyl S-[(ethylthio)methyl] ester
P095	75–44–5	Carbonic dichloride
P095	75–44–5	Phosgene
P096	7803–51–2	Hydrogen phosphide
P096	7803–51–2	Phosphine
P097	52–85–7	Famphur
P097	52–85–7	Phosphorothioic acid, O-[4-[(dimethylamino)sulfonyl]phenyl] O,O-dimethyl ester
P098	151–50–8	Potassium cyanide
P098	151–50–8	Potassium cyanide K(CN)
P099	506–61–6	Argentate(1-), bis(cyano-C)-, potassium
P099	506–61–6	Potassium silver cyanide
P101	107–12–0	Ethyl cyanide

Numerical List

Hazardous waste No.	Chemical abstracts No.	Substance
P101	107–12–0	Propanenitrile
P102	107–19–7	Propargyl alcohol
P102	107–19–7	2-Propyn-1-ol
P103	630–10–4	Selenourea
P104	506–64–9	Silver cyanide
P104	506–64–9	Silver cyanide Ag(CN)
P105	26628–22–8	Sodium azide
P106	143–33–9	Sodium cyanide
P106	143–33–9	Sodium cyanide Na(CN)
P108	[1] 157–24–9	Strychnidin-10-one, & salts
P108	[1] 157–24–9	Strychnine, & salts
P109	3689–24–5	Tetraethyldithiopyrophosphate
P109	3689–24–5	Thiodiphosphoric acid, tetraethyl ester
P110	78–00–2	Plumbane, tetraethyl-
P110	78–00–2	Tetraethyl lead
P111	107–49–3	Diphosphoric acid, tetraethyl ester
P111	107–49–3	Tetraethyl pyrophosphate
P112	509–14–8	Methane, tetranitro-(R)
P112	509–14–8	Tetranitromethane (R)
P113	1314–32–5	Thallic oxide
P113	1314–32–5	Thallium oxide Tl_2O_3
P114	12039–52–0	Selenious acid, dithallium(1+) salt
P114	12039–52–0	Tetraethyldithiopyrophosphate*
P115	7446–18–6	Thiodiphosphoric acid, tetraethyl ester*
P115	7446–18–6	Plumbane, tetraethyl-*
P116	79–19–6	Tetraethyl lead*

* [*Publisher's Note:* These four substances are incorrect and should be replaced with Thallium(I) selenite; Sulfuric acid, dithallium(1+) salt; Thallium(I) sulfate; and Hydrazinecarbothioamide, respectively.]

Hazardous waste No.	Chemical abstracts No.	Substance
P116	79–19–6	Thiosemicarbazide
P118	75–70–7	Methanethiol, trichloro-
P118	75–70–7	Trichloromethanethiol
P119	7803–55–6	Ammonium vanadate
P119	7803–55–6	Vanadic acid, ammonium salt
P120	1314–62–1	Vanadium oxide V_2O_5
P120	1314–62–1	Vanadium pentoxide
P121	557–21–1	Zinc cyanide
P121	557–21–1	Zinc cyanide $Zn(CN)_2$
P122	1314–84–7	Zinc phosphide Zn_3P_2, when present at concentrations greater than 10% (R,T)
P123	8001–35–2	Toxaphene
P127	1563–66–2	7-Benzofuranol, 2,3-dihydro-2,2-dimethyl-, methylcarbamate–
P127	1563–66–2	Carbofuran
P128	315–8–4	Mexacarbate
P128	315–18–4	Phenol, 4-(dimethylamino)-3,5-dimethyl-, methylcarbamate (ester)
P185	26419–73–8	1,3-Dithiolane-2-carboxaldehyde, 2,4-dimethyl-, O-[(methylamino)-carbonyl]oxime
P185	26419–73–8	Tirpate

Numerical List

Hazardous waste No.	Chemical abstracts No.	Substance
P188	57–64–7	Benzoic acid, 2-hydroxy-, compd– with (3aS-cis)-1,2,3,3a,8,8a-hexahydro-1,3a,8-trimethylpyrrolo[2,3-b]indol-5-yl methylcarbamate ester (1:1)
P188	57–64–7	Physostigmine salicylate
P189	55285–14–8	Carbamic acid, [(dibutylamino)-thio]methyl-, 2,3-dihydro-2,2-dimethyl-7-benzofuranyl ester
P189	55285–14–8	Carbosulfan
P190	1129–41–5	Carbamic acid, methyl-, 3-methylphenyl ester
P190	1129–41–5	Metolcarb
P191	644–64–4	Carbamic acid, dimethyl-, 1-[(dimethyl-amino)carbonyl]-5-methyl-1H-pyrazol-3-yl ester
P191	644–64–4	Dimetilan
P192	119–38–0	Carbamic acid, dimethyl-, 3-methyl-1-(1-methylethyl)-1H-pyrazol-5-yl ester
P192	119–38–0	Isolan
P194	23135–22–0	Ethanimidthioic acid, 2-(dimethylamino)-N-[[(methylamino) carbonyl]oxy]-2-oxo-, methyl ester
P194	23135–22–0	Oxamyl
P196	15339–36–3	Manganese, bis(dimethylcarbamodithioato-S,S´)-,
P196	15339–36–3	Manganese dimethyldithiocarbamate
P197	17702–57–7	Formparanate
P197	17702–57–7	Methanimidamide, N,N-dimethyl-N´-[2-methyl-4-[[(methylamino)car-bonyl]oxy]phenyl]-
P198	23422–53–9	Formetanate hydrochloride
P198	23422–53–9	Methanimidamide, N,N-dimethyl-N´-[3-[[(methylamino)-carbonyl]oxy]phenyl]-monohydrochloride
P199	2032–65–7	Methiocarb
P199	2032–65–7	Phenol, (3,5-dimethyl-4-(methylthio)-, methylcarbamate
P201	2631–37–0	Phenol, 3-methyl-5-(1-methylethyl)-, methyl carbamate
P201	2631–37–0	Promecarb
P202	64–00–6	m-Cumenyl methylcarbamate
P202	64–00–6	3-Isopropylphenyl N-methylcarbamate
P202	64–00–6	Phenol, 3-(1-methylethyl)-, methyl carbamate
P203	1646–88–4	Aldicarb sulfone
P203	1646–88–4	Propanal, 2-methyl-2-(methyl-sulfonyl)-, O-[(methylamino)carbonyl] oxime
P204	57–47–6	Physostigmine
P204	57–47–6	Pyrrolo[2,3-b]indol-5-ol, 1,2,3,3a,8,8a-hexahydro-1,3a,8-trimethyl-, methylcarbamate (ester), (3aS-cis)-
P205	137–30–4	Zinc, bis(dimethylcarbamodithioato-S,S´)-,
P205	137–30–4	Ziram

[1] CAS Number given for parent compound only.

(f) The commercial chemical products, manufacturing chemical intermediates, or off-specification commercial chemical products referred to in paragraphs (a) through (d) of this section, are identified as toxic wastes (T), unless otherwise designated and are subject to the small quantity generator exclusion defined in §261.5 (a) and (g). 📖 **1.2.5.4, 3.5, 14.3.1.1**

[*Comment:* For the convenience of the regulated community, the primary hazardous properties of these materials have been indicated by the letters T (Toxicity), R (Reactivity), I (Ignitability) and C (Corrosivity). Absence of a letter indicates that the compound is only listed for toxicity. Wastes are first listed in alphabetical order by substance and then listed again in numerical order by Hazardous Waste Number.]

Publisher's Note: For the convenience of our readers, we have separated the alphabetical list and the numerical list into two tables.

These wastes and their corresponding EPA Hazardous Waste Numbers are:

Alphabetical List

Hazardous waste No.	Chemical abstracts No.	Substance
U394	30558-43-1	A2213
U001	75-07-0	Acetaldehyde (I)
U034	75-87-6	Acetaldehyde, trichloro-
U187	62-44-2	Acetamide, N-(4-ethoxyphenyl)-
U005	53-96-3	Acetamide, N-9H-fluoren-2-yl-
U240	[1]94-75-7	Acetic acid, (2,4-dichlorophenoxy)-, salts & esters
U112	141-78-6	Acetic acid ethyl ester (I)
U144	301-04-2	Acetic acid, lead(2+) salt
U214	563-68-8	Acetic acid, thallium(1+) salt
see F027	93-76-5	Acetic acid, (2,4,5-trichlorophenoxy)-
U002	67-64-1	Acetone (I)
U003	75-05-8	Acetonitrile (I,T)
U004	98-86-2	Acetophenone
U005	53-96-3	2-Acetylaminofluorene
U006	75-36-5	Acetyl chloride (C,R,T)
U007	79-06-1	Acrylamide
U008	79-10-7	Acrylic acid (I)
U009	107-13-1	Acrylonitrile
U011	61-82-5	Amitrole
U012	62-53-3	Aniline (I,T)
U136	75-60-5	Arsinic acid, dimethyl-
U014	492-80-8	Auramine
U015	115-02-6	Azaserine
U010	50-07-7	Azirino[2´,3´:3,4]pyrrolo[1,2- a]indole-4,7-dione, 6-amino-8- [[(amino-carbonyl)oxy]methyl]- 1,1a,2,8,8a,8b-hexahydro-8a-methoxy-5- methyl-, [1aS-(1aalpha, 8beta,8aalpha,8balpha)]-
U280	101-27-9	Barban
U278	22781-23-3	Bendiocarb
U364	22961-82-6	Bendiocarb phenol
U271	17804-35-2	Benomyl
U157	56-49-5	Benz[j]aceanthrylene, 1,2-dihydro-3-methyl-
U016	225-51-4	Benz[c]acridine
U017	98-87-3	Benzal chloride
U192	23950-58-5	Benzamide, 3,5-dichloro-N-(1,1-dimethyl-2-propynyl)-
U018	56-55-3	Benz[a]anthracene
U094	57-97-6	Benz[a]anthracene, 7,12-dimethyl-
U012	62-53-3	Benzenamine (I,T)
U014	492-80-8	Benzenamine, 4,4´-carbonimidoylbis[N,N- dimethyl-
U049	3165-93-3	Benzenamine, 4-chloro-2-methyl-, hydrochloride
U093	60-11-7	Benzenamine, N,N-dimethyl-4-(phenylazo)-
U328	95-53-4	Benzenamine, 2-methyl-
U353	106-49-0	Benzenamine, 4-methyl-
U158	101-14-4	Benzenamine, 4,4´-methylenebis[2-chloro-
U222	636-21-5	Benzenamine, 2-methyl-, hydrochloride
U181	99-55-8	Benzenamine, 2-methyl-5-nitro-
U019	71-43-2	Benzene (I,T)
U038	510-15-6	Benzeneacetic acid, 4-chloro-alpha-(4-chlorophenyl)-alpha-hydroxy-, ethyl ester
U030	101-55-3	Benzene, 1-bromo-4-phenoxy-
U035	305-03-3	Benzenebutanoic acid, 4-[bis(2-chloroethyl)amino]-
U037	108-90-7	Benzene, chloro-
U221	25376-45-8	Benzenediamine, ar-methyl-
U028	117-81-7	1,2-Benzenedicarboxylic acid, bis(2-ethylhexyl) ester
U069	84-74-2	1,2-Benzenedicarboxylic acid, dibutyl ester
U088	84-66-2	1,2-Benzenedicarboxylic acid, diethyl ester
U102	131-11-3	1,2-Benzenedicarboxylic acid, dimethyl ester
U107	117-84-0	1,2-Benzenedicarboxylic acid, dioctyl ester
U070	95-50-1	Benzene, 1,2-dichloro-
U071	541-73-1	Benzene, 1,3-dichloro-
U072	106-46-7	Benzene, 1,4-dichloro-
U060	72-54-8	Benzene, 1,1´-(2,2-dichloroethylidene)bis[4-chloro-
U017	98-87-3	Benzene, (dichloromethyl)-
U223	26471-62-5	Benzene, 1,3-diisocyanatomethyl- (R,T)
U239	1330-20-7	Benzene, dimethyl- (I,T)
U201	108-46-3	1,3-Benzenediol
U127	118-74-1	Benzene, hexachloro-
U056	110-82-7	Benzene, hexahydro- (I)
U220	108-88-3	Benzene, methyl-
U105	121-14-2	Benzene, 1-methyl-2,4-dinitro-
U106	606-20-2	Benzene, 2-methyl-1,3-dinitro-
U055	98-82-8	Benzene, (1-methylethyl)- (I)
U169	98-95-3	Benzene, nitro-
U183	608-93-5	Benzene, pentachloro-
U185	82-68-8	Benzene, pentachloronitro-

Alphabetical List

Hazardous waste No.	Chemical abstracts No.	Substance
U020	98-09-9	Benzenesulfonic acid chloride (C,R)
U020	98-09-9	Benzenesulfonyl chloride (C,R)
U207	95-94-3	Benzene, 1,2,4,5-tetrachloro-
U061	50-29-3	Benzene, 1,1′-(2,2,2-trichloroethylidene)bis[4-chloro-
U247	72-43-5	Benzene, 1,1′-(2,2,2-trichloroethylidene)bis[4- methoxy-
U023	98-07-7	Benzene, (trichloromethyl)-
U234	99-35-4	Benzene, 1,3,5-trinitro-
U021	92-87-5	Benzidine
U202	[1]81-07-2	1,2-Benzisothiazol-3(2H)-one, 1,1-dioxide, & salts
U278	22781-23-3	1,3-Benzodioxol-4-ol, 2,2-dimethyl-, methyl carbamate.
U364	22961-82-6	1,3-Benzodioxol-4-ol, 2,2-dimethyl-,
U203	94-59-7	1,3-Benzodioxole, 5-(2-propenyl)-
U141	120-58-1	1,3-Benzodioxole, 5-(1-propenyl)-
U367	1563-38-8	7-Benzofuranol, 2,3-dihydro-2,2-dimethyl-
U090	94-58-6	1,3-Benzodioxole, 5-propyl-
U064	189-55-9	Benzo[rst]pentaphene
U248	[1]81-81-2	2H-1-Benzopyran-2-one, 4-hydroxy-3-(3-oxo-1-phenyl-butyl)-, & salts, when present at concentrations of 0.3% or less
U022	50-32-8	Benzo[a]pyrene
U197	106-51-4	p-Benzoquinone
U023	98-07-7	Benzotrichloride (C,R,T)
U085	1464-53-5	2,2′-Bioxirane
U021	92-87-5	[1,1′-Biphenyl]-4,4′-diamine
U073	91-94-1	[1,1′-Biphenyl]-4,4′-diamine, 3,3′-dichloro-
U091	119-90-4	[1,1′-Biphenyl]-4,4′-diamine, 3,3′-dimethoxy-
U095	119-93-7	[1,1′-Biphenyl]-4,4′-diamine, 3,3′-dimethyl-
U225	75-25-2	Bromoform
U030	101-55-3	4-Bromophenyl phenyl ether
U128	87-68-3	1,3-Butadiene, 1,1,2,3,4,4-hexachloro-
U172	924-16-3	1-Butanamine, N-butyl-N-nitroso-
U031	71-36-3	1-Butanol (I)
U159	78-93-3	2-Butanone (I,T)
U160	1338-23-4	2-Butanone, peroxide (R,T)
U053	4170-30-3	2-Butenal
U074	764-41-0	2-Butene, 1,4-dichloro- (I,T)
U143	303-34-4	2-Butenoic acid, 2-methyl-, 7-[[2,3-dihydroxy- 2-(1-methoxyethyl)-3-methyl-1- oxobutoxy]methyl]- 2,3,5,7a-tetrahydro-1H-pyrrolizin-1- yl ester, [1S-[1alpha(Z),7(2S*,3R*),7aalpha]]-
U031	71-36-3	n-Butyl alcohol (I)
U136	75-60-5	Cacodylic acid
U032	13765-19-0	Calcium chromate
U372	10605-21-7	Carbamic acid, 1H-benzimidazol-2-yl, methyl ester

Alphabetical List

Hazardous waste No.	Chemical abstracts No.	Substance
U271	17804-35-2	Carbamic acid, [1- [(butylamino)carbonyl]-1H- benzimidazol-2-yl]-, methyl ester
U280	101-27-9	Carbamic acid, (3-chlorophenyl)-, 4- chloro-2-butynyl ester
U238	51-79-6	Carbamic acid, ethyl ester
U178	615-53-2	Carbamic acid, methylnitroso-, ethyl ester
U373	122-42-9	Carbamic acid, phenyl-, 1-methylethyl ester
U409	23564-05-8	Carbamic acid, [1,2-phenylenebis (iminocarbonothioyl)]bis-, dimethyl ester
U097	79-44-7	Carbamic chloride, dimethyl-
U389	2303-17-5	Carbamothioic acid, bis(1-methylethyl)-, S-(2,3,3-trichloro-2-propenyl) ester
U387	52888-80-9	Carbamothioic acid, dipropyl-, S-(phenylmethyl) ester
U114	[1]111-54-6	Carbamodithioic acid, 1,2-ethanediylbis-, salts & esters
U062	2303-16-4	Carbamothioic acid, bis(1-methylethyl)-, S-(2,3-dichloro-2-propenyl) ester
U279	63-25-2	Carbaryl
U372	10605-21-7	Carbendazim
U367	1563-38-8	Carbofuran phenol
U215	6533-73-9	Carbonic acid, dithallium(1+) salt
U033	353-50-4	Carbonic difluoride
U156	79-22-1	Carbonochloridic acid, methyl ester (I, T)
U033	353-50-4	Carbon oxyfluoride (R,T)
U211	56-23-5	Carbon tetrachloride
U034	75-87-6	Chloral
U035	305-03-3	Chlorambucil
U036	57-74-9	Chlordane, alpha & gamma isomers
U026	494-03-1	Chlornaphazin
U037	108-90-7	Chlorobenzene
U038	510-15-6	Chlorobenzilate
U039	59-50-7	p-Chloro-m-cresol
U042	110-75-8	2-Chloroethyl vinyl ether
U044	67-66-3	Chloroform
U046	107-30-2	Chloromethyl methyl ether
U047	91-58-7	beta-Chloronaphthalene
U048	95-57-8	o-Chlorophenol
U049	3165-93-3	4-Chloro-o-toluidine, hydrochloride
U032	13765-19-0	Chromic acid H_2CrO_4, calcium salt
U050	218-01-9	Chrysene
U051		Creosote
U052	1319-77-3	Cresol (Cresylic acid)
U053	4170-30-3	Crotonaldehyde
U055	98-82-8	Cumene (I)
U246	506-68-3	Cyanogen bromide (CN)Br
U197	106-51-4	2,5-Cyclohexadiene-1,4-dione
U056	110-82-7	Cyclohexane (I)
U129	58-89-9	Cyclohexane, 1,2,3,4,5,6-hexachloro-, (1alpha,2alpha,3beta,4alpha,5alpha, 6 beta)-
U057	108-94-1	Cyclohexanone (I)

Alphabetical List

Hazardous waste No.	Chemical abstracts No.	Substance
U130	77-47-4	1,3-Cyclopentadiene, 1,2,3,4,5,5-hexachloro-
U058	50-18-0	Cyclophosphamide
U240	[1]94-75-7	2,4-D, salts & esters
U059	20830-81-3	Daunomycin
U060	72-54-8	DDD
U061	50-29-3	DDT
U062	2303-16-4	Diallate
U063	53-70-3	Dibenz[a,h]anthracene
U064	189-55-9	Dibenzo[a,i]pyrene
U066	96-12-8	1,2-Dibromo-3-chloropropane
U069	84-74-2	Dibutyl phthalate
U070	95-50-1	o-Dichlorobenzene
U071	541-73-1	m-Dichlorobenzene
U072	106-46-7	p-Dichlorobenzene
U073	91-94-1	3,3′-Dichlorobenzidine
U074	764-41-0	1,4-Dichloro-2-butene (I,T)
U075	75-71-8	Dichlorodifluoromethane
U078	75-35-4	1,1-Dichloroethylene
U079	156-60-5	1,2-Dichloroethylene
U025	111-44-4	Dichloroethyl ether
U027	108-60-1	Dichloroisopropyl ether
U024	111-91-1	Dichloromethoxy ethane
U081	120-83-2	2,4-Dichlorophenol
U082	87-65-0	2,6-Dichlorophenol
U084	542-75-6	1,3-Dichloropropene
U085	1464-53-5	1,2:3,4-Diepoxybutane (I,T)
U108	123-91-1	1,4-Diethyleneoxide
U028	117-81-7	Diethylhexyl phthalate
U395	5952-26-1	Diethylene glycol, dicarbamate.
U086	1615-80-1	N,N′-Diethylhydrazine
U087	3288-58-2	O,O-Diethyl S-methyl dithiophosphate
U088	84-66-2	Diethyl phthalate
U089	56-53-1	Diethylstilbesterol
U090	94-58-6	Dihydrosafrole
U091	119-90-4	3,3′-Dimethoxybenzidine
U092	124-40-3	Dimethylamine (I)
U093	60-11-7	p-Dimethylaminoazobenzene
U094	57-97-6	7,12-Dimethylbenz[a]anthracene
U095	119-93-7	3,3′-Dimethylbenzidine
U096	80-15-9	alpha,alpha-Dimethylbenzylhydroperoxide (R)
U097	79-44-7	Dimethylcarbamoyl chloride
U098	57-14-7	1,1-Dimethylhydrazine
U099	540-73-8	1,2-Dimethylhydrazine
U101	105-67-9	2,4-Dimethylphenol
U102	131-11-3	Dimethyl phthalate
U103	77-78-1	Dimethyl sulfate
U105	121-14-2	2,4-Dinitrotoluene
U106	606-20-2	2,6-Dinitrotoluene
U107	117-84-0	Di-n-octyl phthalate
U108	123-91-1	1,4-Dioxane
U109	122-66-7	1,2-Diphenylhydrazine

Alphabetical List

Hazardous waste No.	Chemical abstracts No.	Substance
U110	142-84-7	Dipropylamine (I)
U111	621-64-7	Di-n-propylnitrosamine
U041	106-89-8	Epichlorohydrin
U001	75-07-0	Ethanal (I)
U404	121-44-8	Ethanamine, N,N-diethyl-
U174	55-18-5	Ethanamine, N-ethyl-N-nitroso-
U155	91-80-5	1,2-Ethanediamine, N,N-dimethyl-N′-2-pyridinyl-N′-(2-thienylmethyl)-
U067	106-93-4	Ethane, 1,2-dibromo-
U076	75-34-3	Ethane, 1,1-dichloro-
U077	107-06-2	Ethane, 1,2-dichloro-
U131	67-72-1	Ethane, hexachloro-
U024	111-91-1	Ethane, 1,1′-[methylenebis(oxy)]bis [2-chloro-
U117	60-29-7	Ethane, 1,1′-oxybis-(I)
U025	111-44-4	Ethane, 1,1′-oxybis[2-chloro-
U184	76-01-7	Ethane, pentachloro-
U208	630-20-6	Ethane, 1,1,1,2-tetrachloro-
U209	79-34-5	Ethane, 1,1,2,2-tetrachloro-
U218	62-55-5	Ethanethioamide
U226	71-55-6	Ethane, 1,1,1-trichloro-
U227	79-00-5	Ethane, 1,1,2-trichloro-
U410	59669-26-0	Ethanimidothioic acid, N,N′-[thiobis[(methylimino)carbonyloxy]]bis-, dimethyl ester
U394	30558-43-1	Ethanimidothioic acid, 2-(dimethylamino)-N-hydroxy-2-oxo-, methyl ester
U359	110-80-5	Ethanol, 2-ethoxy-
U173	1116-54-7	Ethanol, 2,2′-(nitrosoimino)bis-
U395	5952-26-1	Ethanol, 2,2′-oxybis-, dicarbamate.
U004	98-86-2	Ethanone, 1-phenyl-
U043	75-01-4	Ethene, chloro-
U042	110-75-8	Ethene, (2-chloroethoxy)-
U078	75-35-4	Ethene, 1,1-dichloro-
U079	156-60-5	Ethene, 1,2-dichloro-, (E)-
U210	127-18-4	Ethene, tetrachloro-
U228	79-01-6	Ethene, trichloro-
U112	141-78-6	Ethyl acetate (I)
U113	140-88-5	Ethyl acrylate (I)
U238	51-79-6	Ethyl carbamate (urethane)
U117	60-29-7	Ethyl ether (I)
U114	[1]111-54-6	Ethylenebisdithiocarbamic acid, salts & esters
U067	106-93-4	Ethylene dibromide
U077	107-06-2	Ethylene dichloride
U359	110-80-5	Ethylene glycol monoethyl ether
U115	75-21-8	Ethylene oxide (I,T)
U116	96-45-7	Ethylenethiourea
U076	75-34-3	Ethylidene dichloride
U118	97-63-2	Ethyl methacrylate
U119	62-50-0	Ethyl methanesulfonate
U120	206-44-0	Fluoranthene
U122	50-00-0	Formaldehyde

Alphabetical List

Hazardous waste No.	Chemical abstracts No.	Substance
U123	64-18-6	Formic acid (C,T)
U124	110-00-9	Furan (I)
U125	98-01-1	2-Furancarboxaldehyde (I)
U147	108-31-6	2,5-Furandione
U213	109-99-9	Furan, tetrahydro-(I)
U125	98-01-1	Furfural (I)
U124	110-00-9	Furfuran (I)
U206	18883-66-4	Glucopyranose, 2-deoxy-2-(3-methyl-3-nitrosoureido)-, D-
U206	18883-66-4	D-Glucose, 2-deoxy-2- [[(methyl-nitrosoamino)- carbonyl]amino]-
U126	765-34-4	Glycidylaldehyde
U163	70-25-7	Guanidine, N-methyl-N'-nitro-N-nitroso-
U127	118-74-1	Hexachlorobenzene
U128	87-68-3	Hexachlorobutadiene
U130	77-47-4	Hexachlorocyclopentadiene
U131	67-72-1	Hexachloroethane
U132	70-30-4	Hexachlorophene
U243	1888-71-7	Hexachloropropene
U133	302-01-2	Hydrazine (R,T)
U086	1615-80-1	Hydrazine, 1,2-diethyl-
U098	57-14-7	Hydrazine, 1,1-dimethyl-
U099	540-73-8	Hydrazine, 1,2-dimethyl-
U109	122-66-7	Hydrazine, 1,2-diphenyl-
U134	7664-39-3	Hydrofluoric acid (C,T)
U134	7664-39-3	Hydrogen fluoride (C,T)
U135	7783-06-4	Hydrogen sulfide
U135	7783-06-4	Hydrogen sulfide H_2 S
U096	80-15-9	Hydroperoxide, 1-methyl-1-phenylethyl- (R)
U116	96-45-7	2-Imidazolidinethione
U137	193-39-5	Indeno[1,2,3-cd]pyrene
U190	85-44-9	1,3-Isobenzofurandione
U140	78-83-1	Isobutyl alcohol (I,T)
U141	120-58-1	Isosafrole
U142	143-50-0	Kepone
U143	303-34-4	Lasiocarpine
U144	301-04-2	Lead acetate
U146	1335-32-6	Lead, bis(acetato-O)tetrahydroxytri-
U145	7446-27-7	Lead phosphate
U146	1335-32-6	Lead subacetate
U129	58-89-9	Lindane
U163	70-25-7	MNNG
U147	108-31-6	Maleic anhydride
U148	123-33-1	Maleic hydrazide
U149	109-77-3	Malononitrile
U150	148-82-3	Melphalan
U151	7439-97-6	Mercury 14.4.4.2
U152	126-98-7	Methacrylonitrile (I, T)
U092	124-40-3	Methanamine, N-methyl- (I)
U029	74-83-9	Methane, bromo-
U045	74-87-3	Methane, chloro- (I, T)
U046	107-30-2	Methane, chloromethoxy-
U068	74-95-3	Methane, dibromo-

Alphabetical List

Hazardous waste No.	Chemical abstracts No.	Substance
U080	75-09-2	Methane, dichloro-
U075	75-71-8	Methane, dichlorodifluoro-
U138	74-88-4	Methane, iodo-
U119	62-50-0	Methanesulfonic acid, ethyl ester
U211	56-23-5	Methane, tetrachloro-
U153	74-93-1	Methanethiol (I, T)
U225	75-25-2	Methane, tribromo-
U044	67-66-3	Methane, trichloro-
U121	75-69-4	Methane, trichlorofluoro-
U036	57-74-9	4,7-Methano-1H-indene, 1,2,4,5,6,7,8,8-octachloro-2,3,3a,4,7,7a-hexahydro-
U154	67-56-1	Methanol (I)
U155	91-80-5	Methapyrilene
U142	143-50-0	1,3,4-Metheno-2H-cyclobuta[cd] pentalen- 2-one, 1,1a,3,3a,4,5,5,5a,5b,6-decachlorooctahydro-
U247	72-43-5	Methoxychlor
U154	67-56-1	Methyl alcohol (I)
U029	74-83-9	Methyl bromide
U186	504-60-9	1-Methylbutadiene (I)
U045	74-87-3	Methyl chloride (I,T)
U156	79-22-1	Methyl chlorocarbonate (I,T)
U226	71-55-6	Methyl chloroform
U157	56-49-5	3-Methylcholanthrene
U158	101-14-4	4,4'-Methylenebis(2-chloroaniline)
U068	74-95-3	Methylene bromide
U080	75-09-2	Methylene chloride
U159	78-93-3	Methyl ethyl ketone (MEK) (I,T)
U160	1338-23-4	Methyl ethyl ketone peroxide (R,T)
U138	74-88-4	Methyl iodide
U161	108-10-1	Methyl isobutyl ketone (I)
U162	80-62-6	Methyl methacrylate (I,T)
U161	108-10-1	4-Methyl-2-pentanone (I)
U164	56-04-2	Methylthiouracil
U010	50-07-7	Mitomycin C
U059	20830-81-3	5,12-Naphthacenedione, 8-acetyl-10-[(3-amino-2,3,6-trideoxy)-alpha-L-lyxo-hexopyranosyl)oxy]-7,8,9,10- tetrahydro-6,8,11-trihydroxy-1-methoxy-, (8S-cis)-
U167	134-32-7	1-Naphthalenamine
U168	91-59-8	2-Naphthalenamine
U026	494-03-1	Naphthalenamine, N,N'-bis(2-chloroethyl)-
U165	91-20-3	Naphthalene
U047	91-58-7	Naphthalene, 2-chloro-
U166	130-15-4	1,4-Naphthalenedione
U236	72-57-1	2,7-Naphthalenedisulfonic acid, 3,3'-[(3,3'- dimethyl[1,1'-biphenyl]-4,4'-diyl)bis(azo)bis[5-amino-4-hydroxy]-, tetrasodium salt
U279	63-25-2	1-Naphthalenol, methylcarbamate.
U166	130-15-4	1,4-Naphthoquinone
U167	134-32-7	alpha-Naphthylamine
U168	91-59-8	beta-Naphthylamine
U217	10102-45-1	Nitric acid, thallium(1+) salt

Alphabetical List

Hazardous waste No.	Chemical abstracts No.	Substance
U169	98-95-3	Nitrobenzene (I,T)
U170	100-02-7	p-Nitrophenol
U171	79-46-9	2-Nitropropane (I,T)
U172	924-16-3	N-Nitrosodi-n-butylamine
U173	1116-54-7	N-Nitrosodiethanolamine
U174	55-18-5	N-Nitrosodiethylamine
U176	759-73-9	N-Nitroso-N-ethylurea
U177	684-93-5	N-Nitroso-N-methylurea
U178	615-53-2	N-Nitroso-N-methylurethane
U179	100-75-4	N-Nitrosopiperidine
U180	930-55-2	N-Nitrosopyrrolidine
U181	99-55-8	5-Nitro-o-toluidine
U193	1120-71-4	1,2-Oxathiolane, 2,2-dioxide
U058	50-18-0	2H-1,3,2-Oxazaphosphorin-2-amine, N,N-bis(2-chloroethyl)tetrahydro-, 2-oxide
U115	75-21-8	Oxirane (I,T)
U126	765-34-4	Oxiranecarboxyaldehyde
U041	106-89-8	Oxirane, (chloromethyl)-
U182	123-63-7	Paraldehyde
U183	608-93-5	Pentachlorobenzene
U184	76-01-7	Pentachloroethane
U185	82-68-8	Pentachloronitrobenzene (PCNB)
See F027	87-86-5	Pentachlorophenol
U161	108-10-1	Pentanol, 4-methyl-
U186	504-60-9	1,3-Pentadiene (I)
U187	62-44-2	Phenacetin
U188	108-95-2	Phenol
U048	95-57-8	Phenol, 2-chloro-
U039	59-50-7	Phenol, 4-chloro-3-methyl-
U081	120-83-2	Phenol, 2,4-dichloro-
U082	87-65-0	Phenol, 2,6-dichloro-
U089	56-53-1	Phenol, 4,4′-(1,2-diethyl-1,2-ethenediyl)bis-, (E)-
U101	105-67-9	Phenol, 2,4-dimethyl-
U052	1319-77-3	Phenol, methyl-
U132	70-30-4	Phenol, 2,2′-methylenebis[3,4,6-trichloro-
U411	114-26-1	Phenol, 2-(1-methylethoxy)-, methylcarbamate.
U170	100-02-7	Phenol, 4-nitro-
See F027	87-86-5	Phenol, pentachloro-
See F027	58-90-2	Phenol, 2,3,4,6-tetrachloro-
See F027	95-95-4	Phenol, 2,4,5-trichloro-
See F027	88-06-2	Phenol, 2,4,6-trichloro-
U150	148-82-3	L-Phenylalanine, 4-[bis(2-chloroethyl)amino]-
U145	7446-27-7	Phosphoric acid, lead(2+) salt (2:3)
U087	3288-58-2	Phosphorodithioic acid, O,O-diethyl S-methyl ester

Alphabetical List

Hazardous waste No.	Chemical abstracts No.	Substance
U189	1314-80-3	Phosphorus sulfide (R)
U190	85-44-9	Phthalic anhydride
U191	109-06-8	2-Picoline
U179	100-75-4	Piperidine, 1-nitroso-
U192	23950-58-5	Pronamide
U194	107-10-8	1-Propanamine (I,T)
U111	621-64-7	1-Propanamine, N-nitroso-N-propyl-
U110	142-84-7	1-Propanamine, N-propyl- (I)
U066	96-12-8	Propane, 1,2-dibromo-3-chloro-
U083	78-87-5	Propane, 1,2-dichloro-
U149	109-77-3	Propanedinitrile
U171	79-46-9	Propane, 2-nitro- (I,T)
U027	108-60-1	Propane, 2,2′-oxybis[2-chloro-
U193	1120-71-4	1,3-Propane sultone
See F027	93-72-1	Propanoic acid, 2-(2,4,5-trichlorophenoxy)-
U235	126-72-7	1-Propanol, 2,3-dibromo-, phosphate (3:1)
U140	78-83-1	1-Propanol, 2-methyl- (I,T)
U002	67-64-1	2-Propanone (I)
U007	79-06-1	2-Propenamide
U084	542-75-6	1-Propene, 1,3-dichloro-
U243	1888-71-7	1-Propene, 1,1,2,3,3,3-hexachloro-
U009	107-13-1	2-Propenenitrile
U152	126-98-7	2-Propenenitrile, 2-methyl- (I,T)
U008	79-10-7	2-Propenoic acid (I)
U113	140-88-5	2-Propenoic acid, ethyl ester (I)
U118	97-63-2	2-Propenoic acid, 2-methyl-, ethyl ester
U162	80-62-6	2-Propenoic acid, 2-methyl-, methyl ester (I,T)
U373	122-42-9	Propham
U411	114-26-1	Propoxur
U387	52888-80-9	Prosulfocarb
U194	107-10-8	n-Propylamine (I,T)
U083	78-87-5	Propylene dichloride
U148	123-33-1	3,6-Pyridazinedione, 1,2-dihydro-
U196	110-86-1	Pyridine
U191	109-06-8	Pyridine, 2-methyl-
U237	66-75-1	2,4-(1H,3H)-Pyrimidinedione, 5-[bis(2-chloroethyl)amino]-
U164	56-04-2	4(1H)-Pyrimidinone, 2,3-dihydro-6-methyl-2-thioxo-
U180	930-55-2	Pyrrolidine, 1-nitroso-
U200	50-55-5	Reserpine
U201	108-46-3	Resorcinol
U202	[1]81-07-2	Saccharin, & salts
U203	94-59-7	Safrole
U204	7783-00-8	Selenious acid
U204	7783-00-8	Selenium dioxide
U205	7488-56-4	Selenium sulfide
U205	7488-56-4	Selenium sulfide SeS_2 (R,T)
U015	115-02-6	L-Serine, diazoacetate (ester)
See F027	93-72-1	Silvex (2,4,5-TP)

Alphabetical List

Hazardous waste No.	Chemical abstracts No.	Substance
U206	18883-66-4	Streptozotocin
U103	77-78-1	Sulfuric acid, dimethyl ester
U189	1314-80-3	Sulfur phosphide (R)
See F027	93-76-5	2,4,5-T
U207	95-94-3	1,2,4,5-Tetrachlorobenzene
U208	630-20-6	1,1,1,2-Tetrachloroethane
U209	79-34-5	1,1,2,2-Tetrachloroethane
U210	127-18-4	Tetrachloroethylene
See F027	58-90-2	2,3,4,6-Tetrachlorophenol
U213	109-99-9	Tetrahydrofuran (I)
U214	563-68-8	Thallium(I) acetate
U215	6533-73-9	Thallium(I) carbonate
U216	7791-12-0	Thallium(I) chloride
U216	7791-12-0	thallium chloride TlCl
U217	10102-45-1	Thallium(I) nitrate
U218	62-55-5	Thioacetamide
U410	59669-26-0	Thiodicarb
U153	74-93-1	Thiomethanol (I,T)
U244	137-26-8	Thioperoxydicarbonic diamide $[(H_2N)C(S)]_2 S_2$, tetramethyl-
U409	23564-05-8	Thiophanate-methyl
U219	62-56-6	Thiourea
U244	137-26-8	Thiram
U220	108-88-3	Toluene
U221	25376-45-8	Toluenediamine
U223	26471-62-5	Toluene diisocyanate (R,T)
U328	95-53-4	o-Toluidine
U353	106-49-0	p-Toluidine
U222	636-21-5	o-Toluidine hydrochloride
U389	2303-17-5	Triallate
U011	61-82-5	1H-1,2,4-Triazol-3-amine
U226	71–55–6	1,1,1-Trichloroethane
U227	79-00-5	1,1,2-Trichloroethane
U228	79-01-6	Trichloroethylene
U121	75-69-4	Trichloromonofluoromethane
See F027	95-95-4	2,4,5-Trichlorophenol
See F027	88-06-2	2,4,6-Trichlorophenol
U404	121-44-8	Triethylamine
U234	99-35-4	1,3,5-Trinitrobenzene (R,T)
U182	123-63-7	1,3,5-Trioxane, 2,4,6-trimethyl-
U235	126-72-7	Tris(2,3-dibromopropyl) phosphate
U236	72-57-1	Trypan blue
U237	66-75-1	Uracil mustard
U176	759-73-9	Urea, N-ethyl-N-nitroso-
U177	684-93-5	Urea, N-methyl-N-nitroso-
U043	75-01-4	Vinyl chloride
U248	[1]81-81-2	Warfarin, & salts, when present at concentrations of 0.3% or less
U239	1330-20-7	Xylene (I)

Alphabetical List

Hazardous waste No.	Chemical abstracts No.	Substance
U200	50-55-5	Yohimban-16-carboxylic acid, 11,17- dimethoxy-18-[(3,4,5- trimethoxybenzoyl)oxy]-, methyl ester, (3beta,16beta,17alpha,18beta,20alpha)-
U249	1314-84-7	Zinc phosphide $Zn_3 P_2$, when present at concentrations of 10% or less

[1]CAS Number given for parent compound only.

Numerical List

Hazardous Waste No.	Chemical abstracts No.	Substance
U001	75–07–0	Acetaldehyde (I)
U001	75–07–0	Ethanal (I)
U002	67–64–1	Acetone (I)
U002	67–64–1	2-Propanone (I)
U003	75–05–8	Acetonitrile (I,T)
U004	98–86–2	Acetophenone
U004	98–86–2	Ethanone, 1-phenyl-
U005	53–96–3	Acetamide, -9H-fluoren-2-yl-
U005	53–96–3	2-Acetylaminofluorene
U006	75–36–5	Acetyl chloride (C,R,T)
U007	79–06–1	Acrylamide
U007	79–06–1	2-Propenamide
U008	79–10–7	Acrylic acid (I)
U008	79–10–7	2-Propenoic acid (I)
U009	107–13–1	Acrylonitrile
U009	107–13–1	2-Propenenitrile
U010	50–07–7	Azirino[2´,3´:3,4]pyrrolo[1,2-a]indole-4,7-dione, 6-amino-8-[[(amino-carbonyl)oxy]methyl]-1,1a,2,8,8a,8b-hexahydro-8a-methoxy-5-methyl-, [1aS-(1aalpha, 8beta,8aalpha,8balpha)]-
U010	50–07–7	Mitomycin C
U011	61–82–5	Amitrole
U011	61–82–5	1H-1,2,4-Triazol-3-amine
U012	62–53–3	Aniline (I,T)
U012	62–53–3	Benzenamine (I,T)
U014	492–80–8	Auramine
U014	492–80–8	Benzenamine, 4,4´-carbonimidoylbis[N,N-dimethyl-
U015	115–02–6	Azaserine
U015	115–02–6	L-Serine, diazoacetate (ester)
U016	225–51–4	Benz[c]acridine
U017	98–87–3	Benzal chloride
U017	98–87–3	Benzene, (dichloromethyl)-
U018	56–55–3	Benz[a]anthracene
U019	71–43–2	Benzene (I,T)
U020	98–09–9	Benzenesulfonic acid chloride (C,R)
U020	98–09–9	Benzenesulfonyl chloride (C,R)
U021	92–87–5	Benzidine
U021	92–87–5	[1,1´-Biphenyl]-4,4´-diamine
U022	50–32–8	Benzo[a]pyrene
U023	98–07–7	Benzene, (trichloromethyl)-

Numerical List

Hazardous Waste No.	Chemical abstracts No.	Substance
U023	98–07–7	Benzotrichloride (C,R,T)
U024	111–91–1	Dichloromethoxy ethane
U024	111–91–1	Ethane, 1,1′-[methylenebis(oxy)]bis[2-chloro-
U025	111–44–4	Dichloroethyl ether
U025	111–44–4	Ethane, 1,1′-oxybis[2-chloro-
U026	494–03–1	Chlornaphazin
U026	494–03–1	Naphthalenamine, N,N′-bis(2-chloroethyl)-
U027	108–60–1	Dichloroisopropyl ether
U027	108–60–1	Propane, 2,2′-oxybis[2-chloro-
U028	117–81–7	1,2-Benzenedicarboxylic acid, bis(2-ethylhexyl) ester
U028	117–81–7	Diethylhexyl phthalate
U029	74–83–9	Methane, bromo-
U029	74–83–9	Methyl bromide
U030	101–55–3	Benzene, 1-bromo-4-phenoxy-
U030	101–55–3	4-Bromophenyl phenyl ether
U031	71–36–3	1-Butanol (I)
U031	71–36–3	n-Butyl alcohol (I)
U032	13765–19–0	Calcium chromate
U032	13765–19–0	Chromic acid H_2CrO_4, calcium salt
U033	353–50–4	Carbonic difluoride
U033	353–50–4	Carbon oxyfluoride (R,T)
U034	75–87–6	Acetaldehyde, trichloro-
U034	75–87–6	Chloral
U035	305–03–3	Benzenebutanoic acid, 4-[bis(2-chloroethyl)amino]-
U035	305–03–3	Chlorambucil
U036	57–74–9	Chlordane, alpha & gamma isomers
U036	57–74–9	4,7-Methano-1H-indene, 1,2,4,5,6,7,8,8-octachloro-2,3,3a,4,7,7a-hexahydro-
U037	108–90–7	Benzene, chloro-
U037	108–90–7	Chlorobenzene
U038	510–15–6	Benzeneacetic acid, 4-chloro-alpha-(4-chlorophenyl)-alpha-hydroxy-, ethyl ester
U038	510–15–6	Chlorobenzilate
U039	59–50–7	p-Chloro-m-cresol
U039	59–50–7	Phenol, 4-chloro-3-methyl-
U041	106–89–8	Epichlorohydrin
U041	106–89–8	Oxirane, (chloromethyl)-
U042	110–75–8	2-Chloroethyl vinyl ether
U042	110–75–8	Ethene, (2-chloroethoxy)-
U043	75–01–4	Ethene, chloro-
U043	75–01–4	Vinyl chloride
U044	67–66–3	Chloroform
U044	67–66–3	Methane, trichloro-
U045	74–87–3	Methane, chloro- (I,T)
U045	74–87–3	Methyl chloride (I,T)
U046	107–30–2	Chloromethyl methyl ether
U046	107–30–2	Methane, chloromethoxy-
U047	91–58–7	beta-Chloronaphthalene
U047	91–58–7	Naphthalene, 2-chloro-
U048	95–57–8	o-Chlorophenol

Numerical List

Hazardous Waste No.	Chemical abstracts No.	Substance
U048	95–57–8	Phenol, 2-chloro-
U049	3165–93–3	Benzenamine, 4-chloro-2-methyl-, hydrochloride
U049	3165–93–3	4-Chloro-o-toluidine, hydrochloride
U050	218–01–9	Chrysene
U051		Creosote
U052	1319–77–3	Cresol (Cresylic acid)
U052	1319–77–3	Phenol, methyl-
U053	4170–30–3	2-Butenal
U053	4170–30–3	Crotonaldehyde
U055	98–82–8	Benzene, (1-methylethyl)-(I)
U055	98–82–8	Cumene (I)
U056	110–82–7	Benzene, hexahydro-(I)
U056	110–82–7	Cyclohexane (I)
U057	108–94–1	Cyclohexanone (I)
U058	50–18–0	Cyclophosphamide
U058	50–18–0	2H-1,3,2-Oxazaphosphorin-2-amine, N,N-bis(2-chloroethyl)tetrahydro-, 2-oxide
U059	20830–81–3	Daunomycin
U059	20830–81–3	5,12-Naphthacenedione, 8-acetyl-10-[(3-amino-2,3,6-trideoxy)-alpha-L-lyxo-hexopyranosyl)oxy]-7,8,9,10-tetrahydro-6,8,11-trihydroxy-1-methoxy-, (8S-cis)-
U060	72–54–8	Benzene, 1,1′-(2,2-dichloroethylidene)bis[4-chloro-
U060	72–54–8	DDD
U061	50–29–3	Benzene, 1,1′-(2,2,2-trichloroethylidene)bis[4-chloro-
U061	50–29–3	DDT
U062	2303–16–4	Carbamothioic acid, bis(1-methylethyl)-, S-(2,3-di chloro-2-propenyl) ester
U062	2303–16–4	Diallate
U063	53–70–3	Dibenz[a,h]anthracene
U064	189–55–9	Benzo[rst]pentaphene
U064	189–55–9	Dibenzo[a,i]pyrene
U066	96–12–8	1,2-Dibromo-3-chloropropane
U066	96–12–8	Propane, 1,2-dibromo-3-chloro-
U067	106–93–4	Ethane, 1,2-dibromo-
U067	106–93–4	Ethylene dibromide
U068	74–95–3	Methane, dibromo-
U068	74–95–3	Methylene bromide
U069	84–74–2	1,2-Benzenedicarboxylic acid, dibutyl ester
U069	84–74–2	Dibutyl phthalate
U070	95–50–1	Benzene, 1,2-dichloro-
U070	95–50–1	o-Dichlorobenzene
U071	541–73–1	Benzene, 1,3-dichloro-
U071	541–73–1	m-Dichlorobenzene
U072	106–46–7	Benzene, 1,4-dichloro-
U072	106–46–7	p-Dichlorobenzene
U073	91–94–1	[1,1′-Biphenyl]-4,4′-diamine, 3,3′-dichloro-
U073	91–94–1	3,3′-Dichlorobenzidine
U074	764–41–0	2-Butene, 1,4-dichloro-(I,T)
U074	764–41–0	1,4-Dichloro-2-butene (I,T)
U075	75–71–8	Dichlorodifluoromethane

PART 261—Subpart D

Numerical List

Hazardous Waste No.	Chemical abstracts No.	Substance
U075	75–71–8	Methane, dichlorodifluoro-
U076	75–34–3	Ethane, 1,1-dichloro-
U076	75–34–3	Ethylidene dichloride
U077	107–06–2	Ethane, 1,2-dichloro-
U077	107–06–2	Ethylene dichloride
U078	75–35–4	1,1-Dichloroethylene
U078	75–35–4	Ethene, 1,1-dichloro-
U079	156–60–5	1,2-Dichloroethylene
U079	156–60–5	Ethene, 1,2-dichloro-, (E)-
U080	75–09–2	Methane, dichloro-
U080	75–09–2	Methylene chloride
U081	120–83–2	2,4-Dichlorophenol
U081	120–83–2	Phenol, 2,4-dichloro-
U082	87–65–0	2,6-Dichlorophenol
U082	87–65–0	Phenol, 2,6-dichloro-
U083	78–87–5	Propane, 1,2-dichloro-
U083	78–87–5	Propylene dichloride
U084	542–75–6	1,3-Dichloropropene
U084	542–75–6	1-Propene, 1,3-dichloro-
U085	1464–53–5	2,2´-Bioxirane
U085	1464–53–5	1,2:3,4-Diepoxybutane (I,T)
U086	1615–80–1	N,N´-Diethylhydrazine
U086	1615–80–1	Hydrazine, 1,2-diethyl-
U087	3288–58–2	O,O-Diethyl S-methyl dithiophosphate
U087	3288–58–2	Phosphorodithioic acid, O,O-diethyl S-methyl ester
U088	84–66–2	1,2-Benzenedicarboxylic acid, diethyl ester
U088	84–66–2	Diethyl phthalate
U089	56–53–1	Diethylstilbesterol
U089	56–53–1	Phenol, 4,4´-(1,2-diethyl-1,2-ethenediyl)bis-, (E)-
U090	94–58–6	1,3-Benzodioxole, 5-propyl-
U090	94–58–6	Dihydrosafrole
U091	119–90–4	[1,1´-Biphenyl]-4,4´-diamine, 3,3´-dimethoxy-
U091	119–90–4	3,3´-Dimethoxybenzidine
U092	124–40–3	Dimethylamine (I)
U092	124–40–3	Methanamine, -methyl-(I)
U093	60–11–7	Benzenamine, N,N-dimethyl-4-(phenylazo)-
U093	60–11–7	p-Dimethylaminoazobenzene
U094	57–97–6	Benz[a]anthracene, 7,12-dimethyl-
U094	57–97–6	7,12-Dimethylbenz[a]anthracene
U095	119–93–7	[1,1´-Biphenyl]-4,4´-diamine, 3,3´-dimethyl-
U095	119–93–7	3,3´-Dimethylbenzidine
U096	80–15–9	alpha,alpha-Dimethylbenzylhydroperoxide (R)
U096	80–15–9	Hydroperoxide, 1-methyl-1-phenylethyl-(R)
U097	79–44–7	Carbamic chloride, dimethyl-
U097	79–44–7	Dimethylcarbamoyl chloride
U098	57–14–7	1,1-Dimethylhydrazine
U098	57–14–7	Hydrazine, 1,1-dimethyl-
U099	540–73–8	1,2-Dimethylhydrazine

Numerical List

Hazardous Waste No.	Chemical abstracts No.	Substance
U099	540–73–8	Hydrazine, 1,2-dimethyl-
U101	105–67–9	2,4-Dimethylphenol
U101	105–67–9	Phenol, 2,4-dimethyl-
U102	131–11–3	1,2-Benzenedicarboxylic acid, dimethyl ester
U102	131–11–3	Dimethyl phthalate
U103	77–78–1	Dimethyl sulfate
U103	77–78–1	Sulfuric acid, dimethyl ester
U105	121–14–2	Benzene, 1-methyl-2,4-dinitro-
U105	121–14–2	2,4-Dinitrotoluene
U106	606–20–2	Benzene, 2-methyl-1,3-dinitro-
U106	606–20–2	2,6-Dinitrotoluene
U107	117–84–0	1,2-Benzenedicarboxylic acid, dioctyl ester
U107	117–84–0	Di-n-octyl phthalate
U108	123–91–1	1,4-Diethyleneoxide
U108	123–91–1	1,4-Dioxane
U109	122–66–7	1,2-Diphenylhydrazine
U109	122–66–7	Hydrazine, 1,2-diphenyl-
U110	142–84–7	Dipropylamine (I)
U110	142–84–7	1-Propanamine, N-propyl-(I)
U111	621–64–7	Di-n-propylnitrosamine
U111	621–64–7	1-Propanamine, N-nitroso-N-propyl-
U112	141–78–6	Acetic acid ethyl ester (I)
U112	141–78–6	Ethyl acetate (I)
U113	140–88–5	Ethyl acrylate (I)
U113	140–88–5	2-Propenoic acid, ethyl ester (I)
U114	1111–54–6	Carbamodithioic acid, 1,2-ethanediylbis-, salts & esters
U114	1111–54–6	Ethylenebisdithiocarbamic acid, salts & esters
U115	75–21–8	Ethylene oxide (I,T)
U115	75–21–8	Oxirane (I,T)
U116	96–45–7	Ethylenethiourea
U116	96–45–7	2-Imidazolidinethione
U117	60–29–7	Ethane, 1,1´-oxybis-(I)
U117	60–29–7	Ethyl ether (I)
U118	97–63–2	Ethyl methacrylate
U118	97–63–2	2-Propenoic acid, 2-methyl-, ethyl ester
U119	62–50–0	Ethyl methanesulfonate
U119	62–50–0	Methanesulfonic acid, ethyl ester
U120	206–44–0	Fluoranthene
U121	75–69–4	Methane, trichlorofluoro-
U121	75–69–4	Trichloromonofluoromethane
U122	50–00–0	Formaldehyde
U123	64–18–6	Formic acid (C,T)
U124	110–00–9	Furan (I)
U124	110–00–9	Furfuran (I)
U125	98–01–1	2-Furancarboxaldehyde (I)
U125	98–01–1	Furfural (I)
U126	765–34–4	Glycidylaldehyde
U126	765–34–4	Oxiranecarboxyaldehyde
U127	118–74–1	Benzene, hexachloro-
U127	118–74–1	Hexachlorobenzene

Numerical List

Hazardous Waste No.	Chemical abstracts No.	Substance
U128	87–68–3	1,3-Butadiene, 1,1,2,3,4,4-hexachloro-
U128	87–68–3	Hexachlorobutadiene
U129	58–89–9	Cyclohexane, 1,2,3,4,5,6-hexachloro-, (1alpha,2alpha,3beta,4alpha,5alpha, 6beta)-
U129	58–89–9	Lindane
U130	77–47–4	1,3-Cyclopentadiene, 1,2,3,4,5,5-hexachloro-
U130	77–47–4	Hexachlorocyclopentadiene
U131	67–72–1	Ethane, hexachloro-
U131	67–72–1	Hexachloroethane
U132	70–30–4	Hexachlorophene
U132	70–30–4	Phenol, 2,2′-methylenebis[3,4,6-trichloro-
U133	302–01–2	Hydrazine (R,T)
U134	7664–39–3	Hydrofluoric acid (C,T)
U134	7664–39–3	Hydrogen fluoride (C,T)
U135	7783–06–4	Hydrogen sulfide
U135	7783–06–4	Hydrogen sulfide H_2S
U136	75–60–5	Arsinic acid, dimethyl-
U136	75–60–5	Cacodylic acid
U137	193–39–5	Indeno[1,2,3-cd]pyrene
U138	74–88–4	Methane, iodo-
U138	74–88–4	Methyl iodide
U140	78–83–1	Isobutyl alcohol (I,T)
U140	78–83–1	1-Propanol, 2-methyl- (I,T)
U141	120–58–1	1,3-Benzodioxole, 5-(1-propenyl)-
U141	120–58–1	Isosafrole
U142	143–50–0	Kepone
U142	143–50–0	1,3,4-Metheno-2H-cyclobuta[cd]pentalen-2-one, 1,1a,3,3a,4,5,5,5a,5b,6-decachlorooctahydro-
U143	303–34–4	2-Butenoic acid, 2-methyl-, 7-[[2,3-dihydroxy-2-(1-methoxyethyl)-3-methyl-1-oxobutoxy]methyl]-2,3,5,7a-tetrahydro-1H-pyrrolizin-1-yl ester, [1S-[1alpha(Z),7(2S*,3R*),7aalpha]]-
U143	303–34–4	Lasiocarpine
U144	301–04–2	Acetic acid, lead(2+) salt
U144	301–04–2	Lead acetate
U145	7446–27–7	Lead phosphate
U145	7446–27–7	Phosphoric acid, lead(2+) salt (2:3)
U146	1335–32–6	Lead, bis(acetato-O)tetrahydroxytri-
U146	1335–32–6	Lead subacetate
U147	108–31–6	2,5-Furandione
U147	108–31–6	Maleic anhydride
U148	123–33–1	Maleic hydrazide
U148	123–33–1	3,6-Pyridazinedione, 1,2-dihydro-
U149	109–77–3	Malononitrile
U149	109–77–3	Propanedinitrile
U150	148–82–3	Melphalan
U150	148–82–3	L-Phenylalanine, 4-[bis(2-chloroethyl)amino]-
U151	7439–97–6	Mercury
U152	126–98–7	Methacrylonitrile (I,T)

Numerical List

Hazardous Waste No.	Chemical abstracts No.	Substance
U152	126–98–7	2-Propenenitrile, 2-methyl- (I,T)
U153	74–93–1	Methanethiol (I,T)
U153	74–93–1	Thiomethanol (I,T)
U154	67–56–1	Methanol (I)
U154	67–56–1	Methyl alcohol (I)
U155	91–80–5	1,2-Ethanediamine, N,N-dimethyl-N′-2-pyridinyl-N′-(2-thienylmethyl)-
U155	91–80–5	Methapyrilene
U156	79–22–1	Carbonochloridic acid, methyl ester (I,T)
U156	79–22–1	Methyl chlorocarbonate (I,T)
U157	56–49–5	Benz[j]aceanthrylene, 1,2-dihydro-3-methyl-
U157	56–49–5	3-Methylcholanthrene
U158	101–14–4	Benzenamine, 4,4′-methylenebis[2-chloro-
U158	101–14–4	4,4′-Methylenebis(2-chloroaniline)
U159	78–93–3	2-Butanone (I,T)
U159	78–93–3	Methyl ethyl ketone (MEK) (I,T)
U160	1338–23–4	2-Butanone, peroxide (R,T)
U160	1338–23–4	Methyl ethyl ketone peroxide (R,T)
U161	108–10–1	Methyl isobutyl ketone (I)
U161	108–10–1	4-Methyl-2-pentanone (I)
U161	108–10–1	Pentanol, 4-methyl-
U162	80–62–6	Methyl methacrylate (I,T)
U162	80–62–6	2-Propenoic acid, 2-methyl-, methyl ester (I,T)
U163	70–25–7	Guanidine, -methyl-N′-nitro-N-nitroso-
U163	70–25–7	MNNG
U164	56–04–2	Methylthiouracil
U164	56–04–2	4(1H)-Pyrimidinone, 2,3-dihydro-6-methyl-2-thioxo-
U165	91–20–3	Naphthalene
U166	130–15–4	1,4-Naphthalenedione
U166	130–15–4	1,4-Naphthoquinone
U167	134–32–7	1-Naphthalenamine
U167	134–32–7	alpha-Naphthylamine
U168	91–59–8	2-Naphthalenamine
U168	91–59–8	beta-Naphthylamine
U169	98–95–3	Benzene, nitro-
U169	98–95–3	Nitrobenzene (I,T)
U170	100–02–7	p-Nitrophenol
U170	100–02–7	Phenol, 4-nitro-
U171	79–46–9	2-Nitropropane (I,T)
U171	79–46–9	Propane, 2-nitro- (I,T)
U172	924–16–3	1-Butanamine, N-butyl-N-nitroso-
U172	924–16–3	N-Nitrosodi-n-butylamine
U173	1116–54–7	Ethanol, 2,2′-(nitrosoimino)bis-
U173	1116–54–7	N-Nitrosodiethanolamine
U174	55–18–5	Ethanamine, -ethyl-N-nitroso-
U174	55–18–5	N-Nitrosodiethylamine
U176	759–73–9	N-Nitroso-N-ethylurea
U176	759–73–9	Urea, N-ethyl-N-nitroso-
U177	684–93–5	N-Nitroso-N-methylurea
U177	684–93–5	Urea, N-methyl-N-nitroso-
U178	615–53–2	Carbamic acid, methylnitroso-, ethyl ester

Numerical List

Hazardous Waste No.	Chemical abstracts No.	Substance
U178	615–53–2	N-Nitroso-N-methylurethane
U179	100–75–4	N-Nitrosopiperidine
U179	100–75–4	Piperidine, 1-nitroso-
U180	930–55–2	N-Nitrosopyrrolidine
U180	930–55–2	Pyrrolidine, 1-nitroso-
U181	99–55–8	Benzenamine, 2-methyl-5-nitro-
U181	99–55–8	5-Nitro-o-toluidine
U182	123–63–7	1,3,5-Trioxane, 2,4,6-trimethyl-
U182	123–63–7	Paraldehyde
U183	608–93–5	Benzene, pentachloro-
U183	608–93–5	Pentachlorobenzene
U184	76–01–7	Ethane, pentachloro-
U184	76–01–7	Pentachloroethane
U185	82–68–8	Benzene, pentachloronitro-
U185	82–68–8	Pentachloronitrobenzene (PCNB)
U186	504–60–9	1-Methylbutadiene (I)
U186	504–60–9	1,3-Pentadiene (I)
U187	62–44–2	Acetamide, -(4-ethoxyphenyl)-
U187	62–44–2	Phenacetin
U188	108–95–2	Phenol
U189	1314–80–3	Phosphorus sulfide (R)
U189	1314–80–3	Sulfur phosphide (R)
U190	85–44–9	1,3-Isobenzofurandione
U190	85–44–9	Phthalic anhydride
U191	109–06–8	2-Picoline
U191	109–06–8	Pyridine, 2-methyl-
U192	23950–58–5	Benzamide, 3,5-dichloro-N-(1,1-dimethyl-2-propynyl)-
U192	23950–58–5	Pronamide
U193	1120–71–4	1,2-Oxathiolane, 2,2-dioxide
U193	1120–71–4	1,3-Propane sultone
U194	107–10–8	1-Propanamine (I,T)
U194	107–10–8	n-Propylamine (I,T)
U196	110–86–1	Pyridine
U197	106–51–4	p-Benzoquinone
U197	106–51–4	2,5-Cyclohexadiene-1,4-dione
U200	50–55–5	Reserpine
U200	50–55–5	Yohimban-16-carboxylic acid, 11,17-dimethoxy-18-[(3,4,5-trimethoxybenzoyl)oxy]-, methyl ester,(3beta,16beta, 17alpha,18beta, 20alpha)-
U201	108–46–3	1,3-Benzenediol
U201	108–46–3	Resorcinol
U202	181–07–2	1,2-Benzisothiazol-3(2H)-one, 1,1-dioxide, & salts
U202	181–07–2	Saccharin, & salts
U203	94–59–7	1,3-Benzodioxole, 5-(2-propenyl)-
U203	94–59–7	Safrole
U204	7783–00–8	Selenious acid
U204	7783–00–8	Selenium dioxide
U205	7488–56–4	Selenium sulfide
U205	7488–56–4	Selenium sulfide SeS_2 (R,T)
U206	18883–66–4	Glucopyranose, 2-deoxy-2-(3-methyl-3-nitrosoureido)-, D-

Numerical List

Hazardous Waste No.	Chemical abstracts No.	Substance
U206	18883–66–4	D-Glucose, 2-deoxy-2-[[(methylnitrosoamino)-carbonyl]amino]-
U206	18883–66–4	Streptozotocin
U207	95–94–3	Benzene, 1,2,4,5-tetrachloro-
U207	95–94–3	1,2,4,5-Tetrachlorobenzene
U208	630–20–6	Ethane, 1,1,1,2-tetrachloro-
U208	630–20–6	1,1,1,2-Tetrachloroethane
U209	79–34–5	Ethane, 1,1,2,2-tetrachloro-
U209	79–34–5	1,1,2,2-Tetrachloroethane
U210	127–18–4	Ethene, tetrachloro-
U210	127–18–4	Tetrachloroethylene
U211	56–23–5	Carbon tetrachloride
U211	56–23–5	Methane, tetrachloro-
U213	109–99–9	Furan, tetrahydro-(I)
U213	109–99–9	Tetrahydrofuran (I)
U214	563–68–8	Acetic acid, thallium(1+) salt
U214	563–68–8	Thallium(I) acetate
U215	6533–73–9	Carbonic acid, dithallium(1+) salt
U215	6533–73–9	Thallium(I) carbonate
U216	7791–12–0	Thallium(I) chloride
U216	7791–12–0	Thallium chloride TlCl
U217	10102–45–1	Nitric acid, thallium(1+) salt
U217	10102–45–1	Thallium(I) nitrate
U218	62–55–5	Ethanethioamide
U218	62–55–5	Thioacetamide
U219	62–56–6	Thiourea
U220	108–88–3	Benzene, methyl-
U220	108–88–3	Toluene
U221	25376–45–8	Benzenediamine, ar-methyl-
U221	25376–45–8	Toluenediamine
U222	636–21–5	Benzenamine, 2-methyl-, hydrochloride
U222	636–21–5	o-Toluidine hydrochloride
U223	26471–62–5	Benzene, 1,3-diisocyanatomethyl- (R,T)
U223	26471–62–5	Toluene diisocyanate (R,T)
U225	75–25–2	Bromoform
U225	75–25–2	Methane, tribromo-
U226	71–55–6	Ethane, 1,1,1-trichloro-
U226	71–55–6	Methyl chloroform
U226	71–55–6	1,1,1-Trichloroethane
U227	79–00–5	Ethane, 1,1,2-trichloro-
U227	79–00–5	1,1,2-Trichloroethane
U228	79–01–6	Ethene, trichloro-
U228	79–01–6	Trichloroethylene
U234	99–35–4	Benzene, 1,3,5-trinitro-
U234	99–35–4	1,3,5-Trinitrobenzene (R,T)
U235	126–72–7	1-Propanol, 2,3-dibromo-, phosphate (3:1)
U235	126–72–7	Tris(2,3-dibromopropyl) phosphate
U236	72–57–1	2,7-Naphthalenedisulfonic acid, 3,3′-[(3,3′-dimethyl[1,1′-biphenyl]-4,4′-diyl)bis(azo)bis[5-amino-4-hydroxy]-, tetrasodium salt
U236	72–57–1	Trypan blue

Numerical List

Hazardous Waste No.	Chemical abstracts No.	Substance
U237	66–75–1	2,4-(1H,3H)-Pyrimidinedione, 5-[bis(2-chloroethyl)amino]-
U237	66–75–1	Uracil mustard
U238	51–79–6	Carbamic acid, ethyl ester
U238	51–79–6	Ethyl carbamate (urethane)
U239	1330–20–7	Benzene, dimethyl- (I,T)
U239	1330–20–7	Xylene (I)
U240	[1] 94–75–7	Acetic acid, (2,4-dichlorophenoxy)-, salts & esters
U240	[1] 94–75–7	2,4-D, salts & esters
U243	1888–71–7	Hexachloropropene
U243	1888–71–7	1-Propene, 1,1,2,3,3,3-hexachloro-
U244	137–26–8	Thioperoxydicarbonic diamide $[(H_2N)C(S)]_2S_2$, tetramethyl-
U244	137–26–8	Thiram
U246	506–68–3	Cyanogen bromide (CN)Br
U247	72–43–5	Benzene, 1,1′-(2,2,2-trichloroethylidene)bis[4- methoxy-
U247	72–43–5	Methoxychlor
U248	[1] 81–81–2	2H-1-Benzopyran-2-one, 4-hydroxy-3-(3-oxo-1-phenyl-butyl)-, & salts, when present at concentrations of 0.3% or less
U248	[1] 81–81–2	Warfarin, & salts, when present at concentrations of 0.3% or less
U249	1314–84–7	Zinc phosphide Zn_3P_2, when present at concentrations of 10% or less
U271	17804–35–2	Benomyl
U271	17804–35–2	Carbamic acid, [1-[(butylamino)carbonyl]-1H-benzimidazol-2-yl]-, methyl ester
U278	22781–23–3	Bendiocarb
U278	22781–23–3	1,3-Benzodioxol-4-ol, 2,2-dimethyl-, methyl carbamate
U279	63–25–2	Carbaryl
U279	63–25–2	1-Naphthalenol, methylcarbamate
U280	101–27–9	Barban
U280	101–27–9	Carbamic acid, (3-chlorophenyl)-, 4-chloro-2-butynyl ester
U328	95–53–4	Benzenamine, 2-methyl-
U328	95–53–4	o-Toluidine
U353	106–49–0	Benzenamine, 4-methyl-
U353	106–49–0	p-Toluidine
U359	110–80–5	Ethanol, 2-ethoxy-
U359	110–80–5	Ethylene glycol monoethyl ether
U364	22961–82–6	Bendiocarb phenol
U364	22961–82–6	1,3-Benzodioxol-4-ol, 2,2-dimethyl-,
U367	1563–38–8	7-Benzofuranol, 2,3-dihydro-2,2-dimethyl-
U367	1563–38–8	Carbofuran phenol
U372	10605–21–7	Carbamic acid, 1H-benzimidazol-2-yl, methyl ester
U372	10605–21–7	Carbendazim
U373	122–42–9	Carbamic acid, phenyl-, 1-methylethyl ester
U373	122–42–9	Propham
U387	52888–80–9	Carbamothioic acid, dipropyl-, S-(phenylmethyl) ester
U387	52888–80–9	Prosulfocarb
U389	2303–17–5	Carbamothioic acid, bis(1-methylethyl)-, S-(2,3,3-trichloro-2-propenyl) ester
U389	2303–17–5	Triallate
U394	30558–43–1	A2213
U394	30558–43–1	Ethanimidothioic acid, 2-(dimethylamino)-N-hydroxy-2-oxo-, methyl ester
U395	5952–26–1	Diethylene glycol, dicarbamate
U395	5952–26–1	Ethanol, 2,2′-oxybis-, dicarbamate
U404	121–44–8	Ethanamine, N,N-diethyl-
U404	121–44–8	Triethylamine
U409	23564–05–8	Carbamic acid, [1,2-phenylenebis (iminocarbonothioyl)]bis-, dimethyl ester
U409	23564–05–8	Thiophanate-methyl
U410	59669–26–0	Ethanimidothioic acid, N,N′-[thiobis[(methylimino)carbonyloxy]]bis-, dimethyl ester
U410	59669–26–0	Thiodicarb
U411	114–26–1	Phenol, 2-(1-methylethoxy)-, methylcarbamate
U411	114–26–1	Propoxur
See F027	93–76–5	Acetic acid, (2,4,5-trichlorophenoxy)-
See F027	87–86–5	Pentachlorophenol
See F027	87–86–5	Phenol, pentachloro-
See F027	58–90–2	Phenol, 2,3,4,6-tetrachloro-
See F027	95–95–4	Phenol, 2,4,5-trichloro-
See F027	88–06–2	Phenol, 2,4,6-trichloro-
See F027	93–72–1	Propanoic acid, 2-(2,4,5-trichlorophenoxy)-
See F027	93–72–1	Silvex (2,4,5-TP)
See F027	93–76–5	2,4,5-T
See F027	58–90–2	2,3,4,6-Tetrachlorophenol
See F027	95–95–4	2,4,5-Trichlorophenol
See F027	88–06–2	2,4,6-Trichlorophenol

[1] CAS Number given for parent compound only.

[45 FR 78529, 78541, Nov. 25, 1980, as amended at 46 FR 27477, May 20, 1981; 49 FR 19923, May 10, 1984; 50 FR 2000, Jan. 14, 1985; 50 FR 28744, July 15, 1985; 50 FR 42942, Oct. 23, 1985; 51 FR 6541, Feb. 25, 1986; 51 FR 10175, Mar. 24, 1986; 51 FR 28298, Aug. 6, 1986; 52 FR 21306, June 5, 1987; 52 FR 26012, July 10, 1987; 53 FR 13383, Apr. 22, 1988; 53 FR 43881, Oct. 31, 1988; 53 FR 43884, Oct. 31, 1988; 55 FR 22684, June 1, 1990; 56 FR 7568, Feb. 25, 1991; 59 FR 31551, June 20, 1994; 60 FR 7849, Feb. 9, 1995; 60 FR 19165, Apr. 17, 1995; 60 FR 25620, May 12, 1995; 62 FR 32977, June 17, 1997; 63 FR 24625, May 4, 1998; 65 FR 14474, Mar. 17, 2000; 71 FR 40259, July 14, 2006]

§261.35 Deletion of certain hazardous waste codes following equipment cleaning and replacement.

(a) Wastes from wood preserving processes at plants that do not resume or initiate use of chlorophenolic preservatives will not meet the listing definition of F032 once the generator has met all of the requirements of paragraphs (b) and (c) of this section. These wastes may, however, continue to meet another hazardous waste listing description or may exhibit one or more of the hazardous waste characteristics.

(b) Generators must either clean or replace all process equipment that may have come into contact with chlorophenolic formulations or constituents thereof, including, but not limited to, treatment cylinders, sumps, tanks, piping systems, drip pads, fork lifts, and trams, in a manner that minimizes or eliminates the escape of hazardous waste or constituents, leachate, contaminated drippage, or hazardous waste decomposition products to the ground water, surface water, or atmosphere.

(1) Generators shall do one of the following:

(i) Prepare and follow an equipment cleaning plan and clean equipment in accordance with this section;

(ii) Prepare and follow an equipment replacement plan and replace equipment in accordance with this section; or

(iii) Document cleaning and replacement in accordance with this section, carried out after termination of use of chlorophenolic preservations.

(2) Cleaning Requirements.

(i) Prepare and sign a written equipment cleaning plan that describes:

(A) The equipment to be cleaned;

(B) How the equipment will be cleaned;

(C) The solvent to be used in cleaning;

(D) How solvent rinses will be tested; and

(E) How cleaning residues will be disposed.

(ii) Equipment must be cleaned as follows:

(A) Remove all visible residues from process equipment;

(B) Rinse process equipment with an appropriate solvent until dioxins and dibenzofurans are not detected in the final solvent rinse.

(iii) Analytical requirements.

(A) Rinses must be tested by using an appropriate method.

(B) "Not detected" means at or below the following lower method calibration limits (MCLs): The 2,3,7,8-TCDD-based MCL—0.01 parts per trillion (ppt), sample weight of 1000 g, IS spiking level of 1 ppt, final extraction volume of 10–50 μL. For other congeners—multiply the values by 1 for TCDF/PeCDD/PeCDF, by 2.5 for HxCDD/HxCDF/HpCDD/HpCDF, and by 5 for OCDD/OCDF.

(iv) The generator must manage all residues from the cleaning process as F032 waste.

(3) Replacement requirements.

(i) Prepare and sign a written equipment replacement plan that describes:

(A) The equipment to be replaced;

(B) How the equipment will be replaced; and

(C) How the equipment will be disposed.

(ii) The generator must manage the discarded equipment as F032 waste.

(4) Documentation requirements.

(i) Document that previous equipment cleaning and/or replacement was performed in accordance with this section and occurred after cessation of use of chlorophenolic preservatives.

(c) The generator must maintain the following records documenting the cleaning and replacement as part of the facility's operating record:

(1) The name and address of the facility;

(2) Formulations previously used and the date on which their use ceased in each process at the plant;

(3) Formulations currently used in each process at the plant;

(4) The equipment cleaning or replacement plan;

(5) The name and address of any persons who conducted the cleaning and replacement;

(6) The dates on which cleaning and replacement were accomplished;

(7) The dates of sampling and testing;

(8) A description of the sample handling and preparation techniques, including techniques used for

extraction, containerization, preservation, and chain-of-custody of the samples;

(9) A description of the tests performed, the date the tests were performed, and the results of the tests;

(10) The name and model numbers of the instrument(s) used in performing the tests;

(11) QA/QC documentation; and

(12) The following statement signed by the generator or his authorized representative:

> I certify under penalty of law that all process equipment required to be cleaned or replaced under 40 CFR 261.35 was cleaned or replaced as represented in the equipment cleaning and replacement plan and accompanying documentation. I am aware that there are significant penalties for providing false information, including the possibility of fine or imprisonment.

[55 FR 50482, Dec. 6, 1990, as amended at 56 FR 30195, July 1, 1991; 70 FR 34561, June 14, 2005]

Subpart E—Exclusions/Exemptions

Source: 71 FR 42948, July 28, 2006, unless otherwise noted.

§261.38 Exclusion of comparable fuel, emission-comparable fuel, and syngas fuel.

(a) *Specifications for excluded fuels.* Materials that meet the specifications for comparable fuel, emission-comparable fuel, or syngas fuel under paragraphs (a)(1), (a)(2), or (a)(3) of this section, respectively, and the other requirements of this section, are not solid wastes.

(1) *Comparable fuel specifications.*—(i) *Physical specifications.*—(A) *Heating value.* The heating value must exceed 5,000 BTU/lbs. (11,500 J/g).

(B) *Viscosity.* The viscosity must not exceed: 50 cs, as-fired.

(ii) *Constituent specifications.* For compounds listed in Table 1 to this section, the specification levels and, where non-detect is the specification, minimum required detection limits are: (*see* Table 1 of this section).

(2) *Emission-comparable fuel specifications*—The specifications shall be met as-generated. (i) *Physical specifications.*—(A) *Heating value.* The heating value must be 8,000 BTU/lbs (18,400 J/g) or greater.

(B) *Viscosity.* The viscosity must not exceed 50 cs.

(ii) *Constituent specifications*—(A) Except as provided by paragraph (a)(2)(ii)(B) of this section, for compounds listed in Table 1 of this section the specification levels and, where nondetect is the specification, minimum required detection limits, are: (*see* Table 1 of this section).

(B) *Specifications not applicable.* The specification levels in Table 1 to this section do not apply for the following hydrocarbons and oxygenates under the special conditions provided under this section for emission-comparable fuel:

(*1*) Benzo(a)anthracene (CAS No. 56–55–3).

(*2*) Benzene (CAS No. 71–43–2).

(*3*) Benzo(b)fluoranthene (CAS No. 205–99–2)

(*4*) Benzo(k)fluoranthene (CAS No. 207–08–9)

(*5*) Benzo(a)pyrene (CAS No. 50–32–8)

(*6*) Chrysene (CAS No. 218–01–9)

(*7*) Dibenzo(a,h)anthracene (CAS No. 52–70–3)

(*8*) 7,12–Dimethylbenz(a)anthracene (CAS No. 57–97–6)

(*9*) Fluoranthene (CAS No. 206–44–0)

(*10*) Indeno(1,2,3-cd)pyrene (CAS No. 193–39–5)

(*11*) 3-Methylcholanthrene (CAS No. 56–49–5)

(*12*) Naphthalene (CAS No. 91–20–3)

(*13*) Toluene (CAS No. 108–88–3).

(*14*) Acetophenone (CAS No. 98–86–2).

(*15*) Acrolein (CAS No. 107–02–8).

(*16*) Allyl alcohol (CAS No. 107–18–6).

(*17*) Bis(2-ethylhexyl)phthalate [Di-2-ethylhexyl phthalate] (CAS No.117–81–7).

(*18*) Butyl benzyl phthalate (CAS No. 85–68–7).

(*19*) o-Cresol [2-Methyl phenol] (CAS No. 95–48–7).

(*20*) m-Cresol [3-Methyl phenol] (CAS No. 108–39–4).

(*21*) p-Cresol [4-Methyl phenol] (CAS No. 106–44–5).

(*22*) Di-n-butyl phthalate (CAS No. 84–74–2).

(*23*) Diethyl phthalate (CAS No. 84–66–2).

(*24*) 2,4-Dimethylphenol (CAS No. 105–67–9).

(*25*) Dimethyl phthalate (CAS No. 131–11–3).

(*26*) Di-n-octyl phthalate (CAS No. 117–84–0).

(*27*) Endothall (CAS No. 145–73–3).

(*28*) Ethyl methacrylate (CAS No. 97–63–2).

(*29*) 2-Ethoxyethanol [Ethylene glycol monoethyl ether] (CAS No. 110–80–5).

(*30*) Isobutyl alcohol (CAS No. 78–83–1).

(*31*) Isosafrole (CAS No. 120–58–1).

(*32*) Methyl ethyl ketone [2-Butanone] (CAS No. 78–93–3).

(*33*) Methyl methacrylate (CAS No. 80–62–6).

(*34*) 1,4-Naphthoquinone (CAS No. 130–15–4).

PART 261—Subpart E

Table 1 to §261.38—Detection and Detection Limit Values for Comparable Fuel Specification

Chemical name	CAS No.	Concentration limit (mg/kg at 10,000 Btu/lb)	Minimum required detection limit (mg/kg)
Total Nitrogen as N	NA	4900	
Total Halogens as Cl	NA	540	
Total Organic Halogens as Cl	NA	([a])	
Polychlorinated biphenyls, total [Arocolors, total]	1336-36-3	ND	1.4
Cyanide, total	57-12-5	ND	1
Metals:			
Antimony, total	7440-36-0	12	
Arsenic, total	7440-38-2	0.23	
Barium, total	7440-39-3	23	
Beryllium, total	7440-41-7	1.2	
Cadmium, total	7440-43-9	1.2	
Chromium, total	7440-47-3	2.3	
Cobalt	7440-48-4	4.6	
Lead, total	7439-92-1	31	
Manganese	7439-96-5	1.2	
Mercury, total	7439-97-6	0.25	
Nickel, total	7440-02-0	58	
Selenium, total	7782-49-2	0.23	
Silver, total	7440-22-4	2.3	
Thallium, total	7440-28-0	23	
Hydrocarbons:			
Benzo[a]anthracene	56-55-3	2400	
Benzene	71-43-2	4100	
Benzo[b]fluoranthene	205-99-2	2400	
Benzo[k]fluoranthene	207-08-9	2400	
Benzo[a]pyrene	50-32-8	2400	
Chrysene	218-01-9	2400	
Dibenzo[a,h]anthracene	52-70-3	2400	
7,12-Dimethylbenz[a]anthracene	57-97-6	2400	
Fluoranthene	206-44-0	2400	
Indeno(1,2,3-cd)pyrene	193-39-5	2400	
3-Methylcholanthrene	56-49-5	2400	
Naphthalene	91-20-3	3200	
Toluene	108-88-3	36000	
Oxygenates:			
Acetophenone	98-86-1	2400	
Acrolein	107-02-8	39	
Allyl alcohol	107-18-6	30	
Bis(2-ethylhexyl)phthalate [Di-2-ethylhexyl phthalate]	117-81-7	2400	
Butyl benzyl phthalate	85-68-7	2400	

Table 1 to §261.38—Detection and Detection Limit Values for Comparable Fuel Specification

Chemical name	CAS No.	Concentration limit (mg/kg at 10,000 Btu/lb)	Minimum required detection limit (mg/kg)
o-Cresol [2-Methyl phenol]	95-48-7	2400	
m-Cresol [3-Methyl phenol]	108-39-4	2400	
p-Cresol [4-Methyl phenol]	106-44-5	2400	
Di-n-butyl phthalate	84-74-2	2400	
Diethyl phthalate	84-66-2	2400	
2,4-Dimethylphenol	105-67-9	2400	
Dimethyl phthalate	131-11-3	2400	
Di-n-octyl phthalate	117-84-0	2400	
Endothall	145-73-3	100	
Ethyl methacrylate	97-63-2	39	
2-Ethoxyethanol [Ethylene glycol monoethyl ether]	110-80-5	100	
Isobutyl alcohol	78-83-1	39	
Isosafrole	120-58-1	2400	
Methyl ethyl ketone [2-Butanone]	78-93-3	39	
Methyl methacrylate	80-62-6	39	
1,4-Naphthoquinone	130-15-4	2400	
Phenol	108-95-2	2400	
Propargyl alcohol [2-Propyn-1-ol]	107-19-7	30	
Safrole	94-59-7	2400	
Sulfonated Organics:			
Carbon disulfide	75-15-0	ND	39
Disulfoton	298-04-4	ND	2400
Ethyl methanesulfonate	62-50-0	ND	2400
Methyl methanesulfonate	66-27-3	ND	2400
Phorate	298-02-2	ND	2400
1,3-Propane sultone	1120-71-4	ND	100
Tetraethyldithiopyrophosphate [Sulfotepp]	3689-24-5	ND	2400
Thiophenol [Benzenethiol]	108-98-5	ND	30
O,O,O-Triethyl phosphorothioate	126-68-1	ND	2400
Nitrogenated Organics:			
Acetonitrile [Methyl cyanide]	75-05-8	ND	39
2-Acetylaminofluorene [2-AAF]	53-96-3	ND	2400
Acrylonitrile	107-13-1	ND	39
4-Aminobiphenyl	92-67-1	ND	2400
4-Aminopyridine	504-24-5	ND	100
Aniline	62-53-3	ND	2400
Benzidine	92-87-5	ND	2400
Dibenz[a,j]acridine	224-42-0	ND	2400

Table 1 to §261.38—Detection and Detection Limit Values for Comparable Fuel Specification

Chemical name	CAS No.	Concentration limit (mg/kg at 10,000 Btu/lb)	Minimum required detection limit (mg/kg)
O,O-Diethyl O-pyrazinyl phosphorothioate [Thionazin]	297-97-2	ND	2400
Dimethoate	60-51-5	ND	2400
p-(Dimethylamino) azobenzene [4-Dimethylaminoazobenzene]	60-11-7	ND	2400
3,3′-Dimethylbenzidine	119-93-7	ND	2400
α,α-Dimethylphenethylamine	122-09-8	ND	2400
3,3′-Dimethoxybenzidine	119-90-4	ND	100
1,3-Dinitrobenzene [m-Dinitrobenzene]	99-65-0	ND	2400
4,6-Dinitro-o-cresol	534-52-1	ND	2400
2,4-Dinitrophenol	51-28-5	ND	2400
2,4-Dinitrotoluene	121-14-2	ND	2400
2,6-Dinitrotoluene	606-20-2	ND	2400
Dinoseb [2-sec-Butyl-4,6-dinitrophenol]	88-85-7	ND	2400
Diphenylamine	122-39-4	ND	2400
Ethyl carbamate [Urethane]	51-79-6	ND	100
Ethylenethiourea (2-Imidazolidinethione)	96-45-7	ND	110
Famphur	52-85-7	ND	2400
Methacrylonitrile	126-98-7	ND	39
Methapyrilene	91-80-5	ND	2400
Methomyl	16752-77-5	ND	57
2-Methyllactonitrile, [Acetone cyanohydrin]	75-86-5	ND	100
Methyl parathion	298-00-0	ND	2400
MNNG (N-Metyl-N-nitroso-N′-nitroguanidine)	70-25-7	ND	110
1-Naphthylamine, [α-Naphthylamine]	134-32-7	ND	2400
2-Naphthylamine, [β-Naphthylamine]	91-59-8	ND	2400
Nicotine	54-11-5	ND	100
4-Nitroaniline, [p-Nitroaniline]	100-01-6	ND	2400
Nitrobenzene	98-96-3	ND	2400
p-Nitrophenol, [p-Nitrophenol]	100-02-7	ND	2400
5-Nitro-o-toluidine	99-55-8	ND	2400
N-Nitrosodi-n-butylamine	924-16-3	ND	2400
N-Nitrosodiethylamine	55-18-5	ND	2400
N-Nitrosodiphenylamine, [Diphenylnitrosamine]	86-30-6	ND	2400
N-Nitroso-N-methylethylamine	10595-95-6	ND	2400
N-Nitrosomorpholine	59-89-2	ND	2400

Table 1 to §261.38—Detection and Detection Limit Values for Comparable Fuel Specification

Chemical name	CAS No.	Concentration limit (mg/kg at 10,000 Btu/lb)	Minimum required detection limit (mg/kg)
N-Nitrosopiperidine	100-75-4	ND	2400
N-Nitrosopyrrolidine	930-55-2	ND	2400
2-Nitropropane	79-46-9	ND	2400
Parathion	56-38-2	ND	2400
Phenacetin	62-44-2	ND	2400
1,4-Phenylene diamine, [p-Phenylenediamine]	106-50-3	ND	2400
N-Phenylthiourea	103-85-5	ND	57
2-Picoline [alpha-Picoline]	109-06-8	ND	2400
Propylthioracil, [6-Propyl-2-thiouracil]	51-52-5	ND	100
Pyridine	110-86-1	ND	2400
Strychnine	57-24-9	ND	100
Thioacetamide	62-55-5	ND	57
Thiofanox	39196-18-4	ND	100
Thiourea	62-56-6	ND	57
Toluene-2,4-diamine [2,4-Diaminotoluene]	95-80-7	ND	57
Toluene-2,6-diamine [2,6-Diaminotoluene]	823-40-5	ND	57
o-Toluidine	95-53-4	ND	2400
p-Toluidine	106-49-0	ND	100
1,3,5-Trinitrobenzene, [sym-Trinitobenzene]	99-35-4	ND	2400
Halogenated Organics:			
Allyl chloride	107-05-1	ND	39
Aramite	140-57-8	ND	2400
Benzal chloride [Dichloromethyl benzene]	98-87-3	ND	100
Benzyl chloride	100-44-77	ND	100
bis(2-Chloroethyl)ether [Dichoroethyl ether]	111-44-4	ND	2400
Bromoform [Tribromomethane]	75-25-2	ND	39
Bromomethane [Methyl bromide]	74-83-9	ND	39
4-Bromophenyl phenyl ether [p-Bromo diphenyl ether]	101-55-3	ND	2400
Carbon tetrachloride	56-23-5	ND	39
Chlordane	57-74-9	ND	14
p-Chloroaniline	106-47-8	ND	2400
Chlorobenzene	108-90-7	ND	39
Chlorobenzilate	510-15-6	ND	2400
p-Chloro-m-cresol	59-50-7	ND	2400
2-Chloroethyl vinyl ether	110-75-8	ND	39

Table 1 to §261.38—Detection and Detection Limit Values for Comparable Fuel Specification

Chemical name	CAS No.	Concentration limit (mg/kg at 10,000 Btu/lb)	Minimum required detection limit (mg/kg)
Chloroform	67-66-3	ND	39
Chloromethane [Methyl chloride]	74-87-3	ND	39
2-Chloronaphthalene [beta-Chloronaphthalene]	91-58-7	ND	2400
2-Chlorophenol [o-Chlorophenol]	95-57-8	ND	2400
Chloroprene [2-Chloro-1,3-butadiene]	1126-99-8	ND	39
2,4-D [2,4-Dichlorophenoxy-acetic acid]	94-75-7	ND	7
Diallate	2303-16-4	ND	3400
1,2-Dibromo-3-chloropropane	96-12-8	ND	39
1,2-Dichlorobenzene [o-Dichlorobenzene]	95-50-1	ND	2400
1,3-Dichlorobenzene [m-Dichlorobenzene]	541-73-1	ND	2400
1,4-Dichlorobenzene [p-Dichlorobenzene]	106-46-7	ND	2400
3,3′-Dichlorobenzidine	91-94-1	ND	2400
Dichlorodifluoromethane [CFC-12]	75-71-8	ND	39
1,2-Dichloroethane [Ethylene dichloride]	107-06-2	ND	39
1,1-Dichloroethylene [Vinylidene chloride]	75-35-4	ND	39
Dichloromethoxy ethane [Bis(2-chloroethoxy)methane]	111-91-1	ND	2400
2,4-Dichlorophenol	120-83-2	ND	2400
2,6-Dichlorophenol	87-65-0	ND	2400
1,2-Dichloropropane [Propylene dichloride]	78-87-5	ND	39
cis-1,3-Dichloropropylene	10061-01-5	ND	39
trans-1,3-Dichloropropylene	10061-02-6	ND	39
1,3-Dichloro-2-propanol	96-23-1	ND	30
Endosulfan I	959-98-8	ND	1.4
Endosulfan II	33213-65-9	ND	1.4
Endrin	72-20-8	ND	1.4
Endrin aldehyde	7421-93-4	ND	1.4
Endrin Ketone	53494-70-5	ND	1.4
Epichlorohydrin [1-Chloro-2,3-epoxy propane]	106-89-8	ND	30
Ethylidene dichloride [1,1-Dichloroethane]	75-34-3	ND	39
2-Fluoroacetamide	640-19-7	ND	100
Heptachlor	76-44-8	ND	1.4
Heptachlor epoxide	1024-57-3	ND	2.8
Hexachlorobenzene	118-74-1	ND	2400

Table 1 to §261.38—Detection and Detection Limit Values for Comparable Fuel Specification

Chemical name	CAS No.	Concentration limit (mg/kg at 10,000 Btu/lb)	Minimum required detection limit (mg/kg)
Hexachloro-1,3-butadiene [Hexachlorobutadiene]	87-68-3	ND	2400
Hexachlorocyclopentadiene	77-47-4	ND	2400
Hexachloroethane	67-72-1	ND	2400
Hexachlorophene	70-30-4	ND	59000
Hexachloropropene [Hexachloropropylene]	1888-71-7	ND	2400
Isodrin	465-73-6	ND	2400
Kepone [Chlordecone]	143-50-0	ND	4700
Lindane [gamma-BHC] [gamma-Hexachlorocyclohexane]	58-89-9	ND	1.4
Methylene chloride [Dichloromethane]	75-09-2	ND	39
4,4′-Methylene-bis(2-chloroaniline)	101-14-4	ND	100
Methyl iodide [Iodomethane]	74-88-4	ND	39
Pentachlorobenzene	608-93-5	ND	2400
Pentachloroethane	76-01-7	ND	39
Pentachloronitrobenzene [PCNB] [Quintobenzene] [Quintozene]	82-68-8	ND	2400
Pentachlorophenol	87-88-5	ND	2400
Pronamide	23950-58-5	ND	2400
Silvex [2,4,5-Trichloro-phenoxypropionic acid]	93-72-1	ND	7
2,3,7,8-Tetrachlorodibenzo-p-dioxin [2,3,7,8- TCDD]	1746-01-6	ND	30
1,2,4,5-Tetrachlorobenzene	95-94-3	ND	2400
1,1,2,2-Tetrachloroethane	79-35-4	ND	39
Tetrachloroethylene [Perchloroethylene]	127-18-4	ND	39
2,3,4,6-Tetrachlorophenol	58-90-2	ND	2400
1,2,4-Trichlorobenzene	120-82-1	ND	2400
1,1,1-Trichloroethane [Methyl chloroform]	71-55-6	ND	39
1,1,2-Trichloroethane [Vinyl trichloride]	79-00-5	ND	39
Trichloroethylene	79-01-6	ND	39
Trichlorofluoromethane [Trichlormonofluoromethane]	75-69-4	ND	39
2,4,5-Trichlorophenol	95-95-4	ND	2400
2,4,6-Trichlorophenol	88-06-2	ND	2400
1,2,3-Trichloropropane	96-18-4	ND	39
Vinyl Chloride	75-01-4	ND	39

Notes:
NA—Not Applicable.
ND—Nondetect.
([a]) 25 or individual halogenated organics listed below.

(*35*) Phenol (CAS No. 108–95–2).

(*36*) Propargyl alcohol [2-Propyn-1-ol] (CAS No. 107–19–7).

(*37*) Safrole (CAS No. 94–59–7).

(3) *Synthesis gas fuel specifications.*—Synthesis gas fuel (*i.e.*, syngas fuel) that is generated from hazardous waste must:

(i) Have a minimum Btu value of 100 Btu/Scf;

(ii) Contain less than 1 ppmv of total halogen;

(iii) Contain less than 300 ppmv of total nitrogen other than diatomic nitrogen (N_2);

(iv) Contain less than 200 ppmv of hydrogen sulfide; and

(v) Contain less than 1 ppmv of each hazardous constituent in the target list of appendix VIII constituents of this part.

(4) *Blending to meet the specifications.* (i) *Comparable fuel.* (A) Hazardous waste shall not be blended to meet the comparable fuel specification under paragraph (a)(1) of this section, except as provided by paragraph (a)(4)(i)(B) of this section:

(B) *Blending to meet the viscosity specification.* A hazardous waste blended to meet the viscosity specification for comparable fuel shall:

(*1*) As generated and prior to any blending, manipulation, or processing, meet the constituent and heating value specifications of paragraphs (a)(1)(i)(A) and (a)(1)(ii) of this section;

(*2*) Be blended at a facility that is subject to the applicable requirements of parts 264 and 265, or §262.34 of this chapter; and

(*3*) Not violate the dilution prohibition of paragraph (a)(7) of this section.

(ii) *Emission-comparable fuel.* Hazardous waste shall not be treated by blending or other means to meet the emission-comparable fuel specifications under paragraph (a)(2) of this section. Emission-comparable fuel must meet those specifications as-generated by the original generator of the material. Emission-comparable fuel that has met the specifications under paragraph (a)(2) of this section as-generated, and that is subsequently commingled with other materials, must continue to meet the specifications.

(5) *Treatment to meet the comparable fuel specifications.* (i) A hazardous waste may be treated to meet the specifications for comparable fuel under paragraph (a)(1) of this section provided the treatment:

(A) Destroys or removes the constituent listed in the specification or raises the heating value by removing or destroying hazardous constituents or materials;

(B) Is performed at a facility that is subject to the applicable requirements of parts 264 and 265, or §262.34 of this chapter; and

(C) Does not violate the dilution prohibition of paragraph (a)(7) of this section.

(ii) Residuals resulting from the treatment of a hazardous waste listed in subpart D of this part to generate a comparable fuel remain a hazardous waste.

(6) *Generation of a syngas fuel.* (i) A syngas fuel can be generated from the processing of hazardous wastes to meet the exclusion specifications of paragraph (a)(3) of this section provided the processing:

(A) Destroys or removes the constituent listed in the specification or raises the heating value by removing or destroying constituents or materials;

(B) Is performed at a facility that is subject to the applicable requirements of parts 264 and 265, or §262.34 of this chapter or is an exempt recycling unit pursuant to §261.6(c); and

(C) Does not violate the dilution prohibition of paragraph (a)(7) of this section.

(ii) Residuals resulting from the treatment of a hazardous waste listed in subpart D of this part to generate a syngas fuel remain a hazardous waste.

(7) *Dilution prohibition for comparable fuel, emission-comparable fuel, and syngas fuel.* (i) *Comparable fuel and syngas fuel.* No generator, transporter, handler, or owner or operator of a treatment, storage, or disposal facility shall in any way dilute a hazardous waste to meet the specifications of paragraphs (a)(1)(i)(A) or (a)(1)(ii) of this section for comparable fuel or paragraph (a)(3) of this section for syngas.

(ii) *Emission-comparable fuel.* Emission-comparable fuel shall not be generated by means of dilution.

(b) *Implementation.*—(1) *General.*—(i) Materials that meet the specifications provided by paragraph (a) of this section for comparable fuel, emission-comparable fuel, or syngas fuel are excluded from the definition of solid waste provided that the conditions under this section are met. For purposes of this section, such materials are called excluded fuel, and the person claiming and qualifying for the exclusion is called the excluded fuel generator and the person burning the excluded fuel is called the excluded fuel burner.

(ii) The person who generates the excluded fuel must claim the exclusion by compliance with the conditions of this section and keep records necessary to document compliance with those conditions.

(2) *Notices.* (i) *Notices to State RCRA and CAA Directors in authorized States or regional RCRA and CAA Directors in unauthorized States.* (A) The generator must submit a one-time notice, except as provided by paragraph (b)(2)(i)(C) of this section, to the Regional or State RCRA and CAA Directors, in whose jurisdiction the exclusion is being claimed and where the excluded fuel will be burned, certifying compliance with the conditions of the exclusion and providing the following documentation:

(*1*) The name, address, and RCRA ID number of the person/facility claiming the exclusion;

(*2*) The applicable EPA Hazardous Waste Codes that would otherwise apply to the excluded fuel;

(*3*) The name and address of the units meeting the requirements of paragraphs (b)(3) and (c) of this section, that will burn the excluded fuel;

(*4*) An estimate of the average and maximum monthly and annual quantity of material for which an exclusion would be claimed, except as provided by paragraph (b)(2)(i)(D) of this section; and

(*5*) The following statement, which shall be signed and submitted by the person claiming the exclusion or his authorized representative:

> Under penalty of criminal and civil prosecution for making or submitting false statements, representations, or omissions, I certify that the requirements of 40 CFR 261.38 have been met for all emission-comparable fuel/comparable fuel (specify which) identified in this notification. Copies of the records and information required at 40 CFR 261.38(b)(8) are available at the generator's facility. Based on my inquiry of the individuals immediately responsible for obtaining the information, the information is, to the best of my knowledge and belief, true, accurate, and complete. I am aware that there are significant penalties for submitting false information, including the possibility of fine and imprisonment for knowing violations.

(B) Generators of emission-comparable fuel must also include in the notices:

(*1*) An estimate of the annual quantity of each material for which an emission-comparable fuel exclusion would be claimed; and

(2) An estimate of the maximum concentration of each compound in Table 2 to this section in each

Table 2 to §261.38—Maximum Allowable Feedrates for Emission-Comparable Fuel Constituents

Chemical name	CAS number	Constituent gas flowrate-normalized feedrate limit (ug/dscm)[1]
Hydrocarbons		
Benzene	71-43-2	5.33E+04
Naphthalene	91-20-3	3.20E+05
Toluene	108-88-3	1.20E+06
Benzo[a]anthracene	56-55-3	1.60E+03
Benzo[b]fluoranthene	205-99-2	2.00E+02
Benzo[k]fluoranthene	207-08-9	1.00E+03
Benzo[a]pyrene	50-32-8	5.00E+01
Chrysene	218-01-9	1.80E+03
Dibenzo[a,h]anthracene	52-70-30	4.00E+02
7,12-Dimethylbenz[a]anthracene	57-97-6	2.00E+02
Fluoranthene	206-44-0	6.10E+03
Indeno(1,2,3-cd)pyrene	193-39-5	1.00E+03
3-Methylcholanthrene	56-49-5	2.00E+02
Oxygenates		
Acetophenone	98-86-2	3.60E+05
Acrolein	107-02-8	3.60E+05
Allyl alcohol	107-18-6	3.60E+05
Bis(2-ethylhexyl)phthalate [Di-2-ethylhexyl phthalate]	117-81-7	3.60E+05
Butyl benzyl phthalate	85-68-7	3.60E+05
o-Cresol [2-Methyl phenol]	95-48-7	3.60E+05
m-Cresol [3-Methyl phenol]	108-39-4	3.60E+05
p-Cresol [4-Methyl phenol]	106-44-5	3.60E+05
Di-n-butyl phthalate	84-74-2	3.60E+05
Diethyl phthalate	84-66-2	3.60E+05
2,4-Dimethylphenol	105-67-9	3.60E+05
Dimethyl phthalate	131-11-3	3.60E+05
Di-n-octyl phthalate	117-84-0	3.60E+05
Endothall	145-73-3	3.60E+05
Ethyl methacrylate	97-63-2	3.60E+05
2-Ethoxyethanol [Ethylene glycol monoethyl ether]	110-80-5	3.60E+05
Isobutyl alcohol	78-83-1	3.60E+05
Isosafrole	120-58-1	3.60E+05
Methyl ethyl ketone [2-Butanone]	78-93-3	3.60E+05
Methyl methacrylate	80-62-6	1.80E+05
1,4-Naphthoquinone	130-15-4	3.60E+05
Phenol	108-95-2	3.60E+04
Propargyl alcohol [2-Propyn-1-ol]	107-19-7	3.60E+05
Safrole	94-59-7	3.60E+05

[1]To determine the maximum allowable mass feedrate per unit time to the combustor, "ug/min," of an emission-comparable fuel constituent, multiply the gas flowrate-normalized feedrate limit, "ug/dscm," times the gas flowrate of the combustor, "dscm/min."

emission-comparable fuel stream for which the fuel exceeds the comparable fuel specifications for those compounds in Table 1 to this section.

(C) If there is a substantive change in the information provided in the notice required under this paragraph (b)(2)(i), the generator must submit a revised notification.

(D) Comparable fuel and syngas fuel generators must include an estimate of the average and maximum monthly and annual quantity of material for which an exclusion would be claimed only in notices submitted after December 19, 2008 for newly excluded comparable fuel or syngas fuel or for revised notices as required by paragraph (b)(2)(i)(C) of this section.

(ii) *Public notice.* Prior to burning an excluded fuel, the burner must publish in a major newspaper of general circulation local to the site where the fuel will be burned, a notice entitled "Notification of Burning a Fuel Excluded Under the Resource Conservation and Recovery Act" and containing the following information:

(A) Name, address, and RCRA ID number of the generating facility(ies);

(B) Name and address of the burner and identification of the unit(s) that will burn the excluded fuel;

(C) A brief, general description of the manufacturing, treatment, or other process generating the excluded fuel;

(D) An estimate of the average and maximum monthly and annual quantity of the excluded fuel to be burned; and

(E) Name and mailing address of the Regional or State Directors to whom the generator submitted a claim for the exclusion.

(3) *Burning.* (i) *Comparable fuel and syngas fuel.* The exclusion for fuels meeting the specifications under paragraphs (a)(1) or (a)(3) of this section applies only if the fuel is burned in the following units that also shall be subject to Federal/State/local air emission requirements, including all applicable requirements implementing Section 112 of the Clean Air Act:

(A) Industrial furnaces as defined in §260.10 of this chapter;

(B) Boilers, as defined in §260.10 of this chapter, that are further defined as follows:

(*1*) Industrial boilers located on the site of a facility engaged in a manufacturing process where substances are transformed into new products, including the component parts of products, by mechanical or chemical processes; or

(*2*) Utility boilers used to produce electric power, steam, heated or cooled air, or other gases or fluids for sale;

(C) Hazardous waste incinerators subject to regulation under subpart O of parts 264 or 265 of this chapter or applicable CAA MACT standards.

(D) Gas turbines used to produce electric power, steam, heated or cooled air, or other gases or fluids for sale.

(ii) *Emission-comparable fuel.* The exclusion for fuel meeting the specifications under paragraph (a)(2) of this section applies only if the fuel is burned under the conditions provided by paragraph (c) of this section.

(4) *Fuel analysis plan for generators.* The generator of an excluded fuel shall develop and follow a written fuel analysis plan which describes the procedures for sampling and analysis of the material to be excluded. The plan shall be followed and retained at the site of the generator claiming the exclusion.

(i) At a minimum, the plan must specify:

(A) The parameters for which each excluded fuel will be analyzed and the rationale for the selection of those parameters;

(B) The test methods which will be used to test for these parameters;

(C) The sampling method which will be used to obtain a representative sample of the excluded fuel to be analyzed;

(D) The frequency with which the initial analysis of the excluded fuel will be reviewed or repeated to ensure that the analysis is accurate and up to date; and

(E) If process knowledge is used in the determination, any information prepared by the generator in making such determination.

(ii) For each analysis, the generator shall document the following:

(A) The dates and times that samples were obtained, and the dates the samples were analyzed;

(B) The names and qualifications of the person(s) who obtained the samples;

(C) A description of the temporal and spatial locations of the samples;

(D) The name and address of the laboratory facility at which analyses of the samples were performed;

(E) A description of the analytical methods used, including any clean-up and sample preparation methods;

(F) All quantitation limits achieved and all other quality control results for the analysis (including method blanks, duplicate analyses, matrix spikes, etc.), laboratory quality assurance data, and the description of any deviations from analytical methods written in the plan or from any other activity written in the plan which occurred;

(G) All laboratory results demonstrating whether the exclusion specifications have been met; and

(H) All laboratory documentation that support the analytical results, unless a contract between the claimant and the laboratory provides for the documentation to be maintained by the laboratory for the period specified in paragraph (b)(9) of this section and also provides for the availability of the documentation to the claimant upon request.

(iii) Syngas fuel generators shall submit for approval, prior to performing sampling, analysis, or any management of an excluded syngas fuel, a fuel analysis plan containing the elements of paragraph (b)(4)(i) of this section to the appropriate regulatory authority. The approval of fuel analysis plans must be stated in writing and received by the facility prior to sampling and analysis to demonstrate the exclusion of a syngas. The approval of the fuel analysis plan may contain such provisions and conditions as the regulatory authority deems appropriate.

(5) *Analysis plans for burners of emission-comparable fuel.* An emission-comparable fuel burner is subject to the fuel analysis plan requirements under paragraph (b)(4) of this section to determine, for each fuel fed to the boiler when burning emission-comparable fuel, the as-fired heating value and the as-fired concentration of each compound listed in paragraph (a)(2)(ii)(B) of this section, except for fuels under the situations described below:

(i) Coal or fuel oil used as primary fuels, when the burner uses the heating values and compound concentrations for these fuels provided in paragraph (c)(2)(ii)(C) of this section and Tables 3 and 4 to §261.38;

(ii) Emission-comparable fuel, when the burner receives documentation of this information from the generator for each shipment of emission-comparable

Table 3 to §261.38—Default Values for the Concentration of Emission-Comparable Fuel Constituents in Fuel Oil

	Chemical name	CAS number	Default concentration (mg/kg)
	Hydrocarbons		
1	Benzene	71-43-2	75
2	Naphthalene	91-20-3	3500
3	Toluene	108-88-3	380
4	Benzo[a]anthracene	56-55-3	2400
5	Benzo[b]fluoranthene	205-99-2	2400
6	Benzo[k]fluoranthene	207-08-9	2400
7	Benzo[a]pyrene	50-32-8	2400
8	Chrysene	218-01-9	2400
9	Dibenzo[a,h]anthracene	52-70-30	2400
10	7,12-Dimethylbenz[a]anthracene	57-97-6	2400
11	Fluoranthene	206-44-0	2400
12	Indeno(1,2,3-cd)pyrene	193-39-5	2400
13	3-Methylcholanthrene	56-49-5	2400
	Oxygenates		
1	Acetophenone	98-86-2	2400
2	Acrolein	107-02-8	39
3	Allyl alcohol	107-18-6	30
4	Bis(2-ethylhexyl)phthalate [Di-2-ethylhexyl phthalate]	117-81-7	2400
5	Butyl benzyl phthalate	85-68-7	2400
6	o-Cresol [2-Methyl phenol]	95-48-7	2400
7	m-Cresol [3-Methyl phenol]	108-39-4	2400
8	p-Cresol [4-Methyl phenol]	106-44-5	2400
9	Di-n-butyl phthalate	84-74-2	2400
10	Diethyl phthalate	84-66-2	2400
11	2,4-Dimethylphenol	105-67-9	2400
12	Dimethyl phthalate	131-11-3	2400
13	Di-n-octyl phthalate	117-84-0	2400
14	Endothall	145-73-3	100
15	Ethyl methacrylate	97-63-2	39
16	2-Ethoxyethanol [Ethylene glycol monoethyl ether]	110-80-5	100
17	Isobutyl alcohol	78-83-1	39
18	Isosafrole	120-58-1	2400
19	Methyl ethyl ketone [2-Butanone]	78-93-3	39
20	Methyl methacrylate	80-62-6	39
21	1,4-Naphthoquinone	130-15-4	2400
22	Phenol	108-95-2	2400
23	Propargyl alcohol [2-Propyn-1-ol]	107-19-7	30
24	Safrole	94-59-7	2400

Table 4 to §261.38—Default Values for the Concentration of Emission-Comparable Fuel Constituents in Coal

Compound	Concentration in coal (mg/kg)
Acetophenone	150
Acrolein	2900
Benzene	217
Bis(2-ethylhexyl)phthalate	730
MEK	3900
Methyl methacrylate	200
Phenol	16
Toluene	120

Note: The default value for other emission-comparable fuel constituents in coal is 0 mg/kg.

fuel, provided that the emission-comparable fuel is not blended with other fuels before firing to the burner.

(iii) Emission-comparable fuel, when the burner receives documentation of this information from the generator for each shipment of emission-comparable fuel, and the emission-comparable fuel is blended with other fuels before firing to the burner, provided that:

(A) The burner has determined the heating value of the other fuels and the concentration of each compound listed in paragraph (a)(2)(ii)(B) of this section for the other fuels; and;

(B) The burner determines by calculation the as-fired heating value of the blended emission-comparable fuel and the as-fired concentration of each compound listed in paragraph (a)(2)(ii)(B) of this section of the blended emission-comparable fuel.

(6) *Excluded fuel sampling and analysis.* (i) *General.* For comparable fuel, emission-comparable fuel, and syngas for which an exclusion is claimed under the specifications provided by paragraphs (a)(1), (a)(2), or (a)(3) of this section, the generator of the material must test for all the constituents in appendix VIII to this part, except those that the generator determines, based on testing or knowledge, should not be present in the fuel. The generator is required to document the basis of each determination that a constituent with an applicable specification should not be present. The generator may not determine that any of the following categories of constituents with a specification in Table 1 to this section should not be present:

(A) A constituent that triggered the toxicity characteristic for the constituents that were the basis for listing the hazardous secondary material as a hazardous waste, or constituents for which there is a treatment standard for the waste code in 40 CFR 268.40;

(B) A constituent detected in previous analysis of the material;

(C) Constituents introduced into the process that generates the material; or

(D) Constituents that are byproducts or side reactions to the process that generates the material.

Note to paragraph (b)(6)(i): Any claim under this section must be valid and accurate for all hazardous constituents; a determination not to test for a hazardous constituent will not shield a generator from liability should that constituent later be found in the fuel/syngas above the exclusion specifications.

(ii) *Use of process knowledge.* (A) *Comparable fuel and syngas.* For each material for which the comparable fuel or syngas exclusion is claimed where the generator of the excluded fuel is not the original generator of the hazardous waste, the generator of the excluded fuel may not use process knowledge pursuant to paragraph (b)(6)(i) of this section and must test to determine that all of the constituent specifications of paragraphs (a)(1) and (a)(3) of this section, as applicable, have been met.

(B) *Emission-comparable fuel.* Emission-comparable fuel must meet the specifications for exclusion as-generated. Thus, the generator may use process knowledge to determine that compounds listed in Appendix VIII to this part are not present in the emission-comparable fuel.

(iii) The excluded fuel generator may use any reliable analytical method to demonstrate that no constituent of concern is present at concentrations above the specification levels. It is the responsibility of the generator to ensure that the sampling and analysis are unbiased, precise, and representative of the excluded fuel. For the fuel to be eligible for exclusion, a generator must demonstrate that:

(A) The 95% upper confidence limit of the mean concentration for each constituent of concern is not above the specification level; and

(B) The analyses could have detected the presence of the constituent at or below the specification level.

(iv) Nothing in this paragraph (b)(6) preempts, overrides or otherwise negates the provision in §262.11 of this chapter, which requires any person who generates a solid waste to determine if that waste is a hazardous waste.

(v) In an enforcement action, the burden of proof to establish conformance with the exclusion specification shall be on the generator claiming the exclusion.

(vi) The generator must conduct sampling and analysis in accordance with the fuel analysis plan developed under paragraph (b)(4) of this section.

(vii) *Viscosity condition for comparable fuel.* (A) Excluded comparable fuel that has not been blended to meet the kinematic viscosity specification shall be analyzed as-generated.

(B) If hazardous waste is blended to meet the kinematic viscosity specification for comparable fuel, the generator shall:

(*1*) Analyze the hazardous waste as-generated to ensure that it meets the constituent and heating value specifications of paragraph (a)(1) of this section; and

(*2*) After blending, analyze the fuel again to ensure that the blended fuel meets all comparable fuel specifications.

(viii) Excluded fuel must be re-tested, at a minimum, annually and must be retested after a process change that could change its chemical or physical properties in a manner that may affect conformance with the specifications.

(ix) An emission-comparable fuel burner must determine, for each fuel fired to the burner, the as-fired heating value of the emission-comparable fuel and the as-fired concentration of each compound listed in paragraph (a)(2)(ii)(B) of this section using information provided by the generator, information provided by paragraph (c)(2)(ii)(C) of this section and Tables 3 and 4 to this section, by sampling and analysis, or by calculation when emission-comparable fuel is commingled with other fuels and the heating value of the emission comparable fuel and the concentration of each compound listed in paragraph (a)(2)(ii)(B) of this section is known for the fuels prior to commingling.

(7) *Speculative accumulation.* Excluded fuel must not be accumulated speculatively, as defined in §261.1(c)(8).

(8) *Operating record.* The generator must maintain an operating record on site containing the following information:

(i) All information required to be submitted to the implementing authority as part of the notification of the claim:

(A) The owner/operator name, address, and RCRA ID number of the person claiming the exclusion;

(B) For each excluded fuel, the EPA Hazardous Waste Codes that would be applicable if the material were discarded; and

(C) The certification signed by the person claiming the exclusion or his authorized representative.

(ii) A brief description of the process that generated the excluded fuel. If the comparable fuel generator is not the generator of the original hazardous waste, provide a brief description of the process that generated the hazardous waste;

(iii) The monthly and annual quantities of each fuel claimed to be excluded;

(iv) Documentation for any claim that a constituent is not present in the excluded fuel as required under paragraph (b)(6) of this section;

(v) The results of all analyses and all detection limits achieved as required under paragraph (b)(4) of this section;

(vi) If the comparable fuel was generated through treatment or blending, documentation of compliance with the applicable provisions of paragraphs (a)(4) and (a)(5) of this section;

(vii) If the excluded fuel is to be shipped off-site, a certification from the burner as required under paragraph (b)(10) of this section;

(viii) The fuel analysis plan and documentation of all sampling and analysis results as required by paragraph (b)(4) of this section; and

(ix) If the generator ships excluded fuel off-site for burning, the generator must retain for each shipment the following information on-site:

(A) The name and address of the facility receiving the excluded fuel for burning;

(B) The quantity of excluded fuel shipped and delivered;

(C) The date of shipment or delivery;

(D) A cross-reference to the record of excluded fuel analysis or other information used to make the determination that the excluded fuel meets the specifications as required under paragraph (b)(4) of this section; and

(E) A one-time certification by the burner as required under paragraph (b)(10) of this section.

(9) *Records retention.* Records must be maintained for a period of three years.

(10) *Burner certification to the generator.*—(i) *Comparable fuel and syngas fuel.* Prior to submitting a notification to the State and Regional Directors, a generator of comparable fuel or syngas fuel excluded under paragraphs (a)(1) or (a)(3) of this section who intends to ship the excluded fuel off-site for burning must obtain a onetime written, signed statement from the burner:

(A) Certifying that the excluded fuel will only be burned in an industrial furnace, industrial boiler, utility boiler, or hazardous waste incinerator, as required under paragraph (b)(3) of this section;

(B) Identifying the name and address of the facility that will burn the excluded fuel; and

(C) Certifying that the state in which the burner is located is authorized to exclude wastes as excluded fuel under the provisions of this section.

(ii) *Emission-comparable fuel.* Prior to submitting a notification to the State and Regional Directors, a generator of emission-comparable fuel who intends to ship the excluded fuel off-site for burning must obtain a one-time written, signed statement from the burner:

(A) Certifying that the excluded fuel will be stored under the conditions of paragraphs (c)(1) or (e) of this section and burned under the conditions of paragraph (c)(2) of this section, and that the burner will comply with the notification, reporting, and recordkeeping conditions of paragraph (c)(5) of this section;

(B) Identifying the name and address of the facility that will burn the excluded fuel; and

(C) Certifying that the state in which the burner is located is authorized to exclude wastes as excluded fuel under the provisions of this section.

(11) *Ineligible waste codes.* Wastes that are listed as hazardous waste because of the presence of dioxins or furans, as set out in appendix VII of this part, are not eligible for these exclusions, and any fuel produced from or otherwise containing these wastes remains a hazardous waste subject to full RCRA hazardous waste management requirements.

(12) *Regulatory status of boiler residues.* Burning excluded fuel that was otherwise a hazardous waste listed under §§261.31 through 261.33 does not subject boiler residues, including bottom ash and emission control residues, to regulation as derived-from hazardous wastes.

(13) *Residues in containers and tank systems upon cessation of operations.* (i) Liquid and accumulated solid residues that remain in a container or tank system for more than 90 days after the container or tank system ceases to be operated for storage or transport of excluded fuel product are subject to regulation under parts 262 through 265, 268, 270, 271, and 124 of this chapter.

(ii) Liquid and accumulated solid residues that are removed from a container or tank system after the container or tank system ceases to be operated for storage or transport of excluded fuel product are solid wastes subject to regulation as hazardous waste if the waste exhibits a characteristic of hazardous waste under §§261.21 through 261.24 or if the fuel were otherwise a hazardous waste listed under §§261.31 through 261.33 when the exclusion was claimed.

(iii) Liquid and accumulated solid residues that are removed from a container or tank system and which do not meet the specifications for exclusion under paragraphs (a)(1) or (a)(2) of this section are solid wastes subject to regulation as hazardous waste if:

(A) The waste exhibits a characteristic of hazardous waste under §§261.21 through 261.24; or

(B) If the fuel were otherwise a hazardous waste listed under §§261.31 through 261.33. The hazardous waste code for the listed waste applies to these liquid and accumulated solid residues.

(14) *Waiver of RCRA Closure Requirements.* Interim status and permitted storage and combustion units, and generator storage units exempt from the permit requirements under §262.34 of this chapter, are not subject to the closure requirements of 40 CFR Parts 264, 265, and 267 provided that the storage and combustion unit has been used to manage only hazardous waste that is subsequently excluded under the conditions of this section, and that afterward will be used only to manage fuel excluded under this section.

(15) *Spills and leaks.* (i) Excluded fuel that is spilled or leaked and that therefore no longer meets the conditions of the exclusion is discarded and must be managed as a hazardous waste if it exhibits a characteristic of hazardous waste under §§261.21 through 261.24 or if the fuel were otherwise a hazardous waste listed in §§261.31 through 261.33.

(ii) For excluded fuel that would have otherwise been a hazardous waste listed in §§261.31 through 261.33 and which is spilled or leaked, the hazardous waste code for the listed waste applies to the spilled or leaked material.

(16) Nothing in this section preempts, overrides, or otherwise negates the provisions in CERCLA Section 103, which establish reporting obligations for releases of hazardous substances, or the Department of Transportation requirements for hazardous materials in 49 CFR parts 171 through 180.

(c) *Special conditions for emission-comparable fuel.* The following additional conditions apply to emission-comparable fuel—fuel that meets the specifications under paragraph (a)(2) of this section.

(1) *Storage.* (i) *General.* Emission-comparable fuel may be stored in a container or tank under the conditions of paragraphs (c)(1)(iii) through (c)(1)(viii) of this section, or alternative conditions under paragraph (e) of this section.

(ii) *Prohibition on underground storage.* Emission-comparable fuel shall not be stored in an underground tank. An underground tank is a tank the volume of which (including the volume of underground pipes connecting thereto) is 10 percent or more beneath the surface of the ground.

(iii) *Spill prevention, control, and countermeasures (SPCC) requirements.* Emission-comparable fuel storage tanks and containers with a capacity equal to or greater than 0.1 m^3 (26 gallons) are subject to the following Spill Prevention, Control, and Countermeasures (SPCC) requirements adopted from 40 CFR Part 112. To satisfy the adopted conditions, you must substitute the term "emission-comparable fuel" for the term "oil," and by substituting the term "release of emission-comparable fuel to the environment" for the term "discharge as described in §112.1(b)."

(A) Section 112.2, Definitions. These definitions apply to the adopted SPCC requirements under paragraphs (c)(1)(iii)(B) through (c)(1)(iii)(D) of this section.

(B) Sections 112.3(d) and 112.3(e) of this chapter, Requirement to Prepare and Implement a Spill Prevention, Control, and Countermeasure Plan. (*1*) You must prepare a SPCC Plan in writing, and in accordance with the adopted provisions of §§112.7 and 112.8 of this chapter;

(*2*) The SPCC Plan must be reviewed and certified according to the provisions of §112.3(d) of this chapter and must be made available to the Regional Administrator according to the provisions of §112.3(e) of this chapter;

(*3*) You must amend your SPCC Plan as directed by the Regional Administrator upon a finding that amendment is necessary to prevent and contain releases of emission-comparable fuel from your facility. You must implement the amended SPCC Plan as soon as possible, but not later than six months after you amend your SPCC Plan, unless the Regional Administrator specifies another date;

(C) Sections 112.5(a) and 112.5(b) of this chapter, Amendment of Spill Prevention, Control, and Countermeasures Plan by Owners or Operators. (*1*) You must comply with the provisions of §112.5(a) and (b) of this chapter by substituting the term "release of emission-comparable fuel to the environment" for the term "discharge as described in §112.1(b);"

(*2*) You must have a Professional Engineer certify any technical amendment to your Plan in accordance with §112.3(d) of this chapter.

(D) Section 112.7 of this chapter, General Requirements for Spill Prevention, Control, and Countermeasure Plans. (*1*) You must comply with the requirements of §112.7, except for paragraphs (a)(2), (c), (d), and (k) of that section.

(*2*) Your Plan may deviate from the requirements §112.7(g), (h)(2), (h)(3) and (i), and the adopted provisions of §112.8, where applicable to a specific facility, if you provide equivalent protection by some other means of spill prevention, control, or countermeasure. Where your Plan does not conform to the applicable requirements in §112.7(g), (h)(2), (h)(3) and (i) and the adopted provisions of §112.8 of this chapter, you must state the reasons for nonconformance in your Plan and describe in detail alternate methods and how you will achieve equivalent environmental protection. If the Regional Administrator determines that the measures described in your Plan do not provide equivalent environmental protection, he may require that you amend your Plan.

(E) Section 112.8 of this chapter, Spill Prevention, Control, and Countermeasure Plan Requirements for Onshore Facilities, except for paragraph (b) of this section (facility drainage), paragraph (c)(2) of this section (secondary containment for bulk storage containers), paragraph (c)(4) of this section (protection of completely buried storage tanks), and paragraph (c)(11) of this section (secondary containment for mobile containers), with the following revisions:

(*1*) You must inspect at least weekly areas where portable containers are stored to look for leaking containers and for deterioration of containers and the containment system caused by corrosion or other factors.

(*2*) Section 112.8(d)(1) of this chapter applies to all buried piping irrespective of the installation or replacement date.

(iv) *Containment and detection of releases*—(A) *Tanks.* To prevent the release of emission comparable fuel or hazardous constituents to the environment, you must provide secondary containment for emission-comparable fuel tank systems as prescribed by the following requirements adopted from §264.193 of this chapter. To satisfy the adopted conditions, you must substitute the term "emission-comparable fuel" for the term "waste," and substitute the term "document in the record" for the term "demonstrate to the Regional Administrator."

(*1*) Section 264.193(b) of this chapter, which prescribes general performance standards for secondary containment systems;

(*2*) Section 264.193(c) of this chapter, which prescribes minimum requirements for secondary containment systems;

(*3*) Section 264.193(d)(1) through (3), which prescribes permissible secondary containment devices;

(*4*) Section 264.193(e) of this chapter, which prescribes design and operating requirements for the permissible secondary containment devices; and

(*5*) Section 264.193(f) of this chapter, which prescribes secondary containment requirements for ancillary equipment.

(B) *Portable containers.* To prevent the release of emission comparable fuel or hazardous constituents to the environment, you must provide containment for emission-comparable fuel container storage units as prescribed by the provisions of §264.175(b) of this chapter, which are hereby adopted for emission-comparable fuel container storage units. To satisfy the adopted condition, you must substitute the term "emission-comparable fuel" for each occurrence of the term "waste."

(v) *Preparedness and prevention, emergency procedures and response to releases.*—(A) *Preparedness and prevention.*—(*1*) *Required equipment.* Your facility must be equipped with the equipment required under §264.32(a) through (d) of this chapter in a manner that it can be used in emergencies associated with storing and handling emission-comparable fuel.

(*2*) *Testing and maintenance of equipment.* You must test and maintain as necessary to assure proper operation in times of emergency all communications or alarm systems, fire protection equipment, spill control equipment, and decontamination equipment required for your emission-comparable fuel tank system or container storage unit.

(*3*) *Access to communications or alarm system.* Whenever emission comparable fuel is distributed into or out of the tank system or container storage unit, all personnel involved in the operation must have immediate access to an internal alarm or emergency communication device, either directly or through visual or voice contact with another employee.

(*4*) *Arrangements with local authorities.* You must comply with §264.37(a) of this chapter. If state or local authorities decline to enter into the arrangements prescribed by §264.37(a) of this chapter, you must keep a record documenting the refusal.

(B) *Emergency procedures.*—(*1*) *Emergency coordinator.* At all times, there must be at least one employee either on the facility premises or on call (*i.e.*, available to respond to an emergency by reaching the facility within a short period of time) with the responsibility for coordinating all emergency response measures. This emergency coordinator must be thoroughly familiar with all aspects of the facility's Spill Prevention, Control, and Countermeasures (SPCC) Plan required under paragraph (c)(1)(iii) of this section, all emission-comparable fuel operations and activities at the facility, the location and characteristics of emission-comparable fuel handled, the location of all records within the facility pertaining to emission-comparable fuel, and the facility layout. In addition, this person must have the authority to commit the resources needed to carry out the SPCC Plan.

(*2*) *Emergency procedures.*—(*i*) Whenever there is an imminent or actual emergency situation relating to the emission-comparable fuel tank system or container storage unit, the emergency coordinator (or his designee when the emergency coordinator is on call) must immediately activate internal facility alarms or communication systems, where applicable, to notify all facility personnel and notify appropriate state or local agencies with designated response roles if their help is needed.

(*ii*) Whenever there is a release, fire, or explosion relating to the emission-comparable fuel tank system or container storage unit, the emergency coordinator must immediately identify the character, exact source, amount, and aerial extent of any released materials. He may do this by observation or review of facility records, and, if necessary, by chemical analysis.

(*iii*) Concurrently, the emergency coordinator must assess possible hazards to human health or the environment that may result from the release, fire, or explosion. This assessment must consider both direct and indirect effects of the release, fire, or explosion (*e.g.*, the effects of any toxic, irritating, or asphyxiating gases that are generated, or the effects of any hazardous surface water run-off from water or chemical agents used to control fire and heat-induced explosions).

(*iv*) If the emergency coordinator determines that the facility has had a release, fire, or explosion associated with the emission-comparable fuel tank system or container storage unit which could threaten human health or the environment outside the facility, he must report his findings as provided by paragraph (c)(1)(v)(B)(2)(v) of this section.

(*v*) If the emergency coordinator's assessment indicates that evacuation of local areas may be advisable, he must immediately notify appropriate local authorities. He must be available to help appropriate officials decide whether local areas should be evacuated, and he must immediately notify either the government official designated as the on-scene coordinator for that geographical area, (in the applicable regional contingency plan under part 300 of this title) or the National Response Center (using their 24-hour toll free number 800/424-8802). The report must include: the name and telephone number of the reporter; the name and address of the facility; the time and type of incident (*e.g.*, release, fire); the name and quantity of material(s) involved, to the extent known; the extent of injuries, if any; and the possible hazards to human health, or the environment, outside the facility.

(*vi*) During an emergency, the emergency coordinator must take all reasonable measures necessary to ensure that fires, explosions, and releases do not occur, recur, or spread to other materials at the facility. These measures must include, where applicable, stopping processes and operations and collecting and containing released emission-comparable fuel.

(*vii*) If the emission-comparable fuel tank system or container storage unit stops operations in response to a fire, explosion, or release, the emergency coordinator must monitor for leaks, pressure buildup, gas generation, or ruptures in valves, pipes, or other equipment, wherever this is appropriate.

(*viii*) Immediately after an emergency, the emergency coordinator must provide for treating, storing, or disposing of recovered emission-comparable fuel, contaminated soil or surface water, or any other material that results from a release, fire, or explosion at the facility.

(*ix*) The emergency coordinator must ensure that, in the affected area(s) of the facility: materials that may be incompatible with the released emission-comparable fuel is treated, stored, or disposed of until cleanup procedures are completed; and all emergency equipment listed in the SPCC Plan is cleaned and fit for its intended use before operations are resumed.

(*x*) You must note in the record the time, date, and details of any incident that requires implementing the SPCC Plan for the emission-comparable fuel tank system or container storage unit. Within 15 days after the incident, you must submit a written report on the incident to the Regional Administrator. The report must include: the name, address, and telephone number of the owner or operator; the name, address, and telephone number of the facility; the date, time, and type of incident (*e.g.*, fire, explosion); the name and quantity of material(s) involved; the extent of injuries, if any; an assessment of actual or potential hazards to human health or the environment, where this is applicable; and the estimated quantity and disposition of recovered material that resulted from the incident.

(C) *Response to leaks or spills and disposition of leaking or unfit-for-use tank systems.* (*1*) You must comply with the provisions of §264.196 of this chapter, except for §264.196(e)(1) and (e)(4) of this chapter.

(*2*) To satisfy the adopted provisions of §264.196, you must substitute the term "emission-comparable fuel" for the terms "hazardous waste" and "waste."

(*3*) Unless you satisfy the requirements of §264.196(e)(2) and (3) of this chapter, you must immediately cease using the tank system to store emission-comparable fuel and remove any liquid and solid residues under the conditions of paragraph (b)(13) of this section.

(vi) *Air emissions conditions adopted from part 63, subpart EEEE.*—(A) *Applicability*—(*1*) If your emission-comparable fuel storage, transfer, and transport equipment is not subject to the controls provided by §63.2346 of this chapter, you must determine whether you are subject to the provisions of paragraphs (c)(1)(vi)(B) and (C) of this section:

(*2*) If your emission-comparable fuel storage tank is subject to the controls provided by §63.2346 of this chapter other than those prescribed by item 6 in Table 2 to subpart EEEE, part 63 of this chapter (*i.e.*, requirements for organic liquids with an annual average true vapor pressure of the total listed organic HAP ≥76.6 kilopascals (11.1 psia)), you must determine whether the tank would be subject to the controls prescribed by item 6 after considering the vapor pressure of the RCRA oxygenates listed in paragraph (c)(1)(vi)(B)(*3*) of this section as well as the organic HAP listed in Table 1 to subpart EEEE, part 63 of this chapter. If the annual average true vapor pressure of the total RCRA oxygenates and Table 1 organic HAP in the emission-comparable fuel is ≥76.6 kilopascals (11.1 psia), you are subject to the requirements of paragraphs (c)(1)(vi)(B) through (C) of this section.

(B) *Conditions of applicability.* To satisfy the conditions under paragraph (c)(1)(vi)(C) of this section that are adopted from part 63, subpart EEEE of this chapter, you must:

(*1*) Satisfy the conditions irrespective of whether your facility is an area source as defined by §63.2 of this chapter.

(*2*) Substitute the term "RCRA oxygenates as well as organic HAP" for each occurrence of the term "organic HAP"; the term "RCRA oxygenates as well as organic HAP listed in Table 1" for each occurrence of the term "organic HAP listed in Table 1"; and the term "RCRA oxygenates as well as Table 1 organic HAP" for each occurrence of the term "Table 1 organic HAP".

(*3*) Use the following definition of RCRA oxygenates: The term "RCRA oxygenates" means the following organic compounds:

(*i*) Allyl alcohol (CAS No. 107–18–6);

(*ii*) Bis(2-ethylhexyl)phthalate [Di–2–ethylhexyl phthalate] (CAS No.117–81–7);

(*iii*) 2,4-Dimethylphenol (CAS No. 105–67–9);

(*iv*) Ethyl methacrylate (CAS No. 97–63–2);

(*v*) 2-Ethoxyethanol [Ethylene glycol monoethyl ether] (CAS No. 110–80–5);

(*vi*) Isobutyl alcohol (CAS No. 78–83–1);

(*vii*) Isosafrole (CAS No. 120–58–1);

(*viii*) Methyl ethyl ketone [2-Butanone] (CAS No. 78–93–3);

(*ix*) 1,4-Naphthoquinone (CAS No. 130–15–4);

(*x*) Propargyl alcohol [2-Propyn-1-ol] (CAS No. 107–19–7); and

(*xi*) Safrole (CAS No. 94–59–7).

(*4*) Use the following definition of organic liquid. Organic liquid means emission comparable fuel that:

(*i*) Contains 5 percent by weight or greater of the RCRA oxygenates as well as organic HAP listed in Table 1 to this subpart, as determined using the procedures specified in §63.2354(c) of this chapter; and

(*ii*) Has an annual average true vapor pressure of 0.7 kilopascals (0.1 psia) or greater.

(*5*) Use the following definition of affected source. Affected source means the collection of activities and equipment used to distribute organic liquids into, out of, or within a facility.

(*6*) Substitute the term "subject to §261.38(c)(1)(vi)(C) of this chapter" for each occurrence of the term "subject to this subpart".

(*7*) Satisfy the conditions if:

(*i*) Your organic liquids transfer equipment is exempt from subpart EEEE, part 63 of this chapter, under the provisions of §63.228(c)(1) of this chapter, which exempts organic liquids transfer equipment at facilities subject to a NESHAP other than subpart EEEE, part 63; and

(*ii*) The requirements applicable to the organic liquids transfer equipment under the other NESHAP are not equivalent to, at a minimum, the conditions under paragraphs (c)(1)(vi)(C), (c)(1)(vii), or (e) of this section. You must document and record your determination whether the requirements under the other NESHAP are less stringent than the conditions under paragraph (c)(1)(vi)(C) of this section. You may contact the RCRA regulatory authority to assist with this determination.

(*8*) Submit all notifications, reports, and other communications to the RCRA regulatory authority rather than the CAA regulatory authority.

(C) *Conditions to control air emissions under provisions adopted from part 63, subpart EEEE of this chapter.* (*1*) The affected source is the equipment identified under §63.2338(b)(1) through (5) of this chapter, except for equipment identified in §63.2338(c)(2) through (3) of this chapter.

(*2*) Definitions of new, reconstructed, and existing affected sources are provided under §63.2338(d) through (f) of this chapter.

(*3*) You must comply with the emission limitations, operating limits, and work practice standards under §63.2346 of this chapter.

(*4*) You must comply with the general requirements under §63.2350 of this chapter. The startup, shutdown, and malfunction plan required by §63.2350(c) of this chapter need not address equipment not subject to paragraph (c)(1)(vi)(C) of this section.

(*5*) You must comply with the performance tests, design evaluation, and performance evaluation requirements under §63.2354 of this chapter. When complying with §63.2354(c) of this chapter, however, you must determine the content of RCRA oxygenates as well as organic HAP in the emission-comparable fuel.

(*6*) You must conduct performance tests and other initial compliance demonstrations prior to managing emission-comparable fuel in the storage unit.

(*7*) You must conduct subsequent performance tests by the dates specified in §63.2362 of this chapter.

(*8*) You must comply with the monitoring, installation, operation, and maintenance requirements under §63.2366 of this chapter.

(*9*) You must demonstrate initial compliance with the emission limitations, operating limits, and work practice standards as required under §63.2370 of this chapter.

(*10*) You must monitor and collect data to demonstrate continuous compliance and use the collected data as required by §63.2374 of this chapter.

(*11*) You must demonstrate continuous compliance with the emission limitations, operating limits, and work practice standards as required by §63.2378 of this chapter.

(*12*) You must submit the notifications and on the schedule required by §63.2382 of this chapter, except that initial notifications must be submitted prior to managing emission-comparable fuel in the storage unit. Notifications must be submitted to the RCRA regulatory authority.

(*13*) You must submit the reports and on the schedule required by §63.2386 of this chapter. Reports must be submitted to the RCRA regulatory authority.

(*14*) You must keep the applicable records required by §63.2390 of this chapter.

(*15*) You must keep records in the form, and for the duration, required by §63.2394 of this chapter.

(*16*) The parts of the General Provisions that apply to you are provided by §63.2398 of this chapter.

(*17*) The definitions that apply to the conditions under paragraph (c)(1)(vi)(C) of this section are provided by §63.2406 of this chapter, and paragraphs (c)(1)(vi)(B)(3) through (5) of this section.

(*18*) You are subject to the requirements in Tables 1–12 to subpart EEEE, part 63 of this chapter.

(vii) *Air emissions conditions for tanks and containers that are not subject to conditions adopted from part 63, subpart EEEE.* Tank and container storage units that are not subject to the conditions adopted from subpart EEEE, part 63 under paragraph (c)(1)(vi) of this section are subject to the conditions of this paragraph.

(A) *Tanks.* (*1*) *Level 1 control.* (*i*) *Applicability criteria.* Tanks that meet the following vapor pressure limitations for emission-comparable fuel for the tank size designations are subject to the air emission controls under paragraph (c)(1)(vii)(A)(*1*)(*ii*) of this section:

(*A*) For a tank design capacity equal to or greater than 151 m^3 (40,000 gallons), the annual average organic vapor pressure limit for the tank is 5.2 kPa (0.75 psia);

(*B*) For a tank design capacity equal to or greater than 75 m^3 (20,000 gallons) but less than 151 m^3 (40,000 gallons), the annual average organic vapor pressure limit for the tank is 27.6 kPa (4.0 psia); and

(*C*) For a tank design capacity less than 75 m^3 (20,000 gallons), the annual average vapor pressure limit for the tank is 76.6 kPa (11.1 psia);

(*ii*) *Conditions to control emissions.* You must comply with the following requirements:

(*A*) *NESHAP provisions for level 1 control under subpart OO, part 63.* Sections 63.901 through 63.907 of this chapter; or

(*B*) *NESHAP provisions for organic liquid distribution under subpart EEEE, part 63.* The provisions under Item 1.a.i or 1.a.ii which require venting to a control device under provisions of subpart SS, part 63 of this chapter, or Level 2 tank emissions control under subpart WW, part 63 of this chapter, or routing emissions to a fuel gas system or back to a process under §63.984 of subpart SS, part 63 of this chapter, or vapor balancing emissions to the transport vehicle from which the storage tank is filled under §63.2346(a)(4); or

(*C*) *Hazardous waste tank controls under subpart CC, part 264.* The provisions for additional options provided for hazardous waste tanks under §264.1084(d)(3), (d)(4), or (d)(5) of this chapter for use of venting to a control device, a pressure tank, or a tank located inside an enclosure that is vented through a closed-vent system to an enclosed combustion control device, and the associated provisions under §§63.1081 (definitions), 264.1083(c) (determination of vapor pressure), 264.1084(j) (transfer to a tank), 264.1087 (closed-vent systems and control devices), and 264.89(b) (recordkeeping) of this chapter. To satisfy these adopted provisions, you must substitute the term "emission-comparable fuel" for the terms "hazardous waste" and "waste."

Publisher's Note: We believe the above reference to 264.89(b) should be to 264.1089(b).

(2) *Level 2 control.* (*i*) *Applicability criteria.* Tanks that do not meet the vapor pressure limitations for emission-comparable fuel for the tank size designations under paragraph (c)(1)(vii)(A)(*1*)(*i*) of this section are subject to the air emission controls under paragraph (c)(1)(vii)(A)(*2*)(*ii*) of this section.

(*ii*) *Conditions to control emissions.* To satisfy the conditions to control emissions, you must comply with the requirements under paragraphs (c)(1)(vii)(A)(*1*)(*ii*)(*B*) or (*C*) of this section.

(*3*) *Equipment leaks.* For each valve, pump, compressor, pressure relief device, sampling connection system, open-ended valve or line, or flange or other connector, and any control devices or systems used to manage emission-comparable fuel in a tank system subject to paragraph (c)(1)(vii)(A) of this section, you must comply with the applicable requirements under 40 CFR part 63, subpart TT (control level 1), except for §63.1000; or subpart UU (control level 2), except for §63.1019; or subpart H, except for §§63.160, 63.162(b) and (e), and 63.183.

(B) *Containers.* (*1*) *Level 1 control.* (*i*) *Applicability criteria.* Containers that meet the following criteria are subject to the air emission controls under paragraph (c)(1)(vii)(B)(*1*)(*ii*) of this section:

(*A*) Containers having a design capacity greater than 0.1 m^3 and less than or equal to 0.46 m^3;

(*B*) Containers having a design capacity greater than 0.46 m^3 that are not in light liquid service, as defined in §264.1031 of this chapter.

(*C*) Containers having a design capacity greater than 0.46 m^3 that are in light liquid service, as defined in §264.1031 of this chapter.

(*ii*) *Conditions to control emissions.* To satisfy the conditions on Level I control of emissions, you must comply with the following requirements:

(*A*) The NESHAP provisions for containers under subpart PP, part 63 at §§63.922 (level 1 control) or 63.923 (level 2 control) of this chapter; and

(*B*) The ancillary provisions under subpart PP, part 63 at §§63.921 (definitions), 63.925 (test methods and procedures), 63.926 (inspection and monitoring requirements), 63.927 (recordkeeping requirements), and 63.928 (reporting requirements) of this chapter.

(*2*) *Level 2 control.* (*i*) *Applicability criteria.* Containers that do not meet the criteria under paragraph (c)(1)(vii)(B)(*1*)(*i*) of this section are subject to the air emission controls under paragraph (c)(1)(vii)(B)(*2*)(*ii*) of this section.

(*ii*) *Conditions to control emissions.* To satisfy the conditions on Level II control of emissions, you must comply with the following requirements:

(*A*) The NESHAP provisions for containers under subpart PP, part 63 at §63.923 (level 2 control) of this chapter; and

(*B*) The ancillary provisions under subpart PP, part 63 at §§63.921 (definitions), 63.925 (test methods and procedures), 63.926 (inspection and monitoring requirements, 63.927 (recordkeeping requirements), and 63.928 (reporting requirements) of this chapter.

(*3*) *Equipment leaks.* For each valve, pump, compressor, pressure relief device, sampling connection system, open-ended valve or line, or flange or other connector, and any control devices or systems used to manage emission-comparable fuel in a container subject to paragraph (c)(1)(vii)(B) of this section, you must comply with the applicable requirements under 40 CFR part 63, subpart TT (control level 1), except for §63.1000; or subpart UU (control level 2), except for §63.1019; or subpart H, except for §§63.160, 63.162(b) and (e), and 63.183.

(viii) *Management of incompatible fuels and other materials*—(A) Generators and burners of emission-comparable fuel must document in the fuel analysis plan under paragraph (b)(4) of this section how (*e.g.*, using trial tests, analytical results, scientific literature, or process knowledge) precautions will be taken to prevent mixing of excluded fuels and other materials which could result in reactions which:

(*1*) Generate extreme heat or pressure, fire or explosions, or violent reactions;

(*2*) Produce uncontrolled toxic mists, fumes, dusts, or gases;

(*3*) Produce uncontrolled flammable fumes or gases; or

(*4*) Damage the structural integrity of the storage unit or facility.

(B) Burners that blend emission-comparable fuel with other fuels but that are exempt from fuel analysis requirements under paragraphs (b)(4) and (b)(5)(iii) of this section must document in the operating record how precautions will be taken to prevent mixing of emission-comparable fuel with other fuels which could result in the reactions listed in paragraph (c)(viii)(A) of this section.

(C) Incompatible fuels must not be placed in the same tank or container.

(2) *Burning.* (i) *Types of combustors that may burn emission-comparable fuel.* Emission-comparable fuel must be burned in a boiler meeting the conditions of paragraph (c)(2)(i)(A) of this section or a hazardous waste combustor under the conditions of paragraph (c)(2)(i)(B) of this section.

(A) *Boilers.* Emission-comparable fuel may be burned in an industrial or utility boiler as defined in paragraph (b)(3) of this section but that is further restricted by being a watertube type of steam boiler that does not feed fuel using a stoker or stoker-type mechanism.

(B) *Hazardous waste combustors.* (*1*) Emission-comparable fuel may be burned in an incinerator, cement kiln, lightweight aggregate kiln, boiler, or halogen acid production furnace operating under a RCRA permit issued under part 270 of this chapter and in compliance with the applicable provisions of subpart O of part 264, subpart H of part 266, or subpart EEE of part 63 of this chapter, provided that the emission-comparable fuel is burned under the same operating requirements that apply to hazardous waste burned by the combustor.

(*2*) When emission-comparable fuel is burned in a hazardous waste combustor under the provisions of paragraph (c)(2)(i)(B) of this section, the operating conditions under paragraph (c)(2)(ii) of this section do not apply, except for:

(*i*) The emission-comparable fuel constituent feedrate conditions under paragraph (c)(2)(ii)(C) of this section continue to apply; and

(*ii*) The emission-comparable fuel automatic feed cutoff system requirements under paragraph (c)(2)(ii)(G) of this section that apply to monitoring the constituent feedrate limits as specified under paragraph (c)(2)(ii)(G)(*1*)(*ii*) of this section continue to apply.

(ii) *Operating conditions*—(A) *Primary fuels.* (*1*) A minimum of 50 percent of fuel fired to the boiler shall be fossil fuel, fuels derived from fossil fuel, tall oil, or comparable fuel meeting the specifications provided by paragraph (a)(1) of this section. Such fuels are termed "primary fuel" for purposes of this section. (Tall oil is a fuel derived from vegetable and rosin fatty acids.) The primary fuel shall comprise at least 50% of the total fuel heat input to the boiler and at least 50% of the total fuel mass input to the boiler.

(*2*) The primary fuel firing rate shall be continuously monitored and the minimum primary fuel firing rate limit shall be achieved on an hourly rolling average basis;

(B) *Fuel heating value.* Primary fuels shall have a minimum as-fired heating value of 8,000 Btu/lb, and each material fired in a firing nozzle where emission-comparable fuel is fired must have a heating value of at least 8,000 Btu/lb, as-fired;

(C) *Feedrate limits for emission-comparable fuel constituents.* The total feedrate, considering all combustor feedstreams, of each emission-comparable fuel constituent listed under paragraph (a)(2)(ii)(B) of this section shall not exceed the limit provided by Table 2 to this section.

(*1*) The feedrate limits are expressed as gas flowrate-normalized feedrates in the units "ug/dscm".

(*2*) The feedrate limit for total combustor feedstreams expressed as mass/unit time (kg/hr) for each emission-comparable fuel constituent is determined by multiplying the gas flowrate-normalized feedrate limit provided by Table 2 to this section times the combustor gas flowrate.

(*3*) The maximum constituent feedrate (kg/hr) attributable to emission-comparable fuel is the total combustor constituent feedrate (kg/hr) minus the constituent feedrate (kg/hr) for all other combustor feedstreams.

(*4*) To account for emission-comparable fuel constituents in primary fuels, burners may use measured concentrations of the constituents, or:

(*i*) If natural gas is used as a primary fuel, burners may assume that natural gas does not contain emission-comparable fuel constituents and that natural gas has a heating value of 22,000 Btu/lb;

(*ii*) If fuel oil is used as a primary fuel, burners may use the default concentrations for emission-comparable fuel constituents provided in Table 3 to this section, and assume that fuel oil has a heating value of 19,200 Btu/lb; and

(*iii*) If coal is used as a primary fuel, burners may use the default concentrations for emission-comparable fuel constituents provided in Table 4 to this section, and assume that coal has a heating value of 11,100 Btu/lb.

(*5*) The feedrate of each emission-comparable fuel constituent shall be continuously monitored (by knowing the concentration of the constituent in each feedstream and by monitoring the feedrate of each feedstream), and the maximum feedrate limit for each constituent shall not be exceeded on an hourly rolling average basis.

(D) *CO CEMS.* When burning emission-comparable fuel, carbon monoxide emissions must not exceed 100 parts per million by volume, over an hourly rolling average (monitored with a continuous emissions monitoring system (CEMS)), dry basis and corrected to 7 percent oxygen. You must use an oxygen CEMS to continuously correct the carbon monoxide level to 7 percent oxygen. You must install, calibrate, maintain, and continuously operate the CEMS in compliance with the quality assurance procedures provided in the appendix to subpart EEE of part 63 of this chapter (Quality Assurance Procedures for Continuous Emissions Monitors Used for Hazardous Waste Combustors) and Performance Specification 4B (carbon monoxide and oxygen) in appendix B, part 60 of this chapter.

(E) *Dioxin/furan control*—(*1*) If the boiler is equipped with a dry particulate matter control device and the primary fuel is not coal, you must continuously monitor the combustion gas temperature at the inlet to the dry particulate matter control device, and the gas temperature must not exceed 400 °F on an hourly rolling average basis.

(*2*) *Calibration of thermocouples.* The calibration of thermocouples must be verified at a frequency and in a manner consistent with manufacturer specifications, but no less frequently than once per year.

(F) *Calculation of rolling averages*—(*1*) *Calculation of rolling averages upon intermittent operations.* You must ignore periods of time when one-minute values are not available for calculating the hourly rolling average. When one-minute values become available again, the first one-minute value is added to the previous 59 values to calculate the hourly rolling average.

(*2*) *Calculation of rolling averages when the emission-comparable fuel feed is cutoff.* You must continue monitoring carbon monoxide and combustion gas temperature at the inlet to the dry particulate matter emission control device when the emission-comparable fuel feed is cutoff, but the source continues operating on other fuels. You must not resume feeding emission-comparable fuel if the emission levels exceed the limits provided in paragraphs (c)(2)(ii)(D) and (E) of this section.

(G) *Automatic fuel feed cutoff system—(1) General.* You must operate the boiler with a functioning system that immediately and automatically cuts off the emission-comparable fuel feed, except as provided by paragraph (c)(2)(ii)(G)(6) of this section:

(*i*) When the hourly rolling average carbon monoxide level exceeds 100 ppmv or the combustion gas temperature at the inlet to the initial dry particulate matter control device (and the primary fuel is not coal) exceeds 400 °F on an hourly rolling average.

(*ii*) When the emission-comparable fuel feedrate limit for a constituent exceeds the limit provided by Table 2 to this section.

(*iii*) When the primary fuel firing rate is below 50 percent on a heat input and mass input basis;

(*iv*) When the steam production rate (or other indicator of boiler load) indicates that the boiler load is below 40 percent;

(*v*) When the span value of the combustion gas temperature detector is exceeded;

(*vi*) Upon malfunction of the carbon monoxide CEMS, the gas temperature detector, the feedrate monitor(s) for the primary fuel, the feedrate monitor(s) used to comply with the maximum feedrate limits for emission-comparable fuel constituents, or the monitor for boiler load; or

(*iv*) When any component of the automatic fuel feed cutoff system fails.

[*Publisher's Note:* We believe that the correct numbering for the paragraph above should be "(vii)." Thus, the references to "paragraphs (c)(2)(ii)(G)(*1*)(*i*) through (*iv*)" in §261.38(c)(2)(ii)(G)(*3*), (*4*), and (*6*) below should be to "paragraphs (c)(2)(ii)(G)(*1*)(*i*) through (*vii*)."]

(*2*) *Failure of the automatic fuel feed cutoff system.* If the automatic emission-comparable fuel feed cutoff system fails to automatically and immediately cut off the flow of emission-comparable fuel (except as provided by paragraph (c)(2)(ii)(G)(*6*) of this section) upon an occurrence of an event linked to the cutoff system as required under paragraph (c)(2)(ii)(G)(*1*) of this section, you have failed to comply with the emission-comparable fuel cutoff conditions of this section. If an equipment failure prevents immediate and automatic cutoff of the emission-comparable fuel feed, however, you must cease feeding emission-comparable fuel as quickly as possible.

(*3*) *Exceedance of a limit.* If, notwithstanding an automatic emission-comparable fuel feed cutoff, a limit linked to the cutoff system under paragraphs (c)(2)(ii)(G)(*1*)(*i*) through(*iv*) of this section is exceeded while emission-comparable fuel remains in the combustion chamber, you have failed to comply with a condition of the exclusion.

(*4*) *Exceedance reporting.* For each exceedance of a limit linked to the cutoff system under paragraphs (c)(2)(ii)(G)(*1*)(*i*) through(*iv*) of this section while emission-comparable fuel remains in the combustion chamber (*i.e.*, when the emission-comparable fuel residence time has not transpired since the emission-comparable fuel feed was cutoff), you must submit to the RCRA regulatory authority a written report within 5 calendar days of the exceedance documenting:

(*i*) The exceedance;

(*ii*) The measures you have taken to manage the material as a hazardous waste; and

(*iii*) The measures you have taken to notify the generator that you have failed to comply with a condition of the exclusion.

(*5*) *Testing.* The automatic emission-comparable fuel feed cutoff system and associated alarms must be tested at least weekly to verify operability, unless you document in the operating record that weekly inspections will unduly restrict or upset operations and that less frequent inspection will be adequate. At a minimum, you must conduct operability testing at least monthly. You must document and record in the operating record automatic emission-comparable fuel feed cutoff system operability test procedures and results.

(*6*) *Ramping down emission-comparable fuel feed.* You may ramp down the emission-comparable fuel feedrate over a period not to exceed one minute. If you elect to ramp down the emission-comparable fuel feed, you must document ramp down procedures in the operating record. The procedures must specify that the ramp down begins immediately upon initiation of automatic emission-comparable fuel feed cutoff and the procedures must prescribe a bona fide ramping down. If a limit linked to the cutoff system under paragraphs (c)(2)(ii)(G)(1)(*i*) through (*iv*) of this section is exceeded during the ramp down, you have failed to comply with that limit.

(H) *Boiler load.* (*1*) Boiler load shall not be less than 40 percent. Boiler load is the ratio at any time of the total heat input to the maximum design heat input.

(*2*) Steam production rate or other measure of boiler load shall be monitored continuously and the minimum 40 percent load shall be maintained on an hourly rolling average basis.

(I) *Fuel atomization.* The emission-comparable fuel shall be fired directly into the primary fuel flame zone of the combustion chamber with an air or steam atomization firing system, mechanical atomization system, or a rotary cup atomization system under the following conditions:

(*1*) *Particle size.* The emission-comparable fuel must pass through a 200 mesh (74 micron) screen, or equivalent;

(*2*) *Mechanical atomization systems.* Fuel pressure within a mechanical atomization system and fuel flow rate shall be maintained within the design range taking into account the viscosity and volatility of the fuel;

(*3*) *Rotary cup atomization systems.* Fuel flow rate through a rotary cup atomization system must be maintained within the design range taking into account the viscosity and volatility of the fuel.

(J) *Definition of continuous monitoring systems.* (*1*) Continuous monitoring systems (CMS) must sample the controlled parameter without interruption, and evaluate the detector response at least once each 15 seconds, and compute and record the average values at least every 60 seconds.

(*2*) For CMS other than the CO CEMS, you must install, operate, and calibrate the other CMS according to the manufacturer's written specifications or recommendations, at a minimum.

(iii) *Boiler operator training.* (A) Boiler operators are personnel that operate or maintain the boiler when emission-comparable fuel is burned, including continuous monitoring systems and the emission-comparable fuel automatic feed cutoff system.

(B) Boiler operators must successfully complete a program that teaches them to perform their duties in a way that ensures the boiler's compliance with the operating conditions under paragraph (c)(2)(ii) of this section. The boiler owner or operator must ensure that this program includes all the elements described in the document required under paragraph (c)(2)(iii)(F) of this section.

(C) This program must be directed by a person trained in boiler operation procedures, and must include instruction which teaches boiler operators procedures relevant to the positions in which they are employed.

(D) At a minimum, the training program must be designed to ensure that boiler operators understand the operating conditions under paragraph (c)(2)(ii) of this section and are able to respond effectively when the emission-comparable fuel automatic feed cutoff system engages an automatic cutoff of the feed of emission-comparable fuel.

(E) Boiler operators must take part in an annual review of the initial training required in paragraph (c)(2)(iii)(B) of this section.

(F) The boiler owner or operator must maintain the following documents and records at the facility:

(*1*) The job title for each boiler operator position, and the name of the employee filling each job;

(*2*) A written job description for each position listed under paragraph (c)(2)(iii)(F)(*1*) of this section. This description may be consistent in its degree of specificity with descriptions for other similar positions in the same company location or bargaining unit, but must include the requisite skill, education, or other qualifications, and duties of employees assigned to each position;

(*3*) A written description of the type and amount of both introductory and continuing training that will be given to each person filling a position listed under paragraph (c)(2)(iii)(F)(*1*) of this section; and

(*4*) Records that document that the training or job experience required under paragraphs (c)(2)(iii)(B), (C), (D), and (E) of this section has been given to, and completed by, boiler operators.

(*5*) Training records on current personnel must be kept until emission-comparable fuel is no longer burned in the boiler. Training records on former boiler operators must be kept for at least three years from the date the employee last worked as a boiler operator at the facility. Personnel training records may accompany personnel transferred within the same company.

(3) *Off-site shipments.* (i) Emission-comparable fuel may not be managed by any entity other than its generator, transporter, and designated burner.

(ii) Emission-comparable fuel may not be exported to a foreign country.

(4) *EPA Identification Number.* A burner that receives emission-comparable fuel from an offsite generator must have or obtain an EPA identification number from the Administrator. A burner who has not received an EPA identification number may obtain one by applying to the Administrator using EPA form 8700–12. Upon receiving the request, the Administrator will assign an EPA identification number to the burner.

(5) *Notification, reporting, and recordkeeping.* Except as provided by paragraph (c)(5)(iv) of this section, burners of emission-comparable fuel are subject to the following conditions:

(i) *Initial Notification.* (A) *Off-site burners.* A burner that receives emission-comparable fuel from an offsite generator must submit an initial notification to the Regional or State RCRA and CAA Directors prior to receiving the first shipment:

(*1*) Providing the name, address, and EPA identification number of the burner;

(*2*) Certifying that the excluded fuel will be stored under the conditions of paragraphs (c)(1) or (e) of this section and burned in a boiler or hazardous waste combustor under the conditions of paragraph (c)(2) of this section, and that the burner will comply with the notification, reporting, and recordkeeping conditions of paragraph (c)(5) of this section;

(*3*) Identifying the specific units that will burn the excluded fuel;

(*4*) Providing an estimate of the maximum annual quantity of emission-comparable fuel that will be burned, and an estimate of the maximum as-fired concentrations of each constituent in Table 2 to this section for which the emission-comparable fuel exceeds the specifications for comparable fuel in Table 1 to this section;

(*5*) Providing documentation that ECF will be fired into the flame zone of the primary fuel; and

(*6*) Certifying that the state in which the burner is located is authorized to exclude wastes as excluded fuel under the provisions of this section.

(B) *On-site burners.* An on-site burner must include in the one-time generator notification required under paragraphs (b)(2)(i)(A) and (B) of this section the information identified under paragraphs (c)(5)(i)(A)(*3*) through (*5*) of this section.

(C) If there is a substantive change in the information provided in the initial notification, the burner must submit a revised notification.

(ii) *Reporting.* The burner must submit to the RCRA regulatory authority reports of exceedances of operating parameter limits that are linked to the emission-comparable fuel automatic feed cutoff system, as required under paragraph (c)(2)(ii)(G)(*4*) of this section.

(iii) *Recordkeeping.* (A) *Records of shipments.* If the burner receives a shipment of emission-comparable fuel from an offsite generator, the burner must retain for each shipment the following information on-site in the operating record:

(*1*) The name, address, and RCRA ID number of the generator shipping the excluded fuel;

(*2*) The quantity of excluded fuel delivered;

(*3*) For ECF that would have otherwise been a hazardous waste listed in §§261.31 through 261.33, the hazardous waste code for the listed waste; and

(*4*) The date of delivery;

(B) *Boiler operating data.* The burner must retain records of information required to comply with the operating conditions of paragraph (c)(2) of this section in an operating record.

(C) *Records retention.* The burner must retain records at the facility for three years.

(iv) *Burners that are hazardous waste combustors.* Hazardous waste combustors that burn emission-comparable fuel under the provisions of paragraph (c)(2)(i)(B) of this section are not subject to the provisions of paragraphs (c)(5)(i) through (iii) of this section, except:

(A) The provisions of paragraphs (c)(5)(i)(A)(*1*) and (*3*), and paragraphs (c)(5)(iii)(A) and (C) apply; and

(B) The initial notification required under paragraphs (c)(5)(i)(A)(*1*) and(*3*) must include a certification that the excluded fuel will be stored under the conditions of paragraphs (c)(1) or (e) of this section.

(d) *Failure to comply with the conditions of the exclusion.* (1) *General.* An excluded fuel loses its exclusion if any person managing the fuel fails to comply with the conditions of the exclusion under this section, and the material must be managed as hazardous waste from the point of generation. In such situations, EPA or an authorized state agency may take enforcement action under RCRA section 3008(a), except as provided in paragraph (d)(2) of this section.

(2) *Emission-comparable fuel burned in an off-site, unaffiliated burner.* If the generator that claims the exclusion

for emission-comparable fuel that is burned in an off-site, unaffiliated burner documents in the operating record that reasonable efforts have been made under this paragraph to ensure that such burner complies with the conditions of exclusion, the burner rather than the generator will be liable for discarding a hazardous waste upon a finding that such burner has not complied with a condition of exclusion.

(i) In making these reasonable efforts, the generator must, at a minimum, affirmatively answer the following questions prior to shipping emission-comparable fuel to the burner:

(A) Has the burner submitted the notification to the RCRA and CAA Directors required under paragraph (c)(5)(i) of this section, and has the burner published the public notice of burning activities required under paragraph (b)(2)(ii) of this section?

(B) Does publicly available information indicate that the burner facility has not had any formal enforcement actions taken against the facility in the previous three years for violations of the RCRA hazardous waste regulations and has not been classified as a significant non-complier with RCRA Subtitle C? In answering this question, the emission-comparable fuel generator can rely on the publicly available information from EPA or the state. If the burner facility has had a formal enforcement action taken against it in the previous three years for violations of the RCRA hazardous waste regulations and has been classified as a significant non-complier with RCRA Subtitle C, does the emission-comparable fuel generator have credible evidence that the burner will manage the emission-comparable fuel properly? In answering this question, the emission-comparable fuel generator can obtain additional information from EPA, the state, or the facility itself that the facility has addressed the violations, taken remedial steps to address the violations and prevent future violations, or that the violations are not relevant to the management of emission-comparable fuel under the conditions of this section.

(C) Does the burner have the equipment and trained personnel to manage the emission-comparable fuel under the conditions of this section?

(ii) In making these reasonable efforts, the generator may use any credible evidence available, including information obtained from the burner and information obtained from a third party;

(iii) The generator must maintain for a minimum of three years documentation and certification that reasonable efforts were made for each burner facility to which emission-comparable fuel is shipped.

(A) Documentation and certification must be made available upon request by a regulatory authority within 72 hours, or within a longer period of time as specified by the regulatory authority.

(B) The certification statement must:

(*1*) Be signed and dated by an authorized representative of the generator company; and

(*2*) Incorporate the following language: "I hereby certify in good faith and to the best of my knowledge that, prior to arranging for transport of emission-comparable fuel to [insert name(s) of burner facility], reasonable efforts were made to ensure that the emission-comparable fuel would be stored and burned under the conditions prescribed by §261.38, and that such efforts were based on current and accurate information."

(iv) Reasonable efforts must be repeated at a minimum of every three years.

(v) An unaffiliated burner is a boiler or hazardous waste combustor located at a facility that is not owned by the same parent company that generated the emission-comparable fuel.

(e) *Alternative storage conditions for emissions-comparable fuel.* Emission-comparable fuel may be stored in a tank or container under the following conditions adopted from 40 CFR Part 264 in lieu of the conditions specified under paragraphs (c)(1)(iii) through (c)(1)(viii) of this section. When satisfying these conditions, you must substitute the term "emission-comparable fuel" for each occurrence of the term "hazardous waste" or "waste." You must document in the operating record whether you are complying with the alternative storage conditions of this paragraph, or the storage conditions under paragraphs (c)(1)(iii) through (c)(1)(viii) of this section.

(1) *Security.* You must comply with the requirements under §264.14 of this chapter to provide security for your emission-comparable fuel storage facility.

(2) *General inspection requirements.* You must comply with the general inspection requirements under §264.15 of this chapter for your emission-comparable fuel storage facility.

(3) *Personnel training.* You must comply with the personnel training requirements under §264.16 of this chapter for emission-comparable fuel storage facility personnel.

(4) *General requirements for ignitable, reactive, or incompatible materials.* You must comply with the requirements for ignitable, reactive, or incompatible materials managed by the emission-comparable fuel storage facility.

(5) *Preparedness and prevention.* You must comply with the preparedness and prevention requirements under §§264.31 through 264.37 of this chapter with respect to your emission-comparable fuel storage facility.

(6) *Contingency plan and emergency procedures.* You must comply with the contingency plan and emergency procedure requirements under §§264.51 through 264.56 of this chapter with respect to your emission-comparable fuel storage facility.

(7) *Air emission requirements for equipment leaks.* You must comply with the requirements under §§264.1051 through 264.1065 of this chapter to control leaks from equipment used to manage emission-comparable fuel;

(8) *Use and management of containers.* If you store emission-comparable fuel in a container, you must comply with the following requirements for use and management of those containers:

(i) *Condition of containers.* You must comply with the requirements to ensure containers are in good condition under §264.171 of this chapter;

(ii) *Compatibility of emission-comparable fuel with containers.* You must comply with the requirements to ensure compatibility of emission-comparable fuel with containers under §264.172 of this chapter;

(iii) *Management of containers.* You must manage containers as prescribed by §264.173 of this chapter;

(iv) *Inspections.* You must inspect containers and the containment system as prescribed by §264.174 of this chapter;

(v) *Containment.* You must comply with the containment provisions under §264.175 of this chapter;

(vi) *Special requirements for ignitable or reactive emission-comparable fuel.* You must comply with the provisions for ignitable or reactive emission-comparable fuel under §264.176 of this chapter; and

(vii) *Air emission standards.* You must comply with the air emission requirements under §§264.1081, 264.1086(b)(1), (c), (d), and (f) through (h), 264.1088, and 264.1089 of this chapter.

(viii) Closed vent systems and control devices. If you use a closed vent system or control device to comply with paragraph (e)(8)(vii) of this section, you must comply with the requirements under §§264.1033(b) through (o), and 264.1034 through 264.1036 of this chapter.

(9) *Tank systems.* If you store emission-comparable fuel in a tank, you must comply with the following requirements:

(i) *Containment and detection of releases.* You must comply with the requirements for containment and detection of releases under §264.193(b), (c), (d), (e), and (f) of this chapter;

(ii) *General operating requirements.* You must comply with the general operating requirements under §264.194 of this chapter;

(iii) *Inspections.* You must comply with the inspection requirements under §264.195 of this chapter;

(iv) *Response to leaks or spills and disposition of leaking or unfit-for-use tank systems.* You must comply with the requirements regarding response to leaks or spills and disposition of leaking or unfit-for-use tank systems under §264.196 of this chapter, except that §264.196(e)(1) reads for emission-comparable fuel tank systems: "Unless the owner/operator satisfies the requirements of paragraphs (e)(2) through (4) of this section, the tank system must be closed".

(v) *Special requirements for ignitable or reactive materials.* You must comply with the requirements for ignitable and reactive materials under §264.198 of this chapter;

(vi) *Special requirements for incompatible materials.* You must comply with the requirements for incompatible materials under §264.199 of this chapter; and

(vii) *Air emissions.* (A) You must comply with the requirements to control air emissions under §§264.1081, 264.1083(c), 264.1084(b) through (l), 264.1087 through 264.1089, and 264.1090(b) through (d) of this chapter.

(B) *Closed vent systems and control devices.* If you use a closed vent system or control device to comply with paragraph (e)(9)(vii) of this section, you must comply with the requirements under §§264.1033(b) through (o), and 264.1034 through 264.1036 of this chapter.

(f) *Notification of closure of an emission-comparable fuel tank or a container storage unit.* If you store emission-comparable fuel in a tank or container, you must submit a notification to the RCRA regulatory authority when a container storage area or a tank system goes out of emission-comparable fuel service which states the date when the tank or container storage area goes out of service.

[63 FR 33823, June 19, 1998, as amended at 64 FR 53070, Sept. 30, 1999; 64 FR 63213, Nov. 19, 1999; 65 FR 42302, July 10, 2000; 70 FR 34562, June 14, 2005; 71 FR 40270, July 14, 2006; 73 FR 77997, Dec. 19, 2008]

§261.39 Conditional Exclusion for Used, Broken Cathode Ray Tubes (CRTs) and Processed CRT Glass Undergoing Recycling.

Used, broken CRTs are not solid wastes if they meet the following conditions: 📖 2.7.3.1

(a) *Prior to processing:* These materials are not solid wastes if they are destined for recycling and if they meet the following requirements:

(1) *Storage.* The broken CRTs must be either:

(i) Stored in a building with a roof, floor, and walls, or

(ii) Placed in a container (*i.e.*, a package or a vehicle) that is constructed, filled, and closed to minimize releases to the environment of CRT glass (including fine solid materials).

(2) *Labeling.* Each container in which the used, broken CRT is contained must be labeled or marked clearly with one of the following phrases: "Used cathode ray tube(s)-contains leaded glass " or "Leaded glass from televisions or computers." It must also be labeled: "Do not mix with other glass materials."

(3) *Transportation.* The used, broken CRTs must be transported in a container meeting the requirements of paragraphs (a)(1)(ii) and (2) of this section.

(4) *Speculative accumulation and use constituting disposal.* The used, broken CRTs are subject to the limitations on speculative accumulation as defined in paragraph (c)(8) of this section. If they are used in a manner constituting disposal, they must comply with the applicable requirements of part 266, subpart C instead of the requirements of this section.

(5) *Exports.* In addition to the applicable conditions specified in paragraphs (a)(1)–(4) of this section, exporters of used, broken CRTs must comply with the following requirements:

(i) Notify EPA of an intended export before the CRTs are scheduled to leave the United States. A complete notification should be submitted sixty (60) days before the initial shipment is intended to be shipped off-site. This notification may cover export activities extending over a twelve (12) month or lesser period. The notification must be in writing, signed by the exporter, and include the following information:

(A) Name, mailing address, telephone number and EPA ID number (if applicable) of the exporter of the CRTs.

(B) The estimated frequency or rate at which the CRTs are to be exported and the period of time over which they are to be exported.

(C) The estimated total quantity of CRTs specified in kilograms.

(D) All points of entry to and departure from each foreign country through which the CRTs will pass.

(E) A description of the means by which each shipment of the CRTs will be transported (*e.g.*, mode of transportation vehicle (air, highway, rail, water, etc.), type(s) of container (drums, boxes, tanks, etc.)).

(F) The name and address of the recycler and any alternate recycler.

(G) A description of the manner in which the CRTs will be recycled in the foreign country that will be receiving the CRTs.

(H) The name of any transit country through which the CRTs will be sent and a description of the approximate length of time the CRTs will remain in such country and the nature of their handling while there.

(ii) Notifications submitted by mail should be sent to the following mailing address: Office of Enforcement and Compliance Assurance, Office of Federal Activities, International Compliance Assurance Division, (Mail Code 2254A), Environmental Protection Agency, 1200 Pennsylvania Ave., NW., Washington, DC 20460. Hand-delivered notifications should be sent to: Office of Enforcement and Compliance Assurance, Office of Federal Activities, International Compliance Assurance Division, (Mail Code 2254A), Environmental Protection Agency, Ariel Rios Bldg., Room 6144, 1200 Pennsylvania Ave., NW., Washington, DC. In both cases, the following shall be prominently displayed on the front of the envelope: "Attention: Notification of Intent to Export CRTs."

(iii) Upon request by EPA, the exporter shall furnish to EPA any additional information which a receiving country requests in order to respond to a notification.

(iv) EPA will provide a complete notification to the receiving country and any transit countries. A notification is complete when EPA receives a notification which EPA determines satisfies the requirements of paragraph (a)(5)(i) of this section. Where a claim of confidentiality is asserted with respect to any notification information required by paragraph (a)(5)(i) of this section, EPA may find the notification not complete until any such claim is resolved in accordance with 40 CFR 260.2.

(v) The export of CRTs is prohibited unless the receiving country consents to the intended export. When the receiving country consents in writing to the receipt of the CRTs, EPA will forward an Acknowledgment of

Consent to Export CRTs to the exporter. Where the receiving country objects to receipt of the CRTs or withdraws a prior consent, EPA will notify the exporter in writing. EPA will also notify the exporter of any responses from transit countries.

(vi) When the conditions specified on the original notification change, the exporter must provide EPA with a written renotification of the change, except for changes to the telephone number in paragraph (a)(5)(i)(A) of this section and decreases in the quantity indicated pursuant to paragraph (a)(5)(i)(C) of this section. The shipment cannot take place until consent of the receiving country to the changes has been obtained (except for changes to information about points of entry and departure and transit countries pursuant to paragraphs (a)(5)(i)(D) and (a)(5)(i)(H) of this section) and the exporter of CRTs receives from EPA a copy of the Acknowledgment of Consent to Export CRTs reflecting the receiving country's consent to the changes.

(vii) A copy of the Acknowledgment of Consent to Export CRTs must accompany the shipment of CRTs. The shipment must conform to the terms of the Acknowledgment.

(viii) If a shipment of CRTs cannot be delivered for any reason to the recycler or the alternate recycler, the exporter of CRTs must renotify EPA of a change in the conditions of the original notification to allow shipment to a new recycler in accordance with paragraph (a)(5)(vi) of this section and obtain another Acknowledgment of Consent to Export CRTs.

(ix) Exporters must keep copies of notifications and Acknowledgments of Consent to Export CRTs for a period of three years following receipt of the Acknowledgment.

(b) *Requirements for used CRT processing:* Used, broken CRTs undergoing CRT processing as defined in §260.10 of this chapter are not solid wastes if they meet the following requirements:

(1) *Storage.* Used, broken CRTs undergoing processing are subject to the requirement of paragraph (a)(4) of this section.

(2) *Processing.*

(i) All activities specified in paragraphs (2) and (3) of the definition of "CRT processing" in §260.10 of this chapter must be performed within a building with a roof, floor, and walls; and

(ii) No activities may be performed that use temperatures high enough to volatilize lead from CRTs.

(c) *Processed CRT glass sent to CRT glass making or lead smelting:* Glass from used CRTs that is destined for recycling at a CRT glass manufacturer or a lead smelter after processing is not a solid waste unless it is speculatively accumulated as defined in §261.1(c)(8).

(d) *Use constituting disposal:* Glass from used CRTs that is used in a manner constituting disposal must comply with the requirements of 40 CFR part 266, subpart C instead of the requirements of this section.

§261.40 Conditional Exclusion for Used, Intact Cathode Ray Tubes (CRTs) Exported for Recycling. 📖 2.7.3.2

Used, intact CRTs exported for recycling are not solid wastes if they meet the notice and consent conditions of §261.39(a)(5), and if they are not speculatively accumulated as defined in §261.1(c)(8).

§261.41 Notification and Recordkeeping for Used, Intact Cathode Ray Tubes (CRTs) Exported for Reuse. 📖 2.7.3.2

(a) Persons who export used, intact CRTs for reuse must send a one-time notification to the Regional Administrator. The notification must include a statement that the notifier plans to export used, intact CRTs for reuse, the notifier's name, address, and EPA ID number (if applicable) and the name and phone number of a contact person.

(b) Persons who export used, intact CRTs for reuse must keep copies of normal business records, such as contracts, demonstrating that each shipment of exported CRTs will be reused. This documentation must be retained for a period of at least three years from the date the CRTs were exported.

Subparts F–G [Reserved]

Subpart H—Financial Requirements for Management of Excluded Hazardous Secondary Materials 📖 1.2.6.3.1, 11.2.3.2

[Source: 73 FR 64764, Oct. 30, 2008, unless otherwise noted.]

§261.140 Applicability.

(a) The requirements of this subpart apply to owners or operators of reclamation and intermediate facilities managing hazardous secondary materials excluded under 40 CFR §261.4(a)(24), except as provided otherwise in this section.

(b) States and the Federal government are exempt from the financial assurance requirements of this subpart.

§261.141 Definitions of terms as used in this subpart.

The terms defined in §265.141(d), (f), (g), and (h) of this chapter have the same meaning in this subpart as they do in §265.141 of this chapter.

§261.142 Cost estimate.

(a) The owner or operator must have a detailed written estimate, in current dollars, of the cost of disposing of any hazardous secondary material as listed or characteristic hazardous waste, and the potential cost of closing the facility as a treatment, storage, and disposal facility.

(1) The estimate must equal the cost of conducting the activities described in paragraph (a) of this section at the point when the extent and manner of the facility's operation would make these activities the most expensive; and

(2) The cost estimate must be based on the costs to the owner or operator of hiring a third party to conduct these activities. A third party is a party who is neither a parent nor a subsidiary of the owner or operator. (See definition of parent corporation in §265.141(d) of this chapter.) The owner or operator may use costs for on-site disposal in accordance with applicable requirements if he can demonstrate that on-site disposal capacity will exist at all times over the life of the facility.

(3) The cost estimate may not incorporate any salvage value that may be realized with the sale of hazardous secondary materials, or hazardous or non-hazardous wastes if applicable under 265.5113(d) of this chapter, facility structures or equipment, land, or other assets associated with the facility.

(4) The owner or operator may not incorporate a zero cost for hazardous secondary materials, or hazardous or non-hazardous wastes if applicable under 265.5113(d) of this chapter that might have economic value.

Publisher's Note: The references to "265.5113(d)" in paragraphs (3) and (4) above should be "265.113(d)".

(b) During the active life of the facility, the owner or operator must adjust the cost estimate for inflation within 60 days prior to the anniversary date of the establishment of the financial instrument(s) used to comply with §261.143. For owners and operators using the financial test or corporate guarantee, the cost estimate must be updated for inflation within 30 days after the close of the firm's fiscal year and before submission of updated information to the Regional Administrator as specified in §261.143(e)(3). The adjustment may be made by recalculating the cost estimate in current dollars, or by using an inflation factor derived from the most recent Implicit Price Deflator for Gross National Product published by the U.S. Department of Commerce in its Survey of Current Business, as specified in paragraphs (b)(1) and (2) of this section. The inflation factor is the result of dividing the latest published annual Deflator by the Deflator for the previous year.

(1) The first adjustment is made by multiplying the cost estimate by the inflation factor. The result is the adjusted cost estimate.

(2) Subsequent adjustments are made by multiplying the latest adjusted cost estimate by the latest inflation factor.

(c) During the active life of the facility, the owner or operator must revise the cost estimate no later than 30 days after a change in a facility's operating plan or design that would increase the costs of conducting the activities described in paragraph (a) or no later than 60 days after an unexpected event which increases the cost of conducting the activities described in paragraph (a) of this section. The revised cost estimate must be adjusted for inflation as specified in paragraph (b) of this section.

(d) The owner or operator must keep the following at the facility during the operating life of the facility: The latest cost estimate prepared in accordance with paragraphs (a) and (c) and, when this estimate has been adjusted in accordance with paragraph (b), the latest adjusted cost estimate.

§261.143 Financial assurance condition.

Per §261.4(a)(24)(vi)(F) of this chapter, an owner or operator of a reclamation or intermediate facility must have financial assurance as a condition of the exclusion as required under §261.4(a)(24) of this chapter. He must choose from the options as specified in paragraphs (a) through (e) of this section.

(a) *Trust fund.* (1) An owner or operator may satisfy the requirements of this section by establishing a trust fund which conforms to the requirements of this paragraph and submitting an originally signed duplicate of the trust agreement to the Regional Administrator. The trustee must be an entity which has the authority to act as a trustee and whose trust operations are regulated and examined by a Federal or State agency.

(2) The wording of the trust agreement must be identical to the wording specified in §261.151(a)(1), and the trust agreement must be accompanied by a formal certification of acknowledgment (for example, see §261.151(a)(2)). Schedule A of the trust agreement must be updated within 60 days after a change

in the amount of the current cost estimate covered by the agreement.

(3) The trust fund must be funded for the full amount of the current cost estimate before it may be relied upon to satisfy the requirements of this section.

(4) Whenever the current cost estimate changes, the owner or operator must compare the new estimate with the trustee's most recent annual valuation of the trust fund. If the value of the fund is less than the amount of the new estimate, the owner or operator, within 60 days after the change in the cost estimate, must either deposit an amount into the fund so that its value after this deposit at least equals the amount of the current cost estimate, or obtain other financial assurance as specified in this section to cover the difference.

(5) If the value of the trust fund is greater than the total amount of the current cost estimate, the owner or operator may submit a written request to the Regional Administrator for release of the amount in excess of the current cost estimate.

(6) If an owner or operator substitutes other financial assurance as specified in this section for all or part of the trust fund, he may submit a written request to the Regional Administrator for release of the amount in excess of the current cost estimate covered by the trust fund.

(7) Within 60 days after receiving a request from the owner or operator for release of funds as specified in paragraph (a) (5) or (6) of this section, the Regional Administrator will instruct the trustee to release to the owner or operator such funds as the Regional Administrator specifies in writing. If the owner or operator begins final closure under subpart G of 40 CFR part 264 or 265, an owner or operator may request reimbursements for partial or final closure expenditures by submitting itemized bills to the Regional Administrator. The owner or operator may request reimbursements for partial closure only if sufficient funds are remaining in the trust fund to cover the maximum costs of closing the facility over its remaining operating life. No later than 60 days after receiving bills for partial or final closure activities, the Regional Administrator will instruct the trustee to make reimbursements in those amounts as the Regional Administrator specifies in writing, if the Regional Administrator determines that the partial or final closure expenditures are in accordance with the approved closure plan, or otherwise justified. If the Regional Administrator has reason to believe that the maximum cost of closure over the remaining life of the facility will be significantly greater than the value of the trust fund, he may withhold reimbursements of such amounts as he deems prudent until he determines, in accordance with §265.143(i) that the owner or operator is no longer required to maintain financial assurance for final closure of the facility. If the Regional Administrator does not instruct the trustee to make such reimbursements, he will provide to the owner or operator a detailed written statement of reasons.

Publisher's Note: The reference to §265.143(i) is incorrect and should refer to §261.143(i).

(8) The Regional Administrator will agree to termination of the trust when:

(i) An owner or operator substitutes alternate financial assurance as specified in this section; or

(ii) The Regional Administrator releases the owner or operator from the requirements of this section in accordance with paragraph (i) of this section.

(b) *Surety bond guaranteeing payment into a trust fund.* (1) An owner or operator may satisfy the requirements of this section by obtaining a surety bond which conforms to the requirements of this paragraph and submitting the bond to the Regional Administrator. The surety company issuing the bond must, at a minimum, be among those listed as acceptable sureties on Federal bonds in Circular 570 of the U.S. Department of the Treasury.

(2) The wording of the surety bond must be identical to the wording specified in §261.151(b).

(3) The owner or operator who uses a surety bond to satisfy the requirements of this section must also establish a standby trust fund. Under the terms of the bond, all payments made thereunder will be deposited by the surety directly into the standby trust fund in accordance with instructions from the Regional Administrator. This standby trust fund must meet the requirements specified in paragraph (a) of this section, except that:

(i) An originally signed duplicate of the trust agreement must be submitted to the Regional Administrator with the surety bond; and

(ii) Until the standby trust fund is funded pursuant to the requirements of this section, the following are not required by these regulations:

(A) Payments into the trust fund as specified in paragraph (a) of this section;

(B) Updating of Schedule A of the trust agreement (see §261.151(a)) to show current cost estimates;

(C) Annual valuations as required by the trust agreement; and

(D) Notices of nonpayment as required by the trust agreement.

(4) The bond must guarantee that the owner or operator will:

(i) Fund the standby trust fund in an amount equal to the penal sum of the bond before loss of the exclusion under §261.4(a)(24) of this chapter or

(ii) Fund the standby trust fund in an amount equal to the penal sum within 15 days after an administrative order to begin closure issued by the Regional Administrator becomes final, or within 15 days after an order to begin closure is issued by a U.S. district court or other court of competent jurisdiction; or

(iii) Provide alternate financial assurance as specified in this section, and obtain the Regional Administrator's written approval of the assurance provided, within 90 days after receipt by both the owner or operator and the Regional Administrator of a notice of cancellation of the bond from the surety.

(5) Under the terms of the bond, the surety will become liable on the bond obligation when the owner or operator fails to perform as guaranteed by the bond.

(6) The penal sum of the bond must be in an amount at least equal to the current cost estimate, except as provided in paragraph (f) of this section.

(7) Whenever the current cost estimate increases to an amount greater than the penal sum, the owner or operator, within 60 days after the increase, must either cause the penal sum to be increased to an amount at least equal to the current cost estimate and submit evidence of such increase to the Regional Administrator, or obtain other financial assurance as specified in this section to cover the increase. Whenever the current cost estimate decreases, the penal sum may be reduced to the amount of the current cost estimate following written approval by the Regional Administrator.

(8) Under the terms of the bond, the surety may cancel the bond by sending notice of cancellation by certified mail to the owner or operator and to the Regional Administrator. Cancellation may not occur, however, during the 120 days beginning on the date of receipt of the notice of cancellation by both the owner or operator and the Regional Administrator, as evidenced by the return receipts.

(9) The owner or operator may cancel the bond if the Regional Administrator has given prior written consent based on his receipt of evidence of alternate financial assurance as specified in this section.

(c) *Letter of credit.* (1) An owner or operator may satisfy the requirements of this section by obtaining an irrevocable standby letter of credit which conforms to the requirements of this paragraph and submitting the letter to the Regional Administrator. The issuing institution must be an entity which has the authority to issue letters of credit and whose letter-of-credit operations are regulated and examined by a Federal or State agency.

(2) The wording of the letter of credit must be identical to the wording specified in §261.151(c).

(3) An owner or operator who uses a letter of credit to satisfy the requirements of this section must also establish a standby trust fund. Under the terms of the letter of credit, all amounts paid pursuant to a draft by the Regional Administrator will be deposited by the issuing institution directly into the standby trust fund in accordance with instructions from the Regional Administrator. This standby trust fund must meet the requirements of the trust fund specified in paragraph (a) of this section, except that:

(i) An originally signed duplicate of the trust agreement must be submitted to the Regional Administrator with the letter of credit; and

(ii) Unless the standby trust fund is funded pursuant to the requirements of this section, the following are not required by these regulations:

(A) Payments into the trust fund as specified in paragraph (a) of this section;

(B) Updating of Schedule A of the trust agreement (see §261.151(a)) to show current cost estimates;

(C) Annual valuations as required by the trust agreement; and

(D) Notices of nonpayment as required by the trust agreement.

(4) The letter of credit must be accompanied by a letter from the owner or operator referring to the letter of credit by number, issuing institution, and date, and providing the following information: The EPA Identification Number (if any issued), name, and address of the facility, and the amount of funds assured for the facility by the letter of credit.

(5) The letter of credit must be irrevocable and issued for a period of at least 1 year. The letter of credit must provide that the expiration date will be automatically extended for a period of at least 1 year unless, at least

120 days before the current expiration date, the issuing institution notifies both the owner or operator and the Regional Administrator by certified mail of a decision not to extend the expiration date. Under the terms of the letter of credit, the 120 days will begin on the date when both the owner or operator and the Regional Administrator have received the notice, as evidenced by the return receipts.

(6) The letter of credit must be issued in an amount at least equal to the current cost estimate, except as provided in paragraph (f) of this section.

(7) Whenever the current cost estimate increases to an amount greater than the amount of the credit, the owner or operator, within 60 days after the increase, must either cause the amount of the credit to be increased so that it at least equals the current cost estimate and submit evidence of such increase to the Regional Administrator, or obtain other financial assurance as specified in this section to cover the increase. Whenever the current cost estimate decreases, the amount of the credit may be reduced to the amount of the current cost estimate following written approval by the Regional Administrator.

(8) Following a determination by the Regional Administrator that the hazardous secondary materials do not meet the conditions of the exclusion under §261.4(a)(24), the Regional Administrator may draw on the letter of credit.

(9) If the owner or operator does not establish alternate financial assurance as specified in this section and obtain written approval of such alternate assurance from the Regional Administrator within 90 days after receipt by both the owner or operator and the Regional Administrator of a notice from the issuing institution that it has decided not to extend the letter of credit beyond the current expiration date, the Regional Administrator will draw on the letter of credit. The Regional Administrator may delay the drawing if the issuing institution grants an extension of the term of the credit. During the last 30 days of any such extension the Regional Administrator will draw on the letter of credit if the owner or operator has failed to provide alternate financial assurance as specified in this section and obtain written approval of such assurance from the Regional Administrator.

(10) The Regional Administrator will return the letter of credit to the issuing institution for termination when:

(i) An owner or operator substitutes alternate financial assurance as specified in this section; or

(ii) The Regional Administrator releases the owner or operator from the requirements of this section in accordance with paragraph (i) of this section.

(d) *Insurance.* (1) An owner or operator may satisfy the requirements of this section by obtaining insurance which conforms to the requirements of this paragraph and submitting a certificate of such insurance to the Regional Administrator. At a minimum, the insurer must be licensed to transact the business of insurance, or eligible to provide insurance as an excess or surplus lines insurer, in one or more States.

(2) The wording of the certificate of insurance must be identical to the wording specified in §261.151(d).

(3) The insurance policy must be issued for a face amount at least equal to the current cost estimate, except as provided in paragraph (f) of this section. The term "face amount" means the total amount the insurer is obligated to pay under the policy. Actual payments by the insurer will not change the face amount, although the insurer's future liability will be lowered by the amount of the payments.

(4) The insurance policy must guarantee that funds will be available whenever needed to pay the cost of removal of all hazardous secondary materials from the unit, to pay the cost of decontamination of the unit, to pay the costs of the performance of activities required under subpart G of 40 CFR parts 264 or 265, as applicable, for the facilities covered by this policy. The policy must also guarantee that once funds are needed, the insurer will be responsible for paying out funds, up to an amount equal to the face amount of the policy, upon the direction of the Regional Administrator, to such party or parties as the Regional Administrator specifies.

(5) After beginning partial or final closure under 40 CFR parts 264 or 265, as applicable, an owner or operator or any other authorized person may request reimbursements for closure expenditures by submitting itemized bills to the Regional Administrator. The owner or operator may request reimbursements only if the remaining value of the policy is sufficient to cover the maximum costs of closing the facility over its remaining operating life. Within 60 days after receiving bills for closure activities, the Regional Administrator will instruct the insurer to make reimbursements in such amounts as the Regional Administrator specifies in writing if the Regional Administrator determines that the expenditures are in accordance with the approved plan or otherwise justified. If the Regional Administrator has reason to believe that the maximum cost over the

remaining life of the facility will be significantly greater than the face amount of the policy, he may withhold reimbursement of such amounts as he deems prudent until he determines, in accordance with paragraph (h) of this section, that the owner or operator is no longer required to maintain financial assurance for the particular facility. If the Regional Administrator does not instruct the insurer to make such reimbursements, he will provide to the owner or operator a detailed written statement of reasons.

(6) The owner or operator must maintain the policy in full force and effect until the Regional Administrator consents to termination of the policy by the owner or operator as specified in paragraph (i)(10) of this section. Failure to pay the premium, without substitution of alternate financial assurance as specified in this section, will constitute a significant violation of these regulations warranting such remedy as the Regional Administrator deems necessary. Such violation will be deemed to begin upon receipt by the Regional Administrator of a notice of future cancellation, termination, or failure to renew due to nonpayment of the premium, rather than upon the date of expiration.

(7) Each policy must contain a provision allowing assignment of the policy to a successor owner or operator. Such assignment may be conditional upon consent of the insurer, provided such consent is not unreasonably refused.

(8) The policy must provide that the insurer may not cancel, terminate, or fail to renew the policy except for failure to pay the premium. The automatic renewal of the policy must, at a minimum, provide the insured with the option of renewal at the face amount of the expiring policy. If there is a failure to pay the premium, the insurer may elect to cancel, terminate, or fail to renew the policy by sending notice by certified mail to the owner or operator and the Regional Administrator. Cancellation, termination, or failure to renew may not occur, however, during the 120 days beginning with the date of receipt of the notice by both the Regional Administrator and the owner or operator, as evidenced by the return receipts. Cancellation, termination, or failure to renew may not occur and the policy will remain in full force and effect in the event that on or before the date of expiration:

(i) The Regional Administrator deems the facility abandoned; or

(ii) Conditional exclusion or interim status is lost, terminated, or revoked; or

(iii) Closure is ordered by the Regional Administrator or a U.S. district court or other court of competent jurisdiction; or

(iv) The owner or operator is named as debtor in a voluntary or involuntary proceeding under Title 11 (Bankruptcy), U.S. Code; or

(v) The premium due is paid.

(9) Whenever the current cost estimate increases to an amount greater than the face amount of the policy, the owner or operator, within 60 days after the increase, must either cause the face amount to be increased to an amount at least equal to the current cost estimate and submit evidence of such increase to the Regional Administrator, or obtain other financial assurance as specified in this section to cover the increase. Whenever the current cost estimate decreases, the face amount may be reduced to the amount of the current cost estimate following written approval by the Regional Administrator.

(10) The Regional Administrator will give written consent to the owner or operator that he may terminate the insurance policy when:

(i) An owner or operator substitutes alternate financial assurance as specified in this section; or

(ii) The Regional Administrator releases the owner or operator from the requirements of this section in accordance with paragraph (i) of this section.

(e) *Financial test and corporate guarantee.* (1) An owner or operator may satisfy the requirements of this section by demonstrating that he passes a financial test as specified in this paragraph. To pass this test the owner or operator must meet the criteria of either paragraph (e)(1)(i) or (ii) of this section:

(i) The owner or operator must have:

(A) Two of the following three ratios: A ratio of total liabilities to net worth less than 2.0; a ratio of the sum of net income plus depreciation, depletion, and amortization to total liabilities greater than 0.1; and a ratio of current assets to current liabilities greater than 1.5; and

(B) Net working capital and tangible net worth each at least six times the sum of the current cost estimates and the current plugging and abandonment cost estimates; and

(C) Tangible net worth of at least $10 million; and

(D) Assets located in the United States amounting to at least 90 percent of total assets or at least six times the sum of the current cost estimates and the current plugging and abandonment cost estimates.

(ii) The owner or operator must have:

(A) A current rating for his most recent bond issuance of AAA, AA, A, or BBB as issued by Standard and Poor's or Aaa, Aa, A, or Baa as issued by Moody's; and

(B) Tangible net worth at least six times the sum of the current cost estimates and the current plugging and abandonment cost estimates; and

(C) Tangible net worth of at least $10 million; and

(D) Assets located in the United States amounting to at least 90 percent of total assets or at least six times the sum of the current cost estimates and the current plugging and abandonment cost estimates.

(2) The phrase "current cost estimates" as used in paragraph (e)(1) of this section refers to the cost estimates required to be shown in paragraphs 1–4 of the letter from the owner's or operator's chief financial officer (§261.151(e)). The phrase "current plugging and abandonment cost estimates" as used in paragraph (e)(1) of this section refers to the cost estimates required to be shown in paragraphs 1–4 of the letter from the owner's or operator's chief financial officer (§144.70(f) of this chapter).

(3) To demonstrate that he meets this test, the owner or operator must submit the following items to the Regional Administrator:

(i) A letter signed by the owner's or operator's chief financial officer and worded as specified in §261.151(e); and

(ii) A copy of the independent certified public accountant's report on examination of the owner's or operator's financial statements for the latest completed fiscal year; and

(iii) If the chief financial officer's letter providing evidence of financial assurance includes financial data showing that the owner or operator satisfies paragraph (e)(1)(i) of this section that are different from the data in the audited financial statements referred to in paragraph (e)(3)(ii) of this section or any other audited financial statement or data filed with the SEC, then a special report from the owner's or operator's independent certified public accountant to the owner or operator is required. The special report shall be based upon an agreed upon procedures engagement in accordance with professional auditing standards and shall describe the procedures performed in comparing the data in the chief financial officer's letter derived from the independently audited, year-end financial statements for the latest fiscal year with the amounts in such financial statements, the findings of the comparison, and the reasons for any differences.

(4) The owner or operator may obtain an extension of the time allowed for submission of the documents specified in paragraph (e)(3) of this section if the fiscal year of the owner or operator ends during the 90 days prior to the effective date of these regulations and if the year-end financial statements for that fiscal year will be audited by an independent certified public accountant. The extension will end no later than 90 days after the end of the owner's or operator's fiscal year. To obtain the extension, the owner's or operator's chief financial officer must send, by the effective date of these regulations, a letter to the Regional Administrator of each Region in which the owner's or operator's facilities to be covered by the financial test are located. This letter from the chief financial officer must:

(i) Request the extension;

(ii) Certify that he has grounds to believe that the owner or operator meets the criteria of the financial test;

(iii) Specify for each facility to be covered by the test the EPA Identification Number (if any issued), name, address, and current cost estimates to be covered by the test;

(iv) Specify the date ending the owner's or operator's last complete fiscal year before the effective date of these regulations in this subpart;

(v) Specify the date, no later than 90 days after the end of such fiscal year, when he will submit the documents specified in paragraph (e)(3) of this section; and

(vi) Certify that the year-end financial statements of the owner or operator for such fiscal year will be audited by an independent certified public accountant.

(5) After the initial submission of items specified in paragraph (e)(3) of this section, the owner or operator must send updated information to the Regional Administrator within 90 days after the close of each succeeding fiscal year. This information must consist of all three items specified in paragraph (e)(3) of this section.

(6) If the owner or operator no longer meets the requirements of paragraph (e)(1) of this section, he must send notice to the Regional Administrator of intent to establish alternate financial assurance as specified in this section. The notice must be sent by certified mail within 90 days after the end of the fiscal year for which the year-end financial data show that the owner or operator no longer meets the requirements.

The owner or operator must provide the alternate financial assurance within 120 days after the end of such fiscal year.

(7) The Regional Administrator may, based on a reasonable belief that the owner or operator may no longer meet the requirements of paragraph (e)(1) of this section, require reports of financial condition at any time from the owner or operator in addition to those specified in paragraph (e)(3) of this section. If the Regional Administrator finds, on the basis of such reports or other information, that the owner or operator no longer meets the requirements of paragraph (e)(1) of this section, the owner or operator must provide alternate financial assurance as specified in this section within 30 days after notification of such a finding.

(8) The Regional Administrator may disallow use of this test on the basis of qualifications in the opinion expressed by the independent certified public accountant in his report on examination of the owner's or operator's financial statements (see paragraph (e)(3)(ii) of this section). An adverse opinion or a disclaimer of opinion will be cause for disallowance. The Regional Administrator will evaluate other qualifications on an individual basis. The owner or operator must provide alternate financial assurance as specified in this section within 30 days after notification of the disallowance.

(9) The owner or operator is no longer required to submit the items specified in paragraph (e)(3) of this section when:

(i) An owner or operator substitutes alternate financial assurance as specified in this section; or

(ii) The Regional Administrator releases the owner or operator from the requirements of this section in accordance with paragraph (i) of this section.

(10) An owner or operator may meet the requirements of this section by obtaining a written guarantee. The guarantor must be the direct or higher-tier parent corporation of the owner or operator, a firm whose parent corporation is also the parent corporation of the owner or operator, or a firm with a "substantial business relationship" with the owner or operator. The guarantor must meet the requirements for owners or operators in paragraphs (e)(1) through (8) of this section and must comply with the terms of the guarantee. The wording of the guarantee must be identical to the wording specified in §261.151(g)(1). A certified copy of the guarantee must accompany the items sent to the Regional Administrator as specified in paragraph (e)(3) of this section. One of these items must be the letter from the guarantor's chief financial officer. If the guarantor's parent corporation is also the parent corporation of the owner or operator, the letter must describe the value received in consideration of the guarantee. If the guarantor is a firm with a "substantial business relationship" with the owner or operator, this letter must describe this "substantial business relationship" and the value received in consideration of the guarantee. The terms of the guarantee must provide that:

(i) Following a determination by the Regional Administrator that the hazardous secondary materials at the owner or operator's facility covered by this guarantee do not meet the conditions of the exclusion under §261.4(a)(24) of this chapter, the guarantor will dispose of any hazardous secondary material as hazardous waste and close the facility in accordance with closure requirements found in parts 264 or 265 of this chapter, as applicable, or establish a trust fund as specified in paragraph (a) of this section in the name of the owner or operator in the amount of the current cost estimate.

(ii) The corporate guarantee will remain in force unless the guarantor sends notice of cancellation by certified mail to the owner or operator and to the Regional Administrator. Cancellation may not occur, however, during the 120 days beginning on the date of receipt of the notice of cancellation by both the owner or operator and the Regional Administrator, as evidenced by the return receipts.

(iii) If the owner or operator fails to provide alternate financial assurance as specified in this section and obtain the written approval of such alternate assurance from the Regional Administrator within 90 days after receipt by both the owner or operator and the Regional Administrator of a notice of cancellation of the corporate guarantee from the guarantor, the guarantor will provide such alternate financial assurance in the name of the owner or operator.

(f) *Use of multiple financial mechanisms.* An owner or operator may satisfy the requirements of this section by establishing more than one financial mechanism per facility. These mechanisms are limited to trust funds, surety bonds, letters of credit, and insurance. The mechanisms must be as specified in paragraphs (a) through (d) of this section, respectively, of this section, except that it is the combination of mechanisms, rather than the single mechanism, which must provide financial assurance for an amount at least equal to the current cost estimate. If an owner or operator uses a trust fund in combination with a surety bond or a letter of credit, he may use the trust fund as the standby trust fund for the other mechanisms. A single standby trust fund may be established for two or more mechanisms. The Regional Administrator may use any or all of the mechanisms to provide for the facility.

(g) *Use of a financial mechanism for multiple facilities.* An owner or operator may use a financial assurance mechanism specified in this section to meet the requirements of this section for more than one facility. Evidence of financial assurance submitted to the Regional Administrator must include a list showing, for each facility, the EPA Identification Number (if any issued), name, address, and the amount of funds assured by the mechanism. If the facilities covered by the mechanism are in more than one Region, identical evidence of financial assurance must be submitted to and maintained with the Regional Administrators of all such Regions. The amount of funds available through the mechanism must be no less than the sum of funds that would be available if a separate mechanism had been established and maintained for each facility. In directing funds available through the mechanism for any of the facilities covered by the mechanism, the Regional Administrator may direct only the amount of funds designated for that facility, unless the owner or operator agrees to the use of additional funds available under the mechanism.

(h) *Removal and Decontamination Plan for Release* (1) An owner or operator of a reclamation facility or an intermediate facility who wishes to be released from his financial assurance obligations under §261.4(a)(24)(vi)(F) of this chapter must submit a plan for removing all hazardous secondary material residues to the Regional Administrator at least 180 days prior to the date on which he expects to cease to operate under the exclusion.

(2) The plan must include, at least:

(A) For each hazardous secondary materials storage unit subject to financial assurance requirements under §261.4(a)(24)(vi)(F), a description of how all excluded hazardous secondary materials will be recycled or sent for recycling, and how all residues, contaminated containment systems (liners, etc.), contaminated soils, subsoils, structures, and equipment will be removed or decontaminated as necessary to protect human health and the environment, and

(B) A detailed description of the steps necessary to remove or decontaminate all hazardous secondary material residues and contaminated containment system components, equipment, structures, and soils including, but not limited to, procedures for cleaning equipment and removing contaminated soils, methods for sampling and testing surrounding soils, and criteria for determining the extent of decontamination necessary to protect human health and the environment; and

(C) A detailed description of any other activities necessary to protect human health and the environment during this timeframe, including, but not limited to, leachate collection, run-on and run-off control, etc; and

(D) A schedule for conducting the activities described which, at a minimum, includes the total time required to remove all excluded hazardous secondary materials for recycling and decontaminate all units subject to financial assurance under §261.4(a)(24)(vi)(F) and the time required for intervening activities which will allow tracking of the progress of decontamination.

(3) The Regional Administrator will provide the owner or operator and the public, through a newspaper notice, the opportunity to submit written comments on the plan and request modifications to the plan no later than 30 days from the date of the notice. He will also, in response to a request or at his discretion, hold a public hearing whenever such a hearing might clarify one or more issues concerning the plan. The Regional Administrator will give public notice of the hearing at least 30 days before it occurs. (Public notice of the hearing may be given at the same time as notice of the opportunity for the public to submit written comments, and the two notices may be combined.) The Regional Administrator will approve, modify, or disapprove the plan within 90 days of its receipt. If the Regional Administrator does not approve the plan, he shall provide the owner or operator with a detailed written statement of reasons for the refusal and the owner or operator must modify the plan or submit a new plan for approval within 30 days after receiving such written statement. The Regional Administrator will approve or modify this plan in writing within 60 days. If the Regional Administrator modifies the plan, this modified plan becomes the approved plan. The Regional Administrator must assure that the approved plan is consistent with paragraph (h) of this section. A copy of the modified plan with a detailed statement of reasons for the modifications must be mailed to the owner or operator.

(4) Within 60 days of completion of the activities described for each hazardous secondary materials management unit, the owner or operator must submit to

the Regional Administrator, by registered mail, a certification that all hazardous secondary materials have been removed from the unit and the unit has been decontaminated in accordance with the specifications in the approved plan. The certification must be signed by the owner or operator and by a qualified Professional Engineer. Documentation supporting the Professional Engineer's certification must be furnished to the Regional Administrator, upon request, until he releases the owner or operator from the financial assurance requirements for §261.4(a)(24)(vi)(F).

(i) *Release of the owner or operator from the requirements of this section.* Within 60 days after receiving certifications from the owner or operator and a qualified Professional Engineer that all hazardous secondary materials have been removed from the facility or a unit at the facility and the facility or a unit has been decontaminated in accordance with the approved plan per paragraph (h), the Regional Administrator will notify the owner or operator in writing that he is no longer required under §261.4(a)(24)(vi)(F) to maintain financial assurance for that facility or a unit at the facility, unless the Regional Administrator has reason to believe that that all hazardous secondary materials have not been removed from the facility or unit at a facility or that the facility or unit has not been decontaminated in accordance with the approved plan. The Regional Administrator shall provide the owner or operator a detailed written statement of any such reason to believe that all hazardous secondary materials have not been removed from the unit or that the unit has not been decontaminated in accordance with the approved plan.

§§261.144–261.146 [Reserved]

§261.147 Liability requirements.

(a) *Coverage for sudden accidental occurrences.* An owner or operator of a hazardous secondary material reclamation facility or an intermediate facility subject to financial assurance requirements under §261.4(a)(24)(vi)(F) of this chapter, or a group of such facilities, must demonstrate financial responsibility for bodily injury and property damage to third parties caused by sudden accidental occurrences arising from operations of the facility or group of facilities. The owner or operator must have and maintain liability coverage for sudden accidental occurrences in the amount of at least $1 million per occurrence with an annual aggregate of at least $2 million, exclusive of legal defense costs. This liability coverage may be demonstrated as specified in paragraphs (a)(1), (2), (3), (4), (5), or (6) of this section:

(1) An owner or operator may demonstrate the required liability coverage by having liability insurance as specified in this paragraph.

(i) Each insurance policy must be amended by attachment of the Hazardous Secondary Material Facility Liability Endorsement, or evidenced by a Certificate of Liability Insurance. The wording of the endorsement must be identical to the wording specified in §261.151(h). The wording of the certificate of insurance must be identical to the wording specified in §261.151(i). The owner or operator must submit a signed duplicate original of the endorsement or the certificate of insurance to the Regional Administrator, or Regional Administrators if the facilities are located in more than one Region. If requested by a Regional Administrator, the owner or operator must provide a signed duplicate original of the insurance policy.

(ii) Each insurance policy must be issued by an insurer which, at a minimum, is licensed to transact the business of insurance, or eligible to provide insurance as an excess or surplus lines insurer, in one or more States.

(2) An owner or operator may meet the requirements of this section by passing a financial test or using the guarantee for liability coverage as specified in paragraphs (f) and (g) of this section.

(3) An owner or operator may meet the requirements of this section by obtaining a letter of credit for liability coverage as specified in paragraph (h) of this section.

(4) An owner or operator may meet the requirements of this section by obtaining a surety bond for liability coverage as specified in paragraph (i) of this section.

(5) An owner or operator may meet the requirements of this section by obtaining a trust fund for liability coverage as specified in paragraph (j) of this section.

(6) An owner or operator may demonstrate the required liability coverage through the use of combinations of insurance, financial test, guarantee, letter of credit, surety bond, and trust fund, except that the owner or operator may not combine a financial test covering part of the liability coverage requirement with a guarantee unless the financial statement of the owner or operator is not consolidated with the financial statement of the guarantor. The amounts of coverage demonstrated must total at least the minimum amounts required by this section. If the owner or operator demonstrates the required coverage through the

use of a combination of financial assurances under this paragraph, the owner or operator shall specify at least one such assurance as "primary" coverage and shall specify other assurance as "excess" coverage.

(7) An owner or operator shall notify the Regional Administrator in writing within 30 days whenever:

(i) A claim results in a reduction in the amount of financial assurance for liability coverage provided by a financial instrument authorized in paragraphs (a)(1) through (a)(6) of this section; or

(ii) A Certification of Valid Claim for bodily injury or property damages caused by a sudden or non-sudden accidental occurrence arising from the operation of a hazardous secondary material reclamation facility or intermediate facility is entered between the owner or operator and third-party claimant for liability coverage under paragraphs (a)(1) through (a)(6) of this section; or

(iii) A final court order establishing a judgment for bodily injury or property damage caused by a sudden or non-sudden accidental occurrence arising from the operation of a hazardous secondary material reclamation facility or intermediate facility is issued against the owner or operator or an instrument that is providing financial assurance for liability coverage under paragraphs (a)(1) through (a)(6) of this section.

(b) *Coverage for nonsudden accidental occurrences.* An owner or operator of a hazardous secondary material reclamation facility or intermediate facility with land-based units, as defined in §260.10 of this chapter, which are used to manage hazardous secondary materials excluded under §261.4(a)(24) of this chapter or a group of such facilities, must demonstrate financial responsibility for bodily injury and property damage to third parties caused by nonsudden accidental occurrences arising from operations of the facility or group of facilities. The owner or operator must have and maintain liability coverage for nonsudden accidental occurrences in the amount of at least $3 million per occurrence with an annual aggregate of at least $6 million, exclusive of legal defense costs. An owner or operator who must meet the requirements of this section may combine the required per-occurrence coverage levels for sudden and nonsudden accidental occurrences into a single per-occurrence level, and combine the required annual aggregate coverage levels for sudden and nonsudden accidental occurrences into a single annual aggregate level. Owners or operators who combine coverage levels for sudden and nonsudden accidental occurrences must maintain liability coverage in the amount of at least $4 million per occurrence and $8 million annual aggregate. This liability coverage may be demonstrated as specified in paragraph (b)(1), (2), (3), (4), (5), or (6) of this section:

(1) An owner or operator may demonstrate the required liability coverage by having liability insurance as specified in this paragraph.

(i) Each insurance policy must be amended by attachment of the Hazardous Secondary Material Facility Liability Endorsement or evidenced by a Certificate of Liability Insurance. The wording of the endorsement must be identical to the wording specified in §261.151(h). The wording of the certificate of insurance must be identical to the wording specified in §261.151(i). The owner or operator must submit a signed duplicate original of the endorsement or the certificate of insurance to the Regional Administrator, or Regional Administrators if the facilities are located in more than one Region. If requested by a Regional Administrator, the owner or operator must provide a signed duplicate original of the insurance policy.

(ii) Each insurance policy must be issued by an insurer which, at a minimum, is licensed to transact the business of insurance, or eligible to provide insurance as an excess or surplus lines insurer, in one or more States.

(2) An owner or operator may meet the requirements of this section by passing a financial test or using the guarantee for liability coverage as specified in paragraphs (f) and (g) of this section.

(3) An owner or operator may meet the requirements of this section by obtaining a letter of credit for liability coverage as specified in paragraph (h) of this section.

(4) An owner or operator may meet the requirements of this section by obtaining a surety bond for liability coverage as specified in paragraph (i) of this section.

(5) An owner or operator may meet the requirements of this section by obtaining a trust fund for liability coverage as specified in paragraph (j) of this section.

(6) An owner or operator may demonstrate the required liability coverage through the use of combinations of insurance, financial test, guarantee, letter of credit, surety bond, and trust fund, except that the owner or operator may not combine a financial test covering part of the liability coverage requirement with a guarantee unless the financial statement of the owner or operator is not consolidated with the financial statement of the guarantor. The amounts of coverage demonstrated must total at least the minimum

amounts required by this section. If the owner or operator demonstrates the required coverage through the use of a combination of financial assurances under this paragraph, the owner or operator shall specify at least one such assurance as "primary" coverage and shall specify other assurance as "excess" coverage.

(7) An owner or operator shall notify the Regional Administrator in writing within 30 days whenever:

(i) A claim results in a reduction in the amount of financial assurance for liability coverage provided by a financial instrument authorized in paragraphs (b)(1) through (b)(6) of this section; or

(ii) A Certification of Valid Claim for bodily injury or property damages caused by a sudden or non-sudden accidental occurrence arising from the operation of a hazardous secondary material treatment and/or storage facility is entered between the owner or operator and third-party claimant for liability coverage under paragraphs (b)(1) through (b)(6) of this section; or

(iii) A final court order establishing a judgment for bodily injury or property damage caused by a sudden or non-sudden accidental occurrence arising from the operation of a hazardous secondary material treatment and/or storage facility is issued against the owner or operator or an instrument that is providing financial assurance for liability coverage under paragraphs (b)(1) through (b)(6) of this section.

(c) *Request for variance.* If an owner or operator can demonstrate to the satisfaction of the Regional Administrator that the levels of financial responsibility required by paragraph (a) or (b) of this section are not consistent with the degree and duration of risk associated with treatment and/or storage at the facility or group of facilities, the owner or operator may obtain a variance from the Regional Administrator. The request for a variance must be submitted in writing to the Regional Administrator. If granted, the variance will take the form of an adjusted level of required liability coverage, such level to be based on the Regional Administrator's assessment of the degree and duration of risk associated with the ownership or operation of the facility or group of facilities. The Regional Administrator may require an owner or operator who requests a variance to provide such technical and engineering information as is deemed necessary by the Regional Administrator to determine a level of financial responsibility other than that required by paragraph (a) or (b) of this section.

(d) *Adjustments by the Regional Administrator.* If the Regional Administrator determines that the levels of financial responsibility required by paragraph (a) or (b) of this section are not consistent with the degree and duration of risk associated with treatment and/or storage at the facility or group of facilities, the Regional Administrator may adjust the level of financial responsibility required under paragraph (a) or (b) of this section as may be necessary to protect human health and the environment. This adjusted level will be based on the Regional Administrator's assessment of the degree and duration of risk associated with the ownership or operation of the facility or group of facilities. In addition, if the Regional Administrator determines that there is a significant risk to human health and the environment from nonsudden accidental occurrences resulting from the operations of a facility that is not a surface impoundment, pile, or land treatment facility, he may require that an owner or operator of the facility comply with paragraph (b) of this section. An owner or operator must furnish to the Regional Administrator, within a reasonable time, any information which the Regional Administrator requests to determine whether cause exists for such adjustments of level or type of coverage.

(e) *Period of coverage.* Within 60 days after receiving certifications from the owner or operator and a qualified Professional Engineer that all hazardous secondary materials have been removed from the facility or a unit at the facility and the facility or a unit has been decontaminated in accordance with the approved plan per §261.143(h), the Regional Administrator will notify the owner or operator in writing that he is no longer required under §261.4(a)(24)(vi)(F) to maintain liability coverage for that facility or a unit at the facility, unless the Regional Administrator has reason to believe that that all hazardous secondary materials have not been removed from the facility or unit at a facility or that the facility or unit has not been decontaminated in accordance with the approved plan.

(f) *Financial test for liability coverage.* (1) An owner or operator may satisfy the requirements of this section by demonstrating that he passes a financial test as specified in this paragraph. To pass this test the owner or operator must meet the criteria of paragraph (f)(1)(i) or (ii) of this section:

(i) The owner or operator must have:

(A) Net working capital and tangible net worth each at least six times the amount of liability coverage to be demonstrated by this test; and

(B) Tangible net worth of at least $10 million; and

(C) Assets in the United States amounting to either:

(*1*) At least 90 percent of his total assets; or

(*2*) at least six times the amount of liability coverage to be demonstrated by this test.

(ii) The owner or operator must have:

(A) A current rating for his most recent bond issuance of AAA, AA, A, or BBB as issued by Standard and Poor's, or Aaa, Aa, A, or Baa as issued by Moody's; and

(B) Tangible net worth of at least $10 million; and

(C) Tangible net worth at least six times the amount of liability coverage to be demonstrated by this test; and

(D) Assets in the United States amounting to either:

(*1*) At least 90 percent of his total assets; or

(*2*) at least six times the amount of liability coverage to be demonstrated by this test.

(2) The phrase "amount of liability coverage" as used in paragraph (f)(1) of this section refers to the annual aggregate amounts for which coverage is required under paragraphs (a) and (b) of this section and the annual aggregate amounts for which coverage is required under paragraphs (a) and (b) of 40 CFR 264.147 and 265.147.

(3) To demonstrate that he meets this test, the owner or operator must submit the following three items to the Regional Administrator:

(i) A letter signed by the owner's or operator's chief financial officer and worded as specified in §261.151(f). If an owner or operator is using the financial test to demonstrate both assurance as specified by §261.143(e), *and* liability coverage, he must submit the letter specified in §261.151(f) to cover both forms of financial responsibility; a separate letter as specified in §261.151(e) is not required.

(ii) A copy of the independent certified public accountant's report on examination of the owner's or operator's financial statements for the latest completed fiscal year.

(iii) If the chief financial officer's letter providing evidence of financial assurance includes financial data showing that the owner or operator satisfies paragraph (f)(1)(i) of this section that are different from the data in the audited financial statements referred to in paragraph (f)(3)(ii) of this section or any other audited financial statement or data filed with the SEC, then a special report from the owner's or operator's independent certified public accountant to the owner or operator is required. The special report shall be based upon an agreed upon procedures engagement in accordance with professional auditing standards and shall describe the procedures performed in comparing the data in the chief financial officer's letter derived from the independently audited, year-end financial statements for the latest fiscal year with the amounts in such financial statements, the findings of the comparison, and the reasons for any difference.

(4) The owner or operator may obtain a one-time extension of the time allowed for submission of the documents specified in paragraph (f)(3) of this section if the fiscal year of the owner or operator ends during the 90 days prior to the effective date of these regulations and if the year-end financial statements for that fiscal year will be audited by an independent certified public accountant. The extension will end no later than 90 days after the end of the owner's or operator's fiscal year. To obtain the extension, the owner's or operator's chief financial officer must send, by the effective date of these regulations, a letter to the Regional Administrator of each Region in which the owner's or operator's facilities to be covered by the financial test are located. This letter from the chief financial officer must:

(i) Request the extension;

(ii) Certify that he has grounds to believe that the owner or operator meets the criteria of the financial test;

(iii) Specify for each facility to be covered by the test the EPA Identification Number, name, address, the amount of liability coverage and, when applicable, current closure and post-closure cost estimates to be covered by the test;

(iv) Specify the date ending the owner's or operator's last complete fiscal year before the effective date of these regulations;

(v) Specify the date, no later than 90 days after the end of such fiscal year, when he will submit the documents specified in paragraph (f)(3) of this section; and

(vi) Certify that the year-end financial statements of the owner or operator for such fiscal year will be audited by an independent certified public accountant.

(5) After the initial submission of items specified in paragraph (f)(3) of this section, the owner or operator must send updated information to the Regional Administrator within 90 days after the close of each succeeding fiscal year. This information must consist of all three items specified in paragraph (f)(3) of this section.

(6) If the owner or operator no longer meets the requirements of paragraph (f)(1) of this section, he must obtain insurance, a letter of credit, a surety bond, a trust fund, or a guarantee for the entire amount of required liability coverage as specified in this section. Evidence of liability coverage must be submitted to the Regional Administrator within 90 days after the end of the fiscal year for which the year-end financial data show that the owner or operator no longer meets the test requirements.

(7) The Regional Administrator may disallow use of this test on the basis of qualifications in the opinion expressed by the independent certified public accountant in his report on examination of the owner's or operator's financial statements (see paragraph (f)(3)(ii) of this section). An adverse opinion or a disclaimer of opinion will be cause for disallowance. The Regional Administrator will evaluate other qualifications on an individual basis. The owner or operator must provide evidence of insurance for the entire amount of required liability coverage as specified in this section within 30 days after notification of disallowance.

(g) *Guarantee for liability coverage.* (1) Subject to paragraph (g)(2) of this section, an owner or operator may meet the requirements of this section by obtaining a written guarantee, hereinafter referred to as "guarantee." The guarantor must be the direct or higher-tier parent corporation of the owner or operator, a firm whose parent corporation is also the parent corporation of the owner or operator, or a firm with a "substantial business relationship" with the owner or operator. The guarantor must meet the requirements for owners or operators in paragraphs (f)(1) through (f)(6) of this section. The wording of the guarantee must be identical to the wording specified in §261.151(g)(2). A certified copy of the guarantee must accompany the items sent to the Regional Administrator as specified in paragraph (f)(3) of this section. One of these items must be the letter from the guarantor's chief financial officer. If the guarantor's parent corporation is also the parent corporation of the owner or operator, this letter must describe the value received in consideration of the guarantee. If the guarantor is a firm with a "substantial business relationship" with the owner or operator, this letter must describe this "substantial business relationship" and the value received in consideration of the guarantee.

(i) If the owner or operator fails to satisfy a judgment based on a determination of liability for bodily injury or property damage to third parties caused by sudden or nonsudden accidental occurrences (or both as the case may be), arising from the operation of facilities covered by this corporate guarantee, or fails to pay an amount agreed to in settlement of claims arising from or alleged to arise from such injury or damage, the guarantor will do so up to the limits of coverage.

(ii) [Reserved]

(2)(i) In the case of corporations incorporated in the United States, a guarantee may be used to satisfy the requirements of this section only if the Attorneys General or Insurance Commissioners of:

(A) The State in which the guarantor is incorporated; and

(B) Each State in which a facility covered by the guarantee is located have submitted a written statement to EPA that a guarantee executed as described in this section and §264.151(g)(2) is a legally valid and enforceable obligation in that State.

Publisher's Note: The reference to §264.151(g)(2) is incorrect and should refer to §261.151(g)(2).

(ii) In the case of corporations incorporated outside the United States, a guarantee may be used to satisfy the requirements of this section only if:

(A) The non-U.S. corporation has identified a registered agent for service of process in each State in which a facility covered by the guarantee is located and in the State in which it has its principal place of business; and if

(B) The Attorney General or Insurance Commissioner of each State in which a facility covered by the guarantee is located and the State in which the guarantor corporation has its principal place of business, has submitted a written statement to EPA that a guarantee executed as described in this section and §261.151(h)(2) is a legally valid and enforceable obligation in that State.

Publisher's Note: The reference to §261.151(h)(2) is incorrect and should refer to §261.151(g)(2).

(h) *Letter of credit for liability coverage.* (1) An owner or operator may satisfy the requirements of this section by obtaining an irrevocable standby letter of credit that conforms to the requirements of this paragraph and submitting a copy of the letter of credit to the Regional Administrator.

(2) The financial institution issuing the letter of credit must be an entity that has the authority to issue letters of credit and whose letter of credit operations are regulated and examined by a Federal or State agency.

(3) The wording of the letter of credit must be identical to the wording specified in §261.151(j).

(4) An owner or operator who uses a letter of credit to satisfy the requirements of this section may also establish a standby trust fund. Under the terms of such a letter of credit, all amounts paid pursuant to a draft by the trustee of the standby trust will be deposited by the issuing institution into the standby trust in accordance with instructions from the trustee. The trustee of the standby trust fund must be an entity which has the authority to act as a trustee and whose trust operations are regulated and examined by a Federal or State agency.

(5) The wording of the standby trust fund must be identical to the wording specified in §261.151(m).

(i) *Surety bond for liability coverage.* (1) An owner or operator may satisfy the requirements of this section by obtaining a surety bond that conforms to the requirements of this paragraph and submitting a copy of the bond to the Regional Administrator.

(2) The surety company issuing the bond must be among those listed as acceptable sureties on Federal bonds in the most recent Circular 570 of the U.S. Department of the Treasury.

(3) The wording of the surety bond must be identical to the wording specified in §261.151(k) of this chapter.

(4) A surety bond may be used to satisfy the requirements of this section only if the Attorneys General or Insurance Commissioners of:

(i) The State in which the surety is incorporated; and

(ii) Each State in which a facility covered by the surety bond is located have submitted a written statement to EPA that a surety bond executed as described in this section and §261.151(k) of this chapter is a legally valid and enforceable obligation in that State.

(j) *Trust fund for liability coverage.* (1) An owner or operator may satisfy the requirements of this section by establishing a trust fund that conforms to the requirements of this paragraph and submitting an originally signed duplicate of the trust agreement to the Regional Administrator.

(2) The trustee must be an entity which has the authority to act as a trustee and whose trust operations are regulated and examined by a Federal or State agency.

(3) The trust fund for liability coverage must be funded for the full amount of the liability coverage to be provided by the trust fund before it may be relied upon to satisfy the requirements of this section. If at any time after the trust fund is created the amount of funds in the trust fund is reduced below the full amount of the liability coverage to be provided, the owner or operator, by the anniversary date of the establishment of the Fund, must either add sufficient funds to the trust fund to cause its value to equal the full amount of liability coverage to be provided, or obtain other financial assurance as specified in this section to cover the difference. For purposes of this paragraph, "the full amount of the liability coverage to be provided" means the amount of coverage for sudden and/or nonsudden occurrences required to be provided by the owner or operator by this section, less the amount of financial assurance for liability coverage that is being provided by other financial assurance mechanisms being used to demonstrate financial assurance by the owner or operator.

(4) The wording of the trust fund must be identical to the wording specified in §261.151(l).

§261.148 Incapacity of owners or operators, guarantors, or financial institutions.

(a) An owner or operator must notify the Regional Administrator by certified mail of the commencement of a voluntary or involuntary proceeding under Title 11 (Bankruptcy), U.S. Code, naming the owner or operator as debtor, within 10 days after commencement of the proceeding. A guarantor of a corporate guarantee as specified in §261.143(e) must make such a notification if he is named as debtor, as required under the terms of the corporate guarantee.

(b) An owner or operator who fulfills the requirements of §261.143 or §261.147 by obtaining a trust fund, surety bond, letter of credit, or insurance policy will be deemed to be without the required financial assurance or liability coverage in the event of bankruptcy of the trustee or issuing institution, or a suspension or revocation of the authority of the trustee institution to act as trustee or of the institution issuing the surety bond, letter of credit, or insurance policy to issue such instruments. The owner or operator must establish other financial assurance or liability coverage within 60 days after such an event.

§261.149 Use of State-required mechanisms.

(a) For a reclamation or intermediate facility located in a State where EPA is administering the requirements of this subpart but where the State has regulations that include requirements for financial assurance of closure or liability coverage, an owner or operator may use State-required financial mechanisms to meet the requirements of §261.143 or §261.147 if the Regional Administrator determines that the State mechanisms are at least equivalent to the financial mechanisms specified in this subpart. The Regional Administrator will evaluate the equivalency of the mechanisms principally in terms of certainty of the availability of: Funds for the required closure activities or liability coverage; and the amount of funds that will be made available. The Regional Administrator may also consider other factors as he deems appropriate. The owner or operator must submit to the Regional Administrator evidence of the establishment of the mechanism together with a letter requesting that the State-required mechanism be considered acceptable for meeting the requirements of this subpart. The submission must include the following information: The facility's EPA Identification Number (if available), name, and address, and the amount of funds for closure or liability coverage assured by the mechanism. The Regional Administrator will notify the owner or operator of his determination regarding the mechanism's acceptability in lieu of financial mechanisms specified in this subpart. The Regional Administrator may require the owner or operator to submit additional information as is deemed necessary to make this determination. Pending this determination, the owner or operator will be deemed to be in compliance with the requirements of §261.143 or §261.147, as applicable.

(b) If a State-required mechanism is found acceptable as specified in paragraph (a) of this section except for the amount of funds available, the owner or operator may satisfy the requirements of this subpart by increasing the funds available through the State-required mechanism or using additional financial mechanisms as specified in this subpart. The amount of funds available through the State and Federal mechanisms must at least equal the amount required by this subpart.

§261.150 State assumption of responsibility.

(a) If a State either assumes legal responsibility for an owner's or operator's compliance with the closure or liability requirements of this part or assures that funds will be available from State sources to cover those requirements, the owner or operator will be in compliance with the requirements of §261.143 or §261.147 if the Regional Administrator determines that the State's assumption of responsibility is at least equivalent to the financial mechanisms specified in this subpart. The Regional Administrator will evaluate the equivalency of State guarantees principally in terms of: Certainty of the availability of funds for the required closure activities or liability coverage; and the amount of funds that will be made available. The Regional Administrator may also consider other factors as he deems appropriate. The owner or operator must submit to the Regional Administrator a letter from the State describing the nature of the State's assumption of responsibility together with a letter from the owner or operator requesting that the State's assumption of responsibility be considered acceptable for meeting the requirements of this subpart. The letter from the State must include, or have attached to it, the following information: The facility's EPA Identification Number (if available), name, and address, and the amount of funds for closure or liability coverage that are guaranteed by the State. The Regional Administrator will notify the owner or operator of his determination regarding the acceptability of the State's guarantee in lieu of financial mechanisms specified in this subpart. The Regional Administrator may require the owner or operator to submit additional information as is deemed necessary to make this determination. Pending this determination, the owner or operator will be deemed to be in compliance with the requirements of §265.143 or §265.147, as applicable.

(b) If a State's assumption of responsibility is found acceptable as specified in paragraph (a) of this section except for the amount of funds available, the owner or operator may satisfy the requirements of this subpart by use of both the State's assurance and additional financial mechanisms as specified in this subpart. The amount of funds available through the State and Federal mechanisms must at least equal the amount required by this subpart.

§261.151 Wording of the instruments.

(a)(1) A trust agreement for a trust fund, as specified in §261.143(a), must be worded as follows, except that instructions in brackets are to be replaced with the relevant information and the brackets deleted:

Trust Agreement

Trust Agreement, the "Agreement," entered into as of [date] by and between [name of the owner or operator], a [name of State] [insert "corporation," "partnership," "association," or "proprietorship"], the "Grantor," and [name of corporate trustee], [insert "incorporated in the State of __________" or "a national bank"], the "Trustee."

Whereas, the United States Environmental Protection Agency, "EPA," an agency of the United States Government, has established certain regulations applicable to the Grantor, requiring that an owner or operator of a facility regulated under parts 264, or 265, or satisfying the conditions of the exclusion under §261.4(a)(24) shall provide assurance that funds will be available if needed for care of the facility under 40 CFR parts 264 or 265, subparts G, as applicable,

Whereas, the Grantor has elected to establish a trust to provide all or part of such financial assurance for the facilities identified herein,

Whereas, the Grantor, acting through its duly authorized officers, has selected the Trustee to be the trustee under this agreement, and the Trustee is willing to act as trustee,

Now, Therefore, the Grantor and the Trustee agree as follows:

Section 1. *Definitions.* As used in this Agreement:

(a) The term "Grantor" means the owner or operator who enters into this Agreement and any successors or assigns of the Grantor.

(b) The term "Trustee" means the Trustee who enters into this Agreement and any successor Trustee.

Section 2. *Identification of Facilities and Cost Estimates.* This Agreement pertains to the facilities and cost estimates identified on attached Schedule A [on Schedule A, for each facility list the EPA Identification Number (if available), name, address, and the current cost estimates, or portions thereof, for which financial assurance is demonstrated by this Agreement].

Section 3. *Establishment of Fund.* The Grantor and the Trustee hereby establish a trust fund, the "Fund," for the benefit of EPA in the event that the hazardous secondary materials of the grantor no longer meet the conditions of the exclusion under §261.4(a)(24). The Grantor and the Trustee intend that no third party have access to the Fund except as herein provided. The Fund is established initially as consisting of the property, which is acceptable to the Trustee, described in Schedule B attached hereto. Such property and any other property subsequently transferred to the Trustee is referred to as the Fund, together with all earnings and profits thereon, less any payments or distributions made by the Trustee pursuant to this Agreement. The Fund shall be held by the Trustee, IN TRUST, as hereinafter provided. The Trustee shall not be responsible nor shall it undertake any responsibility for the amount or adequacy of, nor any duty to collect from the Grantor, any payments necessary to discharge any liabilities of the Grantor established by EPA.

Section 4. *Payments from the Fund.* The Trustee shall make payments from the Fund as the EPA Regional Administrator shall direct, in writing, to provide for the payment of the costs of the performance of activities required under subpart G of 40 CFR parts 264 or 265 for the facilities covered by this Agreement. The Trustee shall reimburse the Grantor or other persons as specified by the EPA Regional Administrator from the Fund for expenditures for such activities in such amounts as the beneficiary shall direct in writing. In addition, the Trustee shall refund to the Grantor such amounts as the EPA Regional Administrator specifies in writing. Upon refund, such funds shall no longer constitute part of the Fund as defined herein.

Section 5. *Payments Comprising the Fund.* Payments made to the Trustee for the Fund shall consist of cash or securities acceptable to the Trustee.

Section 6. *Trustee Management.* The Trustee shall invest and reinvest the principal and income of the Fund and keep the Fund invested as a single fund, without distinction between principal and income, in accordance with general investment policies and guidelines which the Grantor may communicate in writing to the Trustee from time to time, subject, however, to the provisions of this section. In investing, reinvesting, exchanging, selling, and managing the Fund, the Trustee shall discharge his duties with respect to the trust fund solely in the interest of the beneficiary and with the care, skill, prudence, and diligence under the circumstances then prevailing which persons of prudence, acting in a like capacity and familiar with such matters, would use in the conduct of an enterprise of a like character and with like aims; except that:

(i) Securities or other obligations of the Grantor, or any other owner or operator of the facilities, or any of their affiliates as defined in the Investment Company Act of 1940, as amended, 15 U.S.C. 80a-2.(a), shall not be acquired or held, unless they are securities or other obligations of the Federal or a State government;

(ii) The Trustee is authorized to invest the Fund in time or demand deposits of the Trustee, to the extent insured by an agency of the Federal or State government; and

(iii) The Trustee is authorized to hold cash awaiting investment or distribution uninvested for a reasonable time and without liability for the payment of interest thereon.

Section 7. *Commingling and Investment.* The Trustee is expressly authorized in its discretion:

(a) To transfer from time to time any or all of the assets of the Fund to any common, commingled, or collective trust fund created by the Trustee in which the Fund is eligible to participate, subject to all of the provisions thereof, to be commingled with the assets of other trusts participating therein; and

(b) To purchase shares in any investment company registered under the Investment Company Act of 1940, 15 U.S.C. 80a-1 *et seq.*, including one which may be created, managed, underwritten, or to which investment advice is rendered or the shares of which are sold by the Trustee. The Trustee may vote such shares in its discretion.

Section 8. *Express Powers of Trustee.* Without in any way limiting the powers and discretions conferred upon the Trustee by the other provisions of this Agreement or by law, the Trustee is expressly authorized and empowered:

(a) To sell, exchange, convey, transfer, or otherwise dispose of any property held by it, by public or private sale. No person dealing with the Trustee shall be bound to see to the application of the purchase money or to inquire into the validity or expediency of any such sale or other disposition;

(b) To make, execute, acknowledge, and deliver any and all documents of transfer and conveyance and any and all other instruments that may be necessary or appropriate to carry out the powers herein granted;

(c) To register any securities held in the Fund in its own name or in the name of a nominee and to hold any security in bearer form or in book entry, or to combine certificates representing such securities with certificates of the same issue held by the Trustee in other fiduciary capacities, or to deposit or arrange for the deposit of such securities in a qualified central depositary even though, when so deposited, such securities may be merged and held in bulk in the name of the nominee of such depositary with other securities deposited therein by another person, or to deposit or arrange for the deposit of any securities issued by the United States Government, or any agency or instrumentality thereof, with a Federal Reserve bank, but the books and records of the Trustee shall at all times show that all such securities are part of the Fund;

(d) To deposit any cash in the Fund in interest-bearing accounts maintained or savings certificates issued by the Trustee, in its separate corporate capacity, or in any other banking institution affiliated with the Trustee, to the extent insured by an agency of the Federal or State government; and

(e) To compromise or otherwise adjust all claims in favor of or against the Fund.

Section 9. *Taxes and Expenses.* All taxes of any kind that may be assessed or levied against or in respect of the Fund and all brokerage commissions incurred by the Fund shall be paid from the Fund. All other expenses incurred by the Trustee in connection with the administration of this Trust, including fees for legal services rendered to the Trustee, the compensation of the Trustee to the extent not paid directly by the Grantor, and all other proper charges and disbursements of the Trustee shall be paid from the Fund.

Section 10. *Annual Valuation.* The Trustee shall annually, at least 30 days prior to the anniversary date of establishment of the Fund, furnish to the Grantor and to the appropriate EPA Regional Administrator a statement confirming the value of the Trust. Any securities in the Fund shall be valued at market value as of no more than 60 days prior to the anniversary date of establishment of the Fund. The failure of the Grantor to object in writing to the Trustee within 90 days after the statement has been furnished to the Grantor and the EPA Regional Administrator shall constitute a conclusively binding assent by the Grantor, barring the Grantor from asserting any claim or liability against the Trustee with respect to matters disclosed in the statement.

Section 11. *Advice of Counsel.* The Trustee may from time to time consult with counsel, who may be counsel to the Grantor, with respect to any question arising as to the construction of this Agreement or any action to be taken hereunder. The Trustee shall be fully protected, to the extent permitted by law, in acting upon the advice of counsel.

Section 12. *Trustee Compensation.* The Trustee shall be entitled to reasonable compensation for its services as agreed upon in writing from time to time with the Grantor.

Section 13. *Successor Trustee.* The Trustee may resign or the Grantor may replace the Trustee, but such resignation or replacement shall not be effective until the Grantor has appointed a successor trustee and this successor accepts the appointment. The successor trustee shall have the same powers and duties as those conferred upon the Trustee hereunder. Upon the successor trustee's acceptance of the appointment, the Trustee shall assign, transfer, and pay over to the successor trustee the funds and properties then constituting the Fund. If for any reason the Grantor cannot or does not act in the event of the resignation of the Trustee, the Trustee may apply to a court of competent jurisdiction for the appointment of a successor trustee or for instructions. The successor trustee shall specify the date on which it assumes administration of the trust in a writing sent to the Grantor, the EPA Regional Administrator, and the present Trustee by certified mail 10 days before such change becomes effective. Any expenses incurred by the Trustee as a result of any of the acts contemplated by this Section shall be paid as provided in Section 9.

Section 14. *Instructions to the Trustee.* All orders, requests, and instructions by the Grantor to the Trustee shall be in writing, signed by such persons as are designated in the attached Exhibit A or such other designees as the Grantor may designate by amendment to Exhibit A. The Trustee shall be fully protected in acting without inquiry in accordance with the Grantor's orders, requests, and instructions. All orders, requests, and instructions by the EPA Regional Administrator to the Trustee shall be in writing, signed by the EPA Regional Administrators of the Regions in which the facilities are located, or their designees, and the Trustee shall act and shall be fully protected in acting in accordance with such orders, requests, and instructions. The Trustee shall have the right to assume, in the absence of written notice to the contrary, that no event constituting a change or a termination of the authority of any person to act on behalf of the Grantor or EPA hereunder has occurred. The Trustee shall have no duty to act in the absence of such orders, requests, and instructions from the Grantor and/or EPA, except as provided for herein.

Section 15. *Amendment of Agreement.* This Agreement may be amended by an instrument in writing executed by the Grantor, the Trustee, and the appropriate EPA Regional Administrator, or by the Trustee and the appropriate EPA Regional Administrator if the Grantor ceases to exist.

Section 16. *Irrevocability and Termination.* Subject to the right of the parties to amend this Agreement as provided in Section 16, this Trust shall be irrevocable and shall continue until terminated at the written agreement of the Grantor, the Trustee, and the EPA Regional Administrator, or by the Trustee and the EPA Regional Administrator, if the Grantor ceases to exist. Upon termination of the Trust, all remaining trust property, less final trust administration expenses, shall be delivered to the Grantor.

Section 17. *Immunity and Indemnification.* The Trustee shall not incur personal liability of any nature in connection with any act or omission, made in good faith, in the administration of this Trust, or in carrying out any directions by the Grantor or the EPA Regional Administrator issued in accordance with this Agreement. The Trustee shall be indemnified and saved harmless by the Grantor or from the Trust Fund, or both, from and against any personal liability to which the Trustee may be subjected by reason of any act or conduct in its official capacity, including all expenses reasonably incurred in its defense in the event the Grantor fails to provide such defense.

Section 18. *Choice of Law.* This Agreement shall be administered, construed, and enforced according to the laws of the State of [insert name of State].

Section 19. *Interpretation.* As used in this Agreement, words in the singular include the plural and words in the plural include the singular. The descriptive headings for each Section of this Agreement shall not affect the interpretation or the legal efficacy of this Agreement.

In Witness Whereof the parties have caused this Agreement to be executed by their respective officers duly authorized and their corporate seals to be hereunto affixed and attested as of the date first above written: The parties below certify that the wording of this Agreement is identical to the wording specified in 40 CFR 261.151(a)(1) as such regulations were constituted on the date first above written.

[Signature of Grantor]

[Title]

Attest:

[Title]

[Seal]

[Signature of Trustee]

Attest:

[Title]

[Seal]

(2) The following is an example of the certification of acknowledgment which must accompany the trust agreement for a trust fund as specified in §261.143(a) of this chapter. State requirements may differ on the proper content of this acknowledgment.

State of __________

County of __________

On this [date], before me personally came [owner or operator] to me known, who, being by me duly sworn, did depose and say that she/he resides at [address], that she/he is [title] of [corporation], the corporation described in and which executed the above instrument; that she/he knows the seal of said corporation; that the seal affixed to such instrument is such corporate seal; that it was so affixed by order of the Board of Directors of said corporation, and that she/he signed her/his name thereto by like order.

[Signature of Notary Public]

(b) A surety bond guaranteeing payment into a trust fund, as specified in §261.143(b) of this chapter, must be worded as follows, except that instructions in brackets are to be replaced with the relevant information and the brackets deleted:

Financial Guarantee Bond

Date bond executed:

Effective date:

Principal: [legal name and business address of owner or operator]

Type of Organization: [insert "individual," "joint venture," "partnership," or "corporation"]

State of incorporation:__________

Surety(ies): [name(s) and business address(es)]

EPA Identification Number, name, address and amount(s) for each facility guaranteed by this bond: __________

Total penal sum of bond: $ __________

Surety's bond number:__________

Know All Persons By These Presents, That we, the Principal and Surety(ies) are firmly bound to the U.S. EPA in the event that the hazardous secondary materials at the reclamation or intermediate facility listed below no longer meet the conditions of the exclusion under 40 CFR 261.4(a)(24), in the above penal sum for the payment of which we bind ourselves, our heirs, executors, administrators, successors, and assigns jointly and severally; provided that, where the Surety(ies) are corporations acting as co-sureties, we, the Sureties, bind ourselves in such sum "jointly and severally" only for the purpose of allowing a joint action or actions against any or all of us, and for all other purposes each Surety binds itself, jointly and severally with the Principal, for the payment of such sum only as is set forth opposite the name of such Surety, but if no limit of liability is indicated, the limit of liability shall be the full amount of the penal sum.

Whereas said Principal is required, under the Resource Conservation and Recovery Act as amended (RCRA), to have a permit or interim status in order to own or operate each facility identified above, or to meet conditions under 40 CFR sections 261.4(a)(24), and

Whereas said Principal is required to provide financial assurance as a condition of permit or interim status or as a condition of an exclusion under 40 CFR sections 261.4(a)(24) and

Whereas said Principal shall establish a standby trust fund as is required when a surety bond is used to provide such financial assurance;

Now, Therefore, the conditions of the obligation are such that if the Principal shall faithfully, before the beginning of final closure of each facility identified above, fund the standby trust fund in the amount(s) identified above for the facility,

Or, if the Principal shall satisfy all the conditions established for exclusion of hazardous secondary materials from coverage as solid waste under 40 CFR sections 261.4(a)(24),

Or, if the Principal shall fund the standby trust fund in such amount(s) within 15 days after a final order to begin closure is issued by an EPA Regional Administrator or a U.S. district court or other court of competent jurisdiction,

Or, if the Principal shall provide alternate financial assurance, as specified in subpart H of 40 CFR part 261, as applicable, and obtain the EPA Regional Administrator's written approval of such assurance, within 90 days after the date notice of cancellation is received by both the Principal and the EPA Regional Administrator(s) from the Surety(ies), then this obligation shall be null and void; otherwise it is to remain in full force and effect.

The Surety(ies) shall become liable on this bond obligation only when the Principal has failed to fulfill the conditions described above. Upon notification by an EPA Regional Administrator that the Principal has failed to perform as guaranteed by this bond, the Surety(ies) shall place funds in the amount guaranteed for the facility(ies) into the standby trust fund as directed by the EPA Regional Administrator.

The liability of the Surety(ies) shall not be discharged by any payment or succession of payments hereunder, unless and until such payment or payments shall amount in the aggregate to the penal sum of the bond, but in no event shall the obligation of the Surety(ies) hereunder exceed the amount of said penal sum.

The Surety(ies) may cancel the bond by sending notice of cancellation by certified mail to the Principal and to the EPA Regional Administrator(s) for the Region(s) in which the facility(ies) is (are) located, provided, however, that cancellation shall not occur during the 120 days beginning on the date of receipt of the notice of cancellation by both the Principal and the EPA Regional Administrator(s), as evidenced by the return receipts.

The Principal may terminate this bond by sending written notice to the Surety(ies), provided, however, that no such notice shall become effective until the Surety(ies) receive(s) written authorization for termination of the bond by the EPA Regional Administrator(s) of the EPA Region(s) in which the bonded facility(ies) is (are) located.

[The following paragraph is an optional rider that may be included but is not required.]

Principal and Surety(ies) hereby agree to adjust the penal sum of the bond yearly so that it guarantees a new amount, provided that the penal sum does not increase by more than 20 percent in any one year, and no decrease in the penal sum takes place without the written permission of the EPA Regional Administrator(s).

In Witness Whereof, the Principal and Surety(ies) have executed this Financial Guarantee Bond and have affixed their seals on the date set forth above.

The persons whose signatures appear below hereby certify that they are authorized to execute this surety bond on behalf of the Principal and Surety(ies) and that the wording of this surety bond is identical to the wording specified in 40 CFR 261.151(b) as such regulations were constituted on the date this bond was executed.

Principal

[Signature(s)]__________

[Name(s)] __________

[Title(s)] __________

[Corporate seal]__________

Corporate Surety(ies)

[Name and address]

State of incorporation:__________

Liability limit: $ __________

[Signature(s)]

[Name(s) and title(s)]

[Corporate seal]

[For every co-surety, provide signature(s), corporate seal, and other information in the same manner as for Surety above.]

Bond premium: $__________

PART 261—Subpart H

(c) A letter of credit, as specified in §261.143(c) of this chapter, must be worded as follows, except that instructions in brackets are to be replaced with the relevant information and the brackets deleted:

Irrevocable Standby Letter of Credit

Regional Administrator(s) Region(s)________________

U.S. Environmental Protection Agency

Dear Sir or Madam: We hereby establish our Irrevocable Standby Letter of Credit No. ____________ in your favor, in the event that the hazardous secondary materials at the covered reclamation or intermediary facility(ies) no longer meet the conditions of the exclusion under 40 CFR 261.4(a)(24), at the request and for the account of [owner's or operator's name and address] up to the aggregate amount of [in words] U.S. dollars $_________, available upon presentation of

(1) your sight draft, bearing reference to this letter of credit No. _______, and

(2) your signed statement reading as follows: "I certify that the amount of the draft is payable pursuant to regulations issued under authority of the Resource Conservation and Recovery Act of 1976 as amended."

This letter of credit is effective as of [date] and shall expire on [date at least 1 year later], but such expiration date shall be automatically extended for a period of [at least 1 year] on [date] and on each successive expiration date, unless, at least 120 days before the current expiration date, we notify both you and [owner's or operator's name] by certified mail that we have decided not to extend this letter of credit beyond the current expiration date. In the event you are so notified, any unused portion of the credit shall be available upon presentation of your sight draft for 120 days after the date of receipt by both you and [owner's or operator's name], as shown on the signed return receipts.

Whenever this letter of credit is drawn on under and in compliance with the terms of this credit, we shall duly honor such draft upon presentation to us, and we shall deposit the amount of the draft directly into the standby trust fund of [owner's or operator's name] in accordance with your instructions.

We certify that the wording of this letter of credit is identical to the wording specified in 40 CFR 261.151(c) as such regulations were constituted on the date shown immediately below.

[Signature(s) and title(s) of official(s) of issuing institution] [Date]

This credit is subject to [insert "the most recent edition of the Uniform Customs and Practice for Documentary Credits, published and copyrighted by the International Chamber of Commerce," or "the Uniform Commercial Code"].

(d) A certificate of insurance, as specified in §261.143(e) of this chapter, must be worded as follows, except that instructions in brackets are to be replaced with the relevant information and the brackets deleted:

Certificate of Insurance

Name and Address of Insurer (herein called the "Insurer"):

____

Name and Address of Insured (herein called the "Insured"):

____

Facilities Covered: [List for each facility: The EPA Identification Number (if any issued), name, address, and the amount of insurance for all facilities covered, which must total the face amount shown below.

Face Amount: ________________

Policy Number: ________________

Effective Date: ________________

The Insurer hereby certifies that it has issued to the Insured the policy of insurance identified above to provide financial assurance so that in accordance with applicable regulations all hazardous secondary materials can be removed from the facility or any unit at the facility and the facility or any unit at the facility can be decontaminated at the facilities identified above. The Insurer further warrants that such policy conforms in all respects with the requirements of 40 CFR 261.143(d) as applicable and as such regulations were constituted on the date shown immediately below. It is agreed that any provision of the policy inconsistent with such regulations is hereby amended to eliminate such inconsistency.

Whenever requested by the EPA Regional Administrator(s) of the U.S. Environmental Protection Agency, the Insurer agrees to furnish to the EPA Regional Administrator(s) a duplicate original of the policy listed above, including all endorsements thereon.

I hereby certify that the wording of this certificate is identical to the wording specified in 40 CFR 261.151(d) such regulations were constituted on the date shown immediately below.

[Authorized signature for Insurer]

[Name of person signing]

[Title of person signing]

Signature of witness or notary: ________________

[Date]

(e) A letter from the chief financial officer, as specified in §261.143(e) of this chapter, must be worded as follows, except that instructions in brackets are to be replaced with the relevant information and the brackets deleted:

Letter From Chief Financial Officer

[Address to Regional Administrator of every Region in which facilities for which financial responsibility is to be demonstrated through the financial test are located].

I am the chief financial officer of [name and address of firm]. This letter is in support of this firm's use of the financial test to demonstrate financial assurance, as specified in subpart H of 40 CFR part 261.

[Fill out the following nine paragraphs regarding facilities and associated cost estimates. If your firm has no facilities that belong in a particular paragraph, write "None" in the space indicated. For each facility, include its EPA Identification Number (if any issued), name, address, and current cost estimates.]

1. This firm is the owner or operator of the following facilities for which financial assurance is demonstrated through the financial test specified in subpart H of 40 CFR 261. The current cost estimates covered by the test are shown for each facility: ________.
2. This firm guarantees, through the guarantee specified in subpart H of 40 CFR part 261, the following facilities owned or operated by the guaranteed party. The current cost estimates so guaranteed are shown for each facility: ________. The firm identified above is [insert one or more: (1) The direct or higher-tier parent corporation of the owner or operator; (2) owned by the same parent corporation as the parent corporation of the owner or operator, and receiving the following value in consideration of this guarantee ________, or (3) engaged in the following substantial business relationship with

the owner or operator ________, and receiving the following value in consideration of this guarantee ________]. [Attach a written description of the business relationship or a copy of the contract establishing such relationship to this letter].

3. In States where EPA is not administering the financial requirements of subpart H of 40 CFR part 261, this firm, as owner or operator or guarantor, is demonstrating financial assurance for the following facilities through the use of a test equivalent or substantially equivalent to the financial test specified in subpart H of 40 CFR part 261. The current cost estimates covered by such a test are shown for each facility: ________.
4. This firm is the owner or operator of the following hazardous secondary materials management facilities for which financial assurance is not demonstrated either to EPA or a State through the financial test or any other financial assurance mechanism specified in subpart H of 40 CFR part 261 or equivalent or substantially equivalent State mechanisms. The current cost estimates not covered by such financial assurance are shown for each facility: ________.
5. This firm is the owner or operator of the following UIC facilities for which financial assurance for plugging and abandonment is required under part 144. The current closure cost estimates as required by 40 CFR 144.62 are shown for each facility: ________.
6. This firm is the owner or operator of the following facilities for which financial assurance for closure or post-closure care is demonstrated through the financial test specified in subpart H of 40 CFR parts 264 and 265. The current closure and/or post-closure cost estimates covered by the test are shown for each facility: ________.
7. This firm guarantees, through the guarantee specified in subpart H of 40 CFR parts 264 and 265, the closure or post-closure care of the following facilities owned or operated by the guaranteed party. The current cost estimates for the closure or post-closure care so guaranteed are shown for each facility: ________. The firm identified above is [insert one or more: (1) The direct or higher-tier parent corporation of the owner or operator; (2) owned by the same parent corporation as the parent corporation of the owner or operator, and receiving the following value in consideration of this guarantee ________; or (3) engaged in the following substantial business relationship with the owner or operator ll, and receiving the following value in consideration of this guarantee ________]. [Attach a written description of the business relationship or a copy of the contract establishing such relationship to this letter].
8. In States where EPA is not administering the financial requirements of subpart H of 40 CFR parts 264 and 265, this firm, as owner or operator or guarantor, is demonstrating financial assurance for the closure or post-closure care of the following facilities through the use of a test equivalent or substantially equivalent to the financial test specified in subpart H of 40 CFR parts 264 and 265. The current closure and/or post-closure cost estimates covered by such a test are shown for each facility: ________.
9. This firm is the owner or operator of the following hazardous waste management facilities for which financial assurance for closure or, if a disposal facility, post-closure care, is not demonstrated either to EPA or a State through the financial test or any other financial assurance mechanism specified in subpart H of 40 CFR parts 264 and 265 or equivalent or substantially equivalent State mechanisms. The current closure and/or post-closure cost estimates not covered by such financial assurance are shown for each facility: ________.

This firm [insert "is required" or "is not required"] to file a Form 10K with the Securities and Exchange Commission (SEC) for the latest fiscal year.

The fiscal year of this firm ends on [month, day]. The figures for the following items marked with an asterisk are derived from this firm's independently audited, year-end financial statements for the latest completed fiscal year, ended [date].

[Fill in Alternative I if the criteria of paragraph (e)(1)(i) of §261.143 of this chapter are used. Fill in Alternative II if the criteria of paragraph (e)(1)(ii) of §261.143(e) of this chapter are used.]

Alternative I

1. Sum of current cost estimates [total of all cost estimates shown in the nine paragraphs above] $________
*2. Total liabilities [if any portion of the cost estimates is included in total liabilities, you may deduct the amount of that portion from this line and add that amount to lines 3 and 4] $________
*3. Tangible net worth $________
*4. Net worth $________
*5. Current assets $________
*6. Current liabilities $________
7. Net working capital [line 5 minus line 6] $________
*8. The sum of net income plus depreciation, depletion, and amortization $________
*9. Total assets in U.S. (required only if less than 90% of firm's assets are located in the U.S.) $________
10. Is line 3 at least $10 million? (Yes/No) ________
11. Is line 3 at least 6 times line 1? (Yes/ No) ________
12. Is line 7 at least 6 times line 1? (Yes/ No) ________
*13. Are at least 90% of firm's assets located in the U.S.? If not, complete line 14 (Yes/No) ________
14. Is line 9 at least 6 times line 1? (Yes/ No) ________
15. Is line 2 divided by line 4 less than 2.0? (Yes/No) ________
16. Is line 8 divided by line 2 greater than 0.1? (Yes/No) ________
17. Is line 5 divided by line 6 greater than 1.5? (Yes/No) ________

Alternative II

1. Sum of current cost estimates [total of all cost estimates shown in the eight paragraphs above] $________
2. Current bond rating of most recent issuance of this firm and name of rating service________
3. Date of issuance of bond________
4. Date of maturity of bond________
*5. Tangible net worth [if any portion of the cost estimates is included in "total liabilities" on your firm's financial statements, you may add the amount of that portion to this line] $________
*6. Total assets in U.S. (required only if less than 90% of firm's assets are located in the U.S.) $________
7. Is line 5 at least $10 million? (Yes/No) ________
8. Is line 5 at least 6 times line 1? (Yes/ No) ________
*9. Are at least 90% of firm's assets located in the U.S.? If not, complete line 10 (Yes/No) ________
10. Is line 6 at least 6 times line 1? (Yes/ No) ________

I hereby certify that the wording of this letter is identical to the wording specified in 40 CFR 261.151(e) as such regulations were constituted on the date shown immediately below.

[Signature]________________________

[Name] ____________________

[Title] ____________________

[Date] ____________________

(f) A letter from the chief financial officer, as specified in §261.147(f) of this chapter, must be worded as follows, except that instructions in brackets are to be replaced with the relevant information and the brackets deleted.

Letter From Chief Financial Officer

[Address to Regional Administrator of every Region in which facilities for which financial responsibility is to be demonstrated through the financial test are located].

I am the chief financial officer of [firm's name and address]. This letter is in support of the use of the financial test to demonstrate financial responsibility for liability coverage under §261.147 [insert "and costs assured §261.143(e)" if applicable] as specified in subpart H of 40 CFR part 261.

[Fill out the following paragraphs regarding facilities and liability coverage. If there are no facilities that belong in a particular paragraph, write "None" in the space indicated. For each facility, include its EPA Identification Number (if any issued), name, and address].

The firm identified above is the owner or operator of the following facilities for which liability coverage for [insert "sudden" or "nonsudden" or "both sudden and nonsudden"] accidental occurrences is being demonstrated through the financial test specified in subpart H of 40 CFR part 261: ________

The firm identified above guarantees, through the guarantee specified in subpart H of 40 CFR part 261, liability coverage for [insert "sudden" or "nonsudden" or "both sudden and nonsudden"] accidental occurrences at the following facilities owned or operated by the following: ________. The firm identified above is [insert one or more: (1) The direct or higher-tier parent corporation of the owner or operator; (2) owned by the same parent corporation as the parent corporation of the owner or operator, and receiving the following value in consideration of this guarantee ________; or (3) engaged in the following substantial business relationship with the owner or operator ________, and receiving the following value in consideration of this guarantee ________]. [Attach a written description of the business relationship or a copy of the contract establishing such relationship to this letter.]

The firm identified above is the owner or operator of the following facilities for which liability coverage for [insert "sudden" or "nonsudden" or "both sudden and nonsudden"] accidental occurrences is being demonstrated through the financial test specified in subpart H of 40 CFR parts 264 and 265:________

The firm identified above guarantees, through the guarantee specified in subpart H of 40 CFR parts 264 and 265, liability coverage for [insert "sudden" or "nonsudden" or "both sudden and nonsudden"] accidental occurrences at the following facilities owned or operated by the following: _______. The firm identified above is [insert one or more: (1) The direct or higher-tier parent corporation of the owner or operator; (2) owned by the same parent corporation as the parent corporation of the owner or operator, and receiving the following value in consideration of this guarantee ________; or (3) engaged in the following substantial business relationship with the owner or operator ________, and receiving the following value in consideration of this guarantee ________]. [Attach a written description of the business relationship or a copy of the contract establishing such relationship to this letter.]

[If you are using the financial test to demonstrate coverage of both liability and costs assured under §261.143(e) or closure or post-closure care costs under 40 CFR 264.143, 264.145, 265.143 or 265.145, fill in the following nine paragraphs regarding facilities and associated cost estimates. If there are no facilities that belong in a particular paragraph, write "None" in the space indicated. For each facility, include its EPA identification number (if any issued), name, address, and current cost estimates.]

1. This firm is the owner or operator of the following facilities for which financial assurance is demonstrated through the financial test specified in subpart H of 40 CFR 261. The current cost estimates covered by the test are shown for each facility:________.
2. This firm guarantees, through the guarantee specified in subpart H of 40 CFR part 261, the following facilities owned or operated by the guaranteed party. The current cost estimates so guaranteed are shown for each facility: ________. The firm identified above is [insert one or more: (1) The direct or higher-tier parent corporation of the owner or operator; (2) owned by the same parent corporation as the parent corporation of the owner or operator, and receiving the following value in consideration of this guarantee ________, or (3) engaged in the following substantial business relationship with the owner or operator ________, and receiving the following value in consideration of this guarantee ________]. [Attach a written description of the business relationship or a copy of the contract establishing such relationship to this letter].
3. In States where EPA is not administering the financial requirements of subpart H of 40 CFR part 261, this firm, as owner or operator or guarantor, is demonstrating financial assurance for the following facilities through the use of a test equivalent or substantially equivalent to the financial test specified in subpart H of 40 CFR part 261. The current cost estimates covered by such a test are shown for each facility: ________.
4. This firm is the owner or operator of the following hazardous secondary materials management facilities for which financial assurance is not demonstrated either to EPA or a State through the financial test or any other financial assurance mechanism specified in subpart H of 40 CFR part 261 or equivalent or substantially equivalent State mechanisms. The current cost estimates not covered by such financial assurance are shown for each facility: ________.
5. This firm is the owner or operator of the following UIC facilities for which financial assurance for plugging and abandonment is required under part 144. The current closure cost estimates as required by 40 CFR 144.62 are shown for each facility: ________.
6. This firm is the owner or operator of the following facilities for which financial assurance for closure or post-closure care is demonstrated through the financial test specified in subpart H of 40 CFR parts 264 and 265. The current closure and/or post-closure cost estimates covered by the test are shown for each facility: ________.
7. This firm guarantees, through the guarantee specified in subpart H of 40 CFR parts 264 and 265, the closure or post-closure care of the following facilities owned or operated by the guaranteed party. The current cost estimates for the closure or post-closure care so guaranteed are shown for each facility: ________. The firm identified above is [insert one or more: (1) The direct or higher-tier parent corporation of the owner or operator; (2) owned by the same parent corporation as the parent corporation of the owner or operator, and receiving the following value in consideration of this guarantee ________; or (3) engaged in the following substantial business relationship with the

owner or operator ________, and receiving the following value in consideration of this guarantee________].

[Attach a written description of the business relationship or a copy of the contract establishing such relationship to this letter].

8. In States where EPA is not administering the financial requirements of subpart H of 40 CFR part 264 or 265, this firm, as owner or operator or guarantor, is demonstrating financial assurance for the closure or post-closure care of the following facilities through the use of a test equivalent or substantially equivalent to the financial test specified in subpart H of 40 CFR part 264 and 265. The current closure and/or post-closure cost estimates covered by such a test are shown for each facility: _______.
9. This firm is the owner or operator of the following hazardous waste management facilities for which financial assurance for closure or, if a disposal facility, post-closure care, is not demonstrated either to EPA or a State through the financial test or any other financial assurance mechanism specified in subpart H of 40 CFR part 264 and 265 or equivalent or substantially equivalent State mechanisms. The current closure and/or post-closure cost estimates not covered by such financial assurance are shown for each facility: ________.

This firm [insert "is required" or "is not required"] to file a Form 10K with the Securities and Exchange Commission (SEC) for the latest fiscal year.

The fiscal year of this firm ends on [month, day]. The figures for the following items marked with an asterisk are derived from this firm's independently audited, year-end financial statements for the latest completed fiscal year, ended [date].

Part A. Liability Coverage for Accidental Occurrences

[Fill in Alternative I if the criteria of paragraph (f)(1)(i) of Sec. 261.147 are used. Fill in Alternative II if the criteria of paragraph (f)(1)(ii) of Sec. 261.147 are used.]

Alternative I

1. Amount of annual aggregate liability coverage to be demonstrated $________.

*2. Current assets $________.

*3. Current liabilities $________.

4. Net working capital (line 2 minus line 3) $________.

*5. Tangible net worth $________.

*6. If less than 90% of assets are located in the U.S., give total U.S. assets $________.

7. Is line 5 at least $10 million? (Yes/No) ________.

8. Is line 4 at least 6 times line 1? (Yes/ No) ________.

9. Is line 5 at least 6 times line 1? (Yes/ No) ________.

*10. Are at least 90% of assets located in the U.S.? (Yes/No) ______. If not, complete line 11.

11. Is line 6 at least 6 times line 1? (Yes/ No) ________.

Alternative II

1. Amount of annual aggregate liability coverage to be demonstrated $________.

2. Current bond rating of most recent issuance and name of rating service________.

3. Date of issuance of bond________.

4. Date of maturity of bond________.

*5. Tangible net worth $________.

*6. Total assets in U.S. (required only if less than 90% of assets are located in the U.S.) $________.

7. Is line 5 at least $10 million? (Yes/No) ________.

8. Is line 5 at least 6 times line 1? ________.

9. Are at least 90% of assets located in the U.S.? If not, complete line 10. (Yes/No) ________.

10. Is line 6 at least 6 times line 1? ________.

[Fill in part B if you are using the financial test to demonstrate assurance of both liability coverage and costs assured under §261.143(e) or closure or post-closure care costs under 40 CFR 264.143, 264.145, 265.143 or 265.145.]

Part B. Facility Care and Liability Coverage

[Fill in Alternative I if the criteria of paragraphs (e)(1)(i) of Sec. 261.143 and (f)(1)(i) of Sec. 261.147 are used. Fill in Alternative II if the criteria of paragraphs (e)(1)(ii) of Sec. 261.143 and (f)(1)(ii) of Sec. 261.147 are used.]

Alternative I

1. Sum of current cost estimates (total of all cost estimates listed above) $________

2. Amount of annual aggregate liability coverage to be demonstrated $________

3. Sum of lines 1 and 2 $________

*4. Total liabilities (if any portion of your cost estimates is included in your total liabilities, you may deduct that portion from this line and add that amount to lines 5 and 6) $________

*5. Tangible net worth $________

*6. Net worth $________

*7. Current assets $________

*8. Current liabilities $________

9. Net working capital (line 7 minus line 8) $________

*10. The sum of net income plus depreciation, depletion, and amortization $________

*11. Total assets in U.S. (required only if less than 90% of assets are located in the U.S.) $________

12. Is line 5 at least $10 million? (Yes/No)

13. Is line 5 at least 6 times line 3? (Yes/ No)

14. Is line 9 at least 6 times line 3? (Yes/ No)

*15. Are at least 90% of assets located in the U.S.? (Yes/No) If not, complete line 16.

16. Is line 11 at least 6 times line 3? (Yes/ No)

17. Is line 4 divided by line 6 less than 2.0? (Yes/No)

18. Is line 10 divided by line 4 greater than 0.1? (Yes/No)

19. Is line 7 divided by line 8 greater than 1.5? (Yes/No)

Alternative II

1. Sum of current cost estimates (total of all cost estimates listed above) $________

2. Amount of annual aggregate liability coverage to be demonstrated $________

3. Sum of lines 1 and 2 $________

4. Current bond rating of most recent issuance and name of rating service________

5. Date of issuance of bond________

6. Date of maturity of bond________

*7. Tangible net worth (if any portion of the cost estimates is included in "total liabilities" on your financial statements you may add that portion to this line) $________

*8. Total assets in the U.S. (required only if less than 90% of assets are located in the U.S.) $________

9. Is line 7 at least $10 million? (Yes/No)

10. Is line 7 at least 6 times line 3? (Yes/ No)

*11. Are at least 90% of assets located in the U.S.? (Yes/No) If not complete line 12.

12. Is line 8 at least 6 times line 3? (Yes/ No)

I hereby certify that the wording of this letter is identical to the wording specified in 40 CFR 261.151(f) as such regulations were constituted on the date shown immediately below.

[Signature]________________

[Name] ________________

[Title]________________

[Date] ________________

(g)(1) A corporate guarantee, as specified in §261.143(e) of this chapter, must be worded as follows, except that instructions in brackets are to be replaced with the relevant information and the brackets deleted:

Publisher's Note: Paragraph 10 in the Corporate Guarantee for Facility Care below appears to be numbered by mistake. Based on our reading of the guarantee and similar text in §264.151, we believe that paragraph 10 should have no number and the reference to it in paragraph 8 should refer to paragraph 9. However, given that the regulations state that the published wording is mandatory, we recommend consulting EPA or your state agency regarding this issue.

Corporate Guarantee for Facility Care

Guarantee made this [date] by [name of guaranteeing entity], a business corporation organized under the laws of the State of [insert name of State], herein referred to as guarantor. This guarantee is made on behalf of the [owner or operator] of [business address], which is [one of the following: "our subsidiary"; "a subsidiary of [name and address of common parent corporation], of which guarantor is a subsidiary"; or "an entity with which guarantor has a substantial business relationship, as defined in 40 CFR 264.141(h) and 265.141(h)" to the United States Environmental Protection Agency (EPA).

Recitals

1. Guarantor meets or exceeds the financial test criteria and agrees to comply with the reporting requirements for guarantors as specified in 40 CFR 261.143(e).

2. [Owner or operator] owns or operates the following facility(ies) covered by this guarantee: [List for each facility: EPA Identification Number (if any issued), name, and address.

3. "Closure plans" as used below refer to the plans maintained as required by subpart H of 40 CFR part 261 for the care of facilities as identified above.

4. For value received from [owner or operator], guarantor guarantees that in the event of a determination by the Regional Administrator that the hazardous secondary materials at the owner or operator's facility covered by this guarantee do not meet the conditions of the exclusion under §261.4(a)(24), the guarantor will dispose of any hazardous secondary material as hazardous waste, and close the facility in accordance with closure requirements found in parts 264 or 265 of this chapter, as applicable, or establish a trust fund as specified in §261.143(a) in the name of the owner or operator in the amount of the current cost estimate.

5. Guarantor agrees that if, at the end of any fiscal year before termination of this guarantee, the guarantor fails to meet the financial test criteria, guarantor shall send within 90 days, by certified mail, notice to the EPA Regional Administrator(s) for the Region(s) in which the facility(ies) is(are) located and to [owner or operator] that he intends to provide alternate financial assurance as specified in subpart H of 40 CFR part 261, as applicable, in the name of [owner or operator]. Within 120 days after the end of such fiscal year, the guarantor shall establish such financial assurance unless [owner or operator] has done so.

6. The guarantor agrees to notify the EPA Regional Administrator by certified mail, of a voluntary or involuntary proceeding under Title 11 (Bankruptcy), U.S. Code, naming guarantor as debtor, within 10 days after commencement of the proceeding.

7. Guarantor agrees that within 30 days after being notified by an EPA Regional Administrator of a determination that guarantor no longer meets the financial test criteria or that he is disallowed from continuing as a guarantor, he shall establish alternate financial assurance as specified in of 40 CFR parts 264, 265, or subpart H of 40 CFR part 261, as applicable, in the name of [owner or operator] unless [owner or operator] has done so.

8. Guarantor agrees to remain bound under this guarantee notwithstanding any or all of the following: amendment or modification of the closure plan, the extension or reduction of the time of performance, or any other modification or alteration of an obligation of the owner or operator pursuant to 40 CFR parts 264, 265, or Subpart H of 40 CFR part 261.

9. Guarantor agrees to remain bound under this guarantee for as long as [owner or operator] must comply with the applicable financial assurance requirements of 40 CFR parts 264 and 265 or the financial assurance condition of 40 CFR 261.4(a)(24)(vi)(F) for the above-listed facilities, except as provided in paragraph 10 of this agreement.

10. [Insert the following language if the guarantor is (a) a direct or higher-tier corporate parent, or (b) a firm whose parent corporation is also the parent corporation of the owner or operator]:

    Guarantor may terminate this guarantee by sending notice by certified mail to the EPA Regional Administrator(s) for the Region(s) in which the facility(ies) is(are) located and to [owner or operator], provided that this guarantee may not be terminated unless and until [the owner or operator] obtains, and the EPA Regional Administrator(s) approve(s), alternate coverage complying with 40 CFR 261.143.

    [Insert the following language if the guarantor is a firm qualifying as a guarantor due to its "substantial business relationship" with the owner or operator]

    Guarantor may terminate this guarantee 120 days following the receipt of notification, through certified mail, by the EPA Regional Administrator(s) for the Region(s) in which the facility(ies) is(are) located and by [the owner or operator].

11. Guarantor agrees that if [owner or operator] fails to provide alternate financial assurance as specified in 40 CFR parts 264, 265, or subpart H of 40 CFR 261, as applicable, and obtain written approval of such assurance from the EPA Regional Administrator(s) within 90 days after a notice of cancellation by the guarantor is received by an EPA Regional Administrator from guarantor, guarantor shall provide such alternate financial assurance in the name of [owner or operator].

12. Guarantor expressly waives notice of acceptance of this guarantee by the EPA or by [owner or operator]. Guarantor also expressly waives notice of amendments or modifications of the closure plan and of amendments or modifications of the applicable requirements of 40 CFR parts 264, 265, or subpart H of 40 CFR 261.

I hereby certify that the wording of this guarantee is identical to the wording specified in 40 CFR 261.151(g)(1) as such regulations were constituted on the date first above written.

Effective date: ______

[Name of guarantor] ______

[Authorized signature for guarantor] ______

[Name of person signing] ______

[Title of person signing] ______

Signature of witness or notary: ______

(2) A guarantee, as specified in §261.147(g) of this chapter, must be worded as follows, except that instructions in brackets are to be replaced with the relevant information and the brackets deleted:

Guarantee for Liability Coverage

Guarantee made this [date] by [name of guaranteeing entity], a business corporation organized under the laws of [if incorporated within the United States insert "the State of ______" and insert name of State; if incorporated outside the United States insert the name of the country in which incorporated, the principal place of business within the United States, and the name and address of the registered agent in the State of the principal place of business], herein referred to as guarantor. This guarantee is made on behalf of [owner or operator] of [business address], which is one of the following: "our subsidiary;" "a subsidiary of [name and address of common parent corporation], of which guarantor is a subsidiary;" or "an entity with which guarantor has a substantial business relationship, as defined in 40 CFR [either 264.141(h) or 265.141(h)]", to any and all third parties who have sustained or may sustain bodily injury or property damage caused by [sudden and/or nonsudden] accidental occurrences arising from operation of the facility(ies) covered by this guarantee.

Recitals

1. Guarantor meets or exceeds the financial test criteria and agrees to comply with the reporting requirements for guarantors as specified in 40 CFR 261.147(g).
2. [Owner or operator] owns or operates the following facility(ies) covered by this guarantee: [List for each facility: EPA identification number (if any issued), name, and address; and if guarantor is incorporated outside the United States list the name and address of the guarantor's registered agent in each State.] This corporate guarantee satisfies RCRA third-party liability requirements for [insert "sudden" or "nonsudden" or "both sudden and nonsudden"] accidental occurrences in above-named owner or operator facilities for coverage in the amount of [insert dollar amount] for each occurrence and [insert dollar amount] annual aggregate.
3. For value received from [owner or operator], guarantor guarantees to any and all third parties who have sustained or may sustain bodily injury or property damage caused by [sudden and/or nonsudden] accidental occurrences arising from operations of the facility(ies) covered by this guarantee that in the event that [owner or operator] fails to satisfy a judgment or award based on a determination of liability for bodily injury or property damage to third parties caused by [sudden and/or nonsudden] accidental occurrences, arising from the operation of the above-named facilities, or fails to pay an amount agreed to in settlement of a claim arising from or alleged to arise from such injury or damage, the guarantor will satisfy such judgment(s), award(s) or settlement agreement(s) up to the limits of coverage identified above.
4. Such obligation does not apply to any of the following:

   (a) Bodily injury or property damage for which [insert owner or operator] is obligated to pay damages by reason of the assumption of liability in a contract or agreement. This exclusion does not apply to liability for damages that [insert owner or operator] would be obligated to pay in the absence of the contract or agreement.

   (b) Any obligation of [insert owner or operator] under a workers' compensation, disability benefits, or unemployment compensation law or any similar law.

   (c) Bodily injury to:

   (1) An employee of [insert owner or operator] arising from, and in the course of, employment by [insert owner or operator]; or

   (2) The spouse, child, parent, brother, or sister of that employee as a consequence of, or arising from, and in the course of employment by [insert owner or operator]. This exclusion applies:

   (A) Whether [insert owner or operator] may be liable as an employer or in any other capacity; and

   (B) To any obligation to share damages with or repay another person who must pay damages because of the injury to persons identified in paragraphs (1) and (2).

   (d) Bodily injury or property damage arising out of the ownership, maintenance, use, or entrustment to others of any aircraft, motor vehicle or watercraft.

   (e) Property damage to:

   (1) Any property owned, rented, or occupied by [insert owner or operator];

   (2) Premises that are sold, given away or abandoned by [insert owner or operator] if the property damage arises out of any part of those premises;

   (3) Property loaned to [insert owner or operator];

   (4) Personal property in the care, custody or control of [insert owner or operator];

   (5) That particular part of real property on which [insert owner or operator] or any contractors or subcontractors working directly or indirectly on behalf of [insert owner or operator] are performing operations, if the property damage arises out of these operations.
5. Guarantor agrees that if, at the end of any fiscal year before termination of this guarantee, the guarantor fails to meet the financial test criteria, guarantor shall send within 90 days, by certified mail, notice to the EPA Regional Administrator[s] for the Region[s] in which the facility[ies] is[are] located and to [owner or operator] that he intends to provide alternate liability coverage as specified in 40 CFR 261.147, as applicable, in the name of [owner or operator]. Within 120 days after the end of such fiscal year, the guarantor shall establish such liability coverage unless [owner or operator] has done so.
6. The guarantor agrees to notify the EPA Regional Administrator by certified mail of a voluntary or involuntary proceeding under title 11 (Bankruptcy), U.S. Code, naming guarantor as

debtor, within 10 days after commencement of the proceeding. Guarantor agrees that within 30 days after being notified by an EPA Regional Administrator of a determination that guarantor no longer meets the financial test criteria or that he is disallowed from continuing as a guarantor, he shall establish alternate liability coverage as specified in 40 CFR 261.147 in the name of [owner or operator], unless [owner or operator] has done so.

7. Guarantor reserves the right to modify this agreement to take into account amendment or modification of the liability requirements set by 40 CFR 261.147, provided that such modification shall become effective only if a Regional Administrator does not disapprove the modification within 30 days of receipt of notification of the modification.
8. Guarantor agrees to remain bound under this guarantee for so long as [owner or operator] must comply with the applicable requirements of 40 CFR 261.147 for the above-listed facility(ies), except as provided in paragraph 10 of this agreement.
9. [Insert the following language if the guarantor is (a) a direct or higher-tier corporate parent, or (b) a firm whose parent corporation is also the parent corporation of the owner or operator]:
10. Guarantor may terminate this guarantee by sending notice by certified mail to the EPA Regional Administrator(s) for the Region(s) in which the facility(ies) is(are) located and to [owner or operator], provided that this guarantee may not be terminated unless and until [the owner or operator] obtains, and the EPA Regional Administrator(s) approve(s), alternate liability coverage complying with 40 CFR 261.147.

    [Insert the following language if the guarantor is a firm qualifying as a guarantor due to its "substantial business relationship" with the owner or operator]:

    Guarantor may terminate this guarantee 120 days following receipt of notification, through certified mail, by the EPA Regional Administrator(s) for the Region(s) in which the facility(ies) is(are) located and by [the owner or operator].
11. Guarantor hereby expressly waives notice of acceptance of this guarantee by any party.
12. Guarantor agrees that this guarantee is in addition to and does not affect any other responsibility or liability of the guarantor with respect to the covered facilities.
13. The Guarantor shall satisfy a third-party liability claim only on receipt of one of the following documents:

    (a) Certification from the Principal and the third-party claimant(s) that the liability claim should be paid. The certification must be worded as follows, except that instructions in brackets are to be replaced with the relevant information and the brackets deleted:

    Certification of Valid Claim

    The undersigned, as parties [insert Principal] and [insert name and address of third-party claimant(s)], hereby certify that the claim of bodily injury and/or property damage caused by a [sudden or nonsudden] accidental occurrence arising from operating [Principal's] facility should be paid in the amount of $ ______.

    [Signatures] ________________

    Principal ________________

    (Notary) Date ________________

    [Signatures] ________________

    Claimant(s) ________________

    (Notary) Date ________________

    (b) A valid final court order establishing a judgment against the Principal for bodily injury or property damage caused by sudden or nonsudden accidental occurrences arising from the operation of the Principal's facility or group of facilities.
14. In the event of combination of this guarantee with another mechanism to meet liability requirements, this guarantee will be considered [insert "primary" or "excess"] coverage.

I hereby certify that the wording of the guarantee is identical to the wording specified in 40 CFR 261.151(g)(2) as such regulations were constituted on the date shown immediately below.

Effective date: ________________

[Name of guarantor] ________________

[Authorized signature for guarantor] ________________

[Name of person signing] ________________

[Title of person signing] ________________

Signature of witness or notary: ________________

(h) A hazardous waste facility liability endorsement as required §261.147 must be worded as follows, except that instructions in brackets are to be replaced with the relevant information and the brackets deleted:

Hazardous Secondary Material Reclamation/Intermediate Facility Liability Endorsement

1. This endorsement certifies that the policy to which the endorsement is attached provides liability insurance covering bodily injury and property damage in connection with the insured's obligation to demonstrate financial responsibility under 40 CFR 261.147. The coverage applies at [list EPA Identification Number (if any issued), name, and address for each facility] for [insert "sudden accidental occurrences," "nonsudden accidental occurrences," or "sudden and nonsudden accidental occurrences"; if coverage is for multiple facilities and the coverage is different for different facilities, indicate which facilities are insured for sudden accidental occurrences, which are insured for nonsudden accidental occurrences, and which are insured for both]. The limits of liability are [insert the dollar amount of the "each occurrence" and "annual aggregate" limits of the Insurer's liability], exclusive of legal defense costs.
2. The insurance afforded with respect to such occurrences is subject to all of the terms and conditions of the policy; provided, however, that any provisions of the policy inconsistent with subsections (a) through (e) of this Paragraph 2 are hereby amended to conform with subsections (a) through (e):

    (a) Bankruptcy or insolvency of the insured shall not relieve the Insurer of its obligations under the policy to which this endorsement is attached.

    (b) The Insurer is liable for the payment of amounts within any deductible applicable to the policy, with a right of reimbursement by the insured for any such payment made by the Insurer. This provision does not apply with respect to that amount of any deductible for which coverage is demonstrated as specified in 40 CFR 261.147(f).

    (c) Whenever requested by a Regional Administrator of the U.S. Environmental Protection Agency (EPA), the Insurer agrees to furnish to the Regional Administrator a signed duplicate original of the policy and all endorsements.

    (d) Cancellation of this endorsement, whether by the Insurer, the insured, a parent corporation providing insurance coverage for its subsidiary, or by a firm having an insurable interest in and obtaining liability insurance on behalf of the owner or operator of the facility, will be effective only upon written notice and only after the expiration of 60 days after a copy of such written notice is received by the Regional Administrator(s) of the EPA Region(s) in which the facility(ies) is(are) located.

(e) Any other termination of this endorsement will be effective only upon written notice and only after the expiration of thirty (30) days after a copy of such written notice is received by the Regional Administrator(s) of the EPA Region(s) in which the facility(ies) is (are) located.

Attached to and forming part of policy No. ________ issued by [name of Insurer], herein called the Insurer, of [address of Insurer] to [name of insured] of [address] this ______ day of ____________, 19____. The effective date of said policy is _____ day of _________, 19____.

I hereby certify that the wording of this endorsement is identical to the wording specified in 40 CFR 261.151(h) as such regulation was constituted on the date first above written, and that the Insurer is licensed to transact the business of insurance, or eligible to provide insurance as an excess or surplus lines insurer, in one or more States.

[Signature of Authorized Representative of Insurer]

[Type name]

[Title], Authorized Representative of [name of Insurer]

[Address of Representative]

(i) A certificate of liability insurance as required in §261.147 must be worded as follows, except that the instructions in brackets are to be replaced with the relevant information and the brackets deleted:

Hazardous Secondary Material Reclamation/Intermediate Facility Certificate of Liability Insurance

1. [Name of Insurer], (the "Insurer"), of [address of Insurer] hereby certifies that it has issued liability insurance covering bodily injury and property damage to [name of insured], (the "insured"), of [address of insured] in connection with the insured's obligation to demonstrate financial responsibility under 40 CFR parts 264, 265, and the financial assurance condition of 40 CFR 261.4(a)(24)(vi)(F). The coverage applies at [list EPA Identification Number (if any issued), name, and address for each facility] for [insert "sudden accidental occurrences," "nonsudden accidental occurrences," or "sudden and nonsudden accidental occurrences"; if coverage is for multiple facilities and the coverage is different for different facilities, indicate which facilities are insured for sudden accidental occurrences, which are insured for nonsudden accidental occurrences, and which are insured for both]. The limits of liability are [insert the dollar amount of the "each occurrence" and "annual aggregate" limits of the Insurer's liability], exclusive of legal defense costs. The coverage is provided under policy number, issued on [date]. The effective date of said policy is [date].
2. The Insurer further certifies the following with respect to the insurance described in Paragraph 1:

(a) Bankruptcy or insolvency of the insured shall not relieve the Insurer of its obligations under the policy.

(b) The Insurer is liable for the payment of amounts within any deductible applicable to the policy, with a right of reimbursement by the insured for any such payment made by the Insurer. This provision does not apply with respect to that amount of any deductible for which coverage is demonstrated as specified in 40 CFR 261.147.

(c) Whenever requested by a Regional Administrator of the U.S. Environmental Protection Agency (EPA), the Insurer agrees to furnish to the Regional Administrator a signed duplicate original of the policy and all endorsements.

(d) Cancellation of the insurance, whether by the insurer, the insured, a parent corporation providing insurance coverage for its subsidiary, or by a firm having an insurable interest in and obtaining liability insurance on behalf of the owner or operator of the hazardous waste management facility, will be effective only upon written notice and only after the expiration of 60 days after a copy of such written notice is received by the Regional Administrator(s) of the EPA Region(s) in which the facility(ies) is(are) located.

(e) Any other termination of the insurance will be effective only upon written notice and only after the expiration of thirty (30) days after a copy of such written notice is received by the Regional Administrator(s) of the EPA Region(s) in which the facility(ies) is (are) located.

I hereby certify that the wording of this instrument is identical to the wording specified in 40 CFR 261.151(i) as such regulation was constituted on the date first above written, and that the Insurer is licensed to transact the business of insurance, or eligible to provide insurance as an excess or surplus lines insurer, in one or more States.

[Signature of authorized representative of Insurer]

[Type name]

[Title], Authorized Representative of [name of Insurer]

[Address of Representative]

(j) A letter of credit, as specified in §261.147(h) of this chapter, must be worded as follows, except that instructions in brackets are to be replaced with the relevant information and the brackets deleted:

Irrevocable Standby Letter of Credit

Name and Address of Issuing Institution ____________________

Regional Administrator(s) ____________________

Region(s) ____________________

U.S. Environmental Protection Agency ____________________

Dear Sir or Madam: We hereby establish our Irrevocable Standby Letter of Credit No. ________ in the favor of ["any and all third-party liability claimants" or insert name of trustee of the standby trust fund], at the request and for the account of [owner or operator's name and address] for third-party liability awards or settlements up to [in words] U.S. dollars $________ per occurrence and the annual aggregate amount of [in words] U.S. dollars $________, for sudden accidental occurrences and/or for third-party liability awards or settlements up to the amount of [in words] U.S. dollars $________ per occurrence, and the annual aggregate amount of [in words] U.S. dollars $________, for nonsudden accidental occurrences available upon presentation of a sight draft bearing reference to this letter of credit No. ________, and [insert the following language if the letter of credit is being used without a standby trust fund: (1) a signed certificate reading as follows:

Certificate of Valid Claim

The undersigned, as parties [insert principal] and [insert name and address of third party claimant(s)], hereby certify that the claim of bodily injury and/or property damage caused by a [sudden or nonsudden] accidental occurrence arising from operations of [principal's] facility should be paid in the amount of $[ ]. We hereby certify that the claim does not apply to any of the following:

PART 261—Subpart H

(a) Bodily injury or property damage for which [insert principal] is obligated to pay damages by reason of the assumption of liability in a contract or agreement. This exclusion does not apply to liability for damages that [insert principal] would be obligated to pay in the absence of the contract or agreement.

(b) Any obligation of [insert principal] under a workers' compensation, disability benefits, or unemployment compensation law or any similar law.

(c) Bodily injury to:

(1) An employee of [insert principal] arising from, and in the course of, employment by [insert principal]; or

(2) The spouse, child, parent, brother or sister of that employee as a consequence of, or arising from, and in the course of employment by [insert principal].

This exclusion applies:

(A) Whether [insert principal] may be liable as an employer or in any other capacity; and

(B) To any obligation to share damages with or repay another person who must pay damages because of the injury to persons identified in paragraphs (1) and (2).

(d) Bodily injury or property damage arising out of the ownership, maintenance, use, or entrustment to others of any aircraft, motor vehicle or watercraft.

(e) Property damage to:

(1) Any property owned, rented, or occupied by [insert principal];

(2) Premises that are sold, given away or abandoned by [insert principal] if the property damage arises out of any part of those premises;

(3) Property loaned to [insert principal];

(4) Personal property in the care, custody or control of [insert principal];

(5) That particular part of real property on which [insert principal] or any contractors or subcontractors working directly or indirectly on behalf of [insert principal] are performing operations, if the property damage arises out of these operations.

[Signatures] ______

Grantor ______

[Signatures] ______

Claimant(s) ______

or (2) a valid final court order establishing a judgment against the Grantor for bodily injury or property damage caused by sudden or nonsudden accidental occurrences arising from the operation of the Grantor's facility or group of facilities.]

This letter of credit is effective as of [date] and shall expire on [date at least one year later], but such expiration date shall be automatically extended for a period of [at least one year] on [date and on each successive expiration date, unless, at least 120 days before the current expiration date, we notify you, the USEPA Regional Administrator for Region [Region], and [owner's or operator's name] by certified mail that we have decided not to extend this letter of credit beyond the current expiration date.

Whenever this letter of credit is drawn on under and in compliance with the terms of this credit, we shall duly honor such draft upon presentation to us.

[Insert the following language if a standby trust fund is not being used: "In the event that this letter of credit is used in combination with another mechanism for liability coverage, this letter of credit shall be considered [insert "primary" or "excess" coverage]."

We certify that the wording of this letter of credit is identical to the wording specified in 40 CFR 261.151(j) as such regulations were constituted on the date shown immediately below. [Signature(s) and title(s) of official(s) of issuing institution] [Date].

This credit is subject to [insert "the most recent edition of the Uniform Customs and Practice for Documentary Credits, published and copyrighted by the International Chamber of Commerce," or "the Uniform Commercial Code"].

(k) A surety bond, as specified in §261.147(i) of this chapter, must be worded as follows: except that instructions in brackets are to be replaced with the relevant information and the brackets deleted:

Payment Bond

Surety Bond No. [Insert number]

Parties [Insert name and address of owner or operator], Principal, incorporated in [Insert State of incorporation] of [Insert city and State of principal place of business] and [Insert name and address of surety company(ies)], Surety Company(ies), of [Insert surety(ies) place of business].

EPA Identification Number (if any issued), name, and address for each facility guaranteed by this bond: ______

	Sudden accidental occurrences	Nonsudden accidental occurrences
Penal Sum Per Occurrence	[insert amount]	[insert amount]
Annual Aggregate	[insert amount]	[insert amount]

Purpose: This is an agreement between the Surety(ies) and the Principal under which the Surety(ies), its(their) successors and assignees, agree to be responsible for the payment of claims against the Principal for bodily injury and/or property damage to third parties caused by ["sudden" and/or "nonsudden"] accidental occurrences arising from operations of the facility or group of facilities in the sums prescribed herein; subject to the governing provisions and the following conditions.

Governing Provisions:

(1) Section 3004 of the Resource Conservation and Recovery Act of 1976, as amended.

(2) Rules and regulations of the U.S. Environmental Protection Agency (EPA), particularly 40 CFR parts 264, 265, and Subpart H of 40 CFR part 261 (if applicable).

(3) Rules and regulations of the governing State agency (if applicable) [insert citation].

Conditions:

(1) The Principal is subject to the applicable governing provisions that require the Principal to have and maintain liability coverage for bodily injury and property damage to third parties caused by ["sudden" and/or "nonsudden"] accidental occurrences arising from operations of the facility or group of facilities. Such obligation does not apply to any of the following:

(a) Bodily injury or property damage for which [insert Principal] is obligated to pay damages by reason of the assumption of liability in a contract or agreement. This exclusion does not apply to liability for damages that [insert Principal] would be obligated to pay in the absence of the contract or agreement.

(b) Any obligation of [insert Principal] under a workers' compensation, disability benefits, or unemployment compensation law or similar law.

(c) Bodily injury to:

(1) An employee of [insert Principal] arising from, and in the course of, employment by [insert principal]; or

(2) The spouse, child, parent, brother or sister of that employee as a consequence of, or arising from, and in the course of employment by [insert Principal]. This exclusion applies:

(A) Whether [insert Principal] may be liable as an employer or in any other capacity; and

(B) To any obligation to share damages with or repay another person who must pay damages because of the injury to persons identified in paragraphs (1) and (2).

(d) Bodily injury or property damage arising out of the ownership, maintenance, use, or entrustment to others of any aircraft, motor vehicle or watercraft.

(e) Property damage to:

(1) Any property owned, rented, or occupied by [insert Principal];

(2) Premises that are sold, given away or abandoned by [insert Principal] if the property damage arises out of any part of those premises;

(3) Property loaned to [insert Principal];

(4) Personal property in the care, custody or control of [insert Principal];

(5) That particular part of real property on which [insert Principal] or any contractors or subcontractors working directly or indirectly on behalf of [insert Principal] are performing operations, if the property damage arises out of these operations.

(2) This bond assures that the Principal will satisfy valid third party liability claims, as described in condition 1.

(3) If the Principal fails to satisfy a valid third party liability claim, as described above, the Surety(ies) becomes liable on this bond obligation.

(4) The Surety(ies) shall satisfy a third party liability claim only upon the receipt of one of the following documents:

(a) Certification from the Principal and the third party claimant(s) that the liability claim should be paid. The certification must be worded as follows, except that instructions in brackets are to be replaced with the relevant information and the brackets deleted:

Certification of Valid Claim

The undersigned, as parties [insert name of Principal] and [insert name and address of third party claimant(s)], hereby certify that the claim of bodily injury and/or property damage caused by a [sudden or nonsudden] accidental occurrence arising from operating [Principal's] facility should be paid in the amount of $[ ].

[Signature]

Principal

[Notary] Date

[Signature(s)]

Claimant(s)

[Notary] Date

or (b) A valid final court order establishing a judgment against the Principal for bodily injury or property damage caused by sudden or nonsudden accidental occurrences arising from the operation of the Principal's facility or group of facilities.

(5) In the event of combination of this bond with another mechanism for liability coverage, this bond will be considered [insert "primary" or "excess"] coverage.

(6) The liability of the Surety(ies) shall not be discharged by any payment or succession of payments hereunder, unless and until such payment or payments shall amount in the aggregate to the penal sum of the bond. In no event shall the obligation of the Surety(ies) hereunder exceed the amount of said annual aggregate penal sum, provided that the Surety(ies) furnish(es) notice to the Regional Administrator forthwith of all claims filed and payments made by the Surety(ies) under this bond.

(7) The Surety(ies) may cancel the bond by sending notice of cancellation by certified mail to the Principal and the USEPA Regional Administrator for Region [Region], provided, however, that cancellation shall not occur during the 120 days beginning on the date of receipt of the notice of cancellation by the Principal and the Regional Administrator, as evidenced by the return receipt.

(8) The Principal may terminate this bond by sending written notice to the Surety(ies) and to the EPA Regional Administrator(s) of the EPA Region(s) in which the bonded facility(ies) is (are) located.

(9) The Surety(ies) hereby waive(s) notification of amendments to applicable laws, statutes, rules and regulations and agree(s) that no such amendment shall in any way alleviate its (their) obligation on this bond.

(10) This bond is effective from [insert date] (12:01 a.m., standard time, at the address of the Principal as stated herein) and shall continue in force until terminated as described above.

In Witness Whereof, the Principal and Surety(ies) have executed this Bond and have affixed their seals on the date set forth above.

The persons whose signatures appear below hereby certify that they are authorized to execute this surety bond on behalf of the Principal and Surety(ies) and that the wording of this surety bond is identical to the wording specified in 40 CFR 261.151(k), as such regulations were constituted on the date this bond was executed.

PRINCIPAL

[Signature(s)]

[Name(s)]

[Title(s)]

[Corporate Seal]

CORPORATE SURETY[IES]

[Name and address]

State of incorporation: ____________________

Liability Limit: $ ____________________

[Signature(s)]

[Name(s) and title(s)]

[Corporate seal]

[For every co-surety, provide signature(s), corporate seal, and other information in the same manner as for Surety above.]

Bond premium: $____________________

(l)(1) A trust agreement, as specified in §261.147(j) of this chapter, must be worded as follows, except that instructions in brackets are to be replaced with the relevant information and the brackets deleted:

Trust Agreement

Trust Agreement, the "Agreement," entered into as of [date] by and between [name of the owner or operator] a [name of State] [insert "corporation," "partnership," "association," or "proprietorship"], the "Grantor," and [name of corporate trustee], [insert, "incorporated in the State of ____________" or "a national bank"], the "trustee."

Whereas, the United States Environmental Protection Agency, "EPA," an agency of the United States Government, has established certain regulations applicable to the Grantor, requiring that an owner or operator must demonstrate financial responsibility for bodily injury and property damage to third parties caused by sudden accidental and/or nonsudden accidental occurrences arising from operations of the facility or group of facilities.

Whereas, the Grantor has elected to establish a trust to assure all or part of such financial responsibility for the facilities identified herein.

Whereas, the Grantor, acting through its duly authorized officers, has selected the Trustee to be the trustee under this agreement, and the Trustee is willing to act as trustee.

Now, therefore, the Grantor and the Trustee agree as follows:

Section 1. *Definitions.* As used in this Agreement:

(a) The term "Grantor" means the owner or operator who enters into this Agreement and any successors or assigns of the Grantor.

(b) The term "Trustee" means the Trustee who enters into this Agreement and any successor Trustee.

Section 2. *Identification of Facilities.* This agreement pertains to the facilities identified on attached schedule A [on schedule A, for each facility list the EPA Identification Number (if any issued), name, and address of the facility(ies) and the amount of liability coverage, or portions thereof, if more than one instrument affords combined coverage as demonstrated by this Agreement].

Section 3. *Establishment of Fund.* The Grantor and the Trustee hereby establish a trust fund, hereinafter the "Fund," for the benefit of any and all third parties injured or damaged by [sudden and/or nonsudden] accidental occurrences arising from operation of the facility(ies) covered by this guarantee, in the amounts of ________ [up to $1 million] per occurrence and [up to $2 million] annual aggregate for sudden accidental occurrences and ________ [up to $3 million] per occurrence and ________ [up to $6 million] annual aggregate for nonsudden occurrences, except that the Fund is not established for the benefit of third parties for the following:

(a) Bodily injury or property damage for which [insert Grantor] is obligated to pay damages by reason of the assumption of liability in a contract or agreement. This exclusion does not apply to liability for damages that [insert Grantor] would be obligated to pay in the absence of the contract or agreement.

(b) Any obligation of [insert Grantor] under a workers' compensation, disability benefits, or unemployment compensation law or any similar law.

(c) Bodily injury to:

(1) An employee of [insert Grantor] arising from, and in the course of, employment by [insert Grantor]; or

(2) The spouse, child, parent, brother or sister of that employee as a consequence of, or arising from, and in the course of employment by [insert Grantor]. This exclusion applies:

(A) Whether [insert Grantor] may be liable as an employer or in any other capacity; and

(B) To any obligation to share damages with or repay another person who must pay damages because of the injury to persons identified in paragraphs (1) and (2).

(d) Bodily injury or property damage arising out of the ownership, maintenance, use, or entrustment to others of any aircraft, motor vehicle or watercraft.

(e) Property damage to:

(1) Any property owned, rented, or occupied by [insert Grantor];

(2) Premises that are sold, given away or abandoned by [insert Grantor] if the property damage arises out of any part of those premises;

(3) Property loaned to [insert Grantor];

(4) Personal property in the care, custody or control of [insert Grantor];

(5) That particular part of real property on which [insert Grantor] or any contractors or subcontractors working directly or indirectly on behalf of [insert Grantor] are performing operations, if the property damage arises out of these operations.

In the event of combination with another mechanism for liability coverage, the Fund shall be considered [insert "primary" or "excess"] coverage.

The Fund is established initially as consisting of the property, which is acceptable to the Trustee, described in Schedule B attached hereto. Such property and any other property subsequently transferred to the Trustee is referred to as the Fund, together with all earnings and profits thereon, less any payments or distributions made by the Trustee pursuant to this Agreement. The Fund shall be held by the Trustee, IN TRUST, as hereinafter provided. The Trustee shall not be responsible nor shall it undertake any responsibility for the amount or adequacy of, nor any duty to collect from the Grantor, any payments necessary to discharge any liabilities of the Grantor established by EPA.

Section 4. *Payment for Bodily Injury or Property Damage.* The Trustee shall satisfy a third party liability claim by making payments from the Fund only upon receipt of one of the following documents;

(a) Certification from the Grantor and the third party claimant(s) that the liability claim should be paid. The certification must be worded as follows, except that instructions in brackets are to be replaced with the relevant information and the brackets deleted:

Certification of Valid Claim

The undersigned, as parties [insert Grantor] and [insert name and address of third party claimant(s)], hereby certify that the claim of bodily injury and/or property damage caused by a [sudden or nonsudden] accidental occurrence arising from operating [Grantor's] facility or group of facilities should be paid in the amount of $[ ].

[Signatures]

Grantor

[Signatures]

Claimant(s)

(b) A valid final court order establishing a judgment against the Grantor for bodily injury or property damage caused by sudden or nonsudden accidental occurrences arising from the operation of the Grantor's facility or group of facilities.

Section 5. *Payments Comprising the Fund.* Payments made to the Trustee for the Fund shall consist of cash or securities acceptable to the Trustee.

Section 6. *Trustee Management.* The Trustee shall invest and reinvest the principal and income, in accordance with general investment policies and guidelines which the Grantor may communicate in writing to the Trustee from time to time, subject, however, to the provisions of this section. In investing, reinvesting, exchanging, selling, and managing the Fund, the Trustee shall discharge his duties with respect to the trust fund solely in the interest of the beneficiary and with the care, skill, prudence, and diligence under the circumstance then prevailing which persons of prudence, acting in a like capacity and familiar with such matters, would use in the conduct of an enterprise of a like character and with like aims; except that:

(i) Securities or other obligations of the Grantor, or any other owner or operator of the facilities, or any of their affiliates as defined in the Investment Company Act of 1940, as amended, 15 U.S.C. 80a-2.(a), shall not be acquired or held unless they are securities or other obligations of the Federal or a State government;

(ii) The Trustee is authorized to invest the Fund in time or demand deposits of the Trustee, to the extent insured by an agency of the Federal or State government; and

(iii) The Trustee is authorized to hold cash awaiting investment or distribution uninvested for a reasonable time and without liability for the payment of interest thereon.

Section 7. *Commingling and Investment.* The Trustee is expressly authorized in its discretion:

(a) To transfer from time to time any or all of the assets of the Fund to any common commingled, or collective trust fund created by the Trustee in which the fund is eligible to participate, subject to all of the provisions thereof, to be commingled with the assets of other trusts participating therein; and

(b) To purchase shares in any investment company registered under the Investment Company Act of 1940, 15 U.S.C. 81a-1 et seq., including one which may be created, managed, underwritten, or to which investment advice is rendered or the shares of which are sold by the Trustee. The Trustee may vote such shares in its discretion.

Section 8. *Express Powers of Trustee.* Without in any way limiting the powers and discretions conferred upon the Trustee by the other provisions of this Agreement or by law, the Trustee is expressly authorized and empowered:

(a) To sell, exchange, convey, transfer, or otherwise dispose of any property held by it, by public or private sale. No person dealing with the Trustee shall be bound to see to the application of the purchase money or to inquire into the validity or expediency of any such sale or other disposition;

(b) To make, execute, acknowledge, and deliver any and all documents of transfer and conveyance and any and all other instruments that may be necessary or appropriate to carry out the powers herein granted;

(c) To register any securities held in the Fund in its own name or in the name of a nominee and to hold any security in bearer form or in book entry, or to combine certificates representing such securities with certificates of the same issue held by the Trustee in other fiduciary capacities, or to deposit or arrange for the deposit of such securities in a qualified central depository even though, when so deposited, such securities may be merged and held in bulk in the name of the nominee of such depository with other securities deposited therein by another person, or to deposit or arrange for the deposit of any securities issued by the United States Government, or any agency or instrumentality thereof, with a Federal Reserve bank, but the books and records of the Trustee shall at all times show that all such securities are part of the Fund;

(d) To deposit any cash in the Fund in interest-bearing accounts maintained or savings certificates issued by the Trustee, in its separate corporate capacity, or in any other banking institution affiliated with the Trustee, to the extent insured by an agency of the Federal or State government; and

(e) To compromise or otherwise adjust all claims in favor of or against the Fund.

Section 9. *Taxes and Expenses.* All taxes of any kind that may be assessed or levied against or in respect of the Fund and all brokerage commissions incurred by the Fund shall be paid from the Fund. All other expenses incurred by the Trustee in connection with the administration of this Trust, including fees for legal services rendered to the Trustee, the compensation of the Trustee to the extent not paid directly by the Grantor, and all other proper charges and disbursements of the Trustee shall be paid from the Fund.

Section 10. *Annual Valuations.* The Trustee shall annually, at least 30 days prior to the anniversary date of establishment of the Fund, furnish to the Grantor and to the appropriate EPA Regional Administrator a statement confirming the value of the Trust. Any securities in the Fund shall be valued at market value as of no more than 60 days prior to the anniversary date of establishment of the Fund. The failure of the Grantor to object in writing to the Trustee within 90 days after the statement has been furnished to the Grantor and the EPA Regional Administrator shall constitute a conclusively binding assent by the Grantor barring the Grantor from asserting any claim or liability against the Trustee with respect to matters disclosed in the statement.

Section 11. *Advice of Counsel.* The Trustee may from time to time consult with counsel, who may be counsel to the Grantor with respect to any question arising as to the construction of this Agreement or any action to be taken hereunder. The Trustee shall be fully protected, to the extent permitted by law, in acting upon the advice of counsel.

Section 12. *Trustee Compensation.* The Trustee shall be entitled to reasonable compensation for its services as agreed upon in writing from time to time with the Grantor.

Section 13. *Successor Trustee.* The Trustee may resign or the Grantor may replace the Trustee, but such resignation or replacement shall not be effective until the Grantor has appointed a successor trustee and this successor accepts the appointment. The successor trustee shall have the same powers and duties as those conferred upon the Trustee hereunder. Upon the successor trustee's acceptance of the appointment, the Trustee shall assign, transfer, and pay over to the successor trustee the funds and properties then constituting the Fund. If for any reason the Grantor cannot or does not act in the event of the resignation of the Trustee, the Trustee may apply to a court of competent jurisdiction for the appointment of a successor trustee or for instructions. The successor trustee shall specify the date on which it assumes administration of the trust in a writing sent to the Grantor, the EPA Regional Administrator, and the present Trustee by certified mail 10 days before such change becomes effective. Any expenses incurred by the Trustee as a result of any of the acts contemplated by this section shall be paid as provided in Section 9.

Section 14. *Instructions to the Trustee.* All orders, requests, and instructions by the Grantor to the Trustee shall be in writing, signed by such persons as are designated in the attached Exhibit A or such other designees as the Grantor may designate by amendments to

Exhibit A. The Trustee shall be fully protected in acting without inquiry in accordance with the Grantor's orders, requests, and instructions. All orders, requests, and instructions by the EPA Regional Administrator to the Trustee shall be in writing, signed by the EPA Regional Administrators of the Regions in which the facilities are located, or their designees, and the Trustee shall act and shall be fully protected in acting in accordance with such orders, requests, and instructions. The Trustee shall have the right to assume, in the absence of written notice to the contrary, that no event constituting a change or a termination of the authority of any person to act on behalf of the Grantor or EPA hereunder has occurred. The Trustee shall have no duty to act in the absence of such orders, requests, and instructions from the Grantor and/or EPA, except as provided for herein.

Section 15. *Notice of Nonpayment.* If a payment for bodily injury or property damage is made under Section 4 of this trust, the Trustee shall notify the Grantor of such payment and the amount(s) thereof within five (5) working days. The Grantor shall, on or before the anniversary date of the establishment of the Fund following such notice, either make payments to the Trustee in amounts sufficient to cause the trust to return to its value immediately prior to the payment of claims under Section 4, or shall provide written proof to the Trustee that other financial assurance for liability coverage has been obtained equaling the amount necessary to return the trust to its value prior to the payment of claims. If the Grantor does not either make payments to the Trustee or provide the Trustee with such proof, the Trustee shall within 10 working days after the anniversary date of the establishment of the Fund provide a written notice of nonpayment to the EPA Regional Administrator.

Section 16. *Amendment of Agreement.* This Agreement may be amended by an instrument in writing executed by the Grantor, the Trustee, and the appropriate EPA Regional Administrator, or by the Trustee and the appropriate EPA Regional Administrator if the Grantor ceases to exist.

Section 17. *Irrevocability and Termination.* Subject to the right of the parties to amend this Agreement as provided in Section 16, this Trust shall be irrevocable and shall continue until terminated at the written agreement of the Grantor, the Trustee, and the EPA Regional Administrator, or by the Trustee and the EPA Regional Administrator, if the Grantor ceases to exist. Upon termination of the Trust, all remaining trust property, less final trust administration expenses, shall be delivered to the Grantor.

The Regional Administrator will agree to termination of the Trust when the owner or operator substitutes alternate financial assurance as specified in this section.

Section 18. *Immunity and Indemnification.* The Trustee shall not incur personal liability of any nature in connection with any act or omission, made in good faith, in the administration of this Trust, or in carrying out any directions by the Grantor or the EPA Regional Administrator issued in accordance with this Agreement. The Trustee shall be indemnified and saved harmless by the Grantor or from the Trust Fund, or both, from and against any personal liability to which the Trustee may be subjected by reason of any act or conduct in its official capacity, including all expenses reasonably incurred in its defense in the event the Grantor fails to provide such defense.

Section 19. *Choice of Law.* This Agreement shall be administered, construed, and enforced according to the laws of the State of [enter name of State].

Section 20. *Interpretation.* As used in this Agreement, words in the singular include the plural and words in the plural include the singular. The descriptive headings for each section of this Agreement shall not affect the interpretation or the legal efficacy of this Agreement.

In Witness Whereof the parties have caused this Agreement to be executed by their respective officers duly authorized and their corporate seals to be hereunto affixed and attested as of the date first above written. The parties below certify that the wording of this Agreement is identical to the wording specified in 40 CFR 261.151(l) as such regulations were constituted on the date first above written.

[Signature of Grantor]

[Title]

Attest:

[Title]

[Seal]

[Signature of Trustee]

Attest:

[Title]

[Seal]

(2) The following is an example of the certification of acknowledgement which must accompany the trust agreement for a trust fund as specified in §261.147(j) of this chapter. State requirements may differ on the proper

Publisher's Note: The last sentence of the preceding paragraph appears to be truncated. Based on a similar provision in §264.151(m)(2), we believe the final sentence should read: "State requirements may differ on the proper content of this acknowledgement."

State of ____________________

County of ____________________

On this [date], before me personally came [owner or operator] to me known, who, being by me duly sworn, did depose and say that she/he resides at [address], that she/he is [title] of [corporation], the corporation described in and which executed the above instrument; that she/he knows the seal of said corporation; that the seal affixed to such instrument is such corporate seal; that it was so affixed by order of the Board of Directors of said corporation, and that she/he signed her/ his name thereto by like order.

[Signature of Notary Public]

(m)(1) A standby trust agreement, as specified in §261.147(h) of this chapter, must be worded as follows, except that instructions in brackets are to be replaced with the relevant information and the brackets deleted:

Standby Trust Agreement

Trust Agreement, the "Agreement," entered into as of [date] by and between [name of the owner or operator] a [name of a State] [insert "corporation," "partnership," "association," or "proprietorship"], the "Grantor," and [name of corporate trustee], [insert, "incorporated in the State of __________" or "a national bank"], the "trustee."

Whereas the United States Environmental Protection Agency, "EPA," an agency of the United States Government, has established certain regulations applicable to the Grantor, requiring that an owner or operator must demonstrate financial responsibility for bodily injury and property damage to third parties caused by sudden accidental and/or nonsudden accidental occurrences arising from operations of the facility or group of facilities.

Whereas, the Grantor has elected to establish a standby trust into which the proceeds from a letter of credit may be deposited to assure all or part of such financial responsibility for the facilities identified herein.

Whereas, the Grantor, acting through its duly authorized officers, has selected the Trustee to be the trustee under this agreement, and the Trustee is willing to act as trustee.

Now, therefore, the Grantor and the Trustee agree as follows:

Section 1. *Definitions.* As used in this Agreement:

(a) The term Grantor means the owner or operator who enters into this Agreement and any successors or assigns of the Grantor.

(b) The term Trustee means the Trustee who enters into this Agreement and any successor Trustee.

Section 2. *Identification of Facilities.* This Agreement pertains to the facilities identified on attached schedule A [on schedule A, for each facility list the EPA Identification Number (if any issued), name, and address of the facility(ies) and the amount of liability coverage, or portions thereof, if more than one instrument affords combined coverage as demonstrated by this Agreement].

Section 3. *Establishment of Fund.* The Grantor and the Trustee hereby establish a standby trust fund, hereafter the "Fund," for the benefit of any and all third parties injured or damaged by [sudden and/or nonsudden] accidental occurrences arising from operation of the facility(ies) covered by this guarantee, in the amounts of________ [up to $1 million] per occurrence and __________ [up to $2 million] annual aggregate for sudden accidental occurrences and _________ [up to $3 million] per occurrence and __________ [up to $6 million] annual aggregate for nonsudden occurrences, except that the Fund is not established for the benefit of third parties for the following:

(a) Bodily injury or property damage for which [insert Grantor] is obligated to pay damages by reason of the assumption of liability in a contract or agreement. This exclusion does not apply to liability for damages that [insert Grantor] would be obligated to pay in the absence of the contract or agreement.

(b) Any obligation of [insert Grantor] under a workers' compensation, disability benefits, or unemployment compensation law or any similar law.

(c) Bodily injury to:

(1) An employee of [insert Grantor] arising from, and in the course of, employment by [insert Grantor]; or

(2) The spouse, child, parent, brother or sister of that employee as a consequence of, or arising from, and in the course of employment by [insert Grantor].

This exclusion applies:

(A) Whether [insert Grantor] may be liable as an employer or in any other capacity; and

(B) To any obligation to share damages with or repay another person who must pay damages because of the injury to persons identified in paragraphs (1) and (2).

(d) Bodily injury or property damage arising out of the ownership, maintenance, use, or entrustment to others of any aircraft, motor vehicle or watercraft.

(e) Property damage to:

(1) Any property owned, rented, or occupied by [insert Grantor];

(2) Premises that are sold, given away or abandoned by [insert Grantor] if the property damage arises out of any part of those premises;

(3) Property loaned by [insert Grantor];

(4) Personal property in the care, custody or control of [insert Grantor];

(5) That particular part of real property on which [insert Grantor] or any contractors or subcontractors working directly or indirectly on behalf of [insert Grantor] are performing operations, if the property damage arises out of these operations.

In the event of combination with another mechanism for liability coverage, the Fund shall be considered [insert "primary" or "excess"] coverage.

The Fund is established initially as consisting of the proceeds of the letter of credit deposited into the Fund. Such proceeds and any other property subsequently transferred to the Trustee is referred to as the Fund, together with all earnings and profits thereon, less any payments or distributions made by the Trustee pursuant to this Agreement. The Fund shall be held by the Trustee, IN TRUST, as hereinafter provided. The Trustee shall not be responsible nor shall it undertake any responsibility for the amount or adequacy of, nor any duty to collect from the Grantor, any payments necessary to discharge any liabilities of the Grantor established by EPA.

Section 4. *Payment for Bodily Injury or Property Damage.* The Trustee shall satisfy a third party liability claim by drawing on the letter of credit described in Schedule B and by making payments from the Fund only upon receipt of one of the following documents:

(a) Certification from the Grantor and the third party claimant(s) that the liability claim should be paid. The certification must be worded as follows, except that instructions in brackets are to be replaced with the relevant information and the brackets deleted:

Certification of Valid Claim

The undersigned, as parties [insert Grantor] and [insert name and address of third party claimant(s)], hereby certify that the claim of bodily injury and/or property damage caused by a [sudden or nonsudden] accidental occurrence arising from operating [Grantor's] facility should be paid in the amount of $[ ]

[Signature]____________________

Grantor ____________________

[Signatures] ____________________

Claimant(s) ____________________

(b) A valid final court order establishing a judgment against the Grantor for bodily injury or property damage caused by sudden or nonsudden accidental occurrences arising from the operation of the Grantor's facility or group of facilities.

Section 5. *Payments Comprising the Fund.* Payments made to the Trustee for the Fund shall consist of the proceeds from the letter of credit drawn upon by the Trustee in accordance with the requirements of 40 CFR 261.151(k) and Section 4 of this Agreement.

Section 6. *Trustee Management.* The Trustee shall invest and reinvest the principal and income, in accordance with general investment policies and guidelines which the Grantor may communicate in writing to the Trustee from time to time, subject, however, to the provisions of this Section. In investing, reinvesting, exchanging, selling, and managing the Fund, the Trustee shall discharge his duties with respect to the trust fund solely in the interest of the beneficiary and with the care, skill, prudence, and diligence under the circumstances then prevailing which persons of prudence, acting in a like capacity and familiar with such matters, would use in the conduct of an enterprise of a like character and with like aims; except that:

(i) Securities or other obligations of the Grantor, or any other owner or operator of the facilities, or any of their affiliates as defined in the Investment Company Act of 1940, as amended, 15 U.S.C. 80a-2(a), shall not be acquired or held, unless they are securities or other obligations of the Federal or a State government;

(ii) The Trustee is authorized to invest the Fund in time or demand deposits of the Trustee, to the extent insured by an agency of the Federal or a State government; and

(iii) The Trustee is authorized to hold cash awaiting investment or distribution uninvested for a reasonable time and without liability for the payment of interest thereon.

Section 7. *Commingling and Investment.* The Trustee is expressly authorized in its discretion:

(a) To transfer from time to time any or all of the assets of the Fund to any common, commingled, or collective trust fund created by the Trustee in which the Fund is eligible to participate, subject to all of the provisions thereof, to be commingled with the assets of other trusts participating therein; and

(b) To purchase shares in any investment company registered under the Investment Company Act of 1940, 15 U.S.C. 80a-1 et seq., including one which may be created, managed, underwritten, or to which investment advice is rendered or the shares of which are sold by the Trustee. The Trustee may vote such shares in its discretion.

Section 8. *Express Powers of Trustee.* Without in any way limiting the powers and discretions conferred upon the Trustee by the other provisions of this Agreement or by law, the Trustee is expressly authorized and empowered:

(a) To sell, exchange, convey, transfer, or otherwise dispose of any property held by it, by public or private sale. No person dealing with the Trustee shall be bound to see to the application of the purchase money or to inquire into the validity or expediency of any such sale or other disposition;

(b) To make, execute, acknowledge, and deliver any and all documents of transfer and conveyance and any and all other instruments that may be necessary or appropriate to carry out the powers herein granted;

(c) To register any securities held in the Fund in its own name or in the name of a nominee and to hold any security in bearer form or in book entry, or to combine certificates representing such securities with certificates of the same issue held by the Trustee in other fiduciary capacities, or to deposit or arrange for the deposit of such securities in a qualified central depositary even though, when so deposited, such securities may be merged and held in bulk in the name of the nominee of such depositary with other securities deposited therein by another person, or to deposit or arrange for the deposit of any securities issued by the United States Government, or any agency or instrumentality thereof, with a Federal Reserve Bank, but the books and records of the Trustee shall at all times show that all such securities are part of the Fund;

(d) To deposit any cash in the Fund in interest-bearing accounts maintained or savings certificates issued by the Trustee, in its separate corporate capacity, or in any other banking institution affiliated with the Trustee, to the extent insured by an agency of the Federal or State government; and

(e) To compromise or otherwise adjust all claims in favor of or against the Fund.

Section 9. *Taxes and Expenses.* All taxes of any kind that may be assessed or levied against or in respect of the Fund and all brokerage commissions incurred by the Fund shall be paid from the Fund. All other expenses incurred by the Trustee in connection with the administration of this Trust, including fees for legal services rendered to the Trustee, the compensation of the Trustee to the extent not paid directly by the Grantor, and all other proper charges and disbursements to the Trustee shall be paid from the Fund.

Section 10. *Advice of Counsel.* The Trustee may from time to time consult with counsel, who may be counsel to the Grantor, with respect to any question arising as to the construction of this Agreement or any action to be taken hereunder. The Trustee shall be fully protected, to the extent permitted by law, in acting upon the advice of counsel.

Section 11. *Trustee Compensation.* The Trustee shall be entitled to reasonable compensation for its services as agreed upon in writing from time to time with the Grantor.

Section 12. *Successor Trustee.* The Trustee may resign or the Grantor may replace the Trustee, but such resignation or replacement shall not be effective until the Grantor has appointed a successor trustee and this successor accepts the appointment. The successor trustee shall have the same powers and duties as those conferred upon the Trustee hereunder. Upon the successor trustee's acceptance of the appointment, the Trustee shall assign, transfer, and pay over to the successor trustee the funds and properties then constituting the Fund. If for any reason the Grantor cannot or does not act in the event of the resignation of the Trustee, the Trustee may apply to a court of competent jurisdiction for the appointment of a successor trustee or for instructions. The successor trustee shall specify the date on which it assumes administration of the trust in a writing sent to the Grantor, the EPA Regional Administrator and the present Trustee by certified mail 10 days before such change becomes effective. Any expenses incurred by the Trustee as a result of any of the acts contemplated by this Section shall be paid as provided in Section 9.

Section 13. *Instructions to the Trustee.* All orders, requests, certifications of valid claims, and instructions to the Trustee shall be in writing, signed by such persons as are designated in the attached Exhibit A or such other designees as the Grantor may designate by amendments to Exhibit A. The Trustee shall be fully protected in acting without inquiry in accordance with the Grantor's orders, requests, and instructions. The Trustee shall have the right to assume, in the absence of written notice to the contrary, that no event constituting a change or a termination of the authority of any person to act on behalf of the Grantor or the EPA Regional Administrator hereunder has occurred. The Trustee shall have no duty to act in the absence of such orders, requests, and instructions from the Grantor and/or EPA, except as provided for herein.

Section 14. *Amendment of Agreement.* This Agreement may be amended by an instrument in writing executed by the Grantor, the Trustee, and the EPA Regional Administrator, or by the Trustee and the EPA Regional Administrator if the Grantor ceases to exist.

Section 15. *Irrevocability and Termination.* Subject to the right of the parties to amend this Agreement as provided in Section 14, this Trust shall be irrevocable and shall continue until terminated at the written agreement of the Grantor, the Trustee, and the EPA Regional Administrator, or by the Trustee and the EPA Regional Administrator, if the Grantor ceases to exist. Upon termination of the Trust, all remaining trust property, less final trust administration expenses, shall be paid to the Grantor.

The Regional Administrator will agree to termination of the Trust when the owner or operator substitutes alternative financial assurance as specified in this section.

Section 16. *Immunity and indemnification.* The Trustee shall not incur personal liability of any nature in connection with any act or omission, made in good faith, in the administration of this Trust, or in carrying out any directions by the Grantor and the EPA Regional Administrator issued in accordance with this Agreement. The Trustee shall be indemnified and saved harmless by the Grantor or from the Trust Fund, or both, from and against any personal liability to which the Trustee may be subjected by reason of any act or conduct in its official capacity, including all expenses reasonably incurred in its defense in the event the Grantor fails to provide such defense.

Section 17. *Choice of Law.* This Agreement shall be administered, construed, and enforced according to the laws of the State of [enter name of State].

Section 18. *Interpretation.* As used in this Agreement, words in the singular include the plural and words in the plural include the singular. The descriptive headings for each Section of this Agreement shall not affect the interpretation of the legal efficacy of this Agreement.

In Witness Whereof the parties have caused this Agreement to be executed by their respective officers duly authorized and their corporate seals to be hereunto affixed and attested as of the date first above written. The parties below certify that the wording of this Agreement is identical to the wording specified in 40 CFR 261.151(m) as such regulations were constituted on the date first above written.

[Signature of Grantor]

[Title]

Attest:

[Title]

[Seal]

[Signature of Trustee]

Attest:

[Title]

[Seal]

(2) The following is an example of the certification of acknowledgement which must accompany the trust agreement for a standby trust fund as specified in §261.147(h) of this chapter. State requirements may differ on the proper content of this acknowledgement.

State of ____________________

County of ____________________

On this [date], before me personally came [owner or operator] to me known, who, being by me duly sworn, did depose and say that she/he resides at [address], that she/he is [title] of [corporation], the corporation described in and which executed the above instrument; that she/he knows the seal of said corporation; that the seal affixed to such instrument is such corporate seal; that it was so affixed by order of the Board of Directors of said corporation, and that she/he signed her/his name thereto by like order.

[Signature of Notary Public]

Appendices to Part 261

Appendix I to Part 261—Representative Sampling Methods

18.5.1

The methods and equipment used for sampling waste materials will vary with the form and consistency of the waste materials to be sampled. Samples collected using the sampling protocols listed below, for sampling waste with properties similar to the indicated materials, will be considered by the Agency to be representative of the waste.

Extremely viscous liquid—ASTM Standard D140-70 Crushed or powdered material-ASTM Standard D346-75 Soil or rock-like material-ASTM Standard D420-69 Soil-like material-ASTM Standard D1452-65

Fly Ash-like material—ASTM Standard D2234-76 [ASTM Standards are available from ASTM, 1916 Race St., Philadelphia, PA 19103]

Containerized liquid waste—"COLIWASA."

Liquid waste in pits, ponds, lagoons, and similar reservoirs—"Pond Sampler."

This manual also contains additional information on application of these protocols.

45 FR 33119, May 19, 1980, as amended at 70 FR 34562, June 14, 2005]

Appendix II to Part 261 [Reserved]

Appendix III to Part 261 [Reserved]

Appendix IV to Part 261 [Reserved for Radioactive Waste Test Methods]

Appendix V to Part 261 [Reserved for Infectious Waste Treatment Specifications]

Appendix VI to Part 261 [Reserved for Etiologic Agents]

Appendix VII to Part 261—Basis for Listing Hazardous Waste

EPA hazardous waste No.	Hazardous constituents for which listed
F001	Tetrachloroethylene, methylene chloride trichloroethylene, 1,1,1- trichloroethane, carbon tetrachloride, chlorinated fluorocarbons
F002	Tetrachloroethylene, methylene chloride, trichloroethylene, 1,1,1- trichloroethane, 1,1,2- trichloroethane, chlorobenzene, 1,1,2- trichloro-1,2,2-trifluoroethane, ortho-dichlorobenzene, trichlorofluoromethane
F003	N.A.
F004	Cresols and cresylic acid, nitrobenzene
F005	Toluene, methyl ethyl ketone, carbon disulfide, isobutanol, pyridine, 2- ethoxyethanol, benzene, 2-nitropropane
F006	Cadmium, hexavalent chromium, nickel, cyanide (complexed)
F007	Cyanide (salts)
F008	Cyanide (salts)
F009	Cyanide (salts)
F010	Cyanide (salts)
F011	Cyanide (salts)
F012	Cyanide (complexed)
F019	Hexavalent chromium, cyanide (complexed)
F020	Tetra- and pentachlorodibenzo-p-dioxins; tetra and pentachlorodi- benzofurans; tri- and tetrachlorophenols and their chlorophenoxy derivative acids, esters, ethers, amine and other salts
F021	Penta- and hexachlorodibenzo-p- dioxins; penta- and hexachlorodibenzofurans; pentachlorophenol and its derivatives
F022	Tetra-, penta-, and hexachlorodibenzo-p-dioxins; tetra-, penta-, and hexachlorodibenzofurans

EPA hazardous waste No.	Hazardous constituents for which listed
F023	Tetra-, and pentachlorodibenzo-p- dioxins; tetra- and pentachlorodibenzofurans; tri- and tetrachlorophenols and their chlorophenoxy derivative acids, esters, ethers, amine and other salts
F024	Chloromethane, dichloromethane, trichloromethane, carbon tetrachloride, chloroethylene, 1,1- dichloroethane, 1,2-dichloroethane, trans-1-2-dichloroethylene, 1,1- dichloroethylene, 1,1,1- trichloroethane, 1,1,2-trichloroethane, trichloroethylene, 1,1,1,2-tetra-chloroethane, 1,1,2,2- tetrachloroethane, tetrachloroethylene, pentachloroethane, hexachloroethane, allyl chloride (3-chloropropene), dichloropropane, dichloropropene, 2- chloro-1,3-butadiene, hexachloro-1,3- butadiene, hexachlorocyclopentadiene, hexachlorocyclohexane, benzene, chlorbenzene, dichlorobenzenes, 1,2,4-trichlorobenzene, tetrachlorobenzene, pentachlorobenzene, hexachlorobenzene, toluene, naphthalene
F025	Chloromethane; Dichloromethane; Trichloromethane; Carbon tetrachloride; Chloroethylene; 1,1-Dichloroethane; 1,2-Dichloroethane; trans-1,2-Dichloroethylene; 1,1- Dichloroethylene; 1,1,1- Trichloroethane; 1,1,2- Trichloroethane; Trichloroethylene; 1,1,1,2-Tetra chloroethane; 1,1,2,2- Tetrachloroethane; Tetrachloroethylene; Pentachloroethane; Hexachloroethane; Allyl chloride (3-Chloropropene); Dichloropropane; Dichloropropene; 2- Chloro-1,3-butadiene; Hexachloro-1,3- butadiene; Hexachlorocyclopentadiene; Benzene; Chlorobenzene; Dichlorobenzene; 1,2,4- Trichlorobenzene; Tetrachlorobenzene; Pentachlorobenzene; Hexachlorobenzene; Toluene; Naphthalene
F026	Tetra-, penta-, and hexachlorodibenzo- p-dioxins; tetra-, penta-, and hexachlorodibenzofurans
F027	Tetra-, penta-, and hexachlorodibenzo- p- dioxins; tetra-, penta-, and hexachlorodibenzofurans; tri-, tetra-, and pentachlorophenols and their chlorophenoxy derivative acids, esters, ethers, amine and other salts
F028	Tetra-, penta-, and hexachlorodibenzo- p- dioxins; tetra-, penta-, and hexachlorodibenzofurans; tri-, tetra-, and pentachlorophenols and their chlorophenoxy derivative acids, esters, ethers, amine and other salts
F032	Benz(a)anthracene, benzo(a)pyrene, dibenz(a,h)-anthracene, indeno(1,2,3- cd)pyrene, pentachlorophenol, arsenic, chromium, tetra-, penta-, hexa-, heptachlorodibenzo-p-dioxins, tetra-, penta-, hexa-, heptachlorodibenzofurans
F034	Benz(a)anthracene, benzo(k)fluoranthene, benzo(a)pyrene, dibenz(a,h)anthracene, indeno(1,2,3-cd)pyrene, naphthalene, arsenic, chromium
F035	Arsenic, chromium, lead
F037	Benzene, benzo(a)pyrene, chrysene, lead, chromium
F038	Benzene, benzo(a)pyrene, chrysene, lead, chromium
F039	All constituents for which treatment standards are specified for multi-source leachate (wastewaters and nonwastewaters) under 40 CFR 268.43, Table CCW
K001	Pentachlorophenol, phenol, 2- chlorophenol, p-chloro-m-cresol, 2,4-dimethylphenyl, 2,4-dinitrophenol, trichlorophenols, tetrachlorophenols, 2,4-dinitrophenol, creosote, chrysene, naphthalene, fluoranthene, benzo(b)fluoranthene, benzo(a)pyrene, indeno(1,2,3-cd)pyrene, benz(a)anthracene, dibenz(a)anthracene, acenaphthalene
K002	Hexavalent chromium, lead
K003	Hexavalent chromium, lead
K004	Hexavalent chromium
K005	Hexavalent chromium, lead
K006	Hexavalent chromium
K007	Cyanide (complexed), hexavalent chromium
K008	Hexavalent chromium
K009	Chloroform, formaldehyde, methylene chloride, methyl chloride, paraldehyde, formic acid
K010	Chloroform, formaldehyde, methylene chloride, methyl chloride, paraldehyde, formic acid, chloroacetaldehyde
K011	Acrylonitrile, acetonitrile, hydrocyanic acid
K013	Hydrocyanic acid, acrylonitrile, acetonitrile
K014	Acetonitrile, acrylamide
K015	Benzyl chloride, chlorobenzene, toluene, benzotrichloride
K016	Hexachlorobenzene, hexachlorobutadiene, carbon tetrachloride, hexachloroethane, perchloroethylene
K017	Epichlorohydrin, chloroethers [bis(chloromethyl) ether and bis (2- chloroethyl) ethers], trichloropropane, dichloropropanols
K018	1,2-dichloroethane, trichloroethylene, hexachlorobutadiene, hexachlorobenzene
K019	Ethylene dichloride, 1,1,1- trichloroethane, 1,1,2- trichloroethane, tetrachloroethanes (1,1,2,2-tetrachloroethane and 1,1,1,2-tetrachloroethane), trichloroethylene, tetrachloroethylene, carbon tetrachloride, chloroform, vinyl chloride, vinylidene chloride
K020	Ethylene dichloride, 1,1,1- trichloroethane, 1,1,2- trichloroethane, tetrachloroethanes (1,1,2,2-tetrachloroethane and 1,1,1,2-tetrachloroethane), trichloroethylene, tetrachloroethylene, carbon tetrachloride, chloroform, vinyl chloride, vinylidene chloride
K021	Antimony, carbon tetrachloride, chloroform
K022	Phenol, tars (polycyclic aromatic hydrocarbons)
K023	Phthalic anhydride, maleic anhydride
K024	Phthalic anhydride, 1,4- naphthoquinone
K025	Meta-dinitrobenzene, 2,4- dinitrotoluene
K026	Paraldehyde, pyridines, 2-picoline
K027	Toluene diisocyanate, toluene-2, 4- diamine
K028	1,1,1-trichloroethane, vinyl chloride
K029	1,2-dichloroethane, 1,1,1- trichloroethane, vinyl chloride, vinylidene chloride, chloroform
K030	Hexachlorobenzene, hexachlorobutadiene, hexachloroethane, 1,1,1,2- tetrachloroethane, 1,1,2,2-tetrachloroethane, ethylene dichloride
K031	Arsenic
K032	Hexachlorocyclopentadiene
K033	Hexachlorocyclopentadiene
K034	Hexachlorocyclopentadiene
K035	Creosote, chrysene, naphthalene, fluoranthene benzo(b) fluoranthene, benzo(a)pyrene, indeno(1,2,3-cd) pyrene, benzo(a)anthracene, dibenzo(a)anthracene, acenaphthalene
K036	Toluene, phosphorodithioic and phosphorothioic acid esters

EPA hazardous waste No.	Hazardous constituents for which listed
K037	Toluene, phosphorodithioic and phosphorothioic acid esters
K038	Phorate, formaldehyde, phosphorodithioic and phosphorothioic acid esters
K039	Phosphorodithioic and phosphorothioic acid esters
K040	Phorate, formaldehyde, phosphorodithioic and phosphorothioic acid esters
K041	Toxaphene
K042	Hexachlorobenzene, ortho- dichlorobenzene
K043	2,4-dichlorophenol, 2,6- dichlorophenol, 2,4,6-trichlorophenol
K044	N.A.
K045	N.A.
K046	Lead
K047	N.A.
K048	Hexavalent chromium, lead
K049	Hexavalent chromium, lead
K050	Hexavalent chromium
K051	Hexavalent chromium, lead
K052	Lead
K060	Cyanide, napthalene, phenolic compounds, arsenic
K061	Hexavalent chromium, lead, cadmium
K062	Hexavalent chromium, lead
K064	Lead, cadmium
K065	Do
K066	Do
K069	Hexavalent chromium, lead, cadmium
K071	Mercury
K073	Chloroform, carbon tetrachloride, hexachloroethane, trichloroethane, tetrachloroethylene, dichloroethylene, 1,1,2,2- tetrachloroethane
K083	Aniline, diphenylamine, nitrobenzene, phenylenediamine
K084	Arsenic
K085	Benzene, dichlorobenzenes, trichlorobenzenes, tetrachlorobenzenes, pentachlorobenzene, hexachlorobenzene, benzyl chloride
K086	Lead, hexavalent chromium
K087	Phenol, naphthalene
K088	Cyanide (complexes)
K090	Chromium
K091	Do

Publisher's Note: K064, K065, K066, K090, and K091 were removed from the K-wastes in §261.32 (64 FR 56470, Oct. 20, 1999); however, EPA has not removed them from this Appendix VII.

EPA hazardous waste No.	Hazardous constituents for which listed
K093	Phthalic anhydride, maleic anhydride
K094	Phthalic anhydride
K095	1,1,2-trichloroethane, 1,1,1,2-tetrachloroethane, 1,1,2,2-tetrachloroethane
K096	1,2-dichloroethane, 1,1,1-trichloroethane, 1,1,2-trichloroethane
K097	Chlordane, heptachlor
K098	Toxaphene
K099	2,4-dichlorophenol, 2,4,6- trichlorophenol
K100	Hexavalent chromium, lead, cadmium
K101	Arsenic
K102	Arsenic
K103	Aniline, nitrobenzene, phenylenediamine
K104	Aniline, benzene, diphenylamine, nitrobenzene, phenylenediamine
K105	Benzene, monochlorobenzene, dichlorobenzenes, 2,4,6- trichlorophenol
K106	Mercury
K107	1,1-Dimethylhydrazine (UDMH)
K108	1,1-Dimethylhydrazine (UDMH)
K109	1,1-Dimethylhydrazine (UDMH)
K110	1,1-Dimethylhydrazine (UDMH)
K111	2,4-Dinitrotoluene
K112	2,4-Toluenediamine, o-toluidine, p-toluidine, aniline
K113	2,4-Toluenediamine, o-toluidine, p-toluidine, aniline
K114	2,4-Toluenediamine, o-toluidine, p-toluidine
K115	2,4-Toluenediamine
K116	Carbon tetrachloride, tetrachloroethylene, chloroform, phosgene
K117	Ethylene dibromide
K118	Ethylene dibromide
K123	Ethylene thiourea
K124	Ethylene thiourea
K125	Ethylene thiourea
K126	Ethylene thiourea
K131	Dimethyl sulfate, methyl bromide
K132	Methyl bromide
K136	Ethylene dibromide
K141	Benzene, benz(a)anthracene, benzo(a)pyrene, benzo(b)fluoranthene, benzo(k)fluoranthene, dibenz(a,h)anthracene, indeno(1,2,3- cd)pyrene
K142	Benzene, benz(a)anthracene, benzo(a)pyrene, benzo(b)fluoranthene, benzo(k)fluoranthene, dibenz(a,h)anthracene, indeno(1,2,3- cd)pyrene
K143	Benzene, benz(a)anthracene, benzo(b)fluoranthene, benzo(k)fluoranthene
K144	Benzene, benz(a)anthracene, benzo(a)pyrene, benzo(b)fluoranthene, benzo(k)fluoranthene, dibenz(a,h)anthracene
K145	Benzene, benz(a)anthracene, benzo(a)pyrene, dibenz(a,h)anthracene, naphthalene
K147	Benzene, benz(a)anthracene, benzo(a)pyrene, benzo(b)fluoranthene, benzo(k)fluoranthene, dibenz(a,h)anthracene, indeno(1,2,3-cd)pyrene
K148	Benz(a)anthracene, benzo(a)pyrene, benzo(b)fluoranthene, benzo(k)fluoranthene, dibenz(a,h)anthracene, indeno(1,2,3-cd)pyrene
K149	Benzotrichloride, benzyl chloride, chloroform, chloromethane, chlorobenzene, 1,4-dichlorobenzene, hexachlorobenzene, pentachlorobenzene, 1,2,4,5-tetrachlorobenzene, toluene

EPA hazardous waste No.	Hazardous constituents for which listed
K150	Carbon tetrachloride, chloroform, chloromethane, 1,4-dichlorobenzene, hexachlorobenzene, pentachlorobenzene, 1,2,4,5-tetrachlorobenzene, 1,1,2,2-tetrachloroethane, tetrachloroethylene, 1,2,4-trichlorobenzene
K151	Benzene, carbon tetrachloride, chloroform, hexachlorobenzene, pentachlorobenzene, toluene, 1,2,4,5-tetrachlorobenzene, tetrachloroethylene
K156	Benomyl, carbaryl, carbendazim, carbofuran, carbosulfan, formaldehyde, methylene chloride, triethylamine
K157	Carbon tetrachloride, formaldehyde, methyl chloride, methylene chloride, pyridine, triethylamine
K158	Benomyl, carbendazim, carbofuran, carbosulfan, chloroform, methylene chloride
K159	Benzene, butylate, eptc, molinate, pebulate, vernolate
K161	Antimony, arsenic, metam-sodium, ziram
K169	Benzene
K170	Benzo(a)pyrene, dibenz(a,h)anthracene, benzo (a) anthracene, benzo (b)fluoranthene, benzo(k)fluoranthene, 3-methylcholanthrene, 7,12-dimethylbenz(a)anthracene
K171	Benzene, arsenic
K172	Benzene, arsenic
K174	1,2,3,4,6,7,8-Heptachlorodibenzo-p-dioxin (1,2,3,4,6,7,8-HpCDD), 1,2,3,4,6,7,8-Heptachlorodibenzofuran (1,2,3,4,6,7,8-HpCDF), 1,2,3,4,7,8,9-Heptachlorodibenzofuran (1,2,3,6,7,8,9-HpCDF), HxCDDs (All Hexachlorodibenzo-p-dioxins), HxCDFs (All Hexachlorodibenzofurans), PeCDDs (All Pentachlorodibenzo-p-dioxins), OCDD (1,2,3,4,6,7,8,9-Octachlorodibenzo-p-dioxin, OCDF (1,2,3,4,6,7,8,9-Octachlorodibenzofuran), PeCDFs (All Pentachlorodibenzofurans), TCDDs (All tetrachlorodi-benzo-p-dioxins), TCDFs (All tetrachlorodibenzofurans)
K175	Mercury
K176	Arsenic, Lead
K177	Antimony
K178	Thallium
K181	Aniline, o-anisidine, 4-chloroaniline, p-cresidine, 2,4-dimethylaniline, 1,2-phenylenediamine, 1,3-phenylenediamine.

N.A.—Waste is hazardous because it fails the test for the characteristic of ignitability, corrosivity, or reactivity.

[46 FR 4619, Jan. 16, 1981, as amended at 46 FR 27477, May 20, 1981; 49 FR 5312, Feb. 10, 1984; 50 FR 2000, Jan. 14, 1985; 50 FR 42942, Oct. 23, 1985; 51 FR 5330, Feb. 13, 1986; 51 FR 6541, Feb. 25, 1986; 51 FR 37729, Oct. 24, 1986; 53 FR 35421, Sept. 13, 1988; 54 FR 41407, Oct. 6, 1989; 54 FR 50978, Dec. 11, 1989; 55 FR 18505, May 2, 1990; 55 FR 22684, June 1, 1990; 55 FR 46396, Nov. 2, 1990; 55 FR 50483, Dec. 6, 1990; 57 FR 37305, Aug. 18, 1992; 57 FR 47385, Oct. 15, 1992; 60 FR 7853, Feb. 9, 1995; 62 FR 32977, June 17, 1997; 63 FR 24625, May 4, 1998; 63 FR 42186, Aug. 6, 1998; 65 FR 14474, Mar. 17, 2000; 65 FR 67127, Nov. 8, 2000; 66 FR 58298, Nov. 20, 2001; 70 FR 9177, Feb. 24, 2005; 71 FR 40271, July 14, 2006]

Appendix VIII to Part 261—Hazardous Constituents

17.3, 18.2

Common name	Chemical abstracts name	Chemical abstracts No.	Hazardous waste No.
A2213	Ethanimidothioic acid, 2-(dimethylamino) -N-hydroxy-2-oxo-, methyl ester	30558-43-1	U394
Acetonitrile	Same	75-05-8	U003
Acetophenone	Ethanone, 1-phenyl-	98-86-2	U004
2-Acetylamine-fluarone	Acetamide, N-9H-fluoren-2-yl-	53-96-3	U005
Acetyl chloride	Same	75-36-5	U006
1-Acetyl-2-thiourea	Acetamide, N-(amino-thioxomethyl)-	591-08-2	P002
Acrolein	2-Propenal	107-02-8	P003
Acrylamide	2-Propenamide	79-06-1	U007
Acrylonitrile	2-Propenenitrile	107-13-1	U009
Aflatoxins	Same	1402-68-2	
Aldicarb	Propanal, 2-methyl-2-(methylthio)-, O-[(methylamino)carbonyl]oxime	116-06-3	P070
Aldicarb sulfone	Propanal, 2-methyl-2-(methylsulfonyl) -, O-[(methylamino) carbonyl] oxime	1646-88-4	P203
Aldrin	1,4,5,8-Dimethanonaphthalene, 1,2,3,4,10,10-10-hexachloro- 1,4,4a,5,8,8a-hexahydro-, (1alpha, 4alpha, 4abeta, 5alpha, 8alpha, 8abeta)-	309-00-2	P004
Allyl alcohol	2-Propen-1-ol	107-18-6	P005
Allyl chloride	1-Propane, 3-chloro	107-05-1	
Aluminum phosphide	Same	20859-73-8	P006
4-Aminobiphenyl	[1,1′-Biphenyl]-4-amine	92-67-1	
5-(Aminomethyl)-3-isoxazolol	3(2H)-Isoxazolone, 5-(aminomethyl)-	2763-96-4	P007
4-Aminopyridine	4-Pyridinamine	504-24-5	P008
Amitrole	1H-1,2,4-Triazol-3-amine	61-82-5	U011
Ammonium vanadate	Vanadic acid, ammonium salt	7803-55-6	P119
Aniline	Benzenamine	62-53-3	U012
o-Anisidine (2-methoxyaniline)	Benzenamine, 2-Methoxy-	90–04–0	
Antimony	Same	7440-36-0	
Antimony compounds, N.O.S. [1]			
Aramite	Sulfurous acid, 2-chloroethyl 2-[4-(1,1-dimethyl ethyl)phenoxy]-1-methylethyl ester	140-57-8	
Arsenic	Same	7440-38-2	
Arsenic compounds, N.O.S. [1]			

Common name	Chemical abstracts name	Chemical abstracts No.	Hazardous waste No.
Arsenic acid	Arsenic acid $H_3 AsO_4$	7778-39-4	P010
Arsenic pentoxide	Arsenic oxide $As_2 O_5$	1303-28-2	P011
Arsenic trioxide	Arsenic oxide $As_2 O_3$	1327-53-3	P012
Auramine	Benzenamine, 4,4′-carbonimidoylbis[N,N-dimethyl	492-80-8	U014
Azaserine	L-Serine, diazoacetate (ester)	115-02-6	U015
Barban	Carbamic acid, (3-chlorophenyl) -, 4-chloro-2-butynyl ester	101-27-9	U280
Barium	Same	7440-39-3	
Barium compounds, N.O.S. [1]			
Barium cyanide	Same	542-62-1	P013
Bendiocarb	1,3-Benzodioxol-4-ol, 2,2-dimethyl-, methyl carbamate	22781-23-3	U278
Bendiocarb phenol	1,3-Benzodioxol-4-ol, 2,2-dimethyl-,	22961-82-6	U364
Benomyl	Carbamic acid, [1- [(butylamino) carbonyl]- 1H-benzimidazol-2-yl] -, methyl ester	17804-35-2	U271
Benz[c]acridine	Same	225-51-4	U016
Benz[a]anthracene	Same	56-55-3	U018
Benzal chloride	Benzene, (dichloromethyl)-	98-87-3	U017
Benzene	Same	71-43-2	U019
Benzenearsonic acid	Arsonic acid, phenyl-	98-05-5	
Benzidine	[1,1′-Biphenyl]-4,4′-diamine	92-87-5	U021
Benzo[b]fluoranthene	Benz[e]acephenanthrylene	205-99-2	
Benzo[j]fluoranthene	Same	205-82-3	
Benzo(k)fluoranthene	Same	207-08-9	
Benzo[a]pyrene	Same	50-32-8	U022
p-Benzoquinone	2,5-Cyclohexadiene-1,4-dione	106-51-4	U197
Benzotrichloride	Benzene, (trichloromethyl)-	98-07-7	U023
Benzyl chloride	Benzene, (chloromethyl)-	100-44-7	P028
Beryllium powder	Same	7440-41-7	P015
Beryllium compounds, N.O.S. [1]			
Bis(pentamethylene)-thiuram tetrasulfide	Piperidine, 1,1′-(tetrathiodicarbonothioyl)-bis-	120-54-7	
Bromoacetone	2-Propanone, 1-bromo-	598-31-2	P017
Bromoform	Methane, tribromo-	75-25-2	U225
4-Bromophenyl phenyl ether	Benzene, 1-bromo-4-phenoxy-	101-55-3	U030
Brucine	Strychnidin-10-one, 2,3-dimethoxy-	357-57-3	P018
Butyl benzyl phthalate	1,2-Benzenedicarboxylic acid, butyl phenylmethyl ester	85-68-7	
Butylate	Carbamothioic acid, bis(2-methylpropyl)-, S-ethyl ester	2008-41-5	
Cacodylic acid	Arsinic acid, dimethyl-	75-60-5	U136
Cadmium	Same	7440-43-9	
Cadmium compounds, N.O.S. [1]			
Calcium chromate	Chromic acid $H_2 CrO_4$, calcium salt	13765-19-0	U032
Calcium cyanide	Calcium cyanide $Ca(CN)_2$	592-01-8	P021
Carbaryl	1-Naphthalenol, methylcarbamate	63-25-2	U279
Carbendazim	Carbamic acid, 1H-benzimidazol-2-yl, methyl ester	10605-21-7	U372
Carbofuran	7-Benzofuranol, 2,3-dihydro-2,2-dimethyl-, methylcarbamate	1563-66-2	P127
Carbofuran phenol	7-Benzofuranol, 2,3-dihydro-2,2-dimethyl-	1563-38-8	U367
Carbon disulfide	Same	75-15-0	P022
Carbon oxyfluoride	Carbonic difluoride	353-50-4	U033
Carbon tetrachloride	Methane, tetrachloro-	56-23-5	U211
Carbosulfan	Carbamic acid, [(dibutylamino) thio] methyl-, 2,3-dihydro-2,2-dimethyl-7-benzofuranyl ester	55285-14-8	P189
Chloral	Acetaldehyde, trichloro-	75-87-6	U034
Chlorambucil	Benzenebutanoic acid, 4-[bis(2-chloroethyl)amino]-	305-03-3	U035
Chlordane	4,7-Methano-1H-indene, 1,2,4,5,6,7,8,8-octachloro-2,3,3a,4,7,7a-hexahydro-	57-74-9	U036
Chlordane (alpha and gamma isomers)			U036
Chlorinated benzenes, N.O.S.[1]			
Chlorinated ethane, N.O.S. [1]			
Chlorinated fluorocarbons, N.O.S. [1]			
Chlorinated naphthalene, N.O.S. [1]			

PART 261—Appendices

Common name	Chemical abstracts name	Chemical abstracts No.	Hazardous waste No.
Chlorinated phenol, N.O.S. [1]			
Chlornaphazin	Naphthalenamine, N,N'-bis(2-chloroethyl)-	494-03-1	U026
Chloroacetaldehyde	Acetaldehyde, chloro-	107-20-0	P023
Chloroalkyl ethers, N.O.S. [1]			
p-Chloroaniline	Benzenamine, 4-chloro-	106-47-8	P024
Chlorobenzene	Benzene, chloro-	108-90-7	U037
Chlorobenzilate	Benzeneacetic acid, 4-chloro-alpha-(4-chlorophenyl)-alpha-hydroxy-, ethyl ester	510-15-6	U038
p-Chloro-m-cresol	Phenol, 4-chloro-3-methyl-	59-50-7	U039
2-Chloroethyl vinyl ether	Ethene, (2-chloroethoxy)-	110-75-8	U042
Chloroform	Methane, trichloro-	67-66-3	U044
Chloromethyl methyl ether	Methane, chloromethoxy-	107-30-2	U046
beta-Chloronaphthalene	Naphthalene, 2-chloro-	91-58-7	U047
o-Chlorophenol	Phenol, 2-chloro-	95-57-8	U048
1-(o-Chlorophenyl)thiourea	Thiourea, (2-chlorophenyl)-	5344-82-1	P026
Chloroprene	1,3-Butadiene, 2-chloro-	126-99-8	
3-Chloropropionitrile	Propanenitrile, 3-chloro-	542-76-7	P027
Chromium	Same	7440-47-3	
Chromium compounds, N.O.S. [1]			
Chrysene	Same	218-01-9	U050
Citrus red No. 2	2-Naphthalenol, 1-[(2,5-dimethoxyphenyl)azo]-	6358-53-8	
Coal tar creosote	Same	8007-45-2	
Copper cyanide	Copper cyanide CuCN	544-92-3	P029
Copper dimethyldithiocarbamate	Copper, bis(dimethylcarbamodithioato-S,S')-,	137-29-1	
Creosote	Same		U051
p-Cresidine	2-Methoxy-5-methylbenzenamine	120–71–8	
Cresol (Cresylic acid)	Phenol, methyl-	1319-77-3	U052
Crotonaldehyde	2-Butenal	4170-30-3	U053
m-Cumenyl methylcarbamate	Phenol, 3-(methylethyl)-, methyl carbamate	64-00-6	P202
Cyanides (soluble salts and complexes) N.O.S. [1]			P030
Cyanogen	Ethanedinitrile	460-19-5	P031
Cyanogen bromide	Cyanogen bromide (CN)Br	506-68-3	U246
Cyanogen chloride	Cyanogen chloride (CN)Cl	506-77-4	P033
Cycasin	beta-D-Glucopyranoside, (methyl-ONN-azoxy)methyl	14901-08-7	
Cycloate	Carbamothioic acid, cyclohexylethyl-, S-ethyl ester	1134-23-2	
2-Cyclohexyl-4,6-dinitrophenol	Phenol, 2-cyclohexyl-4,6-dinitro-	131-89-5	P034
Cyclophosphamide	2H-1,3,2-Oxazaphosphorin-2-amine, N,N-bis(2-chloroethyl)tetrahydro-, 2-oxide	50-18-0	U058
2,4-D	Acetic acid, (2,4-dichlorophenoxy)-	94-75-7	U240
2,4-D, salts, esters			U240
Daunomycin	5,12-Naphthacenedione, 8-acetyl-10-[(3-amino-2,3,6-trideoxy-alpha-L-lyxo- hexopyranosyl)oxy]-7,8,9,10 tetrahydro-6,8,11-trihydroxy-1-methoxy-, (8S-cis)-	20830-81-3	U059
Dazomet	2H-1,3,5-thiadiazine-2-thione, tetrahydro-3,5-dimethyl	533-74-4	
DDD	Benzene, 1,1'-(2,2-dichloroethylidene)bis[4-chloro-	72-54-8	U060
DDE	Benzene, 1,1'-(dichloroethenylidene)bis[4-chloro-	72-55-9	
DDT	Benzene, 1,1'-(2,2,2-trichloroethylidene)bis[4-chloro-	50-29-3	U061
Diallate	Carbamothioic acid, bis(1-methylethyl)-, S-(2,3-dichloro-2-propenyl) ester	2303-16-4	U062
Dibenz[a,h]acridine	Same	226-36-8	
Dibenz[a,j]acridine	Same	224-42-0	
Dibenz[a,h]anthracene	Same	53-70-3	U063
7H-Dibenzo[c,g]carbazole	Same	194-59-2	
Dibenzo[a,e]pyrene	Naphtho[1,2,3,4-def]chrysene	192-65-4	
Dibenzo[a,h]pyrene	Dibenzo[b,def]chrysene	189-64-0	
Dibenzo[a,i]pyrene	Benzo[rst]pentaphene	189-55-9	U064
1,2-Dibromo-3-chloropropane	Propane, 1,2-dibromo-3-chloro-	96-12-8	U066

Common name	Chemical abstracts name	Chemical abstracts No.	Hazardous waste No.
Dibutyl phthalate	1,2-Benzenedicarboxylic acid, dibutyl ester	84-74-2	U069
o-Dichlorobenzene	Benzene, 1,2-dichloro-	95-50-1	U070
m-Dichlorobenzene	Benzene, 1,3-dichloro-	541-73-1	U071
p-Dichlorobenzene	Benzene, 1,4-dichloro-	106-46-7	U072
Dichlorobenzene, N.O.S. [1]	Benzene, dichloro-	25321-22-6	
3,3′-Dichlorobenzidine	[1,1′-Biphenyl]-4,4′-diamine, 3,3′-dichloro-	91-94-1	U073
1,4-Dichloro-2-butene	2-Butene, 1,4-dichloro-	764-41-0	U074
Dichlorodifluoromethane	Methane, dichlorodifluoro-	75-71-8	U075
Dichloroethylene, N.O.S. [1]	Dichloroethylene	25323-30-2	
1,1-Dichloroethylene	Ethene, 1,1-dichloro-	75-35-4	U078
1,2-Dichloroethylene	Ethene, 1,2-dichloro-, (E)-	156-60-5	U079
Dichloroethyl ether	Ethane, 1,1′oxybis [2-chloro-	111-44-4	U025
Dichloroisopropyl ether	Propane, 2,2′-oxybis[2-chloro-	108-60-1	U027
Dichloromethoxy ethane	Ethane, 1,1′-[methylenebis(oxy)]bis[2-chloro-	111-91-1	U024
Dichloromethyl ether	Methane, oxybis[chloro-	542-88-1	P016
2,4-Dichlorophenol	Phenol, 2,4-dichloro-	120-83-2	U081
2,6-Dichlorophenol	Phenol, 2,6-dichloro-	87-65-0	U082
Dichlorophenylarsine	Arsonous dichloride, phenyl-	696-28-6	P036
Dichloropropane, N.O.S. [1]	Propane, dichloro-	26638-19-7	
Dichloropropanol, N.O.S. [1]	Propanol, dichloro-	26545-73-3	
Dichloropropene, N.O.S. [1]	1-Propene, dichloro-	26952-23-8	
1,3-Dichloropropene	1-Propene, 1,3-dichloro-	542-75-6	U084
Dieldrin	2,7:3,6-Dimethanonaphth[2,3-b]oxirene, 3,4,5,6,9,9-hexachloro-1a,2,2a,3,6,6a,7,7a-octahydro-, (1aalpha,2beta, 2aalpha,3beta,6beta, 6aalpha,7beta,7aalpha)-	60-57-1	P037
1,2:3,4-Diepoxybutane	2,2-Bioxirane	1464-53-5	U085
Diethylarsine	Arsine, diethyl-	692-42-2	P038
Diethylene glycol, dicarbamate	Ethanol, 2,2′-oxybis-, dicarbamate	5952-26-1	U395
1,4-Diethyleneoxide	1,4-Dioxane	123-91-1	U108
Diethylhexyl phthalate	1,2-Benzenedicarboxylic acid, bis(2-ethylhexyl) ester	117-81-7	U028
N,N′-Diethylhydrazine	Hydrazine, 1,2-diethyl-	1615-80-1	U086
O,O-Diethyl S-methyl dithiophosphate	Phosphorodithioic acid, O,O-diethyl S-methyl ester	3288-58-2	U087
Diethyl-p-nitrophenyl phosphate	Phosphoric acid, diethyl 4-nitrophenyl ester	311-45-5	P041
Diethyl phthalate	1,2-Benzenedicarboxylic acid, diethyl ester	84-66-2	U088
O,O-Diethyl O-pyrazinyl phosphorothioate	Phosphorothioic acid, O,O-diethyl O-pyrazinyl ester	297-97-2	P040
Diethylstilbesterol	Phenol, 4,4′-(1,2-diethyl-1,2-ethenediyl)bis-, (E)-	56-53-1	U089
Dihydrosafrole	1,3-Benzodioxole, 5-propyl-	94-58-6	U090
Diisopropylfluorophosphate (DFP)	Phosphorofluoridic acid, bis(1-methylethyl) ester	55-91-4	P043
Dimethoate	Phosphorodithioic acid, O,O-dimethyl S-[2-(methylamino)-2-oxoethyl] ester	60-51-5	P044
3,3′-Dimethoxybenzidine	[1,1′-Biphenyl]-4,4′-diamine, 3,3′-dimethoxy-	119-90-4	U091
p-Dimethylaminoazobenzene	Benzenamine, N,N-dimethyl-4-(phenylazo)-	60-11-7	U093
2,4-Dimethylaniline (2,4-xylidine)	Benzenamine, 2,4-dimethyl-	95–68–1	
7,12-Dimethylbenz[a]anthracene	Benz[a]anthracene, 7,12-dimethyl-	57-97-6	U094
3,3′-Dimethylbenzidine	[1,1′-Biphenyl]-4,4′-diamine, 3,3′-dimethyl-	119-93-7	U095
Dimethylcarbamoyl chloride	Carbamic chloride, dimethyl-	79-44-7	U097
1,1-Dimethylhydrazine	Hydrazine, 1,1-dimethyl-	57-14-7	U098
1,2-Dimethylhydrazine	Hydrazine, 1,2-dimethyl-	540-73-8	U099
alpha,alpha-Dimethylphenethylamine	Benzeneethanamine, alpha,alpha-dimethyl-	122-09-8	P046
2,4-Dimethylphenol	Phenol, 2,4-dimethyl-	105-67-9	U101
Dimethyl phthalate	1,2-Benzenedicarboxylic acid, dimethyl ester	131-11-3	U102
Dimethyl sulfate	Sulfuric acid, dimethyl ester	77-78-1	U103

Common name	Chemical abstracts name	Chemical abstracts No.	Haz-ardous waste No.
Dimetilan	Carbamic acid, dimethyl-, 1-[(dimethylamino) car-bonyl]-5-methyl-1H-pyrazol-3-yl ester	644-64-4	P191
Dinitrobenzene, N.O.S. [1]	Benzene, dinitro-	25154-54-5	
4,6-Dinitro-o-cresol	Phenol, 2-methyl-4,6-dinitro-	534-52-1	P047
4,6-Dinitro-o-cresol salts			P047
2,4-Dinitrophenol	Phenol, 2,4-dinitro-	51-28-5	P048
2,4-Dinitrotoluene	Benzene, 1-methyl-2,4-dinitro-	121-14-2	U105
2,6-Dinitrotoluene	Benzene, 2-methyl-1,3-dinitro-	606-20-2	U106
Dinoseb	Phenol, 2-(1-methyl-propyl)-4,6-dinitro-	88-85-7	P020
Di-n-octyl phthalate	1,2-Benzenedicarboxylic acid, dioctyl ester	117-84-0	U017
Diphenylamine	Benzenamine, N-phenyl-	122-39-4	
1,2-Diphenyl-hydrazine	Hydrazine, 1,2-diphenyl-	122-66-7	U109
Di-n-propylnitros-amine	1-Propanamine, N-nitroso-N-propyl-	621-64-7	U111
Disulfiram	Thioperoxydicarbonic diamide, tetraethyl	97-77-8	
Disulfoton	Phosphorodithioic acid, O,O-diethyl S-[2-(ethylthio)ethyl] ester	298-04-4	P039
Dithiobiuret	Thioimidodicarbonic diamide $[(H_2N)C(S)]_2NH$	541-53-7	P049
Endosulfan	6,9-Methano-2,4,3-benzodioxathiepin, 6,7,8,9,10,10-hexa-chloro-1,5,5a,6,9,9a-hexahydro-, 3-oxide	115-29-7	P050
Endothall	7-Oxabicyclo[2.2.1]hep-tane-2,3-dicarboxylic acid	145-73-3	P088
Endrin	2,7:3,6-Dimethano-naphth[2,3-b]oxirene, 3,4,5,6,9,9-hexachloro-1a,2,2a,3,6,6a,7,7a-octa-hydro-, (1aalpha,2beta, 2abeta,3alpha,6alpha, 6abeta,7beta,7aalpha)-	72-20-8	P051
Endrin metabolites			P051
Epichlorohydrin	Oxirane, (chloromethyl)-	106-89-8	U041
Epinephrine	1,2-Benzenediol, 4-[1-hydroxy-2-(methyl-amino)ethyl]-, (R)-	51-43-4	P042
EPTC	Carbamothioic acid, dipropyl-, S-ethyl ester	759-94-4	
Ethyl carbamate (urethane)	Carbamic acid, ethyl ester	51-79-6	U238
Ethyl cyanide	Propanenitrile	107-12-0	P101
Ethyl Ziram	Zinc, bis(diethyl-carbamodithioato-S,S')-	14324-55-1	
Ethylenebisdithio carbamic acid	Carbamodithioic acid, 1,2-ethanediylbis-	111-54-6	U114
Ethylenebisdithio carbamic acid, salts and esters			U114
Ethylene dibromide	Ethane, 1,2-dibromo-	106-93-4	U067
Ethylene dichloride	Ethane, 1,2-dichloro-	107-06-2	U077
Ethylene glycol monoethyl ether	Ethanol, 2-ethoxy-	110-80-5	U359
Ethyleneimine	Aziridine	151-56-4	P054
Ethylene oxide	Oxirane	75-21-8	U115
Ethylenethiourea	2-Imidazolidinethione	96-45-7	U116
Ethylidene dichloride	Ethane, 1,1-dichloro-	75-34-3	U076
Ethyl methacrylate	2-Propenoic acid, 2-methyl-, ethyl ester	97-63-2	U118
Ethyl methane-sulfonate	Methanesulfonic acid, ethyl ester	62-50-0	U119
Famphur	Phosphorothioic acid, O-[4-[(dimethyl-amino)sulfonyl]phenyl] O,O-dimethyl ester	52-85-7	P097
Ferbam	Iron, tris(dimethyl-carbamodithioato-S,S')-,	14484-64-1	
Fluoranthene	Same	206-44-0	U120
Fluorine	Same	7782-41-4	P056
Fluoroacetamide	Acetamide, 2-fluoro-	640-19-7	P057
Fluoroacetic acid, sodium salt	Acetic acid, fluoro-, sodium salt	62-74-8	P058
Formaldehyde	Same	50-00-0	U122
Formetanate hydrochloride	Methanimidamide, N,N-dimethyl-N'-[3-[[(methylamino) car-bonyl]oxy] phenyl]-, monohydrochloride	23422-53-9	P198
Formic acid	Same	64-18-6	U123
Formparanate	Methanimidamide, N,N-dimethyl-N'-[2-methyl-4-[[(methylamino) car-bonyl] oxy]phenyl]-	17702-57-7	P197
Glycidylaldehyde	Oxiranecarboxyaldehyde	765-34-4	U126
Halomethanes, N.O.S. [1]			
Heptachlor	4,7-Methano-1H-indene,1,4,5,6,7,8,8-heptachloro-3a,4,7,7a-tetrahydro-	76-44-8	P059

Common name	Chemical abstracts name	Chemical abstracts No.	Hazardous waste No.
Heptachlor epoxide	2,5-Methano-2H-indeno[1,2-b]oxirene, 2,3,4,5,6,7,7-hepta-chloro-1a,1b,5,5a,6,6a-hexa-hydro-,(1aalpha, 1bbeta,2alpha,5alpha, 5abeta,6beta,6aalpha)-	1024-57-3	
Heptachlor epoxide (alpha, beta, and gamma isomers)			
Heptachlorodi-benzofurans			
Heptachlorodi-benzo-p-dioxins			
Hexachloroben-zene	Benzene, hexachloro-	118-74-1	U127
Hexachloro-butadiene	1,3-Butadiene, 1,1,2,3,4,4-hexachloro-	87-68-3	U128
Hexachlorocyclo-pentadiene	1,3-Cyclopentadiene, 1,2,3,4,5,5-hexachloro-	77-47-4	U130
Hexachlorodi-benzo-p-dioxins			
Hexachlorodi-benzofurans			
Hexachloroethane	Ethane, hexachloro-	67-72-1	U131
Hexachlorophene	Phenol, 2,2′-methylene-bis[3,4,6-trichloro-	70-30-4	U132
Hexachloro-propene	1-Propene, 1,1,2,3,3,3-hexachloro-	1888-71-7	U243
Hexaethyl tetraphosphate	Tetraphosphoric acid, hexaethyl ester	757-58-4	P062
Hydrazine	Same	302-01-2	U133
Hydrogen cyanide	Hydrocyanic acid	74-90-8	P063
Hydrogen fluoride	Hydrofluoric acid	7664-39-3	U134
Hydrogen sulfide	Hydrogen sulfide H_2S	7783-06-4	U135
Indeno[1,2,3-cd]pyrene	Same	193-39-5	U137
3-Iodo-2-propynyl n-butylcarbamate	Carbamic acid, butyl-, 3-iodo-2-propynyl ester	55406-53-6	
Isobutyl alcohol	1-Propanol, 2-methyl-	78-83-1	U140
Isodrin	1,4,5,8-Dimethano-naphthalene,1,2,3,4,10, 10-hexachloro-1,4,4a,5,8, 8a-hexahydro-, (1alpha, 4alpha,4abeta,5beta, 8beta,8abeta)-	465-73-6	P060
Isolan	Carbamic acid, dimethyl-, 3-methyl-1-(1-methylethyl)-1H-pyrazol-5-yl ester	119-38-0	P192
Isosafrole	1,3-Benzodioxole, 5-(1-propenyl)-	120-58-1	U141
Kepone	1,3,4-Metheno-2H-cyclo-buta[cd]pentalen-2-one, 1,1a,3,3a,4,5,5,5a,5b,6-decachlorooctahydro-	143-50-0	U142

Common name	Chemical abstracts name	Chemical abstracts No.	Hazardous waste No.
Lasiocarpine	2-Butenoic acid, 2-methyl-,7-[[2,3-dihy-droxy-2-(1-methoxy-ethyl)-3-methyl-1- oxo-butoxy]methyl]-2,3,5,7a-tetrahydro-1H-pyrrolizin-1-yl ester, [1S-[1alpha(Z), 7(2S*,3R*), 7aalpha]]-	303-34-4	U143
Lead	Same	7439-92-1	
Lead compounds, N.O.S.[1]			
Lead acetate	Acetic acid, lead(2+) salt	301-04-2	U144
Lead phosphate	Phosphoric acid, lead(2+) salt (2:3)	7446-27-7	U145
Lead subacetate	Lead, bis(acetato-O)tetrahydroxytri-	1335-32-6	U146
Lindane	Cyclohexane, 1,2,3,4,5,6-hexachloro-, (1alpha, 2alpha,3beta,4alpha,5al pha,6beta)-	58-89-9	U129
Maleic anhydride	2,5-Furandione	108-31-6	U147
Maleic hydrazide	3,6-Pyridazinedione, 1,2-dihydro-	123-33-1	U148
Malononitrile	Propanedinitrile	109-77-3	U149
Manganese dimethyldithiocar bamate	Manganese, bis(dimethylcarbamodit hioato-S,S′)-,	15339-36-3	P196
Melphalan	L-Phenylalanine, 4-[bis(2-chloro-ethyl)aminol]-	148-82-3	U150
Mercury	Same	7439-97-6	U151
Mercury com-pounds, N.O.S.[1]			
Mercury fulminate	Fulminic acid, mercury(2+) salt	628-86-4	P065
Metam Sodium	Carbamodithioic acid, methyl-, monosodium salt	137-42-8	
Methacrylonitrile	2-Propenenitrile, 2-methyl-	126-98-7	U152
Methapyrilene	1,2-Ethanediamine, N,N-dimethyl-N′-2-pyridinyl-N′-(2-thienylmethyl)-	91-80-5	U155
Methiocarb	Phenol, (3,5-dimethyl-4-(methylthio)-, methylcarbamate	2032-65-7	P199
Methomyl	Ethanimidothioic acid, N-[[(methylamino)car-bonyl]oxy]-,methyl ester	16752-77-5	P066
Methoxychlor	Benzene, 1,1′-(2,2,2-trichloroethylidene) bis[4-methoxy-	72-43-5	U247
Methyl bromide	Methane, bromo-	74-83-9	U029
Methyl chloride	Methane, chloro-	74-87-3	U045
Methyl chlorocarbonate	Carbonochloridic acid, methyl ester	79-22-1	U156
Methyl chloroform	Ethane, 1,1,1-trichloro-	71-55-6	U226

Common name	Chemical abstracts name	Chemical abstracts No.	Hazardous waste No.
3-Methylcholanthrene	Benz[j]aceanthrylene, 1,2-dihydro-3-methyl-	56-49-5	U157
4,4′-Methylenebis(2-chloroaniline)	Benzenamine, 4,4′-methylenebis[2-chloro-	101-14-4	U158
Methylene bromide	Methane, dibromo-	74-95-3	U068
Methylene chloride	Methane, dichloro-	75-09-2	U080
Methyl ethyl ketone (MEK)	2-Butanone	78-93-3	U159
Methyl ethyl ketone peroxide	2-Butanone, peroxide	1338-23-4	U160
Methyl hydrazine	Hydrazine, methyl-	60-34-4	P068
Methyl iodide	Methane, iodo-	74-88-4	U138
Methyl isocyanate	Methane, isocyanato-	624-83-9	P064
2-Methyllactonitrile	Propanenitrile, 2-hydroxy-2-methyl-	75-86-5	P069
Methyl methacrylate	2-Propenoic acid, 2-methyl-, methyl ester	80-62-6	U162
Methyl methanesulfonate	Methanesulfonic acid, methyl ester	66-27-3	
Methyl parathion	Phosphorothioic acid, O,O-dimethyl O-(4-nitrophenyl) ester	298-00-0	P071
Methylthiouracil	4(1H)-Pyrimidinone, 2,3-dihydro-6-methyl-2-thioxo-	56-04-2	U164
Metolcarb	Carbamic acid, methyl-, 3-methylphenyl ester	1129-41-5	P190
Mexacarbate	Phenol, 4-(dimethylamino)-3,5-dimethyl-, methylcarbamate (ester)	315-18-4	P128
Mitomycin C	Azirino[2′,3′:3,4]pyrrolo[1,2-a]indole-4,7-dione, 6-amino-8-[[(aminocarbonyl)oxy]methyl]-1,1a,2,8,8a,8b-hexahydro-8a-methoxy-5- methyl-, [1aS-(1aalpha,8beta,8aalpha,8balpha)]-	50-07-7	U010
MNNG	Guanidine, N-methyl-N′-nitro-N-nitroso-	70-25-7	U163
Molinate	1H-Azepine-1-carbothioic acid, hexahydro-, S-ethyl ester	2212-67-1	
Mustard gas	Ethane, 1,1′-thiobis[2-chloro-	505-60-2	
Naphthalene	Same	91-20-3	U165
1,4-Naphthoquinone	1,4-Naphthalenedione	130-15-4	U166
alpha-Naphthylamine	1-Naphthalenamine	134-32-7	U167
beta-Naphthylamine	2-Naphthalenamine	91-59-8	U168
alpha-Naphthylthiourea	Thiourea, 1-naphthalenyl-	86-88-4	P072
Nickel	Same	7440-02-0	
Nickel compounds, N.O.S.[1]			
Nickel carbonyl	Nickel carbonyl $Ni(CO)_4$, (T-4)-	13463-39-3	P073
Nickel cyanide	Nickel cyanide $Ni(CN)_2$	557-19-7	P074
Nicotine	Pyridine, 3-(1-methyl-2-pyrrolidinyl)-, (S)-	54-11-5	P075
Nicotine salts			P075
Nitric oxide	Nitrogen oxide NO	10102-43-9	P076
p-Nitroaniline	Benzenamine, 4-nitro-	100-01-6	P077
Nitrobenzene	Benzene, nitro-	98-95-3	U169
Nitrogen dioxide	Nitrogen oxide NO_2	10102-44-0	P078
Nitrogen mustard	Ethanamine, 2-chloro-N-(2-chloroethyl)-N-methyl-	51-75-2	
Nitrogen mustard, hydrochloride salt			
Nitrogen mustard N-oxide	Ethanamine, 2-chloro-N-(2-chloroethyl)-N-methyl-, N-oxide	126-85-2	
Nitrogen mustard, N-oxide, hydrochloride salt			
Nitroglycerin	1,2,3-Propanetriol, trinitrate	55-63-0	P081
p-Nitrophenol	Phenol, 4-nitro-	100-02-7	U170
2-Nitropropane	Propane, 2-nitro-	79-46-9	U171
Nitrosamines, N.O.S. [1]		35576-91-1	
N-Nitrosodi-n-butylamine	1-Butanamine, N-butyl-N-nitroso-	924-16-3	U172
N-Nitrosodiethanolamine	Ethanol, 2,2′-(nitrosoimino)bis-	1116-54-7	U173
N-Nitrosodiethylamine	Ethanamine, N-ethyl-N-nitroso-	55-18-5	U174
N-Nitrosodimethylamine	Methanamine, N-methyl-N-nitroso-	62-75-9	P082
N-Nitroso-N-ethylurea	Urea, N-ethyl-N-nitroso-	759-73-9	U176
N-Nitrosomethylethylamine	Ethanamine, N-methyl-N-nitroso-	10595-95-6	
N-Nitroso-N-methylurea	Urea, N-methyl-N-nitroso-	684-93-5	U177
N-Nitroso-N-methylurethane	Carbamic acid, methylnitroso-,ethyl ester	615-53-2	U178
N-Nitrosomethylvinylamine	Vinylamine, N-methyl-N-nitroso-	4549-40-0	P084
N-Nitrosomorpholine	Morpholine, 4-nitroso-	59-89-2	
N-Nitrosonornicotine	Pyridine, 3-(1-nitroso-2-pyrrolidinyl)-, (S)-	16543-55-8	
N-Nitrosopiperidine	Piperidine, 1-nitroso-	100-75-4	U179

Common name	Chemical abstracts name	Chemical abstracts No.	Hazardous waste No.
N-Nitroso-pyrrolidine	Pyrrolidine, 1-nitroso-	930-55-2	U180
N-Nitroso-sarcosine	Glycine, N-methyl- N-nitroso-	13256-22-9	
5-Nitro-o-toluidine	Benzenamine, 2-methyl-5-nitro-	99-55-8	U181
Octachlorodi-benzo-p-dioxin (OCDD)	1,2,3,4,6,7,8,9-Octa-chlorodibenzo-p-dioxin	3268-87-9	
Octachlorodiben-zofuran (OCDF)	1,2,3,4,6,7,8,9-Octachlorodibenofuran	39001-02-0	
Octamethylpyro-phosphoramide	Diphosphoramide, octamethyl-	152-16-9	P085
Osmium tetroxide	Osmium oxide OsO_4, (T-4)-	20816-12-0	P087
Oxamyl	Ethanimidothioc acid, 2-(dimethylamino)-N-[[(methylamino)car-bonyl]oxy]-2-oxo-, methyl ester	23135-22-0	P194
Paraldehyde	1,3,5-Trioxane, 2,4,6-trimethyl-	123-63-7	U182
Parathion	Phosphorothioic acid, O,O-diethyl O-(4-nitrophenyl) ester	56-38-2	P089
Pebulate	Carbamothioic acid, butyl-ethyl-, S-propyl ester	1114-71-2	
Pentachloro-benzene	Benzene, pentachloro-	608-93-5	U183
Pentachlorodi-benzo-p-dioxins			
Pentachlorodi-benzofurans			
Pentachloro-ethane	Ethane, pentachloro-	76-01-7	U184
Pentachloronitro-benzene (PCNB)	Benzene, pentachloronitro-	82-68-8	U185
Pentachloro-phenol	Phenol, pentachloro-	87-86-5	See F027
Phenacetin	Acetamide, N-(4-ethoxyphenyl)-	62-44-2	U187
Phenol	Same	108-95-2	U188
1,2-Phenylene-diamine	1,2-Benzenediamine	95–54–5	
1,3-Phenylene-diamine	1,3-Benzenediamine	108–45–2	
Phenylenediamine	Benzenediamine	25265-76-3	
Phenylmercury acetate	Mercury, (acetato-O)phenyl-	62-38-4	P092
Phenylthiourea	Thiourea, phenyl-	103-85-5	P093
Phosgene	Carbonic dichloride	75-44-5	P095
Phosphine	Same	7803-51-2	P096
Phorate	Phosphorodithioic acid, O,O-diethyl S-[(ethyl-thio) methyl] ester	298-02-2	P094
Phthalic acid esters, N.O.S. [1]			

Common name	Chemical abstracts name	Chemical abstracts No.	Hazardous waste No.
Phthalic anhydride	1,3-Isobenzofurandione	85-44-9	U190
Physostigmine	Pyrrolo[2,3-b]indol-5-01,1,2,3,3a,8,8a-hexa-hydro-1,3a,8-trimethyl-, methylcarbamate (ester), (3aS-cis)-	57-47-6	P204
Physostigmine salicylate	Benzoic acid, 2-hydroxy-, compd. with (3aS-cis) - 1,2,3,3a,8,8a-hexahydro-1,3a,8-trimethylpyrrolo [2,3-b]indol-5-yl methyl-carbamate ester (1:1)	57-64-7	P188
2-Picoline	Pyridine, 2-methyl-	109-06-8	U191
Polychlorinated biphenyls, N.O.S.[1]			
Potassium cyanide	Potassium cyanide K(CN)	151-50-8	P098
Potassium dimethyldithio-carbamate	Carbamodithioic acid, dimethyl, potassium salt	128-03-0	
Potassium n-hydroxymethyl-n-methyldithio-carbamate	Carbamodithioic acid, (hydroxymethyl)methyl-, monopotassium salt	51026-28-9	
Potassium n-methyldithio-carbamate	Carbamodithioic acid, methyl-monopotassium salt	137-41-7	
Potassium pentachloro-phenate	Pentachlorophenol, potassium salt	7778736	None
Potassium silver cyanide	Argentate(1-), bis(cyano-C)-, potassium	506-61-6	P099
Promecarb	Phenol, 3-methyl-5-(1-methylethyl)-, methyl carbamate	2631-37-0	P201
Pronamide	Benzamide, 3,5-dichloro-N-(1,1-dimethyl- 2-propynyl)-	23950-58-5	U192
1,3-Propane sultone	1,2-Oxathiolane, 2,2-dioxide	1120-71-4	U193
n-Propylamine	1-Propanamine	107-10-8	U194
Propargyl alcohol	2-Propyn-1-ol	107-19-7	P102
Propham	Carbamic acid, phenyl-, 1-methylethyl ester	122-42-9	U373
Propoxur	Phenol, 2-(1-methylethoxy)-, methylcarbamate	114-26-1	U411
Propylene dichloride	Propane, 1,2-dichloro-	78-87-5	U083
1,2-Propylenimine	Aziridine, 2-methyl-	75-55-8	P067
Propylthiouracil	4(1H)-Pyrimidinone, 2,3-dihydro-6-propyl-2-thioxo-	51-52-5	
Prosulfocarb	Carbamothioic acid, dipropyl-, S-(phenylmethyl) ester	52888-80-9	U387
Pyridine	Same	110-86-1	U196

Common name	Chemical abstracts name	Chemical abstracts No.	Hazardous waste No.
Reserpine	Yohimban-16-carboxylic acid, 11,17-dimethoxy-18-[(3,4,5-trimethoxybenzoyl)oxy]-s methyl ester, (3beta,16beta,17alpha,18beta,20alpha)-	50-55-5	U200
Resorcinol	1,3-Benzenediol	108-46-3	U201
Saccharin	1,2-Benzisothiazol-3(2H)-one, 1,1-dioxide	81-07-2	U202
Saccharin salts			U202
Safrole	1,3-Benzodioxole, 5-(2-propenyl)-	94-59-7	U203
Selenium	Same	7782-49-2	
Selenium compounds, N.O.S. [1]			
Selenium dioxide	Selenious acid	7783-00-8	U204
Selenium sulfide	Selenium sulfide SeS_2	7488-56-4	U205
Selenium, tetrakis(dimethyldithiocarbamate)	Carbamodithioic acid, dimethyl-, tetraanhydrosulfide with orthothioselenious acid	144-34-3	
Selenourea	Same	630-10-4	P103
Silver	Same	7440-22-4	
Silver compounds, N.O.S. [1]			
Silver cyanide	Silver cyanide Ag(CN)	506-64-9	P104
Silvex (2,4,5-TP)	Propanoic acid, 2-(2,4,5-trichlorophenoxy)-	93-72-1	See F027
Sodium cyanide	Sodium cyanide Na(CN)	143-33-9	P106
Sodium dibutyldithiocarbamate	Carbamodithioic acid, dibutyl, sodium salt	136-30-1	
Sodium diethyldithiocarbamate	Carbamodithioic acid, diethyl-, sodium salt	148-18-5	
Sodium dimethyldithiocarbamate	Carbamodithioic acid, dimethyl-, sodium salt	128-04-1	
Sodium pentachlorophenate	Pentachlorophenol, sodium salt	131522	None
Streptozotocin	D-Glucose, 2-deoxy-2-[[(methylnitrosoamino)carbonyl]amino]-	18883-66-4	U206
Strychnine	Strychnidin-10-one	57-24-9	P108
Strychnine salts			P108
Sulfallate	Carbamodithioic acid, diethyl-, 2-chloro- 2-propenyl ester	95-06-7	
TCDD	Dibenzo[b,e][1,4]dioxin, 2,3,7,8-tetrachloro-	1746-01-6	
Tetrabutylthiuram disulfide	Thioperoxydicarbonic diamide, tetrabutyl	1634-02-2	
1,2,4,5-Tetrachlorobenzene	Benzene, 1,2,4,5-tetrachloro-	95-94-3	U207
Tetrachlorodibenzo-p-dioxins			
Tetrachlorodibenzofurans			
Tetrachloroethane, N.O.S. [1]	Ethane, tetrachloro-, N.O.S	25322-20-7	
1,1,1,2-Tetrachloroethane	Ethane, 1,1,1,2-tetrachloro-	630-20-6	U208
1,1,2,2-Tetrachloroethane	Ethane, 1,1,2,2-tetrachloro-	79-34-5	U209
Tetrachloroethylene	Ethene, tetrachloro-	127-18-4	U210
2,3,4,6-Tetrachlorophenol	Phenol, 2,3,4,6-tetrachloro-	58-90-2	See F027
2,3,4,6-tetrachlorophenol, potassium salt	same	53535276	None
2,3,4,6-tetrachlorophenol, sodium salt	same	25567559	None
Tetraethyldithiopyrophosphate	Thiodiphosphoric acid, tetraethyl ester	3689-24-5	P109
Tetraethyl lead	Plumbane, tetraethyl-	78-00-2	P110
Tetraethyl pyrophosphate	Diphosphoric acid, tetraethyl ester	107-49-3	P111
Tetramethylthiuram monosulfide	Bis(dimethylthiocarbamoyl) sulfide	97-74-5	
Tetranitromethane	Methane, tetranitro-	509-14-8	P112
Thallium	Same	7440-28-0	
Thallium compounds, N.O.S. [1]			
Thallic oxide	Thallium oxide Tl_2O_3	1314-32-5	P113
Thallium(I) acetate	Acetic acid, thallium(1+) salt	563-68-8	U214
Thallium(I) carbonate	Carbonic acid, dithallium(1+) salt	6533-73-9	U215
Thallium(I) chloride	Thallium chloride TlCl	7791-12-0	U216
Thallium(I) nitrate	Nitric acid, thallium(1+) salt	10102-45-1	U217
Thallium selenite	Selenious acid, dithallium(1+) salt	12039-52-0	P114
Thallium(I) sulfate	Sulfuric acid, dithallium(1+) salt	7446-18-6	P115
Thioacetamide	Ethanethioamide	62-55-5	U218
Thiodicarb	Ethanimidothioic acid, N,N'-[thiobis [(methylimino) carbonyloxy]] bis-, dimethyl ester	59669-26-0	U410
Thiofanox	2-Butanone, 3,3-dimethyl-1-(methylthio)-, 0-[(methylamino)carbonyl] oxime	39196-18-4	P045
Thiomethanol	Methanethiol	74-93-1	U153

Common name	Chemical abstracts name	Chemical abstracts No.	Hazardous waste No.
Thiophanate-methyl	Carbamic acid, [1,2-phyenylenebis (iminocarbonothioyl)] bis-, dimethyl ester	23564-05-8	U409
Thiophenol	Benzenethiol	108-98-5	P014
Thiosemicarbazide	Hydrazinecarbothioamide	79-19-6	P116
Thiourea	Same	62-56-6	U219
Thiram	Thioperoxydicarbonic diamide $[(H_2N)C(S)]_2S_2$, tetramethyl-	137-26-8	U244
Tirpate	1,3-Dithiolane-2-carboxaldehyde, 2,4-dimethyl-, O-[(methylamino) carbonyl] oxime	26419-73-8	P185
Toluene	Benzene, methyl-	108-88-3	U220
Toluenediamine	Benzenediamine, ar-methyl-	25376-45-8	U221
Toluene-2,4-diamine	1,3-Benzenediamine, 4-methyl-	95-80-7	
Toluene-2,6-diamine	1,3-Benzenediamine, 2-methyl-	823-40-5	
Toluene-3,4-diamine	1,2-Benzenediamine, 4-methyl-	496-72-0	
Toluene diisocyanate	Benzene, 1,3-diisocyanatomethyl-	26471-62-5	U223
o-Toluidine	Benzenamine, 2-methyl-	95-53-4	U328
o-Toluidine hydrochloride	Benzenamine, 2-methyl-,hydrochloride	636-21-5	U222
p-Toluidine	Benzenamine, 4-methyl-	106-49-0	U353
Toxaphene	Same	8001-35-2	P123
Triallate	Carbamothioic acid, bis(1-methylethyl)-, S-(2,3,3-trichloro-2-propenyl) ester	2303-17-5	U389
1,2,4-Trichlorobenzene	Benzene, 1,2,4-trichloro-	120-82-1	
1,1,2-Trichloroethane	Ethane, 1,1,2-trichloro-	79-00-5	U227
Trichloroethylene	Ethene, trichloro-	79-01-6	U228
Trichloromethanethiol	Methanethiol, trichloro-	75-70-7	P118
Trichloromonofluoromethane	Methane, trichlorofluoro-	75-69-4	U121
2,4,5-Trichlorophenol	Phenol, 2,4,5-trichloro-	95-95-4	See F027
2,4,6-Trichlorophenol	Phenol, 2,4,6-trichloro-	88-06-2	See F027
2,4,5-T	Acetic acid, (2,4,5-trichlorophenoxy)-	93-76-5	See F027
Trichloropropane, N.O.S. [1]		25735-29-9	
1,2,3-Trichloropropane	Propane, 1,2,3-trichloro-	96-18-4	
Triethylamine	Ethanamine, N,N-diethyl-	121-44-8	U404
O,O,O-Triethyl phosphorothioate	Phosphorothioic acid, O,O,O-triethyl ester	126-68-1	
1,3,5-Trinitrobenzene	Benzene, 1,3,5-trinitro-	99-35-4	U234
Tris(1-aziridinyl) phosphine sulfide	Aziridine, 1,1′,1″-phosphinothioylidynetris-	52-24-4	
Tris(2,3-dibromopropyl) phosphate	1-Propanol, 2,3-dibromo-, phosphate (3:1)	126-72-7	U235
Trypan blue	2,7-Naphthalenedisulfonic acid, 3,3′-[(3,3′-dimethyl[1,1′-biphenyl]-4,4′-diyl)bis(azo)]- bis[5-amino-4-hydroxy-, tetrasodium salt	72-57-1	U236
Uracil mustard	2,4-(1H,3H)-Pyrimidinedione, 5-[bis(2-chloroethyl)amino]-	66-75-1	U237
Vanadium pentoxide	Vanadium oxide V_2O_5	1314-62-1	P120
Vernolate	Carbamothioic acid, dipropyl-,S-propyl ester	1929-77-7	
Vinyl chloride	Ethene, chloro-	75-01-4	U043
Warfarin	2H-1-Benzopyran-2-one, 4-hydroxy-3-(3-oxo-1-phenylbutyl)-, when present at concentrations less than 0.3%	81-81-2	U248
Warfarin	2H-1-Benzopyran-2-one, 4-hydroxy-3-(3-oxo-1-phenylbutyl)-, when present at concentrations greater than 0.3%	81-81-2	P001
Warfarin salts, when present at concentrations less than 0.3%			U248
Warfarin salts, when present at concentrations greater than 0.3%			P001
Zinc cyanide	Zinc cyanide $Zn(CN)_2$	557-21-1	P121
Zinc phosphide	Zinc phosphide Zn_3P_2, when present at concentrations greater than 10%	1314-84-7	P122
Zinc phosphide	Zinc phosphide Zn_3P_2, when present at concentrations of 10% or less	1314-84-7	U249
Ziram	ZInc, bis(dimethylcarbamodithioato-S,S′)-, (T-4)-	137-30-4	P205

[1] The abbreviation N.O.S. (not otherwise specified) signifies those members of the general class not specifically listed by name in this appendix.

[53 FR 13388, Apr. 22, 1988, as amended at 53 FR 43881, Oct. 31, 1988; 54 FR 50978, Dec. 11, 1989; 55 FR 50483, Dec. 6, 1990; 56 FR 7568, Feb. 25, 1991; 59 FR 468, Jan. 4, 1994; 59 FR 31551, June 20, 1994; 60 FR 7853, Feb. 9, 1995; 60 FR 19165, Apr. 17, 1995; 62 FR 32977, June 17, 1997; 63 FR 24625, May 4, 1998; 65 FR 67127, Nov. 8, 2000; 70 FR 9177, Feb. 24, 2005; 71 FR 40271, July 14, 2006]

Appendix IX to Part 261—Wastes Excluded Under §§260.20 and 260.22

Table 1—Wastes Excluded from Non-Specific Sources

Facility	Address	Waste description
Aluminum Company of America	750 Norcold Ave., Sidney, Ohio 45365	Wastewater treatment plant (WWTP) sludges generated from the chemical conversion coating of aluminum (EPA Hazardous Waste No. F019) and WWTP sludges generated from electroplating operations (EPA Hazardous Waste No. F006) and stored in an on-site landfill. This is an exclusion for approximately 16,772 cubic yards of landfilled WWTP filter cake. This exclusion applies only if the waste filter cake remains in place or, if excavated, is disposed of in a Subtitle D landfill which is permitted, licensed, or registered by a state to manage industrial solid waste. This exclusion was published on April 6, 1999. 1. The constituent concentrations measured in the TCLP extract may not exceed the following levels (mg/L): Arsenic—5; Barium—100; Chromium—5; Cobalt—210; Copper—130; Nickel—70; Vanadium—30; Zinc—1000; Fluoride—400; Acetone—400; Methylene Chloride—0.5; Bis(2-ethylhexyl)phthalate—0.6. 2. (a) If, anytime after disposal of the delisted waste, Alcoa possesses or is otherwise made aware of any environmental data (including but not limited to leachate data or groundwater monitoring data) or any other data relevant to the delisted waste indicating that any constituent identified in Condition (1) is at a level in the leachate higher than the delisting level established in Condition (1), or is at a level in the ground water or soil higher than the health based level, then Alcoa must report such data, in writing, to the Regional Administrator within 10 days of first possessing or being made aware of that data. (b) Based on the information described in paragraph (a) and any other information received from any source, the Regional Administrator will make a preliminary determination as to whether the reported information requires Agency action to protect human health or the environment. Further action may include suspending or revoking this exclusion, or other appropriate response necessary to protect human health and the environment. (c) If the Regional Administrator determines that the reported information does require Agency action, the Regional Administrator will notify the facility in writing of the actions the Regional Administrator believes are necessary to protect human health and the environment. The notice shall include a statement of the proposed action and a statement providing the facility with an opportunity to present information as to why the proposed Agency action is not necessary or to suggest an alternative action. The facility shall have 10 days from the date of the Regional Administrator's notice to present such information. (d) Following the receipt of information from the facility described in paragraph (c) or (if no information is presented under paragraph (c) the initial receipt of information described in paragraph (a), the Regional Administrator will issue a final written determination describing the Agency actions that are necessary to protect human health or the environment. Any required action described in the Regional Administrator's determination shall become effective immediately, unless the Regional Administrator provides otherwise.
Alumnitec, Inc. (formerly Profile Extrusion Co. formerly United, Technologies Automotive, Inc.)	Jeffersonville, IN	Dewatered wastewater treatment sludge (EPA Hazardous Waste No. F019) generated from the chemical conversion of aluminum after April 29, 1986.
American Metals Corporation	Westlake, Ohio	Wastewater treatment plant (WWTP) sludges from the chemical conversion coating (phosphating) of aluminum (EPA Hazardous Waste No. F019) and other solid wastes previously disposed in an on-site landfill. This is a one-time exclusion for 12,400 cubic yards of landfilled WWTP sludge. This exclusion is effective on January 15, 2002. 1. *Delisting Levels:* (A) The constituent concentrations measured in the TCLP extract may not exceed the following levels (mg/L): antimony—1.52; arsenic—0.691; barium—100; beryllium—3.07; cadmium—1; chromium—5; cobalt—166; copper—67,300; lead—5; mercury—0.2; nickel—209; selenium—1; silver—5; thallium—0.65; tin—1,660; vanadium—156; and zinc—2,070. (B) The total constituent concentrations in any sample may not exceed the following levels (mg/kg): arsenic—9,280; mercury—94; and polychlorinated biphenyls—0.265. (C) Concentrations of dioxin and furan congeners cannot exceed values which would result in a cancer risk greater than or equal to 10^{-6} as predicted by the model.

Table 1—Wastes Excluded from Non-Specific Sources

Facility	Address	Waste description
		2. *Verification Sampling*—USG shall collect six additional vertically composited samples of sludge from locations that compliment historical data and shall analyze the samples by TCLP for metals including antimony, arsenic, barium, beryllium, cadmium, chromium, lead, mercury, nickel, selenium, silver, thallium, tin, vanadium, and zinc. If the samples exceed the levels in Condition (1)(a), USG must notify EPA. The corresponding sludge and all sludge yet to be disposed remains hazardous until USG has demonstrated by additional sampling that all constituents of concern are below the levels set forth in condition 1. 3. *Reopener Language*—(a) If, anytime after disposal of the delisted waste, USG possesses or is otherwise made aware of any data (including but not limited to leachate data or groundwater monitoring data) or any other data relevant to the delisted waste indicating that any constituent identified in Condition (1) is at a level higher than the delisting level established in Condition (1), or is at a level in the groundwater exceeding maximum allowable point of exposure concentration referenced by the model, then USG must report such data, in writing, to the Regional Administrator within 10 days of first possessing or being made aware of that data. (b) Based on the information described in paragraph (a) and any other information received from any source, the Regional Administrator will make a preliminary determination as to whether the reported information requires Agency action to protect human health or the environment. Further action may include suspending, or revoking the exclusion, or other appropriate response necessary to protect human health and the environment. (c) If the Regional Administrator determines that the reported information does require Agency action, the Regional Administrator will notify USG in writing of the actions the Regional Administrator believes are necessary to protect human health and the environment. The notice shall include a statement of the proposed action and a statement providing USG with an opportunity to present information as to why the proposed Agency action is not necessary or to suggest an alternative action. USG shall have 10 days from the date of the Regional Administrator's notice to present the information. (d) If after 10 days USG presents no further information, the Regional Administrator will issue a final written determination describing the Agency actions that are necessary to protect human health or the environment. Any required action described in the Regional Administrator's determination shall become effective immediately, unless the Regional Administrator provides otherwise. 4. *Notifications*—USG must provide a one- time written notification to any State Regulatory Agency to which or through which the waste described above will be transported for disposal at least 60 days prior to the commencement of such activities. Failure to provide such a notification will result in a violation of the delisting petition and a possible revocation of the decision.
American Steel Cord	Scottsburg, IN	Wastewater treatment plant (WWTP) sludge from electroplating operations (EPA Hazardous Waste No. F006) generated at a maximum annual rate of 3,000 cubic yards per year, after January 26, 1999, and disposed of in a Subtitle D landfill. 1. Verification Testing: American Steel Cord must implement an annual testing program to demonstrate, based on the analysis of a minimum of four representative samples, that the constituent concentrations measured in the TCLP extract of the waste are within specific levels. The constituent concentrations must not exceed the following levels (mg/l) which are back-calculated from the delisting health-based levels and a DAF of 68. Arsenic—3.4; Barium—100; Cadmium—.34; Chromium—5; Copper—88.4.; Lead— 1.02; Mercury—.136; Nickel— 6.8.; Selenium—1; Silver—5; Zinc—680; Cyanide—13.6; Acetone—272; Benzo butyl phthlate—476; Chloroform—.68; 1,4-Dichlorobenzene—.272; cis- 1,2-Dichloroethene—27.2; Methylene chloride—.34; Naphthalene—68; Styrene—6.8; Tetrachloroethene—.34; Toluene— 68; and Xylene—680. American Steel Cord must measure and record the pH of the waste using SW 846 method 9045 and must record all pH measurements performed in accordance with the TCLP. 2. Changes in Operating Conditions: If American Steel Cord significantly changes the manufacturing or treatment process or the chemicals used in the manufacturing or treatment process, American Steel Cord may handle the WWTP filter press sludge generated from the new process under this exclusion only after the facility has demonstrated that the waste meets the levels set forth in paragraph 1 and that no new hazardous constituents listed in Appendix VIII of Part 261 have been introduced. 3. Data Submittals: The data obtained through annual verification testing or compliance with paragraph 2 must be submitted to U.S. EPA Region 5, 77 W. Jackson Blvd., Chicago, IL 60604-3590, within 60 days of sampling. Records of operating conditions and analytical data must be compiled, summarized, and maintained on site for a minimum of five years and must be made available for inspection. All data must be accompanied by a signed copy of the certification statement in 260.22(l)(12).

Table 1—Wastes Excluded from Non-Specific Sources

Facility	Address	Waste description
		4. (a) If, anytime after disposal of the delisted waste, American Steel Cord possesses or is otherwise made aware of any environmental data (including but not limited to leachate data or groundwater monitoring data) or any other data relevant to the delisted waste indicating that any constituent identified in Condition (1) is at a level in the leachate higher than the delisting level established in Condition (1), or is at a level in the ground water or soil higher than the health based level, then American Steel Cord must report such data, in writing, to the Regional Administrator within 10 days of first possessing or being made aware of that data. (b) Based on the information described in paragraph (a) and any other information received from any source, the Regional Administrator will make a preliminary determination as to whether the reported information requires Agency action to protect human health or the environment. Further action may include suspending, or revoking the exclusion, or other appropriate response necessary to protect human health and the environment. (c) If the Regional Administrator determines that the reported information does require Agency action, the Regional Administrator will notify the facility in writing of the actions the Regional Administrator believes are necessary to protect human health and the environment. The notice shall include a statement of the proposed action and a statement providing the facility with an opportunity to present information as to why the proposed Agency action is not necessary or to suggest an alternative action. The facility shall have 10 days from the date of the Regional Administrator's notice to present such information. (d) Following the receipt of information from the facility described in paragraph (c) or (if no information is presented under paragraph (c) the initial receipt of information described in paragraph (a), the Regional Administrator will issue a final written determination describing the Agency actions that are necessary to protect human health or the environment. Any required action described in the Regional Administrator's determination shall become effective immediately, unless the Regional Administrator provides otherwise.
Ampex Recording Media Corporation	Opelika, Alabama	Solvent recovery residues in the powder or pellet form (EPA Hazardous Waste Nos. F003 and F005) generated from the recovery of spent solvents from the manufacture of tape recording media (generated at a maximum annual rate of 1,000 cubic yards in the powder or pellet form) after August 9, 1993. In order to confirm that the characteristics of the wastes do not change significantly, the facility must, on an annual basis, analyze a representative composite sample of the waste (in its final form) for the constituents listed in 40 CFR 261.24 using the method specified therein. The annual analytical results, including quality control information, must be compiled, certified according to 40 CFR 260.22(i)(12), maintained on-site for a minimum of five years, and made available for inspection upon request by any employee or representative of EPA or the State of Alabama. Failure to maintain the required records on-site will be considered by EPA, at its discretion, sufficient basis to revoke the exclusion to the extent directed by EPA.
Aptus, Inc	Coffeyville, Kansas	Kiln residue and spray dryer/baghouse residue (EPA Hazardous Waste No. F027) generated during the treatment of cancelled pesticides containing 2,4,5-T and Silvex and related materials by Aptus' incinerator at Coffeyville, Kansas after December 27, 1991, so long as: (1) The incinerator is monitored continuously and is in compliance with operating permit conditions. Should the incinerator fail to comply with the permit conditions relevant to the mechanical operation of the incinerator, Aptus must test the residues generated during the run when the failure occurred according to the requirements of Conditions (2) through (4), regardless of whether or not the demonstration in Condition (5) has been made. (2) A minimum of four grab samples must be taken from each hopper (or other container) of kiln residue generated during each 24-hour run; all grabs collected during a given 24-hour run must then be composited to form one composite sample. A minimum of four grab samples must also be taken from each hopper (or other container) of spray dryer/ baghouse residue generated during each 24-hour run; all grabs collected during a given 24-hour run must then be composited to form one composite sample. Prior to the disposal of the residues from each 24-hour run, a TCLP leachate test must be performed on these composite samples and the leachate analyzed for the TC toxic metals, nickel, and cyanide. If arsenic, chromium, lead or silver TC leachate test results exceed 1.6 ppm, barium levels exceed 32 ppm, cadmium or selenium levels exceed 0.3 ppm, mercury levels exceed 0.07 ppm, nickel levels exceed 10 ppm, or cyanide levels exceed 6.5 ppm, the wastes must be retreated to achieve these levels or must be disposed in accordance with subtitle C of RCRA. Analyses must be performed according to appropriate methods. As applicable to the method-defined parameters of concern, analyses requiring use of SW–846 methods incorporated by reference in 40 CFR 260.11 must be used without substitution. As applicable, the SW–846 methods might include Methods 0010, 0011, 0020, 0023A, 0030, 0031, 0040, 0050, 0051, 0060, 0061, 1010A, 1020B, 1110A, 1310B, 1311, 1312, 1320, 1330A, 9010C, 9012B, 9040C, 9045D, 9060A, 9070A (uses EPA Method 1664, Rev. A), 9071B, and 9095B.

Table 1—Wastes Excluded from Non-Specific Sources

Facility	Address	Waste description
		(3) Aptus must generate, prior to the disposal of the residues, verification data from each 24 hour run for each treatment residue (i.e., kiln residue, spray dryer/baghouse residue) to demonstrate that the maximum allowable treatment residue concentrations listed below are not exceeded. Samples must be collected as specified in Condition (2). Analyses must be performed according to appropriate methods. As applicable to the method-defined parameters of concern, analyses requiring the use of SW–846 methods incorporated by reference in 40 CFR 260.11 must be used without substitution. As applicable, the SW–846 methods might include Methods 0010, 0011, 0020, 0023A, 0030, 0031, 0040, 0050, 0051, 0060, 0061, 1010A, 1020B, 1110A, 1310B, 1311, 1312, 1320, 1330A, 9010C, 9012B, 9040C, 9045D, 9060A, 9070A (uses EPA Method 1664, Rev. A), 9071B, and 9095B. Any residues which exceed any of the levels listed below must be retreated or must be disposed of as hazardous. Kiln residue and spray dryer/baghouse residue must not exceed the following levels: Aldrin—0.015 ppm Benzene—9.7 ppm Benzo(a)pyrene—0.43 ppm Benzo(b)fluoranthene)—1.8 ppm Chlordane—0.37 ppm Chloroform—5.4 ppm Chrysene—170 ppm Dibenz(a,h)anthracene—0.083 ppm 1.2-Dichloroethane—4.1 ppm Dichloromethane—2.4 ppm 2,4-Dichlorophenol—480 ppm Dichlorvos—260 ppm Disulfaton—23 ppm Endosulfan I—310 ppm Fluorene—120 ppm Indeno(1,2,3,cd)-pyrene—330 ppm Methyl parathion—210 ppm Nitrosodiphenylamine—130 ppm Phenanthrene—150 ppm Polychlorinated biphenyls—0.31 ppm Tetrachlorethylene—59 ppm 2,4,5-TP (silvex)—110 ppm 2,4,6-Trichlorophenol—3.9 ppm
		(4) Aptus must generate, prior to disposal of residues, verification data from each 24-hour run for each treatment residue (i.e., kiln residue, spray dryer/baghouse residue) to demonstrate that the residues do not contain tetra-, penta-, or hexachlorodibenzo-p-dioxins or furans at levels of regulatory concern. Samples must be collected as specified in Condition (2). The TCDD equivalent levels for the solid residues must be less than 5 ppt. Any residues with detected dioxins or furans in excess of this level must be retreated or must be disposed of as acutely hazardous. For tetra- and penta-chlorinated dioxin and furan homologs, the maximum practical quantitation limit must not exceed 15 ppt for the solid residues. For hexachlorinated dioxin and furan homologs, the maximum practical quantitation limit must not exceed 37 ppt for the solid residues.
		(5) The test data from Conditions (1), (2), (3), and (4) must be kept on file by Aptus for inspection purposes and must be compiled, summarized, and submitted to the Director for the Materials Recovery and Waste Management Division, Office of Resource Conservation and Recovery, by certified mail on a monthly basis and when the treatment of the cancelled pesticides and related materials is concluded. The testing requirements for Conditions (2), (3), and (4) will continue until Aptus provides the Director with the results of four consecutive batch analyses for the petitioned wastes, none of which exceed the maximum allowable levels listed in these conditions and the Director notifies Aptus that the conditions have been lifted. All data submitted will be placed in the RCRA public docket.
		(6) Aptus must provide a signed copy of the following certification statement when submitting data in response to the conditions listed above: "Under civil and criminal penalty of law for the making or submission of false or fraudulent statements or representations, I certify that the information contained in or accompanying this document is true, accurate, and complete. As to the (those) identified section(s) of this document for which I cannot personally verify its (their) truth and accuracy, I certify as the company official having supervisory responsibility for the persons who, acting under my direct instructions, made the verification that this information is true, accurate, and complete."

Table 1—Wastes Excluded from Non-Specific Sources

Facility	Address	Waste description
Arco Building Products	Sugarcreek, Ohio	Dewatered wastewater treatment sludge (EPA Hazardous Waste No. F019) generated from the chemical conversion coating of aluminum after August 15, 1986.
Arco Chemical Co.	Miami, FL	Dewatered wastewater treatment sludge (EPA Hazardous Waste No. FO19) generated from the chemical conversion coating of aluminum after April 29, 1986.
Arkansas Department of Pollution Control and Ecology	Vertac Superfund site, Jacksonville, Arkansas	Kiln ash, cyclone ash, and calcium chloride salts from incineration of residues (EPA Hazardous Waste No. F020 and F023) generated from the primary production of 2,4,5-T and 2,4-D after August 24, 1990. This one-time exclusion applies only to the incineration of the waste materials described in the petition, and it is conditional upon the data obtained from ADPC&E's full-scale incineration facility. To ensure that hazardous constituents are not present in the waste at levels of regulatory concern once the full- scale treatment facility is in operation, ADPC&E must implement a testing program for the petitioned waste. This testing program must meet the following conditions for the exclusion to be valid: (1) *Testing:* Sample collection and analyses (including quality control (QC) procedures) must be performed according to appropriate methods. As applicable to the method-defined parameters of concern, analyses requiring the use of SW–846 methods incorporated by reference in 40 CFR 260.11 must be used without substitution. As applicable, the SW–846 methods might include Methods 0010, 0011, 0020, 0023A, 0030, 0031, 0040, 0050, 0051, 0060, 0061, 1010A, 1020B, 1110A, 1310B, 1311, 1312, 1320, 1330A, 9010C, 9012B, 9040C, 9045D, 9060A, 9070A (uses EPA Method 1664, Rev. A), 9071B, and 9095B. (A) *Initial testing:* Representative grab samples must be taken from each drum and kiln ash and cyclone ash generated from each 24 hours of operation, and the grab samples composited to form one composite sample of ash for each 24-hour period Representative grab samples must also be taken from each drum of calcium chloride salts generated from each 24 hours of operation and composited to form one composite sample of calcium chloride salts for each 24- hour period. The initial testing requirements must be fullfilled for the following wastes: (i) Incineration by- products generated prior to and during the incinerator's trial burn; (ii) Incineration by-products from the treatment of 2,4-D wastes for one week (or 7 days if incineration is not on consecutive days) after completion of the trial burn; (iii) Incineration by- products from the treatment of blended 2,4-D and 2,4, 5- T wastes for two weeks (or 14 days if incineration is not on conseutive days) after completion of the trial burn; and (iv) Incineration by-products from the treatment of blended 2,4-D and 2,4,5-T wastes for one week (or 7 days if incineration is not on consecutive days) when the percentage of 2, 4, 5-T wastes exceeds the maximum percentage treated under Condition (1)(A)(iii). Prior to disposal of the residues from each 24-hour sampling period, the daily composite must be analyzed for all the constituents listed in Condition (3). ADPC&E must report the analytical test data, including quality control information, obtained during this initial period no later than 90 days after the start of the operation. (B) *Subsequent testing:* Representative grab samples of each drum of kiln and cyclone ash generated from each week of operation must be composited to form one composite sample of ash for each weekly period Representative grab samples of each drum of calcium chloride salts generated from each week of operation must also be composited to form one composite sample of calcium chloride salts for each weekly period. Prior to disposal of the residues from each weekly sampling period, the weekly composites must be analyzed for all of the constituents listed in Condition (3). The analytical data, including quality control information, must be compiled and maintained on site for a minimum of three years These data must be furnished upon request and made available for inspection by any employee or representative of EPA. (2) *Waste holding:* The incineration residues that are generated must be stored as hazardous until the initial verification analyses or subsequent analyses are completed. If the composite incineration residue samples (from either Condition (1)(A) or Condition (1)(B)) do not exceed any of the delisting levels set in Condition (3), the incineration residues corresponding to these samples may be managed and disposed of in accordance with all applicable solid waste regulations. If any composite incineration residue sample exceeds any of the delisting levels set in Condition (3), the incineration residues generated during the time period corresponding to this sample must be retreated until they meet these levels (analyses must be repeated) or managed and disposed of in accordance with subtitle C of RCRA. Incineration residues which are generated but for which analysis is not complete or valid must be managed and disposed of in accordance with subtitle C of RCRA, until valid analyses demonstrate that the wastes meet the delisting levels.

Table 1—Wastes Excluded from Non-Specific Sources

Facility	Address	Waste description
		(3) *Delisting levels:* If concentrations in one or more of the incineration residues for any of the hazardous constituents listed below exceed their respective maximum allowable concentrations also listed below, the batch of failing waste must either be re- treated until it meets these levels or managed and disposed of in accordance with subtitle C of RCRA. (A) Inorganics (Leachable): Arsenic, 0.32 ppm; Barium, 6.3 ppm; Cadmium, 0.06 ppm; Chromium, 0.32 ppm; Cyanide, 4.4 ppm; Lead, 0.32 ppm; Mercury, 0.01 ppm; Nickel, 4.4 ppm; Selenium, 0.06 ppm; Silver, 0.32 ppm. Metal concentrations must be measured in the waste leachate as per 40 CFR 261.24. Cyanide extractions must be conducted using distilled water. (B) Organics: Benzene, 0.87 ppm; Benzo(a)anthracene, 0.10 ppm; Benzo(a)pyrene, 0.04 ppm; Benzo (b)fluoranthene, 0.16 ppm; Chlorobenzene, 152 ppm; o-Chlorophenol, 44 ppm; Chrysene, 15 ppm; 2,4-D, 107 ppm; DDE, 1.0 ppm; Dibenz(a,h)anthracene, 0.007 ppm; 1, 4-Dichlorobenzene, 265 ppm; 1,1-Dichloroethylene, 1.3 ppm; trans-1,2-Dichloroethylene, 37 ppm; Dichloromethane, 0.23 ppm; 2,4-Dichlorophenol, 43 ppm; Hexachlorobenzene, 0.26 ppm; Indeno (1,2,3-cd) pyrene, 30 ppm; Polychlorinated biphenyls, 12 ppm; 2,4,5-T, 1 x 10^6 ppm; 1,2,4,5-Tetrachlorobenzene, 56 ppm; Tetrachloroethylene, 3.4 ppm; Trichloroethylene, 1.1 ppm; 2,4,5-Trichlorophenol, 21,000 ppm; 2,4,6-Trichlorophenol, 0.35 ppm. (C) *Chlorinated dioxins and furans:* 2,3,7,8-Tetrachlorodibenzo-p-dioxin equivalents, 4 x 10^{-7}ppm. The petitioned by-product must be analyzed for the tetra-, penta-, hexa-, and heptachlorodibenzo-p-dioxins, and the tetra-, penta-, hexa-, and heptachlorodibenzofurans to determine the 2, 3, 7, 8-tetra-chlorodibenzo-p-dioxin equivalent concentration. The analysis must be conducted using a measurement system that achieves practical quantitation limits of 15 parts per trillion (ppt) for the tetra- and penta-homologs, and 37 ppt for the hexa- and hepta-homologs. (4) *Termination of testing:* Due to the possible variability of the incinerator feeds, the testing requirements of Condition (1)(B) will continue indefinitely. (5) *Data submittals:* Within one week of system start-up, ADPC&E must notify the Section Chief, Variances Section (see address below) when the full- scale incineration system is on-line and waste treatment has begun. The data obtained through Condition (1)(A) must be submitted to the Section Chief, Variances Section, PSPD/ OSW (OS-343), U.S. EPA, 1200 Pennsylvania Ave., NW., Washington, DC 20460, within the time period specified. At the Section Chief's request, ADPC&E must submit analytical data obtained through Condition (1)(B) within the time period specified by the Section Chief. Failure to submit the required data obtained from Condition (1)(A) within the specified time period or to maintain the required records for the time specified in Condition (1)(B) (or to submit data within the time specified by the Section Chief) will be considered by the Agency, at its discretion, sufficient basis to revoke ADPC&E's exclusion to the extent directed by EPA. All data must be accompanied by the following certification statement: "Under civil and criminal penalty of law for the making or submission of false or fraudulent statements or representations (pursuant to the applicable provisions of the Federal Code, which include, but may not be limited to, 18 U.S.C. 1001 and 42 U.S.C. 6928), I certify that the information contained in or accompanying this document is true, accurate and complete. As to the (those) identified section(s) of this document for which I cannot personally verify its (their) truth and accuracy, I certify as the company official having supervisory responsibility for the persons who, acting under my direct instructions, made the verification that this information is true, accurate and complete. In the event that any of this information is determined by EPA in its sole discretion to be false, inaccurate or incomplete, and upon conveyance of this fact to the company, I recognize and agree that this exclusion of wastes will be void as if it never had effect or to the extent directed by EPA and that the company will be liable for any actions taken in contravention of the company's RCRA and CERCLA obligations premised upon the company's reliance on the void exclusion."
AutoAlliance International Inc.	Flat Rock, Michigan	Wastewater treatment sludges, F019, that are generated by AutoAlliance International, Inc. (AAI) at Flat Rock, Michigan at a maximum annual rate of 2,000 cubic yards per year. The sludges must be disposed of in a lined landfill with leachate collection which is licensed, permitted, or otherwise authorized to accept the delisted wastewater treatment sludges in accordance with 40 CFR part 258. The exclusion becomes effective as of April 6, 2007. 1. Delisting Levels: (A) The concentrations in a leachate extract of the waste measured in any sample must not exceed the following levels (mg/L): arsenic—0.3; cadmium—0.5; chromium—4.95; lead—5; nickel—90.5; selenium—1; tin—721; zinc—898; p-cresol—11.4; and formaldehyde—84.2. (B) The total concentration measured in any sample must not exceed the following levels (mg/kg): mercury—8.92; and formaldehyde—689.

PART 261—Appendices

Table 1—Wastes Excluded from Non-Specific Sources

Facility	Address	Waste description
		2. Quarterly Verification Testing: To verify that the waste does not exceed the specified delisting levels, AAI must collect and analyze one representative sample of the waste on a quarterly basis. Sample collection and analyses, including quality control procedures, must be performed using appropriate methods. SW–846 Method 1311 must be used for generation of the leachate extract used in the testing of the delisting levels if oil and grease comprise less than 1% of the waste. SW–846 Method 1330A must be used for generation of the leaching extract if oil and grease comprise 1% or more of the waste. SW–846 Method 9071B must be used for determination of oil and grease. SW–846 Methods 1311, 1330A, and 9071B are incorporated by reference in 40 CFR 260.11. 3. Changes in Operating Conditions: AAI must notify the EPA in writing if the manufacturing process, the chemicals used in the manufacturing process, the treatment process, or the chemicals used in the treatment process change significantly. AAI must handle wastes generated after the process change as hazardous until it has demonstrated that the wastes continue to meet the delisting levels and that no new hazardous constituents listed in Appendix VIII of part 261 have been introduced and it has received written approval from EPA. 4. Data Submittals: AAI must submit the data obtained through verification testing or as required by other conditions of this rule to both U.S. EPA Region 5, 77 W. Jackson Blvd., Chicago, IL 60604 and MDEQ, Waste and Hazardous Materials Division, Hazardous Waste Section, at P.O. Box 30241, Lansing, Michigan 48909. The quarterly verification data and certification of proper disposal must be submitted annually upon the anniversary of the effective date of this exclusion. AAI must compile, summarize and maintain on site for a minimum of five years records of operating conditions and analytical data. AAI must make these records available for inspection. A signed copy of the certification statement in 40 CFR 260.22(i)(12) must accompany all data. 5. Reopener Language: (a) If, anytime after disposal of the delisted waste AAI possesses or is otherwise made aware of any data (including but not limited to leachate data or groundwater monitoring data) relevant to the delisted waste indicating that any constituent is at a level in the leachate higher than the specified delisting level, or is in the groundwater at a concentration higher than the maximum allowable groundwater concentration in paragraph (e), then AAI must report such data, in writing, to the Regional Administrator within 10 days of first possessing or being made aware of that data. (b) Based on the information described in paragraph (a) and any other information received from any source, the Regional Administrator will make a preliminary determination as to whether the reported information requires Agency action to protect human health or the environment. Further action may include suspending, or revoking the exclusion, or other appropriate response necessary to protect human health and the environment. (c) If the Regional Administrator determines that the reported information does require Agency action, the Regional Administrator will inform AAI in writing of the actions the Regional Administrator believes are necessary to protect human health and the environment. The notice shall include a statement of the proposed action and a statement providing AAI with an opportunity to present information as to why the proposed Agency action is not necessary or to suggest an alternative action. AAI shall have 30 days from the date of the Regional Administrator's notice to present the information. (d) If after 30 days AAI presents no further information, the Regional Administrator will issue a final written determination describing the Agency actions that are necessary to protect human health or the environment. Any required action described in the Regional Administrator's determination shall become effective immediately, unless the Regional Administrator provides otherwise. (e) Maximum Allowable Groundwater Concentrations (µg/L): arsenic—5; cadmium—5; chromium—100; lead—15; nickel—750; selenium—50; tin—22,500; zinc—11,300; p-cresol—188; and formaldehyde—1,380.
BAE Systems, Inc,	Sealy, TX	Filter Cake (EPA Hazardous Waste Number F019) generated at a maximum rate of 1,200 cubic yards per calendar year after April 15, 2009. For the exclusion to be valid, BAE must implement a verification testing program that meets the following Paragraphs: (1) Delisting Levels: All concentrations for those constituents must not exceed the maximum allowable concentrations in mg/l specified in this paragraph. Filter Cake Leachable Concentrations (mg/l): Acetone—3211; Arsenic—0.052; Barium—100; Bis(2-ethylhexyl)phthalate—103; Cadmium—0.561; Chloroform—0.4924; Chromium—5.0; Copper—149; Cyanide—19; Furans—3.57; Hexavalent Chromium—5.0; Lead— 3.57; Lindane—0.4; Methyl Ethyl Ketone—200; Nickel—82.2; Selenium—1.0; 2,4,5-TP (Silvex)—1.0; 2,4-D—6.65; Tin—9001; Tetrachlorodibenzo-p-dioxin—249; Tetrachloroethylene—0.125685; Zinc—1240.

Table 1—Wastes Excluded from Non-Specific Sources

Facility	Address	Waste description
		(2) Waste Holding and Handling: (A) Waste classification as non-hazardous can not begin until compliance with the limits set in paragraph (1) for filter cake has occurred for two consecutive quarterly sampling events. (B) If constituent levels in any sample taken by BAE exceed any of the delisting levels set in paragraph (1) for the filter cake, BAE must do the following: (i) notify EPA in accordance with paragraph (6) and (ii) manage and dispose the filter cake as hazardous waste generated under Subtitle C of RCRA. (3) Testing Requirements: Upon this exclusion becoming final, BAE may perform quarterly analytical testing by sampling and analyzing the filter cake as follows: (A) Quarterly Testing: (i) Collect two representative composite samples of the filter cake at quarterly intervals after EPA grants the final exclusion. The first composite samples may be taken at any time after EPA grants the final approval. Sampling must be performed in accordance with the sampling plan approved by EPA in support of the exclusion. (ii) Analyze the samples for all constituents listed in paragraph (1). Any composite sample taken that exceeds the delisting levels listed in paragraph (1) for the filter cake must be disposed as hazardous waste in accordance with the applicable hazardous waste requirements. (iii) Within thirty (30) days after taking its first quarterly sample, BAE will report its first quarterly analytical test data to EPA. If levels of constituents measured in the samples of the filter cake do not exceed the levels set forth in paragraph (1) of this exclusion for two consecutive quarters, BAE can manage and dispose the non-hazardous filter cake according to all applicable solid waste regulations. (B) Annual Testing: (i) If BAE completes the quarterly testing specified in paragraph (3) above and no sample contains a constituent at a level which exceeds the limits set forth in paragraph (1), BAE may begin annual testing as follows: BAE must test two representative composite samples of the filter cake for all constituents listed in paragraph (1) at least once per calendar year. (ii) The samples for the annual testing shall be a representative composite sample according to appropriate methods. As applicable to the method-defined parameters of concern, analyses requiring the use of SW–846 methods incorporated by reference in 40 CFR 260.11 must be used without substitution. As applicable, the SW–846 methods might include Methods 0010, 0011, 0020, 0023A, 0030, 0031, 0040, 0050, 0051, 0060, 0061, 1010A, 1020B,1110A, 1310B, 1311, 1312, 1320, 1330A, 9010C, 9012B, 9040C, 9045D, 9060A, 9070A (uses EPA Method 1664, Rev. A), 9071B, and 9095B. Methods must meet Performance Based Measurement System Criteria in which the Data Quality Objectives are to demonstrate that samples of the BAE filter cake are representative for all constituents listed in paragraph (1). (iii) The samples for the annual testing taken for the second and subsequent annual testing events shall be taken within the same calendar month as the first annual sample taken. (iv) The annual testing report should include the total amount of waste in cubic yards disposed during the calendar year. (4) Changes in Operating Conditions: If BAE significantly changes the process described in its petition or starts any processes that generate(s) the waste that may or could affect the composition or type of waste generated (by illustration, but not limitation, changes in equipment or operating conditions of the treatment process), it must notify EPA in writing and it may no longer handle the wastes generated from the new process as non-hazardous until the wastes meet the delisting levels set in paragraph (1) and it has received written approval to do so from EPA. BAE must submit a modification to the petition complete with full sampling and analysis for circumstances where the waste volume changes and/or additional waste codes are added to the waste stream. (5) Data Submittals: BAE must submit the information described below. If BAE fails to submit the required data within the specified time or maintain the required records on-site for the specified time, EPA, at its discretion, will consider this sufficient basis to reopen the exclusion as described in paragraph (6). BAE must: (A) Submit the data obtained through paragraph (3) to the Chief, Corrective Action and Waste Minimization Section, Multimedia Planning and Permitting Division, U.S. Environmental Protection Agency Region 6, 1445 Ross Ave., Dallas, Texas 75202, within the time specified. All supporting data can be submitted on CD–ROM or some comparable electronic media.

Table 1—Wastes Excluded from Non-Specific Sources

Facility	Address	Waste description
		(B) Compile records of analytical data from paragraph (3), summarized, and maintained on-site for a minimum of five years. (C) Furnish these records and data when either EPA or the State of Texas requests them for inspection. (D) Send along with all data a signed copy of the following certification statement, to attest to the truth and accuracy of the data submitted: "Under civil and criminal penalty of law for the making or submission of false or fraudulent statements or representations (pursuant to the applicable provisions of the Federal Code, which include, but may not be limited to, 18 U.S.C. 1001 and 42 U.S.C. 6928), I certify that the information contained in or accompanying this document is true, accurate and complete. As to the (those) identified section(s) of this document for which I cannot personally verify its (their) truth and accuracy, I certify as the company official having supervisory responsibility for the persons who, acting under my direct instructions, made the verification that this information is true, accurate and complete. If any of this information is determined by EPA in its sole discretion to be false, inaccurate or incomplete, and upon conveyance of this fact to the company, I recognize and agree that this exclusion of waste will be void as if it never had effect or to the extent directed by EPA and that the company will be liable for any actions taken in contravention of the company's RCRA and CERCLA obligations premised upon the company's reliance on the void exclusion." (6) Reopener (A) If, anytime after disposal of the delisted waste BAE possesses or is otherwise made aware of any environmental data (including but not limited to leachate data or ground water monitoring data) or any other data relevant to the delisted waste indicating that any constituent identified for the delisting verification testing is at level higher than the delisting level allowed by the Division Director in granting the petition, then the facility must report the data, in writing, to the Division Director within 10 days of first possessing or being made aware of that data. (B) If either the quarterly or annual testing of the waste does not meet the delisting requirements in paragraph (1), BAE must report the data, in writing, to the Division Director within 10 days of first possessing or being made aware of that data. (C) If BAE fails to submit the information described in paragraphs (5), (6)(A) or (6)(B) or if any other information is received from any source, the Division Director will make a preliminary determination as to whether the reported information requires EPA action to protect human health and/or the environment. Further action may include suspending, or revoking the exclusion, or other appropriate response necessary to protect human health and the environment. (D) If the Division Director determines that the reported information requires action by EPA, the Division Director will notify the facility in writing of the actions the Division Director believes are necessary to protect human health and the environment. The notice shall include a statement of the proposed action and a statement providing the facility with an opportunity to present information as to why the proposed EPA action is not necessary. The facility shall have 10 days from the date of the Division Director's notice to present such information. (E) Following the receipt of information from the facility described in paragraph (6)(D) or (if no information is presented under paragraph (6)(D)) the initial receipt of information described in paragraphs (5), (6)(A) or (6)(B), the Division Director will issue a final written determination describing EPA actions that are necessary to protect human health and/or the environment. Any required action described in the Division Director's determination shall become effective immediately, unless the Division Director provides otherwise. (7) Notification Requirements BAE Systems must do the following before transporting the delisted waste. Failure to provide this notification will result in a violation of the delisting petition and a possible revocation of the decision. (A) Provide a one-time written notification to any state Regulatory Agency to which or through which it will transport the delisted waste described above for disposal, 60 days before beginning such activities. (B) Update the one-time written notification if it ships the delisted waste into a different disposal facility. (C) Failure to provide this notification will result in a violation of the delisting variance and possible revocation of the decision.
BBC Brown Boveri, Inc.	Sanford, FL	Dewatered Wastewater treatment sludges (EPA Hazardous Waste No. F006) generated from electroplating operations after October 17, 1986.

Table 1—Wastes Excluded from Non-Specific Sources

Facility	Address	Waste description
Bekaert Corp	Dyersburg, TN	Dewatered wastewater treatment plant (WWTP) sludge (EPA Hazardous Waste Nos. F006) generated at a maximum rate of 1250 cubic yards per calendar year after May 27, 2004, and disposed in a Subtitle D landfill. For the exclusion to be valid, Bekaert must implement a verification testing program that meets the following paragraphs: (1) Delisting Levels: All leachable concentrations for those constituents must not exceed the maximum allowable concentrations in mg/l specified in this paragraph. Bekaert must use the leaching method specified at 40 CFR 261.24 to measure constituents in the waste leachate. (A) Inorganic Constituents TCLP (mg/l): Cadmium—0.672; Chromium—5.0; Nickel—127; Zinc—1260.0. (B) Organic Constituents TCLP (mg/l): Methyl ethyl ketone—200.0. (2) Waste Holding and Handling: (A) Bekaert must accumulate the hazardous waste dewatered WWTP sludge in accordance with the applicable regulations of 40 CFR 262.34 and continue to dispose of the dewatered WWTP sludge as hazardous waste. (B) Once the first quarterly sampling and analyses event described in paragraph (3) is completed and valid analyses demonstrate that no constituent is present in the sample at a level which exceeds the delisting levels set in paragraph (1), Bekaert can manage and dispose of the dewatered WWTP sludge as nonhazardous according to all applicable solid waste regulations. (C) If constituent levels in any sample taken by Bekaert exceed any of the delisting levels set in paragraph (1), Bekaert must do the following: (i) notify EPA in accordance with paragraph (7) and (ii) manage and dispose the dewatered WWTP sludge as hazardous waste generated under Subtitle C of RCRA. (D) Quarterly Verification Testing Requirements: Upon this exclusion becoming final, Bekaert may begin the quarterly testing requirements of paragraph (3) on its dewatered WWTP sludge. (3) Quarterly Testing Requirements: Upon this exclusion becoming final, Bekaert may perform quarterly analytical testing by sampling and analyzing the dewatered WWTP sludge as follows: (A)(i) Collect four representative composite samples of the hazardous waste dewatered WWTP sludge at quarterly (ninety (90) day) intervals after EPA grants the final exclusion. The first composite sample may be taken at any time after EPA grants the final approval. (ii) Analyze the samples for all constituents listed in paragraph (1). Any roll-offs from which the composite sample is taken exceeding the delisting levels listed in paragraph (1) must be disposed as hazardous waste in a Subtitle C landfill. (iii) Within forty-five (45) days after taking its first quarterly sample, Bekaert will report its first quarterly analytical test data to EPA. If levels of constituents measured in the sample of the dewatered WWTP sludge do not exceed the levels set forth in paragraph (1) of this exclusion, Bekaert can manage and dispose the nonhazardous dewatered WWTP sludge according to all applicable solid waste regulations. (4) Annual Testing: (A) If Bekaert completes the quarterly testing specified in paragraph (3) above and no sample contains a constituent with a level which exceeds the limits set forth in paragraph (1), Bekaert may begin annual testing as follows: Bekaert must test one representative composite sample of the dewatered WWTP sludge for all constituents listed in paragraph (1) at least once per calendar year. (B) The sample for the annual testing shall be a representative composite sample for all constituents listed in paragraph (1). (C) The sample for the annual testing taken for the second and subsequent annual testing events shall be taken within the same calendar month as the first annual sample taken. (5) Changes in Operating Conditions: If Bekaert significantly changes the process described in its petition or starts any processes that generate(s) the waste that may or could affect the composition or type of waste generated as established under paragraph (1) (by illustration, but not limitation, changes in equipment or operating conditions of the treatment process), it must notify the EPA in writing; it may no longer handle the wastes generated from the new process as nonhazardous until the wastes meet the delisting levels set in paragraph (1) and it has received written approval to do so from the EPA. (6) Data Submittals: Bekaert must submit the information described below. If Bekaert fails to submit the required data within the specified time or maintain the required records on-site for the specified time, the EPA, at its discretion, will consider this sufficient basis to reopen the exclusion as described in paragraph (7). Bekaert must:

Table 1—Wastes Excluded from Non-Specific Sources

Facility	Address	Waste description
		(A) Submit the data obtained through paragraph (3) to the Chief, North Section, RCRA Enforcement and Compliance Branch, Waste Division, U. S. Environmental Protection Agency Region 4, 61 Forsyth Street, SW., Atlanta, Georgia, 30303, within the time specified. (B) Compile records of analytical data from paragraph (3), summarized, and maintained on-site for a minimum of five years. (C) Furnish these records and data when either the EPA or the State of Tennessee request them for inspection. (D) Send along with all data a signed copy of the following certification statement, to attest to the truth and accuracy of the data submitted: "Under civil and criminal penalty of law for the making or submission of false or fraudulent statements or representations (pursuant to the applicable provisions of the Federal Code, which include, but may not be limited to, 18 U.S.C. 1001 and 42 U.S.C. 6928), I certify that the information contained in or accompanying this document is true, accurate and complete. As to the (those) identified section(s) of this document for which I cannot personally verify its (their) truth and accuracy, I certify as the company official having supervisory responsibility for the persons who, acting under my direct instructions, made the verification that this information is true, accurate and complete. If any of this information is determined by the EPA in its sole discretion to be false, inaccurate or incomplete, and upon conveyance of this fact to the company, I recognize and agree that this exclusion of waste will be void as if it never had effect or to the extent directed by the EPA and that the company will be liable for any actions taken in contravention of the company's RCRA and CERCLA obligations premised upon the company's reliance on the void exclusion." (7) Reopener: (A) If, anytime after disposal of the delisted waste Bekaert possesses or is otherwise made aware of any environmental data (including but not limited to leachate data or ground water monitoring data) or any other data relevant to the delisted waste indicating that any constituent identified for the delisting verification testing is at level higher than the delisting level allowed by the Regional Administrator or his delegate in granting the petition, then the facility must report the data, in writing, to the Regional Administrator or his delegate within ten (10) days of first possessing or being made aware of that data. (B) If either the quarterly or annual testing of the waste does not meet the delisting requirements in paragraph (1), Bekaert must report the data, in writing, to the Regional Administrator or his delegate within ten (10) days of first possessing or being made aware of that data. (C) If Bekaert fails to submit the information described in paragraphs (5), (6)(A) or (6)(B) or if any other information is received from any source, the Regional Administrator or his delegate will make a preliminary determination as to whether the reported information requires the EPA action to protect human health or the environment. Further action may include suspending, or revoking the exclusion, or other appropriate response necessary to protect human health and the environment. (D) If the Regional Administrator or his delegate determines that the reported information requires action the EPA, the Regional Administrator or his delegate will notify the facility in writing of the actions the Regional Administrator or his delegate believes are necessary to protect human health and the environment. The notification shall include a statement of the proposed action and a statement providing the facility with an opportunity to present information as to why the proposed the EPA action is not necessary. The facility shall have ten (10) days from the date of the Regional Administrator or his delegate's notice to present such information. (E) Following the receipt of information from the facility described in paragraph (6)(D) or (if no information is presented under paragraph (6)(D)) the initial receipt of information described in paragraphs (5), (6)(A) or (6)(B), the Regional Administrator or his delegate will issue a final written determination describing the EPA actions that are necessary to protect human health or the environment. Any required action described in the Regional Administrator or his delegate's determination shall become effective immediately, unless the Regional Administrator or his delegate provides otherwise. (8) Notification Requirements: Bekaert must do following before transporting the delisted waste: (A) Provide a one-time written notification to any State Regulatory Agency to which or through which it will transport the delisted waste described above for disposal, sixty (60) days before beginning such activities. (B) Update the one-time written notification if Bekaert ships the delisted waste into a different disposal facility. (C) Failure to provide this notification will result in a violation of the delisting variance and a possible revocation of the decision.

Table 1—Wastes Excluded from Non-Specific Sources

Facility	Address	Waste description
Bethlehem Steel Corporation	Sparrows Point, Maryland	Stabilized filter cake (at a maximum annual rate of 1100 cubic yards) from the treatment of wastewater treatment sludges (EPA Hazardous Waste No. F006) generated from electroplating operations after [insert date of publication in *Federal Register*]. Bethlehem Steel (BSC) must implement a testing program that meets the following conditions for the exclusion to be valid: (1) *Testing:* Sample collection and analyses (including quality control (QC) procedures) must be performed using appropriate methods. As applicable to the method-defined parameters of concern, analyses requiring the use of SW–846 methods incorporated by reference in 40 CFR 260.11 must be used without substitution. As applicable, the SW–846 methods might include Methods 0010, 0011, 0020, 0023A, 0030, 0031, 0040, 0050, 0051, 0060, 0061, 1010A, 1020B, 1110A, 1310B, 1311, 1312, 1320, 1330A, 9010C, 9012B, 9040C, 9045D, 9060A, 9070A (uses EPA Method 1664, Rev. A), 9071B, and 9095B. If EPA judges the stabilization process to be effective under the conditions used during the initial verification testing, BSC may replace the testing required in Condition (1)(A) with the testing required in Condition (1)(B). BSC must continue to test as specified in Condition (1)(A) until and unless notified by EPA in writing that testing in Condition (1)(A) may be replaced by Condition (1)(B) (to the extent directed by EPA). (A) *Initial Verification Testing:* During at least the first eight weeks of operation of the full-scale treatment system, BSC must collect and analyze weekly composites representative of the stabilized waste. Weekly composites must be composed of representative grab samples collected from every batch during each week of stabilization. The composite samples must be collected and analyzed, prior to the disposal of the stabilized filter cake, for all constituents listed in Condition (3). BSC must report the analytical test data, including a record of the ratios of lime kiln dust and fly ash used and quality control information, obtained during this initial period no later than 60 days after the collection of the last composite of stabilized filter cake. (B) *Subsequent Verification Testing:* Following written notification by EPA, BSC may substitute the testing condition in (1)(B) for (1)(A). BSC must collect and analyze at least one composite representative of the stabilized filter cake generated each month. Monthly composites must be comprised of representative samples collected from all batches that are stabilized in a one-month period. The monthly samples must be analyzed prior to the disposal of the stabilized filter cake for chromium, lead and nickel. BSC may, at its discretion, analyze composite samples more frequently to demonstrate that smaller batches of waste are non- hazardous. (C) *Annual Verification Testing:* In order to confirm that the characteristics of the treated waste do not change significantly, BSC must, on an annual basis, analyze a representative composite sample of stabilized filter cake for all TC constituents listed in 40 CFR §261.24 using the method specified therein. This composite sample must represent the stabilized filter cake generated over one week. (2) *Waste Holding and Handling:* BSC must store, as hazardous, all stabilized filter cake generated until verification testing (as specified in Conditions (1)(A) and (1)(B)) is completed and valid analyses demonstrate that the delisting levels set forth in Condition (3) are met. If the levels of hazardous constituents measured in the samples of stabilized filter cake generated are below all the levels set forth in Condition (3), then the stabilized filter cake is non- hazardous and may be managed and disposed of in accordance with all applicable solid waste regulations. If hazardous constituent levels in any weekly or monthly composite sample equal or exceed any of the delisting levels set in Condition (3), the stabilized filter cake generated during the time period corresponding to this sample must be retreated until it is below these levels or managed and disposed of in accordance with Subtitle C of RCRA. (3) *Delisting Levels:* All concentrations must be measured in the waste leachate by the method specified in 40 CFR §261.24. The leachable concentrations for the constituents must be below the following levels (ppm): arsenic— 4.8; barium—100; cadmium—0.48; chromium—5.0; lead—1.4; mercury—0.19; nickel—9.6; selenium—1.0; silver—5.0. (4) *Changes in Operating Conditions:* After completing the initial verification test period in Condition (1)(A), if BSC decides to significantly change the stabilization process (*e.g.*, stabilization reagents) developed under Condition (1), then BSC must notify EPA in writing prior to instituting the change. After written approval by EPA, BSC may manage waste generated from the changed process as non-hazardous under this exclusion, provided the other conditions of this exclusion are fulfilled. (5) *Data Submittals:* Two weeks prior to system start-up, BSC must notify in writing (see address below) when stabilization of the dewatered filter cake will begin. The data obtained through Condition (1)(A) must be submitted to Waste and Chemicals Management Division (Mail Code 3HW11), U.S. EPA Region III, 1650 Arch St., Philadelphia, PA 19103 within the time period specified. The analytical data, including quality control information and records of ratios of lime kiln dust and fly ash used, must be compiled and maintained on site for a minimum of five years. These data must be furnished upon request and made available for inspection by EPA or the State of Maryland. Failure to submit the required data within the specified time period or maintain the required records on site for the specified time will be considered by the Agency, at its discretion, sufficient basis to revoke the exclusion to the extent directed by EPA. All data must be accompanied by a signed copy of the following certification statement to attest to the truth and accuracy of the data submitted:

Table 1—Wastes Excluded from Non-Specific Sources

Facility	Address	Waste description
		"Under civil and criminal penalty of law for the making or submission of false or fraudulent statements or representations (pursuant to the applicable provisions of the Federal Code, which include, but may not be limited to, 18 U.S.C §1001 and 42 U.S.C §6928), I certify that the information contained in or accompanying this document is true, accurate and complete. As to the (those) identified section(s) of this document for which I cannot personally verify its (their) truth and accuracy, I certify as the company official having supervisory responsibility for the persons who, acting under my direct instructions, made the verification that this information is true, accurate and complete. In the event that any of this information is determined by EPA in its sole discretion to be false, inaccurate or incomplete, and upon conveyance of this fact to the company, I recognize and agree that this exclusion of waste will be void as if it never had effect or to the extent directed by EPA and that the company will be liable for any actions taken in contravention of the company's RCRA and CERCLA obligations premised upon the company's reliance on the void exclusion."
BMW Manufacturing Co., LLC	Greer, South Carolina	Wastewater treatment sludge (EPA Hazardous Waste No. F019) that BMW Manufacturing Corporation (BMW) generates by treating wastewater from automobile assembly plant located on Highway 101 South in Greer, South Carolina. This is a conditional exclusion for up to 2,850 cubic yards of waste (hereinafter referred to as "BMW Sludge") that will be generated each year and disposed in a Subtitle D landfill after August 31, 2005. With prior approval by the EPA, following a public comment period, BMW may also beneficially reuse the sludge. BMW must demonstrate that the following conditions are met for the exclusion to be valid. (1) Delisting Levels: All leachable concentrations for these metals and cyanide must not exceed the following levels (ppm): Barium-100; Cadmium-1; Chromium-5; Cyanide-33.6, Lead-5; and Nickel-70.3. These metal and cyanide concentrations must be measured in the waste leachate obtained by the method specified in 40 CFR 260.24, except that for cyanide, deionized water must be the leaching medium. Cyanide concentrations in waste or leachate must be measured by the method specified in 40 CFR 268.40, Note 7. (2) Annual Verification Testing Requirements: Sample collection and analyses, including quality control procedures, must be performed using appropriate methods. As applicable to the method-defined parameters of concern, analyses requiring the use of SW–846 methods incorporated by reference in 40 CFR 260.11 must be used without substitution. As applicable, the SW–846 methods might include Methods 0010, 0011, 0020, 0023A, 0030, 0031, 0040, 0050, 0051, 0060, 0061, 1010A, 1020B, 1110A, 1310B, 1311, 1312, 1320, 1330A, 9010C, 9012B, 9040C, 9045D, 9060A, 9070A, (uses EPA Method 1664, Rev. A), 9071B, and 9095B. Methods must meet Performance Based Measurement System Criteria in which the Data Quality Objectives are to demonstrate that representative samples of the BMW Sludge meet the delisting levels in Condition (1). (A) Annual Verification Testing: BMW must implement an annual testing program to demonstrate that constituent concentrations measured in the TCLP extract do not exceed the delisting levels established in Condition (1). (3) Waste Holding and Handling: BMW must hold sludge containers utilized for verification sampling until composite sample results are obtained. If the levels of constituents measured in the composite samples of BMW Sludge do not exceed the levels set forth in Condition (1), then the BMW Sludge is non-hazardous and must be managed in accordance with all applicable solid waste regulations. If constituent levels in a composite sample exceed any of the delisting levels set forth in Condition (1), the batch of BMW Sludge generated during the time period corresponding to this sample must be managed and disposed of in accordance with Subtitle C of RCRA. (4) Changes in Operating Conditions: BMW must notify EPA in writing when significant changes in the manufacturing or wastewater treatment processes are implemented. EPA will determine whether these changes will result in additional constituents of concern. If so, EPA will notify BMW in writing that the BMW Sludge must be managed as hazardous waste F019 until BMW has demonstrated that the wastes meet the delisting levels set forth in Condition (1) and any levels established by EPA for the additional constituents of concern, and BMW has received written approval from EPA. If EPA determines that the changes do not result in additional constituents of concern, EPA will notify BMW, in writing, that BMW must verify that the BMW Sludge continues to meet Condition (1) delisting levels. (5) Data Retention: Records of analytical data from Condition (2) must be compiled, summarized, and maintained by BMW for a minimum of three years, and must be furnished upon request by EPA or the State of South Carolina, and made available for inspection. Failure to maintain the required records for the specified time will be considered by EPA, at its discretion, sufficient basis to revoke the exclusion to the extent directed by EPA. All data must be accompanied by a signed copy of the certification statement in 40 CFR 260.22(i)(12).

Table 1—Wastes Excluded from Non-Specific Sources

Facility	Address	Waste description
		(6) Reopener Language: (A) If, at any time after disposal of the delisted waste, BMW possesses or is otherwise made aware of any environmental data (including but not limited to leachate data or groundwater monitoring data) or any other data relevant to the delisted waste indicating that any constituent identified in the delisting verification testing is at a level higher than the delisting level allowed by EPA in granting the petition, BMW must report the data, in writing, to EPA and South Carolina within 10 days of first possessing or being made aware of that data. (B) If the testing of the waste, as required by Condition (2)(A), does not meet the delisting requirements of Condition (1), BMW must report the data, in writing, to EPA and South Carolina within 10 days of first possessing or being made aware of that data. (C) Based on the information described in paragraphs (6)(A) or (6)(B) and any other information received from any source, EPA will make a preliminary determination as to whether the reported information requires that EPA take action to protect human health or the environment. Further action may include suspending or revoking the exclusion, or other appropriate response necessary to protect human health and the environment. (D) If EPA determines that the reported information does require Agency action, EPA will notify the facility in writing of the action believed necessary to protect human health and the environment. The notice shall include a statement of the proposed action and a statement providing BMW with an opportunity to present information as to why the proposed action is not necessary. BMW shall have 10 days from the date of EPA's notice to present such information. (E) Following the receipt of information from BMW, as described in paragraph (6)(D), or if no such information is received within 10 days, EPA will issue a final written determination describing the Agency actions that are necessary to protect human health or the environment, given the information received in accordance with paragraphs (6)(A) or (6)(B). Any required action described in EPA's determination shall become effective immediately, unless EPA provides otherwise. (7) Notification Requirements: BMW must provide a one-time written notification to any State Regulatory Agency in a State to which or through which the delisted waste described above will be transported, at least 60 days prior to the commencement of such activities. Failure to provide such a notification will result in a violation of the delisting conditions and a possible revocation of the decision to delist.
Boeing Commercial Airplane Co	Auburn, Washington	Residually contaminated soils in an inactive sludge pile containment area on March 27, 1990, previously used to store wastewater treatment sludges generated from electroplating operations (EPA Hazardous Waste No. F006).
Bommer Industries Inc.	Landrum, SC	Wastewater treatment sludges (EPA Hazardous Waste No. F006) generated from their electroplating operations and contained in evaporation ponds 1 and 2 on August 12, 1987.
BWX Technologies	Lynchburg, VA	Wastewater treatment sludge from electroplating operations (EPA Hazardous Waste No. F006) generated at a maximum annual rate of 500 cubic yards per year, after January 14, 2000, and disposed of in a Subtitle D landfill. BWX Technologies must meet the following conditions for the exclusion to be valid: (1) Delisting Levels: All leachable concentrations for the following constituents measure using the SW-846 method 1311 (the TCLP) must not exceed the following levels (mg/l). (a) Inorganic constituents—Antimony-0.6; Arsenic-5.0; Barium-100; Beryllium-0.4; Cadmium-0.5; Chromium-5.0; Cobalt-210; Copper-130; Lead-1.5; Mercury-0.2; Nickel-70; Silver-5.0; Thallium-0.2; Tin-2100; Zinc-1000; Fluoride-400. (b) Organic constituents—Acetone-400; Methylene Chloride-0.5. (2) Verification testing schedule: BWX Technologies must analyze a representative sample of the filter cake from the pickle acid treatment system on an annual, calendar year basis using methods with appropriate detection levels and quality control procedures. If the level of any constituent measured in the sample of filter cake exceeds the levels set forth in Paragraph 1, then the waste is hazardous and must be managed in accordance with Subtitle C of RCRA. Data from the annual verification testing must be submitted to EPA within 60 days of the sampling event. (3) Changes in Operating Conditions: If BWX Technologies significantly changes the manufacturing or treatment process described in the petition, or the chemicals used in the manufacturing or treatment process, BWX Technologies may not manage the filter cake generated from the new process under this exclusion until it has met the following conditions: (a) BWX Technologies must demonstrate that the waste meets the delisting levels set forth in Paragraph 1; (b) it must demonstrate that no new hazardous constituents listed in appendix VIII of part 261 have been introduced into the manufacturing or treatment process: and (c) it must obtain prior written approval from EPA to manage the waste under this exclusion.

Table 1—Wastes Excluded from Non-Specific Sources

Facility	Address	Waste description
		(4) Data Submittals: The data obtained under Paragraphs 2 and 3 must be submitted to The Waste and Chemicals Management Division, U.S. EPA Region III, 1650 Arch Street, Philadelphia, PA 19103. Records of operating conditions and analytical data must be compiled, summarized, and maintained on site for a minimum of five years and must be furnished upon request by EPA or the Commonwealth of Virginia, and made available for inspection. Failure to submit the required data within the specified time period or to maintain the required records on site for the specified time period will be considered by EPA, at its discretion, sufficient basis to revoke the exclusion to the extent determined necessary by EPA. All data must be accompanied by a signed copy of the certification statement set forth in 40 CFR 260.22(i)(12) to attest to the truth and accuracy of the data submitted. (5) Reopener: (a) If BWX Technologies discovers that a condition at the facility or an assumption related to the disposal of the excluded waste that was modeled or predicted in the petition does not occur as modeled or predicted, then BWX Technologies must report any information relevant to that condition, in writing, to the Regional Administrator or his delegate within 10 days of discovering that condition. (b) Upon receiving information described in paragraph (a) of this section, regardless of its source, the Regional Administrator or his delegate will determine whether the reported condition requires further action. Further action may include repealing the exclusion, modifying the exclusion, or other appropriate response necessary to protect human health and the environment. (6) Notification Requirements: BWX Technologies must provide a one- time written notification to any State Regulatory Agency to which or through which the delisted waste described above will be transported for disposal at least 60 days prior to the commencement of such activities. Failure to provide such a notification will be deemed to be a violation of this exclusion and may result in a revocation of the decision.
Capitol Products Corp	Harrisburg, PA	Dewatered wastewater treatment sludges (EPA Hazardous Waste No. FO19) generated from the chemical conversion coating of aluminum after September 12, 1986.
Capitol Products Corporation	Kentland, IN	Dewatered wastewater treatment sludges (EPA Hazardous Waste No. F019) generated from the chemical conversion coating of aluminum after November 17, 1986.
Care Free Aluminum Products, Inc	Charlotte, Michigan	Wastewater treatment sludge (EPA Hazardous Waste No. F019) generated from the chemical conversion coating of aluminum (generated at a maximum annual rate of 100 cubic yards), after August 21, 1992. In order to confirm that the characteristics of the waste do not change significantly, the facility must, on an annual basis, analyze a representative composite sample for the constituents listed in §261.24 using the method specified therein. The annual analytical results, including quality control information, must be compiled, certified according to §260.22(i)(12), maintained on-site for a minimum of five years, and made available for inspection upon request by any employee or representative of EPA or the State of Michigan. Failure to maintain the required records on-site will be considered by EPA, at its discretion, sufficient basis to revoke the exclusion to the extent directed by EPA.
Chamberlian-Featherlite, Inc	Hot Springs, AR	Dewatered wastewater treatment sludges (EPA Hazardous Waste No. F019) generated from the chemical conversion coating of aluminum after July 16, 1986.
Chrysler Group LLC at the Old Carco LLC Sterling Heights Assembly Plant.	Sterling Heights, Michigan.	Wastewater treatment sludges, F019, that are generated at Old Carco LLC's Sterling Heights Assembly Plant, (SHAP), Sterling Heights, Michigan by Chrysler Group LLC at a maximum annual rate of 3,000 cubic yards per year. The sludges must be disposed of in a lined landfill with leachate collection which is licensed, permitted, or otherwise authorized to accept the delisted wastewater treatment sludges in accordance with 40 CFR part 258. The exclusion becomes effective as of November 6, 2009. 1. *Delisting Levels:* The concentrations in a leachate extract of the waste measured in any sample must not exceed the following levels (mg/L): arsenic—0.22; nickel—67.8; benzene—0.057; hexachlorobenzene—0.0000724; naphthalene—0.00822; and pentachlorophenol—0.00607. 2. *Quarterly Verification Testing:* To verify that the waste does not exceed the specified delisting levels, Chrysler Group LLC or Old Carco LLC must collect and analyze one representative sample of the waste on a quarterly basis. Sample collection and analyses, including quality control procedures, must be performed using appropriate methods. SW–846 Method 1311 must be used for generation of the leachate extract used in the testing of the delisting levels if oil and grease comprise less than 1% of the waste. SW–846 Method 1330A must be used for generation of the leaching extract if oil and grease comprise 1% or more of the waste. SW–846 Method 9071B must be used for determination of oil and grease. SW–846 Methods 1311, 1330A, and 9071B are incorporated by reference in 40 CFR 260.11.

Table 1—Wastes Excluded from Non-Specific Sources

Facility	Address	Waste description
		3. *Changes in Operating Conditions:* Chrysler Group LLC or Old Carco LLC must notify the EPA in writing if the manufacturing process, the chemicals used in the manufacturing process, the treatment process, or the chemicals used in the treatment process change significantly. Chrysler Group LLC or Old Carco LLC must handle wastes generated after the process change as hazardous until it has demonstrated that the wastes continue to meet the delisting levels and that no new hazardous constituents listed in Appendix VIII of part 261 have been introduced and it has received written approval from EPA. 4. *Data Submittals:* Chrysler Group LLC or Old Carco LLC must submit the data obtained through verification testing or as required by other conditions of this rule to both U.S. EPA Region 5, 77 W. Jackson Blvd., Chicago, IL 60604 and MDEQ, Waste and Hazardous Materials Division, Hazardous Waste Section, at P.O. Box 30241, Lansing, Michigan 48909. The quarterly verification data and certification of proper disposal must be submitted annually upon the anniversary of the effective date of this exclusion. Chrysler Group LLC or Old Carco LLC must compile, summarize and maintain on site for a minimum of five years records of operating conditions and analytical data. Chrysler Group LLC or Old Carco LLC must make these records available for inspection. A signed copy of the certification statement in 40 CFR 260.22(i)(12) must accompany all data. 5. *Reopener Language*—(a) If, anytime after disposal of the delisted waste Chrysler Group LLC or Old Carco LLC possesses or is otherwise made aware of any data (including but not limited to leachate data or groundwater monitoring data) relevant to the delisted waste indicating that any constituent is at a level in the leachate higher than the specified delisting level, or is in the groundwater at a concentration higher than the maximum allowable groundwater concentration in paragraph (e), then Chrysler Group LLC or Old Carco LLC must report such data, in writing, to the Regional Administrator within 10 days of first possessing or being made aware of that data. (b) Based on the information described in paragraph (a) and any other information received from any source, the Regional Administrator will make a preliminary determination as to whether the reported information requires Agency action to protect human health or the environment. Further action may include suspending, or revoking the exclusion, or other appropriate response necessary to protect human health and the environment. (c) If the Regional Administrator determines that the reported information does require Agency action, the Regional Administrator will inform Chrysler Group LLC or Old Carco LLC in writing of the actions the Regional Administrator believes are necessary to protect human health and the environment. The notice shall include a statement of the proposed action and a statement providing Chrysler Group LLC or Old Carco LLC with an opportunity to present information as to why the proposed Agency action is not necessary or to suggest an alternative action. Chrysler Group LLC or Old Carco LLC shall have 30 days from the date of the Regional Administrator's notice to present the information. (d) If after 30 days Chrysler Group LLC or Old Carco LLC presents no further information, the Regional Administrator will issue a final written determination describing the Agency actions that are necessary to protect human health or the environment. Any required action described in the Regional Administrator's determination shall become effective immediately, unless the Regional Administrator provides otherwise. (e) Maximum Allowable Groundwater Concentrations (µg/L): arsenic—4.87; nickel—750; benzene—2.5; hexachlorobenzene—0.00168; naphthalene—245; and pentachlorophenol—0.071.
Cincinnati Metropolitan Sewer District	Cincinnati, OH	Sluiced bottom ash (approximately 25,000 cubic yards) contained in the South Lagoon, on September 13, 1985 which contains EPA Hazardous Waste Nos. F001, F002, F003, F004, and F005.
Clay Equipment Corporation	Cedar Falls, Iowa	Dewatered wastewater treatment sludges (EPA Hazardous Waste No. F006) and spent cyanide bath solutions (EPA Hazardous Waste No. F009) generated from electroplating operations and disposed of in an on-site surface impoundment. This is a onetime exclusion. This exclusion was published on August 1, 1989.
Continental Can Co	Olympia, WA	Dewatered wastewater treatment sludges (DPA Hazardous Waste No. FO19) generated from the chemical conversion coating of aluminum after September 12, 1986.
Cooper Crouse-Hinds	Amarillo, TX	Wastewater Treatment Sludge (Hazardous Waste No. F006) generated at a maximum annual rate of 816 cubic yards per calendar year after April 15, 2009 and disposed in Subtitle D Landfill. For the exclusion to be valid, Cooper Crouse-Hinds must implement a verification testing program that meets the following Paragraphs: (1) Delisting Levels: All concentrations for those constituents must not exceed the maximum allowable concentrations in mg/l specified in this paragraph.

Table 1—Wastes Excluded from Non-Specific Sources

Facility	Address	Waste description
		WWTP Sludge Leachable Concentrations (mg/l): (i) Inorganic Constituents: Arsenic-0.0759; Barium-100; Cadmium-0.819; Copper-216; Iron-1.24; Manganese-145; Nickel-119; Zinc-18. (ii) Organic Constituents: Benzene-0.5. (2) Waste Holding and Handling: (A) Waste classification as non-hazardous can not begin until compliance with the limits set in paragraph (1) for WWTP sludge has occurred for two consecutive quarterly sampling events. (B) If constituent levels in any sample taken by Cooper Crouse-Hinds exceed any of the delisting levels set in paragraph (1) for the WWTP sludge, Cooper Crouse-Hinds must do the following: (i) Notify EPA in accordance with paragraph (6) and (ii) Manage and dispose WWTP sludge as hazardous waste generated under Subtitle C of RCRA. (3) Testing Requirements: Upon this exclusion becoming final, Cooper Crouse-Hinds may perform quarterly analytical testing by sampling and analyzing the WWTP sludge as follows: (A) Quarterly Testing: (i) Collect two representative composite samples of the sludge at quarterly intervals after EPA grants the final exclusion. The first composite samples may be taken at any time after EPA grants the final approval. Sampling must be performed in accordance with the sampling plan approved by EPA in support of the exclusion. (ii) Analyze the samples for all constituents listed in paragraph (1). Any composite sample taken that exceeds the delisting levels listed in paragraph (1) for the sludge must be disposed as hazardous waste in accordance with the applicable hazardous waste requirements. (iii) Within thirty (30) days after taking its first quarterly sample, Cooper Crouse-Hinds will report its first quarterly analytical test data to EPA. If levels of constituents measured in the samples of the sludge do not exceed the levels set forth in paragraph (1) of this exclusion for two consecutive quarters, Cooper Crouse-Hinds can manage and dispose the non-hazardous WWTP sludge according to all applicable solid waste regulations. (B) Annual Testing: (i) If Cooper Crouse-Hinds completes the quarterly testing specified in paragraph (3) above and no sample contains a constituent at a level which exceeds the limits set forth in paragraph (1), Cooper Crouse-Hinds may begin annual testing as follows: Cooper Crouse-Hinds must test two representative composite samples of the WWTP sludge for all constituents listed in paragraph (1) at least once per calendar year. (ii) The samples for the annual testing shall be a representative composite sample according to appropriate methods. As applicable to the method-defined parameters of concern, analyses requiring the use of SW–846 methods incorporated by reference in 40 CFR 260.11 must be used without substitution. As applicable, the SW–846 methods might include Methods 0010, 0011, 0020, 0023A, 0030, 0031, 0040, 0050, 0051, 0060, 0061, 1010A, 1020B,1110A, 1310B, 1311, 1312, 1320, 1330A, 9010C, 9012B, 9040C, 9045D, 9060A, 9070A (uses EPA Method 1664, Rev. A), 9071B, and 9095B. Methods must meet Performance Based Measurement System Criteria in which the Data Quality Objectives are to demonstrate that samples of the WWTP sludge is representative for all constituents listed in paragraph (1). (iii) The samples for the annual testing taken for the second and subsequent annual testing events shall be taken within the same calendar month as the first annual sample taken. (iv) The annual testing report should include the total amount of delisted waste in cubic yards disposed as non-hazardous waste during the calendar year. (4) Changes in Operating Conditions: If Cooper Crouse-Hinds significantly changes the process described in its petition or starts any processes that generate(s) the waste that may or could affect the composition or type of waste generated (by illustration, but not limitation, changes in equipment or operating conditions of the treatment process), it must notify EPA in writing and it may no longer handle the wastes generated from the new process as non-hazardous until the wastes meet the delisting levels set in paragraph (1) and it has received written approval to do so from EPA. Cooper Crouse-Hinds must submit a modification to the petition, complete with full sampling and analysis, for circumstances where the waste volume changes and/or additional waste codes are added to the waste stream, if it wishes to dispose of the material as non-hazardous.

Table 1—Wastes Excluded from Non-Specific Sources

Facility	Address	Waste description
		(5) Data Submittals: Cooper Crouse-Hinds must submit the information described below. If Cooper Crouse-Hinds fails to submit the required data within the specified time or maintain the required records on-site for the specified time, EPA, at its discretion, will consider this sufficient basis to re-open the exclusion as described in paragraph (6). Cooper Crouse-Hinds must: (A) Submit the data obtained through paragraph (3) to the Chief, Corrective Action and Waste Minimization Section, Multimedia Planning and Permitting Division, U. S. Environmental Protection Agency Region 6, 1445 Ross Ave., Dallas, Texas, 75202, within the time specified. All supporting data can be submitted on CD–ROM or comparable electronic media. (B) Compile records of analytical data from paragraph (3), summarized, and maintained on-site for a minimum of five years. (C) Furnish these records and data when either EPA or the State of Texas requests them for inspection. (D) Send along with all data a signed copy of the following certification statement, to attest to the truth and accuracy of the data submitted: "Under civil and criminal penalty of law for the making or submission of false or fraudulent statements or representations (pursuant to the applicable provisions of the Federal Code, which include, but may not be limited to, 18 U.S.C. 1001 and 42 U.S.C. 6928), I certify that the information contained in or accompanying this document is true, accurate and complete. "As to the (those) identified section(s) of this document for which I cannot personally verify its (their) truth and accuracy, I certify as the company official having supervisory responsibility for the persons who, acting under my direct instructions, made the verification that this information is true, accurate and complete. "If any of this information is determined by EPA in its sole discretion to be false, inaccurate or incomplete, and upon conveyance of this fact to the company, I recognize and agree that this exclusion of waste will be void as if it never had effect or to the extent directed by EPA and that the company will be liable for any actions taken in contravention of the company's RCRA and CERCLA obligations premised upon the company's reliance on the void exclusion." (6) Re-opener: (A) If, anytime after disposal of the delisted waste Cooper Crouse-Hinds possesses or is otherwise made aware of any environmental data (including but not limited to leachate data or ground water monitoring data) or any other data relevant to the delisted waste indicating that any constituent identified for the delisting verification testing is at level higher than the delisting level allowed by the Division Director in granting the petition, then the facility must report the data, in writing, to the Division Director within 10 days of first possessing or being made aware of that data. (B) If either the quarterly or annual testing of the waste does not meet the delisting requirements in paragraph (1), Cooper Crouse-Hinds must report the data, in writing, to the Division Director within 10 days of first possessing or being made aware of that data. (C) If Cooper Crouse-Hinds fails to submit the information described in paragraphs (5), (6)(A) or (6)(B) or if any other information is received from any source, the Division Director will make a preliminary determination as to whether the reported information requires EPA action to protect human health and/or the environment. Further action may include suspending, or revoking the exclusion, or other appropriate response necessary to protect human health and the environment. (D) If the Division Director determines that the reported information requires action by EPA, the Division Director will notify the facility in writing of the actions the Division Director believes are necessary to protect human health and the environment. The notice shall include a statement of the proposed action and a statement providing the facility with an opportunity to present information as to why the proposed EPA action is not necessary. The facility shall have 10 days from the date of the Division Director's notice to present such information. (E) Following the receipt of information from the facility described in paragraph (6)(D) or (if no information is presented under paragraph (6)(D)) the initial receipt of information described in paragraphs (5), (6)(A) or (6)(B), the Division Director will issue a final written determination describing EPA actions that are necessary to protect human health and/or the environment. Any required action described in the Division Director's determination shall become effective immediately, unless the Division Director provides otherwise. (7) Notification Requirements: Cooper Crouse-Hinds must do the following before transporting the delisted waste. Failure to provide this notification will result in a violation of the delisting petition and a possible revocation of the decision.

Table 1—Wastes Excluded from Non-Specific Sources

Facility	Address	Waste description
		(A) Provide a one-time written notification to any state Regulatory Agency to which or through which it will transport the delisted waste described above for disposal, 60 days before beginning such activities. (B) Update the one-time written notification if it ships the delisted waste into a different disposal facility. (C) Failure to provide this notification will result in a violation of the delisting variance and a possible revocation of the decision.
Daimler Chrysler Corporation	Jefferson North Assembly Plant, Detroit, Michigan	Waste water treatment plant sludge, F019, that is generated by DaimlerChrysler Corporation at the Jefferson North Assembly Plant (DCC–JNAP) at a maximum annual rate of 2,000 cubic yards per year. The sludge must be disposed of in a lined landfill with leachate collection, which is licensed, permitted, or otherwise authorized to accept the delisted wastewater treatment sludge in accordance with 40 CFR part 258. The exclusion becomes effective as of (insert final publication date). 1. *Delisting Levels:* (A) The concentrations in a TCLP extract of the waste measured in any sample may not exceed the following levels (mg/L): Antimony—0.659; Arsenic—0.3; Cadmium—0.48; Chromium—4.95; Lead—5; Nickel—90.5; Selenium—1; Thallium—0.282; Tin—721; Zinc—898; Acetone—228; p-Cresol—11.4; Formaldehyde—84.2; and Methylene chloride—0.288. (B) The total concentrations measured in any sample may not exceed the following levels (mg/kg): Mercury—8.92; and Formaldehyde—689. (C) The sum of the ratios of the TCLP concentrations to the delisting levels for nickel and either thallium or cadmium shall not exceed 1.0. 2. *Quarterly Verification Testing:* To verify that the waste does not exceed the specified delisting levels, DCC–JNAP must collect and analyze one representative sample of the waste on a quarterly basis. 3. *Changes in Operating Conditions:* DCC–JNAP must notify the EPA in writing if the manufacturing process, the chemicals used in the manufacturing process, the treatment process, or the chemicals used in the treatment process significantly change. DCC–JNAP must handle wastes generated after the process change as hazardous until it has demonstrated that the wastes continue to meet the delisting levels and that no new hazardous constituents listed in appendix VIII of part 261 have been introduced and it has received written approval from EPA. 4. *Data Submittals:* DCC–JNAP must submit the data obtained through verification testing or as required by other conditions of this rule to both U.S. EPA Region 5, Waste Management Branch (DW–8J), 77 W. Jackson Blvd., Chicago, IL 60604 and MDEQ, Waste Management Division, Hazardous Waste Program Section, at P.O. Box 30241, Lansing, Michigan 48909. The quarterly verification data and certification of proper disposal must be submitted annually upon the anniversary of the effective date of this exclusion. The facility must compile, summarize, and maintain on site for a minimum of five years records of operating conditions and analytical data. The facility must make these records available for inspection. All data must be accompanied by a signed copy of the certification statement in 40 CFR 260.22(i)(12). 5. *Reopener Language*— (a) If, anytime after disposal of the delisted waste, DCC–JNAP possesses or is otherwise made aware of any data (including but not limited to leachate data or groundwater monitoring data) relevant to the delisted waste indicating that any constituent is at a level in the leachate higher than the specified delisting level, or is in the groundwater at a concentration higher than the maximum allowable groundwater concentration in paragraph (e), then DCC–JNAP must report such data, in writing, to the Regional Administrator within 10 days of first possessing or being made aware of that data. (b) Based on the information described in paragraph (a) and any other information received from any source, the Regional Administrator will make a preliminary determination as to whether the reported information requires Agency action to protect human health or the environment. Further action may include suspending, or revoking the exclusion, or other appropriate response necessary to protect human health and the environment. (c) If the Regional Administrator determines that the reported information does require Agency action, the Regional Administrator will notify DCC–JNAP in writing of the actions the Regional Administrator believes are necessary to protect human health and the environment. The notice shall include a statement of the proposed action and a statement providing DCC–JNAP with an opportunity to present information as to why the proposed Agency action is not necessary or to suggest an alternative action. DCC–JNAP shall have 30 days from the date of the Regional Administrator's notice to present the information.

Table 1—Wastes Excluded from Non-Specific Sources

Facility	Address	Waste description
		(d) If after 30 days the facility presents no further information, the Regional Administrator will issue a final written determination describing the Agency actions that are necessary to protect human health or the environment. Any required action described in the Regional Administrator's determination shall become effective immediately, unless the Regional Administrator provides otherwise. (e) *Maximum Allowable Groundwater Concentrations* (µg/L): Antimony—6; Arsenic—4.87; Cadmium—5; Chromium—100; Lead—15; Nickel—750; Selenium—50; Thallium—2; Tin—22,500; Zinc—11,300; acetone—3,750; p-Cresol—188; Formaldehyde—1,380; and Methylene chloride—5.
Dover Corp., Norris Div	Tulsa, OK	Dewatered wastewater treatment sludge (EPA Hazardous Waste No. FO06) generated from their electroplating operations after April 29, 1986.
DuraTherm, Incorporated	San Leon, Texas	Desorber solids, (at a maximum generation of 20,000 cubic yards per calendar year) generated by DuraTherm using the thermal desorption treatment process, (EPA Hazardous Waste No. F037 and F038) and that is disposed of in subtitle D landfills after April 24, 2000. For the exclusion to be valid, DuraTherm must implement a testing program that meets the following Paragraphs: (1) *Delisting Levels:* All leachable concentrations for those constituents must not exceed the following levels (ppm). The petitioner must use an acceptable leaching method, for example SW-846, Method 1311 to measure constituents in the waste leachate. Desorber solids (i) Inorganic Constituents Arsenic—1.35; Antimony—0.162; Barium—54.0; Beryllium—0.108; Cadmium—0.135; Chromium—0.6; Lead—0.405; Nickel—2.7; Selenium—1.0; Silver—5.0; Vanadium—5.4; Zinc— 270. (ii) Organic Constituents Anthracene—0.28; Benzene—0.135; Benzo(a) anthracene—0.059; Benzo(b)fluoranthene—0.11; Benzo(a)pyrene—0.061; Bis- ethylhexylphthalate—0.28; Carbon Disulfide—3.8; Chlorobenzene— 0.057; Chrysene—0.059; o,m,p Cresols—54; Dibenzo (a,h) anthracene—0.055; 2,4 Dimethyl phenol—18.9; Dioctyl phthalate— 0.017; Ethylbenzene—0.057; Fluoranthene—0.068; Fluorene— 0.059; Naphthalene—0.059; Phenanthrene—0.059; Phenol—6.2; Pyrene—0.067; Styrene—2.7; Trichloroethylene—0.054; Toluene—0.08; Xylene—0.032 (2) *Waste Holding and Handling:* (A) DuraTherm must store the desorber solids as described in its RCRA permit, or continue to dispose of as hazardous all desorber solids generated, until they have completed verification testing described in Paragraph (3)(A) and (B), as appropriate, and valid analyses show that paragraph (1) is satisfied. (B) In order to isolate wastes that have been processed in the unit prior to one of the waste codes to be delisted, DuraTherm must designate the first batch of F037, F038, K048, K049, K050, or K051 wastes as hazardous. Subsequent batches of these wastes which satisfy paragraph (1) are eligible for delisting if they meet the criteria in paragraph (1) and no additional constituents (other than those of the delisted waste streams) from the previously processed wastes are detected. (C) Levels of constituents measured in the samples of the desorber solids that do not exceed the levels set forth in Paragraph (1) are nonhazardous. DuraTherm can manage and dispose the nonhazardous desorber solids according to all applicable solid waste regulations. (D) If constituent levels in a sample exceed any of the delisting levels set in Paragraph (1), DuraTherm must retreat or stabilize the batches of waste used to generate the representative sample until it meets the levels in paragraph(1). DuraTherm must repeat the analyses of the treated waste. (E) If the facility has not treated the waste, DuraTherm must manage and dispose the waste generated under subtitle C of RCRA. (3) *Verification Testing Requirements:* DuraTherm must perform sample collection and analyses, including quality control procedures, using appropriate methods. As applicable to the method-defined parameters of concern, analyses requiring the use of SW–846 methods incorporated by reference in 40 CFR 260.11 must be used without substitution. As applicable, the SW–846 methods might include Methods 0010, 0011, 0020, 0023A, 0030, 0031, 0040, 0050, 0051, 0060, 0061, 1010A, 1020B, 1110A, 1310B, 1311, 1312, 1320, 1330A, 9010C, 9012B, 9040C, 9045D, 9060A, 9070A (uses EPA Method 1664, Rev. A), 9071B, and 9095B. If EPA judges the process to be effective under the operating conditions used during the initial verification testing, DuraTherm may replace the testing required in Paragraph (3)(A) with the testing required in Paragraph (3)(B). DuraTherm must continue to test as specified in Paragraph (3)(A) until and unless notified by EPA in writing that testing in Paragraph (3)(A) may be replaced by Paragraph (3)(B).

Table 1—Wastes Excluded from Non-Specific Sources

Facility	Address	Waste description
		(A) *Initial Verification Testing:* After EPA grants the final exclusion, DuraTherm must do the following: (i) Collect and analyze composites of the desorber solids. (ii) Make two composites of representative grab samples collected. (iii) Analyze the waste, before disposal, for all of the constituents listed in Paragraph 1. (iv) Sixty (60) days after this exclusion becomes final, report the operational and analytical test data, including quality control information. (v) Submit the test plan for conducting the multiple pH leaching procedure to EPA for approval at least 10 days before conducting the analysis. (vi) Conduct a multiple pH leaching procedure on 10 samples collected during the sixty-day test period. (vii) The ten samples should include both non-stabilized and stabilized residual solids. If none of the samples collected during the sixty-day test period need to be stabilized, DuraTherm should provide multiple pH data on the first sample of stabilized wastes generated. (vii) Perform the toxicity characteristic leaching procedure using three different pH extraction fluids to simulate disposal under three conditions and submit the results within 60 days of completion. Simulate an acidic landfill environment, basic landfill environment, and a landfill environment similar to the pH of the waste. (B) *Subsequent Verification Testing:* Following written notification by EPA, DuraTherm may substitute the testing conditions in (3)(B) for (3)(A)(i). DuraTherm must continue to monitor operating conditions, and analyze representative samples each quarter of operation during the first year of waste generation. The samples must represent the waste generated in one quarter. DuraTherm must run the multiple pH procedure on these waste samples. (C) *Termination of Organic Testing:* (i) DuraTherm must continue testing as required under Paragraph (3)(B) for organic constituents in Paragraph (1)(A)(ii), until the analytical results submitted under Paragraph (3)(B) show a minimum of two consecutive samples below the delisting levels in Paragraph (1)(A)(i), DuraTherm may then request that EPA stop quarterly organic testing. After EPA notifies DuraTherm in writing, the company may end quarterly organic testing. (ii) Following cancellation of the quarterly testing, DuraTherm must continue to test a representative composite sample for all constituents listed in Paragraph (1) annually (by twelve months after final exclusion). (4) *Changes in Operating Conditions:* If DuraTherm significantly changes the process described in its petition or starts any processes that generate(s) the waste that may or could affect the composition or type of waste generated as established under Paragraph (1) (by illustration, but not limitation, changes in equipment or operating conditions of the treatment process), they must notify EPA in writing; they may no longer handle the wastes generated from the new process as nonhazardous until the wastes meet the delisting levels set in Paragraph (1) and they have received written approval to do so from EPA. (5) *Data Submittals:* DuraTherm must submit the information described below. If DuraTherm fails to submit the required data within the specified time or maintain the required records on- site for the specified time, EPA, at its discretion, will consider this sufficient basis to reopen the exclusion as described in Paragraph 6. DuraTherm must: (A) Submit the data obtained through Paragraph 3 to Mr. William Gallagher, Chief, Region 6 Delisting Program, EPA, 1445 Ross Avenue, Dallas, Texas 75202- 2733, Mail Code, (6PD-O) within the time specified. (B) Compile records of operating conditions and analytical data from Paragraph (3), summarized, and maintained on-site for a minimum of five years. (C) Furnish these records and data when EPA or the State of Texas request them for inspection. (D) Send along with all data a signed copy of the following certification statement, to attest to the truth and accuracy of the data submitted: Under civil and criminal penalty of law for the making or submission of false or fraudulent statements or representations (pursuant to the applicable provisions of the Federal Code, which include, but may not be limited to, 18 U.S.C. 1001 and 42 U.S.C. 6928), I certify that the information contained in or accompanying this document is true, accurate and complete. As to the (those) identified section(s) of this document for which I cannot personally verify its (their) truth and accuracy, I certify as the company official having supervisory responsibility for the persons who, acting under my direct instructions, made the verification that this information is true, accurate and complete.

Table 1—Wastes Excluded from Non-Specific Sources

Facility	Address	Waste description
		If any of this information is determined by EPA in its sole discretion to be false, inaccurate or incomplete, and upon conveyance of this fact to the company, I recognize and agree that this exclusion of waste will be void as if it never had effect or to the extent directed by EPA and that the company will be liable for any actions taken in contravention of the company's RCRA and CERCLA obligations premised upon the company's reliance on the void exclusion. (6) *Reopener Language:* (A) If, anytime after disposal of the delisted waste, DuraTherm possesses or is otherwise made aware of any environmental data (including but not limited to leachate data or groundwater monitoring data) or any other data relevant to the delisted waste indicating that any constituent identified for the delisting verification testing is at level higher than the delisting level allowed by the Regional Administrator or his delegate in granting the petition, then the facility must report the data, in writing, to the Regional Administrator or his delegate within 10 days of first possessing or being made aware of that data. (B) If the annual testing of the waste does not meet the delisting requirements in Paragraph 1, DuraTherm must report the data, in writing, to the Regional Administrator or his delegate within 10 days of first possessing or being made aware of that data. (C) If DuraTherm fails to submit the information described in paragraphs (5),(6)(A) or (6)(B) or if any other information is received from any source, the Regional Administrator or his delegate will make a preliminary determination as to whether the reported information requires Agency action to protect human health or the environment. Further action may include suspending, or revoking the exclusion, or other appropriate response necessary to protect human health and the environment. (D) If the Regional Administrator or his delegate determines that the reported information does require Agency action, the Regional Administrator or his delegate will notify the facility in writing of the actions the Regional Administrator or his delegate believes are necessary to protect human health and the environment. The notice shall include a statement of the proposed action and a statement providing the facility with an opportunity to present information as to why the proposed Agency action is not necessary. The facility shall have 10 days from the date of the Regional Administrator or his delegate's notice to present such information. (E) Following the receipt of information from the facility described in paragraph (6)(D) or (if no information is presented under paragraph (6)(D)) the initial receipt of information described in paragraphs (5), (6)(A) or (6)(B), the Regional Administrator or his delegate will issue a final written determination describing the Agency actions that are necessary to protect human health or the environment. Any required action described in the Regional Administrator or his delegate's determination shall become effective immediately, unless the Regional Administrator or his delegate provides otherwise. (7) *Notification Requirements:* DuraTherm must do following before transporting the delisted waste: Failure to provide this notification will result in a violation of the delisting petition and a possible revocation of the decision. (A) Provide a one-time written notification to any State Regulatory Agency to which or through which they will transport the delisted waste described above for disposal, 60 days before beginning such activities. (B) Update the one-time written notification if they ship the delisted waste into a different disposal facility.
Eastman Chemical Company	Longview, Texas	Wastewater treatment sludge, (at a maximum generation of 82,100 cubic yards per calendar year) generated by Eastman (EPA Hazardous Waste Nos. F001, F002, F003, F005 generated at Eastman when disposed of in a Subtitle D landfill. Eastman must implement a testing program that meets the following conditions for the exclusion to be valid: (1) *Delisting Levels:* All concentrations for the following constituents must not exceed the following levels (mg/l). For the wastewater treatment sludge constituents must be measured in the waste leachate by the method specified in 40 CFR 261.24—Wastewater treatment sludge: (i) Inorganic Constituents: Antimony—0.0515; Barium—7.30; Cobalt—2.25; Chromium—5.0; Lead—5.0; Mercury—0.0015; Nickel—2.83; Selenium—0.22; Silver—0.384; Vanadium—2.11; Zinc—28.0 (ii) Organic Constituents: Acenaphthene—1.25; Acetone—7.13; bis(2-ethylhexylphthalate—0.28; 2-butanone—42.8; Chloroform—0.0099; Fluorene—0.55; Methanol—35.7; Methylene Chloride—0.486; Naphthalene—0.0321. (2) *Waste Holding and Handling:* If the concentrations of the sludge exceed the levels provided in Condition 1, then the sludge must be treated in the Fluidized Bed Incinerator (FBI) and meet the requirements of that September 25, 1996 delisting exclusion to be non-hazardous (as FBI ash). If the sludge meets the delisting levels provided in Condition 1, then it's non-hazardous (as sludge). If the waste water treatment sludge is not managed in the manner above, Eastman must manage

Table 1—Wastes Excluded from Non-Specific Sources

Facility	Address	Waste description
		it in accordance with applicable RCRA Subtitle C requirements. If the levels of constituents measured in the samples of the waste water treatment sludge do not exceed the levels set forth in Condition (1), then the waste is nonhazardous and may be managed and disposed of in accordance with all applicable solid waste regulations. During the verification period, Eastman must manage the waste in the FBI incinerator prior to disposal.
		(3) *Verification Testing Requirements:* Eastman must perform sample collection and analyses, including quality control procedures, using appropriate methods. As applicable to the method-defined parameters of concern, analyses requiring the use of SW–846 methods incorporated by reference in 40 CFR 260.11 must be used without substitution. As applicable, the SW–846 methods might include Methods 0010, 0011, 0020, 0023A, 0030, 0031, 0040, 0050, 0051, 0060, 0061, 1010A, 1020B, 1110A, 1310B, 1311, 1312, 1320, 1330A, 9010C, 9012B, 9040C, 9045D, 9060A, 9070A (uses EPA Method 1664, Rev. A), 9071B, and 9095B. After completion of the initial verification period, Eastman may replace the testing required in Condition (3)(A) with the testing required in Condition (3)(B). Eastman must continue to test as specified in Condition (3)(A) until and unless notified by EPA in writing that testing in Condition (3)(A) may be replaced by Condition (3)(B).
		(A) *Initial Verification Testing:* At quarterly intervals for one year after the final exclusion is granted, Eastman must collect and analyze composites of the wastewater treatment sludge for constituents listed in Condition (1).
		(B) *Subsequent Verification Testing:* Following termination of the quarterly testing, Eastman must continue to test a representative composite sample for all constituents listed in Condition (1) on an annual basis (no later than twelve months after the final exclusion).
		(4) *Changes in Operating Conditions.* If Eastman significantly changes the process which generate(s) the waste(s) and which may or could affect the composition or type of waste(s) generated as established under Condition (1) (by illustration, but not limitation, change in equipment or operating conditions of the treatment process or generation of volumes in excess 82,100 cubic yards of waste annually), Eastman must (A) notify the EPA in writing of the change and (B) may no longer handle or manage the waste generated from the new process as nonhazardous until Eastman has demonstrated through testing the waste meets the delisting levels set in Condition (1) and (C) Eastman has received written approval to begin managing the wastes as non-hazardous from EPA.
		(5) *Data Submittals.* Eastman must submit or maintain, as applicable, the information described below. If Eastman fails to submit the required data within the specified time or maintain the required records on-site for the specified time, EPA, at its discretion, will consider this sufficient basis to reopen the exclusion as described in Condition (6). Eastman must:
		(A) Submit the data obtained through Condition (3) to Mr. William Gallagher, Chief, Region 6 Delisting Program, EPA, 1445 Ross Avenue, Dallas, Texas 75202–2733, Mail Code, (6PD–O) within the time specified.
		(B) Compile records of operating conditions and analytical data from Condition (3), summarized, and maintained on-site for a minimum of five years.
		(C) Furnish these records and data when EPA or the State of Texas request them for inspection.
		(D) Send along with all data a signed copy of the following certification statement, to attest to the truth and accuracy of the data submitted:
		(i) Under civil and criminal penalty of law for the making or submission of false or fraudulent statements or representations (pursuant to the applicable provisions of the Federal Code, which include, but may not be limited to, 18 U.S.C. 1001 and 42 U.S.C. 6928), I certify that the information contained in or accompanying this document is true, accurate and complete.
		(ii) As to the (those) identified section(s) of this document for which I cannot personally verify its (their) truth and accuracy, I certify as the company official having supervisory responsibility for the persons who, acting under my direct instructions, made the verification that this information is true, accurate and complete.
		(iii) If any of this information is determined by EPA in its sole discretion to be false, inaccurate or incomplete, and upon conveyance of this fact to the company, I recognize and agree that this exclusion of waste will be void as if it never had effect or to the extent directed by EPA and that the company will be liable for any actions taken in contravention of the company's RCRA and CERCLA obligations premised upon the company's reliance on the void exclusion.
		(6) *Reopener Language:*
		(A) If, anytime after disposal of the delisted waste, Eastman possesses or is otherwise made aware of any environmental data (including but not limited to leachate data or groundwater monitoring data) or any other data relevant to the delisted waste indicating that any constituent identified for the delisting verification testing is at level higher than the delisting level allowed by the Regional Administrator or his delegate in granting the petition, then the facility must report the data, in writing, to the Regional Administrator or his delegate within 10 days of first possessing or being made aware of that data.

Table 1—Wastes Excluded from Non-Specific Sources

Facility	Address	Waste description
		(B) If the annual testing of the waste does not meet the delisting requirements in Condition (1), Eastman must report the data, in writing, to the Regional Administrator or his delegate within 10 days of first possessing or being made aware of that data. (C) If Eastman fails to submit the information described in Conditions (5),(6)(A) or (6)(B) or if any other information is received from any source, the Regional Administrator or his delegate will make a preliminary determination as to whether the reported information requires Agency action to protect human health or the environment. Further action may include suspending, or revoking the exclusion, or other appropriate response necessary to protect human health and the environment. (D) If the Regional Administrator or his delegate determines that the reported information does require Agency action, the Regional Administrator or his delegate will notify the facility in writing of the actions the Regional Administrator or his delegate believes are necessary to protect human health and the environment. The notice shall include a statement of the proposed action and a statement providing the facility with an opportunity to present information as to why the proposed Agency action is not necessary. The facility shall have 10 days from the date of the Regional Administrator or his delegate's notice to present such information. (E) Following the receipt of information from the facility described in Condition (6)(D) or (if no information is presented under Condition (6)(D)) the initial receipt of information described in Conditions (5), (6)(A) or (6)(B), the Regional Administrator or his delegate will issue a final written determination describing the Agency actions that are necessary to protect human health or the environment. Any required action described in the Regional Administrator or his delegate's determination shall become effective immediately, unless the Regional Administrator or his delegate provides otherwise. (7) *Notification Requirements.* Eastman must do following before transporting the delisted waste off-site: Failure to provide this notification will result in a violation of the delisting petition and a possible revocation of the exclusion. (A) Provide a one-time written notification to any State Regulatory Agency to which or through which they will transport the delisted waste described above for disposal, 60 days before beginning such activities. (B) Update the one-time written notification if they ship the delisted waste into a different disposal facility.
Eli Lilly and Company	Clinton, Indiana	Incinerator scrubber liquids, entering and contained in their onsite surface impoundment, and solids settling from these liquids originating from the burning of spent solvents (EPA Hazardous Waste Nos. F002, F003, and F005) contained in their onsite surface impoundment and solids retention area on August 18, 1988 and any new incinerator scubber liquids and settled solids generated in the surface impoundment and and disposed of in the retention are after August 12, 1988.
Envirite of Illinois (formerly Envirite Corporation)	Harvey, Illinois	See waste description under Envirite of Pennsylvania.
Envirite of Ohio (formerly Envirite Corporation)	Canton, Ohio	See waste description under Envirite of Pennsylvania.
Envirite of Pennsylvania (formerly Envirite Corporation)	York, Pennsylvania	Dewatered wastewater sludges (EPA Hazardous Waste No .F006) generated from electroplating operations; spent cyanide plating solutions (EPA Hazardous Waste No. F007) generated from electroplating operations; plating bath residues from the bottom of plating baths (EPA Hazardous Waste No. F008) generated from electroplating operations where cyanides are used in the process; spent stripping and cleaning bath solutions (EPA Hazardous Waste No. F009) generated from electroplating operations where cyanides are used in the process; spent cyanide solutions from salt bath pot cleaning (EPA Hazardous Waste No. F011) generated from metal heat treating operations; quenching wastewater treatment sludges (EPA Hazardous Waste No. F012) generated from metal heat treating where cyanides are used in the process; wastewater treatment sludges (EPA Hazardous Waste No. F019) generated from the chemical conversion coating of aluminum after November 14, 1986. To ensure that hazardous constituents are not present in the waste at levels of regulatory concern, the facility must implement a contingency testing program for the petitioned waste. This testing program must meet the following conditions for the exclusions to be valid:

Table 1—Wastes Excluded from Non-Specific Sources

Facility	Address	Waste description
		(1) Each batch of treatment residue must be representatively sampled and tested using the EP Toxicity test for arsenic, barium, cadmium, chromium, lead, selenium, silver, mercury, and nickel. If the extract concentrations for chromium, lead, arsenic, and silver exceed 0.315 ppm; barium levels exceed 6.3 ppm; cadmium and selenium exceed 0.063 ppm; mercury exceeds 0.0126 ppm; or nickel levels exceed 2.205 ppm; the waste must be re-treated or managed and disposed as a hazardous waste under 40 CFR Parts 262 to 265 and the permitting standards of 40 CFR Part 270. (2) Each batch of treatment residue must be tested for leachable cyanide.If the leachable cyanide levels (using the EP Toxicity test without acetic acid adjustment) exceed 1.26 ppm, the waste must be re-treated or managed and disposed as a hazardous waste under 40 CFR Parts 262 to 265 and the permitting standards of 40 CFR Part 270. (3) Each batch of waste must be tested for the total content of specific organic toxicants. If the total content of anthracene exceeds 76.8 ppm, 1,2-diphenyl hydrazine exceeds 0.001 ppm, methylene chloride exceeds 8.18 ppm, methyl ethyl ketone exceeds 326 ppm, n-nitrosodiphenylamine exceeds 11.9 ppm, phenol exceeds 1,566 ppm, tetrachloroethylene exceeds 0.188 ppm, or trichloroethylene exceeds 0.592 ppm, the waste must be managed and disposed as a hazardous waste under 40 CFR Parts 262 to 265 and the permitting standards of 40 CFR 260.11. (4) A grab sample must be collected from each batch to form one monthly composite sample which must be tested using GC/MS analysis for the compounds listed in #3, above, as well as the remaining organics on the priority pollutant list. (See 47 FR 52309, November 19, 1982, for a list of the priority pollutants.) (5) The data from conditions 1-4 must be kept on file at the facility for inspection purposes and must be compiled, summarized, and submitted to the Administrator by certified mail semi-annually. The Agency will review this information and if needed will propose to modify or withdraw the exclusion. The organics testing described in conditions 3 and 4, above, are not required until six months from the date of promulgation. The Agency's decision to conditionally exclude the treatment residue generated from the wastewater treatment systems at these facilities applies only to the wastewater and solids treatment systems as they presently exist as described in the delisting petition. The exclusion does not apply to the proposed process additions described in the petition as recovery including crystallization, electrolytic metals recovery, evaporative recovery, and ion exchange.
EPA's Mobile Incineration System	Denney Farm Site; McDowell, MO	Process wastewater, rotary kiln ash, CHEAF media, and other solids (except spent activated carbon) (EPA Hazardous Waste Nos. F020, F022, F023, F026, F027, and F028) generated during the field demonstration of EPA's Mobile Incinerator at the Denney Farm Site in McDowell, Missouri, after July 25, 1985, so long as: (1) The incinerator is functioning properly; (2) a grab sample is taken from each tank of wastewater generated and the EP leachate values do not exceed 0.03 ppm for mercury, 0.14 ppm for selenium, and 0.68 ppm for chromium; and (3) a grab sample is taken from each drum of soil or ash generated and a core sample is collected from each CHEAF roll generated and the EP leachate values of daily composites do not exceed 0.044 ppm in ash or CHEAF media for mercury or 0.22 ppm in ash or CHEAF media for selenium.
Falconer Glass Indust., Inc	Falconer, NY	Wastewater treatment sludges from the filter press and magnetic drum separator (EPA Hazardous Waste No. F006) generated from electroplating operations after July 16, 1986.
Florida Production Engineering Company	Daytona Beach, Florida	This is a one-time exclusion. Wastewater treatment sludges (EPA Hazardous Waste No. F006) generated from electroplating operations and contained in four on-site trenches on January 23, 1987.
Ford Motor Company, Dearborn Truck Assembly Plant	Dearborn, Michigan	Wastewater treatment assembly plant sludge, F019, that is generated by Ford Motor Company at the Dearborn Truck Assembly Plant at a maximum annual rate of 2,000 cubic yards per year. The sludge must be disposed of in a lined landfill with leachate collection which is licensed, permitted, or otherwise authorized to accept the delisted wastewater treatment sludge in accordance with 40 CFR part 258. The exclusion becomes effective as of April 25, 2005. 1. *Delisting Levels:* (A) The concentrations in a TCLP extract of the waste measured in any sample may not exceed the following levels (mg/L): antimony—0.7; arsenic—0.3; barium—100; cadmium—0.5; chromium—5; lead—5; nickel—90; selenium—1; thallium—0.3; zinc—900; p-cresol—11; di-n-octyl phthlate—0.11; formaldehyde—80; and pentachlorophenol—0.009. (B) The total concentration measured in any sample may not exceed the following levels (mg/kg): mercury—9; and formaldehyde—700. 2. *Quarterly Verification Testing:* To verify that the waste does not exceed the specified delisting levels, Dearborn Truck Assembly Plant must collect and analyze one representative sample of the waste on a quarterly basis.

Table 1—Wastes Excluded from Non-Specific Sources

Facility	Address	Waste description
		3. *Changes in Operating Conditions:* Dearborn Truck Assembly Plant must notify the EPA in writing if the manufacturing process, the chemicals used in the manufacturing process, the treatment process, or the chemicals used in the treatment process change significantly. Dearborn Truck Assembly Plant must handle wastes generated after the process change as hazardous until it has demonstrated that the wastes continue to meet the delisting levels and that no new hazardous constituents listed in appendix VIII of part 261 have been introduced and it has received written approval from EPA. 4. *Data Submittals:* Dearborn Truck Assembly Plant [RedIn Off] must submit the data obtained through verification testing or as required by other conditions of this rule to both U.S. EPA Region 5, Waste Management Branch (DW–8J), 77 W. Jackson Blvd., Chicago, IL 60604 and MDEQ, Waste Management Division, Hazardous Waste Program Section, at P.O. Box 30241, Lansing, Michigan 48909. The quarterly verification data and certification of proper disposal must be submitted annually upon the anniversary of the effective date of this exclusion. Dearborn Truck Assembly Plant must compile, summarize and maintain on site for a minimum of five years records of operating conditions and analytical data. Dearborn Truck Assembly Plant must make these records available for inspection. All data must be accompanied by a signed copy of the certification statement in 40 CFR 260.22(i)(12). 5. *Reopener Language*—(a) If, anytime after disposal of the delisted waste, Dearborn Truck Assembly Plant possesses or is otherwise made aware of any data (including but not limited to leachate data or groundwater monitoring data) relevant to the delisted waste indicating that any constituent is at a level in the leachate higher than the specified delisting level, or is in the groundwater at a concentration higher than the maximum allowable groundwater concentration in paragraph (e), then Dearborn Truck Assembly Plant must report such data, in writing, to the Regional Administrator within 10 days of first possessing or being made aware of that data. (b) Based on the information described in paragraph (a) and any other information received from any source, the Regional Administrator will make a preliminary determination as to whether the reported information requires Agency action to protect human health or the environment. Further action may include suspending, or revoking the exclusion, or other appropriate response necessary to protect human health and the environment. (c) If the Regional Administrator determines that the reported information does require Agency action, the Regional Administrator will notify Dearborn Truck Assembly Plant in writing of the actions the Regional Administrator believes are necessary to protect human health and the environment. The notice shall include a statement of the proposed action and a statement providing Dearborn Truck Assembly Plant with an opportunity to present information as to why the proposed Agency action is not necessary or to suggest an alternative action. Dearborn Truck Assembly Plant shall have 30 days from the date of the Regional Administrator's notice to present the information. (d) If after 30 days the Dearborn Truck Assembly Plant presents no further information, the Regional Administrator will issue a final written determination describing the Agency actions that are necessary to protect human health or the environment. Any required action described in the Regional Administrator's determination shall become effective immediately, unless the Regional Administrator provides otherwise. (e) Maximum Allowable Groundwater Concentrations (µg/L): antimony—6; arsenic—5; barium—2,000; cadmium—5; chromium—100; lead—15; nickel—800; selenium—50; thallium—2; tin—20,000; zinc—11,000; p-Cresol—200; Di-n-octyl phthlate—1.3; Formaldehyde—1,400; and Pentachlorophenol—0.15.
Ford Motor Company, Kansas City Assembly Plant	Claycomo, Missouri	Wastewater treatment sludge, F019, that is generated at the Ford Motor Company (Ford) Kansas City Assembly Plant (KCAP) at a maximum annual rate of 2,000 cubic yards per year. The sludge must be disposed of in a lined landfill with leachate collection, which is licensed, permitted, or otherwise authorized to accept the delisted wastewater treatment sludge in accordance with 40 CFR part 258. The exclusion becomes effective as of June 6, 2007. 1. Delisting Levels: (a) The concentrations in a TCLP extract of the waste measured in any sample may not equal or exceed the following levels (mg/L): barium—100; chromium—5; mercury—0.155; nickel—90; thallium—0.282; zinc—898; cyanides—11.5; ethyl benzene—42.6; toluene—60.8; total xylenes—18.9; bis(2-ethylhexyl) phthalate—0.365; p-cresol—11.4; 2,4-dinitrotoluene—0.13; formaldehyde—343; and napthalene—.728; (b) The total concentrations measured in any sample may not exceed the following levels (mg/kg): chromium 760000; mercury—10.4; thallium—116000; 2,4-dinitrotoluene—100000; and formaldehyde—6880. 2. Quarterly Verification Testing: To verify that the waste does not exceed the specified delisting levels, Ford must collect and analyze one representative sample of KCAP's sludge on a quarterly basis.

Table 1—Wastes Excluded from Non-Specific Sources

Facility	Address	Waste description
		3. Changes in Operating Conditions: Ford must notify the EPA in writing if the manufacturing process, the chemicals used in the manufacturing process, the treatment process, or the chemicals used in the treatment process at KCAP significantly change. Ford must handle wastes generated at KCAP after the process change as hazardous until it has demonstrated that the waste continues to meet the delisting levels and that no new hazardous constituents listed in appendix VIII of part 261 have been introduced and Ford has received written approval from EPA for the changes. 4. Data Submittals: Ford must submit the data obtained through verification testing at KCAP or as required by other conditions of this rule to EPA Region 7, Air, RCRA and Toxics Division, 901 N. 5th, Kansas City, Kansas 66101. The quarterly verification data and certification of proper disposal must be submitted annually upon the anniversary of the effective date of this exclusion. Ford must compile, summarize, and maintain at KCAP records of operating conditions and analytical data for a minimum of five years. Ford must make these records available for inspection. All data must be accompanied by a signed copy of the certification statement in 40 CFR 260.22(i)(12). 5. Reopener Language—(a) If, anytime after disposal of the delisted waste, Ford possesses or is otherwise made aware of any data (including but not limited to leachate data or groundwater monitoring data) relevant to the delisted waste at KCAP indicating that any constituent is at a level in the leachate higher than the specified delisting level, or is in the groundwater at a concentration higher than the maximum allowable groundwater concentration in paragraph (e), then Ford must report such data in writing to the Regional Administrator within 10 days of first possessing or being made aware of that data. (b) Based on the information described in paragraph (a) and any other information received from any source, the Regional Administrator will make a preliminary determination as to whether the reported information requires Agency action to protect human health or the environment. Further action may include suspending, or revoking the exclusion, or other appropriate response necessary to protect human health and the environment. (c) If the Regional Administrator determines that the reported information does require Agency action, the Regional Administrator will notify Ford in writing of the actions the Regional Administrator believes are necessary to protect human health and the environment. The notice shall include a statement of the proposed action and a statement providing Ford with an opportunity to present information as to why the proposed Agency action is not necessary or to suggest an alternative action. Ford shall have 30 days from the date of the Regional Administrator's notice to present the information. (d) If after 30 days Ford presents no further information, the Regional Administrator will issue a final written determination describing the Agency actions that are necessary to protect human health or the environment. Any required action described in the Regional Administrator's determination shall become effective immediately, unless the Regional Administrator provides otherwise.
Ford Motor Company, Michigan Truck Plant and Wayne Integrated Stamping and Assembly Plant	Wayne, Michigan	Waste water treatment plant sludge, F019, that is generated by Ford Motor Company at the Wayne Integrated Stamping and Assembly Plant from wastewaters from both the Wayne Integrated Stamping and Assembly Plant and the Michigan Truck Plant, Wayne, Michigan at a maximum annual rate of 2,000 cubic yards per year. The sludge must be disposed of in a lined landfill with leachate collection, which is licensed, permitted, or otherwise authorized to accept the delisted wastewater treatment sludge in accordance with 40 CFR part 258. The exclusion becomes effective as of July 30, 2003. 1. Delisting Levels: (A) The TCLP concentrations measured in any sample may not exceed the following levels (mg/L): Antimony—0.659; Arsenic—0.3; Cadmium—0.48; Chromium—4.95; Lead—5; Nickel—90.5; Selenium—1; Thallium—0.282; Tin—721; Zinc—898; p-Cresol—11.4; and Formaldehyde—84.2. (B) The total concentrations measured in any sample may not exceed the following levels (mg/kg): Mercury—8.92; and Formaldehyde—689. (C) The sum of the ratios of the TCLP concentrations to the delisting levels for nickel and thallium and for nickel and cadmium shall not exceed 1.0. 2. Quarterly Verification Testing: To verify that the waste does not exceed the specified delisting levels, the facility must collect and analyze one waste sample on a quarterly basis. 3. Changes in Operating Conditions: The facility must notify the EPA in writing if the manufacturing process, the chemicals used in the manufacturing process, the treatment process, or the chemicals used in the treatment process significantly change. The facility must handle wastes generated after the process change as hazardous until it has demonstrated that the wastes continue to meet the delisting levels and that no new hazardous constituents listed in appendix VIII of part 261 have been introduced and it has received written approval from EPA.

Table 1—Wastes Excluded from Non-Specific Sources

Facility	Address	Waste description
		4. Data Submittals: The facility must submit the data obtained through verification testing or as required by other conditions of this rule to both U.S. EPA Region 5, Waste Management Branch (DW–8J), 77 W. Jackson Blvd., Chicago, IL 60604 and MDEQ, Waste Management Division, Hazardous Waste Program Section, at P.O. Box 30241, Lansing, Michigan 48909. The quarterly verification data and certification of proper disposal must be submitted annually upon the anniversary of the effective date of this exclusion. The facility must compile, summarize, and maintain on site for a minimum of five years records of operating conditions and analytical data. The facility must make these records available for inspection. All data must be accompanied by a signed copy of the certification statement in 40 CFR 260.22(i)(12). 5. Reopener Language—(a) If, anytime after disposal of the delisted waste, the facility possesses or is otherwise made aware of any data (including but not limited to leachate data or groundwater monitoring data) relevant to the delisted waste indicating that any constituent is at a level in the leachate higher than the specified delisting level, or is in the groundwater at a concentration higher than the maximum allowable groundwater concentration in paragraph (e), then the facility must report such data, in writing, to the Regional Administrator within 10 days of first possessing or being made aware of that data. (b) Based on the information described in paragraph (a) and any other information received from any source, the Regional Administrator will make a preliminary determination as to whether the reported information requires Agency action to protect human health or the environment. Further action may include suspending, or revoking the exclusion, or other appropriate response necessary to protect human health and the environment. (c) If the Regional Administrator determines that the reported information does require Agency action, the Regional Administrator will notify the facility in writing of the actions the Regional Administrator believes are necessary to protect human health and the environment. The notice shall include a statement of the proposed action and a statement providing the facility with an opportunity to present information as to why the proposed Agency action is not necessary or to suggest an alternative action. The facility shall have 30 days from the date of the Regional Administrator's notice to present the information. (d) If after 30 days the facility presents no further information, the Regional Administrator will issue a final written determination describing the Agency actions that are necessary to protect human health or the environment. Any required action described in the Regional Administrator's determination shall become effective immediately, unless the Regional Administrator provides otherwise. (e) Maximum Allowable Groundwater Concentrations (ug/L): Antimony—6; Arsenic—4.87; Cadmium—5; Chromium—100; Lead—15; Nickel—750; Selenium—50; Thallium—2; Tin—22,500; Zinc—11,300; p-Cresol—188; and Formaldehyde—1,380.
Ford Motor Company, Wixom Assembly Plant	Wixom, Michigan	Waste water treatment plant sludge, F019, that is generated by Ford Motor Company at the Wixom Assembly Plant, Wixom, Michigan at a maximum annual rate of 2,000 cubic yards per year. The sludge must be disposed of in a lined landfill with leachate collection, which is licensed, permitted, or otherwise authorized to accept the delisted wastewater treatment sludge in accordance with 40 CFR Part 258. The exclusion becomes effective as of July 30, 2003. The conditions in paragraphs (2) through (5) for Ford Motor Company—Michigan Truck Plant and Wayne Integrated Stamping Plant—Wayne, Michigan also apply. Delisting Levels: (A) The TCLP concentrations measured in any sample may not exceed the following levels (mg/ L): Antimony—0.659; Arsenic—0.3; Cadmium—0.48; Chromium—4.95; Lead—5; Nickel—90.5; Selenium—1; Thallium—0.282; Tin—721; Zinc—898; p-Cresol—11.4; and Formaldehyde—84.2. (B) The total concentrations measured in any sample may not exceed the following levels (mg/kg): Mercury—8.92; and Formaldehyde—689. (C) The sum of the ratios of the TCLP concentrations to the delisting levels for nickel and thallium and for nickel and cadmium shall not exceed 1.0.
GE's Former RCA del Caribe	Barceloneta, PR	Wastewater treatment plant (WWTP) sludges from chemical etching operation (EPA Hazardous Waste No. F006) and contaminated soil mixed with sludge. This is a one-time exclusion for a range of 5,000 to 15,000 cubic yards of WWTP sludge on condition of disposal in a Subtitle D landfill. This exclusion was published on February 1, 2007. 1. Reopener Language—(a) If, anytime after disposal of the delisted waste, GE discovers that any condition or assumption related to the characterization of the excluded waste which was used in the evaluation of the petition or that was predicted through modeling is not as reported in the petition, then GE must report any information relevant to that condition or assumption, in writing, to the Director of the Division of Environmental Planning and Protection in Region 2 within 10 days of first of discovering that information.

Table 1—Wastes Excluded from Non-Specific Sources

Facility	Address	Waste description
		(b) Upon receiving information described in paragraph (a) of this section, regardless of its source, the Director will determine whether the reported condition requires further action. Further action may include repealing the exclusion, modifying the exclusion, or other appropriate action deemed necessary to protect human health or the environment. 2. Notifications—GE must provide a one-time written notification to any State or Commonwealth Regulatory Agency in any State or Commonwealth to which or through which the waste described above will be transported for disposal at least 60 days prior to the commencement of such activities. Failure to provide such a notification will result in a violation of the waste exclusion and a possible revocation of the decision.
General Electric Company	Shreveport, Louisiana	Wastewater treatment sludges (EPA Hazardous Waste No. F006) generated from electroplating operations and contained in four on-site treatment ponds on August 12, 1987.
General Motors	Arlington, TX	Wastewater Treatment Sludge (WWTP) (EPA Hazardous Waste No. F019) generated at a maximum annual rate of 3,000 cubic yards per calendar year after January 3, 2007 and disposed in a Subtitle D landfill. For the exclusion to be valid, GM-Arlington must implement a verification testing program that meets the following paragraphs: (1) *Delisting Levels:* All leachable concentrations for those constituents must not exceed the following levels (mg/l for TCLP). (i) Inorganic Constituents: Barium-100; Cadmium-0.36; Chromium-5 (3.71) ; Cobalt-18.02; Lead-5; Nickel-67.8; Silver-5; Tin-540; Zinc-673. (ii) Organic Constituents: Acetone-171; Ethylbenzene-31.9; N-Butyl Alcohol-171; Toluene-45.6; Bis(2-Ethylhexyl) Phthalate-0.27; p-Cresol-8.55; Naphthalene-3.11. (2) *Waste Management:* (A) GM-Arlington must manage as hazardous all WWTP sludge generated, until it has completed initial verification testing described in paragraph (3)(A) and (B), as appropriate, and valid analyses show that paragraph(1) is satisfied. (B) Levels of constituents measured in the samples of the WWTP sludge that do not exceed the levels set forth in paragraph (1) are non-hazardous. GM-Arlington can manage and dispose of the non-hazardous WWTP sludge according to all applicable solid waste regulations. (C) If constituent levels in a sample exceed any of the delisting levels set in paragraph (1), GM-Arlington can collect one additional sample and perform expedited analyses to verify if the constituent exceeds the delisting level. If this sample confirms the exceedance, GM-Arlington must, from that point forward, treat the waste as hazardous until it is demonstrated that the waste again meets the levels in paragraph (1). GM-Arlington must manage and dispose of the waste generated under Subtitle C of RCRA from the time it becomes aware of any exceedance. (D) Upon completion of the Verification Testing described in paragraph 3(A) and (B), as appropriate, and the transmittal of the results to EPA, and if the testing results meet the requirements of paragraph (1), GM-Arlington may proceed to manage its WWTP sludge as non-hazardous waste. If subsequent Verification Testing indicates an exceedance of the Delisting Levels in paragraph (1), GM-Arlington must manage the WWTP sludge as a hazardous waste until two consecutive quarterly testing samples show levels below the Delisting Levels in paragraph (1). (3) *Verification Testing Requirements:* GM-Arlington must perform sample collection and analyses, including quality control procedures, according to appropriate methods such as those found in SW–846 or other reliable sources (with the exception of analyses requiring the use of SW–846 methods incorporated by reference in 40 CFR 260.11, which must be used without substitution) for all constituents listed in paragraph (1). If EPA judges the process to be effective under the operating conditions used during the initial verification testing, GM-Arlington may replace the testing required in paragraph (3)(A) with the testing required in paragraph (3)(B). GM-Arlington Plant must continue to test as specified in paragraph (3)(A) until and unless notified by EPA in writing that testing in paragraph (3)(A) may be replaced by paragraph (3)(B). (A) *Initial Verification Testing:* After EPA grants the final exclusion, GM-Arlington must do the following: (i) Within 30 days of this exclusion becoming final, collect two (2) samples, before disposal, of the WWTP sludge. (ii) The samples are to be analyzed and compared against the Delisting Levels in paragraph (1). (iii) Within 60 days of the exclusion becoming final, GM-Arlington must report to EPA the initial verification analytical test data for the WWTP sludge, including analytical quality control information for the first thirty (30) days of operation after this exclusion becomes final.

Table 1—Wastes Excluded from Non-Specific Sources

Facility	Address	Waste description
		If levels of constituents measured in these samples of the WWTP sludge do not exceed the levels set forth in paragraph (1), GM-Arlington can manage and dispose of the WWTP sludge according to all applicable solid waste regulations. (B) *Subsequent Verification Testing:* Following written notification by EPA, GM-Arlington may substitute the testing conditions in paragraph (3)(B) for paragraph (3)(A). GM-Arlington must continue to monitor operating conditions, and analyze two representative samples of the WWTP sludge for the next three quarters of operation during the first year of waste generation. The samples must represent the waste generated during the quarter. Quarterly reports are due to EPA, thirty days after the samples are taken. After the first year of analytical sampling, verification sampling can be performed on a single annual sample of the WWTP sludge. The results are to be compared to the delisting levels in paragraph (1). (C) *Termination of Testing:* (i) After the first year of quarterly testing, if the delisting levels in paragraph (1) are being met, GM-Arlington may then request that EPA not require quarterly testing. (ii) Following cancellation of the quarterly testing by EPA letter, GM-Arlington must continue to test one representative sample for all constituents listed in paragraph (1) annually. Results must be provided to EPA within 30 days of the testing. (4) *Changes in Operating Conditions:* If GM-Arlington significantly changes the process described in its petition or starts any process that generates the waste that may or could significantly affect the composition or type of waste generated as established under paragraph (1) (by illustration, but not limitation, changes in equipment or operating conditions of the treatment process), it must notify EPA in writing; it may no longer handle the wastes generated from the new process as nonhazardous until the wastes meet the delisting levels set in paragraph (1) and it has received written approval to do so from EPA. (5) *Data Submittals:* GM-Arlington must submit the information described below. If GM-Arlington fails to submit the required data within the specified time or maintain the required records on-site for the specified time, EPA, at its discretion, will consider this sufficient basis to reopen the exclusion as described in paragraph 6. GM-Arlington must: (A) Submit the data obtained through paragraph(3) to the Section Chief, Region 6 Corrective Action and Waste Minimization Section, EPA, 1445 Ross Avenue, Dallas, Texas 75202–2733, Mail Code, (6PD–C) within the time specified. (B) Compile records of operating conditions and analytical data from paragraph (3), summarized, and maintained on-site for a minimum of five years. (C) Furnish these records and data when EPA or the State of Texas requests them for inspection. (D) Send along with all data a signed copy of the following certification statement, to attest to the truth and accuracy of the data submitted: "Under civil and criminal penalty of law for the making or submission of false or fraudulent statements or representations (pursuant to the applicable provisions of the Federal Code, which include, but may not be limited to, 18 U.S.C. 1001 and 42 U.S.C. 6928), I certify that the information contained in or accompanying this document is true, accurate and complete. As to the (those) identified section(s) of this document for which I cannot personally verify its (their) truth and accuracy, I certify as the company official having supervisory responsibility for the persons who, acting under my direct instructions, made the verification that this information is true, accurate and complete. If any of this information is determined by EPA in its sole discretion to be false, inaccurate or incomplete, and upon conveyance of this fact to the company, I recognize and agree that this exclusion of waste will be void as if it never had effect or to the extent directed by EPA and that the company will be liable for any actions taken in contravention of the company's RCRA and CERCLA obligations premised upon the company's reliance on the void exclusion." (6) *Re-opener:* (A) If, anytime after disposal of the delisted waste, GM-Arlington possesses or is otherwise made aware of any environmental data (including but not limited to leachate data or groundwater monitoring data) or any other data relevant to the delisted waste indicating that any constituent identified for the delisting verification testing is at a level higher than the delisting level allowed by EPA in granting the petition, then the facility must report the data, in writing, to EPA within 10 days of first possessing or being made aware of that data.

Table 1—Wastes Excluded from Non-Specific Sources

Facility	Address	Waste description
		(B) If either the quarterly or annual testing of the waste does not meet the delisting requirements in paragraph 1, GM-Arlington must report the data, in writing, to EPA within 10 days of first possessing or being made aware of that data. (C) If GM-Arlington fails to submit the information described in paragraphs (5), (6)(A) or (6)(B) or if any other information is received from any source, EPA will make a preliminary determination as to whether the reported information requires action to protect human health and/or the environment. Further action may include suspending, or revoking the exclusion, or other appropriate response necessary to protect human health and the environment. (D) If EPA determines that the reported information requires action, EPA will notify the facility in writing of the actions it believes are necessary to protect human health and the environment. The notice shall include a statement of the proposed action and a statement providing the facility with an opportunity to present information explaining why the proposed EPA action is not necessary. The facility shall have 10 days from the date of EPA's notice to present such information. (E) Following the receipt of information from the facility described in paragraph (6)(D) or (if no information is presented under paragraph (6)(D)) the initial receipt of information described in paragraphs (5), (6)(A) or (6)(B), EPA will issue a final written determination describing the actions that are necessary to protect human health and/or the environment. Any required action described in EPA's determination shall become effective immediately, unless EPA provides otherwise. (7) *Notification Requirements:* GM-Arlington must do the following before transporting the delisted waste. Failure to provide this notification will result in a violation of the delisting petition and a possible revocation of the decision. (A) Provide a one-time written notification to any state Regulatory Agency to which or through which it will transport the delisted waste described above for disposal, 60 days before beginning such activities. (B) Update the one-time written notification if it ships the delisted waste into a different disposal facility. (C) Failure to provide this notification will result in a violation of the delisting variance and a possible revocation of the decision.
General Motors Corp., Fisher Body Division	Elyria, OH	The residue generated from the use of the Chemfix® treatment process on sludge (EPA Hazardous Waste No. F006) generated from electroplating operations and contained in three on-site surface impoundments on November 14, 1986. To assure that stabilization occurs, the following conditions apply to this exclusion: (1) Mixing ratios shall be monitored continuously to assure consistent treatment. (2) One grab sample of the treated waste shall be taken each hour as it is pumped to the holding area (cell) from each trailer unit. At the end of each production day, the grab samples from the individual trailer units will be composited and the EP toxicity test will be run on each composite sample. If lead or total chromium concentrations exceed 0.315 ppm or if nickel exceeds 2.17 ppm, in the EP extract, the waste will be removed and retreated or disposed of as a hazardous waste. (3) The treated waste shall be pumped into bermed cells which are constructed to assure that the treated waste is identifiable and retrievable (*i.e.*, the material can be removed and either disposed of as a hazardous waste or retreated if conditions 1 or 2 are not met). Failure to satisfy any of these conditions would render the exclusion void. This is a one- time exclusion, applicable only to the residue generated from the use of the Chemfix® treatment process on the sludge currently contained in the three on-site surface impoundments.
General Motors Corporation, Flint Truck	Flint, Michigan	Waste water treatment plant sludge, F019, that is generated by General Motors Corporation at Flint Truck, Flint, Michigan at a maximum annual rate of 3,000 cubic yards per year. The sludge must be disposed of in a lined landfill with leachate collection, which is licensed, permitted, or otherwise authorized to accept the delisted wastewater treatment sludge in accordance with 40 CFR part 258. The exclusion becomes effective as of July 30, 2003. The conditions in paragraphs (2) through (5) for Ford Motor Company—Michigan Truck Plant and Wayne Integrated Stamping Plant—Wayne, Michigan also apply. Delisting Levels: (A) The TCLP concentrations measured in any sample may not exceed the following levels (mg/ L): Antimony—0.494; Arsenic—0.224; Cadmium—0.36; Chromium—3.71; Lead—5; Nickel—67.8; Selenium—1; Thallium—0.211; Tin—540; Zinc—673; p-Cresol—8.55; and Formaldehyde—63. (B) The total concentrations measured in any sample may not exceed the following levels (mg/kg): Mercury—6.34; and Formaldehyde—535. (C) The sum of the ratios of the TCLP concentration to the delisting level for nickel and thallium and for nickel and cadmium shall not exceed 1.0.

Table 1—Wastes Excluded from Non-Specific Sources

Facility	Address	Waste description
General Motors Corporation, Hamtramck	Detroit, Michigan	Waste water treatment plant sludge, F019, that is generated by General Motors Corporation at Hamtramck, Detroit, Michigan at a maximum annual rate of 3,000 cubic yards per year. The sludge must be disposed of in a lined landfill with leachate collection, which is licensed, permitted, or otherwise authorized to accept the delisted wastewater treatment sludge in accordance with 40 CFR part 258. The exclusion becomes effective as of July 30, 2003. The conditions in paragraphs (2) through (5) for Ford Motor Company—Michigan Truck Plant and Wayne Integrated Stamping Plant—Wayne, Michigan also apply. A maximum allowable groundwater concentration of 3,750 mg/L for n-butyl alcohol is added to paragraph (5)(e). Delisting Levels: (A) The TCLP concentrations measured in any sample may not exceed the following levels (mg/ L): Antimony—0.494; Arsenic—0.224; Cadmium—0.36; Chromium—3.71; Lead—5; Nickel—67.8; Selenium—1; Thallium—0.211; Tin—540; Zinc—673; p-Cresol—8.55; Formaldehyde—63; and n-Butyl alcohol—171. (B) The total concentrations measured in any sample may not exceed the following levels (mg/kg): Mercury—6.34; and Formaldehyde—535. (C) The sum of the ratios of the TCLP concentration to the delisting level for nickel and thallium and for nickel and cadmium shall not exceed 1.0.
General Motors Corporation Assembly Plant	Lordstown, Ohio	Waste water treatment plant sludge, F019, that is generated at General Motors Corporation's Lordstown Assembly Plant at a maximum annual rate of 2,000 cubic yards per year. The sludge must be disposed of in a Subtitle D landfill which is licensed, permitted, or otherwise authorized by a state to accept the delisted wastewater treatment sludge. The exclusion becomes effective as of (insert final publication date). 1. Delisting Levels: (A) The constituent concentrations measured in the TCLP extract may not exceed the following levels (mg/L): antimony—0.66; arsenic—0.30; chromium—5; lead—5; mercury—0.15; nickel—90; selenium—1; silver—5; thallium—0.28; tin—720; zinc—900; fluoride—130; p-cresol—11; formaldehyde—84; and methylene chloride—0.29 (B) The total constituent concentration measured in any sample of the waste may not exceed the following levels (mg/ kg): chromium—4,100 ; formaldehyde—700; and mercury—10. (C) Maximum allowable groundwater concentrations (mg/L) are as follows: antimony—6; arsenic—4.88; chromium—100; lead—15; mercury—2; nickel—750; selenium—50; silver—188; thallium—2; tin—22,500; zinc—11,300; fluoride—4,000; p-cresol—188; formaldehyde—1,390; and methylene chloride—5. 2. Quarterly Verification Testing: To verify that the waste does not exceed the specified delisting levels, GM must collect and analyze one waste sample on a quarterly basis using methods with appropriate detection levels and elements of quality control. 3. Changes in Operating Conditions: The facility must notify the EPA in writing if the manufacturing process, the chemicals used in the manufacturing process, the treatment process, or the chemicals used in the treatment process significantly change. GM must handle wastes generated after the process change as hazardous until it has demonstrated that the wastes continue to meet the delisting levels and that no new hazardous constituents listed in appendix VIII of part 261 have been introduced and it has received written approval from EPA. 4. Data Submittals: The facility must submit the data obtained through verification testing or as required by other conditions of this rule to U.S. EPA Region 5, Waste Management Branch, RCRA Delisting Program (DW–8J), 77 W. Jackson Blvd., Chicago, IL 60604. The quarterly verification data and certification of proper disposal must be submitted annually upon the anniversary of the effective date of this exclusion. The facility must compile, summarize, and maintain on site for a minimum of five years records of operating conditions and analytical data. The facility must make these records available for inspection. All data must be accompanied by a signed copy of the certification statement in 40 CFR 260.22(i)(12). 5. Reopener Language: (A) If, anytime after disposal of the delisted waste, GM possesses or is otherwise made aware of any data (including but not limited to leachate data or groundwater monitoring data) relevant to the delisted waste indicating that any constituent is at a level in the leachate higher than the specified delisting level, or is in the groundwater at a concentration higher than the maximum allowable groundwater concentration in paragraph (1), then GM must report such data, in writing, to the Regional Administrator within 10 days of first possessing or being made aware of that data. (B) Based on the information described in paragraph (A) and any other information received from any source, the Regional Administrator will make a preliminary determination as to whether the reported information requires Agency action to protect human health or the environment. Further action may include suspending, or revoking the exclusion, or other appropriate response necessary to protect human health and the environment.

Table 1—Wastes Excluded from Non-Specific Sources

Facility	Address	Waste description
		(C) If the Regional Administrator determines that the reported information does require Agency action, the Regional Administrator will notify the facility in writing of the actions the Regional Administrator believes are necessary to protect human health and the environment. The notice shall include a statement of the proposed action and a statement providing GM with an opportunity to present information as to why the proposed Agency action is not necessary or to suggest an alternative action. GM shall have 30 days from the date of the Regional Administrator's notice to present the information. (D) If after 30 days GM presents no further information, the Regional Administrator will issue a final written determination describing the Agency actions that are necessary to protect human health or the environment. Any required action described in the Regional Administrator's determination shall become effective immediately, unless the Regional Administrator provides otherwise.
General Motors Corporation, Pontiac East	Pontiac, Michigan	Waste water treatment plant sludge, F019, that is generated by General Motors Corporation at Pontiac East, Pontiac, Michigan at a maximum annual rate of 3,000 cubic yards per year. The sludge must be disposed of in a lined landfill with leachate collection, which is licensed, permitted, or otherwise authorized to accept the delisted wastewater treatment sludge in accordance with 40 CFR part 258. The exclusion becomes effective as of July 30, 2003. The conditions in paragraphs (2) through (5) for Ford Motor Company—Michigan Truck Plant and Wayne Integrated Stamping Plant—Wayne, Michigan also apply. Delisting Levels: (A) The TCLP concentrations measured in any sample may not exceed the following levels (mg/ L): Antimony—0.494; Arsenic—0.224; Cadmium—0.36; Chromium—3.71; Lead—5; Nickel—67.8; Selenium—1; Thallium—0.211; Tin—540; Zinc—673; p-Cresol—8.55; and Formaldehyde—63. (B) The total concentrations measured in any sample may not exceed the following levels (mg/kg): Mercury—6.34; and Formaldehyde—535. (C) The sum of the ratios of the TCLP concentrations to the delisting levels for nickel and thallium and for nickel and cadmium shall not exceed 1.0.
General Motors Corporation	Lake Orion, Michigan	Wastewater treatment plant (WWTP) sludge from the chemical conversion coating (phosphate coating) of aluminum (EPA Hazardous Waste No. F019) generated at a maximum annual rate of 1,500 tons per year (or 1,500 cubic yards per year), after October 24, 1997 and disposed of in a Subtitle D landfill. 1. Verification Testing: GM must implement an annual testing program to demonstrate, based on the analysis of a minimum of four representative samples, that the constituent concentrations measured in the TCLP (or OWEP, where appropriate) extract of the waste are within specific levels. The constituent concentrations must not exceed the following levels (mg/l) which are back-calculated from the delisting health-based levels and a DAF of 90: Arsenic—4.5; Cobalt—189; Copper—126; Nickel—63; Vanadium—18; Zinc—900; 1,2-Dichloroethane—0.45; Ethylbenzene—63; 4-Methylphenol—16.2; Naphthalene—90; Phenol— 1800; and Xylene—900. The constituent concentrations must also be less than the following levels (mg/l) which are the toxicity characteristic levels: Barium—100.0; and Chromium (total)—5.0. 2. Changes in Operating Conditions: If GM significantly changes the manufacturing or treatment process or the chemicals used in the manufacturing or treatment process, GM may handle the WWTP filter press sludge generated from the new process under this exclusion after the facility has demonstrated that the waste meets the levels set forth in paragraph 1 and that no new hazardous constituents listed in Appendix VIII of Part 261 have been introduced. 3. Data Submittals: The data obtained through annual verification testing or paragraph 2 must be submitted to U.S. EPA Region 5, 77 W. Jackson Blvd., Chicago, IL 60604-3590, within 60 days of sampling. Records of operating conditions and analytical data must be compiled, summarized, and maintained on site for a minimum of five years and must be made available for inspection. All data must be accompanied by a signed copy of the certification statement in 260.22(I)(12).
General Motors Corporation, Janesville Truck Assembly Plant.	Janesville, Wisconsin	Wastewater treatment sludge, F019, that is generated at the General Motors Corporation (GM) Janesville Truck Assembly Plant (JTAP) at a maximum annual rate of 3,000 cubic yards per year. The sludge must be disposed of in a lined landfill with leachate collection, which is licensed, permitted, or otherwise authorized to accept the delisted wastewater treatment sludge in accordance with 40 CFR part 258. The exclusion becomes effective as of January 24, 2006. 1. Delisting Levels: (A) The concentrations in a TCLP extract of the waste measured in any sample may not exceed the following levels (mg/L): antimony—0.49; arsenic—0.22; cadmium—0.36; chromium—3.7; lead—5; nickel—68; selenium—1; thallium—0.21; tin—540; zinc—670; p-cresol—8.5; and formaldehyde—43. (B) The total concentrations measured in any sample may not exceed the following levels (mg/kg): chromium—5,300; mercury—7; and formaldehyde—540. 2. Quarterly Verification Testing: To verify that the waste does not exceed the specified delisting levels, GM must collect and analyze one representative sample of JTAP's sludge on a quarterly basis.

Table 1—Wastes Excluded from Non-Specific Sources

Facility	Address	Waste description
		3. Changes in Operating Conditions: GM must notify the EPA in writing if the manufacturing process, the chemicals used in the manufacturing process, the treatment process, or the chemicals used in the treatment process at JTAP significantly change. GM must handle wastes generated at JTAP after the process change as hazardous until it has demonstrated that the waste continues to meet the delisting levels and that no new hazardous constituents listed in appendix VIII of part 261 have been introduced and GM has received written approval from EPA. 4. Data Submittals: GM must submit the data obtained through verification testing at JTAP or as required by other conditions of this rule to EPA Region 5, Waste Management Branch (DW–8J), 77 W. Jackson Blvd., Chicago, IL 60604. The quarterly verification data and certification of proper disposal must be submitted annually upon the anniversary of the effective date of this exclusion. GM must compile, summarize, and maintain at JTAP records of operating conditions and analytical data for a minimum of five years. GM must make these records available for inspection. All data must be accompanied by a signed copy of the certification statement in 40 CFR 260.22(i)(12). 5. Reopener Language—(a) If, anytime after disposal of the delisted waste, GM possesses or is otherwise made aware of any data (including but not limited to leachate data or groundwater monitoring data) relevant to the delisted waste at JTAP indicating that any constituent is at a level in the leachate higher than the specified delisting level, or is in the groundwater at a concentration higher than the maximum allowable groundwater concentration in paragraph (e), then GM must report such data in writing to the Regional Administrator within 10 days of first possessing or being made aware of that data. (b) Based on the information described in paragraph (a) and any other information received from any source, the Regional Administrator will make a preliminary determination as to whether the reported information requires Agency action to protect human health or the environment. Further action may include suspending, or revoking the exclusion, or other appropriate response necessary to protect human health and the environment. (c) If the Regional Administrator determines that the reported information does require Agency action, the Regional Administrator will notify GM in writing of the actions the Regional Administrator believes are necessary to protect human health and the environment. The notice shall include a statement of the proposed action and a statement providing GM with an opportunity to present information as to why the proposed Agency action is not necessary or to suggest an alternative action. GM shall have 30 days from the date of the Regional Administrator's notice to present the information. (d) If after 30 days GM presents no further information, the Regional Administrator will issue a final written determination describing the Agency actions that are necessary to protect human health or the environment. Any required action described in the Regional Administrator's determination shall become effective immediately, unless the Regional Administrator provides otherwise. (e) Maximum Allowable Groundwater Concentrations (mg/L): antimony—0.006; arsenic— 0.005; cadmium—0.005; chromium—0.1; lead—0.015; nickel—0.750; selenium—0.050; tin—23; zinc—11; p-Cresol—0.190; and formaldehyde—0.950.
General Motors Corporation Lansing Car Assembly—Body Plant	Lansing, Michigan	Wastewater treatment plant (WWTP) sludge from the chemical conversion coating (phosphate coating) of aluminum (EPA Hazardous Waste No. F019) generated at a maximum annual rate of 1,250 cubic yards per year and disposed of in a Subtitle D landfill, after May 16, 2000. 1. Delisting Levels: (A) The constituent concentrations measured in the TCLP extract may not exceed the following levels (mg/L): Antimony—0.576; Arsenic—4.8; Barium—100; Beryllium—0.384; Cadmium—0.48; Chromium (total)—5; Cobalt—201.6; Copper—124.8; Lead—1.44; Mercury—0.192; Nickel—67.2; Selenium—1; Silver—5; Thallium—0.192; Tin—2016; Vanadium—28.8; Zinc—960; Cyanide—19.2; Fluoride—384; Acetone—336; m,p—Cresol— 19.2; 1,1—Dichloroethane— 0.0864; Ethylbenzene—67.2; Formaldehyde—672; Phenol— 1920; Toluene—96; 1,1,1— Trichloroethane—19.2; Xylene— 960 (B) The total concentration of formaldehyde in the waste may not exceed 2100 mg/kg (C) Analysis for determining reactivity from sulfide must be added to verification testing when an EPA-approved method becomes available. 2. Verification Testing: GM must implement an annual testing program to demonstrate that the constituent concentrations measured in the TCLP extract (or OWEP, where appropriate) of the waste do not exceed the delisting levels established in Condition (1).

Table 1—Wastes Excluded from Non-Specific Sources

Facility	Address	Waste description
		3. Changes in Operating Conditions: If GM significantly changes the manufacturing or treatment process or the chemicals used in the manufacturing or treatment process, GM must notify the EPA of the changes in writing. GM must handle wastes generated after the process change as hazardous until GM has demonstrated that the wastes meet the delisting levels set forth in Condition (1), that no new hazardous constituents listed in Appendix VIII of Part 261 have been introduced, and GM has received written approval from EPA. 4. Data Submittals: GM must submit the data obtained through annual verification testing or as required by other conditions of this rule to U.S. EPA Region 5, 77 W. Jackson Blvd. (DW-8J), Chicago, IL 60604, within 60 days of sampling. GM must compile, summarize, and maintain on site for a minimum of five years records of operating conditions and analytical data. GM must make these records available for inspection. All data must be accompanied by a signed copy of the certification statement in 40 CFR 260.22(i)(12). 5. Reopener Language—(a) If, anytime after disposal of the delisted waste, GM possesses or is otherwise made aware of any environmental data (including but not limited to leachate data or groundwater monitoring data) or any other data relevant to the delisted waste indicating that any constituent identified in Condition (1) is at a level in the leachate higher than the delisting level established in Condition (1), or is at a level in the ground water or soil higher than the level predicted by the CML model, then GM must notify the Regional Administrator in writing within 10 days and must report the data within 45 days of first possessing or being made aware of that data. (b) Based on the information described in paragraph (a) and any other information received from any source, the Regional Administrator will make a preliminary determination as to whether the reported information requires Agency action to protect human health or the environment. Further action may include suspending, or revoking the exclusion, or other appropriate response necessary to protect human health and the environment. (c) If the Regional Administrator determines that the reported information does require Agency action, the Regional Administrator will notify GM in writing of the actions the Regional Administrator believes are necessary to protect human health and the environment. The notice shall include a statement of the proposed action and a statement providing GM with an opportunity to present information as to why the proposed Agency action is not necessary or to suggest an alternative action. GM shall have 10 days from the date of the Regional Administrator's notice to present the information. (d) If after 10 days GM presents no further information, the Regional Administrator will issue a final written determination describing the Agency actions that are necessary to protect human health or the environment. Any required action described in the Regional Administrator's determination shall become effective immediately, unless the Regional Administrator provides otherwise.
Geological Reclamation Operations and Waste Systems, Inc	Morrisville, Pennsylvania	Wastewater treatment sludge filter cake from the treatment of EPA Hazardous Waste No. F039, generated at a maximum annual rate of 2000 cubic yards, after December 4, 2001, and disposed of in a Subtitle D landfill. The exclusion covers the filter cake resulting from the treatment of hazardous waste leachate derived from only "old" GROWS and non-hazardous leachate derived from only non-hazardous waste sources. The exclusion does not address the waste disposed of in the "old" GROWS' Landfill or the grit generated during the removal of heavy solids from the landfill leachate. To ensure that hazardous constituents are not present in the filter cake at levels of regulatory concern, GROWS must implement a testing program for the petitioned waste. This testing program must meet the conditions listed below in order for the exclusion to be valid: (1) *Testing:* Sample collection and analyses, including quality control (QC) procedures, must be performed using appropriate methods. As applicable to the method-defined parameters of concern, analyses requiring the use of SW–846 methods incorporated by reference in 40 CFR 260.11 must be used without substitution. As applicable, the SW–846 methods might include Methods 0010, 0011, 0020, 0023A, 0030, 0031, 0040, 0050, 0051, 0060, 0061, 1010A, 1020B, 1110A, 1310B, 1311, 1312, 1320, 1330A, 9010C, 9012B, 9040C, 9045D, 9060A, 9070A (uses EPA Method 1664, Rev. A), 9071B, and 9095B. (A) *Sample Collection:* Each batch of waste generated over a four-week period must be collected in containers with a maximum capacity of 20-cubic yards. At the end of the four-week period, each container must be divided into four quadrants and a single, full-depth core sample shall be collected from each quadrant. All of the full-depth core samples then must be composited under laboratory conditions to produce one representative composite sample for the four-week period.

Table 1—Wastes Excluded from Non-Specific Sources

Facility	Address	Waste description

(B) *Sample Analysis:* Each four-week composite sample must be analyzed for all of the constituents listed in Condition (3). The analytical data, including quality control information, must be submitted to The Waste and Chemicals Management Division, U.S. EPA Region III, 1650 Arch Street, Philadelphia, PA 19103, and the Pennsylvania Department of Environmental Protection, Bureau of Land Recycling and Waste Management, Rachel Carson State Office Building, 400 Market Street, 14th Floor, Harrisburg, PA 17105. Data from the annual verification testing must be compiled and submitted to EPA and the Pennsylvania Department of Environmental Protection within sixty (60) days from the end of the calendar year. All data must be accompanied by a signed copy of the statement set forth in 40 CFR 260.22(i)(12) to certify to the truth and accuracy of the data submitted. Records of operating conditions and analytical data must be compiled, summarized, and maintained on- site for a minimum of three years and must be furnished upon request by any employee or representative of EPA or the Pennsylvania Department of Environmental Protection, and made available for inspection.

(2) *Waste Holding:* The dewatered filter cake must be stored as hazardous until the verification analyses are completed. If the four-week composite sample does not exceed any of the delisting levels set forth in Condition (3), the filter cake waste corresponding to this sample may be managed and disposed of in accordance with all applicable solid waste regulations. If the four-week composite sample exceeds any of the delisting levels set forth in Condition (3), the filter cake waste generated during the time period corresponding to the four- week composite sample must be retreated until it meets these levels (analyses must be repeated) or managed and disposed of in accordance with Subtitle C of RCRA. Filter cake which is generated but for which analyses are not complete or valid must be managed and disposed of in accordance with Subtitle C of RCRA, until valid analyses demonstrate that the waste meets the delisting levels.

(3) *Delisting Levels:* If the concentrations in the four-week composite sample of the filter cake waste for any of the hazardous constituents listed below exceed their respective maximum allowable concentrations (mg/l or mg/kg) also listed below, the four-week batch of failing filter cake waste must either be retreated until it meets these levels or managed and disposed of in accordance with Subtitle C of RCRA. GROWS has the option of determining whether the filter cake waste exceeds the maximum allowable concentrations for the organic constituents by either performing the analysis on a TCLP leachate of the waste or performing total constituent analysis on the waste, and then comparing the results to the corresponding maximum allowable concentration level.

(A) Inorganics

Constituent:	Maximum Allowable Leachate Conc. (mg/l)
Arsenic	3.00e–01
Barium	2.34e+01
Cadmium	1.80e–01
Chromium	5.00e+00
Lead	5.00e+00
Mercury	7.70e–02
Nickel	9.05e+00
Selenium	6.97e–01
Silver	1.23e+00
Cyanide	4.33e+00

Cyanide extractions must be conducted using distilled water in place of the leaching media specified in the TCLP procedure.

(B) Organics

Constituent:	Maximum allowable leachate conc. (mg/l)	Maximum allowable total conc. (mg/kg)
Acetone	2.28e+01	4.56e+02
Acetonitrile	3.92e+00	7.84e+01
Acetophenone	2.28e+01	4.56e+02
Acrolein	1.53e+03	3.06e+04
Acrylonitrile	7.80e–03	1.56e–01
Aldrin	5.81e–06	1.16e–04
Aniline	7.39e–01	1.48e+01
Anthracene	8.00e+00	1.60e+02
Benz(a)anthracene	1.93e–04	3.86e–03
Benzene	1.45e–01	2.90e+00

Table 1—Wastes Excluded from Non-Specific Sources

Facility	Address	Waste description		
		Benzo(a)pyrene	1.18e–05	2.36e–04
		Benzo(b)fluoranthene	1.07e–04	2.14e–03
		Benzo(k)fluoranthene	1.49e–03	2.98e–02
		Bis(2-chloroethyl)ether	3.19e–02	6.38e–01
		Bis(2-ethylhexyl)phthalate	8.96e–02	1.79e+00
		Bromodichloromethane	6.80e–02	1.36e+00
		Bromoform (Tribromomethane)	5.33e–01	1.07e+01
		Butyl-4,6-dinitrophenol, 2-sec-(Dinoseb)	2.28e–01	4.56e+00
		Butylbenzylphthalate	9.29e+00	1.86e+02
		Carbon disulfide	2.28e+01	4.56e+02
		Carbon tetrachloride	4.50e–02	9.00e–01
		Chlordane	5.11e–04	1.02e–02
		Chloro-3-methylphenol 4-	2.97e+02	5.94e+03
		Chloroaniline, p-	9.14e–01	1.83e+01
		Chlorobenzene	6.08e+00	1.22e+02
		Chlorobenzilate	4.85e–02	9.70e–01
		Chlorodibromomethane	5.02e–02	1.00e+00
		Chloroform	7.79e–02	1.56e+00
		Chlorophenol, 2-	1.14e+00	2.28e+01
		Chrysene	2.04e–02	4.08e–01
		Cresol	1.14e+00	2.28e+01
		DDD	5.83e–04	1.17e–02
		DDE	1.37e–04	2.74e–03
		DDT	2.57e–04	5.14e–03
		Dibenz(a,h)anthracene	5.59e–06	1.12e–04
		Dibromo-3-chloropropane, 1,2-	3.51e–03	7.02e–02
		Dichlorobenzene 1,3-	9.35e+00	1.87e+02
		Dichlorobenzene, 1,2-	1.25e+01	2.50e+02
		Dichlorobenzene, 1,4-	1.39e–01	2.78e+00
		Dichlorobenzidine, 3,3'-	9.36e–03	1.87e–01
		Dichlorodifluoromethane	4.57e+01	9.14e+02
		Dichloroethane, 1,1-	1.20e+00	2.40e+01
		Dichloroethane, 1,2-	2.57e–03	5.14e–02
		Dichloroethylene, 1,1-	7.02e–03	1.40e–01
		Dichloroethylene, trans-1,2-	4.57e+00	9.14e+01
		Dichlorophenol, 2,4-	6.85e–01	1.37e+01
		Dichlorophenoxyacetic acid, 2,4-(2,4-D)	2.28e+00	4.56e+01
		Dichloropropane, 1,2-	1.14e–01	2.28e+00
		Dichloropropene, 1,3-	2.34e–02	4.68e–01
		Dieldrin	6.23e+01	1.25e+03
		Diethyl phthalate	2.21e+02	4.42e+03
		Dimethoate	6.01e+01	1.20e+03
		Dimethyl phthalate	1.20e+02	2.40e+03
		Dimethylbenz(a)anthracene, 7,12-	1.55e–06	3.10e–05
		Dimethylphenol, 2,4-	4.57e+00	9.14e+01
		Di-n-butyl phthalate	5.29e+00	1.06e+02
		Dinitrobenzene, 1,3-	2.28e–02	4.56e–01
		Dinitromethylphenol, 4,6-,2-	2.16e–02	4.32e–01
		Dinitrophenol, 2,4-	4.57e–01	9.14e+00
		Dinitrotoluene, 2,6-	6.54e–03	1.31e–01
		Di-n-octyl phthalate	1.12e–02	2.24e–01
		Dioxane, 1,4-	3.83e–01	7.66e+00
		Diphenylamine	3.76e+00	7.52e+01
		Disulfoton	3.80e+02	7.60e+03
		Endosulfan	1.37e+00	2.74e+01
		Endrin	2.00e–02	4.00e–01
		Ethylbenzene	1.66e+01	3.32e+02
		Ethylene Dibromide	4.13e–03	8.26e–02
		Fluoranthene	5.16e–01	1.03e+01

Table 1—Wastes Excluded from Non-Specific Sources

Facility	Address	Waste description		
		Fluorene	1.78e+00	3.56e+01
		Heptachlor	8.00e–03	1.60e–01
		Heptachlor epoxide	8.00e–03	1.60e–01
		Hexachloro-1,3-butadiene	9.61e–03	1.92e–01
		Hexachlorobenzene	9.67e–05	1.93e–03
		Hexachlorocyclohexane, gamma-(Lindane)	4.00e–01	8.00e+00
		Hexachlorocyclopentadiene	1.66e+04	3.32e+05
		Hexachloroethane	1.76e–01	3.52e+00
		Hexachlorophene	3.13e–04	6.26e–03
		Indeno(1,2,3-cd) pyrene	6.04e–05	1.21e–03
		Isobutyl alcohol	6.85e+01	1.37e+03
		Isophorone	4.44e+00	8.88e+01
		Methacrylonitrile	2.28e–02	4.56e–01
		Methoxychlor	1.00e+01	2.00e+02
		Methyl bromide (Bromomethane)	1.28e+02	2.56e+03
		Methyl chloride (Chloromethane)	1.80e–01	3.60e+00
		Methyl ethyl ketone	1.37e+02	2.74e+03
		Methyl isobutyl ketone	1.83e+01	3.66e+02
		Methyl methacrylate	1.03e+03	2.06e+04
		Methyl parathion	1.27e+02	2.54e+03
		Methylene chloride	2.88e–01	5.76e+00
		Naphthalene	1.50e+00	3.00e+01
		Nitrobenzene	1.14e–01	2.28e+00
		Nitrosodiethylamine	2.81e–05	5.62e–04
		Nitrosodimethylamine	8.26e–05	1.65e–03
		Nitrosodi-n-butylamine	7.80e–04	1.56e–02
		N-Nitrosodi-n-propylamine	6.02e–04	1.20e–02
		N-Nitrosodiphenylamine	8.60e–01	1.72e+01
		N-Nitrosopyrrolidine	2.01e–03	4.02e–02
		Pentachlorobenzene	1.15e–02	2.30e–01
		Pentachloronitrobenzene (PCNB)	5.00e–03	1.00e–01
		Pentachlorophenol	4.10e–03	8.20e–02
		Phenanthrene	2.09e–01	4.18e+00
		Phenol	1.37e+02	2.74e+03
		Polychlorinated biphenyls	3.00e–05	6.00e–04
		Pronamide	1.71e+01	3.42e+02
		Pyrene	3.96e–01	7.92e+00
		Pyridine	2.28e–01	4.56e+00
		Styrene	6.08e+00	1.22e+02
		Tetrachlorobenzene, 1,2,4,5-	9.43e–03	1.89e–01
		Tetrachloroethane, 1,1,2,2-	4.39e–01	8.78e+00
		Tetrachloroethylene	8.55e–02	1.71e+00
		Tetrachlorophenol, 2,3,4,6-	1.81e+00	3.62e+01
		Tetraethyl dithiopyrophosphate (Sulfotep)	3.01e+05	6.02e+06
		Toluene	4.57e+01	9.14e+02
		Toxaphene	5.00e–01	1.00e+01
		Trichlorobenzene, 1,2,4-	7.24e–01	1.45e+01
		Trichloroethane, 1,1,1-	7.60e+00	1.52e+02
		Trichloroethane, 1,1,2-	7.80e–02	1.56e+00
		Trichloroethylene	3.04e–01	6.08e+00
		Trichlorofluoromethane	6.85e+01	1.37e+03
		Trichlorophenol, 2,4,5-	9.16e+00	1.83e+02
		Trichlorophenol, 2,4,6-	2.76e–01	5.52e+00
		Trichlorophenoxyacetic acid, 2,4,5-(245-T)	2.28e+00	4.56e+01
		Trichlorophenoxypropionic acid, 2,4,5-(Silvex)	1.00e+00	2.00e+01
		Trichloropropane, 1,2,3-	7.69e–04	1.54e–02
		Trinitrobenzene, sym-	6.49e+00	1.30e+02
		Vinyl chloride	2.34e–03	4.68e–02
		Xylenes (total)	3.20e+02	6.40e+03

Table 1—Wastes Excluded from Non-Specific Sources

Facility	Address	Waste description
		(4) *Changes in Operating Conditions:* If GROWS significantly changes the treatment process or the chemicals used in the treatment process, GROWS may not manage the treatment sludge filter cake generated from the new process under this exclusion until it has met the following conditions: (a) GROWS must demonstrate that the waste meets the delisting levels set forth in Paragraph 3; (b) it must demonstrate that no new hazardous constituents listed in Appendix VIII of Part 261 have been introduced into the manufacturing or treatment process: and (c) it must obtain prior written approval from EPA and the Pennsylvania Department of Environmental Protection to manage the waste under this exclusion. (5)*Reopener:* (a) If GROWS discovers that a condition at the facility or an assumption related to the disposal of the excluded waste that was modeled or predicted in the petition does not occur as modeled or predicted, then GROWS must report any information relevant to that condition, in writing, to the Regional Administrator or his delegate and to the Pennsylvania Department of Environmental Protection within 10 days of discovering that condition. (b) Upon receiving information described in paragraph (a) of this section, regardless of its source, the Regional Administrator or his delegate and the Pennsylvania Department of Environmental Protection will determine whether the reported condition requires further action. Further action may include repealing the exclusion, modifying the exclusion, or other appropriate response necessary to protect human health and the environment.
Goodyear Tire and Rubber Co	Randleman, NC	Dewatered wastewater treatment sludges (EPA Hazardous Waste No. F006) generated from electroplating operations.
Gould, Inc	McConnelsville, OH	Wastewater treatment sludge (EPA Hazardous Waste No. F006) generated from electroplating operations after November 27, 1985.
Hoechst Celanese Corporation	Bucks, Alabama	Distillation bottoms generated (at a maximum annual rate of 31,500 cubic yards) from the production of sodium hydrosulfite (EPA Hazardous Waste No. F003). This exclusion was published on July 17, 1990. This exclusion does not include the waste contained in Hoechst Celanese's on-site surface impoundment.
Hoechst Celanese Corporation	Leeds, South Carolina	Distillation bottoms generated (at a maximum annual rate of 38,500 cubic yards) from the production of sodium hydrosulfite (EPA Hazardous Waste No. F003). This exclusion was published on July 17, 1990.
Hanover Wire Cloth Division	Hanover, Pennsylvania	Dewatered filter cake (EPA Hazardous Waste No. F006) generated from electroplating operations after August 15, 1986.
Holston Army Ammunition Plant	Kingsport, Tennessee	Dewatered wastewater treatment sludges (EPA Hazardous Waste Nos. F003, F005, and K044) generated from the manufacturing and processing of explosives and containing spent non-halogenated solvents after November 14, 1986.
Imperial Clevite	Salem, IN	Solid resin cakes containing EPA Hazardous Waste No. F002 generated after August 27, 1985, from solvent recovery operations.
Indiana Steel & Wire Corporation (formerly General Cable Co.)	Munci, IN	Dewatered wastewater treatment sludges (EPA Hazardous Waste Nos. F006 and K062) generated from electroplating operations and steel finishing operations after October 24, 1986. This exclusion does not apply to sludges in any on-site impoundments as of this date.
International Minerals and Chemical Corporation	Terre Haute, Indiana	Spent non-halogenated solvents and still bottoms (EPA Hazardous Waste No. F003) generated from the recovery of n-butyl alchohol after August 15, 1986.
Kawneer Company, Incorporated	Springdale, Arkansas	Wastewater treatment filter press sludge (EPA Hazardous Waste No. F019) generated (at a maximum annual rate of 26 cubic yards) from the chemical conversion coating of aluminum. This exclusion was published on November 13, 1990.
Kay-Fries, Inc	Stoney Point, NY	Biological aeration lagoon sludge and filter press sludge generated after September 21, 1984, which contain EPA Hazardous Waste Nos. F003 and F005 as well as that disposed of in a holding lagoon as of September 21, 1984.
Keymark Corp	Fonda, NY	Wastewater treatment sludge (EPA Hazardous Waste No. F019) generated from chemical conversion coating of aluminum after November 27, 1985.

Table 1—Wastes Excluded from Non-Specific Sources

Facility	Address	Waste description
Keymark Corp	Fonda, NY	Wastewater treatment sludges (EPA Hazardous Waste No. F019) generated from the chemical conversion coating of aluminum and contained in an on-site impoundment on August 12, 1987. This is a one-time exclusion.
Lawrence Berkeley National Laboratory	Berkeley, California	Treated ignitable and spent halogenated and non-halogenated solvent mixed waste (D001, F002, F003, and F005), and bubbler water on silica gel generated during treatment at the National Tritium Labeling Facility (NTLF) of the Lawrence Berkeley National Laboratory (LBNL). This is a onetime exclusion for 200 U.S. gallons of treatment residues that will be disposed of in a Nuclear Regulatory Commission (NRC) licensed or Department of Energy (DOE) approved low-level radioactive waste disposal facility, after August 7, 2003. (1) Waste Management: The treated waste residue and bubbler water on silica gel must be managed in accordance with DOE or NRC requirements prior to and during disposal. (2) Reopener Language: (A) If, anytime after disposal of the delisted waste, LBNL possesses or is otherwise made aware of any data (including but not limited to leachate data or groundwater monitoring data) relevant to the delisted waste indicating that any organic constituent from the waste is detected in the leachate or the groundwater, then LBNL must report such data, in writing, to the Regional Administrator within 10 days of first possessing or being made aware of that data. (B) Based on the information described in paragraph (2)(A) and any other information received from any source, the Regional Administrator will make a preliminary determination as to whether the reported information requires Agency action to protect human health or the environment. Further action may include suspending, or revoking the exclusion, or other appropriate response necessary to protect human health and the environment. (C) If the Regional Administrator determines that the reported information does require Agency action, the Regional Administrator will notify LBNL in writing of the actions the Regional Administrator believes are necessary to protect human health and the environment. The notice shall include a statement of the proposed action and a statement providing LBNL with an opportunity to present information as to why the proposed Agency action is not necessary or to suggest an alternative action. LBNL shall have 30 days from the date of the Regional Administrator's notice to present the information. (D) If after 30 days LBNL presents no further information, the Regional Administrator will issue a final written determination describing the Agency actions that are necessary to protect human health or the environment. Any required action described in the Regional Administrator's determination shall become effective immediately, unless the Regional Administrator provides otherwise. (3) Notification Requirements: LBNL must do the following before transporting the delisted waste off-site: (A) Provide a one-time written notification to any State Regulatory Agency to which or through which they will transport the delisted waste described above for disposal, 60 days before beginning such activities. (B) Update the one-time written notification if LBNL ships the delisted waste to a different disposal facility. Failure to provide this notification will result in a violation of the delisting petition and a possible revocation of the exclusion.
Lederle Laboratories	Pearl River, NY	Spent non-halogenated solvents and still bottoms (EPA Hazardous Waste Nos. F003 and F005) generated from the recovery of the following solvents: Xylene, acetone, ethyl acetate, ethyl ether, methyl isobutyl ketone, n- butyl alcohol, cyclohexanone, methanol, toluene, and pyridine after August 2, 1988. Excusion applies to primary and secondary filter press sludges and compost soils generated from these sludges.
Lincoln Plating Company	Lincoln, NE	Wastewater treatment sludges (EPA Hazardous Waste No. F006) generated from electroplating operations after November 17, 1986.
Lockheed Martin Aeronautics Company	Fort Worth, TX	Sludge (EPA Hazardous Waste Number F019) generated at a maximum rate of 90 cubic yards per calendar year after October 9, 2008. For the exclusion to be valid, Lockheed Martin Aeronautics Company must implement a verification testing program that meets the following Paragraphs: (1) *Delisting Levels:* All concentrations for those constituents must not exceed the maximum allowable concentrations in mg/l specified in this paragraph. Sludge Leachable Concentrations (mg/l): Antimony—8.45; Arsenic—0.657; Barium—100.0; Cadmium—1.00; Chromium—5.0; Chromium, Hexavalent—5.0; Cobalt—1040; Copper— 1810; Cyanide—240; Lead—5.0; Mercury—0.20; Nickel—1040; Selenium—1.0; Silver— 5.0; Vanadium—51.5; Zinc—15800; Acetone—40600; Acetonitrile—766; Carbon Disulfide—4400; Ethylbenzene—846; Methyl Ethyl Ketone—200.0; Methyl Isobutyl Ketone— 3610; Methylene Chloride—6.16; Toluene—1180; Xylenes—745.

Table 1—Wastes Excluded from Non-Specific Sources

Facility	Address	Waste description
		(2) *Waste Holding and Handling*:

(A) Waste classification as non-hazardous can not begin until compliance with the limits set in paragraph (1) for sludge has occurred for two consecutive quarterly sampling events.

(B) If constituent levels in any sample taken by Lockheed Martin Aeronautics Company exceed any of the delisting levels set in paragraph (1) for the sludge, Lockheed Martin Aeronautics Company must do the following:

(i) notify EPA in accordance with paragraph (6) and

(ii) manage and dispose the sludge as hazardous waste generated under Subtitle C of RCRA.

(3) *Testing Requirements:*

Upon this exclusion becoming final, Lockheed Martin Aeronautics Company may perform quarterly analytical testing by sampling and analyzing the sludge as follows:

(A) Quarterly Testing:

(i) Collect two representative composite samples of the sludge at quarterly intervals after EPA grants the final exclusion. The first composite samples may be taken at any time after EPA grants the final approval. Sampling should be performed in accordance with the sampling plan approved by EPA in support of the exclusion.

(ii) Analyze the samples for all constituents listed in paragraph (1). Any composite sample taken that exceeds the delisting levels listed in paragraph (1) for the sludge must be disposed as hazardous waste in accordance with the applicable hazardous waste requirements.

(iii) Within thirty (30) days after taking each quarterly sample, Lockheed Martin Aeronautics Company will report its quarterly analytical test data to EPA. If levels of constituents measured in the samples of the sludge do not exceed the levels set forth in paragraph (1) of this exclusion for two consecutive quarters or sampling events, Lockheed Martin Aeronautics Company can manage and dispose the non-hazardous sludge according to all applicable solid waste regulations.

(B) Annual Testing:

(i) If Lockheed Martin Aeronautics Company completes the quarterly testing specified in paragraph (3) above and no sample contains a constituent at a level which exceeds the limits set forth in paragraph (1), Lockheed Martin Aeronautics Company may begin annual testing as follows: Lockheed Martin Aeronautics Company must test two representative composite samples of the sludge for all constituents listed in paragraph (1) at least once per calendar year.

(ii) The samples for the annual testing shall be a representative composite sample according to appropriate methods. As applicable to the method-defined parameters of concern, analyses requiring the use of SW–846 methods incorporated by reference in 40 CFR 260.11 must be used without substitution. As applicable, the SW–846 methods might include Methods 0010, 0011, 0020, 0023A, 0030, 0031, 0040, 0050, 0051, 0060, 0061, 1010A, 1020B, 1110A, 1310B, 1311, 1312, 1320, 1330A, 9010C, 9012B, 9040C, 9045D, 9060A, 9070A (uses EPA Method 1664, Rev. A), 9071B, and 9095B. Methods must meet Perform-ance Based Measurement System Criteria in which the Data Quality Objectives are to demonstrate that samples of the Lockheed Martin Aeronautics Company sludge are representative for all constituents listed in paragraph (1).

(iii) The samples for the annual testing taken for the second and subsequent annual testing events shall be taken within the same calendar month as the first annual sample taken.

(iv) The annual testing report should include the total amount of waste in cubic yards disposed during the calendar year.

(4) *Changes in Operating Conditions:* If Lockheed Martin Aeronautics Company significantly changes the process described in its petition or starts any processes that generate(s) the waste that may or could affect the composition or type of waste generated (by illustration, but not limitation, changes in equipment or operating conditions of the treatment process), it must notify EPA in writing and it may no longer handle the wastes generated from the new process as non-hazardous until the wastes meet the delisting levels set in paragraph (1) and it has received written approval to do so from EPA.

Lockheed Martin Aeronautics Company must submit a modification to the petition complete with full sampling and analysis for circumstances where the waste volume changes and/or additional waste codes are added to the waste stream.

Table 1—Wastes Excluded from Non-Specific Sources

Facility	Address	Waste description
		(5) *Data Submittals:*

Lockheed Martin Aeronautics Company must submit the information described below. If Lockheed Martin Aeronautics Company fails to submit the required data within the specified time or maintain the required records on-site for the specified time, EPA, at its discretion, will consider this sufficient basis to reopen the exclusion as described in paragraph (6). Lockheed Martin Aeronautics Company must:

(A) Submit the data obtained through paragraph (3) to the Chief, Corrective Action and Waste Minimization Section, Multimedia Planning and Permitting Division, U.S. Environmental Protection Agency Region 6, 1445 Ross Ave., Dallas, Texas, 75202, within the time specified. All supporting data can be submitted on CD–ROM or some comparable electronic media.

(B) Compile records of analytical data from paragraph (3), summarized, and maintained on-site for a minimum of five years.

(C) Furnish these records and data when either EPA or the State of Texas requests them for inspection.

(D) Send along with all data a signed copy of the following certification statement, to attest to the truth and accuracy of the data submitted:

"Under civil and criminal penalty of law for the making or submission of false or fraudulent statements or representations (pursuant to the applicable provisions of the Federal Code, which include, but may not be limited to, 18 U.S.C. 1001 and 42 U.S.C. 6928), I certify that the information contained in or accompanying this document is true, accurate and complete.

As to the (those) identified section(s) of this document for which I cannot personally verify its (their) truth and accuracy, I certify as the company official having supervisory responsibility for the persons who, acting under my direct instructions, made the verification that this information is true, accurate and complete.

If any of this information is determined by EPA in its sole discretion to be false, inaccurate or incomplete, and upon conveyance of this fact to the company, I recognize and agree that this exclusion of waste will be void as if it never had effect or to the extent directed by EPA and that the company will be liable for any actions taken in contravention of the company's RCRA and CERCLA obligations premised upon the company's reliance on the void exclusion."

(6) *Reopener:*

(A) If, anytime after disposal of the delisted waste Lockheed Martin Aeronautics Company possesses or is otherwise made aware of any environmental data (including but not limited to leachate data or ground water monitoring data) or any other data relevant to the delisted waste indicating that any constituent identified for the delisting verification testing is at level higher than the delisting level allowed by the Division Director in granting the petition, then the facility must report the data, in writing, to the Division Director within 10 days of first possessing or being made aware of that data.

(B) If either the quarterly or annual testing of the waste does not meet the delisting requirements in paragraph 1, Lockheed Martin Aeronautics Company must report the data, in writing, to the Division Director within 10 days of first possessing or being made aware of that data.

(C) If Lockheed Martin Aeronautics Company fails to submit the information described in paragraphs (5), (6)(A) or (6)(B) or if any other information is received from any source, the Division Director will make a preliminary determination as to whether the reported information requires EPA action to protect human health and/or the environment. Further action may include suspending, or revoking the exclusion, or other appropriate response necessary to protect human health and the environment.

(D) If the Division Director determines that the reported information requires action by EPA, the Division Director will notify the facility in writing of the actions the Division Director believes are necessary to protect human health and the environment. The notice shall include a statement of the proposed action and a statement providing the facility with an opportunity to present information as to why the proposed EPA action is not necessary. The facility shall have 10 days from the date of the Division Director's notice to present such information.

(E) Following the receipt of information from the facility described in paragraph (6)(D) or (if no information is presented under paragraph (6)(D)) the initial receipt of information described in paragraphs (5), (6)(A) or (6)(B), the Division Director will issue a final written determination describing EPA actions that are necessary to protect human health and/or the environment. Any required action described in the Division Director's determination shall become effective immediately, unless the Division Director provides otherwise.

(7) *Notification Requirements:* Lockheed Martin Aeronautics Company must do the following before transporting the delisted waste. Failure to provide this notification will result in a violation of the delisting petition and a possible revocation of the decision.

Table 1—Wastes Excluded from Non-Specific Sources

Facility	Address	Waste description
		(A) Provide a one-time written notification to any state Regulatory Agency to which or through which it will transport the delisted waste described above for disposal, 60 days before beginning such activities. (B) Update one-time written notification, if it ships the delisted waste into a different disposal facility. (C) Failure to provide this notification will result in a violation of the delisting variance and a possible revocation of the decision.
Loxcreen Company, Inc	Hayti, MO	Dewatered wastewater treatment sludges (EPA Hazardous Waste No. F019) generated from the chemical conversion coating of aluminum after July 16, 1986.
MAHLE, Inc	Morristown, Tennessee	Wastewater treatment sludge filter cake (EPA Hazardous Waste No. F019) generated from the chemical conversion coating of aluminum (generated at a maximum annual rate of 33 cubic yards), after August 21, 1992. In order to confirm that the characteristics of the waste do not change significantly, the facility must, on an annual basis sample and test for the constituents listed in 40 CFR 261.24 using the method specified therein. The annual analytical results (including quality control information) must be compiled, certified according to 40 CFR 260.22(i)(12), maintained on-site for a minimum of five years, and made available for inspection upon request by representatives of EPA or the State of Tennessee. Failure to maintain the required records on- site will be considered by EPA, at its discretion, sufficient basis to revoke the exclusion to the extent directed by EPA.
Marquette Electronics Incorporated	Milwaukee, Wisconsin	Wastewater treatment sludge (EPA Hazardous Waste No. F006) generated from electroplating operations. This exclusion was published on April 20, 1989.
Martin Marietta Aerospace	Ocala, Florida	Dewatered wastewater treatment sludges (EPA Hazardous Waste No. F006) generated from electroplating operations after January 23, 1987.
Mason Chamberlain, Incorporated	Bay St. Louis, Mississippi	Wastewater treatment sludge filter cake (EPA Hazardous Waste No. F019) generated (at a maximum annual rate of 1,262 cubic yards) from the chemical conversion coating of aluminum. This exclusion was published on October 27, 1989.
Maytag Company	Newton, IA	Wastewater treatment sludges (EPA Hazardous Waste No. F006) generated from electroplating operations and wastewater treatment sludges (EPA Hazardous Waste No. F019) generated from the chemical conversion coating of aluminum November 17, 1986.
McDonnell Douglas Corporation	Tulsa, Oklahoma	Stabilized wastewater treatment sludges from surface impoundments previously closed as a landfill (at a maximum generation of 85,000 cubic yards on a one-time basis). EPA Hazardous Waste No. F019, F002, F003, and F005 generated at U.S. Air Force Plant No. 3, Tulsa, Oklahoma and is disposed of in Subtitle D landfills after February 26, 1999. McDonnell Douglas must implement a testing program that meets the following conditions for the exclusion to be valid: (1) *Delisting Levels:* All leachable concentrations for the constituents in Conditions (1)(A) and (1)(B) in the approximately 5,000 cubic yards of combined stabilization materials and excavated sludges from the bottom portion of the northwest lagoon of the surface impoundments which are closed as a landfill must not exceed the following levels (ppm) after the stabilization process is completed in accordance with Condition (3). Constituents must be measured in the waste leachate by the method specified in 40 CFR 261.24. Cyanide extractions must be conducted using distilled water in the place of the leaching media per 40 CFR 261.24. Constituents in Condition (1)(C) must be measured as the total concentrations in the waste(ppm) (A) Inorganic Constituents (leachate) Antimony-0.336; Cadmium-0.280; Chromium (total)-5.0; Lead-0.84; Cyanide-11.2; (B) Organic Constituents (leachate) Benzene-0.28; trans-1,2- Dichloroethene-5.6; Tetrachloroethylene-0.280; Trichloroethylene-0.280 (C) Organic Constituents (total analysis) Benzene-10.; Ethylbenzene-10.; Toluene-30.; Xylenes-30.; trans- 1,2-Dichloroethene-30.; Tetrachloroethylene-6.0; Trichloroethylene-6.0 McDonnell Douglas Corporation shall control volatile emissions from the stabilization process by collection of the volatile chemicals as they are emitted from the waste but before release to the ambient air. and the facility shall use dust control measures. These two controls must be adequate to protect human health and the environment. The approximately 80,000 cubic yards of previously stabilized waste in the upper northwest lagoon, entire northeast lagoon, and entire south lagoon of the surface impoundments which were closed as a landfill requires no verification testing.

Table 1—Wastes Excluded from Non-Specific Sources

Facility	Address	Waste description
		(2) *Waste Holding and Handling:* McDonnell Douglas must store as hazardous all stabilized waste from the bottom portion of the northwest lagoon area of the closed landfill as generated until verification testing as specified in Condition (3), is completed and valid analyses demonstrate that Condition (1) is satisfied. If the levels of constituents measured in the samples of the stabilized waste do not exceed the levels set forth in Condition (1), then the waste is nonhazardous and may be managed and disposed of in a Subtitle D landfill in accordance with all applicable solid waste regulations. If constituent levels in a sample exceed any of the delisting levels set in Condition (1), the waste generated during the time period corresponding to this sample must be restabilized until delisting levels are met or managed and disposed of in accordance with Subtitle C of RCRA.
		(3) *Verification Testing Requirements:* Sample collection and analyses, including quality control procedures, must be performed using appropriate methods. As applicable to the method-defined parameters of concern, analyses requiring the use of SW–846 methods incorporated by reference in 40 CFR 260.11 must be used without substitution. As applicable, the SW–846 methods might include Methods 0010, 0011, 0020, 0023A, 0030, 0031, 0040, 0050, 0051, 0060, 0061, 1010A, 1020B, 1110A, 1310B, 1311, 1312, 1320, 1330A, 9010C, 9012B, 9040C, 9045D, 9060A, 9070A (uses EPA Method 1664, Rev. A), 9071B, and 9095B. McDonnell Douglas must stabilize the previously unstabilized waste from the bottom portion of the northwest lagoon of the surface impoundment (which was closed as a landfill) using fly ash, kiln dust or similar accepted materials in batches of 500 cubic yards or less. McDonnell Douglas must analyze one composite sample from each batch of 500 cubic yards or less. A minimum of four grab samples must be taken from each waste pile (or other designated holding area) of stabilized waste generated from each batch run. Each composited batch sample must be analyzed, prior to disposal of the waste in the batch represented by that sample, for constituents listed in Condition (1). There are no verification testing requirements for the stabilized wastes in the upper portions of the northwest lagoon, the entire northeast lagoon, and the entire south lagoon of the surface impoundments which were closed as a landfill.
		(4) *Changes in Operating Conditions:* If McDonnell Douglas significantly changes the stabilization process established under Condition (3) (*e.g.*, use of new stabilization agents), McDonnell Douglas must notify the Agency in writing. After written approval by EPA, McDonnell Douglas may handle the wastes generated as non-hazardous, if the wastes meet the delisting levels set in Condition (1).
		(5) *Data Submittals:* Records of operating conditions and analytical data from Condition (3) must be compiled, summarized, and maintained on site for a minimum of five years. These records and data must be furnished upon request by EPA, or the State of Oklahoma, or both, and made available for inspection. Failure to submit the required data within the specified time period or maintain the required records on site for the specified time will be considered by EPA, at its discretion, sufficient basis to revoke the exclusion to the extent directed by EPA. All data must be accompanied by a signed copy of the following certification statement to attest to the truth and accuracy of the data submitted: Under civil and criminal penalty of law for the making or submission of false or fraudulent statements or representations (pursuant to the applicable provisions of the Federal Code, which include, but may not be limited to, 18 U.S.C. §1001 and 42 U.S.C. §6928), I certify that the information contained in or accompanying this document is true, accurate and complete. As to the (those) identified section(s) of this document for which I cannot personally verify its (their) truth and accuracy, I certify as the company official having supervisory responsibility for the persons who, acting under my direct instructions, made the verification that this information is true, accurate and complete. In the event that any of this information is determined by EPA in its sole discretion to be false, inaccurate or incomplete, and upon conveyance of this fact to the company, I recognize and agree that this exclusion of waste will be void as if it never had effect or to the extent directed by EPA and that the company will be liable for any actions taken in contravention of the company's RCRA and CERCLA obligations premised upon the company's reliance on the void exclusion.
		(6) *Reopener Language* (a) If McDonnell Douglas discovers that a condition at the facility or an assumption related to the disposal of the excluded waste that was modeled or predicted in the petition does not occur as modeled or predicted, then McDonnell Douglas must report any information relevant to that condition, in writing, to the Regional Administrator or his delegate within 10 days of discovering that condition. (b) Upon receiving information described in paragraph (a) from any source, the Regional Administrator or his delegate will determine whether the reported condition requires further action. Further action may include revoking the exclusion, modifying the exclusion, or other appropriate response necessary to protect human health and the environment.

Table 1—Wastes Excluded from Non-Specific Sources

Facility	Address	Waste description
		(7) *Notification Requirements:* McDonnell Douglas must provide a one-time written notification to any State Regulatory Agency to which or through which the delisted waste described above will be transported for disposal at least 60 days prior to the commencement of such activity. The one-time written notification must be updated if the delisted waste is shipped to a different disposal facility. Failure to provide such a notification will result in a violation of the delisting petition and a possible revocation of the decision.
Merck & Company, Incorporated	Elkton, Virginia	One-time exclusion for fly ash (EPA Hazardous Waste No. F002) from the incineration of wastewater treatment sludge generated from pharmaceutical production processes and stored in an on-site fly ash lagoon. This exclusion was published on May 12, 1989.
Metropolitan Sewer District of Greater Cincinnati	Cincinnati, OH	Sluiced bottom ash sludge (approximately 25,000 cubic yards), contained in the North Lagoon, on September 21, 1984, which contains EPA Hazardous Wastes Nos. F001, F002, F003, F004, and F005.
Michelin Tire Corp	Sandy Springs, South Carolina	Dewatered wastewater treatment sludge (EPA Hazardous Wastes No. F006) generated from electroplating operations after November 14, 1986.
Monroe Auto Equipment	Paragould, AR	Wastewater treatment sludge (EPA Hazardous Waste No. F006) generated from electroplating operations after vacuum filtration after November 27, 1985. This exclusion does not apply to the sludge contained in the on-site impoundment.
Nissan North America, Inc.	Smyrna, Tennessee	Wastewater treatment sludge (EPA Hazardous Waste No. F019) that Nissan North American, Inc. (Nissan) generates by treating wastewater from automobile assembly plant located on 983 Nissan Drive in Smyrna, Tennessee. This is a conditional exclusion for up to 3,500 cubic yards of waste (hereinafter referred to as "Nissan Sludge") that will be generated each year and disposed in a Subtitle D landfill after February 27, 2006. Nissan must continue to demonstrate that the following conditions are met for the exclusion to be valid. (1) *Delisting Levels:* All leachable concentrations for these metals, cyanide, and organic constituents must not exceed the following levels (ppm): Barium-100.0; Cadmium-0.422; Chromium-5.0; Cyanide-7.73, Lead-5.0; and Nickel-60.7; Bis-(2- ethylhexyl) phthalate-0.601; Di-n-octyl phthalate-0.0752; and 4–Methylphenol-7.66. These concentrations must be measured in the waste leachate obtained by the method specified in 40 CFR 261.24, except that for cyanide, deionized water must be the leaching medium. Cyanide concentrations in waste or leachate must be measured by the method specified in 40 CFR 268.40, Note 7. (2) *Verification Testing Requirements:* Sample collection and analyses, including quality control procedures, must be performed using appropriate methods. As applicable to the method-defined parameters of concern, analyses requiring the use of SW–846 methods incorporated by reference in 40 CFR 260.11 must be used without substitution. As applicable, the SW–846 methods might include Methods 0010, 0011, 0020, 0023A, 0030, 0031, 0040, 0050, 0051, 0060, 0061, 1010A, 1020B, 1110A, 1310B, 1311, 1312, 1320, 1330A, 9010C, 9012B, 9040C, 9045D, 9060A, 9070A, (uses EPA Method 1664, Rev. A), 9071B, and 9095B. Methods must meet Performance Based Measurement System Criteria in which the Data Quality Objectives are to demonstrate that representative samples of the Nissan Sludge meet the delisting levels in Condition (1). Nissan must perform an annual testing program to demonstrate that constituent concentrations measured in the TCLP extract do not exceed the delisting levels established in Condition (1). (3) *Waste Holding and Handling:* Nissan must hold sludge containers utilized for verification sampling until composite sample results are obtained. If the levels of constituents measured in Nissan's annual testing program do not exceed the levels set forth in Condition (1), then the Nissan Sludge is non-hazardous and must be managed in accordance with all applicable solid waste regulations. If constituent levels in a composite sample exceed any of the delisting levels set forth in Condition (1), the batch of Nissan Sludge generated during the time period corresponding to this sample must be managed and disposed of in accordance with Subtitle C of RCRA. (4) *Changes in Operating Conditions:* Nissan must notify EPA in writing when significant changes in the manufacturing or wastewater treatment processes are implemented. EPA will determine whether these changes will result in additional constituents of concern. If so, EPA will notify Nissan in writing that the Nissan Sludge must be managed as hazardous waste F019 until Nissan has demonstrated that the wastes meet the delisting levels set forth in Condition (1) and any levels established by EPA for the additional constituents of concern, and Nissan has received written approval from EPA. If EPA determines that the changes do not result in additional constituents of concern, EPA will notify Nissan, in writing, that Nissan must verify that the Nissan Sludge continues to meet Condition (1) delisting levels.

Table 1—Wastes Excluded from Non-Specific Sources

Facility	Address	Waste description
		(5) *Data Submittals:* Data obtained in accordance with Condition (2) must be submitted to Narindar M. Kumar, Chief, RCRA Enforcement and Compliance Branch, Mail Code: 4WD–RCRA, U.S. EPA, Region 4, Sam Nunn Atlanta Federal Center, 61 Forsyth Street, SW., Atlanta, Georgia 30303. The submission is due no later than 60 days after taking each annual verification samples in accordance with delisting Conditions (1) through (7). Records of analytical data from Condition (2) must be compiled, summarized, and maintained by Nissan for a minimum of three years, and must be furnished upon request by EPA or the State of Tennessee, and made available for inspection. Failure to submit the required data within the specified time period or maintain the required records for the specified time will be considered by EPA, at its discretion, sufficient basis to revoke the exclusion to the extent directed by EPA. All data must be accompanied by a signed copy of the certification statement in 40 CFR 260.22(i)(12). (6) *Reopener Language:* (A) If, at any time after disposal of the delisted waste, Nissan possesses or is otherwise made aware of any environmental data (including but not limited to leachate data or groundwater monitoring data) or any other data relevant to the delisted waste indicating that any constituent identified in the delisting verification testing is at a level higher than the delisting level allowed by EPA in granting the petition, Nissan must report the data, in writing, to EPA and Tennessee within 10 days of first possessing or being made aware of that data.. (B) If the testing of the waste, as required by Condition (2), does not meet the delisting requirements of Condition (1), Nissan must report the data, in writing, to EPA and Tennessee within 10 days of first possessing or being made aware of that data. (C) Based on the information described in paragraphs (6)(A) or (6)(B) and any other information received from any source, EPA will make a preliminary determination as to whether the reported information requires that EPA take action to protect human health or the environment. Further action may include suspending or revoking the exclusion, or other appropriate response necessary to protect human health and the environment. (D) If EPA determines that the reported information does require Agency action, EPA will notify the facility in writing of the action believed necessary to protect human health and the environment. The notice shall include a statement of the proposed action and a statement providing Nissan with an opportunity to present information as to why the proposed action is not necessary. Nissan shall have 10 days from the date of EPA's notice to present such information. (E) Following the receipt of information from Nissan, as described in paragraph (6)(D), or if no such information is received within 10 days, EPA will issue a final written determination describing the Agency actions that are necessary to protect human health or the environment, given the information received in accordance with paragraphs (6)(A) or (6)(B). Any required action described in EPA's determination shall become effective immediately, unless EPA provides otherwise. (7) *Notification Requirements:* Nissan must provide a one-time written notification to any State Regulatory Agency in a State to which or through which the delisted waste described above will be transported, at least 60 days prior to the commencement of such activities. Failure to provide such a notification will result in a violation of the delisting conditions and a possible revocation of the decision to delist.
North American Philips Consumer Electronics Corporation	Greenville, Tennessee	Wastewater treatment sludges (EPA Hazardous Waste No. F006) generated from electroplating operations. This exclusion was published on April 20, 1989.
Occidental Chemical	Ingleside, Texas	Limestone Sludge, (at a maximum generation 1,114 cubic yards per calender year) Rockbox Residue, (at a maximum generation of 1,000 cubic yards per calender year) generated by Occidental Chemical using the wastewater treatment process to treat the Rockbox Residue and the Limestone Sludge (EPA Hazardous Waste No. F025, F001, F003, and F005) generated at Occidental Chemical. Occidental Chemical must implement a testing program that meets the following conditions for the exclusion to be valid: (1) *Delisting Levels:* All concentrations for the following constituents must not exceed the following levels (ppm). The Rockbox Residue and the Limestone Sludge, must be measured in the waste leachate by the method specified in 40 CFR Part 261.24. (A) Rockbox Residue (i) Inorganic Constituents: Barium-100; Chromium-5; Copper-130; Lead- 1.5; Selenium-1; Tin-2100; Vanadium-30; Zinc-1,000 (ii) Organic Constituents: Acetone- 400; Bromodichloromethane-0.14; Bromoform-1.0; Chlorodibromethane- 0.1; Chloroform-1.0; Dichloromethane-1.0; Ethylbenzene- 7,000; 2,3,7,8-TCDD Equivalent- 0.00000006

Table 1—Wastes Excluded from Non-Specific Sources

Facility	Address	Waste description
		(B) Limestone Sludge
		(i) Inorganic Constituents: Antimony-0.6; Arsenic-5; Barium- 100; Beryllium-0.4; Chromium-5; Cobalt-210; Copper-130; Lead-1.5; Nickel-70; Selenium-5; Silver-5; Vanadium-30; Zinc-1,000
		(ii) Organic Constituents Acetone- 400; Bromoform-1.0; Chlorodibromomethane-0.1; Dichloromethane-1.0; Diethyl phthalate-3,000, Ethylbenzene- 7,000; 1,1,1-Trichloroethane-20; Toluene-700; Trichlorofluoromethane-1,000, Xylene-10,000, 2,3,7,8-TCDD Equivalent-0.00000006;
		(2) *Waste Holding and Handling:* Occidental Chemical must store in accordance with its RCRA permit, or continue to dispose of as hazardous waste all Rockbox Residue and the Limestone Sludge generated until the verification testing described in Condition (3)(B), as appropriate, is completed and valid analyses demonstrate that condition (3) is satisfied. If the levels of constituents measured in the samples of the Rockbox Residue and the Limestone Sludge do not exceed the levels set forth in Condition (1), then the waste is nonhazardous and may be managed and disposed of in accordance with all applicable solid waste regulations. If constituent levels in a sample exceed any of the delisting levels waste generated during the time period corresponding to this sample must be managed and disposed of in accordance with Subtitle C of RCRA.
		(3) *Verification Testing Requirements:* Sample collection and analyses, including quality control procedures, must be performed using appropriate methods. As applicable to the method-defined parameters of concern, any analyses requiring use of SW–846 methods incorporated by reference in 40 CFR 260.11 must use those methods without substitution. As applicable, the SW–846 methods might include Methods 0010, 0011, 0020, 0023A, 0030, 0031, 0040, 0050, 0051, 0060, 0061, 1010A, 1020B, 1110A, 1310B, 1311, 1312, 1320, 1330A, 9010C, 9012B, 9040C, 9045D, 9060A, 9070A (uses EPA Method 1664, Rev. A), 9071B, and 9095B. If EPA judges the incineration process to be effective under the operating conditions used during the initial verification testing, Occidental Chemical may replace the testing required in Condition (3)(A) with the testing required in Condition (3)(B). Occidental Chemical must continue to test as specified in Condition (3)(A) until and unless notified by EPA in writing that testing in Condition (3)(A) may be replaced by Condition (3)(B).
		(A) *Initial Verification Testing:* (i) During the first 40 operating days of the Incinerator Offgas Treatment System after the final exclusion is granted, Occidental Chemical must collect and analyze composites of the Limestone Sludge. Daily composites must be representative grab samples collected every 6 hours during each unit operating cycle. The two wastes must be analyzed, prior to disposal, for all of the constituents listed in Paragraph 1. The waste must also be analyzed for pH. Occidental Chemical must report the operational and analytical test data, including quality control information, obtained during this initial period no later than 90 days after the generation of the two wastes.
		(ii) When the Rockbox unit is decommissioned for cleanout, after the final exclusion is granted, Occidental Chemical must collect and analyze composites of the Rockbox Residue. Two composites must be composed of representative grab samples collected from the Rockbox unit. The waste must be analyzed, prior to disposal, for all of the constituents listed in Paragraph 1. The waste must be analyzed for pH. No later than 90 days after the Rockbox is decommissioned for cleanout the first two times after this exclusion becomes final, Occidental Chemical must report the operational and analytical test data, including quality control information.
		(B) *Subsequent Verification Testing:* Following written notification by EPA, Occidental Chemical may substitute the testing conditions in (3)(B) for (3)(A)(i). Occidental Chemical must continue to monitor operating conditions, analyze samples representative of each quarter of operation during the first year of waste generation. The samples must represent the waste generated over one quarter. (This provision does not apply to the Rockbox Residue.)
		(C) *Termination of Organic Testing for the Limestone Sludge:* Occidental Chemical must continue testing as required under Condition (3)(B) for organic constituents specified under Condition (3)(B) for organic constituents specified in Condition (1)(A)(ii) and (1)(B)(ii) until the analyses submitted under Condition (3)(B) show a minimum of two consecutive quarterly samples below the delisting levels in Condition (1)(A)(ii) and (1)(B)(ii), Occidental Chemical may then request that quarterly organic testing be terminated. After EPA notifies Occidental Chemical in writing it may terminate quarterly organic testing. Following termination of the quarterly testing, Occidental Chemical must continue to test a representative composite sample for all constituents listed in Condition (1) on an annual basis (no later than twelve months after exclusion).
		(4) *Changes in Operating Conditions:* If Occidental Chemical significantly changes the process which generate(s) the waste(s) and which may or could affect the composition or type waste(s) generated as established under Condition (1) (by illustration, but not limitation, change in equipment or operating conditions of the treatment process), Occidental Chemical must notify the EPA in writing and may no longer handle the wastes generated from the new process or no longer discharges as nonhazardous until the wastes meet the delisting levels set Condition (1) and it has received written approval to do so from EPA.

Table 1—Wastes Excluded from Non-Specific Sources

Facility	Address	Waste description
		(5) *Data Submittals:* The data obtained through Condition 3 must be submitted to Mr. William Gallagher, Chief, Region 6 Delisting Program, U.S. EPA, 1445 Ross Avenue, Dallas, Texas 75202-2733, Mail Code, (6PD-O) within the time period specified. Records of operating conditions and analytical data from Condition (1) must be compiled, summarized, and maintained on site for a minimum of five years. These records and data must be furnished upon request by EPA, or the State of Texas, and made available for inspection. Failure to submit the required data within the specified time period or maintain the required records on site for the specified time will be considered by EPA, at its discretion, sufficient basis to revoke the exclusion to the extent directed by EPA. All data must be accompanied by a signed copy of the following certification statement to attest to the truth and accuracy of the data submitted: Under civil and criminal penalty of law for the making or submission of false or fraudulent statements or representations (pursuant to the applicable provisions of the Federal Code, which include, but may not be limited to, 18 U.S.C. §1001 and 42 U.S.C. §6928), I certify that the information contained in or accompanying this document is true, accurate and complete. As to the (those) identified section(s) of this document for which I cannot personally verify its (their) truth and accuracy, I certify as the company official having supervisory responsibility for the persons who, acting under my direct instructions, made the verification that this information is true, accurate and complete. In the event that any of this information is determined by EPA in its sole discretion to be false, inaccurate or incomplete, and upon conveyance of this fact to the company, I recognize and agree that this exclusion of waste will be void as if it never had effect or to the extent directed by EPA and that the company will be liable for any actions taken in contravention of the company's RCRA and CERCLA obligations premised upon the company's reliance on the void exclusion. (6) *Reopener:* (a) If Occidental Chemical discovers that a condition at the facility or an assumption related to the disposal of the excluded waste that was modeled or predicted in the petition does not occur as modeled or predicted, then Occidental Chemical must report any information relevant to that condition, in writing, to the Director of the Multimedia Planning and Permitting Division or his delegate within 10 days of discovering that condition. (b) Upon receiving information described in paragraph (a) from any source, the Director or his delegate will determine whether the reported condition requires further action. Further action may include revoking the exclusion, modifying the exclusion, or other appropriate response necessary to protect human health and the environment. (7) *Notification Requirements:* Occidental Chemical must provide a one-time written notification to any State Regulatory Agency to which or through which the delisted waste described above will be transported for disposal at least 60 days prior to the commencement of such activities. Failure to provide such a notification will result in a violation of the delisting petition and a possible revocation of the decision.
Philway Products, Incorporated	Ashland, Ohio	Filter press sludge generated (at a maximum annual rate of 96 cubic yards) during the treatment of electroplating wastewaters using lime (EPA Hazardous Waste No. F006). This exclusion was published on October 26, 1990.
Plastene Supply Company	Portageville, Missouri	Dewatered wastewater treatment sludges (EPA Hazardous Waste No. F006) generated from electroplating operations after August 15, 1986.
POP Fasteners	Shelton, Connecticut	Wastewater treatment sludge (EPA Hazardous Waste No. F006) generated from electroplating operations (at a maximum annual rate of 1,000 cubic yards) after September 19, 1994. In order to confirm that the characteristics of the waste do not change significantly, the facility must, on an annual basis, analyze a representative composite sample for the constituents listed in §261.24 using the method specified therein. The annual analytical results, including quality control information, must be compiled, certified according to §260.22(i)(12), maintained on site for a minimum of five years, and made available for inspection upon request by any employee or representative of EPA or the State of Connecticut. Failure to maintain the required records on site will be considered by EPA, at its discretion, sufficient basis to revoke the exclusion to the extent directed by EPA.
Reynolds Metals Company	Sheffield, AL	Dewatered wastewater treatment sludges (EPA Hazardous Waste No. F019) generated from the chemical conversion coating of aluminum after August 15, 1986.
Reynolds Metals Company	Sheffield, AL	Wastewater treatment filter press sludge (EPA Hazardous Waste No. F019) generated (at a maximum annual rate of 3,840 cubic yards) from the chemical conversion coating of aluminum. This exclusion was published on July 17, 1990.

Table 1—Wastes Excluded from Non-Specific Sources

Facility	Address	Waste description
Rhodia	Houston, Texas	Filter-cake Sludge, (at a maximum generation of 1,200 cubic yards per calendar year) generated by Rhodia using the SARU and AWT treatment process to treat the filter-cake sludge (EPA Hazardous Waste Nos. D001-D43, F001-F012, F019, F024, F025, F032, F034, F037-F039) generated at Rhodia. Rhodia must implement a testing program that meets the following conditions for the exclusion to be valid: (1) *Delisting Levels:* All concentrations for the following constituents must not exceed the following levels (mg/l). For the filter-cake constituents must be measured in the waste leachate by the method specified in 40 CFR 261.24. (A) Filter-cake Sludge (i) Inorganic Constituents: Antimony-1.15; Arsenic-1.40; Barium-21.00; Beryllium-1.22; Cadmium-0.11; Cobalt-189.00; Copper-90.00; Chromium-0.60; Lead- 0.75; Mercury-0.025; Nickel-9.00; Selenium-4.50; Silver-0.14; Thallium-0.20; Vanadium-1.60; Zinc-4.30 (ii) Organic Constituents: Chlorobenzene-Non Detect; Carbon Tetrachloride-Non Detect; Acetone- 360; Chloroform-0.9 (2) *Waste Holding and Handling:* Rhodia must store in accordance with its RCRA permit, or continue to dispose of as hazardous waste all Filter-cake Sludge until the verification testing described in Condition (3)(A), as appropriate, is completed and valid analyses demonstrate that condition (3) is satisfied. If the levels of constituents measured in the samples of the Filter-cake Sludge do not exceed the levels set forth in Condition (1), then the waste is nonhazardous and may be managed and disposed of in accordance with all applicable solid waste regulations. (3) *Verification Testing Requirements:* Rhodia must perform sample collection and analyses, including quality control procedures, using appropriate methods. As applicable to the method-defined parameters of concern, analyses requiring the use of SW–846 methods incorporated by reference in 40 CFR 260.11 must be used without substitution. As applicable, the SW–846 methods might include Methods 0010, 0011, 0020, 0023A, 0030, 0031, 0040, 0050, 0051, 0060, 0061, 1010A, 1020B, 1110A, 1310B, 1311, 1312, 1320, 1330A, 9010C, 9012B, 9040C, 9045D, 9060A, 9070A (uses EPA Method 1664, Rev. A), 9071B, and 9095B. If EPA judges the process to be effective under the operating conditions used during the initial verification testing, Rhodia may replace the testing required in Condition (3)(A) with the testing required in Condition (3)(B). Rhodia must continue to test as specified in Condition (3)(A) until and unless notified by EPA in writing that testing in Condition (3)(A) may be replaced by Condition (3)(B). (A) *Initial Verification Testing:* At quarterly intervals for one year after the final exclusion is granted, Rhodia must collect and analyze composites of the filter- cake sludge. From Paragraph 1 TCLP must be run on all waste and any constituents for which total concentrations have been identified. Rhodia must conduct a multiple pH leaching procedure on samples collected during the quarterly intervals. Rhodia must perform the TCLP procedure using distilled water and three different pH extraction fluids to simulate disposal under three conditions. Simulate an acidic landfill environment, basic landfill environment and a landfill environment similar to the pH of the waste. Rhodia must report the operational and analytical test data, including quality control information, obtained during this initial period no later than 90 days after the generation of the waste. (B) *Subsequent Verification Testing:* Following termination of the quarterly testing, Rhodia must continue to test a representative composite sample for all constituents listed in Condition (1) on an annual basis (no later than twelve months after the final exclusion). (4) *Changes in Operating Conditions:* If Rhodia significantly changes the process which generate(s) the waste(s) and which may or could affect the composition or type waste(s) generated as established under Condition (1) (by illustration, but not limitation, change in equipment or operating conditions of the treatment process), or its NPDES permit is changed, revoked or not reissued, Rhodia must notify the EPA in writing and may no longer handle the waste generated from the new process or no longer discharge as nonhazardous until the waste meet the delisting levels set in Condition (1) and it has received written approval to do so from EPA. (5) *Data Submittals:* Rhodia must submit the information described below. If Rhodia fails to submit the required data within the specified time or maintain the required records on-site for the specified time, EPA, at its discretion, will consider this sufficient basis to reopen the exclusion as described in Paragraph 6. Rhodia must: (A) Submit the data obtained through Paragraph 3 to Mr. William Gallagher, Chief, Region 6 Delisting Program, EPA, 1445 Ross Avenue, Dallas, Texas 75202- 2733, Mail Code, (6PD-O) within the time specified. (B) Compile records of operating conditions and analytical data from Paragraph (3), summarized, and maintained on-site for a minimum of five years. (C) Furnish these records and data when EPA or the State of Texas request them for inspection.

Table 1—Wastes Excluded from Non-Specific Sources

Facility	Address	Waste description
		(D) Send along with all data a signed copy of the following certification statement, to attest to the truth and accuracy of the data submitted: (i) Under civil and criminal penalty of law for the making or submission of false or fraudulent statements or representations (pursuant to the applicable provisions of the Federal Code, which include, but may not be limited to, 18 U.S.C. 1001 and 42 U.S.C. 6928), I certify that the information contained in or accompanying this document is true, accurate and complete. (ii) As to the (those) identified section(s) of this document for which I cannot personally verify its (their) truth and accuracy, I certify as the company official having supervisory responsibility for the persons who, acting under my direct instructions, made the verification that this information is true, accurate and complete. (iii) If any of this information is determined by EPA in its sole discretion to be false, inaccurate or incomplete, and upon conveyance of this fact to the company, I recognize and agree that this exclusion of waste will be void as if it never had effect or to the extent directed by EPA and that the company will be liable for any actions taken in contravention of the company's RCRA and CERCLA obligations premised upon the company's reliance on the void exclusion. (6) *Reopener Language* (A) If, anytime after disposal of the delisted waste, Rhodia possesses or is otherwise made aware of any environmental data (including but not limited to leachate data or groundwater monitoring data) or any other data relevant to the delisted waste indicating that any constituent identified for the delisting verification testing is at level higher than the delisting level allowed by the Regional Administrator or his delegate in granting the petition, then the facility must report the data, in writing, to the Regional Administrator or his delegate within 10 days of first possessing or being made aware of that data. (B) If the annual testing of the waste does not meet the delisting requirements in Paragraph 1, Rhodia must report the data, in writing, to the Regional Administrator or his delegate within 10 days of first possessing or being made aware of that data. (C) If Rhodia fails to submit the information described in paragraphs (5), (6)(A) or (6)(B) or if any other information is received from any source, the Regional Administrator or his delegate will make a preliminary determination as to whether the reported information requires Agency action to protect human health or the environment. Further action may include suspending, or revoking the exclusion, or other appropriate response necessary to protect human health and the environment. (D) If the Regional Administrator or his delegate determines that the reported information does require Agency action, the Regional Administrator or his delegate will notify the facility in writing of the actions the Regional Administrator or his delegate believes are necessary to protect human health and the environment. The notice shall include a statement of the proposed action and a statement providing the facility with an opportunity to present information as to why the proposed Agency action is not necessary. The facility shall have 10 days from the date of the Regional Administrator or his delegate's notice to present such information. (E) Following the receipt of information from the facility described in paragraph (6)(D) or (if no information is presented under paragraph (6)(D)) the initial receipt of information described in paragraphs (5), (6)(A) or (6)(B), the Regional Administrator or his delegate will issue a final written determination describing the Agency actions that are necessary to protect human health or the environment. Any required action described in the Regional Administrator or his delegate's determination shall become effective immediately, unless the Regional Administrator or his delegate provides otherwise. (7) *Notification Requirements:* Rhodia must do following before transporting the delisted waste: Failure to provide this notification will result in a violation of the delisting petition and a possible revocation of the decision. (A) Provide a one-time written notification to any State Regulatory Agency to which or through which they will transport the delisted waste described above for disposal, 60 days before beginning such activities. (B) Update the one-time written notification if they ship the delisted waste into a different disposal facility.
Saturn Corporation	Spring Hill, Tennessee	Dewatered wastewater treatment plant (WWTP) sludge (EPA Hazardous Waste No. F019) generated at a maximum rate of 3,000 cubic yards per calendar year. The sludge must be disposed in a lined, Subtitle D landfill with leachate collection that is licensed, permitted, or otherwise authorized to accept the delisted WWTP sludge in accordance with 40 CFR part 258. The exclusion becomes effective on December 23, 2005.

Table 1—Wastes Excluded from Non-Specific Sources

Facility	Address	Waste description
		For the exclusion to be valid, Saturn must implement a verification testing program that meets the following conditions:

1. Delisting Levels: The constituent concentrations in an extract of the waste must not exceed the following maximum allowable concentrations in mg/l: antimony—0.494; arsenic—0.224; total chromium—3.71; lead—5.0; nickel—68; thallium—0.211; and zinc—673. Sample collection and analyses, including quality control procedures, must be performed using appropriate methods. As applicable to the method-defined parameters of concern, analyses requiring the use of SW–846 methods incorporated by reference in 40 CFR 260.11 must be used without substitution. As applicable, the SW–846 methods might include Methods 0010, 0011, 0020, 0023A, 0030, 0031, 0040, 0050, 0051, 0060, 0061, 1010A, 1020B, 1110A, 1310B, 1311, 1312, 1320, 1330A, 9010C, 9012B, 9040C, 9045D, 9060A, 9070A, (uses EPA Method 1664, Rev. A), 9071B, and 9095B. Methods must meet Performance Based Measurement System Criteria in which the Data Quality Objectives are to demonstrate that representative samples of Saturn's sludge meet the delisting levels in this condition.
2. Waste Holding and Handling:
   (a) Saturn must accumulate the hazardous waste dewatered WWTP sludge in accordance with the applicable regulations of 40 CFR 262.34 and continue to dispose of the dewatered WWTP sludge as hazardous waste until the results of the first quarterly verification testing are available.
   (b) After the first quarterly verification sampling event described in Condition (3) has been completed and the laboratory data demonstrates that no constituent is present in the sample at a level which exceeds the delisting levels set in Condition (1), Saturn can manage and dispose of the dewatered WWTP sludge as nonhazardous according to all applicable solid waste regulations.
   (c) If constituent levels in any sample taken by Saturn exceed any of the delisting levels set in Condition (1), Saturn must do the following:
      (i) Notify EPA in accordance with Condition (7) and
      (ii) Manage and dispose the dewatered WWTP sludge as hazardous waste generated under Subtitle C of RCRA.
3. Quarterly Testing Requirements: Upon this exclusion becoming final, Saturn may perform quarterly analytical testing by sampling and analyzing the dewatered WWTP sludge as follows:
   (i) Collect one representative composite sample (consisting of four grab samples) of the hazardous waste dewatered WWTP sludge at any time after EPA grants the final delisting. In addition, collect the second, third, and fourth quarterly samples at approximately ninety (90)-day intervals after EPA grants the final exclusion.
   (ii) Analyze the samples for all constituents listed in Condition (1). Any roll-offs from which the composite sample is taken exceeding the delisting levels listed in Condition (1) must be disposed as hazardous waste in a Subtitle C landfill.
   (iii) Within forty-five (45) days after taking its first quarterly sample, Saturn will report its first quarterly analytical test data to EPA and will include the certification statement required in condition (6). If levels of constituents measured in the sample of the dewatered WWTP sludge do not exceed the levels set forth in Condition (1) of this exclusion, Saturn can manage and dispose the nonhazardous dewatered WWTP sludge according to all applicable solid waste regulations.
4. Annual Verification Testing:
   (i) If Saturn completes the quarterly testing specified in Condition (3) above, and no sample contains a constituent with a level which exceeds the limits set forth in Condition (1), Saturn may begin annual verification testing on an annual basis. Saturn must collect and analyze one sample of the WWTP sludge on an annual basis as follows: Saturn must test one representative composite sample of the dewatered WWTP sludge for all constituents listed in Condition (1) at least once per calendar year.
   (ii) The sample collected for annual verification testing shall be a representative composite sample consisting of four grab samples that will be collected in accordance with the appropriate methods described in Condition (1).
   (iii) The sample for the annual testing for the second and subsequent annual testing events shall be collected within the same calendar month as the first annual verification sample. Saturn will report the results of the annual verification testing to EPA on an annual basis and will include the certification statement required by Condition (6).

Table 1—Wastes Excluded from Non-Specific Sources

Facility	Address	Waste description
		5. Changes in Operating Conditions: Saturn must notify EPA in writing when significant changes in the manufacturing or wastewater treatment processes are implemented. EPA will determine whether these changes will result in additional constituents of concern. If so, EPA will notify Saturn in writing that Saturn's sludge must be managed as hazardous waste F019 until Saturn has demonstrated that the wastes meet the delisting levels set forth in Condition (1) and any levels established by EPA for the additional constituents of concern, and Saturn has received written approval from EPA. If EPA determines that the changes do not result in additional constituents of concern, EPA will notify Saturn, in writing, that Saturn must verify that Saturn's sludge continues to meet Condition (1) delisting levels. 6. Data Submittals: Saturn must submit data obtained through verification testing at Saturn or as required by other conditions of this rule to: Chief, North Section, RCRA Enforcement and Compliance Branch, Waste Management Division, U.S. Environmental Protection Agency Region 4, Sam Nunn Atlanta Federal Center, 61 Forsyth Street SW., Atlanta, Georgia 30303. If Saturn fails to submit the required data within the specified time or maintain the required records on-site for the specified time, the EPA, at its discretion, will consider this sufficient basis to re-open the exclusion as described in Condition (7). Saturn must: (A) Submit the data obtained through Condition (3) within the time specified. The quarterly verification data must be submitted to EPA in accordance with Condition (3). The annual verification data and certification statement of proper disposal must be submitted to EPA annually upon the anniversary of the effective date of this exclusion. All data must be accompanied by a signed copy of the certification statement in 40 CFR 260.22(i)(12). (B) Compile, Summarize, and Maintain Records: Saturn must compile, summarize, and maintain at Saturn records of operating conditions and analytical data records of analytical data from Condition (3), summarized, and maintained on-site for a minimum of five years. Saturn must furnish these records and data when either the EPA or the State of Tennessee requests them for inspection. (C) Send along with all data a signed copy of the following certification statement, to attest to the truth and accuracy of the data submitted: "I certify under penalty of law that I have personally examined and am familiar with the information submitted in this demonstration and all attached documents, and that, based on my inquiry of those individuals immediately responsible for getting the information, I believe that the submitted information is true, accurate, and complete. I am aware that there are significant penalties for sending false information, including the possibility of fine and imprisonment." 7. Reopener. (A) If, at any time after disposal of the delisted waste, Saturn possesses or is otherwise made aware of any data (including but not limited to leachate data or groundwater monitoring data) relevant to the delisted WWTP sludge at Saturn indicating that any constituent is at a level in the leachate higher than the specified delisting level or TCLP regulatory level, then Saturn must report the data, in writing, to the Regional Administrator within ten (10) days of first possessing or being made aware of that data. (B) Based upon the information described in Paragraph (A) and any other information received from any source, the EPA Regional Administrator will make a preliminary determination as to whether the reported information requires EPA action to protect human health or the environment. Further action may include suspending, or revoking the exclusion, or other appropriate response necessary to protect human health and the environment. (C) If the Regional Administrator determines that the reported information does require EPA action, the Regional Administrator will notify Saturn in writing of the actions the Regional Administrator believes are necessary to protect human health and the environment. The notification shall include a statement of the proposed action and a statement providing Saturn with an opportunity to present information as to why the proposed EPA action is not necessary. Saturn shall have ten (10) days from the date of the Regional Administrator's notice to present the information. (D) Following the receipt of information from Saturn, or if Saturn presents no further information after 10 days, the Regional Administrator will issue a final written determination describing the EPA actions that are necessary to protect human health or the environment. Any required action described in the Regional Administrator's determination shall become effective immediately, unless the Regional Administrator provides otherwise. 8. Notification Requirements: Before transporting the delisted waste, Saturn must provide a one-time written notification to any State Regulatory Agency to which or through which it will transport the delisted WWTP sludge for disposal. The notification will be updated if Saturn transports the delisted WWTP sludge to a different disposal facility. Failure to provide this notification will result in a violation of the delisting variance and a possible revocation of the decision.

Table 1—Wastes Excluded from Non-Specific Sources

Facility	Address	Waste description
Savannah River Site (SRS)	Aiken, South Carolina	Vitrified waste (EPA Hazardous Waste Nos. F006 and F028) that the United States Department of Energy Savannah River Operations Office (DOE–SR) generated by treating the following waste streams from the M-Area of the Savannah River Site (SRS) in Aiken, South Carolina, as designated in the SRS Site Treatment Plan: W–004, Plating Line Sludge from Supernate Treatment; W–995, Mark 15 Filter Cake; W–029, Sludge Treatability Samples (glass and cementitious); W–031, Uranium/ Chromium Solution; W–037, High Nickel Plating Line Sludge; W–038, Plating Line Sump Material; W–039, Nickel Plating Line Solution; W–048, Soils from Spill Remediation and Sampling Programs; W–054, Uranium/Lead Solution; W–082, Soils from Chemicals, Metals, and Pesticides Pits Excavation; and Dilute Effluent Treatment Facility (DETF) Filtercake (no Site Treatment Plan code). This is a onetime exclusion for 538 cubic yards of waste (hereinafter referred to as "DOE–SR Vitrified Waste") that was generated from 1996 through 1999 and 0.12 cubic yard of cementitious treatability samples (hereinafter referred to as "CTS") generated from 1988 through 1991 (EPA Hazardous Waste No. F006). The one-time exclusion for these wastes is contingent on their being disposed in a low-level radioactive waste landfill, in accordance with the Atomic Energy Act, after [insert date of final rule.] DOE–SR has demonstrated that concentrations of toxic constituents in the DOE–SR Vitrified Waste and CTS do not exceed the following levels: (1) *TCLP Concentrations:* All leachable concentrations for these metals did not exceed the Land Disposal Restrictions (LDR) Universal Treatment Standards (UTS): (mg/l TCLP): Arsenic—5.0; Barium—21; Beryllium—1.22; Cadmium— 0.11; Chromium—0.60; Lead—0.75; Nickel—11; and Silver—0.14. In addition, none of the metals in the DOE–SR Vitrified Waste exceeded the allowable delisting levels of the EPA, Region 6 Delisting Risk Assessment Software (DRAS): (mg/l TCLP): Arsenic—0.0649; Barium—100.0; Beryllium—0.40; Cadmium—1.0; Chromium—5.0; Lead—5.0; Nickel—10.0; and Silver—5.0. These metal concentrations were measured in the waste leachate obtained by the method specified in 40 CFR 261.24. *Total Concentrations in Unextracted Waste:* The total concentrations in the DOE–SR Vitrified Waste, not the waste leachate, did not exceed the following levels (mg/kg): Arsenic—10; Barium—200; Beryllium—10; Cadmium—10; Chromium—500; Lead—200; Nickel—10,000; Silver—20; Acetonitrile—1.0, which is below the LDR UTS of 38 mg/kg; and Fluoride—1.0 (2) *Data Records:* Records of analytical data for the petitioned waste must be maintained by DOE–SR for a minimum of three years, and must be furnished upon request by EPA or the State of South Carolina, and made available for inspection. Failure to maintain the required records for the specified time will be considered by EPA, at its discretion, sufficient basis to revoke the exclusion to the extent directed by EPA. All data must be maintained with a signed copy of the certification statement in 40 CFR 260.22(i)(12). (3) *Reopener Language:* (A) If, at any time after disposal of the delisted waste, DOE–SR possesses or is otherwise made aware of any environmental data (including but not limited to leachate data or groundwater monitoring data) or any other data relevant to the delisted waste indicating that any constituent is identified at a level higher than the delisting level allowed by EPA in granting the petition, DOE–SR must report the data, in writing, to EPA within 10 days of first possessing or being made aware of that data. (B) Based on the information described in paragraph (3)(A) and any other information received from any source, EPA will make a preliminary determination as to whether the reported information requires that EPA take action to protect human health or the environment. Further action may include suspending or revoking the exclusion, or other appropriate response necessary to protect human health and the environment. (C) If EPA determines that the reported information does require Agency action, EPA will notify the facility in writing of the action believed necessary to protect human health and the environment. The notice shall include a statement of the proposed action and a statement providing DOE–SR with an opportunity to present information as to why the proposed action is not necessary. DOE–SR shall have 10 days from the date of EPA's notice to present such information. *Publisher's Note:* The reference to paragraph (3)(D) in the following paragraph should reference paragraph (3)(C) instead and paragraph (3)(E) below has been mislabeled and should be paragraph (3)(D). (E) Following the receipt of information from DOE–SR, as described in paragraph (3)(D), or if no such information is received within 10 days, EPA will issue a final written determination describing the Agency actions that are necessary to protect human health or the environment, given the information received in accordance with paragraphs (3)(A) or (3)(B). Any required action described in EPA's determination shall become effective immediately, unless EPA provides otherwise. (4) *Notification Requirements:* DOE–SR must provide a one-time written notification to any State Regulatory Agency in a State to which or through which the delisted waste described above will be transported, at least 60 days prior to the commencement of such activities. Failure to provide such a notification will result in a violation of the delisting conditions and a possible revocation of the decision to delist.

Table 1—Wastes Excluded from Non-Specific Sources

Facility	Address	Waste description
Shell Oil Company	Deer Park, TX	North Pond Sludge (EPA Hazardous Waste No. F037) generated one time at a volume of 15,000 cubic yards August 23, 2005 and disposed in a Subtitle D landfill. This is a one time exclusion and applies to 15,000 cubic yards of North Pond Sludge. (1) Reopener: (A) If, anytime after disposal of the delisted waste, Shell possesses or is otherwise made aware of any environmental data (including but not limited to leachate data or ground water monitoring data) or any other data relevant to the delisted waste indicating that any constituent identified for the delisting verification testing is at level higher than the delisting level allowed by the Division Director in granting the petition, then the facility must report the data, in writing, to the Division Director within 10 days of first possessing or being made aware of that data. (B) If Shell fails to submit the information described in paragraph (A) or if any other information is received from any source, the Division Director will make a preliminary determination as to whether the reported information requires EPA action to protect human health or the environment. Further action may include suspending, or revoking the exclusion, or other appropriate response necessary to protect human health and the environment. (C) If the Division Director determines that the reported information does require EPA action, the Division Director will notify the facility in writing of the actions the Division Director believes are necessary to protect human health and the environment. The notice shall include a statement of the proposed action and a statement providing the facility with an opportunity to present information as to why the proposed EPA action is not necessary. The facility shall have 10 days from the date of the Division Director's notice to present such information. (D) Following the receipt of information from the facility described in paragraph (C) or if no information is presented under paragraph (C), the Division Director will issue a final written determination describing the actions that are necessary to protect human health or the environment. Any required action described in the Division Director's determination shall become effective immediately, unless the Division Director provides otherwise. (2) Notification Requirements: Shell must do the following before transporting the delisted waste: Failure to provide this notification will result in a violation of the delisting petition and a possible revocation of the decision. (A) Provide a one-time written notification to any state regulatory agency to which or through which they will transport the delisted waste described above for disposal, 60 days before beginning such activities. (B) Update the one-time written notification, if they ship the delisted waste to a different disposal facility. (C) Failure to provide this notification will result in a violation of the delisting variance and a possible revocation of the decision.
Shell Oil Company	Deer Park, TX	Multi-source landfill leachate (EPA Hazardous Waste No. F039) generated at a maximum annual rate of 3.36 million gallons (16,619 cu. yards) per calendar year after August 23, 2005 and disposed in accordance with the TPDES permit. The delisting levels set do not relieve Shell Oil Company of its duty to comply with the limits set in its TPDES permit. For the exclusion to be valid, Shell Oil Company must implement a verification testing program that meets the following paragraphs: (1) Delisting Levels: All total concentrations for those constituents must not exceed the following levels (mg/l). The petitioner must analyze the aqueous waste on a total basis to measure constituents in the multi-source landfill leachate. Multi-source landfill leachate (i) Inorganic Constituents Antimony—0.0204; Arsenic—0.385; Barium—2.92; Copper—418.00; Chromium—5.0; Cobalt—2.25; Nickel—1.13; Selenium—0.0863; Thallium—0.005; Vanadium—0.838 (ii) Organic Constituents Acetone—1.46; Acetophenone—1.58; Benzene—0.0222; p-Cresol—0.0788; Bis(2-ethylhexyl)phthlate—15800.00; Dichloroethane, 1,2—0.0803; Ethylbenzene—4.51; Fluorene—1.87; Napthalene—1.05; Phenol—9.46; Phenanthrene—1.36; Pyridine—0.0146; 2,3,7,8-TCDD equivalents as TEQ—0.0000926; Toluene—4.43; Trichloropropane—0.000574; Xylenes (total)—97.60 (2) Waste Management: (A) Shell Oil Company must manage as hazardous all multi-source landfill leachate generated, until it has completed initial verification testing described in paragraph (3)(A) and (B), as appropriate, and valid analyses show that paragraph (1) is satisfied.

Table 1—Wastes Excluded from Non-Specific Sources

Facility	Address	Waste description
		(B) Levels of constituents measured in the samples of the multi-source landfill leachate that do not exceed the levels set forth in paragraph (1) are non-hazardous. Shell Oil Company can manage and dispose of the non-hazardous multi-source landfill leachate according to all applicable solid waste regulations. (C) If constituent levels in a sample exceed any of the delisting levels set in paragraph (1), Shell Oil Company can collect one additional sample and perform expedited analyses to verify if the constituent exceeds the delisting level. If this sample confirms the exceedance, Shell Oil Company must, from that point forward, treat the waste as hazardous until it is demonstrated that the waste again meets the levels in paragraph (1). (D) If the facility has not treated the waste, Shell Oil Company must manage and dispose of the waste generated under Subtitle C of RCRA from the time that it becomes aware of any exceed-ance. (E) Upon completion of the Verification Testing described in paragraph 3(A) and (B) as appropriate and the transmittal of the results to EPA, and if the testing results meet the requirements of paragraph (1), Shell Oil Company may proceed to manage its multi-source landfill leachate as non-hazardous waste. If Subsequent Verification Testing indicates an exceedance of the delisting levels in paragraph (1), Shell Oil Company must manage the multi-source landfill leachate as a hazardous waste until two consecutive quarterly testing samples show levels below the delisting levels in Table I. (3) Verification Testing Requirements: Shell Oil Company must perform sample collection and analyses, including quality control procedures, using appropriate methods. As applicable to the method-defined parameters of concern, analyses requiring the use of SW–846 methods incorporated by reference in 40 CFR 260.11 must be used without substitution. As applicable, the SW–846 methods might include Methods 0010, 0011, 0020, 0023A, 0030, 0031, 0040, 0050, 0051, 0060, 0061, 1010A, 1020B, 1110A, 1310B, 1311, 1312, 1320, 1330A, 9010C, 9012B, 9040C, 9045D, 9060A, 9070A (uses EPA Method 1664, Rev. A), 9071B, and 9095B. Methods used must meet Performance Based Measurement System Criteria in which the Data Quality Objectives demonstrate that representative samples of the Shell-Deer Park multi-source landfill leachate are collected and meet the delisting levels in paragraph (1). (A) Initial Verification Testing: After EPA grants the final exclusion, Shell Oil Company must do the following: (i) Within 60 days of this exclusions becoming final, collect four samples, before disposal, of the multi-source landfill leachate. (ii) The samples are to be analyzed and compared against the delisting levels in paragraph (1). (iii) Within sixty (60) days after this exclusion becomes final, Shell Oil Company will report initial verification analytical test data for the multi-source landfill leachate, including analytical quality control information for the first thirty (30) days of operation after this exclusion becomes final. If levels of constituents measured in the samples of the multi-source landfill leachate that do not exceed the levels set forth in paragraph (1) are also non-hazardous in two consecutive quarters after the first thirty (30) days of operation after this exclusion become effective, Shell Oil Company can manage and dispose of the multi-source landfill leachate according to all applicable solid waste regulations. (B) Subsequent Verification Testing: Following written notification by EPA, Shell Oil Company may substitute the testing conditions in (3)(B) for (3)(A). Shell Oil Company must continue to monitor operating conditions, and analyze one representative sample of the multi-source landfill leachate for each quarter of operation during the first year of waste generation. The sample must represent the waste generated during the quarter. After the first year of analytical sampling verification sampling can be performed on a single annual sample of the multi-source landfill leachate. The results are to be compared to the delisting levels in paragraph (1). (C) Termination of Testing: (i) After the first year of quarterly testing, if the delisting levels in paragraph (1) are being met, Shell Oil Company may then request that EPA not require quarterly testing. After EPA notifies Shell Oil Company in writing, the company may end quarterly testing. (ii) Following cancellation of the quarterly testing, Shell Oil Company must continue to test a representative sample for all constituents listed in paragraph (1) annually. (4) Changes in Operating Conditions: If Shell Oil Company significantly changes the process described in its petition or starts any processes that generate(s) the waste that may or could significantly affect the composition or type of waste generated as established under paragraph (1) (by illustration, but not limitation, changes in equipment or operating conditions of the treatment process), it must notify EPA in writing; it may no longer handle the wastes generated from the new process as nonhazardous until the wastes meet the delisting levels set in paragraph (1) and it has received written approval to do so from EPA.

Table 1—Wastes Excluded from Non-Specific Sources

Facility	Address	Waste description
		(5) Data Submittals: Shell Oil Company must submit the information described below. If Shell Oil Company fails to submit the required data within the specified time or maintain the required records on-site for the specified time, EPA, at its discretion, will consider this sufficient basis to reopen the exclusion as described in paragraph 6. Shell Oil Company must: (A) Submit the data obtained through paragraph 3 to the Section Chief, Region 6 Corrective Action and Waste Minimization Section, EPA, 1445 Ross Avenue, Dallas, Texas 75202–2733, Mail Code, (6PD–C) within the time specified. (B) Compile records of operating conditions and analytical data from paragraph (3), summarized, and maintained on-site for a minimum of five years. (C) Furnish these records and data when EPA or the state of Texas request them for inspection. (D) Send along with all data a signed copy of the following certification statement, to attest to the truth and accuracy of the data submitted: Under civil and criminal penalty of law for the making or submission of false or fraudulent statements or representations (pursuant to the applicable provisions of the Federal Code, which include, but may not be limited to, 18 U.S.C. 1001 and 42 U.S.C. 6928), I certify that the information contained in or accompanying this document is true, accurate and complete. As to the (those) identified section(s) of this document for which I cannot personally verify its (their) truth and accuracy, I certify as the company official having supervisory responsibility for the persons who, acting under my direct instructions, made the verification that this information is true, accurate and complete. If any of this information is determined by EPA in its sole discretion to be false, inaccurate or incomplete, and upon conveyance of this fact to the company, I recognize and agree that this exclusion of waste will be void as if it never had effect or to the extent directed by EPA and that the company will be liable for any actions taken in contravention of the company's RCRA and CERCLA obligations premised upon the company's reliance on the void exclusion. (6) Reopener: (A) If, anytime after disposal of the delisted waste, Shell Oil Company possesses or is otherwise made aware of any environmental data (including but not limited to leachate data or groundwater monitoring data) or any other data relevant to the delisted waste indicating that any constituent identified for the delisting verification testing is at a level higher than the delisting level allowed by the Division Director in granting the petition, then the facility must report the data, in writing, to the Division Director within 10 days of first possessing or being made aware of that data. (B) If the annual testing of the waste does not meet the delisting requirements in paragraph 1, Shell Oil Company must report the data, in writing, to the Division Director within 10 days of first possessing or being made aware of that data. (C) If Shell Oil Company fails to submit the information described in paragraphs (5),(6)(A) or (6)(B) or if any other information is received from any source, the Division Director will make a preliminary determination as to whether the reported information requires EPA action to protect human health and/or the environment. Further action may include suspending, or revoking the exclusion, or other appropriate response necessary to protect human health and the environment. (D) If the Division Director determines that the reported information does require action, he will notify the facility in writing of the actions the Division Director believes are necessary to protect human health and the environment. The notice shall include a statement of the proposed action and a statement providing the facility with an opportunity to present information as to why the proposed action by EPA is not necessary. The facility shall have 10 days from the date of the Division Director's notice to present such information. (E) Following the receipt of information from the facility described in paragraph (6)(D) or if no information is presented under paragraph (6)(D), the Division Director will issue a final written determination describing the actions that are necessary to protect human health and/or the environment. Any required action described in the Division Director's determination shall become effective immediately, unless the Division Director provides otherwise. (7) Notification Requirements: Shell Oil Company must do the following before transporting the delisted waste. Failure to provide this notification will result in a violation of the delisting petition and a possible revocation of the decision. (A) Provide a one-time written notification to any state regulatory agency to which or through which it will transport the delisted waste described above for disposal, 60 days before beginning such activities.

Table 1—Wastes Excluded from Non-Specific Sources

Facility	Address	Waste description
		(B) Update the one-time written notification if it ships the delisted waste into a different disposal facility. (C) Failure to provide this notification will result in a violation of the delisting exclusion and a possible revocation of the decision.
Siegel-Robert, Inc	St. Louis, MO	Wastewater treatment sludge (EPA Hazardous Waste No. F006) generated from electroplating operations after November 27, 1985.
Southeastern Public Service Authority (SPSA) and Onyx Environmental Service (Onyx)	Suffolk, Virginia	Combustion ash generated from the burning of spent solvent methyl ethyl ketone (Hazardous Waste Number F005) and disposed in a Subtitle D landfill. This is a one-time exclusion for 1410 cubic yards of ash and is effective after September 11, 2003. (1) *Reopener Language* (a) If SPSA and/or Onyx discovers that any condition or assumption related to the characterization of the excluded waste which was used in the evaluation of the petition or that was predicted through modeling is not as reported in the petition, then SPSA and/or Onyx must report any information relevant to that condition or assumption, in writing, to the Regional Administrator and the Virginia Department of Environmental Quality within 10 calendar days of discovering that information. (b) Upon receiving information described in paragraph (a) of this section, regardless of its source, the Regional Administrator will determine whether the reported condition requires further action. Further action may include repealing the exclusion, modifying the exclusion, or other appropriate action deemed necessary to protect human health or the environment. (2) *Notification Requirements* In the event that the delisted waste is transported off-site for disposal, SPSA/Onyx must provide a one-time written notification to any State Regulatory Agency to which or through which the delisted waste described above will be transported at least sixty (60) calendar days prior to the commencement of such activities. Failure to provide such notification will be deemed to be a violation of this exclusion and may result in revocation of the decision and other enforcement action.
Square D Company	Oxford, Ohio	Dewatered filter press sludge (EPA Hazardous Waste No. F006) generated from electroplating operations after August 15, 1986.
Syntex Agribusiness	Springfield, MO	Kiln ash, cyclone ash, separator sludge, and filtered wastewater (except spent activiated carbon) (EPA Hazardous Waste No. F020 generated during the treatment of wastewater treatment sludge by the EPA's Mobile Incineration System at the Denney Farm Site in McDowell, Missouri after June 2, 1988, so long as: (1) The incinerator is monitored continuously and is in compliance with operating permit conditions. Should the incinerator fail to comply with the permit conditions relevant to the mechanical operation of the incinerator, Syntex must test the residues generated during the run when the failure occurred according to the requirements of Conditions (2) through (6), regardless of whether or not the demonstration in Condition (7) has been made. (2) Four grab samples of wastewater must be composited from the volume of filtered wastewater collected after each eight hour run and, prior to disposal the composite samples must be analyzed for the EP toxic metals, nickel, and cyanide. If arsenic, chromium, lead, and silver EP leachate test results exceed 0.61 ppm; barium levels exceed 12 ppm; cadmium and selenium levels exceed 0.12 ppm; mercury levels exceed 0.02 ppm; nickel levels exceed 6.1 ppm; or cyanide levels exceed 2.4 ppm, the wastewater must be retreated to achieve these levels or must be disposed in accordance with all applicable hazardous waste regulations. Analyses must be performed using appropriate methods. As applicable to the method- defined parameters of concern, analyses requiring the use of SW–846 methods incorporated by reference in 40 CFR 260.11 must be used without substitution. As applicable, the SW–846 methods might include Methods 0010, 0011, 0020, 0023A, 0030, 0031, 0040, 0050, 0051, 0060, 0061, 1010A, 1020B, 1110A, 1310B, 1311, 1312, 1320, 1330A, 9010C, 9012B, 9040C, 9045D, 9060A, 9070A (uses EPA Method 1664, Rev. A), 9071B, and 9095B.

Table 1—Wastes Excluded from Non-Specific Sources

Facility	Address	Waste description
		(3) One grab sample must be taken from each drum of kiln and cyclone ash generated during each eight-hour run; all grabs collected during a given eight-hour run must then be composited to form one composite sample. A composite sample of four grab samples of the separator sludge must be collected at the end of each eight-hour run. Prior to the disposal of the residues from each eight-hour run, an EP leachate test must be performed on these composite samples and the leachate analyzed for the EP toxic metals, nickel, and cyanide (using a distilled water extraction for the cyanide extraction) to demonstrate that the following maximum allowable treatment residue concentrations listed below are not exceeded. Analyses must be performed using appropriate methods. As applicable to the method-defined parameters of concern, analyses requiring the use of SW–846 methods incorporated by reference in 40 CFR 260.11 must be used without substitution. As applicable, the SW–846 methods might include Methods 0010, 0011, 0020, 0023A, 0030, 0031, 0040, 0050, 0051, 0060, 0061, 1010A, 1020B, 1110A, 1310B, 1311, 1312, 1320, 1330A, 9010C, 9012B, 9040C, 9045D, 9060A, 9070A (uses EPA Method 1664, Rev. A), 9071B, and 9095B. Any residues which exceed any of the levels listed below must be retreated to achieve these levels or must be disposed in accordance with all applicable hazardous waste regulations. Maximum Allowable Solids Treatment Residue EP Leachate Concentrations (mg/L) Arsenic—1.6, Barium—32, Cadmium—0.32, Chromium—1.6, Lead—1.6, Mercury—0.065, Nickel—16, Selenium—0.32, Silver—1.6, Cyanide—6.5.
		(4) If Syntex stabilizes any of the kiln and cyclone ash or separator sludge, a Portland cement-type stabilization process must be used and Syntex must collect a composite sample of four grab samples from each batch of stabilized waste. An MEP leachate test must be performed on these composite samples and the leachate analyzed for the EP toxic metals, nickel, and cyanide (using a distilled water extraction for the cyanide leachate analysis) to demonstrate that the maximum allowable treatment residue concentrations listed in condition (3) are not exceeded during any run of the MEP extraction. Analyses must be performed using appropriate methods. As applicable to the method-defined parameters of concern, analyses requiring the use of SW–846 methods incorporated by reference in 40 CFR 260.11 must be used without substitution. As applicable, the SW–846 methods might include Methods 0010, 0011, 0020, 0023A, 0030, 0031, 0040, 0050, 0051, 0060, 0061, 1010A, 1020B, 1110A, 1310B, 1311, 1312, 1320, 1330A, 9010C, 9012B, 9040C 9045D, 9060A, 9070A (uses EPA Method 1664, Rev. A), 9071B, and 9095B. Any residues which exceed any of the levels listed in Condition (3) must be retreated to achieve these levels or must be disposed in accordance with all applicable hazardous waste regulations. (If the residues are stabilized, the analyses required in this condition supercede the analyses required in Condition (3).)
		(5) Syntex must generate, prior to disposal of residues, verification data from each eight hour run from each treatment residue (i.e., kiln and cyclone ash, separator sludge, and filtered wastewater) to demonstrate that the maximum allowable treatment residue concentrations listed below are not exceeded. Samples must be collected as specified in Conditions (2) and (3). Analyses must be performed using appropriate methods. As applicable to the method-defined parameters of concern, analyses requiring the use of SW–846 methods incorporated by reference in 40 CFR 260.11 must be used without substitution. As applicable, the SW–846 methods might include Methods 0010, 0011, 0020, 0023A, 0030, 0031, 0040, 0050, 0051, 0060, 0061, 1010A, 1020B, 1110A, 1310B, 1311, 1312, 1320, 1330A, 9010C, 9012B, 9040C, 9045D, 9060A, 9070A (uses EPA Method 1664, Rev. A), 9071B, and 9095B. Any solid or liquid residues which exceed any of the levels listed below must be retreated to achieve these levels or must be disposed in accordance with Subtitle C of RCRA. Maximum Allowable Wastewater Concentrations (ppm): Benz(a)anthracene—1×10^{-4} Benzo(a)pyrene—4×10^{-5} Benzo(b)fluoranthene—2×10^{-4} Chloroform—0.07 Chrysene—0.002 Dibenz(a,h)anthracene—9×10^{-6} 1,2-Dichloroethane—0.06 Dichloromethane—0.06 Indeno(1,2,3-cd)pyrene—0.002 Polychlorinated biphenyls—1×10^{-4} 1,2,4,5-Tetrachlorobenzene—0.13 2,3,4,6-Tetrachlorophenol—12 Toluene—120 Trichloroethylene—0.04 2,4,5-Trichlorophenol—49 2,4,6-Trichlorophenol—0.02

Table 1—Wastes Excluded from Non-Specific Sources

Facility	Address	Waste description
		Maximum Allowable Solid Treatment Residue Concentrations (ppm): Benz(a)anthracene—1.1 Benzo(a)pyrene—0.43 benzo(b)fluoranthene—1.8 Chloroform—5.4 Chrysene—170 Dibenz(a,h)anthracene—0.083 Dichloromethane—2.4 1,2-Dichloroethane—4.1 Indeno(1,2,3-cd)pyrene—330 Polychlorinated biphenyls—0.31 1,2,4,5-Tetrachlorobenzene—720 Trichloroethylene—6.6 2,4,6-Trichlorophenol—3.9 (6) Syntex must generate, prior to disposal of residues, verification data from each eight-hour run for each treatment residue (i.e., kiln and cyclone ash, separator sludge, and filtered wastewater) to demonstrate that the residues do not contain tetra-, penta-, or hexachlorodibenzo-p-dioxins or furans at levels of regulatory concern. Samples must be collected as specified in Conditions (2) and (3). The TCDD equivalent levels for wastewaters must be less than 2 ppq and less than 5 ppt for the solid treatment residues. Any residues with detected dioxins or furans in excess of these levels must be retreated or must be disposed as acutely hazardous. For this analysis, Syntex must use appropriate methods. For tetra- and pentachloronated dioxin and furan homologs, the maximum practical quantitation limit must not exceed 15 ppt for solids and 120 ppq for wastewaters. For hexachlorinated homologs, the maximum practical quantitation limit must not exceed 37 ppt for solids and 300 ppq for wastewaters. (7)(A) The test data from Conditions (1), (2), (3), (4), (5) and (6) must be kept on file by Syntex for inspection purposes and must be compiled, summarized, and submitted to the Section Chief, Variances Section, PSPD/ OSW (WH-563), US EPA, 1200 Pennsylvania Ave., NW, Washington, DC 20460 by certified mail on a monthly basis and when the treatment of the lagoon sludge is concluded. All data submitted will be placed in the RCRA docket. (B) The testing requirements for Conditions (2), (3), (4), (5), and (6) will continue until Syntex provides the Section Chief, Variances Section, with the results of four consecutive batch analyses for the petitioned wastes, none of which exceed the maximum allowable treatment residue concentrations listed in these conditions and the Section Chief, Variances Section, notifies Syntex that the conditions have been lifted. (8) Syntex must provide a signed copy of the following certification statement when submitting data in response to the conditions listed above: "Under civil and criminal penalty of law for the making or submission of false or fraudulent statements or representations, I certify that the information contained in or accompanying this document is true, accurate, and complete. As to the (those) identified section(s) of this document for which I cannot personally verify its (their) accuracy, I certify as the company official having supervisory responsibility for the persons who, acting under my direct instructions, made the verification that this information is true, accurate and complete."
SR of Tennessee	Ripley, TN	Dewatered wastewater treatment sludges (EPA Hazardous Waste No. F006) generated from the copper, nickel, and chromium electroplating of plastic parts after November 17, 1986.
Tenneco Automotive	Paragould, AR	Stabilized sludge from electroplating operations, excavated from the Finch Road Landfill and currently stored in containment cells by Tenneco (EPA Hazardous Waste Nos. F006). This is a one-time exclusion for 1,800 cubic yards of stabilized sludge when it is disposed of in a Subtitle D landfill. This exclusion was published on August 9, 2001. (1) *Reopener Language:* (A) If, anytime after disposal of the delisted waste, Tenneco possesses or is otherwise made aware of any environmental data (including but not limited to leachate data or groundwater monitoring data) or any other data relevant to the delisted waste indicating that any constituent identified for the delisting verification testing is at level higher than the delisting level allowed by the Regional Administrator or his delegate in granting the petition, then the facility must report the data, in writing, to the Regional Administrator or his delegate within 10 days of first possessing or being made aware of that data. (B) If Tenneco fails to submit the information described in (2)(A) or if any other information is received from any source, the Regional Administrator or his delegate will make a preliminary determination as to whether the reported information requires Agency action to protect human health or the environment. Further action may include suspending, or revoking the exclusion, or other appropriate response necessary to protect human health and the environment.

Table 1—Wastes Excluded from Non-Specific Sources

Facility	Address	Waste description
		(C) If the Regional Administrator or his delegate determines the reported information does require Agency action, the Regional Administrator or his delegate will notify the facility in writing of the actions the Regional Administrator or his delegate believes are necessary to protect human health and the environment. The notice shall include a statement of the proposed action and a statement providing the facility with an opportunity to present information as to why the proposed Agency action is not necessary. The facility shall have 10 days from the date of the Regional Administrator or his delegate's notice to present such information. (D) Following the receipt of information from the facility described in (1)(C) or (if no information is presented under (1)(C)) the initial receipt of information described in (1)(A), the Regional Administrator or his delegate will issue a final written determination describing the Agency actions that are necessary to protect human health or the environment. Any required action described in the Regional Administrator or his delegate's determination shall become effective immediately, unless the Regional Administrator or his delegate provides otherwise. (2) *Notification Requirements:* Tenneco must do following before transporting the delisted waste off-site: Failure to provide this notification will result in a violation of the delisting petition and a possible revocation of the exclusion. (A) Provide a one-time written notification to any State Regulatory Agency to which or through which they will transport the delisted waste described above for disposal, 60 days before beginning such activities. (B) Update the one-time written notification if Tenneco ships the delisted waste to a different disposal facility.
Tennessee Electroplating	Ripley, Tennessee	Dewatered wastewater treatment sludges (EPA Hazardous Waste Nos. F006) generated from electroplating operations after November 17, 1986. To ensure chromium levels do not exceed the regulatory standards there must be continuous batch testing of the filter press sludge for chromium for 45 days after the exclusion is granted. Each batch of treatment residue must be representatively sampled and tested using the EP toxicity test for chromium. This data must be kept on file at the facility for inspection purposes. If the extract levels exceed 0.922 ppm of chromium the waste must be managed and disposed of as hazardous. If these conditions are not met, the exclusion does not apply. This exclusion does not apply to sludges in any on- site impoundments as of this date.
Tennessee Electroplating	Ripley, TN	Wastewater treatment sludge (EPA Hazardous Waste No. F006) generated from electroplating operations and contained in an on- site surface impoundment (maximum volume of 6,300 cubic yards). This is a one-time exclusion. This exclusion was published on April 8, 1991.
Texas Eastman	Longview, Texas	Incinerator ash (at a maximum generation of 7,000 cubic yards per calendar year) generated from the incineration of sludge from the wastewater treatment plant (EPA Hazardous Waste No. D001, D003, D018, D019, D021, D022, D027, D028, D029, D030, D032, D033, D034, D035, D036, D038, D039, D040, F001, F002, F003, F005, and that is disposed of in Subtitle D landfills after September 25, 1996. Texas Eastman must implement a testing program that meets the following conditions for the petition to be valid: 1. *Delisting Levels:* All leachable concentrations for those metals must not exceed the following levels (mg/l). Metal concentrations must be measured in the waste leachate by the method specified in 40 CFR §261.24. (A) Inorganic Constituents Antimony—0.27; Arsenic—2.25; Barium—90.0; Beryllium—0.0009; Cadmium—0.225; Chromium—4.5; Cobalt—94.5; Copper—58.5; Lead— 0.675; Mercury—0.045; Nickel— 4.5; Selenium—1.0; Silver—5.0; Thallium—0.135; Tin—945.0; Vanadium—13.5; Zinc—450.0 (B) Organic Constituents Acenaphthene—90.0; Acetone—180.0; Benzene—0.135; Benzo(a)anthracene—0.00347; Benzo(a)pyrene—0.00045; Benzo(b) fluoranthene—0.00320; Bis(2 ethylhexyl) phthalate—0.27; Butylbenzyl phthalate—315.0; Chloroform—0.45; Chlorobenzene—31.5; Carbon Disulfide—180.0; Chrysene—0.1215; 1,2- Dichlorobenzene—135.0; 1,4- Dichlorobenzene—0.18; Di-n-butyl phthalate—180.0; Di-n-octyl phthalate—35.0; 1,4 Dioxane— 0.36; Ethyl Acetate—1350.0; Ethyl Ether—315.0; Ethylbenzene—180.0; Flouranthene—45.0; Fluorene—45.0; 1-Butanol—180.0; Methyl Ethyl Ketone—200.0; Methylene Chloride—0.45; Methyl Isobutyl Ketone—90.0; Naphthalene—45.0; Pyrene—45.0; Toluene—315.0; Xylenes—3150.0

Table 1—Wastes Excluded from Non-Specific Sources

Facility	Address	Waste description
		2. *Waste Holding and Handling:* Texas Eastman must store in accordance with its RCRA permit, or continue to dispose of as hazardous all FBI ash generated until the Initial and Subsequent Verification Testing described in Paragraph 4 and 5 below is completed and valid analyses demonstrate that all Verification Testing Conditions are satisfied. After completion of Initial and Subsequent Verification Testing, if the levels of constituents measured in the samples of the FBI ash do not exceed the levels set forth in Paragraph 1 above, and written notification is given by EPA, then the waste is non- hazardous and may be managed and disposed of in accordance with all applicable solid waste regulations.
		3. *Verification Testing Requirements:* Sample collection and analyses, including quality control procedures, must be performed using appropriate methods. As applicable to the method-defined parameters of concern, analyses requiring the use of SW–846 methods incorporated by reference in 40 CFR 260.11 must be used without substitution. As applicable, the SW–846 methods might include Methods 0010, 0011, 0020, 0023A, 0030, 0031, 0040, 0050, 0051, 0060, 0061, 1010A, 1020B, 1110A, 1310B, 1311, 1312, 1320, 1330A, 9010C, 9012B, 9040C, 9045D, 9060A, 9070A (uses EPA Method 1664, Rev. A), 9071B, and 9095B. If EPA judges the incineration process to be effective under the operating conditions used during the initial verification testing described in Condition (4), Texas Eastman may replace the testing required in Condition (4) with the testing required in Condition (5) below. Texas Eastman must, however, continue to test as specified in Condition (4) until notified by EPA in writing that testing in Condition (4) may be replaced by the testing described in Condition (5).
		4. *Initial Verification Testing:* During the first 40 operating days of the FBI incinerator after the final exclusion is granted, Texas Eastman must collect and analyze daily composites of the FBI ash. Daily composites must be composed of representative grab samples collected every 6 hours during each 24-hour FBI operating cycle. The FBI ash must be analyzed, prior to disposal of the ash, for all constituents listed in Paragraph 1. Texas Eastman must report the operational and analytical test data, including quality control information, obtained during this initial period no later than 90 days after receipt of the validated analytical results.
		5. *Subsequent Verification Testing:* Following the completion of the Initial Verification Testing, Texas Eastman may request to monitor operating conditions and analyze samples representative of each quarter of operation during the first year of ash generation. The samples must represent the untreated ash generated over one quarter. Following written notification from EPA, Texas Eastman may begin the quarterly testing described in this Paragraph.
		6. *Termination of Organic Testing:* Texas Eastman must continue testing as required under Paragraph 5 for organic constituents specified in Paragraph 1 until the analyses submitted under Paragraph 5 show a minimum of two consecutive quarterly samples below the delisting levels in Paragraph 1. Texas Eastman may then request that quarterly organic testing be terminated. After EPA notifies Texas Eastman in writing it may terminate quarterly organic testing.
		7. *Annual Testing:* Following termination of quarterly testing under either Paragraphs 5 or 6, Texas Eastman must continue to test a representative composite sample for all constituents listed in Paragraph 1 (including organics) on an annual basis (no later than twelve months after the date that the final exclusion is effective).
		8. *Changes in Operating Conditions:* If Texas Eastman significantly changes the incineration process described in its petition or implements any new manufacturing or production process(es) which generate(s) the ash and which may or could affect the composition or type of waste generated established under Paragraph 3 (by illustration { but not limitation}, use of stabilization reagents or operating conditions of the fluidized bed incinerator), Texas Eastman must notify the EPA in writing and may no longer handle the wastes generated from the new process as non-hazardous until the wastes meet the delisting levels set in Paragraph 1 and it has received written approval to do so from EPA.
		9. *Data Submittals:* The data obtained through Paragraph 3 must be submitted to Mr. William Gallagher, Chief, Region 6 Delisting Program, U.S. EPA, 1445 Ross Avenue, Dallas, Texas 75202-2733, Mail Code, (6PD-O) within the time period specified. Records of operating conditions and analytical data from Paragraph 3 must be compiled, summarized, and maintained on site for a minimum of five years. These records and data must be furnished upon request by EPA, or the State of Texas, and made available for inspection. Failure to submit the required data within the specified time period or maintain the required records on site for the specified time will be considered by EPA, at its discretion, sufficient basis to revoke the exclusion to the extent directed by EPA. All data must be accompanied by a signed copy of the following certification statement to attest to the truth and accuracy of the data submitted: Under civil and criminal penalty of law for the making or submission of false or fraudulent statements or representations (pursuant to the applicable provisions of the Federal Code, which include, but may not be limited to, 18 USC 1001 and 42 USC 6928), I certify that the information contained in or accompanying this document is true, accurate and complete.

Table 1—Wastes Excluded from Non-Specific Sources

Facility	Address	Waste description
		As to the (those) identified section(s) of this document for which I cannot personally verify its (their) truth and accuracy, I certify as the company official having supervisory responsibility for the persons who, acting under my direct instructions, made the verification that this information is true, accurate and complete. In the event that any of this information is determined by EPA in its sole discretion to be false, inaccurate or incomplete, and upon conveyance of this fact to the company, I recognize and agree that this exclusion of waste will be void as if it never had effect or to the extent directed by EPA and that the company will be liable for any actions taken in contravention of the company's RCRA and CERCLA obligations premised upon the company's reliance on the void exclusion. 10. *Notification Requirements:* Texas Eastman must provide a one-time written notification to any State Regulatory Agency to which or through which the delisted waste described above will be transported for disposal at least 60 days prior to the commencement of such activities. Failure to provide such a notification will result in a violation of the delisting petition and a possible revocation of the decision.
Trigen/ Cinergy-USFOS of Lansing LLC at General Motors Corporation, Lansing Grand River	Lansing, Michigan	Waste water treatment plant sludge, F019, that is generated at General Motors Corporation's Lansing Grand River (GM-Grand River) facility by Trigen/Cinergy-USFOS of Lansing LLC exclusively from wastewaters from GM-Grand River, Lansing, Michigan at a maximum annual rate of 2,000 cubic yards per year. The sludge must be disposed of in a lined landfill with leachate collection, which is licensed, permitted, or otherwise authorized to accept the delisted wastewater treatment sludge in accordance with 40 CFR Part 258. The exclusion becomes effective as of July 30, 2003. The conditions in paragraphs (2) through (5) for Ford Motor Company—Michigan Truck Plant and Wayne Integrated Stamping Plant—Wayne, Michigan also apply. Delisting Levels: (A) The TCLP concentrations measured in any sample may not exceed the following levels (mg/ L): Antimony—0.659; Arsenic—0.3; Cadmium—0.48; Chromium—4.95; Lead—5; Nickel—90.5; Selenium—1; Thallium—0.282; Tin—721; Zinc—898; p-Cresol—11.4; and Formaldehyde—84.2. (B) The total concentrations measured in any sample may not exceed the following levels (mg/kg): Mercury—8.92; and Formaldehyde—689. (C) The sum of the ratios of the TCLP concentrations to the delisting levels for nickel and thallium and for nickel and cadmium shall not exceed 1.0.
Tyco Printed Circuit Group, Melbourne Division	Melbourne, Florida	Wastewater treatment sludge (EPA Hazardous Waste No. F006) that Tyco Printed Circuit Group, Melbourne Division (Tyco) generates by treating wastewater from its circuit board manufacturing plant located on John Rodes Blvd. in Melbourne, Florida. This is a conditional exclusion for up to 590 cubic yards of waste (hereinafter referred to as "Tyco Sludge") that will be generated each year and disposed in a Subtitle D landfill or shipped to a smelter for metal recovery after May 14, 2001. Tyco must demonstrate that the following conditions are met for the exclusion to be valid. (Please see Condition (8) for certification and recordkeeping requirements that must be met in order for the exclusion to be valid for waste that is sent to a smelter for metal recovery.) (1) *Verification Testing Requirements:* Sample collection and analyses, including quality control procedures must be performed using appropriate methods. As applicable to the method-defined parameters of concern, analyses requiring the use of SW–846 methods incorporated by reference in 40 CFR 260.11 must be used without substitution. As applicable, the SW–846 methods might include Methods 0010, 0011, 0020, 0023A, 0030, 0031, 0040, 0050, 0051, 0060, 0061, 1010A, 1020B, 1110A, 1310B, 1311, 1312, 1320, 1330A, 9010C, 9012B, 9040C, 9045D, 9060A, 9070A (uses EPA Method 1664, Rev. A), 9071B, and 9095B. Methods must meet Performance Based Measurement System Criteria in which the Data Quality Objectives are to demonstrate that representative samples of the Tyco Sludge meet the delisting levels in Condition (3). (A) *Initial Verification Testing:* Tyco must collect and analyze a representative sample of every batch, for eight sequential batches of Tyco sludge generated in its wastewater treatment system after May 14, 2001. A batch is the Tyco Sludge generated during one day of wastewater treatment. Tyco must analyze for the constituents listed in Condition (3). A minimum of four composite samples must be collected as representative of each batch. Tyco must report analytical test data, including quality control information, no later than 60 days after generating the first batch of Tyco Sludge to be disposed in accordance with the delisting Conditions (1) through (7). (B) *Subsequent Verification Testing:* If the initial verification testing in Condition (1)(A) is successful, i.e., delisting levels of condition (3) are met for all of the eight initial batches, Tyco must test a minimum of 5% of the Tyco Sludge generated each year. Tyco must collect and analyze at least one composite sample representative of that 5%. The composite must be made up of representative samples collected from each batch included in the 5%. Tyco may, at its discretion, analyze composite samples gathered more frequently to demonstrate that smaller batches of waste are non-hazardous.

Table 1—Wastes Excluded from Non-Specific Sources

Facility	Address	Waste description
		(2) *Waste Holding and Handling:* Tyco must store as hazardous all Tyco Sludge generated until verification testing as specified in Condition (1)(A) or (1)(B), as appropriate, is completed and valid analyses demonstrate that Condition (3) is satisfied. If the levels of constituents measured in the samples of Tyco Sludge do not exceed the levels set forth in Condition (3), then the Tyco Sludge is non-hazardous and must be managed in accordance with all applicable solid waste regulations. If constituent levels in a sample exceed any of the delisting levels set forth in Condition (3), the batch of Tyco Sludge generated during the time period corresponding to this sample must be retreated until it meets the delisting levels set forth in Condition (3), or managed and disposed of in accordance with Subtitle C of RCRA. (3) *Delisting Levels:* All leachable concentrations for these metals and cyanide must not exceed the following levels (ppm): Barium—100; Cadmium—0.5; Chromium—5.0; Cyanide—20, Lead—1.5; and Nickel—73. These metal and cyanide concentrations must be measured in the waste leachate obtained by the method specified in 40 CFR 261.24, except that for cyanide, deionized water must be the leaching medium. The total concentration of cyanide (total, not amenable) in the waste, not the waste leachate, must not exceed 200 mg/kg. Cyanide concentrations in waste or leachate must be measured by the method specified in 40 CFR 268.40, Note 7. The total concentrations of metals in the waste, not the waste leachate, must not exceed the following levels (ppm): Barium—2,000; Cadmium—500; Chromium—1,000; Lead—2,000; and Nickel—20,000. (4) *Changes in Operating Conditions:* Tyco must notify EPA in writing when significant changes in the manufacturing or wastewater treatment processes are necessary (*e.g.*, use of new chemicals not specified in the petition). EPA will determine whether these changes will result in additional constituents of concern. If so, EPA will notify Tyco in writing that the Tyco sludge must be managed as hazardous waste F006, pending receipt and evaluation of a new delisting petition. If EPA determines that the changes do not result in additional constituents of concern, EPA will notify Tyco, in writing, that Tyco must repeat Condition (1)(A) to verify that the Tyco Sludge continues to meet Condition (3) delisting levels. (5) *Data Submittals:* Data obtained in accordance with Condition (1)(A) must be submitted to Jewell Grubbs, Chief, RCRA Enforcement and Compliance Branch, Mail Code: 4WD-RCRA, U.S. EPA, Region 4, Sam Nunn Atlanta Federal Center, 61 Forsyth Street, Atlanta, Georgia 30303. This notification is due no later than 60 days after generating the first batch of Tyco Sludge to be disposed in accordance with delisting Conditions (1) through (7). Records of analytical data from Condition (1) must be compiled, summarized, and maintained by Tyco for a minimum of three years, and must be furnished upon request by EPA or the State of Florida, and made available for inspection. Failure to submit the required data within the specified time period or maintain the required records for the specified time will be considered by EPA, at its discretion, sufficient basis to revoke the exclusion to the extent directed by EPA. All data must be accompanied by a signed copy of the following certification statement to attest to the truth and accuracy of the data submitted: Under civil and criminal penalty of law for the making or submission of false or fraudulent statements or representations (pursuant to the applicable provisions of the Federal Code, which include, but may not be limited to, 18 U.S.C. 1001 and 42 U.S.C. 6928), I certify that the information contained or accompanying this document is true, accurate and complete. As to the (those) identified section(s) of this document for which I cannot personally verify its (their) truth and accuracy, I certify as the company official having supervisory responsibility for the persons who, acting under my direct instructions, made the verification that this information is true, accurate and complete. In the event that any of this information is determined by EPA in its sole discretion to be false, inaccurate or incomplete, and upon conveyance of this fact to the company, I recognize and agree that this exclusion of waste will be void as if it never had effect or to the extent directed by EPA and that the company will be liable for any actions taken in contravention of the company's RCRA and CERCLA obligations premised upon the company's void exclusion. (6) *Reopener Language:* (A) If, anytime after disposal or shipment to a smelter of the delisted waste, Tyco possesses or is otherwise made aware of any environmental data (including but not limited to leachate data or groundwater monitoring data) or any other data relevant to the delisted waste indicating that any constituent identified in the delisting verification testing is at a level higher than the delisting level allowed by EPA in granting the petition, Tyco must report the data, in writing, to EPA within 10 days of first possessing or being made aware of that data. (B) If the testing of the waste, as required by Condition (1)(B), does not meet the delisting requirements of Condition (3), Tyco must report the data, in writing, to EPA within 10 days of first possessing or being made aware of that data.

Table 1—Wastes Excluded from Non-Specific Sources

Facility	Address	Waste description
		(C) Based on the information described in paragraphs (6)(A) or (6)(B) and any other information received from any source, EPA will make a preliminary determination as to whether the reported information requires that EPA take action to protect human health or the environment. Further action may include suspending, or revoking the exclusion, or other appropriate response necessary to protect human health and the environment. (D) If EPA determines that the reported information does require Agency action, EPA will notify the facility in writing of the action believed necessary to protect human health and the environment. The notice shall include a statement of the proposed action and a statement providing Tyco with an opportunity to present information as to why the proposed action is not necessary. Tyco shall have 10 days from the date of EPA's notice to present such information. (E) Following the receipt of information from Tyco, as described in paragraph (6)(D) or if no such information is received within 10 days, EPA will issue a final written determination describing the Agency actions that are necessary to protect human health or the environment, given the information received in accordance with paragraphs (6)(A) or (6)(B). Any required action described in EPA's determination shall become effective immediately. (7) *Notification Requirements:* Tyco must provide a one-time written notification to any State Regulatory Agency in a State to which or through which the delisted waste described above will be transported, at least 60 days prior to the commencement of such activities. Failure to provide such a notification will result in a violation of the delisting conditions and a possible revocation of the decision to delist. (8) *Recordkeeping and Certification Requirements for Waste to be Smelted for Metal Recovery:* Tyco must maintain in its facility files, and make available for inspection by EPA and the Florida Department of Environmental Protection (FDEP), records that include the name, address, telephone number, and contact person of each smelting facility used by Tyco for its delisted waste, quantities of waste shipped, analytical data for demonstrating that the delisting levels of Condition (3) are met, and a certification that the smelter(s) is(are) subject to regulatory controls on discharges to air, water, and land. The certification statement must be signed by a responsible official and contain the following language: Under civil and criminal penalty of law for the making or submission of false or fraudulent statements or representations (pursuant to the applicable provisions of the Federal Code, which include, but may not be limited to, 18 U.S.C. 1001 and 42 U.S.C. 6928), I certify that the smelter(s) used for Tyco's delisted waste is(are) subject to regulatory controls on discharges to air, water, and land. As the company official having supervisory responsibility for plant operations, I certify that to the best of my knowledge this information is true, accurate and complete. In the event that any of this information is determined by EPA in its sole discretion to be false, inaccurate or incomplete, and upon conveyance of this fact to the company, I recognize and agree that this exclusion of waste will be void as if it never had effect or to the extent directed by EPA and that the company will be liable for any actions taken in contravention of the company's RCRA and CERCLA obligations premised upon the company's void exclusion.
Universal Oil Products	Decatur, Alabama	Wastewater treatment sludges (EPA Hazardous Waste No. F006) generated from electroplating operations and contained in two on-site lagoons on August 15, 1986. This is a one-time exclusion.
U.S. EPA Combustion Research Facility	Jefferson, Arkansas	One-time exclusion for scrubber water (EPA Hazardous Waste No. F020) generated in 1985 from the incineration of Vertac still bottoms. This exclusion was published on June 28, 1989.
U.S. Nameplate Company, Inc	Mount Vernon, Iowa	Retreated wastewater treatment sludges (EPA Hazardous Waste No. F006) previously generated from electroplating operations and currently contained in an on-site surface impoundment after September 28, 1988. This is a one-time exclusion for the retreated wastes only. This exclusion does not relieve the waste unit from regulatory compliance under Subtitle C.
VAW of America Incorporated	St. Augustine, Florida	Wastewater treatment sludge filter cake (EPA Hazardous Waste No. F019) generated from the chemical conversion coating of aluminum. This exclusion was published on February 1, 1989.
Vermont American, Corp	Newark, OH	Wastewater treatment sludge (EPA Hazardous Waste No. F006) generated from electroplating operations after November 27, 1985.

Table 1—Wastes Excluded from Non-Specific Sources

Facility	Address	Waste description
Waterloo Industries	Pocahontas, AR	Wastewater treatment sludges (EPA Hazardous Waste No. F006) generated from electroplating operations after dewatering and held on-site on July 17, 1986 and any such sludge generated (after dewatering) after July 17, 1986.
Watervliet Arsenal	Watervliet, NY	Wastewater treatment sludges (EPA Hazardous Waste No. F006) generated from electroplating operations after January 10, 1986.
Weirton Steel Corporation	Weirton, West Virginia	Wastewater treatment sludge (known as C&E sludge) containing EPA Hazardous Waste Numbers F007 and F008, subsequent to its excavation from the East Lagoon and the Figure 8 tanks for the purpose of transportation and disposal in a Subtitle D landfill after May 23, 2002. This is a one-time exclusion for a maximum volume of 18,000 cubic yards of C&E sludge. (1) Reopener language. (a) If Weirton discovers that any condition or assumption related to the characterization of the excluded waste which was used in the evaluation of the petition or that was predicted through modeling is not as reported in the petition, then Weirton must report any information relevant to that condition or assumption, in writing, to the Regional Administrator and the West Virginia Department of Environmental Protection within 10 calendar days of discovering that information. (b) Upon receiving information described in paragraph (a) of this section, regardless of its source, the Regional Administrator and the West Virginia Department of Environmental Protection will determine whether the reported condition requires further action. Further action may include repealing the exclusion, modifying the exclusion, or other appropriate response necessary to protect human health or the environment. (2) Notification Requirements. Weirton must provide a one-time written notification to any State Regulatory Agency to which or through which the delisted waste described above will be transported for disposal at least 60 calendar days prior to the commencement of such activities. Failure to provide such notification will be deemed to be a violation of this exclusion and may result in revocation of the decision and other enforcement action.
William L Bonnell Co	Newnan, Georgia	Dewatered wastewater treatment sludges (EPA Hazardous Waste No. F019) generated from the chemical conversion coating of aluminum after November 14, 1986. This exclusion does not include sludges contained in Bonnell's on-site surface impoundments.
Windsor Plastics, Inc	Evansville, IN	Spent non-halogenated solvents and still bottoms (EPA Hazardous Waste No. F003) generated from the recovery of acetone after November 17, 1986.
WRB Refining, LLC	Borger, TX	Thermal desorber residual solids (Hazardous Waste Nos. F037, F038, K048, K049, K050, and K051) generated at a maximum annual rate of 5,000 cubic yards per calendar year after September 29, 2009 and disposed in Subtitle D Landfill. For the exclusion to be valid, WRB Refining LLC must implement a verification testing program that meets the following Paragraphs: (1) Delisting Levels: All concentrations for those constituents must not exceed the maximum allowable concentrations in mg/l specified in this paragraph. Thermal Desorber Residual Solid Leachable Concentrations (mg/l): Antimony–0.165; Arsenic–0.0129; Barium–54.8; Beryllium–0.119; Cadmium–0.139; Chromium–3.23; Chromium, Hexavalent–3.23; Cobalt–20.7; Copper–38.6; Cyanide–4.69; Lead–1.07; Mercury–0.104; Nickel–20.6; Selenium–1.0; Silver–5.0; Tin–3790.00; Vanadium–1.46; Zinc–320.0; Acenapthene–16.2; Anthracene–39.5; Benzene–0.117; Carbon Disulfide–86.0; 2-chlorophenol–4.41; Dibenzofuran–0.0226; 1,4-Dichlororbenzene–0.518; Ethylbenzene–16.5; Fluoranthene–3.75; Methylene Chloride–0.077; Naphthalene–0.0498; Phenol–264.0; Pyrene–6.78; Toluene–23.0; 1,2,4-Trichlorobenzene–1.51; Trichlorofluoromethane–23.5; Xylenes–14.6. (2) Waste Holding and Handling: (A) Waste classification as non-hazardous can not begin until compliance with the limits set in paragraph (1) for thermal desorber residual solids has occurred for two consecutive quarterly sampling events. (B) If constituent levels in any sample taken by WRB Refining LLC exceed any of the delisting levels set in paragraph (1) for the thermal desorber residual solids, WRB Refining LLC must do the following: (i) Notify EPA in accordance with paragraph (6) and

Table 1—Wastes Excluded from Non-Specific Sources

Facility	Address	Waste description

(ii) Manage and dispose the thermal desorber residual solids as hazardous waste generated under Subtitle C of RCRA.

(3) Testing Requirements:

Upon this exclusion becoming final, WRB Refining LLC may perform quarterly analytical testing by sampling and analyzing the desorber residual solids as follows:

(A) Quarterly Testing:

(i) Collect two representative composite samples of the sludge at quarterly intervals after EPA grants the final exclusion. The first composite samples may be taken at any time after EPA grants the final approval. Sampling should be performed in accordance with the sampling plan approved by EPA in support of the exclusion.

(ii) Analyze the samples for all constituents listed in paragraph (1). Any composite sample taken that exceeds the delisting levels listed in paragraph (1) for the sludge must be disposed as hazardous waste in accordance with the applicable hazardous waste requirements.

(iii) Within thirty (30) days after taking its first quarterly sample, WRB Refining LLC will report its first quarterly analytical test data to EPA. If levels of constituents measured in the samples of the sludge do not exceed the levels set forth in paragraph (1) of this exclusion for two consecutive quarters, WRB Refining LLC can manage and dispose the non-hazardous thermal desorber residual solids according to all applicable solid waste regulations.

(B) Annual Testing: (i) If WRB Refining LLC completes the quarterly testing specified in paragraph (3) above and no sample contains a constituent at a level which exceeds the limits set forth in paragraph (1), WRB Refining LLC may begin annual testing as follows: WRB Refining LLC must test two representative composite samples of the thermal desorber residual solids for all constituents listed in paragraph (1) at least once per calendar year.

(ii) The samples for the annual testing shall be a representative composite sample according to appropriate methods. As applicable to the method-defined parameters of concern, analyses requiring the use of SW–846 methods incorporated by reference in 40 CFR 260.11 must be used without substitution. As applicable, the SW–846 methods might include Methods 0010, 0011, 0020, 0023A, 0030, 0031, 0040, 0050, 0051, 0060, 0061, 1010A, 1020B,1110A, 1310B, 1311, 1312, 1320, 1330A, 9010C, 9012B, 9040C, 9045D, 9060A, 9070A (uses EPA Method 1664, Rev. A), 9071B, and 9095B. Methods must meet Performance Based Measurement System Criteria in which the Data Quality Objectives are to demonstrate that samples of the WRB Refining thermal desorber residual solids are representative for all constituents listed in paragraph (1).

(iii) The samples for the annual testing taken for the second and subsequent annual testing events shall be taken within the same calendar month as the first annual sample taken.

(iv) The annual testing report should include the total amount of delisted waste in cubic yards disposed as non-hazardous waste during the calendar year.

(4) Changes in Operating Conditions: If WRB Refining LLC significantly changes the process described in its petition or starts any processes that generate(s) the waste that may or could affect the composition or type of waste generated (by illustration, but not limitation, changes in equipment or operating conditions of the treatment process), it must notify EPA in writing and it may no longer handle the wastes generated from the new process as non-hazardous until the wastes meet the delisting levels set in paragraph (1) and it has received written approval to do so from EPA.

WRB Refining LLC must submit a modification to the petition, complete with full sampling and analysis, for circumstances where the waste volume changes and/or additional waste codes are added to the waste stream, if it wishes to dispose of the material as non-hazardous.

(5) Data Submittals:

WRB Refining LLC must submit the information described below. If WRB Refining LLC fails to submit the required data within the specified time or maintain the required records on-site for the specified time, EPA, at its discretion, will consider this sufficient basis to reopen the exclusion as described in paragraph (6). WRB Refining LLC must:

(A) Submit the data obtained through paragraph (3) to the Chief, Corrective Action and Waste Minimization Section, Multimedia Planning and Permitting Division, U.S. Environmental Protection Agency Region 6, 1445 Ross Ave., Dallas, Texas, 75202, within the time specified. All supporting data can be submitted on CD–ROM or comparable electronic media.

(B) Compile records of analytical data from paragraph (3), summarized, and maintained on-site for a minimum of five years.

(C) Furnish these records and data when either EPA or the State of Texas requests them for inspection.

Table 1—Wastes Excluded from Non-Specific Sources

Facility	Address	Waste description
		(D) Send along with all data a signed copy of the following certification statement, to attest to the truth and accuracy of the data submitted: "Under civil and criminal penalty of law for the making or submission of false or fraudulent statements or representations (pursuant to the applicable provisions of the Federal Code, which include, but may not be limited to, 18 U.S.C. §1001 and 42 U.S.C. §6928), I certify that the information contained in or accompanying this document is true, accurate and complete. As to the (those) identified section(s) of this document for which I cannot personally verify its (their) truth and accuracy, I certify as the company official having supervisory responsibility for the persons who, acting under my direct instructions, made the verification that this information is true, accurate and complete. If any of this information is determined by EPA in its sole discretion to be false, inaccurate or incomplete, and upon conveyance of this fact to the company, I recognize and agree that this exclusion of waste will be void as if it never had effect or to the extent directed by EPA and that the company will be liable for any actions taken in contravention of the company's RCRA and CERCLA obligations premised upon the company's reliance on the void exclusion." (6) Re-opener (A) If, anytime after disposal of the delisted waste WRB Refining LLC possesses or is otherwise made aware of any environmental data (including but not limited to leachate data or ground water monitoring data) or any other data relevant to the delisted waste indicating that any constituent identified for the delisting verification testing is at level higher than the delisting level allowed by the Division Director in granting the petition, then the facility must report the data, in writing, to the Division Director within 10 days of first possessing or being made aware of that data. (B) If either the quarterly or annual testing of the waste does not meet the delisting requirements in paragraph 1, WRB Refining LLC must report the data, in writing, to the Division Director within 10 days of first possessing or being made aware of that data. (C) If WRB Refining LLC fails to submit the information described in paragraphs (5), (6)(A) or (6)(B) or if any other information is received from any source, the Division Director will make a preliminary determination as to whether the reported information requires EPA action to protect human health and/or the environment. Further action may include suspending, or revoking the exclusion, or other appropriate response necessary to protect human health and the environment. (D) If the Division Director determines that the reported information requires action by EPA, the Division Director will notify the facility in writing of the actions the Division Director believes are necessary to protect human health and the environment. The notice shall include a statement of the proposed action and a statement providing the facility with an opportunity to present information as to why the proposed EPA action is not necessary. The facility shall have 10 days from the date of the Division Director's notice to present such information. (E) Following the receipt of information from the facility described in paragraph (6)(D) or (if no information is presented under paragraph (6)(D)) the initial receipt of information described in paragraphs (5), (6)(A) or (6)(B), the Division Director will issue a final written determination describing EPA actions that are necessary to protect human health and/or the environment. Any required action described in the Division Director's determination shall become effective immediately, unless the Division Director provides otherwise. (7) Notification Requirements WRB Refining LLC must do the following before transporting the delisted waste. Failure to provide this notification will result in a violation of the delisting petition and a possible revocation of the decision. (A) Provide a one-time written notification to any state Regulatory Agency to which or through which it will transport the delisted waste described above for disposal, 60 days before beginning such activities. (B) Update the one-time written notification if it ships the delisted waste into a different disposal facility. (C) Failure to provide this notification will result in a violation of the delisting variance and a possible revocation of the decision.

Table 2—Wastes Excluded From Specific Sources

Facility	Address	Waste description
American Chrome & Chemical	Corpus Christi, Texas	Dewatered sludge (the EPA Hazardous Waste No. K006) generated at a maximum generation of 1450 cubic yards per calendar year after September 21, 2004 and disposed in a Subtitle D landfill. ACC must implement a verification program that meets the following Paragraphs: (1) Delisting Levels: All leachable constituent concentrations must not exceed the following levels (mg/l). The petitioner must use the method specified in 40 CFR 261.24 to measure constituents in the waste leachate. Dewatered wastewater sludge: Arsenic-0.0377; Barium-100.0; Chromium-5.0; Thallium-0.355; Zinc-1130.0. (2) Waste Holding and Handling: (A) ACC is a 90 day facility and does not have a RCRA permit, therefore, ACC must store the dewatered sludge following the requirements specified in 40 CFR 262.34, or continue to dispose of as hazardous all dewatered sludge generated, until they have completed verification testing described in Paragraph (3), as appropriate, and valid analyses show that paragraph (1) is satisfied. (B) Levels of constituents measured in the samples of the dewatered sludge that do not exceed the levels set forth in Paragraph (1) are non-hazardous. ACC can manage and dispose the non-hazardous dewatered sludge according to all applicable solid waste regulations. (C) If constituent levels in a sample exceed any of the delisting levels set in Paragraph (1), ACC must retreat the batches of waste used to generate the representative sample until it meets the levels. ACC must repeat the analyses of the treated waste. (D) If the facility does not treat the waste or retreat it until it meets the delisting levels in Paragraph (1), ACC must manage and dispose the waste generated under Subtitle C of RCRA. (E) The dewatered sludge must pass paint filter test as described in SW 846, Method 9095 or another appropriate method found in a reliable source before it is allowed to leave the facility. ACC must maintain a record of the actual volume of the dewatered sludge to be disposed off-site according to the requirements in Paragraph (5). (3) Verification Testing Requirements: ACC must perform sample collection and analyses, including quality control procedures, according to appropriate methods such as those found in SW–846 or other reliable sources (with the exception of analyses requiring the use of SW–846 methods incorporated by reference in 40 CFR 260.11, which must be used without substitution. ACC must conduct verification testing each time it decides to evacuate the tank contents. Four (4) representative composite samples shall be collected from the dewatered sludge. ACC shall analyze the verification samples according to the constituent list specified in Paragraph (1) and submit the analytical results to EPA within 10 days of receiving the analytical results. If the EPA determines that the data collected under this Paragraph do not support the data provided for the petition, the exclusion will not cover the generated wastes. The EPA will notify ACC the decision in writing within two weeks of receiving this information. (4) Changes in Operating Conditions: If ACC significantly changes the process described in its petition or starts any processes that may or could affect the composition or type of waste generated as established under Paragraph (1) (by illustration, but not limitation, changes in equipment or operating conditions of the treatment process), they must notify the EPA in writing; they may no longer handle the wastes generated from the new process as nonhazardous until the test results of the wastes meet the delisting levels set in Paragraph (1) and they have received written approval to do so from the EPA. (5) Data Submittals: ACC must submit the information described below. If ACC fails to submit the required data within the specified time or maintain the required records on-site for the specified time, the EPA, at its discretion, will consider this sufficient basis to reopen the exclusion as described in Paragraph 6. ACC must: (A) Submit the data obtained through Paragraph 3 to the Section Chief, Corrective Action and Waste Minimization Section, Environmental Protection Agency, 1445 Ross Avenue, Dallas, Texas 75202–2733, Mail Code, (6PD–C) within the time specified. (B) Compile records of operating conditions and analytical data from Paragraph (3), summarized, and maintained on-site for a minimum of five years. (C) Furnish these records and data when the EPA or the State of Texas request them for inspection. (D) Send along with all data a signed copy of the following certification statement, to attest to the truth and accuracy of the data submitted: Under civil and criminal penalty of law for the making or submission of false or fraudulent statements or representations (pursuant to the applicable provisions of the Federal Code, which include, but may not be limited to, 18 U.S.C. 1001 and 42 U.S.C. 6928), I certify that the information contained in or accompanying this document is true, accurate and complete. As to the (those) identified section(s) of this document for which I cannot personally verify its (their) truth and accuracy, I certify as the company official having supervisory responsibility for the persons who, acting under my direct instructions, made the verification that this information is true, accurate and complete. If any of this information is determined by the EPA in its sole discretion to be false, inaccurate or incomplete, and

Table 2—Wastes Excluded From Specific Sources

Facility	Address	Waste description
		upon conveyance of this fact to the company, I recognize and agree that this exclusion of waste will be void as if it never had effect or to the extent directed by the EPA and that the company will be liable for any actions taken in contravention of the company's RCRA and CERCLA obligations premised upon the company's reliance on the void exclusion. (6) Reopener: (A) If, anytime after disposal of the delisted waste, ACC possesses or is otherwise made aware of any environmental data (including but not limited to leachate data or ground water monitoring data) or any other data relevant to the delisted waste indicating that any constituent identified for the delisting verification testing is at level higher than the delisting level allowed by the Division Director in granting the petition, then the facility must report the data, in writing, to the Division Director within 10 days of first possessing or being made aware of that data. (B) If the verification testing of the waste does not meet the delisting requirements in Paragraph 1, ACC must report the data, in writing, to the Division Director within 10 days of first possessing or being made aware of that data. (C) If ACC fails to submit the information described in paragraphs (5),(6)(A) or (6)(B) or if any other information is received from any source, the Division Director will make a preliminary determination as to whether the reported information requires Agency action to protect human health or the environment. Further action may include suspending, or revoking the exclusion, or other appropriate response necessary to protect human health and the environment. (D) If the Division Director determines that the reported information does require Agency action, the Division Director will notify the facility in writing of the actions the Division Director believes are necessary to protect human health and the environment. The notice shall include a statement of the proposed action and a statement providing the facility with an opportunity to present information as to why the proposed Agency action is not necessary. The facility shall have 10 days from the date of the Division Director's notice to present such information. (E) Following the receipt of information from the facility described in paragraph (6)(D) or (if no information is presented under paragraph (6)(D)) the initial receipt of information described in paragraphs (5), (6)(A) or (6)(B), the Division Director will issue a final written determination describing the Agency actions that are necessary to protect human health or the environment. Any required action described in the Division Director's determination shall become effective immediately, unless the Division Director provides otherwise. (7) Notification Requirements: ACC must do the following before transporting the delisted waste: Failure to provide this notification will result in a violation of the delisting petition and a possible revocation of the decision. (A) Provide a one-time written notification to any State Regulatory Agency to which or through which they will transport the delisted waste described above for disposal, 60 days before beginning such activities. If ACC transports the excluded waste to or manages the waste in any state with delisting authorization, ACC must obtain delisting authorization from that state before it can manage the waste as nonhazardous in the state. (B) Update the one-time written notification if they ship the delisted waste to a different disposal facility. (C) Failure to provide the notification will result in a violation of the delisting variance and a possible revocation of the exclusion.
American Cyanamid	Hannibal, Missouri	Wastewater and sludge (EPA Hazardous Waste No. K038) generated from the washing and stripping of phorate production and contained in on-site lagoons on May 8, 1987, and such wastewater and sludge generated after May 8, 1987.
Amoco Oil Co	Wood River, IL	150 million gallons of DAF from petroleum refining contained in in four surge ponds after treatment with the Chemifix© stabilization process. This waste contains EPA Hazardous Waste No. K048. This exclusion applies to the 150 million gallons of waste after chemical stabilization as long as the mixing ratios of the reagent with the waste are monitored continuously and do not vary outside of the limits presented in the demonstration samples; one grab sample is taken each hour from each treatment unit, composited, and EP toxicity tests performed on each sample. If the levels of lead or total chromium exceed 0.5 ppm in the EP extract, then the waste that was processed during the compositing period is considered hazardous; the treatment residue shall be pumped into bermed cells to ensure that the waste is identifiable in the event that removal is necessary.
Akzo Chemicals Inc. (formerly Stauffer Chemical Company)	Axis, AL	Brine purification muds generated from their chlor-alkali manufacturing operations (EPA Hazardous Waste No. K071) and disposed of in brine mud pond HWTF: 5 EP-201.

Table 2—Wastes Excluded From Specific Sources

Facility	Address	Waste description
Bayer Material Science LLC	Baytown, TX	Outfall 007 Treated Effluent (EPA Hazardous Waste Nos. K027, K104, K111, and K112) generated at a maximum rate of 18,071,150 cubic yards (5.475 billion gallons) per calendar year after July 25, 2005 as it exits the Outfall Tank and disposed in accordance with the TPDES permit. The delisting levels set do not relieve Bayer of its duty to comply with the limits set in its TPDES permit. For the exclusion to be valid, Bayer must implement a verification testing program that meets the following Paragraphs: (1) Delisting Levels: All concentrations for those constituents must not exceed the maximum allowable concentrations in mg/kg specified in this paragraph. Outfall 007 Treated Effluent Total Concentrations (mg/kg): Antimony—0.0816; Arsenic—0.385, Barium—22.2; Chromium—153.0; Copper—3620.0; Cyanide—0.46; Mercury—0.0323; Nickel—11.3; Selenium—0.23; Thallium—0.0334; Vanadium—8.38; Zinc—112.0; Acetone—14.6; Acetophenone—15.8; Aniline—0.680; Benzene—0.0590; Bis (2-ethylhexyl)phthalate—1260.0; Bromodichloromethane—0.0719; Chloroform—0.077; Din-octyl phthalate—454.0; 2,4-Dinitrotoluene—0.00451; Diphenylamine—11.8; 1,4-Dioxane—1.76; Di-n-butyl phthalate—149.0; Fluoranthene—24.6; Methylene chloride—0.029; Methyl ethyl ketone—87.9; Nitrobenzene—0.0788; m-phenylenediamine—0.879; Pyrene—39.0; 1,1,1,2-Tetrachloroethane—0.703; o-Toluidine—0.0171; p-Toluidine—0.215; 2,4-Toluenediamine—0.00121. Toluene diisocyanate—0.001. (2) Waste Holding and Handling: (A) Waste classification as non-hazardous can not begin until compliance with the limits set in paragraph (1) for the treated effluent has occurred for two consecutive quarterly sampling events and those reports have been approved by EPA. The delisting for the treated effluent applies only during periods of TPDES compliance. (B) If constituent levels in any sample taken by Bayer exceed any of the delisting levels set in paragraph (1) for the treated effluent, Bayer must do the following: (i) notify EPA in accordance with paragraph (6) and (ii) Manage and dispose the treated effluent as hazardous waste generated under Subtitle C of RCRA. (iii) Routine inspection and regular maintenance of the effluent pipe line must occur to prevent spills and leaks of the treated effluent prior to discharge. (3) Testing Requirements: Sample collection and analyses, including quality control procedures, must be performed using appropriate methods. As applicable to the method-defined parameters of concern, analyses requiring the use of SW–846 methods incorporated by reference in 40 CFR 260.11 must be used without substitution. As applicable, the SW–846 methods might include Methods 0010, 0011, 0020, 0023A, 0030, 0031, 0040, 0050, 0051, 0060, 0061, 1010A, 1020B, 1110A, 1310B, 1311, 1312, 1320, 1330A, 9010C, 9012B, 9040C, 9045D, 9060A, 9070A (uses EPA Method 1664, Rev. A), 9071B, and 9095B. Methods must meet Performance Based Measurement System Criteria in which the Data Quality Objectives are to demonstrate that representative samples of the Bayer treated effluent meet the delisting levels in paragraph (1). (A) Quarterly Testing: Upon this exclusion becoming final, Bayer may perform quarterly analytical testing by sampling and analyzing the treated effluent as follows: (i) Collect two representative composite samples of the treated effluent at quarterly intervals after EPA grants the final exclusion. The first composite samples may be taken at any time after EPA grants the final approval. Sampling should be performed in accordance with the sampling plan approved by EPA in support of the exclusion. (ii) Analyze the samples for all constituents listed in paragraph (1). Any composite sample taken that exceeds the delisting levels listed in paragraph (1) for the treated effluent must be disposed of as hazardous waste in accordance with the applicable hazardous waste requirements in its TPDES discharge permit. (iii) Within thirty (30) days after taking its first quarterly sample, Bayer will report its first quarterly analytical test data to EPA. If levels of constituents measured in the samples of the treated effluent do not exceed the levels set forth in paragraph (1) of this exclusion for two consecutive quarters, Bayer can manage and dispose the nonhazardous treated effluent according to all applicable solid waste regulations. (B) Annual Testing: (i) If Bayer completes the four (4) quarterly testing events specified in paragraph (3)(A) above and no sample contains a constituent with a level which exceeds the limits set forth in paragraph (1), Bayer may begin annual testing as follows: Bayer must test two representative composite samples of the treated effluent for all constituents listed in paragraph (1) at least once per calendar year.

Table 2—Wastes Excluded From Specific Sources

Facility	Address	Waste description
		(ii) The samples for the annual testing shall be a representative composite sample according to appropriate methods. As applicable to the method-defined parameters of concern, analyses requiring the use of SW–846 methods incorporated by reference in 40 CFR 260.11 must be used without substitution. As applicable, the SW–846 methods might include Methods 0010, 0011, 0020, 0023A, 0030, 0031, 0040, 0050, 0051, 0060, 0061, 1010A, 1020B, 1110A, 1310B, 1311, 1312, 1320, 1330A, 9010C, 9012B, 9040C, 9045D, 9060A, 9070A (uses EPA Method 1664, Rev. A), 9071B, and 9095B. Methods must meet Performance Based Measurement System Criteria in which the Data Quality Objectives are to demonstrate that representative samples of the Bayer treated effluent for all constituents listed in paragraph (1). (iii) The samples for the annual testing taken for the second and subsequent annual testing events shall be taken within the same calendar month as the first annual sample taken. (4) Changes in Operating Conditions: If Bayer significantly changes the process described in its petition or starts any processes that generate(s) the waste that may or could affect the composition or type of waste generated as established under paragraph (1) (by illustration, but not limitation, changes in equipment or operating conditions of the treatment process), it must notify EPA in writing; it may no longer handle the wastes generated from the new process as nonhazardous until the wastes meet the delisting levels set in paragraph (1) and it has received written approval to do so from EPA. Bayer must submit a modification to the petition complete with full sampling and analysis for circumstances where the waste volume changes and/or additional waste codes are added to the waste stream. (5) Data Submittals: Bayer must submit the information described below. If Bayer fails to submit the required data within the specified time or maintain the required records on-site for the specified time, EPA, at its discretion, will consider this sufficient basis to reopen the exclusion as described in paragraph (6). Bayer must: (i) Submit the data obtained through paragraph (3) to the Chief, Corrective Action and Waste Minimization Section, Multimedia Planning and Permitting Division, U.S. Environmental Protection Agency Region 6, 1445 Ross Ave., Dallas, Texas, 75202, within the time specified. All supporting data can be submitted on CD–ROM or some comparable electronic media. (ii) Compile records of analytical data from paragraph (3), summarized, and maintained on-site for a minimum of five years. (iii) Furnish these records and data when either EPA or the State of Texas request them for inspection. (iv) Send along with all data a signed copy of the following certification statement, to attest to the truth and accuracy of the data submitted: "Under civil and criminal penalty of law for the making or submission of false or fraudulent statements or representations (pursuant to the applicable provisions of the Federal Code, which include, but may not be limited to, 18 U.S.C. 1001 and 42 U.S.C. 6928), I certify that the information contained in or accompanying this document is true, accurate and complete. As to the (those) identified section(s) of this document for which I cannot personally verify its (their) truth and accuracy, I certify as the company official having supervisory responsibility for the persons who, acting under my direct instructions, made the verification that this information is true, accurate and complete. If any of this information is determined by EPA in its sole discretion to be false, inaccurate or incomplete, and upon conveyance of this fact to the company, I recognize and agree that this exclusion of waste will be void as if it never had effect or to the extent directed by EPA and that the company will be liable for any actions taken in contravention of the company's RCRA and CERCLA obligations premised upon the company's reliance on the void exclusion." (6) Reopener: (i) If, anytime after disposal of the delisted waste Bayer possesses or is otherwise made aware of any environmental data (including but not limited to leachate data or ground water monitoring data) or any other data relevant to the delisted waste indicating that any constituent identified for the delisting verification testing is at level higher than the delisting level allowed by the Division Director in granting the petition, then the facility must report the data, in writing, to the Division Director within 10 days of first possessing or being made aware of that data. (ii) If either the quarterly or annual testing of the waste does not meet the delisting requirements in paragraph (1), Bayer must report the data, in writing, to the Division Director within 10 days of first possessing or being made aware of that data.

Table 2—Wastes Excluded From Specific Sources

Facility	Address	Waste description
		(iii) If Bayer fails to submit the information described in paragraphs (5), (6)(i) or (6)(ii) or if any other information is received from any source, the Division Director will make a preliminary determination as to whether the reported information requires EPA action to protect human health and/or the environment. Further action may include suspending, or revoking the exclusion, or other appropriate response necessary to protect human health and the environment. (iv) If the Division Director determines that the reported information requires action by EPA, the Division Director will notify the facility in writing of the actions the Division Director believes are necessary to protect human health and the environment. The notice shall include a statement of the proposed action and a statement providing the facility with an opportunity to present information as to why the proposed EPA action is not necessary. The facility shall have 10 days from the date of the Division Director's notice to present such information. (v) Following the receipt of information from the facility described in paragraph (6)(iv) or (if no information is presented under paragraph (6)(iv)) the initial receipt of information described in paragraphs (5), (6)(i) or (6)(ii), the Division Director will issue a final written determination describing EPA actions that are necessary to protect human health and/ or the environment. Any required action described in the Division Director's determination shall become effective immediately, unless the Division Director provides otherwise.
Bayer Material Science LLC	Baytown, TX	Spent Carbon (EPA Hazardous Waste Nos. K027, K104, K111, and K112) generated at a maximum rate of 7,728 cubic yards per calendar year after May 16, 2006. For the exclusion to be valid, Bayer must implement a verification testing program that meets the following Paragraphs: (1) Delisting Levels: All concentrations for those constituents must not exceed the maximum allowable concentrations in mg/l specified in this paragraph. Spent Carbon Leachable Concentrations (mg/l): Antimony–0.251; Arsenic–0.385, Barium– 8.93; Beryllium–0.953; Cadmium–0.687; Chromium–5.0; Cobalt–2.75; Copper–128.0; Cyanide–1.65; Lead–5.0; Mercury–0.0294; Nickel–3.45; Selenium–0.266; Tin–2.75; Vanadium–2.58; Zinc–34.2; Aldrin–0.0000482; Acetophenone–87.1; Aniline–2.82; Benzene–0.554; Bis(2-ethylhexyl)phthalate–0.342; Benzyl alcohol–261; Butylbenzylphthalate–3.54; Chloroform–0.297; Di-n-octyl phthalate–0.00427; 2,4-Dinitrotoluene–0.0249; 2,6-Dinitrotoluene–0.0249; Diphenylamine–1.43; 1,4-Dioxane–14.6; Di-n-butylphthalate–2.02; Kepone– 0.000373; 2-Nitrophenol–87.9; N-Nitrodiphenylamine–3.28; Phenol–52.2; 2,4-Toluenediamine–0.00502; Toluene diisocyanate–0.001. (2) Waste Holding and Handling: (A) Waste classification as non-hazardous can not begin until compliance with the limits set in paragraph (1) for spent carbon has occurred for two consecutive quarterly sampling events and the reports have been approved by EPA. (B) If constituent levels in any sample taken by Bayer exceed any of the delisting levels set in paragraph (1) for the spent carbon, Bayer must do the following: (i) notify EPA in accordance with paragraph (6) and (ii) manage and dispose the spent carbon as hazardous waste generated under Subtitle C of RCRA. (3) Testing Requirements: Upon this exclusion becoming final, Bayer must perform quarterly analytical testing by sampling and analyzing the spent carbon as follows: (A) Quarterly Testing: (i) Collect two representative composite samples of the spent carbon at quarterly intervals after EPA grants the final exclusion. The first composite samples may be taken at any time after EPA grants the final approval. Sampling should be performed in accordance with the sampling plan approved by EPA in support of the exclusion. (ii) Analyze the samples for all constituents listed in paragraph (1). Any composite sample taken that exceeds the delisting levels listed in paragraph (1) for the spent carbon must be disposed as hazardous waste in accordance with the applicable hazardous waste requirements. (iii) Within thirty (30) days after taking its first quarterly sample, Bayer will report its first quarterly analytical test data to EPA. If levels of constituents measured in the samples of the spent carbon do not exceed the levels set forth in paragraph (1) of this exclusion for two consecutive quarters, Bayer can manage and dispose the non-hazardous spent carbon according to all applicable solid waste regulations.

Table 2—Wastes Excluded From Specific Sources

Facility	Address	Waste description
		(B) Annual Testing:

(i) If Bayer completes the quarterly testing specified in paragraph (3) above and no sample contains a constituent at a level which exceeds the limits set forth in paragraph (1), Bayer can begin annual testing as follows: Bayer must test two representative composite samples of the spent carbon for all constituents listed in paragraph (1) at least once per calendar year.

(ii) The samples for the annual testing shall be a representative composite sample according to appropriate methods. As applicable to the method-defined parameters of concern, analyses requiring the use of SW–846 methods incorporated by reference in 40 CFR 260.11 must be used without substitution. As applicable, the SW–846 methods might include Methods 0010, 0011, 0020, 0023A, 0030, 0031, 0040, 0050, 0051, 0060, 0061, 1010A, 1020B, 1110A, 1310B, 1311, 1312, 1320, 1330A, 9010C, 9012B, 9040C, 9045D, 9060A, 9070A (uses EPA Method 1664, Rev. A), 9071B, and 9095B.

Methods must meet Performance Based Measurement System Criteria in which the Data Quality Objectives are to demonstrate that samples of the Bayer spent carbon are representative for all constituents listed in paragraph (1).

(iii) The samples for the annual testing taken for the second and subsequent annual testing events shall be taken within the same calendar month as the first annual sample taken.

(iv) The annual testing report must include the total amount of waste in cubic yards disposed during the calendar year.

(4) Changes in Operating Conditions:

If Bayer significantly changes the process described in its petition or starts any process that generates the waste that may or could affect the composition or type of waste generated (by illustration, but not limitation, changes in equipment or operating conditions of the treatment process), it must notify EPA in writing and it may no longer handle the wastes generated from the new process as non-hazardous until the wastes meet the delisting levels set in paragraph (1) and it has received written approval to do so from EPA.

Bayer must submit a modification to the petition complete with full sampling and analysis for circumstances where the waste volume changes and/or additional waste codes are added to the waste stream.

(5) Data Submittals:

Bayer must submit the information described below. If Bayer fails to submit the required data within the specified time or maintain the required records on-site for the specified time, EPA, at its discretion, will consider this sufficient basis to reopen the exclusion as described in paragraph (6). Bayer must:

(A) Submit the data obtained through paragraph 3 to the Chief, Corrective Action and Waste Minimization Section, Multimedia Planning and Permitting Division, U. S. Environmental Protection Agency Region 6, 1445 Ross Ave., Dallas, Texas, 75202, within the time specified. All supporting data can be submitted on CD–ROM or some comparable electronic media.

(B) Compile records of analytical data from paragraph (3), summarized, and maintained onsite for a minimum of five years.

(C) Furnish these records and data when either EPA or the State of Texas requests them for inspection.

(D) Send along with all data a signed copy of the following certification statement, to attest to the truth and accuracy of the data submitted:

"Under civil and criminal penalty of law for the making or submission of false or fraudulent statements or representations (pursuant to the applicable provisions of the Federal Code, which include, but may not be limited to, 18 U.S.C. 1001 and 42 U.S.C. 6928), I certify that the information contained in or accompanying this document is true, accurate and complete.

As to the (those) identified section(s) of this document for which I cannot personally verify its (their) truth and accuracy, I certify as the company official having supervisory responsibility for the persons who, acting under my direct instructions, made the verification that this information is true, accurate and complete.

If any of this information is determined by EPA in its sole discretion to be false, inaccurate or incomplete, and upon conveyance of this fact to the company, I recognize and agree that this exclusion of waste will be void as if it never had effect or to the extent directed by EPA and that the company will be liable for any actions taken in contravention of the company's RCRA and CERCLA obligations premised upon the company's reliance on the void exclusion."

Table 2—Wastes Excluded From Specific Sources

Facility	Address	Waste description
		(6) Reopener: (A) If, anytime after disposal of the delisted waste Bayer possesses or is otherwise made aware of any environmental data (including but not limited to leachate data or ground water monitoring data) or any other data relevant to the delisted waste indicating that any constituent identified for the delisting verification testing is at a level higher than the delisting level allowed by EPA in granting the petition, then the facility must report the data, in writing, to EPA within 10 days of first possessing or being made aware of that data. (B) If either the quarterly or annual testing of the waste does not meet the delisting requirements in paragraph 1, Bayer must report the data, in writing, to EPA within 10 days of first possessing or being made aware of that data. (C) If Bayer fails to submit the information described in paragraphs (5),(6)(A) or (6)(B) or if any other information is received from any source, EPA will make a preliminary determination as to whether the reported information requires action to protect human health and/or the environment. Further action may include suspending, or revoking the exclusion, or other appropriate response necessary to protect human health and the environment. (D) If EPA determines that the reported information requires action, EPA will notify the facility in writing of the actions it believes are necessary to protect human health and the environment. The notice shall include a statement of the proposed action and a statement providing the facility with an opportunity to present information explaining why the proposed EPA action is not necessary. The facility shall have 10 days from the date of EPA's notice to present such information. (E) Following the receipt of information from the facility described in paragraph (6)(D) or (if no information is presented under paragraph (6)(D)) the initial receipt of information described in paragraphs (5), (6)(A) or (6)(B), EPA will issue a final written determination describing the actions that are necessary to protect human health and/or the environment. Any required action described in EPA's determination shall become effective immediately, unless EPA provides otherwise.
Bayer Material Science LLC	Baytown, TX	Toluene Diisocyanate (TDI) Residue (EPA Hazardous Waste No. K027) generated at a maximum rate of 9,780 cubic yards per calendar year after March 12, 2009. For the exclusion to be valid, Bayer must implement a verification testing program that meets the following Paragraphs: (1) Delisting Levels: All concentrations for those constituents must not exceed the maximum allowable concentrations in mg/l specified in this paragraph. TDI Residue Leachable Concentrations (mg/l): Arsenic—0.10, Barium—36.0; Chloromethane—6.06; Chromium—2.27; Cobalt—13.6; Copper—25.9; Cyanide—3.08; Dichlorophenoxyacetic acid—1.08; Diethyl phthalate—1000.0; Endrin—0.02; Lead—0.702; Nickel—13.5; ortho-dichlorobenzene—9.72; Selenium—0.89; Tin—22.5; Vanadium—0.976; Zinc—197.0; 2,4-Toluenediamine—0.0459; Toluene Diisocyanate—0.039. (2) Waste Holding and Handling: (A) Bayer must manage the TDI residue in a manner to ensure that the residues are offloaded safely and opportunities for chemical self-reaction and expansion are minimized. The TDI residue must be handled to ensure that contact with water is minimized. (B) Waste classification as non-hazardous cannot begin until compliance with the limits set in paragraph (1) for the TDI residue has occurred for two consecutive quarterly sampling events and the reports have been approved by EPA. (C) If constituent levels in any sample taken by Bayer exceed any of the delisting levels set in paragraph (1) for the TDI residue, Bayer must do the following: (i) notify EPA in accordance with paragraph (6) and (ii) manage and dispose the TDI residue as hazardous waste generated under Subtitle C of RCRA. (3) Testing Requirements: Upon this exclusion becoming final, Bayer must perform quarterly analytical testing by sampling and analyzing the TDI residue as follows: (A) Quarterly Testing: (i) Collect two representative composite samples of the TDI residue at quarterly intervals after EPA grants the final exclusion. The first composite samples may be taken at any time after EPA grants the final approval. Sampling should be performed in accordance with the sampling plan approved by EPA in support of the exclusion.

Table 2—Wastes Excluded From Specific Sources

Facility	Address	Waste description
		(ii) Analyze the samples for all constituents listed in paragraph (1). Any composite sample taken that exceeds the delisting levels listed in paragraph (1) for the TDI residue must be disposed as hazardous waste in accordance with the applicable hazardous waste requirements. (iii) Within thirty (30) days after taking its first quarterly sample, Bayer will report its first quarterly analytical test data to EPA. If levels of constituents measured in the samples of the TDI residue do not exceed the levels set forth in paragraph (1) of this exclusion for two consecutive quarters, Bayer can manage and dispose the non-hazardous TDI residue according to all applicable solid waste regulations. (B) Annual Testing: (i) If Bayer completes the quarterly testing specified in paragraph (3) above and no sample contains a constituent at a level which exceeds the limits set forth in paragraph (1), Bayer can begin annual testing as follows: Bayer must test two representative composite samples of the TDI residue for all constituents listed in paragraph (1) at least once per calendar year. (ii) The samples for the annual testing shall be a representative composite sample according to appropriate methods. As applicable to the method-defined parameters of concern, analyses requiring the use of SW–846 methods incorporated by reference in 40 CFR 260.11 must be used without substitution. As applicable, the SW–846 methods might include Methods 0010, 0011, 0020, 0023A, 0030, 0031, 0040, 0050, 0051, 0060, 0061, 1010A, 1020B, 1110A, 1310B, 1311, 1312, 1320, 1330A, 9010C, 9012B, 9040C, 9045D, 9060A, 9070A (uses EPA Method 1664, Rev. A), 9071B, and 9095B. Methods must meet Performance Based Measurement System Criteria in which the Data Quality Objectives are to demonstrate that samples of the Bayer spent carbon are representative for all constituents listed in paragraph (1). (iii) The samples for the annual testing taken for the second and subsequent annual testing events shall be taken within the same calendar month as the first annual sample taken. (iv) The annual testing report must include the total amount of waste in cubic yards disposed during the calendar year. (4) Changes in Operating Conditions: If Bayer significantly changes the process described in its petition or starts any process that generates the waste that may or could affect the composition or type of waste generated (by illustration, but not limitation, changes in equipment or operating conditions of the treatment process), it must notify EPA in writing and it may no longer handle the wastes generated from the new process as non-hazardous until the wastes meet the delisting levels set in paragraph (1) and it has received written approval to do so from EPA. Bayer must submit a modification to the petition complete with full sampling and analysis for circumstances where the waste volume changes and/or additional waste codes are added to the waste stream. (5) Data Submittals: Bayer must submit the information described below. If Bayer fails to submit the required data within the specified time or maintain the required records on-site for the specified time, EPA, at its discretion, will consider this sufficient basis to reopen the exclusion as described in paragraph (6). Bayer must: (A) Submit the data obtained through paragraph 3 to the Chief, Corrective Action and Waste Minimization Section, Multimedia Planning and Permitting Division, U.S. Environmental Protection Agency Region 6, 1445 Ross Ave., Dallas, Texas 75202, within the time specified. All supporting data can be submitted on CD–ROM or some comparable electronic media. (B) Compile records of analytical data from paragraph (3), summarized, and maintained on-site for a minimum of five years. (C) Furnish these records and data when either EPA or the State of Texas requests them for inspection. (D) Send along with all data a signed copy of the following certification statement, to attest to the truth and accuracy of the data submitted. "Under civil and criminal penalty of law for the making or submission of false or fraudulent statements or representations (pursuant to the applicable provisions of the Federal Code, which include, but may not be limited to, 18 U.S.C. 1001 and 42 U.S.C. 6928), I certify that the information contained in or accompanying this document is true, accurate and complete. As to the (those) identified section(s) of this document for which I cannot personally verify its (their) truth and accuracy, I certify as the company official having supervisory responsibility for the persons who, acting under my direct instructions, made the verification that this information is true, accurate and complete.

PART 261—Appendices

Table 2—Wastes Excluded From Specific Sources

Facility	Address	Waste description
		If any of this information is determined by EPA in its sole discretion to be false, inaccurate or incomplete, and upon conveyance of this fact to the company, I recognize and agree that this exclusion of waste will be void as if it never had effect or to the extent directed by EPA and that the company will be liable for any actions taken in contravention of the company's RCRA and CERCLA obligations premised upon the company's reliance on the void exclusion." (6) Reopener: (A) If, anytime after disposal of the delisted waste Bayer possesses or is otherwise made aware of any environmental data (including but not limited to leachate data or ground water monitoring data) or any other data relevant to the delisted waste indicating that any constituent identified for the delisting verification testing is at a level higher than the delisting level allowed by EPA in granting the petition, then the facility must report the data, in writing, to EPA within 10 days of first possessing or being made aware of that data. (B) If either the quarterly or annual testing of the waste does not meet the delisting requirements in paragraph 1, Bayer must report the data, in writing, to EPA within 10 days of first possessing or being made aware of that data. (C) If Bayer fails to submit the information described in paragraphs (5), (6)(A) or (6)(B) or if any other information is received from any source, EPA will make a preliminary determination as to whether the reported information requires action to protect human health and/or the environment. Further action may include suspending, or revoking the exclusion, or other appropriate response necessary to protect human health and the environment. (D) If EPA determines that the reported information requires action, EPA will notify the facility in writing of the actions it believes are necessary to protect human health and the environment. The notice shall include a statement of the proposed action and a statement providing the facility with an opportunity to present information explaining why the proposed EPA action is not necessary. The facility shall have 10 days from the date of EPA's notice to present such information. (E) Following the receipt of information from the facility described in paragraph (6)(D) or (if no information is presented under paragraph (6)(D)) the initial receipt of information described in paragraphs (5), (6)(A) or (6)(B), EPA will issue a final written determination describing the actions that are necessary to protect human health and/or the environment. Any required action described in EPA's determination shall become effective immediately, unless EPA provides otherwise. (7) Notification Requirements Bayer must do the following before transporting the delisted waste. Failure to provide this notification will result in a violation of the delisting petition and a possible revocation of the decision. (A) Provide a one-time written notification to any state Regulatory Agency to which or through which it will transport the delisted waste described above for disposal, 60 days before beginning such activities. (B) Update the one-time written notification if it ships the delisted waste into a different disposal facility. (C) Failure to provide this notification will result in a violation of the delisting variance and a possible revocation of the decision.
Bekaert Steel Corporation	Rogers, Arkansas	Wastewater treatment sludge (EPA Hazardous Waste No. F006) generated from electroplating operations (at a maximum annual rate of 1250 cubic yards to be measured on a calendar year basis) after [insert publication date of the final rule]. In order to confirm that the characteristics of the waste do not change significantly, the facility must, on an annual basis, before July 1 of each year, analyze a representative composite sample for the constituents listed in §261.24 as well as antimony, copper, nickel, and zinc using the method specified therein. The annual analytical results, including quality control information, must be compiled, certified according to §260.22(i)(12) of this chapter, maintained on site for a minimum of five years, and made available for inspection upon request of any employee or representative of EPA or the State of Arkansas. Failure to maintain the required documents on site will be considered by EPA, at its discretion, sufficient basis to revoke the exclusion to the extent directed by EPA. *Notification Requirements:* Bekaert Steel Corporation must provide a one-time written notification to any State Regulatory Agency to which or through which the delisted waste described above will be transported for disposal at least 60 days prior to the commencement of such activities. Failure to provide such a notification will result in a violation of the delisting petition and a possible revocation of the decision.
Bethlehem Steel Corporation	Lackawanna, New York	Ammonia still lime sludge (EPA Hazardous Waste No. K060) and other solid waste generated from primary metal-making and coking operations. This is a one-time exclusion for 118,000 cubic yards of waste contained in the on-site landfill referred to as HWM-2. This exclusion was published on April 24, 1996.

Table 2—Wastes Excluded From Specific Sources

Facility	Address	Waste description
Bethlehem Steel Corp	Johnstown, PA	Uncured and cured chemically stabilized electric arc furnace dust/sludge (CSEAFD) treatment residue (K061) generated from the primary production of steel after May 22, 1989. This exclusion is conditioned upon the data obtained from Bethlehem's full- scale CSEAFD treatment facility because Bethlehem's original data were obtained from a labortory- scale CSEAFD treatment process. To ensure that hazardous constituents are not present in the waste at levels of regulatory concern once the full-scale treatment facility is in operation, Bethlehem must implement a testing program for the petitioned waste. This testing program must meet the following conditions for the exclusion to be valid:

(1) *Testing:*

(A) *Initial Testing:* During the first four weeks of operation of the full-scale treatment system, Bethlehem must collect representative grab samples of each treated batch of the CSEAFD and composite the grab samples daily. The daily composites, prior to disposal, must be analyzed for the EP leachate concentrations of all the EP toxic metals, nickel, and cyanide (using distilled water in the cyanide extractions). Analyses must be performed using appropriate methods. As applicable to the method-defined parameters of concern, analyses requiring the use of SW–846 methods incorporated by reference in 40 CFR 260.11 must be used without substitution. As applicable, the SW–846 methods might include Methods 0010, 0011, 0020, 0023A, 0030, 0031, 0040, 0050, 0051, 0060, 0061, 1010A, 1020B, 1110A, 1310B, 1311, 1312, 1320, 1330A, 9010C, 9012B, 9040C, 9045D, 9060A, 9070A (uses EPA Method 1664, Rev. A), 9071B, and 9095B. Bethlehem must report the analytical test data obtained during this initial period no later than 90 days after the treatment of the first full-scale batch.

(B) *Subsequent Testing:* Bethlehem must collect representative grab samples from every treated batch of CSEAFD generated daily and composite all of the grab samples to produce a weekly composite sample. Bethlehem then must analyze each weekly composite sample for the EP leachate concentrations of all the EP toxic metals and nickel. Analyses must be performed using appropriate methods. As applicable to the method-defined parameters of concern, analyses requiring the use of SW–846 methods incorporated by reference in 40 CFR 260.11 must be used without substitution. As applicable, the SW–846 methods might include Methods 0010, 0011, 0020, 0023A, 0030, 0031, 0040, 0050, 0051, 0060, 0061, 1010A, 1020B, 1110A, 1310B, 1311, 1312, 1320, 1330A, 9010C, 9012B, 9040C, 9045D, 9060A, 9070A (uses EPA Method 1664, Rev. A), 9071B, and 9095B. The analytical data, including all quality control information, must be compiled and maintained on site for a minimum of three years. These data must be furnished upon request and made available for inspection by any employee or representative of EPA or the State of Pennsylvania.

(2) *Delisting Levels:* If the EP extract concentrations resulting from the testing in condition (1)(A) or (1)(B) for chromium, lead, arsenic, or silver exceed 0.315 mg/l; for barium exceeds 6.3 mg/l; for cadmium or selenium exceed 0.063 mg/l; for mercury exceeds 0.0126 mg/l; for nickel exceeds 3.15 mg/l; or for cyanide exceeds 4.42 mg/l, the waste must either be retreated until it meets these levels or managed and disposed in accordance with subtitle C of RCRA.

(3) *Data submittals:* Within one week of system start-up, Bethlehem must notify the Section Chief, Variances Section (see address below) when their full- scale stabilization system is on- line and waste treatment has begun. All data obtained through the initial testing condition (1)(A), must be submitted to the Section Chief, Variances Section, PSPD/OSW, (OS-343), U.S. EPA, 1200 Pennsylvania Ave., NW., Washington, DC 20406 within the time period specified in condition (1)(A). At the Section Chief's request, Bethlehem must submit analytical data obtained through condition (1)(B) to the above address, within the time period specified by the Section Chief. Failure to submit the required data obtained from either condition (1)(A) or (1)(B) within the specified time periods will be considered by the Agency sufficient basis to revoke Bethlehem's exclusion to the extent directed by EPA. All data must be accompanied by the following certification statement:

"Under civil and criminal penalty of law for the making or submission of false or fraudulent statements or representations (pursuant to the applicable provisions of the Federal Code which include, but may not be limited to, 18 U.S.C. 6928), I certify that the information contained in or accompanying this document is true, accurate and complete.

"As to the (those) identified section(s) of this document for which I cannot personally verify its (their) truth and accuracy, I certify as the company official having supervisory responsibility for the persons who, acting under my direct instructions, made the verification that this information is true, accurate and complete.

"In the event that any of this information is determined by EPA in its sole discretion to be false, inaccurate or incomplete, and upon conveyance of this fact to the company, I recognize and agree that this exclusion of wastes will be void as if it never had effect or to the extent directed by EPA and that the company will be liable for any actions taken in contravention of the company's RCRA and CERCLA obligations premised upon the company's reliance on the void exclusion."

Table 2—Wastes Excluded From Specific Sources

Facility	Address	Waste description
Bethlehem Steel Corp	Steelton, PA	Uncured and cured chemically stabilized electric arc furnace dust/sludge (CSEAFD) treatment residue (K061) generated from the primary production of steel after May 22, 1989. This exclusion is conditioned upon the data obtained from Bethlehem's full- scale CSEAFD treatment facility because Bethlehem's original data were obtained from a laboratory- scale CSEAFD treatment process. To ensure that hazardous constituents are not present in the waste at levels of regulatory concern once the full-scale treatment facility is in operation, Bethlehem must implement a testing program for the petitioned waste. This testing program must meet the following conditions for the exclusion to be valid: (1) *Testing:* (A) *Initial Testing:* During the first four weeks of operation of the full-scale treatment system, Bethlehem must collect representative grab samples of each treated batch of the CSEAFD and composite the grab samples daily. The daily composites, prior to disposal, must be analyzed for the EP leachate concentrations of all the EP toxic metals, nickel and cyanide (using distilled water in the cyanide extractions). Analyses must be performed using appropriate methods. As applicable to the method-defined parameters of concern, analyses requiring the use of SW–846 methods incorporated by reference in 40 CFR 260.11 must be used without substitution. As applicable, the SW–846 methods might include Methods 0010, 0011, 0020, 0023A, 0030, 0031, 0040, 0050, 0051, 0060, 0061, 1010A, 1020B, 1110A, 1310B, 1311, 1312, 1320, 1330A, 9010C, 9012B, 9040C, 9045D, 9060A, 9070A (uses EPA Method 1664, Rev. A), 9071B, and 9095B. Bethlehem must report the analytical test data obtained during this initial period no later than 90 days after the treatment of the first full-scale batch. (B) *Subsequent Testing:* Bethlehem must collect representative grab samples from every treated batch of CSEAFD generated daily and composite all of the grab samples to produce a weekly composite sample. Bethlehem then must analyze each weekly composite sample for the EP leachate concentrations of all the EP toxic metals and nickel. Analyses must be performed using appropriate methods. As applicable to the method-defined parameters of concern, analyses requiring the use of SW–846 methods incorporated by reference in 40 CFR 260.11 must be used without substitution. As applicable, the SW–846 methods might include Methods 0010, 0011, 0020, 0023A, 0030, 0031, 0040, 0050, 0051, 0060, 0061, 1010A, 1020B, 1110A, 1310B, 1311, 1312, 1320, 1330A, 9010C, 9012B, 9040C, 9045D, 9060A, 9070A (uses EPA Method 1664, Rev. A), 9071B, and 9095B. The analytical data, including all quality control information, must be compiled and maintained on site for a minimum of three years. These data must be furnished upon request and made available for inspection by any employee or representative of EPA or the State of Pennsylvania. (2) *Delisting Levels:* If the EP extract concentrations resulting from the testing in condition (1)(A) or (1)(B) for chromium, lead, arsenic, or silver exceeds 0.315 mg/l; for barium exceeds 6.3 mg/l; for cadmium or selenium exceed 0.063 mg/l; for mercury exceeds 0.0126 mg/l; for nickel exceeds 3.15 mg/l; or for cyanide exceeds 4.42 mg/l, the waste must either be re-treated or managed and disposed in accordance with subtitle C of RCRA. (3) *Data submittals:* Within one week of system start-up, Bethlehem must notify the Section Chief, Variances Section (see address below) when their full- scale stabilization system is on- line and waste treatment has begun. All data obtained through the initial testing condition (1)(A), must be submitted to the PSPD/OSW (5303W), U.S. EPA, 1200 Pennsylvania Ave., NW, Washington, DC 20460 within the time period specified in condition (1)(A). At the Section Chief's request, Bethlehem must submit analytical data obtained through condition (1)(B) to the above address, within the time period specified by the Section Chief. Failure to submit the required data obtained from either condition (1)(A) or (1)(B) within the specified time periods will be considered by the Agency sufficient basis to revoke Bethlehem's exclusion to the extent directed by EPA. All data must be accompanied by the following certification statement: "Under civil and criminal penalty of law for the making or submission of false or fraudulent statements or representations (pursuant to the applicable provisions of the Federal Code which include, but may not be limited to, 18 U.S.C. 6928), I certify that the information contained in or accompanying this document is true, accurate and complete. "As to the (those) identified section(s) of this document for which I cannot personally verify its (their) truth and accuracy, I certify as the company official having supervisory responsibility for the persons who, acting under my direct instructions, made the verification that this information is true, accurate and complete. "In the event that any of this information is determined by EPA in its sole discretion to be false, inaccurate or incomplete, and upon conveyance of this fact to the company, I recognize and agree that this exclusion of wastes will be void as if it never had effect or to the extent directed by EPA and that the company will be liable for any actions taken in contravention of the company's RCRA and CERCLA obligations premised upon the company's reliance on the void exclusion."

Table 2—Wastes Excluded From Specific Sources

Facility	Address	Waste description
BF Goodrich Intermediates Company, Inc	Calvert City, Kentucky	Brine purification muds and saturator insolubles (EPA Hazardous Waste No. K071) after August 18, 1989. This exclusion is conditional upon the collection and submission of data obtained from BFG's full-scale treatment system because BFG's original data was based on data presented by another petitioner using an identical treatment process. To ensure that hazardous constituents are not present in the waste at levels of regulatory concern once the full-scale treatment facility is in operation, BFG must implement a testing program. All sampling and analyses (including quality control procedures) must be performed using appropriate methods. As applicable to the method-defined parameters of concern, analyses requiring the use of SW–846 methods incorporated by reference in 40 CFR 260.11 must be used without substitution. As applicable, the SW–846 methods might include Methods 0010, 0011, 0020, 0023A, 0030, 0031, 0040, 0050, 0051, 0060, 0061, 1010A, 1020B, 1110A, 1310B, 1311, 1312, 1320, 1330A, 9010C, 9012B, 9040C, 9045D, 9060A, 9070A (uses EPA Method 1664, Rev. A), 9071B, and 9095B. This testing program must meet the following conditions for the exclusion to be valid: (1) Initial Testing: During the first four weeks of full-scale operation, BFG must do the following: (A) Collect representative grab samples from every batch of the treated mercury brine purification muds and treated saturator insolubles on a daily basis and composite the grab samples to produce two separate daily composite samples (one of the treated mercury brine purification muds and one of the treated saturator insolubles). Prior to disposal of the treated batches, two daily composite samples must be analyzed for EP leachate concentration of mercury. BFG must report the analytical test data, including all quality control data, within 90 days after the treatment of the first full-scale batch. (B) Collect representative grab samples from every batch of treated mercury brine purification muds and treated saturator insolubles on a daily basis and composite the grab samples to produce two separate weekly composite samples (one of the treated mercury brine muds and one of the treated saturator insolubles). Prior to disposal of the treated batches, two weekly composite samples must be analyzed for the EP leachate concentrations of all the EP toxic metals (except mercury), nickel, and cyanide (using distilled water in the cyanide extractions). BFG must report the analytical test data, including all quality control data, obtained during this initial period no later than 90 days after the treatment of the first full-scale batch. (2) Subsequent Testing: After the first four weeks of full-scale operation, BFG must do the following: (A) Continue to sample and test as described in condition (1)(A). BFG must compile and store on-site for a minimum of three years all analytical data and quality control data. These data must be furnished upon request and made available for inspection by any employee or representative of EPA or the State of Kentucky. (B) Continue to sample and test as described in condition (1)(B). BFG must compile and store on- site for a minimum of three years all analytical data and quality control data. These data must be furnished upon request and made available for inspection by any employee or representative of EPA or the State of Kentucky. These testing requirements shall be terminated by EPA when the results of four consecutive weekly composite samples of both the treated mercury brine muds and treated saturator insolubles, obtained from either the initial testing or subsequent testing, show the maximum allowable levels in condition (3) are not exceeded and the Section Chief, Variances Section, notifies BFG that the requirements of this condition have been lifted. (3) If, under condition (1) or (2), the EP leachate concentrations for chromium, lead, arsenic, or silver exceed 0.316 mg/l; for barium exceeds 6.31 mg/l; for cadmium or selenium exceed 0.063 mg/l; for mercury exceeds 0.0126 mg/l, for nickel exceeds 3.16 mg/l; or for cyanide exceeds 4.42 mg/l, the waste must either be retreated until it meets these levels or managed and disposed of in accordance with subtitle C of RCRA. (4) Within one week of system start-up, BFG must notify the Section Chief, Variances Section (see address below) when the full- scale system is on-line and waste treatment has begun. All data obtained through condition (1) must be submitted to the Section Chief, Variances Section, PSPD/ OSW (OS-343), U.S. EPA, 1200 Pennsylvania Ave., NW., Washington, DC 20460 within the time period specified in condition (1). At the Section Chief's request, BFG must submit any other analytical data obtained through condition (2) to the above address, within the time period specified by the Section Chief. Failure to submit the required data will be considered by the Agency sufficient basis to revoke BFG's exclusion to the extent directed by EPA. All data must be accompanied by the following certification statement: "Under civil and criminal penalty of law for the making or submission of false or fraudulent statements or representations (pursuant to the applicable provisions of the Federal Code which include, but may not be limited to, 18 U.S.C. §6928), I certify that the information contained in or accompanying this document is true, accurate and complete. As to the (those) identified section(s) of this document for which I cannot personally verify its (their) truth and accuracy, I certify as the company official having supervisory responsibility for the persons who, acting under my direct instructions, made the verification that this information is true, accurate and complete.

Table 2—Wastes Excluded From Specific Sources

Facility	Address	Waste description
		In the event that any of this information is determined by EPA in its sole discretion to be false, inaccurate or incomplete, and upon conveyance of this fact to the company, I recognize and agree that this exclusion of wastes will be void as if it never had effect or to the extent directed by EPA and that the company will be liable for any actions taken in contravention of the company's RCRA and CERCLA obligations premised upon the company's reliance on the void exclusion."
CF&I Steel Corporation	Pueblo, Colorado	Fully-cured chemically stabilized electric arc furnace dust/sludge (CSEAFD) treatment residue (EPA Hazardous Waste No. K061) generated from the primary production of steel after May 9, 1989. This exclusion is conditioned upon the data obtained from CF&I's full-scale CSEAFD treatment facility because CF&I's original data was obtained from a laboratory-scale CSEAFD treatment process. To ensure that hazardous constituents are not present in the waste at levels of regulatory concern once the full- scale treatment facility is in operation, CF&I must implement a testing program for the petitioned waste. This testing program must meet the following conditions for the exclusion to be valid: (1) *Testing:* (A) *Initial Testing:* During the first four weeks of operation of the full-scale treatment system, CF&I must collect representative grab samples of each treated batch of the CSEAFD and composite the grab samples daily. The daily composites, prior to disposal, must be analyzed for the EP leachate concentrations of all the EP toxic metals, nickel, and cyanide (using distilled water in the cyanide extractions). Analyses must be performed using appropriate methods. As applicable to the method-defined parameters of concern, analyses requiring the use of SW–846 methods incorporated by reference in 40 CFR 260.11 must be used without substitution. As applicable, the SW–846 methods might include Methods 0010, 0011, 0020, 0023A, 0030, 0031, 0040, 0050, 0051, 0060, 0061, 1010A, 1020B, 1110A, 1310B, 1311, 1312, 1320, 1330A, 9010C, 9012B, 9040C, 9045D, 9060A, 9070A (uses EPA Method 1664, Rev. A), 9071B, and 9095B. CF&I must report the analytical test data obtained during this initial period no later than 90 days after the treatment of the first full-scale batch. (B) *Subsequent Testing:* CF&I must collect representative grab samples from every treated batch of CSEAFD generated daily and composite all of the grab samples to produce a weekly composite sample. CF&I then must analyze each weekly composite sample for the EP leachate concentrations of all of the EP toxic metals and nickel. Analyses must be performed using appropriate methods. As applicable to the method-defined parameters of concern, analyses requiring the use of SW–846 methods incorporated by reference in 40 CFR 260.11 must be used without substitution. As applicable, the SW–846 methods might include Methods 0010, 0011, 0020, 0023A, 0030, 0031, 0040, 0050, 0051, 0060, 0061, 1010A, 1020B, 1110A, 1310B, 1311, 1312, 1320, 1330A, 9010C, 9012B, 9040C, 9045D, 9060A, 9070A (uses EPA Method 1664, Rev. A), 9071B, and 9095B. The analytical data, including all quality control information, must be compiled and maintained on site for a minimum of three years. These data must be furnished upon request and made available for inspection by any employee or representative of EPA or the State of Colorado. (2) *Delisting levels:* If the EP extract concentrations determined in conditions (1)(A) or (1)(B) for chromium, lead, arsenic, or silver exceed 0.315 mg/l; for barium exceeds 6.3 mg/l; for cadmium or selenium exceed 0.063 mg/l; for mercury exceeds 0.0126 mg/l; for nickel exceeds 3.15 mg/l; or for cyanide exceeds 4.42 mg/l, the waste must either be re-treated or managed and disposed in accordance with Subtitle C of RCRA. (3) *Data submittals:* Within one week of system start-up, CF&I must notify the Section Chief, Variances Section (see address below) when their full-scale stabilization system is on-line and waste treatment has begun. All data obtained through the initial testing condition (1)(A), must be submitted to the Section Chief, Variances Section, PSPD/OSW, (OS-343), U.S. EPA, 1200 Pennsylvania Ave., NW., Washington, DC 20460 within the time period specified in condition (1)(A). At the Section Chief's request, CF&I must submit analytical data obtained through condition (1)(B) to the above address, within the time period specified by the Section Chief. Failure to submit the required data obtained from either condition (1)(A) or (1)(B) within the specified time periods will be considered by the Agency sufficient basis to revoke CF&I's exclusion to the extent directed by EPA. All data must be accompanied by the following certification statement: "Under civil and criminal penalty of law for the making of submission of false or fraudulent statements or representations (pursuant to the applicable provisions of the Federal Code which include, but may not be limited to, 18 U.S.C. 6928), I certify that the information contained in or accompanying this document is true, accurate and complete. As to the (those) identified section(s) of this document for which I cannot personally verify its (their) truth and accuracy, I certify as the company official having supervisory responsibility for the persons who, acting under my direct instructions, made the verification that this information is true, accurate and complete. In the event that any of this information is determined by EPA in its sole discretion to be false, inaccurate or incomplete, and upon conveyance of this fact to the company, I recognize and agree that this exclusion of wastes will be void as if it never had effect or to the extent directed by EPA and that the company will be liable for any actions taken in contravention of the company's RCRA and CERCLA obligations premised upon the company's reliance on the void exclusion."

Table 2—Wastes Excluded From Specific Sources

Facility	Address	Waste description
Chaparral Steel Midlothian, L.P.	Midlothian, Texas	Leachate from Landfill No. 3, storm water from the baghouse area, and other K061 wastewaters which have been pumped to tank storage (at a maximum generation of 2500 cubic yards or 500,000 gallons per calender year) (EPA Hazardous Waste No. K061) generated at Chaparral Steel Midlothian, L.P., Midlothian, Texas, and is managed as nonhazardous solid waste after February 23, 2000. Chaparral Steel must implement a testing program that meets the following conditions for the exclusion to be valid: (1) *Delisting Levels:* All concentrations for the constituent total lead in the approximately 2,500 cubic yards (500,000 gallons) per calender year of raw leachate from Landfill No. 3, storm water from the baghouse area, and other K061 wastewaters that is transferred from the storage tank to non-hazardous management must not exceed 0.69 mg/l (ppm). Constituents must be measured in the waste by appropriate methods. As applicable to the method-defined parameters of concern, analyses requiring the use of SW–846 methods incorporated by reference in 40 CFR 260.11 must be used without substitution. As applicable, the SW–846 methods might include Methods 0010, 0011, 0020, 0023A, 0030, 0031, 0040, 0050, 0051, 0060, 0061, 1010A, 1020B, 1110A, 1310B, 1311, 1312, 1320, 1330A, 9010C, 9012B, 9040C, 9045D, 9060A, 9070A (uses EPA Method 1664, Rev. A), 9071B, and 9095B. (2) *Waste Holding and Handling:* Chaparral Steel must store as hazardous all leachate waste from Landfill No. 3, storm water from the bag house area, and other K061 wastewaters until verification testing as specified in Condition (3), is completed and valid analyses demonstrate that condition (1) is satisfied. If the levels of constituents measured in the samples of the waste do not exceed the levels set forth in Condition (1), then the waste is nonhazardous and may be managed and disposed of in accordance with all applicable solid waste regulations. If constituent levels in a sample exceed the delisting levels set in Condition (1), the waste volume corresponding to this sample must be treated until delisting levels are met or returned to the original storage tank. Treatment is designated as precipitation, flocculation, and filtering in a wastewater treatment system to remove metals from the wastewater. Treatment residuals precipitated will be designated as a hazardous waste. If the delisting level cannot be met, then the waste must be managed and disposed of in accordance with subtitle C of RCRA. (3) *Verification Testing Requirements:* Sample collection and analyses, including quality control procedures, must be performed using appropriate methods. As applicable to the method-defined parameters of concern, analyses requiring the use of SW–846 methods incorporated by reference in 40 CFR 260.11 must be used without substitution. As applicable, the SW–846 methods might include Methods 0010, 0011, 0020, 0023A, 0030, 0031, 0040, 0050, 0051, 0060, 0061, 1010A, 1020B, 1110A, 1310B, 1311, 1312, 1320, 1330A, 9010C, 9012B, 9040C, 9045D, 9060A, 9070A (uses EPA Method 1664, Rev. A), 9071B, and 9095B. Chaparral Steel must analyze one composite sample from each batch of untreated wastewater transferred from the hazardous waste storage tank to non-hazardous waste management. Each composited batch sample must be analyzed, prior to non-hazardous management of the waste in the batch represented by that sample, for the constituent lead as listed in Condition (1). Chaparral may treat the waste as specified in Condition (2). If EPA judges the treatment process to be effective during the operating conditions used during the initial verification testing, Chaparral Steel may replace the testing requirement in Condition (3)(A) with the testing requirement in Condition (3)(B). Chaparral must continue to test as specified in (3)(A) until and unless notified by EPA or designated authority that testing in Condition (3)(A) may be replaced by Condition (3)(B). (A) Initial Verification Testing: Representative composite samples from the first eight (8) full- scale treated batches of wastewater from the K061 leachate/ wastewater storage tank must be analyzed for the constituent lead as listed in Condition (1), Chaparral must report to EPA the operational and analytical test data, including quality control information, obtained from these initial full scale treatment batches within 90 days of the eighth treatment batch. (B) Subsequent Verification Testing: Following notification by EPA, Chaparral Steel may substitute the testing conditions in (3)(B) for (3)(A). Chaparral Steel must analyze representative composite samples from the treated full scale batches on an annual basis. If delisting levels for any constituent listed in Condition (1) are exceeded in the annual sample, Chaparral must reinstitute complete testing as required in Condition (3)(A). As stated in Condition (3) Chaparral must continue to test all batches of untreated waste to determine if delisting criteria are met before managing the wastewater from the K061 tank as nonhazardous. (4) *Changes in Operating Conditions:* If Chaparral Steel significantly changes the treatment process established under Condition (3) (*e.g.,* use of new treatment agents), Chaparral Steel must notify the Agency in writing. After written approval by EPA, Chaparral Steel may handle the wastes generated as non-hazardous, if the wastes meet the delisting levels set in Condition (1).

Table 2—Wastes Excluded From Specific Sources

Facility	Address	Waste description
		(5) *Data Submittals:* Records of operating conditions and analytical data from Condition (3) must be compiled, summarized, and maintained on site for a minimum of five years. These records and data must be furnished upon request by EPA, or the State of Texas, or both, and be made available for inspection. Failure to submit the required data within the specified time period or maintain the required records on site for the specified time will be considered by EPA, at its discretion, sufficient basis to reopen the exclusion as described in Paragraph (6). All data must be accompanied by a signed copy of the following certification statement to attest to the truth and accuracy of the data submitted: Under civil and criminal penalty of law for the making or submission of false or fraudulent statements or representations (pursuant to the applicable provisions of the Federal Code, which include, but may not be limited to, 18 U.S.C. 1001 and 42 U.S.C. 6928), I certify that the information contained in or accompanying this document is true, accurate and complete. As to the (those) identified section(s) of this document for which I cannot personally verify its (their) truth and accuracy, I certify as the company official having supervisory responsibility for the persons who, acting under my direct instructions, made the verification that this information is true, accurate and complete. In the event that any of this information is determined by EPA in its sole discretion to be false, inaccurate or incomplete, and upon conveyance of this fact to the company, I recognize and agree that this exclusion of waste will be void as if it never had effect or to the extent directed by EPA and that the company will be liable for any actions taken in contravention of the company's RCRA and CERCLA obligations premised upon the company's reliance on the void exclusion. (6) *Reopener Language* (A) If, anytime after disposal of the delisted waste, Chaparral Steel possesses or is otherwise made aware of any environmental data (including but not limited to leachate data or groundwater monitoring data) or any other data relevant to the delisted waste indicating that any constituent identified for the delisting verification testing is at level higher than the delisting level allowed by the Regional Administrator or his delegate in granting the petition, then the facility must report the data, in writing, to the Regional Administrator or his delegate within 10 days of first possessing or being made aware of that data. (B) Based on the information described in paragraphs (5), or (6)(A) and any other information received from any source, the Regional Administrator or his delegate will make a preliminary determination as to whether the reported information requires Agency action to protect human health or the environment. Further action may include suspending, or revoking the exclusion, or other appropriate response necessary to protect human health and the environment. (C) If the Regional Administrator or his delegate determines that the reported information does require Agency action, the Regional Administrator or his delegate will notify the facility in writing of the actions the Regional Administrator or his delegate believes are necessary to protect human health and the environment. The notice shall include a statement of the proposed action and a statement providing the facility with an opportunity to present information as to why the proposed Agency action is not necessary. The facility shall have 10 days from the date of the Regional Administrator or delegate's notice to present such information. (D) Following the receipt of information from the facility described in paragraph (6)(C) or (if no information is presented under paragraph (6)(C)) the initial receipt of information described in paragraph (5) or (6)(A), the Regional Administrator or his delegate will issue a final written determination describing the Agency actions that are necessary to protect human health or the environment. Any required action described in the Regional Administrator or delegate's determination shall become effective immediately, unless the Regional Administrator or his delegate provides otherwise. (7) *Notification Requirements:* Chaparral Steel must provide a one-time written notification to any State Regulatory Agency to which or through which the delisted waste described above will be transported for disposal at least 60 days prior to the commencement of such activity. The one-time written notification must be updated if the delisted waste is shipped to a different disposal facility. Failure to provide such a notification will result in a violation of the delisting petition and a possible revocation of the decision.
Conversion Systems, Inc	Horsham, Pennsylvania	Chemically Stabilized Electric Arc Furnace Dust (CSEAFD) that is generated by Conversion Systems, Inc. (CSI) (using the Super Detox™ treatment process as modified by CSI to treat EAFD (EPA Hazardous Waste No. K061)) at the following sites and that is disposed of in Subtitle D landfills: Northwestern Steel, Sterling, Illinois after June 13, 1995. CSI must implement a testing program for each site that meets the following conditions for the exclusion to be valid:

Table 2—Wastes Excluded From Specific Sources

Facility	Address	Waste description
		(1) *Verification Testing Requirements:* Sample collection and analyses, including quality control procedures, must be performed using appropriate methods. As applicable to the method-defined parameters of concern, analyses requiring the use of SW–846 methods incorporated by reference in 40 CFR 260.11 must be used without substitution. As applicable, the SW–846 methods might include Methods 0010, 0011, 0020, 0023A, 0030, 0031, 0040, 0050, 0051, 0060, 0061, 1010A, 1020B, 1110A, 1310B, 1311, 1312, 1320, 1330A, 9010C, 9012B, 9040C, 9045D, 9060A, 9070A (uses EPA Method 1664, Rev. A), 9071B, and 9095B. (A) *Initial Verification Testing:* During the first 20 operating days of full-scale operation of a newly constructed Super Detox™ treatment facility, CSI must analyze a minimum of four (4) composite samples of CSEAFD representative of the full 20-day period. Composites must be comprised of representative samples collected from every batch generated. The CSEAFD samples must be analyzed for the constituents listed in Condition (3). CSI must report the operational and analytical test data, including quality control information, obtained during this initial period no later than 60 days after the generation of the first batch of CSEAFD. (B) *Addition of New Super Detox™ Treatment Facilities to Exclusion:* If the Agency's review of the data obtained during initial verification testing indicates that the CSEAFD generated by a specific Super Detox™ treatment facility consistently meets the delisting levels specified in Condition (3), the Agency will publish a notice adding to this exclusion the location of the new Super Detox™ treatment facility and the name of the steel mill contracting CSI's services. If the Agency's review of the data obtained during initial verification testing indicates that the CSEAFD generated by a specific Super Detox™ treatment facility fails to consistently meet the conditions of the exclusion, the Agency will not publish the notice adding the new facility. (C) *Subsequent Verification Testing:* For the Sterling, Illinois facility and any new facility subsequently added to CSI's conditional multiple-site exclusion, CSI must collect and analyze at least one composite sample of CSEAFD each month. The composite samples must be composed of representative samples collected from all batches treated in each month. These monthly representative samples must be analyzed, prior to the disposal of the CSEAFD, for the constituents listed in Condition (3). CSI may, at its discretion, analyze composite samples gathered more frequently to demonstrate that smaller batches of waste are nonhazardous. (2) *Waste Holding and Handling:* CSI must store as hazardous all CSEAFD generated until verification testing as specified in Conditions (1)(A) and (1)(C), as appropriate, is completed and valid analyses demonstrate that Condition (3) is satisfied. If the levels of constituents measured in the samples of CSEAFD do not exceed the levels set forth in Condition (3), then the CSEAFD is non-hazardous and may be disposed of in Subtitle D landfills. If constituent levels in a sample exceed any of the delisting levels set in Condition (3), the CSEAFD generated during the time period corresponding to this sample must be retreated until it meets these levels, or managed and disposed of in accordance with Subtitle C of RCRA. CSEAFD generated by a new CSI treatment facility must be managed as a hazardous waste prior to the addition of the name and location of the facility to the exclusion. After addition of the new facility to the exclusion, CSEAFD generated during the verification testing in Condition (1)(A) is also non- hazardous, if the delisting levels in Condition (3) are satisfied. (3) *Delisting Levels:* All leachable concentrations for those metals must not exceed the following levels (ppm): Antimony— 0.06; arsenic—0.50; barium—7.6; beryllium—0.010; cadmium—0.050; chromium—0.33; lead—0.15; mercury—0.009; nickel—1; selenium—0.16; silver—0.30; thallium—0.020; vanadium—2; and zinc—70. Metal concentrations must be measured in the waste leachate by the method specified in 40 CFR 261.24. (4) *Changes in Operating Conditions:* After initiating subsequent testing as described in Condition (1)(C), if CSI significantly changes the stabilization process established under Condition (1) (*e.g.*, use of new stabilization reagents), CSI must notify the Agency in writing. After written approval by EPA, CSI may handle CSEAFD wastes generated from the new process as non-hazardous, if the wastes meet the delisting levels set in Condition (3). (5) *Data Submittals:* At least one month prior to operation of a new Super Detox™ treatment facility, CSI must notify, in writing, the Chief of the Waste Identification Branch (see address below) when the Super Detox™ treatment facility is scheduled to be on- line. The data obtained through Condition (1)(A) must be submitted to the Branch Chief of the Waste Identification Branch, OSW (Mail Code 5304), U.S. EPA, 1200 Pennsylvania Ave., NW, Washington, DC 20460 within the time period specified. Records of operating conditions and analytical data from Condition (1) must be compiled, summarized, and maintained on site for a minimum of five years. These records and data must be furnished upon request by EPA, or the State in which the CSI facility is located, and made available for inspection. Failure to submit the required data within the specified time period or maintain the required records on site for the specified time will be considered by EPA, at its discretion, sufficient basis to revoke the exclusion to the extent directed by EPA. All data must be accompanied by a signed copy of the following certification statement to attest to the truth and accuracy of the data submitted:

Table 2—Wastes Excluded From Specific Sources

Facility	Address	Waste description
		Under civil and criminal penalty of law for the making or submission of false or fraudulent statements or representations (pursuant to the applicable provisions of the Federal Code, which include, but may not be limited to, 18 U.S.C. 1001 and 42 U.S.C. 6928), I certify that the information contained in or accompanying this document is true, accurate and complete. As to the (those) identified section(s) of this document for which I cannot personally verify its (their) truth and accuracy, I certify as the company official having supervisory responsibility for the persons who, acting under my direct instructions, made the verification that this information is true, accurate and complete. In the event that any of this information is determined by EPA in its sole discretion to be false, inaccurate or incomplete, and upon conveyance of this fact to the company, I recognize and agree that this exclusion of waste will be void as if it never had effect or to the extent directed by EPA and that the company will be liable for any actions taken in contravention of the company's RCRA and CERCLA obligations premised upon the company's reliance on the void exclusion.
Conversion Systems, Inc.	Willow Grove, PA	Chemically Stabilized Electric Arc Furnace Dust (CSEAFD) that is generated by Conversion Systems Inc. (CSI) using the Super Detox™ process as modified by CSI to treat EAFD (EPA Hazardous Waste No. K061) at the following sites and that is disposed of in Subtitle C landfills: Northwestern Steel, Sterling, Illinois after June 13, 1995. Structural Metals, Inc. treated at U.S. Ecology, Robstown, Texas after September 23, 2008. (1) *Verification Testing Requirements:* Sample collection and analyses, including quality control procedures must be performed using appropriate methods. As applicable to the method-defined parameters of concern, analyses requiring the use of SW–846 methods incorporated by reference in 40 CFR 260.11 must be used without substitution. As applicable, the SW–846 methods might include Methods 0010, 0011, 0020, 0023A, 0030, 0031, 0040, 0050, 0051, 0060, 0061, 1010A, 1020B, 1110A, 1310B, 1311, 1312, 1320, 1330A, 9010C, 9012B, 9040C, 9045D, 9060A, 9070A (uses EPA Method 1664, Rev. A), 9071B, and 9095B. (A) *Initial Verification Testing:* During the first 20 operating days of full scale operation of a newly constructed Super Detox™ treatment facility, CSI must analyze a minimum of four (4) composite samples of CSEAFD representative of the full 20-day period. Composites must be comprised of representative samples collected from every batch generated. The CSEAFD samples must be analyzed for the constituents listed in Condition (3). CSI must report the operational and analytical test data, including quality control information, obtained during this initial period no later than 60 days after the generation of the first batch of CSEAFD. (B) *Addition of New Super Detox™ Treatment Facilities to Exclusion:* If the Agency's review of the data obtained during initial verification testing indicates that the CSEAFD generated by a specific Super Detox™ treatment facility consistently meets the delisting levels specified in Condition (3), the Agency will publish a notice adding to this exclusion the location of the new Super Detox™ treatment facility and the name of the steel mill contracting CSI's services. If the Agency's review of the data obtained during initial verification testing indicates that the CSEAFD generated by a specific Super Detox™ treatment facility fails to consistently meet the conditions of this exclusion, the Agency will not publish the notice adding the new facility. (C) *Subsequent Verification Testing:* For the Sterling, Illinois facility and any new facility subsequently added to CSI's conditional multiple-site exclusion, CSI must collect and analyze at least one composite sample of CSEAFD each month. The composite samples must be composed of representative samples collected from all batches treated in each month. The composite samples must be composed rep-resentative samples collected from all batches treated in each month. These monthly representative samples must be analyzed, prior to disposal of the CSEAFD, for the constituents listed in Condition (3). CSI may, at its discretion, analyze composite samples gathered more frequently to demonstrate that smaller batches of waste are non-hazardous. (2) *Waste Holding and Handling:* CSI must store as hazardous all CSEAFD generated until verification testing as specified in Conditions (1)(A) and (1)(C), as appropriate, is completed and valid analyses demonstrate that Condition (3) is satisfied. If the levels of constituents measured in the samples of CSEAFD do not exceed the levels set forth in Condition (3), then the CSEAFD is non-hazardous and may be managed and disposed of in Subtitle D landfills. If constituent levels in a sample exceed any of the delisting levels set in Condition (3), the CSEAFD generated during the time period corresponding to this sample must be retreated until it meets these levels, or managed and disposed of in accordance with Subtitle C of RCRA. CSEAFD generated by a new CSI treatment facility must be managed as a hazardous waste prior to the addition of the name and location of the facility to the exclusion. After addition of the new facility to the exclusion, CSEAFD generated during the verification testing in Condition (1)(A) is also non-hazardous, if the delisting levels in Condition (3) are satisfied.

Table 2—Wastes Excluded From Specific Sources

Facility	Address	Waste description
		(3) *Delisting Levels:* All leachable constituents for those metals must not exceed the following levels (ppm): Antimony–0.06; Arsenic–0.50; Barium–7.6; Beryllium–0.010; Cadmium–0.050; Chromium–0.33; Lead–0.15; Mercury–0.009; Nickel–1.00; Selenium–0.16; Silver–0.30; Thallium–0.020; Vanadium–2.0; Zinc–70. Metal concentrations must be measured in the waste leachate by the method specified in 40 CFR 261.24.
		(4) *Changes in Operating Conditions:* After initiating subsequent testing described in Condition (1)(C), if CSI significantly changes the stabilization process established under Condition (1) (e.g., use of new stabilization reagents), CSI must notify the Agency in writing. After written approval by EPA, CSI may handle CSEAFD generated from the new process as non-hazardous, if the wastes meet the delisting levels set in Condition (3).
		(5) *Data Submittals:* CSI must submit the information described below. If CSI fails to submit the required data within the specified time or maintain the required records on-site for the specified time, EPA, at its discretion, will consider this sufficient basis to reopen the exclusion as described in paragraph (6). CSI must:
		(A) At least one month prior to operation of a new Super Detox™ treatment facility, CSI must notify, in writing, the EPA Regional Administrator or his designee, when the new Super Detox™ treatment facility is scheduled to be on-line. The data obtained through paragraph 1(A) must be submitted to the Regional Administrator or his designee within the time period specified. All supporting data can be submitted on CD–ROM or some comparable electronic media.
		(B) CSI shall submit and receive EPA approval of the Quality Assurance Project Plan for data collection for each new facility added to this exclusion prior to conducting sampling events in paragraph 1(A).
		(C) Compile records of analytical data from paragraph (3), summarized, and maintained on-site for a minimum of five years.
		(D) Furnish these records and data when either EPA or the State agency requests them for inspection.
		(E) Send along with all data a signed copy of the following certification statement, to attest to the truth and accuracy of the data submitted. "Under civil and criminal penalty of law for the making or submission of false or fraudulent statements or representations (pursuant to the applicable provisions of the Federal Code, which include, but may not be limited to, 18 U.S.C. 1001 and 42 U.S.C. 6928), I certify that the information contained in or accompanying this document is true, accurate and complete. As to the (those) identified section(s) of this document for which I cannot personally verify its (their) truth and accuracy, I certify as the company official having supervisory responsibility for the persons who, acting under my direct instructions, made the verification that this information is true, accurate and complete. If any of this information is determined by EPA in its sole discretion to be false, inaccurate or incomplete, and upon conveyance of this fact to the company, I recognize and agree that this exclusion of waste will be void as if it never had effect or to the extent directed by EPA and that the company will be liable for any actions taken in contravention of the company's RCRA and CERCLA obligations premised upon the company's reliance on the void exclusion."
		(6) *Reopener:* (A) If, anytime after disposal of the delisted waste CSI, the treatment facility, or the steel mill possess or is otherwise made aware of any data (including but not limited to leachate data or ground water monitoring data) relevant to the delisted waste indicating that any constituent identified for the delisting verification testing is at a level higher than the delisting level allowed by EPA in granting the petition, then the facility must report the data, in writing, to EPA within 10 days of first possessing or being made aware of that data.
		(B) If subsequent verification testing of the waste as required by paragraph 1(C) does not meet the delisting requirements in paragraph 3 and the waste is subsequently managed as non-hazardous waste, CSI must report the data, in writing, to EPA within 10 days of first possessing or being made aware of that data.
		(C) If CSI fails to submit the information described in paragraphs (5), (6)(A) or (6)(B) or if any other information is received from any source, EPA will make a preliminary determination as to whether the reported information requires action to protect human health and/or the environment. Further action may include suspending, or revoking the exclusion, or other appropriate response necessary to protect human health and the environment.
		(D) If EPA determines that the reported information requires action, EPA will notify the facility in writing of the actions it believes are necessary to protect human health and the environment. The notice shall include a statement of the proposed action and a statement providing the facility with an opportunity to present information explaining why the proposed EPA action is not necessary. The facility shall have 10 days from the date of EPA's notice to present such information.

Table 2—Wastes Excluded From Specific Sources

Facility	Address	Waste description
		(E) Following the receipt of information from the facility described in paragraph (6)(D) or (if no information is presented under paragraph (6)(D)) the initial receipt of information described in paragraphs (5), (6)(A) or (6)(B), EPA will issue a final written determination describing the actions that are necessary to protect human health and/or the environment. Any required action described in EPA's determination shall become effective immediately, unless EPA provides otherwise. (7) *Notification Requirements:* CSI or the treatment facility must do the following before transporting the delisted waste. Failure to provide this notification will result in a violation of the delisting petition and a possible revocation of the decision. (A) Provide a one-time written notification to any state Regulatory Agency to which or through which it will transport the delisted waste described above for disposal, 60 days before beginning such activities. (B) Update the one-time written notification if it ships the delisted waste into a different disposal facility. (C) Failure to provide this notification will result in a violation of the delisting exclusion and a possible revocation of the decision.
United States Department of Energy (Energy)	Richland, Washington	Treated effluents bearing the waste numbers identified below, from the 200 Area Effluent Treatment Facility (ETF) located at the Hanford Facility, at a maximum generation rate of 210 million liters per year, subject to Conditions 1–7: This conditional exclusion applies to Environmental Protection Agency (EPA) Hazardous Waste Nos. F001, F002, F003, F004, F005, and F039. This exclusion also applies to EPA Hazardous Waste Nos. F006–F012, F019 and F027 provided that the as-generated waste streams bearing these waste numbers prior to treatment in the 200 Area ETF is in the form of dilute wastewater containing a maximum of 1.0 weight percent of any hazardous constituent. In addition, this conditional exclusion applies to all other U- and P-listed waste numbers that meet the following criteria: The U/P listed substance has a treatment standard established for wastewater forms of F039 multi-source leachate under 40 CFR 268.40,"Treatment Standards for Hazardous Wastes"; and the as-generated waste stream prior to treatment in the 200 Area ETF is in the form of dilute wastewater containing a maximum of 1.0 weight percent of any hazardous constituent. This exclusion shall apply at the point of discharge from the 200 Area ETF verification tanks after satisfaction of Conditions 1–7. Conditions: (1) Waste Influent Characterization and Processing Strategy Preparation (a) Prior to treatment of any waste stream in the 200 Area ETF, Energy must: (i) Complete sufficient characterization of the waste stream to demonstrate that the waste stream is within the treatability envelope of 200 Area ETF as specified in Tables C–1 and C–2 of the delisting petition dated November 29, 2001. Results of the waste stream characterization and the treatability evaluation must be in writing and placed in the facility operating record, along with a copy of the November 29, 2001 petition. Waste stream characterization may be carried out in whole or in part using the waste analysis procedures in the Hanford Facility RCRA Permit, WA7 89000 8967; (ii) Prepare a written waste processing strategy specific to the waste stream, based on the ETF process model documented in the November 29, 2001 petition. For waste processing strategies applicable to waste streams for which inorganic envelope data is provided in Table C–2 of the November 29, 2001 petition, Energy shall use envelope data specific to that waste stream, if available. Otherwise, Energy shall use the minimum envelope in Table C–2. (b) Energy may modify the 200 Area ETF treatability envelope specified in Tables C–1 and C–2 of the November 29, 2001 delisting petition to reflect changes in treatment technology or operating practices upon written approval of the Regional Administrator. Requests for modification shall be accompanied by an engineering report detailing the basis for a modified treatment envelope. Data supporting modified envelopes must be based on at least four influent waste stream characterization data points and corresponding treated effluent verification sample data points for wastes managed under a particular waste processing strategy. Treatment efficiencies must be calculated based on a comparison of upper 95 percent confidence level constituent concentrations. Upon written EPA approval of the engineering report, the associated inorganic treatment efficiency data may be used in lieu of those in Tables C–1 and C–2 for purposes of condition (1)(a)(i). (c) Energy shall conduct all 200 Area ETF treatment operations for a particular waste stream according to the written waste processing strategy, as may be modified by Condition 3(b)(i). (d) The following definitions apply: (i) A waste stream is defined as all wastewater received by the 200 Area ETF that meet the 200 Area ETF waste acceptance criteria as defined by the Hanford Facility RCRA Permit, WA7 89000 8967 and are managed under the same 200 Area ETF waste processing strategy.

Table 2—Wastes Excluded From Specific Sources

Facility	Address	Waste description

(ii) A waste processing strategy is defined as a specific 200 Area ETF unit operation configuration, primary operating parameters and expected maximum influent total dissolved solids (TDS) and total organic carbon (TOC). Each waste processing strategy shall require monitoring and recording of treated effluent conductivity for purposes of Condition (2)(b)(i)(E), and for monitoring and recording of primary operating parameters as necessary to demonstrate that 200 Area ETF operations are in accordance with the associated waste processing strategy.

(iii) Primary operating parameters are defined as ultraviolet oxidation (UV/OX) peroxide addition rate, reverse osmosis reject ratio, and processing flow rate as measured at the 200 Area ETF surge tank outlet.

(iv) Key unit operations are defined as filtration, UV/OX, reverse osmosis, ion exchange, and secondary waste treatment.

(2) Testing. Energy shall perform verification testing of treated effluents according to Conditions (a), (b), and (c) below.

(a) No later than 45 days after the effective date of this rule, or such other time as may be approved of in advance and in writing by EPA, Energy shall submit to EPA a report proposing required data quality parameters and data acceptance criteria (parameter values) for sampling and analysis which may be conducted pursuant to the requirements of this rule. This report shall explicitly consider verification sampling and analysis for purposes of demonstrating compliance with exclusion limits in Condition 5, as well as any sampling and analysis which may be required pursuant to Conditions (1)(a)(i) and (1)(d)(ii). This report shall contain a detailed justification for the proposed data quality parameters and data acceptance criteria. Following review and approval of this report, the proposed data quality parameters and data acceptance criteria shall become enforceable conditions of this exclusion. Pending EPA approval of this report, Energy may demonstrate compliance with sampling and analysis requirements of this rule through application of methods appearing in EPA Publication SW–846 or equivalent methods. Energy shall maintain a written sampling and analysis plan, including QA/QC requirements and procedures, based upon these enforceable data quality parameters and data acceptance criteria in the facility operating record, and shall conduct all sampling and analysis conducted pursuant to this rule according to this written plan. Records of all sampling and analysis, including quality assurance QA/QC information, shall be placed in the facility operating record. As applicable to the method-defined parameters of concern, analyses requiring the use of SW–846 methods incorporated by reference in 40 CFR 260.11 must be used without substitution. As applicable, the SW–846 methods might include Methods 0010, 0011, 0020, 0023A, 0030, 0031, 0040, 0050, 0051, 0060, 0061, 1010A, 1020B, 1110A, 1310B, 1311, 1312, 1320, 1330A, 9010C, 9012B, 9040C, 9045D, 9060A, 9070A (uses EPA Method 1664, Rev. A), 9071B, and 9095B.

(b) Initial verification testing.

(i) Verification sampling shall consist of a representative sample of one filled effluent discharge tank, analyzed for all constituents in Condition (5), and for conductivity for purposes of establishing a conductivity baseline with respect to Condition (2)(b)(i)(E). Verification sampling shall be required under each of the following conditions:

(A) Any new or modified waste strategy;

(B) Influent wastewater total dissolved solids or total organic carbon concentration increases by an order of magnitude or more above values established in the waste processing strategy;

(C) Changes in primary operating parameters;

(D) Changes in influent flow rate outside a range of 150 to 570 liters per minute;

(E) Increase greater than a factor of ten (10) in treated effluent conductivity (conductivity changes indicate changes in dissolved ionic constituents, which in turn are a good indicator of 200 Area ETF treatment efficiency).

(F) Any failure of initial verification required by this condition, or subsequent verification required by Condition (2)(c).

(ii) Treated effluents shall be managed according to Condition 3. Once Condition (3)(a) is satisfied, subsequent verification testing shall be performed according to Condition (2)(c).

(c) Subsequent Verification: Following successful initial verification associated with a specific waste processing strategy, Energy must continue to monitor primary operating parameters, and collect and analyze representative samples from every fifteenth (15th) verification tank filled with 200 Area ETF effluents processed according to the associated waste processing strategy. These representative samples must be analyzed prior to disposal of 200 Area ETF effluents for all constituents in Condition (5). Treated effluent from tanks sampled according to this condition must be managed according to Condition (3).

(3) Waste Holding and Handling: Energy must store as hazardous waste all 200 Area ETF effluents subject to verification testing in Condition (2)(b) and (2)(c), that is, until valid analyses demonstrate Condition (5) is satisfied.

Table 2—Wastes Excluded From Specific Sources

Facility	Address	Waste description

(a) If the levels of hazardous constituents in the samples of 200 Area ETF effluent are equal to or below the levels set forth in Condition (5), the 200 Area ETF effluents are not listed as hazardous wastes provided they are disposed of in the State Authorized Land Disposal Site (SALDS) (except as provided pursuant to Condition (7)) according to applicable requirements and permits. Subsequent treated effluent batches shall be subject to verification requirements of Condition (2)(c).

(b) If hazardous constituent levels in any representative sample collected from a verification tank exceed any of the delisting levels set in Condition (5), Energy must:

(i) Review waste characterization data, and review and change accordingly the waste processing strategy as necessary to ensure subsequent batches of treated effluent do not exceed delisting criteria;

(ii) Retreat the contents of the failing verification tank;

(iii) Perform verification testing on the retreated effluent. If constituent concentrations are at or below delisting levels in Condition (5), the treated effluent are not listed hazardous waste provided they are disposed at SALDS according to applicable requirements and permits (except as provided pursuant to Condition (7)), otherwise repeat the requirements of Condition (3)(b).

(iv) Perform initial verification sampling according to Condition (2)(b) on the next treated effluent tank once testing required by Condition (3)(b)(iii) demonstrates compliance with delisting requirements.

(4) Re-opener Language

(a) If, anytime before, during, or after treatment of waste in the 200 Area ETF, Energy possesses or is otherwise made aware of any data (including but not limited to groundwater monitoring data, as well as data concerning the accuracy of site conditions or the validity of assumptions upon which the November 29, 2001 petition was based) relevant to the delisted waste indicating that the treated effluent no longer meets delisting criteria (excluding record keeping and data submissions required by Condition (6)), or that groundwater affected by discharge of the treated effluent exhibits hazardous constituent concentrations above health-based limits, Energy must report such data, in writing, to the Regional Administrator within 10 days of first possessing or being made aware of that data.

(b) Energy shall provide written notification to the Regional Administrator no less than 180 days prior to any planned or proposed substantial modifications to the 200 Area ETF, exclusive of routine maintenance activities, that could affect waste processing strategies or primary operating parameters. This condition shall specifically include, but not be limited to, changes that do or would require Class II or III modification to the Hanford Facility RCRA Permit WA7 89000 8967 (in the case of permittee-initiated modifications) or equivalent modifications in the case of agency-initiated permit modifications operations. Energy may request a modification to the 180-day notification requirement of this condition in the instance of agency-initiated permit modifications for purposes of ensuring coordination with permitting activities.

(c) Based on the information described in paragraph (4)(a) or (4)(b) or any other relevant information received from any source, the Regional Administrator will make a preliminary determination as to whether the reported information requires Agency action to protect human health or the environment. Further action could include suspending or revoking the exclusion, or other appropriate response necessary to protect human health and the environment.

(5) Delisting Levels: All total constituent concentrations in treated effluents managed under this exclusion must be equal to or less than the following levels, expressed as mg/L:

Inorganic Constituents
Ammonia—6.0
Barium—1.6
Beryllium—4.5×10^{-2}
Nickel—$4.5\ 10^{-1}$
Silver—1.1×10^{-1}
Vanadium—1.6×10^{-1}
Zinc—6.8
Arsenic—1.5×10^{-2}
Cadmium—1.1×10^{-2}
Chromium—6.8×10^{-2}
Lead—9.0×10^{-2}
Mercury—6.8×10^{-3}
Selenium—1.1×10^{-1}
Fluoride—1.2
Cyanides—4.8×10^{-1}

Table 2—Wastes Excluded From Specific Sources

Facility	Address	Waste description
		Organic Constituents: Cresol—1.2 2,4,6 Trichlorophenol—3.6×10^{-1} Benzene—6.0×10^{-2} Chrysene—5.6×10^{-1} Hexachlorobenzne—2.0×10^{-3} Hexachlorocyclopentadiene—1.8×10^{-1} Dichloroisopropyl ether [Bis(2-Chloroisopropyl) either]—6.0×10^{-2} Di-n-octylphthalate—4.8×10^{-1} 1-Butanol—2.4 Isophorone—4.2 Diphenylamine—5.6×10^{-1} p-Chloroaniline—1.2×10^{-1} Acetonitrile—1.2 Carbazole—1.8×10^{-1} N-Nitrosodimethylamine—2.0×10^{-2} Pyridine—2.4×10^{-2} Lindane [gamma-BHC]—3.0×10^{-3} Arochlor [total of Arochlors 1016, 1221, 1232, 1242, 1248, 1254, 1260]—5.0×10^{-4} Carbon tetrachloride—1.8×10^{-2} Tetrahydrofuran—5.6×10^{-1} Acetone—2.4 Carbon disulfide—2.3 Tributyl phosphate—1.2×10^{-1} (6) Recordkeeping and Data Submittals. (a) Energy shall maintain records of all waste characterization, and waste processing strategies required by Condition (1), and verification sampling data, including QA/QC results, in the facility operating record for a period of no less than three (3) years. However, this period is automatically extended during the course of any unresolved enforcement action regarding the 200 Area ETF or as requested by EPA. (b) No less than thirty (30) days after receipt of verification data indicating a failure to meet delisting criteria of Condition (5), Energy shall notify the Regional Administrator. This notification shall include a summary of waste characterization data for the associated influent, verification data, and any corrective actions taken according to Condition (3)(b)(i). (c) Records required by Condition (6)(a) must be furnished on request by EPA or the State of Washington and made available for inspection. All data must be accompanied by a signed copy of the following certification statement to attest to the truth and accuracy of the data submitted: "Under civil and criminal penalty of law for the making or submission of false or fraudulent statements or representations (pursuant to the applicable provisions of the Federal Code, which include, but may not be limited to, 18 U.S.C. 1001 and 42 U.S.C. 6928). I certify that the information contained in or accompanying this document is true, accurate, and complete. As to the (those) identified section(s) of the document for which I cannot personally verify its (their) truth and accuracy, I certify as the official having supervisory responsibility of the persons who, acting under my direct instructions, made the verification that this information is true, accurate, and complete. In the event that any of this information is determined by EPA in its sole discretion to be false, inaccurate, or incomplete, and upon conveyance of this fact to Energy, I recognize and agree that this exclusion of waste will be void as if it never had effect to the extent directed by EPA and that the Energy will be liable for Energy's reliance on the void exclusion." (7) Treated Effluent Disposal Requirements. Energy may at any time propose alternate reuse practices for treated effluent managed under terms of this exclusion in lieu of disposal at the SALDS. Such proposals must be in writing to the Regional Administrator, and demonstrate that the risks and potential human health or environmental exposures from alternate treated effluent disposal or reuse practices do not warrant retaining the waste as a hazardous waste. Upon written approval by EPA of such a proposal, nonhazardous treated effluents may be managed according to the proposed alternate practices in lieu of the SALDS disposal requirement in paragraph (3)(a). The effect of such approved proposals shall be explicitly limited to approving alternate disposal practices in lieu of the requirements in paragraph (3)(a) to dispose of treated effluent in SALDS.

Table 2—Wastes Excluded From Specific Sources

Facility	Address	Waste description
DuraTherm, Incorporated	San Leon, Texas	Desorber Solids, (at a maximum generation of 20,000 cubic yards per calendar year) generated by DuraTherm using the treatment process to treat the Desorber solids, (EPA Hazardous Waste No. K048, K049, K050, and K051 and disposed of in a subtitle D landfill. DuraTherm must implement the testing program found in Table 1. Wastes Excluded From Non-Specific Sources, for the petition to be valid.
Eastman Chemical Company	Longview, Texas	Wastewater treatment sludge, (at a maximum generation of 82,100 cubic yards per calendar year) (EPA Hazardous Waste Nos. K009, K010) generated at Eastman. Eastman must implement the testing program described in Table 1—Waste Excluded From Non-Specific Sources for the petition to be valid.
Envirite of Illinois (formerly Envirite Corporation)	Harvey, Illinois	See waste description under Envirite of Pennsylvania.
Envirite of Ohio (formerly Envirite Corporation)	Canton, Ohio	See waste description under Envirite of Pennsylvania.
Envirite of Pennsylvania (formerly Envirite Corporation)	York, Pennsylvania	Spent pickle liquor (EPA Hazardous Waste No. K062) generated from steel finishing operations of facilities within the iron and steel industry (SIC Codes 331 and 332); wastewater treatment sludge (EPA Hazardous Waste No. K002) generated from the production of chrome yellow and orange pigments; wastewater treatment sludge (EPA Hazardous Waste No. K003) generated from the production of molybdate orange pigments; wastewater treatment sludge (EPA Hazardous Waste No. K004) generated from the production of zinc yellow pigments; wastewater treatment sludge (EPA Hazardous Waste K005) generated from the production of chrome green pigments; wastewater treatment sludge (EPA Hazardous Waste No. K006) generated from the production of chrome oxide green pigments (anhydrous and hydrated); wastewater treatment sludge (EPA Hazardous Waste No. K007) generated from the production of iron blue pigments; oven residues (EPA Hazardous Waste No. K008) generated from the production of chrome oxide green pigments after November 14, 1986. To ensure that hazardous constituents are not present in the waste at levels of regulatory concern, the facility must implement a contingency testing program for the petitioned wastes. This testing program must meet the following conditions for the exclusions to be valid: (1) Each batch of treatment residue must be representatively sampled and tested using the EP Toxicity test for arsenic, barium, cadmium, chromium, lead, selenium, silver, mercury, and nickel. If the extract concentrations for chromium, lead, arsenic, and silver exceed 0.315 ppm; barium levels exceed 6.3 ppm; cadmium and selenium exceed 0.063 ppm; mercury exceeds 0.0126 ppm; or nickel levels exceed 2.205 ppm, the waste must be retreated or managed and disposed as a hazardous waste under 40 CFR Parts 262 to 265 and the permitting standards of 40 CFR Part 270. (2) Each batch of treatment residue (formerly must be tested for leachable cyanide. If the leachable cyanide levels Corporation) (using the EP Toxicity test without acetic acid adjustment) exceed 1.26 ppm, the waste must be re-treated or managed and disposed as a hazardous waste under 40 CFR Parts 262 to 265 and the permitting standards of 40 CFR Part 270. (3) Each batch of waste must be tested for the total content of specific organic toxicants. If the total content of anthracene exceeds 76.8 ppm, 1.2-diphenyl hydrazine exceeds 0.001 ppm, methylene chloride exceeds 8.18 ppm, methyl ethyl ketone exceeds 326 ppm, n-nitrosodiphenylamine exceeds 11.9 ppm, phenol exceeds 1,566 ppm, tetrachloroethylene exceeds 0.188 ppm, or trichloroethylene exceeds 0.592 ppm, the waste must be managed and disposed as a hazardous waste under 40 CFR Parts 262 to 265 and the permitting standards of 40 CFR Part 270. (4) A grab sample must be collected from each batch to form one monthly composite sample which must be tested using GC/MS analysis for the compounds listed in #3, above, as well as the remaining organics on the priority pollutant list. (See 47 FR 52309, November 19, 1982, for a list of the priority pollutants.) (5) The data from conditions 1-4 must be kept on file at the facility for inspection purposes and must be compiled, summarized, and submitted to the Administrator by certified mail semi-annually. The Agency will review this information and if needed will propose to modify or withdraw the exclusion. The organics testing described in conditions 3 and 4, above, is not required until six months from the date of promulgation. The Agency's decision to conditionally exclude the treatment residue generated from the wastewater treatment systems at these facilities applies only to the wastewater and solids treatment systems as they presently exist as described in the delisting petition. The exclusion does not apply to the proposed process additions described in the petition as recovery, including crystallization, electrolytic metals recovery, evaporative recovery, and ion exchange.

Table 2—Wastes Excluded From Specific Sources

Facility	Address	Waste description
ERCO Worldwide (USA) Inc. (formerly Vulcan Materials Company)	Port Edwards, Wisconsin	Brine purification muds (EPA Hazardous Waste No. K071) generated from the mercury cell process in chlorine production, where separately purified brine is not used after November 17, 1986. To assure that mercury levels in this waste are maintained at acceptable levels, the following conditions apply to this exclusion: Each batch of treated brine clarifier muds and saturator insolubles must be tested (by the extraction procedure) prior to disposal and the leachate concentration of mercury must be less than or equal to 0.0129 ppm. If the waste does not meet this requirement, then it must be retreated or disposed of as hazardous. This exclusion does not apply to wastes for which either of these conditions is not satisfied.
Giant Refining Company, Inc	Bloomfield, New Mexico	Waste generated during the excavation of soils from two wastewater treatment impoundments (referred to as the South and North Oily Water Ponds) used to contain water outflow from an API separator (EPA Hazardous Waste No. K051). This is a one-time exclusion for approximately 2,000 cubic yards of stockpiled waste. This exclusion was published on September 3, 1996. Notification Requirements: Giant Refining Company must provide a one-time written notification to any State Regulatory Agency to which or through which the delisted waste described above will be transported for disposal at least 60 days prior to the commencement of such activities. Failure to provide such a notification will result in a violation of the delisting petition and a possible revocation of the decision.
Heritage Environmental Services, LLC, at the Nucor Steel facility	Crawfordsville, Indiana	Electric arc furnace dust (EAFD) that has been generated by Nucor Steel at its Crawfordsville, Indiana facility and treated on site by Heritage Environmental Services, LLC (Heritage) at a maximum annual rate of 30,000 cubic yards per year and disposed of in a Subtitle D landfill which has groundwater monitoring, after January 15, 2002. (1) *Delisting Levels:* (A) The constituent concentrations measured in either of the extracts specified in Paragraph (2) may not exceed the following levels (mg/L): Antimony-0.206; Arsenic-0.0936; Barium-55.7; Beryllium-0.416; Cadmium-0.15; Chromium (total)-1.55; Lead-5.0; Mercury-0.149; Nickel- 28.30; Selenium-0.58; Silver-3.84; Thallium-0.088; Vanadium-21.1; Zinc- 280.0. (B) Total mercury may not exceed 1 mg/ kg. (2) *Verification Testing:* On a monthly basis, Heritage or Nucor must analyze two samples of the waste using the TCLP, SW–846 Method 1311, with an extraction fluid of pH 12 ± 0.05 standard units and for the mercury determinative analysis of the leachate using an appropriate method. The constituent concentrations measured must be less than the delisting levels established in Paragraph (1). (3) *Changes in Operating Conditions:* If Nucor significantly changes the manufacturing process or chemicals used in the manufacturing process or Heritage significantly changes the treatment process or the chemicals used in the treatment process, Heritage or Nucor must notify the EPA of the changes in writing. Heritage and Nucor must handle wastes generated after the process change as hazardous until Heritage or Nucor has demonstrated that the wastes continue to meet the delisting levels set forth in Paragraph (1) and that no new hazardous constituents listed in Appendix VIII of Part 261 have been introduced and Heritage and Nucor have received written approval from EPA. (4) *Data Submittals:* Heritage must submit the data obtained through monthly verification testing or as required by other conditions of this rule to U.S. EPA Region 5, Waste Management Branch (DW-8J), 77 W. Jackson Blvd., Chicago, IL 60604 by February 1 of each calendar year for the prior calendar year. Heritage or Nucor must compile, summarize, and maintain on site for a minimum of five years records of operating conditions and analytical data. Heritage or Nucor must make these records available for inspection. All data must be accompanied by a signed copy of the certification statement in 40 CFR 260.22(i)(12). (5) *Reopener Language*—(A) If, anytime after disposal of the delisted waste, Heritage or Nucor possesses or is otherwise made aware of any data (including but not limited to leachate data or groundwater monitoring data) relevant to the delisted waste indicating that any constituent identified in Paragraph (1) is at a level in the leachate higher than the delisting level established in Paragraph (1), or is at a level in the groundwater higher than the maximum allowable point of exposure concentration predicted by the CMTP model, then Heritage or Nucor must report such data, in writing, to the Regional Administrator within 10 days of first possessing or being made aware of that data. (B) Based on the information described in paragraph (5)(A) and any other information received from any source, the Regional Administrator will make a preliminary determination as to whether the reported information requires Agency action to protect human health or the environment. Further action may include suspending, or revoking the exclusion, or other appropriate response necessary to protect human health and the environment.

Table 2—Wastes Excluded From Specific Sources

Facility	Address	Waste description
		(C) If the Regional Administrator determines that the reported information does require Agency action, the Regional Administrator will notify Heritage and Nucor in writing of the actions the Regional Administrator believes are necessary to protect human health and the environment. The notice shall include a statement of the proposed action and a statement providing Heritage and Nucor with an opportunity to present information as to why the proposed Agency action is not necessary or to suggest an alternative action. Heritage and Nucor shall have 30 days from the date of the Regional Administrator's notice to present the information. (D) If after 30 days Heritage or Nucor presents no further information, the Regional Administrator will issue a final written determination describing the Agency actions that are necessary to protect human health or the environment. Any required action described in the Regional Administrator's determination shall become effective immediately, unless the Regional Administrator provides otherwise.
LCP Chemical	Orrington, ME	Brine purification muds and wastewater treatment sludges generated after August 27, 1985 from their chlor-alkali manufacturing operations (EPA Hazardous Waste Nos. K071 and K106) that have been batch tested for mercury using the EP toxicity procedures and have been found to contain less than 0.05 ppm mercury in the EP extract. Brine purification muds and wastewater treatment sludges that exceed this level will be considered a hazardous waste.
Marathon Oil Co	Texas City, TX	Residual solids (at a maximum annual generation rate of 1,000 cubic yards) generated from the thermal desorption treatment and, where necessary, stabilization of wastewater treatment plant API/ DAF filter cake (EPA Hazardous Waste Nos. K048 and K051), after [insert date of publication]. Marathon must implement a testing program that meets the following conditions for the exclusion to be valid: (1) *Testing:* Sample collection and analyses (including quality control (QC) procedures) must be performed using appropriate methods. As applicable to the method-defined parameters of concern, analyses requiring the use of SW–846 methods incorporated by reference in 40 CFR 260.11 must be used without substitution. As applicable, the SW–846 methods might include Methods 0010, 0011, 0020, 0023A, 0030, 0031, 0040, 0050, 0051, 0060, 0061, 1010A, 1020B, 1110A, 1310B, 1311, 1312, 1320, 1330A, 9010C, 9012B, 9040C, 9045D, 9060A, 9070A (uses EPA Method 1664, Rev. A), 9071B, and 9095B. If EPA judges the treatment process to be effective under the operating conditions used during the initial verification testing, Marathon may replace the testing required in Condition (1)(A) with the testing required in Condition (1)(B). Marathon must continue to test as specified in Condition (1)(A), including testing for organics in Conditions (3)(B) and (3)(C), until and unless notified by EPA in writing that testing in Condition (1)(A) may be replaced by Condition (1)(B), or that testing for organics may be terminated as described in (1)(C) (to the extent directed by EPA). (A) *Initial Verification Testing:* During at least the first 40 operating days of full-scale operation of the thermal desorption unit, Marathon must monitor the operating conditions and analyze 5-day composites of residual solids. 5-day composites must be composed of representative grab samples collected from every batch during each 5-day period of operation. The samples must be analyzed prior to disposal of the residual solids for constituents listed in Condition (3). Marathon must report the operational and analytical test data, including quality control information, obtained during this initial period no later than 90 days after the treatment of the first full-scale batch. (B) *Subsequent Verification Testing:* Following notification by EPA, Marathon may substitute the testing conditions in (1)(B) for (1)(A). Marathon must continue to monitor operating conditions, and analyze samples representative of each month of operation. The samples must be composed of representative grab samples collected during at least the first five days of operation of each month. These monthly representative samples must be analyzed for the constituents listed in Condition (3) prior to the disposal of the residual solids. Marathon may, at its discretion, analyze composite samples gathered more frequently to demonstrate that smaller batches of waste are nonhazardous. (C) *Termination of Organic Testing:* Marathon must continue testing as required under Condition (1)(B) for organic constituents specified in Conditions (3)(B) and (3)(C) until the analyses submitted under Condition (1)(B) show a minimum of four consecutive monthly representative samples with levels of specific constituents significantly below the delisting levels in Conditions (3)(B) and (3)(C), and EPA notifies Marathon in writing that monthly testing for specific organic constituents may be terminated. Following termination of monthly testing, Marathon must continue to test a representative 5-day composite sample for all constituents listed in Conditions (3)(B) and (3)(C) on an annual basis. If delisting levels for any constituents listed in Conditions (3)(B) and (3)(C) are exceeded in the annual sample, Marathon must reinstitute complete testing as required in Condition (1)(B).

Table 2—Wastes Excluded From Specific Sources

Facility	Address	Waste description
		(2) *Waste Holding and Handling:* Marathon must store as hazardous all residual solids generated until verification testing (as specified in Conditions (1)(A) and (1)(B)) is completed and valid analysis demonstrates that Condition (3) is satisfied. If the levels of hazardous constituents in the samples of residual solids are below all of the levels set forth in Condition (3), then the residual solids are non-hazardous and may be managed and disposed of in accordance with all applicable solid waste regulations. If hazardous constituent levels in any 5-day composite or other representative sample equal or exceed any of the delisting levels set in Condition (3), the residual solids generated during the corresponding time period must be retreated and/or stabilized as allowed below, until the residual solids meet these levels, or managed and disposed of in accordance with Subtitle C of RCRA. If the residual solids contain leachable inorganic concentrations at or above the delisting levels set forth in Condition (3)(A), then Marathon may stabilize the material with Type 1 portland cement as demonstrated in the petition to immobilize the metals. Following stabilization, Marathon must repeat analyses in Condition (3)(A) prior to disposal. (3) *Delisting Levels:* Leachable concentrations in Conditions (3)(A) and (3)(B) must be measured in the waste leachate by the method specified in 40 CFR 261.24. The indicator parameters in Condition (3)(C) must be measured as the total concentration in the waste. Concentrations must be less than the following levels (ppm): (A) *Inorganic Constituents:* antimony-0.6; arsenic, chromium, or silver-5.0; barium-100.0; beryllium-0.4; cadmium-0.5; lead- 1.5; mercury-0.2; nickel-10.0; selenium-1.0; vanadium-20.0. (B) *Organic Constituents:* acenaphthene-200; benzene-0.5; benzo(a)anthracene-0.01; benzo(a)pyrene-0.02; benzo(b)fluoranthene-0.02; chrysene-0.02; ethyl benzene-70; fluoranthene-100; fluorene-100; naphthalene-100; pyrene-100; toluene-100. (C)*Indicator Parameters:* 1-methyl naphthalene-3; benzo(a)pyrene-3. (4) *Changes in Operating Conditions:* After completing the initial verification test period in Condition (1)(A), if Marathon significantly changes the operating conditions established under Condition (1), Marathon must notify the Agency in writing. After written approval by EPA, Marathon must re- institute the testing required in Condition (1)(A) for a minimum of four 5-day operating periods. Marathon must report the operations and test data, required by Condition (1)(A), including quality control data, obtained during this period no later than 60 days after the changes take place. Following written notification by EPA, Marathon may replace testing Condition (1)(A) with (1)(B). Marathon must fulfill all other requirements in Condition (1), as appropriate. (5) *Data Submittals:* At least two weeks prior to system start-up, Marathon must notify in writing the Section Chief Delisting Section (see address below) when the thermal desorption and stabilization units will be on- line and waste treatment will begin. The data obtained through Condition (1)(A) must be submitted to HWIDOSW (5304W) (OS-333), U.S. EPA, 1200 Pennsylvania Ave., NW., Washington, DC 20460 within the time period specified. Records of operating conditions and analytical data from Condition (1) must be compiled, summarized, and maintained on site for a minimum of five years. These records and data must be furnished upon request by EPA or the State of Texas and made available for inspection. Failure to submit the required data within the specified time period or maintain the required records on site for the specified time will be considered by EPA, at its discretion, sufficient basis to revoke the exclusion to the extent directed by EPA. All data must be accompanied by a signed copy of the following certification statement to attest to the truth and accuracy of the data submitted: "Under civil and criminal penalty of law for the making or submission of false or fraudulent statements or representations (pursuant to the applicable provisions of the Federal Code, which include, but may not be limited to, 18 U.S.C. 1001 and 42 U.S.C 6928), I certify that the information contained in or accompanying this document is true, accurate, and complete. As to the (those) identified sections(s) of this document for which I cannot personally verify its (their) truth and accuracy, I certify as the company official having supervisory responsibility for the persons who, acting under my direct instructions, made the verification that this information is true, accurate, and complete. In the event that any of this information is determined by EPA in its sole discretion to be false, inaccurate, or incomplete, and upon conveyance of this fact to the company, I recognize and agree that this exclusion of waste will be void as if it never had effect or to the extent directed by EPA and that the company will be liable for any actions taken in contravention of the company's RCRA and CERCLA obligations premised upon the company's reliance on the void exclusion."
Mearl Corp	Peekskill, NY	Wastewater treatment sludge (EPA Hazardous Waste Nos. K006 and K007) generated from the production of chrome oxide green and iron blue pigments after November 27, 1985.
Monsanto Industrial Chemicals Company	Sauget, Illinois	Brine purification muds (EPA Hazardous Waste No. K071) generated from the mercury cell process in chlorine production, where separately prepurified brine is not used after August 15, 1986.

Table 2—Wastes Excluded From Specific Sources

Facility	Address	Waste description
Occidental Chemical	Ingleside, Texas	Limestone Sludge, (at a maximum generation of 1,114 cubic yards per calendar year) Rockbox Residue, (at a maximum generation of 1,000 cubic yards per calendar year) generated by Occidental Chemical using the wastewater treatment process to treat the Rockbox Residue and the Limestone Sludge (EPA Hazardous Waste No. K019, K020). Occidental Chemical must implement a testing program that meets conditions found in Table 1. Wastes Excluded From Non- Specific Sources from the petition to be valid.
Occidental Chemical Corp Muscle Shoals Plant	Sheffield, Alabama	Retorted wastewater treatment sludge from the mercury cell process in chlorine production (EPA Hazardous Plant Waste No. K106) after September 19, 1989. This exclusion is conditional upon the submission of data obtained from Occidental's full-scale retort treatment system because Occidental's original data were based on a pilot-scale retort system. To ensure that hazardous constituents are not present in the waste at levels of regulatory concern once the full-scale treatment facility is in operation, Occidental must implement a testing program. All sampling and analyses (including quality control procedures) must be performed using appropriate methods. As applicable to the method-defined parameters of concern, analyses requiring the use of SW–846 methods incorporated by reference in 40 CFR 260.11 must be used without substitution. As applicable, the SW–846 methods might include Methods 0010, 0011, 0020, 0023A, 0030, 0031, 0040, 0050, 0051, 0060, 0061, 1010A, 1020B, 1110A, 1310B, 1311, 1312, 1320, 1330A, 9010C, 9012B, 9040C, 9045D, 9060A, 9070A (uses EPA Method 1664, Rev. A), 9071B, and 9095B. This testing program must meet the following conditions for the exclusion to be valid: (1) Initial Testing—During the first four weeks of full-scale retort operation, Occidental must do the following: (A) Collect representative grab samples from every batch of retorted material and composite the grab samples to produce a weekly composite sample. The weekly composite samples, prior to disposal or recycling, must be analyzed for the EP leachate concentrations of all the EP toxic metals (except mercury), nickel, and cyanide (using distilled water in the cyanide extractions). Occidental must report the analytical test data, including all quality control data, obtained during this initial period no later than 90 days after the treatment of the first full-scale batch. (B) Collect representative grab samples of every batch of retorted material prior to its disposal or recycling and analyze the sample for EP leachate concentration of mercury. Occidental must report the analytical test data, including all quality control data, within 90 days after the treatment of the first full-scale batch. (2) Subsequent Testing—After the first four weeks of full-scale retort operation, Occidental must do the following: (A) Continue to sample and test as described in condition (1)(A). Occidental must compile and store on-site for a minimum of three years all analytical data and quality control data. These data must be furnished upon request and made available for inspection by any employee or representative of EPA or the State of Alabama. These testing requirements shall be terminated by EPA when the results of four consecutive weekly composite samples of the petitioned waste, obtained from either the initial testing or subsequent testing show the maximum allowable levels in condition (3) are not exceeded and the Section Chief, Variances Section, notifies Occidental that the requirements of this condition have been lifted. (B) Continue to sample and test for mercury as described in condition (1)(B). Occidental must compile and store on-site for a minimum of three years all analytical data and quality control data. These data must be furnished upon request and made available for inspection by any employee or representative of EPA or the State of Alabama. These testing requirements shall remain in effect until Occidental provides EPA with analytical and quality control data for thirty consecutive batches of retorted material, collected as described in condition (1)(B), demonstrating that the EP leachable levels of mercury are below the maximum allowable level in condition (3) and the Section Chief, Variances Section, notifies Occidental that the testing in condition (2)(B) may be replaced with (2)(C). (C) [If the conditions in (2)(B) are satisfied, the testing requirements for mercury in (2)(B) shall be replaced with the following condition]. Collect representative grab samples from every batch of retorted material on a daily basis and composite the grab samples to produce a weekly composite sample. Occidental must analyze each weekly composite sample prior to its disposal or recycling for the EP leachate concentration of mercury. Occidental must compile and store on-site for a minimum of three years all analytical data and quality control data. These data must be furnished upon request and made available for inspection by any employee or representative of EPA or the State of Alabama. (3) If, under condition (1) or (2), the EP leachate concentrations for chromium, lead, arsenic, or silver exceed 1.616 mg/l; for barium exceeds 32.3 mg/l; for cadmium or selenium exceed 0.323 mg/l; for mercury exceeds 0.065 mg/l, for nickel exceeds 16.15 mg/l; or for cyanide exceeds 22.61 mg/l, the waste must either be retreated until it meets these levels or managed and disposed of in accordance with subtitle C of RCRA.

Table 2—Wastes Excluded From Specific Sources

Facility	Address	Waste description
		(4) Within one week of system start-up, Occidental must notify the Section Chief, Variances Section (see address below) when the full-scale retort system is on-line and waste treatment has begun. All data obtained through condition (1) must be submitted to the Section Chief, Variances Section, PSPD/OSW (OS-343), U.S. EPA, 1200 Pennsylvania Ave., NW., Washington, DC 20460 within the time period specified in condition (1). At the Section Chief's request, Occidental must submit any other analytical data obtained through condition (2) to the above address, within the time period specified by the Section Chief. Failure to submit the required data will be considered by the Agency sufficient basis to revoke Occidental's exclusion to the extent directed by EPA. All data must be accompanied by the following certification statement: "Under civil and criminal penalty of law for the making or submission of false or fraudulent statements or representations (pursuant to the applicable provisions of the Federal Code which include, but may not be limited to, 18 U.S.C. 6928), I certify that the information contained in or accompanying this document is true, accurate and complete. As to the (those) identified section(s) of this document for which I cannot personally verify its (their) truth and accuracy, I certify as the company official having supervisory responsibility for the persons who, acting under my direct instructions, made the verification that this information is true, accurate and complete. In the event that any of this information is determined by EPA in its sole discretion to be false, inaccurate or incomplete, and upon conveyance of this fact to the company, I recognize and agree that this exclusion of wastes will be void as if it never had effect or to the extent directed by EPA and that the company will be liable for any actions taken in contravention of the company's RCRA and CERCLA obligations premised upon the company's reliance on the void exclusion."
Occidental Chemical Corporation	Delaware City, Delaware	Sodium chloride treatment muds (NaCl-TM), sodium chloride saturator cleanings (NaCl-SC), and potassium chloride treatment muds (KCl-TM) (all classified as EPA Hazardous Waste No. K071) generated at a maximum combined rate (for all three wastes) of 1,018 tons per year. This exclusion was published on April 29, 1991 and is conditioned upon the collection of data from Occidental's full-scale brine treatment system because Occidental's request for exclusion was based on data from a laboratory-scale brine treatment process. To ensure that hazardous constituents are not present in the waste at levels of regulatory concern once the full-scale treatment system is in operation, Occidental must implement a testing program for the petitioned waste. All sampling and analyses (including quality control (QC) procedures) must be performed using appropriate methods. As applicable to the method-defined parameters of concern, analyses requiring the use of SW–846 methods incorporated by reference in 40 CFR 260.11 must be used without substitution. As applicable, the SW–846 methods might include Methods 0010, 0011, 0020, 0023A, 0030, 0031, 0040, 0050, 0051, 0060, 0061, 1010A, 1020B, 1110A, 1310B, 1311, 1312, 1320, 1330A, 9010C, 9012B, 9040C, 9045D, 9060A, 9070A (uses EPA Method 1664, Rev. A), 9071B, and 9095B. This testing program must meet the following conditions for the exclusion to be valid: (1) *Initial Testing:* During the first four weeks of full-scale treatment system operation, Occidental must do the following: (A) Collect representative grab samples from each batch of the three treated wastestreams (sodium chloride saturator cleanings (NaCl-SC), sodium chloride treatment muds (NaCl-TM) and potassium chloride treatment muds (KCl-TM)) on an as generated basis and composite the samples to produce three separate weekly composite samples (of each type of K071 waste). The three weekly composite samples, prior to disposal, must be analyzed for the EP leachate concentrations of all the EP toxic metals (except mercury), nickel, and cyanide (using distilled water in the cyanide extractions). Occidental must report the waste volumes produced and the analytical test data, including all quality control data, obtained during this initial period, no later than 90 days after the treatment of the first full-scale batch. (B) Collect representative grab samples of each batch of the three treated wastestreams (NaCl-SC, NACl-TM and KCl-TM) and composite the grab samples to produce three separate daily composite samples (of each type of K071 waste) on an as generated basis. The three daily composite samples, prior to disposal, must be analyzed for the EP leachate concentration of mercury. Occidental must report the waste volumes produced and the analytical test data, including all quality control data, obtained during this initial period, no later than 90 days after the treatment of the first full-scale batch. (2) *Subsequent Testing:* After the first four weeks of full-scale treatment operations, Occidental must do the following; all sampling and analyses (including quality control procedures) must be performed using appropriate methods, and as applicable to the method-defined parameters of concern, analyses requiring the use of SW–846 methods incorporated by reference in 40 CFR 260.11 must be used without substitution. As applicable, the SW–846 methods might include Methods 0010, 0011, 0020, 0023A, 0030, 0031, 0040, 0050, 0051, 0060, 0061, 1010A, 1020B, 1110A, 1310B, 1311, 1312, 1320, 1330A, 9010C, 9012B, 9040C, 9045D, 9060A, 9070A (uses EPA Method 1664, Rev. A), 9071B, and 9095B:

Table 2—Wastes Excluded From Specific Sources

Facility	Address	Waste description
		(A) Continue to sample and test as described in condition (1)(A). Occidental must compile and store on-site for a minimum of three years the records of waste volumes produced and all analytical data and quality control data. These data must be furnished upon request and made available for inspection by any employee or representative of EPA or the State of Delaware. These testing requirements shall be terminated by EPA when the results of four consecutive weekly composite samples of the petitioned waste, obtained from either the initial testing or subsequent testing, show the maximum allowable levels in condition (3) are not exceeded and the Section Chief, Variances Section, notifies Occidental that the requirements of this condition have been lifted. (B) Continue to sample and test for mercury as described in condition (1)(B). Occidental must compile and store on-site for a minimum of three years the records of waste volumes produced and all analytical data and quality control data. These data must be furnished upon request and made available for inspection by any employee or representative of EPA or the State of Delaware. These testing requirements shall be terminated and replaced with the requirements of condition (2)(C) if Occidental provides EPA with analytical and quality control data for thirty consecutive batches of treated material, collected as described in condition (1)(B), demonstrating that the EP leachable level of mercury in condition (3) is not exceeded (in all three treated wastes), and the Section Chief, Variances Section, notifies Occidental that the testing in condition (2)(B) may be replaced with (2)(C). (C) [If the conditions in (2)(B) are satisfied, the testing requirements for mercury in (2)(B) shall be replaced with the following condition.] Collect representative grab samples from each batch of the three treated wastestreams (NaCl-SC, NaCl-TM and KCl-TM) on an as generated basis and composite the grab samples to produce three separate weekly composite samples (of each type of K071 waste). The three weekly composite samples, prior to disposal, must be analyzed for the EP leachate concentration of mercury. Occidental must compile and store on-site for a minimum of three years the records of waste volumes produced and all analytical data and quality control data. These data must be furnished upon request and made available for inspection by any employee or representative of EPA or the State of Delaware. (3) If, under conditions (1) or (2), the EP leachate concentrations for chromium, lead, arsenic, or silver exceed 0.77 mg/l; for barium exceeds 15.5 mg/l; for cadmium or selenium exceed 0.16 mg/l; for mercury exceeds 0.031 mg/l, or for nickel or total cyanide exceed 10.9 mg/ l, the waste must either be retreated or managed and disposed of in accordance with all applicable hazardous waste regulations. (4) Within one week of system start-up, Occidental must notify the Section Chief, Variances Section (see address below) when the full-scale system is on-line and waste treatment has begun. All data obtained through condition (1) must be submitted to the Section Chief, Variances Section, PSPD/OSW, (OS-333), U.S. EPA, 1200 Pennsylvania Ave., NW., Washington, DC 20460 within the time period required in condition (1). At the Section Chief's request, Occidental must submit any other analytical data obtained through conditions (1) and (2) to the above address within the time period specified by the Section Chief. Failure to submit the required data will be considered by the Agency sufficient basis to revoke Occidental's exclusion to the extent directed by EPA. All data (either submitted to EPA or maintained at the site) must be accompanied by the following statement: "Under civil and criminal penalty of law for the making or submission of false or fraudulent statements or representations (pursuant to the applicable provisions of the Federal Code, which include, but may not be limited to 18 U.S.C. 1001 and 42 U.S.C. 6926), I certify that the information contained in or accompanying this document is true, accurate and complete. As to the (those) identified section(s) of this document for which I cannot personally verify its (their) truth and accuracy, I certify as the company official having supervisory responsibility for the persons who, acting under my direct instructions, made the verification that this information is true, accurate and complete. In the event that any of this information is determined by EPA in its sole discretion to be false, inaccurate or incomplete, and upon conveyance of this fact to the company, I recognize and agree that this exclusion of wastes will be void as if it never had effect or to the extent directed by EPA and that the company will be liable for any actions taken in contravention of the company's RCRA and CERCLA obligations premised upon the company's reliance on the void exclusion."
Olin Corporation	Charleston, TN	Sodium chloride purification muds and potassium chloride purification muds (both classified as EPA Hazardous Waste No. K071) that have been batch tested using EPA's Toxicity Characteristic Leaching Procedure and have been found to contain less than 0.05 ppm mercury. Purification muds that have been found to contain less than 0.05 ppm mercury will be disposed in Olin's on-site non-hazardous waste landfill or another Subtitle D landfill. Purification muds that exceed this level will be considered a hazardous waste.

Table 2—Wastes Excluded From Specific Sources

Facility	Address	Waste description
Ormet Primary Aluminum Corporation	Hannibal, OH	Vitrified spent potliner (VSP), K088, that is generated by Ormet Primary Aluminum Corporation in Hannibal (Ormet), Ohio at a maximum annual rate of 8,500 cubic yards per year and disposed of in a Subtitle D landfill, licensed, permitted, or registered by a state. The exclusion becomes effective as of July 25, 2002. 1. *Delisting Levels:* (A) The constituent concentrations measured in any of the extracts specified in paragraph (2) may not exceed the following levels (mg/L): Antimony-0.235; Arsenic-0.107; Barium-63.5; Beryllium-0.474; Cadmium-0.171; Chromium (total)-1.76; Lead-5; Mercury-0.17; Nickel-32.2; Selenium-0.661; Silver-4.38; Thallium-0.1; Tin-257; Vanadium-24.1; Zinc-320; Cyanide-4.11. (B) Land disposal restrictions (LDR) treatment standards for K088 must also be met before the VSP can be land disposed. Ormet must comply with any future LDR treatment standards promulgated under 40 CFR 268.40 for K088. 2. *Verification Testing:* (A) On a quarterly basis, Ormet must collect two samples of the waste and analyze them for the constituents listed in paragraph (1) using the methodologies specified in an EPA-approved sampling plan specifying (a) the TCLP method, and (b) the TCLP procedure with an extraction fluid of 0.1 Normal sodium hydroxide solution. The constituent concentrations measured in the extract must be less than the delisting levels established in paragraph (1). Ormet must also comply with LDR treatment standards in accordance with 40 CFR 268.40. (B) If the quarterly testing of the waste does not meet the delisting levels set forth in paragraph (1), Ormet must notify the Agency in writing in accordance with paragraph (5). The exclusion will be suspended and the waste managed as hazardous until Ormet has received written approval for the exclusion from the Agency. Ormet may provide sampling results that support the continuation of the delisting exclusion. 3. *Changes in Operating Conditions:* If Ormet significantly changes the manufacturing process, the treatment process, or the chemicals used, Ormet must notify the EPA of the changes in writing. Ormet must handle wastes generated after the process change as hazardous until Ormet has demonstrated that the wastes continue to meet the delisting levels set forth in paragraph (1) and that no new hazardous constituents listed in Appendix VIII of Part 261 have been introduced and Ormet has received written approval from EPA. 4. *Data Submittals:* Ormet must submit the data obtained through quarterly verification testing or as required by other conditions of this rule to U.S. EPA Region 5, Waste Management Branch (DW-8J), 77 W. Jackson Blvd., Chicago, IL 60604 by February 1 of each calendar year for the prior calendar year. Ormet must compile, summarize, and maintain on site for a minimum of five years records of operating conditions and analytical data. Ormet must make these records available for inspection. All data must be accompanied by a signed copy of the certification statement in 40 CFR 260.22(i)(12). 5. *Reopener Language*—(a) If, anytime after disposal of the delisted waste, Ormet possesses or is otherwise made aware of any data (including but not limited to leachate data or groundwater monitoring data) relevant to the delisted waste indicating that any constituent identified in paragraph (1) is at a level in the leachate higher than the delisting level established in paragraph (1), or is at a level in the groundwater higher than the point of exposure groundwater levels referenced by the model, then Ormet must report such data, in writing, to the Regional Administrator within 10 days of first possessing or being made aware of that data. (b) Based on the information described in paragraph (5)(a) or any other information received from any source, the Regional Administrator will make a preliminary determination as to whether the reported information requires Agency action to protect human health or the environment. Further action may include suspending, or revoking the exclusion, or other appropriate response necessary to protect human health and the environment. (c) If the Regional Administrator determines that the information does require Agency action, the Regional Administrator will notify Ormet in writing of the actions the Regional Administrator believes are necessary to protect human health and the environment. The notice shall include a statement of the proposed action and a statement providing Ormet with an opportunity to present information as to why the proposed Agency action is not necessary or to suggest an alternative action. Ormet shall have 30 days from the date of the Regional Administrator's notice to present the information. (d) If after 30 days Ormet presents no further information, the Regional Administrator will issue a final written determination describing the Agency actions that are necessary to protect human health or the environment. Any required action described in the Regional Administrator's determination shall become effective immediately, unless the Regional Administrator provides otherwise.
Oxy Vinyls	Deer Park, Texas	Rockbox Residue, (at a maximum generation of 1,000 cubic yards per calender year) generated by Oxy Vinyls using the wastewater treatment process to treat the Rockbox Residue (EPA Hazardous Waste No. K017, K019, and K020).

Table 2—Wastes Excluded From Specific Sources

Facility	Address	Waste description

Oxy Vinyls must implement a testing program that meets the following conditions for the exclusion to be valid:

(1) *Delisting Levels:* All concentrations for the following constituents must not exceed the following levels (ppm). The Rockbox Residue must be measured in the waste leachate by the method specified in 40 CFR 261.24.

(A) Rockbox Residue:

(i) Inorganic Constituents: Barium—200; Chromium—5.0; Copper—130; Lead+1.5; Tin—2,100; Vanadium—30; Zinc—1,000

(ii) Organic Constituents: Acetone—400; Dichloromethane—1.0; Dimethylphthalate—4,000; Xylene—10,000; 2,3,7,8-TCDD Equivalent—0.00000006

(2) *Waste Holding and Handling:* Oxy Vinyls must store in accordance with its RCRA permit, or continue to dispose of as hazardous waste all Rockbox Residue generated until the verification testing described in Condition (3)(B), as appropriate, is completed and valid analyses demonstrate that condition (3) is satisfied. If the levels of constituents measured in the samples of the Rockbox Residue do not exceed the levels set forth in Condition (1), then the waste is nonhazardous and may be managed and disposed of in accordance with all applicable solid waste regulations. If constituent levels in a sample exceed any of the delisting levels set in Condition 1, waste generated during the time period corresponding to this sample must be managed and disposed of in accordance with subtitle C of RCRA.

(3) *Verification Testing Requirements:* Sample collection and analyses, including quality control procedures, must be performed using appropriate methods. As applicable to the method-defined parameters of concern, analyses requiring the use of SW–846 methods incorporated by reference in 40 CFR 260.11 must be used without substitution. As applicable, the SW–846 methods might include Methods 0010, 0011, 0020, 0023A, 0030, 0031, 0040, 0050, 0051, 0060, 0061, 1010A, 1020B, 1110A, 1310B, 1311, 1312, 1320, 1330A, 9010C, 9012B, 9040C, 9045D, 9060A, 9070A (uses EPA Method 1664, Rev. A), 9071B, and 9095B. If EPA judges the incineration process to be effective under the operating conditions used during the initial verification testing, OxyVinyls may replace the testing required in Condition (3)(A) with the testing required in Condition (3)(B). OxyVinyls must continue to test as specified in Condition (3)(A) until and unless notified by EPA in writing that testing in Condition (3)(A) may be replaced by Condition (3)(B).

(A) *Initial Verification Testing:* (i) When the Rockbox unit is decommissioned for clean out, after the final exclusion is granted, Oxy Vinyls must collect and analyze composites of the Rockbox Residue. Two composites must be composed of representative grab samples collected from the Rockbox unit. The waste must be analyzed, prior to disposal, for all of the constituents listed in Condition 1. No later than 90 days after the Rockbox unit is decommissioned for clean out the first two times after this exclusion becomes final, Oxy Vinyls must report the operational and analytical test data, including quality control information.

(B) *Subsequent Verification Testing:* Following written notification by EPA, Oxy Vinyls may substitute the testing conditions in (3)(B) for (3)(A)(i). Oxy Vinyls must continue to monitor operating conditions, analyze samples representative of each cleanout of the Rockbox of operation during the first year of waste generation.

(C) *Termination of Organic Testing for the Rockbox Residue:* Oxy Vinyls must continue testing as required under Condition (3)(B) for organic constituents specified under Condition (3)(B) for organic constituents specified in Condition (1)(A)(ii) until the analyses submitted under Condition (3)(B) show a minimum of two consecutive annual samples below the delisting levels in Condition (1)(A)(ii), Oxy Vinyls may then request that annual organic testing be terminated. Following termination of the quarterly testing, Oxy Vinyls must continue to test a representative composite sample for all constituents listed in Condition (1) on an annual basis (no later than twelve months after exclusion).

(4) *Changes in Operating Conditions:* If Oxy Vinyls significantly changes the process which generate(s) the waste(s) and which may or could affect the composition or type waste(s) generated as established under Condition (1) (by illustration, but not limitation, change in equipment or operating conditions of the treatment process), Oxy Vinyls must notify the EPA in writing and may no longer handle the wastes generated from the new process or no longer discharges as nonhazardous until the wastes meet the delisting levels set Condition (1) and it has received written approval to do so from EPA.

Table 2—Wastes Excluded From Specific Sources

Facility	Address	Waste description
		(5) *Data Submittals:* The data obtained through Condition 3 must be submitted to Mr. William Gallagher, Chief, Region 6 Delisting Program, U.S. EPA, 1445 Ross Avenue, Dallas, Texas 75202-2733, Mail Code, (6PD-O) within the time period specified. Records of operating conditions and analytical data from Condition (1) must be compiled, summarized, and maintained on site for a minimum of five years. These records and data must be furnished upon request by EPA, or the State of Texas, and made available for inspection. Failure to submit the required data within the specified time period or maintain the required records on site for the specified time will be considered by EPA, at its discretion, sufficient basis to revoke the exclusion to the extent directed by EPA. All data must be accompanied by a signed copy of the following certification statement to attest to the truth and accuracy of the data submitted: Under civil and criminal penalty of law for the making or submission of false or fraudulent statements or representations (pursuant to the applicable provisions of the Federal Code, which include, but may not be limited to, 18 U.S.C. 1001 and 42 U.S.C. 6928), I certify that the information contained in or accompanying this document is true, accurate and complete. As to the (those) identified section(s) of this document for which I cannot personally verify its (their) truth and accuracy, I certify as the company official having supervisory responsibility for the persons who, acting under my direct instructions, made the verification that this information is true, accurate and complete. In the event that any of this information is determined by EPA in its sole discretion to be false, inaccurate or incomplete, and upon conveyance of this fact to the company, I recognize and agree that this exclusion of waste will be void as if it never had effect or to the extent directed by EPA and that the company will be liable for any actions taken in contravention of the company's RCRA and CERCLA obligations premised upon the company's reliance on the void exclusion. (6) *Reopener Language:* (A) If, anytime after disposal of the delisted waste, Oxy Vinyls possesses or is otherwise made aware of any environmental data (including but not limited to leachate data or groundwater monitoring data) or any other data relevant to the delisted waste indicating that any constituent identified for the delisting verification testing is at level higher than the delisting level allowed by the Director in granting the petition, then the facility must report the data, in writing, to the Director within 10 days of first possessing or being made aware of that data. (B) If the annual testing of the waste does not meet the delisting requirements in Paragraph 1, Oxy Vinyls must report the data, in writing, to the Director within 10 days of first possessing or being made aware of that data. (C) Based on the information described in paragraphs (A) or (B) and any other information received from any source, the Director will make a preliminary determination as to whether the reported information requires Agency action to protect human health or the environment. Further action may include suspending, or revoking the exclusion, or other appropriate response necessary to protect human health and the environment. (D) If the Director determines that the reported information does require Agency action, the Director will notify the facility in writing of the actions the Director believes are necessary to protect human health and the environment. The notice shall include a statement of the proposed action and a statement providing the facility with an opportunity to present information as to why the proposed Agency action is not necessary. The facility shall have 10 days from the date of the Director's notice to present such information. (E) Following the receipt of information from the facility described in paragraph (D) or (if no information is presented under paragraph (D)) the initial receipt of information described in paragraphs (A) or (B), the Director will issue a final written determination describing the Agency actions that are necessary to protect human health or the environment. Any required action described in the Director's determination shall become effective immediately, unless the Director provides otherwise. (7) *Notification Requirements:* Oxy Vinyls must provide a one-time written notification to any State Regulatory Agency to which or through which the delisted waste described above will be transported for disposal at least 60 days prior to the commencement of such activities. Failure to provide such a notification will result in a violation of the delisting petition and a possible revocation of the decision.
OxyVinyls, L.P.	Deer Park, TX	Incinerator Offgas Scrubber Water (EPA Hazardous Waste Nos. K017, K019 and K020) generated at a maximum annual rate of 919,990 cubic yards per calendar year after April 22, 2004, and disposed in accordance with the TPDES permit. For the exclusion to be valid, OxyVinyls must implement a testing program that meets the following Paragraphs:

Table 2—Wastes Excluded From Specific Sources

Facility	Address	Waste description
		(1) *Delisting Levels:* All total concentrations for those constituents must not exceed the following levels (mg/kg) in the incinerator offgas scrubber water. Incinerator offgas treatment scrubber water (i) Inorganic Constituents Antimony—0.0204; Arsenic—0.385; Barium—2.92; Beryllium—0.166; Cadmium—0.0225; Chromium—5.0; Cobalt—13.14; Copper—418.00; Lead—5.0; Nickel—1.13; Mercury—0.0111; Vanadium—0.838; Zinc—2.61 (ii) Organic Constituents Acetone—1.46; Bromoform—0.481; Bromomethane—8.2; Bromodichloromethane—0.0719; Chloroform—0.683; Dibromochloromethane—0.057; Iodomethane—0.19; Methylene Chloride—0.029; 2,3,7,8—TCDD equivalents as TEQ—0.0000926 (2) *Waste Management:* (A) OxyVinyls must manage as hazardous all incinerator offgas treatment scrubber water generated, until it has completed initial verification testing described in Paragraphs (3)(A) and (B), as appropriate, and valid analyses show that paragraph (1) is satisfied. (B) Levels of constituents measured in the samples of the incinerator offgas treatment scrubber water that do not exceed the levels set forth in Paragraph (1) are non-hazardous. OxyVinyls can manage and dispose the non-hazardous incinerator offgas treatment scrubber water according to all applicable solid waste regulations. (C) If constituent levels in a sample exceed any of the delisting levels set in Paragraph (1), OxyVinyls must collect one additional sample and perform the expedited analyses to confirm if the constituent exceeds the delisting level. If this sample confirms the exceedance, OxyVinyls must, from that point forward, treat the waste as hazardous until it is demonstrated that the waste again meets the levels set in Paragraph (1). OxyVinyls must notify EPA of the exceedance and resampling analytical results prior to disposing of the waste. (D) If the waste exceeds the levels in paragraph (1) OxyVinyls must manage and dispose of the waste generated under Subtitle C of RCRA from the time that it becomes aware of any exceedance. (E) Upon completion of the Verification Testing described in Paragraphs 3(A) and (B) as appropriate and the transmittal of the results to EPA, and if the testing results meet the requirements of Paragraph (1), OxyVinyls may proceed to manage its incinerator offgas treatment scrubber water as non-hazardous waste. If subsequent verification testing indicates an exceedance of the Delisting Levels in Paragraph (1), OxyVinyls must manage the incinerator offgas treatment scrubber water as a hazardous waste until two consecutive quarterly testing samples show levels below the Delisting Levels. (3) *Verification Testing Requirements:* OxyVinyls must perform sample collection and analyses, including quality control procedures, using appropriate methods. As applicable to the method-defined parameters of concern, analyses requiring the use of SW–846 methods incorporated by reference in 40 CFR 260.11 must be used without substitution. As applicable, the SW–846 methods might include Methods 0010, 0011, 0020, 0023A, 0030, 0031, 0040, 0050, 0051, 0060, 0061, 1010A, 1020B, 1110A, 1310B, 1311, 1312, 1320, 1330A, 9010C, 9012B, 9040C, 9045D, 9060A, 9070A (uses EPA Method 1664, Rev. A), 9071B, and 9095B. If EPA judges the process to be effective under the operating conditions used during the initial verification testing, OxyVinlys may replace the testing required in Paragraph (3)(A) with the testing required in Paragraph (3)(B). OxyVinyls must continue to test as specified in Paragraph (3)(A) until and unless notified by EPA in writing that testing in Paragraph (3)(A) may be replaced by Paragraph (3)(B). (A) *Initial Verification Testing:* After EPA grants the final exclusion, OxyVinyls must do the following: (i) Within 60 days of this exclusion becoming final, collect four samples, before disposal, of the incinerator offgas treatment scrubber water. (ii) The samples are to be analyzed and compared against the delisting levels in Paragraph (1) (iii). Within sixty (60) days after the exclusion becomes final, OxyVinyls will report initial verification analytical test data, including analytical quality control information for the first sixty (30) days of operation after this exclusion becomes final of the incinerator offgas treatment scrubber water. If levels of constituents measured in the samples of the incinerator offgas treatment scrubber water that do not exceed the levels set forth in Paragraph (1) and are also non-hazardous in two consecutive quarters after the first thirty (30) days of operation after this exclusion, OxyVinyls can manage and dispose of the incinerator offgas treatment scrubber water according to all applicable solid water regulations after reporting the analytical results to EPA.

Table 2—Wastes Excluded From Specific Sources

Facility	Address	Waste description
		(B) *Subsequent Verification Testing:* Following written notification by EPA, OxyVinyls may substitute the testing conditions in Paragraph (3)(B) for (3)(A). OxyVinyls must continue to monitor operating conditions, and analyze representative samples of each quarter of operation during the first year of waste generation. The samples must represent the waste generated during the quarter. After the first year of analytical sampling verification sampling can be performed on a single annual composite sample of the incinerator offgas treatment scrubber water. The results are to be compared to the delisting levels in Condition (1). (C) *Termination of Testing:* (i) After the first year of quarterly testing, if the Delisting Levels in Paragraph (1) are being met, OxyVinyls may then request that EPA stop requiring quarterly testing. After EPA notifies OxyVinyls in writing, the company may end quarterly testing. (ii) Following cancellation of the quarterly testing, OxyVinyls must continue to test a representative sample for all constituents listed in Paragraph (1) annually. (4) Changes in Operating Conditions: If OxyVinyls significantly changes the process described in its petition or starts any processes that generate(s) the waste that may or could significantly affect the composition or type of waste generated as established under Paragraph (1) (by illustration, but not limitation, changes in equipment or operating conditions of the treatment process), it must notify EPA in writing; OxyVinyls may no longer handle the wastes generated from the new process as nonhazardous until the wastes meet the delisting levels set in Paragraph (1) and it has received written approval to do so from EPA. (5) Data Submittals: OxyVinyls must submit the information described below. If OxyVinyls fails to submit the required data within the specified time or maintain the required records on-site for the specified time, EPA, at its discretion, will consider this sufficient basis to reopen the exclusion as described in Paragraph 6. OxyVinyls must: (A) Submit the data obtained through Paragraph 3 to the Section Chief, EPA Region 6 Corrective Action and Waste Minimization Section, 1445 Ross Avenue, Dallas, Texas 75202–2733, Mail Code, (6PD–C) within the time specified. (B) Compile records of operating conditions and analytical data from Paragraph (3), summarized, and maintained on-site for a minimum of five years. (C) Finish these records and data when EPA or the State of Texas request them for inspection. (D) Send along with all data a signed copy of the following certification statement, to attest to the truth and accuracy of the data submitted: Under civil and criminal penalty of law for the making or submission of false or fraudulent statements or representations (pursuant to the applicable provisions of the Federal Code, which include, but may not be limited to, 18 U.S.C. 1001 and 42 U.S.C. 6928), I certify that the information contained in or accompanying this document is true, accurate and complete. As to the (those) identified section(s) of this document for which I cannot personally verify its (their) truth and accuracy, I certify as the company official having supervisory responsibility for the persons who, acting under my direct instructions, made the verification that this information is true, accurate and complete. If any of this information is determined by EPA in its sole discretion to be false, inaccurate or incomplete, and upon conveyance of this fact to the company, I recognize and agree that this exclusion of waste will be void as if its never had effect or to the extent directed by EPA and that the company will be liable for any actions taken in contravention of the company's RCRA and CERCLA obligations premised upon the company's reliance on the void exclusion. (6) *Reopener:* (A) If, anytime after disposal of the delisted waste OxyVinyls possesses or is otherwise made aware of any environmental data (including but not limited to leachate data or groundwater monitoring data) or any other data relevant to the delisted waste indicating that any constituent identified for the delisting verification testing is at a level higher than the delisting level allowed by the Regional Administrator or his delegate in granting the petition, then the facility must report the data, in writing, to the Regional Administrator or his delegate within 10 days of first possessing or being made aware of that data. (B) If the annual testing of the waste does not meet the delisting requirements in Paragraph 1, OxyVinyls must report the data, in writing, to the Regional Administrator or his delegate within 10 days of first possessing or being made aware of that data. (C) If OxyVinyls fails to submit the information described in paragraphs (5), (6)(A) or (6)(B) or if any other information is received from any source, the Regional Administrator or his delegate will make a preliminary determination as to whether the reported information requires EPA action to protect human health or the environment. Further action may include suspending, or revoking the exclusion, or other appropriate response necessary to protect human health and environment.

Table 2—Wastes Excluded From Specific Sources

Facility	Address	Waste description
		(D) If the Regional Administrator or his delegate determines that the reported information does require action by EPA's Regional Administrator or his delegate will notify the facility in writing of the actions the Regional Administrator or his delegate believes are necessary to protect human health and the environment. The notice shall include a statement of the proposed action and a statement providing the facility with an opportunity to present information as to why the proposed EPA action is not necessary. The facility shall have 10 days from the date of the Regional Administrator or his delegate's notice to present such information. (E) Following the receipt of information from the facility described in paragraph (6)(D) or (of no information is presented under paragraph (6)(D)) the initial receipt of information described in paragraphs (5), (6)(A) or (6)(B), the Regional Administrator or his delegate will issue a final written determination describing EPA actions that are necessary to protect human health or the environment. Any require action described in the Regional Administrator or his delegate's determination shall become effective immediately, unless the Regional Administrator or his delegate provides otherwise. (7) *Notification Requirements:* OxyVinyls must do the following before transporting the delisted waste. Failure to provide this notification will result in a violation of the delisting petition and a possible revocation of the decision. (A) Provide a one-time written notification to any State Regulatory Agency to which or through which it will transport the delisted waste described above for disposal, 60 days before beginning such activities. (B) Update the one-time written notification if it ships the delisted waste into a different disposal facility. (C) Failure to provide this notification will result in a violation of the delisting variance and a possible revocation of the decision.
Perox, Incorporated	Sharon, Pennsylvania	Iron oxide (EPA Hazardous Waste No. K062) generated (at a maximum annual rate of 4800 cubic yards) from a spent hydrochloric acid pickle liquor regeneration plant for spent pickle liquor generated from steel finishing operations. This exclusion was published on November 13, 1990.
Pioneer Chlor Alkai Company, Inc. (formerly Stauffer Chemical Company)	St. Gabriel, LA	Brine purification muds, which have been washed and vacuum filtered, generated after August 27, 1985 from their chlor-alkali manufacturing operations (EPA Hazardous Waste No. K071) that have been batch tested for mercury using the EP toxicity procedure and have been found to contain less than 0.05 ppm in mercury in the EP extract. Brine purification muds that exceed this level will be considered a hazardous waste.
POP Fasteners	Shelton, Connecticut	Wastewater treatment sludge (EPA Hazardous Waste No. F006) generated from electroplating operations (at a maximum annual rate of 300 cubic yards) after December 7, 1992. In order to confirm that the characteristics of the waste do not change significantly, the facility must, on an annual basis, analyze a representative composite sample for the constituents listed in §261.24 using the method specified therein. The annual analytical results, including quality control information, must be compiled, certified according to §260.22(i)(12) of this chapter, maintained on site for a minimum of five years, and made available for inspection upon request by any employee or representative of EPA or the State of Connecticut. Failure to maintain the required records on site will be considered by EPA, at its discretion, sufficient basis to revoke the exclusion to the extent directed by EPA.
Rhodia	Houston, Texas	Filter-cake Sludge, (at a maximum generation of 1,200 cubic yards per calendar year) generated by Rhodia using the SARU and AWT treatment process to treat the filter-cake sludge (EPA Hazardous Waste Nos. K002-004, K006-K011, K013-K052, K060-K062, K064-K066, K069, K071, K073, K083-K088, K090- K091, K093-K118, K123-K126, K131- K133, K136, K141-K145, K147-K151, K156-K161) generated at Rhodia. Rhodia must implement the testing program described in Table 1. Waste Excluded From Non-Specific Sources for the petition to be valid.
Roanoke Electric Steel Corp	Roanoke, VA	Fully-cured chemically stabilized electric arc furnace dust/sludge (CSEAFD) treatment residue (EPA Hazardous Waste No. K061) generated from the primary production of steel after March 22, 1989. This exclusion is conditioned upon the data obtained from Roanoke's full-scale CSEAFD treatment facility because Roanoke's original data were obtained from a laboratory-scale CSEAFD treatment process. To ensure that hazardous constituents are not present in the waste at levels of regulatory concern once the full-scale treatment facility is in operation, Roanoke must implement a testing program for the petitioned waste. This testing program must meet the following conditions for the exclusion to be valid:

Table 2—Wastes Excluded From Specific Sources

Facility	Address	Waste description
		(1) *Testing:* (A) *Initial Testing:* During the first four weeks of operation of the full-scale treatment system, Roanoke must collect representative grab samples of each treated batch of the CSEAFD and composite the grab samples daily. The daily composites, prior to disposal, must be analyzed for the EP leachate concentrations of all the EP toxic metals, nickel and cyanide (using distilled water in the cyanide extractions). Analyses must be performed using appropriate methods. As applicable to the method-defined parameters of concern, analyses requiring the use of SW–846 methods incorporated by reference in 40 CFR 260.11 must be used without substitution. As applicable, the SW–846 methods might include Methods 0010, 0011, 0020, 0023A, 0030, 0031, 0040, 0050, 0051, 0060, 0061, 1010A, 1020B, 1110A, 1310B, 1311, 1312, 1320, 1330A, 9010C, 9012B, 9040C, 9045D, 9060A, 9070A (uses EPA Method 1664, Rev. A), 9071B, and 9095B. Roanoke must report the analytical test data obtained during this initial period no later than 90 days after the treatment of the first full-scale batch. (B) Subsequent Testing: Roanoke must collect representative grab samples from every treated batch of CSEAFD generated daily and composite all of the grab samples to produce a weekly composite sample. Roanoke then must analyze each weekly composite sample for all of the EP toxic metals and nickel. Analyses must be performed using appropriate methods. As applicable to the method-defined parameters of concern, analyses requiring the use of SW–846 methods incorporated by reference in 40 CFR 260.11 must be used without substitution. As applicable, the SW–846 methods might include Methods 0010, 0011, 0020, 0023A, 0030, 0031, 0040, 0050, 0051, 0060, 0061, 1010A, 1020B, 1110A, 1310B, 1311, 1312, 1320, 1330A, 9010C, 9012B, 9040C, 9045D, 9060A, 9070A (uses EPA Method 1664, Rev. A), 9071B, and 9095B. The analytical data, including all quality control information, must be compiled and maintained on site for a minimum of three years. These data must be furnished upon request and made available for inspection for any employee or representative of EPA or the State of Virginia. (2) *Delistiing levels:* If the EP extract concentrations for chromium, lead, arsenic, or silver exceed 0.315 mg/l; for barium exceeds 6.3 mg/l; for cadmium or selenium exceed 0.063 mg/l; for mercury exceeds 0.0126 mg/l, for nickel exceeds 3.15 mg/l, or for cyanide exceeds 1.26 mg/l, the waste must either be re-treated or managed and disposed in accordance with subtitle C of RCRA. (3) *Data submittals:* Within one week of system start-up, Roanoke must notify the Section Chief, Variances Section (see address below) when their full-scale stabilization system in on-line and waste treatment has begun. All data obtained through the initial testing condition (1)(A), must be submitted to the Section Chief, Variances Section, PSPD/ OSW, (OS-343), U.S. EPA, 1200 Pennsylvania Ave., NW., Washington, DC 20460 within the time period specified in condition (1)(A). Failure to submit the required data or keep the required records will be considered by the Agency, at its discretion, sufficient basis to revoke Roanoke's exclusion. All data must be accompanied by the following certification statement: "Under civil and criminal penalty of law for the making or submission of false or fraudulent statements or representations (pursuant to the applicable provisions of the Federal Code which include, but may not be limited to, 18 USC 6928), I certify that the information contained in or accompanying this document is true, accurate and complete. As to the (those) identified section(s) of this document for which I cannot personally verify its (their) truth and accuracy, I certify as the company official having supervisory responsibility for the persons who, acting under my direct instructions, made the verification that this information is true, accurate and complete. In the event that any of this information is determined by EPA in its sole discretion to be false, inaccurate or incomplete, and upon conveyance of this fact to the company, I recognize and agree that this exclusion of wastes will be void as if it never had effect or to the extent directed by EPA and that the company will be liable for any actions taken in contravention of the company's RCRA and CERCLA obligations premised upon the company's reliance on the void exclusion."
Texas Eastman	Longview, Texas	Incinerator ash (at a maximum generation of 7,000 cubic yards per calendar year) generated from the incineration of sludge from the wastewater treatment plant (EPA Hazardous Waste No. K009 and K010, and that is disposed of in Subtitle D landfills after September 25, 1996. Texas Eastman must implement a testing program that meets conditions found in Table 1. Wastes Excluded From Non-Specific Sources for the petition to be valid.
USX Steel Corporation, USS Division, Southworks Plant, Gary Works	Chicago, Illinois	Fully-cured chemically stabilized electric arc furnace dust/sludge (CSEAFD) treatment residue (EPA Hazardous Waste No. K061) generated from the primary production of steel after April 29, 1991. This exclusion (for 35,000 tons of CSEAFD per year) is conditioned upon the data obtained from USX's full-scale CSEAFD treatment facility. To ensure that hazardous constituents are not present in the waste at levels of regulatory concern once the full-scale treatment facility is in operation, USX must implement a testing program for the petitioned waste. This testing program must meet the following conditions for the exclusion to be valid:

PART 261—Appendices

Table 2—Wastes Excluded From Specific Sources

Facility	Address	Waste description
		(1) *Testing:* Sample collection and analyses (including quality control (QC) procedures) must be performed using appropriate methods. As applicable to the method-defined parameters of concern, analyses requiring the use of SW–846 methods incorporated by reference in 40 CFR 260.11 must be used without substitution. As applicable, the SW–846 methods might include Methods 0010, 0011, 0020, 0023A, 0030, 0031, 0040, 0050, 0051, 0060, 0061,1010A, 1020B, 1110A, 1310B, 1311, 1312, 1320, 1330A, 9010C, 9012B, 9040C, 9045D, 9060A, 9070A (uses EPA Method 1664, Rev. A), 9071B, and 9095B. (A) *Initial Testing:* During the first four weeks of operation of the full-scale treatment system, USX must collect representative grab samples of each treated batch of the CSEAFD and composite the grab samples daily. The daily composites, prior to disposal, must be analyzed for the EP leachate concentrations of all the EP toxic metals, nickel, and cyanide (using distilled water in the cyanide extractions). USX must report the analytical test data, including quality control information, obtained during this initial period no later than 90 days after the treatment of the first full-scale batch. (B) *Subsequent Testing:* USX must collect representative grab samples from every treated batch of CSEAFD generated daily and composite all of the grab samples to produce a weekly composite sample. USX then must analyze each weekly composite sample for all of the EP toxic metals, and nickel. The analytical data, including quality control information, must be compiled and maintained on site for a minimum of three years. These data must be furnished upon request and made available for inspection by any employee or representative of EPA or the State of Illinois. (2) *Delisting levels:* If the EP extract concentrations for chromium, lead, arsenic, or silver exceed 0.315 mg/l; for barium exceeds 6.3 mg/l; for cadmium or selenium exceed 0.063 mg/l; for mercury exceeds 0.0126 mg/l; for nickel exceeds 3.15 mg/l; or for cyanide exceeds 4.42 mg/l, the waste must either be re-treated until it meets these levels or managed and disposed in accordance with subtitle C of RCRA. (3) *Data submittals:* Within one week of system start-up USX must notify the Section Chief, Delisting Section (see address below) when their full-scale stabilization system is on-line and waste treatment has begun. The data obtained through condition (1)(A) must be submitted to the Section Chief, Delisting Section, CAD/OSW (OS- 333), U.S. EPA, 1200 Pennsylvania Ave., NW, Washington, DC 20460 within the time period specified. At the Section Chief's request, USX must submit any other analytical data obtained through conditions (1)(A) or (1)(B) within the time period specified by the Section Chief. Failure to submit the required data obtained from conditions (1)(A) or (1)(B) within the specified time period or maintain the required records for the specified time will be considered by the Agency, at its discretion, sufficient basis to revoke USX's exclusion to the extent directed by EPA. All data must be accompanied by the following certification statement: "Under civil and criminal penalty of law for the making or submission of false or fraudulent statements or representations (pursuant to the applicable provisions of the Federal Code which include, but may not be limited to, 18 U.S.C. §6928), I certify that the information contained in or accompanying this document is true, accurate and complete. As to the (those) identified section(s) of this document for which I cannot personally verify its (their) truth and accuracy, I certify as the company official having supervisory responsibility for the persons who, acting under my direct instructions, made the verification that this information is true, accurate and complete. In the event that any of this information is determined by EPA in its sole discretion to be false, inaccurate or incomplete, and upon conveyance of this fact to the company, I recognize and agree that this exclusion of wastes will be void as if it never had effect or to the extent directed by EPA and that the company will be liable for any actions taken in contravention of the company's RCRA and CERCLA obligations premised upon the company's reliance on the void exclusion."

Table 3—Wastes Excluded From Commercial Chemical Products, Off-Specification Species, Container Residues, and Soil Residues Thereof

Facility	Address	Waste description
Eastman Chemical Company	Longview, Texas	Wastewater treatment sludge, (at a maximum generation of 82,100 cubic yards per calendar year) generated by Eastman (EPA Hazardous Waste Nos. U001, U002, U028, U031, U069, U088, U112, U115, U117, U122, U140, U147, U154, U159, U161, U220, U226, U239, U359). Eastman must implement the testing program described in Table 1—Waste Excluded From Non-Specific Sources for the petition to be valid.
Rhodia	Houston, Texas	Filter-cake Sludge, (at a maximum generation of 1,200 cubic yards per calendar year) generated by Rhodia using the SARU and AWT treatment process to treat the filter-cake sludge (EPA Hazardous Waste Nos. P001-P024, P026-P031, P033-P034, P036-P051, P054, P056- P060, P062-P078, P081-P082, P084- P085, P087-P089, P092-P116, P118- P123, P127-P128, P185, P188-P192, P194, P196-P199, P201-P205, U001- U012, U014-U039, U041-U053, U055- U064, U066-U099, U101-U103, U105- U138, U140-U174, U176-U194, U196- U197, U200-U211, U213-U223, U225- U228, U234-U240, U243-U244, U246- U249, U271, U277-U280, U328, U353, U359, U364-U367, U372-U373, U375-U379, U381-U396, U400-U404, U407, U409-U411) generated at Rhodia. Rhodia must implement the testing program described in Table 1—Waste Excluded From Non- Specific Sources for the petition to be valid.
Texas Eastman	Longview, Texas	Incinerator ash (at a maximum generation of 7,000 cubic yards per calendar year) generated from the incineration of sludge from the wastewater treatment plant (EPA Hazardous Waste No. U001, U002, U003, U019, U028, U031, U037, U044, U056, U069, U070, U107, U108, U112, U113, U115, U117, U122, U140, U147, U151, U154, U159, U161, U169, U190, U196, U211, U213, U226, U239, and U359, and that is disposed of in Subtitle D landfills after September 25, 1996. Texas Eastman must implement the testing program described in Table 1—Wastes Excluded From Non-Specific Sources for the petition to be valid.
Union Carbide Corp	Taft, LA	Contaminated soil (approximately 11,000 cubic yards), which contains acrolein in concentrations of less than 9 ppm.

[49 FR 37070, Sept. 21, 1984, as amended at 50 FR 30274, July 25, 1985; 50 FR 34692, Aug. 27, 1985; 50 FR 48910, Nov. 27, 1985; 51 FR 1254, Jan. 10, 1986; 51 FR 15889, Apr. 29, 1986; 51 FR 27039, July 29, 1986; 51 FR 25701, July 16, 1986; 51 FR 25891, July 17, 1986; 51 FR 29219, 29222, Aug. 15, 1986; 51 FR 27038, July 29, 1986; 51 FR 32460, Sept. 12, 1986; 51 FR 37021, Oct. 17, 1986; 51 FR 37725, Oct. 24, 1986; 51 FR 41308, 41310, 41313, 41327, Nov. 14, 1986; 51 FR 41483, 41486, 41490, 41499, Nov. 17, 1986; 52 FR 2522, Jan. 23, 1987; 52 FR 17403, May 8, 1987; 52 FR 29848, Aug. 12, 1987; 52 FR 29851, Aug. 12, 1987; 53 FR 4850, Feb. 18, 1988; 53 FR 7913, Mar. 11, 1988; 53 FR 15170, Apr. 27, 1988; 53 FR 20117, June 2, 1988; 53 FR 29045, Aug. 2, 1988; 53 FR 31334, Aug. 18, 1988; 53 FR 37761, Sept. 28, 1988; 53 FR 47693, Nov. 25, 1988; 54 FR 5085, Feb. 1, 1989; 54 FR 11712, Mar. 22, 1989; 54 FR 15938, Apr. 20, 1989; 54 FR 15939, Apr. 20, 1989; 54 FR 19893, May 9, 1989; 54 FR 20589, May 12, 1989; 54 FR 21951, May 22, 1989; 54 FR 27169, June 28, 1989; 54 FR 31680, Aug. 1, 1989; 54 FR 34180, Aug. 18, 1989; 54 FR 38524, Sept. 19, 1989; 54 FR 39359, Sept. 26, 1989; 54 FR 40239, Sept. 29, 1989; 54 FR 43821, Oct. 27, 1989; 55 FR 11192, Mar. 27, 1990; 55 FR 23634, June 11, 1990; 55 FR 29018, July 17, 1990; 55 FR 29020, July 17, 1990; 55 FR 29022, July 17, 1990; 55 FR 29359, July 19, 1990; 55 FR 34718, Aug. 24, 1990; 55 FR 43132, Oct. 26, 1990; 55 FR 47329, Nov. 13, 1990; 55 FR 47335, Nov. 13, 1990; 56 FR 14202, Apr. 8, 1991; 56 FR 19587, 19593, Apr. 29, 1991; 56 FR 41289, Aug. 20, 1991; 56 FR 67000, Dec. 27, 1991; 56 FR 67207, Dec. 30, 1991; 57 FR 37885, 37888, Aug. 21, 1992; 57 FR 57674, Dec. 7, 1992; 58 FR 40070, July 27, 1993; 58 FR 42244, Aug. 9, 1993; 59 FR 5726, Feb. 8, 1994; 59 FR 47814, Sept. 19, 1994; 59 FR 52862, Oct. 19, 1994; 60 FR 1746, Jan. 5, 1995; 60 FR 31114, June 13, 1995; 60 FR 31118, June 13, 1995; 60 FR 54312, Oct. 23, 1995; 61 FR 18091, Apr. 24, 1996; 61 FR 37401, July 18, 1996; 61 FR 40520, Aug. 5, 1996; 61 FR 46383, Sept. 3, 1996; 61 FR 48638, Sept. 16, 1996; 61 FR 50242, Sept. 25, 1996; 61 FR 57334, Nov. 6, 1996; 62 FR 1678, Jan. 13, 1997; 62 FR 7684, Feb. 20, 1997; 62 FR 8632, Feb. 26, 1997; 62 FR 55347, Oct. 24, 1997; 62 FR 63463, Dec. 1, 1997; 64 FR 3872, Jan. 26, 1999; 64 Fr 4594, Jan. 29, 1999; 64 FR 9443, Feb. 26, 1999; 64 FR 16646, Apr. 6, 1999; 64 FR 31987, June 15, 1999; 64 FR 42037, Aug. 3, 1999; 64 FR 56256, Oct. 19, 1999; 65 FR 2341, Jan. 14, 2000; 65 FR 8879, Feb. 23, 2000; 65 FR 18922, Apr. 10, 2000; 65 FR 21655, Apr. 24, 2000; 65 FR 31099, May 16, 2000; 65 FR 47325, Aug. 2, 2000; 66 FR 21884, May 2, 2001; 66 FR 24278, May 14, 2001; 66 FR 34376, June 28, 2001; 66 FR 41800, Aug. 9, 2001; 66 FR 43061, Aug. 16, 2001; 66 FR 62975, Dec. 4, 2001; 67 FR 1895, Jan. 15, 2002; 67 FR 1898, Jan. 15, 2002; 67 FR 36112, May 23, 2002; 67 FR 42196, June 21, 2002; 67 FR 48557, July 25, 2002; 67 FR 54131, Aug. 21, 2002; 67 FR 79877, Dec. 31, 2002; 68 FR 44656, July 30, 2003; 68 FR 46955, Aug. 7, 2003; 68 FR 53520, Sept. 11, 2003; 69 FR 8832, Feb. 26, 2004; 69 FR 21757, Apr. 22, 2004; 69 FR 30230, May 27, 2004; 69 FR 56361, Sept. 21, 2004; 69 FR 60559, Oct. 12, 2004; 70 FR 21157, Apr. 25, 2005; 70 FR 34562, June 14, 2005; 70 FR 42502, July 25, 2005; 70 FR 44150, Aug. 1, 2005; 70 FR 44501, Aug. 3, 2005; 70 FR 49190, Aug. 23, 2005; 70 FR 51641; Aug. 31, 2005; 70 FR 60217, Oct. 17, 2005; 70 FR 71002, Nov. 25, 2005; 70 FR 71005, Nov. 25, 2005; 70 FR 76172, Dec. 23, 2005; 71 FR 9726, Feb. 27, 2006; 71 FR 28277, May 16, 2006; 71 FR 35396, June 20, 2006; 71 FR 43071, July 31, 2006; 72 FR 47, Jan. 3, 2007; 72 FR 4648, Feb. 1, 2007; 72 FR 17031, Apr. 6, 2007; 72 FR 31188, June 6, 2007; 73 FR 54715, Sept. 23, 2008; 73 FR 59525, Oct. 9, 2008; 74 FR 10683, Mar. 12, 2009; 74 FR 17416, Apr. 15, 2009; 74 FR 17421, Apr. 15, 2009; 74 FR 30230, June 25, 2009; 74 FR 38112, July 31, 2009; 74 FR 57423, Nov. 6, 2009]

PART 262—STANDARDS APPLICABLE TO GENERATORS OF HAZARDOUS WASTE

262.215 Unwanted material that is not solid or hazardous waste.

262.216 Non-laboratory hazardous waste generated at an eligible academic entity.

Appendix to Part 262—Uniform Hazardous Waste Manifest and Instructions (EPA Forms 8700-22 and 8700-22A and Their Instructions)

Authority: 42 U.S.C. 6906, 6912, 6922–6925, 6937, and 6938.

Source: 45 FR 33142, May 19, 1980, unless otherwise noted.

Subpart A—General

§262.10 Purpose, scope, and applicability.

(a) These regulations establish standards for generators of hazardous waste.

(b) 40 CFR 261.5(c) and (d) must be used to determine the applicability of provisions of this part that are dependent on calculations of the quantity of hazardous waste generated per month. 📖 6.1.2

(c) A generator who treats, stores, or disposes of hazardous waste on-site must only comply with the following sections of this part with respect to that waste: Section 262.11 for determining whether or not he has a hazardous waste, §262.12 for obtaining an EPA identification number, §262.34 for accumulation of hazardous waste, §262.40 (c) and (d) for recordkeeping, §262.43 for additional reporting, and if applicable, §262.70 for farmers.

(d) Any person who exports or imports hazardous waste subject to the Federal manifesting requirements of part 262, or subject to the universal waste management standards of 40 CFR Part 273, or subject to State requirements analogous to 40 CFR Part 273, to or from the countries listed in §262.58(a)(1) for recovery must comply with subpart H of this part.

(e) Any person who imports hazardous waste into the United States must comply with the standards applicable to generators established in this part.

(f) A farmer who generates waste pesticides which are hazardous waste and who complies with all of the requirements of §262.70 is not required to comply with other standards in this part or 40 CFR parts 270, 264, 265, or 268 with respect to such pesticides.

(g) A person who generates a hazardous waste as defined by 40 CFR part 261 is subject to the compliance requirements and penalties prescribed in section 3008 of the Act if he does not comply with the requirements of this part.

(h) An owner or operator who initiates a shipment of hazardous waste from a treatment, storage, or disposal facility must comply with the generator standards established in this part.

(i) Persons responding to an explosives or munitions emergency in accordance with 40 CFR 264.1(g)(8)(i)(D) or (iv) or 265.1(c)(11)(i)(D) or (iv), and 270.1(c)(3)(i)(D) or (iii) are not required to comply with the standards of this part.

(j)(1) Universities that are participating in the Laboratory XL project are the University of Massachusetts Boston in Boston, Massachusetts, Boston College in Chestnut Hill, Massachusetts, and the University of Vermont in Burlington, Vermont ("Universities"). The Universities generate laboratory wastes (as defined in §262.102), some of which will be hazardous wastes. As long as the Universities comply with all the requirements of subpart J of this part the Universities' laboratories that are participating in the University Laboratories XL Project as identified in Table 1 of this section, are not subject to the provisions of §§262.11, 262.34(c), 40 CFR Parts 264 and 265, and the permit requirements of 40 CFR Part 270 with respect to said laboratory wastes.

(2) Each University shall have the right to change its respective departments or the on-site location of its hazardous waste accumulation areas listed in Table 1 of this section upon written notice to the Regional Administrator for EPA-Region I and the appropriate state

Table 1—Laboratory XL Project Participant Information

Institution	Approx. number of labs	Departments participating	Location of current hazardous waste accumulation areas
Boston College, Chestnut Hill, MA	120	Chemistry, Biology, Geology, Physics, Psychology	Merkert Chemistry Building, 2609 Beacon St., Boston, MA, Higgins Building, 140 Commonwealth Ave., Chestnut Hill, MA.
University of Massachusetts Boston, Boston, MA	150	Chemistry, Biology, Psychology, Anthropology, Geology and Earth Sciences, and Environmental, Coastal and Ocean Sciences	Science Building (Bldg. #080); McCormack Building (Bldg. #020); and Wheatley Building (Bldg. #010), 100 Morrissey Blvd., Boston, MA.
University of Vermont, Burlington, VT	400	Colleges of: Agriculture and Life Sciences, Arts and Sciences, Medicine, and Engineering and Mathematics; and Schools of: Nursing, Allied Heath Sciences, and Natural Resources.	Given Bunker, 89 Beaumont Ave., Burlington, VT.

agency. Such written notice will be provided at least ten days prior to the effective date of any such changes.

(k) Generators in the Commonwealth of Massachusetts may comply with the State regulations regarding Class A recyclable materials in 310 C.M.R. 30.200, when authorized by the EPA under 40 CFR part 271, with respect to those recyclable materials and matters covered by the authorization, instead of complying with the hazardous waste accumulation requirements of §262.34, the reporting requirements of §262.41, the storage facility operator requirements of 40 CFR parts 264 and 265 and the permitting requirements of 40 CFR part 270. Such generators must also comply with any other applicable requirements, including any applicable authorized State regulations governing hazardous wastes not being recycled and any applicable Federal requirements which are being directly implemented by the EPA within Massachusetts pursuant to the Hazardous and Solid Waste Amendments of 1984.

(l) The laboratories owned by an eligible academic entity that chooses to be subject to the requirements of Subpart K of this part are not subject to (for purposes of this paragraph, the terms "laboratory" and "eligible academic entity" shall have the meaning as defined in §262.200 of Subpart K of this part).:

(1) The requirements of §262.11 or §262.34(c), for large quantity generators and small quantity generators, except as provided in Subpart K, and

(2) The conditions of §261.5(b), for conditionally exempt small quantity generators, except as provided in Subpart K.

Note 1: The provisions of §262.34 are applicable to the on-site accumulation of hazardous waste by generators. Therefore, the provisions of §262.34 only apply to owners or operators who are shipping hazardous waste which they generated at that facility.

Note 2: A generator who treats, stores, or disposes of hazardous waste on-site must comply with the applicable standards and permit requirements set forth in 40 CFR parts 264, 265, 266, 268, and 270.

[45 FR 33142, May 19, 1980, as amended at 45 FR 86970, Dec. 31, 1980; 47 FR 1251, Jan. 11, 1982; 48 FR 14294, Apr. 1, 1983; 53 FR 27164, July 19, 1988; 56 FR 3877, Jan. 31, 1991; 60 FR 25541, May 11, 1995; 61 FR 16309, Apr. 12, 1996; 62 FR 6651, Feb. 12, 1997; 64 FR 52392, Sept. 28, 1999; 69 FR 11813, Mar. 12, 2004; 73 FR 72954, Dec. 1, 2008]

§262.11 Hazardous waste determination.

A person who generates a solid waste, as defined in 40 CFR 261.2, must determine if that waste is a hazardous waste using the following method: 📖 **2.1, 14.1, 16.1.4, 18.1**

(a) He should first determine if the waste is excluded from regulation under 40 CFR 261.4. 📖 **4.1–4.21, 18.1.2**

(b) He must then determine if the waste is listed as a hazardous waste in subpart D of 40 CFR part 261. 📖 **3.1, 14.3, 18.1.3, 18.3.2**

Note: Even if the waste is listed, the generator still has an opportunity under 40 CFR 260.22 to demonstrate to the Administrator that the waste from his particular facility or operation is not a hazardous waste.

(c) For purposes of compliance with 40 CFR part 268, or if the waste is not listed in subpart D of 40 CFR part 261, the generator must then determine whether the waste is identified in subpart C of 40 CFR part 261 by either: 📖 **2.2–2.8, 13.6, 18.1.4**

(1) Testing the waste according to the methods set forth in subpart C of 40 CFR part 261, or according to an equivalent method approved by the Administrator under 40 CFR 260.21; or 📖 **18.2.2**

(2) Applying knowledge of the hazard characteristic of the waste in light of the materials or the processes used. 📖 **2.1.1.1, 18.3.1, 18.3.3**

(d) If the waste is determined to be hazardous, the generator must refer to parts 261, 264, 265, 266, 268, and 273 of this chapter for possible exclusions or restrictions pertaining to management of the specific waste.

[45 FR 33142, May 19, 1980, as amended at 45 FR 76624, Nov. 19, 1980; 51 FR 40637, Nov. 7, 1986; 55 FR 22684, June 1, 1990; 56 FR 3877, Jan. 31, 1991; 60 FR 25541, May 11, 1995]

§262.12 EPA identification numbers.

(a) A generator must not treat, store, dispose of, transport, or offer for transportation, hazardous waste without having received an EPA identification number from the Administrator.

(b) A generator who has not received an EPA identification number may obtain one by applying to the Administrator using EPA form 8700-12. Upon receiving the request the Administrator will assign an EPA identification number to the generator.

(c) A generator must not offer his hazardous waste to transporters or to treatment, storage, or disposal facilities that have not received an EPA identification number.

Subpart B—The Manifest 📖 **6.5.2, 6.6**

§262.20 General requirements.

(a)(1) A generator who transports, or offers for transport a hazardous waste for offsite treatment, storage, or disposal, or a treatment, storage, and disposal facility who offers for transport a rejected hazardous waste load, must prepare a Manifest (OMB Control number 2050–0039) on EPA Form 8700–22, and, if necessary, EPA Form 8700–22A, according to the instructions included in the appendix to this part. 📖 **6.6.3, 6.6.7**

(2) The revised manifest form and procedures in 40 CFR 260.10, 261.7, 262.20, 262.21, 262.27, 262.32, 262.34, 262.54, 262.60, and the appendix to part 262, shall not apply until September 5, 2006. The manifest form and procedures in 40 CFR 260.10, 261.7, 262.20, 262.21, 262.32, 262.34, 262.54, 262.60, and the Appendix to part 262, contained in the 40 CFR, parts 260 to 265, edition revised as of July 1, 2004, shall be applicable until September 5, 2006.

(b) A generator must designate on the manifest one facility which is permitted to handle the waste described on the manifest. 📖 6.6.3.4, 7.2.2.6, 7.4.1.1

(c) A generator may also designate on the manifest one alternate facility which is permitted to handle his waste in the event an emergency prevents delivery of the waste to the primary designated facility.

(d) If the transporter is unable to deliver the hazardous waste to the designated facility or the alternate facility, the generator must either designate another facility or instruct the transporter to return the waste.

(e) The requirements of this subpart do not apply to hazardous waste produced by generators of greater than 100 kg but less than 1000 kg in a calendar month where: 📖 6.6.2.1

(1) The waste is reclaimed under a contractual agreement pursuant to which:

(i) The type of waste and frequency of shipments are specified in the agreement;

(ii) The vehicle used to transport the waste to the recycling facility and to deliver regenerated material back to the generator is owned and operated by the reclaimer of the waste; and

(2) The generator maintains a copy of the reclamation agreement in his files for a period of at least three years after termination or expiration of the agreement.

(f) The requirements of this subpart and §262.32(b) do not apply to the transport of hazardous wastes on a public or private right-of-way within or along the border of contiguous property under the control of the same person, even if such contiguous property is divided by a public or private right-of-way. Notwithstanding 40 CFR 263.10(a), the generator or transporter must comply with the requirements for transporters set forth in 40 CFR 263.30 and 263.31 in the event of a discharge of hazardous waste on a public or private right-of-way. 📖 6.6.2.2

[45 FR 33142, May 19, 1980, as amended at 49 FR 10500, Mar. 20, 1984; 51 FR 10175, Mar. 24, 1986; 53 FR 45090, Nov. 8, 1988; 62 FR 6651, Feb. 12, 1997; 70 FR 10815, Mar. 4, 2005; 70 FR 35037, June 16, 2005]

§262.21 Manifest tracking numbers, manifest printing, and obtaining manifests.

(a)(1) A registrant may not print, or have printed, the manifest for use of distribution unless it has received approval from the EPA Director of the Office of Resource Conservation and Recovery to do so under paragraphs (c) and (e) of this section.

(2) The approved registrant is responsible for ensuring that the organizations identified in its application are in compliance with the procedures of its approved application and the requirements of this section. The registrant is responsible for assigning manifest tracking numbers to its manifests.

(b) A registrant must submit an initial application to the EPA Director of the Office of Resource Conservation and Recovery that contains the following information:

(1) Name and mailing address of registrant;

(2) Name, telephone number and email address of contact person;

(3) Brief description of registrant's government or business activity;

(4) EPA identification number of the registrant, if applicable;

(5) Description of the scope of the operations that the registrant plans to undertake in printing, distributing, and using its manifests, including:

(i) A description of the printing operation. The description should include an explanation of whether the registrant intends to print its manifests in-house (*i.e.*, using its own printing establishments) or through a separate (*i.e.*, unaffiliated) printing company. If the registrant intends to use a separate printing company to print the manifest on its behalf, the application must identify this printing company and discuss how the registrant will oversee the company. If this includes the use of intermediaries (*e.g.*, prime and subcontractor relationships), the role of each must be discussed. The application must provide the name and mailing address of each company. It also must provide the name and telephone number of the contact person at each company.

(ii) A description of how the registrant will ensure that its organization and unaffiliated companies, if any, comply with the requirements of this section. The application must discuss how the registrant will ensure that a unique manifest tracking number will be preprinted on each manifest. The application must describe the internal control procedures to be followed by the registrant and unaffiliated companies to ensure that numbers are tightly controlled and remain unique. In particular, the application must describe how the registrant will assign manifest tracking numbers to its manifests. If computer systems or other infrastructure will be used to maintain, track, or assign numbers, these should be indicated. The application must also indicate how the printer will pre-print a unique number on each form (*e.g.*, crash or press numbering). The application also must explain the other quality procedures to be followed by each establishment and printing company to ensure that all required print specifications are consistently achieved and that printing violations are identified and corrected at the earliest practicable time.

(iii) An indication of whether the registrant intends to use the manifests for its own business operations or to distribute the manifests to a separate company or to the general public (*e.g.*, for purchase).

(6) A brief description of the qualifications of the company that will print the manifest. The registrant may use readily available information to do so (*e.g.*, corporate brochures, product samples, customer references, documentation of ISO certification), so long as such information pertains to the establishments or company being proposed to print the manifest.

(7) Proposed unique three-letter manifest tracking number suffix. If the registrant is approved to print the manifest, the registrant must use this suffix to pre-print a unique manifest tracking number on each manifest.

(8) A signed certification by a duly authorized employee of the registrant that the organizations and companies in its application will comply with the procedures of its approved application and the requirements of this section and that it will notify the EPA Director of the Office of Resource Conservation and Recovery of any duplicated manifest tracking numbers on manifests that have been used or distributed to other parties as soon as this becomes known.

(c) EPA will review the application submitted under paragraph (b) of this section and either approve it or request additional information or modification before approving it.

(d)(1) Upon EPA approval of the application under paragraph (c) of this section, EPA will provide the registrant an electronic file of the manifest, continuation sheet, and manifest instructions and ask the registrant to submit three fully assembled manifests and continuation sheet samples, except as noted in paragraph (d)(3) of this section. The registrant's samples must meet all of the specifications in paragraph (f) of this section and be printed by the company that will print the manifest as identified in the application approved under paragraph (c) of this section.

(2) The registrant must submit a description of the manifest samples as follows:

(i) Paper type (*i.e.*, manufacturer and grade of the manifest paper);

(ii) Paper weight of each copy;

(iii) Ink color of the manifest's instructions. If screening of the ink was used, the registrant must indicate the extent of the screening; and

(iv) Method of binding the copies.

(3) The registrant need not submit samples of the continuation sheet if it will print its continuation sheet using the same paper type, paper weight of each copy, ink color of the instructions, and binding method as its manifest form samples.

(e) EPA will evaluate the forms and either approve the registrant to print them as proposed or request additional information or modification to them before approval. EPA will notify the registrant of its decision by mail. The registrant cannot use or distribute its forms until EPA approves them. An approved registrant must print the manifest and continuation sheet according to its application approved under paragraph (c) of this section and the manifest specifications in paragraph (f) of this section. It also must print the forms according to the paper type, paper weight, ink color of the manifest instructions and binding method of its approved forms.

(f) Paper manifests and continuation sheets must be printed according to the following specifications:

(1) The manifest and continuation sheet must be printed with the exact format and appearance as EPA Forms 8700–22 and 8700–22A, respectively. However, information required to complete the manifest may be preprinted on the manifest form.

(2) A unique manifest tracking number assigned in accordance with a numbering system approved by EPA must be pre-printed in Item 4 of the manifest. The tracking number must consist of a unique three-letter suffix following nine digits.

(3) The manifest and continuation sheet must be printed on 8 1/2 x 11-inch white paper, excluding common stubs (*e.g.*, top- or side-bound stubs). The paper must be durable enough to withstand normal use.

(4) The manifest and continuation sheet must be printed in black ink that can be legibly photocopied, scanned, and faxed, except that the marginal words indicating copy distribution must be in red ink.

(5) The manifest and continuation sheet must be printed as six-copy forms. Copy-to-copy registration must be exact within 1/32nd of an inch. Handwritten and typed impressions on the form must be legible on all six copies. Copies must be bound together by one or more common stubs that reasonably ensure that they will not become detached inadvertently during normal use.

(6) Each copy of the manifest and continuation sheet must indicate how the copy must be distributed, as follows:

(i) Page 1 (top copy): "Designated facility to destination State (if required)".

(ii) Page 2: "Designated facility to generator State (if required)".

(iii) Page 3: "Designated facility to generator".

(iv) Page 4: "Designated facility's copy".

(v) Page 5: "Transporter's copy".

(vi) Page 6 (bottom copy): "Generator's initial copy".

(7) The instructions in the appendix to 40 CFR part 262 must appear legibly on the back of the copies of the manifest and continuation sheet as provided in this paragraph (f). The instructions must not be visible through the front of the copies when photocopied or faxed.

(i) Manifest Form 8700–22.

(A) The "Instructions for Generators" on Copy 6;

(B) The "Instructions for International Shipment Block" and "Instructions for Transporters" on Copy 5; and

(C) The "Instructions for Treatment, Storage, and Disposal Facilities" on Copy 4.

(ii) Manifest Form 8700–22A.

(A) The "Instructions for Generators" on Copy 6;

(B) The "Instructions for Transporters" on Copy 5; and

(C) The "Instructions for Treatment, Storage, and Disposal Facilities" on Copy 4.

(g)(1) A generator may use manifests printed by any source so long as the source of the printed form has received approval from EPA to print the manifest under paragraphs (c) and (e) of this section. A registered source may be a:

(i) State agency;

(ii) Commercial printer;

(iii) Hazardous waste generator, transporter or TSDF; or

(iv) Hazardous waste broker or other preparer who prepares or arranges shipments of hazardous waste for transportation.

(2) A generator must determine whether the generator state or the consignment state for a shipment regulates any additional wastes (beyond those regulated Federally) as hazardous wastes under these states' authorized programs. Generators also must determine whether the consignment state or generator state requires the generator to submit any copies of the manifest to these states. In cases where the generator must supply copies to either the generator's state or the consignment state, the generator is responsible for supplying legible photocopies of the manifest to these states.

(h)(1) If an approved registrant would like to update any of the information provided in its application approved under paragraph (c) of this section (e.g., to update a company phone number or name of contact person), the registrant must revise the application and submit it to the EPA Director of the Office of Resource Conservation and Recovery, along with an indication or explanation of the update, as soon as practicable after the change occurs. The Agency either will approve or deny the revision. If the Agency denies the revision, it will explain the reasons for the denial, and it will contact the registrant and request further modification before approval.

(2) If the registrant would like a new tracking number suffix, the registrant must submit a proposed suffix to the EPA Director of the Office of Resource Conservation and Recovery, along with the reason for requesting it. The Agency will either approve the suffix or deny the suffix and provide an explanation why it is not acceptable.

(3) If a registrant would like to change the paper type, paper weight, ink color of the manifest instructions, or binding method of its manifest or continuation sheet subsequent to approval under paragraph (e) of this section, then the registrant must submit three samples of the revised form for EPA review and approval. If the approved registrant would like to use a new printer, the registrant must submit three manifest samples printed by the new printer, along with a brief description of the printer's qualifications to print the manifest. EPA will evaluate the manifests and either approve the registrant to print the forms as proposed or request additional information or modification to them before approval. EPA will notify the registrant of its decision by

mail. The registrant cannot use or distribute its revised forms until EPA approves them.

(i) If, subsequent to its approval under paragraph (e) of this section, a registrant typesets its manifest or continuation sheet instead of using the electronic file of the forms provided by EPA, it must submit three samples of the manifest or continuation sheet to the registry for approval. EPA will evaluate the manifests or continuation sheets and either approve the registrant to print them as proposed or request additional information or modification to them before approval. EPA will notify the registrant of its decision by mail. The registrant cannot use or distribute its typeset forms until EPA approves them.

(j) EPA may exempt a registrant from the requirement to submit form samples under paragraph (d) or (h)(3) of this section if the Agency is persuaded that a separate review of the registrant's forms would serve little purpose in informing an approval decision (*e.g.*, a registrant certifies that it will print the manifest using the same paper type, paper weight, ink color of the instructions and binding method of the form samples approved for some other registrant). A registrant may request an exemption from EPA by indicating why an exemption is warranted.

(k) An approved registrant must notify EPA by phone or email as soon as it becomes aware that it has duplicated tracking numbers on any manifests that have been used or distributed to other parties.

(l) If, subsequent to approval of a registrant under paragraph (e) of this section, EPA becomes aware that the approved paper type, paper weight, ink color of the instructions, or binding method of the registrant's form is unsatisfactory, EPA will contact the registrant and require modifications to the form.

(m)(1) EPA may suspend and, if necessary, revoke printing privileges if we find that the registrant:

(i) Has used or distributed forms that deviate from its approved form samples in regard to paper weight, paper type, ink color of the instructions, or binding method; or

(ii) Exhibits a continuing pattern of behavior in using or distributing manifests that contain duplicate manifest tracking numbers.

(2) EPA will send a warning letter to the registrant that specifies the date by which it must come into compliance with the requirements. If the registrant does not come in compliance by the specified date, EPA will send a second letter notifying the registrant that EPA has suspended or revoked its printing privileges. An approved registrant must provide information on its printing activities to EPA if requested.

[49 FR 10500, Mar. 20, 1984; 70 FR 10815, Mar. 4, 2005; 74 FR 30230, June 25, 2009]

§262.22 Number of copies.

The manifest consists of at least the number of copies which will provide the generator, each transporter, and the owner or operator of the designated facility with one copy each for their records and another copy to be returned to the generator.

§262.23 Use of the manifest.

(a) The generator must:

(1) Sign the manifest certification by hand; and

📖 6.6.3.11

(2) Obtain the handwritten signature of the initial transporter and date of acceptance on the manifest; and

(3) Retain one copy, in accordance with §262.40(a).

(b) The generator must give the transporter the remaining copies of the manifest.

(c) For shipments of hazardous waste within the United States solely by water (bulk shipments only), the generator must send three copies of the manifest dated and signed in accordance with this section to the owner or operator of the designated facility or the last water (bulk shipment) transporter to handle the waste in the United States if exported by water. Copies of the manifest are not required for each transporter.

(d) For rail shipments of hazardous waste within the United States which originate at the site of generation, the generator must send at least three copies of the manifest dated and signed in accordance with this section to:

📖 6.6.6

(1) The next non-rail transporter, if any; or

(2) The designated facility if transported solely by rail; or

(3) The last rail transporter to handle the waste in the United States if exported by rail.

(e) For shipments of hazardous waste to a designated facility in an authorized State which has not yet obtained authorization to regulate that particular waste as hazardous, the generator must assure that the designated facility agrees to sign and return the manifest to the generator, and that any out-of-state transporter signs and forwards the manifest to the designated facility.

Note: See §263.20(e) and (f) for special provisions for rail or water (bulk shipment) transporters.

[45 FR 33142, May 19, 1980, as amended at 45 FR 86973, Dec. 31, 1980; 55 FR 2354, Jan. 23, 1990]

§262.27 Waste minimization certification. 📖 6.3.9, 6.6.3.11

A generator who initiates a shipment of hazardous waste must certify to one of the following statements in Item 15 of the uniform hazardous waste manifest:

(a) "I am a large quantity generator. I have a program in place to reduce the volume and toxicity of waste generated to the degree I have determined to be economically practicable and I have selected the practicable method of treatment, storage, or disposal currently available to me which minimizes the present and future threat to human health and the environment;" or

(b) "I am a small quantity generator. I have made a good faith effort to minimize my waste generation and select the best waste management method that is available to me and that I can afford."

[70 FR 10817, Mar. 4, 2005]

Subpart C—Pre-Transport Requirements

§262.30 Packaging.

Before transporting hazardous waste or offering hazardous waste for transportation off-site, a generator must package the waste in accordance with the applicable Department of Transportation regulations on packaging under 49 CFR parts 173, 178, and 179.

§262.31 Labeling. 📖 9.3

Before transporting or offering hazardous waste for transportation off-site, a generator must label each package in accordance with the applicable Department of Transportation regulations on hazardous materials under 49 CFR part 172.

§262.32 Marking.

(a) Before transporting or offering hazardous waste for transportation off-site, a generator must mark each package of hazardous waste in accordance with the applicable Department of Transportation regulations on hazardous materials under 49 CFR part 172;

(b) Before transporting hazardous waste or offering hazardous waste for transportation off-site, a generator must mark each container of 119 gallons or less used in such transportation with the following words and information in accordance with the requirements of 49 CFR 172.304: 📖 9.3

HAZARDOUS WASTE—Federal Law Prohibits Improper Disposal. If found, contact the nearest police or public safety authority or the U.S. Environmental Protection Agency.

Generator's Name and Address_______________.

Generator's EPA Identification Number_______.

Manifest Tracking Number________.

[45 FR 33142, May 19, 1980, as amended at 70 FR 10817, Mar. 4, 2005]

§262.33 Placarding.

Before transporting hazardous waste or offering hazardous waste for transportation off-site, a generator must placard or offer the initial transporter the appropriate placards according to Department of Transportation regulations for hazardous materials under 49 CFR part 172, subpart F.

[70 FR 10817, Mar. 4, 2005; 70 FR 35037, June 16, 2005]

§262.34 Accumulation time. 📖 6.3

(a) Except as provided in paragraphs (d), (e), and (f) of this section, a generator may accumulate hazardous waste on-site for 90 days or less without a permit or without having interim status, provided that: 📖 7.3, 14.1.4, 14.3.2

(1) The waste is placed:

(i) In containers and the generator complies with the applicable requirements of subparts I, AA, BB, and CC of 40 CFR part 265; and/or 📖 6.3.4.2, 9.3

(ii) In tanks and the generator complies with the applicable requirements of subparts J, AA, BB, and CC of 40 CFR part 265 except §§265.197(c) and 265.200; and/or 📖 6.3.4.1, 10.2.4, 10.4.1

(iii) On drip pads and the generator complies with subpart W of 40 CFR part 265 and maintains the following records at the facility: 📖 6.3.4.3

(A) A description of procedures that will be followed to ensure that all wastes are removed from the drip pad and associated collection system at least once every 90 days; and

(B) Documentation of each waste removal, including the quantity of waste removed from the drip pad and the sump or collection system and the date and time of removal; and/or

(iv) In containment buildings and the generator complies with subpart DD of 40 CFR part 265, has placed its professional engineer certification that the building complies with the design standards specified in 40 CFR 265.1101 in the facility's operating record no later than 60 days after the date of initial operation of the unit. After February 18, 1993, PE certification will be required prior to operation of the unit. The owner or operator shall maintain the following records at the facility: 📖 6.3.4.4, 13.8.4.1.1

(A) A written description of procedures to ensure that each waste volume remains in the unit for no more than 90 days, a written description of the waste generation and management practices for the facility showing that they are consistent with respecting the 90 day limit, and documentation that the procedures are complied with; or

(B) Documentation that the unit is emptied at least once every 90 days.

In addition, such a generator is exempt from all the requirements in subparts G and H of 40 CFR part 265, except for §§265.111 and 265.114. 📖 6.3.13–14

(2) The date upon which each period of accumulation begins is clearly marked and visible for inspection on each container; 📖 6.3.6, 16.1.3, 9.3

(3) While being accumulated on-site, each container and tank is labeled or marked clearly with the words, "Hazardous Waste"; and 📖 6.3.2, 16.1.3, 9.3

(4) The generator complies with the requirements for owners or operators in Subparts C and D in 40 CFR part 265, with §265.16, and with 40 CFR 268.7(a)(5). 📖 6.3.7–8, 6.4, 6.7.4, 14.4.2.1, 16.1.2, 16.1.8, 18.2.3.1

(b) A generator who accumulates hazardous waste for more than 90 days is an operator of a storage facility and is subject to the requirements of 40 CFR parts 264 and 265 and the permit requirements of 40 CFR part 270 unless he has been granted an extension to the 90-day period. Such extension may be granted by EPA if hazardous wastes must remain on-site for longer than 90 days due to unforeseen, temporary, and uncontrollable circumstances. An extension of up to 30 days may be granted at the discretion of the Regional Administrator on a case-by-case basis. 📖 6.3.6.4

(c)(1) A generator may accumulate as much as 55 gallons of hazardous waste or one quart of acutely hazardous waste listed in §261.33(e) in containers at or near any point of generation where wastes initially accumulate, which is under the control of the operator of the process generating the waste, without a permit or interim status and without complying with paragraph (a) of this section provided he: 📖 6.2.1–2

(i) Complies with §§265.171, 265.172, and 265.173(a) of this chapter; and 📖 6.2.3

(ii) Marks his containers either with the words "Hazardous Waste" or with other words that identify the contents of the containers. 📖 6.2.1, 9.3.1, 16.1.3

(2) A generator who accumulates either hazardous waste or acutely hazardous waste listed in §261.33(e) in excess of the amounts listed in paragraph (c)(1) of this section at or near any point of generation must, with respect to that amount of excess waste, comply within three days with paragraph (a) of this section or other applicable provisions of this chapter. During the three day period the generator must continue to comply with paragraphs (c)(1)(i) through (ii) of this section. The generator must mark the container holding the excess accumulation of hazardous waste with the date the excess amount began accumulating. 📖 6.2.4

(d) A generator who generates greater than 100 kilograms but less than 1000 kilograms of hazardous waste in a calendar month may accumulate hazardous waste on-site for 180 days or less without a permit or without having interim status provided that: 📖 6.3.16, 7.3.2.1

(1) The quantity of waste accumulated on-site never exceeds 6000 kilograms;

(2) The generator complies with the requirements of subpart I of part 265 of this chapter, except for §§265.176 and 265.178;

(3) The generator complies with the requirements of §265.201 in subpart J of part 265;

(4) The generator complies with the requirements of paragraphs (a)(2) and (a)(3) of this section, the requirements of subpart C of part 265, the requirements of 40 CFR 268.7(a)(5); and 📖 6.3.7, 6.7.4, 16.1.3, 16.1.8, 18.2.3.1

(5) The generator complies with the following requirements: 📖 6.3.7–8, 16.1.11

(i) At all times there must be at least one employee either on the premises or on call (*i.e.*, available to respond to an emergency by reaching the facility within a short period of time) with the responsibility for coordinating all emergency response measures specified in paragraph (d)(5)(iv) of this section. This employee is the emergency coordinator.

(ii) The generator must post the following information next to the telephone:

(A) The name and telephone number of the emergency coordinator;

(B) Location of fire extinguishers and spill control material, and, if present, fire alarm; and

(C) The telephone number of the fire department, unless the facility has a direct alarm.

(iii) The generator must ensure that all employees are thoroughly familiar with proper waste handling and emergency procedures, relevant to their responsibilities during normal facility operations and emergencies; 📖 6.4.2, 16.1.1

(iv) The emergency coordinator or his designee must respond to any emergencies that arise. The applicable responses are as follows:

(A) In the event of a fire, call the fire department or attempt to extinguish it using a fire extinguisher;

(B) In the event of a spill, contain the flow of hazardous waste to the extent possible, and as soon as is practicable, clean up the hazardous waste and any contaminated materials or soil;

(C) In the event of a fire, explosion, or other release which could threaten human health outside the facility or when the generator has knowledge that a spill has reached surface water, the generator must immediately notify the National Response Center (using their 24-hour toll free number 800/424-8802). The report must include the following information:

(*1*) The name, address, and U.S. EPA Identification Number of the generator;

(*2*) Date, time, and type of incident (*e.g.*, spill or fire);

(*3*) Quantity and type of hazardous waste involved in the incident;

(*4*) Extent of injuries, if any; and

(*5*) Estimated quantity and disposition of recovered materials, if any.

(e) A generator who generates greater than 100 kilograms but less than 1000 kilograms of hazardous waste in a calendar month and who must transport his waste, or offer his waste for transportation, over a distance of 200 miles or more for off-site treatment, storage or disposal may accumulate hazardous waste on-site for 270 days or less without a permit or without having interim status provided that he complies with the requirements of paragraph (d) of this section. 📖 6.3.16.3

(f) A generator who generates greater than 100 kilograms but less than 1000 kilograms of hazardous waste in a calendar month and who accumulates hazardous waste in quantities exceeding 6000 kg or accumulates hazardous waste for more than 180 days (or for more than 270 days if he must transport his waste, or offer his waste for transportation, over a distance of 200 miles or more) is an operator of a storage facility and is subject to the requirements of 40 CFR parts 264 and 265 and the permit requirements of 40 CFR part 270 unless he has been granted an extension to the 180-day (or 270-day if applicable) period. Such extension may be granted by EPA if hazardous wastes must remain on-site for longer than 180 days (or 270 days if applicable) due to unforeseen, temporary, and uncontrollable circumstances. An extension of up to 30 days may be granted at the discretion of the Regional Administrator on a case-by-case basis. 📖 6.3.6.4

(g) A generator who generates 1,000 kilograms or greater of hazardous waste per calendar month who also generates wastewater treatment sludges from electroplating operations that meet the listing description for the RCRA hazardous waste code F006, may accumulate F006 waste on-site for more than 90 days, but not more than 180 days without a permit or without having interim status provided that: 📖 3.4.2.6

(1) The generator has implemented pollution prevention practices that reduce the amount of any hazardous substances, pollutants or contaminants entering F006 or otherwise released to the environment prior to its recycling;

(2) The F006 waste is legitimately recycled through metals recovery;

(3) No more than 20,000 kilograms of F006 waste is accumulated on-site at any one time; and

(4) The F006 waste is managed in accordance with the following:

(i) The F006 waste is placed:

(A) In containers and the generator complies with the applicable requirements of subparts I, AA, BB, and CC of 40 CFR part 265; and/or

(B) In tanks and the generator complies with the applicable requirements of subparts J, AA, BB, and CC of 40 CFR part 265, except §§265.197(c) and 265.200; and/or

(C) In containment buildings and the generator complies with subpart DD of 40 CFR part 265, and has placed its professional engineer certification that the building complies with the design standards specified in 40 CFR 265.1101 in the facility's operating record prior to operation of the unit. The owner or operator must maintain the following records at the facility:

(*1*) A written description of procedures to ensure that the F006 waste remains in the unit for no more than 180 days, a written description of the waste generation and management practices for the facility showing that they are consistent with the 180-day limit, and documentation that the generator is complying with the procedures; or

(*2*) Documentation that the unit is emptied at least once every 180 days.

(ii) In addition, such a generator is exempt from all the requirements in subparts G and H of 40 CFR part 265, except for §§265.111 and 265.114.

(iii) The date upon which each period of accumulation begins is clearly marked and visible for inspection on each container;

(iv) While being accumulated on-site, each container and tank is labeled or marked clearly with the words, "Hazardous Waste;" and

(v) The generator complies with the requirements for owners or operators in subparts C and D in 40 CFR part 265, with 40 CFR 265.16, and with 40 CFR 268.7(a)(5).

(h) A generator who generates 1,000 kilograms or greater of hazardous waste per calendar month who also generates wastewater treatment sludges from electroplating operations that meet the listing description for the RCRA hazardous waste code F006, and who must transport this waste, or offer this waste for transportation, over a distance of 200 miles or more for off-site metals recovery, may accumulate F006 waste on-site for more than 90 days, but not more than 270 days without a permit or without having interim status if the generator complies with the requirements of paragraphs (g)(1) through (g)(4) of this section.

(i) A generator accumulating F006 in accordance with paragraphs (g) and (h) of this section who accumulates F006 waste on-site for more than 180 days (or for more than 270 days if the generator must transport this waste, or offer this waste for transportation, over a distance of 200 miles or more), or who accumulates more than 20,000 kilograms of F006 waste on-site is an operator of a storage facility and is subject to the requirements of 40 CFR parts 264 and 265 and the permit requirements of 40 CFR part 270 unless the generator has been granted an extension to the 180-day (or 270-day if applicable) period or an exception to the 20,000 kilogram accumulation limit. Such extensions and exceptions may be granted by EPA if F006 waste must remain on-site for longer than 180 days (or 270 days if applicable) or if more than 20,000 kilograms of F006 waste must remain on-site due to unforeseen, temporary, and uncontrollable circumstances. An extension of up to 30 days or an exception to the accumulation limit may be granted at the discretion of the Regional Administrator on a case-by-case basis.

(j) A member of the Performance Track Program who generates 1000 kg or greater of hazardous waste per month (or one kilogram or more of acute hazardous waste) may accumulate hazardous waste on-site without a permit or interim status for an extended period of time, provided that: 📖 6.3.6.5

(1) The generator accumulates the hazardous waste for no more than 180 days, or for no more than 270 days if the generator must transport the waste (or offer the waste for transport) more than 200 miles from the generating facility; and

(2) The generator first notifies the Regional Administrator and the Director of the authorized State in writing of its intent to begin accumulation of hazardous waste for extended time periods under the provisions of this section. Such advance notice must include:

(i) Name and EPA ID number of the facility, and specification of when the facility will begin accumulation of hazardous wastes for extended periods of time in accordance with this section; and

(ii) A description of the types of hazardous wastes that will be accumulated for extended periods of time, and the units that will be used for such extended accumulation; and

(iii) A Statement that the facility has made all changes to its operations, procedures, including emergency preparedness procedures, and equipment, including equipment needed for emergency preparedness, that will be necessary to accommodate extended time periods for accumulating hazardous wastes; and

(iv) If the generator intends to accumulate hazardous wastes on-site for up to 270 days, a certification that a facility that is permitted (or operating under interim status) under part 270 of this chapter to receive these wastes is not available within 200 miles of the generating facility; and

(3) The waste is managed in:

(i) Containers, in accordance with the applicable requirements of subparts I, AA, BB, and CC of 40 CFR part 265 and 40 CFR 264.175; or

(ii) Tanks, in accordance with the applicable requirements of subparts J, AA, BB, and CC of 40 CFR part 265, except for §§265.197(c) and 265.200; or

(iii) Drip pads, in accordance with subpart W of 40 CFR part 265; or

(iv) Containment buildings, in accordance with subpart DD of 40 CFR part 265; and

(4) The quantity of hazardous waste that is accumulated for extended time periods at the facility does not exceed 30,000 kg; and

(5) The generator maintains the following records at the facility for each unit used for extended accumulation times:

(i) A written description of procedures to ensure that each waste volume remains in the unit for no more than 180 days (or 270 days, as applicable), a description of the waste generation and management practices at the facility showing that they are consistent with the extended accumulation time limit, and documentation that the procedures are complied with; or

(ii) Documentation that the unit is emptied at least once every 180 days (or 270 days, if applicable); and

(6) Each container or tank that is used for extended accumulation time periods is labeled or marked clearly with the words "Hazardous Waste," and for each container the date upon which each period of accumulation begins is clearly marked and visible for inspection; and

(7) The generator complies with the requirements for owners and operators in subparts C and D in 40 CFR part 265, with §265.16, and with §268.7(a)(5). In addition, such a generator is exempt from all the requirements in subparts G and H of part 265 of this chapter, except for §§265.111 and 265.114; and

(8) The generator has implemented pollution prevention practices that reduce the amount of any hazardous substances, pollutants, or contaminants released to the environment prior to its recycling, treatment, or disposal; and

(9) The generator includes the following with its Performance Track Annual Performance Report, which must be submitted to the Regional Administrator and the Director of the authorized State:

(i) Information on the total quantity of each hazardous waste generated at the facility that has been managed in the previous year according to extended accumulation time periods; and

(ii) Information for the previous year on the number of off-site shipments of hazardous wastes generated at the facility, the types and locations of destination facilities, how the wastes were managed at the destination facilities (e.g., recycling, treatment, storage, or disposal), and what changes in on-site or off-site waste management practices have occurred as a result of extended accumulation times or other pollution prevention provisions of this section; and

(iii) Information for the previous year on any hazardous waste spills or accidents occurring at extended accumulation units at the facility, or during off-site transport of accumulated wastes; and

(iv) If the generator intends to accumulate hazardous wastes on-site for up to 270 days, a certification that a facility that is permitted (or operating under interim status) under part 270 of this chapter to receive these wastes is not available within 200 miles of the generating facility; and

(k) If hazardous wastes must remain on-site at a Performance Track member facility for longer than 180 days (or 270 days, if applicable) due to unforseen, temporary, and uncontrollable circumstances, an extension to the extended accumulation time period of up to 30 days may be granted at the discretion of the Regional Administrator on a case-by-case basis.

(l) If a generator who is a member of the Performance Track Program withdraws from the Performance Track Program, or if the Regional Administrator terminates a generator's membership, the generator must return to compliance with all otherwise applicable hazardous waste regulations as soon as possible, but no later than six months after the date of withdrawal or termination.

(m) A generator who sends a shipment of hazardous waste to a designated facility with the understanding that the designated facility can accept and manage the waste and later receives that shipment back as a rejected load or residue in accordance with the manifest discrepancy provisions of §264.72 or §265.72 of this chapter may accumulate the returned waste on-site in accordance with paragraphs (a) and (b) or (d), (e) and (f) of this section, depending on the amount of hazardous waste on-site in that calendar month. Upon receipt of the returned shipment, the generator must: 📖 6.3.6.5, 6.6.3.12.2, 9.5.6.1

(1) Sign Item 18c of the manifest, if the transporter returned the shipment using the original manifest; or

(2) Sign Item 20 of the manifest, if the transporter returned the shipment using a new manifest.

[47 FR 1251, Jan. 11, 1982, as amended at 48 FR 14294, Apr. 1, 1983; 49 FR 49571, Dec. 20, 1984; 51 FR 10175, Mar. 24, 1986; 51 FR 25472, July 14, 1986; 55 FR 22684, June 1, 1990; 55 FR 50483, Dec. 6, 1990; 56 FR 3877, Jan. 31, 1991; 56 FR 30195, July 1, 1991; 57 FR 37264, Aug. 18, 1992; 59 FR 62926, Dec. 6, 1994; 61 FR 4911, Feb. 9, 1996; 61 FR 59950, Nov. 25, 1996; 64 FR 3388, Jan. 21, 1999; 64 FR 25414, May 11, 1999; 64 FR 56471, Oct. 20, 1999; 65 FR 12397, Mar. 8, 2000; 69 FR 21753, Apr. 22, 2004; 69 FR 62224, Oct. 25, 2004; 70 FR 10817, Mar. 4, 2005; 71 FR 40271, July 14, 2006]

Subpart D—Recordkeeping and Reporting

§262.40 Recordkeeping.

📖 16.1.12

(a) A generator must keep a copy of each manifest signed in accordance with §262.23(a) for three years or until he receives a signed copy from the designated facility which received the waste. This signed copy must be retained as a record for at least three years from the date the waste was accepted by the initial transporter. 📖 6.6.5, 6.7.1

(b) A generator must keep a copy of each Biennial Report and Exception Report for a period of at least three years from the due date of the report. 📖 6.7.1

(c) A generator must keep records of any test results, waste analyses, or other determinations made in accordance with §262.11 for at least three years from the date that the waste was last sent to on-site or off-site treatment, storage, or disposal. 📖 6.7.3

(d) The periods or retention referred to in this section are extended automatically during the course of any unresolved enforcement action regarding the regulated activity or as requested by the Administrator.

[45 FR 33142, May 19, 1980, as amended at 48 FR 3981, Jan. 28, 1983]

§262.41 Biennial report. 📖 6.7.9, 6.8

(a) A generator who ships any hazardous waste off-site to a treatment, storage or disposal facility within the United States must prepare and submit a single copy of a Biennial Report to the Regional Administrator by March 1 of each even numbered year. The Biennial Report must be submitted on EPA Form 8700-13A, must cover generator activities during the previous year, and must include the following information:

(1) The EPA identification number, name, and address of the generator;

(2) The calendar year covered by the report;

(3) The EPA identification number, name, and address for each off-site treatment, storage, or disposal facility in the United States to which waste was shipped during the year;

(4) The name and EPA identification number of each transporter used during the reporting year for shipments to a treatment, storage or disposal facility within the United States;

(5) A description, EPA hazardous waste number (from 40 CFR part 261, subpart C or D), DOT hazard class, and quantity of each hazardous waste shipped off-site for shipments to a treatment, storage or disposal facility within the United States. This information must be listed by EPA identification number of each such off-site facility to which waste was shipped. 📖 9.1.2.2, 9.7

(6) A description of the efforts undertaken during the year to reduce the volume and toxicity of waste generated.

(7) A description of the changes in volume and toxicity of waste actually achieved during the year in comparison to previous years to the extent such information is available for years prior to 1984.

(8) The certification signed by the generator or authorized representative.

(b) Any generator who treats, stores, or disposes of hazardous waste on-site must submit a biennial report covering those wastes in accordance with the provisions of 40 CFR parts 270, 264, 265, and 266. Reporting for exports of hazardous waste is not required on the Biennial Report form. A separate annual report requirement is set forth at 40 CFR 262.56.

[48 FR 3981, Jan. 28, 1983, as amended at 48 FR 14294, Apr. 1, 1983; 50 FR 28746, July 15, 1985; 51 FR 28682, Aug. 8, 1986]

§262.42 Exception reporting. 📖 6.6.4, 6.7.1

(a)(1) A generator of greater than 1000 kilograms of hazardous waste in a calendar month who does not receive a copy of the manifest with the handwritten signature of the owner or operator of the designated facility within 35 days of the date the waste was accepted by the initial transporter must contact the transporter and/or the owner or operator of the designated facility to determine the status of the hazardous waste.

(2) A generator of greater than 1000 kilograms of hazardous waste in a calendar month must submit an Exception Report to the EPA Regional Administrator for the Region in which the generator is located if he has not received a copy of the manifest with the handwritten signature of the owner or operator of the designated facility within 45 days of the date the waste was accepted by the initial transporter. The Exception Report must include:

(i) A legible copy of the manifest for which the generator does not have confirmation of delivery;

(ii) A cover letter signed by the generator or his authorized representative explaining the efforts taken to locate the hazardous waste and the results of those efforts.

(b) A generator of greater than 100 kilograms but less than 1000 kilograms of hazardous waste in a calendar month who does not receive a copy of the manifest with the handwritten signature of the owner or operator of the designated facility within 60 days of the date the waste was accepted by the initial transporter must submit a legible copy of the manifest, with some indication that the generator has not received confirmation of delivery, to the EPA Regional Administrator for the Region in which the generator is located.

Note: The submission to EPA need only be a handwritten or typed note on the manifest itself, or on an attached sheet of paper, stating that the return copy was not received.

[52 FR 35898, Sept. 23, 1987]

§262.43 Additional reporting.

The Administrator, as he deems necessary under sections 2002(a) and 3002(6) of the Act, may require generators to furnish additional reports concerning the quantities and disposition of wastes identified or listed in 40 CFR part 261.

§262.44 Special requirements for generators of between 100 and 1000 kg/mo. 📖 6.7, 16.1.12

A generator of greater than 100 kilograms but less than 1000 kilograms of hazardous waste in a calendar month is subject only to the following requirements in this subpart:

(a) Section 262.40(a), (c), and (d), recordkeeping;

(b) Section 262.42(b), exception reporting; and

(c) Section 262.43, additional reporting.

[52 FR 35899, Sept. 23, 1987]

Subpart E—Exports of Hazardous Waste

Source: 51 FR 28682, Aug. 8, 1986, unless otherwise noted.

§262.50 Applicability. 📖 6.6.9

This subpart establishes requirements applicable to exports of hazardous waste. Except to the extent §262.58 provides otherwise, a primary exporter of hazardous waste must comply with the special requirements of this subpart and a transporter transporting hazardous waste for export must comply with applicable requirements of part 263. Section 262.58 sets forth the requirements of international agreements between the United States and receiving countries which establish different notice, export, and enforcement procedures for the transportation, treatment, storage and disposal of hazardous waste for shipments between the United States and those countries.

§262.51 Definitions.

In addition to the definitions set forth at 40 CFR 260.10, the following definitions apply to this subpart:

Consignee means the ultimate treatment, storage or disposal facility in a receiving country to which the hazardous waste will be sent.

EPA Acknowledgement of Consent means the cable sent to EPA from the U.S. Embassy in a receiving country that acknowledges the written consent of the receiving country to accept the hazardous waste and describes the terms and conditions of the receiving country's consent to the shipment.

Primary Exporter means any person who is required to originate the manifest for a shipment of hazardous waste in accordance with 40 CFR part 262, subpart B, or equivalent State provision, which specifies a treatment, storage, or disposal facility in a receiving country as the facility to which the hazardous waste will be sent and any intermediary arranging for the export.

Receiving country means a foreign country to which a hazardous waste is sent for the purpose of treatment, storage or disposal (except short-term storage incidental to transportation).

Transit country means any foreign country, other than a receiving country, through which a hazardous waste is transported.

[53 FR 27164, July 19, 1988]

§262.52 General requirements. 📖 6.6.9

Exports of hazardous waste are prohibited except in compliance with the applicable requirements of this subpart and part 263. Exports of hazardous waste are prohibited unless:

(a) Notification in accordance with §262.53 has been provided;

(b) The receiving country has consented to accept the hazardous waste;

(c) A copy of the EPA Acknowledgment of Consent to the shipment accompanies the hazardous waste shipment and, unless exported by rail, is attached to the manifest (or shipping paper for exports by water (bulk shipment)).

(d) The hazardous waste shipment conforms to the terms of the receiving country's written consent as reflected in the EPA Acknowledgment of Consent.

§262.53 Notification of intent to export.

(a) A primary exporter of hazardous waste must notify EPA of an intended export before such waste is scheduled to leave the United States. A complete notification should be submitted sixty (60) days before the initial shipment is intended to be shipped off site. This notification may cover export activities extending over a twelve (12) month or lesser period. The notification must be in writing, signed by the primary exporter, and include the following information:

(1) Name, mailing address, telephone number and EPA ID number of the primary exporter;

(2) By consignee, for each hazardous waste type:

(i) A description of the hazardous waste and the EPA hazardous waste number (from 40 CFR part 261, subparts C and D), U.S. DOT proper shipping name, hazard class and ID number (UN/NA) for each hazardous waste as identified in 49 CFR parts 171 through 177;

(ii) The estimated frequency or rate at which such waste is to be exported and the period of time over which such waste is to be exported.

(iii) The estimated total quantity of the hazardous waste in units as specified in the instructions to the Uniform Hazardous Waste Manifest Form (8700-22);

(iv) All points of entry to and departure from each foreign country through which the hazardous waste will pass;

(v) A description of the means by which each shipment of the hazardous waste will be transported (*e.g.,* mode of transportation vehicle (air, highway, rail, water, etc.), type(s) of container (drums, boxes, tanks, etc.));

(vi) A description of the manner in which the hazardous waste will be treated, stored or disposed of in the receiving country (*e.g.,* land or ocean incineration, other land disposal, ocean dumping, recycling);

(vii) The name and site address of the consignee and any alternate consignee; and

(viii) The name of any transit countries through which the hazardous waste will be sent and a description of the approximate length of time the hazardous waste will remain in such country and the nature of its handling while there;

(b) Notifications submitted by mail should be sent to the following mailing address: Office of Enforcement and Compliance Assurance, Office of Federal Activities, International Compliance Assurance Division (2254A), Environmental Protection Agency, 1200 Pennsylvania Ave., NW., Washington, DC 20460. Hand-delivered notifications should be sent to: Office of Enforcement and Compliance Assurance, Office of Federal Activities, International Compliance Assurance Division, Environmental Protection Agency, Ariel Rios Bldg., Room 6144, 12th St. and Pennsylvania Ave., NW., Washington, DC 20004. In both cases, the following shall be prominently displayed on the front of the envelope: "Attention: Notification of Intent to Export.".

(c) Except for changes to the telephone number in paragraph (a)(1) of this section, changes to paragraph (a)(2)(v) of this section and decreases in the quantity indicated pursuant to paragraph (a)(2)(iii) of this section when the conditions specified on the original notification change (including any exceedance of the estimate of the quantity of hazardous waste specified in the original notification), the primary exporter must provide EPA with a written renotification of the change. The shipment cannot take place until consent of the receiving country to the changes (except for changes to paragraph (a)(2)(viii) of this section and in the ports of entry to and departure from transit countries pursuant to paragraph (a)(2)(iv) of this section) has been obtained and the primary exporter receives an EPA Acknowledgment of Consent reflecting the receiving country's consent to the changes.

(d) Upon request by EPA, a primary exporter shall furnish to EPA any additional information which a receiving country requests in order to respond to a notification.

(e) In conjunction with the Department of State, EPA will provide a complete notification to the receiving country and any transit countries. A notification is complete when EPA receives a notification which EPA determines satisfies the requirements of paragraph (a) of this section. Where a claim of confidentiality is asserted with respect to any notification information required by paragraph (a) of this section, EPA may find the notification not complete until any such claim is resolved in accordance with 40 CFR 260.2.

(f) Where the receiving country consents to the receipt of the hazardous waste, EPA will forward an EPA Acknowledgment of Consent to the primary exporter for purposes of §262.54(h). Where the receiving country objects to receipt of the hazardous waste or withdraws a prior consent, EPA will notify the primary exporter in writing. EPA will also notify the primary exporter of any responses from transit countries.

[51 FR 28682, Aug. 8, 1986, as amended at 56 FR 43705, Sept. 4, 1991; 61 FR 16309, Apr. 12, 1996; 71 FR 40271, July 14, 2006]

§262.54 Special manifest requirements.

A primary exporter must comply with the manifest requirements of 40 CFR 262.20 through 262.23 except that:

(a) In lieu of the name, site address and EPA ID number of the designated permitted facility, the primary exporter must enter the name and site address of the consignee;

(b) In lieu of the name, site address and EPA ID number of a permitted alternate facility, the primary exporter may enter the name and site address of any alternate consignee.

(c) In the International Shipments block, the primary exporter must check the export box and enter the point of exit (city and State) from the United States.

(d) The following statement must be added to the end of the first sentence of the certification set forth in Item 16 of the Uniform Hazardous Waste Manifest Form: "and conforms to the terms of the attached EPA Acknowledgment of Consent";

(e) The primary exporter may obtain the manifest from any source that is registered with the U.S. EPA as a supplier of manifests (*e.g.,* states, waste handlers, and/or commercial forms printers).

(f) The primary exporter must require the consignee to confirm in writing the delivery of the hazardous waste to that facility and to describe any significant discrepancies (as defined in 40 CFR 264.72(a)) between the manifest and the shipment. A copy of the manifest signed by such facility may be used to confirm delivery of the hazardous waste.

(g) In lieu of the requirements of §262.20(d), where a shipment cannot be delivered for any reason to the designated or alternate consignee, the primary exporter must:

(1) Renotify EPA of a change in the conditions of the original notification to allow shipment to a new consignee in accordance with §262.53(c) and obtain an EPA Acknowledgment of Consent prior to delivery; or

(2) Instruct the transporter to return the waste to the primary exporter in the United States or designate another facility within the United States; and

(3) Instruct the transporter to revise the manifest in accordance with the primary exporter's instructions.

(h) The primary exporter must attach a copy of the EPA Acknowledgment of Consent to the shipment to the manifest which must accompany the hazardous waste shipment. For exports by rail or water (bulk shipment), the primary exporter must provide the transporter with an EPA Acknowledgment of Consent which must accompany the hazardous waste but which need not be attached to the manifest except that for exports by water (bulk shipment) the primary exporter must attach the copy of the EPA Acknowledgment of Consent to the shipping paper.

(i) The primary exporter shall provide the transporter with an additional copy of the manifest for delivery to the U.S. Customs official at the point the hazardous waste leaves the United States in accordance with §263.20(g)(4).

[51 FR 28682, Aug. 8, 1986, as amended at 70 FR 10818, Mar. 4, 2005]

§262.55 Exception reports.

In lieu of the requirements of §262.42, a primary exporter must file an exception report with the Administrator if:

(a) He has not received a copy of the manifest signed by the transporter stating the date and place of departure from the United States within forty-five (45) days from the date it was accepted by the initial transporter;

(b) Within ninety (90) days from the date the waste was accepted by the initial transporter, the primary exporter has not received written confirmation from the consignee that the hazardous waste was received;

(c) The waste is returned to the United States.

§262.56 Annual reports.

6.7.10

(a) Primary exporters of hazardous waste shall file with the Administrator no later than March 1 of each year, a report summarizing the types, quantities, frequency, and ultimate destination of all hazardous waste exported during the previous calendar year. Such reports shall include the following:

(1) The EPA identification number, name, and mailing and site address of the exporter;

(2) The calendar year covered by the report;

(3) The name and site address of each consignee;

(4) By consignee, for each hazardous waste exported, a description of the hazardous waste, the EPA hazardous waste number (from 40 CFR part 261, subpart C or D), DOT hazard class, the name and US EPA ID number (where applicable) for each transporter used, the total amount of waste shipped and number of shipments pursuant to each notification;

(5) Except for hazardous waste produced by exporters of greater than 100 kg but less than 1000 kg in a calendar month, unless provided pursuant to §262.41, in even numbered years:

(i) A description of the efforts undertaken during the year to reduce the volume and toxicity of waste generated; and

(ii) A description of the changes in volume and toxicity of waste actually achieved during the year in comparison to previous years to the extent such information is available for years prior to 1984.

(6) A certification signed by the primary exporter which states:

I certify under penalty of law that I have personally examined and am familiar with the information submitted in this and all attached documents, and that based on my inquiry of those individuals immediately responsible for obtaining the information, I believe that the submitted information is true, accurate, and complete. I am aware that there are significant penalties for submitting false information including the possibility of fine and imprisonment.

(b) Annual reports submitted by mail should be sent to the following mailing address: Office of Enforcement and Compliance Assurance, Office of Federal Activities, International Compliance Assurance Division (2254A), Environmental Protection Agency, 1200 Pennsylvania Ave., NW., Washington, DC 20460. Hand-delivered reports should be sent to: Office of Enforcement and Compliance Assurance, Office of Federal Activities, International Compliance Assurance Division, Environmental Protection Agency, Ariel Rios Bldg., Room 6144, 12th St. and Pennsylvania Ave., NW., Washington, DC 20004.

[51 FR 28682, Aug. 8, 1986, as amended at 56 FR 43705, Sept. 4, 1991; 61 FR 16309, Apr. 12, 1996; 71 FR 40271, July 14, 2006]

§262.57 Recordkeeping.

(a) For all exports a primary exporter must:

(1) Keep a copy of each notification of intent to export for a period of at least three years from the date the hazardous waste was accepted by the initial transporter;

(2) Keep a copy of each EPA Acknowledgment of Consent for a period of at least three years from the date the hazardous waste was accepted by the initial transporter;

(3) Keep a copy of each confirmation of delivery of the hazardous waste from the consignee for at least three years from the date the hazardous waste was accepted by the initial transporter; and

(4) Keep a copy of each annual report for a period of at least three years from the due date of the report.

(b) The periods of retention referred to in this section are extended automatically during the course of any unresolved enforcement action regarding the regulated activity or as requested by the Administrator.

§262.58 International agreements.

(a) Any person who exports or imports hazardous waste subject to Federal manifest requirements of Part 262, or subject to the universal waste management standards of 40 CFR Part 273, or subject to State requirements analogous to 40 CFR Part 273, to or from designated member countries of the Organization for Economic Cooperation and Development (OECD) as defined in paragraph (a)(1) of this section for purposes of recovery is subject to Subpart H of this part. The requirements of Subparts E and F do not apply.

(1) For the purposes of subpart H, the designated OECD Member countries consist of Australia, Austria, Belgium, the Czech Republic, Denmark, Finland, France, Germany, Greece, Hungary, Iceland, Ireland, Italy, Japan, Luxembourg, the Netherlands, New Zealand, Norway, Poland, Portugal, the Slovak Republic, South Korea, Spain, Sweden, Switzerland, Turkey, the United Kingdom, and the United States.

(2) For the purposes of this Subpart, Canada and Mexico are considered OECD member countries only for the purpose of transit.

(b) Any person who exports hazardous waste to or imports hazardous waste from: a designated OECD member country for purposes other than recovery (*e.g.*, incineration, disposal), Mexico (for any purpose), or Canada (for any purpose) remains subject to the requirements of subparts E and F of this part.

[61 FR 16310, Apr. 12, 1996, as amended at 71 FR 40271, July 14, 2006]

Subpart F—Imports of Hazardous Waste

§262.60 Imports of hazardous waste. 📖 6.6.8

(a) Any person who imports hazardous waste from a foreign country into the United States must comply with the requirements of this part and the special requirements of this subpart.

(b) When importing hazardous waste, a person must meet all the requirements of §262.20(a) for the manifest except that:

(1) In place of the generator's name, address and EPA identification number, the name and address of the foreign generator and the importer's name, address and EPA identification number must be used.

(2) In place of the generator's signature on the certification statement, the U.S. importer or his agent must sign and date the certification and obtain the signature of the initial transporter.

(c) A person who imports hazardous waste may obtain the manifest form from any source that is registered with the U.S. EPA as a supplier of manifests (*e.g.*, states, waste handlers, and/or commercial forms printers).

(d) In the International Shipments block, the importer must check the import box and enter the point of entry (city and State) into the United States.

(e) The importer must provide the transporter with an additional copy of the manifest to be submitted by the receiving facility to U.S. EPA in accordance with §264.71(a)(3) and §265.71(a)(3) of this chapter.

[51 FR 28685, Aug. 8, 1986, as amended at 70 FR 10818, Mar. 4, 2005]

Subpart G—Farmers

§262.70 Farmers.

A farmer disposing of waste pesticides from his own use which are hazardous wastes is not required to comply with the standards in this part or other standards in 40 CFR parts 264, 265, 268, or 270 for those wastes provided he triple rinses each emptied pesticide container in accordance with §261.7(b)(3) and disposes of the pesticide residues on his own farm in a manner consistent with the disposal instructions on the pesticide label.

[53 FR 27165, July 19, 1988, as amended at 71 FR 40271, July 14, 2006]

Subpart H—Transfrontier Shipments of Hazardous Waste for Recovery within the OECD

Source: 61 FR 16310, Apr. 12, 1996, unless otherwise noted.

§262.80 Applicability.

(a) The requirements of this subpart apply to imports and exports of wastes that are considered hazardous under U.S. national procedures and are destined for recovery operations in the countries listed in §262.58(a)(1). A waste is considered hazardous under U.S. national procedures if it meets the Federal definition of hazardous waste in 40 CFR 261.3 and it is subject to either the Federal manifesting requirements at 40 CFR Part 262, Subpart B, to the universal waste management standards of 40 CFR Part 273, or to State requirements analogous to 40 CFR Part 273.

(b) Any person (notifier, consignee, or recovery facility operator) who mixes two or more wastes (including hazardous and non-hazardous wastes) or otherwise subjects two or more wastes (including hazardous and non-hazardous wastes) to physical or chemical transformation operations, and thereby creates a new hazardous waste, becomes a generator and assumes all subsequent generator duties under RCRA and any notifier duties, if applicable, under this subpart.

§262.81 Definitions.

The following definitions apply to this subpart.

(a) *Competent authorities* means the regulatory authorities of concerned countries having jurisdiction over transfrontier movements of wastes destined for recovery operations.

(b) *Concerned countries* means the exporting and importing OECD member countries and any OECD member countries of transit.

(c) *Consignee* means the person to whom possession or other form of legal control of the waste is assigned at the time the waste is received in the importing country.

(d) *Country of transit* means any designated OECD country in §262.58(a)(1) and (a)(2) other than the exporting or importing country across which a transfrontier movement of wastes is planned or takes place.

(e) *Exporting country* means any designated OECD member country in §262.58(a)(1) from which a transfrontier movement of wastes is planned or has commenced.

(f) *Importing country* means any designated OECD country in §262.58(a)(1) to which a transfrontier movement of wastes is planned or takes place for the purpose of submitting the wastes to recovery operations therein.

(g) *Notifier* means the person under the jurisdiction of the exporting country who has, or will have at the time the planned transfrontier movement commences, possession or other forms of legal control of the wastes and who proposes their transfrontier movement for the ultimate purpose of submitting them to recovery operations. When the United States (U.S.) is the exporting country, notifier is interpreted to mean a person domiciled in the U.S.

(h) *OECD area* means all land or marine areas under the national jurisdiction of any designated OECD member country in §262.58. When the regulations refer to shipments to or from an OECD country, this means OECD area.

(i) *Recognized trader* means a person who, with appropriate authorization of concerned countries, acts in the role of principal to purchase and subsequently sell wastes; this person has legal control of such wastes from time of purchase to time of sale; such a person may act to arrange and facilitate transfrontier movements of wastes destined for recovery operations.

(j) *Recovery facility* means an entity which, under applicable domestic law, is operating or is authorized to operate in the importing country to receive wastes and to perform recovery operations on them.

(k) *Recovery operations* means activities leading to resource recovery, recycling, reclamation, direct re-use or alternative uses as listed in Table 2.B of the Annex of OECD Council Decision C(88)90(Final) of 27 May 1988, (available from the Environmental Protection Agency, RCRA Docket, EPA/DC, EPA West, Room B102, 1301 Constitution Ave., NW., Washington, DC 20460 (Docket # F-94-IEHF-FFFFF) and the Organisation for Economic Co-operation and Development, Environment Direcorate, 2 rue Andre Pascal, 75775 Paris Cedex 16, France) which include:

R1 Use as a fuel (other than in direct incineration) or other means to generate energy

R2 Solvent reclamation/regeneration

R3 Recycling/reclamation of organic substances which are not used as solvents

R4 Recycling/reclamation of metals and metal compounds

R5 Recycling/reclamation of other inorganic materials

R6 Regeneration of acids or bases

R7 Recovery of components used for pollution control

R8 Recovery of components from catalysts

R9 Used oil re-refining or other reuses of previously used oil

R10 Land treatment resulting in benefit to agriculture or ecological improvement

R11 Uses of residual materials obtained from any of the operations numbered R1-R10

R12 Exchange of wastes for submission to any of the operations numbered R1-R11

6R13 Accumulation of material intended for any operation in Table 2.B

(l) *Transfrontier movement* means any shipment of wastes destined for recovery operations from an area under the national jurisdiction of one OECD member country to an area under the national jurisdiction of another OECD member country.

[61 FR 16310, Apr. 12, 1996, as amended at 71 FR 40271, July 14, 2006]

§262.82 General conditions.

(a) *Scope.* The level of control for exports and imports of waste is indicated by assignment of the waste to a green, amber, or red list and by U.S. national procedures as defined in §262.80(a). The green, amber, and red lists are incorporated by reference in §262.89 (e).

(1) Wastes on the green list are subject to existing controls normally applied to commercial transactions, except as provided below:

(i) Green-list wastes that are considered hazardous under U.S. national procedures are subject to amber-list controls.

(ii) Green-list wastes that are sufficiently contaminated or mixed with amber-list wastes, such that the waste or waste mixture is considered hazardous under U.S. national procedures, are subject to amber-list controls.

(iii) Green-list wastes that are sufficiently contaminated or mixed with other wastes subject to red-list controls such that the waste or waste mixture is considered hazardous under U.S. national procedures must be handled in accordance with the red-list controls.

(2) Wastes on the amber list that are considered hazardous under U.S. national procedures as defined in §262.80(a) are subject to the amber-list controls of this Subpart.

(i) If amber-list wastes are sufficiently contaminated or mixed with other wastes subject to red-list controls such that the waste or waste mixture is considered hazardous under U.S. national procedures, the wastes must be handled in accordance with the red-list controls.

(ii) [Reserved].

(3) Wastes on the red list that are considered hazardous under U.S. national procedures as defined in §262.80(a) are subject to the red-list controls of this subpart.

Note to paragraph (a)(3): Some wastes on the amber or red lists are not listed or otherwise identified as hazardous under RCRA (*e.g.*, polychlorinated biphenyls) and therefore are not subject to the amber- or red-list controls of this subpart. Regardless of the status of the waste under RCRA, however, other Federal environmental statutes (*e.g.*, the Toxic Substances Control Act) may restrict certain waste imports or exports. Such restrictions continue to apply without regard to this Subpart.

(4) Wastes not yet assigned to a list are eligible for transfrontier movements, as follows:

(i) If such wastes are considered hazardous under U.S. national procedures as defined in §262.80(a), these wastes are subject to the red-list controls; or

(ii) If such wastes are not considered hazardous under U.S. national procedures as defined in §262.80(a), such wastes may move as though they appeared on the green list.

(b) *General conditions applicable to transfrontier movements of hazardous waste.*

(1) The waste must be destined for recovery operations at a facility that, under applicable domestic law, is operating or is authorized to operate in the importing country;

(2) The transfrontier movement must be in compliance with applicable international transport agreements; and

Note to paragraph (b)(2): These international agreements include, but are not limited to, the Chicago Convention (1944), ADR (1957), ADNR (1970), MARPOL Convention (1973/1978), SOLAS Convention (1974), IMDG Code (1985), COTIF (1985), and RID (1985).

(3) Any transit of waste through a non-OECD member country must be conducted in compliance with all applicable international and national laws and regulations.

(c) *Provisions relating to re-export for recovery to a third country.*

(1) Re-export of wastes subject to the amber-list control system from the U.S., as the importing country, to a third country listed in §262.58(a)(1) may occur only after a notifier in the U.S. provides notification to and obtains consent of the competent authorities in the third country, the original exporting country, and new transit countries. The notification must comply with the notice and consent procedures in §262.83 for all concerned countries and the original exporting country. The competent authorities of the original exporting country as well as the competent authorities of all other concerned countries have 30 days to object to the proposed movement.

(i) The 30-day period begins once the competent authorities of both the initial exporting country and new importing country issue Acknowledgements of Receipt of the notification.

(ii) The transfrontier movement may commence if no objection has been lodged after the 30-day period has passed or immediately after written consent is received from all relevant OECD importing and transit countries.

(2) Re-export of waste subject to the red-list control system from the original importing country to a third

country listed in §262.58(a)(1) may occur only following notification of the competent authorities of the third country, the original exporting country, and new transit countries by a notifier in the original importing country in accordance with §262.83. The transfrontier movement may not proceed until receipt by the original importing country of written consent from the competent authorities of the third country, the original exporting country, and new transit countries.

(3) In the case of re-export of amber or red-list wastes to a country other than those in §262.58(a)(1), notification to and consent of the competent authorities of the original OECD member country of export and any OECD member countries of transit is required as specified in paragraphs (c)(1) and (c)(2) of this section in addition to compliance with all international agreements and arrangements to which the first importing OECD member country is a party and all applicable regulatory requirements for exports from the first importing country.

[61 FR 16310, Apr. 12, 1996, as amended at 71 FR 40271, July 14, 2006]

§262.83 Notification and consent.

(a) *Applicability.* Consent must be obtained from the competent authorities of the relevant OECD importing and transit countries prior to exporting hazardous waste destined for recovery operations subject to this Subpart. Hazardous wastes subject to amber-list controls are subject to the requirements of paragraph (b) of this section; hazardous wastes subject to red-list controls are subject to the requirements of paragraph (c) of this section; and wastes not identified on any list are subject to the requirements of paragraph (d) of this section.

(b) *Amber-list wastes.* The export from the U.S. of hazardous wastes as described in §262.80(a) that appear on the amber list is prohibited unless the notification and consent requirements of paragraph (b)(1) or paragraph (b)(2) of this section are met.

(1) Transactions requiring specific consent:

(i) *Notification.* At least 45 days prior to commencement of the transfrontier movement, the notifier must provide written notification in English of the proposed transfrontier movement to the Office of Enforcement and Compliance Assurance, Office of Federal Activities, International Compliance Assurance Division (2254A), Environmental Protection Agency, 1200 Pennsylvania Ave., NW., Washington, DC 20460, with the words "Attention: OECD Export Notification" prominently displayed on the envelope. This notification must include all of the information identified in paragraph (e) of this section. In cases where wastes having similar physical and chemical characteristics, the same United Nations classification, and the same RCRA waste codes are to be sent periodically to the same recovery facility by the same notifier, the notifier may submit one notification of intent to export these wastes in multiple shipments during a period of up to one year.

(ii) *Tacit consent.* If no objection has been lodged by any concerned country (*i.e.*, exporting, importing, or transit countries) to a notification provided pursuant to paragraph (b)(1)(i) of this section within 30 days after the date of issuance of the Acknowledgment of Receipt of notification by the competent authority of the importing country, the transfrontier movement may commence. Tacit consent expires one calendar year after the close of the 30 day period; renotification and renewal of all consents is required for exports after that date.

(iii) *Written consent.* If the competent authorities of all the relevant OECD importing and transit countries provide written consent in a period less than 30 days, the transfrontier movement may commence immediately after all necessary consents are received. Written consent expires for each relevant OECD importing and transit country one calendar year after the date of that country's consent unless otherwise specified; renotification and renewal of each expired consent is required for exports after that date.

(2) Shipments to facilities pre-approved by the competent authorities of the importing countries to accept specific wastes for recovery:

(i) The notifier must provide EPA the information identified in paragraph (e) of this section in English, at least 10 days in advance of commencing shipment to a pre-approved facility. The notification should indicate that the recovery facility is pre-approved, and may apply to a single specific shipment or to multiple shipments as described in paragraph (b)(1)(i) of this section. This information must be sent to the Office of Enforcement and Compliance Assurance, Office of Federal Activities, International Compliance Assurance Division (2254A), Environmental Protection Agency, 1200 Pennsylvania Ave., NW., Washington, DC 20460, with the words "Attention: OECD Export Notification—Pre-approved Facility" prominently displayed on the envelope.

(ii) Shipments may commence after the notification required in paragraph (b)(1)(i) of this section has been received by the competent authorities of all concerned countries, unless the notifier has received information indicating that the competent authorities of one or more concerned countries objects to the shipment.

(c) *Red-list wastes.* The export from the U.S. of hazardous wastes as described in §262.80(a) that appear on the red list is prohibited unless notice is given pursuant to paragraph (b)(1)(i) of this section and the notifier receives written consent from the importing country and any transit countries prior to commencement of the transfrontier movement.

(d) *Unlisted wastes.* Wastes not assigned to the green, amber, or red list that are considered hazardous under U.S. national procedures as defined in §262.80(a) are subject to the notification and consent requirements established for red-list wastes in accordance with paragraph (c) of this section. Unlisted wastes that are not considered hazardous under U.S. national procedures as defined in §262.80(a) are not subject to amber or red controls when exported or imported.

(e) *Notification information.* Notifications submitted under this section must include:

(1) Serial number or other accepted identifier of the notification form;

(2) Notifier name and EPA identification number (if applicable), address, and telephone and telefax numbers;

(3) Importing recovery facility name, address, telephone and telefax numbers, and technologies employed;

(4) Consignee name (if not the owner or operator of the recovery facility) address, and telephone and telefax numbers; whether the consignee will engage in waste exchange or storage prior to delivering the waste to the final recovery facility and identification of recovery operations to be employed at the final recovery facility;

(5) Intended transporters and/or their agents;

(6) Country of export and relevant competent authority, and point of departure;

(7) Countries of transit and relevant competent authorities and points of entry and departure;

(8) Country of import and relevant competent authority, and point of entry;

(9) Statement of whether the notification is a single notification or a general notification. If general, include period of validity requested;

(10) Date foreseen for commencement of transfrontier movement;

(11) Designation of waste type(s) from the appropriate list (amber or red and waste list code), descriptions of each waste type, estimated total quantity of each, RCRA waste code, and United Nations number for each waste type; and

(12) Certification/Declaration signed by the notifier that states:

I certify that the above information is complete and correct to the best of my knowledge. I also certify that legally-enforceable written contractual obligations have been entered into, and that any applicable insurance or other financial guarantees are or shall be in force covering the transfrontier movement.

Name:____________________

Signature:____________________

Date:____________________

Note to paragraph (e)(12): The U.S. does not currently require financial assurance; however, U.S. exporters may be asked by other governments to provide and certify to such assurance as a condition of obtaining consent to a proposed movement.

[61 FR 16310, Apr. 12, 1996, as amended at 71 FR 40271, July 14, 2006]

§262.84 Tracking document.

(a) All U.S. parties subject to the contract provisions of §262.85 must ensure that a tracking document meeting the conditions of §262.84(b) accompanies each transfrontier shipment of wastes subject to amber-list or red-list controls from the initiation of the shipment until it reaches the final recovery facility, including cases in which the waste is stored and/or exchanged by the consignee prior to shipment to the final recovery facility, except as provided in §§262.84(a)(1) and (2).

(1) For shipments of hazardous waste within the U.S. solely by water (bulk shipments only) the generator must forward the tracking document with the manifest to the last water (bulk shipment) transporter to handle the waste in the U.S. if exported by water, (in accordance with the manifest routing procedures at §262.23(c)).

(2) For rail shipments of hazardous waste within the U.S. which originate at the site of generation, the generator must forward the tracking document with the manifest (in accordance with the routing procedures for the manifest in §262.23(d)) to the next non-rail transporter, if any, or the last rail transporter to handle the waste in the U.S. if exported by rail.

(b) The tracking document must include all information required under §262.83 (for notification), and the following:

(1) Date shipment commenced.

(2) Name (if not notifier), address, and telephone and telefax numbers of primary exporter.

(3) Company name and EPA ID number of all transporters.

(4) Identification (license, registered name or registration number) of means of transport, including types of packaging.

(5) Any special precautions to be taken by transporters.

(6) Certification/declaration signed by notifier that no objection to the shipment has been lodged as follows:

I certify that the above information is complete and correct to the best of my knowledge. I also certify that legally-enforceable written contractual obligations have been entered into, that any applicable insurance or other financial guarantees are or shall be in force covering the transfrontier movement, and that:

1. All necessary consents have been received; OR

2. The shipment is directed at a recovery facility within the OECD area and no objection has been received from any of the concerned countries within the 30 day tacit consent period; OR

3. The shipment is directed at a recovery facility pre-authorized for that type of waste within the OECD area; such an authorization has not been revoked, and no objection has been received from any of the concerned countries.

(delete sentences that are not applicable)

Name:____________________

Signature:____________________

Date:____________________

(7) Appropriate signatures for each custody transfer (*e.g.* transporter, consignee, and owner or operator of the recovery facility).

(c) Notifiers also must comply with the special manifest requirements of 40 CFR 262.54(a), (b), (c), (e), and (i) and consignees must comply with the import requirements of 40 CFR part 262, subpart F.

(d) Each U.S. person that has physical custody of the waste from the time the movement commences until it arrives at the recovery facility must sign the tracking document (*e.g.* transporter, consignee, and owner or operator of the recovery facility).

(e) Within three working days of the receipt of imports subject to this Subpart, the owner or operator of the U.S. recovery facility must send signed copies of the tracking document to the notifier, to the Office of Enforcement and Compliance Assurance, Office of Federal Activities, International Compliance Assurance Division (2254A), Environmental Protection Agency, 1200 Pennsylvania Ave., NW., Washington, DC 20460, and to the competent authorities of the exporting and transit countries.

[61 FR 16310, Apr. 12, 1996, as amended at 71 FR 40271, July 14, 2006]

§262.85 Contracts.

(a) Transfrontier movements of hazardous wastes subject to amber or red control procedures are prohibited unless they occur under the terms of a valid written contract, chain of contracts, or equivalent arrangements (when the movement occurs between parties controlled by the same corporate or legal entity). Such contracts or equivalent arrangements must be executed by the notifier and the owner or operator of the recovery facility, and must specify responsibilities for each. Contracts or equivalent arrangements are valid for the purposes of this section only if persons assuming obligations under the contracts or equivalent arrangements have appropriate legal status to conduct the operations specified in the contract or equivalent arrangement.

(b) Contracts or equivalent arrangements must specify the name and EPA ID number, where available, of:

(1) The generator of each type of waste;

(2) Each person who will have physical custody of the wastes;

(3) Each person who will have legal control of the wastes; and

(4) The recovery facility.

(c) Contracts or equivalent arrangements must specify which party to the contract will assume responsibility for alternate management of the wastes if its disposition cannot be carried out as described in the notification of intent to export. In such cases, contracts must specify that:

(1) The person having actual possession or physical control over the wastes will immediately inform the notifier and the competent authorities of the exporting and importing countries and, if the wastes are located in a country of transit, the competent authorities of that country; and

(2) The person specified in the contract will assume responsibility for the adequate management of the wastes in compliance with applicable laws and regulations including, if necessary, arranging their return to the original country of export.

(d) Contracts must specify that the consignee will provide the notification required in §262.82(c) prior to re-export of controlled wastes to a third country.

(e) Contracts or equivalent arrangements must include provisions for financial guarantees, if required by the competent authorities of any concerned country, in accordance with applicable national or international law requirements.

Note to paragraph (e): Financial guarantees so required are intended to provide for alternate recycling, disposal or other means of sound management of the wastes in cases where arrangements for the shipment and the recovery operations cannot be carried out as foreseen. The U.S. does not require such financial guarantees at this time; however, some OECD countries do. It is the responsibility of the notifier to ascertain and comply with such requirements; in some cases, transporters or consignees may refuse to enter into the necessary contracts absent specific references or certifications to financial guarantees.

(f) Contracts or equivalent arrangements must contain provisions requiring each contracting party to comply with all applicable requirements of this subpart.

(g) Upon request by EPA, U.S. notifiers, consignees, or recovery facilities must submit to EPA copies of contracts, chain of contracts, or equivalent arrangements (when the movement occurs between parties controlled by the same corporate or legal entity). Information contained in the contracts or equivalent arrangements for which a claim of confidentiality is asserted accordance with 40 CFR 2.203(b) will be treated as confidential and will be disclosed by EPA only as provided in 40 CFR 260.2.

Note to paragraph (g): Although the U.S. does not require routine submission of contracts at this time, OECD Council Decision C(92)39/FINAL allows members to impose such requirements. When other OECD countries require submission of partial or complete copies of the contract as a condition to granting consent to proposed movements, EPA will request the required information; absent submission of such information, some OECD countries may deny consent for the proposed movement.

§262.86 Provisions relating to recognized traders.

(a) A recognized trader who takes physical custody of a waste and conducts recovery operations (including storage prior to recovery) is acting as the owner or operator of a recovery facility and must be so authorized in accordance with all applicable Federal laws.

(b) A recognized trader acting as a notifier or consignee for transfrontier shipments of waste must comply with all the requirements of this Subpart associated with being a notifier or consignee.

§262.87 Reporting and recordkeeping.

(a) *Annual reports.* For all waste movements subject to this Subpart, persons (*e.g.,* notifiers, recognized traders) who meet the definition of primary exporter in §262.51 shall file an annual report with the Office of Enforcement and Compliance Assurance, Office of Federal Activities, International Compliance Assurance Division (2254A), Environmental Protection Agency, 1200 Pennsylvania Ave., NW., Washington, DC 20460, no later than March 1 of each year summarizing the types, quantities, frequency, and ultimate destination of all such hazardous waste exported during the previous calendar year. (If the primary exporter is required to file an annual report for waste exports that are not covered under this Subpart, he may include all export information in one report provided the following information on exports of waste destined for recovery within the designated OECD member countries is contained in a separate section). Such reports shall include the following:

(1) The EPA identification number, name, and mailing and site address of the notifier filing the report;

(2) The calendar year covered by the report;

(3) The name and site address of each final recovery facility;

(4) By final recovery facility, for each hazardous waste exported, a description of the hazardous waste, the EPA hazardous waste number (from 40 CFR part 261, subpart C or D), designation of waste type(s) from OECD waste list and applicable waste code from the OECD lists, DOT hazard class, the name and U.S. EPA identification number (where applicable) for each transporter used, the total amount of hazardous waste shipped pursuant to this Subpart, and number of shipments pursuant to each notification;

(5) In even numbered years, for each hazardous waste exported, except for hazardous waste produced by exporters of greater than 100 kg but less than 1000 kg in a calendar month, and except for hazardous waste for which information was already provided pursuant to §262.41:

(i) A description of the efforts undertaken during the year to reduce the volume and toxicity of waste generated; and

(ii) A description of the changes in volume and toxicity of the waste actually achieved during the year in comparison to previous years to the extent such information is available for years prior to 1984; and

(6) A certification signed by the person acting as primary exporter that states:

I certify under penalty of law that I have personally examined and am familiar with the information submitted in this and all attached documents, and that based on my inquiry of those individuals immediately responsible for obtaining the information, I believe that the submitted information is true, accurate, and complete. I am aware that there are significant penalties for submitting false information including the possibility of fine and imprisonment.

(b) *Exception reports.* Any person who meets the definition of primary exporter in §262.51 must file an exception report in lieu of the requirements of §262.42 with the Administrator if any of the following occurs:

(1) He has not received a copy of the tracking documentation signed by the transporter stating point of departure of the waste from the United States, within

forty-five (45) days from the date it was accepted by the initial transporter;

(2) Within ninety (90) days from the date the waste was accepted by the initial transporter, the notifier has not received written confirmation from the recovery facility that the hazardous waste was received;

(3) The waste is returned to the United States.

(c) *Recordkeeping.* (1) Persons who meet the definition of primary exporter in §262.51 shall keep the following records: §262.89

(i) A copy of each notification of intent to export and all written consents obtained from the competent authorities of concerned countries for a period of at least three years from the date the hazardous waste was accepted by the initial transporter;

(ii) A copy of each annual report for a period of at least three years from the due date of the report; and

(iii) A copy of any exception reports and a copy of each confirmation of delivery (*i.e.,* tracking documentation) sent by the recovery facility to the notifier for at least three years from the date the hazardous waste was accepted by the initial transporter or received by the recovery facility, whichever is applicable.

(2) The periods of retention referred to in this section are extended automatically during the course of any unresolved enforcement action regarding the regulated activity or as requested by the Administrator.

[61 FR 16310, Apr. 12, 1996, as amended at 71 FR 40272, July 14, 2006]

§262.88 Pre-approval for U.S. Recovery Facilities (Reserved).

§262.89 OECD Waste Lists.

(a) *General.* For the purposes of this Subpart, a waste is considered hazardous under U.S. national procedures, and hence subject to this Subpart, if the waste:

(1) Meets the Federal definition of hazardous waste in 40 CFR 261.3; and

(2) Is subject to either the Federal RCRA manifesting requirements at 40 CFR part 262, subpart B, to the universal waste management standards of 40 CFR part 273, or to State requirements analogous to 40 CFR part 273.

(b) If a waste is hazardous under paragraph (a) of this section and it appears on the amber or red list, it is subject to amber- or red-list requirements respectively;

(c) If a waste is hazardous under paragraph (a) of this section and it does not appear on either amber or red lists, it is subject to red-list requirements.

(d) The appropriate control procedures for hazardous wastes and hazardous waste mixtures are addressed in §262.82.

(e) The OECD Green List of Wastes (revised May 1994), Amber List of Wastes and Red List of Wastes (both revised May 1993) as set forth in Appendix 3, Appendix 4 and Appendix 5, respectively, to the OECD Council Decision C(92)39/FINAL (Concerning the Control of Transfrontier Movements of Wastes Destined for Recovery Operations) are incorporated by reference. These incorporations by reference were approved by the Director of the Federal Register in accordance with 5 U.S.C. 552(a) and 1 CFR part 51 on July 11, 1996. These materials are incorporated as they exist on the date of the approval and a notice of any change in these materials will be published in the *Federal Register.* The materials are available for inspection at: the Office of the Federal Register, 800 North Capitol Street, NW., suite 700, Washington, DC; the U.S. Environmental Protection Agency, RCRA Information Center (RIC), 1235 Jefferson-Davis Highway, first floor, Arlington, VA 22203 (Docket # F-94-IEHF-FFFFF) and may be obtained from the Organisation for Economic Co-operation and Development, Environment Direcorate, 2 rue Andre Pascal, 75775 Paris Cedex 16, France.

Subpart I—New York State Public Utilities

Source: 64 FR 37636, July 12, 1999, unless otherwise noted.

§262.90 Project XL for Public Utilities in New York State.

(a) The following definitions apply to this section:

(1) A *Utility* is any company that operates wholesale and/or retail oil and gas pipelines, or any company that provides electric power or telephone service and is regulated by New York State's Public Service Commission or the New York Power Authority.

(2) A *right-of-way* is a fixed, integrated network of aboveground or underground conveyances, including land structures, fixed equipment, and other appurtenances, controlled or owned by a Utility, and used for the purpose of conveying its products or services to customers.

(3) A *remote location* is a location in New York State within a Utility's right-of-way network that is not permanently staffed.

(4) A *Utility's central collection facility (UCCF)* is a Utility-owned facility within the Utility's right-of-way network to which hazardous waste, generated by the Utility at remote locations within the same right-of-way network, is brought.

(b) A UCCF designated pursuant to paragraph (e) of this section may consolidate hazardous waste (with the exception of mixed waste) generated by that Utility at its remote locations (and at that UCCF) for up to 90 days without a permit or without having interim status, provided that:

(1) The Utility complies with all applicable requirements for generators in 40 CFR part 262 (except §262.34 (d) through (f)) for hazardous waste generated at its remote locations and at the UCCF, including the manifest and pretransport requirements for all shipments greater than 100 kilograms sent from a remote location to a UCCF.

(2) The Utility transports the hazardous waste from the remote location to a UCCF immediately after collection of all hazardous waste at the remote location is complete or when the staff collecting the hazardous waste leave the remote location, whichever comes first.

(3) The Utility complies with all applicable requirements for transporters in 40 CFR part 263 for each shipment of hazardous waste greater than 100 kilograms which is sent from remote location to the UCCF, and all applicable Department of Transportation requirements.

(4)(i) The Utility complies with 40 CFR 262.34 (a) through (c), regardless of the total quantity of hazardous waste generated or consolidated at the UCCF per calendar month;

(ii) The Utility complies with 40 CFR 264.178; and

(iii) Secondary containment is provided for all liquid hazardous waste consolidated in containers if:

(A) The UCCF is consolidating 8,800 gallons or more of liquid hazardous waste, or

(B) The UCCF is consolidating 185 gallons or more of liquid hazardous waste and is located in an area designated by New York State that overlays a sole-source aquifer.

(5) The Utility submits a biennial report in accordance with 40 CFR 262.41 including all hazardous waste shipped from remote locations to the UCCF. This UCCF biennial report may be submitted in lieu of submitting a biennial report for each remote location. However, for hazardous waste generated at a particular remote location that exceeds 1000 kg per calendar month and that is not sent to the UCCF, the Utility must submit a separate biennial report.

(6) Waste generated at a remote location that is not sent to a UCCF is managed according to the requirements of parts 260 through 270 of this chapter.

(7) The Utility maintains records at the UCCF in accordance with all the recordkeeping requirements set forth in subpart D of 40 CFR part 262, including 40 CFR 262.40, and maintains records on any PCB test results for hazardous wastes brought to the facility from remote locations.

(8) The UCCF obtains an EPA identification number.

(9) The UCCF receives hazardous waste only from its remote location.

(10) The Utility reinvests at least one-third of the direct savings described in paragraph (h) of this section in one or more environmentally beneficial projects, such as remediation or pollution prevention, that are over and above existing legal requirements and that have not been initiated prior to the Utility's receipt of approval to consolidate hazardous waste pursuant to this section.

(c) Utilities seeking to have UCCFs designated under paragraph (e) of this section must comply with the following requirements:

(1) Any New York State Utility seeking approval to consolidate hazardous waste under this section must notify local governments and communities of the Utility's intent to designate specific UCCFs.

(2) In carrying out paragraph (c)(1) of this section, the Utility must solicit public comment. In soliciting public comment, the Utility must use the notice method set forth in paragraph (c)(2)(i) of this section, as well as at least two of the methods set forth in paragraphs (c)(2)(ii) through (vii) of this section. Each Utility must also notify by mail all parties who commented on the proposed rule for this XL project.

(i) A public notice in a newspaper of general circulation within the area in which each proposed UCCF is located;

(ii) A radio announcement in each affected community during peak listening hours;

(iii) Mailings to all citizens within a five-mile radius of proposed UCCF;

(iv) Well-publicized community meetings;

(v) Presentations to the local community board;

(vi) Placement of copies of this section and the Final Project Agreement that explains the regulatory relief outlined in this section in the local library nearest the proposed UCCF, and inclusion of the name and address of the library in the newspaper notice; and

(vii) Placement of copies of this section and the Final Project Agreement that explains the regulatory relief outlined in this section on the Utility's web site, and inclusion of the web site's address in the newspaper notice.

(3) All outreach efforts made under paragraph (c)(2) of this section shall be prepared in English (and any other language spoken by a large number of persons in the community of concern) and at a minimum shall include the following information:

(i) A brief description of the XL project, the intended new use of the facility, and a request for comments on the proposed UCCF.

(ii) The name, if any, and address of the proposed UCCF and its current status under the RCRA Subtitle C program.

(iii) The intended duration of use of the UCCF under the requirements of this section.

(iv) Names, addresses, and telephone numbers of contact persons, representing the Utility, to whom questions or comments may be directed.

(v) Notification of when the comment period of no less than 30 days will close.

(4) Prior to the solicitation of public comment pursuant to paragraph (c)(2) of this section, the Utility must submit copies of each notice, announcement or mailing directly to local governments and to EPA.

(5) At the close of the comment period, the Utility shall prepare a Responsiveness Package containing a summary of public outreach efforts, all comments and questions received as a result of its outreach efforts, and the Utility's written responses to all comments and questions. The Utility shall provide copies of its Responsiveness Package to any citizens that participated in the public notice process, local governments and EPA.

(d) Upon completion of the public notice procedures described in paragraph (c) of this section, the Utility must provide written notice to EPA of its intent to participate. The Notice of Intent must contain the following information:

(1) The name of the Utility, corporate address, and corporate mailing address, if different.

(2) The name, mailing address, and telephone number of a corporate-level contact person to whom communications and inquiries may be directed. This contact person may be changed by written notification to EPA.

(3) A list of the names, addresses, and EPA identification numbers, if applicable, of all Utility-owned facilities in New York State that are proposed UCCFs and the names and telephone numbers of a designated contact person at each facility.

(4) A summary of public outreach efforts undertaken pursuant to paragraph (c) of this section.

(5) A commitment that one-third of the direct cost savings outlined in paragraph (h) of this section due to project participation will be reinvested in one or more environmentally beneficial projects which are over and above existing legal requirements and which have not been initiated prior to the Utility's receipt of approval to consolidate hazardous waste pursuant to this section.

(6) An acknowledgment that the signatory is personally familiar with the terms and conditions of this section and has the authority to obligate and does obligate the Utility to comply with all such terms and conditions. The Utility shall comply with the signatory requirements set forth in 40 CFR 270.11(a)(1).

(e) The procedures for designating UCCFs are as follows:

(1) Subject to paragraphs (e)(2) through (5) of this section, the Utility and specified UCCF shall receive approval to comply with the requirements set forth in paragraph (b) of this section upon the receipt of written acknowledgment from EPA that the Notice of Intent described in paragraph (d) of this section has been received and found to be complete and in compliance with all the requirements set forth in paragraph (d) of this section. This acknowledgment will state whether the UCCF has been designated under this section and any additional limitations which have been placed on the UCCF.

(2) Based on information provided and comments received during the public notice and comment period, EPA shall prepare a response to the comments received. The response to comments shall be attached to the acknowledgment described in paragraph (e)(1). Both the acknowledgment and the response to comments shall be sent to all persons who commented on the designation of the UCCF(s) that are the subject of the acknowledgment.

(3) Based on information provided and comments received during or after the public notice and comment period, designated UCCFs may be rejected for the

PART 262—Subpart I

proposed use, or, if EPA determines that acceptance for the proposed use under the conditions of paragraph (b) of this section may not fully protect human health and the environment based on the Utility's compliance history or other appropriate factors, the acknowledgment may impose conditions in addition to those in paragraph (b) of this section.

(4) If EPA determines that a site-specific informational public meeting is warranted prior to determining the acceptability of a designated UCCF, the acknowledgment will so state.

(5) Subsequent to any public meeting, EPA may reject or prohibit UCCFs from participating in this project based on information provided or comments received during or after the public notice process or based on a determination that acceptance for the proposed use under the conditions of paragraph (b) of this section may not fully protect human health and the environment based on the Utility's compliance history or other appropriate factors.

(f) At any time, a Utility may add or remove UCCF designations by complying with the following requirements:

(1) A Utility may notify EPA of its intent to designate additional UCCFs. Such a notification shall be submitted to, and processed by, EPA, in the manner indicated in paragraphs (d) and (e) of this section.

(2) To have one or more additional UCCFs designated, the Utility must comply with paragraph (c) of this section.

(3) A Utility can discontinue use of a facility as a UCCF by notifying EPA in writing.

(g) Each Utility that receives approval to consolidate hazardous waste pursuant to this section shall submit an Annual Progress Report with the following information for the preceding year:

(1) The number of remote locations statewide for which hazardous waste was handled in accordance with paragraph (b) of this section.

(2) The total tonnage of each type of hazardous waste handled by each UCCF.

(3) The number of remote locations statewide from which 1,000 kilograms or more of hazardous waste were collected per calendar month.

(4) The number of remote locations statewide from which between 100 and 1,000 kilograms of hazardous waste were collected per calendar month.

(5) An estimate of the monetary value, on a Utility-wide basis, of the direct savings realized by participation in this project. Direct savings at a minimum include those outlined in paragraph (h) of this section.

(6) Descriptions of the environmental compliance, remediation, or pollution prevention projects or activities into which the savings, described in paragraph (h) of this section, have been reinvested, with an estimate of the savings reinvested in each. Any such projects must consist of activities that are over and above existing legal requirements and that have not been initiated prior to the Utility's receipt of approval to consolidate hazardous waste pursuant to this section.

(7) The addresses and EPA identification numbers for all facilities that served as UCCFs for hazardous waste from remote locations.

(h) Utilities that receive approval to consolidate hazardous waste pursuant to this section must assess the direct savings realized as a result. Cost estimates shall include direct savings based on relief from any regulatory requirements, which the facility expects to be relieved from due to compliance with the provisions of this section including, but not limited to, the following:

(1) Database management for each remote location as an individual generator;

(2) Biennial Report preparation costs; and/or

(3) Cost savings realized from consolidation of waste for economical shipment (including no longer shipping waste directly to a TSD from remote locations).

(i) If any UCCF or Utility that receives approval under this section fails to comply with any of the requirements of this section, EPA may terminate or suspend the UCCF's or Utility's participation. EPA will provide a UCCF or Utility with 15 days written notice of its intent to terminate or suspend participation. During this period, the UCCF will have the opportunity to come back into compliance or provide a written explanation as to why it was not in compliance with the terms of this section and how it will come back into compliance. If EPA then issues a written notice terminating or suspending participation, the Utility must take immediate action to come into compliance with all otherwise applicable federal requirements. EPA may also take enforcement action against a Utility for non-compliance with the provisions of this section.

(j) This section will expire on May 24, 2011.

[64 FR 37636, July 12, 1999, as amended at 70 FR 29913, May 24, 2005; 71 FR 40272, July 14, 2006]

Subpart J—University Laboratories XL Project—Laboratory Environmental Management Standard

Source: 64 FR 53292, Sept. 28, 1999, unless otherwise noted.

§262.100 To what organizations does this subpart apply?

This subpart applies to an organization that meets all three of the following conditions:

(a) It is one of the three following academic institutions: The University of Massachusetts Boston in Boston, Massachusetts, Boston College in Chestnut Hill, Massachusetts, or the University of Vermont in Burlington, Vermont ("Universities"); and

(b) It is a laboratory at one of the Universities (identified pursuant to §262.105(c)(2)(ii)) where laboratory scale activities, as defined in §262.102, result in laboratory waste; and

(c) It complies with all the requirements of this subpart.

§262.101 What is in this subpart?

This subpart provides a framework for a new management system for wastes that are generated in University laboratories. This framework is called the Laboratory Environmental Management Standard. The standard includes some specific definitions that apply to the University laboratories. It contains specific requirements for how to handle laboratory waste that are called Minimum Performance Criteria. The standard identifies the requirements for developing and implementing an environmental management plan. It outlines the responsibilities of the management staff of each participating university. Finally, the standard identifies requirements for training people who will work in the laboratories or manage laboratory waste. This Subpart contains requirements for RCRA solid and hazardous waste determination, and circumstances for termination and expiration of this pilot.

§262.102 What special definitions are included in this subpart?

For purposes of this subpart, the following definitions apply:

Acutely Hazardous Laboratory Waste means a laboratory waste, defined in the Environmental Management Plan as posing significant potential hazards to human health or the environment and which must include RCRA "P" wastes, and may include particularly hazardous substances as designated in a University's Chemical Hygiene Plan under OSHA, or Extremely Hazardous Substances under the Emergency Planning and Community Right to Know Act.

Emergency means any occurrence such as, but not limited to, equipment failure, rupture of containers or failure of control equipment which results in the potential uncontrolled release of a hazardous chemical into the environment and which requires agency or fire department notification and/or reporting.

Environmental Management Plan (EMP) means a written program developed and implemented by the university which sets forth standards and procedures, responsibilities, pollution control equipment, performance criteria, resources and work practices that both protect human health and the environment from the hazards presented by laboratory wastes within a laboratory and between a laboratory and the hazardous waste accumulation area, and satisfies the plan requirements defined elsewhere in this Subpart. Certain requirements of this plan are satisfied through the use of the Chemical Hygiene Plan (see, 29 CFR 1910.1450), or equivalent, and other relevant plans, including a waste minimization plan. The elements of the Environmental Management Plan must be easily accessible, but may be integrated into existing plans, incorporated as an attachment, or developed as a separate document.

Environmental Objective means an overall environmental goal of the organization which is verifiable.

Environmental Performance means results of the data collected pursuant to implementation of the Environmental Management Plan as measured against policy, objectives and targets.

Environmental Target means an environmental performance requirement of the organization which is quantifiable, where practicable, verifiable and designed to be achieved within a specified time frame.

Hazardous Chemical means any chemical which is a physical hazard or a health hazard. A physical hazard means a chemical for which there is scientifically valid evidence that it is a combustible liquid, a compressed gas, explosive, flammable, an organic peroxide, an oxidizer, pyrophoric, unstable (reactive) or water-reactive. A health hazard means a chemical for which there is statistically significant evidence based on at least one study conducted in accordance with established scientific principles that acute or chronic health effects may occur in exposed employees. The term "health hazard" includes chemicals which are carcinogens, toxic or highly toxic agents, reproductive toxins, irritants, corrosives, sensitizers, hepatotoxins, nephrotoxins, neurotoxins, agents which act on the hematopoietic system and agents which damage the lungs, skin, eyes or mucous membranes.

Hazardous Chemical of Concern means a chemical that the organization has identified as having the potential to be of significant risk to human health or the environment if not managed in accordance with procedures or practices defined by the organization.

Hazardous Waste Accumulation Area means the on-site area at a University where the University will make a solid and hazardous waste determination with respect to laboratory wastes.

In-Line Waste Collection means a system for the automatic collection of laboratory waste which is directly connected to or part of a laboratory scale activity and which is constructed or operated in a manner which prevents the release of any laboratory waste therein into the environment during collection.

Laboratory means, for the purpose of this Subpart, an area within a facility where the laboratory use of hazardous chemicals occurs. It is a workplace where relatively small quantities of hazardous chemicals are used on a non-production basis. The physical extent of individual laboratories within an organization will be defined by the Environmental Management Plan. A laboratory may include more than a single room if the rooms are in the same building and under the common supervision of a laboratory supervisor.

Laboratory Clean-Out means an evaluation of the chemical inventory of a laboratory as a result of laboratory renovation, relocation or a change in laboratory supervision that may result in the transfer of laboratory wastes to the hazardous waste accumulation area.

Laboratory Environmental Management Standard means the provisions of this Subpart and includes the requirements for preparation of Environmental Management Plans and the inclusion of Minimum Performance Criteria within each Environmental Management Plan.

Laboratory Scale means work with substances in which containers used for reactions, transfers and other handling of substances are designed to be safely and easily manipulated by one person. "Laboratory Scale" excludes those workplaces whose function is to produce commercial quantities of chemicals.

Laboratory Waste means a hazardous chemical that results from laboratory scale activities and includes the following: excess or unused hazardous chemicals that may or may not be reused outside their laboratory of origin; hazardous chemicals determined to be RCRA hazardous waste as defined in 40 CFR Part 261; and hazardous chemicals that will be determined not to be RCRA hazardous waste pursuant to §262.106.

Laboratory Worker means a person who is assigned to handle hazardous chemicals in the laboratory and may include researchers, students or technicians.

Legal and Other Requirements means requirements imposed by, or as a result of, governmental permits, governmental laws and regulations, judicial and administrative enforcement orders, non-governmental legally enforceable contracts, research grants and agreements, certification specifications, formal voluntary commitments and organizational policies and standards.

Senior Management means senior personnel with overall responsibility, authority and accountability for managing laboratory activities within the organization.

Universities means the following academic institutions; University of Vermont, Boston College, and the University of Massachusetts Boston, which are participants in this Laboratory XL project and which are subject to the requirements set forth in this Subpart J.

§262.103 What is the scope of the laboratory environmental management standard?

The Laboratory Environmental Management Standard will not affect or supersede any legal requirements other than those described in §262.10(j). The requirements that continue to apply include, but are not limited to, OSHA, Fire Codes, wastewater permit limitations, emergency response notification provisions, or other legal requirements applicable to University laboratories.

§262.104 What are the minimum performance criteria?

The Minimum Performance Criteria that each University must meet in managing its Laboratory Waste are:

(a) Each University must label all laboratory waste with the general hazard class and either the words "laboratory waste" or with the chemical name of the contents. If the container is too small to hold a label, the label must be placed on a secondary container.

(b) Each University may temporarily hold up to 55 gallons of laboratory waste or one quart of acutely hazardous laboratory waste, or weight equivalent, in each laboratory, but upon reaching these thresholds, each University must mark that laboratory waste with the date when this threshold requirement was met (by dating the container(s) or secondary container(s)).

(c) Each university must remove all of the dated laboratory waste from the laboratory for delivery to a location identified in paragraph (i) of this section within 30 days of reaching the threshold amount identified in paragraph (b) of this section.

(d) In no event shall the excess laboratory waste that a laboratory temporarily holds before dated laboratory waste is removed exceed an additional 55 gallons of laboratory waste (or one additional quart of acutely hazardous laboratory waste). No more than 110 gallons of laboratory waste total (or no more than two quarts of acutely hazardous laboratory waste total) may be temporarily held in a laboratory at any one time. Excess laboratory waste must be dated and removed in accordance with the requirements of paragraphs (b) and (c) of this section.

(e) Containers of laboratory wastes must be:

(1) Closed at all times except when wastes are being added to (including during in-line waste collection) or removed from the container;

(2) Maintained in good condition and stored in the laboratory in a manner to avoid leaks;

(3) Compatible with their contents to avoid reactions between the waste and its container; and must be made of, or lined with, materials which are compatible with the laboratory wastes to be temporarily held in the laboratory so that the container is not impaired; and

(4) Inspected regularly (at least annually) to ensure that they meet requirements for container management.

(f) The management of laboratory waste must not result in the release of hazardous constituents into the land, air and water where such release is prohibited under federal law.

(g) The requirements for emergency response are:

(1) Each University must post notification procedures, location of emergency response equipment to be used by laboratory workers and evacuation procedures;

(2) Emergency response equipment and procedures for emergency response must be appropriate to the hazards in the laboratory such that hazards to human health and the environment will be minimized in the event of an emergency;

(3) In the event of a fire, explosion or other release of laboratory waste which could threaten human health or the environment, the laboratory worker must follow the notification procedures under paragraph (g)(1) of this section.

(h) Each University must investigate, document, and take actions to correct and prevent future incidents of hazardous chemical spills, exposures and other incidents that trigger a reportable emergency or that require reporting under paragraph (g) of this section.

(i) Each University may only transfer laboratory wastes from a laboratory:

(1) Directly to an on-site designated hazardous waste accumulation area. Notwithstanding 40 CFR 263.10(a), each University must comply with requirements for transporters set forth in 40 CFR 263.30 and 263.31 in the event of a discharge of laboratory waste en route from a laboratory to an on-site hazardous waste accumulation area; or

(2) To a treatment, storage or disposal (TSD) facility permitted to handle the waste under 40 CFR part 270 or in interim status under 40 CFR parts 265 and 270 (or authorized to handle the waste by a state with a hazardous waste management program approved under 40 CFR part 271) if it is determined in the laboratory by the individuals identified in §262.105(b)(3) to be responsible for waste management decisions that the waste is a hazardous waste and that it is prudent to transfer it directly to a treatment, storage, and disposal facility rather than an on-site accumulation area.

(j) Each University must ensure that laboratory workers receive training and are provided with information so that they can implement and comply with these Minimum Performance Criteria.

§262.105 What must be included in the laboratory environmental management plan?

(a) Each University must include specific measures it will take to protect human health and the environment from hazards associated with the management of laboratory wastes and from the reuse, recycling or disposal of such materials outside the laboratory.

(b) Each University must write, implement and comply with an Environmental Management Plan that includes the following:

(1) The specific procedures to assure compliance with each of the Minimum Performance Criteria set forth in §262.104.

(2) An environmental policy, or environmental, health and safety policy, signed by the University's senior management, which must include commitments to regulatory compliance, waste minimization, risk reduction and continual improvement of the environmental management system.

(3) A description of roles and responsibilities for the implementation and maintenance of the Laboratory Environmental Management Plan.

(4) A system for identifying and tracking legal and other requirements applicable to laboratory waste, including the procedures for providing updates to laboratory supervisors.

(5) Criteria for the identification of physical and chemical hazards and the control measures to reduce the potential for releases of laboratory wastes to the environment, including engineering controls, the use of personal protective equipment and hygiene practices, containment strategies and other control measures.

(6) A pollution prevention plan, including, but not limited to, roles and responsibilities, training, pollution prevention activities, and performance review.

(7) A system for conducting and updating annual surveys of hazardous chemicals of concern and procedures for identifying acutely hazardous laboratory waste.

(8) The procedures for conducting laboratory cleanouts with regard to the safe management and disposal of laboratory wastes.

(9) The criteria that laboratory workers must comply with for managing, containing and labeling laboratory wastes, including: an evaluation of the need for and the use of any special containers or labeling circumstances, and the use of laboratory wastes secondary containers including packaging, bottles, or test tube racks.

(10) The procedures relevant to the safe and timely removal of laboratory wastes from the laboratory.

(11) The emergency preparedness and response procedures to be implemented for laboratory waste.

(12) Provisions for information dissemination and training, provided for in paragraph (d) of this section.

(13) The procedures for the development and approval of changes to the Environmental Management Plan.

(14) The procedures and work practices for safely transferring or moving laboratory wastes from a laboratory to a location identified in §262.104(i).

(15) The procedures for regularly inspecting a laboratory to assess conformance with the requirements of the Environmental Management Plan.

(16) The procedures for the identification of environmental management plan noncompliance, and the assignment of responsibility, timelines and corrective actions to prevent their reoccurrence.

(17) The record keeping requirements to document conformance with this Plan.

(c) Organizational responsibilities for each university. Each University must:

(1) Develop and oversee implementation of its Laboratory Environmental Management Plan.

(2) Identify the following:

(i) Annual environmental objectives and targets;

(ii) Those laboratories covered by the requirements of the Laboratory Environmental Management Plan.

(3) Assign roles and responsibilities for the effective implementation of the Environmental Management Plan.

(4) Determine whether laboratory wastes are solid wastes under RCRA and, if so, whether they are hazardous.

(5) Develop, implement, and maintain:

(i) Policies, procedures and practices governing its compliance with the Environmental Management Plan and applicable federal and state hazardous waste regulations.

(ii) Procedures to monitor and measure relevant conformance and environmental performance data for the purpose of supporting continual improvement of the Environmental Management Plan.

(iii) Policies and procedures for managing environmental documents and records applicable to this Environmental Management Standard.

(6) Ensure that:

(i) Its Environmental Management Plan is available to laboratory workers, vendors, employee representatives, visitors, on-site contractors, and upon request, to governmental representatives.

(ii) Personnel designated by each University to handle laboratory wastes and RCRA hazardous waste receive appropriate training.

(iii) The Environmental Management Plan is reviewed at least annually by senior management to ensure its continuing suitability, adequacy and effectiveness. The reviews may include, but not be limited to, a consideration of monitoring and measuring information, Laboratory Environmental Management Standard performance data, assessment and audit results and other relevant information and data.

(d) What are the Information and Training Requirements for Each University?

(1) Each University must ensure that laboratory workers receive training and are provided with the information to understand and implement the elements of each University's Environmental Management Plan that are relevant to the laboratory workers' responsibilities.

(2) When must each University ensure that laboratory workers receive training and information?

(i) Each University must provide the information to each laboratory worker when he/she is first assigned to a work area where laboratory wastes may be generated.

(ii) Each University must ensure that each laboratory worker has had training within six months of when he/she is first assigned to a work area where laboratory wastes may be generated. Each University must retrain a laboratory worker when a laboratory waste poses a new or unique hazard for which the laboratory worker has not received prior training and as frequently as needed to maintain knowledge of the procedures of the Environmental Management Plan.

(3) Each University must provide an outline of training and specify who is to receive training in its Environmental Management Plan.

(4) Each University must ensure that laboratory workers are informed of:

(i) The contents of this Subpart and the Laboratory Environmental Management Plan(s) for the laboratory(ies) in which they will be performing work;

(ii) The location and availability of the Environmental Management Plan;

(iii) Emergency response measures applicable to laboratories;

(iv) Signs and indicators of a hazardous substance release;

(v) The location and availability of known reference materials relevant to implementation of the Environmental Management Plan; and

(vi) Environmental training requirements applicable to laboratory workers.

(5) Each University must ensure that Laboratory workers have received training in:

(i) Methods and observations that may be used to detect the presence or release of a hazardous substance;

(ii) The chemical and physical hazards associated with laboratory wastes in their work area;

(iii) The relevant measures a laboratory worker can take to protect human health and the environment; and

(iv) Details of the Environmental Management Plan sufficient to ensure they manage laboratory waste in accordance with the requirements of this Subpart.

(6) Requirements pertaining to Laboratory visitors:

(i) Laboratory visitors, such as on-site contractors or environmental vendors, that require information and training under this standard must be identified in the Environmental Management Plan.

(ii) Laboratory visitors identified in the Environmental Management Plan must be informed of the existence and location of the Environmental Management Plan.

(iii) Laboratory visitors identified in the Environmental Management Plan must be informed of relevant policies, procedures or work practices to ensure compliance with the requirements of the Environmental Management Plan.

(7) Each University must define methods of providing objective evidence and records of training and information dissemination in its Environmental Management Plan.

§262.106 When must a hazardous waste determination be made?

(a) For laboratory waste sent from a laboratory to an on-site hazardous waste accumulation area, each University must evaluate the laboratory wastes to determine whether they are solid wastes under RCRA and, if so, determine pursuant to §262.11 (a) through (d) whether they are hazardous wastes, as soon as the laboratory wastes reach the University's Hazardous Waste Accumulation area(s). At this point each University must determine whether the laboratory waste will be reused or whether it must be managed as RCRA solid or hazardous waste.

(b) For laboratory waste that will be sent from a laboratory to a TSD facility permitted to handle the waste, each University must evaluate such laboratory wastes to determine whether they are solid wastes under RCRA and, if so, determine pursuant to §262.11 (a) through (d) whether they are hazardous wastes, prior to the 30-day deadline for removing dated laboratory waste from the laboratory.

(c) Laboratory waste that is determined to be hazardous waste is no longer subject to the provisions of this subpart and must be managed in accordance with all applicable provisions of 40 CFR Parts 260 through 270.

§262.107 Under what circumstances will a university's participation in this environmental management standard pilot be terminated?

(a) EPA retains the right to terminate a University's participation in this Laboratory XL project if the University:

(1) Is in non-compliance with the Minimum Performance Criteria in §262.104; or

(2) Has actual environmental management practices in the laboratory that do not conform to its Environmental Management Plan; or

(3) Is in non-compliance with the Hazardous Waste Determination requirements of §262.106.

(b) In the event of termination, EPA will provide the University with 15 days written notice of its intent to terminate. During this period, which commences upon receipt of the notice, the University will have the opportunity to come back into compliance with the Minimum Performance Criteria, its Environmental Management Plan, or the requirements for making a hazardous waste determination at §262.106 or to provide a written explanation as to why it was not in compliance and how it intends to return to compliance. If, upon review of the University's written explanation, EPA then reissues a written notice terminating the University from this XL Project, the provisions of paragraph (c) of this section will immediately apply and the University shall have 90 days to come into compliance with the applicable RCRA requirements deferred by §262.10(j). During the 90-day transition period, the provisions of this subpart shall continue to apply to the University.

(c) If a University withdraws from this XL project, or receives a notice of termination pursuant to this section, it must submit to EPA and the state a schedule for returning to full compliance with RCRA requirements at the laboratory level. The schedule must show how the University will return to full compliance with RCRA within 90 days from the date of the notice of termination or withdrawal.

§262.108 When will this subpart expire?

This subpart will expire on April 15, 2009.

[71 FR 35550, June 21, 2006]

Subpart K—Alternative Requirements for Hazardous Waste Determination and Accumulation of Unwanted Material for Laboratories Owned by Eligible Academic Entities

Source: 73 FR 72954, Dec. 1, 2008, unless otherwise noted.

§262.200 Definitions for this subpart.

The following definitions apply to this subpart:

Central accumulation area means an on-site hazardous waste accumulation area subject to either §262.34(a) (or 262.34(j) and (k) for Performance Track members) of this part (large quantity generators); or §262.34(d)–(f) of this part (small quantity generators). A central accumulation area at an eligible academic entity that chooses to be subject to this subpart must also comply with §262.211 when accumulating unwanted material and/or hazardous waste.

College/University means a private or public, post-secondary, degree-granting, academic institution, that is accredited by an accrediting agency listed annually by the U.S. Department of Education.

Eligible academic entity means a college or university, or a non-profit research institute that is owned by or has a formal written affiliation agreement with a college or university, or a teaching hospital that is owned by or has a formal written affiliation agreement with a college or university.

Formal written affiliation agreement for a non-profit research institute means a written document that establishes a relationship between institutions for the purposes of research and/or education and is signed by authorized representatives, as defined by §260.10, from each institution. A relationship on a project-by-project or grant-by-grant basis is not considered a formal written affiliation agreement. A *formal written affiliation agreement* for a teaching hospital means a master affiliation agreement and program letter of agreement, as defined by the Accreditation Council for Graduate Medical Education, with an accredited medical program or medical school.

Laboratory means an area owned by an eligible academic entity where relatively small quantities of chemicals and other substances are used on a nonproduction basis for teaching or research (or diagnostic purposes at a teaching hospital) and are stored and used in containers that are easily manipulated by one person. Photo laboratories, art studios, and field laboratories are considered laboratories. Areas such as chemical stockrooms and preparatory laboratories that provide a support function to teaching or research laboratories (or diagnostic laboratories at teaching hospitals) are also considered laboratories.

Laboratory clean-out means an evaluation of the inventory of chemicals and other materials in a laboratory that are no longer needed or that have expired and the subsequent removal of those chemicals or other unwanted materials from the laboratory. A cleanout may occur for several reasons. It may be on a routine basis (e.g., at the end of a semester or academic year) or as a result of a renovation, relocation, or change in laboratory supervisor/ occupant. A regularly scheduled removal of unwanted material as required by §262.208 does not qualify as a laboratory clean-out.

Laboratory worker means a person who handles chemicals and/or unwanted material in a laboratory and may include, but is not limited to, faculty, staff, post-doctoral fellows, interns, researchers, technicians, supervisors/managers, and principal investigators. A person does not need to be paid or otherwise compensated for his/her work in the laboratory to be considered a laboratory worker. Undergraduate and graduate students in a supervised classroom setting are not laboratory workers.

Non-profit research institute means an organization that conducts research as its primary function and files as a non-profit organization under the tax code of 26 U.S.C. 501(c)(3).

Reactive acutely hazardous unwanted material means an unwanted material that is one of the acutely hazardous commercial chemical products listed in §261.33(e) for reactivity.

Teaching hospital means a hospital that trains students to become physicians, nurses or other health or laboratory personnel.

Trained professional means a person who has completed the applicable RCRA training requirements of §265.16 for large quantity generators, or is knowledgeable about normal operations and emergencies in accordance with §262.34(d)(5)(iii) for small quantity generators and conditionally exempt small quantity generators. A trained professional may be an employee of the eligible academic entity or may be a contractor or vendor who meets the requisite training requirements.

Unwanted material means any chemical, mixtures of chemicals, products of experiments or other material from a laboratory that is no longer needed, wanted or usable in the laboratory and that is destined for hazardous waste determination by a trained professional. Unwanted materials include reactive acutely hazardous unwanted materials and materials that may eventually be determined not to be solid waste pursuant to §261.2, or a hazardous waste pursuant to §261.3. If an eligible academic entity elects to use another equally effective term in lieu of "unwanted material," as allowed by §262.206(a)(1)(i), the equally effective term has the same meaning and is subject to the same requirements as "unwanted material" under this subpart.

Working container means a small container (*i.e.*, two gallons or less) that is in use at a laboratory bench, hood, or other work station, to collect unwanted material from a laboratory experiment or procedure.

§262.201 Applicability for this subpart.

(a) Large quantity generators and small quantity generators. This subpart provides alternative requirements to the requirements in §§262.11 and 262.34(c) for the hazardous waste determination and accumulation of hazardous waste in laboratories owned by eligible academic entities that choose to be subject to this subpart, provided that they complete the notification requirements of §262.203.

(b) Conditionally exempt small quantity generators. This subpart provides alternative requirements to the conditional exemption in §261.5(b) for the accumulation of hazardous waste in laboratories owned by eligible academic entities that choose to be subject to this subpart, provided that they complete the notification requirements of §262.203.

§262.202 This subpart is optional.

(a) Large quantity generators and small quantity generators: Eligible academic entities have the option of complying with this subpart with respect to its laboratories, as an alternative to complying with the requirements of §§262.11 and 262.34(c).

(b) Conditionally exempt small quantity generators. Eligible academic entities have the option of complying with this subpart with respect to its laboratories, as an alternative to complying with the conditional exemption of §261.5(b).

§262.203 How an eligible academic entity indicates it will be subject to the requirements of this subpart.

(a) An eligible academic entity must notify the appropriate EPA Regional Administrator in writing, using the RCRA Subtitle C Site Identification Form (EPA Form 8700–12), that it is electing to be subject to the requirements of this subpart for all the laboratories owned by the eligible academic entity under the same EPA Identification Number. An eligible academic entity that is a conditionally exempt small quantity generator and does not have an EPA Identification Number must notify that it is electing to be subject to the requirements of this subpart for all the laboratories owned by the eligible academic entity that are onsite, as defined by §260.10. An eligible academic entity must submit a separate notification (Site Identification Form) for each EPA Identification Number (or site, for conditionally exempt small quantity generators) that is electing to be subject to the requirements of this subpart, and must submit the Site Identification Form before it begins operating under this subpart.

(b) When submitting the Site Identification Form, the eligible academic entity must, at a minimum, fill out the following fields on the form:

(1) Reason for Submittal.

(2) Site EPA Identification Number (except for conditionally exempt small quantity generators).

(3) Site Name.

PART 262—Subpart K

(4) Site Location Information.

(5) Site Land Type.

(6) North American Industry Classification System (NAICS) Code(s) for the Site.

(7) Site Mailing Address.

(8) Site Contact Person.

(9) Operator and Legal Owner of the Site.

(10) Type of Regulated Waste Activity.

(11) Certification.

(c) An eligible academic entity must keep a copy of the notification on file at the eligible academic entity for as long as its laboratories are subject to this subpart.

(d) A teaching hospital that is not owned by a college or university must keep a copy of its formal written affiliation agreement with a college or university on file at the teaching hospital for as long as its laboratories are subject to this subpart.

(e) A non-profit research institute that is not owned by a college or university must keep a copy of its formal written affiliation agreement with a college or university on file at the non-profit research institute for as long as its laboratories are subject to this subpart.

§262.204 How an eligible academic entity indicates it will withdraw from the requirements of this subpart.

(a) An eligible academic entity must notify the appropriate EPA Regional Administrator in writing, using the RCRA Subtitle C Site Identification Form (EPA Form 8700–12), that it is electing to no longer be subject to the requirements of this subpart for all the laboratories owned by the eligible academic entity under the same EPA Identification Number and that it will comply with the requirements of §§262.11 and 262.34(c) for small quantity generators and large quantity generators. An eligible academic entity that is a conditionally exempt small quantity generator and does not have an EPA Identification Number must notify that it is withdrawing from the requirements of this subpart for all the laboratories owned by the eligible academic entity that are on-site and that it will comply with the conditional exemption in §261.5(b). An eligible academic entity must submit a separate notification (Site Identification Form) for each EPA Identification Number (or site, for conditionally exempt small quantity generators) that is withdrawing from the requirements of this subpart and must submit the Site Identification Form before it begins operating under the requirements of §§262.11 and 262.34(c) for small quantity generators and large quantity generators, or §261.5(b) for conditionally exempt small quantity generators.

(b) When submitting the Site Identification Form, the eligible academic entity must, at a minimum, fill out the following fields on the form:

(1) Reason for Submittal.

(2) Site EPA Identification Number (except for conditionally exempt small quantity generators).

(3) Site Name.

(4) Site Location Information.

(5) Site Land Type.

(6) North American Industry Classification System (NAICS) Code(s) for the Site.

(7) Site Mailing Address.

(8) Site Contact Person.

(9) Operator and Legal Owner of the Site.

(10) Type of Regulated Waste Activity.

(11) Certification.

(c) An eligible academic entity must keep a copy of the withdrawal notice on file at the eligible academic entity for three years from the date of the notification.

§262.205 Summary of the requirements of this subpart.

An eligible academic entity that chooses to be subject to this subpart is not required to have interim status or a RCRA Part B permit for the accumulation of unwanted material and hazardous waste in its laboratories, provided the laboratories comply with the provisions of this subpart and the eligible academic entity has a Laboratory Management Plan (LMP) in accordance with §262.214 that describes how the laboratories owned by the eligible academic entity will comply with the requirements of this subpart.

§262.206 Labeling and management standards for containers of unwanted material in the laboratory.

An eligible academic entity must manage containers of unwanted material while in the laboratory in accordance with the requirements in this section.

(a) Labeling: Label unwanted material as follows:

(1) The following information must be affixed or attached to the container:

(i) The words "unwanted material" or another equally effective term that is to be used consistently by the eligible academic entity and that is identified in Part I of the Laboratory Management Plan, and

(ii) Sufficient information to alert emergency responders to the contents of the container. Examples of information that would be sufficient to alert emergency responders to the contents of the container include, but are not limited to:

(A) The name of the chemical(s),

(B) The type or class of chemical, such as organic solvents or halogenated organic solvents.

(2) The following information may be affixed or attached to the container, but must at a minimum be associated with the container:

(i) The date that the unwanted material first began accumulating in the container, and

(ii) Information sufficient to allow a trained professional to properly identify whether an unwanted material is a solid and hazardous waste and to assign the proper hazardous waste code(s), pursuant to §262.11. Examples of information that would allow a trained professional to properly identify whether an unwanted material is a solid or hazardous waste include, but are not limited to:

(A) The name and/or description of the chemical contents or composition of the unwanted material, or, if known, the product of the chemical reaction,

(B) Whether the unwanted material has been used or is unused,

(C) A description of the manner in which the chemical was produced or processed, if applicable.

(b) Management of Containers in the Laboratory: An eligible academic entity must properly manage containers of unwanted material in the laboratory to assure safe storage of the unwanted material, to prevent leaks, spills, emissions to the air, adverse chemical reactions, and dangerous situations that may result in harm to human health or the environment. Proper container management must include the following:

(1) Containers are maintained and kept in good condition and damaged containers are replaced, overpacked, or repaired, and

(2) Containers are compatible with their contents to avoid reactions between the contents and the container; and are made of, or lined with, material that is compatible with the unwanted material so that the container's integrity is not impaired, and

(3) Containers must be kept closed at all times, except:

(i) When adding, removing or consolidating unwanted material, or

(ii) A working container may be open until the end of the procedure or work shift, or until it is full, whichever comes first, at which time the working container must either be closed or the contents emptied into a separate container that is then closed, or

(iii) When venting of a container is necessary.

(A) For the proper operation of laboratory equipment, such as with inline collection of unwanted materials from high performance liquid chromatographs, or

(B) To prevent dangerous situations, such as build-up of extreme pressure.

§262.207 Training.

An eligible academic entity must provide training to all individuals working in a laboratory at the eligible academic entity, as follows:

(a) Training for laboratory workers and students must be commensurate with their duties so they understand the requirements in this subpart and can implement them.

(b) An eligible academic entity can provide training for laboratory workers and students in a variety of ways, including, but not limited to:

(1) Instruction by the professor or laboratory manager before or during an experiment; or

(2) Formal classroom training; or

(3) Electronic/written training; or

(4) On-the-job training; or

(5) Written or oral exams.

(c) An eligible academic entity that is a large quantity generator must maintain documentation for the durations specified in §265.16(e) demonstrating training for all laboratory workers that is sufficient to determine whether laboratory workers have been trained. Examples of documentation demonstrating training can include, but are not limited to, the following:

(1) Sign-in/attendance sheet(s) for training session(s); or

(2) Syllabus for training session; or

(3) Certificate of training completion; or

(4) Test results.

(d) A trained professional must:

(1) Accompany the transfer of unwanted material and hazardous waste when the unwanted material and hazardous waste is removed from the laboratory, and

(2) Make the hazardous waste determination, pursuant to §262.11, for unwanted material.

§262.208 Removing containers of unwanted material from the laboratory.

(a) Removing containers of unwanted material on a regular schedule. An eligible academic entity must either:

(1) Remove all containers of unwanted material from each laboratory on a regular interval, not to exceed 6 months; or

(2) Remove containers of unwanted material from each laboratory within 6 months of each container's accumulation start date.

(b) The eligible academic entity must specify in Part I of its Laboratory Management Plan whether it will comply with paragraph (a)(1) or (a)(2) of this section for the regular removal of unwanted material from its laboratories.

(c) The eligible academic entity must specify in Part II of its Laboratory Management Plan how it will comply with paragraph (a)(1) or (a)(2) of this section and develop a schedule for regular removals of unwanted material from its laboratories.

(d) Removing containers of unwanted material when volumes are exceeded.

(1) If a laboratory accumulates a total volume of unwanted material (including reactive acutely hazardous unwanted material) in excess of 55 gallons before the regularly scheduled removal, the eligible academic entity must ensure that all containers of unwanted material in the laboratory (including reactive acutely hazardous unwanted material):

(i) Are marked on the label that is associated with the container (or on the label that is affixed or attached to the container, if that is preferred) with the date that 55 gallons is exceeded; and

(ii) Are removed from the laboratory within 10 calendar days of the date that 55 gallons was exceeded, or at the next regularly scheduled removal, whichever comes first.

(2) If a laboratory accumulates more than 1 quart of reactive acutely hazardous unwanted material before the regularly scheduled removal, then the eligible academic entity must ensure that all containers of reactive acutely hazardous unwanted material:

(i) Are marked on the label that is associated with the container (or on the label that is affixed or attached to the container, if that is preferred) with the date that 1 quart is exceeded; and

(ii) Are removed from the laboratory within 10 calendar days of the date that 1 quart was exceeded, or at the next regularly scheduled removal, whichever comes first.

§262.209 Where and when to make the hazardous waste determination and where to send containers of unwanted material upon removal from the laboratory.

(a) Large quantity generators and small quantity generators—an eligible academic entity must ensure that a trained professional makes a hazardous waste determination, pursuant to §262.11, for unwanted material in any of the following areas:

(1) In the laboratory before the unwanted material is removed from the laboratory, in accordance with §262.210;

(2) Within 4 calendar days of arriving at an on-site central accumulation area, in accordance with §262.211; and

(3) Within 4 calendar days of arriving at an on-site interim status or permitted treatment, storage or disposal facility, in accordance with §262.212.

(b) Conditionally exempt small quantity generators—an eligible academic entity must ensure that a trained professional makes a hazardous waste determination, pursuant to §262.11, for unwanted material in the laboratory before the unwanted material is removed from the laboratory, in accordance with §262.210.

§262.210 Making the hazardous waste determination in the laboratory before the unwanted material is removed from the laboratory.

If an eligible academic entity makes the hazardous waste determination, pursuant to §262.11, for unwanted material in the laboratory, it must comply with the following:

(a) A trained professional must make the hazardous waste determination, pursuant to §262.11, before the unwanted material is removed from the laboratory.

(b) If an unwanted material is a hazardous waste, the eligible academic entity must:

(1) Write the words "hazardous waste" on the container label that is affixed or attached to the container, before the hazardous waste may be removed from the laboratory; and

(2) Write the appropriate hazardous waste code(s) on the label that is associated with the container (or on the label that is affixed or attached to the container, if that is preferred) before the hazardous waste is transported off-site.

(3) Count the hazardous waste toward the eligible academic entity's generator status, pursuant to §261.5(c) and (d), in the calendar month that the hazardous waste determination was made.

(c) A trained professional must accompany all hazardous waste that is transferred from the laboratory(ies) to an on-site central accumulation area or onsite interim status or permitted treatment, storage or disposal facility.

(d) When hazardous waste is removed from the laboratory:

(1) Large quantity generators and small quantity generators must ensure it is taken directly from the laboratory(ies) to an on-site central accumulation area, or on-site interim status or permitted treatment, storage or disposal facility, or transported off-site.

(2) Conditionally exempt small quantity generators must ensure it is taken directly from the laboratory(ies) to any of the types of facilities listed in §261.5(f)(3) for acute hazardous waste, or §261.5(g)(3) for hazardous waste.

(e) An unwanted material that is a hazardous waste is subject to all applicable hazardous waste regulations when it is removed from the laboratory.

§262.211 Making the hazardous waste determination at an on-site central accumulation area.

If an eligible academic entity makes the hazardous waste determination, pursuant to §262.11, for unwanted material at an on-site central accumulation area, it must comply with the following:

(a) A trained professional must accompany all unwanted material that is transferred from the laboratory(ies) to an on-site central accumulation area.

(b) All unwanted material removed from the laboratory(ies) must be taken directly from the laboratory(ies) to the on-site central accumulation area.

(c) The unwanted material becomes subject to the generator accumulation regulations of §262.34(a) (or §262.34(j) and (k) for Performance Track members) for large quantity generators or §262.34(d)–(f) for small quantity generators as soon as it arrives in the central accumulation area, except for the "hazardous waste" labeling requirements of §262.34(a)(3) (or §262.34(j)(6) for Performance Track members).

(d) A trained professional must determine, pursuant to §262.11, if the unwanted material is a hazardous waste within 4 calendar days of the unwanted materials' arrival at the on-site central accumulation area.

(e) If the unwanted material is a hazardous waste, the eligible academic entity must:

(1) Write the words "hazardous waste" on the container label that is affixed or attached to the container, within 4 calendar days of arriving at the on-site central accumulation area and before the hazardous waste may be removed from the on-site central accumulation area, and

(2) Write the appropriate hazardous waste code(s) on the container label that is associated with the container (or on the label that is affixed or attached to the container, if that is preferred) before the hazardous waste may be treated or disposed of on-site or transported offsite, and

(3) Count the hazardous waste toward the eligible academic entity's generator status, pursuant to §261.5(c) and (d) in the calendar month that the hazardous waste determination was made, and

(4) Manage the hazardous waste according to all applicable hazardous waste regulations.

§262.212 Making the hazardous waste determination at an on-site interim status or permitted treatment, storage or disposal facility.

If an eligible academic entity makes the hazardous waste determination, pursuant to §262.11, for unwanted material at an on-site interim status or permitted treatment, storage or disposal facility, it must comply with the following:

(a) A trained professional must accompany all unwanted material that is transferred from the laboratory(ies) to an on-site interim status or permitted treatment, storage or disposal facility.

(b) All unwanted material removed from the laboratory(ies) must be taken directly from the laboratory(ies) to the on-site interim status or permitted treatment, storage or disposal facility.

(c) The unwanted material becomes subject to the terms of the eligible academic entity's hazardous waste permit or interim status as soon as it arrives in the on-site treatment, storage or disposal facility.

(d) A trained professional must determine, pursuant to §262.11, if the unwanted material is a hazardous waste within 4 calendar days of the unwanted materials' arrival at an on-site interim status or permitted treatment, storage or disposal facility.

(e) If the unwanted material is a hazardous waste, the eligible academic entity must:

(1) Write the words "hazardous waste" on the container label that is affixed or attached to the container (or on the label that is affixed or attached to the container, if that is preferred) within 4 calendar days of arriving at the on-site interim status or permitted treatment, storage or disposal facility and before the hazardous waste may be removed from the on-site interim status or permitted treatment, storage or disposal facility, and

(2) Write the appropriate hazardous waste code(s) on the container label that is associated with the container (or on the label that is affixed or attached to the

container, if that is preferred) before the hazardous waste may be treated or disposed on-site or transported off-site, and

(3) Count the hazardous waste toward the eligible academic entity's generator status, pursuant to §261.5(c) and (d) in the calendar month that the hazardous waste determination was made, and

(4) Manage the hazardous waste according to all applicable hazardous waste regulations.

§262.213 Laboratory clean-outs.

(a) One time per 12 month period for each laboratory, an eligible academic entity may opt to conduct a laboratory clean-out that is subject to all the applicable requirements of this subpart, except that:

(1) If the volume of unwanted material in the laboratory exceeds 55 gallons (or 1 quart of reactive acutely hazardous unwanted material), the eligible academic entity is not required to remove all unwanted materials from the laboratory within 10 calendar days of exceeding 55 gallons (or 1 quart of reactive acutely hazardous unwanted material), as required by §262.208. Instead, the eligible academic entity must remove all unwanted materials from the laboratory within 30 calendar days from the start of the laboratory clean-out; and

(2) For the purposes of on-site accumulation, an eligible academic entity is not required to count a hazardous waste that is an unused commercial chemical product (listed in 40 CFR part 261, subpart D or exhibiting one or more characteristics in 40 CFR part 261, subpart C) generated solely during the laboratory clean-out toward its hazardous waste generator status, pursuant to §261.5(c) and (d). An unwanted material that is generated prior to the beginning of the laboratory clean-out and is still in the laboratory at the time the laboratory clean-out commences must be counted toward hazardous waste generator status, pursuant to §261.5(c) and (d), if it is determined to be hazardous waste; and

(3) For the purposes of off-site management, an eligible academic entity must count all its hazardous waste, regardless of whether the hazardous waste was counted toward generator status under paragraph (a)(2) of this section, and if it generates more than 1 kg/month of acute hazardous waste or more than 100 kg/month of hazardous waste (i.e., the conditionally exempt small quantity generator limits of §261.5), the hazardous waste is subject to all applicable hazardous waste regulations when it is transported off-site; and

(4) An eligible academic entity must document the activities of the laboratory clean-out. The documentation must, at a minimum, identify the laboratory being cleaned out, the date the laboratory clean-out begins and ends, and the volume of hazardous waste generated during the laboratory clean-out. The eligible academic entity must maintain the records for a period of three years from the date the clean-out ends; and

(b) For all other laboratory clean-outs conducted during the same 12-month period, an eligible academic entity is subject to all the applicable requirements of this subpart, including, but not limited to:

(1) The requirement to remove all unwanted materials from the laboratory within 10 calendar days of exceeding 55 gallons (or 1 quart of reactive acutely hazardous unwanted material), as required by §262.208; and

(2) The requirement to count all hazardous waste, including unused hazardous waste, generated during the laboratory clean-out toward its hazardous waste generator status, pursuant to §261.5(c) and (d).

§262.214 Laboratory management plan.

An eligible academic entity must develop and retain a written Laboratory Management Plan, or revise an existing written plan. The Laboratory Management Plan is a site-specific document that describes how the eligible academic entity will manage unwanted materials in compliance with this subpart. An eligible academic entity may write one Laboratory Management Plan for all the laboratories owned by the eligible academic entity that have opted into this subpart, even if the laboratories are located at sites with different EPA Identification Numbers. The Laboratory Management Plan must contain two parts with a total of nine elements identified in paragraphs (a) and (b) of this section. In Part I of its Laboratory Management Plan, an eligible academic entity must describe its procedures for each of the elements listed in paragraph (a) of this section. An eligible academic entity must implement and comply with the specific provisions that it develops to address the elements in Part I of the Laboratory Management Plan. In Part II of its Laboratory Management Plan, an eligible academic entity must describe its best management practices for each of the elements listed in paragraph (b) of this section. The specific actions taken by an eligible academic entity to implement each element in Part II of its Laboratory Management Plan may vary from the procedures described in the eligible academic entity's Laboratory Management Plan, without constituting a violation of this subpart. An eligible academic entity may include additional elements and best management practices in Part II of its Laboratory Management Plan if it chooses.

(a) The eligible academic entity must implement and comply with the specific provisions of Part I of its Laboratory Management Plan. In Part I of its Laboratory Management Plan, an eligible academic entity must:

(1) Describe procedures for container labeling in accordance with §262.206(a), including:

(i) Identifying whether the eligible academic entity will use the term "unwanted material" on the containers in the laboratory. If not, identify an equally effective term that will be used in lieu of "unwanted material" and consistently by the eligible academic entity. The equally effective term, if used, has the same meaning and is subject to the same requirements as "unwanted material."

(ii) Identifying the manner in which information that is "associated with the container" will be imparted.

(2) Identify whether the eligible academic entity will comply with §262.208(a)(1) or (a)(2) for regularly scheduled removals of unwanted material from the laboratory.

(b) In Part II of its Laboratory Management Plan, an eligible academic entity must:

(1) Describe its intended best practices for container labeling and management, including how the eligible academic entity will manage containers used for in-line collection of unwanted materials, such as with high performance liquid chromatographs and other laboratory equipment (see the required standards at §262.206).

(2) Describe its intended best practices for providing training for laboratory workers and students commensurate with their duties (see the required standards at §262.207(a)).

(3) Describe its intended best practices for providing training to ensure safe on-site transfers of unwanted material and hazardous waste by trained professionals (see the required standards at §262.207(d)(1)).

(4) Describe its intended best practices for removing unwanted material from the laboratory, including:

(i) For regularly scheduled removals—Develop a regular schedule for identifying and removing unwanted materials from its laboratories (see the required standards at §262.208(a)(1) and (a)(2)).

(ii) For removals when maximum volumes are exceeded:

(A) Describe its intended best practices for removing unwanted materials from the laboratory within 10 calendar days when unwanted materials have exceeded their maximum volumes (see the required standards at §262.208(d)).

(B) Describe its intended best practices for communicating that unwanted materials have exceeded their maximum volumes.

(5) Describe its intended best practices for making hazardous waste determinations, including specifying the duties of the individuals involved in the process (see the required standards at §262.11 and §§262.209 through 262.212).

(6) Describe its intended best practices for laboratory clean-outs, if the eligible academic entity plans to use the incentives for laboratory clean-outs provided in §262.213, including:

(i) Procedures for conducting laboratory clean-outs (see the required standards at §262.213(a)(1) through (3)); and

(ii) Procedures for documenting laboratory clean-outs (see the required standards at §262.213(a)(4)).

(7) Describe its intended best practices for emergency prevention, including:

(i) Procedures for emergency prevention, notification, and response, appropriate to the hazards in the laboratory; and

(ii) A list of chemicals that the eligible academic entity has, or is likely to have, that become more dangerous when they exceed their expiration date and/or as they degrade; and

(iii) Procedures to safely dispose of chemicals that become more dangerous when they exceed their expiration date and/or as they degrade; and

(iv) Procedures for the timely characterization of unknown chemicals.

(c) An eligible academic entity must make its Laboratory Management Plan available to laboratory workers, students, or any others at the eligible academic entity who request it.

(d) An eligible academic entity must review and revise its Laboratory Management Plan, as needed.

§262.215 Unwanted material that is not solid or hazardous waste.

(a) If an unwanted material does not meet the definition of solid waste in §261.2, it is no longer subject to this subpart or to the RCRA hazardous waste regulations.

(b) If an unwanted material does not meet the definition of hazardous waste in §261.3, it is no longer subject to this subpart or to the RCRA hazardous waste regulations, but must be managed in compliance with any other applicable regulations and/or conditions.

§262.216 Non-laboratory hazardous waste generated at an eligible academic entity.

An eligible academic entity that generates hazardous waste outside of a laboratory is not eligible to manage that hazardous waste under this subpart; and

(a) Remains subject to the generator requirements of §§262.11 and 262.34(c) for large quantity generators and small quantity generators (if the hazardous waste is managed in a satellite accumulation area), and all other applicable generator requirements of 40 CFR part 262, with respect to that hazardous waste; or

(b) Remains subject to the conditional exemption of §261.5(b) for conditionally exempt small quantity generators, with respect to that hazardous waste.

Appendix

Appendix to Part 262—Uniform Hazardous Waste Manifest and Instructions (EPA Forms 8700-22 and 8700-22A and Their Instructions)

📖 6.6.1.1, 6.6.3

U.S. EPA Form 8700-22

Read all instructions before completing this form.

1. This form has been designed for use on a 12-pitch (elite) typewriter which is also compatible with standard computer printers; a firm point pen may also be used—press down hard.
2. Federal regulations require generators and transporters of hazardous waste and owners or operators of hazardous waste treatment, storage, and disposal facilities to complete this form (FORM 8700–22) and, if necessary, the continuation sheet (FORM 8700–22A) for both inter- and intrastate transportation of hazardous waste.

Publisher's Note: U.S. EPA Form 8700-22 has been reduced to fit in this book; in its present form, it must be enlarged 110% for use on a 12-pitch (elite) typewriter. See the form on the following page.

Manifest 8700–22

The following statement must be included with each Uniform Hazardous Waste Manifest, either on the form, in the instructions to the form, or accompanying the form:

> Public reporting burden for this collection of information is estimated to average: 30 minutes for generators, 10 minutes for transporters, and 25 minutes for owners or operators of treatment, storage, and disposal facilities. This includes time for reviewing instructions, gathering data, completing, reviewing and transmitting the form. Any correspondence regarding the PRA burden statement for the manifest must be sent to the Director of the Collection Strategies Division in EPA's Office of Information Collection at the following address: U.S. Environmental Protection Agency (2822T), 1200 Pennsylvania Ave., NW., Washington, DC 20460. Do not send the completed form to this address.

I. Instructions for Generators

Item 1. *Generator's U.S. EPA Identification Number*

Enter the generator's U.S. EPA twelve digit identification number, or the State generator identification number if the generator site does not have an EPA identification number.

Item 2. *Page 1 of___*

Enter the total number of pages used to complete this Manifest (*i.e.*, the first page (EPA Form 8700–22) plus the number of Continuation Sheets (EPA Form 8700–22A), if any).

Item 3. *Emergency Response Phone Number*

Enter a phone number for which emergency response information can be obtained in the event of an incident during transportation. The emergency response phone number must:

1. Be the number of the generator or the number of an agency or organization who is capable of and accepts responsibility for providing detailed information about the shipment;
2. Reach a phone that is monitored 24 hours a day at all times the waste is in transportation (including transportation related storage); and
3. Reach someone who is either knowledgeable of the hazardous waste being shipped and has comprehensive emergency response and spill cleanup/incident mitigation information for the material being shipped or has immediate access to a person who has that knowledge and information about the shipment.

Note: Emergency Response phone number information should only be entered in Item 3 when there is one phone number that applies to all the waste materials described in Item 9b. If a situation (*e.g.*, consolidated shipments) arises where more than one Emergency Response phone number applies to the various wastes listed on the manifest, the phone numbers associated with each specific material should be entered after its description in Item 9b.

Item 4. *Manifest Tracking Number*

This unique tracking number must be preprinted on the manifest by the forms printer.

Item 5. *Generator's Mailing Address, Phone Number and Site Address*

Enter the name of the generator, the mailing address to which the completed manifest signed by the designated facility should be mailed, and the generator's telephone number. Note, the telephone number (including area code) should be the normal business number for the generator, or the number where the generator or his authorized agent may be reached to provide instructions in the event the designated and/or alternate (if any) facility rejects some or all of the shipment. Also enter the physical site address from which the shipment originates only if this address is different than the mailing address.

Item 6. *Transporter 1 Company Name, and U.S. EPA ID Number*

Enter the company name and U.S. EPA ID number of the first transporter who will transport the waste. Vehicle or driver information may not be entered here.

Item 7. *Transporter 2 Company Name and U.S. EPA ID Number*

If applicable, enter the company name and U.S. EPA ID number of the second transporter who will transport the waste. Vehicle or driver information may not be entered here.

If more than two transporters are needed, use a Continuation Sheet(s) (EPA Form 8700– 22A).

Please print or type. (Form designed for use on elite (12-pitch) typewriter.)

Form Approved. OMB No. 2050-0039

UNIFORM HAZARDOUS WASTE MANIFEST | 1. Generator ID Number | 2. Page 1 of | 3. Emergency Response Phone | **4. Manifest Tracking Number**

GENERATOR

5. Generator's Name and Mailing Address — Generator's Site Address (if different than mailing address)

Generator's Phone:

6. Transporter 1 Company Name — U.S. EPA ID Number

7. Transporter 2 Company Name — U.S. EPA ID Number

8. Designated Facility Name and Site Address — U.S. EPA ID Number

Facility's Phone:

9a. HM	9b. U.S. DOT Description (including Proper Shipping Name, Hazard Class, ID Number, and Packing Group (if any))	10. Containers No.	10. Containers Type	11. Total Quantity	12. Unit Wt./Vol.	13. Waste Codes
	1.					
	2.					
	3.					
	4.					

14. Special Handling Instructions and Additional Information

15. **GENERATOR'S/OFFEROR'S CERTIFICATION:** I hereby declare that the contents of this consignment are fully and accurately described above by the proper shipping name, and are classified, packaged, marked and labeled/placarded, and are in all respects in proper condition for transport according to applicable international and national governmental regulations. If export shipment and I am the Primary Exporter, I certify that the contents of this consignment conform to the terms of the attached EPA Acknowledgment of Consent.
I certify that the waste minimization statement identified in 40 CFR 262.27(a) (if I am a large quantity generator) or (b) (if I am a small quantity generator) is true.

Generator's/Offeror's Printed/Typed Name — Signature — Month Day Year

INT'L

16. International Shipments ☐ Import to U.S. ☐ Export from U.S. Port of entry/exit: ______

Transporter signature (for exports only): Date leaving U.S.:

TRANSPORTER

17. Transporter Acknowledgment of Receipt of Materials

Transporter 1 Printed/Typed Name — Signature — Month Day Year

Transporter 2 Printed/Typed Name — Signature — Month Day Year

DESIGNATED FACILITY

18. Discrepancy

18a. Discrepancy Indication Space ☐ Quantity ☐ Type ☐ Residue ☐ Partial Rejection ☐ Full Rejection

Manifest Reference Number:

18b. Alternate Facility (or Generator) — U.S. EPA ID Number

Facility's Phone:

18c. Signature of Alternate Facility (or Generator) — Month Day Year

19. Hazardous Waste Report Management Method Codes (i.e., codes for hazardous waste treatment, disposal, and recycling systems)

1.	2.	3.	4.

20. Designated Facility Owner or Operator: Certification of receipt of hazardous materials covered by the manifest except as noted in Item 18a

Printed/Typed Name — Signature — Month Day Year

EPA Form 8700-22 (Rev. 3-05) Previous editions are obsolete.

DESIGNATED FACILITY TO DESTINATION STATE (IF REQUIRED)

Item 8. *Designated Facility Name, Site Address, and U.S. EPA ID Number*

Enter the company name and site address of the facility designated to receive the waste listed on this manifest. Also enter the facility's phone number and the U.S. EPA twelve digit identification number of the facility.

Item 9. *U.S. DOT Description (Including Proper Shipping Name, Hazard Class or Division, Identification Number, and Packing Group)*

Item 9a. If the wastes identified in Item 9b consist of both hazardous and nonhazardous materials, then identify the hazardous materials by entering an "X" in this Item next to the corresponding hazardous material identified in Item 9b.

Item 9b. Enter the U.S. DOT Proper Shipping Name, Hazard Class or Division, Identification Number (UN/NA) and Packing Group for each waste as identified in 49 CFR 172. Include technical name(s) and reportable quantity references, if applicable.

Note: If additional space is needed for waste descriptions, enter these additional descriptions in Item 27 on the Continuation Sheet (EPA Form 8700–22A). Also, if more than one Emergency Response phone number applies to the various wastes described in either Item 9b or Item 27, enter applicable Emergency Response phone numbers immediately following the shipping descriptions for those Items.

Item 10. *Containers (Number and Type)*

Enter the number of containers for each waste and the appropriate abbreviation from Table I (below) for the type of container.

TABLE I—TYPES OF CONTAINERS

BA = Burlap, cloth, paper, or plastic bags.

CF = Fiber or plastic boxes, cartons, cases.

CM = Metal boxes, cartons, cases (including roll-offs).

CW = Wooden boxes, cartons, cases.

CY = Cylinders.

DF = Fiberboard or plastic drums, barrels, kegs.

DM = Metal drums, barrels, kegs.

DT = Dump truck.

DW = Wooden drums, barrels, kegs.

HG = Hopper or gondola cars.

TC = Tank cars.

TP = Portable tanks.

TT = Cargo tanks (tank trucks).

Item 11. *Total Quantity*

Enter, in designated boxes, the total quantity of waste. Round partial units to the nearest whole unit, and *do not* enter decimals or fractions. To the extent practical, report quantities using appropriate units of measure that will allow you to report quantities with precision. Waste quantities entered should be based on actual measurements or reasonably accurate estimates of actual quantities shipped. Container capacities are not acceptable as estimates.

Item 12. *Units of Measure (Weight/Volume)*

Enter, in designated boxes, the appropriate abbreviation from Table II (below) for the unit of measure.

TABLE II—UNITS OF MEASURE

G = Gallons (liquids only).

K = Kilograms.

L = Liters (liquids only).

M = Metric Tons (1000 kilograms).

N = Cubic Meters.

P = Pounds.

T = Tons (2000 pounds).

Y = Cubic Yards.

Note: Tons, Metric Tons, Cubic Meters, and Cubic Yards should only be reported in connection with very large bulk shipments, such as rail cars, tank trucks, or barges.

Item 13. *Waste Codes*

Enter up to six federal and state waste codes to describe each waste stream identified in Item 9b. State waste codes that are not redundant with federal codes must be entered here, in addition to the federal waste codes which are most representative of the properties of the waste.

Item 14. *Special Handling Instructions and Additional Information.*

1. Generators may enter any special handling or shipment-specific information necessary for the proper management or tracking of the materials under the generator's or other handler's business processes, such as waste profile numbers, container codes, bar codes, or response guide numbers. Generators also may use this space to enter additional descriptive information about their shipped materials, such as chemical names, constituent percentages, physical state, or specific gravity of wastes identified with volume units in Item 12.
2. This space may be used to record limited types of federally required information for which there is no specific space provided on the manifest, including any alternate facility designations; the manifest tracking number of the original manifest for rejected wastes and residues that are re-shipped under a second manifest; and the specification of PCB waste descriptions and PCB out-of-service dates required under 40 CFR 761.207. Generators, however, cannot be required to enter information in this space to meet state regulatory requirements.

Item 15. *Generator's/Offeror's Certifications*

1. The generator must read, sign, and date the waste minimization certification statement. In signing the waste minimization certification statement, those generators who have not been exempted by statute or regulation from the duty to make a waste minimization certification under section 3002(b) of RCRA are also certifying that they have complied with the waste minimization requirements. The Generator's Certification also contains the required attestation that the shipment has been properly prepared and is in proper condition for transportation (the shipper's certification). The content of the shipper's certification statement is as follows: "I hereby declare that the contents of this consignment are fully and accurately described above by the proper shipping name, and are classified, packaged, marked, and labeled/placarded, and are in all respects in proper condition for transport by highway according to applicable international and national governmental regulations. If export shipment and I am the Primary Exporter, I certify that the contents of this consignment conform to the terms of the attached EPA Acknowledgment of Consent." When a party other than the generator prepares the shipment for transportation, this party may also sign the shipper's certification statement as the offeror of the shipment.
2. Generator or Offeror personnel may preprint the words, "On behalf of" in the signature block or may hand write this

statement in the signature block prior to signing the generator/offeror certification, to indicate that the individual signs as the employee or agent of the named principal.

Note: All of the above information except the handwritten signature required in Item 15 may be pre-printed.

II. Instructions for International Shipment Block

Item 16. *International Shipments*

For export shipments, the primary exporter must check the export box, and enter the point of exit (city and state) from the United States. For import shipments, the importer must check the import box and enter the point of entry (city and state) into the United States. For exports, the transporter must sign and date the manifest to indicate the day the shipment left the United States. Transporters of hazardous waste shipments must deliver a copy of the manifest to the U.S. Customs when exporting the waste across U.S. borders.

III. Instructions for Transporters

Item 17. *Transporters' Acknowledgments of Receipt*

Enter the name of the person accepting the waste on behalf of the first transporter. That person must acknowledge acceptance of the waste described on the manifest by signing and entering the date of receipt. Only one signature per transportation company is required. Signatures are not required to track the movement of wastes in and out of transfer facilities, unless there is a change of custody between transporters.

If applicable, enter the name of the person accepting the waste on behalf of the second transporter. That person must acknowledge acceptance of the waste described on the manifest by signing and entering the date of receipt.

Note: Transporters carrying imports, who are acting as importers, may have responsibilities to enter information in the International Shipments Block. Transporters carrying exports may also have responsibilities to enter information in the International Shipments Block. See above instructions for Item 16.

IV. Instructions for Owners and Operators of Treatment, Storage, and Disposal Facilities

Item 18. *Discrepancy*

Item 18a. Discrepancy Indication Space

1. The authorized representative of the designated (or alternate) facility's owner or operator must note in this space any discrepancies between the waste described on the Manifest and the waste actually received at the facility. Manifest discrepancies are: significant differences (as defined by §§264.72(b) and 265.72(b)) between the quantity or type of hazardous waste designated on the manifest or shipping paper, and the quantity and type of hazardous waste a facility actually receives, rejected wastes, which may be a full or partial shipment of hazardous waste that the TSDF cannot accept, or container residues, which are residues that exceed the quantity limits for "empty" containers set forth in 40 CFR 261.7(b).
2. For rejected loads and residues (40 CFR 264.72(d), (e), and (f), or 40 CFR 265.72(d), (e), or (f)), check the appropriate box if the shipment is a rejected load (*i.e.*, rejected by the designated and/or alternate facility and is sent to an alternate facility or returned to the generator) or a regulated residue that cannot be removed from a container. Enter the reason for the rejection or the inability to remove the residue and a description of the waste. Also, reference the manifest tracking number for any additional manifests being used to track the rejected waste or residue shipment on the original manifest. Indicate the original manifest tracking number in Item 14, the Special Handling Block and Additional Information Block of the additional manifests.
3. Owners or operators of facilities located in unauthorized States (*i.e.*, states in which the U.S. EPA administers the hazardous waste management program) who cannot resolve significant differences in quantity or type within 15 days of receiving the waste must submit to their Regional Administrator a letter with a copy of the Manifest at issue describing the discrepancy and attempts to reconcile it (40 CFR 264.72(c) and 265.72(c)).
4. Owners or operators of facilities located in authorized States (*i.e.*, those States that have received authorization from the U.S. EPA to administer the hazardous waste management program) should contact their State agency for information on where to report discrepancies involving "significant differences" to state officials.

Item 18b. Alternate Facility (or Generator) for Receipt of Full Load Rejections

Enter the name, address, phone number, and EPA Identification Number of the Alternate Facility which the rejecting TSDF has designated, after consulting with the generator, to receive a fully rejected waste shipment. In the event that a fully rejected shipment is being returned to the generator, the rejecting TSDF may enter the generator's site information in this space. This field is not to be used to forward partially rejected loads or residue waste shipments.

Item 18c. Alternate Facility (or Generator) Signature

The authorized representative of the alternate facility (or the generator in the event of a returned shipment) must sign and date this field of the form to acknowledge receipt of the fully rejected wastes or residues identified by the initial TSDF.

Item 19. *Hazardous Waste Report Management Method Codes*

Enter the most appropriate Hazardous Waste Report Management Method code for each waste listed in Item 9. The Hazardous Waste Report Management Method code is to be entered by the first treatment, storage, or disposal facility (TSDF) that receives the waste and is the code that best describes the way in which the waste is to be managed when received by the TSDF.

Item 20. *Designated Facility Owner or Operator Certification of Receipt (Except as Noted in Item 18a)*

Enter the name of the person receiving the waste on behalf of the owner or operator of the facility. That person must acknowledge receipt or rejection of the waste described on the Manifest by signing and entering the date of receipt or rejection where indicated. Since the Facility Certification acknowledges receipt of the waste except as noted in the Discrepancy Space in Item 18a, the certification should be signed for both waste receipt and waste rejection, with the rejection being noted and described in the space provided in Item 18a. Fully rejected wastes may be forwarded or returned using Item 18b after consultation with the generator. Enter the name of the person accepting the waste on behalf of the owner or operator of the alternate facility or the original generator. That person must acknowledge receipt or rejection of the waste described on the Manifest by signing and entering the date they received or rejected the waste in Item 18c. Partially rejected wastes and residues must be re-shipped under a new manifest, to be initiated and signed by the rejecting TSDF as offeror of the shipment.

Manifest Continuation Sheet

Instructions—Continuation Sheet, U.S. EPA Form 8700–22A

Read all instructions before completing this form. This form has been designed for use on a 12-pitch (elite) typewriter; a firm point pen may also be used—press down hard.

This form must be used as a continuation sheet to U.S. EPA Form 8700–22 if:

- More than two transporters are to be used to transport the waste; or
- More space is required for the U.S. DOT descriptions and related information in Item 9 of U.S. EPA Form 8700–22.

Federal regulations require generators and transporters of hazardous waste and owners or operators of hazardous waste treatment, storage, or disposal facilities to use the uniform hazardous waste manifest (EPA Form 8700–22) and, if necessary, this continuation sheet (EPA Form 8700–22A) for both interstate and intrastate transportation.

Item 21. *Generator's ID Number*

Enter the generator's U.S. EPA twelve digit identification number or, the State generator identification number if the generator site does not have an EPA identification number.

Item 22. *Page___—*

Enter the page number of this Continuation Sheet.

Item 23. *Manifest Tracking Number*

Enter the Manifest Tracking number from Item 4 of the Manifest form to which this continuation sheet is attached.

Item 24. *Generator's Name—*

Enter the generator's name as it appears in Item 5 on the first page of the Manifest.

Item 25. *Transporter—Company Name*

If additional transporters are used to transport the waste described on this Manifest, enter the company name of each additional transporter in the order in which they will transport the waste. Enter after the word "Transporter" the order of the transporter. For example, Transporter 3 Company Name. Also enter the U.S. EPA twelve digit identification number of the transporter described in Item 25.

Item 26. *Transporter—Company Name*

If additional transporters are used to transport the waste described on this Manifest, enter the company name of each additional transporter in the order in which they will transport the waste. Enter after the word "Transporter" the order of the transporter. For example, Transporter 4 Company Name. Each Continuation Sheet can record the names of two additional transporters. Also enter the U.S. EPA twelve digit identification number of the transporter named in Item 26.

Item 27. *U.S. D.O.T. Description Including Proper Shipping Name, Hazardous Class, and ID Number (UN/NA)*

For each row enter a sequential number under Item 27b that corresponds to the order of waste codes from one continuation sheet to the next, to reflect the total number of wastes being shipped. Refer to instructions for Item 9 of the manifest for the information to be entered.

Item 28. *Containers (No. And Type)*

Refer to the instructions for Item 10 of the manifest for information to be entered.

Item 29. *Total Quantity*

Refer to the instructions for Item 11 of the manifest form.

Item 30. *Units of Measure (Weight/Volume)*

Refer to the instructions for Item 12 of the manifest form.

Item 31. *Waste Codes*

Refer to the instructions for Item 13 of the manifest form.

Item 32. *Special Handling Instructions and Additional Information*

Refer to the instructions for Item 14 of the manifest form.

Transporters

Item 33. *Transporter—Acknowledgment of Receipt of Materials*

Enter the same number of the Transporter as identified in Item 25. Enter also the name of the person accepting the waste on behalf of the Transporter (Company Name) identified in Item 25. That person must acknowledge acceptance of the waste described on the Manifest by signing and entering the date of receipt.

Item 34. *Transporter—Acknowledgment of Receipt of Materials*

Enter the same number of the Transporter as identified in Item 26. Enter also the name of the person accepting the waste on behalf of the Transporter (Company Name) identified in Item 26. That person must acknowledge acceptance of the waste described on the Manifest by signing and entering the date of receipt.

Owner and Operators of Treatment, Storage, or Disposal Facilities

Item 35. *Discrepancy Indication Space*

Refer to Item 18. This space may be used to more fully describe information on discrepancies identified in Item 18a of the manifest form.

Item 36. *Hazardous Waste Report Management Method Codes*

For each field here, enter the sequential number that corresponds to the waste materials described under Item 27, and enter the appropriate process code that describes how the materials will be processed when received. If additional continuation sheets are attached, continue numbering the waste materials and process code fields sequentially, and enter on each sheet the process codes corresponding to the waste materials identified on that sheet.

[49 FR 10501, Mar. 20, 1984, as amended at 51 FR 28685, Aug. 8, 1986; 51 FR 35192, Oct. 1, 1986; 53 FR 45091, Nov. 8, 1988; 62 FR 1834, Jan. 14, 1997; 70 FR 10818, Mar. 4, 2005; 70 FR 35037, June 16, 2005]

Please print or type. (Form designed for use on elite (12-pitch) typewriter.)

Form Approved. OMB No. 2050-0039

UNIFORM HAZARDOUS WASTE MANIFEST (Continuation Sheet)	21. Generator ID Number	22. Page	**23. Manifest Tracking Number**

GENERATOR

24. Generator's Name

25. Transporter ______ Company Name | U.S. EPA ID Number

26. Transporter ______ Company Name | U.S. EPA ID Number

27a. HM	27b. U.S. DOT Description (including Proper Shipping Name, Hazard Class, ID Number, and Packing Group (if any))	28. Containers No.	28. Containers Type	29. Total Quantity	30. Unit Wt./Vol.	31. Waste Codes

32. Special Handling Instructions and Additional Information

TRANSPORTER

33. Transporter ______ Acknowledgment of Receipt of Materials
Printed/Typed Name | Signature | Month | Day | Year

34. Transporter ______ Acknowledgment of Receipt of Materials
Printed/Typed Name | Signature | Month | Day | Year

DESIGNATED FACILITY

35. Discrepancy

36. Hazardous Waste Report Management Method Codes (i.e., codes for hazardous waste treatment, disposal, and recycling systems)

EPA Form 8700-22A (Rev. 3-05) Previous editions are obsolete.

DESIGNATED FACILITY TO DESTINATION STATE (IF REQUIRED)

PART 263—STANDARDS APPLICABLE TO TRANSPORTERS OF HAZARDOUS WASTE

Authority: 42 U.S.C. 6906, 6912, 6922-6925, 6937, and 6938.

Source: 45 FR 33151, May 19, 1980, unless otherwise noted.

Subpart A—General

§263.10 Scope.

(a) These regulations establish standards which apply to persons transporting hazardous waste within the United States if the transportation requires a manifest under 40 CFR part 262. 📖 6.6, 14.4.11.3

Note: The regulations set forth in parts 262 and 263 establish the responsibilities of generators and transporters of hazardous waste in the handling, transportation, and management of that waste. In these regulations, EPA has expressly adopted certain regulations of the Department of Transportation (DOT) governing the transportation of hazardous materials. These regulations concern, among other things, labeling, marking, placarding, using proper containers, and reporting discharges. EPA has expressly adopted these regulations in order to satisfy its statutory obligation to promulgate regulations which are necessary to protect human health and the environment in the transportation of hazardous waste. EPA's adoption of these DOT regulations ensures consistency with the requirements of DOT and thus avoids the establishment of duplicative or conflicting requirements with respect to these matters. These EPA regulations which apply to both interstate and intrastate transportation of hazardous waste are enforceable by EPA.

DOT has revised its hazardous materials transportation regulations in order to encompass the transportation of hazardous waste and to regulate intrastate, as well as interstate, transportation of hazardous waste. Transporters of hazardous waste are cautioned that DOT's regulations are fully applicable to their activities and enforceable by DOT. These DOT regulations are codified in title 49, Code of Federal Regulations, subchapter C.

EPA and DOT worked together to develop standards for transporters of hazardous waste in order to avoid conflicting requirements. Except for transporters of bulk shipments of hazardous waste by water, a transporter who meets all applicable requirements of 49 CFR parts 171 through 179 and the requirements of 40 CFR 263.11 and 263.31 will be deemed in compliance with this part. Regardless of DOT's action, EPA retains its authority to enforce these regulations.

(b) These regulations do not apply to on-site transportation of hazardous waste by generators or by owners or operators of permitted hazardous waste management facilities.

(c) A transporter of hazardous waste must also comply with 40 CFR part 262, Standards Applicable to Generators of Hazardous Waste, if he: 📖 6.3.3

(1) Transports hazardous waste into the United States from abroad; or 📖 6.6.8

(2) Mixes hazardous wastes of different DOT shipping descriptions by placing them into a single container. 📖 7.1.2.1

(d) A transporter of hazardous waste subject to the Federal manifesting requirements of 40 CFR part 262, or subject to the waste management standards of 40 CFR part 273, or subject to State requirements analogous to 40 CFR part 273, that is being imported from or exported to any of the countries listed in 40 CFR 262.58(a)(1) for purposes of recovery is subject to this Subpart and to all other relevant requirements of subpart H of 40 CFR part 262, including, but not limited to, 40 CFR 262.84 for tracking documents.

(e) The regulations in this part do not apply to transportation during an explosives or munitions emergency response, conducted in accordance with 40 CFR 264.1(g)(8)(i)(D) or (iv) or 265.1(c)(11)(i)(D) or (iv), and 270.1(c)(3)(i)(D) or (iii).

(f) Section 266.203 of this chapter identifies how the requirements of this part apply to military munitions classified as solid waste under 40 CFR 266.202.

[45 FR 33151, May 19, 1980, as amended at 45 FR 86968, Dec. 31, 1980; 61 FR 16314, Apr. 12, 1996; 62 FR 6651, Feb. 12, 1997]

§263.11 EPA identification number.

(a) A transporter must not transport hazardous wastes without having received an EPA identification number from the Administrator.

(b) A transporter who has not received an EPA identification number may obtain one by applying to the Administrator using EPA Form 8700-12. Upon receiving the request, the Administrator will assign an EPA identification number to the transporter.

§263.12 Transfer facility requirements. 📖 6.3.3, 6.6.3.3.1

A transporter who stores manifested shipments of hazardous waste in containers meeting the requirements of §262.30 at a transfer facility for a period of ten days or less is not subject to regulation under parts 270, 264, 265, and 268 of this chapter with respect to the storage of those wastes.

[45 FR 86968, Dec. 31, 1980, as amended at 48 FR 14294, Apr. 1, 1983; 51 FR 40637, Nov. 7, 1986]

Subpart B—Compliance With the Manifest System and Recordkeeping

§263.20 The manifest system. 6.6

(a)(1) *Manifest requirement.* A transporter may not accept hazardous waste from a generator unless the transporter is also provided with a manifest signed in accordance with the requirements of §262.23.

(2) *Exports.* In the case of exports other than those subject to subpart H of 40 CFR part 262, a transporter may not accept such waste from a primary exporter or other person if he knows the shipment does not conform to the EPA Acknowledgment of Consent; and unless, in addition to a manifest signed by the generator as provided in this section, the transporter shall also be provided with an EPA Acknowledgment of Consent which, except for shipments by rail, is attached to the manifest (or shipping paper for exports by water (bulk shipment)). For exports of hazardous waste subject to the requirements of subpart H of 40 CFR part 262, a transporter may not accept hazardous waste without a tracking document that includes all information required by 40 CFR 262.84.

(3) *Compliance Date for Form Revisions.* The revised Manifest form and procedures in 40 CFR 260.10, 261.7, 263.20, and 263.21, shall not apply until September 5, 2006. The Manifest form and procedures in 40 CFR 260.10, 261.7, 263.20, and 263.21, contained in the 40 CFR, parts 260 to 265, edition revised as of July 1, 2004, shall be applicable until September 5, 2006.

(b) Before transporting the hazardous waste, the transporter must sign and date the manifest acknowledging acceptance of the hazardous waste from the generator. The transporter must return a signed copy to the generator before leaving the generator's property.

(c) The transporter must ensure that the manifest accompanies the hazardous waste. In the case of exports, the transporter must ensure that a copy of the EPA Acknowledgment of Consent also accompanies the hazardous waste.

(d) A transporter who delivers a hazardous waste to another transporter or to the designated facility must:

(1) Obtain the date of delivery and the handwritten signature of that transporter or of the owner or operator of the designated facility on the manifest; and

(2) Retain one copy of the manifest in accordance with §263.22; and

(3) Give the remaining copies of the manifest to the accepting transporter or designated facility.

(e) The requirements of paragraphs (c), (d) and (f) of this section do not apply to water (bulk shipment) transporters if:

(1) The hazardous waste is delivered by water (bulk shipment) to the designated facility; and

(2) A shipping paper containing all the information required on the manifest (excluding the EPA identification numbers, generator certification, and signatures) and, for exports, an EPA Acknowledgment of Consent accompanies the hazardous waste; and

(3) The delivering transporter obtains the date of delivery and handwritten signature of the owner or operator of the designated facility on either the manifest or the shipping paper; and

(4) The person delivering the hazardous waste to the initial water (bulk shipment) transporter obtains the date of delivery and signature of the water (bulk shipment) transporter on the manifest and forwards it to the designated facility; and

(5) A copy of the shipping paper or manifest is retained by each water (bulk shipment) transporter in accordance with §263.22.

(f) For shipments involving rail transportation, the requirements of paragraphs (c), (d) and (e) do not apply and the following requirements do apply: 6.6.6

(1) When accepting hazardous waste from a non-rail transporter, the initial rail transporter must:

(i) Sign and date the manifest acknowledging acceptance of the hazardous waste;

(ii) Return a signed copy of the manifest to the non-rail transporter;

(iii) Forward at least three copies of the manifest to:

(A) The next non-rail transporter, if any; or,

(B) The designated facility, if the shipment is delivered to that facility by rail; or

(C) The last rail transporter designated to handle the waste in the United States;

(iv) Retain one copy of the manifest and rail shipping paper in accordance with §263.22.

(2) Rail transporters must ensure that a shipping paper containing all the information required on the manifest (excluding the EPA identification numbers, generator certification, and signatures) and, for exports an EPA

Acknowledgment of Consent accompanies the hazardous waste at all times.

Note: Intermediate rail transporters are not required to sign either the manifest or shipping paper.

(3) When delivering hazardous waste to the designated facility, a rail transporter must:

(i) Obtain the date of delivery and handwritten signature of the owner or operator of the designated facility on the manifest or the shipping paper (if the manifest has not been received by the facility); and

(ii) Retain a copy of the manifest or signed shipping paper in accordance with §263.22.

(4) When delivering hazardous waste to a non-rail transporter a rail transporter must:

(i) Obtain the date of delivery and the handwritten signature of the next non-rail transporter on the manifest; and

(ii) Retain a copy of the manifest in accordance with §263.22.

(5) Before accepting hazardous waste from a rail transporter, a non-rail transporter must sign and date the manifest and provide a copy to the rail transporter.

(g) Transporters who transport hazardous waste out of the United States must:

(1) Sign and date the manifest in the International Shipments block to indicate the date that the shipment left the United States;

(2) Retain one copy in accordance with §263.22(d);

(3) Return a signed copy of the manifest to the generator; and

(4) Give a copy of the manifest to a U.S. Customs official at the point of departure from the United States.

(h) A transporter transporting hazardous waste from a generator who generates greater than 100 kilograms but less than 1000 kilograms of hazardous waste in a calendar month need not comply with the requirements of this section or those of §263.22 provided that:

(1) The waste is being transported pursuant to a reclamation agreement as provided for in §262.20(e);

(2) The transporter records, on a log or shipping paper, the following information for each shipment:

(i) The name, address, and U.S. EPA Identification Number of the generator of the waste;

(ii) The quantity of waste accepted;

(iii) All DOT-required shipping information;

(iv) The date the waste is accepted; and

(3) The transporter carries this record when transporting waste to the reclamation facility; and

(4) The transporter retains these records for a period of at least three years after termination or expiration of the agreement.

[45 FR 33151, May 19, 1980, as amended at 45 FR 86973, Dec. 31, 1980; 51 FR 10176, Mar. 24, 1986; 51 FR 28685, Aug. 8, 1986; 61 FR 16315, Apr. 12, 1996; 70 FR 10821, Mar. 4, 2005]

§263.21 Compliance with the manifest.

📖 6.6

(a) The transporter must deliver the entire quantity of hazardous waste which he has accepted from a generator or a transporter to:

(1) The designated facility listed on the manifest; or

(2) The alternate designated facility, if the hazardous waste cannot be delivered to the designated facility because an emergency prevents delivery; or

(3) The next designated transporter; or

(4) The place outside the United States designated by the generator.

(b)(1) If the hazardous waste cannot be delivered in accordance with paragraph (a) of this section because of an emergency condition other than rejection of the waste by the designated facility, then the transporter must contact the generator for further directions and must revise the manifest according to the generator's instructions. 📖 6.6.3.3

(2) If hazardous waste is rejected by the designated facility while the transporter is on the facility's premises, then the transporter must obtain the following:

(i) For a partial load rejection or for regulated quantities of container residues, a copy of the original manifest that includes the facility's date and signature, and the Manifest Tracking Number of the new manifest that will accompany the shipment, and a description of the partial rejection or container residue in the discrepancy block of the original manifest. The transporter must retain a copy of this manifest in accordance with §263.22, and give the remaining copies of the original manifest to the rejecting designated facility. If the transporter is forwarding the rejected part of the shipment or a regulated container residue to an alternate facility or returning it to the generator, the transporter must obtain a new manifest to accompany the shipment, and the new manifest must include all of the information required in 40 CFR 264.72(e)(1) through (6) or (f)(1) through (6) or 40 CFR 265.72(e)(1) through (6) or (f)(1) through (6).

(ii) For a full load rejection that will be taken back by the transporter, a copy of the original manifest that includes the rejecting facility's signature and date attesting to the rejection, the description of the rejection in the discrepancy block of the manifest, and the name, address, phone number, and Identification Number for the alternate facility or generator to whom the shipment must be delivered. The transporter must retain a copy of the manifest in accordance with §263.22, and give a copy of the manifest containing this information to the rejecting designated facility. If the original manifest is not used, then the transporter must obtain a new manifest for the shipment and comply with 40 CFR 264.72(e)(1) through (6) or 40 CFR 265.72(e)(1) through (6).

[45 FR 33151, May 19, 1980, as amended at 70 FR 10821, Mar. 4, 2005]

§263.22 Recordkeeping.

(a) A transporter of hazardous waste must keep a copy of the manifest signed by the generator, himself, and the next designated transporter or the owner or operator of the designated facility for a period of three years from the date the hazardous waste was accepted by the initial transporter.

(b) For shipments delivered to the designated facility by water (bulk shipment), each water (bulk shipment) transporter must retain a copy of the shipping paper containing all the information required in §263.20(e)(2) for a period of three years from the date the hazardous waste was accepted by the initial transporter.

(c) For shipments of hazardous waste by rail within the United States:

(1) The initial rail transporter must keep a copy of the manifest and shipping paper with all the information required in §263.20(f)(2) for a period of three years from the date the hazardous waste was accepted by the initial transporter; and

(2) The final rail transporter must keep a copy of the signed manifest (or the shipping paper if signed by the designated facility in lieu of the manifest) for a period of three years from the date the hazardous waste was accepted by the initial transporter.

Note: Intermediate rail transporters are not required to keep records pursuant to these regulations.

(d) A transporter who transports hazardous waste out of the United States must keep a copy of the manifest indicating that the hazardous waste left the United States for a period of three years from the date the hazardous waste was accepted by the initial transporter.

(e) The periods of retention referred to in this Section are extended automatically during the course of any unresolved enforcement action regarding the regulated activity or as requested by the Administrator.

[45 FR 33151, May 19, 1980, as amended at 45 FR 86973, Dec. 31, 1980]

Subpart C—Hazardous Waste Discharges

§263.30 Immediate action.

14.4.2.3

(a) In the event of a discharge of hazardous waste during transportation, the transporter must take appropriate immediate action to protect human health and the environment (*e.g.*, notify local authorities, dike the discharge area).

(b) If a discharge of hazardous waste occurs during transportation and an official (State or local government or a Federal Agency) acting within the scope of his official responsibilities determines that immediate removal of the waste is necessary to protect human health or the environment, that official may authorize the removal of the waste by transporters who do not have EPA identification numbers and without the preparation of a manifest.

(c) An air, rail, highway, or water transporter who has discharged hazardous waste must: 14.4.10

(1) Give notice, if required by 49 CFR 171.15, to the National Response Center (800-424-8802 or 202-426-2675); and

(2) Report in writing as required by 49 CFR 171.16 to the Director, Office of Hazardous Materials Regulations, Materials Transportation Bureau, Department of Transportation, Washington, DC 20590.

(d) A water (bulk shipment) transporter who has discharged hazardous waste must give the same notice as required by 33 CFR 153.203 for oil and hazardous substances.

§263.31 Discharge clean up.

A transporter must clean up any hazardous waste discharge that occurs during transportation or take such action as may be required or approved by Federal, State, or local officials so that the hazardous waste discharge no longer presents a hazard to human health or the environment. 14.4.2.3

PART 264—STANDARDS FOR OWNERS AND OPERATORS OF HAZARDOUS WASTE TREATMENT, STORAGE, AND DISPOSAL FACILITIES

Subpart J—Tank Systems

Subpart K—Surface Impoundments

Subpart L—Waste Piles

Subpart M—Land Treatment

Subpart N—Landfills

Subpart O—Incinerators

Subparts P–R [Reserved]

Subpart S—Special Provisions for Cleanup

Authority: 42 U.S.C. 6905, 6912(a), 6924, and 6925.

Source: 45 FR 33221, May 19, 1980, unless otherwise noted.

Subpart A—General

§264.1 Purpose, scope and applicability.

(a) The purpose of this part is to establish minimum national standards which define the acceptable management of hazardous waste.

(b) The standards in this part apply to owners and operators of all facilities which treat, store, or dispose of hazardous waste, except as specifically provided otherwise in this part or part 261 of this chapter. 📖 14.2.1

(c) The requirements of this part apply to a person disposing of hazardous waste by means of ocean disposal subject to a permit issued under the Marine Protection, Research, and Sanctuaries Act only to the extent they are included in a RCRA permit by rule granted to such a person under part 270 of this chapter.

[*Comment:* These part 264 regulations do apply to the treatment or storage of hazardous waste before it is loaded onto an ocean vessel for incineration or disposal at sea.]

(d) The requirements of this part apply to a person disposing of hazardous waste by means of underground injection subject to a permit issued under an Underground Injection Control (UIC) program approved or promulgated under the Safe Drinking Water Act only to the extent they are required by §144.14 of this chapter.

[*Comment:* These part 264 regulations do apply to the above-ground treatment or storage of hazardous waste before it is injected underground.]

(e) The requirements of this part apply to the owner or operator of a POTW which treats, stores, or disposes of hazardous waste only to the extent they are included in a RCRA permit by rule granted to such a person under part 270 of this chapter.

(f) The requirements of this part do not apply to a person who treats, stores, or disposes of hazardous waste in a State with a RCRA hazardous waste program authorized under subpart A of part 271 of this chapter, or in a State authorized under subpart B of part 271 of this chapter for the component or components of Phase II interim authorization which correspond to the person's treatment, storage or disposal processes; except that this part will apply:

(1) As stated in paragraph (d) of this section, if the authorized State RCRA program does not cover disposal of hazardous waste by means of underground injection; and

(2) To a person who treats, stores or disposes of hazardous waste in a State authorized under subpart A of part 271 of this chapter, at a facility which was not covered by standards under this part when the State obtained authorization, and for which EPA promulgates standards under this part after the State is authorized. This paragraph will only apply until the State is authorized to permit such facilities under subpart A of part 271 of this chapter.

(3) To a person who treats, stores, or disposes of hazardous waste in a State which is authorized under subpart A or B of part 271 of this chapter if the State has not been authorized to carry out the requirements and prohibitions applicable to the treatment, storage, or disposal of hazardous waste at his facility which are imposed pursuant to the Hazardous and Solid Waste Amendments of 1984. The requirements and prohibitions that are applicable until a State receives authorization to carry them out include all Federal program requirements identified in §271.1(j).

(g) The requirements of this part do not apply to:

(1) The owner or operator of a facility permitted, licensed, or registered by a State to manage municipal or industrial solid waste, if the only hazardous waste the facility treats, stores, or disposes of is excluded from regulation under this part by §261.5 of this chapter;

(2) The owner or operator of a facility managing recyclable materials described in §261.6 (a)(2), (3), and (4) of this chapter (except to the extent they are referred to in part 279 or subparts C, F, G, or H of part 266 of this chapter). 📖 7.4

(3) A generator accumulating waste on-site in compliance with §262.34 of this chapter; 📖 6.3, 7.3

(4) A farmer disposing of waste pesticides from his own use in compliance with §262.70 of this chapter; or

(5) The owner or operator of a totally enclosed treatment facility, as defined in §260.10. 📖 7.5.2

(6) The owner or operator of an elementary neutralization unit or a wastewater treatment unit as defined in §260.10 of this chapter, provided that if the owner or operator is diluting hazardous ignitable (D001) wastes (other than the D001 High TOC Subcategory defined in §268.40 of this chapter, Table Treatment Standards for Hazardous Wastes), or reactive (D003) waste, to remove the characteristic before land disposal, the owner/operator must comply with the requirements set out in §264.17(b). 📖 5.2.3.7, 7.2, 7.5.1

(7) [Reserved]

(8)(i) Except as provided in paragraph (g)(8)(ii) of this section, a person engaged in treatment or containment activities during immediate response to any of the following situations: 📖 7.5.4, 10.1.2.4, 10.2.1, 14.4.2.5

(A) A discharge of a hazardous waste;

(B) An imminent and substantial threat of a discharge of hazardous waste;

(C) A discharge of a material which, when discharged, becomes a hazardous waste.

(D) An immediate threat to human health, public safety, property, or the environment, from the known or suspected presence of military munitions, other explosive material, or an explosive device, as determined by an explosive or munitions emergency response specialist as defined in 40 CFR 260.10.

(ii) An owner or operator of a facility otherwise regulated by this part must comply with all applicable requirements of subparts C and D.

(iii) Any person who is covered by paragraph (g)(8)(i) of this section and who continues or initiates hazardous waste treatment or containment activities after the immediate response is over is subject to all applicable requirements of this part and parts 122 through 124 of this chapter for those activities.

(iv) In the case of an explosives or munitions emergency response, if a Federal, State, Tribal or local official acting within the scope of his or her official responsibilities, or an explosives or munitions emergency response specialist, determines that immediate removal of the material or waste is necessary to protect human health or the environment, that official or specialist may authorize the removal of the material or waste by transporters who do not have EPA identification numbers and without the preparation of a manifest. In the case of emergencies involving military munitions, the responding military emergency response specialist's organizational unit must retain records for three years identifying the dates of the response, the responsible persons responding, the type and description of material addressed, and its disposition.

(9) A transporter storing manifested shipments of hazardous waste in containers meeting the requirements of 40 CFR 262.30 at a transfer facility for a period of ten days or less. 📖 6.6.3.3.1

(10) The addition of absorbent material to waste in a container (as defined in §260.10 of this chapter) or the addition of waste to absorbent material in a container, provided that these actions occur at the time waste is first placed in the container; and §§264.17(b), 264.171, and 264.172 are complied with. 📖 7.5.3

(11) Universal waste handlers and universal waste transporters (as defined in 40 CFR 260.10) handling the wastes listed below. These handlers are subject to regulation under 40 CFR part 273, when handling the below listed universal wastes. 📖 8.3, 8.4.1

(i) Batteries as described in 40 CFR 273.2;

(ii) Pesticides as described in §273.3 of this chapter;

(iii) Mercury-containing equipment as described in §273.4 of this chapter; and

(iv) Lamps as described in §273.5 of this chapter.

(12) A New York State Utility central collection facility consolidating hazardous waste in accordance with 40 CFR 262.90.

(h) The requirements of this part apply to owners or operators of all facilities which treat, store, or dispose of hazardous wastes referred to in part 268.

(i) Section 266.205 of this chapter identifies when the requirements of this part apply to the storage of military munitions classified as solid waste under §266.202 of this chapter. The treatment and disposal of hazardous waste military munitions are subject to the applicable permitting, procedural, and technical standards in 40 CFR parts 260 through 270.

(j) The requirements of subparts B, C, and D of this part and §264.101 do not apply to remediation waste management sites. (However, some remediation waste management sites may be a part of a facility that is subject to a traditional RCRA permit because the facility is also treating, storing or disposing of hazardous wastes that are not remediation wastes. In these cases, Subparts B, C, and D of this part, and §264.101 do apply to the facility subject to the traditional RCRA permit.) Instead of the requirements of subparts B, C, and D of this part, owners or operators of remediation waste management sites must:

(1) Obtain an EPA identification number by applying to the Administrator using EPA Form 8700-12;

(2) Obtain a detailed chemical and physical analysis of a representative sample of the hazardous remediation wastes to be managed at the site. At a minimum, the analysis must contain all of the information which must be known to treat, store or dispose of the waste according to this part and part 268 of this chapter, and must be kept accurate and up to date;

(3) Prevent people who are unaware of the danger from entering, and minimize the possibility for unauthorized people or livestock to enter onto the active portion of the remediation waste management site, unless the owner or operator can demonstrate to the Director that:

(i) Physical contact with the waste, structures, or equipment within the active portion of the remediation waste management site will not injure people or livestock who may enter the active portion of the remediation waste management site; and

(ii) Disturbance of the waste or equipment by people or livestock who enter onto the active portion of the remediation waste management site, will not cause a violation of the requirements of this part;

(4) Inspect the remediation waste management site for malfunctions, deterioration, operator errors, and discharges that may be causing, or may lead to, a release of hazardous waste constituents to the environment, or a

threat to human health. The owner or operator must conduct these inspections often enough to identify problems in time to correct them before they harm human health or the environment, and must remedy the problem before it leads to a human health or environmental hazard. Where a hazard is imminent or has already occurred, the owner/operator must take remedial action immediately;

(5) Provide personnel with classroom or on-the-job training on how to perform their duties in a way that ensures the remediation waste management site complies with the requirements of this part, and on how to respond effectively to emergencies;

(6) Take precautions to prevent accidental ignition or reaction of ignitable or reactive waste, and prevent threats to human health and the environment from ignitable, reactive and incompatible waste;

(7) For remediation waste management sites subject to regulation under subparts I through O and subpart X of this part, the owner/operator must design, construct, operate, and maintain a unit within a 100-year floodplain to prevent washout of any hazardous waste by a 100-year flood, unless the owner/operator can meet the demonstration of §264.18(b);

(8) Not place any non-containerized or bulk liquid hazardous waste in any salt dome formation, salt bed formation, underground mine or cave;

(9) Develop and maintain a construction quality assurance program for all surface impoundments, waste piles and landfill units that are required to comply with §§264.221(c) and (d), 264.251(c) and (d), and 264.301(c) and (d) at the remediation waste management site, according to the requirements of §264.19;

(10) Develop and maintain procedures to prevent accidents and a contingency and emergency plan to control accidents that occur. These procedures must address proper design, construction, maintenance, and operation of remediation waste management units at the site. The goal of the plan must be to minimize the possibility of, and the hazards from a fire, explosion, or any unplanned sudden or non-sudden release of hazardous waste or hazardous waste constituents to air, soil, or surface water that could threaten human health or the environment. The plan must explain specifically how to treat, store and dispose of the hazardous remediation waste in question, and must be implemented immediately whenever a fire, explosion, or release of hazardous waste or hazardous waste constituents which could threaten human health or the environment;

(11) Designate at least one employee, either on the facility premises or on call (that is, available to respond to an emergency by reaching the facility quickly), to coordinate all emergency response measures. This emergency coordinator must be thoroughly familiar with all aspects of the facility's contingency plan, all operations and activities at the facility, the location and characteristics of waste handled, the location of all records within the facility, and the facility layout. In addition, this person must have the authority to commit the resources needed to carry out the contingency plan;

(12) Develop, maintain and implement a plan to meet the requirements in paragraphs (j)(2) through (j)(6) and (j)(9) through (j)(10) of this section; and

(13) Maintain records documenting compliance with paragraphs (j)(1) through (j)(12) of this section.

[45 FR 33221, May 19, 1980, as amended at 45 FR 76075, Nov. 17, 1980; 45 FR 86968, Dec. 31, 1980; 46 FR 27480, May 20, 1981; 47 FR 8306, Feb. 25, 1982; 47 FR 32384, July 26, 1982; 48 FR 2511, Jan. 19, 1983; 48 FR 14294, Apr. 1, 1983; 50 FR 665, Jan. 4, 1985; 50 FR 28746, July 15, 1985; 52 FR 21016, June 4, 1987; 53 FR 27165, July 19, 1988; 58 FR 26424, May 3, 1993; 58 FR 29884, May 24, 1993; 59 FR 48042, Sept. 19, 1994; 60 FR 25542, May 11, 1995; 62 FR 6651, Feb. 12, 1997; 63 FR 65938, Nov. 30, 1998; 64 FR 36487, July 6, 1999; 64 FR 37638, July 12, 1999; 70 FR 45520, Aug. 5, 2005; 71 FR 40272, July 14, 2006]

§264.2 [Reserved]

§264.3 Relationship to interim status standards.

A facility owner or operator who has fully complied with the requirements for interim status—as defined in section 3005(e) of RCRA and regulations under §270.70 of this chapter—must comply with the regulations specified in part 265 of this chapter in lieu of the regulations in this part, until final administrative disposition of his permit application is made, except as provided under 40 CFR part 264 subpart S.

[*Comment:* As stated in section 3005(a) of RCRA, after the effective date of regulations under that section, *i.e.*, parts 270 and 124 of this chapter, the treatment, storage, or disposal of hazardous waste is prohibited except in accordance with a permit. Section 3005(e) of RCRA provides for the continued operation of an existing facility which meets certain conditions until final administrative disposition of the owner's or operator's permit application is made.]

[45 FR 33221, May 19, 1980, as amended at 48 FR 14294, Apr. 1, 1983; 58 FR 8683, Feb. 16, 1993]

§264.4 Imminent hazard action.

Notwithstanding any other provisions of these regulations, enforcement actions may be brought pursuant to section 7003 of RCRA.

[45 FR 33221, May 19, 1980, as amended at 71 FR 40272, July 14, 2006]

Subpart B—General Facility Standards

§264.10 Applicability.

(a) The regulations in this subpart apply to owners and operators of all hazardous waste facilities, except as provided in §264.1 and in paragraph (b) of this section.

(b) Section 264.18(b) applies only to facilities subject to regulation under subparts I through O and subpart X of this part.

[46 FR 2848, Jan. 12, 1981, as amended at 52 FR 46963, Dec. 10, 1987]

§264.11 Identification number.

Every facility owner or operator must apply to EPA for an EPA identification number in accordance with the EPA notification procedures (45 FR 12746).

[45 FR 33221, May 19, 1980, as amended at 50 FR 4514, Jan. 31, 1985]

§264.12 Required notices.

(a)(1) The owner or operator of a facility that has arranged to receive hazardous waste from a foreign source must notify the Regional Administrator in writing at least four weeks in advance of the date the waste is expected to arrive at the facility. Notice of subsequent shipments of the same waste from the same foreign source is not required.

(2) The owner or operator of a recovery facility that has arranged to receive hazardous waste subject to 40 CFR part 262, subpart H must provide a copy of the tracking document bearing all required signatures to the notifier, to the Office of Enforcement and Compliance Assurance, Office of Compliance, Enforcement Planning, Targeting and Data Division (2222A), Environmental Protection Agency, 401 M St., SW., Washington, DC 20460; and to the competent authorities of all other concerned countries within three working days of receipt of the shipment. The original of the signed tracking document must be maintained at the facility for at least three years.

(b) The owner or operator of a facility that receives hazardous waste from an off-site source (except where the owner or operator is also the generator) must inform the generator in writing that he has the appropriate permit(s) for, and will accept, the waste the generator is shipping. The owner or operator must keep a copy of this written notice as part of the operating record.

(c) Before transferring ownership or operation of a facility during its operating life, or of a disposal facility during the post-closure care period, the owner or operator must notify the new owner or operator in writing of the requirements of this part and part 270 of this chapter.

[*Comment:* An owner's or operator's failure to notify the new owner or operator of the requirements of this part in no way relieves the new owner or operator of his obligation to comply with all applicable requirements.]

[45 FR 33221, May 19, 1980, as amended at 48 FR 14294, Apr. 1, 1983; 50 FR 4514, Jan. 31, 1985; 61 FR 16315, Apr. 12, 1996]

§264.13 General waste analysis.

18.2.3.2

(a)(1) Before an owner or operator treats, stores, or disposes of any hazardous wastes, or nonhazardous wastes if applicable under §264.113(d), he must obtain a detailed chemical and physical analysis of a representative sample of the wastes. At a minimum, the analysis must contain all the information which must be known to treat, store, or dispose of the waste in accordance with this part and part 268 of this chapter.

(2) The analysis may include data developed under part 261 of this chapter, and existing published or documented data on the hazardous waste or on hazardous waste generated from similar processes.

[*Comment:* For example, the facility's records of analyses performed on the waste before the effective date of these regulations, or studies conducted on hazardous waste generated from processes similar to that which generated the waste to be managed at the facility, may be included in the data base required to comply with paragraph (a)(1) of this section. The owner or operator of an off-site facility may arrange for the generator of the hazardous waste to supply part of the information required by paragraph (a)(1) of this section, except as otherwise specified in 40 CFR 268.7 (b) and (c). If the generator does not supply the information, and the owner or operator chooses to accept a hazardous waste, the owner or operator is responsible for obtaining the information required to comply with this section.]

(3) The analysis must be repeated as necessary to ensure that it is accurate and up to date. At a minimum, the analysis must be repeated:

(i) When the owner or operator is notified, or has reason to believe, that the process or operation generating the hazardous wastes, or non-hazardous wastes if applicable under §264.113(d), has changed; and

(ii) For off-site facilities, when the results of the inspection required in paragraph (a)(4) of this section indicate that the hazardous waste received at the facility does not match the waste designated on the accompanying manifest or shipping paper.

(4) The owner or operator of an off-site facility must inspect and, if necessary, analyze each hazardous waste movement received at the facility to determine whether it matches the identity of the waste specified on the accompanying manifest or shipping paper. 18.2.3.2.1

(b) The owner or operator must develop and follow a written waste analysis plan which describes the procedures which he will carry out to comply with paragraph (a) of this section. He must keep this plan at the facility. At a minimum, the plan must specify:

(1) The parameters for which each hazardous waste, or non-hazardous waste if applicable under §264.113(d), will be analyzed and the rationale for the selection of these parameters (*i.e.*, how analysis for these parameters will provide sufficient information on the waste's properties to comply with paragraph (a) of this section);

(2) The test methods which will be used to test for these parameters;

(3) The sampling method which will be used to obtain a representative sample of the waste to be analyzed. A representative sample may be obtained using either:

(i) One of the sampling methods described in appendix I of part 261 of this chapter; or

(ii) An equivalent sampling method.

[*Comment:* See §260.21 of this chapter for related discussion.]

(4) The frequency with which the initial analysis of the waste will be reviewed or repeated to ensure that the analysis is accurate and up to date; and

(5) For off-site facilities, the waste analyses that hazardous waste generators have agreed to supply.

(6) Where applicable, the methods that will be used to meet the additional waste analysis requirements for specific waste management methods as specified in §§264.17, 264.314, 264.341, 264.1034(d), 264.1063(d), 264.1083, and 268.7 of this chapter.

(7) For surface impoundments exempted from land disposal restrictions under §268.4(a), the procedures and schedules for:

(i) The sampling of impoundment contents;

(ii) The analysis of test data; and,

(iii) The annual removal of residues which are not delisted under §260.22 of this chapter or which exhibit a characteristic of hazardous waste and either:

(A) Do not meet applicable treatment standards of part 268, subpart D; or

(B) Where no treatment standards have been established:

(*1*) Such residues are prohibited from land disposal under §268.32 or RCRA section 3004(d); or

(*2*) Such residues are prohibited from land disposal under §268.33(f).

Publisher's Note: The section referenced above, §268.33(f), is no longer in the RCRA regulations.

(8) For owners and operators seeking an exemption to the air emission standards of subpart CC in accordance with §264.1082—

(i) If direct measurement is used for the waste determination, the procedures and schedules for waste sampling and analysis, and the results of the analysis of test data to verify the exemption.

(ii) If knowledge of the waste is used for the waste determination, any information prepared by the facility owner or operator or by the generator of the hazardous waste, if the waste is received from off-site, that is used as the basis for knowledge of the waste.

(c) For off-site facilities, the waste analysis plan required in paragraph (b) of this section must also specify the procedures which will be used to inspect and, if necessary, analyze each movement of hazardous waste received at the facility to ensure that it matches the identity of the waste designated on the accompanying manifest or shipping paper. At a minimum, the plan must describe: 📖 18.2.3.2.1

(1) The procedures which will be used to determine the identity of each movement of waste managed at the facility; and

(2) The sampling method which will be used to obtain a representative sample of the waste to be identified, if the identification method includes sampling.

(3) The procedures that the owner or operator of an off-site landfill receiving containerized hazardous waste will use to determine whether a hazardous waste generator or treater has added a biodegradable sorbent to the waste in the container.

[*Comment:* Part 270 of this chapter requires that the waste analysis plan be submitted with part B of the permit application.]

[45 FR 33221, May 19, 1980, as amended at 46 FR 2848, Jan. 12, 1981; 50 FR 4514, Jan. 31, 1985; 51 FR 40637, Nov. 7, 1986; 53 FR 31211, Aug. 17, 1988; 54 FR 33394, Aug. 14, 1989; 55 FR 22685, June 1, 1990; 55 FR 25494, June 21, 1990; 57 FR 8088, Mar. 6, 1992; 57 FR 54460, Nov. 18, 1992; 59 FR 62926, Dec. 6, 1994; 61 FR 4911, Feb. 9, 1996; 71 FR 40272, July 14, 2006]

§264.14 Security.

(a) The owner or operator must prevent the unknowing entry, and minimize the possibility for the unauthorized entry, of persons or livestock onto the active portion of his facility, unless he can demonstrate to the Regional Administrator that:

(1) Physical contact with the waste, structures, or equipment within the active portion of the facility will not injure unknowing or unauthorized persons or livestock which may enter the active portion of a facility; and

(2) Disturbance of the waste or equipment, by the unknowing or unauthorized entry of persons or livestock onto the active portion of a facility, will not cause a violation of the requirements of this part.

[*Comment:* Part 270 of this chapter requires that an owner or operator who wishes to make the demonstration referred to above must do so with part B of the permit application.]

(b) Unless the owner or operator has made a successful demonstration under paragraphs (a) (1) and (2) of this section, a facility must have:

(1) A 24-hour surveillance system (*e.g.*, television monitoring or surveillance by guards or facility personnel) which continuously monitors and controls entry onto the active portion of the facility; or

(2)(i) An artificial or natural barrier (*e.g.*, a fence in good repair or a fence combined with a cliff), which completely surrounds the active portion of the facility; and

(ii) A means to control entry, at all times, through the gates or other entrances to the active portion of the facility (*e.g.*, an attendant, television monitors, locked entrance, or controlled roadway access to the facility).

[*Comment:* The requirements of paragraph (b) of this section are satisfied if the facility or plant within which the active portion is located itself has a surveillance system, or a barrier and a means to control entry, which complies with the requirements of paragraph (b) (1) or (2) of this section.]

(c) Unless the owner or operator has made a successful demonstration under paragraphs (a) (1) and (2) of this section, a sign with the legend, "Danger—Unauthorized Personnel Keep Out", must be posted at each entrance to the active portion of a facility, and at other locations, in sufficient numbers to be seen from any approach to this active portion. The legend must be written in English and in any other language predominant in the area surrounding the facility (*e.g.*, facilities in counties bordering the Canadian province of Quebec must post signs in French; facilities in counties bordering Mexico must post signs in Spanish), and must be legible from a distance of at least 25 feet. Existing signs with a legend other than "Danger—Unauthorized Personnel Keep Out" may be used if the legend on the sign indicates that only authorized personnel are allowed to enter the active portion, and that entry onto the active portion can be dangerous.

[*Comment:* See §264.117(b) for discussion of security requirements at disposal facilities during the post-closure care period.]

[45 FR 33221, May 19, 1980, as amended at 46 FR 2848, Jan. 12, 1981; 48 FR 14294, Apr. 1, 1983; 50 FR 4514, Jan. 31, 1985]

§264.15 General inspection requirements.

(a) The owner or operator must inspect his facility for malfunctions and deterioration, operator errors, and discharges which may be causing—or may lead to—(1) release of hazardous waste constituents to the environment or (2) a threat to human health. The owner or operator must conduct these inspections often enough to identify problems in time to correct them before they harm human health or the environment.

(b)(1) The owner or operator must develop and follow a written schedule for inspecting monitoring equipment, safety and emergency equipment, security devices, and operating and structural equipment (such as dikes and sump pumps) that are important to preventing, detecting, or responding to environmental or human health hazards.

(2) He must keep this schedule at the facility.

(3) The schedule must identify the types of problems (*e.g.*, malfunctions or deterioration) which are to be looked for during the inspection (*e.g.*, inoperative sump pump, leaking fitting, eroding dike, etc.).

(4) The frequency of inspection may vary for the items on the schedule. However, the frequency should be based on the rate of deterioration of the equipment and the probability of an environmental or human health incident if the deterioration, malfunction, or operator error goes undetected between inspections. Areas subject to spills, such as loading and unloading areas, must be inspected daily when in use, except for Performance Track member facilities, that must inspect at least once each month, upon approval by the Director, as described in paragraph (b)(5) of this section. At a minimum, the inspection schedule must include the items and frequencies called for in §§264.174, 264.193, 264.195, 264.226, 264.254, 264.278, 264.303, 264.347, 264.602, 264.1033, 264.1052, 264.1053, 264.1058, and 264.1083 through 264.1089 of this part, where applicable.

[*Comment:* Part 270 of this chapter requires the inspection schedule to be submitted with part B of the permit application. EPA will evaluate the schedule along with the rest of the application to ensure that it adequately protects human health and the environment. As part of this review, EPA may modify or amend the schedule as may be necessary.]

(5) Performance Track member facilities that choose to reduce their inspection frequency must:

(i) Submit a request for a Class I permit modification with prior approval to the Director. The modification request must identify the facility as a member of the National Environmental Performance Track Program and identify the management units for reduced inspections and the proposed frequency of inspections. The modification request must also specify, in writing, that the reduced inspection frequency will apply for as long as the facility is a Performance Track member facility, and that within seven calendar days of ceasing to be a Performance Track member, the facility will revert to the non-Performance Track inspection frequency. Inspections must be conducted at least once each month.

(ii) Within 60 days, the Director will notify the Performance Track member facility, in writing, if the request is approved, denied, or if an extension to the 60-day deadline is needed. This notice must be placed in the facility's operating record. The Performance Track member facility should consider the application approved if the Director does not: deny the application; or notify the Performance Track member facility of an extension to the 60-day deadline. In these situations, the Performance Track member facility must adhere to the revised inspection schedule outlined in its request for a Class 1 permit modification and keep a copy of the application in the facility's operating record.

(iii) Any Performance Track member facility that discontinues their membership or is terminated from the program must immediately notify the Director of their change in status. The facility must place in its operating record a dated copy of this notification and revert back to the non-Performance Track inspection frequencies within seven calendar days.

(c) The owner or operator must remedy any deterioration or malfunction of equipment or structures which the inspection reveals on a schedule which ensures that the problem does not lead to an environmental or human health hazard. Where a hazard is imminent or has already occurred, remedial action must be taken immediately.

(d) The owner or operator must record inspections in an inspection log or summary. He must keep these records for at least three years from the date of inspection. At a minimum, these records must include the date and time of the inspection, the name of the inspector, a notation of the observations made, and the date and nature of any repairs or other remedial actions.

[45 FR 33221, May 19, 1980, as amended at 48 FR 14294, Apr. 1, 1983; 50 FR 4514, Jan. 31, 1985; 57 FR 3486, Jan. 29, 1992; 59 FR 62926, Dec. 6, 1994; 62 FR 64656, Dec. 8, 1997; 71 FR 16903, Apr. 4, 2006]

§264.16 Personnel training.

📖 6.4.4, 16.1.1

(a)(1) Facility personnel must successfully complete a program of classroom instruction or on-the-job training that teaches them to perform their duties in a way that ensures the facility's compliance with the requirements of this part. The owner or operator must ensure that this program includes all the elements described in the document required under paragraph (d)(3) of this section. 📖 6.4.1.1, 6.5.4

[*Comment:* Part 270 of this chapter requires that owners and operators submit with part B of the RCRA permit application, an outline of the training program used (or to be used) at the facility and a brief description of how the training program is designed to meet actual job tasks.]

(2) This program must be directed by a person trained in hazardous waste management procedures, and must include instruction which teaches facility personnel hazardous waste management procedures (including contingency plan implementation) relevant to the positions in which they are employed. 📖 6.4.1.3–4

(3) At a minimum, the training program must be designed to ensure that facility personnel are able to respond effectively to emergencies by familiarizing them with emergency procedures, emergency equipment, and emergency systems, including, where applicable: 📖 6.4.1.3, 14.4.11.2

(i) Procedures for using, inspecting, repairing, and replacing facility emergency and monitoring equipment;

(ii) Key parameters for automatic waste feed cut-off systems;

(iii) Communications or alarm systems;

(iv) Response to fires or explosions;

(v) Response to ground-water contamination incidents; and

(vi) Shutdown of operations.

(4) For facility employees that receive emergency response training pursuant to Occupational Safety and Health Administration (OSHA) regulations 29 CFR 1910.120(p)(8) and 1910.120(q), the facility is not required to provide separate emergency response training pursuant to this section, provided that the overall facility training meets all the requirements of this section.

(b) Facility personnel must successfully complete the program required in paragraph (a) of this section within six months after the effective date of these regulations or six months after the date of their employment or assignment to a facility, or to a new position at a facility, whichever is later. Employees hired after the effective date of these regulations must not work in unsupervised positions until they have completed the training requirements of paragraph (a) of this section. 📖 6.4.1.2

(c) Facility personnel must take part in an annual review of the initial training required in paragraph (a) of this section. 📖 6.4.1.2

(d) The owner or operator must maintain the following documents and records at the facility: 6.4.1.5

(1) The job title for each position at the facility related to hazardous waste management, and the name of the employee filling each job;

(2) A written job description for each position listed under paragraph (d)(1) of this section. This description may be consistent in its degree of specificity with descriptions for other similar positions in the same company location or bargaining unit, but must include the requisite skill, education, or other qualifications, and duties of employees assigned to each position;

(3) A written description of the type and amount of both introductory and continuing training that will be given to each person filling a position listed under paragraph (d)(1) of this section;

(4) Records that document that the training or job experience required under paragraphs (a), (b), and (c) of this section has been given to, and completed by, facility personnel.

(e) Training records on current personnel must be kept until closure of the facility; training records on former employees must be kept for at least three years from the date the employee last worked at the facility. Personnel training records may accompany personnel transferred within the same company. 6.4.1.5

[45 FR 33221, May 19, 1980, as amended at 46 FR 2848, Jan. 12, 1981; 48 FR 14294, Apr. 1, 1983; 50 FR 4514, Jan. 31, 1985; 71 FR 16903, Apr. 4, 2006]

§264.17 General requirements for ignitable, reactive, or incompatible wastes.

(a) The owner or operator must take precautions to prevent accidental ignition or reaction of ignitable or reactive waste. This waste must be separated and protected from sources of ignition or reaction including but not limited to: open flames, smoking, cutting and welding, hot surfaces, frictional heat, sparks (static, electrical, or mechanical), spontaneous ignition (*e.g.*, from heat-producing chemical reactions), and radiant heat. While ignitable or reactive waste is being handled, the owner or operator must confine smoking and open flame to specially designated locations. "No Smoking" signs must be conspicuously placed wherever there is a hazard from ignitable or reactive waste.

(b) Where specifically required by other sections of this part, the owner or operator of a facility that treats, stores or disposes ignitable or reactive waste, or mixes incompatible waste or incompatible wastes and other materials, must take precautions to prevent reactions which:

(1) Generate extreme heat or pressure, fire or explosions, or violent reactions;

(2) Produce uncontrolled toxic mists, fumes, dusts, or gases in sufficient quantities to threaten human health or the environment;

(3) Produce uncontrolled flammable fumes or gases in sufficient quantities to pose a risk of fire or explosions;

(4) Damage the structural integrity of the device or facility;

(5) Through other like means threaten human health or the environment.

(c) When required to comply with paragraph (a) or (b) of this section, the owner or operator must document that compliance. This documentation may be based on references to published scientific or engineering literature, data from trial tests (*e.g.*, bench scale or pilot scale tests), waste analyses (as specified in §264.13), or the results of the treatment of similar wastes by similar treatment processes and under similar operating conditions.

[46 FR 2848, Jan. 12, 1981, as amended at 50 FR 4514, Jan. 31, 1985; 71 FR 40272, July 14, 2006]

§264.18 Location standards.

(a) *Seismic considerations.* (1) Portions of new facilities where treatment, storage, or disposal of hazardous waste will be conducted must not be located within 61 meters (200 feet) of a fault which has had displacement in Holocene time.

(2) As used in paragraph (a)(1) of this section:

(i) "Fault" means a fracture along which rocks on one side have been displaced with respect to those on the other side.

(ii) "Displacement" means the relative movement of any two sides of a fault measured in any direction.

(iii) "Holocene" means the most recent epoch of the Quaternary period, extending from the end of the Pleistocene to the present.

[*Comment:* Procedures for demonstrating compliance with this standard in part B of the permit application are specified in §270.14(b)(11). Facilities which are located in political jurisdictions other than those listed in appendix VI of this part, are assumed to be in compliance with this requirement.]

(b) *Floodplains.* (1) A facility located in a 100-year floodplain must be designed, constructed, operated, and maintained to prevent washout or any hazardous waste by a 100-year flood, unless the owner or operator can demonstrate to the Regional Administrator's satisfaction that:

(i) Procedures are in effect which will cause the waste to be removed safely, before flood waters can reach the facility, to a location where the wastes will not be vulnerable to flood waters; or

(ii) For existing surface impoundments, waste piles, land treatment units, landfills, and miscellaneous units, no adverse effects on human health or the environment will result if washout occurs, considering:

(A) The volume and physical and chemical characteristics of the waste in the facility;

(B) The concentration of hazardous constituents that would potentially affect surface waters as a result of washout;

(C) The impact of such concentrations on the current or potential uses of and water quality standards established for the affected surface waters; and

(D) The impact of hazardous constituents on the sediments of affected surface waters or the soils of the 100-year floodplain that could result from washout.

[*Comment:* The location where wastes are moved must be a facility which is either permitted by EPA under part 270 of this chapter, authorized to manage hazardous waste by a State with a hazardous waste management program authorized under part 271 of this chapter, or in interim status under parts 270 and 265 of this chapter.]

(2) As used in paragraph (b)(1) of this section:

(i) "100-year floodplain" means any land area which is subject to a one percent or greater chance of flooding in any given year from any source.

(ii) "Washout" means the movement of hazardous waste from the active portion of the facility as a result of flooding.

(iii) "100-year flood" means a flood that has a one percent chance of being equalled or exceeded in any given year.

[*Comment:* (1) Requirements pertaining to other Federal laws which affect the location and permitting of facilities are found in §270.3 of this chapter. For details relative to these laws, see EPA's manual for SEA (special environmental area) requirements for hazardous waste facility permits. Though EPA is responsible for complying with these requirements, applicants are advised to consider them in planning the location of a facility to help prevent subsequent project delays.]

(c) *Salt dome formations, salt bed formations, underground mines and caves.* The placement of any noncontainerized or bulk liquid hazardous waste in any salt dome formation, salt bed formation, underground mine or cave is prohibited, except for the Department of Energy Waste Isolation Pilot Project in New Mexico.

[46 FR 2848, Jan. 12, 1981, as amended at 47 FR 32350, July 26, 1982; 48 FR 14294, Apr. 1, 1983; 48 FR 30115, June 30, 1983; 50 FR 4514, Jan. 31, 1985; 50 FR 28746, July 15, 1985; 52 FR 46963, Dec. 10, 1987; 71 FR 40272, July 14, 2006]

§264.19 Construction quality assurance program.

(a) *CQA program.* (1) A construction quality assurance (CQA) program is required for all surface impoundment, waste pile, and landfill units that are required to comply with §§264.221 (c) and (d), 264.251 (c) and (d), and 264.301 (c) and (d). The program must ensure that the constructed unit meets or exceeds all design criteria and specifications in the permit. The program must be developed and implemented under the direction of a CQA officer who is a registered professional engineer.

(2) The CQA program must address the following physical components, where applicable:

(i) Foundations;

(ii) Dikes;

(iii) Low-permeability soil liners;

(iv) Geomembranes (flexible membrane liners);

(v) Leachate collection and removal systems and leak detection systems; and

(vi) Final cover systems.

(b) *Written CQA plan.* The owner or operator of units subject to the CQA program under paragraph (a) of this section must develop and implement a written CQA plan. The plan must identify steps that will be used to monitor and document the quality of materials and the condition and manner of their installation. The CQA plan must include:

(1) Identification of applicable units, and a description of how they will be constructed.

(2) Identification of key personnel in the development and implementation of the CQA plan, and CQA officer qualifications.

(3) A description of inspection and sampling activities for all unit components identified in paragraph (a)(2) of this section, including observations and tests that will be used before, during, and after construction to ensure that the construction materials and the installed unit components meet the design specifications. The description must cover: Sampling size and locations; frequency of testing; data evaluation procedures; acceptance and rejection criteria for construction materials; plans for implementing corrective measures; and data or other

information to be recorded and retained in the operating record under §264.73.

(c) *Contents of program.* (1) The CQA program must include observations, inspections, tests, and measurements sufficient to ensure:

(i) Structural stability and integrity of all components of the unit identified in paragraph (a)(2) of this section;

(ii) Proper construction of all components of the liners, leachate collection and removal system, leak detection system, and final cover system, according to permit specifications and good engineering practices, and proper installation of all components (*e.g.*, pipes) according to design specifications;

(iii) Conformity of all materials used with design and other material specifications under §§264.221, 264.251, and 264.301.

(2) The CQA program shall include test fills for compacted soil liners, using the same compaction methods as in the full scale unit, to ensure that the liners are constructed to meet the hydraulic conductivity requirements of §§264.221(c)(1)(i)(B), 264.251(c)(1)(i)(B), and 264.301(c)(1)(i)(B) in the field. Compliance with the hydraulic conductivity requirements must be verified by using in-situ testing on the constructed test fill. The Regional Administrator may accept an alternative demonstration, in lieu of a test fill, where data are sufficient to show that a constructed soil liner will meet the hydraulic conductivity requirements of §§264.221(c)(1)(i)(B), 264.251(c)(1)(i)(B), and 264.301(c)(1)(i)(B) in the field.

(d) *Certification.* Waste shall not be received in a unit subject to §264.19 until the owner or operator has submitted to the Regional Administrator by certified mail or hand delivery a certification signed by the CQA officer that the approved CQA plan has been successfully carried out and that the unit meets the requirements of §§264.221 (c) or (d), 264.251 (c) or (d), or 264.301 (c) or (d); and the procedure in §270.30(l)(2)(ii) of this chapter has been completed. Documentation supporting the CQA officer's certification must be furnished to the Regional Administrator upon request.

[57 FR 3486, Jan. 29, 1992]

Subpart C—Preparedness and Prevention

§264.30 Applicability.

📖 6.3.7

The regulations in this subpart apply to owners and operators of all hazardous waste facilities, except as §264.1 provides otherwise.

§264.31 Design and operation of facility.

Facilities must be designed, constructed, maintained, and operated to minimize the possibility of a fire, explosion, or any unplanned sudden or non-sudden release of hazardous waste or hazardous waste constituents to air, soil, or surface water which could threaten human health or the environment.

§264.32 Required equipment.

All facilities must be equipped with the following, unless it can be demonstrated to the Regional Administrator that none of the hazards posed by waste handled at the facility could require a particular kind of equipment specified below:

(a) An internal communications or alarm system capable of providing immediate emergency instruction (voice or signal) to facility personnel;

(b) A device, such as a telephone (immediately available at the scene of operations) or a hand-held two-way radio, capable of summoning emergency assistance from local police departments, fire departments, or State or local emergency response teams;

(c) Portable fire extinguishers, fire control equipment (including special extinguishing equipment, such as that using foam, inert gas, or dry chemicals), spill control equipment, and decontamination equipment; and

(d) Water at adequate volume and pressure to supply water hose streams, or foam producing equipment, or automatic sprinklers, or water spray systems.

[*Comment:* Part 270 of this chapter requires that an owner or operator who wishes to make the demonstration referred to above must do so with part B of the permit application.]

[45 FR 33221, May 19, 1980, as amended at 48 FR 14294, Apr. 1, 1983]

§264.33 Testing and maintenance of equipment.

All facility communications or alarm systems, fire protection equipment, spill control equipment, and decontamination equipment, where required, must be tested and maintained as necessary to assure its proper operation in time of emergency.

§264.34 Access to communications or alarm system.

(a) Whenever hazardous waste is being poured, mixed, spread, or otherwise handled, all personnel involved in the operation must have immediate access to an internal alarm or emergency communication device, either directly or through visual or voice contact with another employee, unless the Regional Administrator has ruled that such a device is not required under §264.32.

(b) If there is ever just one employee on the premises while the facility is operating, he must have immediate access to a device, such as a telephone (immediately available at the scene of operation) or a hand-held two-way radio, capable of summoning external emergency assistance, unless the Regional Administrator has ruled that such a device is not required under §264.32.

§264.35 Required aisle space.

The owner or operator must maintain aisle space to allow the unobstructed movement of personnel, fire protection equipment, spill control equipment, and decontamination equipment to any area of facility operation in an emergency, unless it can be demonstrated to the Regional Administrator that aisle space is not needed for any of these purposes.

[*Comment:* Part 270 of this chapter requires that an owner or operator who wishes to make the demonstration referred to above must do so with part B of the permit application.]

[45 FR 33221, May 19, 1980, as amended at 48 FR 14294, Apr. 1, 1983]

§264.36 [Reserved]

§264.37 Arrangements with local authorities.

(a) The owner or operator must attempt to make the following arrangements, as appropriate for the type of waste handled at his facility and the potential need for the services of these organizations:

(1) Arrangements to familiarize police, fire departments, and emergency response teams with the layout of the facility, properties of hazardous waste handled at the facility and associated hazards, places where facility personnel would normally be working, entrances to and roads inside the facility, and possible evacuation routes;

(2) Where more than one police and fire department might respond to an emergency, agreements designating primary emergency authority to a specific police and a specific fire department, and agreements with any others to provide support to the primary emergency authority;

(3) Agreements with State emergency response teams, emergency response contractors, and equipment suppliers; and

(4) Arrangements to familiarize local hospitals with the properties of hazardous waste handled at the facility and the types of injuries or illnesses which could result from fires, explosions, or releases at the facility.

(b) Where State or local authorities decline to enter into such arrangements, the owner or operator must document the refusal in the operating record.

Subpart D—Contingency Plan and Emergency Procedures

§264.50 Applicability.

The regulations in this subpart apply to owners and operators of all hazardous waste facilities, except as §264.1 provides otherwise. 📖 **6.3.8, 14.4.2.2**

§264.51 Purpose and implementation of contingency plan.

(a) Each owner or operator must have a contingency plan for his facility. The contingency plan must be designed to minimize hazards to human health or the environment from fires, explosions, or any unplanned sudden or non-sudden release of hazardous waste or hazardous waste constituents to air, soil, or surface water.

(b) The provisions of the plan must be carried out immediately whenever there is a fire, explosion, or release of hazardous waste or hazardous waste constituents which could threaten human health or the environment.

[45 FR 33221, May 19, 1980, as amended at 50 FR 4514, Jan. 31, 1985]

§264.52 Content of contingency plan.

(a) The contingency plan must describe the actions facility personnel must take to comply with §§264.51 and 264.56 in response to fires, explosions, or any unplanned sudden or non-sudden release of hazardous waste or hazardous waste constituents to air, soil, or surface water at the facility.

(b) If the owner or operator has already prepared a Spill Prevention, Control, and Countermeasures (SPCC) Plan in accordance with part 112 of this chapter, or part 1510 of chapter V, or some other emergency or contingency plan, he need only amend that plan to incorporate hazardous waste management provisions that are sufficient to comply with the requirements of this part. The owner or operator may develop one contingency plan which meets all regulatory requirements. EPA recommends that the plan be based on the National Response Team's Integrated Contingency Plan Guidance ("One Plan"). When modifications are made to non-RCRA provisions in an integrated contingency plan, the changes do not trigger the need for a RCRA permit modification.

(c) The plan must describe arrangements agreed to by local police departments, fire departments, hospitals, contractors, and State and local emergency response teams to coordinate emergency services, pursuant to §264.37.

(d) The plan must list names, addresses, and phone numbers (office and home) of all persons qualified to act as emergency coordinator (see §264.55), and this list must be kept up to date. Where more than one person is listed, one must be named as primary emergency coordinator and others must be listed in the order in which they will assume responsibility as alternates. *For new facilities,* this information must be supplied to the Regional Administrator at the time of certification, rather than at the time of permit application. 16.1.2

(e) The plan must include a list of all emergency equipment at the facility (such as fire extinguishing systems, spill control equipment, communications and alarm systems (internal and external), and decontamination equipment), where this equipment is required. This list must be kept up to date. In addition, the plan must include the location and a physical description of each item on the list, and a brief outline of its capabilities.

(f) The plan must include an evacuation plan for facility personnel where there is a possibility that evacuation could be necessary. This plan must describe signal(s) to be used to begin evacuation, evacuation routes, and alternate evacuation routes (in cases where the primary routes could be blocked by releases of hazardous waste or fires).

[45 FR 33221, May 19, 1980, as amended at 46 FR 27480, May 20, 1981; 50 FR 4514, Jan. 31, 1985; 71 FR 16903, Apr. 4, 2006]

§264.53 Copies of contingency plan.

A copy of the contingency plan and all revisions to the plan must be:

(a) Maintained at the facility; and

(b) Submitted to all local police departments, fire departments, hospitals, and State and local emergency response teams that may be called upon to provide emergency services.

[*Comment:* The contingency plan must be submitted to the Regional Administrator with Part B of the permit application under part 270, of this chapter and, after modification or approval, will become a condition of any permit issued.]

[45 FR 33221, May 19, 1980, as amended at 48 FR 30115, June 30, 1983; 50 FR 4514, Jan. 31, 1985]

§264.54 Amendment of contingency plan.

The contingency plan must be reviewed, and immediately amended, if necessary, whenever:

(a) The facility permit is revised;

(b) The plan fails in an emergency;

(c) The facility changes—in its design, construction, operation, maintenance, or other circumstances—in a way that materially increases the potential for fires, explosions, or releases of hazardous waste or hazardous waste constituents, or changes the response necessary in an emergency;

(d) The list of emergency coordinators changes; or

(e) The list of emergency equipment changes.

[45 FR 33221, May 19, 1980, as amended at 50 FR 4514, Jan. 31, 1985; 53 FR 37935, Sept. 28, 1988]

§264.55 Emergency coordinator.

At all times, there must be at least one employee either on the facility premises or on call (*i.e.,* available to respond to an emergency by reaching the facility within a short period of time) with the responsibility for coordinating all emergency response measures. This emergency coordinator must be thoroughly familiar with all aspects of the facility's contingency plan, all operations and activities at the facility, the location and characteristics of waste handled, the location of all records within the facility, and the facility layout. In addition, this person must have the authority to commit the resources needed to carry out the contingency plan.

[*Comment:* The emergency coordinator's responsibilities are more fully spelled out in §264.56. Applicable responsibilities for the emergency coordinator vary, depending on factors such as type and variety of waste(s) handled by the facility, and type and complexity of the facility.]

§264.56 Emergency procedures.

(a) Whenever there is an imminent or actual emergency situation, the emergency coordinator (or his designee when the emergency coordinator is on call) must immediately:

(1) Activate internal facility alarms or communication systems, where applicable, to notify all facility personnel; and

(2) Notify appropriate State or local agencies with designated response roles if their help is needed.

(b) Whenever there is a release, fire, or explosion, the emergency coordinator must immediately identify the character, exact source, amount, and areal extent of any released materials. He may do this by observation or review of facility records or manifests, and, if necessary, by chemical analysis.

(c) Concurrently, the emergency coordinator must assess possible hazards to human health or the environment that may result from the release, fire, or explosion. This assessment must consider both direct and indirect effects of the release, fire, or explosion (*e.g.,* the effects of any toxic, irritating, or asphyxiating gases that are generated, or the effects of any hazardous surface water runoff from water or chemical agents used to control fire and heat-induced explosions).

(d) If the emergency coordinator determines that the facility has had a release, fire, or explosion which could threaten human health, or the environment, outside the facility, he must report his findings as follows: 14.4.10

(1) If his assessment indicates that evacuation of local areas may be advisable, he must immediately notify appropriate local authorities. He must be available to help appropriate officials decide whether local areas should be evacuated; and

(2) He must immediately notify either the government official designated as the on-scene coordinator for that geographical area, (in the applicable regional contingency plan under part 1510 of this title) or the National Response Center (using their 24-hour toll free number 800/424-8802). The report must include:

(i) Name and telephone number of reporter;

(ii) Name and address of facility;

(iii) Time and type of incident (*e.g.*, release, fire);

(iv) Name and quantity of material(s) involved, to the extent known;

(v) The extent of injuries, if any; and

(vi) The possible hazards to human health, or the environment, outside the facility.

(e) During an emergency, the emergency coordinator must take all reasonable measures necessary to ensure that fires, explosions, and releases do not occur, recur, or spread to other hazardous waste at the facility. These measures must include, where applicable, stopping processes and operations, collecting and containing release waste, and removing or isolating containers.

(f) If the facility stops operations in response to a fire, explosion, or release, the emergency coordinator must monitor for leaks, pressure buildup, gas generation, or ruptures in valves, pipes, or other equipment, wherever this is appropriate.

(g) Immediately after an emergency, the emergency coordinator must provide for treating, storing, or disposing of recovered waste, contaminated soil or surface water, or any other material that results from a release, fire, or explosion at the facility.

[*Comment:* Unless the owner or operator can demonstrate, in accordance with §261.3(c) or (d) of this chapter, that the recovered material is not a hazardous waste, the owner or operator becomes a generator of hazardous waste and must manage it in accordance with all applicable requirements of parts 262, 263, and 264 of this chapter.]

(h) The emergency coordinator must ensure that, in the affected area(s) of the facility:

(1) No waste that may be incompatible with the released material is treated, stored, or disposed of until cleanup procedures are completed; and

(2) All emergency equipment listed in the contingency plan is cleaned and fit for its intended use before operations are resumed.

(i) The owner or operator must note in the operating record the time, date, and details of any incident that requires implementing the contingency plan. Within 15 days after the incident, he must submit a written report on the incident to the Regional Administrator. The report must include:

(1) Name, address, and telephone number of the owner or operator;

(2) Name, address, and telephone number of the facility;

(3) Date, time, and type of incident (*e.g.*, fire, explosion);

(4) Name and quantity of material(s) involved;

(5) The extent of injuries, if any;

(6) An assessment of actual or potential hazards to human health or the environment, where this is applicable; and

(7) Estimated quantity and disposition of recovered material that resulted from the incident.

[45 FR 33221, May 19, 1980, as amended at 50 FR 4514, Jan. 31, 1985; 71 FR 16903, Apr. 4, 2006]

Subpart E—Manifest System, Recordkeeping, and Reporting

§264.70 Applicability.

(a) The regulations in this subpart apply to owners and operators of both on-site and off-site facilities, except as §264.1 provides otherwise. Sections 264.71, 264.72, and 264.76 do not apply to owners and operators of on-site facilities that do not receive any hazardous waste from off-site sources, nor to owners and operators of off-site facilities with respect to waste military munitions exempted from manifest requirements under 40 CFR 266.203(a). Section 264.73(b) only applies to permittees who treat, store, or dispose of hazardous wastes on-site where such wastes were generated.

(b) The revised Manifest form and procedures in 40 CFR 260.10, 261.7, 264.70, 264.71. 264.72, and 264.76, shall not apply until September 5, 2006. The Manifest form and procedures in 40 CFR 260.10, 261.7, 264.70, 264.71. 264.72, and 264.76, contained in the 40 CFR, parts 260 to 265, edition revised as of July 1, 2004, shall be applicable until September 5, 2006.

[62 FR 6652, Feb. 12, 1997; 70 FR 10821, Mar. 4, 2005]

§264.71 Use of manifest system. 6.6

(a)(1) If a facility receives hazardous waste accompanied by a manifest, the owner, operator or his/her agent must sign and date the manifest as indicated in paragraph (a)(2) of this section to certify that the hazardous waste covered by the manifest was received, that the hazardous waste was received except as noted in the discrepancy space of the manifest, or that the hazardous waste was rejected as noted in the manifest discrepancy space.

(2) If a facility receives a hazardous waste shipment accompanied by a manifest, the owner, operator or his agent must:

(i) Sign and date, by hand, each copy of the manifest;

(ii) Note any discrepancies (as defined in §264.72(a)) on each copy of the manifest;

(iii) Immediately give the transporter at least one copy of the manifest;

(iv) Within 30 days of delivery, send a copy of the manifest to the generator; and

(v) Retain at the facility a copy of each manifest for at least three years from the date of delivery.

(3) If a facility receives hazardous waste imported from a foreign source, the receiving facility must mail a copy of the manifest to the following address within 30 days of delivery: International Compliance Assurance Division, OFA/OECA (2254A), U.S. Environmental Protection Agency, Ariel Rios Building, 1200 Pennsylvania Avenue, NW., Washington, DC 20460.

(b) If a facility receives, from a rail or water (bulk shipment) transporter, hazardous waste which is accompanied by a shipping paper containing all the information required on the manifest (excluding the EPA identification numbers, generator's certification, and signatures), the owner or operator, or his agent, must:

(1) Sign and date each copy of the manifest or shipping paper (if the manifest has not been received) to certify that the hazardous waste covered by the manifest or shipping paper was received;

(2) Note any significant discrepancies (as defined in §264.72(a)) in the manifest or shipping paper (if the manifest has not been received) on each copy of the manifest or shipping paper.

[*Comment:* The Agency does not intend that the owner or operator of a facility whose procedures under §264.13(c) include waste analysis must perform that analysis before signing the shipping paper and giving it to the transporter. Section 264.72(b), however, requires reporting an unreconciled discrepancy discovered during later analysis.]

(3) Immediately give the rail or water (bulk shipment) transporter at least one copy of the manifest or shipping paper (if the manifest has not been received);

(4) Within 30 days after the delivery, send a copy of the signed and dated manifest or a signed and dated copy of the shipping paper (if the manifest has not been received within 30 days after delivery) to the generator; and

[*Comment:* Section 262.23(c) of this chapter requires the generator to send three copies of the manifest to the facility when hazardous waste is sent by rail or water (bulk shipment).]

(5) Retain at the facility a copy of the manifest and shipping paper (if signed in lieu of the manifest at the time of delivery) for at least three years from the date of delivery.

(c) Whenever a shipment of hazardous waste is initiated from a facility, the owner or operator of that facility must comply with the requirements of part 262 of this chapter.

[*Comment:* The provisions of §262.34 are applicable to the on-site accumulation of hazardous wastes by generators. Therefore, the provisions of §262.34 only apply to owners or operators who are shipping hazardous waste which they generated at that facility.]

(d) Within three working days of the receipt of a shipment subject to 40 CFR part 262, subpart H, the owner or operator of the facility must provide a copy of the tracking document bearing all required signatures to the notifier, to the Office of Enforcement and Compliance Assurance, Office of Compliance, Enforcement Planning, Targeting and Data Division (2222A), Environmental Protection Agency, 401 M St., SW., Washington, DC 20460, and to competent authorities of all other concerned countries. The original copy of the tracking document must be maintained at the facility for at least three years from the date of signature.

(e) A facility must determine whether the consignment state for a shipment regulates any additional wastes (beyond those regulated Federally) as hazardous wastes under its state hazardous waste program. Facilities must also determine whether the consignment state or generator state requires the facility to submit any copies of the manifest to these states.

[45 FR 33221, May 19, 1980, as amended at 45 FR 86970, 86974, Dec. 31, 1980; 61 FR 16315, Apr. 12, 1996; 70 FR 10821, Mar. 4, 2005]

§264.72 Manifest discrepancies.

📖 6.6.3.12, 9.5.6.1

(a) Manifest discrepancies are:

(1) Significant differences (as defined by paragraph (b) of this section) between the quantity or type of hazardous waste designated on the manifest or shipping paper, and the quantity and type of hazardous waste a facility actually receives;

(2) Rejected wastes, which may be a full or partial shipment of hazardous waste that the TSDF cannot accept; or

(3) Container residues, which are residues that exceed the quantity limits for "empty" containers set forth in 40 CFR 261.7(b).

(b) Significant differences in quantity are: For bulk waste, variations greater than 10 percent in weight; for batch waste, any variation in piece count, such as a discrepancy of one drum in a truckload. Significant differences in type are obvious differences which can be discovered by inspection or waste analysis, such as waste solvent substituted for waste acid, or toxic constituents not reported on the manifest or shipping paper.

(c) Upon discovering a significant difference in quantity or type, the owner or operator must attempt to reconcile the discrepancy with the waste generator or transporter (*e.g.*, with telephone conversations). If the discrepancy is not resolved within 15 days after receiving the waste, the owner or operator must immediately submit to the Regional Administrator a letter describing the discrepancy and attempts to reconcile it, and a copy of the manifest or shipping paper at issue.

(d)(1) Upon rejecting waste or identifying a container residue that exceeds the quantity limits for "empty" containers set forth in 40 CFR 261.7(b), the facility must consult with the generator prior to forwarding the waste to another facility that can manage the waste. If it is impossible to locate an alternative facility that can receive the waste, the facility may return the rejected waste or residue to the generator. The facility must send the waste to the alternative facility or to the generator within 60 days of the rejection or the container residue identification.

(2) While the facility is making arrangements for forwarding rejected wastes or residues to another facility under this section, it must ensure that either the delivering transporter retains custody of the waste, or, the facility must provide for secure, temporary custody of the waste, pending delivery of the waste to the first transporter designated on the manifest prepared under paragraph (e) or (f) of this section.

(e) Except as provided in paragraph (e)(7) of this section, for full or partial load rejections and residues that are to be sent off-site to an alternate facility, the facility is required to prepare a new manifest in accordance with §262.20(a) of this chapter and the following instructions:

(1) Write the generator's U.S. EPA ID number in Item 1 of the new manifest. Write the generator's name and mailing address in Item 5 of the new manifest. If the mailing address is different from the generator's site address, then write the generator's site address in the designated space for Item 5.

(2) Write the name of the alternate designated facility and the facility's U.S. EPA ID number in the designated facility block (Item 8) of the new manifest.

(3) Copy the manifest tracking number found in Item 4 of the old manifest to the Special Handling and Additional Information Block of the new manifest, and indicate that the shipment is a residue or rejected waste from the previous shipment.

(4) Copy the manifest tracking number found in Item 4 of the new manifest to the manifest reference number line in the Discrepancy Block of the old manifest (Item 18a).

(5) Write the DOT description for the rejected load or the residue in Item 9 (U.S. DOT Description) of the new manifest and write the container types, quantity, and volume(s) of waste.

(6) Sign the Generator's/Offeror's Certification to certify, as the offeror of the shipment, that the waste has been properly packaged, marked and labeled and is in proper condition for transportation.

(7) For full load rejections that are made while the transporter remains present at the facility, the facility may forward the rejected shipment to the alternate facility by completing Item 18b of the original manifest and supplying the information on the next destination facility in the Alternate Facility space. The facility must retain a copy of this manifest for its records, and then give the remaining copies of the manifest to the transporter to accompany the shipment. If the original manifest is not used, then the facility must use a new manifest and comply with paragraphs (e)(1), (2), (3), (4), (5), and (6) of this section.

(f) Except as provided in paragraph (f)(7) of this section, for rejected wastes and residues that must be sent back to the generator, the facility is required to prepare a new manifest in accordance with §262.20(a) of this chapter and the following instructions:

(1) Write the facility's U.S. EPA ID number in Item 1 of the new manifest. Write the generator's name and mailing address in Item 5 of the new manifest. If the mailing address is different from the generator's site address, then write the generator's site address in the designated space for Item 5.

Publisher's Note: EPA's intention is to require the designated facility to enter its own information in Item 5, not the generator's name and mailing address, since the designated facility originates the shipment of rejected wastes. The generator's information should go in Item 8. The agency also intends to make this correction to the regulations in a formal rulemaking but hasn't done so as of the printing of this book. [May 14, 2007 memo from Matt Hale to EPA regional waste directors]

(2) Write the name of the initial generator and the generator's U.S. EPA ID number in the designated facility block (Item 8) of the new manifest.

(3) Copy the manifest tracking number found in Item 4 of the old manifest to the Special Handling and Additional Information Block of the new manifest, and indicate that the shipment is a residue or rejected waste from the previous shipment.

(4) Copy the manifest tracking number found in Item 4 of the new manifest to the manifest reference number line in the Discrepancy Block of the old manifest (Item 18a).

(5) Write the DOT description for the rejected load or the residue in Item 9 (U.S. DOT Description) of the new manifest and write the container types, quantity, and volume(s) of waste.

(6) Sign the Generator's/Offeror's Certification to certify, as offeror of the shipment, that the waste has been properly packaged, marked and labeled and is in proper condition for transportation.

(7) For full load rejections that are made while the transporter remains at the facility, the facility may return the shipment to the generator with the original manifest by completing Item 18a and 18b of the manifest and supplying the generator's information in the Alternate Facility space. The facility must retain a copy for its records and then give the remaining copies of the manifest to the transporter to accompany the shipment. If the original manifest is not used, then the facility must use a new manifest and comply with paragraphs (f)(1), (2), (3), (4), (5), and (6) of this section.

(g) If a facility rejects a waste or identifies a container residue that exceeds the quantity limits for "empty" containers set forth in 40 CFR 261.7(b) after it has signed, dated, and returned a copy of the manifest to the delivering transporter or to the generator, the facility must amend its copy of the manifest to indicate the rejected wastes or residues in the discrepancy space of the amended manifest. The facility must also copy the manifest tracking number from Item 4 of the new manifest to the Discrepancy space of the amended manifest, and must re-sign and date the manifest to certify to the information as amended. The facility must retain the amended manifest for at least three years from the date of amendment, and must within 30 days, send a copy of the amended manifest to the transporter and generator that received copies prior to their being amended.

[45 FR 33221, May 19, 1980, as amended at 50 FR 4514, Jan. 31, 1985; 70 FR 10822, Mar. 4, 2005; 70 FR 35041, June 16, 2005]

§264.73 Operating record.

(a) The owner or operator must keep a written operating record at his facility.

(b) The following information must be recorded, as it becomes available, and maintained in the operating record for three years unless noted as follows:

(1) A description and the quantity of each hazardous waste received, and the method(s) and date(s) of its treatment, storage, or disposal at the facility as required by appendix I of this part. This information must be maintained in the operating record until closure of the facility;

(2) The location of each hazardous waste within the facility and the quantity at each location. For disposal facilities, the location and quantity of each hazardous waste must be recorded on a map or diagram that shows each cell or disposal area. For all facilities, this information must include cross-references to manifest document numbers if the waste was accompanied by a manifest. This information must be maintained in the operating record until closure of the facility.

[*Comment:* See §264.119 for related requirements.]

(3) Records and results of waste analyses and waste determinations performed as specified in §§264.13, 264.17, 264.314, 264.341, 264.1034, 264.1063, 264.1083, 268.4(a), and 268.7 of this chapter.

(4) Summary reports and details of all incidents that require implementing the contingency plan as specified in §264.56(j);

Publisher's Note: The above reference to §264.56(j) is incorrect and should refer to §264.56(i).

(5) Records and results of inspections as required by §264.15(d) (except these data need be kept only three years);

(6) Monitoring, testing or analytical data, and corrective action where required by subpart F of this part and §§264.19, 264.191, 264.193, 264.195, 264.222, 264.223, 264.226, 264.252–264.254, 264.276, 264.278, 264.280, 264.302–264.304, 264.309, 264.602, 264.1034(c)–264.1034(f), 264.1035, 264.1063(d)–264.1063(i), 264.1064, and 264.1082 through 264.1090 of this part. Maintain in the operating record for three years, except for records and results pertaining to ground-water monitoring and cleanup which must be maintained in the operating record until closure of the facility.

(7) For off-site facilities, notices to generators as specified in §264.12(b); and

(8) All closure cost estimates under §264.142, and for disposal facilities, all post-closure cost estimates under §264.144 of this part. This information must be maintained in the operating record until closure of the facility.

(9) A certification by the permittee no less often than annually, that the permittee has a program in place to reduce the volume and toxicity of hazardous waste that he generates to the degree determined by the permittee to be economically practicable; and the proposed method of treatment, storage or disposal is that practicable method currently available to the permittee which minimizes the present and future threat to human health and the environment.

(10) Records of the quantities and date of placement for each shipment of hazardous waste placed in land disposal units under an extension to the effective date of any land disposal restriction granted pursuant to §268.5 of this chapter, a petition pursuant to §268.6 of this chapter, or a certification under §268.8 of this chapter, and the applicable notice required by a generator under §268.7(a) of this chapter. This information must be maintained in the operating record until closure of the facility.

(11) For an off-site treatment facility, a copy of the notice, and the certification and demonstration, if applicable, required by the generator or the owner or operator under §268.7 or §268.8;

(12) For an on-site treatment facility, the information contained in the notice (except the manifest number), and the certification and demonstration if applicable, required by the generator or the owner or operator under §268.7 or §268.8;

(13) For an off-site land disposal facility, a copy of the notice, and the certification and demonstration if applicable, required by the generator or the owner or operator of a treatment facility under §§268.7 and 268.8, whichever is applicable; and

(14) For an on-site land disposal facility, the information contained in the notice required by the generator or owner or operator of a treatment facility under §268.7, except for the manifest number, and the certification and demonstration if applicable, required under §268.8, whichever is applicable.

(15) For an off-site storage facility, a copy of the notice, and the certification and demonstration if applicable, required by the generator or the owner or operator under §268.7 or §268.8; and

(16) For an on-site storage facility, the information contained in the notice (except the manifest number), and the certification and demonstration if applicable, required by the generator or the owner or operator under §268.7 or §268.8.

(17) Any records required under §264.1(j)(13).

(18) Monitoring, testing or analytical data where required by §264.347 must be maintained in the operating record for five years.

(19) Certifications as required by §264.196(f) must be maintained in the operating record until closure of the facility.

[45 FR 33221, May 19, 1980, as amended at 46 FR 2849, Jan. 12, 1981; 46 FR 7678, Jan. 23, 1981; 50 FR 4514, Jan. 31, 1985; 50 FR 18374, Apr. 30, 1985; 50 FR 28746, July 15, 1985; 51 FR 40637, Nov. 7, 1986; 52 FR 21016, June 4, 1987; 53 FR 31211, Aug. 17, 1988; 54 FR 26647, June 23, 1989; 55 FR 25494, June 21, 1990; 57 FR 3487, Jan. 29, 1992; 59 FR 62926, Dec. 6, 1994; 62 FR 64656, Dec. 8, 1997; 63 FR 65938, Nov. 30, 1998; 71 FR 16903, Apr. 4, 2006]

§264.74 Availability, retention, and disposition of records.

(a) All records, including plans, required under this part must be furnished upon request, and made available at all reasonable times for inspection, by any officer, employee, or representative of EPA who is duly designated by the Administrator.

(b) The retention period for all records required under this part is extended automatically during the course of any unresolved enforcement action regarding the facility or as requested by the Administrator.

(c) A copy of records of waste disposal locations and quantities under §264.73(b)(2) must be submitted to the Regional Administrator and local land authority upon closure of the facility.

§264.75 Biennial report. 📖 6.8

The owner or operator must prepare and submit a single copy of a biennial report to the Regional Administrator by March 1 of each even numbered year. The biennial report must be submitted on EPA form 8700-13B. The report must cover facility activities during the previous calendar year and must include:

(a) The EPA identification number, name, and address of the facility;

(b) The calendar year covered by the report;

(c) For off-site facilities, the EPA identification number of each hazardous waste generator from which the facility received a hazardous waste during the year; for imported shipments, the report must give the name and address of the foreign generator;

(d) A description and the quantity of each hazardous waste the facility received during the year. For off-site facilities, this information must be listed by EPA identification number of each generator;

(e) The method of treatment, storage, or disposal for each hazardous waste;

(f) [Reserved]

(g) The most recent closure cost estimate under §264.142, and, for disposal facilities, the most recent post-closure cost estimate under §264.144; and

(h) For generators who treat, store, or dispose of hazardous waste on-site, a description of the efforts undertaken during the year to reduce the volume and toxicity of waste generated.

(i) For generators who treat, store, or dispose of hazardous waste on-site, a description of the changes in volume and toxicity of waste actually achieved during the year in comparison to previous years to the extent such information is available for the years prior to 1984.

(j) The certification signed by the owner or operator of the facility or his authorized representative.

[45 FR 33221, May 19, 1980, as amended at 46 FR 2849, Jan. 12, 1981; 48 FR 3982, Jan. 28, 1983; 50 FR 4514, Jan. 31, 1985; 51 FR 28556, Aug. 8, 1986]

§264.76 Unmanifested waste report.

6.6

(a) If a facility accepts for treatment, storage, or disposal any hazardous waste from an off-site source without an accompanying manifest, or without an accompanying shipping paper as described by §263.20(e) of this chapter, and if the waste is not excluded from the manifest requirement by this chapter, then the owner or operator must prepare and submit a letter to the Regional Administrator within 15 days after receiving the waste. The unmanifested waste report must contain the following information:

(1) The EPA identification number, name and address of the facility;

(2) The date the facility received the waste;

(3) The EPA identification number, name and address of the generator and the transporter, if available;

(4) A description and the quantity of each unmanifested hazardous waste the facility received;

(5) The method of treatment, storage, or disposal for each hazardous waste;

(6) The certification signed by the owner or operator of the facility or his authorized representative; and,

(7) A brief explanation of why the waste was unmanifested, if known.

(b) [Reserved]

[45 FR 33221, May 19, 1980, as amended at 48 FR 3982, Jan. 28, 1983; 50 FR 4514, Jan. 31, 1985; 70 FR 10823, Mar. 4, 2005]

§264.77 Additional reports.

In addition to submitting the biennial reports and unmanifested waste reports described in §§264.75 and 264.76, the owner or operator must also report to the Regional Administrator:

(a) Releases, fires, and explosions as specified in §264.56(j);

Publisher's Note: The above reference to §264.56(j) is incorrect and should refer to §264.56(i).

(b) Facility closures specified in §264.115; and

(c) As otherwise required by subparts F, K through N, AA, BB, and CC of this part.

[46 FR 2849, Jan. 12, 1981, as amended at 47 FR 32350, July 26, 1982; 48 FR 3982, Jan. 28, 1983; 55 FR 25494, June 21, 1990; 59 FR 62926, Dec. 6, 1994]

Subpart F—Releases From Solid Waste Management Units

Source: 47 FR 32350, July 26, 1982, unless otherwise noted.

§264.90 Applicability.

(a)(1) Except as provided in paragraph (b) of this section, the regulations in this subpart apply to owners or operators of facilities that treat, store or dispose of hazardous waste. The owner or operator must satisfy the requirements identified in paragraph (a)(2) of this section for all wastes (or constituents thereof) contained in solid waste management units at the facility, regardless of the time at which waste was placed in such units.

(2) All solid waste management units must comply with the requirements in §264.101. A surface impoundment, waste pile, and land treatment unit or landfill that receives hazardous waste after July 26, 1982 (hereinafter referred to as a "regulated unit") must comply with the requirements of §§264.91 through 264.100 in lieu of §264.101 for purposes of detecting, characterizing and responding to releases to the uppermost aquifer. The financial responsibility requirements of §264.101 apply to regulated units.

(b) The owner or operator's regulated unit or units are not subject to regulation for releases into the uppermost aquifer under this subpart if:

(1) The owner or operator is exempted under §264.1; or

(2) He operates a unit which the Regional Administrator finds:

(i) Is an engineered structure,

(ii) Does not receive or contain liquid waste or waste containing free liquids,

(iii) Is designed and operated to exclude liquid, precipitation, and other run-on and run-off,

(iv) Has both inner and outer layers of containment enclosing the waste,

(v) Has a leak detection system built into each containment layer,

(vi) The owner or operator will provide continuing operation and maintenance of these leak detection systems during the active life of the unit and the closure and post-closure care periods, and

(vii) To a reasonable degree of certainty, will not allow hazardous constituents to migrate beyond the outer containment layer prior to the end of the post-closure care period.

(3) The Regional Administrator finds, pursuant to §264.280(d), that the treatment zone of a land treatment unit that qualifies as a regulated unit does not contain levels of hazardous constituents that are above background levels of those constituents by an amount that is statistically significant, and if an unsaturated zone monitoring program meeting the requirements of §264.278 has not shown a statistically significant increase in hazardous constituents below the treatment zone during the operating life of the unit. An exemption under this paragraph can only relieve an owner or operator of responsibility to meet the requirements of this subpart during the post-closure care period; or

(4) The Regional Administrator finds that there is no potential for migration of liquid from a regulated unit to the uppermost aquifer during the active life of the regulated unit (including the closure period) and the post-closure care period specified under §264.117. This demonstration must be certified by a qualified geologist or geotechnical engineer. In order to provide an adequate margin of safety in the prediction of potential migration of liquid, the owner or operator must base any predictions made under this paragraph on assumptions that maximize the rate of liquid migration.

(5) He designs and operates a pile in compliance with §264.250(c).

(c) The regulations under this subpart apply during the active life of the regulated unit (including the closure period). After closure of the regulated unit, the regulations in this subpart:

(1) Do not apply if all waste, waste residues, contaminated containment system components, and contaminated subsoils are removed or decontaminated at closure;

(2) Apply during the post-closure care period under §264.117 if the owner or operator is conducting a detection monitoring program under §264.98; or

(3) Apply during the compliance period under §264.96 if the owner or operator is conducting a compliance monitoring program under §264.99 or a corrective action program under §264.100.

(d) Regulations in this subpart may apply to miscellaneous units when necessary to comply with §§264.601 through 264.603.

(e) The regulations of this subpart apply to all owners and operators subject to the requirements of 40 CFR 270.1(c)(7), when the Agency issues either a post-closure permit or an enforceable document (as defined in 40 CFR 270.1(c)(7)) at the facility. When the Agency issues an enforceable document, references in this subpart to "in the permit" mean "in the enforceable document."

(f) The Regional Administrator may replace all or part of the requirements of §§264.91 through 264.100 applying to a regulated unit with alternative requirements for groundwater monitoring and corrective action for releases to groundwater set out in the permit (or in an enforceable document) (as defined in 40 CFR 270.1(c)(7)) where the Regional Administrator determines that:

(1) The regulated unit is situated among solid waste management units (or areas of concern), a release has occurred, and both the regulated unit and one or more solid waste management unit(s) (or areas of concern) are likely to have contributed to the release; and

(2) It is not necessary to apply the groundwater monitoring and corrective action requirements of §§264.91 through 264.100 because alternative requirements will protect human health and the environment.

[47 FR 32350, July 26, 1982, as amended at 50 FR 28746, July 15, 1985; 52 FR 46963, Dec. 10, 1987; 63 FR 56733, Oct. 22, 1998]

§264.91 Required programs.

(a) Owners and operators subject to this subpart must conduct a monitoring and response program as follows:

(1) Whenever hazardous constituents under §264.93 from a regulated unit are detected at a compliance point under §264.95, the owner or operator must institute a compliance monitoring program under §264.99. Detected is defined as statistically significant evidence of contamination as described in §264.98(f);

(2) Whenever the ground-water protection standard under §264.92 is exceeded, the owner or operator must institute a corrective action program under §264.100.

Exceeded is defined as statistically significant evidence of increased contamination as described in §264.99(d);

(3) Whenever hazardous constituents under §264.93 from a regulated unit exceed concentration limits under §264.94 in ground water between the compliance point under §264.95 and the downgradient facility property boundary, the owner or operator must institute a corrective action program under §264.100; or

(4) In all other cases, the owner or operator must institute a detection monitoring program under §264.98.

(b) The Regional Administrator will specify in the facility permit the specific elements of the monitoring and response program. The Regional Administrator may include one or more of the programs identified in paragraph (a) of this section in the facility permit as may be necessary to protect human health and the environment and will specify the circumstances under which each of the programs will be required. In deciding whether to require the owner or operator to be prepared to institute a particular program, the Regional Administrator will consider the potential adverse effects on human health and the environment that might occur before final administrative action on a permit modification application to incorporate such a program could be taken.

[47 FR 32350, July 26, 1982, as amended at 53 FR 39728, Oct. 11, 1988]

§264.92 Ground-water protection standard.

The owner or operator must comply with conditions specified in the facility permit that are designed to ensure that hazardous constituents under §264.93 detected in the ground water from a regulated unit do not exceed the concentration limits under §264.94 in the uppermost aquifer underlying the waste management area beyond the point of compliance under §264.95 during the compliance period under §264.96. The Regional Administrator will establish this ground-water protection standard in the facility permit when hazardous constituents have been detected in the ground water.

[53 FR 39728, Oct. 11, 1988]

§264.93 Hazardous constituents.

(a) The Regional Administrator will specify in the facility permit the hazardous constituents to which the ground-water protection standard of §264.92 applies. Hazardous constituents are constituents identified in appendix VIII of part 261 of this chapter that have been detected in ground water in the uppermost aquifer underlying a regulated unit and that are reasonably expected to be in or derived from waste contained in a regulated unit, unless the Regional Administrator has excluded them under paragraph (b) of this section.

(b) The Regional Administrator will exclude an appendix VIII constituent from the list of hazardous constituents specified in the facility permit if he finds that the constituent is not capable of posing a substantial present or potential hazard to human health or the environment. In deciding whether to grant an exemption, the Regional Administrator will consider the following:

(1) Potential adverse effects on ground-water quality, considering:

(i) The physical and chemical characteristics of the waste in the regulated unit, including its potential for migration;

(ii) The hydrogeological characteristics of the facility and surrounding land;

(iii) The quantity of ground water and the direction of ground-water flow;

(iv) The proximity and withdrawal rates of ground-water users;

(v) The current and future uses of ground water in the area;

(vi) The existing quality of ground water, including other sources of contamination and their cumulative impact on the ground-water quality;

(vii) The potential for health risks caused by human exposure to waste constituents;

(viii) The potential damage to wildlife, crops, vegetation, and physical structures caused by exposure to waste constituents;

(ix) The persistence and permanence of the potential adverse effects; and

(2) Potential adverse effects on hydraulically-connected surface water quality, considering:

(i) The volume and physical and chemical characteristics of the waste in the regulated unit;

(ii) The hydrogeological characteristics of the facility and surrounding land;

(iii) The quantity and quality of ground water, and the direction of ground-water flow;

(iv) The patterns of rainfall in the region;

(v) The proximity of the regulated unit to surface waters;

(vi) The current and future uses of surface waters in the area and any water quality standards established for those surface waters;

(vii) The existing quality of surface water, including other sources of contamination and the cumulative impact on surface-water quality;

(viii) The potential for health risks caused by human exposure to waste constituents;

(ix) The potential damage to wildlife, crops, vegetation, and physical structures caused by exposure to waste constituents; and

(x) The persistence and permanence of the potential adverse effects.

(c) In making any determination under paragraph (b) of this section about the use of ground water in the area around the facility, the Regional Administrator will consider any identification of underground sources of drinking water and exempted aquifers made under §144.8 of this chapter.

[47 FR 32350, July 26, 1982, as amended at 48 FR 14294, Apr. 1, 1983]

§264.94 Concentration limits.

(a) The Regional Administrator will specify in the facility permit concentration limits in the ground water for hazardous constituents established under §264.93. The concentration of a hazardous constituent:

(1) Must not exceed the background level of that constituent in the ground water at the time that limit is specified in the permit; or

(2) For any of the constituents listed in Table 1, must not exceed the respective value given in that table if the background level of the constituent is below the value given in Table 1; or

Table 1—Maximum Concentration of Constituents for Ground-water Protection

Constituent	Maximum concentration[1]
Arsenic	0.05
Barium	1.0
Cadmium	0.01
Chromium	0.05
Lead	0.05
Mercury	0.002
Selenium	0.01
Silver	0.05
Endrin (1,2,3,4,10,10-hexachloro-1,7-epoxy 1,4,4a,5,6,7,8,9a-octahydro-1, 4-endo, endo-5,8-dimethano naphthalene)	0.0002
Lindane (1,2,3,4,5,6-hexachlorocyclohexane, gamma isomer)	0.004
Methoxychlor (1,1,1-Trichloro-2,2-bis (p-methoxyphenylethane)	0.1
Toxaphene ($C_{10}H_{10}Cl_6$, Technical chlorinated camphene, 67-69 percent chlorine)	0.005
2,4-D (2,4-Dichlorophenoxyacetic acid)	0.1
2,4,5-TP Silvex (2,4,5-Trichlorophenoxypropionic acid)	0.01

[1]Milligrams per liter.

(3) Must not exceed an alternate limit established by the Regional Administrator under paragraph (b) of this section.

(b) The Regional Administrator will establish an alternate concentration limit for a hazardous constituent if he finds that the constituent will not pose a substantial present or potential hazard to human health or the environment as long as the alternate concentration limit is not exceeded. In establishing alternate concentration limits, the Regional Administrator will consider the following factors:

(1) Potential adverse effects on ground-water quality, considering:

(i) The physical and chemical characteristics of the waste in the regulated unit, including its potential for migration;

(ii) The hydrogeological characteristics of the facility and surrounding land;

(iii) The quantity of ground water and the direction of ground-water flow;

(iv) The proximity and withdrawal rates of ground-water users;

(v) The current and future uses of ground water in the area;

(vi) The existing quality of ground water, including other sources of contamination and their cumulative impact on the ground-water quality;

(vii) The potential for health risks caused by human exposure to waste constituents;

(viii) The potential damage to wildlife, crops, vegetation, and physical structures caused by exposure to waste constituents;

(ix) The persistence and permanence of the potential adverse effects; and

(2) Potential adverse effects on hydraulically-connected surface-water quality, considering:

(i) The volume and physical and chemical characteristics of the waste in the regulated unit;

(ii) The hydrogeological characteristics of the facility and surrounding land;

(iii) The quantity and quality of ground water, and the direction of ground-water flow;

(iv) The patterns of rainfall in the region;

(v) The proximity of the regulated unit to surface waters;

(vi) The current and future uses of surface waters in the area and any water quality standards established for those surface waters;

(vii) The existing quality of surface water, including other sources of contamination and the cumulative impact on surface water quality;

(viii) The potential for health risks caused by human exposure to waste constituents;

(ix) The potential damage to wildlife, crops, vegetation, and physical structures caused by exposure to waste constituents; and

(x) The persistence and permanence of the potential adverse effects.

(c) In making any determination under paragraph (b) of this section about the use of ground water in the area around the facility the Regional Administrator will consider any identification of underground sources of drinking water and exempted aquifers made under §144.8 of this chapter.

[47 FR 32350, July 26, 1982, as amended at 48 FR 14294, Apr. 1, 1983]

§264.95 Point of compliance.

(a) The Regional Administrator will specify in the facility permit the point of compliance at which the ground-water protection standard of §264.92 applies and at which monitoring must be conducted. The point of compliance is a vertical surface located at the hydraulically downgradient limit of the waste management area that extends down into the uppermost aquifer underlying the regulated units.

(b) The waste management area is the limit projected in the horizontal plane of the area on which waste will be placed during the active life of a regulated unit.

(1) The waste management area includes horizontal space taken up by any liner, dike, or other barrier designed to contain waste in a regulated unit.

(2) If the facility contains more than one regulated unit, the waste management area is described by an imaginary line circumscribing the several regulated units.

§264.96 Compliance period.

(a) The Regional Administrator will specify in the facility permit the compliance period during which the ground-water protection standard of §264.92 applies. The compliance period is the number of years equal to the active life of the waste management area (including any waste management activity prior to permitting, and the closure period.)

(b) The compliance period begins when the owner or operator initiates a compliance monitoring program meeting the requirements of §264.99.

(c) If the owner or operator is engaged in a corrective action program at the end of the compliance period specified in paragraph (a) of this section, the compliance period is extended until the owner or operator can demonstrate that the ground-water protection standard of §264.92 has not been exceeded for a period of three consecutive years.

§264.97 General ground-water monitoring requirements.

The owner or operator must comply with the following requirements for any ground-water monitoring program developed to satisfy §264.98, §264.99, or §264.100:

(a) The ground-water monitoring system must consist of a sufficient number of wells, installed at appropriate locations and depths to yield ground-water samples from the uppermost aquifer that:

(1) Represent the quality of background ground water that has not been affected by leakage from a regulated unit;

(i) A determination of background ground-water quality may include sampling of wells that are not hydraulically upgradient of the waste management area where:

(A) Hydrogeologic conditions do not allow the owner or operator to determine what wells are hydraulically upgradient; and

(B) Sampling at other wells will provide an indication of background ground-water quality that is representative or more representative than that provided by the upgradient wells; and

(2) Represent the quality of ground water passing the point of compliance.

(3) Allow for the detection of contamination when hazardous waste or hazardous constituents have migrated from the waste management area to the uppermost aquifer.

(b) If a facility contains more than one regulated unit, separate ground-water monitoring systems are not required for each regulated unit provided that provisions for sampling the ground water in the uppermost aquifer will enable detection and measurement at the compliance point of hazardous constituents from the regulated units that have entered the ground water in the uppermost aquifer.

(c) All monitoring wells must be cased in a manner that maintains the integrity of the monitoring-well bore hole. This casing must be screened or perforated and packed with gravel or sand, where necessary, to enable collection of ground-water samples. The annular space (*i.e.*, the space between the bore hole and well casing) above the sampling depth must be sealed to prevent contamination of samples and the ground water.

(d) The ground-water monitoring program must include consistent sampling and analysis procedures that are designed to ensure monitoring results that provide a reliable indication of ground-water quality below the waste management area. At a minimum the program must include procedures and techniques for:

(1) Sample collection;

(2) Sample preservation and shipment;

(3) Analytical procedures; and

(4) Chain of custody control.

(e) The ground-water monitoring program must include sampling and analytical methods that are appropriate for ground-water sampling and that accurately measure hazardous constituents in ground-water samples.

(f) The ground-water monitoring program must include a determination of the ground-water surface elevation each time ground water is sampled.

(g) In detection monitoring or where appropriate in compliance monitoring, data on each hazardous constituent specified in the permit will be collected from background wells and wells at the compliance point(s). The number and kinds of samples collected to establish background shall be appropriate for the form of statistical test employed, following generally accepted statistical principles. The sample size shall be as large as necessary to ensure with reasonable confidence that a contaminant release to ground water from a facility will be detected. The owner or operator will determine an appropriate sampling procedure and interval for each hazardous constituent listed in the facility permit which shall be specified in the unit permit upon approval by the Regional Administrator. This sampling procedure shall be:

(1) A sequence of at least four samples, taken at an interval that assures, to the greatest extent technically feasible, that an independent sample is obtained, by reference to the uppermost aquifer's effective porosity, hydraulic conductivity, and hydraulic gradient, and the fate and transport characteristics of the potential contaminants, or

(2) an alternate sampling procedure proposed by the owner or operator and approved by the Regional Administrator.

(h) The owner or operator will specify one of the following statistical methods to be used in evaluating groundwater monitoring data for each hazardous constituent which, upon approval by the Regional Administrator, will be specified in the unit permit. The statistical test chosen shall be conducted separately for each hazardous constituent in each well. Where practical quantification limits (pql's) are used in any of the following statistical procedures to comply with §264.97(i)(5), the pql must be proposed by the owner or operator and approved by the Regional Administrator. Use of any of the following statistical methods must be protective of human health and the environment and must comply with the performance standards outlined in paragraph (i) of this section.

(1) A parametric analysis of variance (ANOVA) followed by multiple comparisons procedures to identify statistically significant evidence of contamination. The method must include estimation and testing of the contrasts between each compliance well's mean and the background mean levels for each constituent.

(2) An analysis of variance (ANOVA) based on ranks followed by multiple comparisons procedures to identify statistically significant evidence of contamination. The method must include estimation and testing of the contrasts between each compliance well's median and the background median levels for each constituent.

(3) A tolerance or prediction interval procedure in which an interval for each constituent is established from the distribution of the background data, and the level of each constituent in each compliance well is compared to the upper tolerance or prediction limit.

(4) A control chart approach that gives control limits for each constituent.

(5) Another statistical test method submitted by the owner or operator and approved by the Regional Administrator.

(i) Any statistical method chosen under §264.97(h) for specification in the unit permit shall comply with the following performance standards, as appropriate:

(1) The statistical method used to evaluate ground-water monitoring data shall be appropriate for the distribution of chemical parameters or hazardous constituents. If the distribution of the chemical parameters or hazardous constituents is shown by the owner or operator to be inappropriate for a normal theory test, then the data should be transformed or a distribution-free theory test should be used. If the distributions for the constituents differ, more than one statistical method may be needed.

(2) If an individual well comparison procedure is used to compare an individual compliance well constituent

concentration with background constituent concentrations or a ground-water protection standard, the test shall be done at a Type I error level no less than 0.01 for each testing period. If a multiple comparisons procedure is used, the Type I experimentwise error rate for each testing period shall be no less than 0.05; however, the Type I error of no less than 0.01 for individual well comparisons must be maintained. This performance standard does not apply to tolerance intervals, prediction intervals or control charts.

(3) If a control chart approach is used to evaluate ground-water monitoring data, the specific type of control chart and its associated parameter values shall be proposed by the owner or operator and approved by the Regional Administrator if he or she finds it to be protective of human health and the environment.

(4) If a tolerance interval or a prediction interval is used to evaluate groundwater monitoring data, the levels of confidence and, for tolerance intervals, the percentage of the population that the interval must contain, shall be proposed by the owner or operator and approved by the Regional Administrator if he or she finds these parameters to be protective of human health and the environment. These parameters will be determined after considering the number of samples in the background data base, the data distribution, and the range of the concentration values for each constituent of concern.

(5) The statistical method shall account for data below the limit of detection with one or more statistical procedures that are protective of human health and the environment. Any practical quantification limit (pql) approved by the Regional Administrator under §264.97(h) that is used in the statistical method shall be the lowest concentration level that can be reliably achieved within specified limits of precision and accuracy during routine laboratory operating conditions that are available to the facility.

(6) If necessary, the statistical method shall include procedures to control or correct for seasonal and spatial variability as well as temporal correlation in the data.

(j) Ground-water monitoring data collected in accordance with paragraph (g) of this section including actual levels of constituents must be maintained in the facility operating record. The Regional Administrator will specify in the permit when the data must be submitted for review.

[47 FR 32350, July 26, 1982, as amended at 50 FR 4514, Jan. 31, 1985; 53 FR 39728, Oct. 11, 1988; 71 FR 40272, July 14, 2006]

§264.98 Detection monitoring program.

An owner or operator required to establish a detection monitoring program under this subpart must, at a minimum, discharge the following responsibilities:

(a) The owner or operator must monitor for indicator parameters (*e.g.*, specific conductance, total organic carbon, or total organic halogen), waste constituents, or reaction products that provide a reliable indication of the presence of hazardous constituents in ground water. The Regional Administrator will specify the parameters or constituents to be monitored in the facility permit, after considering the following factors:

(1) The types, quantities, and concentrations of constituents in wastes managed at the regulated unit;

(2) The mobility, stability, and persistence of waste constituents or their reaction products in the unsaturated zone beneath the waste management area;

(3) The detectability of indicator parameters, waste constituents, and reaction products in ground water; and

(4) The concentrations or values and coefficients of variation of proposed monitoring parameters or constituents in the ground-water background.

(b) The owner or operator must install a ground-water monitoring system at the compliance point as specified under §264.95. The ground-water monitoring system must comply with §264.97(a)(2), (b), and (c).

(c) The owner or operator must conduct a ground-water monitoring program for each chemical parameter and hazardous constituent specified in the permit pursuant to paragraph (a) of this section in accordance with §264.97(g). The owner or operator must maintain a record of ground-water analytical data as measured and in a form necessary for the determination of statistical significance under §264.97(h).

(d) The Regional Administrator will specify the frequencies for collecting samples and conducting statistical tests to determine whether there is statistically significant evidence of contamination for any parameter or hazardous constituent specified in the permit conditions under paragraph (a) of this section in accordance with §264.97(g).

(e) The owner or operator must determine the groundwater flow rate and direction in the uppermost aquifer at least annually.

(f) The owner or operator must determine whether there is statistically significant evidence of contamination for any chemical parameter of hazardous constituent specified in the permit pursuant to paragraph (a) of this section at a frequency specified under paragraph (d) of this section.

(1) In determining whether statistically significant evidence of contamination exists, the owner or operator must use the method(s) specified in the permit under §264.97(h). These method(s) must compare data collected at the compliance point(s) to the background ground-water quality data.

(2) The owner or operator must determine whether there is statistically significant evidence of contamination at each monitoring well as the compliance point within a reasonable period of time after completion of sampling. The Regional Administrator will specify in the facility permit what period of time is reasonable, after considering the complexity of the statistical test and the availability of laboratory facilities to perform the analysis of ground-water samples.

(g) If the owner or operator determines pursuant to paragraph (f) of this section that there is statistically significant evidence of contamination for chemical parameters or hazardous constituents specified pursuant to paragraph (a) of this section at any monitoring well at the compliance point, he or she must:

(1) Notify the Regional Administrator of this finding in writing within seven days. The notification must indicate what chemical parameters or hazardous constituents have shown statistically significant evidence of contamination;

(2) Immediately sample the ground water in all monitoring wells and determine whether constituents in the list of appendix IX of this part are present, and if so, in what concentration. However, the Regional Administrator, on a discretionary basis, may allow sampling for a site-specific subset of constituents from the Appendix IX list of this part and other representative/related waste constituents.

(3) For any appendix IX compounds found in the analysis pursuant to paragraph (g)(2) of this section, the owner or operator may resample within one month or at an alternative site-specific schedule approved by the Administrator and repeat the analysis for those compounds detected. If the results of the second analysis confirm the initial results, then these constituents will form the basis for compliance monitoring. If the owner or operator does not resample for the compounds in paragraph (g)(2) of this section, the hazardous constituents found during this initial appendix IX analysis will form the basis for compliance monitoring.

(4) Within 90 days, submit to the Regional Administrator an application for a permit modification to establish a compliance monitoring program meeting the requirements of §264.99. The application must include the following information:

(i) An identification of the concentration of any appendix IX constituent detected in the ground water at each monitoring well at the compliance point;

(ii) Any proposed changes to the ground-water monitoring system at the facility necessary to meet the requirements of §264.99;

(iii) Any proposed additions or changes to the monitoring frequency, sampling and analysis procedures or methods, or statistical methods used at the facility necessary to meet the requirements of §264.99;

(iv) For each hazardous constituent detected at the compliance point, a proposed concentration limit under §264.94(a) (1) or (2), or a notice of intent to seek an alternate concentration limit under §264.94(b); and

(5) Within 180 days, submit to the Regional Administrator:

(i) All data necessary to justify an alternate concentration limit sought under §264.94(b); and

(ii) An engineering feasibility plan for a corrective action program necessary to meet the requirement of §264.100, unless:

(A) All hazardous constituents identified under paragraph (g)(2) of this section are listed in Table 1 of §264.94 and their concentrations do not exceed the respective values given in that Table; or

(B) The owner or operator has sought an alternate concentration limit under §264.94(b) for every hazardous constituent identified under paragraph (g)(2) of this section.

(6) If the owner or operator determines, pursuant to paragraph (f) of this section, that there is a statistically significant difference for chemical parameters or hazardous constituents specified pursuant to paragraph (a) of this section at any monitoring well at the compliance point, he or she may demonstrate that a source other than a regulated unit caused the contamination or that the detection is an artifact caused by an error in sampling, analysis, or statistical evaluation or natural variation in the ground water. The owner operator may make a demonstration under this paragraph in addition to, or in lieu of, submitting a permit modification application under paragraph (g)(4) of this section; however, the

owner or operator is not relieved of the requirement to submit a permit modification application within the time specified in paragraph (g)(4) of this section unless the demonstration made under this paragraph successfully shows that a source other than a regulated unit caused the increase, or that the increase resulted from error in sampling, analysis, or evaluation. In making a demonstration under this paragraph, the owner or operator must:

(i) Notify the Regional Administrator in writing within seven days of determining statistically significant evidence of contamination at the compliance point that he intends to make a demonstration under this paragraph;

(ii) Within 90 days, submit a report to the Regional Administrator which demonstrates that a source other than a regulated unit caused the contamination or that the contamination resulted from error in sampling, analysis, or evaluation;

(iii) Within 90 days, submit to the Regional Administrator an application for a permit modification to make any appropriate changes to the detection monitoring program facility; and

(iv) Continue to monitor in accordance with the detection monitoring program established under this section.

(h) If the owner or operator determines that the detection monitoring program no longer satisfies the requirements of this section, he or she must, within 90 days, submit an application for a permit modification to make any appropriate changes to the program.

[47 FR 32350, July 26, 1982, as amended at 50 FR 4514, Jan. 31, 1985; 52 FR 25946, July 9, 1987; 53 FR 39729, Oct. 11, 1988; 71 FR 16904, Apr. 4, 2006; 71 FR 40272, July 14, 2006]

§264.99 Compliance monitoring program.

An owner or operator required to establish a compliance monitoring program under this subpart must, at a minimum, discharge the following responsibilities:

(a) The owner or operator must monitor the ground water to determine whether regulated units are in compliance with the ground-water protection standard under §264.92. The Regional Administrator will specify the ground-water protection standard in the facility permit, including:

(1) A list of the hazardous constituents identified under §264.93;

(2) Concentration limits under §264.94 for each of those hazardous constituents;

(3) The compliance point under §264.95; and

(4) The compliance period under §264.96.

(b) The owner or operator must install a ground-water monitoring system at the compliance point as specified under §264.95. The ground-water monitoring system must comply with §264.97(a)(2), (b), and (c).

(c) The Regional Administrator will specify the sampling procedures and statistical methods appropriate for the constituents and the facility, consistent with §264.97 (g) and (h).

(1) The owner or operator must conduct a sampling program for each chemical parameter or hazardous constituent in accordance with §264.97(g).

(2) The owner or operator must record ground-water analytical data as measured and in form necessary for the determination of statistical significance under §264.97(h) for the compliance period of the facility.

(d) The owner or operator must determine whether there is statistically significant evidence of increased contamination for any chemical parameter or hazardous constituent specified in the permit, pursuant to paragraph (a) of this section, at a frequency specified under paragraph (f) under this section.

(1) In determining whether statistically significant evidence of increased contamination exists, the owner or operator must use the method(s) specified in the permit under §264.97(h). The methods(s) must compare data collected at the compliance point(s) to a concentration limit developed in accordance with §264.94.

(2) The owner or operator must determine whether there is statistically significant evidence of increased contamination at each monitoring well at the compliance point within a reasonable time period after completion of sampling. The Regional Administrator will specify that time period in the facility permit, after considering the complexity of the statistical test and the availability of laboratory facilities to perform the analysis of ground-water samples.

(e) The owner or operator must determine the ground-water flow rate and direction in the uppermost aquifer at least annually.

(f) The Regional Administrator will specify the frequencies for collecting samples and conducting statistical tests to determine statistically significant evidence of increased contamination in accordance with §264.97(g).

(g) Annually, the owner or operator must determine whether additional hazardous constituents from Appendix IX of this part, which could possibly be present but are not on the detection monitoring list in the permit, are actually present in the uppermost aquifer and, if so, at what concentration, pursuant to procedures in §264.98(f). To accomplish this, the owner or operator must consult with the Regional Administrator to determine on a case-by-case basis: which sample collection event during the year will involve enhanced sampling; the number of monitoring wells at the compliance point to undergo enhanced sampling; the number of samples to be collected from each of these monitoring wells; and, the specific constituents from Appendix IX of this part for which these samples must be analyzed. If the enhanced sampling event indicates that Appendix IX constituents are present in the ground water that are not already identified in the permit as monitoring constituents, the owner or operator may resample within one month or at an alternative site-specific schedule approved by the Regional Administrator, and repeat the analysis. If the second analysis confirms the presence of new constituents, the owner or operator must report the concentration of these additional constituents to the Regional Administrator within seven days after the completion of the second analysis and add them to the monitoring list. If the owner or operator chooses not to resample, then he or she must report the concentrations of these additional constituents to the Regional Administrator within seven days after completion of the initial analysis, and add them to the monitoring list.

(h) If the owner or operator determines pursuant to paragraph (d) of this section that any concentration limits under §264.94 are being exceeded at any monitoring well at the point of compliance he or she must:

(1) Notify the Regional Administrator of this finding in writing within seven days. The notification must indicate what concentration limits have been exceeded.

(2) Submit to the Regional Administrator an application for a permit modification to establish a corrective action program meeting the requirements of §264.100 within 180 days, or within 90 days if an engineering feasibility study has been previously submitted to the Regional Administrator under §264.98(g)(5). The application must at a minimum include the following information:

(i) A detailed description of corrective actions that will achieve compliance with the ground-water protection standard specified in the permit under paragraph (a) of this section; and

(ii) A plan for a ground-water monitoring program that will demonstrate the effectiveness of the corrective action. Such a ground-water monitoring program may be based on a compliance monitoring program developed to meet the requirements of this section.

(i) If the owner or operator determines, pursuant to paragraph (d) of this section, that the ground-water concentration limits under this section are being exceeded at any monitoring well at the point of compliance, he or she may demonstrate that a source other than a regulated unit caused the contamination or that the detection is an artifact caused by an error in sampling, analysis, or statistical evaluation or natural variation in the ground water. In making a demonstration under this paragraph, the owner or operator must:

(1) Notify the Regional Administrator in writing within seven days that he intends to make a demonstration under this paragraph;

(2) Within 90 days, submit a report to the Regional Administrator which demonstrates that a source other than a regulated unit caused the standard to be exceeded or that the apparent noncompliance with the standards resulted from error in sampling, analysis, or evaluation;

(3) Within 90 days, submit to the Regional Administrator an application for a permit modification to make any appropriate changes to the compliance monitoring program at the facility; and

(4) Continue to monitor in accord with the compliance monitoring program established under this section.

(j) If the owner or operator determines that the compliance monitoring program no longer satisfies the requirements of this section, he must, within 90 days, submit an application for a permit modification to make any appropriate changes to the program.

[47 FR 32350, July 26, 1982, as amended at 50 FR 4514, Jan. 31, 1985; 52 FR 25946, July 9, 1987; 53 FR 39730, Oct. 11, 1988; 71 FR 16904, Apr. 4, 2006; 71 FR 40272, July 14, 2006]

§264.100 Corrective action program.

An owner or operator required to establish a corrective action program under this subpart must, at a minimum, discharge the following responsibilities:

(a) The owner or operator must take corrective action to ensure that regulated units are in compliance with the ground-water protection standard under §264.92. The Regional Administrator will specify the ground-water protection standard in the facility permit, including:

(1) A list of the hazardous constituents identified under §264.93;

(2) Concentration limits under §264.94 for each of those hazardous constituents;

(3) The compliance point under §264.95; and

(4) The compliance period under §264.96.

(b) The owner or operator must implement a corrective action program that prevents hazardous constituents from exceeding their respective concentration limits at the compliance point by removing the hazardous waste constituents or treating them in place. The permit will specify the specific measures that will be taken.

(c) The owner or operator must begin corrective action within a reasonable time period after the ground-water protection standard is exceeded. The Regional Administrator will specify that time period in the facility permit. If a facility permit includes a corrective action program in addition to a compliance monitoring program, the permit will specify when the corrective action will begin and such a requirement will operate in lieu of §264.99(i)(2).

(d) In conjunction with a corrective action program, the owner or operator must establish and implement a ground-water monitoring program to demonstrate the effectiveness of the corrective action program. Such a monitoring program may be based on the requirements for a compliance monitoring program under §264.99 and must be as effective as that program in determining compliance with the ground-water protection standard under §264.92 and in determining the success of a corrective action program under paragraph (e) of this section, where appropriate.

(e) In addition to the other requirements of this section, the owner or operator must conduct a corrective action program to remove or treat in place any hazardous constituents under §264.93 that exceed concentration limits under §264.94 in groundwater:

(1) Between the compliance point under §264.95 and the downgradient property boundary; and

(2) Beyond the facility boundary, where necessary to protect human health and the environment, unless the owner or operator demonstrates to the satisfaction of the Regional Administrator that, despite the owner's or operator's best efforts, the owner or operator was unable to obtain the necessary permission to undertake such action. The owner/operator is not relieved of all responsibility to clean up a release that has migrated beyond the facility boundary where off-site access is denied. On-site measures to address such releases will be determined on a case-by-case basis.

(3) Corrective action measures under this paragraph must be initiated and completed within a reasonable period of time considering the extent of contamination.

(4) Corrective action measures under this paragraph may be terminated once the concentration of hazardous constituents under §264.93 is reduced to levels below their respective concentration limits under §264.94.

(f) The owner or operator must continue corrective action measures during the compliance period to the extent necessary to ensure that the ground-water protection standard is not exceeded. If the owner or operator is conducting corrective action at the end of the compliance period, he must continue that corrective action for as long as necessary to achieve compliance with the ground-water protection standard. The owner or operator may terminate corrective action measures taken beyond the period equal to the active life of the waste management area (including the closure period) if he can demonstrate, based on data from the ground-water monitoring program under paragraph (d) of this section, that the ground-water protection standard of §264.92 has not been exceeded for a period of three consecutive years.

(g) The owner or operator must report in writing to the Regional Administrator on the effectiveness of the corrective action program. The owner or operator must submit these reports annually.

(h) If the owner or operator determines that the corrective action program no longer satisfies the requirements of this section, he must, within 90 days, submit an application for a permit modification to make any appropriate changes to the program.

[47 FR 32350, July 26, 1985, as amended at 50 FR 4514, Jan. 31, 1985; 52 FR 45798, Dec. 1, 1987; 71 FR 16904, Apr. 4, 2006]

§264.101 Corrective action for solid waste management units.

(a) The owner or operator of a facility seeking a permit for the treatment, storage or disposal of hazardous waste must institute corrective action as necessary to protect human health and the environment for all releases of hazardous waste or constituents from any solid waste management unit at the facility, regardless of the time at which waste was placed in such unit. 📖 **4.17.4, 6.3.12, 7.2.3.3, 14.4.8, 17.2-5**

(b) Corrective action will be specified in the permit in accordance with this section and subpart S of this part. The permit will contain schedules of compliance for such corrective action (where such corrective action cannot be completed prior to issuance of the permit) and assurances of financial responsibility for completing such corrective action. 📖 17.6, 17.8

(c) The owner or operator must implement corrective actions beyond the facility property boundary, where necessary to protect human health and the environment, unless the owner or operator demonstrates to the satisfaction of the Regional Administrator that, despite the owner's or operator's best efforts, the owner or operator was unable to obtain the necessary permission to undertake such actions. The owner/operator is not relieved of all responsibility to clean up a release that has migrated beyond the facility boundary where off-site access is denied. On-site measures to address such releases will be determined on a case-by-case basis. Assurances of financial responsibility for such corrective action must be provided. 📖 17.6.2

(d) This section does not apply to remediation waste management sites unless they are part of a facility subject to a permit for treating, storing or disposing of hazardous wastes that are not remediation wastes. 📖 17.15

[50 FR 28747, July 15, 1985, as amended at 52 FR 45798, Dec. 1, 1987; 58 FR 8683, Feb. 16, 1993; 63 FR 65938, Nov. 30, 1998; 71 FR 40272, July 14, 2006]

Subpart G—Closure and Post-Closure

Source: 51 FR 16444, May 2, 1986, unless otherwise noted.

§264.110 Applicability.

Except as §264.1 provides otherwise:

(a) Sections 264.111 through 264.115 (which concern closure) apply to the owners and operators of all hazardous waste management facilities; and

(b) Sections 264.116 through 264.120 (which concern post-closure care) apply to the owners and operators of:

(1) All hazardous waste disposal facilities;

(2) Waste piles and surface impoundments from which the owner or operator intends to remove the wastes at closure to the extent that these sections are made applicable to such facilities in §264.228 or §264.258;

(3) Tank systems that are required under §264.197 to meet the requirements for landfills; and

(4) Containment buildings that are required under §264.1102 to meet the requirement for landfills.

(c) The Regional Administrator may replace all or part of the requirements of this subpart (and the unit-specific standards referenced in §264.111(c) applying to a regulated unit), with alternative requirements set out in a permit or in an enforceable document (as defined in 40 CFR 270.1(c)(7)), where the Regional Administrator determines that:

(1) The regulated unit is situated among solid waste management units (or areas of concern), a release has occurred, and both the regulated unit and one or more solid waste management unit(s) (or areas of concern) are likely to have contributed to the release; and

(2) It is not necessary to apply the closure requirements of this subpart (and those referenced herein) because the alternative requirements will protect human health and the environment and will satisfy the closure performance standard of §264.111 (a) and (b).

[51 FR 16444, May 2, 1986, as amended at 51 FR 25472, July 14, 1986; 57 FR 37264, Aug. 18, 1992; 63 FR 56733, Oct. 22, 1998]

§264.111 Closure performance standard.

The owner or operator must close the facility in a manner that:

(a) Minimizes the need for further maintenance; and

(b) Controls, minimizes or eliminates, to the extent necessary to protect human health and the environment, post-closure escape of hazardous waste, hazardous constituents, leachate, contaminated run-off, or hazardous waste decomposition products to the ground or surface waters or to the atmosphere; and

(c) Complies with the closure requirements of this part, including, but not limited to, the requirements of §§264.178, 264.197, 264.228, 264.258, 264.280, 264.310, 264.351, 264.601 through 264.603, and 264.1102.

[51 FR 16444, May 2, 1986, as amended at 52 FR 46963, Dec. 10, 1987; 57 FR 37265, Aug. 18, 1992; 71 FR 40272, July 14, 2006]

§264.112 Closure plan; amendment of plan.

(a) *Written plan.* (1) The owner or operator of a hazardous waste management facility must have a written closure plan. In addition, certain surface impoundments and waste piles from which the owner or operator intends to remove or decontaminate the hazardous waste at partial or final closure are required by §§264.228(c)(1)(i) and 264.258(c)(1)(i) to have contingent closure plans. The plan must be submitted with the permit application, in accordance with §270.14(b)(13) of this chapter, and approved by the Regional Administrator as part of the permit issuance procedures under part 124 of this chapter. In accordance with §270.32 of this chapter, the approved closure plan will become a condition of any RCRA permit.

(2) The Director's approval of the plan must ensure that the approved closure plan is consistent with §§264.111 through 264.115 and the applicable requirements of subpart F of this part, §§264.178, 264.197,

264.228, 264.258, 264.280, 264.310, 264.351, 264.601, and 264.1102. Until final closure is completed and certified in accordance with §264.115, a copy of the approved plan and all approved revisions must be furnished to the Director upon request, including requests by mail.

(b) *Content of plan.* The plan must identify steps necessary to perform partial and/or final closure of the facility at any point during its active life. The closure plan must include, at least:

(1) A description of how each hazardous waste management unit at the facility will be closed in accordance with §264.111;

(2) A description of how final closure of the facility will be conducted in accordance with §264.111. The description must identify the maximum extent of the operations which will be unclosed during the active life of the facility; and

(3) An estimate of the maximum inventory of hazardous wastes ever on-site over the active life of the facility and a detailed description of the methods to be used during partial closures and final closure, including, but not limited to, methods for removing, transporting, treating, storing, or disposing of all hazardous wastes, and identification of the type(s) of the off-site hazardous waste management units to be used, if applicable; and

(4) A detailed description of the steps needed to remove or decontaminate all hazardous waste residues and contaminated containment system components, equipment, structures, and soils during partial and final closure, including, but not limited to, procedures for cleaning equipment and removing contaminated soils, methods for sampling and testing surrounding soils, and criteria for determining the extent of decontamination required to satisfy the closure performance standard; and

(5) A detailed description of other activities necessary during the closure period to ensure that all partial closures and final closure satisfy the closure performance standards, including, but not limited to, ground-water monitoring, leachate collection, and run-on and run-off control; and

(6) A schedule for closure of each hazardous waste management unit and for final closure of the facility. The schedule must include, at a minimum, the total time required to close each hazardous waste management unit and the time required for intervening closure activities which will allow tracking of the progress of partial and final closure. (For example, in the case of a landfill unit, estimates of the time required to treat or dispose of all hazardous waste inventory and of the time required to place a final cover must be included.)

(7) For facilities that use trust funds to establish financial assurance under §264.143 or §264.145 and that are expected to close prior to the expiration of the permit, an estimate of the expected year of final closure.

(8) For facilities where the Regional Administrator has applied alternative requirements at a regulated unit under §§264.90(f), 264.110(c), and/or §264.140(d), either the alternative requirements applying to the regulated unit, or a reference to the enforceable document containing those alternative requirements.

(c) *Amendment of plan.* The owner or operator must submit a written notification of or request for a permit modification to authorize a change in operating plans, facility design, or the approved closure plan in accordance with the applicable procedures in parts 124 and 270. The written notification or request must include a copy of the amended closure plan for review or approval by the Regional Administrator.

(1) The owner or operator may submit a written notification or request to the Regional Administrator for a permit modification to amend the closure plan at any time prior to the notification of partial or final closure of the facility.

(2) The owner or operator must submit a written notification of or request for a permit modification to authorize a change in the approved closure plan whenever:

(i) Changes in operating plans or facility design affect the closure plan, or

(ii) There is a change in the expected year of closure, if applicable, or

(iii) In conducting partial or final closure activities, unexpected events require a modification of the approved closure plan.

(iv) The owner or operator requests the Regional Administrator to apply alternative requirements to a regulated unit under §§264.90(f), 264.110(c), and/or §264.140(d).

(3) The owner or operator must submit a written request for a permit modification including a copy of the amended closure plan for approval at least 60 days prior to the proposed change in facility design or operation, or no later than 60 days after an unexpected event has occurred which has affected the closure plan. If an unexpected event occurs during the partial or final closure period, the owner or operator must request a permit

modification no later than 30 days after the unexpected event. An owner or operator of a surface impoundment or waste pile that intends to remove all hazardous waste at closure and is not otherwise required to prepare a contingent closure plan under §264.228(c)(1)(i) or §264.258(c)(1)(i), must submit an amended closure plan to the Regional Administrator no later than 60 days from the date that the owner or operator or Regional Administrator determines that the hazardous waste management unit must be closed as a landfill, subject to the requirements of §264.310, or no later than 30 days from that date if the determination is made during partial or final closure. The Regional Administrator will approve, disapprove, or modify this amended plan in accordance with the procedures in parts 124 and 270. In accordance with §270.32 of this chapter, the approved closure plan will become a condition of any RCRA permit issued.

(4) The Regional Administrator may request modifications to the plan under the conditions described in §264.112(c)(2). The owner or operator must submit the modified plan within 60 days of the Regional Administrator's request, or within 30 days if the change in facility conditions occurs during partial or final closure. Any modifications requested by the Regional Administrator will be approved in accordance with the procedures in parts 124 and 270.

(d) *Notification of partial closure and final closure.* (1) The owner or operator must notify the Regional Administrator in writing at least 60 days prior to the date on which he expects to begin closure of a surface impoundment, waste pile, land treatment or landfill unit, or final closure of a facility with such a unit. The owner or operator must notify the Regional Administrator in writing at least 45 days prior to the date on which he expects to begin final closure of a facility with only treatment or storage tanks, container storage, or incinerator units to be closed. The owner or operator must notify the Regional Administrator in writing at least 45 days prior to the date on which he expects to begin partial or final closure of a boiler or industrial furnace, whichever is earlier.

(2) The date when he "expects to begin closure" must be either:

(i) No later than 30 days after the date on which any hazardous waste management unit receives the known final volume of hazardous wastes, or if there is a reasonable possibility that the hazardous waste management unit will receive additional hazardous wastes, no later than one year after the date on which the unit received the most recent volume of hazardous wastes. If the owner or operator of a hazardous waste management unit can demonstrate to the Regional Administrator that the hazardous waste management unit or facility has the capacity to receive additional hazardous wastes and he has taken all steps to prevent threats to human health and the environment, including compliance with all applicable permit requirements, the Regional Administrator may approve an extension to this one-year limit; or

(ii) For units meeting the requirements of §264.113(d), no later than 30 days after the date on which the hazardous waste management unit receives the known final volume of non-hazardous wastes, or if there is a reasonable possibility that the hazardous waste management unit will receive additional non-hazardous wastes, no later than one year after the date on which the unit received the most recent volume of non-hazardous wastes. If the owner or operator can demonstrate to the Regional Administrator that the hazardous waste management unit has the capacity to receive additional non-hazardous wastes and he has taken, and will continue to take, all steps to prevent threats to human health and the environment, including compliance with all applicable permit requirements, the Regional Administrator may approve an extension to this one-year limit.

(3) If the facility's permit is terminated, or if the facility is otherwise ordered, by judicial decree or final order under section 3008 of RCRA, to cease receiving hazardous wastes or to close, then the requirements of this paragraph do not apply. However, the owner or operator must close the facility in accordance with the deadlines established in §264.113.

(e) *Removal of wastes and decontamination or dismantling of equipment.* Nothing in this section shall preclude the owner or operator from removing hazardous wastes and decontaminating or dismantling equipment in accordance with the approved partial or final closure plan at any time before or after notification of partial or final closure.

[51 FR 16444, May 2, 1986, as amended at 52 FR 46963, Dec. 10, 1987; 53 FR 37935, Sept. 28, 1988; 54 FR 33394, Aug. 14, 1989; 56 FR 7207, Feb. 21, 1991; 57 FR 37265, Aug. 18, 1992; 63 FR 56733, Oct. 22, 1998; 71 FR 40272, July 14, 2006]

§264.113 Closure; time allowed for closure.

(a) Within 90 days after receiving the final volume of hazardous wastes, or the final volume of non-hazardous wastes if the owner or operator complies with all applicable requirements in paragraphs (d) and (e) of this section, at a hazardous waste management unit or facility, the owner or operator must treat, remove from the unit or facility, or dispose of on-site, all hazardous wastes in accordance with the approved closure plan. The Regional Administrator may approve a longer period if the owner or operator complies with all applicable requirements for requesting a modification to the permit and demonstrates that:

(1)(i) The activities required to comply with this paragraph will, of necessity, take longer than 90 days to complete; or

(ii)(A) The hazardous waste management unit or facility has the capacity to receive additional hazardous wastes, or has the capacity to receive non-hazardous wastes if the owner or operator complies with paragraphs (d) and (e) of this section; and

(B) There is a reasonable likelihood that he or another person will recommence operation of the hazardous waste management unit or the facility within one year; and

(C) Closure of the hazardous waste management unit or facility would be incompatible with continued operation of the site; and

(2) He has taken and will continue to take all steps to prevent threats to human health and the environment, including compliance with all applicable permit requirements.

(b) The owner or operator must complete partial and final closure activities in accordance with the approved closure plan and within 180 days after receiving the final volume of hazardous wastes, or the final volume of non-hazardous wastes if the owner or operator complies with all applicable requirements in paragraphs (d) and (e) of this section, at the hazardous waste management unit or facility. The Regional Administrator may approve an extension to the closure period if the owner or operator complies with all applicable requirements for requesting a modification to the permit and demonstrates that:

(1)(i) The partial or final closure activities will, of necessity, take longer than 180 days to complete; or

(ii)(A) The hazardous waste management unit or facility has the capacity to receive additional hazardous wastes, or has the capacity to receive non-hazardous wastes if the owner or operator complies with paragraphs (d) and (e) of this section; and

(B) There is reasonable likelihood that he or another person will recommence operation of the hazardous waste management unit or the facility within one year; and

(C) Closure of the hazardous waste management unit or facility would be incompatible with continued operation of the site; and

(2) He has taken and will continue to take all steps to prevent threats to human health and the environment from the unclosed but not operating hazardous waste management unit or facility, including compliance with all applicable permit requirements.

(c) The demonstrations referred to in paragraphs (a)(1) and (b)(1) of this section must be made as follows:

(1) The demonstrations in paragraph (a)(1) of this section must be made at least 30 days prior to the expiration of the 90-day period in paragraph (a) of this section; and

(2) The demonstration in paragraph (b)(1) of this section must be made at least 30 days prior to the expiration of the 180-day period in paragraph (b) of this section, unless the owner or operator is otherwise subject to the deadlines in paragraph (d) of this section.

(d) The Regional Administrator may allow an owner or operator to receive only non-hazardous wastes in a landfill, land treatment, or surface impoundment unit after the final receipt of hazardous wastes at that unit if:

(1) The owner or operator requests a permit modification in compliance with all applicable requirements in parts 270 and 124 of this title and in the permit modification request demonstrates that:

(i) The unit has the existing design capacity as indicated on the part A application to receive non-hazardous wastes; and

(ii) There is a reasonable likelihood that the owner or operator or another person will receive non-hazardous wastes in the unit within one year after the final receipt of hazardous wastes; and

(iii) The non-hazardous wastes will not be incompatible with any remaining wastes in the unit, or with the facility design and operating requirements of the unit or facility under this part; and

(iv) Closure of the hazardous waste management unit would be incompatible with continued operation of the unit or facility; and

(v) The owner or operator is operating and will continue to operate in compliance with all applicable permit requirements; and

(2) The request to modify the permit includes an amended waste analysis plan, ground-water monitoring and response program, human exposure assessment required under RCRA section 3019, and closure

and post-closure plans, and updated cost estimates and demonstrations of financial assurance for closure and post-closure care as necessary and appropriate, to reflect any changes due to the presence of hazardous constituents in the non-hazardous wastes, and changes in closure activities, including the expected year of closure if applicable under §264.112(b)(7), as a result of the receipt of non-hazardous wastes following the final receipt of hazardous wastes; and

(3) The request to modify the permit includes revisions, as necessary and appropriate, to affected conditions of the permit to account for the receipt of non-hazardous wastes following receipt of the final volume of hazardous wastes; and

(4) The request to modify the permit and the demonstrations referred to in paragraphs (d)(1) and (d)(2) of this section are submitted to the Regional Administrator no later than 120 days prior to the date on which the owner or operator of the facility receives the known final volume of hazardous wastes at the unit, or no later than 90 days after the effective date of this rule in the state in which the unit is located, whichever is later.

(e) In addition to the requirements in paragraph (d) of this section, an owner or operator of a hazardous waste surface impoundment that is not in compliance with the liner and leachate collection system requirements in 42 U.S.C. 3004(o)(1) and 3005(j)(1) or 42 U.S.C. 3004(o)(2) or (3) or 3005(j)(2), (3), (4) or (13) must:

(1) Submit with the request to modify the permit:

(i) A contingent corrective measures plan, unless a corrective action plan has already been submitted under §264.99; and

(ii) A plan for removing hazardous wastes in compliance with paragraph (e)(2) of this section; and

(2) Remove all hazardous wastes from the unit by removing all hazardous liquids, and removing all hazardous sludges to the extent practicable without impairing the integrity of the liner(s), if any.

(3) Removal of hazardous wastes must be completed no later than 90 days after the final receipt of hazardous wastes. The Regional Administrator may approve an extension to this deadline if the owner or operator demonstrates that the removal of hazardous wastes will, of necessity, take longer than the allotted period to complete and that an extension will not pose a threat to human health and the environment.

(4) If a release that is a statistically significant increase (or decrease in the case of pH) over background values for detection monitoring parameters or constituents specified in the permit or that exceeds the facility's ground-water protection standard at the point of compliance, if applicable, is detected in accordance with the requirements in subpart F of this part, the owner or operator of the unit:

(i) Must implement corrective measures in accordance with the approved contingent corrective measures plan required by paragraph (e)(1) of this section no later than one year after detection of the release, or approval of the contingent corrective measures plan, whichever is later;

(ii) May continue to receive wastes at the unit following detection of the release only if the approved corrective measures plan includes a demonstration that continued receipt of wastes will not impede corrective action; and

(iii) May be required by the Regional Administrator to implement corrective measures in less than one year or to cease the receipt of wastes until corrective measures have been implemented if necessary to protect human health and the environment.

(5) During the period of corrective action, the owner or operator shall provide annual reports to the Regional Administrator describing the progress of the corrective action program, compile all ground-water monitoring data, and evaluate the effect of the continued receipt of non-hazardous wastes on the effectiveness of the corrective action.

(6) The Regional Administrator may require the owner or operator to commence closure of the unit if the owner or operator fails to implement corrective action measures in accordance with the approved contingent corrective measures plan within one year as required in paragraph (e)(4) of this section, or fails to make substantial progress in implementing corrective action and achieving the facility's ground-water protection standard or background levels if the facility has not yet established a ground-water protection standard.

(7) If the owner or operator fails to implement corrective measures as required in paragraph (e)(4) of this section, or if the Regional Administrator determines that substantial progress has not been made pursuant to paragraph (e)(6) of this section he shall:

(i) Notify the owner or operator in writing that the owner or operator must begin closure in accordance with the deadlines in paragraphs (a) and (b) of this section and provide a detailed statement of reasons for this determination, and

(ii) Provide the owner or operator and the public, through a newspaper notice, the opportunity to submit written comments on the decision no later than 20 days after the date of the notice.

(iii) If the Regional Administrator receives no written comments, the decision will become final five days after the close of the comment period. The Regional Administrator will notify the owner or operator that the decision is final, and that a revised closure plan, if necessary, must be submitted within 15 days of the final notice and that closure must begin in accordance with the deadlines in paragraphs (a) and (b) of this section.

(iv) If the Regional Administrator receives written comments on the decision, he shall make a final decision within 30 days after the end of the comment period, and provide the owner or operator in writing and the public through a newspaper notice, a detailed statement of reasons for the final decision. If the Regional Administrator determines that substantial progress has not been made, closure must be initiated in accordance with the deadlines in paragraphs (a) and (b) of this section.

(v) The final determinations made by the Regional Administrator under paragraphs (e)(7) (iii) and (iv) of this section are not subject to administrative appeal.

[51 FR 16444, May 2, 1986, as amended at 54 FR 33394, Aug. 14, 1989; 71 FR 16904, Apr. 4, 2006]

§264.114 Disposal or decontamination of equipment, structures and soils.

During the partial and final closure periods, all contaminated equipment, structures and soils must be properly disposed of or decontaminated unless otherwise specified in §§264.197, 264.228, 264.258, 264.280 or §264.310. By removing any hazardous wastes or hazardous constituents during partial and final closure, the owner or operator may become a generator of hazardous waste and must handle that waste in accordance with all applicable requirements of part 262 of this chapter.

[51 FR 16444, May 2, 1986, as amended at 52 FR 46963, Dec. 10, 1987; 53 FR 34086, Sept. 2, 1988]

§264.115 Certification of closure.

Within 60 days of completion of closure of each hazardous waste surface impoundment, waste pile, land treatment, and landfill unit, and within 60 days of the completion of final closure, the owner or operator must submit to the Regional Administrator, by registered mail, a certification that the hazardous waste management unit or facility, as applicable, has been closed in accordance with the specifications in the approved closure plan. The certification must be signed by the owner or operator and by a qualified Professional Engineer. Documentation supporting the Professional Engineer's certification must be furnished to the Regional Administrator upon request until he releases the owner or operator from the financial assurance requirements for closure under §264.143(i).

[71 FR 16904, Apr. 4, 2006, as amended at 71 FR 40272, July 14, 2006]

§264.116 Survey plat.

No later than the submission of the certification of closure of each hazardous waste disposal unit, the owner or operator must submit to the local zoning authority, or the authority with jurisdiction over local land use, and to the Regional Administrator, a survey plat indicating the location and dimensions of landfill cells or other hazardous waste disposal units with respect to permanently surveyed benchmarks. This plat must be prepared and certified by a professional land surveyor. The plat filed with the local zoning authority, or the authority with jurisdiction over local land use, must contain a note, prominently displayed, which states the owner's or operator's obligation to restrict disturbance of the hazardous waste disposal unit in accordance with the applicable subpart G regulations.

[51 FR 16444, May 2, 1986, as amended at 71 FR 40272, July 14, 2006]

§264.117 Post-closure care and use of property.

(a)(1) Post-closure care for each hazardous waste management unit subject to the requirements of §§264.117 through 264.120 must begin after completion of closure of the unit and continue for 30 years after that date and must consist of at least the following:

(i) Monitoring and reporting in accordance with the requirements of subparts F, K, L, M, N, and X of this part; and

(ii) Maintenance and monitoring of waste containment systems in accordance with the requirements of subparts F, K, L, M, N, and X of this part.

(2) Any time preceding partial closure of a hazardous waste management unit subject to post-closure care requirements or final closure, or any time during the post-closure period for a particular unit, the Regional Administrator may, in accordance with the permit modification procedures in parts 124 and 270:

(i) Shorten the post-closure care period applicable to the hazardous waste management unit, or facility, if all disposal units have been closed, if he finds that the reduced period is sufficient to protect human health and the environment (*e.g.*, leachate or ground-water monitoring results, characteristics of the hazardous wastes, application of advanced technology, or alternative disposal, treatment, or re-use techniques indicate that the hazardous waste management unit or facility is secure); or

(ii) Extend the post-closure care period applicable to the hazardous waste management unit or facility if he finds that the extended period is necessary to protect human health and the environment (*e.g.*, leachate or ground-water monitoring results indicate a potential for migration of hazardous wastes at levels which may be harmful to human health and the environment).

(b) The Regional Administrator may require, at partial and final closure, continuation of any of the security requirements of §264.14 during part or all of the post-closure period when:

(1) Hazardous wastes may remain exposed after completion of partial or final closure; or

(2) Access by the public or domestic livestock may pose a hazard to human health.

(c) Post-closure use of property on or in which hazardous wastes remain after partial or final closure must never be allowed to disturb the integrity of the final cover, liner(s), or any other components of the containment system, or the function of the facility's monitoring systems, unless the Regional Administrator finds that the disturbance:

(1) Is necessary to the proposed use of the property, and will not increase the potential hazard to human health or the environment; or

(2) Is necessary to reduce a threat to human health or the environment.

(d) All post-closure care activities must be in accordance with the provisions of the approved post-closure plan as specified in §264.118.

[51 FR 16444, May 2, 1986, as amended at 52 FR 46963, Dec. 10, 1987]

§264.118 Post-closure plan; amendment of plan.

(a) *Written Plan.* The owner or operator of a hazardous waste disposal unit must have a written post-closure plan. In addition, certain surface impoundments and waste piles from which the owner or operator intends to remove or decontaminate the hazardous wastes at partial or final closure are required by §§264.228(c)(1)(ii) and 264.258(c)(1)(ii) to have contingent post-closure plans. Owners or operators of surface impoundments and waste piles not otherwise required to prepare contingent post-closure plans under §§264.228(c)(1)(ii) and 264.258(c)(1)(ii) must submit a post-closure plan to the Regional Administrator within 90 days from the date that the owner or operator or Regional administrator determines that the hazardous waste management unit must be closed as a landfill, subject to the requirements of §§264.117 through 264.120. The plan must be submitted with the permit application, in accordance with §270.14(b)(13) of this chapter, and approved by the Regional Administrator as part of the permit issuance procedures under part 124 of this chapter. In accordance with §270.32 of this chapter, the approved post-closure plan will become a condition of any RCRA permit issued.

(b) For each hazardous waste management unit subject to the requirements of this section, the post-closure plan must identify the activities that will be carried on after closure of each disposal unit and the frequency of these activities, and include at least:

(1) A description of the planned monitoring activities and frequencies at which they will be performed to comply with subparts F, K, L, M, N, and X of this part during the post-closure care period; and

(2) A description of the planned maintenance activities, and frequencies at which they will be performed, to ensure:

(i) The integrity of the cap and final cover or other containment systems in accordance with the requirements of subparts F, K, L, M, N, and X of this part; and

(ii) The function of the monitoring equipment in accordance with the requirements of subparts, F, K, L, M, N, and X of this part; and

(3) The name, address, and phone number of the person or office to contact about the hazardous waste disposal unit or facility during the post-closure care period.

(4) For facilities where the Regional Administrator has applied alternative requirements at a regulated unit under §§264.90(f), 264.110(c), and/or §§264.140(d), either the alternative requirements that apply to the regulated unit, or a reference to the enforceable document containing those requirements.

(c) Until final closure of the facility, a copy of the approved post-closure plan must be furnished to the Regional Administrator upon request, including request by mail. After final closure has been certified, the person or office specified in §264.118(b)(3) must keep the approved post-closure plan during the remainder of the post-closure period.

(d) *Amendment of plan.* The owner or operator must submit a written notification of or request for a permit modification to authorize a change in the approved post-closure plan in accordance with the applicable requirements in parts 124 and 270. The written notification or request must include a copy of the amended post-closure plan for review or approval by the Regional Administrator.

(1) The owner or operator may submit a written notification or request to the Regional Administrator for a permit modification to amend the post-closure plan at any time during the active life of the facility or during the post-closure care period.

(2) The owner or operator must submit a written notification of or request for a permit modification to authorize a change in the approved post-closure plan whenever:

(i) Changes in operating plans or facility design affect the approved post-closure plan, or

(ii) There is a change in the expected year of final closure, if applicable, or

(iii) Events which occur during the active life of the facility, including partial and final closures, affect the approved post-closure plan.

(iv) The owner or operator requests the Regional Administrator to apply alternative requirements to a regulated unit under §§264.90(f), 264.110(c), and/or §264.140(d).

(3) The owner or operator must submit a written request for a permit modification at least 60 days prior to the proposed change in facility design or operation, or no later than 60 days after an unexpected event has occurred which has affected the post-closure plan. An owner or operator of a surface impoundment or waste pile that intends to remove all hazardous waste at closure and is not otherwise required to submit a contingent post-closure plan under §§264.228(c)(1)(ii) and 264.258(c)(1)(ii) must submit a post-closure plan to the Regional Administrator no later than 90 days after the date that the owner or operator or Regional Administrator determines that the hazardous waste management unit must be closed as a landfill, subject to the requirements of §264.310. The Regional Administrator will approve, disapprove or modify this plan in accordance with the procedures in parts 124 and 270. In accordance with §270.32 of this chapter, the approved post-closure plan will become a permit condition.

(4) The Regional Administrator may request modifications to the plan under the conditions described in §264.118(d)(2). The owner or operator must submit the modified plan no later than 60 days after the Regional Administrator's request, or no later than 90 days if the unit is a surface impoundment or waste pile not previously required to prepare a contingent post-closure plan. Any modifications requested by the Regional Administrator will be approved, disapproved, or modified in accordance with the procedures in parts 124 and 270.

[51 FR 16444, May 2, 1986, as amended at 52 FR 46964, Dec. 10, 1987; 53 FR 37935, Sept. 28,1988; 63 FR 56733, Oct. 22, 1998; 71 FR 40272, July 14, 2006]

§264.119 Post-closure notices.

(a) No later than 60 days after certification of closure of each hazardous waste disposal unit, the owner or operator must submit to the local zoning authority, or the authority with jurisdiction over local land use, and to the Regional Administrator a record of the type, location, and quantity of hazardous wastes disposed of within each cell or other disposal unit of the facility. For hazardous wastes disposed of before January 12, 1981, the owner or operator must identify the type, location, and quantity of the hazardous wastes to the best of his knowledge and in accordance with any records he has kept.

(b) Within 60 days of certification of closure of the first hazardous waste disposal unit and within 60 days of certification of closure of the last hazardous waste disposal unit, the owner or operator must:

(1) Record, in accordance with State law, a notation on the deed to the facility property—or on some other instrument which is normally examined during title search—that will in perpetuity notify any potential purchaser of the property that:

(i) The land has been used to manage hazardous wastes; and

(ii) Its use is restricted under 40 CFR part 264, subpart G regulations; and

(iii) The survey plat and record of the type, location, and quantity of hazardous wastes disposed of within each cell or other hazardous waste disposal unit of the facility required by §§264.116 and 264.119(a) have been filed with the local zoning authority or the authority with jurisdiction over local land use and with the Regional Administrator; and

(2) Submit a certification, signed by the owner or operator, that he has recorded the notation specified in

paragraph (b)(1) of this section, including a copy of the document in which the notation has been placed, to the Regional Administrator.

(c) If the owner or operator or any subsequent owner or operator of the land upon which a hazardous waste disposal unit is located wishes to remove hazardous wastes and hazardous waste residues, the liner, if any, or contaminated soils, he must request a modification to the post-closure permit in accordance with the applicable requirements in parts 124 and 270. The owner or operator must demonstrate that the removal of hazardous wastes will satisfy the criteria of §264.117(c). By removing hazardous waste, the owner or operator may become a generator of hazardous waste and must manage it in accordance with all applicable requirements of this chapter. If he is granted a permit modification or otherwise granted approval to conduct such removal activities, the owner or operator may request that the Regional Administrator approve either:

(1) The removal of the notation on the deed to the facility property or other instrument normally examined during title search; or

(2) The addition of a notation to the deed or instrument indicating the removal of the hazardous waste.

[51 FR 16444, May 2, 1986, as amended at 71 FR 40272, July 14, 2006]

§264.120 Certification of completion of post-closure care.

No later than 60 days after completion of the established post-closure care period for each hazardous waste disposal unit, the owner or operator must submit to the Regional Administrator, by registered mail, a certification that the post-closure care period for the hazardous waste disposal unit was performed in accordance with the specifications in the approved post-closure plan. The certification must be signed by the owner or operator and a qualified Professional Engineer. Documentation supporting the Professional Engineer's certification must be furnished to the Regional Administrator upon request until he releases the owner or operator from the financial assurance requirements for post-closure care under §264.145(i).

[71 FR 16904, Apr. 4, 2006]

Subpart H—Financial Requirements

Source: 47 FR 15047, Apr. 7, 1982, unless otherwise noted.

§264.140 Applicability.

(a) The requirements of §§264.142, 264.143, and 264.147 through 264.151 apply to owners and operators of all hazardous waste facilities, except as provided otherwise in this section or in §264.1.

(b) The requirements of §§264.144 and 264.145 apply only to owners and operators of:

(1) Disposal facilities;

(2) Piles, and surface impoundments from which the owner or operator intends to remove the wastes at closure, to the extent that these sections are made applicable to such facilities in §§264.228 and 264.258;

(3) Tank systems that are required under §264.197 to meet the requirements for landfills; and

(4) Containment buildings that are required under §264.1102 to meet the requirements for landfills.

(c) States and the Federal government are exempt from the requirements of this subpart.

(d) The Regional Administrator may replace all or part of the requirements of this subpart applying to a regulated unit with alternative requirements for financial assurance set out in the permit or in an enforceable document (as defined in 40 CFR 270.1(c)(7)), where the Regional Administrator:

(1) Prescribes alternative requirements for the regulated unit under §264.90(f) and/or §264.110(c); and

(2) Determines that it is not necessary to apply the requirements of this subpart because the alternative financial assurance requirements will protect human health and the environment.

[47 FR 15047, Apr. 7, 1982, as amended at 47 FR 32357, July 26, 1982; 51 FR 25472, July 14, 1986; 57 FR 37265, Aug. 18, 1992; 63 FR 56733, Oct. 22, 1998; 71 FR 40272, July 14, 2006]

§264.141 Definitions of terms as used in this subpart.

(a) *Closure plan* means the plan for closure prepared in accordance with the requirements of §264.112.

(b) *Current closure cost estimate* means the most recent of the estimates prepared in accordance with §264.142 (a), (b), and (c).

(c) *Current post-closure cost estimate* means the most recent of the estimates prepared in accordance with §264.144 (a), (b), and (c).

(d) *Parent corporation* means a corporation which directly owns at least 50 percent of the voting stock of the corporation which is the facility owner or operator; the latter corporation is deemed a "subsidiary" of the parent corporation.

(e) *Post-closure plan* means the plan for post-closure care prepared in accordance with the requirements of §§264.117 through 264.120.

(f) The following terms are used in the specifications for the financial tests for closure, post-closure care, and liability coverage. The definitions are intended to assist in the understanding of these regulations and are not intended to limit the meanings of terms in a way that conflicts with generally accepted accounting practices.

Assets means all existing and all probable future economic benefits obtained or controlled by a particular entity.

Current assets means cash or other assets or resources commonly identified as those which are reasonably expected to be realized in cash or sold or consumed during the normal operating cycle of the business.

Current liabilities means obligations whose liquidation is reasonably expected to require the use of existing resources properly classifiable as current assets or the creation of other current liabilities.

Current plugging and abandonment cost estimate means the most recent of the estimates prepared in accordance with §144.62(a), (b), and (c) of this title.

Independently audited refers to an audit performed by an independent certified public accountant in accordance with generally accepted auditing standards.

Liabilities means probable future sacrifices of economic benefits arising from present obligations to transfer assets or provide services to other entities in the future as a result of past transactions or events.

Net working capital means current assets minus current liabilities.

Net worth means total assets minus total liabilities and is equivalent to owner's equity.

Tangible net worth means the tangible assets that remain after deducting liabilities; such assets would not include intangibles such as goodwill and rights to patents or royalties.

(g) In the liability insurance requirements the terms *bodily injury* and *property damage* shall have the meanings given these terms by applicable State law. However, these terms do not include those liabilities which, consistent with standard industry practices, are excluded from coverage in liability policies for bodily injury and property damage. The Agency intends the meanings of other terms used in the liability insurance requirements to be consistent with their common meanings within the insurance industry. The definitions given below of several of the terms are intended to assist in the understanding of these regulations and are not intended to limit their meanings in a way that conflicts with general insurance industry usage.

Accidental occurrence means an accident, including continuous or repeated exposure to conditions, which results in bodily injury or property damage neither expected nor intended from the standpoint of the insured.

Legal defense costs means any expenses that an insurer incurs in defending against claims of third parties brought under the terms and conditions of an insurance policy.

Nonsudden accidental occurrence means an occurrence which takes place over time and involves continuous or repeated exposure.

Sudden accidental occurrence means an occurrence which is not continuous or repeated in nature.

(h) *Substantial business relationship* means the extent of a business relationship necessary under applicable State law to make a guarantee contract issued incident to that relationship valid and enforceable. A "substantial business relationship" must arise from a pattern of recent or ongoing business transactions, in addition to the guarantee itself, such that a currently existing business relationship between the guarantor and the owner or operator is demonstrated to the satisfaction of the applicable EPA Regional Administrator.

[47 FR 16554, Apr. 16, 1982, as amended at 51 FR 16447, May 2, 1986; 53 FR 33950, Sept. 1, 1988]

§264.142 Cost estimate for closure.

(a) The owner or operator must have a detailed written estimate, in current dollars, of the cost of closing the facility in accordance with the requirements in §§264.111 through 264.115 and applicable closure requirements in §§264.178, 264.197, 264.228, 264.258, 264.280, 264.310, 264.351, 264.601 through 264.603, and 264.1102.

(1) The estimate must equal the cost of final closure at the point in the facility's active life when the extent and manner of its operation would make closure the most expensive, as indicated by its closure plan (see §264.112(b)); and

(2) The closure cost estimate must be based on the costs to the owner or operator of hiring a third party to close the facility. A third party is a party who is neither a parent nor a subsidiary of the owner or operator. (See definition of parent corporation in §264.141(d).) The owner or operator may use costs for on-site disposal if he can demonstrate that on-site disposal capacity will exist at all times over the life of the facility.

(3) The closure cost estimate may not incorporate any salvage value that may be realized with the sale of hazardous wastes, or non-hazardous wastes if applicable under §264.113(d), facility structures or equipment,

land, or other assets associated with the facility at the time of partial or final closure.

(4) The owner or operator may not incorporate a zero cost for hazardous wastes, or non-hazardous wastes if applicable under §264.113(d), that might have economic value.

(b) During the active life of the facility, the owner or operator must adjust the closure cost estimate for inflation within 60 days prior to the anniversary date of the establishment of the financial instrument(s) used to comply with §264.143. For owners and operators using the financial test or corporate guarantee, the closure cost estimate must be updated for inflation within 30 days after the close of the firm's fiscal year and before submission of updated information to the Regional Administrator as specified in §264.143(f)(3). The adjustment may be made by recalculating the maximum costs of closure in current dollars, or by using an inflation factor derived from the most recent Implicit Price Deflator for Gross National Product published by the U.S. Department of Commerce in its *Survey of Current Business*, as specified in paragraphs (b)(1) and (2) of this section. The inflation factor is the result of dividing the latest published annual Deflator by the Deflator for the previous year.

(1) The first adjustment is made by multiplying the closure cost estimate by the inflation factor. The result is the adjusted closure cost estimate.

(2) Subsequent adjustments are made by multiplying the latest adjusted closure cost estimate by the latest inflation factor.

(c) During the active life of the facility, the owner or operator must revise the closure cost estimate no later than 30 days after the Regional Administrator has approved the request to modify the closure plan, if the change in the closure plan increases the cost of closure. The revised closure cost estimate must be adjusted for inflation as specified in §264.142(b).

(d) The owner or operator must keep the following at the facility during the operating life of the facility: The latest closure cost estimate prepared in accordance with §264.142 (a) and (c) and, when this estimate has been adjusted in accordance with §264.142(b), the latest adjusted closure cost estimate.

[47 FR 15047, Apr. 7, 1982, as amended at 50 FR 4514, Jan. 31, 1985; 51 FR 16447, May 2, 1986; 52 FR 46964, Dec. 10, 1987; 54 FR 33395, Aug. 14, 1989; 57 FR 37265, Aug. 18, 1992; 71 FR 40272, July 14, 2006]

§264.143 Financial assurance for closure.

An owner or operator of each facility must establish financial assurance for closure of the facility. He must choose from the options as specified in paragraphs (a) through (f) of this section.

(a) *Closure trust fund.* (1) An owner or operator may satisfy the requirements of this section by establishing a closure trust fund which conforms to the requirements of this paragraph and submitting an originally signed duplicate of the trust agreement to the Regional Administrator. An owner or operator of a new facility must submit the originally signed duplicate of the trust agreement to the Regional Administrator at least 60 days before the date on which hazardous waste is first received for treatment, storage, or disposal. The trustee must be an entity which has the authority to act as a trustee and whose trust operations are regulated and examined by a Federal or State agency.

(2) The wording of the trust agreement must be identical to the wording specified in §264.151(a)(1), and the trust agreement must be accompanied by a formal certification of acknowledgment (for example, see §264.151(a)(2)). Schedule A of the trust agreement must be updated within 60 days after a change in the amount of the current closure cost estimate covered by the agreement.

(3) Payments into the trust fund must be made annually by the owner or operator over the term of the initial RCRA permit or over the remaining operating life of the facility as estimated in the closure plan, whichever period is shorter; this period is hereafter referred to as the "pay-in period." The payments into the closure trust fund must be made as follows:

(i) For a new facility, the first payment must be made before the initial receipt of hazardous waste for treatment, storage, or disposal. A receipt from the trustee for this payment must be submitted by the owner or operator to the Regional Administrator before this initial receipt of hazardous waste. The first payment must be at least equal to the current closure cost estimate, except as provided in §264.143(g), divided by the number of years in the pay-in period. Subsequent payments must be made no later than 30 days after each anniversary date of the first payment. The amount of each subsequent payment must be determined by this formula:

$$\text{Next payment} = \frac{CE - CV}{Y}$$

where CE is the current closure cost estimate, CV is the current value of the trust fund, and Y is the number of years remaining in the pay-in period.

(ii) If an owner or operator establishes a trust fund as specified in §265.143(a) of this chapter, and the value of that trust fund is less than the current closure cost estimate when a permit is awarded for the facility, the amount of the current closure cost estimate still to be paid into the trust fund must be paid in over the pay-in period as defined in paragraph (a)(3) of this section. Payments must continue to be made no later than 30 days after each anniversary date of the first payment made pursuant to part 265 of this chapter. The amount of each payment must be determined by this formula:

$$\text{Next payment} = \frac{CE - CV}{Y}$$

where CE is the current closure cost estimate, CV is the current value of the trust fund, and Y is the number of years remaining in the pay-in period.

(4) The owner or operator may accelerate payments into the trust fund or he may deposit the full amount of the current closure cost estimate at the time the fund is established. However, he must maintain the value of the fund at no less than the value that the fund would have if annual payments were made as specified in paragraph (a)(3) of this section.

(5) If the owner or operator establishes a closure trust fund after having used one or more alternate mechanisms specified in this section or in §265.143 of this chapter, his first payment must be in at least the amount that the fund would contain if the trust fund were established initially and annual payments made according to specifications of this paragraph and §265.143(a) of this chapter, as applicable.

(6) After the pay-in period is completed, whenever the current closure cost estimate changes, the owner or operator must compare the new estimate with the trustee's most recent annual valuation of the trust fund. If the value of the fund is less than the amount of the new estimate, the owner or operator, within 60 days after the change in the cost estimate, must either deposit an amount into the fund so that its value after this deposit at least equals the amount of the current closure cost estimate, or obtain other financial assurance as specified in this section to cover the difference.

(7) If the value of the trust fund is greater than the total amount of the current closure cost estimate, the owner or operator may submit a written request to the Regional Administrator for release of the amount in excess of the current closure cost estimate.

(8) If an owner or operator substitutes other financial assurance as specified in this section for all or part of the trust fund, he may submit a written request to the Regional Administrator for release of the amount in excess of the current closure cost estimate covered by the trust fund.

(9) Within 60 days after receiving a request from the owner or operator for release of funds as specified in paragraph (a) (7) or (8) of this section, the Regional Administrator will instruct the trustee to release to the owner or operator such funds as the Regional Administrator specifies in writing.

(10) After beginning partial or final closure, an owner or operator or another person authorized to conduct partial or final closure may request reimbursements for partial or final closure expenditures by submitting itemized bills to the Regional Administrator. The owner or operator may request reimbursements for partial closure only if sufficient funds are remaining in the trust fund to cover the maximum costs of closing the facility over its remaining operating life. Within 60 days after receiving bills for partial or final closure activities, the Regional Administrator will instruct the trustee to make reimbursements in those amounts as the Regional Administrator specifies in writing, if the Regional Administrator determines that the partial or final closure expenditures are in accordance with the approved closure plan, or otherwise justified. If the Regional Administrator has reason to believe that the maximum cost of closure over the remaining life of the facility will be significantly greater than the value of the trust fund, he may withhold reimbursements of such amounts as he deems prudent until he determines, in accordance with §264.143(i) that the owner or operator is no longer required to maintain financial assurance for final closure of the facility. If the Regional Administrator does not instruct the trustee to make such reimbursements, he will provide the owner or operator with a detailed written statement of reasons.

(11) The Regional Administrator will agree to termination of the trust when:

(i) An owner or operator substitutes alternate financial assurance as specified in this section; or

(ii) The Regional Administrator releases the owner or operator from the requirements of this section in accordance with §264.143(i).

(b) *Surety bond guaranteeing payment into a closure trust fund.* (1) An owner or operator may satisfy the requirements of this section by obtaining a surety bond which conforms to the requirements of this paragraph and submitting the bond to the Regional Administrator. An owner or operator of a new facility must submit the bond to the Regional Administrator at least 60 days before the date on which hazardous waste is first received for treatment, storage, or disposal. The bond must be effective before this initial receipt of hazardous waste. The surety company issuing the bond must, at a minimum, be among those listed as acceptable sureties on Federal bonds in Circular 570 of the U.S. Department of the Treasury.

(2) The wording of the surety bond must be identical to the wording specified in §264.151(b).

(3) The owner or operator who uses a surety bond to satisfy the requirements of this section must also establish a standby trust fund. Under the terms of the bond, all payments made thereunder will be deposited by the surety directly into the standby trust fund in accordance with instructions from the Regional Administrator. This standby trust fund must meet the requirements specified in §264.143(a), except that:

(i) An originally signed duplicate of the trust agreement must be submitted to the Regional Administrator with the surety bond; and

(ii) Until the standby trust fund is funded pursuant to the requirements of this section, the following are not required by these regulations:

(A) Payments into the trust fund as specified in §264.143(a);

(B) Updating of Schedule A of the trust agreement (see §264.151(a)) to show current closure cost estimates;

(C) Annual valuations as required by the trust agreement; and

(D) Notices of nonpayment as required by the trust agreement.

(4) The bond must guarantee that the owner or operator will:

(i) Fund the standby trust fund in an amount equal to the penal sum of the bond before the beginning of final closure of the facility; or

(ii) Fund the standby trust fund in an amount equal to the penal sum within 15 days after an administrative order to begin final closure issued by the Regional Administrator becomes final, or within 15 days after an order to begin final closure is issued by a U.S. district court or other court of competent jurisdiction; or

(iii) Provide alternate financial assurance as specified in this section, and obtain the Regional Administrator's written approval of the assurance provided, within 90 days after receipt by both the owner or operator and the Regional Administrator of a notice of cancellation of the bond from the surety.

(5) Under the terms of the bond, the surety will become liable on the bond obligation when the owner or operator fails to perform as guaranteed by the bond.

(6) The penal sum of the bond must be in an amount at least equal to the current closure cost estimate, except as provided in §264.143(g).

(7) Whenever the current closure cost estimate increases to an amount greater than the penal sum, the owner or operator, within 60 days after the increase, must either cause the penal sum to be increased to an amount at least equal to the current closure cost estimate and submit evidence of such increase to the Regional Administrator, or obtain other financial assurance as specified in this section to cover the increase. Whenever the current closure cost estimate decreases, the penal sum may be reduced to the amount of the current closure cost estimate following written approval by the Regional Administrator.

(8) Under the terms of the bond, the surety may cancel the bond by sending notice of cancellation by certified mail to the owner or operator and to the Regional Administrator. Cancellation may not occur, however, during the 120 days beginning on the date of receipt of the notice of cancellation by both the owner or operator and the Regional Administrator, as evidenced by the return receipts.

(9) The owner or operator may cancel the bond if the Regional Administrator has given prior written consent based on his receipt of evidence of alternate financial assurance as specified in this section.

(c) *Surety bond guaranteeing performance of closure.* (1) An owner or operator may satisfy the requirements of this section by obtaining a surety bond which conforms to the requirements of this paragraph and submitting the bond to the Regional Administrator. An owner or operator of a new facility must submit the bond to the Regional Administrator at least 60 days before the date on which hazardous waste is first received for treatment, storage, or disposal. The bond must be effective before this initial receipt of hazardous waste. The surety company issuing the bond must, at a minimum, be among those listed as acceptable sureties on

Federal bonds in Circular 570 of the U.S. Department of the Treasury.

(2) The wording of the surety bond must be identical to the wording specified in §264.151(c).

(3) The owner or operator who uses a surety bond to satisfy the requirements of this section must also establish a standby trust fund. Under the terms of the bond, all payments made thereunder will be deposited by the surety directly into the standby trust fund in accordance with instructions from the Regional Administrator. This standby trust must meet the requirements specified in §264.143(a), except that:

(i) An originally signed duplicate of the trust agreement must be submitted to the Regional Administrator with the surety bond; and

(ii) Unless the standby trust fund is funded pursuant to the requirements of this section, the following are not required by these regulations:

(A) Payments into the trust fund as specified in §264.143(a);

(B) Updating of Schedule A of the trust agreement (see §264.151(a)) to show current closure cost estimates;

(C) Annual valuations as required by the trust agreement; and

(D) Notices of nonpayment as required by the trust agreement.

(4) The bond must guarantee that the owner or operator will:

(i) Perform final closure in accordance with the closure plan and other requirements of the permit for the facility whenever required to do so; or

(ii) Provide alternate financial assurance as specified in this section, and obtain the Regional Administrator's written approval of the assurance provided, within 90 days after receipt by both the owner or operator and the Regional Administrator of a notice of cancellation of the bond from the surety.

(5) Under the terms of the bond, the surety will become liable on the bond obligation when the owner or operator fails to perform as guaranteed by the bond. Following a final administrative determination pursuant to section 3008 of RCRA that the owner or operator has failed to perform final closure in accordance with the approved closure plan and other permit requirements when required to do so, under the terms of the bond the surety will perform final closure as guaranteed by the bond or will deposit the amount of the penal sum into the standby trust fund.

(6) The penal sum of the bond must be in an amount at least equal to the current closure cost estimate.

(7) Whenever the current closure cost estimate increases to an amount greater than the penal sum, the owner or operator, within 60 days after the increase, must either cause the penal sum to be increased to an amount at least equal to the current closure cost estimate and submit evidence of such increase to the Regional Administrator, or obtain other financial assurance as specified in this section. Whenever the current closure cost estimate decreases, the penal sum may be reduced to the amount of the current closure cost estimate following written approval by the Regional Administrator.

(8) Under the terms of the bond, the surety may cancel the bond by sending notice of cancellation by certified mail to the owner or operator and to the Regional Administrator. Cancellation may not occur, however, during the 120 days beginning on the date of receipt of the notice of cancellation by both the owner or operator and the Regional Administrator, as evidenced by the return receipts.

(9) The owner or operator may cancel the bond if the Regional Administrator has given prior written consent. The Regional Administrator will provide such written consent when:

(i) An owner or operator substitutes alternate financial assurance as specified in this section; or

(ii) The Regional Administrator releases the owner or operator from the requirements of this section in accordance with §264.143(i).

(10) The surety will not be liable for deficiencies in the performance of closure by the owner or operator after the Regional Administrator releases the owner or operator from the requirements of this section in accordance with §264.143(i).

(d) *Closure letter of credit.* (1) An owner or operator may satisfy the requirements of this section by obtaining an irrevocable standby letter of credit which conforms to the requirements of this paragraph and submitting the letter to the Regional Administrator. An owner or operator of a new facility must submit the letter of credit to the Regional Administrator at least 60 days before the date on which hazardous waste is first received for treatment, storage, or disposal. The letter of credit must be effective before this initial receipt of hazardous waste. The issuing institution must be an entity which has the authority to issue letters of credit and whose letter-of-credit operations are regulated and examined by a Federal or State agency.

(2) The wording of the letter of credit must be identical to the wording specified in §264.151(d).

(3) An owner or operator who uses a letter of credit to satisfy the requirements of this section must also establish a standby trust fund. Under the terms of the letter of credit, all amounts paid pursuant to a draft by the Regional Administrator will be deposited by the issuing institution directly into the standby trust fund in accordance with instructions from the Regional Administrator. This standby trust fund must meet the requirements of the trust fund specified in §264.143(a), except that:

(i) An originally signed duplicate of the trust agreement must be submitted to the Regional Administrator with the letter of credit; and

(ii) Unless the standby trust fund is funded pursuant to the requirements of this section, the following are not required by these regulations:

(A) Payments into the trust fund as specified in §264.143(a);

(B) Updating of Schedule A of the trust agreement (see §264.151(a)) to show current closure cost estimates;

(C) Annual valuations as required by the trust agreement; and

(D) Notices of nonpayment as required by the trust agreement.

(4) The letter of credit must be accompanied by a letter from the owner or operator referring to the letter of credit by number, issuing institution, and date, and providing the following information: the EPA Identification Number, name, and address of the facility, and the amount of funds assured for closure of the facility by the letter of credit.

(5) The letter of credit must be irrevocable and issued for a period of at least 1 year. The letter of credit must provide that the expiration date will be automatically extended for a period of at least 1 year unless, at least 120 days before the current expiration date, the issuing institution notifies both the owner or operator and the Regional Administrator by certified mail of a decision not to extend the expiration date. Under the terms of the letter of credit, the 120 days will begin on the date when both the owner or operator and the Regional Administrator have received the notice, as evidenced by the return receipts.

(6) The letter of credit must be issued in an amount at least equal to the current closure cost estimate, except as provided in §264.143(g).

(7) Whenever the current closure cost estimate increases to an amount greater than the amount of the credit, the owner or operator, within 60 days after the increase, must either cause the amount of the credit to be increased so that it at least equals the current closure cost estimate and submit evidence of such increase to the Regional Administrator, or obtain other financial assurance as specified in this section to cover the increase. Whenever the current closure cost estimate decreases, the amount of the credit may be reduced to the amount of the current closure cost estimate following written approval by the Regional Administrator.

(8) Following a final administrative determination pursuant to section 3008 of RCRA that the owner or operator has failed to perform final closure in accordance with the closure plan and other permit requirements when required to do so, the Regional Administrator may draw on the letter of credit.

(9) If the owner or operator does not establish alternate financial assurance as specified in this section and obtain written approval of such alternate assurance from the Regional Administrator within 90 days after receipt by both the owner or operator and the Regional Administrator of a notice from issuing institution that it has decided not to extend the letter of credit beyond the current expiration date, the Regional Administrator will draw on the letter of credit. The Regional Administrator may delay the drawing if the issuing institution grants an extension of the term of the credit. During the last 30 days of any such extension the Regional Administrator will draw on the letter of credit if the owner or operator has failed to provide alternate financial assurance as specified in this section and obtain written approval of such assurance from the Regional Administrator.

(10) The Regional Administrator will return the letter of credit to the issuing institution for termination when:

(i) An owner or operator substitutes alternate financial assurance as specified in this section; or

(ii) The Regional Administrator releases the owner or operator from the requirements of this section in accordance with §264.143(i).

(e) *Closure insurance.* (1) An owner or operator may satisfy the requirements of this section by obtaining closure insurance which conforms to the requirements of this paragraph and submitting a certificate of such insurance to the Regional Administrator. An owner or operator of a new facility must submit the certificate of insurance to the Regional Administrator at least 60 days before the date on which hazardous waste is first received for treatment, storage, or disposal. The insurance must be effective before this initial receipt of hazardous waste. At a minimum, the insurer must be licensed to transact the business of insurance, or eligible to provide insurance as an excess or surplus lines insurer, in one or more States.

(2) The wording of the certificate of insurance must be identical to the wording specified in §264.151(e).

(3) The closure insurance policy must be issued for a face amount at least equal to the current closure cost estimate, except as provided in §264.143(g). The term "face amount" means the total amount the insurer is obligated to pay under the policy. Actual payments by the insurer will not change the face amount, although the insurer's future liability will be lowered by the amount of the payments.

(4) The closure insurance policy must guarantee that funds will be available to close the facility whenever final closure occurs. The policy must also guarantee that once final closure begins, the insurer will be responsible for paying out funds, up to an amount equal to the face amount of the policy, upon the direction of the Regional Administrator, to such party or parties as the Regional Administrator specifies.

(5) After beginning partial or final closure, an owner or operator or any other person authorized to conduct closure may request reimbursements for closure expenditures by submitting itemized bills to the Regional Administrator. The owner or operator may request reimbursements for partial closure only if the remaining value of the policy is sufficient to cover the maximum costs of closing the facility over its remaining operating life. Within 60 days after receiving bills for closure activities, the Regional Administrator will instruct the insurer to make reimbursements in such amounts as the Regional Administrator specifies in writing, if the Regional Administrator determines that the partial or final closure expenditures are in accordance with the approved closure plan or otherwise justified. If the Regional Administrator has reason to believe that the maximum cost of closure over the remaining life of the facility will be significantly greater than the face amount of the policy, he may withhold reimbursements of such amounts as he deems prudent until he determines, in accordance with §264.143(i), that the owner or operator is no longer required to maintain financial assurance for final closure of the facility. If the Regional Administrator does not instruct the insurer to make such reimbursements, he will provide the owner or operator with a detailed written statement of reasons.

(6) The owner or operator must maintain the policy in full force and effect until the Regional Administrator consents to termination of the policy by the owner or operator as specified in paragraph (e)(10) of this section. Failure to pay the premium, without substitution of alternate financial assurance as specified in this section, will constitute a significant violation of these regulations, warranting such remedy as the Regional Administrator deems necessary. Such violation will be deemed to begin upon receipt by the Regional Administrator of a notice of future cancellation, termination, or failure to renew due to nonpayment of the premium, rather than upon the date of expiration.

(7) Each policy must contain a provision allowing assignment of the policy to a successor owner or operator. Such assignment may be conditional upon consent of the insurer, provided such consent is not unreasonably refused.

(8) The policy must provide that the insurer may not cancel, terminate, or fail to renew the policy except for failure to pay the premium. The automatic renewal of the policy must, at a minimum, provide the insured with the option of renewal at the face amount of the expiring policy. If there is a failure to pay the premium, the insurer may elect to cancel, terminate, or fail to renew the policy by sending notice by certified mail to the owner or operator and the Regional Administrator. Cancellation, termination, or failure to renew may not occur, however, during the 120 days beginning with the date of receipt of the notice by both the Regional Administrator and the owner or operator, as evidenced by the return receipts. Cancellation, termination, or failure to renew may not occur and the policy will remain in full force and effect in the event that on or before the date of expiration:

(i) The Regional Administrator deems the facility abandoned; or

(ii) The permit is terminated or revoked or a new permit is denied; or

(iii) Closure is ordered by the Regional Administrator or a U.S. district court or other court of competent jurisdiction; or

(iv) The owner or operator is named as debtor in a voluntary or involuntary proceeding under Title 11 (Bankruptcy), U.S. Code; or

(v) The premium due is paid.

(9) Whenever the current closure cost estimate increases to an amount greater than the face amount of the policy, the owner or operator, within 60 days after the increase, must either cause the face amount to be increased to an amount at least equal to the current closure cost estimate and submit evidence of such increase to the Regional Administrator, or obtain other financial assurance as specified in this section to cover the increase. Whenever the current closure cost estimate decreases, the face amount may be reduced to the amount of the current closure cost estimate following written approval by the Regional Administrator.

(10) The Regional Administrator will give written consent to the owner or operator that he may terminate the insurance policy when:

(i) An owner or operator substitutes alternate financial assurance as specified in this section; or

(ii) The Regional Administrator releases the owner or operator from the requirements of this section in accordance with §264.143(i).

(f) *Financial test and corporate guarantee for closure.* (1) An owner or operator may satisfy the requirements of this section by demonstrating that he passes a financial test as specified in this paragraph. To pass this test the owner or operator must meet the criteria of either paragraph (f)(1)(i) or (ii) of this section:

(i) The owner or operator must have:

(A) Two of the following three ratios: a ratio of total liabilities to net worth less than 2.0; a ratio of the sum of net income plus depreciation, depletion, and amortization to total liabilities greater than 0.1; and a ratio of current assets to current liabilities greater than 1.5; and

(B) Net working capital and tangible net worth each at least six times the sum of the current closure and post-closure cost estimates and the current plugging and abandonment cost estimates; and

(C) Tangible net worth of at least $10 million; and

(D) Assets located in the United States amounting to at least 90 percent of total assets or at least six times the sum of the current closure and post-closure cost estimates and the current plugging and abandonment cost estimates.

(ii) The owner or operator must have:

(A) A current rating for his most recent bond issuance of AAA, AA, A, or BBB as issued by Standard and Poor's or Aaa, Aa, A, or Baa as issued by Moody's; and

(B) Tangible net worth at least six times the sum of the current closure and post-closure cost estimates and the current plugging and abandonment cost estimates; and

(C) Tangible net worth of at least $10 million; and

(D) Assets located in the United States amounting to at least 90 percent of total assets or at least six times the sum of the current closure and post-closure cost estimates and the current plugging and abandonment cost estimates.

(2) The phrase "current closure and post-closure cost estimates" as used in paragraph (f)(1) of this section refers to the cost estimates required to be shown in paragraphs 1-4 of the letter from the owner's or operator's chief financial officer (§264.151(f)). The phrase "current plugging and abandonment cost estimates" as used in paragraph (f)(1) of this section refers to the cost estimates required to be shown in paragraphs 1-4 of the letter from the owner's or operator's chief financial officer (§144.70(f) of this title).

(3) To demonstrate that he meets this test, the owner or operator must submit the following items to the Regional Administrator:

(i) A letter signed by the owner's or operator's chief financial officer and worded as specified in §264.151(f); and

(ii) A copy of the independent certified public accountant's report on examination of the owner's or operator's financial statements for the latest completed fiscal year; and

(iii) A special report from the owner's or operator's independent certified public accountant to the owner or operator stating that:

(A) He has compared the data which the letter from the chief financial officer specifies as having been derived from the independently audited, year-end financial statements for the latest fiscal year with the amounts in such financial statements; and

(B) In connection with that procedure, no matters came to his attention which caused him to believe that the specified data should be adjusted.

(4) An owner or operator of a new facility must submit the items specified in paragraph (f)(3) of this section

to the Regional Administrator at least 60 days before the date on which hazardous waste is first received for treatment, storage, or disposal.

(5) After the initial submission of items specified in paragraph (f)(3) of this section, the owner or operator must send updated information to the Regional Administrator within 90 days after the close of each succeeding fiscal year. This information must consist of all three items specified in paragraph (f)(3) of this section.

(6) If the owner or operator no longer meets the requirements of paragraph (f)(1) of this section, he must send notice to the Regional Administrator of intent to establish alternate financial assurance as specified in this section. The notice must be sent by certified mail within 90 days after the end of the fiscal year for which the year-end financial data show that the owner or operator no longer meets the requirements. The owner or operator must provide the alternate financial assurance within 120 days after the end of such fiscal year.

(7) The Regional Administrator may, based on a reasonable belief that the owner or operator may no longer meet the requirements of paragraph (f)(1) of this section, require reports of financial condition at any time from the owner or operator in addition to those specified in paragraph (f)(3) of this section. If the Regional Administrator finds, on the basis of such reports or other information, that the owner or operator no longer meets the requirements of paragraph (f)(1) of this section, the owner or operator must provide alternate financial assurance as specified in this section within 30 days after notification of such a finding.

(8) The Regional Administrator may disallow use of this test on the basis of qualifications in the opinion expressed by the independent certified public accountant in his report on examination of the owner's or operator's financial statements (see paragraph (f)(3)(ii) of this section). An adverse opinion or a disclaimer of opinion will be cause for disallowance. The Regional Administrator will evaluate other qualifications on an individual basis. The owner or operator must provide alternate financial assurance as specified in this section within 30 days after notification of the disallowance.

(9) The owner or operator is no longer required to submit the items specified in paragraph (f)(3) of this section when:

(i) An owner or operator substitutes alternate financial assurance as specified in this section; or

(ii) The Regional Administrator releases the owner or operator from the requirements of this section in accordance with §264.143(i).

(10) An owner or operator may meet the requirements of this section by obtaining a written guarantee. The guarantor must be the direct or higher-tier parent corporation of the owner or operator, a firm whose parent corporation is also the parent corporation of the owner or operator, or a firm with a "substantial business relationship" with the owner or operator. The guarantor must meet the requirements for owners or operators in paragraphs (f)(1) through (8) of this section and must comply with the terms of the guarantee. The wording of the guarantee must be identical to the wording specified in §264.151(h). The certified copy of the guarantee must accompany the items sent to the Regional Administrator as specified in paragraph (f)(3) of this section. One of these items must be the letter from the guarantor's chief financial officer. If the guarantor's parent corporation is also the parent corporation of the owner or operator, the letter must describe the value received in consideration of the guarantee. If the guarantor is a firm with a "substantial business relationship" with the owner or operator, this letter must describe this "substantial business relationship" and the value received in consideration of the guarantee. The terms of the guarantee must provide that:

(i) If the owner or operator fails to perform final closure of a facility covered by the corporate guarantee in accordance with the closure plan and other permit requirements whenever required to do so, the guarantor will do so or establish a trust fund as specified in §264.143(a) in the name of the owner or operator.

(ii) The corporate guarantee will remain in force unless the guarantor sends notice of cancellation by certified mail to the owner or operator and to the Regional Administrator. Cancellation may not occur, however, during the 120 days beginning on the date of receipt of the notice of cancellation by both the owner or operator and the Regional Administrator, as evidenced by the return receipts.

(iii) If the owner or operator fails to provide alternate financial assurance as specified in this section and obtain the written approval of such alternate assurance from the Regional Administrator within 90 days after receipt by both the owner or operator and the Regional Administrator of a notice of cancellation of the corporate guarantee from the guarantor, the guarantor will provide such alternative financial assurance in the name of the owner or operator.

(g) *Use of multiple financial mechanisms.* An owner or operator may satisfy the requirements of this section by establishing more than one financial mechanism per facility. These mechanisms are limited to trust funds, surety bonds guaranteeing payment into a trust fund, letters of credit, and insurance. The mechanisms must be as specified in paragraphs (a), (b), (d), and (e), respectively, of this section, except that it is the combination of mechanisms, rather than the single mechanism, which must provide financial assurance for an amount at least equal to the current closure cost estimate. If an owner or operator uses a trust fund in combination with a surety bond or a letter of credit, he may use the trust fund as the standby trust fund for the other mechanisms. A single standby trust fund may be established for two or more mechanisms. The Regional Administrator may use any or all of the mechanisms to provide for closure of the facility.

(h) *Use of a financial mechanism for multiple facilities.* An owner or operator may use a financial assurance mechanism specified in this section to meet the requirements of this section for more than one facility. Evidence of financial assurance submitted to the Regional Administrator must include a list showing, for each facility, the EPA Identification Number, name, address, and the amount of funds for closure assured by the mechanism. If the facilities covered by the mechanism are in more than one Region, identical evidence of financial assurance must be submitted to and maintained with the Regional Administrators of all such Regions. The amount of funds available through the mechanism must be no less than the sum of funds that would be available if a separate mechanism had been established and maintained for each facility. In directing funds available through the mechanism for closure of any of the facilities covered by the mechanism, the Regional Administrator may direct only the amount of funds designated for that facility, unless the owner or operator agrees to the use of additional funds available under the mechanism.

(i) *Release of the owner or operator from the requirements of this section.* Within 60 days after receiving certifications from the owner or operator and a qualified Professional Engineer that final closure has been completed in accordance with the approved closure plan, the Regional Administrator will notify the owner or operator in writing that he is no longer required by this section to maintain financial assurance for final closure of the facility, unless the Regional Administrator has reason to believe that final closure has not been in accordance with the approved closure plan. The Regional Administrator shall provide the owner or operator a detailed written statement of any such reason to believe that closure has not been in accordance with the approved closure plan.

[47 FR 15047, Apr. 7, 1982, as amended at 51 FR 16448, May 2, 1986; 57 FR 42835, Sept. 16, 1992; 71 FR 16905, Apr. 4, 2006; 71 FR 40272, July 14, 2006]

§264.144 Cost estimate for post-closure care.

(a) The owner or operator of a disposal surface impoundment, disposal miscellaneous unit, land treatment unit, or landfill unit, or of a surface impoundment or waste pile required under §§264.228 and 264.258 to prepare a contingent closure and post-closure plan, must have a detailed written estimate, in current dollars, of the annual cost of post-closure monitoring and maintenance of the facility in accordance with the applicable post-closure regulations in §§264.117 through 264.120, 264.228, 264.258, 264.280, 264.310, and 264.603.

(1) The post-closure cost estimate must be based on the costs to the owner or operator of hiring a third party to conduct post-closure care activities. A third party is a party who is neither a parent nor a subsidiary of the owner or operator. (See definition of parent corporation in §264.141(d).)

(2) The post-closure cost estimate is calculated by multiplying the annual post-closure cost estimate by the number of years of post-closure care required under §264.117.

(b) During the active life of the facility, the owner or operator must adjust the post-closure cost estimate for inflation within 60 days prior to the anniversary date of the establishment of the financial instrument(s) used to comply with §264.145. For owners or operators using the financial test or corporate guarantee, the post-closure cost estimate must be updated for inflation within 30 days after the close of the firm's fiscal year and before the submission of updated information to the Regional Administrator as specified in §264.145(f)(5). The adjustment may be made by recalculating the post-closure cost estimate in current dollars or by using an inflation factor derived from the most recent Implicit Price Deflator for Gross National Product published by the U.S. Department of Commerce in its Survey of Current Business as specified in §264.145(b)(1) and (2). The inflation factor is the result of dividing the latest published annual Deflator by the Deflator for the previous year.

(1) The first adjustment is made by multiplying the post-closure cost estimate by the inflation factor. The result is the adjusted post-closure cost estimate.

(2) Subsequent adjustments are made by multiplying the latest adjusted post-closure cost estimate by the latest inflation factor.

(c) During the active life of the facility, the owner or operator must revise the post-closure cost estimate within 30 days after the Regional Administrator has approved the request to modify the post-closure plan, if the change in the post-closure plan increases the cost of post-closure care. The revised post-closure cost estimate must be adjusted for inflation as specified in §264.144(b).

(d) The owner or operator must keep the following at the facility during the operating life of the facility: The latest post-closure cost estimate prepared in accordance with §264.144 (a) and (c) and, when this estimate has been adjusted in accordance with §264.144(b), the latest adjusted post-closure cost estimate.

[47 FR 15047, Apr. 7, 1982, as amended at 47 FR 32357, July 26, 1982; 50 FR 4514, Jan. 31, 1985; 51 FR 16449, May 2, 1986; 52 FR 46964, Dec. 10, 1987]

§264.145 Financial assurance for post-closure care.

The owner or operator of a hazardous waste management unit subject to the requirements of §264.144 must establish financial assurance for post-closure care in accordance with the approved post-closure plan for the facility 60 days prior to the initial receipt of hazardous waste or the effective date of the regulation, whichever is later. He must choose from the following options:

(a) *Post-closure trust fund.* (1) An owner or operator may satisfy the requirements of this section by establishing a post-closure trust fund which conforms to the requirements of this paragraph and submitting an originally signed duplicate of the trust agreement to the Regional Administrator. An owner or operator of a new facility must submit the originally signed duplicate of the trust agreement to the Regional Administrator at least 60 days before the date on which hazardous waste is first received for disposal. The trustee must be an entity which has the authority to act as a trustee and whose trust operations are regulated and examined by a Federal or State agency.

(2) The wording of the trust agreement must be identical to the wording specified in §264.151(a)(1), and the trust agreement must be accompanied by a formal certification of acknowledgment (for example, see §264.151(a)(2)). Schedule A of the trust agreement must be updated within 60 days after a change in the amount of the current post-closure cost estimate covered by the agreement.

(3) Payments into the trust fund must be made annually by the owner or operator over the term of the initial RCRA permit or over the remaining operating life of the facility as estimated in the closure plan, whichever period is shorter; this period is hereafter referred to as the "pay-in period." The payments into the post-closure trust fund must be made as follows:

(i) For a new facility, the first payment must be made before the initial receipt of hazardous waste for disposal. A receipt from the trustee for this payment must be submitted by the owner or operator to the Regional Administrator before this initial receipt of hazardous waste. The first payment must be at least equal to the current post-closure cost estimate, except as provided in §264.145(g), divided by the number of years in the pay-in period. Subsequent payments must be made no later than 30 days after each anniversary date of the first payment. The amount of each subsequent payment must be determined by this formula:

$$\text{Next payment} = \frac{CE - CV}{Y}$$

where CE is the current post-closure cost estimate, CV is the current value of the trust fund, and Y is the number of years remaining in the pay-in period.

(ii) If an owner or operator establishes a trust fund as specified in §265.145(a) of this chapter, and the value of that trust fund is less than the current post-closure cost estimate when a permit is awarded for the facility, the amount of the current post-closure cost estimate still to be paid into the fund must be paid in over the pay-in period as defined in paragraph (a)(3) of this section. Payments must continue to be made no later than 30 days after each anniversary date of the first payment made pursuant to Part 265 of this chapter. The amount of each payment must be determined by this formula:

$$\text{Next payment} = \frac{CE - CV}{Y}$$

where CE is the current post-closure cost estimate, CV is the current value of the trust fund, and Y is the number of years remaining in the pay-in period.

(4) The owner or operator may accelerate payments into the trust fund or he may deposit the full amount

of the current post-closure cost estimate at the time the fund is established. However, he must maintain the value of the fund at no less than the value that the fund would have if annual payments were made as specified in paragraph (a)(3) of this section.

(5) If the owner or operator establishes a post-closure trust fund after having used one or more alternate mechanisms specified in this section or in §265.145 of this chapter, his first payment must be in at least the amount that the fund would contain if the trust fund were established initially and annual payments made according to specifications of this paragraph and §265.145(a) of this chapter, as applicable.

(6) After the pay-in period is completed, whenever the current post-closure cost estimate changes during the operating life of the facility, the owner or operator must compare the new estimate with the trustee's most recent annual valuation of the trust fund. If the value of the fund is less than the amount of the new estimate, the owner or operator, within 60 days after the change in the cost estimate, must either deposit an amount into the fund so that its value after this deposit at least equals the amount of the current post-closure cost estimate, or obtain other financial assurance as specified in this section to cover the difference.

(7) During the operating life of the facility, if the value of the trust fund is greater than the total amount of the current post-closure cost estimate, the owner or operator may submit a written request to the Regional Administrator for release of the amount in excess of the current post-closure cost estimate.

(8) If an owner or operator substitutes other financial assurance as specified in this section for all or part of the trust fund, he may submit a written request to the Regional Administrator for release of the amount in excess of the current post-closure cost estimate covered by the trust fund.

(9) Within 60 days after receiving a request from the owner or operator for release of funds as specified in paragraph (a) (7) or (8) of this section, the Regional Administrator will instruct the trustee to release to the owner or operator such funds as the Regional Administrator specifies in writing.

(10) During the period of post-closure care, the Regional Administrator may approve a release of funds if the owner or operator demonstrates to the Regional Administrator that the value of the trust fund exceeds the remaining cost of post-closure care.

(11) An owner or operator or any other person authorized to conduct post-closure care may request reimbursements for post-closure care expenditures by submitting itemized bills to the Regional Administrator. Within 60 days after receiving bills for post-closure care activities, the Regional Administrator will instruct the trustee to make reimbursements in those amounts as the Regional Administrator specifies in writing, if the Regional Administrator determines that the post-closure care expenditures are in accordance with the approved post-closure plan or otherwise justified. If the Regional Administrator does not instruct the trustee to make such reimbursements, he will provide the owner or operator with a detailed written statement of reasons.

(12) The Regional Administrator will agree to termination of the trust when:

(i) An owner or operator substitutes alternate financial assurance as specified in this section; or

(ii) The Regional Administrator releases the owner or operator from the requirements of this section in accordance with §264.145(i).

(b) *Surety bond guaranteeing payment into a post-closure trust fund.* (1) An owner or operator may satisfy the requirements of this section by obtaining a surety bond which conforms to the requirements of this paragraph and submitting the bond to the Regional Administrator. An owner or operator of a new facility must submit the bond to the Regional Administrator at least 60 days before the date on which hazardous waste is first received for disposal. The bond must be effective before this initial receipt of hazardous waste. The surety company issuing the bond must, at a minimum, be among those listed as acceptable sureties on Federal bonds in Circular 570 of the U.S. Department of the Treasury.

(2) The wording of the surety bond must be identical to the wording specified in §264.151(b).

(3) The owner or operator who uses a surety bond to satisfy the requirements of this section must also establish a standby trust fund. Under the terms of the bond, all payments made thereunder will be deposited by the surety directly into the standby trust fund in accordance with instructions from the Regional Administrator. This standby trust fund must meet the requirements specified in §264.145(a), except that:

(i) An originally signed duplicate of the trust agreement must be submitted to the Regional Administrator with the surety bond; and

(ii) Until the standby trust fund is funded pursuant to the requirements of this section, the following are not required by these regulations:

(A) Payments into the trust fund as specified in §264.145(a);

(B) Updating of Schedule A of the trust agreement (see §264.151(a)) to show current post-closure cost estimates;

(C) Annual valuations as required by the trust agreement; and

(D) Notices of nonpayment as required by the trust agreement.

(4) The bond must guarantee that the owner or operator will:

(i) Fund the standby trust fund in an amount equal to the penal sum of the bond before the beginning of final closure of the facility; or

(ii) Fund the standby trust fund in an amount equal to the penal sum within 15 days after an administrative order to begin final closure issued by the Regional Administrator becomes final, or within 15 days after an order to begin final closure is issued by a U.S. district court or other court of competent jurisdiction; or

(iii) Provide alternate financial assurance as specified in this section, and obtain the Regional Administrator's written approval of the assurance provided, within 90 days after receipt by both the owner or operator and the Regional Administrator of a notice of cancellation of the bond from the surety.

(5) Under the terms of the bond, the surety will become liable on the bond obligation when the owner or operator fails to perform as guaranteed by the bond.

(6) The penal sum of the bond must be in an amount at least equal to the current post-closure cost estimate, except as provided in §264.145(g).

(7) Whenever the current post-closure cost estimate increases to an amount greater than the penal sum, the owner or operator, within 60 days after the increase, must either cause the penal sum to be increased to an amount at least equal to the current post-closure cost estimate and submit evidence of such increase to the Regional Administrator, or obtain other financial assurance as specified in this section to cover the increase. Whenever the current post-closure cost estimate decreases, the penal sum may be reduced to the amount of the current post-closure cost estimate following written approval by the Regional Administrator.

(8) Under the terms of the bond, the surety may cancel the bond by sending notice of cancellation by certified mail to the owner or operator and to the Regional Administrator. Cancellation may not occur, however, during the 120 days beginning on the date of receipt of the notice of cancellation by both the owner or operator and the Regional Administrator, as evidenced by the return receipts.

(9) The owner or operator may cancel the bond if the Regional Administrator has given prior written consent based on his receipt of evidence of alternate financial assurance as specified in this section.

(c) *Surety bond guaranteeing performance of post-closure care.* (1) An owner or operator may satisfy the requirements of this section by obtaining a surety bond which conforms to the requirements of this paragraph and submitting the bond to the Regional Administrator. An owner or operator of a new facility must submit the bond to the Regional Administrator at least 60 days before the date on which hazardous waste is first received for disposal. The bond must be effective before this initial receipt of hazardous waste. The surety company issuing the bond must, at a minimum, be among those listed as acceptable sureties on Federal bonds in Circular 570 of the U.S. Department of the Treasury.

(2) The wording of the surety bond must be identical to the wording specified in §264.151(c).

(3) The owner or operator who uses a surety bond to satisfy the requirements of this section must also establish a standby trust fund. Under the terms of the bond, all payments made thereunder will be deposited by the surety directly into the standby trust fund in accordance with instructions from the Regional Administrator. This standby trust fund must meet the requirements specified in §264.145(a), except that:

(i) An originally signed duplicate of the trust agreement must be submitted to the Regional Administrator with the surety bond; and

(ii) Unless the standby trust fund is funded pursuant to the requirements of this section, the following are not required by these regulations:

(A) Payments into the trust fund as specified in §264.145(a);

(B) Updating of Schedule A of the trust agreement (see §264.151(a)) to show current post-closure cost estimates;

(C) Annual valuations as required by the trust agreement; and

(D) Notices of nonpayment as required by the trust agreement.

(4) The bond must guarantee that the owner or operator will:

(i) Perform post-closure care in accordance with the post-closure plan and other requirements of the permit for the facility; or

(ii) Provide alternate financial assurance as specified in this section, and obtain the Regional Administrator's written approval of the assurance provided, within 90 days of receipt by both the owner or operator and the Regional Administrator of a notice of cancellation of the bond from the surety.

(5) Under the terms of the bond, the surety will become liable on the bond obligation when the owner or operator fails to perform as guaranteed by the bond. Following a final administrative determination pursuant to section 3008 of RCRA that the owner or operator has failed to perform post-closure care in accordance with the approved post-closure plan and other permit requirements, under the terms of the bond the surety will perform post-closure care in accordance with the post-closure plan and other permit requirements or will deposit the amount of the penal sum into the standby trust fund.

(6) The penal sum of the bond must be in an amount at least equal to the current post-closure cost estimate.

(7) Whenever the current post-closure cost estimate increases to an amount greater than the penal sum during the operating life of the facility, the owner or operator, within 60 days after the increase, must either cause the penal sum to be increased to an amount at least equal to the current post-closure cost estimate and submit evidence of such increase to the Regional Administrator, or obtain other financial assurance as specified in this section. Whenever the current post-closure cost estimate decreases during the operating life of the facility, the penal sum may be reduced to the amount of the current post-closure cost estimate following written approval by the Regional Administrator.

(8) During the period of post-closure care, the Regional Administrator may approve a decrease in the penal sum if the owner or operator demonstrates to the Regional Administrator that the amount exceeds the remaining cost of post-closure care.

(9) Under the terms of the bond, the surety may cancel the bond by sending notice of cancellation by certified mail to the owner or operator and to the Regional Administrator. Cancellation may not occur, however, during the 120 days beginning on the date of receipt of the notice of cancellation by both the owner or operator and the Regional Administrator, as evidenced by the return receipts.

(10) The owner or operator may cancel the bond if the Regional Administrator has given prior written consent. The Regional Administrator will provide such written consent when:

(i) An owner or operator substitutes alternate financial assurance as specified in this section; or

(ii) The Regional Administrator releases the owner or operator from the requirements of this section in accordance with §264.145(i).

(11) The surety will not be liable for deficiencies in the performance of post-closure care by the owner or operator after the Regional Administrator releases the owner or operator from the requirements of this section in accordance with §264.145(i).

(d) *Post-closure letter of credit.* (1) An owner or operator may satisfy the requirements of this section by obtaining an irrevocable standby letter of credit which conforms to the requirements of this paragraph and submitting the letter to the Regional Administrator. An owner or operator of a new facility must submit the letter of credit to the Regional Administrator at least 60 days before the date on which hazardous waste is first received for disposal. The letter of credit must be effective before this initial receipt of hazardous waste. The issuing institution must be an entity which has the authority to issue letters of credit and whose letter-of-credit operations are regulated and examined by a Federal or State agency.

(2) The wording of the letter of credit must be identical to the wording specified in §264.151(d).

(3) An owner or operator who uses a letter of credit to satisfy the requirements of this section must also establish a standby trust fund. Under the terms of the letter of credit, all amounts paid pursuant to a draft by the Regional Administrator will be deposited by the issuing institution directly into the standby trust fund in accordance with instructions from the Regional Administrator. This standby trust fund must meet the requirements of the trust fund specified in §264.145(a), except that:

(i) An originally signed duplicate of the trust agreement must be submitted to the Regional Administrator with the letter of credit; and

(ii) Unless the standby trust fund is funded pursuant to the requirements of this section, the following are not required by these regulations:

(A) Payments into the trust fund as specified in §264.145(a);

(B) Updating of Schedule A of the trust agreement (see §264.151(a)) to show current post-closure cost estimates;

(C) Annual valuations as required by the trust agreement; and

(D) Notices of nonpayment as required by the trust agreement.

(4) The letter of credit must be accompanied by a letter from the owner or operator referring to the letter of credit by number, issuing institution, and date, and providing the following information: the EPA Identification Number, name, and address of the facility, and the amount of funds assured for post-closure care of the facility by the letter of credit.

(5) The letter of credit must be irrevocable and issued for a period of at least 1 year. The letter of credit must provide that the expiration date will be automatically extended for a period of at least 1 year unless, at least 120 days before the current expiration date, the issuing institution notifies both the owner or operator and the Regional Administrator by certified mail of a decision not to extend the expiration date. Under the terms of the letter of credit, the 120 days will begin on the date when both the owner or operator and the Regional Administrator have received the notice, as evidenced by the return receipts.

(6) The letter of credit must be issued in an amount at least equal to the current post-closure cost estimate, except as provided in §264.145(g).

(7) Whenever the current post-closure cost estimate increases to an amount greater than the amount of the credit during the operating life of the facility, the owner or operator, within 60 days after the increase, must either cause the amount of the credit to be increased so that it at least equals the current post-closure cost estimate and submit evidence of such increase to the Regional Administrator, or obtain other financial assurance as specified in this section to cover the increase. Whenever the current post-closure cost estimate decreases during the operating life of the facility, the amount of the credit may be reduced to the amount of the current post-closure cost estimate following written approval by the Regional Administrator.

(8) During the period of post-closure care, the Regional Administrator may approve a decrease in the amount of the letter of credit if the owner or operator demonstrates to the Regional Administrator that the amount exceeds the remaining cost of post-closure care.

(9) Following a final administrative determination pursuant to section 3008 of RCRA that the owner or operator has failed to perform post-closure care in accordance with the approved post-closure plan and other permit requirements, the Regional Administrator may draw on the letter of credit.

(10) If the owner or operator does not establish alternate financial assurance as specified in this section and obtain written approval of such alternate assurance from the Regional Administrator within 90 days after receipt by both the owner or operator and the Regional Administrator of a notice from the issuing institution that it has decided not to extend the letter of credit beyond the current expiration date, the Regional Administrator will draw on the letter of credit. The Regional Administrator may delay the drawing if the issuing institution grants an extension of the term of the credit. During the last 30 days of any such extension the Regional Administrator will draw on the letter of credit if the owner or operator has failed to provide alternate financial assurance as specified in this section and obtain written approval of such assurance from the Regional Administrator.

(11) The Regional Administrator will return the letter of credit to the issuing institution for termination when:

(i) An owner or operator substitutes alternate financial assurance as specified in this section; or

(ii) The Regional Administrator releases the owner or operator from the requirements of this section in accordance with §264.145(i).

(e) *Post-closure insurance.* (1) An owner or operator may satisfy the requirements of this section by obtaining post-closure insurance which conforms to the requirements of this paragraph and submitting a certificate of such insurance to the Regional Administrator. An owner or operator of a new facility must submit the certificate of insurance to the Regional Administrator at least 60 days before the date on which hazardous waste is first received for disposal. The insurance must be effective before this initial receipt of hazardous waste. At a minimum, the insurer must be licensed to transact the business of insurance, or eligible to provide insurance as an excess or surplus lines insurer, in one or more States.

(2) The wording of the certificate of insurance must be identical to the wording specified in §264.151(e).

(3) The post-closure insurance policy must be issued for a face amount at least equal to the current post-closure cost estimate, except as provided in §264.145(g). The term "face amount" means the total amount the insurer is obligated to pay under the policy. Actual payments by the insurer will not change the face amount, although the insurer's future liability will be lowered by the amount of the payments.

(4) The post-closure insurance policy must guarantee that funds will be available to provide post-closure care of the facility whenever the post-closure period begins. The policy must also guarantee that once post-closure care begins, the insurer will be responsible for paying out funds, up to an amount equal to the face amount of the policy, upon the direction of the Regional Administrator, to such party or parties as the Regional Administrator specifies.

(5) An owner or operator or any other person authorized to conduct post-closure care may request reimbursements for post-closure care expenditures by submitting itemized bills to the Regional Administrator. Within 60 days after receiving bills for post-closure care activities, the Regional Administrator will instruct the insurer to make reimbursements in those amounts as the Regional Administrator specifies in writing, if the Regional Administrator determines that the post-closure care expenditures are in accordance with the approved post-closure plan or otherwise justified. If the Regional Administrator does not instruct the insurer to make such reimbursements, he will provide the owner or operator with a detailed written statement of reasons.

(6) The owner or operator must maintain the policy in full force and effect until the Regional Administrator consents to termination of the policy by the owner or operator as specified in paragraph (e)(11) of this section. Failure to pay the premium, without substitution of alternate financial assurance as specified in this section, will constitute a significant violation of these regulations, warranting such remedy as the Regional Administrator deems necessary. Such violation will be deemed to begin upon receipt by the Regional Administrator of a notice of future cancellation, termination, or failure to renew due to nonpayment of the premium, rather than upon the date of expiration.

(7) Each policy must contain a provision allowing assignment of the policy to a successor owner or operator. Such assignment may be conditional upon consent of the insurer, provided such consent is not unreasonably refused.

(8) The policy must provide that the insurer may not cancel, terminate, or fail to renew the policy except for failure to pay the premium. The automatic renewal of the policy must, at a minimum, provide the insured with the option of renewal at the face amount of the expiring policy. If there is a failure to pay the premium, the insurer may elect to cancel, terminate, or fail to renew the policy by sending notice by certified mail to the owner or operator and the Regional Administrator. Cancellation, termination, or failure to renew may not occur, however, during the 120 days beginning with the date of receipt of the notice by both the Regional Administrator and the owner or operator, as evidenced by the return receipts. Cancellation, termination, or failure to renew may not occur and the policy will remain in full force and effect in the event that on or before the date of expiration:

(i) The Regional Administrator deems the facility abandoned; or

(ii) The permit is terminated or revoked or a new permit is denied; or

(iii) Closure is ordered by the Regional Administrator or a U.S. district court or other court of competent jurisdiction; or

(iv) The owner or operator is named as debtor in a voluntary or involuntary proceeding under Title 11 (Bankruptcy), U.S. Code; or

(v) The premium due is paid.

(9) Whenever the current post-closure cost estimate increases to an amount greater than the face amount of the policy during the operating life of the facility, the owner or operator, within 60 days after the increase, must either cause the face amount to be increased to an amount at least equal to the current post-closure cost estimate and submit evidence of such increase to the Regional Administrator, or obtain other financial assurance as specified in this section to cover the increase. Whenever the current post-closure cost estimate decreases during the operating life of the facility, the face amount may be reduced to the amount of the current post-closure cost estimate following written approval by the Regional Administrator.

(10) Commencing on the date that liability to make payments pursuant to the policy accrues, the insurer will thereafter annually increase the face amount of the policy. Such increase must be equivalent to the face

amount of the policy, less any payments made, multiplied by an amount equivalent to 85 percent of the most recent investment rate or of the equivalent coupon-issue yield announced by the U.S. Treasury for 26-week Treasury securities.

(11) The Regional Administrator will give written consent to the owner or operator that he may terminate the insurance policy when:

(i) An owner or operator substitutes alternate financial assurance as specified in this section; or

(ii) The Regional Administrator releases the owner or operator from the requirements of this section in accordance with §264.145(i).

(f) *Financial test and corporate guarantee for post-closure care.* (1) An owner or operator may satisfy the requirements of this section by demonstrating that he passes a financial test as specified in this paragraph. To pass this test the owner or operator must meet the criteria of either paragraph (f)(1)(i) or (ii) of this section:

(i) The owner or operator must have:

(A) Two of the following three ratios: a ratio of total liabilities to net worth less than 2.0; a ratio of the sum of net income plus depreciation, depletion, and amortization to total liabilities greater than 0.1; and a ratio of current assets to current liabilities greater than 1.5; and

(B) Net working capital and tangible net worth each at least six times the sum of the current closure and post-closure cost estimates and the current plugging and abandonment cost estimates; and

(C) Tangible net worth of at least $10 million; and

(D) Assets in the United States amounting to at least 90 percent of his total assets or at least six times the sum of the current closure and post-closure cost estimates and the current plugging and abandonment cost estimates.

(ii) The owner or operator must have:

(A) A current rating for his most recent bond issuance of AAA, AA, A, or BBB as issued by Standard and Poor's or Aaa, Aa, A or Baa as issued by Moody's; and

(B) Tangible net worth at least six times the sum of the current closure and post-closure cost estimates and the current plugging and abandonment cost estimates; and

(C) Tangible net worth of at least $10 million; and

(D) Assets located in the United States amounting to at least 90 percent of his total assets or at least six times the sum of the current closure and post-closure cost estimates and the current plugging and abandonment cost estimates.

(2) The phrase "current closure and post-closure cost estimates" as used in paragraph (f)(1) of this section refers to the cost estimates required to be shown in paragraphs 1-4 of the letter from the owner's or operator's chief financial officer (§264.151(f)). The phrase "current plugging and abandonment cost estimates" as used in paragraph (f)(1) of this section refers to the cost estimates required to be shown in paragraphs 1-4 of the letter from the owner's or operator's chief financial officer (§144.70(f) of this title).

(3) To demonstrate that he meets this test, the owner or operator must submit the following items to the Regional Administrator:

(i) A letter signed by the owner's or operator's chief financial officer and worded as specified in §264.151(f); and

(ii) A copy of the independent certified public accountant's report on examination of the owner's or operator's financial statements for the latest completed fiscal year; and

(iii) A special report from the owner's or operator's independent certified public accountant to the owner or operator stating that:

(A) He has compared the data which the letter from the chief financial officer specifies as having been derived from the independently audited, year-end financial statements for the latest fiscal year with the amounts in such financial statements; and

(B) In connection with that procedure, no matters came to his attention which caused him to believe that the specified data should be adjusted.

(4) An owner or operator of a new facility must submit the items specified in paragraph (f)(3) of this section to the Regional Administrator at least 60 days before the date on which hazardous waste is first received for disposal.

(5) After the initial submission of items specified in paragraph (f)(3) of this section, the owner or operator must send updated information to the Regional Administrator within 90 days after the close of each succeeding fiscal year. This information must consist of all three items specified in paragraph (f)(3) of this section.

(6) If the owner or operator no longer meets the requirements of paragraph (f)(1) of this section, he must send notice to the Regional Administrator of intent to establish alternate financial assurance as specified in this section. The notice must be sent by certified mail within 90 days after the end of the fiscal year for which the year-end financial data show that the owner or operator no longer meets the requirements. The owner or operator must provide the alternate financial assurance within 120 days after the end of such fiscal year.

(7) The Regional Administrator may, based on a reasonable belief that the owner or operator may no longer meet the requirements of paragraph (f)(1) of this section, require reports of financial condition at any time from the owner or operator in addition to those specified in paragraph (f)(3) of this section. If the Regional Administrator finds, on the basis of such reports or other information, that the owner or operator no longer meets the requirements of paragraph (f)(1) of this section, the owner or operator must provide alternate financial assurance as specified in this section within 30 days after notification of such a finding.

(8) The Regional Administrator may disallow use of this test on the basis of qualifications in the opinion expressed by the independent certified public accountant in his report on examination of the owner's or operator's financial statements (see paragraph (f)(3)(ii) of this section). An adverse opinion or a disclaimer of opinion will be cause for disallowance. The Regional Administrator will evaluate other qualifications on an individual basis. The owner or operator must provide alternate financial assurance as specified in this section within 30 days after notification of the disallowance.

(9) During the period of post-closure care, the Regional Administrator may approve a decrease in the current post-closure cost estimate for which this test demonstrates financial assurance if the owner or operator demonstrates to the Regional Administrator that the amount of the cost estimate exceeds the remaining cost of post-closure care.

(10) The owner or operator is no longer required to submit the items specified in paragraph (f)(3) of this section when:

(i) An owner or operator substitutes alternate financial assurance as specified in this section; or

(ii) The Regional Administrator releases the owner or operator from the requirements of this section in accordance with §264.145(i).

(11) An owner or operator may meet the requirements of this section by obtaining a written guarantee. The guarantor must be the direct or higher-tier parent corporation of the owner or operator, a firm whose parent corporation is also the parent corporation of the owner or operator, or a firm with a "substantial business relationship" with the owner or operator. The guarantor must meet the requirements for owners or operators in paragraphs (f)(1) through (9) of this section and must comply with the terms of the guarantee. The wording of the guarantee must be identical to the wording specified in §264.151(h). A certified copy of the guarantee must accompany the items sent to the Regional Administrator as specified in paragraph (f)(3) of this section. One of these items must be the letter from the guarantor's chief financial officer. If the guarantor's parent corporation is also the parent corporation of the owner or operator, the letter must describe the value received in consideration of the guarantee. If the guarantor is a firm with a "substantial business relationship" with the owner or operator, this letter must describe this "substantial business relationship" and the value received in consideration of the guarantee. The terms of the guarantee must provide that:

(i) If the owner or operator fails to perform post-closure care of a facility covered by the corporate guarantee in accordance with the post-closure plan and other permit requirements whenever required to do so, the guarantor will do so or establish a trust fund as specified in §264.145(a) in the name of the owner or operator.

(ii) The corporate guarantee will remain in force unless the guarantor sends notice of cancellation by certified mail to the owner or operator and to the Regional Administrator. Cancellation may not occur, however, during the 120 days beginning on the date of receipt of the notice of cancellation by both the owner or operator and the Regional Administrator, as evidenced by the return receipts.

(iii) If the owner or operator fails to provide alternate financial assurance as specified in this section and obtain the written approval of such alternate assurance from the Regional Administrator within 90 days after receipt by both the owner or operator and the Regional Administrator of a notice of cancellation of the corporate guarantee from the guarantor, the guarantor will provide such alternate financial assurance in the name of the owner or operator.

(g) *Use of multiple financial mechanisms.* An owner or operator may satisfy the requirements of this section by establishing more than one financial mechanism per facility. These mechanisms are limited to trust funds, surety bonds guaranteeing payment into a trust fund, letters of credit, and insurance. The mechanisms must be as specified in paragraphs (a), (b), (d), and (e), respectively, of this section, except that it is the combination of mechanisms, rather than the single mechanism, which must provide financial assurance for an amount at least equal to the current post-closure cost estimate. If an owner or operator uses a trust fund in combination with a surety bond or a letter of credit, he may use the trust fund as the standby trust fund for the other mechanisms. A single standby trust fund may be established for two or more mechanisms. The Regional Administrator may use any or all of the mechanisms to provide for post-closure care of the facility.

(h) *Use of a financial mechanism for multiple facilities.* An owner or operator may use a financial assurance mechanism specified in this section to meet the requirements of this section for more than one facility. Evidence of financial assurance submitted to the Regional Administrator must include a list showing, for each facility, the EPA Identification Number, name, address, and the amount of funds for post-closure care assured by the mechanism. If the facilities covered by the mechanism are in more than one Region, identical evidence of financial assurance must be submitted to and maintained with the Regional Administrators of all such Regions. The amount of funds available through the mechanism must be no less than the sum of funds that would be available if a separate mechanism had been established and maintained for each facility. In directing funds available through the mechanism for post-closure care of any of the facilities covered by the mechanism, the Regional Administrator may direct only the amount of funds designated for that facility, unless the owner or operator agrees to the use of additional funds available under the mechanism.

(i) *Release of the owner or operator from the requirements of this section.* Within 60 days after receiving certifications from the owner or operator and a qualified Professional Engineer that the post-closure care period has been completed for a hazardous waste disposal unit in accordance with the approved plan, the Regional Administrator will notify the owner or operator that he is no longer required to maintain financial assurance for post-closure of that unit, unless the Regional Administrator has reason to believe that post-closure care has not been in accordance with the approved post-closure plan. The Regional Administrator shall provide the owner or operator a detailed written statement of any such reason to believe that post-closure care has not been in accordance with the approved post-closure plan.

[47 FR 15047, Apr. 7, 1982, as amended at 51 FR 16449, May 2, 1986; 57 FR 42836, Sept. 16, 1992; 71 FR 16905, Apr. 4, 2006; 71 FR 40272, July 14, 2006]

§264.146 Use of a mechanism for financial assurance of both closure and post-closure care.

An owner or operator may satisfy the requirements for financial assurance for both closure and post-closure care for one or more facilities by using a trust fund, surety bond, letter of credit, insurance, financial test, or corporate guarantee that meets the specifications for the mechanism in both §§264.143 and 264.145. The amount of funds available through the mechanism must be no less than the sum of funds that would be available if a separate mechanism had been established and maintained for financial assurance of closure and of post-closure care.

§264.147 Liability requirements.

(a) *Coverage for sudden accidental occurrences.* An owner or operator of a hazardous waste treatment, storage, or disposal facility, or a group of such facilities, must demonstrate financial responsibility for bodily injury and property damage to third parties caused by sudden accidental occurrences arising from operations of the facility or group of facilities. The owner or operator must have and maintain liability coverage for sudden accidental occurrences in the amount of at least $1 million per occurrence with an annual aggregate of at least $2 million, exclusive of legal defense costs. This liability coverage may be demonstrated as specified in paragraphs (a)(1), (2), (3), (4), (5), or (6) of this section:

(1) An owner or operator may demonstrate the required liability coverage by having liability insurance as specified in this paragraph.

(i) Each insurance policy must be amended by attachment of the Hazardous Waste Facility Liability Endorsement or evidenced by a Certificate of Liability Insurance. The wording of the endorsement must be identical to the wording specified in §264.151(i). The wording of the certificate of insurance must be identical to the wording specified in §264.151(j). The owner or operator must submit a signed duplicate original of the endorsement or the certificate of insurance to the Regional Administrator, or Regional Administrators if the facilities are located in more than one Region. If requested by a Regional Administrator, the owner or operator must provide a signed duplicate original of the insurance policy. An owner or operator of a new facility must submit the signed duplicate original of the Hazardous Waste Facility Liability Endorsement or the Certificate of Liability Insurance to the Regional Administrator at least 60 days before the date on which hazardous waste is first received for treatment, storage, or disposal. The insurance must be effective before this initial receipt of hazardous waste.

(ii) Each insurance policy must be issued by an insurer which, at a minimum, is licensed to transact the business of insurance, or eligible to provide insurance as an excess or surplus lines insurer, in one or more States.

(2) An owner or operator may meet the requirements of this section by passing a financial test or using the guarantee for liability coverage as specified in paragraphs (f) and (g) of this section.

(3) An owner or operator may meet the requirements of this section by obtaining a letter of credit for liability coverage as specified in paragraph (h) of this section.

(4) An owner or operator may meet the requirements of this section by obtaining a surety bond for liability coverage as specified in paragraph (i) of this section.

(5) An owner or operator may meet the requirements of this section by obtaining a trust fund for liability coverage as specified in paragraph (j) of this section.

(6) An owner or operator may demonstrate the required liability coverage through the use of combinations of insurance, financial test, guarantee, letter of credit, surety bond, and trust fund, except that the owner or operator may not combine a financial test covering part of the liability coverage requirement with a guarantee unless the financial statement of the owner or operator is not consolidated with the financial statement of the guarantor. The amounts of coverage demonstrated must total at least the minimum amounts required by this section. If the owner or operator demonstrates the required coverage through the use of a combination of financial assurances under this paragraph, the owner or operator shall specify at least one such assurance as "primary" coverage and shall specify other assurance as "excess" coverage.

(7) An owner or operator shall notify the Regional Administrator in writing within 30 days whenever:

(i) A claim results in a reduction in the amount of financial assurance for liability coverage provided by a financial instrument authorized in paragraphs (a)(1) through (a)(6) of this section; or

(ii) A Certification of Valid Claim for bodily injury or property damages caused by a sudden or non-sudden accidental occurrence arising from the operation of a hazardous waste treatment, storage, or disposal facility is entered between the owner or operator and third-party claimant for liability coverage under paragraphs (a)(1) through (a)(6) of this section; or

(iii) A final court order establishing a judgment for bodily injury or property damage caused by a sudden or non-sudden accidental occurrence arising from the operation of a hazardous waste treatment, storage, or disposal facility is issued against the owner or operator or an instrument that is providing financial assurance for liability coverage under paragraphs (a)(1) through (a)(6) of this section.

(b) *Coverage for nonsudden accidental occurrences.* An owner or operator of a surface impoundment, landfill, land treatment facility, or disposal miscellaneous unit that is used to manage hazardous waste, or a group of such facilities, must demonstrate financial responsibility for bodily injury and property damage to third parties caused by nonsudden accidental occurrences arising from operations of the facility or group of facilities. The owner or operator must have and maintain liability coverage for nonsudden accidental occurrences in the amount of at least $3 million per occurrence with an annual aggregate of at least $6 million, exclusive of legal defense costs. An owner or operator who must meet the requirements of this section may combine the required per-occurrence coverage levels for sudden and nonsudden accidental occurrences into a single per-occurrence level, and combine the required annual aggregate coverage levels for sudden and nonsudden accidental occurrences into a single annual aggregate level. Owners or operators who combine coverage levels for sudden and nonsudden accidental occurrences must maintain liability coverage in the amount of at least $4 million per occurrence and $8 million annual aggregate. This liability coverage may be demonstrated as specified in paragraphs (b) (1), (2), (3), (4), (5), or (6), of this section:

(1) An owner or operator may demonstrate the required liability coverage by having liability insurance as specified in this paragraph.

(i) Each insurance policy must be amended by attachment of the Hazardous Waste Facility Liability Endorsement or evidenced by a Certificate of Liability Insurance. The wording of the endorsement must be identical to the wording specified in §264.151(i). The wording of the certificate of insurance must be identical to the wording specified in §264.151(j). The owner or operator must submit a signed duplicate original of the endorsement or the certificate of insurance to the Regional Administrator, or Regional Administrators if the facilities are located in more than one Region. If requested by a Regional Administrator, the owner or operator must provide a signed duplicate original of the insurance policy. An owner or operator of a new facility must submit the signed duplicate original of the Hazardous Waste Facility Liability Endorsement or the Certificate of Liability Insurance to the Regional Administrator at least 60 days before the date on which hazardous waste is first received for treatment, storage, or disposal. The insurance must be effective before this initial receipt of hazardous waste.

(ii) Each insurance policy must be issued by an insurer which, at a minimum, is licensed to transact the business of insurance, or eligible to provide insurance as an excess or surplus lines insurer, in one or more States.

(2) An owner or operator may meet the requirements of this section by passing a financial test or using the guarantee for liability coverage as specified in paragraphs (f) and (g) of this section.

(3) An owner or operator may meet the requirements of this section by obtaining a letter of credit for liability coverage as specified in paragraph (h) of this section.

(4) An owner or operator may meet the requirements of this section by obtaining a surety bond for liability coverage as specified in paragraph (i) of this section.

(5) An owner or operator may meet the requirements of this section by obtaining a trust fund for liability coverage as specified in paragraph (j) of this section.

(6) An owner or operator may demonstrate the required liability coverage through the use of combinations of insurance, financial test, guarantee, letter of credit, surety bond, and trust fund, except that the owner or operator may not combine a financial test covering part of the liability coverage requirement with a guarantee unless the financial statement of the owner or operator is not consolidated with the financial statement of the guarantor. The amounts of coverage demonstrated must total at least the minimum amount required by this section. If the owner or operator demonstrates the required coverage through the use of a combination of financial assurances under this paragraph, the owner or operator shall specify at least one such assurance as "primary" coverage and shall specify other assurance as "excess" coverage.

(7) An owner or operator shall notify the Regional Administrator in writing within 30 days whenever:

(i) A Claim results in a reduction in the amount of financial assurance for liability coverage provided by a financial instrument authorized in paragraphs (b)(1) through (b)(6) of this section; or

(ii) A Certification of Valid Claim for bodily injury or property damages caused by a sudden or non-sudden accidental occurrence arising from the operation of a hazardous waste treatment, storage, or disposal facility is entered between the owner or operator and third-party claimant for liability coverage under paragraphs (b)(1) through (b)(6) of this section; or

(iii) A final court order establishing a judgment for bodily injury or property damage caused by a sudden or non-sudden accidental occurrence arising from the operation of a hazardous waste treatment, storage, or disposal facility is issued against the owner or operator or an instrument that is providing financial assurance for liability coverage under paragraphs (b)(1) through (b)(6) of this section.

(c) *Request for variance.* If an owner or operator can demonstrate to the satisfaction of the Regional Administrator that the levels of financial responsibility required by paragraph (a) or (b) of this section are not consistent with the degree and duration of risk associated with treatment, storage, or disposal at the facility or group of facilities, the owner or operator may obtain a variance from the Regional Administrator. The request for a variance must be submitted to the Regional Administrator as part of the application under §270.14 of this chapter for a facility that does not have a permit, or pursuant to the procedures for permit modification under §124.5 of this chapter for a facility that has a permit. If granted, the variance will take the form of an adjusted level of required liability coverage, such level to be based on the Regional Administrator's assessment of the degree and duration of risk associated with the ownership or operation of the facility or group of facilities. The Regional Administrator may require an owner or operator who requests a variance to provide such technical and engineering information as is deemed necessary by the Regional Administrator to determine a level of financial responsibility other than that required by paragraph (a) or (b) of this section. Any request for a variance for a permitted facility will be treated as a request for a permit modification under §§270.41(a)(5) and 124.5 of this chapter.

(d) *Adjustments by the Regional Administrator.* If the Regional Administrator determines that the levels of financial responsibility required by paragraph (a) or (b) of this section are not consistent with the degree and duration of risk associated with treatment, storage, or disposal at the facility or group of facilities, the Regional Administrator may adjust the level of financial responsibility required under paragraph (a) or (b) of this section as may be necessary to protect human health and the environment. This adjusted level will be based on the Regional Administrator's assessment of the degree and duration of risk associated with the ownership or operation of the facility or group of facilities. In addition, if the Regional Administrator determines that there is a significant risk to human health and the environment from nonsudden accidental occurrences resulting from the operations of a facility that is not a surface impoundment, landfill, or land treatment facility, he may require that an owner or operator of the facility comply with paragraph (b) of this section. An owner or operator must furnish to the Regional Administrator, within a reasonable time, any information which the Regional Administrator requests to determine whether cause exists for such adjustments of level or type of coverage. Any adjustment of the level or type of coverage for a facility that has a permit will be treated as a permit modification under §§270.41(a)(5) and 124.5 of this chapter.

(e) *Period of coverage.* Within 60 days after receiving certifications from the owner or operator and a qualified Professional Engineer that final closure has been completed in accordance with the approved closure plan, the Regional Administrator will notify the owner or operator in writing that he is no longer required by this section to maintain liability coverage for that facility, unless the Regional Administrator has reason to believe that closure has not been in accordance with the approved closure plan.

(f) *Financial test for liability coverage.* (1) An owner or operator may satisfy the requirements of this section by demonstrating that he passes a financial test as specified in this paragraph. To pass this test the owner or operator must meet the criteria of paragraph (f)(1)(i) or (ii):

(i) The owner or operator must have:

(A) Net working capital and tangible net worth each at least six times the amount of liability coverage to be demonstrated by this test; and

(B) Tangible net worth of at least $10 million; and

(C) Assets in the United States amounting to either: (1) At least 90 percent of his total assets; or (2) at least six times the amount of liability coverage to be demonstrated by this test.

(ii) The owner or operator must have:

(A) A current rating for his most recent bond issuance of AAA, AA, A, or BBB as issued by Standard and Poor's, or Aaa, Aa, A, or Baa as issued by Moody's; and

(B) Tangible net worth of at least $10 million; and

(C) Tangible net worth at least six times the amount of liability coverage to be demonstrated by this test; and

(D) Assets in the United States amounting to either: (1) At least 90 percent of his total assets; or (2) at least six times the amount of liability coverage to be demonstrated by this test.

(2) The phrase "amount of liability coverage" as used in paragraph (f)(1) of this section refers to the annual aggregate amounts for which coverage is required under paragraphs (a) and (b) of this section.

(3) To demonstrate that he meets this test, the owner or operator must submit the following three items to the Regional Administrator:

(i) A letter signed by the owner's or operator's chief financial officer and worded as specified in §264.151(g). If an owner or operator is using the financial test to demonstrate both assurance for closure or post-closure care, as specified by §§264.143(f), 264.145(f), 265.143(e), and 265.145(e), and liability coverage, he must submit the letter specified in §264.151(g) to cover both forms of financial responsibility; a separate letter as specified in §264.151(f) is not required.

(ii) A copy of the independent certified public accountant's report on examination of the owner's or operator's financial statements for the latest completed fiscal year.

(iii) A special report from the owner's or operator's independent certified public accountant to the owner or operator stating that:

(A) He has compared the data which the letter from the chief financial officer specifies as having been derived from the independently audited, year-end financial statements for the latest fiscal year with the amounts in such financial statements; and

(B) In connection with that procedure, no matters came to his attention which caused him to believe that the specified data should be adjusted.

(4) An owner or operator of a new facility must submit the items specified in paragraph (f)(3) of this section

to the Regional Administrator at least 60 days before the date on which hazardous waste is first received for treatment, storage, or disposal.

(5) After the initial submission of items specified in paragraph (f)(3) of this section, the owner or operator must send updated information to the Regional Administrator within 90 days after the close of each succeeding fiscal year. This information must consist of all three items specified in paragraph (f)(3) of this section.

(6) If the owner or operator no longer meets the requirements of paragraph (f)(1) of this section, he must obtain insurance, a letter of credit, a surety bond, a trust fund, or a guarantee for the entire amount of required liability coverage as specified in this section. Evidence of liability coverage must be submitted to the Regional Administrator within 90 days after the end of the fiscal year for which the year-end financial data show that the owner or operator no longer meets the test requirements.

(7) The Regional Administrator may disallow use of this test on the basis of qualifications in the opinion expressed by the independent certified public accountant in his report on examination of the owner's or operator's financial statements (see paragraph (f)(3)(ii) of this section). An adverse opinion or a disclaimer of opinion will be cause for disallowance. The Regional Administrator will evaluate other qualifications on an individual basis. The owner or operator must provide evidence of insurance for the entire amount of required liability coverage as specified in this section within 30 days after notification of disallowance.

(g) *Guarantee for liability coverage.* (1) Subject to paragraph (g)(2) of this section, an owner or operator may meet the requirements of this section by obtaining a written guarantee, hereinafter referred to as "guarantee." The guarantor must be the direct or higher-tier parent corporation of the owner or operator, a firm whose parent corporation is also the parent corporation of the owner or operator, or a firm with a "substantial business relationship" with the owner or operator. The guarantor must meet the requirements for owners or operators in paragraphs (f)(1) through (f)(6) of this section. The wording of the guarantee must be identical to the wording specified in §264.151(h)(2) of this part. A certified copy of the guarantee must accompany the items sent to the Regional Administrator as specified in paragraph (f)(3) of this section. One of these items must be the letter from the guarantor's chief financial officer. If the guarantor's parent corporation is also the parent corporation of the owner or operator, this letter must describe the value received in consideration of the guarantee. If the guarantor is a firm with a "substantial business relationship" with the owner or operator, this letter must describe this "substantial business relationship" and the value received in consideration of the guarantee.

(i) If the owner or operator fails to satisfy a judgment based on a determination of liability for bodily injury or property damage to third parties caused by sudden or nonsudden accidental occurrences (or both as the case may be), arising from the operation of facilities covered by this corporate guarantee, or fails to pay an amount agreed to in settlement of claims arising from or alleged to arise from such injury or damage, the guarantor will do so up to the limits of coverage.

(ii) [Reserved]

(2)(i) In the case of corporations incorporated in the United States, a guarantee may be used to satisfy the requirements of this section only if the Attorneys General or Insurance Commissioners of (A) the State in which the guarantor is incorporated, and (B) each State in which a facility covered by the guarantee is located have submitted a written statement to EPA that a guarantee executed as described in this section and §264.151(h)(2) is a legally valid and enforceable obligation in that State.

(ii) In the case of corporations incorporated outside the United States, a guarantee may be used to satisfy the requirements of this section only if (A) the non-U.S. corporation has identified a registered agent for service of process in each State in which a facility covered by the guarantee is located and in the State in which it has its principal place of business, and (B) the Attorney General or Insurance Commissioner of each State in which a facility covered by the guarantee is located and the State in which the guarantor corporation has its principal place of business, has submitted a written statement to EPA that a guarantee executed as described in this section and §264.151(h)(2) is a legally valid and enforceable obligation in that State.

(h) *Letter of credit for liability coverage.* (1) An owner or operator may satisfy the requirements of this section by obtaining an irrevocable standby letter of credit that conforms to the requirements of this paragraph and submitting a copy of the letter of credit to the Regional Administrator.

(2) The financial institution issuing the letter of credit must be an entity that has the authority to issue letters of credit and whose letter of credit operations are regulated and examined by a Federal or State agency.

(3) The wording of the letter of credit must be identical to the wording specified in §264.151(k) of this part.

(4) An owner or operator who uses a letter of credit to satisfy the requirements of this section may also establish a standby trust fund. Under the terms of such a letter of credit, all amounts paid pursuant to a draft by the trustee of the standby trust will be deposited by the issuing institution into the standby trust in accordance with instructions from the trustee. The trustee of the standby trust fund must be an entity which has the authority to act as a trustee and whose trust operations are regulated and examined by a Federal or State agency.

(5) The wording of the standby trust fund must be identical to the wording specified in §264.151(n).

(i) *Surety bond for liability coverage.* (1) An owner or operator may satisfy the requirements of this section by obtaining a surety bond that conforms to the requirements of this paragraph and submitting a copy of the bond to the Regional Administrator.

(2) The surety company issuing the bond must be among those listed as acceptable sureties on Federal bonds in the most recent Circular 570 of the U.S. Department of the Treasury.

(3) The wording of the surety bond must be identical to the wording specified in §264.151(l) of this part.

(4) A surety bond may be used to satisfy the requirements of this section only if the Attorneys General or Insurance Commissioners of (i) the State in which the surety is incorporated, and (ii) each State in which a facility covered by the surety bond is located have submitted a written statement to EPA that a surety bond executed as described in this section and §264.151(l) of this part is a legally valid and enforceable obligation in that State.

(j) *Trust fund for liability coverage.* (1) An owner or operator may satisfy the requirements of this section by establishing a trust fund that conforms to the requirements of this paragraph and submitting an originally signed duplicate of the trust agreement to the Regional Administrator.

(2) The trustee must be an entity which has the authority to act as a trustee and whose trust operations are regulated and examined by a Federal or State agency.

(3) The trust fund for liability coverage must be funded for the full amount of the liability coverage to be provided by the trust fund before it may be relied upon to satisfy the requirements of this section. If at any time after the trust fund is created the amount of funds in the trust fund is reduced below the full amount of the liability coverage to be provided, the owner or operator, by the anniversary date of the establishment of the fund, must either add sufficient funds to the trust fund to cause its value to equal the full amount of liability coverage to be provided, or obtain other financial assurance as specified in this section to cover the difference. For purposes of this paragraph, "the full amount of the liability coverage to be provided" means the amount of coverage for sudden and/or nonsudden occurrences required to be provided by the owner or operator by this section, less the amount of financial assurance for liability coverage that is being provided by other financial assurance mechanisms being used to demonstrate financial assurance by the owner or operator.

(4) The wording of the trust fund must be identical to the wording specified in §264.151(m) of this part.

(k) Notwithstanding any other provision of this part, an owner or operator using liability insurance to satisfy the requirements of this section may use, until October 16, 1982, a Hazardous Waste Facility Liability Endorsement or Certificate of Liability Insurance that does not certify that the insurer is licensed to transact the business of insurance, or eligible as an excess or surplus lines insurer, in one or more States.

[47 FR 16554, Apr. 16, 1982, as amended at 47 FR 28627, July 1, 1982; 47 FR 30447, July 13, 1982; 48 FR 30115, June 30, 1983; 51 FR 16450, May 2, 1986; 51 FR 25354, July 11, 1986; 52 FR 44320, Nov. 18, 1987; 52 FR 46964, Dec. 10, 1987; 53 FR 33950, Sept. 1, 1988; 56 FR 30200, July 1, 1991; 57 FR 42836, Sept. 16, 1992; 71 FR 16905, Apr. 4, 2006; 71 FR 40272, July 14, 2006]

§264.148 Incapacity of owners or operators, guarantors, or financial institutions.

(a) An owner or operator must notify the Regional Administrator by certified mail of the commencement of a voluntary or involuntary proceeding under Title 11 (Bankruptcy), U.S. Code, naming the owner or operator as debtor, within 10 days after commencement of the proceeding. A guarantor of a corporate guarantee as specified in §§264.143(f) and 264.145(f) must make such a notification if he is named as debtor, as required under the terms of the corporate guarantee (§264.151(h)).

(b) An owner or operator who fulfills the requirements of §264.143, §264.145, or §264.147 by obtaining a trust fund, surety bond, letter of credit, or insurance policy will be deemed to be without the required financial assurance or liability coverage in the event of bankruptcy of the trustee or issuing institution, or a suspension or revocation of the authority of the trustee institution to act as trustee or of the institution issuing the surety bond, letter of credit, or insurance policy to issue such instruments. The owner or operator must establish other financial assurance or liability coverage within 60 days after such an event.

§264.149 Use of State-required mechanisms.

(a) For a facility located in a State where EPA is administering the requirements of this subpart but where the State has hazardous waste regulations that include requirements for financial assurance of closure or post-closure care or liability coverage, an owner or operator may use State-required financial mechanisms to meet the requirements of §264.143, §264.145, or §264.147, if the Regional Administrator determines that the State mechanisms are at least equivalent to the financial mechanism specified in this subpart. The Regional Administrator will evaluate the equivalency of the mechanisms principally in terms of (1) certainty of the availability of funds for the required closure or post-closure care activities or liability coverage and (2) the amount of funds that will be made available. The Regional Administrator may also consider other factors as he deems appropriate. The owner or operator must submit to the Regional Administrator evidence of the establishment of the mechanism together with a letter requesting that the State-required mechanism be considered acceptable for meeting the requirements of this subpart. The submission must include the following information: The facility's EPA Identification Number, name, and address, and the amount of funds for closure or post-closure care or liability coverage assured by the mechanism. The Regional Administrator will notify the owner or operator of his determination regarding the mechanism's acceptability in lieu of financial mechanisms specified in this subpart. The Regional Administrator may require the owner or operator to submit additional information as is deemed necessary to make this determination. Pending this determination, the owner or operator will be deemed to be in compliance with the requirements of §264.143, §264.145, or §264.147, as applicable.

(b) If a State-required mechanism is found acceptable as specified in paragraph (a) of this section except for the amount of funds available, the owner or operator may satisfy the requirements of this subpart by increasing the funds available through the State-required mechanism or using additional financial mechanisms as specified in this subpart. The amount of funds available through the State and Federal mechanisms must at least equal the amount required by this subpart.

§264.150 State assumption of responsibility.

(a) If a State either assumes legal responsibility for an owner's or operator's compliance with the closure, post-closure care, or liability requirements of this part or assures that funds will be available from State sources to cover those requirements, the owner or operator will be in compliance with the requirements of §264.143, §264.145, or §264.147 if the Regional Administrator determines that the State's assumption of responsibility is at least equivalent to the financial mechanisms specified in this subpart. The Regional Administrator will evaluate the equivalency of State guarantees principally in terms of (1) certainty of the availability of funds for the required closure or post-closure care activities or liability coverage and (2) the amount of funds that will be made available. The Regional Administrator may also consider other factors as he deems appropriate. The owner or operator must submit to the Regional Administrator a letter from the State describing the nature of the State's assumption of responsibility together with a letter from the owner or operator requesting that the State's assumption of responsibility be considered acceptable for meeting the requirements of this subpart. The letter from the State must include, or have attached to it, the following information: the facility's EPA Identification Number, name, and address, and the amount of funds for closure or post-closure care or liability coverage that are guaranteed by the State. The Regional Administrator will notify the owner or operator of his determination regarding the acceptability of the State's guarantee in lieu of financial mechanisms specified in this subpart. The Regional Administrator may require the owner or operator to submit additional information as is deemed necessary to make this determination. Pending this determination, the owner or operator will be deemed to be in compliance with the requirements of §264.143, §264.145, or §264.147, as applicable.

(b) If a State's assumption of responsibility is found acceptable as specified in paragraph (a) of this section except for the amount of funds available, the owner or operator may satisfy the requirements of this subpart by use of both the State's assurance and additional financial mechanisms as specified in this subpart. The amount of funds available through the State and Federal mechanisms must at least equal the amount required by this subpart.

§264.151 Wording of the instruments.

(a)(1) A trust agreement for a trust fund, as specified in §264.143(a) or §264.145(a) or §265.143(a) or §265.145(a) of this chapter, must be worded as follows, except that instructions in brackets are to be replaced with the relevant information and the brackets deleted:

Trust Agreement

Trust Agreement, the "Agreement," entered into as of [date] by and between [name of the owner or operator], a [name of State] [insert "corporation," "partnership," "association," or "proprietorship"], the "Grantor," and [name of corporate trustee], [insert "incorporated in the State of ________" or "a national bank"], the "Trustee."

Whereas, the United States Environmental Protection Agency, "EPA," an agency of the United States Government, has established certain regulations applicable to the Grantor, requiring that an owner or operator of a hazardous waste management facility shall provide assurance that funds will be available when needed for closure and/or post-closure care of the facility,

Whereas, the Grantor has elected to establish a trust to provide all or part of such financial assurance for the facilities identified herein,

Whereas, the Grantor, acting through its duly authorized officers, has selected the Trustee to be the trustee under this agreement, and the Trustee is willing to act as trustee,

Now, Therefore, the Grantor and the Trustee agree as follows:

Section 1. *Definitions.* As used in this Agreement:

(a) The term "Grantor" means the owner or operator who enters into this Agreement and any successors or assigns of the Grantor.

(b) The term "Trustee" means the Trustee who enters into this Agreement and any successor Trustee.

Section 2. *Identification of Facilities and Cost Estimates.* This Agreement pertains to the facilities and cost estimates identified on attached Schedule A [on Schedule A, for each facility list the EPA Identification Number, name, address, and the current closure and/or post-closure cost estimates, or portions thereof, for which financial assurance is demonstrated by this Agreement].

Section 3. *Establishment of Fund.* The Grantor and the Trustee hereby establish a trust fund, the "Fund," for the benefit of EPA. The Grantor and the Trustee intend that no third party have access to the Fund except as herein provided. The Fund is established initially as consisting of the property, which is acceptable to the Trustee, described in Schedule B attached hereto. Such property and any other property subsequently transferred to the Trustee is referred to as the Fund, together with all earnings and profits thereon, less any payments or distributions made by the Trustee pursuant to this Agreement. The Fund shall be held by the Trustee, IN TRUST, as hereinafter provided. The Trustee shall not be responsible nor shall it undertake any responsibility for the amount or adequacy of, nor any duty to collect from the Grantor, any payments necessary to discharge any liabilities of the Grantor established by EPA.

Section 4. *Payment for Closure and Post-Closure Care.* The Trustee shall make payments from the Fund as the EPA Regional Administrator shall direct, in writing, to provide for the payment of the costs of closure and/or post-closure care of the facilities covered by this Agreement. The Trustee shall reimburse the Grantor or other persons as specified by the EPA Regional Administrator from the Fund for closure and post-closure expenditures in such amounts as the EPA Regional Administrator shall direct in writing. In addition, the Trustee shall refund to the Grantor such amounts as the EPA Regional Administrator specifies in writing. Upon refund, such funds shall no longer constitute part of the Fund as defined herein.

Section 5. *Payments Comprising the Fund.* Payments made to the Trustee for the Fund shall consist of cash or securities acceptable to the Trustee.

Section 6. *Trustee Management.* The Trustee shall invest and reinvest the principal and income of the Fund and keep the Fund invested as a single fund, without distinction between principal and income, in accordance with general investment policies and guidelines which the Grantor may communicate in writing to the Trustee from time to time, subject, however, to the provisions of this section. In investing, reinvesting, exchanging, selling, and managing the Fund, the Trustee shall discharge his duties with respect to the trust fund solely in the interest of the beneficiary and with the care, skill, prudence, and diligence under the circumstances then prevailing which persons of prudence, acting in a like capacity and familiar with such matters, would use in the conduct of an enterprise of a like character and with like aims; *except that:*

(i) Securities or other obligations of the Grantor, or any other owner or operator of the facilities, or any of their affiliates as defined in the Investment Company Act of 1940, as amended, 15 U.S.C. 80a-2.(a), shall not be acquired or held, unless they are securities or other obligations of the Federal or a State government;

(ii) The Trustee is authorized to invest the Fund in time or demand deposits of the Trustee, to the extent insured by an agency of the Federal or State government; and

(iii) The Trustee is authorized to hold cash awaiting investment or distribution uninvested for a reasonable time and without liability for the payment of interest thereon.

Section 7. *Commingling and Investment.* The Trustee is expressly authorized in its discretion:

(a) To transfer from time to time any or all of the assets of the Fund to any common, commingled, or collective trust fund created by the Trustee in which the Fund is eligible to participate, subject to all of the provisions thereof, to be commingled with the assets of other trusts participating therein; and

(b) To purchase shares in any investment company registered under the Investment Company Act of 1940, 15 U.S.C. 80a-1 *et seq.*, including one which may be created, managed, underwritten, or to which investment advice is rendered or the shares of which are sold by the Trustee. The Trustee may vote such shares in its discretion.

Section 8. *Express Powers of Trustee.* Without in any way limiting the powers and discretions conferred upon the Trustee by the other provisions of this Agreement or by law, the Trustee is expressly authorized and empowered:

(a) To sell, exchange, convey, transfer, or otherwise dispose of any property held by it, by public or private sale. No person dealing with the Trustee shall be bound to see to the application of the purchase money or to inquire into the validity or expediency of any such sale or other disposition;

(b) To make, execute, acknowledge, and deliver any and all documents of transfer and conveyance and any and all other instruments that may be necessary or appropriate to carry out the powers herein granted;

(c) To register any securities held in the Fund in its own name or in the name of a nominee and to hold any security in bearer form or in book entry, or to combine certificates representing such securities with certificates of the same issue held by the Trustee in other fiduciary capacities, or to deposit or arrange for the deposit of such securities in a qualified central depositary even though, when so deposited, such securities may be merged and held in bulk in the name of the nominee of such depositary with other securities deposited therein by another person, or to deposit or arrange for the deposit of any securities issued by the United States Government, or any agency or instrumentality thereof, with a Federal Reserve bank, but the books and records of the Trustee shall at all times show that all such securities are part of the Fund;

(d) To deposit any cash in the Fund in interest-bearing accounts maintained or savings certificates issued by the Trustee, in its separate corporate capacity, or in any other banking institution affiliated with the Trustee, to the extent insured by an agency of the Federal or State government; and

(e) To compromise or otherwise adjust all claims in favor of or against the Fund.

Section 9. *Taxes and Expenses.* All taxes of any kind that may be assessed or levied against or in respect of the Fund and all brokerage commissions incurred by the Fund shall be paid from the Fund. All other expenses incurred by the Trustee in connection with the administration of this Trust, including fees for legal services rendered to the Trustee, the compensation of the Trustee to the extent not paid directly by the Grantor, and all other proper charges and disbursements of the Trustee shall be paid from the Fund.

Section 10. *Annual Valuation.* The Trustee shall annually, at least 30 days prior to the anniversary date of establishment of the Fund, furnish to the Grantor and to the appropriate EPA Regional Administrator a statement confirming the value of the Trust. Any securities in the Fund shall be valued at market value as of no more than 60 days prior to the anniversary date of establishment of the Fund. The failure of the Grantor to object in writing to the Trustee within 90 days after the statement has been furnished to the Grantor and the EPA Regional Administrator shall constitute a conclusively binding assent by the Grantor, barring the Grantor from asserting any claim or liability against the Trustee with respect to matters disclosed in the statement.

Section 11. *Advice of Counsel.* The Trustee may from time to time consult with counsel, who may be counsel to the Grantor, with respect to any question arising as to the construction of this Agreement or any action to be taken hereunder. The Trustee shall be fully protected, to the extent permitted by law, in acting upon the advice of counsel.

Section 12. *Trustee Compensation.* The Trustee shall be entitled to reasonable compensation for its services as agreed upon in writing from time to time with the Grantor.

Section 13. *Successor Trustee.* The Trustee may resign or the Grantor may replace the Trustee, but such resignation or replacement shall not be effective until the Grantor has appointed a successor trustee and this successor accepts the appointment. The successor trustee shall have the same powers and duties as those conferred upon the Trustee hereunder. Upon the successor trustee's acceptance of the appointment, the Trustee shall assign, transfer, and pay over to the successor trustee the funds and properties then constituting the Fund. If for any reason the Grantor cannot or does not act in the event of the resignation of the Trustee, the Trustee may apply to a court of competent jurisdiction for the appointment of a successor trustee or for instructions. The successor trustee shall specify the date on which it assumes administration of the trust in a writing sent to the Grantor, the EPA Regional Administrator, and the present Trustee by certified mail 10 days before such change becomes effective. Any expenses incurred by the Trustee as a result of any of the acts contemplated by this Section shall be paid as provided in Section 9.

Section 14. *Instructions to the Trustee.* All orders, requests, and instructions by the Grantor to the Trustee shall be in writing, signed by such persons as are designated in the attached Exhibit A or such other designees as the Grantor may designate by amendment to Exhibit A. The Trustee shall be fully protected in acting without inquiry in accordance with the Grantor's orders, requests, and instructions. All orders, requests, and instructions by the EPA Regional Administrator to the Trustee shall be in writing, signed by the EPA Regional Administrators of the Regions in which the facilities are located, or their designees, and the Trustee shall act and shall be fully protected in acting in accordance with such orders, requests, and instructions. The Trustee shall have the right to assume, in the absence of written notice to the contrary, that no event constituting a change or a termination of the authority of any person to act on behalf of the Grantor or EPA hereunder has occurred. The Trustee shall have no duty to act in the absence of such orders, requests, and instructions from the Grantor and/or EPA, except as provided for herein.

Section 15. *Notice of Nonpayment.* The Trustee shall notify the Grantor and the appropriate EPA Regional Administrator, by certified mail within 10 days following the expiration of the 30-day period after the anniversary of the establishment of the Trust, if no payment is received from the Grantor during that period. After the pay-in period is completed, the Trustee shall not be required to send a notice of nonpayment.

Section 16. *Amendment of Agreement.* This Agreement may be amended by an instrument in writing executed by the Grantor, the Trustee, and the appropriate EPA Regional Administrator, or by the Trustee and the appropriate EPA Regional Administrator if the Grantor ceases to exist.

Section 17. *Irrevocability and Termination.* Subject to the right of the parties to amend this Agreement as provided in Section 16, this Trust shall be irrevocable and shall continue until terminated at the written agreement of the Grantor, the Trustee, and the EPA Regional Administrator, or by the Trustee and the EPA Regional Administrator, if the Grantor ceases to exist. Upon termination of the Trust, all remaining trust property, less final trust administration expenses, shall be delivered to the Grantor.

Section 18. *Immunity and Indemnification.* The Trustee shall not incur personal liability of any nature in connection with any act or omission, made in good faith, in the administration of this Trust, or in carrying out any directions by the Grantor or the EPA Regional Administrator issued in accordance with this Agreement. The Trustee shall be indemnified and saved harmless by the Grantor or from the Trust Fund, or both, from and against any personal liability to which the Trustee may be subjected by reason of any act or conduct in its official capacity, including all expenses reasonably incurred in its defense in the event the Grantor fails to provide such defense.

Section 19. *Choice of Law.* This Agreement shall be administered, construed, and enforced according to the laws of the State of [insert name of State].

Section 20. *Interpretation.* As used in this Agreement, words in the singular include the plural and words in the plural include the singular. The descriptive headings for each Section of this Agreement shall not affect the interpretation or the legal efficacy of this Agreement.

In Witness Whereof the parties have caused this Agreement to be executed by their respective officers duly authorized and their corporate seals to be hereunto affixed and attested as of the date first above written: The parties below certify that the wording of this Agreement is identical to the wording specified in 40 CFR

264.151(a)(1) as such regulations were constituted on the date first above written.

[Signature of Grantor]

[Title]

Attest:

[Title]

[Seal]

[Signature of Trustee]

Attest:

[Title]

[Seal]

(2) The following is an example of the certification of acknowledgment which must accompany the trust agreement for a trust fund as specified in §§264.143(a) and 264.145(a) or §§265.143(a) or 265.145(a) of this chapter. State requirements may differ on the proper content of this acknowledgment.

State of __________

County of __________

On this [date], before me personally came [owner or operator] to me known, who, being by me duly sworn, did depose and say that she/he resides at [address], that she/he is [title] of [corporation], the corporation described in and which executed the above instrument; that she/he knows the seal of said corporation; that the seal affixed to such instrument is such corporate seal; that it was so affixed by order of the Board of Directors of said corporation, and that she/he signed her/his name thereto by like order.

[Signature of Notary Public]

(b) A surety bond guaranteeing payment into a trust fund, as specified in §264.143(b) or §264.145(b) or §265.143(b) or §265.145(b) of this chapter, must be worded as follows, except that instructions in brackets are to be replaced with the relevant information and the brackets deleted:

Financial Guarantee Bond

Date bond executed:

Effective date:

Principal: [legal name and business address of owner or operator]

Type of Organization: [insert "individual," "joint venture," "partnership," or "corporation"]

State of incorporation: __________

Surety(ies): [name(s) and business address(es)]

EPA Identification Number, name, address and closure and/or post-closure amount(s) for each facility guaranteed by this bond [indicate closure and post-closure amounts separately]: __________

Total penal sum of bond: $ __________

Surety's bond number: __________

Know All Persons By These Presents, That we, the Principal and Surety(ies) hereto are firmly bound to the U.S. Environmental Protection Agency (hereinafter called EPA), in the above penal sum for the payment of which we bind ourselves, our heirs, executors, administrators, successors, and assigns jointly and severally; provided that, where the Surety(ies) are corporations acting as co-sureties, we, the Sureties, bind ourselves in such sum "jointly and severally" only for the purpose of allowing a joint action or actions against any or all of us, and for all other purposes each Surety binds itself, jointly and severally with the Principal, for the payment of such sum only as is set forth opposite the name of such Surety, but if no limit of liability is indicated, the limit of liability shall be the full amount of the penal sum.

Whereas said Principal is required, under the Resource Conservation and Recovery Act as amended (RCRA), to have a permit or interim status in order to own or operate each hazardous waste management facility identified above, and

Whereas said Principal is required to provide financial assurance for closure, or closure and post-closure care, as a condition of the permit or interim status, and

Whereas said Principal shall establish a standby trust fund as is required when a surety bond is used to provide such financial assurance;

Now, Therefore, the conditions of the obligation are such that if the Principal shall faithfully, before the beginning of final closure of each facility identified above, fund the standby trust fund in the amount(s) identified above for the facility,

Or, if the Principal shall fund the standby trust fund in such amount(s) within 15 days after a final order to begin closure is issued by an EPA Regional Administrator or a U.S. district court or other court of competent jurisdiction,

Or, if the Principal shall provide alternate financial assurance, as specified in subpart H of 40 CFR part 264 or 265, as applicable, and obtain the EPA Regional Administrator's written approval of such assurance, within 90 days after the date notice of cancellation is received by both the Principal and the EPA Regional Administrator(s) from the Surety(ies), then this obligation shall be null and void; otherwise it is to remain in full force and effect.

The Surety(ies) shall become liable on this bond obligation only when the Principal has failed to fulfill the conditions described above. Upon notification by an EPA Regional Administrator that the Principal has failed to perform as guaranteed by this bond, the Surety(ies) shall place funds in the amount guaranteed for the facility(ies) into the standby trust fund as directed by the EPA Regional Administrator.

The liability of the Surety(ies) shall not be discharged by any payment or succession of payments hereunder, unless and until such payment or payments shall amount in the aggregate to the penal sum of the bond, but in no event shall the obligation of the Surety(ies) hereunder exceed the amount of said penal sum.

The Surety(ies) may cancel the bond by sending notice of cancellation by certified mail to the Principal and to the EPA Regional Administrator(s) for the Region(s) in which the facility(ies) is (are) located, provided, however, that cancellation shall not occur during the 120 days beginning on the date of receipt of the notice of cancellation by both the Principal and the EPA Regional Administrator(s), as evidenced by the return receipts.

The Principal may terminate this bond by sending written notice to the Surety(ies), provided, however, that no such notice shall become effective until the Surety(ies) receive(s) written authorization for termination of the bond by the EPA Regional Administrator(s) of the EPA Region(s) in which the bonded facility(ies) is (are) located.

[The following paragraph is an optional rider that may be included but is not required.]

Principal and Surety(ies) hereby agree to adjust the penal sum of the bond yearly so that it guarantees a new closure and/or post-closure amount, provided that the penal sum does not increase by more than 20 percent in any one year, and no decrease in the penal sum takes place without the written permission of the EPA Regional Administrator(s).

In Witness Whereof, the Principal and Surety(ies) have executed this Financial Guarantee Bond and have affixed their seals on the date set forth above.

The persons whose signatures appear below hereby certify that they are authorized to execute this surety bond on behalf of the Principal and Surety(ies) and that the wording of this surety bond is identical to the wording specified in 40 CFR 264.151(b) as such regulations were constituted on the date this bond was executed.

Principal

[Signature(s)] ____

[Name(s)] ____

[Title(s)] ____

[Corporate seal] ____

Corporate Surety(ies)

[Name and address]

State of incorporation: ____

Liability limit: $ ____

[Signature(s)]

[Name(s) and title(s)]

[Corporate seal]

[For every co-surety, provide signature(s), corporate seal, and other information in the same manner as for Surety above.]

Bond premium: $____

(c) A surety bond guaranteeing performance of closure and/or post-closure care, as specified in §264.143(c) or §264.145(c), must be worded as follows, except that the instructions in brackets are to be replaced with the relevant information and the brackets deleted:

Performance Bond

Date bond executed: ____

Effective date: ____

Principal: [legal name and business address of owner or operator]

Type of organization: [insert "individual," "joint venture," "partnership," or "corporation"]

State of incorporation: ____

Surety(ies): [name(s) and business address(es)] ____

EPA Identification Number, name, address, and closure and/or post-closure amount(s) for each facility guaranteed by this bond [indicate closure and post-closure amounts separately]: ____

Total penal sum of bond: $ ____

Surety's bond number: ____

Know All Persons By These Presents, That we, the Principal and Surety(ies) hereto are firmly bound to the U.S. Environmental Protection Agency (hereinafter called EPA), in the above penal sum for the payment of which we bind ourselves, our heirs, executors, administrators, successors, and assigns jointly and severally; provided that, where the Surety(ies) are corporations acting as co-sureties, we, the Sureties, bind ourselves in such sum "jointly and severally" only for the purpose of allowing a joint action or actions against any or all of us, and for all other purposes each Surety binds itself, jointly and severally with the Principal, for the payment of such sum only as is set forth opposite the name of such Surety, but if no limit of liability is indicated, the limit of liability shall be the full amount of the penal sum.

Whereas said Principal is required, under the Resource Conservation and Recovery Act as amended (RCRA), to have a permit in order to own or operate each hazardous waste management facility identified above, and

Whereas said Principal is required to provide financial assurance for closure, or closure and post-closure care, as a condition of the permit, and

Whereas said Principal shall establish a standby trust fund as is required when a surety bond is used to provide such financial assurance;

Now, Therefore, the conditions of this obligation are such that if the Principal shall faithfully perform closure, whenever required to do so, of each facility for which this bond guarantees closure, in accordance with the closure plan and other requirements of the permit as such plan and permit may be amended, pursuant to all applicable laws, statutes, rules, and regulations, as such laws, statutes, rules, and regulations may be amended,

And, if the Principal shall faithfully perform post-closure care of each facility for which this bond guarantees post-closure care, in accordance with the post-closure plan and other requirements of the permit, as such plan and permit may be amended, pursuant to all applicable laws, statutes, rules, and regulations, as such laws, statutes, rules, and regulations may be amended,

Or, if the Principal shall provide alternate financial assurance as specified in subpart H of 40 CFR part 264, and obtain the EPA Regional Administrator's written approval of such assurance, within 90 days after the date notice of cancellation is received by both the Principal and the EPA Regional Administrator(s) from the Surety(ies), then this obligation shall be null and void, otherwise it is to remain in full force and effect.

The Surety(ies) shall become liable on this bond obligation only when the Principal has failed to fulfill the conditions described above.

Upon notification by an EPA Regional Administrator that the Principal has been found in violation of the closure requirements of 40 CFR part 264, for a facility for which this bond guarantees performance of closure, the Surety(ies) shall either perform closure in accordance with the closure plan and other permit requirements or place the closure amount guaranteed for the facility into the standby trust fund as directed by the EPA Regional Administrator.

Upon notification by an EPA Regional Administrator that the Principal has been found in violation of the post-closure requirements of 40 CFR part 264 for a facility for which this bond guarantees performance of post-closure care, the Surety(ies) shall either perform post-closure care in accordance with the post-closure plan and other permit requirements or place the post-closure amount guaranteed for the facility into the standby trust fund as directed by the EPA Regional Administrator.

Upon notification by an EPA Regional Administrator that the Principal has failed to provide alternate financial assurance as specified in subpart H of 40 CFR part 264, and obtain written approval of such assurance from the EPA Regional Administrator(s) during the 90 days following receipt by both the Principal and the EPA Regional Administrator(s) of a notice of cancellation of the bond, the Surety(ies) shall place funds in the amount guaranteed for the facility(ies) into the standby trust fund as directed by the EPA Regional Administrator.

The surety(ies) hereby waive(s) notification of amendments to closure plans, permits, applicable laws, statutes, rules, and regulations and agrees that no such amendment shall in any way alleviate its (their) obligation on this bond.

The liability of the Surety(ies) shall not be discharged by any payment or succession of payments hereunder, unless and until such payment or payments shall amount in the aggregate to the penal sum of the bond, but in no event shall the obligation of the Surety(ies) hereunder exceed the amount of said penal sum.

The Surety(ies) may cancel the bond by sending notice of cancellation by certified mail to the owner or operator and to the EPA Regional Administrator(s) for the Region(s) in which the facility(ies) is (are) located, provided, however, that cancellation shall not occur during the 120 days beginning on the date of receipt of the notice of cancellation by both the Principal and the EPA Regional Administrator(s), as evidenced by the return receipts.

The principal may terminate this bond by sending written notice to the Surety(ies), provided, however, that no such notice shall become effective until the Surety(ies) receive(s) written authorization for termination of the bond by the EPA Regional Administrator(s) of the EPA Region(s) in which the bonded facility(ies) is (are) located.

[The following paragraph is an *optional* rider that may be included but is not required.]

Principal and Surety(ies) hereby agree to adjust the penal sum of the bond yearly so that it guarantees a new closure and/or post-closure amount, provided that the penal sum does not increase by more than 20 percent in any one year, and no decrease in the penal sum takes place without the written permission of the EPA Regional Administrator(s).

In Witness Whereof, The Principal and Surety(ies) have executed this Performance Bond and have affixed their seals on the date set forth above.

The persons whose signatures appear below hereby certify that they are authorized to execute this surety bond on behalf of the Principal and Surety(ies) and that the wording of this surety bond is identical to the wording specified in 40 CFR 264.151(c) as such regulation was constituted on the date this bond was executed.

Principal

[Signature(s)]

[Name(s)]

[Title(s)]

[Corporate seal]

Corporate Surety(ies)

[Name and address]

State of incorporation: ______

Liability limit: $ ______

[Signature(s)]

[Name(s) and title(s)]

[Corporate seal]

[For every co-surety, provide signature(s), corporate seal, and other information in the same manner as for Surety above.]

Bond premium: $______

(d) A letter of credit, as specified in §264.143(d) or §264.145(d) or §265.143(c) or §265.145(c) of this chapter, must be worded as follows, except that instructions in brackets are to be replaced with the relevant information and the brackets deleted:

Irrevocable Standby Letter of Credit

Regional Administrator(s) Region(s)______

U.S. Environmental Protection Agency

Dear Sir or Madam: We hereby establish our Irrevocable Standby Letter of Credit No. ______ in your favor, at the request and for the account of [owner's or operator's name and address] up to the aggregate amount of [in words] U.S. dollars $______, available upon presentation [insert, if more than one Regional Administrator is a beneficiary, "by any one of you"] of

(1) your sight draft, bearing reference to this letter of credit No. ______, and

(2) your signed statement reading as follows: "I certify that the amount of the draft is payable pursuant to regulations issued under authority of the Resource Conservation and Recovery Act of 1976 as amended."

This letter of credit is effective as of [date] and shall expire on [date at least 1 year later], but such expiration date shall be automatically extended for a period of [at least 1 year] on [date] and on each successive expiration date, unless, at least 120 days before the current expiration date, we notify both you and [owner's or operator's name] by certified mail that we have decided not to extend this letter of credit beyond the current expiration date. In the event you are so notified, any unused portion of the credit shall be available upon presentation of your sight draft for 120 days after the date of receipt by both you and [owner's or operator's name], as shown on the signed return receipts.

Whenever this letter of credit is drawn on under and in compliance with the terms of this credit, we shall duly honor such draft upon presentation to us, and we shall deposit the amount of the draft directly into the standby trust fund of [owner's or operator's name] in accordance with your instructions.

We certify that the wording of this letter of credit is identical to the wording specified in 40 CFR 264.151(d) as such regulations were constituted on the date shown immediately below.

[Signature(s) and title(s) of official(s) of issuing institution] [Date]

This credit is subject to [insert "the most recent edition of the Uniform Customs and Practice for Documentary Credits, published and copyrighted by the International Chamber of Commerce," or "the Uniform Commercial Code"].

(e) A certificate of insurance, as specified in §264.143(e) or §264.145(e) or §265.143(d) or §265.145(d) of this chapter, must be worded as follows, except that instructions in brackets are to be replaced with the relevant information and the brackets deleted:

Certificate of Insurance for Closure or Post-Closure Care

Name and Address of Insurer (herein called the "Insurer"):

______

Name and Address of Insured (herein called the "Insured"):

______

Facilities Covered: [List for each facility: The EPA Identification Number, name, address, and the amount of insurance for closure and/or the amount for post-closure care (these amounts for all facilities covered must total the face amount shown below).]

Face Amount: ______

Policy Number: ______

Effective Date: ______

The Insurer hereby certifies that it has issued to the Insured the policy of insurance identified above to provide financial assurance for [insert "closure" or "closure and post-closure care" or "post-closure care"] for the facilities identified above. The Insurer further warrants that such policy conforms in all respects with the requirements of 40 CFR 264.143(e), 264.145(e), 265.143(d), and 265.145(d), as applicable and as such regulations were constituted on the date shown immediately below. It is agreed that any provision of the policy inconsistent with such regulations is hereby amended to eliminate such inconsistency.

Whenever requested by the EPA Regional Administrator(s) of the U.S. Environmental Protection Agency, the Insurer agrees to furnish to the EPA Regional Administrator(s) a duplicate original of the policy listed above, including all endorsements thereon.

I hereby certify that the wording of this certificate is identical to the wording specified in 40 CFR 264.151(e) as such regulations were constituted on the date shown immediately below.

[Authorized signature for Insurer]

[Name of person signing]

[Title of person signing]

Signature of witness or notary: ______________________

[Date]

(f) A letter from the chief financial officer, as specified in §264.143(f) or 264.145(f), or 265.143(e) or §265.145(e) of this chapter, must be worded as follows, except that instructions in brackets are to be replaced with the relevant information and the brackets deleted:

Letter From Chief Financial Officer

[Address to Regional Administrator of every Region in which facilities for which financial responsibility is to be demonstrated through the financial test are located].

I am the chief financial officer of [name and address of firm]. This letter is in support of this firm's use of the financial test to demonstrate financial assurance for closure and/or post-closure costs, as specified in subpart H of 40 CFR parts 264 and 265.

[Fill out the following five paragraphs regarding facilities and associated cost estimates. If your firm has no facilities that belong in a particular paragraph, write "None" in the space indicated. For each facility, include its EPA Identification Number, name, address, and current closure and/or post-closure cost estimates. Identify each cost estimate as to whether it is for closure or post-closure care].

1. This firm is the owner or operator of the following facilities for which financial assurance for closure or post-closure care is demonstrated through the financial test specified in subpart H of 40 CFR parts 264 and 265. The current closure and/or post-closure cost estimates covered by the test are shown for each facility: ________.
2. This firm guarantees, through the guarantee specified in subpart H of 40 CFR parts 264 and 265, the closure or post-closure care of the following facilities owned or operated by the guaranteed party. The current cost estimates for the closure or post-closure care so guaranteed are shown for each facility: _______. The firm identified above is [insert one or more: (1) The direct or higher-tier parent corporation of the owner or operator; (2) owned by the same parent corporation as the parent corporation of the owner or operator, and receiving the following value in consideration of this guarantee ________; or (3) engaged in the following substantial business relationship with the owner or operator ________, and receiving the following value in consideration of this guarantee ________]. [Attach a written description of the business relationship or a copy of the contract establishing such relationship to this letter].
3. In States where EPA is not administering the financial requirements of subpart H of 40 CFR part 264 or 265, this firm, as owner or operator or guarantor, is demonstrating financial assurance for the closure or post-closure care of the following facilities through the use of a test equivalent or substantially equivalent to the financial test specified in subpart H of 40 CFR parts 264 and 265. The current closure and/or post-closure cost estimates covered by such a test are shown for each facility: ________.
4. This firm is the owner or operator of the following hazardous waste management facilities for which financial assurance for closure or, if a disposal facility, post-closure care, is not demonstrated either to EPA or a State through the financial test or any other financial assurance mechanism specified in subpart H of 40 CFR parts 264 and 265 or equivalent or substantially equivalent State mechanisms. The current closure and/or post-closure cost estimates not covered by such financial assurance are shown for each facility: ________.
5. This firm is the owner or operator of the following UIC facilities for which financial assurance for plugging and abandonment is required under part 144. The current closure cost estimates as required by 40 CFR 144.62 are shown for each facility: ________.

This firm [insert "is required" or "is not required"] to file a Form 10K with the Securities and Exchange Commission (SEC) for the latest fiscal year.

The fiscal year of this firm ends on [month, day]. The figures for the following items marked with an asterisk are derived from this firm's independently audited, year-end financial statements for the latest completed fiscal year, ended [date].

[Fill in Alternative I if the criteria of paragraph (f)(1)(i) of §264.143 or §264.145, or of paragraph (e)(1)(i) of §265.143 or §265.145 of this chapter are used. Fill in Alternative II if the criteria of paragraph (f)(1)(ii) of §264.143 or §264.145, or of paragraph (e)(1)(ii) of §265.143 or §265.145 of this chapter are used.]

Alternative I

1. Sum of current closure and post-closure cost estimate [total of all cost estimates shown in the five paragraphs above] $________

*2. Total liabilities [if any portion of the closure or post-closure cost estimates is included in total liabilities, you may deduct the amount of that portion from this line and add that amount to lines 3 and 4] $________

*3. Tangible net worth $________

*4. Net worth $________

*5. Current assets $________

*6. Current liabilities $________

7. Net working capital [line 5 minus line 6] $________

*8. The sum of net income plus depreciation, depletion, and amortization $________

*9. Total assets in U.S. (required only if less than 90% of firm's assets are located in the U.S.) $________

10. Is line 3 at least $10 million? (Yes/No) ________

11. Is line 3 at least 6 times line 1? (Yes/No) ________

12. Is line 7 at least 6 times line 1? (Yes/No) ________

*13. Are at least 90% of firm's assets located in the U.S.? If not, complete line 14 (Yes/No) ________

14. Is line 9 at least 6 times line 1? (Yes/No) ________

15. Is line 2 divided by line 4 less than 2.0? (Yes/No) ________

16. Is line 8 divided by line 2 greater than 0.1? (Yes/No) ________

17. Is line 5 divided by line 6 greater than 1.5? (Yes/No) ________

Alternative II

1. Sum of current closure and post-closure cost estimates [total of all cost estimates shown in the five paragraphs above] $________
2. Current bond rating of most recent issuance of this firm and name of rating service________
3. Date of issuance of bond________
4. Date of maturity of bond________

*5. Tangible net worth [if any portion of the closure and post-closure cost estimates is included in "total liabilities" on your firm's financial statements, you may add the amount of that portion to this line] $________

*6. Total assets in U.S. (required only if less than 90% of firm's assets are located in the U.S.) $________

7. Is line 5 at least $10 million ? (Yes/No) ________
8. Is line 5 at least 6 times line 1? (Yes/No) ________

*9. Are at least 90% of firm's assets located in the U.S.? If not, complete line 10 (Yes/No) ________

10. Is line 6 at least 6 times line 1? (Yes/No) ________

I hereby certify that the wording of this letter is identical to the wording specified in 40 CFR 264.151(f) as such regulations were constituted on the date shown immediately below.

[Signature]________

[Name] ________

[Title]________

[Date] ________

(g) A letter from the chief financial officer, as specified in §264.147(f) or §265.147(f) of this chapter, must be worded as follows, except that instructions in brackets are to be replaced with the relevant information and the brackets deleted.

Letter From Chief Financial Officer

[Address to Regional Administrator of every Region in which facilities for which financial responsibility is to be demonstrated through the financial test are located].

I am the chief financial officer of [firm's name and address]. This letter is in support of the use of the financial test to demonstrate financial responsibility for liability coverage [insert "and closure and/or post-closure care" if applicable] as specified in subpart H of 40 CFR parts 264 and 265.

[Fill out the following paragraphs regarding facilities and liability coverage. If there are no facilities that belong in a particular paragraph, write "None" in the space indicated. For each facility, include its EPA Identification Number, name, and address].

The firm identified above is the owner or operator of the following facilities for which liability coverage for [insert "sudden" or "nonsudden" or "both sudden and nonsudden"] accidental occurrences is being demonstrated through the financial test specified in subpart H of 40 CFR parts 264 and 265:________

The firm identified above guarantees, through the guarantee specified in subpart H of 40 CFR parts 264 and 265, liability coverage for [insert "sudden" or "nonsudden" or "both sudden and nonsudden"] accidental occurrences at the following facilities owned or operated by the following: ________. The firm identified above is [insert one or more: (1) The direct or higher-tier parent corporation of the owner or operator; (2) owned by the same parent corporation as the parent corporation of the owner or operator, and receiving the following value in consideration of this guarantee ________; or (3) engaged in the following substantial business relationship with the owner or operator ________, and receiving the following value in consideration of this guarantee ________]. [Attach a written description of the business relationship or a copy of the contract establishing such relationship to this letter.]

[If you are using the financial test to demonstrate coverage of both liability and closure and post-closure care, fill in the following five paragraphs regarding facilities and associated closure and post-closure cost estimates. If there are no facilities that belong in a particular paragraph, write "None" in the space indicated. For each facility, include its EPA identification number, name, address, and current closure and/or post-closure cost estimates. Identify each cost estimate as to whether it is for closure or post-closure care.]

1. The firm identified above owns or operates the following facilities for which financial assurance for closure or post-closure care or liability coverage is demonstrated through the financial test specified in subpart H of 40 CFR parts 264 and 265. The current closure and/or post-closure cost estimate covered by the test are shown for each facility: ________.
2. The firm identified above guarantees, through the guarantee specified in subpart H of 40 CFR parts 264 and 265, the closure and post-closure care or liability coverage of the following facilities owned or operated by the guaranteed party. The current cost estimates for closure or post-closure care so guaranteed are shown for each facility: ________.
3. In States where EPA is not administering the financial requirements of subpart H of 40 CFR parts 264 and 265, this firm is demonstrating financial assurance for the closure or post-closure care of the following facilities through the use of a test equivalent or substantially equivalent to the financial test specified in subpart H of 40 CFR parts 264 and 265. The current closure or post-closure cost estimates covered by such a test are shown for each facility: ________.
4. The firm identified above owns or operates the following hazardous waste management facilities for which financial assurance for closure or, if a disposal facility, post-closure care, is not demonstrated either to EPA or a State through the financial test or any other financial assurance mechanisms specified in subpart H of 40 CFR parts 264 and 265 or equivalent or substantially equivalent State mechanisms. The current closure and/or post-closure cost estimates not covered by such financial assurance are shown for each facility: ________.
5. This firm is the owner or operator or guarantor of the following UIC facilities for which financial assurance for plugging and abandonment is required under part 144 and is assured through a financial test. The current closure cost estimates as required by 40 CFR 144.62 are shown for each facility:________.

This firm [insert "is required" or "is not required"] to file a Form 10K with the Securities and Exchange Commission (SEC) for the latest fiscal year.

The fiscal year of this firm ends on [month, day]. The figures for the following items marked with an asterisk are derived from this firm's independently audited, year-end financial statements for the latest completed fiscal year, ended [date].

Part A. Liability Coverage for Accidental Occurrences

[Fill in Alternative I if the criteria of paragraph (f)(1)(i) of §264.147 or §265.147 are used. Fill in Alternative II if the criteria of paragraph (f)(1)(ii) of §264.147 or §265.147 are used.]

Alternative I

1. Amount of annual aggregate liability coverage to be demonstrated $ ______.
*2. Current assets $ ________.
*3. Current liabilities $ ________.
4. Net working capital (line 2 minus line 3) $ ________.
*5. Tangible net worth $ ________.
*6. If less than 90% of assets are located in the U.S., give total U.S. assets $ ________.
7. Is line 5 at least $10 million? (Yes/No) ________.
8. Is line 4 at least 6 times line 1? (Yes/No) ________.
9. Is line 5 at least 6 times line 1? (Yes/No) ________.
*10. Are at least 90% of assets located in the U.S.? (Yes/No) ______. If not, complete line 11.
11. Is line 6 at least 6 times line 1? (Yes/No) ________.

Alternative II

1. Amount of annual aggregate liability coverage to be demonstrated $ ________.
2. Current bond rating of most recent issuance and name of rating service________.
3. Date of issuance of bond________.
4. Date of maturity of bond________.
*5. Tangible net worth $ ________.
*6. Total assets in U.S. (required only if less than 90% of assets are located in the U.S.) $ ________.
7. Is line 5 at least $10 million? (Yes/No) ________.
8. Is line 5 at least 6 times line 1? ________.
9. Are at least 90% of assets located in the U.S.? If not, complete line 10. (Yes/No) ________.
10. Is line 6 at least 6 times line 1? ________.

[Fill in part B if you are using the financial test to demonstrate assurance of both liability coverage and closure or post-closure care.]

Part B. Closure or Post-Closure Care and Liability Coverage

[Fill in Alternative I if the criteria of paragraphs (f)(1)(i) of §264.143 or §264.145 and (f)(1)(i) of §264.147 are used or if the criteria of paragraphs (e)(1)(i) of §265.143 or §265.145 and (f)(1)(i) of §265.147 are used. Fill in Alternative II if the criteria of paragraphs (f)(1)(ii) of §264.143 or §264.145 and (f)(1)(ii) of §264.147 are used or if the criteria of paragraphs (e)(1)(i) of §265.143 or §265.145 and (f)(1)(ii) of §265.147 are used.]

Alternative I

1. Sum of current closure and post-closure cost estimates (total of all cost estimates listed above) $ ________
2. Amount of annual aggregate liability coverage to be demonstrated $ ________
3. Sum of lines 1 and 2 $ ________
*4. Total liabilities (if any portion of your closure or post-closure cost estimates is included in your total liabilities, you may deduct that portion from this line and add that amount to lines 5 and 6) $ ________
*5. Tangible net worth $ ________
*6. Net worth $ ________
*7. Current assets $ ________
*8. Current liabilities $ ________
9. Net working capital (line 7 minus line 8) $ ________
*10. The sum of net income plus depreciation, depletion, and amortization $________
*11. Total assets in U.S. (required only if less than 90% of assets are located in the U.S.) $ ________
12. Is line 5 at least $10 million? (Yes/No)
13. Is line 5 at least 6 times line 3? (Yes/No)
14. Is line 9 at least 6 times line 3? (Yes/No)
*15. Are at least 90% of assets located in the U.S.? (Yes/No) If not, complete line 16.
16. Is line 11 at least 6 times line 3? (Yes/No)
17. Is line 4 divided by line 6 less than 2.0? (Yes/No)
18. Is line 10 divided by line 4 greater than 0.1? (Yes/No)
19. Is line 7 divided by line 8 greater than 1.5? (Yes/No)

Alternative II

1. Sum of current closure and post-closure cost estimates (total of all cost estimates listed above) $ ________
2. Amount of annual aggregate liability coverage to be demonstrated $ ________
3. Sum of lines 1 and 2 $ ________
4. Current bond rating of most recent issuance and name of rating service________
5. Date of issuance of bond________
6. Date of maturity of bond________
*7. Tangible net worth (if any portion of the closure or post-closure cost estimates is included in "total liabilities" on your financial statements you may add that portion to this line) $ ________
*8. Total assets in the U.S. (required only if less than 90% of assets are located in the U.S.) $ ________
9. Is line 7 at least $10 million? (Yes/No)
10. Is line 7 at least 6 times line 3? (Yes/No)
*11. Are at least 90% of assets located in the U.S.? (Yes/No) If not complete line 12.
12. Is line 8 at least 6 times line 3? (Yes/No) I hereby certify that the wording of this letter is identical to the wording specified in 40 CFR 264.151(g) as such regulations were constituted on the date shown immediately below.

[Signature]________________________

[Name] ________________________

[Title]________________________

[Date] ________________________

(h)(1) A corporate guarantee, as specified in §264.143(f) or §264.145(f), or §265.143(e) or §265.145(e) of this chapter, must be worded as follows, except that instructions in brackets are to be replaced with the relevant information and the brackets deleted:

Corporate Guarantee for Closure or Post-Closure Care

Guarantee made this [date] by [name of guaranteeing entity], a business corporation organized under the laws of the State of [insert name of State], herein referred to as guarantor. This guarantee is made on behalf of the [owner or operator] of [business address], which is [one of the following: "our subsidiary"; "a subsidiary of [name and address of common parent corporation], of which guarantor is a subsidiary"; or "an entity with which guarantor has a substantial business relationship, as defined in 40 CFR [either 264.141(h) or 265.141(h)]" to the United States Environmental Protection Agency (EPA).

Recitals

1. Guarantor meets or exceeds the financial test criteria and agrees to comply with the reporting requirements for guarantors as specified in 40 CFR 264.143(f), 264.145(f), 265.143(e), and 265.145(e).
2. [Owner or operator] owns or operates the following hazardous waste management facility(ies) covered by this guarantee: [List for each facility: EPA Identification Number, name, and address. Indicate for each whether guarantee is for closure, post-closure care, or both.]
3. "Closure plans" and "post-closure plans" as used below refer to the plans maintained as required by subpart G of 40 CFR parts 264 and 265 for the closure and post-closure care of facilities as identified above.
4. For value received from [owner or operator], guarantor guarantees to EPA that in the event that [owner or operator] fails to perform [insert "closure," "post-closure care" or "closure and post-closure care"] of the above facility(ies) in accordance with the closure or post-closure plans and other permit or interim status requirements whenever required to do so, the guarantor shall do so or establish a trust fund as specified in subpart H of 40 CFR part 264 or 265, as applicable, in the name of [owner or operator] in the amount of the current closure or post-closure cost estimates as specified in subpart H of 40 CFR parts 264 and 265.
5. Guarantor agrees that if, at the end of any fiscal year before termination of this guarantee, the guarantor fails to meet the financial test criteria, guarantor shall send within 90 days, by certified mail, notice to the EPA Regional Administrator(s) for the Region(s) in which the facility(ies) is(are) located and to [owner or operator] that he intends to provide alternate financial assurance as specified in subpart H of 40 CFR part 264 or 265, as applicable, in the name of [owner or operator]. Within 120 days after the end of such fiscal year, the guarantor shall establish such financial assurance unless [owner or operator] has done so.
6. The guarantor agrees to notify the EPA Regional Administrator by certified mail, of a voluntary or involuntary proceeding under Title 11 (Bankruptcy), U.S. Code, naming guarantor as debtor, within 10 days after commencement of the proceeding.
7. Guarantor agrees that within 30 days after being notified by an EPA Regional Administrator of a determination that guarantor no longer meets the financial test criteria or that he is disallowed from continuing as a guarantor of closure or post-closure care, he shall establish alternate financial assurance as specified in subpart H of 40 CFR part 264 or 265, as applicable, in the name of [owner or operator] unless [owner or operator] has done so.
8. Guarantor agrees to remain bound under this guarantee notwithstanding any or all of the following: amendment or modification of the closure or post-closure plan, amendment or modification of the permit, the extension or reduction of the time of performance of closure or post-closure, or any other modification or alteration of an obligation of the owner or operator pursuant to 40 CFR part 264 or 265.
9. Guarantor agrees to remain bound under this guarantee for as long as [owner or operator] must comply with the applicable financial assurance requirements of subpart H of 40 CFR parts 264 and 265 for the above-listed facilities, except as provided in paragraph 10 of this agreement.
10. [Insert the following language if the guarantor is (a) a direct or higher-tier corporate parent, or (b) a firm whose parent corporation is also the parent corporation of the owner or operator]:

    Guarantor may terminate this guarantee by sending notice by certified mail to the EPA Regional Administrator(s) for the Region(s) in which the facility(ies) is(are) located and to [owner or operator], provided that this guarantee may not be terminated unless and until [the owner or operator] obtains, and the EPA Regional Administrator(s) approve(s), alternate closure and/or post-closure care coverage complying with 40 CFR 264.143, 264.145, 265.143, and/or 265.145.

    [Insert the following language if the guarantor is a firm qualifying as a guarantor due to its "substantial business relationship" with its owner or operator]

    Guarantor may terminate this guarantee 120 days following the receipt of notification, through certified mail, by the EPA Regional Administrator(s) for the Region(s) in which the facility(ies) is(are) located and by [the owner or operator].
11. Guarantor agrees that if [owner or operator] fails to provide alternate financial assurance as specified in subpart H of 40 CFR part 264 or 265, as applicable, and obtain written approval of such assurance from the EPA Regional Administrator(s) within 90 days after a notice of cancellation by the guarantor is received by an EPA Regional Administrator from guarantor, guarantor shall provide such alternate financial assurance in the name of [owner or operator].
12. Guarantor expressly waives notice of acceptance of this guarantee by the EPA or by [owner or operator]. Guarantor also expressly waives notice of amendments or modifications of the closure and/or post-closure plan and of amendments or modifications of the facility permit(s).

I hereby certify that the wording of this guarantee is identical to the wording specified in 40 CFR 264.151(h) as such regulations were constituted on the date first above written.

Effective date: ____________________

[Name of guarantor] ____________________

[Authorized signature for guarantor] ____________________

[Name of person signing] ____________________

[Title of person signing] ____________________

Signature of witness or notary: ____________________

(2) A guarantee, as specified in §264.147(g) or §265.147(g) of this chapter, must be worded as follows, except that instructions in brackets are to be replaced with the relevant information and the brackets deleted:

Guarantee for Liability Coverage

Guarantee made this [date] by [name of guaranteeing entity], a business corporation organized under the laws of [if incorporated within the United States insert "the State of ________" and insert name of State; if incorporated outside the United States insert the name of the country in which incorporated, the principal place of business within the United States, and the name and address of the registered agent in the State of the principal place of business], herein referred to as guarantor. This guarantee is made on behalf of [owner or operator] of [business address], which is one of the following: "our subsidiary;" "a subsidiary of [name and address of common parent corporation], of which guarantor is a subsidiary;" or "an entity with which guarantor has a substantial business relationship, as defined in 40 CFR [either 264.141(h) or 265.141(h)]", to any and all third parties who have sustained or may sustain bodily injury or property damage caused by [sudden and/or nonsudden] accidental occurrences arising from operation of the facility(ies) covered by this guarantee.

Recitals

1. Guarantor meets or exceeds the financial test criteria and agrees to comply with the reporting requirements for guarantors as specified in 40 CFR 264.147(g) and 265.147(g).
2. [Owner or operator] owns or operates the following hazardous waste management facility(ies) covered by this guarantee: [List for each facility: EPA identification number, name, and address; and if guarantor is incorporated outside the United States list the name and address of the guarantor's registered agent in each State.] This corporate guarantee satisfies RCRA third-party liability requirements for [insert "sudden" or "nonsudden" or "both sudden and nonsudden"] accidental occurrences in above-named owner or operator facilities for coverage in the amount of [insert dollar amount] for each occurrence and [insert dollar amount] annual aggregate.
3. For value received from [owner or operator], guarantor guarantees to any and all third parties who have sustained or may sustain bodily injury or property damage caused by [sudden and/or nonsudden] accidental occurrences arising from operations of the facility(ies) covered by this guarantee that in the event that [owner or operator] fails to satisfy a judgment or award based on a determination of liability for bodily injury or property damage to third parties caused by [sudden and/or nonsudden] accidental occurrences, arising from the operation of the above-named facilities, or fails to pay an amount agreed to in settlement of a claim arising from or alleged to arise from such injury or damage, the guarantor will satisfy such judgment(s), award(s) or settlement agreement(s) up to the limits of coverage identified above.
4. Such obligation does not apply to any of the following:

   (a) Bodily injury or property damage for which [insert owner or operator] is obligated to pay damages by reason of the assumption of liability in a contract or agreement. This exclusion does not apply to liability for damages that [insert owner or operator] would be obligated to pay in the absence of the contract or agreement.

   (b) Any obligation of [insert owner or operator] under a workers' compensation, disability benefits, or unemployment compensation law or any similar law.

   (c) Bodily injury to:

   (1) An employee of [insert owner or operator] arising from, and in the course of, employment by [insert owner or operator]; or

   (2) The spouse, child, parent, brother, or sister of that employee as a consequence of, or arising from, and in the course of employment by [insert owner or operator]. This exclusion applies:

   (A) Whether [insert owner or operator] may be liable as an employer or in any other capacity; and

   (B) To any obligation to share damages with or repay another person who must pay damages because of the injury to persons identified in paragraphs (1) and (2).

   (d) Bodily injury or property damage arising out of the ownership, maintenance, use, or entrustment to others of any aircraft, motor vehicle or watercraft.

   (e) Property damage to:

   (1) Any property owned, rented, or occupied by [insert owner or operator];

   (2) Premises that are sold, given away or abandoned by [insert owner or operator] if the property damage arises out of any part of those premises;

   (3) Property loaned to [insert owner or operator];

   (4) Personal property in the care, custody or control of [insert owner or operator];

   (5) That particular part of real property on which [insert owner or operator] or any contractors or subcontractors working directly or indirectly on behalf of [insert owner or operator] are performing operations, if the property damage arises out of these operations.
5. Guarantor agrees that if, at the end of any fiscal year before termination of this guarantee, the guarantor fails to meet the financial test criteria, guarantor shall send within 90 days, by certified mail, notice to the EPA Regional Administrator[s] for the Region[s] in which the facility[ies] is[are] located and to [owner or operator] that he intends to provide alternate liability coverage as specified in 40 CFR 264.147 and 265.147, as applicable, in the name of [owner or operator]. Within 120 days after the end of such fiscal year, the guarantor shall establish such liability coverage unless [owner or operator] has done so.
6. The guarantor agrees to notify the EPA Regional Administrator by certified mail of a voluntary or involuntary proceeding under title 11 (Bankruptcy), U.S. Code, naming guarantor as debtor, within 10 days after commencement of the proceeding.
7. Guarantor agrees that within 30 days after being notified by an EPA Regional Administrator of a determination that guarantor no longer meets the financial test criteria or that he is disallowed from continuing as a guarantor, he shall establish alternate liability coverage as specified in 40 CFR 264.147 or 265.147 in the name of [owner or operator], unless [owner or operator] has done so.
8. Guarantor reserves the right to modify this agreement to take into account amendment or modification of the liability requirements set by 40 CFR 264.147 and 265.147, provided that such modification shall become effective only if a Regional Administrator does not disapprove the modification within 30 days of receipt of notification of the modification.
9. Guarantor agrees to remain bound under this guarantee for so long as [owner or operator] must comply with the applicable requirements of 40 CFR 264.147 and 265.147 for the above-listed facility(ies), except as provided in paragraph 10 of this agreement.
10. [Insert the following language if the guarantor is (a) a direct or higher-tier corporate parent, or (b) a firm whose parent corporation is also the parent corporation of the owner or operator]:

    Guarantor may terminate this guarantee by sending notice by certified mail to the EPA Regional Administrator(s) for the Region(s) in which the facility(ies) is(are) located and to [owner or operator], provided that this guarantee may not be terminated unless and until [the owner or operator] obtains, and the EPA Regional Administrator(s) approve(s), alternate liability coverage complying with 40 CFR 264.147 and/or 265.147.

    [Insert the following language if the guarantor is a firm qualifying as a guarantor due to its "substantial business relationship" with the owner or operator]:

    Guarantor may terminate this guarantee 120 days following receipt of notification, through certified mail, by the EPA Regional Administrator(s) for the Region(s) in which the facility(ies) is(are) located and by [the owner or operator].

11. Guarantor hereby expressly waives notice of acceptance of this guarantee by any party.
12. Guarantor agrees that this guarantee is in addition to and does not affect any other responsibility or liability of the guarantor with respect to the covered facilities.
13. The Guarantor shall satisfy a third-party liability claim only on receipt of one of the following documents:

(a) Certification from the Principal and the third-party claimant(s) that the liability claim should be paid. The certification must be worded as follows, except that instructions in brackets are to be replaced with the relevant information and the brackets deleted:

Certification of Valid Claim

The undersigned, as parties [insert Principal] and [insert name and address of third-party claimant(s)], hereby certify that the claim of bodily injury and/or property damage caused by a [sudden or nonsudden] accidental occurrence arising from operating [Principal's] hazardous waste treatment, storage, or disposal facility should be paid in the amount of $ ______.

[Signatures] ______

Principal ______

(Notary) Date ______

[Signatures] ______

Claimant(s) ______

(Notary) Date ______

(b) A valid final court order establishing a judgment against the Principal for bodily injury or property damage caused by sudden or nonsudden accidental occurrences arising from the operation of the Principal's facility or group of facilities.

14. In the event of combination of this guarantee with another mechanism to meet liability requirements, this guarantee will be considered [insert "primary" or "excess"] coverage.

I hereby certify that the wording of the guarantee is identical to the wording specified in 40 CFR 264.151(h)(2) as such regulations were constituted on the date shown immediately below.

Effective date: ______

[Name of guarantor] ______

[Authorized signature for guarantor] ______

[Name of person signing] ______

[Title of person signing] ______

Signature of witness or notary: ______

(i) A hazardous waste facility liability endorsement as required in §264.147 or §265.147 must be worded as follows, except that instructions in brackets are to be replaced with the relevant information and the brackets deleted:

Hazardous Waste Facility Liability Endorsement

1. This endorsement certifies that the policy to which the endorsement is attached provides liability insurance covering bodily injury and property damage in connection with the insured's obligation to demonstrate financial responsibility under 40 CFR 264.147 or 265.147. The coverage applies at [list EPA Identification Number, name, and address for each facility] for [insert "sudden accidental occurrences," "nonsudden accidental occurrences," or "sudden and nonsudden accidental occurrences"; if coverage is for multiple facilities and the coverage is different for different facilities, indicate which facilities are insured for sudden accidental occurrences, which are insured for nonsudden accidental occurrences, and which are insured for both]. The limits of liability are [insert the dollar amount of the "each occurrence" and "annual aggregate" limits of the Insurer's liability], exclusive of legal defense costs.
2. The insurance afforded with respect to such occurrences is subject to all of the terms and conditions of the policy; provided, however, that any provisions of the policy inconsistent with subsections (a) through (e) of this Paragraph 2 are hereby amended to conform with subsections (a) through (e):

(a) Bankruptcy or insolvency of the insured shall not relieve the Insurer of its obligations under the policy to which this endorsement is attached.

(b) The Insurer is liable for the payment of amounts within any deductible applicable to the policy, with a right of reimbursement by the insured for any such payment made by the Insurer. This provision does not apply with respect to that amount of any deductible for which coverage is demonstrated as specified in 40 CFR 264.147(f) or 265.147(f).

(c) Whenever requested by a Regional Administrator of the U.S. Environmental Protection Agency (EPA), the Insurer agrees to furnish to the Regional Administrator a signed duplicate original of the policy and all endorsements.

(d) Cancellation of this endorsement, whether by the Insurer, the insured, a parent corporation providing insurance coverage for its subsidiary, or by a firm having an insurable interest in and obtaining liability insurance on behalf of the owner or operator of the hazardous waste management facility, will be effective only upon written notice and only after the expiration of 60 days after a copy of such written notice is received by the Regional Administrator(s) of the EPA Region(s) in which the facility(ies) is(are) located.

(e) Any other termination of this endorsement will be effective only upon written notice and only after the expiration of thirty (30) days after a copy of such written notice is received by the Regional Administrator(s) of the EPA Region(s) in which the facility(ies) is (are) located.

Attached to and forming part of policy No. ______ issued by [name of Insurer], herein called the Insurer, of [address of Insurer] to [name of insured] of [address] this ____ day of ______, 19__. The effective date of said policy is ____ day of ______, 19__.

I hereby certify that the wording of this endorsement is identical to the wording specified in 40 CFR 264.151(i) as such regulation was constituted on the date first above written, and that the Insurer is licensed to transact the business of insurance, or eligible to provide insurance as an excess or surplus lines insurer, in one or more States.

[Signature of Authorized Representative of Insurer]

[Type name]

[Title], Authorized Representative of [name of Insurer]

[Address of Representative]

(j) A certificate of liability insurance as required in §264.147 or §265.147 must be worded as follows, except that the instructions in brackets are to be replaced with the relevant information and the brackets deleted:

Hazardous Waste Facility Certificate of Liability Insurance

1. [Name of Insurer], (the "Insurer"), of [address of Insurer] hereby certifies that it has issued liability insurance covering bodily injury and property damage to [name of insured], (the

"insured"), of [address of insured] in connection with the insured's obligation to demonstrate financial responsibility under 40 CFR 264.147 or 265.147. The coverage applies at [list EPA Identification Number, name, and address for each facility] for [insert "sudden accidental occurrences," "nonsudden accidental occurrences," or "sudden and nonsudden accidental occurrences"; if coverage is for multiple facilities and the coverage is different for different facilities, indicate which facilities are insured for sudden accidental occurrences, which are insured for nonsudden accidental occurrences, and which are insured for both]. The limits of liability are [insert the dollar amount of the "each occurrence" and "annual aggregate" limits of the Insurer's liability], exclusive of legal defense costs. The coverage is provided under policy number ______, issued on [date]. The effective date of said policy is [date].

2. The Insurer further certifies the following with respect to the insurance described in Paragraph 1:

(a) Bankruptcy or insolvency of the insured shall not relieve the Insurer of its obligations under the policy.

(b) The Insurer is liable for the payment of amounts within any deductible applicable to the policy, with a right of reimbursement by the insured for any such payment made by the Insurer. This provision does not apply with respect to that amount of any deductible for which coverage is demonstrated as specified in 40 CFR 264.147(f) or 265.147(f).

(c) Whenever requested by a Regional Administrator of the U.S. Environmental Protection Agency (EPA), the Insurer agrees to furnish to the Regional Administrator a signed duplicate original of the policy and all endorsements.

(d) Cancellation of the insurance, whether by the insurer, the insured, a parent corporation providing insurance coverage for its subsidiary, or by a firm having an insurable interest in and obtaining liability insurance on behalf of the owner or operator of the hazardous waste management facility, will be effective only upon written notice and only after the expiration of 60 days after a copy of such written notice is received by the Regional Administrator(s) of the EPA Region(s) in which the facility(ies) is(are) located.

(e) Any other termination of the insurance will be effective only upon written notice and only after the expiration of thirty (30) days after a copy of such written notice is received by the Regional Administrator(s) of the EPA Region(s) in which the facility(ies) is (are) located.

I hereby certify that the wording of this instrument is identical to the wording specified in 40 CFR 264.151(j) as such regulation was constituted on the date first above written, and that the Insurer is licensed to transact the business of insurance, or eligible to provide insurance as an excess or surplus lines insurer, in one or more States.

[Signature of authorized representative of Insurer]

[Type name]

[Title], Authorized Representative of [name of Insurer]

[Address of Representative]

(k) A letter of credit, as specified in §264.147(h) or 265.147(h) of this chapter, must be worded as follows, except that instructions in brackets are to be replaced with the relevant information and the brackets deleted:

Irrevocable Standby Letter of Credit

Name and Address of Issuing Institution____________________

Regional Administrator(s)____________________

Region(s)____________________

U.S. Environmental Protection Agency____________________

Dear Sir or Madam: We hereby establish our Irrevocable Standby Letter of Credit No. ____________ in the favor of ["any and all third-party liability claimants" or insert name of trustee of the standby trust fund], at the request and for the account of [owner or operator's name and address] for third-party liability awards or settlements up to [in words] U.S. dollars $____________ per occurrence and the annual aggregate amount of [in words] U.S. dollars $____________, for sudden accidental occurrences and/or for third-party liability awards or settlements up to the amount of [in words] U.S. dollars $____________ per occurrence, and the annual aggregate amount of [in words] U.S. dollars $____________, for nonsudden accidental occurrences available upon presentation of a sight draft bearing reference to this letter of credit No. ____________, and [insert the following language if the letter of credit is being used without a standby trust fund: (1) a signed certificate reading as follows:

Certificate of Valid Claim

The undersigned, as parties [insert principal] and [insert name and address of third party claimant(s)], hereby certify that the claim of bodily injury and/or property damage caused by a [sudden or nonsudden] accidental occurrence arising from operations of [principal's] hazardous waste treatment, storage, or disposal facility should be paid in the amount of $[ ]. We hereby certify that the claim does not apply to any of the following:

(a) Bodily injury or property damage for which [insert principal] is obligated to pay damages by reason of the assumption of liability in a contract or agreement. This exclusion does not apply to liability for damages that [insert principal] would be obligated to pay in the absence of the contract or agreement.

(b) Any obligation of [insert principal] under a workers' compensation, disability benefits, or unemployment compensation law or any similar law.

(c) Bodily injury to:

(1) An employee of [insert principal] arising from, and in the course of, employment by [insert principal]; or

(2) The spouse, child, parent, brother or sister of that employee as a consequence of, or arising from, and in the course of employment by [insert principal].

This exclusion applies:

(A) Whether [insert principal] may be liable as an employer or in any other capacity; and

(B) To any obligation to share damages with or repay another person who must pay damages because of the injury to persons identified in paragraphs (1) and (2).

(d) Bodily injury or property damage arising out of the ownership, maintenance, use, or entrustment to others of any aircraft, motor vehicle or watercraft.

(e) Property damage to:

(1) Any property owned, rented, or occupied by [insert principal];

(2) Premises that are sold, given away or abandoned by [insert principal] if the property damage arises out of any part of those premises;

(3) Property loaned to [insert principal];

(4) Personal property in the care, custody or control of [insert principal];

(5) That particular part of real property on which [insert principal] or any contractors or subcontractors working directly or indirectly on behalf of [insert principal] are performing operations, if the property damage arises out of these operations.

[Signatures] ______________________________

Grantor ______________________________

[Signatures] ______________________________

Claimant(s) ______________________________

or (2) a valid final court order establishing a judgment against the Grantor for bodily injury or property damage caused by sudden or nonsudden accidental occurrences arising from the operation of the Grantor's facility or group of facilities.]

This letter of credit is effective as of [date] and shall expire on [date at least one year later], but such expiration date shall be automatically extended for a period of [at least one year] on [date and on each successive expiration date, unless, at least 120 days before the current expiration date, we notify you, the USEPA Regional Administrator for Region [Region _], and [owner's or operator's name] by certified mail that we have decided not to extend this letter of credit beyond the current expiration date.

Whenever this letter of credit is drawn on under and in compliance with the terms of this credit, we shall duly honor such draft upon presentation to us.

[Insert the following language if a standby trust fund is not being used: "In the event that this letter of credit is used in combination with another mechanism for liability coverage, this letter of credit shall be considered [insert "primary" or "excess" coverage]."

We certify that the wording of this letter of credit is identical to the wording specified in 40 CFR 264.151(k) as such regulations were constituted on the date shown immediately below. [Signature(s) and title(s) of official(s) of issuing institution] [Date].

This credit is subject to [insert "the most recent edition of the Uniform Customs and Practice for Documentary Credits, published and copyrighted by the International Chamber of Commerce," or "the Uniform Commercial Code"].

(l) A surety bond, as specified in §264.147(i) or §265.147(i) of this chapter, must be worded as follows: except that instructions in brackets are to be replaced with the relevant information and the brackets deleted:

Payment Bond

Surety Bond No. [Insert number]

Parties [Insert name and address of owner or operator], Principal, incorporated in [Insert State of incorporation] of [Insert city and State of principal place of business] and [Insert name and address of surety company(ies)], Surety Company(ies), of [Insert surety(ies) place of business].

EPA Identification Number, name, and address for each facility guaranteed by this bond: ________

	Sudden accidental occurrences	Nonsudden accidental occurrences
Penal Sum Per Occurrence	[insert amount]	[insert amount]
Annual Aggregate	[insert amount]	[insert amount]

Purpose: This is an agreement between the Surety(ies) and the Principal under which the Surety(ies), its(their) successors and assignees, agree to be responsible for the payment of claims against the Principal for bodily injury and/or property damage to third parties caused by ["sudden" and/or "nonsudden"] accidental occurrences arising from operations of the facility or group of facilities in the sums prescribed herein; subject to the governing provisions and the following conditions.

Governing Provisions:

(1) Section 3004 of the Resource Conservation and Recovery Act of 1976, as amended.

(2) Rules and regulations of the U.S. Environmental Protection Agency (EPA), particularly 40 CFR ["§264.147" or "§265.147"] (if applicable).

(3) Rules and regulations of the governing State agency (if applicable) [insert citation].

Conditions:

(1) The Principal is subject to the applicable governing provisions that require the Principal to have and maintain liability coverage for bodily injury and property damage to third parties caused by ["sudden" and/or "nonsudden"] accidental occurrences arising from operations of the facility or group of facilities. Such obligation does not apply to any of the following:

(a) Bodily injury or property damage for which [insert principal] is obligated to pay damages by reason of the assumption of liability in a contract or agreement. This exclusion does not apply to liability for damages that [insert principal] would be obligated to pay in the absence of the contract or agreement.

(b) Any obligation of [insert principal] under a workers' compensation, disability benefits, or unemployment compensation law or similar law.

(c) Bodily injury to:

(1) An employee of [insert principal] arising from, and in the course of, employment by [insert principal]; or

(2) The spouse, child, parent, brother or sister of that employee as a consequence of, or arising from, and in the course of employment by [insert principal]. This exclusion applies:

(A) Whether [insert principal] may be liable as an employer or in any other capacity; and

(B) To any obligation to share damages with or repay another person who must pay damages because of the injury to persons identified in paragraphs (1) and (2).

(d) Bodily injury or property damage arising out of the ownership, maintenance, use, or entrustment to others of any aircraft, motor vehicle or watercraft.

(e) Property damage to:

(1) Any property owned, rented, or occupied by [insert principal];

(2) Premises that are sold, given away or abandoned by [insert principal] if the property damage arises out of any part of those premises;

(3) Property loaned to [insert principal];

(4) Personal property in the care, custody or control of [insert principal];

(5) That particular part of real property on which [insert principal] or any contractors or subcontractors working directly or indirectly on behalf of [insert principal] are performing operations, if the property damage arises out of these operations.

(2) This bond assures that the Principal will satisfy valid third party liability claims, as described in condition 1.

(3) If the Principal fails to satisfy a valid third party liability claim, as described above, the Surety(ies) becomes liable on this bond obligation.

(4) The Surety(ies) shall satisfy a third party liability claim only upon the receipt of one of the following documents:

(a) Certification from the Principal and the third party claimant(s) that the liability claim should be paid. The certification must be worded as follows, except that instructions in brackets are to be replaced with the relevant information and the brackets deleted:

Certification of Valid Claim

The undersigned, as parties [insert name of Principal] and [insert name and address of third party claimant(s)], hereby certify that the claim of bodily injury and/or property damage caused by a [sudden or nonsudden] accidental occurrence arising from operating [Principal's] hazardous waste treatment, storage, or disposal facility should be paid in the amount of $[ ].

[Signature]

Principal

[Notary] Date

[Signature(s)]

Claimant(s)

[Notary] Date

or (b) A valid final court order establishing a judgment against the Principal for bodily injury or property damage caused by sudden or nonsudden accidental occurrences arising from the operation of the Principal's facility or group of facilities.

(5) In the event of combination of this bond with another mechanism for liability coverage, this bond will be considered [insert "primary" or "excess"] coverage.

(6) The liability of the Surety(ies) shall not be discharged by any payment or succession of payments hereunder, unless and until such payment or payments shall amount in the aggregate to the penal sum of the bond. In no event shall the obligation of the Surety(ies) hereunder exceed the amount of said annual aggregate penal sum, provided that the Surety(ies) furnish(es) notice to the Regional Administrator forthwith of all claims filed and payments made by the Surety(ies) under this bond.

(7) The Surety(ies) may cancel the bond by sending notice of cancellation by certified mail to the Principal and the USEPA Regional Administrator for Region [Region _], provided, however, that cancellation shall not occur during the 120 days beginning on the date of receipt of the notice of cancellation by the Principal and the Regional Administrator, as evidenced by the return receipt.

(8) The Principal may terminate this bond by sending written notice to the Surety(ies) and to the EPA Regional Administrator(s) of the EPA Region(s) in which the bonded facility(ies) is (are) located.

(9) The Surety(ies) hereby waive(s) notification of amendments to applicable laws, statutes, rules and regulations and agree(s) that no such amendment shall in any way alleviate its (their) obligation on this bond.

(10) This bond is effective from [insert date] (12:01 a.m., standard time, at the address of the Principal as stated herein) and shall continue in force until terminated as described above.

In Witness Whereof, the Principal and Surety(ies) have executed this Bond and have affixed their seals on the date set forth above.

The persons whose signatures appear below hereby certify that they are authorized to execute this surety bond on behalf of the Principal and Surety(ies) and that the wording of this surety bond is identical to the wording specified in 40 CFR 264.151(1), as such regulations were constituted on the date this bond was executed.

PRINCIPAL

[Signature(s)]

[Name(s)]

[Title(s)]

[Corporate Seal]

CORPORATE SURETY[IES]

[Name and address]

State of incorporation: ____________

Liability Limit: $ ____________

[Signature(s)]

[Name(s) and title(s)]

[Corporate seal]

[For every co-surety, provide signature(s), corporate seal, and other information in the same manner as for Surety above.]

Bond premium: $____________

(m)(1) A trust agreement, as specified in §264.147(j) or §265.147(j) of this chapter, must be worded as follows, except that instructions in brackets are to be replaced with the relevant information and the brackets deleted:

Trust Agreement

Trust Agreement, the "Agreement," entered into as of [date] by and between [name of the owner or operator] a [name of State] [insert "corporation," "partnership," "association," or "proprietorship"], the "Grantor," and [name of corporate trustee], [insert, "incorporated in the State of ________" or "a national bank"], the "trustee."

Whereas, the United States Environmental Protection Agency, "EPA," an agency of the United States Government, has established certain regulations applicable to the Grantor, requiring that an owner or operator of a hazardous waste management facility or group of facilities must demonstrate financial responsibility for bodily injury and property damage to third parties caused by sudden accidental and/or nonsudden accidental occurrences arising from operations of the facility or group of facilities.

Whereas, the Grantor has elected to establish a trust to assure all or part of such financial responsibility for the facilities identified herein.

Whereas, the Grantor, acting through its duly authorized officers, has selected the Trustee to be the trustee under this agreement, and the Trustee is willing to act as trustee.

Now, therefore, the Grantor and the Trustee agree as follows:

Section 1. *Definitions.* As used in this Agreement:

(a) The term "Grantor" means the owner or operator who enters into this Agreement and any successors or assigns of the Grantor.

(b) The term "Trustee" means the Trustee who enters into this Agreement and any successor Trustee.

Section 2. *Identification of Facilities.* This agreement pertains to the facilities identified on attached schedule A [on schedule A, for each facility list the EPA Identification Number, name, and address of the facility(ies) and the amount of liability coverage, or portions thereof, if more than one instrument affords combined coverage as demonstrated by this Agreement].

Section 3. *Establishment of Fund.* The Grantor and the Trustee hereby establish a trust fund, hereinafter the "Fund," for the benefit of any and all third parties injured or damaged by [sudden and/or nonsudden] accidental occurrences arising from operation of the facility(ies) covered by this guarantee, in the amounts of ________ [up to $1 million] per occurrence and ________ [up to $2 million] annual aggregate for sudden accidental occurrences and ________ [up to $3 million] per occurrence and ________ [up to $6 million] annual aggregate for nonsudden occurrences, except that the Fund is not established for the benefit of third parties for the following:

(a) Bodily injury or property damage for which [insert Grantor] is obligated to pay damages by reason of the assumption of liability in a contract or agreement. This exclusion does not apply to liability for damages that [insert Grantor] would be obligated to pay in the absence of the contract or agreement.

(b) Any obligation of [insert Grantor] under a workers' compensation, disability benefits, or unemployment compensation law or any similar law.

(c) Bodily injury to:

(1) An employee of [insert Grantor] arising from, and in the course of, employment by [insert Grantor]; or

(2) The spouse, child, parent, brother or sister of that employee as a consequence of, or arising from, and in the course of employment by [insert Grantor].

This exclusion applies:

(A) Whether [insert Grantor] may be liable as an employer or in any other capacity; and

(B) To any obligation to share damages with or repay another person who must pay damages because of the injury to persons identified in paragraphs (1) and (2).

(d) Bodily injury or property damage arising out of the ownership, maintenance, use, or entrustment to others of any aircraft, motor vehicle or watercraft.

(e) Property damage to:

(1) Any property owned, rented, or occupied by [insert Grantor];

(2) Premises that are sold, given away or abandoned by [insert Grantor] if the property damage arises out of any part of those premises;

(3) Property loaned to [insert Grantor];

(4) Personal property in the care, custody or control of [insert Grantor];

(5) That particular part of real property on which [insert Grantor] or any contractors or subcontractors working directly or indirectly on behalf of [insert Grantor] are performing operations, if the property damage arises out of these operations.

In the event of combination with another mechanism for liability coverage, the fund shall be considered [insert "primary" or "excess"] coverage.

The Fund is established initially as consisting of the property, which is acceptable to the Trustee, described in Schedule B attached hereto. Such property and any other property subsequently transferred to the Trustee is referred to as the Fund, together with all earnings and profits thereon, less any payments or distributions made by the Trustee pursuant to this Agreement. The Fund shall be held by the Trustee, IN TRUST, as hereinafter provided. The Trustee shall not be responsible nor shall it undertake any responsibility for the amount or adequacy of, nor any duty to collect from the Grantor, any payments necessary to discharge any liabilities of the Grantor established by EPA.

Section 4. *Payment for Bodily Injury or Property Damage.* The Trustee shall satisfy a third party liability claim by making payments from the Fund only upon receipt of one of the following documents;

(a) Certification from the Grantor and the third party claimant(s) that the liability claim should be paid. The certification must be worded as follows, except that instructions in brackets are to be replaced with the relevant information and the brackets deleted:

Certification of Valid Claim

The undersigned, as parties [insert Grantor] and [insert name and address of third party claimant(s)], hereby certify that the claim of bodily injury and/or property damage caused by a [sudden or nonsudden] accidental occurrence arising from operating [Grantor's] hazardous waste treatment, storage, or disposal facility should be paid in the amount of $[ ].

[Signatures]

Grantor

[Signatures]

Claimant(s)

(b) A valid final court order establishing a judgment against the Grantor for bodily injury or property damage caused by sudden or nonsudden accidental occurrences arising from the operation of the Grantor's facility or group of facilities.

Section 5. *Payments Comprising the Fund.* Payments made to the Trustee for the Fund shall consist of cash or securities acceptable to the Trustee.

Section 6. *Trustee Management.* The Trustee shall invest and reinvest the principal and income, in accordance with general investment policies and guidelines which the Grantor may communicate in writing to the Trustee from time to time, subject, however, to the provisions of this section. In investing, reinvesting, exchanging, selling, and managing the Fund, the Trustee shall discharge his duties with respect to the trust fund solely in the interest of the beneficiary and with the care, skill, prudence, and diligence under the circumstance then prevailing which persons of prudence, acting in a like capacity and familiar with such matters, would use in the conduct of an enterprise of a like character and with like aims; *except that:*

(i) Securities or other obligations of the Grantor, or any other owner or operator of the facilities, or any of their affiliates as defined in the Investment Company Act of 1940, as amended, 15 U.S.C. 80a-2.(a), shall not be acquired or *held* unless they are securities or other obligations of the Federal or a State government;

(ii) The Trustee is authorized to invest the Fund in time or demand deposits of the Trustee, to the extent insured by an agency of the Federal or State government; and

(iii) The Trustee is authorized to hold cash awaiting investment or distribution uninvested for a reasonable time and without liability for the payment of interest thereon.

Section 7. *Commingling and Investment.* The Trustee is expressly authorized in its discretion:

(a) To transfer from time to time any or all of the assets of the Fund to any common commingled, or collective trust fund created by the Trustee in which the fund is eligible to participate, subject to all of the provisions thereof, to be commingled with the assets of other trusts participating therein; and

(b) To purchase shares in any investment company registered under the Investment Company Act of 1940, 15 U.S.C. 81a-1 *et seq.*, including one which may be created, managed, underwritten, or to which investment advice is rendered or the shares of which are sold by the Trustee. The Trustee may vote such shares in its discretion.

Section 8. *Express Powers of Trustee.* Without in any way limiting the powers and discretions conferred upon the Trustee by the other provisions of this Agreement or by law, the Trustee is expressly authorized and empowered:

(a) To sell, exchange, convey, transfer, or otherwise dispose of any property held by it, by public or private sale. No person dealing with the Trustee shall be bound to see to the application of the purchase money or to inquire into the validity or expediency of any such sale or other disposition;

(b) To make, execute, acknowledge, and deliver any and all documents of transfer and conveyance and any and all other instruments that may be necessary or appropriate to carry out the powers herein granted;

(c) To register any securities held in the Fund in its own name or in the name of a nominee and to hold any security in bearer form or in book entry, or to combine certificates representing such securities with certificates of the same issue held by the Trustee in other fiduciary capacities, or to deposit or arrange for the deposit of such securities in a qualified central depository even though, when so deposited, such securities may be merged and held in bulk in the name of the nominee of such depository with other securities deposited therein by another person, or to deposit or arrange for the deposit of any securities issued by the United States Government, or any agency or instrumentality thereof, with a Federal Reserve bank, but the books and records of the Trustee shall at all times show that all such securities are part of the Fund;

(d) To deposit any cash in the Fund in interest-bearing accounts maintained or savings certificates issued by the Trustee, in its separate corporate capacity, or in any other banking institution affiliated with the Trustee, to the extent insured by an agency of the Federal or State government; and

(e) To compromise or otherwise adjust all claims in favor of or against the Fund.

Section 9. *Taxes and Expenses.* All taxes of any kind that may be assessed or levied against or in respect of the Fund and all brokerage commissions incurred by the Fund shall be paid from the Fund. All other expenses incurred by the Trustee in connection with the administration of this Trust, including fees for legal services rendered to the Trustee, the compensation of the Trustee to the extent not paid directly by the Grantor, and all other proper charges and disbursements of the Trustee shall be paid from the Fund.

Section 10. *Annual Valuations.* The Trustee shall annually, at least 30 days prior to the anniversary date of establishment of the Fund, furnish to the Grantor and to the appropriate EPA Regional Administrator a statement confirming the value of the Trust. Any securities in the Fund shall be valued at market value as of no more than 60 days prior to the anniversary date of establishment of the Fund. The failure of the Grantor to object in writing to the Trustee within 90 days after the statement has been furnished to the Grantor and the EPA Regional Administrator shall constitute a conclusively binding assent by the Grantor barring the Grantor from asserting any claim or liability against the Trustee with respect to matters disclosed in the statement.

Section 11. *Advice of Counsel.* The Trustee may from time to time consult with counsel, who may be counsel to the Grantor with respect to any question arising as to the construction of this Agreement or any action to be taken hereunder. The Trustee shall be fully protected, to the extent permitted by law, in acting upon the advice of counsel.

Section 12. *Trustee Compensation.* The Trustee shall be entitled to reasonable compensation for its services as agreed upon in writing from time to time with the Grantor.

Section 13. *Successor Trustee.* The Trustee may resign or the Grantor may replace the Trustee, but such resignation or replacement shall not be effective until the Grantor has appointed a successor trustee and this successor accepts the appointment. The successor trustee shall have the same powers and duties as those conferred upon the Trustee hereunder. Upon the successor trustee's acceptance of the appointment, the Trustee shall assign, transfer, and pay over to the successor trustee the funds and properties then constituting the Fund. If for any reason the Grantor cannot or does not act in the event of the resignation of the Trustee, the Trustee may apply to a court of competent jurisdiction for the appointment of a successor trustee or for instructions. The successor trustee shall specify the date on which it assumes administration of the trust in a writing sent to the Grantor, the EPA Regional Administrator, and the present Trustee by certified mail 10 days before such change becomes effective. Any expenses incurred by the Trustee as a result of any of the acts contemplated by this section shall be paid as provided in Section 9.

Section 14. *Instructions to the Trustee.* All orders, requests, and instructions by the Grantor to the Trustee shall be in writing, signed by such persons as are designated in the attached Exhibit A or such other designees as the Grantor may designate by amendments to Exhibit A. The Trustee shall be fully protected in acting without inquiry in accordance with the Grantor's orders, requests, and instructions. All orders, requests, and instructions by the EPA Regional Administrator to the Trustee shall be in writing, signed by the EPA Regional Administrators of the Regions in which the facilities are located, or their designees, and the Trustee shall act and shall be fully protected in acting in accordance with such orders, requests, and instructions. The Trustee shall have the right to assume, in the absence of written notice to the contrary, that no event constituting a change or a termination of the authority of any person to act on behalf of the Grantor or EPA hereunder has occurred. The Trustee shall have no duty to act in the absence of such orders, requests, and instructions from the Grantor and/or EPA, except as provided for herein.

Section 15. *Notice of Nonpayment.* If a payment for bodily injury or property damage is made under Section 4 of this trust, the Trustee shall notify the Grantor of such payment and the amount(s) thereof within five (5) working days. The Grantor shall, on or before the anniversary date of the establishment of the Fund following such notice, either make payments to the Trustee in amounts sufficient to cause the trust to return to its value immediately prior to the payment of claims under Section 4, or shall provide written proof to the Trustee that other financial assurance for liability coverage has been obtained equalling the amount necessary to return the trust to its value prior to the payment of claims. If the Grantor does not either make payments to the Trustee or provide the Trustee with such proof, the Trustee shall within 10 working days after the anniversary date of the establishment of the Fund provide a written notice of nonpayment to the EPA Regional Administrator.

Section 16. *Amendment of Agreement.* This Agreement may be amended by an instrument in writing executed by the Grantor, the Trustee, and the appropriate EPA Regional Administrator, or by the Trustee and the appropriate EPA Regional Administrator if the Grantor ceases to exist.

Section 17. *Irrevocability and Termination.* Subject to the right of the parties to amend this Agreement as provided in Section 16, this Trust shall be irrevocable and shall continue until terminated at the written agreement of the Grantor, the Trustee, and the EPA Regional Administrator, or by the Trustee and the EPA Regional Administrator, if the Grantor ceases to exist. Upon termination of the Trust, all remaining trust property, less final trust administration expenses, shall be delivered to the Grantor.

The Regional Administrator will agree to termination of the Trust when the owner or operator substitutes alternate financial assurance as specified in this section.

Section 18. *Immunity and Indemnification.* The Trustee shall not incur personal liability of any nature in connection with any act or omission, made in good faith, in the administration of this Trust, or in carrying out any directions by the Grantor or the EPA Regional Administrator issued in accordance with this Agreement. The Trustee shall be indemnified and saved harmless by the Grantor or from the Trust Fund, or both, from and against any personal liability to which the Trustee may be subjected by reason of any act or conduct in its official capacity, including all expenses reasonably incurred in its defense in the event the Grantor fails to provide such defense.

Section 19. *Choice of Law.* This Agreement shall be administered, construed, and enforced according to the laws of the State of [enter name of State].

Section 20. *Interpretation.* As used in this Agreement, words in the singular include the plural and words in the plural include the singular. The descriptive headings for each section of this Agreement shall not affect the interpretation or the legal efficacy of this Agreement.

In Witness Whereof the parties have caused this Agreement to be executed by their respective officers duly authorized and their corporate seals to be hereunto affixed and attested as of the date first above written. The parties below certify that the wording of this Agreement is identical to the wording specified in 40 CFR 264.151(m) as such regulations were constituted on the date first above written.

____

[Signature of Grantor]

[Title]

Attest:

[Title]

[Seal]

____

[Signature of Trustee]

Attest:

[Title]

[Seal]

(2) The following is an example of the certification of acknowledgement which must accompany the trust agreement for a trust fund as specified in §§264.147(j) or 265.147(j) of this chapter. State requirements may differ on the proper content of this acknowledgement.

State of ________________________

County of ________________________

On this [date], before me personally came [owner or operator] to me known, who, being by me duly sworn, did depose and say that she/he resides at [address], that she/he is [title] of [corporation], the corporation described in and which executed the above instrument; that she/he knows the seal of said corporation; that the seal affixed to such instrument is such corporate seal; that it was so affixed by order of the Board of Directors of said corporation, and that she/he signed her/his name thereto by like order.

____

[Signature of Notary Public]

(n)(1) A standby trust agreement, as specified in §264.147(h) or 265.147(h) of this chapter, must be worded as follows, except that instructions in brackets are to be replaced with the relevant information and the brackets deleted:

Standby Trust Agreement

Trust Agreement, the "Agreement," entered into as of [date] by and between [name of the owner or operator] a [name of a State] [insert "corporation," "partnership," "association," or "proprietorship"], the "Grantor," and [name of corporate trustee], [insert, "incorporated in the State of ____________" or "a national bank"], the "trustee."

Whereas the United States Environmental Protection Agency, "EPA," an agency of the United States Government, has established certain regulations applicable to the Grantor, requiring that an owner or operator of a hazardous waste management facility or group of facilities must demonstrate financial responsibility for bodily injury and property damage to third parties caused by sudden accidental and/or nonsudden accidental occurrences arising from operations of the facility or group of facilities.

Whereas, the Grantor has elected to establish a standby trust into which the proceeds from a letter of credit may be deposited to assure all or part of such financial responsibility for the facilities identified herein.

Whereas, the Grantor, acting through its duly authorized officers, has selected the Trustee to be the trustee under this agreement, and the Trustee is willing to act as trustee.

Now, therefore, the Grantor and the Trustee agree as follows:

Section 1. *Definitions.* As used in this Agreement:

(a) The term *Grantor* means the owner or operator who enters into this Agreement and any successors or assigns of the Grantor.

(b) The term *Trustee* means the Trustee who enters into this Agreement and any successor Trustee.

Section 2. *Identification of Facilities.* This agreement pertains to the facilities identified on attached schedule A [on schedule A, for each facility list the EPA Identification Number, name, and address of the facility(ies) and the amount of liability coverage, or portions thereof, if more than one instrument affords combined coverage as demonstrated by this Agreement].

Section 3. *Establishment of Fund.* The Grantor and the Trustee hereby establish a standby trust fund, hereafter the "Fund," for the benefit of any and all third parties injured or damaged by [sudden and/or nonsudden] accidental occurrences arising from operation of the facility(ies) covered by this guarantee, in the amounts of __________ [up to $1 million] per occurrence and __________ [up to $2 million] annual aggregate for sudden accidental occurrences and __________ [up to $3 million] per occurrence and __________ [up to $6 million] annual aggregate for nonsudden occurrences, except that the Fund is not established for the benefit of third parties for the following:

(a) Bodily injury or property damage for which [insert Grantor] is obligated to pay damages by reason of the assumption of liability in a contract or agreement. This exclusion does not apply to liability for damages that [insert Grantor] would be obligated to pay in the absence of the contract or agreement.

(b) Any obligation of [insert Grantor] under a workers' compensation, disability benefits, or unemployment compensation law or any similar law.

(c) Bodily injury to:

(1) An employee of [insert Grantor] arising from, and in the course of, employment by [insert Grantor]; or

(2) The spouse, child, parent, brother or sister of that employee as a consequence of, or arising from, and in the course of employment by [insert Grantor].

This exclusion applies:

(A) Whether [insert Grantor] may be liable as an employer or in any other capacity; and

(B) To any obligation to share damages with or repay another person who must pay damages because of the injury to persons identified in paragraphs (1) and (2).

(d) Bodily injury or property damage arising out of the ownership, maintenance, use, or entrustment to others of any aircraft, motor vehicle or watercraft.

(e) Property damage to:

(1) Any property owned, rented, or occupied by [insert Grantor];

(2) Premises that are sold, given away or abandoned by [insert Grantor] if the property damage arises out of any part of those premises;

(3) Property loaned by [insert Grantor];

(4) Personal property in the care, custody or control of [insert Grantor];

(5) That particular part of real property on which [insert Grantor] or any contractors or subcontractors working directly or indirectly on behalf of [insert Grantor] are performing operations, if the property damage arises out of these operations.

In the event of combination with another mechanism for liability coverage, the fund shall be considered [insert "primary" or "excess"] coverage.

The Fund is established initially as consisting of the proceeds of the letter of credit deposited into the Fund. Such proceeds and any other property subsequently transferred to the Trustee is referred to as the Fund, together with all earnings and profits thereon, less any payments or distributions made by the Trustee pursuant to this Agreement. The Fund shall be held by the Trustee, IN TRUST, as hereinafter provided. The Trustee shall not be responsible nor shall it undertake any responsibility for the amount or adequacy of, nor any duty to collect from the Grantor, any payments necessary to discharge any liabilities of the Grantor established by EPA.

Section 4. *Payment for Bodily Injury or Property Damage.* The Trustee shall satisfy a third party liability claim by drawing on the letter of credit described in Schedule B and by making payments from the Fund only upon receipt of one of the following documents:

(a) Certification from the Grantor and the third party claimant(s) that the liability claim should be paid. The certification must be worded as follows, except that instructions in brackets are to be replaced with the relevant information and the brackets deleted:

Certification of Valid Claim

The undersigned, as parties [insert Grantor] and [insert name and address of third party claimant(s)], hereby certify that the claim of bodily injury and/or property damage caused by a [sudden or nonsudden] accidental occurrence arising from operating [Grantor's] hazardous waste treatment, storage, or disposal facility should be paid in the amount of $[ ].

[Signature] ______

Grantor ______

[Signatures] ______

Claimant(s) ______

(b) A valid final court order establishing a judgment against the Grantor for bodily injury or property damage caused by sudden or nonsudden accidental occurrences arising from the operation of the Grantor's facility or group of facilities.

Section 5. *Payments Comprising the Fund.* Payments made to the Trustee for the Fund shall consist of the proceeds from the letter of credit drawn upon by the Trustee in accordance with the requirements of 40 CFR 264.151(k) and Section 4 of this Agreement.

Section 6. *Trustee Management.* The Trustee shall invest and reinvest the principal and income, in accordance with general investment policies and guidelines which the Grantor may communicate in writing to the Trustee from time to time, subject, however, to the provisions of this Section. In investing, reinvesting, exchanging, selling, and managing the Fund, the Trustee shall discharge his duties with respect to the trust fund solely in the interest of the beneficiary and with the care, skill, prudence, and diligence under the circumstances then prevailing which persons of prudence, acting in a like capacity and familiar with such matters, would use in the conduct of an enterprise of a like character and with like aims; except that:

(i) Securities or other obligations of the Grantor, or any other owner or operator of the facilities, or any of their affiliates as defined in the Investment Company Act of 1940, as amended, 15 U.S.C. 80a-2(a), shall not be acquired or held, unless they are securities or other obligations of the Federal or a State government;

(ii) The Trustee is authorized to invest the Fund in time or demand deposits of the Trustee, to the extent insured by an agency of the Federal or a State government; and

(iii) The Trustee is authorized to hold cash awaiting investment or distribution uninvested for a reasonable time and without liability for the payment of interest thereon.

Section 7. *Commingling and Investment.* The Trustee is expressly authorized in its discretion:

(a) To transfer from time to time any or all of the assets of the Fund to any common, commingled, or collective trust fund created by the Trustee in which the Fund is eligible to participate, subject to all of the provisions thereof, to be commingled with the assets of other trusts participating therein; and

(b) To purchase shares in any investment company registered under the Investment Company Act of 1940, 15 U.S.C. 80a-1 *et seq.*, including one which may be created, managed, underwritten, or to which investment advice is rendered or the shares of which are sold by the Trustee. The Trustee may vote such shares in its discretion.

Section 8. *Express Powers of Trustee.* Without in any way limiting the powers and discretions conferred upon the Trustee by the other provisions of this Agreement or by law, the Trustee is expressly authorized and empowered:

(a) To sell, exchange, convey, transfer, or otherwise dispose of any property held by it, by public or private sale. No person dealing with the Trustee shall be bound to see to the application of the purchase money or to inquire into the validity or expediency of any such sale or other disposition;

(b) To make, execute, acknowledge, and deliver any and all documents of transfer and conveyance and any and all other instruments that may be necessary or appropriate to carry out the powers herein granted;

(c) To register any securities held in the Fund in its own name or in the name of a nominee and to hold any security in bearer form or in book entry, or to combine certificates representing such securities with certificates of the same issue held by the Trustee in other fiduciary capacities, or to deposit or arrange for the deposit of such securities in a qualified central depositary even though, when so deposited, such securities may be merged and held in bulk in the name of the nominee of such depositary with other securities deposited therein by another person, or to deposit or arrange for the deposit of any securities issued by the United States Government, or any agency or instrumentality thereof, with a Federal Reserve Bank, but the books and records of the Trustee shall at all times show that all such securities are part of the Fund;

(d) To deposit any cash in the Fund in interest-bearing accounts maintained or savings certificates issued by the Trustee, in its separate corporate capacity, or in any other banking institution affiliated with the Trustee, to the extent insured by an agency of the Federal or State government; and

(e) To compromise or otherwise adjust all claims in favor of or against the Fund.

Section 9. *Taxes and Expenses.* All taxes of any kind that may be assessed or levied against or in respect of the Fund and all brokerage commissions incurred by the Fund shall be paid from the Fund. All other expenses incurred by the Trustee in connection with the administration of this Trust, including fees for legal services rendered to the Trustee, the compensation of the Trustee to the extent not paid directly by the Grantor, and all other proper charges and disbursements to the Trustee shall be paid from the Fund.

Section 10. *Advice of Counsel.* The Trustee may from time to time consult with counsel, who may be counsel to the Grantor, with respect to any question arising as to the construction of this Agreement or any action to be taken hereunder. The Trustee shall be fully protected, to the extent permitted by law, in acting upon the advice of counsel.

Section 11. *Trustee Compensation.* The Trustee shall be entitled to reasonable compensation for its services as agreed upon in writing from time to time with the Grantor.

Section 12. *Successor Trustee.* The Trustee may resign or the Grantor may replace the Trustee, but such resignation or replacement shall not be effective until the Grantor has appointed a successor trustee and this successor accepts the appointment. The successor trustee shall have the same powers and duties as those conferred upon the Trustee hereunder. Upon the successor trustee's acceptance of the appointment, the Trustee shall assign, transfer, and pay over to the successor trustee the funds and properties then constituting the Fund. If for any reason the Grantor cannot or does not act in the event of the resignation of the Trustee, the Trustee may apply to a court of competent jurisdiction for the appointment of a successor trustee or for instructions. The successor trustee shall specify the date on which it assumes administration of the trust in a writing sent to the Grantor, the EPA Regional Administrator and the present Trustee by certified mail 10 days before such change becomes effective. Any expenses incurred by the Trustee as a result of any of the acts contemplated by this Section shall be paid as provided in Section 9.

Section 13. *Instructions to the Trustee.* All orders, requests, certifications of valid claims, and instructions to the Trustee shall be in writing, signed by such persons as are designated in the attached Exhibit A or such other designees as the Grantor may designate by amendments to Exhibit A. The Trustee shall be fully protected in acting without inquiry in accordance with the Grantor's orders, requests, and instructions. The Trustee shall have the right to assume, in the absence of written notice to the contrary, that no event constituting a change or a termination of the authority of any person to act on behalf of the Grantor or the EPA Regional Administrator hereunder has occurred. The Trustee shall have no duty to act in the absence of such orders, requests, and instructions from the Grantor and/or EPA, except as provided for herein.

Section 14. *Amendment of Agreement.* This Agreement may be amended by an instrument in writing executed by the Grantor, the Trustee, and the EPA Regional Administrator, or by the Trustee and the EPA Regional Administrator if the Grantor ceases to exist.

Section 15. *Irrevocability and Termination.* Subject to the right of the parties to amend this Agreement as provided in Section 14, this Trust shall be irrevocable and shall continue until terminated at the written agreement of the Grantor, the Trustee, and the EPA Regional Administrator, or by the Trustee and the EPA Regional Administrator, if the Grantor ceases to exist. Upon termination of the Trust, all remaining trust property, less final trust administration expenses, shall be paid to the Grantor.

The Regional Administrator will agree to termination of the Trust when the owner or operator substitutes alternative financial assurance as specified in this section.

Section 16. *Immunity and indemnification.* The Trustee shall not incur personal liability of any nature in connection with any act or omission, made in good faith, in the administration of this Trust, or in carrying out any directions by the Grantor and the EPA Regional Administrator issued in accordance with this Agreement. The Trustee shall be indemnified and saved harmless by the Grantor or from the Trust Fund, or both, from and against any personal liability to which the Trustee may be subjected by reason of any act or conduct in its official capacity, including all expenses reasonably incurred in its defense in the event the Grantor fails to provide such defense.

Section 17. *Choice of Law.* This Agreement shall be administered, construed, and enforced according to the laws of the State of [enter name of State].

Section 18. *Interpretation.* As used in this Agreement, words in the singular include the plural and words in the plural include the singular. The descriptive headings for each Section of this Agreement shall not affect the interpretation of the legal efficacy of this Agreement.

In Witness Whereof the parties have caused this Agreement to be executed by their respective officers duly authorized and their corporate seals to be hereunto affixed and attested as of the date first above written. The parties below certify that the wording of this Agreement is identical to the wording specified in 40 CFR 264.151(n) as such regulations were constituted on the date first above written.

____

[Signature of Grantor]

[Title]

Attest:

[Title]

[Seal]

____

[Signature of Trustee]

Attest:

[Title]

[Seal]

(2) The following is an example of the certification of acknowledgement which must accompany the trust agreement for a standby trust fund as specified in section 264.147(h) or 265.147(h) of this chapter. State requirements may differ on the proper content of this acknowledgement.

State of ____________________

County of ____________________

On this [date], before me personally came [owner or operator] to me known, who, being by me duly sworn, did depose and say that she/he resides at [address], that she/he is [title] of [corporation], the corporation described in and which executed the above instrument; that she/he knows the seal of said corporation; that the seal affixed to such instrument is such corporate seal; that it was so affixed by order of the Board of Directors of said corporation, and that she/he signed her/his name thereto by like order.

[Signature of Notary Public]

[47 FR 15059, Apr. 7, 1982, as amended at 47 FR 16556, Apr. 16, 1982; 47 FR 17989, Apr. 27, 1982; 47 FR 19995, May 10, 1982; 47 FR 28627, July 1, 1982; 51 FR 16450, May 2, 1986; 51 FR 25354, July 11, 1986; 52 FR 44320, Nov. 18, 1987; 53 FR 33952, Sept. 1, 1988; 57 FR 42836, Sept. 16, 1992; 59 FR 29960, June 10, 1994; 71 FR 40272, July 14, 2006]

Subpart I—Use and Management of Containers

Source: 46 FR 2866, Jan. 12, 1981, unless otherwise noted.

§264.170 Applicability. 📖 9.1

The regulations in this subpart apply to owners and operators of all hazardous waste facilities that store containers of hazardous waste, except as §264.1 provides otherwise.

[*Comment:* Under §261.7 and §261.33(c), if a hazardous waste is emptied from a container the residue remaining in the container is not considered a hazardous waste if the container is "empty" as defined in §261.7. In that event, management of the container is exempt from the requirements of this subpart.]

§264.171 Condition of containers.

If a container holding hazardous waste is not in good condition (*e.g.*, severe rusting, apparent structural defects) or if it begins to leak, the owner or operator must transfer the hazardous waste from this container to a container that is in good condition or manage the waste in some other way that complies with the requirements of this part.

§264.172 Compatibility of waste with containers.

The owner or operator must use a container made of or lined with materials which will not react with, and are otherwise compatible with, the hazardous waste to be stored, so that the ability of the container to contain the waste is not impaired.

§264.173 Management of containers.

(a) A container holding hazardous waste must always be closed during storage, except when it is necessary to add or remove waste. 📖 9.2, 16.1.7

(b) A container holding hazardous waste must not be opened, handled, or stored in a manner which may rupture the container or cause it to leak.

[*Comment:* Reuse of containers in transportation is governed by U.S. Department of Transportation regulations including those set forth in 49 CFR 173.28.]

§264.174 Inspections. 📖 9.6, 16.1.9

At least weekly, the owner or operator must inspect areas where containers are stored, except for Performance Track member facilities, that may conduct inspections at least once each month, upon approval by the Director. To apply for reduced inspection frequencies, the Performance Track member facility must follow the procedures identified in §264.15(b)(5) of this part. The owner or operator must look for leaking containers and for deterioration of containers and the containment system caused by corrosion or other factors.

[Comment: See §§264.15(c) and 264.171 for remedial action required if deterioration or leaks are detected.]

[71 FR 16905, Apr. 4, 2006]

§264.175 Containment. 📖 9.4

(a) Container storage areas must have a containment system that is designed and operated in accordance with paragraph (b) of this section, except as otherwise provided by paragraph (c) of this section.

(b) A containment system must be designed and operated as follows:

(1) A base must underlie the containers which is free of cracks or gaps and is sufficiently impervious to contain leaks, spills, and accumulated precipitation until the collected material is detected and removed;

(2) The base must be sloped or the containment system must be otherwise designed and operated to drain and remove liquids resulting from leaks, spills, or precipitation, unless the containers are elevated or are otherwise protected from contact with accumulated liquids;

(3) The containment system must have sufficient capacity to contain 10% of the volume of containers or the volume of the largest container, whichever is greater. Containers that do not contain free liquids need not be considered in this determination;

(4) Run-on into the containment system must be prevented unless the collection system has sufficient excess capacity in addition to that required in paragraph (b)(3) of this section to contain any run-on which might enter the system; and

(5) Spilled or leaked waste and accumulated precipitation must be removed from the sump or collection

area in as timely a manner as is necessary to prevent overflow of the collection system.

[*Comment:* If the collected material is a hazardous waste under part 261 of this Chapter, it must be managed as a hazardous waste in accordance with all applicable requirements of parts 262 through 266 of this chapter. If the collected material is discharged through a point source to waters of the United States, it is subject to the requirements of section 402 of the Clean Water Act, as amended.]

(c) Storage areas that store containers holding only wastes that do not contain free liquids need not have a containment system defined by paragraph (b) of this section, except as provided by paragraph (d) of this section or provided that:

(1) The storage area is sloped or is otherwise designed and operated to drain and remove liquid resulting from precipitation, or

(2) The containers are elevated or are otherwise protected from contact with accumulated liquid.

(d) Storage areas that store containers holding the wastes listed below that do not contain free liquids must have a containment system defined by paragraph (b) of this section:

(1) F020, F021, F022, F023, F026, and F027.

(2) [Reserved]

[46 FR 55112, Nov. 6, 1981, as amended at 50 FR 2003, Jan. 14, 1985; 71 FR 40273, July 14, 2006]

§264.176 Special requirements for ignitable or reactive waste.

Containers holding ignitable or reactive waste must be located at least 15 meters (50 feet) from the facility's property line.

[*Comment:* See §264.17(a) for additional requirements.]

§264.177 Special requirements for incompatible wastes.

(a) Incompatible wastes, or incompatible wastes and materials (see appendix V for examples), must not be placed in the same container, unless §264.17(b) is complied with.

(b) Hazardous waste must not be placed in an unwashed container that previously held an incompatible waste or material.

[*Comment:* As required by §264.13, the waste analysis plan must include analyses needed to comply with §264.177. Also, §264.17(c) requires wastes analyses, trial tests or other documentation to assure compliance with §264.17(b). As required by §264.73, the owner or operator must place the results of each waste analysis and trial test, and any documented information, in the operating record of the facility.]

(c) A storage container holding a hazardous waste that is incompatible with any waste or other materials stored nearby in other containers, piles, open tanks, or surface impoundments must be separated from the other materials or protected from them by means of a dike, berm, wall, or other device.

[*Comment:* The purpose of this section is to prevent fires, explosions, gaseous emission, leaching, or other discharge of hazardous waste or hazardous waste constituents which could result from the mixing of incompatible wastes or materials if containers break or leak.]

§264.178 Closure.

At closure, all hazardous waste and hazardous waste residues must be removed from the containment system. Remaining containers, liners, bases, and soil containing or contaminated with hazardous waste or hazardous waste residues must be decontaminated or removed.

[*Comment:* At closure, as throughout the operating period, unless the owner or operator can demonstrate in accordance with §261.3(d) of this chapter that the solid waste removed from the containment system is not a hazardous waste, the owner or operator becomes a generator of hazardous waste and must manage it in accordance with all applicable requirements of parts 262 through 266 of this chapter].

§264.179 Air emission standards. 📖 15.1–3

The owner or operator shall manage all hazardous waste placed in a container in accordance with the applicable requirements of subparts AA, BB, and CC of this part.

[61 FR 59950, Nov. 25, 1996]

Subpart J—Tank Systems

Source: 51 FR 25472, July 14, 1986, unless otherwise noted.

§264.190 Applicability. 📖 10.1–2

The requirements of this subpart apply to owners and operators of facilities that use tank systems for storing or treating hazardous waste except as otherwise provided in paragraphs (a), (b), and (c) of this section or in §264.1 of this part.

(a) Tank systems that are used to store or treat hazardous waste which contains no free liquids and are situated inside a building with an impermeable floor are exempted from the requirements in §264.193. To demonstrate the absence or presence of free liquids in the stored/ treated waste, the following test must be used: Method 9095B (Paint Filter Liquids Test) as described in "Test Methods for Evaluating Solid Waste, Physical/ Chemical Methods," EPA Publication SW–846, as incorporated by reference in §260.11 of this chapter.

(b) Tank systems, including sumps, as defined in §260.10, that serve as part of a secondary containment system to collect or contain releases of hazardous wastes are exempted from the requirements in §264.193(a). 📖 7.5.4.1.1, 10.2.2

(c) Tanks, sumps, and other such collection devices or systems used in conjunction with drip pads, as defined in §260.10 of this chapter and regulated under 40 CFR part 264 subpart W, must meet the requirements of this subpart. 📖 10.1.3.4

[51 FR 25472, July 14, 1986; 51 FR 29430, Aug. 15, 1986, as amended at 53 FR 34086, Sept. 2, 1988; 55 FR 50484, Dec. 6, 1990; 58 FR 46050, Aug. 31, 1993; 70 FR 34581, June 14, 2005]

§264.191 Assessment of existing tank system's integrity.

📖 10.1.5.1

(a) For each existing tank system that does not have secondary containment meeting the requirements of §264.193, the owner or operator must determine that the tank system is not leaking or is unfit for use. Except as provided in paragraph (c) of this section, the owner or operator must obtain and keep on file at the facility a written assessment reviewed and certified by a qualified Professional Engineer, in accordance with §270.11(d) of this chapter, that attests to the tank system's integrity by January 12, 1988.

(b) This assessment must determine that the tank system is adequately designed and has sufficient structural strength and compatibility with the waste(s) to be stored or treated, to ensure that it will not collapse, rupture, or fail. At a minimum, this assessment must consider the following:

(1) Design standard(s), if available, according to which the tank and ancillary equipment were constructed;

(2) Hazardous characteristics of the waste(s) that have been and will be handled;

(3) Existing corrosion protection measures;

(4) Documented age of the tank system, if available (otherwise, an estimate of the age); and

(5) Results of a leak test, internal inspection, or other tank integrity examination such that:

(i) For non-enterable underground tanks, the assessment must include a leak test that is capable of taking into account the effects of temperature variations, tank end deflection, vapor pockets, and high water table effects, and

(ii) For other than non-enterable underground tanks and for ancillary equipment, this assessment must include either a leak test, as described above, or other integrity examination that is certified by a qualified Professional Engineer in accordance with §270.11(d) of this chapter, that addresses cracks, leaks, corrosion, and erosion.

[*Note:* The practices described in the American Petroleum Institute (API) Publication, Guide for Inspection of Refinery Equipment, Chapter XIII, "Atmospheric and Low-Pressure Storage Tanks," 4th edition, 1981, may be used, where applicable, as guidelines in conducting other than a leak test.]

(c) Tank systems that store or treat materials that become hazardous wastes subsequent to July 14, 1986, must conduct this assessment within 12 months after the date that the waste becomes a hazardous waste.

(d) If, as a result of the assessment conducted in accordance with paragraph (a), a tank system is found to be leaking or unfit for use, the owner or operator must comply with the requirements of §264.196.

[51 FR 25472, July 14, 1986; 51 FR 29430, Aug. 15, 1986; 71 FR 16905, Apr. 4, 2006]

§264.192 Design and installation of new tank systems or components.

📖 10.1.5.1

(a) Owners or operators of new tank systems or components must obtain and submit to the Regional Administrator, at time of submittal of part B information, a written assessment, reviewed and certified by a qualified Professional Engineer, in accordance with §270.11(d) of this chapter, attesting that the tank system has sufficient structural integrity and is acceptable for the storing and treating of hazardous waste. The assessment must show that the foundation, structural support, seams, connections, and pressure controls (if applicable) are adequately designed and that the tank system has sufficient structural strength, compatibility with the waste(s) to be stored or treated, and corrosion protection to ensure that it will not collapse, rupture, or fail. This assessment, which will be used by the Regional Administrator to review and approve or disapprove the acceptability of the tank system design, must include, at a minimum, the following information:

(1) Design standard(s) according to which tank(s) and/or the ancillary equipment are constructed;

(2) Hazardous characteristics of the waste(s) to be handled;

(3) For new tank systems or components in which the external shell of a metal tank or any external metal component of the tank system will be in contact with the soil or with water, a determination by a corrosion expert of:

(i) Factors affecting the potential for corrosion, including but not limited to:

(A) Soil moisture content;

(B) Soil pH;

(C) Soil sulfides level;

(D) Soil resistivity;

(E) Structure to soil potential;

(F) Influence of nearby underground metal structures (*e.g.*, piping);

(G) Existence of stray electric current;

(H) Existing corrosion-protection measures (*e.g.*, coating, cathodic protection), and

(ii) The type and degree of external corrosion protection that are needed to ensure the integrity of the tank system during the use of the tank system or component, consisting of one or more of the following:

(A) Corrosion-resistant materials of construction such as special alloys, fiberglass reinforced plastic, etc.;

(B) Corrosion-resistant coating (such as epoxy, fiberglass, etc.) with cathodic protection (*e.g.*, impressed current or sacrificial anodes); and

(C) Electrical isolation devices such as insulating joints, flanges, etc.

[*Note:* The practices described in the National Association of Corrosion Engineers (NACE) standard, "Recommended Practice (RP-02-85)—Control of External Corrosion on Metallic Buried, Partially Buried, or Submerged Liquid Storage Systems," and the American Petroleum Institute (API) Publication 1632, "Cathodic Protection of Underground Petroleum Storage Tanks and Piping Systems," may be used, where applicable, as guidelines in providing corrosion protection for tank systems.]

(4) For underground tank system components that are likely to be adversely affected by vehicular traffic, a determination of design or operational measures that will protect the tank system against potential damage; and

(5) Design considerations to ensure that:

(i) Tank foundations will maintain the load of a full tank;

(ii) Tank systems will be anchored to prevent flotation or dislodgment where the tank system is placed in a saturated zone, or is located within a seismic fault zone subject to the standards of §264.18(a); and

(iii) Tank systems will withstand the effects of frost heave.

(b) The owner or operator of a new tank system must ensure that proper handling procedures are adhered to in order to prevent damage to the system during installation. Prior to covering, enclosing, or placing a new tank system or component in use, an independent, qualified, installation inspector or a qualified Professional Engineer, either of whom is trained and experienced in the proper installation of tanks systems or components, must inspect the system for the presence of any of the following items:

(1) Weld breaks;

(2) Punctures;

(3) Scrapes of protective coatings;

(4) Cracks;

(5) Corrosion;

(6) Other structural damage or inadequate construction/installation.

All discrepancies must be remedied before the tank system is covered, enclosed, or placed in use.

(c) New tank systems or components that are placed underground and that are backfilled must be provided with a backfill material that is a noncorrosive, porous, homogeneous substance and that is installed so that the backfill is placed completely around the tank and compacted to ensure that the tank and piping are fully and uniformly supported.

(d) All new tanks and ancillary equipment must be tested for tightness prior to being covered, enclosed, or placed in use. If a tank system is found not to be tight, all repairs necessary to remedy the leak(s) in the system must be performed prior to the tank system being covered, enclosed, or placed into use.

(e) Ancillary equipment must be supported and protected against physical damage and excessive stress due to settlement, vibration, expansion, or contraction.

[*Note:* The piping system installation procedures described in American Petroleum Institute (API) Publication 1615 (November 1979), "Installation of Underground Petroleum Storage Systems," or ANSI Standard B31.3, "Petroleum Refinery Piping," and ANSI Standard B31.4 "Liquid Petroleum Transportation Piping System," may be used, where applicable, as guidelines for proper installation of piping systems.]

(f) The owner or operator must provide the type and degree of corrosion protection recommended by an independent corrosion expert, based on the information provided under paragraph (a)(3) of this section, or other corrosion protection if the Regional Administrator believes other corrosion protection is necessary to ensure the integrity of the tank system during use of the tank system. The installation of a corrosion protection system that is field fabricated must be supervised by an independent corrosion expert to ensure proper installation.

(g) The owner or operator must obtain and keep on file at the facility written statements by those persons required to certify the design of the tank system and supervise the installation of the tank system in accordance with the requirements of paragraphs (b) through (f) of this section, that attest that the tank system was properly designed and installed and that repairs, pursuant to paragraphs (b) and (d) of this section, were performed. These written statements must also include the certification statement as required in §270.11(d) of this chapter.

[51 FR 25472, July 14, 1986; 51 FR 29430, Aug. 15, 1986; 71 FR 16905, Apr. 4, 2006]

§264.193 Containment and detection of releases. 10.3

(a) In order to prevent the release of hazardous waste or hazardous constituents to the environment, secondary containment that meets the requirements of this section must be provided (except as provided in paragraphs (f) and (g) of this section): 10.3.4

(1) For all new and existing tank systems or components, prior to their being put into service.

(2) For tank systems that store or treat materials that become hazardous wastes, within two years of the hazardous waste listing, or when the tank system has reached 15 years of age, whichever comes later.

(b) Secondary containment systems must be:

(1) Designed, installed, and operated to prevent any migration of wastes or accumulated liquid out of the system to the soil, ground water, or surface water at any time during the use of the tank system; and

(2) Capable of detecting and collecting releases and accumulated liquids until the collected material is removed.

(c) To meet the requirements of paragraph (b) of this section, secondary containment systems must be at a minimum:

(1) Constructed of or lined with materials that are compatible with the wastes(s) to be placed in the tank system and must have sufficient strength and thickness to prevent failure owing to pressure gradients (including static head and external hydrological forces), physical contact with the waste to which it is exposed, climatic conditions, and the stress of daily operation (including stresses from nearby vehicular traffic).

(2) Placed on a foundation or base capable of providing support to the secondary containment system, resistance to pressure gradients above and below the system, and capable of preventing failure due to settlement, compression, or uplift;

(3) Provided with a leak-detection system that is designed and operated so that it will detect the failure of either the primary or secondary containment structure or the presence of any release of hazardous waste or accumulated liquid in the secondary containment system within 24 hours, or at the earliest practicable time if the owner or operator can demonstrate to the Regional Administrator that existing detection technologies or site conditions will not allow detection of a release within 24 hours; and 10.3.3

(4) Sloped or otherwise designed or operated to drain and remove liquids resulting from leaks, spills, or precipitation. Spilled or leaked waste and accumulated precipitation must be removed from the secondary containment system within 24 hours, or in as timely a manner as is possible to prevent harm to human health and the environment, if the owner or operator can demonstrate to the Regional Administrator that removal of the released waste or accumulated precipitation cannot be accomplished within 24 hours.

[*Note:* If the collected material is a hazardous waste under part 261 of this chapter, it is subject to management as a hazardous waste in accordance with all applicable requirements of parts 262 through 265 of this chapter. If the collected material is discharged through a point source to waters of the United States, it is subject to the requirements of sections 301, 304, and 402 of the Clean Water Act, as amended. If discharged to a Publicly Owned Treatment Works (POTW), it is subject to the requirements of section 307 of the Clean Water Act, as amended. If the collected material is released to the environment, it may be subject to the reporting requirements of 40 CFR part 302.]

(d) Secondary containment for tanks must include one or more of the following devices:

(1) A liner (external to the tank);

(2) A vault;

(3) A double-walled tank; or

(4) An equivalent device as approved by the Regional Administrator.

(e) In addition to the requirements of paragraphs (b), (c), and (d) of this section, secondary containment systems must satisfy the following requirements:

(1) External liner systems must be:

(i) Designed or operated to contain 100 percent of the capacity of the largest tank within its boundary; 10.3.2.1

(ii) Designed or operated to prevent run-on or infiltration of precipitation into the secondary containment system unless the collection system has sufficient excess capacity to contain run-on or infiltration. Such additional capacity must be sufficient to contain precipitation from a 25-year, 24-hour rainfall event.

(iii) Free of cracks or gaps; and

(iv) Designed and installed to surround the tank completely and to cover all surrounding earth likely to come into contact with the waste if the waste is released from the tank(s) (*i.e.*, capable of preventing lateral as well as vertical migration of the waste).

(2) Vault systems must be:

(i) Designed or operated to contain 100 percent of the capacity of the largest tank within its boundary; 10.3.2.1

(ii) Designed or operated to prevent run-on or infiltration of precipitation into the secondary containment system unless the collection system has sufficient excess capacity to contain run-on or infiltration. Such additional capacity must be sufficient to contain precipitation from a 25-year, 24-hour rainfall event;

(iii) Constructed with chemical-resistant water stops in place at all joints (if any);

(iv) Provided with an impermeable interior coating or lining that is compatible with the stored waste and that will prevent migration of waste into the concrete; 📖 10.3.2.2

(v) Provided with a means to protect against the formation of and ignition of vapors within the vault, if the waste being stored or treated:

(A) Meets the definition of ignitable waste under §261.21 of this chapter; or

(B) Meets the definition of reactive waste under §261.23 of this chapter, and may form an ignitable or explosive vapor; and

(vi) Provided with an exterior moisture barrier or be otherwise designed or operated to prevent migration of moisture into the vault if the vault is subject to hydraulic pressure.

(3) Double-walled tanks must be:

(i) Designed as an integral structure (*i.e.*, an inner tank completely enveloped within an outer shell) so that any release from the inner tank is contained by the outer shell;

(ii) Protected, if constructed of metal, from both corrosion of the primary tank interior and of the external surface of the outer shell; and

(iii) Provided with a built-in continuous leak detection system capable of detecting a release within 24 hours, or at the earliest practicable time, if the owner or operator can demonstrate to the Regional Administrator, and the Regional Administrator concludes, that the existing detection technology or site conditions would not allow detection of a release within 24 hours.

[*Note:* The provisions outlined in the Steel Tank Institute's (STI) "Standard for Dual Wall Underground Steel Storage Tanks" may be used as guidelines for aspects of the design of underground steel double-walled tanks.]

(f) Ancillary equipment must be provided with secondary containment (*e.g.*, trench, jacketing, double-walled piping) that meets the requirements of paragraphs (b) and (c) of this section except for: 📖 10.3.2.4

(1) Aboveground piping (exclusive of flanges, joints, valves, and other connections) that are visually inspected for leaks on a daily basis;

(2) Welded flanges, welded joints, and welded connections, that are visually inspected for leaks on a daily basis;

(3) Sealless or magnetic coupling pumps and sealless valves, that are visually inspected for leaks on a daily basis; and

(4) Pressurized aboveground piping systems with automatic shut-off devices (*e.g.*, excess flow check valves, flow metering shutdown devices, loss of pressure actuated shut-off devices) that are visually inspected for leaks on a daily basis.

(g) The owner or operator may obtain a variance from the requirements of this section if the Regional Administrator finds, as a result of a demonstration by the owner or operator that alternative design and operating practices, together with location characteristics, will prevent the migration of any hazardous waste or hazardous constituents into the ground water; or surface water at least as effectively as secondary containment during the active life of the tank system or that in the event of a release that does migrate to ground water or surface water, no substantial present or potential hazard will be posed to human health or the environment. New underground tank systems may not, per a demonstration in accordance with paragraph (g)(2) of this section, be exempted from the secondary containment requirements of this section. 📖 10.3.5

(1) In deciding whether to grant a variance based on a demonstration of equivalent protection of ground water and surface water, the Regional Administrator will consider:

(i) The nature and quantity of the wastes;

(ii) The proposed alternate design and operation;

(iii) The hydrogeologic setting of the facility, including the thickness of soils present between the tank system and ground water; and

(iv) All other factors that would influence the quality and mobility of the hazardous constituents and the potential for them to migrate to ground water or surface water.

(2) In deciding whether to grant a variance based on a demonstration of no substantial present or potential hazard, the Regional Administrator will consider:

(i) The potential adverse effects on ground water, surface water, and land quality taking into account:

(A) The physical and chemical characteristics of the waste in the tank system, including its potential for migration,

(B) The hydrogeological characteristics of the facility and surrounding land,

(C) The potential for health risks caused by human exposure to waste constituents,

(D) The potential for damage to wildlife, crops, vegetation, and physical structures caused by exposure to waste constituents, and

(E) The persistence and permanence of the potential adverse effects;

(ii) The potential adverse effects of a release on ground-water quality, taking into account:

(A) The quantity and quality of ground water and the direction of ground-water flow,

(B) The proximity and withdrawal rates of ground-water users,

(C) The current and future uses of ground water in the area, and

(D) The existing quality of ground water, including other sources of contamination and their cumulative impact on the ground-water quality;

(iii) The potential adverse effects of a release on surface water quality, taking into account:

(A) The quantity and quality of ground water and the direction of ground-water flow,

(B) The patterns of rainfall in the region,

(C) The proximity of the tank system to surface waters,

(D) The current and future uses of surface waters in the area and any water quality standards established for those surface waters, and

(E) The existing quality of surface water, including other sources of contamination and the cumulative impact on surface-water quality; and

(iv) The potential adverse effects of a release on the land surrounding the tank system, taking into account:

(A) The patterns of rainfall in the region, and

(B) The current and future uses of the surrounding land.

(3) The owner or operator of a tank system, for which a variance from secondary containment had been granted in accordance with the requirements of paragraph (g)(1) of this section, at which a release of hazardous waste has occurred from the primary tank system but has not migrated beyond the zone of engineering control (as established in the variance), must:

(i) Comply with the requirements of §264.196, except paragraph (d), and

(ii) Decontaminate or remove contaminated soil to the extent necessary to:

(A) Enable the tank system for which the variance was granted to resume operation with the capability for the detection of releases at least equivalent to the capability it had prior to the release; and

(B) Prevent the migration of hazardous waste or hazardous constituents to ground water or surface water; and

(iii) If contaminated soil cannot be removed or decontaminated in accordance with paragraph (g)(3)(ii) of this section, comply with the requirement of §264.197(b).

(4) The owner or operator of a tank system, for which a variance from secondary containment had been granted in accordance with the requirements of paragraph (g)(1) of this section, at which a release of hazardous waste has occurred from the primary tank system and has migrated beyond the zone of engineering control (as established in the variance), must:

(i) Comply with the requirements of §264.196 (a), (b), (c), and (d); and

(ii) Prevent the migration of hazardous waste or hazardous constituents to ground water or surface water, if possible, and decontaminate or remove contaminated soil. If contaminated soil cannot be decontaminated or removed or if ground water has been contaminated, the owner or operator must comply with the requirements of §264.197(b); and

(iii) If repairing, replacing, or reinstalling the tank system, provide secondary containment in accordance with the requirements of paragraphs (a) through (f) of this section or reapply for a variance from secondary containment and meet the requirements for new tank systems in §264.192 if the tank system is replaced. The owner or operator must comply with these requirements even if contaminated soil can be decontaminated or removed and ground water or surface water has not been contaminated.

(h) The following procedures must be followed in order to request a variance from secondary containment:

(1) The Regional Administrator must be notified in writing by the owner or operator that he intends to conduct and submit a demonstration for a variance from secondary containment as allowed in paragraph (g) of this section according to the following schedule:

(i) For existing tank systems, at least 24 months prior to the date that secondary containment must be provided in accordance with paragraph (a) of this section.

(ii) For new tank systems, at least 30 days prior to entering into a contract for installation.

(2) As part of the notification, the owner or operator must also submit to the Regional Administrator a description of the steps necessary to conduct the demonstration and a timetable for completing each of the steps. The demonstration must address each of the factors listed in paragraph (g)(1) or paragraph (g)(2) of this section;

(3) The demonstration for a variance must be completed within 180 days after notifying the Regional Administrator of an intent to conduct the demonstration; and

(4) If a variance is granted under this paragraph, the Regional Administrator will require the permittee to construct and operate the tank system in the manner that was demonstrated to meet the requirements for the variance.

(i) All tank systems, until such time as secondary containment that meets the requirements of this section is provided, must comply with the following: 📖 10.3.4.1

(1) For non-enterable underground tanks, a leak test that meets the requirements of §264.191(b)(5) or other tank integrity method, as approved or required by the Regional Administrator, must be conducted at least annually.

(2) For other than non-enterable underground tanks, the owner or operator must either conduct a leak test as in paragraph (i)(1) of this section or develop a schedule and procedure for an assessment of the overall condition of the tank system by a qualified Professional Engineer. The schedule and procedure must be adequate to detect obvious cracks, leaks, and corrosion or erosion that may lead to cracks and leaks. The owner or operator must remove the stored waste from the tank, if necessary, to allow the condition of all internal tank surfaces to be assessed. The frequency of these assessments must be based on the material of construction of the tank and its ancillary equipment, the age of the system, the type of corrosion or erosion protection used, the rate of corrosion or erosion observed during the previous inspection, and the characteristics of the waste being stored or treated.

(3) For ancillary equipment, a leak test or other integrity assessment as approved by the Regional Administrator must be conducted at least annually.

[*Note:* The practices described in the American Petroleum Institute (API) Publication Guide for Inspection of Refinery Equipment, Chapter XIII, "Atmospheric and Low-Pressure Storage Tanks," 4th edition, 1981, may be used, where applicable, as guidelines for assessing the overall condition of the tank system.]

(4) The owner or operator must maintain on file at the facility a record of the results of the assessments conducted in accordance with paragraphs (i)(1) through (i)(3) of this section.

(5) If a tank system or component is found to be leaking or unfit for use as a result of the leak test or assessment in paragraphs (i)(1) through (i)(3) of this section, the owner or operator must comply with the requirements of §264.196.

[51 FR 25472, July 14, 1986; 51 FR 29430, Aug. 15, 1986, as amended at 53 FR 34086, Sept. 2, 1988; 71 FR 16905, Apr. 4, 2006; 71 FR 40273, July 14, 2006]

§264.194 General operating requirements. 📖 10.4

(a) Hazardous wastes or treatment reagents must not be placed in a tank system if they could cause the tank, its ancillary equipment, or the containment system to rupture, leak, corrode, or otherwise fail.

(b) The owner or operator must use appropriate controls and practices to prevent spills and overflows from tank or containment systems. These include at a minimum:

(1) Spill prevention controls (*e.g.*, check valves, dry disconnect couplings);

(2) Overfill prevention controls (*e.g.*, level sensing devices, high level alarms, automatic feed cutoff, or bypass to a standby tank); and

(3) Maintenance of sufficient freeboard in uncovered tanks to prevent overtopping by wave or wind action or by precipitation.

(c) The owner or operator must comply with the requirements of §264.196 if a leak or spill occurs in the tank system.

§264.195 Inspections. 📖 10.5

(a) The owner or operator must develop and follow a schedule and procedure for inspecting overfill controls.

(b) The owner or operator must inspect at least once each operating day data gathered from monitoring and leak detection equipment (*e.g.*, pressure or temperature gauges, monitoring wells) to ensure that the tank system is being operated according to its design.

[*Note:* Section 264.15(c) requires the owner or operator to remedy any deterioration or malfunction he finds. Section 264.196 requires the owner or operator to notify the Regional Administrator within 24 hours of confirming a leak. Also, 40 CFR part 302 may require the owner or operator to notify the National Response Center of a release.]

(c) In addition, except as noted under paragraph (d) of this section, the owner or operator must inspect at least once each operating day:

(1) Above ground portions of the tank system, if any, to detect corrosion or releases of waste.

(2) The construction materials and the area immediately surrounding the externally accessible portion of the tank system, including the secondary containment system (*e.g.*, dikes) to detect erosion or signs of releases of hazardous waste (*e.g.*, wet spots, dead vegetation).

(d) Owners or operators of tank systems that either use leak detection systems to alert facility personnel to leaks, or implement established workplace practices to ensure leaks are promptly identified, must inspect at least weekly those areas described in paragraphs (c)(1) and (c)(2) of this section. Use of the alternate inspection schedule must be documented in the facility's operating record. This documentation must include a description of the established workplace practices at the facility.

(e) Performance Track member facilities may inspect on a less frequent basis, upon approval by the Director, but must inspect at least once each month. To apply for a less than weekly inspection frequency, the Performance Track member facility must follow the procedures described in §264.15(b)(5).

(f) Ancillary equipment that is not provided with secondary containment, as described in §264.193(f)(1) through (4), must be inspected at least once each operating day.

(g) The owner or operator must inspect cathodic protection systems, if present, according to, at a minimum, the following schedule to ensure that they are functioning properly:

(1) The proper operation of the cathodic protection system must be confirmed within six months after initial installation and annually thereafter; and

(2) All sources of impressed current must be inspected and/or tested, as appropriate, at least bimonthly (*i.e.*, every other month).

[*Note:* The practices described in the National Association of Corrosion Engineers (NACE) standard, "Recommended Practice (RP-02-85)—Control of External Corrosion on Metallic Buried, Partially Buried, or Submerged Liquid Storage Systems," and the American Petroleum Institute (API) Publication 1632, "Cathodic Protection of Underground Petroleum Storage Tanks and Piping Systems," may be used, where applicable, as guidelines in maintaining and inspecting cathodic protection systems.]

(h) The owner or operator must document in the operating record of the facility an inspection of those items in paragraphs (a) through (c) of this section.

[51 FR 25472, July 14, 1986, as amended at 71 FR 16906, Apr. 4, 2006]

§264.196 Response to leaks or spills and disposition of leaking or unfit-for-use tank systems.

📖 10.3.3.1

A tank system or secondary containment system from which there has been a leak or spill, or which is unfit for use, must be removed from service immediately, and the owner or operator must satisfy the following requirements:

(a) *Cessation of use; prevent flow or addition of wastes.* The owner or operator must immediately stop the flow of hazardous waste into the tank system or secondary containment system and inspect the system to determine the cause of the release.

(b) *Removal of waste from tank system or secondary containment system.* (1) If the release was from the tank system, the owner/operator must, within 24 hours after detection of the leak or, if the owner/operator demonstrates that it is not possible, at the earliest practicable time, remove as much of the waste as is necessary to prevent further release of hazardous waste to the environment and to allow inspection and repair of the tank system to be performed.

(2) If the material released was to a secondary containment system, all released materials must be removed within 24 hours or in as timely a manner as is possible to prevent harm to human health and the environment.

(c) *Containment of visible releases to the environment.* The owner/operator must immediately conduct a visual inspection of the release and, based upon that inspection:

(1) Prevent further migration of the leak or spill to soils or surface water; and

(2) Remove, and properly dispose of, any visible contamination of the soil or surface water.

(d) *Notifications, reports.* (1) Any release to the environment, except as provided in paragraph (d)(2) of this section, must be reported to the Regional Administrator within 24 hours of its detection. If the release has been reported pursuant to 40 CFR part 302, that report will satisfy this requirement. 📖 10.3.3.1.1, 14.4.10

(2) A leak or spill of hazardous waste is exempted from the requirements of this paragraph if it is:

(i) Less than or equal to a quantity of one (1) pound, and

(ii) Immediately contained and cleaned up.

(3) Within 30 days of detection of a release to the environment, a report containing the following information must be submitted to the Regional Administrator:

(i) Likely route of migration of the release;

(ii) Characteristics of the surrounding soil (soil composition, geology, hydrogeology, climate);

(iii) Results of any monitoring or sampling conducted in connection with the release (if available). If sampling or monitoring data relating to the release are not available within 30 days, these data must be submitted to the Regional Administrator as soon as they become available.

(iv) Proximity to downgradient drinking water, surface water, and populated areas; and

(v) Description of response actions taken or planned.

(e) *Provision of secondary containment, repair, or closure.* (1) Unless the owner/operator satisfies the requirements of paragraphs (e)(2) through (4) of this section, the tank system must be closed in accordance with §264.197.

(2) If the cause of the release was a spill that has not damaged the integrity of the system, the owner/operator may return the system to service as soon as the released waste is removed and repairs, if necessary, are made.

(3) If the cause of the release was a leak from the primary tank system into the secondary containment system, the system must be repaired prior to returning the tank system to service.

(4) If the source of the release was a leak to the environment from a component of a tank system without secondary containment, the owner/operator must provide the component of the system from which the leak occurred with secondary containment that satisfies the requirements of §264.193 before it can be returned to service, unless the source of the leak is an aboveground portion of a tank system that can be inspected visually. If the source is an aboveground component that can be inspected visually, the component must be repaired and may be returned to service without secondary containment as long as the requirements of paragraph (f) of this section are satisfied. If a component is replaced to comply with the requirements of this subparagraph, that component must satisfy the requirements for new tank systems or components in §§264.192 and 264.193. Additionally, if a leak has occurred in any portion of a tank system component that is not readily accessible for visual inspection (*e.g.*, the bottom of an inground or onground tank), the entire component must be provided with secondary containment in accordance with §264.193 prior to being returned to use.

(f) *Certification of major repairs.* If the owner/operator has repaired a tank system in accordance with paragraph (e) of this section, and the repair has been extensive (*e.g.*, installation of an internal liner; repair of a ruptured primary containment or secondary containment vessel), the tank system must not be returned to service unless the owner/operator has obtained a certification by a qualified Professional Engineer in accordance with §270.11(d) of this chapter that the repaired system is capable of handling hazardous wastes without release for the intended life of the system. This certification must be placed in the operating record and maintained until closure of the facility.

[*Note:* The Regional Administrator may, on the basis of any information received that there is or has been a release of hazardous waste or hazardous constituents into the environment, issue an order under RCRA section 3004(v), 3008(h), or 7003(a) requiring corrective action or such other response as deemed necessary to protect human health or the environment.]

[*Note:* See §264.15(c) for the requirements necessary to remedy a failure. Also, 40 CFR part 302 may require the owner or operator to notify the National Response Center of certain releases.]

[51 FR 25472, July 14, 1986; 51 FR 29430, Aug. 15, 1986, as amended at 53 FR 34086, Sept. 2, 1988; 71 FR 16906, Apr. 4, 2006]

§264.197 Closure and post-closure care.

(a) At closure of a tank system, the owner or operator must remove or decontaminate all waste residues, contaminated containment system components (liners, etc.), contaminated soils, and structures and equipment contaminated with waste, and manage them as hazardous waste, unless §261.3(d) of this chapter applies. The closure plan, closure activities, cost estimates for closure, and financial responsibility for tank systems must meet all of the requirements specified in subparts G and H of this part.

(b) If the owner or operator demonstrates that not all contaminated soils can be practicably removed or decontaminated as required in paragraph (a) of this section, then the owner or operator must close the tank system and perform post-closure care in accordance with the closure and post-closure care requirements that apply to landfills (§264.310). In addition, for the purposes of closure, post-closure, and financial responsibility, such a tank system is then considered to be a landfill, and the owner or operator must meet all of the requirements for landfills specified in subparts G and H of this part.

(c) If an owner or operator has a tank system that does not have secondary containment that meets the requirements of §264.193 (b) through (f) and has not been granted a variance from the secondary containment requirements in accordance with §264.193(g), then:

(1) The closure plan for the tank system must include both a plan for complying with paragraph (a) of this section and a contingent plan for complying with paragraph (b) of this section.

(2) A contingent post-closure plan for complying with paragraph (b) of this section must be prepared and submitted as part of the permit application.

(3) The cost estimates calculated for closure and post-closure care must reflect the costs of complying with the contingent closure plan and the contingent post-closure plan, if those costs are greater than the costs of complying with the closure plan prepared for the expected closure under paragraph (a) of this section.

(4) Financial assurance must be based on the cost estimates in paragraph (c)(3) of this section.

(5) For the purposes of the contingent closure and post-closure plans, such a tank system is considered to be a landfill, and the contingent plans must meet all of the closure, post-closure, and financial responsibility requirements for landfills under subparts G and H of this part.

[51 FR 25472, July 14, 1986; 51 FR 29430, Aug. 15, 1986]

§264.198 Special requirements for ignitable or reactive wastes.

(a) Ignitable or reactive waste must not be placed in tank systems, unless:

(1) The waste is treated, rendered, or mixed before or immediately after placement in the tank system so that:

(i) The resulting waste, mixture, or dissolved material no longer meets the definition of ignitable or reactive waste under §§261.21 or 261.23 of this chapter, and

(ii) Section 264.17(b) is complied with; or

(2) The waste is stored or treated in such a way that it is protected from any material or conditions that may cause the waste to ignite or react; or

(3) The tank system is used solely for emergencies.

(b) The owner or operator of a facility where ignitable or reactive waste is stored or treated in a tank must comply with the requirements for the maintenance of protective distances between the waste management area and any public ways, streets, alleys, or an adjoining property line that can be built upon as required in Tables 2-1 through 2-6 of the National Fire Protection Association's "Flammable and Combustible Liquids Code," (1977 or 1981), (incorporated by reference, see §260.11).

§264.199 Special requirements for incompatible wastes.

(a) Incompatible wastes, or incompatible wastes and materials, must not be placed in the same tank system, unless §264.17(b) is complied with.

(b) Hazardous waste must not be placed in a tank system that has not been decontaminated and that previously held an incompatible waste or material, unless §264.17(b) is complied with.

§264.200 Air emission standards.

📖 15.1–3

The owner or operator shall manage all hazardous waste placed in a tank in accordance with the applicable requirements of subparts AA, BB, and CC of this part.

[61 FR 59950, Nov. 25, 1996]

Subpart K—Surface Impoundments

Source: 47 FR 32357, July 26, 1982, unless otherwise noted.

§264.220 Applicability.

📖 2.4.4, 10.1.3.2, 14.1.2, 14.2.1.3

The regulations in this subpart apply to owners and operators of facilities that use surface impoundments to treat, store, or dispose of hazardous waste except as §264.1 provides otherwise.

§264.221 Design and operating requirements.

(a) Any surface impoundment that is not covered by paragraph (c) of this section or §265.221 of this chapter must have a liner for all portions of the impoundment (except for existing portions of such impoundments). The liner must be designed, constructed, and installed to prevent any migration of wastes out of the impoundment to the adjacent subsurface soil or ground water or surface water at any time during the active life (including the closure period) of the impoundment. The liner may be constructed of materials that may allow wastes to migrate into the liner (but not into the adjacent subsurface soil or ground water or surface water) during the active life of the facility, provided that the impoundment is closed in accordance with §264.228(a)(1). For impoundments that will be closed in accordance with §264.228(a)(2), the liner must be constructed of materials that can prevent wastes from migrating into the liner during the active life of the facility. The liner must be:

(1) Constructed of materials that have appropriate chemical properties and sufficient strength and thickness to prevent failure due to pressure gradients (including static head and external hydrogeologic forces), physical contact with the waste or leachate to which they are exposed, climatic conditions, the stress of installation, and the stress of daily operation;

(2) Placed upon a foundation or base capable of providing support to the liner and resistance to pressure gradients above and below the liner to prevent failure of the liner due to settlement, compression, or uplift; and

(3) Installed to cover all surrounding earth likely to be in contact with the waste or leachate.

(b) The owner or operator will be exempted from the requirements of paragraph (a) of this section if the Regional Administrator finds, based on a demonstration by the owner or operator, that alternate design and operating practices, together with location characteristics, will prevent the migration of any hazardous constituents (see §264.93) into the ground water or surface water at any future time. In deciding whether to grant an exemption, the Regional Administrator will consider:

(1) The nature and quantity of the wastes;

(2) The proposed alternate design and operation;

(3) The hydrogeologic setting of the facility, including the attenuative capacity and thickness of the liners and soils present between the impoundment and ground water or surface water; and

(4) All other factors which would influence the quality and mobility of the leachate produced and the potential for it to migrate to ground water or surface water.

(c) The owner or operator of each new surface impoundment unit on which construction commences after January 29, 1992, each lateral expansion of a surface impoundment unit on which construction commences after July 29, 1992 and each replacement of an existing surface impoundment unit that is to commence reuse after July 29, 1992 must install two or more liners and a leachate collection and removal system between such liners. "Construction commences" is as defined in §260.10 of this chapter under "existing facility".

(1)(i) The *liner system* must include:

(A) A top liner designed and constructed of materials (*e.g.*, a geomembrane) to prevent the migration of hazardous constituents into such liner during the active life and post-closure care period; and

(B) A composite bottom liner, consisting of at least two components. The upper component must be designed and constructed of materials (*e.g.*, a geomembrane) to prevent the migration of hazardous constituents into this component during the active life and post-closure care period. The lower component must be designed and constructed of materials to minimize the migration of hazardous constituents if a breach in the upper component were to occur. The lower component must be constructed of at least 3 feet (91 cm) of compacted soil material with a hydraulic conductivity of no more than 1×10^{-7} cm/sec.

(ii) The liners must comply with paragraphs (a) (1), (2), and (3) of this section.

(2) The *leachate collection and removal system* between the liners, and immediately above the bottom composite liner in the case of multiple leachate collection and removal systems, is also a *leak detection system*. This leak detection system must be capable of detecting, collecting, and removing leaks of hazardous constituents at the earliest practicable time through all areas of the top liner likely to be exposed to waste or leachate during the active life and post-closure care period. The requirements for a leak detection system in this paragraph are satisfied by installation of a system that is, at a minimum:

(i) Constructed with a bottom slope of one percent or more;

(ii) Constructed of granular drainage materials with a hydraulic conductivity of 1×10^{-1} cm/sec or more and a thickness of 12 inches (30.5 cm) or more; or constructed of synthetic or geonet drainage materials with a transmissivity of 3×10^{-4} m^2/sec or more;

(iii) Constructed of materials that are chemically resistant to the waste managed in the surface impoundment and the leachate expected to be generated, and of sufficient strength and thickness to prevent collapse under the pressures exerted by overlying wastes and any waste cover materials or equipment used at the surface impoundment;

(iv) Designed and operated to minimize clogging during the active life and post-closure care period; and

(v) Constructed with sumps and liquid removal methods (*e.g.*, pumps) of sufficient size to collect and remove liquids from the sump and prevent liquids from backing up into the drainage layer. Each unit must have its own sump(s). The design of each sump and removal system must provide a method for measuring and recording the volume of liquids present in the sump and of liquids removed. 10.2.3–4

(3) The owner or operator shall collect and remove pumpable liquids in the sumps to minimize the head on the bottom liner.

(4) The owner or operator of a leak detection system that is not located completely above the seasonal high water table must demonstrate that the operation of the leak detection system will not be adversely affected by the presence of ground water.

(d) The Regional Administrator may approve alternative design or operating practices to those specified in paragraph (c) of this section if the owner or operator demonstrates to the Regional Administrator that such design and operating practices, together with location characteristics:

(1) Will prevent the migration of any hazardous constituent into the ground water or surface water at least as effectively as the liners and leachate collection and removal system specified in paragraph (c) of this section; and

(2) Will allow detection of leaks of hazardous constituents through the top liner at least as effectively.

(e) The double liner requirement set forth in paragraph (c) of this section may be waived by the Regional Administrator for any monofill, if:

(1) The monofill contains only hazardous wastes from foundry furnace emission controls or metal casting molding sand, and such wastes do not contain constituents which would render the wastes hazardous for reasons other than the toxicity characteristic in §261.24 of this chapter; and

(2)(i)(A) The monofill has at least one liner for which there is no evidence that such liner is leaking. For the purposes of this paragraph, the term "liner" means a liner designed, constructed, installed, and operated to prevent hazardous waste from passing into the liner at any time during the active life of the facility, or a liner designed, constructed, installed, and operated to prevent hazardous waste from migrating beyond the liner to adjacent subsurface soil, ground water, or surface water at any time during the active life of the facility. In the case of any surface impoundment which has been exempted from the requirements of paragraph (c) of this section on the basis of a liner designed, constructed, installed, and operated to prevent hazardous waste from passing beyond the liner, at the closure of such impoundment, the owner or operator must remove or decontaminate all waste residues, all contaminated liner material, and contaminated soil to the extent practicable. If all contaminated soil is not removed or decontaminated, the owner or operator of such impoundment will comply with appropriate post-closure requirements, including but not limited to ground-water monitoring and corrective action;

(B) The monofill is located more than one-quarter mile from an "underground source of drinking water" (as that term is defined in 40 CFR 270.2); and

(C) The monofill is in compliance with generally applicable ground-water monitoring requirements for facilities with permits under RCRA section 3005(c); or

(ii) The owner or operator demonstrates that the monofill is located, designed and operated so as to assure that there will be no migration of any hazardous constituent into ground water or surface water at any future time.

(f) The owner or operator of any replacement surface impoundment unit is exempt from paragraph (c) of this section if:

(1) The existing unit was constructed in compliance with the design standards of sections 3004 (o)(1)(A)(i) and (o)(5) of the Resource Conservation and Recovery Act; and

(2) There is no reason to believe that the liner is not functioning as designed.

(g) A surface impoundment must be designed, constructed, maintained, and operated to prevent overtopping resulting from normal or abnormal operations; overfilling; wind and wave action; rainfall; run-on; malfunctions of level controllers, alarms, and other equipment; and human error.

(h) A surface impoundment must have dikes that are designed, constructed, and maintained with sufficient structural integrity to prevent massive failure of the dikes. In ensuring structural integrity, it must not be presumed that the liner system will function without leakage during the active life of the unit.

(i) The Regional Administrator will specify in the permit all design and operating practices that are necessary to ensure that the requirements of this section are satisfied.

[47 FR 32357, July 26, 1982, as amended at 50 FR 4514, Jan. 31, 1985; 50 FR 28747, July 15, 1985; 57 FR 3487, Jan. 29, 1992; 71 FR 40273, July 14, 2006]

§264.222 Action leakage rate.

(a) The Regional Administrator shall approve an action leakage rate for surface impoundment units subject to §264.221 (c) or (d). The action leakage rate is the maximum design flow rate that the leak detection system (LDS) can remove without the fluid head on the bottom liner exceeding 1 foot. The action leakage rate must include an adequate safety margin to allow for uncertainties in the design (*e.g.*, slope, hydraulic conductivity, thickness of drainage material), construction, operation, and location of the LDS, waste and leachate characteristics, likelihood and amounts of other sources of liquids in the LDS, and proposed response actions (*e.g.*, the action leakage rate must consider decreases in the flow capacity of the system over time resulting from siltation and clogging, rib layover and creep of synthetic components of the system, overburden pressures, etc.).

(b) To determine if the action leakage rate has been exceeded, the owner or operator must convert the weekly or monthly flow rate from the monitoring data obtained under §264.226(d) to an average daily flow rate (gallons per acre per day) for each sump. Unless the Regional Administrator approves a different calculation, the average daily flow rate for each sump must be calculated weekly during the active life and closure period, and if the unit is closed in accordance with §264.228(b), monthly during the post-closure care period when monthly monitoring is required under §264.226(d).

[57 FR 3487, Jan. 29, 1992]

§264.223 Response actions.

(a) The owner or operator of surface impoundment units subject to §264.221 (c) or (d) must have an approved response action plan before receipt of waste. The response action plan must set forth the actions to be taken if the action leakage rate has been exceeded. At a minimum, the response action plan must describe the actions specified in paragraph (b) of this section.

(b) If the flow rate into the leak detection system exceeds the action leakage rate for any sump, the owner or operator must:

(1) Notify the Regional Administrator in writing of the exceedance within 7 days of the determination;

(2) Submit a preliminary written assessment to the Regional Administrator within 14 days of the determination, as to the amount of liquids, likely sources of liquids, possible location, size, and cause of any leaks, and short-term actions taken and planned;

(3) Determine to the extent practicable the location, size, and cause of any leak;

(4) Determine whether waste receipt should cease or be curtailed, whether any waste should be removed from the unit for inspection, repairs, or controls, and whether or not the unit should be closed;

(5) Determine any other short-term and longer-term actions to be taken to mitigate or stop any leaks; and

(6) Within 30 days after the notification that the action leakage rate has been exceeded, submit to the Regional Administrator the results of the analyses specified in paragraphs (b) (3), (4), and (5) of this section, the results of actions taken, and actions planned. Monthly thereafter, as long as the flow rate in the leak detection system exceeds the action leakage rate, the owner or operator must submit to the Regional Administrator a report summarizing the results of any remedial actions taken and actions planned.

(c) To make the leak and/or remediation determinations in paragraphs (b) (3), (4), and (5) of this section, the owner or operator must:

(1)(i) Assess the source of liquids and amounts of liquids by source,

(ii) Conduct a fingerprint, hazardous constituent, or other analyses of the liquids in the leak detection system to identify the source of liquids and possible location of any leaks, and the hazard and mobility of the liquid; and

(iii) Assess the seriousness of any leaks in terms of potential for escaping into the environment; or

(2) Document why such assessments are not needed.

[57 FR 3488, Jan. 29, 1992, as amended at 71 FR 40273, July 14, 2006]

§§264.224–264.225 [Reserved]

§264.226 Monitoring and inspection.

(a) During construction and installation, liners (except in the case of existing portions of surface impoundments exempt from §264.221(a)) and cover systems (*e.g.*, membranes, sheets, or coatings) must be inspected for uniformity, damage, and imperfections (*e.g.*, holes, cracks, thin spots, or foreign materials). Immediately after construction or installation:

(1) Synthetic liners and covers must be inspected to ensure tight seams and joints and the absence of tears, punctures, or blisters; and

(2) Soil-based and admixed liners and covers must be inspected for imperfections including lenses, cracks, channels, root holes, or other structural non-uniformities that

may cause an increase in the permeability of the liner or cover.

(b) While a surface impoundment is in operation, it must be inspected weekly and after storms to detect evidence of any of the following:

(1) Deterioration, malfunctions, or improper operation of overtopping control systems;

(2) Sudden drops in the level of the impoundment's contents; and

(3) Severe erosion or other signs of deterioration in dikes or other containment devices.

(c) Prior to the issuance of a permit, and after any extended period of time (at least six months) during which the impoundment was not in service, the owner or operator must obtain a certification from a qualified engineer that the impoundment's dike, including that portion of any dike which provides freeboard, has structural integrity. The certification must establish, in particular, that the dike:

(1) Will withstand the stress of the pressure exerted by the types and amounts of wastes to be placed in the impoundment; and

(2) Will not fail due to scouring or piping, without dependence on any liner system included in the surface impoundment construction.

(d)(1) An owner or operator required to have a leak detection system under §264.221 (c) or (d) must record the amount of liquids removed from each leak detection system sump at least once each week during the active life and closure period.

(2) After the final cover is installed, the amount of liquids removed from each leak detection system sump must be recorded at least monthly. If the liquid level in the sump stays below the pump operating level for two consecutive months, the amount of liquids in the sumps must be recorded at least quarterly. If the liquid level in the sump stays below the pump operating level for two consecutive quarters, the amount of liquids in the sumps must be recorded at least semi-annually. If at any time during the post-closure care period the pump operating level is exceeded at units on quarterly or semi-annual recording schedules, the owner or operator must return to monthly recording of amounts of liquids removed from each sump until the liquid level again stays below the pump operating level for two consecutive months.

(3) "Pump operating level" is a liquid level proposed by the owner or operator and approved by the Regional Administrator based on pump activation level, sump dimensions, and level that avoids backup into the drainage layer and minimizes head in the sump.

[47 FR 32357, July 26, 1982, as amended at 50 FR 4514, Jan. 31, 1985; 50 FR 28748, July 15, 1985; 57 FR 3488, Jan. 29, 1992; 71 FR 40273, July 14, 2006]

§264.227 Emergency repairs; contingency plans.

(a) A surface impoundment must be removed from service in accordance with paragraph (b) of this section when:

(1) The level of liquids in the impoundment suddenly drops and the drop is not known to be caused by changes in the flows into or out of the impoundment; or

(2) The dike leaks.

(b) When a surface impoundment must be removed from service as required by paragraph (a) of this section, the owner or operator must:

(1) Immediately shut off the flow or stop the addition of wastes into the impoundment;

(2) Immediately contain any surface leakage which has occurred or is occurring;

(3) Immediately stop the leak;

(4) Take any other necessary steps to stop or prevent catastrophic failure;

(5) If a leak cannot be stopped by any other means, empty the impoundment; and

(6) Notify the Regional Administrator of the problem in writing within seven days after detecting the problem.

(c) As part of the contingency plan required in subpart D of this part, the owner or operator must specify a procedure for complying with the requirements of paragraph (b) of this section.

(d) No surface impoundment that has been removed from service in accordance with the requirements of this section may be restored to service unless the portion of the impoundment which was failing is repaired and the following steps are taken:

(1) If the impoundment was removed from service as the result of actual or imminent dike failure, the dike's structural integrity must be recertified in accordance with §264.226(c).

(2) If the impoundment was removed from service as the result of a sudden drop in the liquid level, then:

(i) For any existing portion of the impoundment, a liner must be installed in compliance with §264.221(a); and

(ii) For any other portion of the impoundment, the repaired liner system must be certified by a qualified engineer as meeting the design specifications approved in the permit.

(e) A surface impoundment that has been removed from service in accordance with the requirements of this section and that is not being repaired must be closed in accordance with the provisions of §264.228.

[47 FR 32357, July 26, 1982, as amended at 50 FR 28748, July 15, 1985]

§264.228 Closure and post-closure care.

(a) At closure, the owner or operator must:

(1) Remove or decontaminate all waste residues, contaminated containment system components (liners, etc.), contaminated subsoils, and structures and equipment contaminated with waste and leachate, and manage them as hazardous waste unless §261.3(d) of this chapter applies; or

(2)(i) Eliminate free liquids by removing liquid wastes or solidifying the remaining wastes and waste residues;

(ii) Stabilize remaining wastes to a bearing capacity sufficient to support final cover; and

(iii) Cover the surface impoundment with a final cover designed and constructed to:

(A) Provide long-term minimization of the migration of liquids through the closed impoundment;

(B) Function with minimum maintenance;

(C) Promote drainage and minimize erosion or abrasion of the final cover;

(D) Accommodate settling and subsidence so that the cover's integrity is maintained; and

(E) Have a permeability less than or equal to the permeability of any bottom liner system or natural subsoils present.

(b) If some waste residues or contaminated materials are left in place at final closure, the owner or operator must comply with all post-closure requirements contained in §§264.117 through 264.120, including maintenance and monitoring throughout the post-closure care period (specified in the permit under §264.117). The owner or operator must:

(1) Maintain the integrity and effectiveness of the final cover, including making repairs to the cap as necessary to correct the effects of settling, subsidence, erosion, or other events;

(2) Maintain and monitor the leak detection system in accordance with §§264.221(c)(2)(iv) and (3) and 264.226(d), and comply with all other applicable leak detection system requirements of this part;

(3) Maintain and monitor the ground-water monitoring system and comply with all other applicable requirements of subpart F of this part; and

(4) Prevent run-on and run-off from eroding or otherwise damaging the final cover.

(c)(1) If an owner or operator plans to close a surface impoundment in accordance with paragraph (a)(1) of this section, and the impoundment does not comply with the liner requirements of §264.221(a) and is not exempt from them in accordance with §264.221(b), then:

(i) The closure plan for the impoundment under §264.112 must include both a plan for complying with paragraph (a)(1) of this section and a contingent plan for complying with paragraph (a)(2) of this section in case not all contaminated subsoils can be practicably removed at closure; and

(ii) The owner or operator must prepare a contingent post-closure plan under §264.118 for complying with paragraph (b) of this section in case not all contaminated subsoils can be practicably removed at closure.

(2) The cost estimates calculated under §§264.142 and 264.144 for closure and post-closure care of an impoundment subject to this paragraph must include the cost of complying with the contingent closure plan and the contingent post-closure plan, but are not required to include the cost of expected closure under paragraph (a)(1) of this section.

[47 FR 32357, July 26, 1982, as amended at 50 FR 28748, July 15, 1985; 57 FR 3488, Jan. 29, 1992]

§264.229 Special requirements for ignitable or reactive waste.

Ignitable or reactive waste must not be placed in a surface impoundment, unless the waste and impoundment satisfy all applicable requirements of 40 CFR part 268, and:

(a) The waste is treated, rendered, or mixed before or immediately after placement in the impoundment so that:

(1) The resulting waste, mixture, or dissolution of material no longer meets the definition of ignitable or reactive waste under §261.21 or §261.23 of this chapter; and

(2) Section 264.17(b) is complied with; or

(b) The waste is managed in such a way that it is protected from any material or conditions which may cause it to ignite or react; or

(c) The surface impoundment is used solely for emergencies.

[47 FR 32357, July 26, 1982, as amended at 55 FR 22685, June 1, 1990]

§264.230 Special requirements for incompatible wastes.

Incompatible wastes, or incompatible wastes and materials, (see appendix V of this part for examples) must not be placed in the same surface impoundment, unless §264.17(b) is complied with.

§264.231 Special requirements for hazardous wastes F020, F021, F022, F023, F026, and F027.

(a) Hazardous Wastes F020, F021, F022, F023, F026, and F027 must not be placed in a surface impoundment unless the owner or operator operates the surface impoundment in accordance with a management plan for these wastes that is approved by the Regional Administrator pursuant to the standards set out in this paragraph, and in accord with all other applicable requirements of this part. The factors to be considered are:

(1) The volume, physical, and chemical characteristics of the wastes, including their potential to migrate through soil or to volatilize or escape into the atmosphere;

(2) The attenuative properties of underlying and surrounding soils or other materials;

(3) The mobilizing properties of other materials codisposed with these wastes; and

(4) The effectiveness of additional treatment, design, or monitoring techniques.

(b) The Regional Administrator may determine that additional design, operating, and monitoring requirements are necessary for surface impoundments managing hazardous wastes F020, F021, F022, F023, F026, and F027 in order to reduce the possibility of migration of these wastes to ground water, surface water, or air so as to protect human health and the environment.

[50 FR 2004, Jan. 14, 1985]

§264.232 Air emission standards. 15.2–3

The owner or operator shall manage all hazardous waste placed in a surface impoundment in accordance with the applicable requirements of subparts BB and CC of this part.

[61 FR 59950, Nov. 25, 1996]

Subpart L—Waste Piles

Source: 47 FR 32359, July 26, 1982, unless otherwise noted.

§264.250 Applicability. 10.1.3.1

(a) The regulations in this subpart apply to owners and operators of facilities that store or treat hazardous waste in piles, except as §264.1 provides otherwise.

(b) The regulations in this subpart do not apply to owners or operators of waste piles that are closed with wastes left in place. Such waste piles are subject to regulation under subpart N of this part (Landfills).

(c) The owner or operator of any waste pile that is inside or under a structure that provides protection from precipitation so that neither run-off nor leachate is generated is not subject to regulation under §264.251 or under subpart F of this part, provided that:

(1) Liquids or materials containing free liquids are not placed in the pile;

(2) The pile is protected from surface water run-on by the structure or in some other manner;

(3) The pile is designed and operated to control dispersal of the waste by wind, where necessary, by means other than wetting; and

(4) The pile will not generate leachate through decomposition or other reactions.

§264.251 Design and operating requirements.

(a) A waste pile (except for an existing portion of a waste pile) must have:

(1) A liner that is designed, constructed, and installed to prevent any migration of wastes out of the pile into the adjacent subsurface soil or ground water or surface water at any time during the active life (including the closure period) of the waste pile. The liner may be constructed of materials that may allow waste to migrate into the liner itself (but not into the adjacent subsurface soil or ground water or surface water) during the active life of the facility. The liner must be:

(i) Constructed of materials that have appropriate chemical properties and sufficient strength and thickness to prevent failure due to pressure gradients (including static head and external hydrogeologic forces), physical contact with the waste or leachate to which they are exposed, climatic conditions, the stress of installation, and the stress of daily operation;

(ii) Placed upon a foundation or base capable of providing support to the liner and resistance to pressure gradients above and below the liner to prevent failure of the liner due to settlement, compression, or uplift; and

(iii) Installed to cover all surrounding earth likely to be in contact with the waste or leachate; and

(2) A leachate collection and removal system immediately above the liner that is designed, constructed, maintained, and operated to collect and remove leachate from the pile. The Regional Administrator will specify design and operating conditions in the permit to ensure that the leachate depth over the liner does not exceed 30 cm (one foot). The leachate collection and removal system must be:

(i) Constructed of materials that are:

(A) Chemically resistant to the waste managed in the pile and the leachate expected to be generated; and

(B) Of sufficient strength and thickness to prevent collapse under the pressures exerted by overlaying wastes, waste cover materials, and by any equipment used at the pile; and

(ii) Designed and operated to function without clogging through the scheduled closure of the waste pile.

(b) The owner or operator will be exempted from the requirements of paragraph (a) of this section, if the Regional Administrator finds, based on a demonstration by the owner or operator, that alternate design and operating practices, together with location characteristics, will prevent the migration of any hazardous constituents (see §264.93) into the ground water or surface water at any future time. In deciding whether to grant an exemption, the Regional Administrator will consider:

(1) The nature and quantity of the wastes;

(2) The proposed alternate design and operation;

(3) The hydrogeologic setting of the facility, including attenuative capacity and thickness of the liners and soils present between the pile and ground water or surface water; and

(4) All other factors which would influence the quality and mobility of the leachate produced and the potential for it to migrate to ground water or surface water.

(c) The owner or operator of each new waste pile unit, each lateral expansion of a waste pile unit, and each replacement of an existing waste pile unit must install two or more liners and a leachate collection and removal system above and between such liners.

(1)(i) The liner system must include:

(A) A top liner designed and constructed of materials (*e.g.*, a geomembrane) to prevent the migration of hazardous constituents into such liner during the active life and post-closure care period; and

(B) A composite bottom liner, consisting of at least two components. The upper component must be designed and constructed of materials (*e.g.*, a geomembrane) to prevent the migration of hazardous constituents into this component during the active life and post-closure care period. The lower component must be designed and constructed of materials to minimize the migration of hazardous constituents if a breach in the upper component were to occur. The lower component must be constructed of at least 3 feet (91 cm) of compacted soil material with a hydraulic conductivity of no more than 1×10^{-7} cm/sec.

(ii) The liners must comply with paragraphs (a)(1)(i), (ii), and (iii) of this section.

(2) The *leachate collection and removal system* immediately above the top liner must be designed, constructed, operated, and maintained to collect and remove leachate from the waste pile during the active life and post-closure care period. The Regional Administrator will specify design and operating conditions in the permit to ensure that the leachate depth over the liner does not exceed 30 cm (one foot). The leachate collection and removal system must comply with paragraphs (c)(3)(iii) and (iv) of this section.

(3) The *leachate collection and removal system* between the liners, and immediately above the bottom composite liner in the case of multiple leachate collection and removal systems, is also a *leak detection system*. This leak detection system must be capable of detecting, collecting, and removing leaks of hazardous constituents at the earliest practicable time through all areas of the top liner likely to be exposed to waste or leachate during the active life and post-closure care period. The requirements for a leak detection system in this paragraph are satisfied by installation of a system that is, at a minimum:

(i) Constructed with a bottom slope of one percent or more;

(ii) Constructed of granular drainage materials with a hydraulic conductivity of 1×10^{-2} cm/sec or more and a thickness of 12 inches (30.5 cm) or more; or constructed of synthetic or geonet drainage materials with a transmissivity of 3×10^{-5} m^2/sec or more:

(iii) Constructed of materials that are chemically resistant to the waste managed in the waste pile and the leachate expected to be generated, and of sufficient strength and thickness to prevent collapse under the pressures exerted by overlying wastes, waste cover materials, and equipment used at the waste pile;

(iv) Designed and operated to minimize clogging during the active life and post-closure care period; and

(v) Constructed with sumps and liquid removal methods (*e.g.*, pumps) of sufficient size to collect and remove liquids from the sump and prevent liquids from backing up into the drainage layer. Each unit must have its own sump(s). The design of each sump and removal system must provide a method for measuring and recording the volume of liquids present in the sump and of liquids removed. 📖 10.2.3–4

(4) The owner or operator shall collect and remove pumpable liquids in the leak detection system sumps to minimize the head on the bottom liner.

(5) The owner or operator of a leak detection system that is not located completely above the seasonal high water table must demonstrate that the operation of the leak detection system will not be adversely affected by the presence of ground water.

(d) The Regional Administrator may approve alternative design or operating practices to those specified in paragraph (c) of this section if the owner or operator demonstrates to the Regional Administrator that such design and operating practices, together with location characteristics:

(1) Will prevent the migration of any hazardous constituent into the ground water or surface water at least as effectively as the liners and leachate collection and removal systems specified in paragraph (c) of this section; and

(2) Will allow detection of leaks of hazardous constituents through the top liner at least as effectively.

(e) Paragraph (c) of this section does not apply to monofills that are granted a waiver by the Regional Administrator in accordance with §264.221(e).

(f) The owner or operator of any replacement waste pile unit is exempt from paragraph (c) of this section if:

(1) The existing unit was constructed in compliance with the design standards of section 3004(o)(1)(A)(i) and (o)(5) of the Resource Conservation and Recovery Act; and

(2) There is no reason to believe that the liner is not functioning as designed.

(g) The owner or operator must design, construct, operate, and maintain a run-on control system capable of preventing flow onto the active portion of the pile during peak discharge from at least a 25-year storm.

(h) The owner or operator must design, construct, operate, and maintain a run-off management system to collect and control at least the water volume resulting from a 24-hour, 25-year storm.

(i) Collection and holding facilities (*e.g.*, tanks or basins) associated with run-on and run-off control systems must be emptied or otherwise managed expeditiously after storms to maintain design capacity of the system.

(j) If the pile contains any particulate matter which may be subject to wind dispersal, the owner or operator must cover or otherwise manage the pile to control wind dispersal.

(k) The Regional Administrator will specify in the permit all design and operating practices that are necessary to ensure that the requirements of this section are satisfied.

[47 FR 32359, July 26, 1982, as amended at 50 FR 4514, Jan. 31, 1985; 57 FR 3488, Jan. 29, 1992; 71 FR 16906, Apr. 4, 2006; 71 FR 40273, July 14, 2006]

§264.252 Action leakage rate.

(a) The Regional Administrator shall approve an action leakage rate for waste pile units subject to §264.251(c) or (d). The action leakage rate is the maximum design flow rate that the leak detection system (LDS) can remove without the fluid head on the bottom liner exceeding 1 foot. The action leakage rate must include an adequate safety margin to allow for uncertainties in the design (*e.g.*, slope, hydraulic conductivity, thickness of drainage material), construction, operation, and location of the LDS, waste and leachate characteristics, likelihood and amounts of other sources of liquids in the LDS, and proposed response actions (*e.g.*, the action leakage rate must consider decreases in the flow capacity of the system over time resulting from siltation and clogging, rib layover and creep of synthetic components of the system, overburden pressures, etc.).

(b) To determine if the action leakage rate has been exceeded, the owner or operator must convert the weekly flow rate from the monitoring data obtained under §264.254(c) to an average daily flow rate (gallons per acre per day) for each sump. Unless the Regional Administrator approves a different calculation, the average daily flow rate for each sump must be calculated weekly during the active life and closure period.

[57 FR 3489, Jan. 29, 1992, as amended at 71 FR 40273, July 14, 2006]

§264.253 Response actions.

(a) The owner or operator of waste pile units subject to §264.251 (c) or (d) must have an approved response action plan before receipt of waste. The response action plan must set forth the actions to be taken if the action leakage rate has been exceeded. At a minimum, the response action plan must describe the actions specified in paragraph (b) of this section.

(b) If the flow rate into the leak detection system exceeds the action leakage rate for any sump, the owner or operator must:

(1) Notify the Regional Administrator in writing of the exceedance within 7 days of the determination;

(2) Submit a preliminary written assessment to the Regional Administrator within 14 days of the determination, as to the amount of liquids, likely sources of liquids, possible location, size, and cause of any leaks, and short-term actions taken and planned;

(3) Determine to the extent practicable the location, size, and cause of any leak;

(4) Determine whether waste receipt should cease or be curtailed, whether any waste should be removed from the unit for inspection, repairs, or controls, and whether or not the unit should be closed;

(5) Determine any other short-term and long-term actions to be taken to mitigate or stop any leaks; and

(6) Within 30 days after the notification that the action leakage rate has been exceeded, submit to the Regional Administrator the results of the analyses specified in paragraphs (b) (3), (4), and (5) of this section, the results of actions taken, and actions planned. Monthly thereafter, as long as the flow rate in the leak detection system exceeds the action leakage rate, the owner or operator must submit to the Regional Administrator a report summarizing the results of any remedial actions taken and actions planned.

(c) To make the leak and/or remediation determinations in paragraphs (b) (3), (4), and (5) of this section, the owner or operator must:

(1)(i) Assess the source of liquids and amounts of liquids by source,

(ii) Conduct a fingerprint, hazardous constituent, or other analyses of the liquids in the leak detection system to identify the source of liquids and possible location of any leaks, and the hazard and mobility of the liquid; and

(iii) Assess the seriousness of any leaks in terms of potential for escaping into the environment; or

(2) Document why such assessments are not needed.

[57 FR 3489, Jan. 29, 1992]

§264.254 Monitoring and inspection.

(a) During construction or installation, liners (except in the case of existing portions of piles exempt from §264.251(a)) and cover systems (*e.g.*, membranes, sheets, or coatings) must be inspected for uniformity, damage, and imperfections (*e.g.*, holes, cracks, thin spots, or foreign materials). Immediately after construction or installation:

(1) Synthetic liners and covers must be inspected to ensure tight seams and joints and the absence of tears, punctures, or blisters; and

(2) Soil-based and admixed liners and covers must be inspected for imperfections including lenses, cracks, channels, root holes, or other structural non-uniformities that may cause an increase in the permeability of the liner or cover.

(b) While a waste pile is in operation, it must be inspected weekly and after storms to detect evidence of any of the following:

(1) Deterioration, malfunctions, or improper operation of run-on and run-off control systems;

(2) Proper functioning of wind dispersal control systems, where present; and

(3) The presence of leachate in and proper functioning of leachate collection and removal systems, where present.

(c) An owner or operator required to have a leak detection system under §264.251(c) must record the amount of liquids removed from each leak detection system sump at least once each week during the active life and closure period.

[47 FR 32359, July 26, 1982, as amended at 50 FR 4514, Jan. 31, 1985; 50 FR 28748, July 15, 1985; 57 FR 3489, Jan. 29, 1992]

§264.255 [Reserved]

§264.256 Special requirements for ignitable or reactive waste.

Ignitable or reactive waste must not be placed in a waste pile unless the waste and waste pile satisfy all applicable requirements of 40 CFR part 268, and:

(a) The waste is treated, rendered, or mixed before or immediately after placement in the pile so that:

(1) The resulting waste, mixture, or dissolution of material no longer meets the definition of ignitable or reactive waste under §261.21 or §261.23 of this chapter; and

(2) Section 264.17(b) is complied with; or

(b) The waste is managed in such a way that it is protected from any material or conditions which may cause it to ignite or react.

[47 FR 32359, July 26, 1982, as amended at 55 FR 22685, June 1, 1990]

§264.257 Special requirements for incompatible wastes.

(a) Incompatible wastes, or incompatible wastes and materials, (see appendix V of this part for examples) must not be placed in the same pile, unless §264.17(b) is complied with.

(b) A pile of hazardous waste that is incompatible with any waste or other material stored nearby in containers, other piles, open tanks, or surface impoundments must be separated from the other materials, or protected from them by means of a dike, berm, wall, or other device.

(c) Hazardous waste must not be piled on the same base where incompatible wastes or materials were previously piled, unless the base has been decontaminated sufficiently to ensure compliance with §264.17(b).

§264.258 Closure and post-closure care.

(a) At closure, the owner or operator must remove or decontaminate all waste residues, contaminated containment system components (liners, etc.), contaminated subsoils, and structures and equipment contaminated with waste and leachate, and manage them as hazardous waste unless §261.3(d) of this chapter applies.

(b) If, after removing or decontaminating all residues and making all reasonable efforts to effect removal or decontamination of contaminated components, subsoils, structures, and equipment as required in paragraph (a) of this section, the owner or operator finds that not all contaminated subsoils can be practicably removed or decontaminated, he must close the facility and perform post-closure care in accordance with the closure and post-closure care requirements that apply to landfills (§264.310).

(c)(1) The owner or operator of a waste pile that does not comply with the liner requirements of §264.251(a)(1) and is not exempt from them in accordance with §264.250(c) or §264.251(b), must:

(i) Include in the closure plan for the pile under §264.112 both a plan for complying with paragraph (a) of this section and a contingent plan for complying with paragraph (b) of this section in case not all contaminated subsoils can be practicably removed at closure; and

(ii) Prepare a contingent post-closure plan under §264.118 for complying with paragraph (b) of this section in case not all contaminated subsoils can be practicably removed at closure.

(2) The cost estimates calculated under §§264.142 and 264.144 for closure and post-closure care of a pile subject to this paragraph must include the cost of complying with the contingent closure plan and the contingent post-closure plan, but are not required to include the cost of expected closure under paragraph (a) of this section.

§264.259 Special requirements for hazardous wastes F020, F021, F022, F023, F026, and F027.

(a) Hazardous Wastes F020, F021, F022, F023, F026, and F027 must not be placed in waste piles that are not enclosed (as defined in §264.250(c)) unless the owner or operator operates the waste pile in accordance with a management plan for these wastes that is approved by the Regional Administrator pursuant to the standards set out in this paragraph, and in accord with all other applicable requirements of this part. The factors to be considered are:

(1) The volume, physical, and chemical characteristics of the wastes, including their potential to migrate through soil or to volatilize or escape into the atmosphere;

(2) The attenuative properties of underlying and surrounding soils or other materials;

(3) The mobilizing properties of other materials codisposed with these wastes; and

(4) The effectiveness of additional treatment, design, or monitoring techniques.

(b) The Regional Administrator may determine that additional design, operating, and monitoring requirements are necessary for piles managing hazardous wastes F020, F021, F022, F023, F026, and F027 in order to reduce the possibility of migration of these wastes to ground water, surface water, or air so as to protect human health and the environment.

[50 FR 2004, Jan. 14, 1985, as amended at 71 FR 40273, July 14, 2006]

Subpart M—Land Treatment

Source: 47 FR 32361, July 26, 1982, unless otherwise noted.

§264.270 Applicability.

The regulations in this subpart apply to owners and operators of facilities that treat or dispose of hazardous waste in land treatment units, except as §264.1 provides otherwise.

§264.271 Treatment program.

(a) An owner or operator subject to this subpart must establish a land treatment program that is designed to ensure that hazardous constituents placed in or on the treatment zone are degraded, transformed, or immobilized within the treatment zone. The Regional Administrator will specify in the facility permit the elements of the treatment program, including:

(1) The wastes that are capable of being treated at the unit based on a demonstration under §264.272;

(2) Design measures and operating practices necessary to maximize the success of degradation, transformation, and immobilization processes in the treatment zone in accordance with §264.273(a); and

(3) Unsaturated zone monitoring provisions meeting the requirements of §264.278.

(b) The Regional Administrator will specify in the facility permit the hazardous constituents that must be degraded, transformed, or immobilized under this subpart. Hazardous constituents are constituents identified in appendix VIII of part 261 of this chapter that are reasonably expected to be in, or derived from, waste placed in or on the treatment zone.

(c) The Regional Administrator will specify the vertical and horizontal dimensions of the treatment zone in the facility permit. The treatment zone is the portion of the unsaturated zone below and including the land surface in which the owner or operator intends to maintain the conditions necessary for effective degradation, transformation, or immobilization of hazardous constituents. The maximum depth of the treatment zone must be:

(1) No more than 1.5 meters (5 feet) from the initial soil surface; and

(2) More than 1 meter (3 feet) above the seasonal high water table.

[47 FR 32361, July 26, 1982, as amended at 50 FR 4514, Jan. 31, 1985]

§264.272 Treatment demonstration.

(a) For each waste that will be applied to the treatment zone, the owner or operator must demonstrate, prior to application of the waste, that hazardous constituents in the waste can be completely degraded, transformed, or immobilized in the treatment zone.

(b) In making this demonstration, the owner or operator may use field tests, laboratory analyses, available data, or, in the case of existing units, operating data. If the owner or operator intends to conduct field tests or laboratory analyses in order to make the demonstration required under paragraph (a) of this section, he must obtain a treatment or disposal permit under §270.63. The Regional Administrator will specify in this permit the testing, analytical, design, and operating requirements (including the duration of the tests and analyses, and, in the case of field tests, the horizontal and vertical dimensions of the treatment zone, monitoring procedures, closure and clean-up activities) necessary to meet the requirements in paragraph (c) of this section.

(c) Any field test or laboratory analysis conducted in order to make a demonstration under paragraph (a) of this section must:

(1) Accurately simulate the characteristics and operating conditions for the proposed land treatment unit including:

(i) The characteristics of the waste (including the presence of appendix VIII of part 261 of this chapter constituents);

(ii) The climate in the area;

(iii) The topography of the surrounding area;

(iv) The characteristics of the soil in the treatment zone (including depth); and

(v) The operating practices to be used at the unit.

(2) Be likely to show that hazardous constituents in the waste to be tested will be completely degraded, transformed, or immobilized in the treatment zone of the proposed land treatment unit; and

(3) Be conducted in a manner that protects human health and the environment considering:

(i) The characteristics of the waste to be tested;

(ii) The operating and monitoring measures taken during the course of the test;

(iii) The duration of the test;

(iv) The volume of waste used in the test;

(v) In the case of field tests, the potential for migration of hazardous constituents to ground water or surface water.

[47 FR 32361, July 26, 1982, as amended at 48 FR 14294, Apr. 1, 1983]

§264.273 Design and operating requirements.

The Regional Administrator will specify in the facility permit how the owner or operator will design, construct, operate, and maintain the land treatment unit in compliance with this section.

(a) The owner or operator must design, construct, operate, and maintain the unit to maximize the degradation, transformation, and immobilization of hazardous constituents in the treatment zone. The owner or operator must design, construct, operate, and maintain the unit in accord with all design and operating conditions that were used in the treatment demonstration under §264.272. At a minimum, the Regional Administrator will specify the following in the facility permit:

(1) The rate and method of waste application to the treatment zone;

(2) Measures to control soil pH;

(3) Measures to enhance microbial or chemical reactions (*e.g.*, fertilization, tilling); and

(4) Measures to control the moisture content of the treatment zone.

(b) The owner or operator must design, construct, operate, and maintain the treatment zone to minimize runoff of hazardous constituents during the active life of the land treatment unit.

(c) The owner or operator must design, construct, operate, and maintain a run-on control system capable of preventing flow onto the treatment zone during peak discharge from at least a 25-year storm.

(d) The owner or operator must design, construct, operate, and maintain a run-off management system to collect and control at least the water volume resulting from a 24-hour, 25-year storm.

(e) Collection and holding facilities (*e.g.*, tanks or basins) associated with run-on and run-off control systems must be emptied or otherwise managed expeditiously after storms to maintain the design capacity of the system.

(f) If the treatment zone contains particulate matter which may be subject to wind dispersal, the owner or operator must manage the unit to control wind dispersal.

(g) The owner or operator must inspect the unit weekly and after storms to detect evidence of:

(1) Deterioration, malfunctions, or improper operation of run-on and run-off control systems; and

(2) Improper functioning of wind dispersal control measures.

[47 FR 32361, July 26, 1982, as amended at 50 FR 4514, Jan. 31, 1985]

§§264.274–264.275 [Reserved]

§264.276 Food-chain crops.

The Regional Administrator may allow the growth of food-chain crops in or on the treatment zone only if the owner or operator satisfies the conditions of this section. The Regional Administrator will specify in the facility permit the specific food-chain crops which may be grown.

(a)(1) The owner or operator must demonstrate that there is no substantial risk to human health caused by the growth of such crops in or on the treatment zone by demonstrating, prior to the planting of such crops, that hazardous constituents other than cadmium:

(i) Will not be transferred to the food or feed portions of the crop by plant uptake or direct contact, and will not otherwise be ingested by food-chain animals (*e.g.*, by grazing); or

(ii) Will not occur in greater concentrations in or on the food or feed portions of crops grown on the treatment zone than in or on identical portions of the same crops grown on untreated soils under similar conditions in the same region.

(2) The owner or operator must make the demonstration required under this paragraph prior to the planting of crops at the facility for all constituents identified in appendix VIII of part 261 of this chapter that are reasonably expected to be in, or derived from, waste placed in or on the treatment zone.

(3) In making a demonstration under this paragraph, the owner or operator may use field tests, greenhouse studies, available data, or, in the case of existing units, operating data, and must:

(i) Base the demonstration on conditions similar to those present in the treatment zone, including soil characteristics (*e.g.*, pH, cation exchange capacity), specific wastes, application rates, application methods, and crops to be grown; and

(ii) Describe the procedures used in conducting any tests, including the sample selection criteria, sample size, analytical methods, and statistical procedures.

(4) If the owner or operator intends to conduct field tests or greenhouse studies in order to make the demonstration required under this paragraph, he must obtain a permit for conducting such activities.

(b) The owner or operator must comply with the following conditions if cadmium is contained in wastes applied to the treatment zone:

(1)(i) The pH of the waste and soil mixture must be 6.5 or greater at the time of each waste application, except for waste containing cadmium at concentrations of 2 mg/kg (dry weight) or less;

(ii) The annual application of cadmium from waste must not exceed 0.5 kilograms per hectare (kg/ha) on land used for production of tobacco, leafy vegetables, or root crops grown for human consumption.

For other food-chain crops, the annual cadmium application rate must not exceed:

Time period	Annual Cd application rate (kilograms per hectare)
Present to June 30, 1984	2.0
July 1, 1984 to December 31, 1986	1.25
Beginning January 1, 1987	0.5

(iii) The cumulative application of cadmium from waste must not exceed 5 kg/ha if the waste and soil mixture has a pH of less than 6.5; and

(iv) If the waste and soil mixture has a pH of 6.5 or greater or is maintained at a pH of 6.5 or greater during crop growth, the cumulative application of cadmium from waste must not exceed: 5 kg/ha if soil cation exchange capacity (CEC) is less than 5 meq/100g; 10 kg/ha if soil CEC is 5-15 meq/100g; and 20 kg/ha if soil CEC is greater than 15 meq/100g; or

(2)(i) Animal feed must be the only food-chain crop produced;

(ii) The pH of the waste and soil mixture must be 6.5 or greater at the time of waste application or at the time the crop is planted, whichever occurs later, and this pH level must be maintained whenever food-chain crops are grown;

(iii) There must be an operating plan which demonstrates how the animal feed will be distributed to preclude ingestion by humans. The operating plan must describe the measures to be taken to safeguard against possible health hazards from cadmium entering the food chain, which may result from alternative land uses; and

(iv) Future property owners must be notified by a stipulation in the land record or property deed which states that the property has received waste at high cadmium application rates and that food-chain crops must not be grown except in compliance with paragraph (b)(2) of this section.

§264.277 [Reserved]

§264.278 Unsaturated zone monitoring.

An owner or operator subject to this subpart must establish an unsaturated zone monitoring program to discharge the following responsibilities:

(a) The owner or operator must monitor the soil and soil-pore liquid to determine whether hazardous constituents migrate out of the treatment zone.

(1) The Regional Administrator will specify the hazardous constituents to be monitored in the facility permit. The hazardous constituents to be monitored are those specified under §264.271(b).

(2) The Regional Administrator may require monitoring for principal hazardous constituents (PHCs) in lieu of the constituents specified under §264.271(b). PHCs are hazardous constituents contained in the wastes to be applied at the unit that are the most difficult to treat, considering the combined effects of degradation, transformation, and immobilization. The Regional Administrator will establish PHCs if he finds, based on waste analyses, treatment demonstrations, or other data, that effective degradation, transformation, or immobilization of the PHCs will assure treatment at at least equivalent levels for the other hazardous constituents in the wastes.

(b) The owner or operator must install an unsaturated zone monitoring system that includes soil monitoring using soil cores and soil-pore liquid monitoring using devices such as lysimeters. The unsaturated zone monitoring system must consist of a sufficient number of sampling points at appropriate locations and depths to yield samples that:

(1) Represent the quality of background soil-pore liquid quality and the chemical make-up of soil that has not been affected by leakage from the treatment zone; and

(2) Indicate the quality of soil-pore liquid and the chemical make-up of the soil below the treatment zone.

(c) The owner or operator must establish a background value for each hazardous constituent to be monitored under paragraph (a) of this section. The permit will specify the background values for each constituent or specify the procedures to be used to calculate the background values.

(1) Background soil values may be based on a one-time sampling at a background plot having characteristics similar to those of the treatment zone.

(2) Background soil-pore liquid values must be based on at least quarterly sampling for one year at a background plot having characteristics similar to those of the treatment zone.

(3) The owner or operator must express all background values in a form necessary for the determination of statistically significant increases under paragraph (f) of this section.

(4) In taking samples used in the determination of all background values, the owner or operator must use an unsaturated zone monitoring system that complies with paragraph (b)(1) of this section.

(d) The owner or operator must conduct soil monitoring and soil-pore liquid monitoring immediately below the treatment zone. The Regional Administrator will specify the frequency and timing of soil and soil-pore liquid monitoring in the facility permit after considering the frequency, timing, and rate of waste application, and the soil permeability. The owner or operator must express the results of soil and soil-pore liquid monitoring in a form necessary for the determination of statistically significant increases under paragraph (f) of this section.

(e) The owner or operator must use consistent sampling and analysis procedures that are designed to ensure sampling results that provide a reliable indication of soil-pore liquid quality and the chemical make-up of the soil below the treatment zone. At a minimum, the owner or operator must implement procedures and techniques for:

(1) Sample collection;

(2) Sample preservation and shipment;

(3) Analytical procedures; and

(4) Chain of custody control.

(f) The owner or operator must determine whether there is a statistically significant change over background values for any hazardous constituent to be monitored under paragraph (a) of this section below the treatment zone each time he conducts soil monitoring and soil-pore liquid monitoring under paragraph (d) of this section.

(1) In determining whether a statistically significant increase has occurred, the owner or operator must compare the value of each constituent, as determined under paragraph (d) of this section, to the background value for that constituent according to the statistical procedure specified in the facility permit under this paragraph.

(2) The owner or operator must determine whether there has been a statistically significant increase below the treatment zone within a reasonable time period after completion of sampling. The Regional Administrator will specify that time period in the facility permit after considering the complexity of the statistical test and the availability of laboratory facilities to perform the analysis of soil and soil-pore liquid samples.

(3) The owner or operator must determine whether there is a statistically significant increase below the treatment zone using a statistical procedure that provides reasonable confidence that migration from the treatment zone will be identified. The Regional Administrator will specify a statistical procedure in the facility permit that he finds:

(i) Is appropriate for the distribution of the data used to establish background values; and

(ii) Provides a reasonable balance between the probability of falsely identifying migration from the treatment zone and the probability of failing to identify real migration from the treatment zone.

(g) If the owner or operator determines, pursuant to paragraph (f) of this section, that there is a statistically significant increase of hazardous constituents below the treatment zone, he must:

(1) Notify the Regional Administrator of this finding in writing within seven days. The notification must indicate what constituents have shown statistically significant increases.

(2) Within 90 days, submit to the Regional Administrator an application for a permit modification to modify the operating practices at the facility in order to maximize the success of degradation, transformation, or immobilization processes in the treatment zone.

(h) If the owner or operator determines, pursuant to paragraph (f) of this section, that there is a statistically significant increase of hazardous constituents below the treatment zone, he may demonstrate that a source other than regulated units caused the increase or that the increase resulted from an error in sampling, analysis, or evaluation. While the owner or operator may make a demonstration under this paragraph in addition to, or in lieu of, submitting a permit modification application under paragraph (g)(2) of this section, he is not relieved of the requirement to submit a permit modification application within the time specified in paragraph (g)(2) of this section unless the demonstration made under this paragraph successfully shows that a source other than regulated units caused the increase or that the increase resulted from an error in sampling, analysis, or evaluation. In making a demonstration under this paragraph, the owner or operator must:

(1) Notify the Regional Administrator in writing within seven days of determining a statistically significant increase below the treatment zone that he intends to make a determination under this paragraph;

(2) Within 90 days, submit a report to the Regional Administrator demonstrating that a source other than the regulated units caused the increase or that the increase resulted from error in sampling, analysis, or evaluation;

(3) Within 90 days, submit to the Regional Administrator an application for a permit modification to make any appropriate changes to the unsaturated zone monitoring program at the facility; and

(4) Continue to monitor in accordance with the unsaturated zone monitoring program established under this section.

[47 FR 32361, July 26, 1982, as amended at 50 FR 4514, Jan. 31, 1985]

§264.279 Recordkeeping.

The owner or operator must include hazardous waste application dates and rates in the operating record required under §264.73.

[47 FR 32361, July 26, 1982, as amended at 50 FR 4514, Jan. 31, 1985]

§264.280 Closure and post-closure care.

(a) During the closure period the owner or operator must:

(1) Continue all operations (including pH control) necessary to maximize degradation, transformation, or immobilization of hazardous constituents within the treatment zone as required under §264.273(a), except to the extent such measures are inconsistent with paragraph (a)(8) of this section.

(2) Continue all operations in the treatment zone to minimize run-off of hazardous constituents as required under §264.273(b);

(3) Maintain the run-on control system required under §264.273(c);

(4) Maintain the run-off management system required under §264.273(d);

(5) Control wind dispersal of hazardous waste if required under §264.273(f);

(6) Continue to comply with any prohibitions or conditions concerning growth of food-chain crops under §264.276;

(7) Continue unsaturated zone monitoring in compliance with §264.278, except that soil-pore liquid monitoring may be terminated 90 days after the last application of waste to the treatment zone; and

(8) Establish a vegetative cover on the portion of the facility being closed at such time that the cover will not substantially impede degradation, transformation, or immobilization of hazardous constituents in the treatment zone. The vegetative cover must be capable of maintaining growth without extensive maintenance.

(b) For the purpose of complying with §264.115 of this chapter, when closure is completed the owner or operator may submit to the Regional Administrator certification by an independent, qualified soil scientist, in lieu of a qualified Professional Engineer, that the facility has been closed in accordance with the specifications in the approved closure plan.

(c) During the post-closure care period the owner or operator must:

(1) Continue all operations (including pH control) necessary to enhance degradation and transformation and sustain immobilization of hazardous constituents in the treatment zone to the extent that such measures are consistent with other post-closure care activities;

(2) Maintain a vegetative cover over closed portions of the facility;

(3) Maintain the run-on control system required under §264.273(c);

(4) Maintain the run-off management system required under §264.273(d);

(5) Control wind dispersal of hazardous waste if required under §264.273(f);

(6) Continue to comply with any prohibitions or conditions concerning growth of food-chain crops under §264.276; and

(7) Continue unsaturated zone monitoring in compliance with §264.278, except that soil-pore liquid monitoring may be terminated 90 days after the last application of waste to the treatment zone.

(d) The owner or operator is not subject to regulation under paragraphs (a)(8) and (c) of this section if the Regional Administrator finds that the level of hazardous constituents in the treatment zone soil does not exceed the background value of those constituents by an amount that is statistically significant when using the test specified in paragraph (d)(3) of this section. The owner or operator may submit such a demonstration to the Regional Administrator at any time during the closure or post-closure care periods. For the purposes of this paragraph:

(1) The owner or operator must establish background soil values and determine whether there is a statistically significant increase over those values for all hazardous constituents specified in the facility permit under §264.271 (b).

(i) Background soil values may be based on a one-time sampling of a background plot having characteristics similar to those of the treatment zone.

(ii) The owner or operator must express background values and values for hazardous constituents in the treatment zone in a form necessary for the determination of statistically significant increases under paragraph (d)(3) of this section.

(2) In taking samples used in the determination of background and treatment zone values, the owner or operator must take samples at a sufficient number of sampling points and at appropriate locations and depths to yield samples that represent the chemical make-up of soil that has not been affected by leakage from the treatment zone and the soil within the treatment zone, respectively.

(3) In determining whether a statistically significant increase has occurred, the owner or operator must compare the value of each constituent in the treatment zone to the background value for that constituent using a statistical procedure that provides reasonable confidence that constituent presence in the treatment zone will be identified. The owner or operator must use a statistical procedure that:

(i) Is appropriate for the distribution of the data used to establish background values; and

(ii) Provides a reasonable balance between the probability of falsely identifying hazardous constituent presence in the treatment zone and the probability of failing to identify real presence in the treatment zone.

(e) The owner or operator is not subject to regulation under Subpart F of this chapter if the Regional Administrator finds that the owner or operator satisfies paragraph (d) of this section and if unsaturated zone monitoring under §264.278 indicates that hazardous constituents have not migrated beyond the treatment zone during the active life of the land treatment unit.

[47 FR 32361, July 26, 1982, as amended at 71 FR 16906, Apr. 4, 2006; 71 FR 40273, July 14, 2006]

§264.281 Special requirements for ignitable or reactive waste.

The owner or operator must not apply ignitable or reactive waste to the treatment zone unless the waste and the treatment zone meet all applicable requirements of 40 CFR part 268, and:

(a) The waste is immediately incorporated into the soil so that:

(1) The resulting waste, mixture, or dissolution of material no longer meets the definition of ignitable or reactive waste under §261.21 or §261.23 of this chapter; and

(2) Section 264.17(b) is complied with; or

(b) The waste is managed in such a way that it is protected from any material or conditions which may cause it to ignite or react.

[47 FR 32361, July 26, 1982, as amended at 55 FR 22685, June 1, 1990]

§264.282 Special requirements for incompatible wastes.

The owner or operator must not place incompatible wastes, or incompatible wastes and materials (see appendix V of this part for examples), in or on the same treatment zone, unless §264.17(b) is complied with.

§264.283 Special requirements for hazardous wastes F020, F021, F022, F023, F026, and F027.

(a) Hazardous Wastes F020, F021, F022, F023, F026 and F027 must not be placed in a land treatment unit unless the owner or operator operates the facility in accordance with a management plan for these wastes that is approved by the Regional Administrator pursuant to the standards set out in this paragraph, and in accord with all other applicable requirements of this part. The factors to be considered are:

(1) The volume, physical, and chemical characteristics of the wastes, including their potential to migrate through soil or to volatilize or escape into the atmosphere;

(2) The attenuative properties of underlying and surrounding soils or other materials;

(3) The mobilizing properties of other materials co-disposed with these wastes; and

(4) The effectiveness of additional treatment, design, or monitoring techniques.

(b) The Regional Administrator may determine that additional design, operating, and monitoring requirements are necessary for land treatment facilities managing hazardous wastes F020, F021, F022, F023, F026, and F027 in order to reduce the possibility of migration of these wastes to ground water, surface water, or air so as to protect human health and the environment.

[50 FR 2004, Jan. 14, 1985, as amended at 71 FR 40273, July 14, 2006]

Subpart N—Landfills

Source: 47 FR 32365, July 26, 1982, unless otherwise noted.

§264.300 Applicability.

The regulations in this subpart apply to owners and operators of facilities that dispose of hazardous waste in landfills, except as §264.1 provides otherwise.

§264.301 Design and operating requirements.

(a) Any landfill that is not covered by paragraph (c) of this section or §265.301(a) of this chapter must have a liner system for all portions of the landfill (except for existing portions of such landfill). The liner system must have:

(1) A liner that is designed, constructed, and installed to prevent any migration of wastes out of the landfill to the adjacent subsurface soil or ground water or surface water at anytime during the active life (including the closure period) of the landfill. The liner must be constructed of materials that prevent wastes from passing into the liner during the active life of the facility. The liner must be:

(i) Constructed of materials that have appropriate chemical properties and sufficient strength and thickness to prevent failure due to pressure gradients (including static head and external hydrogeologic forces), physical contact with the waste or leachate to which they are exposed, climatic conditions, the stress of installation, and the stress of daily operation;

(ii) Placed upon a foundation or base capable of providing support to the liner and resistance to pressure gradients above and below the liner to prevent failure of the liner due to settlement, compression, or uplift; and

(iii) Installed to cover all surrounding earth likely to be in contact with the waste or leachate; and

(2) A leachate collection and removal system immediately above the liner that is designed, constructed, maintained, and operated to collect and remove leachate from the landfill. The Regional Administrator will specify design and operating conditions in the permit to ensure that the leachate depth over the liner does not exceed 30 cm (one foot). The leachate collection and removal system must be:

(i) Constructed of materials that are:

(A) Chemically resistant to the waste managed in the landfill and the leachate expected to be generated; and

(B) Of sufficient strength and thickness to prevent collapse under the pressures exerted by overlying wastes, waste cover materials, and by any equipment used at the landfill; and

(ii) Designed and operated to function without clogging through the scheduled closure of the landfill.

(b) The owner or operator will be exempted from the requirements of paragraph (a) of this section if the Regional Administrator finds, based on a demonstration by the owner or operator, that alternative design and operating practices, together with location characteristics, will prevent the migration of any hazardous constituents (see §264.93) into the ground water or surface water at any future time. In deciding whether to grant an exemption, the Regional Administrator will consider:

(1) The nature and quantity of the wastes;

(2) The proposed alternate design and operation;

(3) The hydrogeologic setting of the facility, including the attenuative capacity and thickness of the liners and soils present between the landfill and ground water or surface water; and

(4) All other factors which would influence the quality and mobility of the leachate produced and the potential for it to migrate to ground water or surface water.

(c) The owner or operator of each new landfill unit on which construction commences after January 29, 1992, each lateral expansion of a landfill unit on which construction commences after July 29, 1992, and each replacement of an existing landfill unit that is to commence reuse after July 29, 1992 must install two or more liners and a leachate collection and removal system above and between such liners. "Construction commences" is as defined in §260.10 of this chapter under "existing facility".

(1)(i) The *liner system* must include:

(A) A top liner designed and constructed of materials (*e.g.*, a geomembrane) to prevent the migration of hazardous constituents into such liner during the active life and post-closure care period; and

(B) A composite bottom liner, consisting of at least two components. The upper component must be designed and constructed of materials (*e.g.*, a geomembrane) to prevent the migration of hazardous constituents into this component during the active life and post-closure care period. The lower component must be designed and constructed of materials to minimize the migration of hazardous constituents if a breach in the upper component were to occur. The lower component must be constructed of at least 3 feet (91 cm) of compacted soil material with a hydraulic conductivity of no more than 1×10^{-7} cm/sec.

(ii) The liners must comply with paragraphs (a)(1)(i), (ii), and (iii) of this section.

(2) The *leachate collection and removal system* immediately above the top liner must be designed, constructed, operated, and maintained to collect and remove leachate from the landfill during the active life and post-closure care period. The Regional Administrator will specify design and operating conditions in the permit to ensure that the leachate depth over the liner does not exceed 30 cm (one foot). The leachate collection and removal system must comply with paragraphs (c)(3) (iii) and (iv) of this section.

(3) The *leachate collection and removal system* between the liners, and immediately above the bottom composite liner in the case of multiple leachate collection and removal systems, is also a *leak detection system*. This leak detection system must be capable of detecting, collecting, and removing leaks of hazardous constituents at the earliest practicable time through all areas of the top liner likely to be exposed to waste or leachate during the active life and post-closure care period. The requirements for a leak detection system in this paragraph are satisfied by installation of a system that is, at a minimum:

(i) Constructed with a bottom slope of one percent or more;

(ii) Constructed of granular drainage materials with a hydraulic conductivity of 1×10^{-2} cm/sec or more and a thickness of 12 inches (30.5 cm) or more; or constructed of synthetic or geonet drainage materials with a transmissivity of 3×10^{-5} m^2/sec or more;

(iii) Constructed of materials that are chemically resistant to the waste managed in the landfill and the leachate expected to be generated, and of sufficient strength and thickness to prevent collapse under the pressures exerted by overlying wastes, waste cover materials, and equipment used at the landfill;

(iv) Designed and operated to minimize clogging during the active life and post-closure care period; and

(v) Constructed with sumps and liquid removal methods (*e.g.*, pumps) of sufficient size to collect and remove liquids from the sump and prevent liquids from backing up into the drainage layer. Each unit must have its own sump(s). The design of each sump and removal system must provide a method for measuring and recording the volume of liquids present in the sump and of liquids removed. 📖 10.2.3–4

(4) The owner or operator shall collect and remove pumpable liquids in the leak detection system sumps to minimize the head on the bottom liner.

(5) The owner or operator of a leak detection system that is not located completely above the seasonal high water table must demonstrate that the operation of the leak detection system will not be adversely affected by the presence of ground water.

(d) The Regional Administrator may approve alternative design or operating practices to those specified in paragraph (c) of this section if the owner or operator demonstrates to the Regional Administrator that such design and operating practices, together with location characteristics:

(1) Will prevent the migration of any hazardous constituent into the ground water or surface water at least as effectively as the liners and leachate collection and removal systems specified in paragraph (c) of this section; and

(2) Will allow detection of leaks of hazardous constituents through the top liner at least as effectively.

(e) The double liner requirement set forth in paragraph (c) of this section may be waived by the Regional Administrator for any monofill, if:

(1) The monofill contains only hazardous wastes from foundry furnace emission controls or metal casting molding sand, and such wastes do not contain constituents which would render the wastes hazardous for reasons other than the Toxicity Characteristic in §261.24 of this chapter, with EPA Hazardous Waste Numbers D004 through D017; and

(2)(i)(A) The monofill has at least one liner for which there is no evidence that such liner is leaking;

(B) The monofill is located more than one-quarter mile from an "underground source of drinking water" (as that term is defined in 40 CFR 270.2); and

(C) The monofill is in compliance with generally applicable ground-water monitoring requirements for facilities with permits under RCRA 3005(c); or

(ii) The owner or operator demonstrates that the monofill is located, designed and operated so as to assure that there will be no migration of any hazardous constituent into ground water or surface water at any future time.

(f) The owner or operator of any replacement landfill unit is exempt from paragraph (c) of this section if:

(1) The existing unit was constructed in compliance with the design standards of section 3004(o)(1)(A)(i) and (o)(5) of the Resource Conservation and Recovery Act; and

(2) There is no reason to believe that the liner is not functioning as designed.

(g) The owner or operator must design, construct, operate, and maintain a run-on control system capable of preventing flow onto the active portion of the landfill during peak discharge from at least a 25-year storm.

(h) The owner or operator must design, construct, operate, and maintain a run-off management system to collect and control at least the water volume resulting from a 24-hour, 25-year storm.

(i) Collection and holding facilities (*e.g.*, tanks or basins) associated with run-on and run-off control systems must be emptied or otherwise managed expeditiously after storms to maintain design capacity of the system.

(j) If the landfill contains any particulate matter which may be subject to wind dispersal, the owner or operator must cover or otherwise manage the landfill to control wind dispersal.

(k) The Regional Administrator will specify in the permit all design and operating practices that are necessary to ensure that the requirements of this section are satisfied.

(l) Any permit under RCRA 3005(c) which is issued for a landfill located within the State of Alabama shall require the installation of two or more liners and a leachate collection system above and between such liners, notwithstanding any other provision of RCRA.

[47 FR 32365, July 26, 1982, as amended at 50 FR 4514, Jan. 31, 1985; 50 FR 28748, July 15, 1985; 55 FR 11875, Mar. 29, 1990; 57 FR 3489, Jan. 29, 1992; 71 FR 40273, July 14, 2006]

§264.302 Action leakage rate.

(a) The Regional Administrator shall approve an action leakage rate for landfill units subject to §264.301(c) or (d). The action leakage rate is the maximum design flow rate that the leak detection system (LDS) can remove without the fluid head on the bottom liner exceeding 1 foot. The action leakage rate must include an adequate safety margin to allow for uncertainties in the design (*e.g.*, slope, hydraulic conductivity, thickness of drainage material), construction, operation, and location of the LDS, waste and leachate characteristics, likelihood and amounts of other sources of liquids in the LDS, and proposed response actions (*e.g.*, the action leakage rate must consider decreases in the flow capacity of the system over time resulting from siltation and clogging, rib layover and creep of synthetic components of the system, overburden pressures, etc.).

(b) To determine if the action leakage rate has been exceeded, the owner or operator must convert the weekly or monthly flow rate from the monitoring data obtained under §264.303(c) to an average daily flow rate (gallons per acre per day) for each sump. Unless the Regional Administrator approves a different calculation, the average daily flow rate for each sump must be calculated weekly during the active life and closure period, and monthly during the post-closure care period when monthly monitoring is required under §264.303(c).

[57 FR 3490, Jan. 29, 1992, as amended at 71 FR 40273, July 14, 2006]

§264.303 Monitoring and inspection.

(a) During construction or installation, liners (except in the case of existing portions of landfills exempt from §264.301(a)) and cover systems (*e.g.*, membranes, sheets, or coatings) must be inspected for uniformity, damage, and imperfections (*e.g.*, holes, cracks, thin spots, or foreign materials). Immediately after construction or installation:

(1) Synthetic liners and covers must be inspected to ensure tight seams and joints and the absence of tears, punctures, or blisters; and

(2) Soil-based and admixed liners and covers must be inspected for imperfections including lenses, cracks, channels, root holes, or other structural non-uniformities that may cause an increase in the permeability of the liner or cover.

(b) While a landfill is in operation, it must be inspected weekly and after storms to detect evidence of any of the following:

(1) Deterioration, malfunctions, or improper operation of run-on and run-off control systems;

(2) Proper functioning of wind dispersal control systems, where present; and

(3) The presence of leachate in and proper functioning of leachate collection and removal systems, where present.

(c)(1) An owner or operator required to have a leak detection system under §264.301(c) or (d) must record the amount of liquids removed from each leak detection system sump at least once each week during the active life and closure period.

(2) After the final cover is installed, the amount of liquids removed from each leak detection system sump must be recorded at least monthly. If the liquid level in

the sump stays below the pump operating level for two consecutive months, the amount of liquids in the sumps must be recorded at least quarterly. If the liquid level in the sump stays below the pump operating level for two consecutive quarters, the amount of liquids in the sumps must be recorded at least semi-annually. If at any time during the post-closure care period the pump operating level is exceeded at units on quarterly or semi-annual recording schedules, the owner or operator must return to monthly recording of amounts of liquids removed from each sump until the liquid level again stays below the pump operating level for two consecutive months.

(3) "Pump operating level" is a liquid level proposed by the owner or operator and approved by the Regional Administrator based on pump activation level, sump dimensions, and level that avoids backup into the drainage layer and minimizes head in the sump.

[47 FR 32365, July 26, 1982, as amended at 50 FR 28748, July 15, 1985; 57 FR 3490, Jan. 29, 1992]

§264.304 Response actions.

(a) The owner or operator of landfill units subject to §264.301(c) or (d) must have an approved response action plan before receipt of waste. The response action plan must set forth the actions to be taken if the action leakage rate has been exceeded. At a minimum, the response action plan must describe the actions specified in paragraph (b) of this section.

(b) If the flow rate into the leak detection system exceeds the action leakage rate for any sump, the owner or operator must:

(1) Notify the Regional Administrator in writing of the exceedance within 7 days of the determination;

(2) Submit a preliminary written assessment to the Regional Administrator within 14 days of the determination, as to the amount of liquids, likely sources of liquids, possible location, size, and cause of any leaks, and short-term actions taken and planned;

(3) Determine to the extent practicable the location, size, and cause of any leak;

(4) Determine whether waste receipt should cease or be curtailed, whether any waste should be removed from the unit for inspection, repairs, or controls, and whether or not the unit should be closed;

(5) Determine any other short-term and longer-term actions to be taken to mitigate or stop any leaks; and

(6) Within 30 days after the notification that the action leakage rate has been exceeded, submit to the Regional Administrator the results of the analyses specified in paragraphs (b)(3), (4), and (5) of this section, the results of actions taken, and actions planned. Monthly thereafter, as long as the flow rate in the leak detection system exceeds the action leakage rate, the owner or operator must submit to the Regional Administrator a report summarizing the results of any remedial actions taken and actions planned.

(c) To make the leak and/or remediation determinations in paragraphs (b)(3), (4), and (5) of this section, the owner or operator must:

(1)(i) Assess the source of liquids and amounts of liquids by source,

(ii) Conduct a fingerprint, hazardous constituent, or other analyses of the liquids in the leak detection system to identify the source of liquids and possible location of any leaks, and the hazard and mobility of the liquid; and

(iii) Assess the seriousness of any leaks in terms of potential for escaping into the environment; or

(2) Document why such assessments are not needed.

[57 FR 3491, Jan. 29, 1992, as amended at 71 FR 40273, July 14, 2006]

§§264.305–264.308 [Reserved]

§264.309 Surveying and recordkeeping.

The owner or operator of a landfill must maintain the following items in the operating record required under §264.73:

(a) On a map, the exact location and dimensions, including depth, of each cell with respect to permanently surveyed benchmarks; and

(b) The contents of each cell and the approximate location of each hazardous waste type within each cell.

[47 FR 32365, July 26, 1982, as amended at 50 FR 4514, Jan. 31, 1985]

§264.310 Closure and post-closure care.

(a) At final closure of the landfill or upon closure of any cell, the owner or operator must cover the landfill or cell with a final cover designed and constructed to:

(1) Provide long-term minimization of migration of liquids through the closed landfill;

(2) Function with minimum maintenance;

(3) Promote drainage and minimize erosion or abrasion of the cover;

(4) Accommodate settling and subsidence so that the cover's integrity is maintained; and

(5) Have a permeability less than or equal to the permeability of any bottom liner system or natural subsoils present.

(b) After final closure, the owner or operator must comply with all post-closure requirements contained in §§264.117 through 264.120, including maintenance and monitoring throughout the post-closure care period (specified in the permit under §264.117). The owner or operator must:

(1) Maintain the integrity and effectiveness of the final cover, including making repairs to the cap as necessary to correct the effects of settling, subsidence, erosion, or other events;

(2) Continue to operate the leachate collection and removal system until leachate is no longer detected;

(3) Maintain and monitor the leak detection system in accordance with §§264.301(c)(3)(iv) and (4) and 264.303(c), and comply with all other applicable leak detection system requirements of this part;

(4) Maintain and monitor the ground-water monitoring system and comply with all other applicable requirements of subpart F of this part;

(5) Prevent run-on and run-off from eroding or otherwise damaging the final cover; and

(6) Protect and maintain surveyed benchmarks used in complying with §264.309.

[47 FR 32365, July 26, 1982, as amended at 50 FR 28748, July 15, 1985; 57 FR 3491, Jan. 29, 1992]

§264.311 [Reserved]

§264.312 Special requirements for ignitable or reactive waste.

(a) Except as provided in paragraph (b) of this section, and in §264.316, ignitable or reactive waste must not be placed in a landfill, unless the waste and landfill meet all applicable requirements of part 268, and:

(1) The resulting waste, mixture, or dissolution of material no longer meets the definition of ignitable or reactive waste under §261.21 or §261.23 of this chapter; and

(2) Section 264.17(b) is complied with.

(b) Except for prohibited wastes which remain subject to treatment standards in subpart D of part 268, ignitable wastes in containers may be landfilled without meeting the requirements of paragraph (a) of this section, provided that the wastes are disposed of in such a way that they are protected from any material or conditions which may cause them to ignite. At a minimum, ignitable wastes must be disposed of in non-leaking containers which are carefully handled and placed so as to avoid heat, sparks, rupture, or any other condition that might cause ignition of the wastes; must be covered daily with soil or other non-combustible material to minimize the potential for ignition of the wastes; and must not be disposed of in cells that contain or will contain other wastes which may generate heat sufficient to cause ignition of the waste.

[47 FR 32365, July 26, 1982, as amended at 55 FR 22685, June 1, 1990]

§264.313 Special requirements for incompatible wastes.

Incompatible wastes, or incompatible wastes and materials, (see appendix V of this part for examples) must not be placed in the same landfill cell, unless §264.17(b) is complied with.

§264.314 Special requirements for bulk and containerized liquids. 📖 7.5.3

(a) The placement of bulk or noncontainerized liquid hazardous waste or hazardous waste containing free liquids (whether or not sorbents have been added) in any landfill is prohibited.

(b) To demonstrate the absence or presence of free liquids in either a containerized or a bulk waste, the following test must be used: Method 9095B (Paint Filter Liquids Test) as described in "Test Methods for Evaluating Solid Waste, Physical/Chemical Methods," EPA Publication SW–846, as incorporated by reference in §260.11 of this chapter.

(c) Containers holding free liquids must not be placed in a landfill unless: 📖 9.1.2.4

(1) All free-standing liquid:

(i) Has been removed by decanting, or other methods;

(ii) Has been mixed with sorbent or solidified so that free-standing liquid is no longer observed; or

(iii) Has been otherwise eliminated; or

(2) The container is very small, such as an ampule; or

(3) The container is designed to hold free liquids for use other than storage, such as a battery or capacitor; or

(4) The container is a lab pack as defined in §264.316 and is disposed of in accordance with §264.316. 📖 9.7, 13.13.1

(d) Sorbents used to treat free liquids to be disposed of in landfills must be nonbiodegradable. Nonbiodegradable sorbents are: materials listed or described in paragraph (e)(1) of this section; materials that pass one of the tests in paragraph (e)(2) of this section; or materials that are determined by EPA to be nonbiodegradable through the part 260 petition process.

Publisher's Note: The references to "paragraph (e)(1)" and "paragraph (e)(2)" in the above paragraph are incorrect and should refer to "paragraph (d)(1)" and "paragraph (d)(2)".

(1) Nonbiodegradable sorbents. (i) Inorganic minerals, other inorganic materials, and elemental carbon (*e.g.*, aluminosilicates, clays, smectites, Fuller's earth, bentonite, calcium bentonite, montmorillonite, calcined montmorillonite, kaolinite, micas (illite), vermiculites, zeolites; calcium carbonate (organic free limestone); oxides/hydroxides, alumina, lime, silica (sand), diatomaceous earth; perlite (volcanic glass); expanded volcanic rock; volcanic ash; cement kiln dust; fly ash; rice hull ash; activated charcoal/activated carbon); or

(ii) High molecular weight synthetic polymers (*e.g.*, polyethylene, high density polyethylene (HDPE), polypropylene, polystyrene, polyurethane, polyacrylate, polynorborene, polyisobutylene, ground synthetic rubber, cross-linked allylstyrene and tertiary butyl copolymers). This does not include polymers derived from biological material or polymers specifically designed to be degradable; or

(iii) Mixtures of these nonbiodegradable materials.

(2) Tests for nonbiodegradable sorbents. (i) The sorbent material is determined to be nonbiodegradable under ASTM Method G21-70 (1984a)—Standard Practice for Determining Resistance of Synthetic Polymer Materials to Fungi; or

(ii) The sorbent material is determined to be nonbiodegradable under ASTM Method G22-76 (1984b)—Standard Practice for Determining Resistance of Plastics to Bacteria; or

(iii) The sorbent material is determined to be nonbiodegradable under OECD test 301B: [CO_2 Evolution (Modified Sturm Test)].

(e) The placement of any liquid which is not a hazardous waste in a landfill is prohibited unless the owner or operator of such landfill demonstrates to the Regional Administrator, or the Regional Administrator determines that:

(1) The only reasonably available alternative to the placement in such landfill is placement in a landfill or unlined surface impoundment, whether or not permitted or operating under interim status, which contains, or may reasonably be anticipated to contain, hazardous waste; and

(2) Placement in such owner or operator's landfill will not present a risk of contamination of any "underground source of drinking water" (as that term is defined in 40 CFR 270.2).

[47 FR 32365, July 26, 1982, as amended at 50 FR 18374, Apr. 30, 1985; 50 FR 28748, July 15, 1985; 57 FR 54460, Nov. 18, 1992; 58 FR 46050, Aug. 31, 1993; 60 FR 35705, July 11, 1995; 70 FR 34581, June 14, 2005; 71 FR 16906, Apr. 4, 2006; 71 FR 40273, July 14, 2006]

§264.315 Special requirements for containers.

Unless they are very small, such as an ampule, containers must be either:

(a) At least 90 percent full when placed in the landfill; or

(b) Crushed, shredded, or similarly reduced in volume to the maximum practical extent before burial in the landfill.

§264.316 Disposal of small containers of hazardous waste in overpacked drums (lab packs).

📖 9.7

Small containers of hazardous waste in overpacked drums (lab packs) may be placed in a landfill if the following requirements are met:

(a) Hazardous waste must be packaged in non-leaking inside containers. The inside containers must be of a design and constructed of a material that will not react dangerously with, be decomposed by, or be ignited by the contained waste. Inside containers must be tightly and securely sealed. The inside containers must be of the size and type specified in the Department of Transportation (DOT) hazardous materials regulations (49 CFR parts 173, 178, and 179), if those regulations specify a particular inside container for the waste.

(b) The inside containers must be overpacked in an open head DOT-specification metal shipping container (49 CFR parts 178 and 179) of no more than 416-liter (110 gallon) capacity and surrounded by, at a minimum, a sufficient quantity of sorbent material, determined to be nonbiodegradable in accordance with §264.314(e), to completely sorb all of the liquid contents of the inside containers. The metal outer container must be full after it has been packed with inside containers and sorbent material.

Publisher's Note: The above reference to §264.314(e) is incorrect and should refer to §264.314(d).

(c) The sorbent material used must not be capable of reacting dangerously with, being decomposed by, or being ignited by the contents of the inside containers, in accordance with §264.17(b).

(d) Incompatible wastes, as defined in §260.10 of this chapter, must not be placed in the same outside container.

(e) Reactive wastes, other than cyanide- or sulfide-bearing waste as defined in §261.23(a)(5) of this chapter, must be treated or rendered non-reactive prior to packaging in accordance with paragraphs (a) through (d) of this section. Cyanide- and sulfide-bearing reactive waste may be packed in accordance with paragraphs (a) through (d) of this section without first being treated or rendered non-reactive.

(f) Such disposal is in compliance with the requirements of part 268. Persons who incinerate lab packs according to the requirements in 40 CFR 268.42(c)(1) may use fiber drums in place of metal outer containers. Such fiber drums must meet the DOT specifications in 49 CFR 173.12 and be overpacked according to the requirements in paragraph (b) of this section.

13.13.1

[47 FR 32365, July 26, 1982, as amended at 55 FR 22685, June 1, 1990; 57 FR 54460, Nov. 18, 1992]

§264.317 Special requirements for hazardous wastes F020, F021, F022, F023, F026, and F027.

(a) Hazardous Wastes F020, F021, F022, F023, F026, and F027 must not be placed in a landfill unless the owner or operator operates the landfill in accord with a management plan for these wastes that is approved by the Regional Administrator pursuant to the standards set out in this paragraph, and in accord with all other applicable requirements of this part. The factors to be considered are:

(1) The volume, physical, and chemical characteristics of the wastes, including their potential to migrate through the soil or to volatilize or escape into the atmosphere;

(2) The attenuative properties of underlying and surrounding soils or other materials;

(3) The mobilizing properties of other materials co-disposed with these wastes; and

(4) The effectiveness of additional treatment, design, or monitoring requirements.

(b) The Regional Administrator may determine that additional design, operating, and monitoring requirements are necessary for landfills managing hazardous wastes F020, F021, F022, F023, F026, and F027 in order to reduce the possibility of migration of these wastes to ground water, surface water, or air so as to protect human health and the environment.

[50 FR 2004, Jan. 14, 1985, as amended at 71 FR 40273, July 14, 2006]

Subpart O—Incinerators

§264.340 Applicability.

(a) The regulations of this subpart apply to owners and operators of hazardous waste incinerators (as defined in §260.10 of this chapter), except as §264.1 provides otherwise.

(b) *Integration of the MACT standards.* (1) Except as provided by paragraphs (b)(2) through (b)(4) of this section, the standards of this part do not apply to a new hazardous waste incineration unit that becomes subject to RCRA permit requirements after October 12, 2005; or no longer apply when an owner or operator of an existing hazardous waste incineration unit demonstrates compliance with the maximum achievable control technology (MACT) requirements of part 63, subpart EEE, of this chapter by conducting a comprehensive performance test and submitting to the Administrator a Notification of Compliance under §§63.1207(j) and 63.1210(d) of this chapter documenting compliance with the requirements of part 63, subpart EEE, of this chapter. Nevertheless, even after this demonstration of compliance with the MACT standards, RCRA permit conditions that were based on the standards of this part will continue to be in effect until they are removed from the permit or the permit is terminated or revoked, unless the permit expressly provides otherwise.

(2) The MACT standards do not replace the closure requirements of §264.351 or the applicable requirements of subparts A through H, BB and CC of this part.

(3) The particulate matter standard of §264.343(c) remains in effect for incinerators that elect to comply with the alternative to the particulate matter standard under §§63.1206(b)(14) and 63.1219(e) of this chapter.

(4) The following requirements remain in effect for startup, shutdown, and malfunction events if you elect to comply with §270.235(a)(1)(i) of this chapter to minimize emissions of toxic compounds from these events:

(i) Section 264.345(a) requiring that an incinerator operate in accordance with operating requirements specified in the permit; and

(ii) Section 264.345(c) requiring compliance with the emission standards and operating requirements during startup and shutdown if hazardous waste is in the combustion chamber, except for particular hazardous wastes.

(c) After consideration of the waste analysis included with part B of the permit application, the Regional Administrator, in establishing the permit conditions, must exempt the applicant from all requirements of this subpart except §264.341 (Waste analysis) and §264.351 (Closure),

(1) If the Regional Administrator finds that the waste to be burned is:

(i) Listed as a hazardous waste in part 261, subpart D, of this chapter solely because it is ignitable (Hazard Code I), corrosive (Hazard Code C), or both; or

(ii) Listed as a hazardous waste in part 261, subpart D, of this chapter solely because it is reactive (Hazard Code R) for characteristics other than those listed in §261.23(a) (4) and (5), and will not be burned when other hazardous wastes are present in the combustion zone; or

(iii) A hazardous waste solely because it possesses the characteristic of ignitability, corrosivity, or both, as determined by the test for characteristics of hazardous wastes under part 261, subpart C, of this chapter; or

(iv) A hazardous waste solely because it possesses any of the reactivity characteristics described by §261.23(a)(1), (2), (3), (6), (7), and (8) of this chapter, and will not be burned when other hazardous wastes are present in the combustion zone; and

(2) If the waste analysis shows that the waste contains none of the hazardous constituents listed in part 261, appendix VIII, of this chapter, which would reasonably be expected to be in the waste.

(d) If the waste to be burned is one which is described by paragraphs (b)(1)(i), (ii), (iii), or (iv) of this section and contains insignificant concentrations of the hazardous constituents listed in part 261, appendix VIII, of this chapter, then the Regional Administrator may, in establishing permit conditions, exempt the applicant from all requirements of this subpart, except §264.341 (Waste analysis) and §264.351 (Closure), after consideration of the waste analysis included with part B of the permit application, unless the Regional Administrator finds that the waste will pose a threat to human health and the environment when burned in an incinerator.

Publisher's Note: The above reference to "paragraphs (b)(1)(i), (ii), (iii), or (iv)" is incorrect and should refer to "paragraphs (c)(1)(i), (ii), (iii), (iv)".

(e) The owner or operator of an incinerator may conduct trial burns subject only to the requirements of §270.62 of this chapter (Short term and incinerator permits).

[46 FR 7678, Jan. 23, 1981, as amended at 47 FR 27532, June 24, 1982; 48 FR 14295, Apr. 1, 1983; 50 FR 665, Jan. 4, 1985; 50 FR 49203, Nov. 29, 1985; 56 FR 7207, Feb. 21, 1991; 64 FR 53074, Sept. 30, 1999; 66 FR 35106, July 3, 2001; 67 FR 6815, Feb. 13, 2002; 70 FR 59575, Oct. 12, 2005; 73 FR 18983, Apr. 8, 2008]

§264.341 Waste analysis.

(a) As a portion of the trial burn plan required by §270.62 of this chapter, or with part B of the permit application, the owner or operator must have included an analysis of the waste feed sufficient to provide all information required by §270.62(b) or §270.19 of this chapter. Owners or operators of new hazardous waste incinerators must provide the information required by §270.62(c) or §270.19 of this chapter to the greatest extent possible.

(b) Throughout normal operation the owner or operator must conduct sufficient waste analysis to verify that waste feed to the incinerator is within the physical and chemical composition limits specified in his permit (under §264.345(b)).

[46 FR 7678, Jan. 23, 1981, as amended at 47 FR 27532, June 24, 1982; 48 FR 14295, Apr. 1, 1983; 48 FR 30115, June 30, 1983; 50 FR 4514, Jan. 31, 1985]

§264.342 Principal organic hazardous constituents (POHCs).

(a) Principal Organic Hazardous Constituents (POHCs) in the waste feed must be treated to the extent required by the performance standard of §264.343.

(b)(1) One or more POHCs will be specified in the facility's permit, from among those constituents listed in part 261, appendix VIII of this chapter, for each waste feed to be burned. This specification will be based on the degree of difficulty of incineration of the organic constituents in the waste and on their concentration or mass in the waste feed, considering the results of waste analyses and trial burns or alternative data submitted with part B of the facility's permit application. Organic constituents which represent the greatest degree of difficulty of incineration will be those most likely to be designated as POHCs. Constituents are more likely to be designated as POHCs if they are present in large quantities or concentrations in the waste.

(2) Trial POHCs will be designated for performance of trial burns in accordance with the procedure specified in §270.62 of this chapter for obtaining trial burn permits.

[46 FR 7678, Jan. 23, 1981, as amended at 48 FR 14295, Apr. 1, 1983]

§264.343 Performance standards.

An incinerator burning hazardous waste must be designed, constructed, and maintained so that, when operated in accordance with operating requirements specified under §264.345, it will meet the following performance standards:

(a)(1) Except as provided in paragraph (a)(2) of this section, an incinerator burning hazardous waste must achieve a destruction and removal efficiency (DRE) of 99.99% for each principal organic hazardous constituent (POHC) designated (under §264.342) in its permit for each waste feed. DRE is determined for each POHC from the following equation:

$$DRE = \frac{(W_{in} - W_{out})}{W_{in}} \times 100\%$$

where:

W_{in} = mass feed rate of one principal organic hazardous constituent (POHC) in the waste stream feeding the incinerator

and

W_{out} = mass emission rate of the same POHC present in exhaust emissions prior to release to the atmosphere.

(2) An incinerator burning hazardous wastes F020, F021, F022, F023, F026, or F027 must achieve a destruction and removal efficiency (DRE) of 99.9999% for each principal organic hazardous constituent (POHC) designated (under §264.342) in its permit. This performance must be demonstrated on POHCs that are more difficult to incinerate than tetra-, penta-, and hexachlorodibenzo-p-dioxins and dibenzofurans. DRE is determined for each POHC from the equation in §264.343(a)(1).

(b) An incinerator burning hazardous waste and producing stack emissions of more than 1.8 kilograms per hour (4 pounds per hour) of hydrogen chloride (HCl) must control HCl emissions such that the rate of emission is no greater than the larger of either 1.8 kilograms per hour or 1% of the HCl in the stack gas prior to entering any pollution control equipment.

(c) An incinerator burning hazardous waste must not emit particulate matter in excess of 180 milligrams per dry standard cubic meter (0.08 grains per dry standard cubic foot) when corrected for the amount of oxygen in the stack gas according to the formula:

$$P_c = P_m \times \frac{14}{21 - Y}$$

Where P_c is the corrected concentration of particulate matter, P_m is the measured concentration of particulate matter, and Y is the measured concentration of oxygen in the stack gas, using the Orsat method for oxygen analysis of dry flue gas, presented in part 60, appendix A (Method 3), of this chapter. This correction procedure is to be used by all hazardous waste incinerators except those operating under conditions of oxygen enrichment. For these facilities, the Regional Administrator will select an appropriate correction procedure, to be specified in the facility permit.

(d) For purposes of permit enforcement, compliance with the operating requirements specified in the permit (under §264.345) will be regarded as compliance with this section. However, evidence that compliance with those permit conditions is insufficient to ensure compliance with the performance requirements of this section may be "information" justifying modification, revocation, or reissuance of a permit under §270.41 of this chapter.

[46 FR 7678, Jan. 23, 1981, as amended at 47 FR 27532, June 24, 1982; 48 FR 14295, Apr. 1, 1983; 50 FR 2005, Jan. 14, 1985; 71 FR 16906, Apr. 4, 2006]

§264.344 Hazardous waste incinerator permits.

(a) The owner or operator of a hazardous waste incinerator may burn only wastes specified in his permit and only under operating conditions specified for those wastes under §264.345, except:

(1) In approved trial burns under §270.62 of this chapter; or

(2) Under exemptions created by §264.340.

(b) Other hazardous wastes may be burned only after operating conditions have been specified in a new permit or a permit modification as applicable. Operating requirements for new wastes may be based on either trial burn results or alternative data included with part B of a permit application under §270.19 of this chapter.

(c) The permit for a new hazardous waste incinerator must establish appropriate conditions for each of the applicable requirements of this subpart, including but not limited to allowable waste feeds and operating conditions necessary to meet the requirements of §264.345, sufficient to comply with the following standards:

(1) For the period beginning with initial introduction of hazardous waste to the incinerator and ending with initiation of the trial burn, and only for the minimum time required to establish operating conditions required in paragraph (c)(2) of this section, not to exceed a duration of 720 hours operating time for treatment of hazardous waste, the operating requirements must be those most likely to ensure compliance with the performance standards of §264.343, based on the Regional Administrator's engineering judgment. The Regional Administrator may extend the duration of this period once for up to 720 additional hours when good cause for the extension is demonstrated by the applicant.

(2) For the duration of the trial burn, the operating requirements must be sufficient to demonstrate compliance with the performance standards of §264.343 and must be in accordance with the approved trial burn plan;

(3) For the period immediately following completion of the trial burn, and only for the minimum period sufficient to allow sample analysis, data computation, and submission of the trial burn results by the applicant, and review of the trial burn results and modification of the facility permit by the Regional Administrator, the operating requirements must be those most likely to ensure compliance with the performance standards of §264.343, based on the Regional Administrator's engineering judgement.

(4) For the remaining duration of the permit, the operating requirements must be those demonstrated, in a trial burn or by alternative data specified in §270.19(c) of this chapter, as sufficient to ensure compliance with the performance standards of §264.343.

[46 FR 7678, Jan. 23, 1981, as amended at 47 FR 27532, June 24, 1982; 48 FR 14295, Apr. 1, 1983; 50 FR 4514, Jan. 31, 1985; 71 FR 40273, July 14, 2006]

§264.345 Operating requirements.

(a) An incinerator must be operated in accordance with operating requirements specified in the permit. These will be specified on a case-by-case basis as those demonstrated (in a trial burn or in alternative data as specified in §264.344(b) and included with part B of a facility's permit application) to be sufficient to comply with the performance standards of §264.343.

(b) Each set of operating requirements will specify the composition of the waste feed (including acceptable variations in the physical or chemical properties of the waste feed which will not affect compliance with the performance requirement of §264.343) to which the operating requirements apply. For each such waste feed, the permit will specify acceptable operating limits including the following conditions:

(1) Carbon monoxide (CO) level in the stack exhaust gas;

(2) Waste feed rate;

(3) Combustion temperature;

(4) An appropriate indicator of combustion gas velocity;

(5) Allowable variations in incinerator system design or operating procedures; and

(6) Such other operating requirements as are necessary to ensure that the performance standards of §264.343 are met.

(c) During start-up and shut-down of an incinerator, hazardous waste (except wastes exempted in accordance with §264.340) must not be fed into the incinerator unless the incinerator is operating within the conditions of operation (temperature, air feed rate, etc.) specified in the permit.

(d) Fugitive emissions from the combustion zone must be controlled by:

(1) Keeping the combustion zone totally sealed against fugitive emissions; or

(2) Maintaining a combustion zone pressure lower than atmospheric pressure; or

(3) An alternate means of control demonstrated (with part B of the permit application) to provide fugitive emissions control equivalent to maintenance of combustion zone pressure lower than atmospheric pressure.

(e) An incinerator must be operated with a functioning system to automatically cut off waste feed to the incinerator when operating conditions deviate from limits established under paragraph (a) of this section.

(f) An incinerator must cease operation when changes in waste feed, incinerator design, or operating conditions exceed limits designated in its permit.

[46 FR 7678, Jan. 23, 1981, as amended at 47 FR 27532, June 24, 1982; 50 FR 4514, Jan. 31, 1985]

§264.346 [Reserved]

§264.347 Monitoring and inspections.

(a) The owner or operator must conduct, as a minimum, the following monitoring while incinerating hazardous waste:

(1) Combustion temperature, waste feed rate, and the indicator of combustion gas velocity specified in the facility permit must be monitored on a continuous basis.

(2) CO must be monitored on a continuous basis at a point in the incinerator downstream of the combustion zone and prior to release to the atmosphere.

(3) Upon request by the Regional Administrator, sampling and analysis of the waste and exhaust emissions must be conducted to verify that the operating requirements established in the permit achieve the performance standards of §264.343.

(b) The incinerator and associated equipment (pumps, valves, conveyors, pipes, etc.) must be subjected to thorough visual inspection, at least daily, for leaks, spills, fugitive emissions, and signs of tampering.

(c) The emergency waste feed cutoff system and associated alarms must be tested at least weekly to verify operability, unless the applicant demonstrates to the Regional Administrator that weekly inspections will unduly restrict or upset operations and that less frequent inspection will be adequate. At a minimum, operational testing must be conducted at least monthly.

(d) This monitoring and inspection data must be recorded and the records must be placed in the operating record required by §264.73 of this part and maintained in the operating record for five years.

[46 FR 7678, Jan. 23, 1981, as amended at 47 FR 27533, June 24, 1982; 50 FR 4514, Jan. 31, 1985; 71 FR 16907, Apr. 4, 2006]

§§264.348–264.350 [Reserved]

§264.351 Closure.

At closure the owner or operator must remove all hazardous waste and hazardous waste residues (including, but not limited to, ash, scrubber waters, and scrubber sludges) from the incinerator site.

[*Comment:* At closure, as throughout the operating period, unless the owner or operator can demonstrate, in accordance with §261.3(d) of this chapter, that the residue removed from the incinerator is not a hazardous waste, the owner or operator becomes a generator of hazardous waste and must manage it in accordance with applicable requirements of parts 262 through 266 of this chapter.]

[46 FR 7678, Jan. 23, 1981]

Subparts P–R [Reserved]

Subpart S—Special Provisions for Cleanup

§264.550 Applicability of Corrective Action Management Unit (CAMU) Regulations. 📖 17.11

(a) Except as provided in paragraph (b) of this section, CAMUs are subject to the requirements of §264.552.

(b) CAMUs that were approved before April 22, 2002, or for which substantially complete applications (or equivalents) were submitted to the Agency on or before November 20, 2000, are subject to the requirements in §264.551 for grandfathered CAMUs; CAMU waste, activities, and design will not be subject to the standards in §264.552, so long as the waste, activities, and design remain within the general scope of the CAMU as approved.

[67 FR 3024, Jan. 22, 2002]

§264.551 Grandfathered Corrective Action Management Units (CAMUs). 📖 17.11

(a) To implement remedies under §264.101 or RCRA Section 3008(h), or to implement remedies at a permitted facility that is not subject to §264.101, the Regional Administrator may designate an area at the facility as a corrective action management unit under the requirements in this section. Corrective action management unit means an area within a facility that is used only for managing remediation wastes for implementing corrective action or cleanup at the facility. A CAMU must be located within the contiguous property under the control of the owner or operator where the wastes to be managed in the CAMU originated. One or more CAMUs may be designated at a facility.

(1) Placement of remediation wastes into or within a CAMU does not constitute land disposal of hazardous wastes. 📖 13.1.3.1

(2) Consolidation or placement of remediation wastes into or within a CAMU does not constitute creation of a unit subject to minimum technology requirements.

(b)(1) The Regional Administrator may designate a regulated unit (as defined in §264.90(a)(2)) as a CAMU, or may incorporate a regulated unit into a CAMU, if:

(i) The regulated unit is closed or closing, meaning it has begun the closure process under §264.113 or §265.113; and

(ii) Inclusion of the regulated unit will enhance implementation of effective, protective and reliable remedial actions for the facility.

(2) The subpart F, G, and H requirements and the unit-specific requirements of part 264 or 265 that applied to that regulated unit will continue to apply to that portion of the CAMU after incorporation into the CAMU.

(c) The Regional Administrator shall designate a CAMU in accordance with the following:

(1) The CAMU shall facilitate the implementation of reliable, effective, protective, and cost-effective remedies;

(2) Waste management activities associated with the CAMU shall not create unacceptable risks to humans or to the environment resulting from exposure to hazardous wastes or hazardous constituents;

(3) The CAMU shall include uncontaminated areas of the facility, only if including such areas for the purpose of managing remediation waste is more protective than management of such wastes at contaminated areas of the facility;

(4) Areas within the CAMU, where wastes remain in place after closure of the CAMU, shall be managed and contained so as to minimize future releases, to the extent practicable;

(5) The CAMU shall expedite the timing of remedial activity implementation, when appropriate and practicable;

(6) The CAMU shall enable the use, when appropriate, of treatment technologies (including innovative technologies) to enhance the long-term effectiveness of remedial actions by reducing the toxicity, mobility, or volume of wastes that will remain in place after closure of the CAMU; and

(7) The CAMU shall, to the extent practicable, minimize the land area of the facility upon which wastes will remain in place after closure of the CAMU.

(d) The owner/operator shall provide sufficient information to enable the Regional Administrator to designate a CAMU in accordance with the criteria in §264.552.

(e) The Regional Administrator shall specify, in the permit or order, requirements for CAMUs to include the following:

(1) The areal configuration of the CAMU.

(2) Requirements for remediation waste management to include the specification of applicable design, operation and closure requirements.

(3) Requirements for ground water monitoring that are sufficient to:

(i) Continue to detect and to characterize the nature, extent, concentration, direction, and movement of existing releases of hazardous constituents in ground water from sources located within the CAMU; and

(ii) Detect and subsequently characterize releases of hazardous constituents to ground water that may occur from areas of the CAMU in which wastes will remain in place after closure of the CAMU.

(4) Closure and post-closure requirements.

(i) Closure of corrective action management units shall:

(A) Minimize the need for further maintenance; and

(B) Control, minimize, or eliminate, to the extent necessary to protect human health and the environment, for areas where wastes remain in place, post-closure escape of hazardous waste, hazardous constituents, leachate, contaminated runoff, or hazardous waste decomposition products to the ground, to surface waters, or to the atmosphere.

(ii) Requirements for closure of CAMUs shall include the following, as appropriate and as deemed necessary by the Regional Administrator for a given CAMU:

(A) Requirements for excavation, removal, treatment or containment of wastes;

(B) For areas in which wastes will remain after closure of the CAMU, requirements for capping of such areas; and

(C) Requirements for removal and decontamination of equipment, devices, and structures used in remediation waste management activities within the CAMU.

(iii) In establishing specific closure requirements for CAMUs under §264.552(e), the Regional Administrator shall consider the following factors:

(A) CAMU characteristics;

(B) Volume of wastes which remain in place after closure;

(C) Potential for releases from the CAMU;

(D) Physical and chemical characteristics of the waste;

(E) Hydrological and other relevant environmental conditions at the facility which may influence the migration of any potential or actual releases; and

(F) Potential for exposure of humans and environmental receptors if releases were to occur from the CAMU.

(iv) Post-closure requirements as necessary to protect human health and the environment, to include, for areas where wastes will remain in place, monitoring and maintenance activities, and the frequency with which such activities shall be performed to ensure the integrity of any cap, final cover, or other containment system.

(f) The Regional Administrator shall document the rationale for designating CAMUs and shall make such documentation available to the public.

(g) Incorporation of a CAMU into an existing permit must be approved by the Regional Administrator according to the procedures for Agency-initiated permit modifications under §270.41 of this chapter, or according to the permit modification procedures of §270.42 of this chapter.

(h) The designation of a CAMU does not change EPA's existing authority to address clean-up levels, media-specific points of compliance to be applied to remediation at a facility, or other remedy selection decisions.

[58 FR 8683, Feb. 16, 1993, as amended at 63 FR 65939, Nov. 30, 1998; 67 FR 3025, Jan. 22, 2002]

§264.552 Corrective Action Management Units (CAMU).

📖 17.11.3

(a) To implement remedies under §264.101 or RCRA Section 3008(h), or to implement remedies at a permitted facility that is not subject to §264.101, the Regional Administrator may designate an area at the facility as a corrective action management unit under the requirements in this section. Corrective action management unit means an area within a facility that is used only for managing CAMU-eligible wastes for implementing corrective action or cleanup at the facility. A CAMU must be located within the contiguous property under the control of the owner or operator where the wastes to be managed in the CAMU originated. One or more CAMUs may be designated at a facility.

(1) *CAMU-eligible waste* means:

(i) All solid and hazardous wastes, and all media (including ground water, surface water, soils, and sediments) and debris, that are managed for implementing cleanup. As-generated wastes (either hazardous or non-hazardous) from ongoing industrial operations at a site are not CAMU-eligible wastes. 📖 17.11.2

(ii) Wastes that would otherwise meet the description in paragraph (a)(1)(i) of this section are not "CAMU-Eligible Wastes" where:

(A) The wastes are hazardous wastes found during cleanup in intact or substantially intact containers, tanks, or other non-land-based units found above ground, unless the wastes are first placed in the tanks, containers or non-land-based units as part of cleanup, or the containers or tanks are excavated during the course of cleanup; or

(B) The Regional Administrator exercises the discretion in paragraph (a)(2) of this section to prohibit the wastes from management in a CAMU.

(iii) Notwithstanding paragraph (a)(1)(i) of this section, where appropriate, as-generated non-hazardous waste may be placed in a CAMU where such waste is being used to facilitate treatment or the performance of the CAMU.

(2) The Regional Administrator may prohibit, where appropriate, the placement of waste in a CAMU where the Regional Administrator has or receives information that such wastes have not been managed in compliance with applicable land disposal treatment standards of part 268 of this chapter, or applicable unit design requirements of this part, or applicable unit design requirements of part 265 of this chapter, or that non-compliance with other applicable requirements of this chapter likely contributed to the release of the waste.

(3) *Prohibition against placing liquids in CAMUs.* 📖 17.11.2

(i) The placement of bulk or noncontainerized liquid hazardous waste or free liquids contained in hazardous waste (whether or not sorbents have been added) in any CAMU is prohibited except where placement of such wastes facilitates the remedy selected for the waste.

(ii) The requirements in §264.314(d) for placement of containers holding free liquids in landfills apply to placement in a CAMU except where placement facilitates the remedy selected for the waste.

Publisher's Note: The above reference to §264.314(d) is incorrect and should refer to §264.314(c).

(iii) The placement of any liquid which is not a hazardous waste in a CAMU is prohibited unless such placement facilitates the remedy selected for the waste or a demonstration is made pursuant to §264.314(f).

Publisher's Note: The above reference to §264.314(f) is incorrect and should refer to §264.314(e).

(iv) The absence or presence of free liquids in either a containerized or a bulk waste must be determined in accordance with §264.314(c). Sorbents used to treat free liquids in CAMUs must meet the requirements of §264.314(e).

Publisher's Note: The above references to §264.314(c) and §264.314(e) are incorrect and should refer to §264.314(b) and §264.314(d), respectively.

(4) Placement of CAMU-eligible wastes into or within a CAMU does not constitute land disposal of hazardous wastes. 📖 13.1.3.1

(5) Consolidation or placement of CAMU-eligible wastes into or within a CAMU does not constitute creation of a unit subject to minimum technology requirements.

(b)(1) The Regional Administrator may designate a regulated unit (as defined in §264.90(a)(2)) as a CAMU, or may incorporate a regulated unit into a CAMU, if:

(i) The regulated unit is closed or closing, meaning it has begun the closure process under §264.113 or §265.113 of this chapter; and

(ii) Inclusion of the regulated unit will enhance implementation of effective, protective and reliable remedial actions for the facility.

(2) The subpart F, G, and H requirements and the unit-specific requirements of this part 264 or part 265 of this chapter that applied to the regulated unit will continue to apply to that portion of the CAMU after incorporation into the CAMU.

(c) The Regional Administrator shall designate a CAMU that will be used for storage and/or treatment only in accordance with paragraph (f) of this section. The

Regional Administrator shall designate all other CAMUs in accordance with the following: 17.11.3

(1) The CAMU shall facilitate the implementation of reliable, effective, protective, and cost-effective remedies;

(2) Waste management activities associated with the CAMU shall not create unacceptable risks to humans or to the environment resulting from exposure to hazardous wastes or hazardous constituents;

(3) The CAMU shall include uncontaminated areas of the facility, only if including such areas for the purpose of managing CAMU-eligible waste is more protective than management of such wastes at contaminated areas of the facility;

(4) Areas within the CAMU, where wastes remain in place after closure of the CAMU, shall be managed and contained so as to minimize future releases, to the extent practicable;

(5) The CAMU shall expedite the timing of remedial activity implementation, when appropriate and practicable;

(6) The CAMU shall enable the use, when appropriate, of treatment technologies (including innovative technologies) to enhance the long-term effectiveness of remedial actions by reducing the toxicity, mobility, or volume of wastes that will remain in place after closure of the CAMU; and

(7) The CAMU shall, to the extent practicable, minimize the land area of the facility upon which wastes will remain in place after closure of the CAMU.

(d) The owner/operator shall provide sufficient information to enable the Regional Administrator to designate a CAMU in accordance with the criteria in this section. This must include, unless not reasonably available, information on:

(1) The origin of the waste and how it was subsequently managed (including a description of the timing and circumstances surrounding the disposal and/or release);

(2) Whether the waste was listed or identified as hazardous at the time of disposal and/or release; and

(3) Whether the disposal and/or release of the waste occurred before or after the land disposal requirements of part 268 of this chapter were in effect for the waste listing or characteristic.

(e) The Regional Administrator shall specify, in the permit or order, requirements for CAMUs to include the following:

(1) The areal configuration of the CAMU.

(2) Except as provided in paragraph (g) of this section, requirements for CAMU-eligible waste management to include the specification of applicable design, operation, treatment and closure requirements.

(3) Minimum design requirements. CAMUs, except as provided in paragraph (f) of this section, into which wastes are placed must be designed in accordance with the following: 17.11.4

(i) Unless the Regional Administrator approves alternate requirements under paragraph (e)(3)(ii) of this section, CAMUs that consist of new, replacement, or laterally expanded units must include a composite liner and a leachate collection system that is designed and constructed to maintain less than a 30-cm depth of leachate over the liner. For purposes of this section, *composite liner* means a system consisting of two components; the upper component must consist of a minimum 30-mil flexible membrane liner (FML), and the lower component must consist of at least a two-foot layer of compacted soil with a hydraulic conductivity of no more than 1×10^{-7} cm/sec. FML components consisting of high density polyethylene (HDPE) must be at least 60 mil thick. The FML component must be installed in direct and uniform contact with the compacted soil component;

(ii) Alternate requirements. The Regional Administrator may approve alternate requirements if:

(A) The Regional Administrator finds that alternate design and operating practices, together with location characteristics, will prevent the migration of any hazardous constituents into the ground water or surface water at least as effectively as the liner and leachate collection systems in paragraph (e)(3)(i) of this section; or

(B) The CAMU is to be established in an area with existing significant levels of contamination, and the Regional Administrator finds that an alternative design, including a design that does not include a liner, would prevent migration from the unit that would exceed long-term remedial goals.

(4) Minimum treatment requirements: Unless the wastes will be placed in a CAMU for storage and/or treatment only in accordance with paragraph (f) of this section, CAMU-eligible wastes that, absent this section, would be subject to the treatment requirements of part 268 of this chapter, and that the Regional Administrator determines contain principal

hazardous constituents must be treated to the standards specified in paragraph (e)(4)(iii) of this section.

17.11.5

(i) Principal hazardous constituents are those constituents that the Regional Administrator determines pose a risk to human health and the environment substantially higher than the cleanup levels or goals at the site.

(A) In general, the Regional Administrator will designate as principal hazardous constituents:

(*1*) Carcinogens that pose a potential direct risk from ingestion or inhalation at the site at or above 10^{-3}; and

(*2*) Non-carcinogens that pose a potential direct risk from ingestion or inhalation at the site an order of magnitude or greater over their reference dose.

(B) The Regional Administrator will also designate constituents as principal hazardous constituents, where appropriate, when risks to human health and the environment posed by the potential migration of constituents in wastes to ground water are substantially higher than cleanup levels or goals at the site; when making such a designation, the Regional Administrator may consider such factors as constituent concentrations, and fate and transport characteristics under site conditions.

(C) The Regional Administrator may also designate other constituents as principal hazardous constituents that the Regional Administrator determines pose a risk to human health and the environment substantially higher than the cleanup levels or goals at the site.

(ii) In determining which constituents are "principal hazardous constituents," the Regional Administrator must consider all constituents which, absent this section, would be subject to the treatment requirements in 40 CFR part 268.

(iii) Waste that the Regional Administrator determines contains principal hazardous constituents must meet treatment standards determined in accordance with paragraph (e)(4)(iv) or (e)(4)(v) of this section.

(iv) Treatment standards for wastes placed in CAMUs.

(A) For non-metals, treatment must achieve 90 percent reduction in total principal hazardous constituent concentrations, except as provided by paragraph (e)(4)(iv)(C) of this section.

(B) For metals, treatment must achieve 90 percent reduction in principal hazardous constituent concentrations as measured in leachate from the treated waste or media (tested according to the TCLP) or 90 percent reduction in total constituent concentrations (when a metal removal treatment technology is used), except as provided by paragraph (e)(4)(iv)(C) of this section.

(C) When treatment of any principal hazardous constituent to a 90 percent reduction standard would result in a concentration less than 10 times the Universal Treatment Standard for that constituent, treatment to achieve constituent concentrations less than 10 times the Universal Treatment Standard is not required. Universal Treatment Standards are identified in §268.48 Table UTS of this chapter.

(D) For waste exhibiting the hazardous characteristic of ignitability, corrosivity or reactivity, the waste must also be treated to eliminate these characteristics.

(E) For debris, the debris must be treated in accordance with §268.45 of this chapter, or by methods or to levels established under paragraphs (e)(4)(iv)(A) through (D) or paragraph (e)(4)(v) of this section, whichever the Regional Administrator determines is appropriate.

(F) Alternatives to TCLP. For metal bearing wastes for which metals removal treatment is not used, the Regional Administrator may specify a leaching test other than the TCLP (SW846 Method 1311, 40 CFR 260.11(a)(11)) to measure treatment effectiveness, provided the Regional Administrator determines that an alternative leach testing protocol is appropriate for use, and that the alternative more accurately reflects conditions at the site that affect leaching.

Publisher's Note: The above reference to 40 CFR 260.11(a)(11) is incorrect and should refer to 40 CFR 260.11(c)(3)(v).

(v) Adjusted standards. The Regional Administrator may adjust the treatment level or method in paragraph (e)(4)(iv) of this section to a higher or lower level, based on one or more of the following factors, as appropriate. The adjusted level or method must be protective of human health and the environment:

(A) The technical impracticability of treatment to the levels or by the methods in paragraph (e)(4)(iv) of this section;

(B) The levels or methods in paragraph (e)(4)(iv) of this section would result in concentrations of principal hazardous constituents (PHCs) that are significantly above or below cleanup standards applicable to the site (established either site-specifically, or promulgated under state or federal law);

(C) The views of the affected local community on the treatment levels or methods in paragraph (e)(4)(iv) of this section as applied at the site, and, for treatment levels, the treatment methods necessary to achieve these levels;

(D) The short-term risks presented by the on-site treatment method necessary to achieve the levels or treatment methods in paragraph (e)(4)(iv) of this section;

(E) The long-term protection offered by the engineering design of the CAMU and related engineering controls:

(*1*) Where the treatment standards in paragraph (e)(4)(iv) of this section are substantially met and the principal hazardous constituents in the waste or residuals are of very low mobility; or

(*2*) Where cost-effective treatment has been used and the CAMU meets the Subtitle C liner and leachate collection requirements for new land disposal units at §264.301(c) and (d); or

(*3*) Where, after review of appropriate treatment technologies, the Regional Administrator determines that cost-effective treatment is not reasonably available, and the CAMU meets the Subtitle C liner and leachate collection requirements for new land disposal units at §264.301(c) and (d); or

(*4*) Where cost-effective treatment has been used and the principal hazardous constituents in the treated wastes are of very low mobility; or

(*5*) Where, after review of appropriate treatment technologies, the Regional Administrator determines that cost-effective treatment is not reasonably available, the principal hazardous constituents in the wastes are of very low mobility, and either the CAMU meets or exceeds the liner standards for new, replacement, or laterally expanded CAMUs in paragraphs (e)(3)(i) and (ii) of this section, or the CAMU provides substantially equivalent or greater protection.

(vi) The treatment required by the treatment standards must be completed prior to, or within a reasonable time after, placement in the CAMU.

(vii) For the purpose of determining whether wastes placed in CAMUs have met site-specific treatment standards, the Regional Administrator may, as appropriate, specify a subset of the principal hazardous constituents in the waste as analytical surrogates for determining whether treatment standards have been met for other principal hazardous constituents. This specification will be based on the degree of difficulty of treatment and analysis of constituents with similar treatment properties.

(5) Except as provided in paragraph (f) of this section, requirements for ground water monitoring and corrective action that are sufficient to:

(i) Continue to detect and to characterize the nature, extent, concentration, direction, and movement of existing releases of hazardous constituents in ground water from sources located within the CAMU; and

(ii) Detect and subsequently characterize releases of hazardous constituents to ground water that may occur from areas of the CAMU in which wastes will remain in place after closure of the CAMU; and

(iii) Require notification to the Regional Administrator and corrective action as necessary to protect human health and the environment for releases to ground water from the CAMU.

(6) Except as provided in paragraph (f) of this section, closure and post-closure requirements:

(i) Closure of corrective action management units shall:

(A) Minimize the need for further maintenance; and

(B) Control, minimize, or eliminate, to the extent necessary to protect human health and the environment, for areas where wastes remain in place, post-closure escape of hazardous wastes, hazardous constituents, leachate, contaminated runoff, or hazardous waste decomposition products to the ground, to surface waters, or to the atmosphere.

(ii) Requirements for closure of CAMUs shall include the following, as appropriate and as deemed necessary by the Regional Administrator for a given CAMU:

(A) Requirements for excavation, removal, treatment or containment of wastes; and

(B) Requirements for removal and decontamination of equipment, devices, and structures used in CAMU-eligible waste management activities within the CAMU.

(iii) In establishing specific closure requirements for CAMUs under paragraph (e) of this section, the

Regional Administrator shall consider the following factors:

(A) CAMU characteristics;

(B) Volume of wastes which remain in place after closure;

(C) Potential for releases from the CAMU;

(D) Physical and chemical characteristics of the waste;

(E) Hydrogeological and other relevant environmental conditions at the facility which may influence the migration of any potential or actual releases; and

(F) Potential for exposure of humans and environmental receptors if releases were to occur from the CAMU.

(iv) Cap requirements:

(A) At final closure of the CAMU, for areas in which wastes will remain after closure of the CAMU, with constituent concentrations at or above remedial levels or goals applicable to the site, the owner or operator must cover the CAMU with a final cover designed and constructed to meet the following performance criteria, except as provided in paragraph (e)(6)(iv)(B) of this section:

(*1*) Provide long-term minimization of migration of liquids through the closed unit;

(*2*) Function with minimum maintenance;

(*3*) Promote drainage and minimize erosion or abrasion of the cover;

(*4*) Accommodate settling and subsidence so that the cover's integrity is maintained; and

(*5*) Have a permeability less than or equal to the permeability of any bottom liner system or natural subsoils present.

(B) The Regional Administrator may determine that modifications to paragraph (e)(6)(iv)(A) of this section are needed to facilitate treatment or the performance of the CAMU (e.g., to promote biodegradation).

(v) Post-closure requirements as necessary to protect human health and the environment, to include, for areas where wastes will remain in place, monitoring and maintenance activities, and the frequency with which such activities shall be performed to ensure the integrity of any cap, final cover, or other containment system.

(f) CAMUs used for storage and/or treatment only are CAMUs in which wastes will not remain after closure. Such CAMUs must be designated in accordance with all of the requirements of this section, except as follows.

📖 17.11.6

(1) CAMUs that are used for storage and/or treatment only and that operate in accordance with the time limits established in the staging pile regulations at §264.554(d)(1)(iii), (h), and (i) are subject to the requirements for staging piles at §264.554(d)(1)(i) and (ii), §264.554(d)(2), §264.554(e) and (f), and §264.554(j) and (k) in lieu of the performance standards and requirements for CAMUs in this section at paragraphs (c) and (e)(3) through (6).

(2) CAMUs that are used for storage and/or treatment only and that do not operate in accordance with the time limits established in the staging pile regulations at §264.554(d)(1)(iii), (h), and (i):

(i) Must operate in accordance with a time limit, established by the Regional Administrator, that is no longer than necessary to achieve a timely remedy selected for the waste, and

(ii) Are subject to the requirements for staging piles at §264.554(d)(1)(i) and (ii), §264.554(d)(2), §264.554(e) and (f), and §264.554(j) and (k) in lieu of the performance standards and requirements for CAMUs in this section at paragraphs (c) and (e)(4) and (6).

(g) CAMUs into which wastes are placed where all wastes have constituent levels at or below remedial levels or goals applicable to the site do not have to comply with the requirements for liners at paragraph (e)(3)(i) of this section, caps at paragraph (e)(6)(iv) of this section, ground water monitoring requirements at paragraph (e)(5) of this section or, for treatment and/or storage-only CAMUs, the design standards at paragraph (f) of this section.

(h) The Regional Administrator shall provide public notice and a reasonable opportunity for public comment before designating a CAMU. Such notice shall include the rationale for any proposed adjustments under paragraph (e)(4)(v) of this section to the treatment standards in paragraph (e)(4)(iv) of this section.

(i) Notwithstanding any other provision of this section, the Regional Administrator may impose additional requirements as necessary to protect human health and the environment.

(j) Incorporation of a CAMU into an existing permit must be approved by the Regional Administrator according to the procedures for Agency-initiated permit modifications under §270.41 of this chapter, or according to the permit modification procedures of §270.42 of this chapter.

(k) The designation of a CAMU does not change EPA's existing authority to address clean-up levels, media-specific points of compliance to be applied to remediation at a facility, or other remedy selection decisions.

[67 FR 3025, Jan. 22, 2002, as amended at 71 FR 40273, July 14, 2006]

§264.553 Temporary Units (TU).

17.12

(a) For temporary tanks and container storage areas used to treat or store hazardous remediation wastes during remedial activities required under §264.101 or RCRA 3008(h), or at a permitted facility that is not subject to §264.101, the Regional Administrator may designate a unit at the facility, as a temporary unit. A temporary unit must be located within the contiguous property under the control of the owner/operator where the wastes to be managed in the temporary unit originated. For temporary units, the Regional Administrator may replace the design, operating, or closure standard applicable to these units under this part 264 or part 265 of this chapter with alternative requirements which protect human health and the environment.

(b) Any temporary unit to which alternative requirements are applied in accordance with paragraph (a) of this section shall be:

(1) Located within the facility boundary; and

(2) Used only for treatment or storage of remediation wastes.

(c) In establishing standards to be applied to a temporary unit, the Regional Administrator shall consider the following factors:

(1) Length of time such unit will be in operation;

(2) Type of unit;

(3) Volumes of wastes to be managed;

(4) Physical and chemical characteristics of the wastes to be managed in the unit;

(5) Potential for releases from the unit;

(6) Hydrogeological and other relevant environmental conditions at the facility which may influence the migration of any potential releases; and

(7) Potential for exposure of humans and environmental receptors if releases were to occur from the unit.

(d) The Regional Administrator shall specify in the permit or order the length of time a temporary unit will be allowed to operate, to be no longer than a period of one year. The Regional Administrator shall also specify the design, operating, and closure requirements for the unit.

(e) The Regional Administrator may extend the operational period of a temporary unit once for no longer than a period of one year beyond that originally specified in the permit or order, if the Regional Administrator determines that:

(1) Continued operation of the unit will not pose a threat to human health and the environment; and

(2) Continued operation of the unit is necessary to ensure timely and efficient implementation of remedial actions at the facility.

(f) Incorporation of a temporary unit or a time extension for a temporary unit into an existing permit shall be:

(1) Approved in accordance with the procedures for Agency-initiated permit modifications under §270.41; or

(2) Requested by the owner/operator as a Class II modification according to the procedures under §270.42 of this chapter.

(g) The Regional Administrator shall document the rationale for designating a temporary unit and for granting time extensions for temporary units and shall make such documentation available to the public.

[58 FR 8683, Feb. 16, 1993, as amended at 63 FR 65939, Nov. 30, 1998; 71 FR 40273, July 14, 2006]

§264.554 Staging piles.

13.1.3.1, 17.13

This section is written in a special format to make it easier to understand the regulatory requirements. Like other Environmental Protection Agency (EPA) regulations, this establishes enforceable legal requirements. For this "I" and "you" refer to the owner/operator.

(a) *What is a staging pile?* A staging pile is an accumulation of solid, non-flowing remediation waste (as defined in §260.10 of this chapter) that is not a containment building and is used only during remedial operations for temporary storage at a facility. A staging pile must be located within the contiguous property under the control of the owner/operator where the wastes to be managed in the staging pile originated. Staging piles must be designated by the Director according to the requirements in this section.

(1) For the purposes of this section, storage includes mixing, sizing, blending, or other similar physical operations as long as they are intended to prepare the wastes for subsequent management or treatment.

(2) [Reserved]

(b) *When may I use a staging pile?* You may use a staging pile to store hazardous remediation waste (or remediation waste otherwise subject to land disposal restrictions) only if you follow the standards and design criteria the Director has designated for that staging pile. The Director must designate the staging pile in a permit or, at an interim status facility, in a closure plan or order (consistent with §270.72(a)(5) and (b)(5) of this chapter). The Director must establish conditions in the permit, closure plan, or order that comply with paragraphs (d) through (k) of this section.

(c) *What information must I provide to get a staging pile designated?* When seeking a staging pile designation, you must provide:

(1) Sufficient and accurate information to enable the Director to impose standards and design criteria for your staging pile according to paragraphs (d) through (k) of this section;

(2) Certification by a qualified Professional Engineer for technical data, such as design drawings and specifications, and engineering studies, unless the Director determines, based on information that you provide, that this certification is not necessary to ensure that a staging pile will protect human health and the environment; and

(3) Any additional information the Director determines is necessary to protect human health and the environment.

(d) *What performance criteria must a staging pile satisfy?* The Director must establish the standards and design criteria for the staging pile in the permit, closure plan, or order.

(1) The standards and design criteria must comply with the following:

(i) The staging pile must facilitate a reliable, effective and protective remedy;

(ii) The staging pile must be designed so as to prevent or minimize releases of hazardous wastes and hazardous constituents into the environment, and minimize or adequately control cross-media transfer, as necessary to protect human health and the environment (for example, through the use of liners, covers, run-off/run-on controls, as appropriate); and

(iii) The staging pile must not operate for more than two years, except when the Director grants an operating term extension under paragraph (i) of this section (entitled "May I receive an operating extension for a staging pile?"). You must measure the two-year limit, or other operating term specified by the Director in the permit, closure plan, or order, from the first time you place remediation waste into a staging pile. You must maintain a record of the date when you first placed remediation waste into the staging pile for the life of the permit, closure plan, or order, or for three years, whichever is longer.

(2) In setting the standards and design criteria, the Director must consider the following factors:

(i) Length of time the pile will be in operation;

(ii) Volumes of wastes you intend to store in the pile;

(iii) Physical and chemical characteristics of the wastes to be stored in the unit;

(iv) Potential for releases from the unit;

(v) Hydrogeological and other relevant environmental conditions at the facility that may influence the migration of any potential releases; and

(vi) Potential for human and environmental exposure to potential releases from the unit;

(e) *May a staging pile receive ignitable or reactive remediation waste?* You must not place ignitable or reactive remediation waste in a staging pile unless:

(1) You have treated, rendered or mixed the remediation waste before you placed it in the staging pile so that:

(i) The remediation waste no longer meets the definition of ignitable or reactive under §261.21 or §261.23 of this chapter; and

(ii) You have complied with §264.17(b); or

(2) You manage the remediation waste to protect it from exposure to any material or condition that may cause it to ignite or react.

(f) *How do I handle incompatible remediation wastes in a staging pile?* The term "incompatible waste" is defined in §260.10 of this chapter. You must comply with the following requirements for incompatible wastes in staging piles:

(1) You must not place incompatible remediation wastes in the same staging pile unless you have complied with §264.17(b);

(2) If remediation waste in a staging pile is incompatible with any waste or material stored nearby in containers, other piles, open tanks or land disposal units (for example, surface impoundments), you must separate the incompatible materials, or protect them from one another by using a dike, berm, wall or other device; and

(3) You must not pile remediation waste on the same base where incompatible wastes or materials were previously piled, unless the base has been decontaminated sufficiently to comply with §264.17(b).

(g) *Are staging piles subject to Land Disposal Restrictions (LDR) and Minimum Technological Requirements (MTR)?* No. Placing hazardous remediation wastes into a staging pile does not constitute land disposal of hazardous wastes or create a unit that is subject to the minimum technological requirements of RCRA 3004(o).

(h) *How long may I operate a staging pile?* The Director may allow a staging pile to operate for up to two years after hazardous remediation waste is first placed into the pile. You must use a staging pile no longer than the length of time designated by the Director in the permit, closure plan, or order (the "operating term"), except as provided in paragraph (i) of this section.

(i) *May I receive an operating extension for a staging pile?* (1) The Director may grant one operating term extension of up to 180 days beyond the operating term limit contained in the permit, closure plan, or order (see paragraph (l) of this section for modification procedures). To justify to the Director the need for an extension, you must provide sufficient and accurate information to enable the Director to determine that continued operation of the staging pile:

(i) Will not pose a threat to human health and the environment; and

(ii) Is necessary to ensure timely and efficient implementation of remedial actions at the facility.

(2) The Director may, as a condition of the extension, specify further standards and design criteria in the permit, closure plan, or order, as necessary, to ensure protection of human health and the environment.

(j) *What is the closure requirement for a staging pile located in a previously contaminated area?* (1) Within 180 days after the operating term of the staging pile expires, you must close a staging pile located in a previously contaminated area of the site by removing or decontaminating all:

(i) Remediation waste;

(ii) Contaminated containment system components; and

(iii) Structures and equipment contaminated with waste and leachate.

(2) You must also decontaminate contaminated subsoils in a manner and according to a schedule that the Director determines will protect human health and the environment.

(3) The Director must include the above requirements in the permit, closure plan, or order in which the staging pile is designated.

(k) *What is the closure requirement for a staging pile located in an uncontaminated area?* (1) Within 180 days after the operating term of the staging pile expires, you must close a staging pile located in an uncontaminated area of the site according to §§264.258(a) and 264.111; or according to §§265.258(a) and 265.111 of this chapter.

(2) The Director must include the above requirement in the permit, closure plan, or order in which the staging pile is designated.

(l) *How may my existing permit (for example, RAP), closure plan, or order be modified to allow me to use a staging pile?* (1) To modify a permit, other than a RAP, to incorporate a staging pile or staging pile operating term extension, either:

(i) The Director must approve the modification under the procedures for Agency-initiated permit modifications in §270.41 of this chapter; or

(ii) You must request a Class 2 modification under §270.42 of this chapter.

(2) To modify a RAP to incorporate a staging pile or staging pile operating term extension, you must comply with the RAP modification requirements under §§270.170 and 270.175 of this chapter.

(3) To modify a closure plan to incorporate a staging pile or staging pile operating term extension, you must follow the applicable requirements under §264.112(c) or §265.112(c) of this chapter.

(4) To modify an order to incorporate a staging pile or staging pile operating term extension, you must follow the terms of the order and the applicable provisions of §270.72(a)(5) or (b)(5) of this chapter.

(m) *Is information about the staging pile available to the public?* The Director must document the rationale for designating a staging pile or staging pile operating term extension and make this documentation available to the public.

[63 FR 65939, Nov. 30, 1998; 67 FR 3028, Jan. 22, 2002; 71 FR 16907, Apr. 4, 2006; 71 FR 40273, July 14, 2006]

§264.555 Disposal of CAMU-eligible wastes in permitted hazardous waste landfills.

📖 17.11.7

(a) The Regional Administrator with regulatory oversight at the location where the cleanup is taking place may approve placement of CAMU-eligible wastes in hazardous waste landfills not located at the site from which the waste originated, without the wastes meeting the requirements of RCRA 40 CFR part 268, if the conditions in paragraphs (a)(1) through (3) of this section are met:

(1) The waste meets the definition of CAMU-eligible waste in §264.552(a)(1) and (2).

(2) The Regional Administrator with regulatory oversight at the location where the cleanup is taking place identifies principal hazardous constitutes in such waste, in accordance with §264.552(e)(4)(i) and (ii), and requires that such principal hazardous constituents are treated to any of the following standards specified for CAMU-eligible wastes:

(i) The treatment standards under §264.552(e)(4)(iv); or

(ii) Treatment standards adjusted in accordance with §264.552(e)(4)(v)(A), (C), (D) or (E)(1); or

(iii) Treatment standards adjusted in accordance with §264.552(e)(4)(v)(E)(2), where treatment has been used and that treatment significantly reduces the toxicity or mobility of the principal hazardous constituents in the waste, minimizing the short-term and long-term threat posed by the waste, including the threat at the remediation site.

(3) The landfill receiving the CAMU-eligible waste must have a RCRA hazardous waste permit, meet the requirements for new landfills in Subpart N of this part, and be authorized to accept CAMU-eligible wastes; for the purposes of this requirement, "permit" does not include interim status.

(b) The person seeking approval shall provide sufficient information to enable the Regional Administrator with regulatory oversight at the location where the cleanup is taking place to approve placement of CAMU-eligible waste in accordance with paragraph (a) of this section. Information required by §264.552(d)(1) through (3) for CAMU applications must be provided, unless not reasonably available.

(c) The Regional Administrator with regulatory oversight at the location where the cleanup is taking place shall provide public notice and a reasonable opportunity for public comment before approving CAMU eligible waste for placement in an off-site permitted hazardous waste landfill, consistent with the requirements for CAMU approval at §264.552(h). The approval must be specific to a single remediation.

(d) Applicable hazardous waste management requirements in this part, including recordkeeping requirements to demonstrate compliance with treatment standards approved under this section, for CAMU-eligible waste must be incorporated into the receiving facility permit through permit issuance or a permit modification, providing notice and an opportunity for comment and a hearing. Notwithstanding 40 CFR 270.4(a), a landfill may not receive hazardous CAMU-eligible waste under this section unless its permit specifically authorizes receipt of such waste.

(e) For each remediation, CAMU-eligible waste may not be placed in an off-site landfill authorized to receive CAMU-eligible waste in accordance with paragraph (d) of this section until the following additional conditions have been met:

(1) The landfill owner/operator notifies the Regional Administrator responsible for oversight of the landfill and persons on the facility mailing list, maintained in accordance with 40 CFR 124.10(c)(1)(ix), of his or her intent to receive CAMU-eligible waste in accordance with this section; the notice must identify the source of the remediation waste, the principal hazardous constituents in the waste, and treatment requirements.

(2) Persons on the facility mailing list may provide comments, including objections to the receipt of the CAMU-eligible waste, to the Regional Administrator within 15 days of notification.

(3) The Regional Administrator may object to the placement of the CAMU-eligible waste in the landfill within 30 days of notification; the Regional Administrator may extend the review period an additional 30 days because of public concerns or insufficient information.

(4) CAMU-eligible wastes may not be placed in the landfill until the Regional Administrator has notified the facility owner/operator that he or she does not object to its placement.

(5) If the Regional Administrator objects to the placement or does not notify the facility owner/operator that he or she has chosen not to object, the facility may not receive the waste, notwithstanding 40 CFR 270.4(a), until the objection has been resolved, or the owner/operator obtains a permit modification in accordance with the procedures of §270.42 specifically authorizing receipt of the waste.

(6) As part of the permit issuance or permit modification process of paragraph (d) of this section, the Regional Administrator may modify, reduce, or eliminate the notification requirements of this paragraph as

they apply to specific categories of CAMU-eligible waste, based on minimal risk.

(f) Generators of CAMU-eligible wastes sent off-site to a hazardous waste landfill under this section must comply with the requirements of 40 CFR 268.7(a)(4); off-site facilities treating CAMU-eligible wastes to comply with this section must comply with the requirements of §268.7(b)(4), except that the certification must be with respect to the treatment requirements of paragraph (a)(2) of this section.

(g) For the purposes of this section only, the "design of the CAMU" in 40 CFR 264.552(e)(4)(v)(E) means design of the permitted Subtitle C landfill.

[67 FR 3028, Jan. 22, 2002, as amended at 71 FR 40274, July 14, 2006]

Subparts T–V [Reserved]

Subpart W—Drip Pads

10.1.3.4

Source: 56 FR 30196, July 1, 1991, unless otherwise noted.

§264.570 Applicability.

(a) The requirements of this subpart apply to owners and operators of facilities that use new or existing drip pads to convey treated wood drippage, precipitation, and/or surface water run-off to an associated collection system. Existing drip pads are those constructed before December 6, 1990 and those for which the owner or operator has a design and has entered into binding financial or other agreements for construction prior to December 6, 1990. All other drip pads are new drip pads. The requirement at §264.573(b)(3) to install a leak collection system applies only to those drip pads that are constructed after December 24, 1992 except for those constructed after December 24, 1992 for which the owner or operator has a design and has entered into binding financial or other agreements for construction prior to December 24, 1992.

(b) The owner or operator of any drip pad that is inside or under a structure that provides protection from precipitation so that neither run-off nor run-on is generated is not subject to regulation under §264.573(e) or §264.573(f), as appropriate.

(c) The requirements of this subpart are not applicable to the management of infrequent and incidental drippage in storage yards provided that:

(1) The owner or operator maintains and complies with a written contingency plan that describes how the owner or operator will respond immediately to the discharge of such infrequent and incidental drippage. At a minimum, the contingency plan must describe how the owner or operator will do the following:

(i) Clean up the drippage;

(ii) Document the cleanup of the drippage;

(iii) Retain documents regarding cleanup for three years; and

(iv) Manage the contaminated media in a manner consistent with Federal regulations.

[56 FR 30196, July 1, 1991, as amended at 57 FR 61502, Dec. 24, 1992]

§264.571 Assessment of existing drip pad integrity.

(a) For each existing drip pad as defined in §264.570 of this subpart, the owner or operator must evaluate the drip pad and determine whether it meets all of the requirements of this subpart, except the requirements for liners and leak detection systems of §264.573(b). No later than the effective date of this rule, the owner or operator must obtain and keep on file at the facility a written assessment of the drip pad, reviewed and certified by a qualified Professional Engineer that attests to the results of the evaluation. The assessment must be reviewed, updated and re-certified annually until all upgrades, repairs, or modifications necessary to achieve compliance with all the standards of §264.573 are complete. The evaluation must document the extent to which the drip pad meets each of the design and operating standards of §264.573, except the standards for liners and leak detection systems, specified in §264.573(b).

(b) The owner or operator must develop a written plan for upgrading, repairing, and modifying the drip pad to meet the requirements of §264.573(b) and submit the plan to the Regional Administrator no later than 2 years before the date that all repairs, upgrades, and modifications are complete. This written plan must describe all changes to be made to the drip pad in sufficient detail to document compliance with all the requirements of §264.573. The plan must be reviewed and certified by a qualified Professional Engineer.

(c) Upon completion of all upgrades, repairs, and modifications, the owner or operator must submit to the Regional Administrator or state Director, the as-built drawings for the drip pad together with a certification by a qualified Professional Engineer attesting that the drip pad conforms to the drawings.

(d) If the drip pad is found to be leaking or unfit for use, the owner or operator must comply with the provisions of §264.573 (m) of this subpart or close the drip pad in accordance with §264.575 of this subpart.

[56 FR 30196, July 1, 1991, as amended at 57 FR 61503, Dec. 24, 1992; 71 FR 16907, Apr. 4, 2006]

§264.572 Design and installation of new drip pads.

Owners and operators of new drip pads must ensure that the pads are designed, installed, and operated in accordance with one of the following:

(a) all of the requirements of §§264.573 (except 264.573(a)(4)), 264.574 and 264.575 of this subpart, or

(b) all of the requirements of §§264.573 (except §264.573(b)), 264.574 and 264.575 of this subpart.

[57 FR 61503, Dec. 24, 1992]

§264.573 Design and operating requirements.

(a) Drip pads must: (1) Be constructed of non-earthen materials, excluding wood and non-structurally supported asphalt;

(2) Be sloped to free-drain treated wood drippage, rain and other waters, or solutions of drippage and water or other wastes to the associated collection system;

(3) Have a curb or berm around the perimeter;

(4)(i) Have a hydraulic conductivity of less than or equal to 1 x 10^{-7} centimeters per second, *e.g.*, existing concrete drip pads must be sealed, coated, or covered with a surface material with a hydraulic conductivity of less than or equal to 1 x 10^{-7} centimeters per second such that the entire surface where drippage occurs or may run across is capable of containing such drippage and mixtures of drippage and precipitation, materials, or other wastes while being routed to an associated collection system. This surface material must be maintained free of cracks and gaps that could adversely affect its hydraulic conductivity, and the material must be chemically compatible with the preservatives that contact the drip pad. The requirements of this provision apply only to existing drip pads and those drip pads for which the owner or operator elects to comply with §264.572(b) instead of §264.572(a).

(ii) The owner or operator must obtain and keep on file at the facility a written assessment of the drip pad, reviewed and certified by a qualified Professional Engineer that attests to the results of the evaluation. The assessment must be reviewed, updated and recertified annually. The evaluation must document the extent to which the drip pad meets the design and operating standards of this section, except for paragraph (b) of this section.

(5) Be of sufficient structural strength and thickness to prevent failure due to physical contact, climatic conditions, the stress of daily operations, *e.g.*, variable and moving loads such as vehicle traffic, movement of wood, etc.

[*Note:* EPA will generally consider applicable standards established by professional organizations generally recognized by the industry such as the American Concrete Institute (ACI) or the American Society of Testing and Materials (ASTM) in judging the structural integrity requirement of this paragraph.]

(b) If an owner/operator elects to comply with §264.572(a) instead of §264.572(b), the drip pad must have:

(1) A synthetic liner installed below the drip pad that is designed, constructed, and installed to prevent leakage from the drip pad into the adjacent subsurface soil or groundwater or surface water at any time during the active life (including the closure period) of the drip pad. The liner must be constructed of materials that will prevent waste from being absorbed into the liner and to prevent releases into the adjacent subsurface soil or groundwater or surface water during the active life of the facility. The liner must be:

(i) Constructed of materials that have appropriate chemical properties and sufficient strength and thickness to prevent failure due to pressure gradients (including static head and external hydrogeologic forces), physical contact with the waste or drip pad leakage to which they are exposed, climatic conditions, the stress of installation, and the stress of daily operation (including stresses from vehicular traffic on the drip pad);

(ii) Placed upon a foundation or base capable of providing support to the liner and resistance to pressure gradients above and below the liner to prevent failure of the liner due to settlement, compression or uplift; and

(iii) Installed to cover all surrounding earth that could come in contact with the waste or leakage; and

(2) A leakage detection system immediately above the liner that is designed, constructed, maintained and operated to detect leakage from the drip pad. The leakage detection system must be:

(i) Constructed of materials that are:

(A) Chemically resistant to the waste managed in the drip pad and the leakage that might be generated; and

(B) Of sufficient strength and thickness to prevent collapse under the pressures exerted by overlaying materials and by any equipment used at the drip pad;

(ii) Designed and operated to function without clogging through the scheduled closure of the drip pad; and

(iii) Designed so that it will detect the failure of the drip pad or the presence of a release of hazardous waste or accumulated liquid at the earliest practicable time.

(3) A leakage collection system immediately above the liner that is designed, constructed, maintained and operated to collect leakage from the drip pad such that it can be removed from below the drip pad. The date, time, and quantity of any leakage collected in this system and removed must be documented in the operating log.

(c) Drip pads must be maintained such that they remain free of cracks, gaps, corrosion, or other deterioration that could cause hazardous waste to be released from the drip pad.

[*Note:* See §264.573(m) for remedial action required if deterioration or leakage is detected.]

(d) The drip pad and associated collection system must be designed and operated to convey, drain, and collect liquid resulting from drippage or precipitation in order to prevent run-off.

(e) Unless protected by a structure, as described in §264.570(b) of this subpart, the owner or operator must design, construct, operate and maintain a run-on control system capable of preventing flow onto the drip pad during peak discharge from at least a 24-hour, 25-year storm, unless the system has sufficient excess capacity to contain any run-off that might enter the system.

(f) Unless protected by a structure or cover as described in §264.570(b) of this subpart, the owner or operator must design, construct, operate and maintain a run-off management system to collect and control at least the water volume resulting from a 24-hour, 25-year storm.

(g) The drip pad must be evaluated to determine that it meets the requirements of paragraphs (a) through (f) of this section and the owner or operator must obtain a statement from a qualified Professional Engineer certifying that the drip pad design meets the requirements of this section.

(h) Drippage and accumulated precipitation must be removed from the associated collection system as necessary to prevent overflow onto the drip pad.

(i) The drip pad surface must be cleaned thoroughly in a manner and frequency such that accumulated residues of hazardous waste or other materials are removed, with residues being properly managed as hazardous waste, so as to allow weekly inspections of the entire drip pad surface without interference or hindrance from accumulated residues of hazardous waste or other materials on the drip pad. The owner or operator must document the date and time of each cleaning and the cleaning procedure used in the facility's operating log. The owner/operator must determine if the residues are hazardous as per 40 CFR 262.11 and, if so, must manage them under parts 261–268, 270, and section 3010 of RCRA.

(j) Drip pads must be operated and maintained in a manner to minimize tracking of hazardous waste or hazardous waste constituents off the drip pad as a result of activities by personnel or equipment.

(k) After being removed from the treatment vessel, treated wood from pressure and non-pressure processes must be held on the drip pad until drippage has ceased. The owner or operator must maintain records sufficient to document that all treated wood is held on the pad following treatment in accordance with this requirement.

(l) Collection and holding units associated with run-on and run-off control systems must be emptied or otherwise managed as soon as possible after storms to maintain design capacity of the system.

(m) Throughout the active life of the drip pad and as specified in the permit, if the owner or operator detects a condition that may have caused or has caused a release of hazardous waste, the condition must be repaired within a reasonably prompt period of time following discovery, in accordance with the following procedures:

(1) Upon detection of a condition that may have caused or has caused a release of hazardous waste (*e.g.*, upon detection of leakage in the leak detection system), the owner or operator must:

(i) Enter a record of the discovery in the facility operating log;

(ii) Immediately remove the portion of the drip pad affected by the condition from service;

(iii) Determine what steps must be taken to repair the drip pad and clean up any leakage from below the drip pad, and establish a schedule for accomplishing the repairs;

(iv) Within 24 hours after discovery of the condition, notify the Regional Administrator of the condition and, within 10 working days, provide written notice to the Regional Administrator with a description of the steps that will be taken to repair the drip pad and clean up any leakage, and the schedule for accomplishing this work.

(2) The Regional Administrator will review the information submitted, make a determination regarding whether the pad must be removed from service completely or partially until repairs and cleanup are complete and notify the owner or operator of the determination and the underlying rationale in writing.

(3) Upon completing all repairs and cleanup, the owner or operator must notify the Regional Administrator in writing and provide a certification signed by an independent, qualified registered professional engineer, that the repairs and cleanup have been completed according to the written plan submitted in accordance with paragraph (m)(1)(iv) of this section.

(n) Should a permit be necessary, the Regional Administrator will specify in the permit all design and operating practices that are necessary to ensure that the requirements of this section are satisfied.

(o) The owner or operator must maintain, as part of the facility operating log, documentation of past operating and waste handling practices. This must include identification of preservative formulations used in the past, a description of drippage management practices, and a description of treated wood storage and handling practices.

[56 FR 30196, July 1, 1991, as amended at 57 FR 5861, Feb. 18, 1992; 57 FR 61503, Dec. 24, 1992; 71 FR 16907, Apr. 4, 2006; 71 FR 40274, July 14, 2006]

§264.574 Inspections.

(a) During construction or installation, liners and cover systems (*e.g.*, membranes, sheets, or coatings) must be inspected for uniformity, damage and imperfections (*e.g.*, holes, cracks, thin spots, or foreign materials). Immediately after construction or installation, liners must be inspected and certified as meeting the requirements in §264.573 of this subpart by a qualified Professional Engineer. This certification must be maintained at the facility as part of the facility operating record. After installation, liners and covers must be inspected to ensure tight seams and joints and the absence of tears, punctures, or blisters.

(b) While a drip pad is in operation, it must be inspected weekly and after storms to detect evidence of any of the following:

(1) Deterioration, malfunctions or improper operation of run-on and run-off control systems;

(2) The presence of leakage in and proper functioning of leak detection system.

(3) Deterioration or cracking of the drip pad surface.

Note: See §264.573(m) for remedial action required if deterioration or leakage is detected.

[56 FR 30196, July 1, 1991, as amended at 71 FR 16907, Apr. 4, 2006]

§264.575 Closure.

(a) At closure, the owner or operator must remove or decontaminate all waste residues, contaminated containment system components (pad, liners, etc.), contaminated subsoils, and structures and equipment contaminated with waste and leakage, and manage them as hazardous waste.

(b) If, after removing or decontaminating all residues and making all reasonable efforts to effect removal or decontamination of contaminated components, subsoils, structures, and equipment as required in paragraph (a) of this section, the owner or operator finds that not all contaminated subsoils can be practicably removed or decontaminated, he must close the facility and perform post-closure care in accordance with closure and post-closure care requirements that apply to landfills (§264.310). For permitted units, the requirement to have a permit continues throughout the post-closure period. In addition, for the purpose of closure, post-closure, and financial responsibility, such a drip pad is then considered to be landfill, and the owner or operator must meet all of the requirements for landfills specified in subparts G and H of this part.

(c)(1) The owner or operator of an existing drip pad, as defined in §264.570 of this subpart, that does not comply with the liner requirements of §264.573(b)(1) must:

(i) Include in the closure plan for the drip pad under §264.112 both a plan for complying with paragraph (a) of this section and a contingent plan for complying with paragraph (b) of this section in case not all contaminated subsoils can be practicably removed at closure; and

(ii) Prepare a contingent post-closure plan under §264.118 of this part for complying with paragraph (b) of this section in case not all contaminated subsoils can be practicably removed at closure.

(2) The cost estimates calculated under §§264.112 and 264.144 of this part for closure and post-closure care of a drip pad subject to this paragraph must include the cost of complying with the contingent closure plan and the contingent post-closure plan, but are not required to include the cost of expected closure under paragraph (a) of this section.

Subpart X—Miscellaneous Units

Source: 52 FR 46964, Dec. 10, 1987, unless otherwise noted.

§264.600 Applicability.

10.1.3

The requirements in this subpart apply to owners and operators of facilities that treat, store, or dispose of hazardous waste in miscellaneous units, except as §264.1 provides otherwise.

[52 FR 46964, Dec. 10, 1987, as amended at 71 FR 40274, July 14, 2006]

§264.601 Environmental performance standards.

A miscellaneous unit must be located, designed, constructed, operated, maintained, and closed in a manner that will ensure protection of human health and the environment. Permits for miscellaneous units are to contain such terms and provisions as necessary to protect human health and the environment, including, but not limited to, as appropriate, design and operating requirements, detection and monitoring requirements, and requirements for responses to releases of hazardous waste or hazardous constituents from the unit. Permit terms and provisions must include those requirements of subparts I through O and subparts AA through CC of this part, part 270, part 63 subpart EEE, and part 146 of this chapter that are appropriate for the miscellaneous unit being permitted. Protection of human health and the environment includes, but is not limited to:

(a) Prevention of any releases that may have adverse effects on human health or the environment due to migration of waste constituents in the ground water or subsurface environment, considering:

(1) The volume and physical and chemical characteristics of the waste in the unit, including its potential for migration through soil, liners, or other containing structures;

(2) The hydrologic and geologic characteristics of the unit and the surrounding area;

(3) The existing quality of ground water, including other sources of contamination and their cumulative impact on the ground water;

(4) The quantity and direction of ground-water flow;

(5) The proximity to and withdrawal rates of current and potential ground-water users;

(6) The patterns of land use in the region;

(7) The potential for deposition or migration of waste constituents into subsurface physical structures, and into the root zone of food-chain crops and other vegetation;

(8) The potential for health risks caused by human exposure to waste constituents; and

(9) The potential for damage to domestic animals, wildlife, crops, vegetation, and physical structures caused by exposure to waste constituents;

(b) Prevention of any releases that may have adverse effects on human health or the environment due to migration of waste constituents in surface water, or wetlands or on the soil surface considering:

(1) The volume and physical and chemical characteristics of the waste in the unit;

(2) The effectiveness and reliability of containing, confining, and collecting systems and structures in preventing migration;

(3) The hydrologic characteristics of the unit and the surrounding area, including the topography of the land around the unit;

(4) The patterns of precipitation in the region;

(5) The quantity, quality, and direction of ground-water flow;

(6) The proximity of the unit to surface waters;

(7) The current and potential uses of nearby surface waters and any water quality standards established for those surface waters;

(8) The existing quality of surface waters and surface soils, including other sources of contamination and their cumulative impact on surface waters and surface soils;

(9) The patterns of land use in the region;

(10) The potential for health risks caused by human exposure to waste constituents; and

(11) The potential for damage to domestic animals, wildlife, crops, vegetation, and physical structures caused by exposure to waste constituents.

(c) Prevention of any release that may have adverse effects on human health or the environment due to migration of waste constituents in the air, considering:

(1) The volume and physical and chemical characteristics of the waste in the unit, including its potential for the emission and dispersal of gases, aerosols and particulates;

(2) The effectiveness and reliability of systems and structures to reduce or prevent emissions of hazardous constituents to the air;

(3) The operating characteristics of the unit;

(4) The atmospheric, meteorologic, and topographic characteristics of the unit and the surrounding area;

(5) The existing quality of the air, including other sources of contamination and their cumulative impact on the air;

(6) The potential for health risks caused by human exposure to waste constituents; and

(7) The potential for damage to domestic animals, wildlife, crops, vegetation, and physical structures caused by exposure to waste constituents.

[59 FR 62927, Dec. 6, 1994, as amended at 64 FR 53074, Sept. 30, 1999; 71 FR 40274, July 14, 2006]

§264.602 Monitoring, analysis, inspection, response, reporting, and corrective action.

Monitoring, testing, analytical data, inspections, response, and reporting procedures and frequencies must ensure compliance with §§264.601, 264.15, 264.33, 264.75, 264.76, 264.77, and 264.101 as well as meet any additional requirements needed to protect human health and the environment as specified in the permit.

§264.603 Post-closure care.

A miscellaneous unit that is a disposal unit must be maintained in a manner that complies with §264.601 during the post-closure care period. In addition, if a treatment or storage unit has contaminated soils or ground water that cannot be completely removed or decontaminated during closure, then that unit must also meet the requirements of §264.601 during post-closure care. The post-closure plan under §264.118 must specify the procedures that will be used to satisfy this requirement.

Subparts Y–Z [Reserved]

Subpart AA—Air Emission Standards for Process Vents

Source: 55 FR 25494, June 21, 1990, unless otherwise noted.

§264.1030 Applicability. 15.1.1

(a) The regulations in this subpart apply to owners and operators of facilities that treat, store, or dispose of hazardous wastes (except as provided in §264.1). 15.1.1.1

(b) Except for §264.1034, paragraphs (d) and (e), this subpart applies to process vents associated with distillation, fractionation, thin-film evaporation, solvent extraction, or air or steam stripping operations that manage hazardous wastes with organic concentrations of at least 10 ppmw, if these operations are conducted in one of the following: 15.1.1.2–5

(1) A unit that is subject to the permitting requirements of 40 CFR part 270, or

(2) A unit (including a hazardous waste recycling unit) that is not exempt from permitting under the provisions of 40 CFR 262.34(a) (*i.e.*, a hazardous waste recycling unit that is not a 90-day tank or container) and that is located at a hazardous waste management facility otherwise subject to the permitting requirements of 40 CFR part 270, or

(3) A unit that is exempt from permitting under the provisions of 40 CFR 262.34(a) (*i.e.*, a "90-day" tank or container) and is not a recycling unit under the provisions of 40 CFR 261.6.

(c) For the owner and operator of a facility subject to this subpart and who received a final permit under RCRA section 3005 prior to December 6, 1996, the requirements of this subpart shall be incorporated into the permit when the permit is reissued in accordance with the requirements of 40 CFR 124.15 or reviewed in accordance with the requirements of 40 CFR 270.50(d). Until such date when the owner and operator receive a final permit incorporating the requirements of this subpart, the owner and operator are subject to the requirements of 40 CFR 265, subpart AA.

[*Note:* The requirements of §§264.1032 through 264.1036 apply to process vents on hazardous waste recycling units previously exempt under §261.6(c)(1). Other exemptions under §§261.4, and 264.1(g) are not affected by these requirements.]

(d) The requirements of this subpart do not apply to the pharmaceutical manufacturing facility, commonly referred to as the Stonewall Plant, located at Route 340 South, Elkton, Virginia, provided that facility is operated in compliance with the requirements contained in a Clean Air Act permit issued pursuant to 40 CFR 52.2454. The requirements of this subpart shall apply to the facility upon termination of the Clean Air Act permit issued pursuant to 40 CFR 52.2454.

(e) The requirements of this subpart do not apply to the process vents at a facility where the facility owner or operator certifies that all of the process vents that would otherwise be subject to this subpart are equipped with and operating air emission controls in accordance with the process vent requirements of an applicable Clean Air Act regulation codified under 40 CFR part 60, part 61, or part 63. The documentation of compliance under regulations at 40 CFR part 60, part 61, or part 63 shall be kept with, or made readily available with, the facility operating record. 15.1.1.6

[55 FR 25494, June 21, 1990, as amended at 56 FR 19290, Apr. 26, 1991; 61 FR 59950, Nov. 25, 1996; 62 FR 52641, Oct. 8, 1997; 62 FR 64656, Dec. 8, 1997; 71 FR 40274, July 14, 2006]

§264.1031 Definitions.

As used in this subpart, all terms not defined herein shall have the meaning given them in the Act and parts 260-266.

Air stripping operation is a desorption operation employed to transfer one or more volatile components from a liquid mixture into a gas (air) either with or without the application of heat to the liquid. Packed towers, spray towers, and bubble-cap, sieve, or valve-type plate towers are among the process configurations used for contacting the air and a liquid.

Bottoms receiver means a container or tank used to receive and collect the heavier bottoms fractions of the distillation feed stream that remain in the liquid phase.

Closed-vent system means a system that is not open to the atmosphere and that is composed of piping, connections, and, if necessary, flow-inducing devices that transport gas or vapor from a piece or pieces of equipment to a control device.

Condenser means a heat-transfer device that reduces a thermodynamic fluid from its vapor phase to its liquid phase.

Connector means flanged, screwed, welded, or other joined fittings used to connect two pipelines or a pipeline and a piece of equipment. For the purposes of reporting and recordkeeping, connector means flanged fittings that are not covered by insulation or other materials that prevent location of the fittings.

Continuous recorder means a data-recording device recording an instantaneous data value at least once every 15 minutes.

Control device means an enclosed combustion device, vapor recovery system, or flare. Any device the primary function of which is the recovery or capture of solvents or other organics for use, reuse, or sale (*e.g.*, a primary condenser on a solvent recovery unit) is not a control device.

Control device shutdown means the cessation of operation of a control device for any purpose.

Distillate receiver means a container or tank used to receive and collect liquid material (condensed) from the overhead condenser of a distillation unit and from which the condensed liquid is pumped to larger storage tanks or other process units.

Distillation operation means an operation, either batch or continuous, separating one or more feed stream(s) into two or more exit streams, each exit stream having component concentrations different from those in the feed stream(s). The separation is achieved by the redistribution of the components between the liquid and vapor phase as they approach equilibrium within the distillation unit.

Double block and bleed system means two block valves connected in series with a bleed valve or line that can vent the line between the two block valves.

Equipment means each valve, pump, compressor, pressure relief device, sampling connection system, open-ended valve or line, or flange or other connector, and any control devices or systems required by this subpart.

Flame zone means the portion of the combustion chamber in a boiler occupied by the flame envelope.

Flow indicator means a device that indicates whether gas flow is present in a vent stream.

First attempt at repair means to take rapid action for the purpose of stopping or reducing leakage of organic material to the atmosphere using best practices.

Fractionation operation means a distillation operation or method used to separate a mixture of several volatile components of different boiling points in successive stages, each stage removing from the mixture some proportion of one of the components.

Hazardous waste management unit shutdown means a work practice or operational procedure that stops operation of a hazardous waste management unit or part of a hazardous waste management unit. An unscheduled work practice or operational procedure that stops operation of a hazardous waste management unit or part of a hazardous waste management unit for less than 24 hours is not a hazardous waste management unit shutdown. The use of spare equipment and technically feasible bypassing of equipment without stopping operation are not hazardous waste management unit shutdowns.

Hot well means a container for collecting condensate as in a steam condenser serving a vacuum-jet or steam-jet ejector.

In gas/vapor service means that the piece of equipment contains or contacts a hazardous waste stream that is in the gaseous state at operating conditions.

In heavy liquid service means that the piece of equipment is not in gas/vapor service or in light liquid service.

In light liquid service means that the piece of equipment contains or contacts a waste stream where the vapor pressure of one or more of the organic components in the stream is greater than 0.3 kilopascals (kPa) at 20° C, the total concentration of the pure organic components having a vapor pressure greater than 0.3 kilopascals (kPa) at 20° C is equal to or greater than 20 percent by weight, and the fluid is a liquid at operating conditions.

📖 15.2.2.1

In situ sampling systems means nonextractive samplers or in-line samplers.

In vacuum service means that equipment is operating at an internal pressure that is at least 5 kPa below ambient pressure.

Malfunction means any sudden failure of a control device or a hazardous waste management unit or failure of a hazardous waste management unit to operate in a normal or usual manner, so that organic emissions are increased.

Open-ended valve or *line* means any valve, except pressure relief valves, having one side of the valve seat in contact with hazardous waste and one side open to the atmosphere, either directly or through open piping.

Pressure release means the emission of materials resulting from the system pressure being greater than the set pressure of the pressure relief device.

Process heater means a device that transfers heat liberated by burning fuel to fluids contained in tubes, including all fluids except water that are heated to produce steam.

Process vent means any open-ended pipe or stack that is vented to the atmosphere either directly, through a vacuum-producing system, or through a tank (*e.g.*, distillate receiver, condenser, bottoms receiver, surge control tank, separator tank, or hot well) associated with hazardous waste distillation, fractionation, thin-film evaporation, solvent extraction, or air or steam stripping operations.

15.1.1.5

Repaired means that equipment is adjusted, or otherwise altered, to eliminate a leak.

Sampling connection system means an assembly of equipment within a process or waste management unit used during periods of representative operation to take samples of the process or waste fluid. Equipment used to take non-routine grab samples is not considered a sampling connection system.

Sensor means a device that measures a physical quantity or the change in a physical quantity, such as temperature, pressure, flow rate, pH, or liquid level.

Separator tank means a device used for separation of two immiscible liquids.

Solvent extraction operation means an operation or method of separation in which a solid or solution is contacted with a liquid solvent (the two being mutually insoluble) to preferentially dissolve and transfer one or more components into the solvent.

Startup means the setting in operation of a hazardous waste management unit or control device for any purpose.

Steam stripping operation means a distillation operation in which vaporization of the volatile constituents of a liquid mixture takes place by the introduction of steam directly into the charge.

Surge control tank means a large-sized pipe or storage reservoir sufficient to contain the surging liquid discharge of the process tank to which it is connected.

Thin-film evaporation operation means a distillation operation that employs a heating surface consisting of a large diameter tube that may be either straight or tapered, horizontal or vertical. Liquid is spread on the tube wall by a rotating assembly of blades that maintain a close clearance from the wall or actually ride on the film of liquid on the wall.

Vapor incinerator means any enclosed combustion device that is used for destroying organic compounds and does not extract energy in the form of steam or process heat.

Vented means discharged through an opening, typically an open-ended pipe or stack, allowing the passage of a stream of liquids, gases, or fumes into the atmosphere. The passage of liquids, gases, or fumes is caused by mechanical means such as compressors or vacuum-producing systems or by process-related means such as evaporation produced by heating and not caused by tank loading and unloading (working losses) or by natural means such as diurnal temperature changes.

[55 FR 25494, June 21, 1990, as amended at 62 FR 64657, Dec. 8, 1997; 64 FR 3389, Jan. 21, 1999]

§264.1032 Standards: Process vents.

15.1.2.1

(a) The owner or operator of a facility with process vents associated with distillation, fractionation, thin-film evaporation, solvent extraction, or air or steam stripping operations managing hazardous wastes with organic concentrations of at least 10 ppmw shall either:

(1) Reduce total organic emissions from all affected process vents at the facility below 1.4 kg/h (3 lb/h) and 2.8 Mg/yr (3.1 tons/yr), or

(2) Reduce, by use of a control device, total organic emissions from all affected process vents at the facility by 95 weight percent.

(b) If the owner or operator installs a closed-vent system and control device to comply with the provisions of paragraph (a) of this section the closed-vent system and control device must meet the requirements of §264.1033.

(c) Determinations of vent emissions and emission reductions or total organic compound concentrations achieved by add-on control devices may be based on engineering calculations or performance tests. If performance tests are used to determine vent emissions, emission reductions, or total organic compound concentrations achieved by add-on control devices, the performance tests must conform with the requirements of §264.1034(c).

(d) When an owner or operator and the Regional Administrator do not agree on determinations of vent emissions and/or emission reductions or total organic compound concentrations achieved by add-on control devices based on engineering calculations, the procedures in §264.1034(c) shall be used to resolve the disagreement.

§264.1033 Standards: Closed-vent systems and control devices. 📖 15.1.2.2

(a)(1) Owners or operators of closed-vent systems and control devices used to comply with provisions of this part shall comply with the provisions of this section.

(2)(i) The owner or operator of an existing facility who cannot install a closed-vent system and control device to comply with the provisions of this subpart on the effective date that the facility becomes subject to the provisions of this subpart must prepare an implementation schedule that includes dates by which the closed-vent system and control device will be installed and in operation. The controls must be installed as soon as possible, but the implementation schedule may allow up to 30 months after the effective date that the facility becomes subject to this subpart for installation and startup.

(ii) Any unit that begins operation after December 21, 1990, and is subject to the provisions of this subpart when operation begins, must comply with the rules immediately (*i.e.*, must have control devices installed and operating on startup of the affected unit); the 30-month implementation schedule does not apply.

(iii) The owner or operator of any facility in existence on the effective date of a statutory or EPA regulatory amendment that renders the facility subject to this subpart shall comply with all requirements of this subpart as soon as practicable but no later than 30 months after the amendment's effective date. When control equipment required by this subpart can not be installed and begin operation by the effective date of the amendment, the facility owner or operator shall prepare an implementation schedule that includes the following information: Specific calendar dates for award of contracts or issuance of purchase orders for the control equipment, initiation of on-site installation of the control equipment, completion of the control equipment installation, and performance of any testing to demonstrate that the installed equipment meets the applicable standards of this subpart. The owner or operator shall enter the implementation schedule in the operating record or in a permanent, readily available file located at the facility.

(iv) Owners and operators of facilities and units that become newly subject to the requirements of this subpart after December 8, 1997, due to an action other than those described in paragraph (a)(2)(iii) of this section must comply with all applicable requirements immediately (*i.e.*, must have control devices installed and operating on the date the facility or unit becomes subject to this subpart; the 30-month implementation schedule does not apply).

(b) A control device involving vapor recovery (*e.g.*, a condenser or adsorber) shall be designed and operated to recover the organic vapors vented to it with an efficiency of 95 weight percent or greater unless the total organic emission limits of §264.1032(a)(1) for all affected process vents can be attained at an efficiency less than 95 weight percent.

(c) An enclosed combustion device (*e.g.*, a vapor incinerator, boiler, or process heater) shall be designed and operated to reduce the organic emissions vented to it by 95 weight percent or greater; to achieve a total organic compound concentration of 20 ppmv, expressed as the sum of the actual compounds, not carbon equivalents, on a dry basis corrected to 3 percent oxygen; or to provide a minimum residence time of 0.50 seconds at a minimum temperature of 760° C. If a boiler or process heater is used as the control device, then the vent stream shall be introduced into the flame zone of the boiler or process heater.

(d)(1) A flare shall be designed for and operated with no visible emissions as determined by the methods specified in paragraph (e)(1) of this section, except for periods not to exceed a total of 5 minutes during any 2 consecutive hours.

(2) A flare shall be operated with a flame present at all times, as determined by the methods specified in paragraph (f)(2)(iii) of this section.

(3) A flare shall be used only if the net heating value of the gas being combusted is 11.2 MJ/scm (300 Btu/scf) or greater if the flare is steam-assisted or air-assisted; or if the net heating value of the gas being combusted is 7.45 MJ/scm (200 Btu/scf) or greater if the flare is

nonassisted. The net heating value of the gas being combusted shall be determined by the methods specified in paragraph (e)(2) of this section.

(4)(i) A steam-assisted or nonassisted flare shall be designed for and operated with an exit velocity, as determined by the methods specified in paragraph (e)(3) of this section, less than 18.3 m/s (60 ft/s), except as provided in paragraphs (d)(4) (ii) and (iii) of this section.

(ii) A steam-assisted or nonassisted flare designed for and operated with an exit velocity, as determined by the methods specified in paragraph (e)(3) of this section, equal to or greater than 18.3 m/s (60 ft/s) but less than 122 m/s (400 ft/s) is allowed if the net heating value of the gas being combusted is greater than 37.3 MJ/scm (1,000 Btu/scf).

(iii) A steam-assisted or nonassisted flare designed for and operated with an exit velocity, as determined by the methods specified in paragraph (e)(3) of this section, less than the velocity, V_{max}, as determined by the method specified in paragraph (e)(4) of this section and less than 122 m/s (400 ft/s) is allowed.

(5) An air-assisted flare shall be designed and operated with an exit velocity less than the velocity, V_{max}, as determined by the method specified in paragraph (e)(5) of this section.

(6) A flare used to comply with this section shall be steam-assisted, air-assisted, or nonassisted.

(e)(1) Reference Method 22 in 40 CFR part 60 shall be used to determine the compliance of a flare with the visible emission provisions of this subpart. The observation period is 2 hours and shall be used according to Method 22.

(2) The net heating value of the gas being combusted in a flare shall be calculated using the following equation:

$$H_T = K\left[\sum_{i=1}^{n} C_i H_i\right]$$

where:

H_T = Net heating value of the sample, MJ/scm; where the net enthalpy per mole of offgas is based on combustion at 25° C and 760 mm Hg, but the standard temperature for determining the volume corresponding to 1 mol is 20° C;

K = Constant, 1.74×10^{-7} (1/ppm) (g mol/scm) (MJ/kcal) where standard temperature for (g mol/scm) is 20° C;

C_i = Concentration of sample component i in ppm on a wet basis, as measured for organics by Reference Method 18 in 40 CFR part 60 and measured for hydrogen and carbon monoxide by ASTM D 1946-82 (incorporated by reference as specified in §260.11); and

H_i = Net heat of combustion of sample component i, kcal/9 mol at 25° C and 760 mm Hg. The heats of combustion may be determined using ASTM D 2382-83 (incorporated by reference as specified in §260.11) if published values are not available or cannot be calculated.

(3) The actual exit velocity of a flare shall be determined by dividing the volumetric flow rate (in units of standard temperature and pressure), as determined by Reference Methods 2, 2A, 2C, or 2D in 40 CFR part 60 as appropriate, by the unobstructed (free) cross-sectional area of the flare tip.

(4) The maximum allowed velocity in m/s, V_{max}, for a flare complying with paragraph (d)(4)(iii) of this section shall be determined by the following equation:

$$\text{Log}_{10}(V_{max}) = (H_T + 28.8) / 31.7$$

where:

28.8 = Constant,

31.7 = Constant,

H_T = The net heating value as determined in paragraph (e)(2) of this section.

(5) The maximum allowed velocity in m/s, V_{max}, for an air-assisted flare shall be determined by the following equation:

$$V_{max} = 8.706 + 0.7084(H_T)$$

where:

8.706 = Constant,

0.7084 = Constant,

H_T = The net heating value as determined in paragraph (e)(2) of this section.

(f) The owner or operator shall monitor and inspect each control device required to comply with this section to ensure proper operation and maintenance of the control device by implementing the following requirements:

15.1.2.3

(1) Install, calibrate, maintain, and operate according to the manufacturer's specifications a flow indicator that provides a record of vent stream flow from each affected process vent to the control device at least once every hour. The flow indicator sensor shall be installed in the vent stream at the nearest feasible point to the control device inlet but before the point at which the vent streams are combined.

(2) Install, calibrate, maintain, and operate according to the manufacturer's specifications a device to continuously monitor control device operation as specified below:

(i) For a thermal vapor incinerator, a temperature monitoring device equipped with a continuous recorder. The device shall have an accuracy of ±1 percent of the temperature being monitored in ° C or ±0.5° C, whichever is greater. The temperature sensor shall be installed at a location in the combustion chamber downstream of the combustion zone.

(ii) For a catalytic vapor incinerator, a temperature monitoring device equipped with a continuous recorder. The device shall be capable of monitoring temperature at two locations and have an accuracy of ±1 percent of the temperature being monitored in ° C or ±0.5° C, whichever is greater. One temperature sensor shall be installed in the vent stream at the nearest feasible point to the catalyst bed inlet and a second temperature sensor shall be installed in the vent stream at the nearest feasible point to the catalyst bed outlet.

(iii) For a flare, a heat sensing monitoring device equipped with a continuous recorder that indicates the continuous ignition of the pilot flame.

(iv) For a boiler or process heater having a design heat input capacity less than 44 MW, a temperature monitoring device equipped with a continuous recorder. The device shall have an accuracy of ±1 percent of the temperature being monitored in ° C or ±0.5° C, whichever is greater. The temperature sensor shall be installed at a location in the furnace downstream of the combustion zone.

(v) For a boiler or process heater having a design heat input capacity greater than or equal to 44 MW, a monitoring device equipped with a continuous recorder to measure a parameter(s) that indicates good combustion operating practices are being used.

(vi) For a condenser, either:

(A) A monitoring device equipped with a continuous recorder to measure the concentration level of the organic compounds in the exhaust vent stream from the condenser, or

(B) A temperature monitoring device equipped with a continuous recorder. The device shall be capable of monitoring temperature with an accuracy of ±1 percent of the temperature being monitored in degrees Celsius (° C) or ±0.5° C, whichever is greater. The temperature sensor shall be installed at a location in the exhaust vent stream from the condenser exit (*i.e.*, product side).

(vii) For a carbon adsorption system that regenerates the carbon bed directly in the control device such as a fixed-bed carbon adsorber, either:

(A) A monitoring device equipped with a continuous recorder to measure the concentration level of the organic compounds in the exhaust vent stream from the carbon bed, or

(B) A monitoring device equipped with a continuous recorder to measure a parameter that indicates the carbon bed is regenerated on a regular, predetermined time cycle.

(3) Inspect the readings from each monitoring device required by paragraphs (f)(1) and (2) of this section at least once each operating day to check control device operation and, if necessary, immediately implement the corrective measures necessary to ensure the control device operates in compliance with the requirements of this section.

(g) An owner or operator using a carbon adsorption system such as a fixed-bed carbon adsorber that regenerates the carbon bed directly onsite in the control device shall replace the existing carbon in the control device with fresh carbon at a regular, predetermined time interval that is no longer than the carbon service life established as a requirement of §264.1035(b)(4)(iii)(F).

(h) An owner or operator using a carbon adsorption system such as a carbon canister that does not regenerate the carbon bed directly onsite in the control device shall replace the existing carbon in the control device with fresh carbon on a regular basis by using one of the following procedures:

(1) Monitor the concentration level of the organic compounds in the exhaust vent stream from the carbon adsorption system on a regular schedule, and replace the existing carbon with fresh carbon immediately when carbon breakthrough is indicated. The monitoring frequency shall be daily or at an interval no greater than 20 percent of the time required to consume the total carbon working capacity established as a requirement of §264.1035(b)(4)(iii)(G), whichever is longer.

(2) Replace the existing carbon with fresh carbon at a regular, predetermined time interval that is less than the design carbon replacement interval established as a requirement of §264.1035(b)(4)(iii)(G).

(i) An alternative operational or process parameter may be monitored if it can be demonstrated that another parameter will ensure that the control device is operated in conformance with these standards and the control device's design specifications.

(j) An owner or operator of an affected facility seeking to comply with the provisions of this part by using a control device other than a thermal vapor incinerator, catalytic vapor incinerator, flare, boiler, process heater, condenser, or carbon adsorption system is required to develop documentation including sufficient information to describe the control device operation and identify the process parameter or parameters that indicate proper operation and maintenance of the control device.

(k) A closed-vent system shall meet either of the following design requirements:

(1) A closed-vent system shall be designed to operate with no detectable emissions, as indicated by an instrument reading of less than 500 ppmv above background as determined by the procedure in §264.1034(b) of this subpart, and by visual inspections; or

(2) A closed-vent system shall be designed to operate at a pressure below atmospheric pressure. The system shall be equipped with at least one pressure gauge or other pressure measurement device that can be read from a readily accessible location to verify that negative pressure is being maintained in the closed-vent system when the control device is operating.

(l) The owner or operator shall monitor and inspect each closed-vent system required to comply with this section to ensure proper operation and maintenance of the closed-vent system by implementing the following requirements: 15.1.2.3

(1) Each closed-vent system that is used to comply with paragraph (k)(1) of this section shall be inspected and monitored in accordance with the following requirements:

(i) An initial leak detection monitoring of the closed-vent system shall be conducted by the owner or operator on or before the date that the system becomes subject to this section. The owner or operator shall monitor the closed-vent system components and connections using the procedures specified in §264.1034(b) of this subpart to demonstrate that the closed-vent system operates with no detectable emissions, as indicated by an instrument reading of less than 500 ppmv above background.

(ii) After initial leak detection monitoring required in paragraph (l)(1)(i) of this section, the owner or operator shall inspect and monitor the closed-vent system as follows:

(A) Closed-vent system joints, seams, or other connections that are permanently or semi-permanently sealed (*e.g.*, a welded joint between two sections of hard piping or a bolted and gasketed ducting flange) shall be visually inspected at least once per year to check for defects that could result in air pollutant emissions. The owner or operator shall monitor a component or connection using the procedures specified in §264.1034(b) of this subpart to demonstrate that it operates with no detectable emissions following any time the component is repaired or replaced (*e.g.*, a section of damaged hard piping is replaced with new hard piping) or the connection is unsealed (e.g., a flange is unbolted).

(B) Closed-vent system components or connections other than those specified in paragraph (l)(1)(ii)(A) of this section shall be monitored annually and at other times as requested by the Regional Administrator, except as provided for in paragraph (o) of this section, using the procedures specified in §264.1034(b) of this subpart to demonstrate that the components or connections operate with no detectable emissions.

(iii) In the event that a defect or leak is detected, the owner or operator shall repair the defect or leak in accordance with the requirements of paragraph (l)(3) of this section.

(iv) The owner or operator shall maintain a record of the inspection and monitoring in accordance with the requirements specified in §264.1035 of this subpart.

(2) Each closed-vent system that is used to comply with paragraph (k)(2) of this section shall be inspected and monitored in accordance with the following requirements:

(i) The closed-vent system shall be visually inspected by the owner or operator to check for defects that could result in air pollutant emissions. Defects include, but are not limited to, visible cracks, holes, or gaps in ductwork or piping or loose connections.

(ii) The owner or operator shall perform an initial inspection of the closed-vent system on or before the date that the system becomes subject to this section. Thereafter, the owner or operator shall perform the inspections at least once every year.

(iii) In the event that a defect or leak is detected, the owner or operator shall repair the defect in accordance with the requirements of paragraph (l)(3) of this section.

(iv) The owner or operator shall maintain a record of the inspection and monitoring in accordance with the requirements specified in §264.1035 of this subpart.

(3) The owner or operator shall repair all detected defects as follows:

(i) Detectable emissions, as indicated by visual inspection, or by an instrument reading greater than 500 ppmv above background, shall be controlled as soon as practicable, but not later than 15 calendar days after the emission is detected, except as provided for in paragraph (l)(3)(iii) of this section.

(ii) A first attempt at repair shall be made no later than 5 calendar days after the emission is detected.

(iii) Delay of repair of a closed-vent system for which leaks have been detected is allowed if the repair is technically infeasible without a process unit shutdown, or if the owner or operator determines that emissions resulting from immediate repair would be greater than the fugitive emissions likely to result from delay of repair. Repair of such equipment shall be completed by the end of the next process unit shutdown.

(iv) The owner or operator shall maintain a record of the defect repair in accordance with the requirements specified in §264.1035 of this subpart.

(m) Closed-vent systems and control devices used to comply with provisions of this subpart shall be operated at all times when emissions may be vented to them.

(n) The owner or operator using a carbon adsorption system to control air pollutant emissions shall document that all carbon that is a hazardous waste and that is removed from the control device is managed in one of the following manners, regardless of the average volatile organic concentration of the carbon:

(1) Regenerated or reactivated in a thermal treatment unit that meets one of the following:

(i) The owner or operator of the unit has been issued a final permit under 40 CFR part 270 which implements the requirements of subpart X of this part; or

(ii) The unit is equipped with and operating air emission controls in accordance with the applicable requirements of subparts AA and CC of either this part or of 40 CFR part 265; or

(iii) The unit is equipped with and operating air emission controls in accordance with a national emission standard for hazardous air pollutants under 40 CFR part 61 or 40 CFR part 63.

(2) Incinerated in a hazardous waste incinerator for which the owner or operator either:

(i) Has been issued a final permit under 40 CFR part 270 which implements the requirements of subpart O of this part; or

(ii) Has designed and operates the incinerator in accordance with the interim status requirements of 40 CFR part 265, subpart O.

(3) Burned in a boiler or industrial furnace for which the owner or operator either:

(i) Has been issued a final permit under 40 CFR part 270 which implements the requirements of 40 CFR part 266, subpart H; or

(ii) Has designed and operates the boiler or industrial furnace in accordance with the interim status requirements of 40 CFR part 266, subpart H.

(o) Any components of a closed-vent system that are designated, as described in §264.1035(c)(9) of this subpart, as unsafe to monitor are exempt from the requirements of paragraph (l)(1)(ii)(B) of this section if:

(1) The owner or operator of the closed-vent system determines that the components of the closed-vent system are unsafe to monitor because monitoring personnel would be exposed to an immediate danger as a consequence of complying with paragraph (l)(1)(ii)(B) of this section; and

(2) The owner or operator of the closed-vent system adheres to a written plan that requires monitoring the closed-vent system components using the procedure specified in paragraph (l)(1)(ii)(B) of this section as frequently as practicable during safe-to-monitor times.

[55 FR 25494, June 21, 1990, as amended at 56 FR 19290, Apr. 26, 1991; 59 FR 62927, Dec. 6, 1994; 61 FR 4911, Feb. 9, 1996; 61 FR 59950, Nov. 25, 1996; 62 FR 64657, Dec. 8, 1997; 71 FR 40274, July 14, 2006]

§264.1034 Test methods and procedures.

(a) Each owner or operator subject to the provisions of this subpart shall comply with the test methods and procedures requirements provided in this section.

(b) When a closed-vent system is tested for compliance with no detectable emissions, as required in §264.1033(l) of this subpart, the test shall comply with the following requirements:

(1) Monitoring shall comply with Reference Method 21 in 40 CFR part 60.

(2) The detection instrument shall meet the performance criteria of Reference Method 21.

(3) The instrument shall be calibrated before use on each day of its use by the procedures specified in Reference Method 21.

(4) Calibration gases shall be:

(i) Zero air (less than 10 ppm of hydrocarbon in air).

(ii) A mixture of methane or n-hexane and air at a concentration of approximately, but less than, 10,000 ppm methane or n-hexane.

(5) The background level shall be determined as set forth in Reference Method 21.

(6) The instrument probe shall be traversed around all potential leak interfaces as close to the interface as possible as described in Reference Method 21.

(7) The arithmetic difference between the maximum concentration indicated by the instrument and the background level is compared with 500 ppm for determining compliance.

(c) Performance tests to determine compliance with §264.1032(a) and with the total organic compound concentration limit of §264.1033(c) shall comply with the following:

(1) Performance tests to determine total organic compound concentrations and mass flow rates entering and exiting control devices shall be conducted and data reduced in accordance with the following reference methods and calculation procedures:

(i) Method 2 in 40 CFR part 60 for velocity and volumetric flow rate.

(ii) Method 18 or Method 25A in 40 CFR part 60, appendix A, for organic content. If Method 25A is used, the organic HAP used as the calibration gas must be the single organic HAP representing the largest percent by volume of the emissions. The use of Method 25A is acceptable if the response from the high-level calibration gas is at least 20 times the standard deviation of the response from the zero calibration gas when the instrument is zeroed on the most sensitive scale.

(iii) Each performance test shall consist of three separate runs; each run conducted for at least 1 hour under the conditions that exist when the hazardous waste management unit is operating at the highest load or capacity level reasonably expected to occur. For the purpose of determining total organic compound concentrations and mass flow rates, the average of results of all runs shall apply. The average shall be computed on a time-weighted basis.

(iv) Total organic mass flow rates shall be determined by the following equation:

(A) For sources utilizing Method 18.

$$E_h = Q_{2sd}\left\{\sum_{i=1}^{n} C_i MW_i\right\}[0.0416]\,[10^{-6}]$$

where:

E_h = Total organic mass flow rate, kg/h;

Q_{2sd} = Volumetric flow rate of gases entering or exiting control device, as determined by Method 2, dscm/h;

n = Number of organic compounds in the vent gas;

C_i = Organic concentration in ppm, dry basis, of compound i in the vent gas, as determined by Method 18;

MW_i = Molecular weight of organic compound i in the vent gas, kg/kg-mol;

0.0416 = Conversion factor for molar volume, kg-mol/m^3 (@ 293 K and 760 mm Hg);

10^{-6} = Conversion from ppm

(B) For sources utilizing Method 25A.

$$E_h = (Q)(C)(MW)(0.0416)(10^{-6})$$

where:

E_h = Total organic mass flow rate, kg/h;

Q = Volumetric flow rate of gases entering or exiting control device, as determined by Method 2, dscm/h;

C = Organic concentration in ppm, dry basis, as determined by Method 25A;

MW = Molecular weight of propane, 44;

0.0416 = Conversion factor for molar volume, kg-mol/m^3 (@ 293 K and 760 mm Hg);

10^{-6} = Conversion from ppm.

(v) The annual total organic emission rate shall be determined by the following equation:

$$E_A = (E_h)(H)$$

where:

E_A = Total organic mass emission rate, kg/y;

E_h = Total organic mass flow rate for the process vent, kg/h;

H = Total annual hours of operations for the affected unit, h.

(vi) Total organic emissions from all affected process vents at the facility shall be determined by summing the hourly total organic mass emission rates (E_h as determined in paragraph (c)(1)(iv) of this section) and by summing the annual total organic mass emission rates (E_A, as determined in paragraph (c)(1)(v) of this section) for all affected process vents at the facility.

(2) The owner or operator shall record such process information as may be necessary to determine the conditions of the performance tests. Operations during periods of startup, shutdown, and malfunction shall not constitute representative conditions for the purpose of a performance test.

(3) The owner or operator of an affected facility shall provide, or cause to be provided, performance testing facilities as follows:

(i) Sampling ports adequate for the test methods specified in paragraph (c)(1) of this section.

(ii) Safe sampling platform(s).

(iii) Safe access to sampling platform(s).

(iv) Utilities for sampling and testing equipment.

(4) For the purpose of making compliance determinations, the time-weighted average of the results of the three runs shall apply. In the event that a sample is accidentally lost or conditions occur in which one of the three runs must be discontinued because of forced shutdown, failure of an irreplaceable portion of the sample train, extreme meteorological conditions, or other circumstances beyond the owner or operator's control, compliance may, upon the Regional Administrator's approval, be determined using the average of the results of the two other runs.

(d) To show that a process vent associated with a hazardous waste distillation, fractionation, thin-film evaporation, solvent extraction, or air or steam stripping operation is not subject to the requirements of this subpart, the owner or operator must make an initial determination that the time-weighted, annual average total organic concentration of the waste managed by the waste management unit is less than 10 ppmw using one of the following two methods:

(1) Direct measurement of the organic concentration of the waste using the following procedures:

(i) The owner or operator must take a minimum of four grab samples of waste for each waste stream managed in the affected unit under process conditions expected to cause the maximum waste organic concentration.

(ii) For waste generated onsite, the grab samples must be collected at a point before the waste is exposed to the atmosphere such as in an enclosed pipe or other closed system that is used to transfer the waste after generation to the first affected distillation, fractionation, thin-film evaporation, solvent extraction, or air or steam stripping operation. For waste generated offsite, the grab samples must be collected at the inlet to the first waste management unit that receives the waste provided the waste has been transferred to the facility in a closed system such as a tank truck and the waste is not diluted or mixed with other waste.

(iii) Each sample shall be analyzed and the total organic concentration of the sample shall be computed using Method 9060A (incorporated by reference under 40 CFR 260.11) of "Test Methods for Evaluating Solid Waste, Physical/Chemical Methods," EPA Publication SW–846, or analyzed for its individual organic constituents.

(iv) The arithmetic mean of the results of the analyses of the four samples shall apply for each waste stream managed in the unit in determining the time-weighted, annual average total organic concentration of the waste. The time-weighted average is to be calculated using the annual quantity of each waste stream processed and the mean organic concentration of each waste stream managed in the unit.

(2) Using knowledge of the waste to determine that its total organic concentration is less than 10 ppmw. Documentation of the waste determination is required. Examples of documentation that shall be used to support a determination under this provision include production process information documenting that no organic compounds are used, information that the waste is generated by a process that is identical to a process at the same or another facility that has previously been demonstrated by direct measurement to generate a waste stream having a total organic content less than 10 ppmw, or prior speciation analysis results on the same waste stream where it can also be documented that no process changes have occurred since that analysis that could affect the waste total organic concentration.

(e) The determination that distillation, fractionation, thin-film evaporation, solvent extraction, or air or steam stripping operations manage hazardous wastes with time-weighted, annual average total organic concentrations less than 10 ppmw shall be made as follows:

(1) By the effective date that the facility becomes subject to the provisions of this subpart or by the date when the waste is first managed in a waste management unit, whichever is later, and

(2) For continuously generated waste, annually, or

(3) Whenever there is a change in the waste being managed or a change in the process that generates or treats the waste.

(f) When an owner or operator and the Regional Administrator do not agree on whether a distillation, fractionation, thin-film evaporation, solvent extraction, or air or steam stripping operation manages a hazardous waste with organic concentrations of at least 10 ppmw based on knowledge of the waste, the dispute may be resolved by using direct measurement as specified at paragraph (d)(1) of this section.

[55 FR 25494, June 21, 1990, as amended at 61 FR 59951, Nov. 25, 1996; 62 FR 32462, June 13, 1997; 70 FR 34581, June 14, 2005; 71 FR 40274, July 14, 2006]

§264.1035 Recordkeeping requirements.

15.1.2.4

(a)(1) Each owner or operator subject to the provisions of this subpart shall comply with the recordkeeping requirements of this section.

(2) An owner or operator of more than one hazardous waste management unit subject to the provisions of this subpart may comply with the recordkeeping requirements for these hazardous waste management units in one recordkeeping system if the system identifies each record by each hazardous waste management unit.

(b) Owners and operators must record the following information in the facility operating record:

(1) For facilities that comply with the provisions of §264.1033(a)(2), an implementation schedule that includes dates by which the closed-vent system and control device will be installed and in operation. The schedule must also include a rationale of why the installation cannot be completed at an earlier date. The implementation schedule must be in the facility operating record by the effective date that the facility becomes subject to the provisions of this subpart.

(2) Up-to-date documentation of compliance with the process vent standards in §264.1032, including:

(i) Information and data identifying all affected process vents, annual throughput and operating hours of each affected unit, estimated emission rates for each affected vent and for the overall facility (*i.e.*, the total emissions for all affected vents at the facility), and the approximate location within the facility of each affected unit (*e.g.*, identify the hazardous waste management units on a facility plot plan).

(ii) Information and data supporting determinations of vent emissions and emission reductions achieved by add-on control devices based on engineering calculations or source tests. For the purpose of determining compliance, determinations of vent emissions and emission reductions must be made using operating parameter values (*e.g.*, temperatures, flow rates, or vent stream organic compounds and concentrations) that represent the conditions that result in maximum organic emissions, such as when the waste management unit is operating at the highest load or capacity level reasonably expected to occur. If the owner or operator takes any action (*e.g.*, managing a waste of different composition or increasing operating hours of affected waste management units) that would result in an increase in total organic emissions from affected process vents at the facility, then a new determination is required.

(3) Where an owner or operator chooses to use test data to determine the organic removal efficiency or total organic compound concentration achieved by the control device, a performance test plan. The test plan must include:

(i) A description of how it is determined that the planned test is going to be conducted when the hazardous waste management unit is operating at the highest load or capacity level reasonably expected to occur. This shall include the estimated or design flow rate and organic content of each vent stream and define the acceptable operating ranges of key process and control device parameters during the test program.

(ii) A detailed engineering description of the closed-vent system and control device including:

(A) Manufacturer's name and model number of control device.

(B) Type of control device.

(C) Dimensions of the control device.

(D) Capacity.

(E) Construction materials.

(iii) A detailed description of sampling and monitoring procedures, including sampling and monitoring locations in the system, the equipment to be used, sampling and monitoring frequency, and planned analytical procedures for sample analysis.

(4) Documentation of compliance with §264.1033 shall include the following information:

(i) A list of all information references and sources used in preparing the documentation.

(ii) Records, including the dates, of each compliance test required by §264.1033(k).

(iii) If engineering calculations are used, a design analysis, specifications, drawings, schematics, and piping and instrumentation diagrams based on the appropriate sections of "APTI Course 415: Control of Gaseous Emissions" (incorporated by reference as specified in §260.11) or other engineering texts acceptable to the Regional Administrator that present basic control device design information. Documentation provided by the control device manufacturer or vendor that describes the control device design in accordance with paragraphs (b)(4)(iii)(A) through (b)(4)(iii)(G) of this section may be used to comply with this requirement. The design analysis shall address the vent stream characteristics and control device operation parameters as specified below.

(A) For a thermal vapor incinerator, the design analysis shall consider the vent stream composition, constituent concentrations, and flow rate. The design analysis shall also establish the design minimum and average temperature in the combustion zone and the combustion zone residence time.

(B) For a catalytic vapor incinerator, the design analysis shall consider the vent stream composition, constituent concentrations, and flow rate. The design analysis shall also establish the design minimum and average temperatures across the catalyst bed inlet and outlet.

(C) For a boiler or process heater, the design analysis shall consider the vent stream composition, constituent concentrations, and flow rate. The design analysis shall also establish the design minimum and average flame zone temperatures, combustion zone residence time, and description of method and location where the vent stream is introduced into the combustion zone.

(D) For a flare, the design analysis shall consider the vent stream composition, constituent concentrations, and flow rate. The design analysis shall also consider the requirements specified in §264.1033(d).

(E) For a condenser, the design analysis shall consider the vent stream composition, constituent concentrations, flow rate, relative humidity, and temperature. The design analysis shall also establish the design outlet organic compound concentration level, design average temperature of the condenser exhaust vent stream, and design average temperatures of the coolant fluid at the condenser inlet and outlet.

(F) For a carbon adsorption system such as a fixed-bed adsorber that regenerates the carbon bed directly onsite in the control device, the design analysis shall consider the vent stream composition, constituent concentrations, flow rate, relative humidity, and temperature. The design analysis shall also establish the design exhaust vent stream organic compound concentration level, number and capacity of carbon beds, type and working capacity of activated carbon used for carbon beds, design total steam flow over the period of each complete carbon bed regeneration cycle, duration of the carbon bed steaming and cooling/drying cycles, design carbon bed temperature after regeneration, design carbon bed regeneration time, and design service life of carbon.

(G) For a carbon adsorption system such as a carbon canister that does not regenerate the carbon bed directly onsite in the control device, the design analysis shall consider the vent stream composition, constituent concentrations, flow rate, relative humidity, and temperature. The design analysis shall also establish the design outlet organic concentration level, capacity of carbon bed, type and working capacity of activated carbon used for carbon bed, and design carbon replacement interval based on the total carbon working capacity of the control device and source operating schedule.

(iv) A statement signed and dated by the owner or operator certifying that the operating parameters used in the design analysis reasonably represent the conditions that exist when the hazardous waste management unit is or would be operating at the highest load or capacity level reasonably expected to occur.

(v) A statement signed and dated by the owner or operator certifying that the control device is designed to operate at an efficiency of 95 percent or greater unless the total organic concentration limit of §264.1032(a) is achieved at an efficiency less than 95 weight percent or the total organic emission limits of §264.1032(a) for affected process vents at the facility can be attained by a control device involving vapor recovery at an efficiency less than 95 weight percent. A statement provided by the control device manufacturer or vendor certifying that the control equipment meets the design specifications may be used to comply with this requirement.

(vi) If performance tests are used to demonstrate compliance, all test results.

(c) Design documentation and monitoring, operating, and inspection information for each closed-vent system and control device required to comply with the provisions of this part shall be recorded and kept up-to-date in the facility operating record. The information shall include:

(1) Description and date of each modification that is made to the closed-vent system or control device design.

(2) Identification of operating parameter, description of monitoring device, and diagram of monitoring sensor location or locations used to comply with §264.1033 (f)(1) and (f)(2).

(3) Monitoring, operating, and inspection information required by paragraphs (f) through (k) of §264.1033.

(4) Date, time, and duration of each period that occurs while the control device is operating when any monitored parameter exceeds the value established in the control device design analysis as specified below:

(i) For a thermal vapor incinerator designed to operate with a minimum residence time of 0.50 second at a minimum temperature of 760° C, period when the combustion temperature is below 760° C.

(ii) For a thermal vapor incinerator designed to operate with an organic emission reduction efficiency of 95 weight percent or greater, period when the combustion zone temperature is more than 28° C below the design average combustion zone temperature established as a requirement of paragraph (b)(4)(iii)(A) of this section.

(iii) For a catalytic vapor incinerator, period when:

(A) Temperature of the vent stream at the catalyst bed inlet is more than 28° C below the average temperature of the inlet vent stream established as a requirement of paragraph (b)(4)(iii)(B) of this section, or

(B) Temperature difference across the catalyst bed is less than 80 percent of the design average temperature difference established as a requirement of paragraph (b)(4)(iii)(B) of this section.

(iv) For a boiler or process heater, period when:

(A) Flame zone temperature is more than 28° C below the design average flame zone temperature established as a requirement of paragraph (b)(4)(iii)(C) of this section, or

(B) Position changes where the vent stream is introduced to the combustion zone from the location established as a requirement of paragraph (b)(4)(iii)(C) of this section.

(v) For a flare, period when the pilot flame is not ignited.

(vi) For a condenser that complies with §264.1033 (f)(2)(vi)(A), period when the organic compound concentration level or readings of organic compounds in the exhaust vent stream from the condenser are more than 20 percent greater than the design outlet organic compound concentration level established as a requirement of paragraph (b)(4)(iii)(E) of this section.

(vii) For a condenser that complies with §264.1033 (f)(2)(vi)(B), period when:

(A) Temperature of the exhaust vent stream from the condenser is more than 6° C above the design average exhaust vent stream temperature established as a requirement of paragraph (b)(4)(iii)(E) of this section; or

(B) Temperature of the coolant fluid exiting the condenser is more than 6° C above the design average coolant fluid temperature at the condenser outlet established as a requirement of paragraph (b)(4)(iii)(E) of this section.

(viii) For a carbon adsorption system such as a fixed-bed carbon adsorber that regenerates the carbon bed directly onsite in the control device and complies with §264.1033(f)(2)(vii)(A), period when the organic compound concentration level or readings of organic compounds in the exhaust vent stream from the carbon bed are more than 20 percent greater than the design exhaust vent stream organic compound concentration level established as a requirement of paragraph (b)(4)(iii)(F) of this section.

(ix) For a carbon adsorption system such as a fixed-bed carbon adsorber that regenerates the carbon bed directly onsite in the control device and complies with §264.1033(f)(2)(vii)(B), period when the vent stream continues to flow through the control device beyond the predetermined carbon bed regeneration time established as a requirement of paragraph (b)(4)(iii)(F) of this section.

(5) Explanation for each period recorded under paragraph (4) of the cause for control device operating parameter exceeding the design value and the measures implemented to correct the control device operation.

(6) For a carbon adsorption system operated subject to requirements specified in §264.1033(g) or §264.1033(h)(2),

date when existing carbon in the control device is replaced with fresh carbon.

(7) For a carbon adsorption system operated subject to requirements specified in §264.1033(h)(1), a log that records:

(i) Date and time when control device is monitored for carbon breakthrough and the monitoring device reading.

(ii) Date when existing carbon in the control device is replaced with fresh carbon.

(8) Date of each control device startup and shutdown.

(9) An owner or operator designating any components of a closed-vent system as unsafe to monitor pursuant to §264.1033(o) of this subpart shall record in a log that is kept in the facility operating record the identification of closed-vent system components that are designated as unsafe to monitor in accordance with the requirements of §264.1033(o) of this subpart, an explanation for each closed-vent system component stating why the closed-vent system component is unsafe to monitor, and the plan for monitoring each closed-vent system component.

(10) When each leak is detected as specified in §264.1033(l) of this subpart, the following information shall be recorded:

(i) The instrument identification number, the closed-vent system component identification number, and the operator name, initials, or identification number.

(ii) The date the leak was detected and the date of first attempt to repair the leak.

(iii) The date of successful repair of the leak.

(iv) Maximum instrument reading measured by Method 21 of 40 CFR part 60, appendix A after it is successfully repaired or determined to be nonrepairable.

(v) "Repair delayed" and the reason for the delay if a leak is not repaired within 15 calendar days after discovery of the leak.

(A) The owner or operator may develop a written procedure that identifies the conditions that justify a delay of repair. In such cases, reasons for delay of repair may be documented by citing the relevant sections of the written procedure.

(B) If delay of repair was caused by depletion of stocked parts, there must be documentation that the spare parts were sufficiently stocked on-site before depletion and the reason for depletion.

(d) Records of the monitoring, operating, and inspection information required by paragraphs (c)(3) through (c)(10) of this section shall be maintained by the owner or operator for at least 3 years following the date of each occurrence, measurement, maintenance, corrective action, or record.

(e) For a control device other than a thermal vapor incinerator, catalytic vapor incinerator, flare, boiler, process heater, condenser, or carbon adsorption system, the Regional Administrator will specify the appropriate recordkeeping requirements.

(f) Up-to-date information and data used to determine whether or not a process vent is subject to the requirements in §264.1032 including supporting documentation as required by §264.1034(d)(2) when application of the knowledge of the nature of the hazardous waste stream or the process by which it was produced is used, shall be recorded in a log that is kept in the facility operating record.

[55 FR 25494, June 21, 1990, as amended at 56 FR 19290, Apr. 26, 1991; 61 FR 59952, Nov. 25, 1996; 71 FR 40274, July 14, 2006]

§264.1036 Reporting requirements.

📖 15.1.2.4

(a) A semiannual report shall be submitted by owners and operators subject to the requirements of this subpart to the Regional Administrator by dates specified by the Regional Administrator. The report shall include the following information:

(1) The Environmental Protection Agency identification number, name, and address of the facility.

(2) For each month during the semiannual reporting period, dates when the control device exceeded or operated outside of the design specifications as defined in §264.1035(c)(4) and as indicated by the control device monitoring required by §264.1033(f) and such exceedances were not corrected within 24 hours, or that a flare operated with visible emissions as defined in §264.1033(d) and as determined by Method 22 monitoring, the duration and cause of each exceedance or visible emissions, and any corrective measures taken.

(b) If, during the semiannual reporting period, the control device does not exceed or operate outside of the design specifications as defined in §264.1035(c)(4) for more than 24 hours or a flare does not operate with visible emissions as defined in §264.1033(d), a report to the Regional Administrator is not required.

§§264.1037–264.1049 [Reserved]

Subpart BB—Air Emission Standards for Equipment Leaks

Source: 55 FR 25501, June 21, 1990, unless otherwise noted.

§264.1050 Applicability.

15.2.1

(a) The regulations in this subpart apply to owners and operators of facilities that treat, store, or dispose of hazardous wastes (except as provided in §264.1). 15.2.1.1

(b) Except as provided in §264.1064(k), this subpart applies to equipment that contains or contacts hazardous wastes with organic concentrations of at least 10 percent by weight that are managed in one of the following: 15.2.1.2–5

(1) A unit that is subject to the permitting requirements of 40 CFR part 270, or

(2) A unit (including a hazardous waste recycling unit) that is not exempt from permitting under the provisions of 40 CFR 262.34(a) (*i.e.*, a hazardous waste recycling unit that is not a "90-day" tank or container) and that is located at a hazardous waste management facility otherwise subject to the permitting requirements of 40 CFR part 270, or

(3) A unit that is exempt from permitting under the provisions of 40 CFR 262.34(a) (*i.e.*, a "90-day" tank or container) and is not a recycling unit under the provisions of 40 CFR 261.6.

(c) For the owner or operator of a facility subject to this subpart and who received a final permit under RCRA section 3005 prior to December 6, 1996, the requirements of this subpart shall be incorporated into the permit when the permit is reissued in accordance with the requirements of 40 CFR 124.15 or reviewed in accordance with the requirements of 40 CFR 270.50(d). Until such date when the owner or operator receives a final permit incorporating the requirements of this subpart, the owner or operator is subject to the requirements of 40 CFR part 265, subpart BB.

(d) Each piece of equipment to which this subpart applies shall be marked in such a manner that it can be distinguished readily from other pieces of equipment.

(e) Equipment that is in vacuum service is excluded from the requirements of §264.1052 to §264.1060 if it is identified as required in §264.1064(g)(5).

(f) Equipment that contains or contacts hazardous waste with an organic concentration of at least 10 percent by weight for less than 300 hours per calendar year is excluded from the requirements of §§264.1052 through 264.1060 of this subpart if it is identified, as required in §264.1064(g)(6) of this subpart. 15.2.1.4

(g) The requirements of this subpart do not apply to the pharmaceutical manufacturing facility, commonly referred to as the Stonewall Plant, located at Route 340 South, Elkton, Virginia, provided that facility is operated in compliance with the requirements contained in a Clean Air Act permit issued pursuant to 40 CFR 52.2454. The requirements of this subpart shall apply to the facility upon termination of the Clean Air Act permit issued pursuant to 40 CFR 52.2454.

(h) Purged coatings and solvents from surface coating operations subject to the national emission standards for hazardous air pollutants (NESHAP) for the surface coating of automobiles and light-duty trucks at 40 CFR part 63, subpart IIII, are not subject to the requirements of this subpart.

[*Note:* The requirements of §§264.1052 through 264.1065 apply to equipment associated with hazardous waste recycling units previously exempt under §261.6(c)(1). Other exemptions under §§261.4, and 264.1(g) are not affected by these requirements.]

[55 FR 25501, June 21, 1990, as amended at 61 FR 59952, Nov. 25, 1996; 62 FR 52641, Oct. 8, 1997; 62 FR 64657, Dec. 8, 1997; 69 FR 22661, Apr. 26, 2004; 71 FR 40274, July 14, 2006]

§264.1051 Definitions.

As used in this subpart, all terms shall have the meaning given them in §264.1031, the Act, and parts 260-266.

§264.1052 Standards: Pumps in light liquid service. 15.2.2.2

(a)(1) Each pump in light liquid service shall be monitored monthly to detect leaks by the methods specified in §264.1063(b), except as provided in paragraphs (d), (e), and (f) of this section.

(2) Each pump in light liquid service shall be checked by visual inspection each calendar week for indications of liquids dripping from the pump seal.

(b)(1) If an instrument reading of 10,000 ppm or greater is measured, a leak is detected.

(2) If there are indications of liquids dripping from the pump seal, a leak is detected.

(c)(1) When a leak is detected, it shall be repaired as soon as practicable, but not later than 15 calendar days after it is detected, except as provided in §264.1059.

(2) A first attempt at repair (*e.g.*, tightening the packing gland) shall be made no later than 5 calendar days after each leak is detected.

(d) Each pump equipped with a dual mechanical seal system that includes a barrier fluid system is exempt from the requirements of paragraph (a) of this section, provided the following requirements are met:

(1) Each dual mechanical seal system must be:

(i) Operated with the barrier fluid at a pressure that is at all times greater than the pump stuffing box pressure, or

(ii) Equipped with a barrier fluid degassing reservoir that is connected by a closed-vent system to a control device that complies with the requirements of §264.1060, or

(iii) Equipped with a system that purges the barrier fluid into a hazardous waste stream with no detectable emissions to the atmosphere.

(2) The barrier fluid system must not be a hazardous waste with organic concentrations 10 percent or greater by weight.

(3) Each barrier fluid system must be equipped with a sensor that will detect failure of the seal system, the barrier fluid system, or both.

(4) Each pump must be checked by visual inspection, each calendar week, for indications of liquids dripping from the pump seals.

(5)(i) Each sensor as described in paragraph (d)(3) of this section must be checked daily or be equipped with an audible alarm that must be checked monthly to ensure that it is functioning properly.

(ii) The owner or operator must determine, based on design considerations and operating experience, a criterion that indicates failure of the seal system, the barrier fluid system, or both.

(6)(i) If there are indications of liquids dripping from the pump seal or the sensor indicates failure of the seal system, the barrier fluid system, or both based on the criterion determined in paragraph (d)(5)(ii) of this section, a leak is detected.

(ii) When a leak is detected, it shall be repaired as soon as practicable, but not later than 15 calendar days after it is detected, except as provided in §264.1059.

(iii) A first attempt at repair (*e.g.*, relapping the seal) shall be made no later than 5 calendar days after each leak is detected.

(e) Any pump that is designated, as described in §264.1064(g)(2), for no detectable emissions, as indicated by an instrument reading of less than 500 ppm above background, is exempt from the requirements of paragraphs (a), (c), and (d) of this section if the pump meets the following requirements:

(1) Must have no externally actuated shaft penetrating the pump housing.

(2) Must operate with no detectable emissions as indicated by an instrument reading of less than 500 ppm above background as measured by the methods specified in §264.1063(c).

(3) Must be tested for compliance with paragraph (e)(2) of this section initially upon designation, annually, and at other times as requested by the Regional Administrator.

(f) If any pump is equipped with a closed-vent system capable of capturing and transporting any leakage from the seal or seals to a control device that complies with the requirements of §264.1060, it is exempt from the requirements of paragraphs (a) through (e) of this section.

[55 FR 25501, June 21, 1990, as amended at 56 FR 19290, Apr. 26, 1991]

§264.1053 Standards: Compressors. 📖 15.2.2.2

(a) Each compressor shall be equipped with a seal system that includes a barrier fluid system and that prevents leakage of total organic emissions to the atmosphere, except as provided in paragraphs (h) and (i) of this section.

(b) Each compressor seal system as required in paragraph (a) of this section shall be:

(1) Operated with the barrier fluid at a pressure that is at all times greater than the compressor stuffing box pressure, or

(2) Equipped with a barrier fluid system that is connected by a closed-vent system to a control device that complies with the requirements of §264.1060, or

(3) Equipped with a system that purges the barrier fluid into a hazardous waste stream with no detectable emissions to atmosphere.

(c) The barrier fluid must not be a hazardous waste with organic concentrations 10 percent or greater by weight.

(d) Each barrier fluid system as described in paragraphs (a) through (c) of this section shall be equipped with a sensor that will detect failure of the seal system, barrier fluid system, or both.

(e)(1) Each sensor as required in paragraph (d) of this section shall be checked daily or shall be equipped with an audible alarm that must be checked monthly to ensure that it is functioning properly unless the compressor is located within the boundary of an unmanned plant site, in which case the sensor must be checked daily.

(2) The owner or operator shall determine, based on design considerations and operating experience, a criterion that indicates failure of the seal system, the barrier fluid system, or both.

(f) If the sensor indicates failure of the seal system, the barrier fluid system, or both based on the criterion determined under paragraph (e)(2) of this section, a leak is detected.

(g)(1) When a leak is detected, it shall be repaired as soon as practicable, but not later than 15 calendar days after it is detected, except as provided in §264.1059.

(2) A first attempt at repair (*e.g.*, tightening the packing gland) shall be made no later than 5 calendar days after each leak is detected.

(h) A compressor is exempt from the requirements of paragraphs (a) and (b) of this section if it is equipped with a closed-vent system capable of capturing and transporting any leakage from the seal to a control device that complies with the requirements of §264.1060, except as provided in paragraph (i) of this section.

(i) Any compressor that is designated, as described in §264.1064(g)(2), for no detectable emissions as indicated by an instrument reading of less than 500 ppm above background is exempt from the requirements of paragraphs (a) through (h) of this section if the compressor:

(1) Is determined to be operating with no detectable emissions, as indicated by an instrument reading of less than 500 ppm above background, as measured by the method specified in §264.1063(c).

(2) Is tested for compliance with paragraph (i)(1) of this section initially upon designation, annually, and at other times as requested by the Regional Administrator.

§264.1054 Standards: Pressure relief devices in gas/vapor service. 15.2.2.2

(a) Except during pressure releases, each pressure relief device in gas/vapor service shall be operated with no detectable emissions, as indicated by an instrument reading of less than 500 ppm above background, as measured by the method specified in §264.1063(c).

(b)(1) After each pressure release, the pressure relief device shall be returned to a condition of no detectable emissions, as indicated by an instrument reading of less than 500 ppm above background, as soon as practicable, but no later than 5 calendar days after each pressure release, except as provided in §264.1059.

(2) No later than 5 calendar days after the pressure release, the pressure relief device shall be monitored to confirm the condition of no detectable emissions, as indicated by an instrument reading of less than 500 ppm above background, as measured by the method specified in §264.1063(c).

(c) Any pressure relief device that is equipped with a closed-vent system capable of capturing and transporting leakage from the pressure relief device to a control device as described in §264.1060 is exempt from the requirements of paragraphs (a) and (b) of this section.

§264.1055 Standards: Sampling connection systems. 15.2.2.2

(a) Each sampling connection system shall be equipped with a closed-purge, closed-loop, or closed-vent system. This system shall collect the sample purge for return to the process or for routing to the appropriate treatment system. Gases displaced during filling of the sample container are not required to be collected or captured.

(b) Each closed-purge, closed-loop, or closed-vent system as required in paragraph (a) of this section shall meet one of the following requirements:

(1) Return the purged process fluid directly to the process line;

(2) Collect and recycle the purged process fluid; or

(3) Be designed and operated to capture and transport all the purged process fluid to a waste management unit that complies with the applicable requirements of §264.1084 through §264.1086 of this subpart or a control device that complies with the requirements of §264.1060 of this subpart.

(c) *In-situ* sampling systems and sampling systems without purges are exempt from the requirements of paragraphs (a) and (b) of this section.

[61 FR 59952, Nov. 25, 1996]

§264.1056 Standards: Open-ended valves or lines. 15.2.2.2

(a)(1) Each open-ended valve or line shall be equipped with a cap, blind flange, plug, or a second valve.

(2) The cap, blind flange, plug, or second valve shall seal the open end at all times except during operations requiring hazardous waste stream flow through the open-ended valve or line.

(b) Each open-ended valve or line equipped with a second valve shall be operated in a manner such that the valve on the hazardous waste stream end is closed before the second valve is closed.

(c) When a double block and bleed system is being used, the bleed valve or line may remain open during operations that require venting the line between the block valves but shall comply with paragraph (a) of this section at all other times.

§264.1057 Standards: Valves in gas/vapor service or in light liquid service. 15.2.2.2

(a) Each valve in gas/vapor or light liquid service shall be monitored monthly to detect leaks by the methods specified in §264.1063(b) and shall comply with paragraphs (b) through (e) of this section, except as provided in paragraphs (f), (g), and (h) of this section, and §§264.1061 and 264.1062.

(b) If an instrument reading of 10,000 ppm or greater is measured, a leak is detected.

(c)(1) Any valve for which a leak is not detected for two successive months may be monitored the first month of every succeeding quarter, beginning with the next quarter, until a leak is detected.

(2) If a leak is detected, the valve shall be monitored monthly until a leak is not detected for two successive months,

(d)(1) When a leak is detected, it shall be repaired as soon as practicable, but no later than 15 calendar days after the leak is detected, except as provided in §264.1059.

(2) A first attempt at repair shall be made no later than 5 calendar days after each leak is detected.

(e) First attempts at repair include, but are not limited to, the following best practices where practicable:

(1) Tightening of bonnet bolts.

(2) Replacement of bonnet bolts.

(3) Tightening of packing gland nuts.

(4) Injection of lubricant into lubricated packing.

(f) Any valve that is designated, as described in §264.1064(g)(2), for no detectable emissions, as indicated by an instrument reading of less than 500 ppm above background, is exempt from the requirements of paragraph (a) of this section if the valve:

(1) Has no external actuating mechanism in contact with the hazardous waste stream.

(2) Is operated with emissions less than 500 ppm above background as determined by the method specified in §264.1063(c).

(3) Is tested for compliance with paragraph (f)(2) of this section initially upon designation, annually, and at other times as requested by the Regional Administrator.

(g) Any valve that is designated, as described in §264.1064(h)(1), as an unsafe-to-monitor valve is exempt from the requirements of paragraph (a) of this section if:

(1) The owner or operator of the valve determines that the valve is unsafe to monitor because monitoring personnel would be exposed to an immediate danger as a consequence of complying with paragraph (a) of this section.

(2) The owner or operator of the valve adheres to a written plan that requires monitoring of the valve as frequently as practicable during safe-to-monitor times.

(h) Any valve that is designated, as described in §264.1064(h)(2), as a difficult-to-monitor valve is exempt from the requirements of paragraph (a) of this section if:

(1) The owner or operator of the valve determines that the valve cannot be monitored without elevating the monitoring personnel more than 2 meters above a support surface.

(2) The hazardous waste management unit within which the valve is located was in operation before June 21, 1990.

(3) The owner or operator of the valve follows a written plan that requires monitoring of the valve at least once per calendar year.

§264.1058 Standards: Pumps and valves in heavy liquid service, pressure relief devices in light liquid or heavy liquid service, and flanges and other connectors. 15.2.2.2

(a) Pumps and valves in heavy liquid service, pressure relief devices in light liquid or heavy liquid service, and flanges and other connectors shall be monitored within 5 days by the method specified in §264.1063(b) if evidence of a potential leak is found by visual, audible, olfactory, or any other detection method.

(b) If an instrument reading of 10,000 ppm or greater is measured, a leak is detected.

(c)(1) When a leak is detected, it shall be repaired as soon as practicable, but not later than 15 calendar days after it is detected, except as provided in §264.1059.

(2) The first attempt at repair shall be made no later than 5 calendar days after each leak is detected.

(d) First attempts at repair include, but are not limited to, the best practices described under §264.1057(e).

(e) Any connector that is inaccessible or is ceramic or ceramic-lined (*e.g.*, porcelain, glass, or glass-lined) is exempt from the monitoring requirements of paragraph (a) of this section and from the recordkeeping requirements of §264.1064 of this subpart.

[55 FR 25501, June 21, 1990, as amended at 61 FR 59952, Nov. 25, 1996; 71 FR 40274, July 14, 2006]

§264.1059 Standards: Delay of repair.

(a) Delay of repair of equipment for which leaks have been detected will be allowed if the repair is technically infeasible without a hazardous waste management unit shutdown. In such a case, repair of this equipment shall occur before the end of the next hazardous waste management unit shutdown.

(b) Delay of repair of equipment for which leaks have been detected will be allowed for equipment that is isolated from the hazardous waste management unit and that does not continue to contain or contact hazardous waste with organic concentrations at least 10 percent by weight.

(c) Delay of repair for valves will be allowed if:

(1) The owner or operator determines that emissions of purged material resulting from immediate repair are greater than the emissions likely to result from delay of repair.

(2) When repair procedures are effected, the purged material is collected and destroyed or recovered in a control device complying with §264.1060.

(d) Delay of repair for pumps will be allowed if:

(1) Repair requires the use of a dual mechanical seal system that includes a barrier fluid system.

(2) Repair is completed as soon as practicable, but not later than 6 months after the leak was detected.

(e) Delay of repair beyond a hazardous waste management unit shutdown will be allowed for a valve if valve assembly replacement is necessary during the hazardous waste management unit shutdown, valve assembly supplies have been depleted, and valve assembly supplies had been sufficiently stocked before the supplies were depleted. Delay of repair beyond the next hazardous waste management unit shutdown will not be allowed unless the next hazardous waste management unit shutdown occurs sooner than 6 months after the first hazardous waste management unit shutdown.

§264.1060 Standards: Closed-vent systems and control devices.

(a) Owners and operators of closed-vent systems and control devices subject to this subpart shall comply with the provisions of §264.1033 of this part.

(b)(1) The owner or operator of an existing facility who cannot install a closed-vent system and control device to comply with the provisions of this subpart on the effective date that the facility becomes subject to the provisions of this subpart must prepare an implementation schedule that includes dates by which the closed-vent system and control device will be installed and in operation. The controls must be installed as soon as possible, but the implementation schedule may allow up to 30 months after the effective date that the facility becomes subject to this subpart for installation and startup.

(2) Any unit that begins operation after December 21, 1990, and is subject to the provisions of this subpart when operation begins, must comply with the rules immediately (*i.e.*, must have control devices installed and operating on startup of the affected unit); the 30-month implementation schedule does not apply.

(3) The owner or operator of any facility in existence on the effective date of a statutory or EPA regulatory amendment that renders the facility subject to this subpart shall comply with all requirements of this subpart as soon as practicable but no later than 30 months after the amendment's effective date. When control equipment required by this subpart can not be installed and begin operation by the effective date of the amendment, the facility owner or operator shall prepare an implementation schedule that includes the following information: Specific calendar dates for award or contracts or issuance of purchase orders for the control equipment, initiation of on-site installation of the control equipment, completion of the control equipment installation, and performance of any testing to demonstrate that the installed equipment meets the applicable standards of this subpart. The owner or operator shall enter the implementation schedule in the operating record or in a permanent, readily available file located at the facility.

(4) Owners and operators of facilities and units that become newly subject to the requirements of this subpart after December 8, 1997, due to an action other than those described in paragraph (b)(3) of this section must comply with all applicable requirements immediately (*i.e.*, must have control devices installed and operating on the date the facility or unit becomes subject to this subpart; the 30-month implementation schedule does not apply).

[62 FR 64657, Dec. 8, 1997]

§264.1061 Alternative standards for valves in gas/vapor service or in light liquid service: percentage of valves allowed to leak.

(a) An owner or operator subject to the requirements of §264.1057 may elect to have all valves within a hazardous waste management unit comply with an alternative standard that allows no greater than 2 percent of the valves to leak.

(b) The following requirements shall be met if an owner or operator decides to comply with the alternative standard of allowing 2 percent of valves to leak:

(1) A performance test as specified in paragraph (c) of this section shall be conducted initially upon designation, annually, and at other times requested by the Regional Administrator.

(2) If a valve leak is detected, it shall be repaired in accordance with §264.1057(d) and (e).

(c) Performance tests shall be conducted in the following manner:

(1) All valves subject to the requirements in §264.1057 within the hazardous waste management unit shall be monitored within 1 week by the methods specified in §264.1063(b).

(2) If an instrument reading of 10,000 ppm or greater is measured, a leak is detected.

(3) The leak percentage shall be determined by dividing the number of valves subject to the requirements in §264.1057 for which leaks are detected by the total number of valves subject to the requirements in §264.1057 within the hazardous waste management unit.

[55 FR 25501, June 21, 1990, as amended at 71 FR 16907, Apr. 4, 2006]

§264.1062 Alternative standards for valves in gas/vapor service or in light liquid service: skip period leak detection and repair.

(a) An owner or operator subject to the requirements of §264.1057 may elect for all valves within a hazardous waste management unit to comply with one of the alternative work practices specified in paragraphs (b) (2) and (3) of this section.

(b)(1) An owner or operator shall comply with the requirements for valves, as described in §264.1057, except as described in paragraphs (b)(2) and (b)(3) of this section.

(2) After two consecutive quarterly leak detection periods with the percentage of valves leaking equal to or less than 2 percent, an owner or operator may begin to skip one of the quarterly leak detection periods (*i.e.*, monitor for leaks once every six months) for the valves subject to the requirements in §264.1057 of this subpart.

(3) After five consecutive quarterly leak detection periods with the percentage of valves leaking equal to or less than 2 percent, an owner or operator may begin to skip three of the quarterly leak detection periods (*i.e.*, monitor for leaks once every year) for the valves subject to the requirements in §264.1057 of this subpart.

(4) If the percentage of valves leaking is greater than 2 percent, the owner or operator shall monitor monthly in compliance with the requirements in §264.1057, but may again elect to use this section after meeting the requirements of §264.1057(c)(1).

[55 FR 25501, June 21, 1990, as amended at 62 FR 64658, Dec. 8, 1997; 71 FR 16907, Apr. 4, 2006]

§264.1063 Test methods and procedures.

(a) Each owner or operator subject to the provisions of this subpart shall comply with the test methods and procedures requirements provided in this section.

(b) Leak detection monitoring, as required in §§264.1052-264.1062, shall comply with the following requirements:

(1) Monitoring shall comply with Reference Method 21 in 40 CFR part 60.

(2) The detection instrument shall meet the performance criteria of Reference Method 21.

(3) The instrument shall be calibrated before use on each day of its use by the procedures specified in Reference Method 21.

(4) Calibration gases shall be:

(i) Zero air (less than 10 ppm of hydrocarbon in air).

(ii) A mixture of methane or n-hexane and air at a concentration of approximately, but less than, 10,000 ppm methane or n-hexane.

(5) The instrument probe shall be traversed around all potential leak interfaces as close to the interface as possible as described in Reference Method 21.

(c) When equipment is tested for compliance with no detectable emissions, as required in §§264.1052(e), 264.1053(i), 264.1054, and 264.1057(f), the test shall comply with the following requirements:

(1) The requirements of paragraphs (b)(1) through (4) of this section shall apply.

(2) The background level shall be determined as set forth in Reference Method 21.

(3) The instrument probe shall be traversed around all potential leak interfaces as close to the interface as possible as described in Reference Method 21.

(4) The arithmetic difference between the maximum concentration indicated by the instrument and the background level is compared with 500 ppm for determining compliance.

(d) In accordance with the waste analysis plan required by §264.13(b), an owner or operator of a facility must determine, for each piece of equipment, whether the equipment contains or contacts a hazardous waste with organic concentration that equals or exceeds 10 percent by weight using the following:

(1) Methods described in ASTM Methods D 2267-88, E 169-87, E 168-88, E 260-85 (incorporated by reference under §260.11);

(2) Method 9060A (incorporated by reference under 40 CFR 260.11) of "Test Methods for Evaluating Solid Waste," EPA Publication SW–846, for computing total organic concentration of the sample, or analyzed for its individual organic constituents; or

(3) Application of the knowledge of the nature of the hazardous waste stream or the process by which it was produced. Documentation of a waste determination by knowledge is required. Examples of documentation that shall be used to support a determination under this provision include production process information documenting that no organic compounds are used, information that the waste is generated by a process that is identical to a process at the same or another facility that has previously been demonstrated by direct measurement to have a total organic content less than 10 percent, or prior speciation analysis results on the same waste stream where it can also be documented that no process changes have occurred since that analysis that could affect the waste total organic concentration.

(e) If an owner or operator determines that a piece of equipment contains or contacts a hazardous waste with organic concentrations at least 10 percent by weight, the determination can be revised only after following the procedures in paragraph (d)(1) or (d)(2) of this section.

(f) When an owner or operator and the Regional Administrator do not agree on whether a piece of equipment contains or contacts a hazardous waste with organic concentrations at least 10 percent by weight, the procedures in paragraph (d)(1) or (d)(2) of this section can be used to resolve the dispute.

(g) Samples used in determining the percent organic content shall be representative of the highest total organic content hazardous waste that is expected to be contained in or contact the equipment.

(h) To determine if pumps or valves are in light liquid service, the vapor pressures of constituents may be obtained from standard reference texts or may be determined by ASTM D-2879-86 (incorporated by reference under §260.11).

(i) Performance tests to determine if a control device achieves 95 weight percent organic emission reduction shall comply with the procedures of §264.1034(c)(1) through (c)(4).

[55 FR 25501, June 21, 1990, as amended at 62 FR 32462, June 13, 1997; 70 FR 34581, June 14, 2005]

§264.1064 Recordkeeping requirements.

15.2.2.3

(a)(1) Each owner or operator subject to the provisions of this subpart shall comply with the recordkeeping requirements of this section.

(2) An owner or operator of more than one hazardous waste management unit subject to the provisions of this subpart may comply with the recordkeeping requirements for these hazardous waste management units in one recordkeeping system if the system identifies each record by each hazardous waste management unit.

(b) Owners and operators must record the following information in the facility operating record:

(1) For each piece of equipment to which subpart BB of part 264 applies:

(i) Equipment identification number and hazardous waste management unit identification.

(ii) Approximate locations within the facility (*e.g.*, identify the hazardous waste management unit on a facility plot plan).

(iii) Type of equipment (*e.g.*, a pump or pipeline valve).

(iv) Percent-by-weight total organics in the hazardous waste stream at the equipment.

(v) Hazardous waste state at the equipment (*e.g.*, gas/vapor or liquid).

(vi) Method of compliance with the standard (*e.g.*, "monthly leak detection and repair" or "equipped with dual mechanical seals").

(2) For facilities that comply with the provisions of §264.1033(a)(2), an implementation schedule as specified in §264.1033(a)(2).

(3) Where an owner or operator chooses to use test data to demonstrate the organic removal efficiency or total organic compound concentration achieved by the control device, a performance test plan as specified in §264.1035(b)(3).

(4) Documentation of compliance with §264.1060, including the detailed design documentation or performance test results specified in §264.1035(b)(4).

(c) When each leak is detected as specified in §§264.1052, 264.1053, 264.1057, and 264.1058, the following requirements apply:

(1) A weatherproof and readily visible identification, marked with the equipment identification number, the date evidence of a potential leak was found in accordance with §264.1058(a), and the date the leak was detected, shall be attached to the leaking equipment.

(2) The identification on equipment, except on a valve, may be removed after it has been repaired.

(3) The identification on a valve may be removed after it has been monitored for 2 successive months as specified in §264.1057(c) and no leak has been detected during those 2 months.

(d) When each leak is detected as specified in §§264.1052, 264.1053, 264.1057, and 264.1058, the following information shall be recorded in an inspection log and shall be kept in the facility operating record:

(1) The instrument and operator identification numbers and the equipment identification number.

(2) The date evidence of a potential leak was found in accordance with §264.1058(a).

(3) The date the leak was detected and the dates of each attempt to repair the leak.

(4) Repair methods applied in each attempt to repair the leak.

(5) "Above 10,000" if the maximum instrument reading measured by the methods specified in §264.1063(b) after each repair attempt is equal to or greater than 10,000 ppm.

(6) "Repair delayed" and the reason for the delay if a leak is not repaired within 15 calendar days after discovery of the leak.

(7) Documentation supporting the delay of repair of a valve in compliance with §264.1059(c).

(8) The signature of the owner or operator (or designate) whose decision it was that repair could not be effected without a hazardous waste management unit shutdown.

(9) The expected date of successful repair of the leak if a leak is not repaired within 15 calendar days.

(10) The date of successful repair of the leak.

(e) Design documentation and monitoring, operating, and inspection information for each closed-vent system and control device required to comply with the provisions of §264.1060 shall be recorded and kept up-to-date in the facility operating record as specified in §264.1035(c). Design documentation is specified in §264.1035 (c)(1) and (c)(2) and monitoring, operating, and inspection information in §264.1035 (c)(3)-(c)(8).

(f) For a control device other than a thermal vapor incinerator, catalytic vapor incinerator, flare, boiler, process heater, condenser, or carbon adsorption system, the Regional Administrator will specify the appropriate recordkeeping requirements.

(g) The following information pertaining to all equipment subject to the requirements in §§264.1052 through 264.1060 shall be recorded in a log that is kept in the facility operating record:

(1) A list of identification numbers for equipment (except welded fittings) subject to the requirements of this subpart.

(2)(i) A list of identification numbers for equipment that the owner or operator elects to designate for no detectable emissions, as indicated by an instrument reading of less than 500 ppm above background, under the provisions of §§264.1052(e), 264.1053(i), and 264.1057(f).

(ii) The designation of this equipment as subject to the requirements of §§264.1052(e), 264.1053(i), or 264.1057(f) shall be signed by the owner or operator.

(3) A list of equipment identification numbers for pressure relief devices required to comply with §264.1054(a).

(4)(i) The dates of each compliance test required in §§264.1052(e), 264.1053(i), 264.1054, and 264.1057(f).

(ii) The background level measured during each compliance test.

(iii) The maximum instrument reading measured at the equipment during each compliance test.

(5) A list of identification numbers for equipment in vacuum service.

(6) Identification, either by list or location (area or group) of equipment that contains or contacts hazardous waste with an organic concentration of at least 10 percent by weight for less than 300 hours per calendar year.

(h) The following information pertaining to all valves subject to the requirements of §264.1057 (g) and (h) shall be recorded in a log that is kept in the facility operating record:

(1) A list of identification numbers for valves that are designated as unsafe to monitor, an explanation for

each valve stating why the valve is unsafe to monitor, and the plan for monitoring each valve.

(2) A list of identification numbers for valves that are designated as difficult to monitor, an explanation for each valve stating why the valve is difficult to monitor, and the planned schedule for monitoring each valve.

(i) The following information shall be recorded in the facility operating record for valves complying with §264.1062:

(1) A schedule of monitoring.

(2) The percent of valves found leaking during each monitoring period.

(j) The following information shall be recorded in a log that is kept in the facility operating record:

(1) Criteria required in §264.1052(d)(5)(ii) and §264.1053(e)(2) and an explanation of the design criteria.

(2) Any changes to these criteria and the reasons for the changes.

(k) The following information shall be recorded in a log that is kept in the facility operating record for use in determining exemptions as provided in the applicability section of this subpart and other specific subparts:

(1) An analysis determining the design capacity of the hazardous waste management unit.

(2) A statement listing the hazardous waste influent to and effluent from each hazardous waste management unit subject to the requirements in §§264.1052 through 264.1060 and an analysis determining whether these hazardous wastes are heavy liquids.

(3) An up-to-date analysis and the supporting information and data used to determine whether or not equipment is subject to the requirements in §§264.1052 through 264.1060. The record shall include supporting documentation as required by §264.1063(d)(3) when application of the knowledge of the nature of the hazardous waste stream or the process by which it was produced is used. If the owner or operator takes any action (*e.g.*, changing the process that produced the waste) that could result in an increase in the total organic content of the waste contained in or contacted by equipment determined not to be subject to the requirements in §§264.1052 through 264.1060, then a new determination is required.

(l) Records of the equipment leak information required by paragraph (d) of this section and the operating information required by paragraph (e) of this section need be kept only 3 years.

(m) The owner or operator of a facility with equipment that is subject to this subpart and to regulations at 40 CFR part 60, part 61, or part 63 may elect to determine compliance with this subpart either by documentation pursuant to §264.1064 of this subpart, or by documentation of compliance with the regulations at 40 CFR part 60, part 61, or part 63 pursuant to the relevant provisions of the regulations at 40 part 60, part 61, or part 63. The documentation of compliance under regulations at 40 CFR part 60, part 61, or part 63 shall be kept with or made readily available with the facility operating record. 📖 15.2.1.6

[55 FR 25501, June 21, 1990, as amended at 61 FR 59952, Nov. 25, 1996; 62 FR 64658, Dec. 8, 1997; 71 FR 40274, July 14, 2006]

§264.1065 Reporting requirements. 📖 15.2.2.3

(a) A semiannual report shall be submitted by owners and operators subject to the requirements of this subpart to the Regional Administrator by dates specified by the Regional Administrator. The report shall include the following information:

(1) The Environmental Protection Agency identification number, name, and address of the facility.

(2) For each month during the semiannual reporting period:

(i) The equipment identification number of each valve for which a leak was not repaired as required in §264.1057(d).

(ii) The equipment identification number of each pump for which a leak was not repaired as required in §264.1052 (c) and (d)(6).

(iii) The equipment identification number of each compressor for which a leak was not repaired as required in §264.1053(g).

(3) Dates of hazardous waste management unit shutdowns that occurred within the semiannual reporting period.

(4) For each month during the semiannual reporting period, dates when the control device installed as required by §264.1052, 264.1053, 264.1054, or 264.1055 exceeded or operated outside of the design specifications as defined in §264.1064(e) and as indicated by the control device monitoring required by §264.1060 and was not corrected within 24 hours, the duration and cause of each exceedance, and any corrective measures taken.

(b) If, during the semiannual reporting period, leaks from valves, pumps, and compressors are repaired as required in §§264.1057 (d), 264.1052 (c) and (d)(6), and

264.1053 (g), respectively, and the control device does not exceed or operate outside of the design specifications as defined in §264.1064(e) for more than 24 hours, a report to the Regional Administrator is not required.

§§264.1066–264.1079 [Reserved]

Subpart CC—Air Emission Standards for Tanks, Surface Impoundments, and Containers

Source: 59 FR 62927, Dec. 6, 1994, unless otherwise noted.

§264.1080 Applicability. 15.3.1

(a) The requirements of this subpart apply to owners and operators of all facilities that treat, store, or dispose of hazardous waste in tanks, surface impoundments, or containers subject to either subpart I, J, or K of this part except as §264.1 and paragraph (b) of this section provide otherwise. 15.3.1.1–2

(b) The requirements of this subpart do not apply to the following waste management units at the facility: 15.3.1.2.1

(1) A waste management unit that holds hazardous waste placed in the unit before December 6, 1996, and in which no hazardous waste is added to the unit on or after December 6, 1996.

(2) A container that has a design capacity less than or equal to 0.1 m^3.

(3) A tank in which an owner or operator has stopped adding hazardous waste and the owner or operator has begun implementing or completed closure pursuant to an approved closure plan.

(4) A surface impoundment in which an owner or operator has stopped adding hazardous waste (except to implement an approved closure plan) and the owner or operator has begun implementing or completed closure pursuant to an approved closure plan.

(5) A waste management unit that is used solely for on-site treatment or storage of hazardous waste that is placed in the unit as a result of implementing remedial activities required under the corrective action authorities of RCRA sections 3004(u), 3004(v), or 3008(h); CERCLA authorities; or similar Federal or State authorities.

(6) A waste management unit that is used solely for the management of radioactive mixed waste in accordance with all applicable regulations under the authority of the Atomic Energy Act and the Nuclear Waste Policy Act.

(7) A hazardous waste management unit that the owner or operator certifies is equipped with and operating air emission controls in accordance with the requirements of an applicable Clean Air Act regulation codified under 40 CFR part 60, part 61, or part 63. For the purpose of complying with this paragraph, a tank for which the air emission control includes an enclosure, as opposed to a cover, must be in compliance with the enclosure and control device requirements of §264.1084(i), except as provided in §264.1082(c)(5).

(8) A tank that has a process vent as defined in 40 CFR 264.1031.

(c) For the owner and operator of a facility subject to this subpart who received a final permit under RCRA section 3005 prior to December 6, 1996, the requirements of this subpart shall be incorporated into the permit when the permit is reissued in accordance with the requirements of 40 CFR 124.15 of this chapter or reviewed in accordance with the requirements of 40 CFR 270.50(d) of this chapter. Until such date when the permit is reissued in accordance with the requirements of 40 CFR 124.15 or reviewed in accordance with the requirements of 40 CFR 270.50(d), the owner and operator are subject to the requirements of 40 CFR part 265, subpart CC.

(d) The requirements of this subpart, except for the recordkeeping requirements specified in §264.1089(i) of this subpart, are administratively stayed for a tank or a container used for the management of hazardous waste generated by organic peroxide manufacturing and its associated laboratory operations when the owner or operator of the unit meets all of the following conditions: 15.3.1.2.1

(1) The owner or operator identifies that the tank or container receives hazardous waste generated by an organic peroxide manufacturing process producing more than one functional family of organic peroxides or multiple organic peroxides within one functional family, that one or more of these organic peroxides could potentially undergo self-accelerating thermal decomposition at or below ambient temperatures, and that organic peroxides are the predominant products manufactured by the process. For the purpose of meeting the conditions of this paragraph, "organic peroxide" means an organic compound that contains the bivalent —O—O— structure and which may be considered to be a structural derivative of hydrogen peroxide where one or both of the hydrogen atoms has been replaced by an organic radical.

(2) The owner or operator prepares documentation, in accordance with the requirements of §264.1089(i) of this subpart, explaining why an undue safety hazard would be created if air emission controls specified in §§264.1084 through 264.1087 of this subpart are installed and operated on the tanks and containers used at the facility to manage the hazardous waste generated by the organic peroxide manufacturing process or processes meeting the conditions of paragraph (d)(1) of this section.

(3) The owner or operator notifies the Regional Administrator in writing that hazardous waste generated by an organic peroxide manufacturing process or processes meeting the conditions of paragraph (d)(1) of this section are managed at the facility in tanks or containers meeting the conditions of paragraph (d)(2) of this section. The notification shall state the name and address of the facility, and be signed and dated by an authorized representative of the facility owner or operator.

(e)(1) Except as provided in paragraph (e)(2) of this section, the requirements of this subpart do not apply to the pharmaceutical manufacturing facility, commonly referred to as the Stonewall Plant, located at Route 340 South, Elkton, Virginia, provided that facility is operated in compliance with the requirements contained in a Clean Air Act permit issued pursuant to 40 CFR 52.2454. The requirements of this subpart shall apply to the facility upon termination of the Clean Air Act permit issued pursuant to 40 CFR 52.2454.

(2) Notwithstanding paragraph (e)(1) of this section, any hazardous waste surface impoundment operated at the Stonewall Plant is subject to:

(i) The standards in §264.1085 and all requirements related to hazardous waste surface impoundments that are referenced in or by §264.1085, including the closed-vent system and control device requirements of §264.1087 and the recordkeeping requirements of §264.1089(c); and

(ii) The reporting requirements of §264.1090 that are applicable to surface impoundments and/or to closed-vent systems and control devices associated with a surface impoundment.

(f) This section applies only to the facility commonly referred to as the OSi Specialties Plant, located on State Route 2, Sistersville, West Virginia ("Sistersville Plant").

(1)(i) Provided that the Sistersville Plant is in compliance with the requirements of paragraph (f)(2) of this section, the requirements referenced in paragraphs (f)(1)(iii) and (f)(1)(iv) of this section are temporarily deferred, as specified in paragraph (f)(3) of this section, with respect to the two hazardous waste surface impoundments at the Sistersville Plant. Beginning on the date that paragraph (f)(1)(ii) of this section is first implemented, the temporary deferral of this paragraph shall no longer be effective.

(ii)(A) In the event that a notice of revocation is issued pursuant to paragraph (f)(3)(iv) of this section, the requirements referenced in paragraphs (f)(1)(iii) and (f)(1)(iv) of this section are temporarily deferred, with respect to the two hazardous waste surface impoundments, provided that the Sistersville Plant is in compliance with the requirements of paragraphs (f)(2)(ii), (f)(2)(iii), (f)(2)(iv), (f)(2)(v), (f)(2)(vi) and (g) of this section, except as provided under paragraph (f)(1)(ii)(B) of this section. The temporary deferral of the previous sentence shall be effective beginning on the date the Sistersville Plant receives written notification of revocation, and continuing for a maximum period of 18 months from that date, provided that the Sistersville Plant is in compliance with the requirements of paragraphs (f)(2)(ii), (f)(2)(iii), (f)(2)(iv), (f)(2)(v), (f)(2)(vi) and (g) of this section at all times during that 18-month period. In no event shall the temporary deferral continue to be effective after the MON Compliance Date.

(B) In the event that a notification of revocation is issued pursuant to paragraph (f)(3)(iv) of this section as a result of the permanent removal of the capper unit from methyl capped polyether production service, the requirements referenced in paragraphs (f)(1)(iii) and (f)(1)(iv) of this section are temporarily deferred, with respect to the two hazardous waste surface impoundments, provided that the Sistersville Plant is in compliance with the requirements of paragraphs (f)(2)(vi), and (g) of this section. The temporary deferral of the previous sentence shall be effective beginning on the date the Sistersville Plant receives written notification of revocation, and continuing for a maximum period of 18 months from that date, provided that the Sistersville Plant is in compliance with the requirements of paragraphs (f)(2)(vi) and (g) of this section at all times during that 18-month period. In no event shall the temporary deferral continue to be effective after the MON Compliance Date.

(iii) The standards in §264.1085 of this part, and all requirements referenced in or by §264.1085 that otherwise would apply to the two hazardous waste surface impoundments, including the closed-vent system and control device requirements of §264.1087 of this part.

(iv) The reporting requirements of §264.1090 that are applicable to surface impoundments and/or to closed-vent systems and control devices associated with a surface impoundment.

(2) Notwithstanding the effective period and revocation provisions in paragraph (f)(3) of this section, the temporary deferral provided in paragraph (f)(1)(i) of this section is effective only if the Sistersville Plant meets the requirements of paragraph (f)(2) of this section.

(i) The Sistersville Plant shall install an air pollution control device on the polyether methyl capper unit ("capper unit"), implement a methanol recovery operation, and implement a waste minimization/pollution prevention ("WMPP") project. The installation and implementation of these requirements shall be conducted according to the schedule described in paragraphs (f)(2)(i) and (f)(2)(vi) of this section.

(A) The Sistersville Plant shall complete the initial start-up of a thermal incinerator on the capper unit's process vents from the first stage vacuum pump, from the flash pot and surge tank, and from the water stripper, no later than April 1, 1998.

(B) The Sistersville Plant shall provide to the EPA and the West Virginia Department of Environmental Protection, written notification of the actual date of initial start-up of the thermal incinerator, and commencement of the methanol recovery operation. The Sistersville Plant shall submit this written notification as soon as practicable, but in no event later than 15 days after such events.

(ii) The Sistersville Plant shall install and operate the capper unit process vent thermal incinerator according to the requirements of paragraphs (f)(2)(ii)(A) through (f)(2)(ii)(D) of this section.

(A) Capper unit process vent thermal incinerator.

(*1*) Except as provided under paragraph (f)(2)(ii)(D) of this section, the Sistersville Plant shall operate the process vent thermal incinerator such that the incinerator reduces the total organic compounds ("TOC") from the process vent streams identified in paragraph (f)(2)(i)(A) of this section, by 98 weight-percent, or to a concentration of 20 parts per million by volume, on a dry basis, corrected to 3 percent oxygen, whichever is less stringent.

(*i*) Prior to conducting the initial performance test required under paragraph (f)(2)(ii)(B) of this section, the Sistersville Plant shall operate the thermal incinerator at or above a minimum temperature of 1600 Fahrenheit.

(*ii*) After the initial performance test required under paragraph (f)(2)(ii)(B) of this section, the Sistersville Plant shall operate the thermal incinerator at or above the minimum temperature established during that initial performance test.

(*iii*) The Sistersville Plant shall operate the process vent thermal incinerator at all times that the capper unit is being operated to manufacture product.

(*2*) The Sistersville Plant shall install, calibrate, and maintain all air pollution control and monitoring equipment described in paragraphs (f)(2)(i)(A) and (f)(2)(ii)(B)(*3*) of this section, according to the manufacturer's specifications, or other written procedures that provide adequate assurance that the equipment can reasonably be expected to control and monitor accurately, and in a manner consistent with good engineering practices during all periods when emissions are routed to the unit.

(B) The Sistersville Plant shall comply with the requirements of paragraphs (f)(2)(ii)(B)(*1*) through (f)(2)(ii)(B)(*3*) of this section for performance testing and monitoring of the capper unit process vent thermal incinerator.

(*1*) Within sixty (120) days after thermal incinerator initial start-up, the Sistersville Plant shall conduct a performance test to determine the minimum temperature at which compliance with the emission reduction requirement specified in paragraph (f)(4) of this section is achieved. This determination shall be made by measuring TOC minus methane and ethane, according to the procedures specified in paragraph (f)(2)(ii)(B) of this section.

(*2*) The Sistersville Plant shall conduct the initial performance test in accordance with the standards set forth in paragraph (f)(4) of this section.

(*3*) Upon initial start-up, the Sistersville Plant shall install, calibrate, maintain and operate, according to manufacturer's specifications and in a manner consistent with good engineering practices, the monitoring equipment described in paragraphs (f)(2)(ii)(B)(*3*)(*i*) through (f)(2)(ii)(B)(*3*)(*iii*) of this section.

(*i*) A temperature monitoring device equipped with a continuous recorder. The temperature monitoring device shall be installed in the firebox or in the duct work immediately downstream of the firebox in a position before any substantial heat exchange is encountered.

(*ii*) A flow indicator that provides a record of vent stream flow to the incinerator at least once every fifteen minutes. The flow indicator shall be installed in the vent stream from the process vent at a point closest to the inlet of the incinerator.

(*iii*) If the closed-vent system includes bypass devices that could be used to divert the gas or vapor stream to the atmosphere before entering the control device, each bypass device shall be equipped with either a bypass flow indicator or a seal or locking device as specified in this paragraph. For the purpose of complying with this paragraph, low leg drains, high point bleeds, analyzer vents, open-ended valves or lines, spring-loaded pressure relief valves, and other fittings used for safety purposes are not considered to be bypass devices. If a bypass flow indicator is used to comply with this paragraph, the bypass flow indicator shall be installed at the inlet to the bypass line used to divert gases and vapors from the closed-vent system to the atmosphere at a point upstream of the control device inlet. If a seal or locking device (*e.g.* car-seal or lock-and-key configuration) is used to comply with this paragraph, the device shall be placed on the mechanism by which the bypass device position is controlled (*e.g.*, valve handle, damper levels) when the bypass device is in the closed position such that the bypass device cannot be opened without breaking the seal or removing the lock. The Sistersville Plant shall visually inspect the seal or locking device at least once every month to verify that the bypass mechanism is maintained in the closed position.

(C) The Sistersville Plant shall keep on-site an up-to-date, readily accessible record of the information described in paragraphs (f)(2)(ii)(C)(*1*) through (f)(2)(ii)(C)(*4*) of this section.

(*1*) Data measured during the initial performance test regarding the firebox temperature of the incinerator and the percent reduction of TOC achieved by the incinerator, and/or such other information required in addition to or in lieu of that information by the WVDEP in its approval of equivalent test methods and procedures.

(*2*) Continuous records of the equipment operating procedures specified to be monitored under paragraph (f)(2)(ii)(B)(*3*) of this section, as well as records of periods of operation during which the firebox temperature falls below the minimum temperature established under paragraph (f)(2)(ii)(A)(*1*) of this section.

(*3*) Records of all periods during which the vent stream has no flow rate to the extent that the capper unit is being operated during such period.

(*4*) Records of all periods during which there is flow through a bypass device.

(D) The Sistersville Plant shall comply with the start-up, shutdown, maintenance and malfunction requirements contained in paragraphs (f)(2)(ii)(D)(*1*) through (f)(2)(ii)(D)(*6*) of this section, with respect to the capper unit process vent incinerator.

(*1*) The Sistersville Plant shall develop and implement a Start-up, Shutdown and Malfunction Plan as required by the provisions set forth in paragraph (f)(2)(ii)(D) of this section. The plan shall describe, in detail, procedures for operating and maintaining the thermal incinerator during periods of start-up, shutdown and malfunction, and a program of corrective action for malfunctions of the thermal incinerator.

(*2*) The plan shall include a detailed description of the actions the Sistersville Plant will take to perform the functions described in paragraphs (f)(2)(ii)(D)(*2*)(*i*) through (f)(2)(ii)(D)(*2*)(*iii*) of this section.

(*i*) Ensure that the thermal incinerator is operated in a manner consistent with good air pollution control practices.

(*ii*) Ensure that the Sistersville Plant is prepared to correct malfunctions as soon as practicable after their occurrence in order to minimize excess emissions.

(*iii*) Reduce the reporting requirements associated with periods of start-up, shutdown and malfunction.

(*3*) During periods of start-up, shutdown and malfunction, the Sistersville Plant shall maintain the process unit and the associated thermal incinerator in accordance with the procedures set forth in the plan.

(*4*) The plan shall contain record keeping requirements relating to periods of start-up, shutdown or malfunction, actions taken during such periods in conformance with the plan, and any failures to act in conformance with the plan during such periods.

(*5*) During periods of maintenance or malfunction of the thermal incinerator, the Sistersville Plant may continue to operate the capper unit, provided that operation of the capper unit without the thermal incinerator shall be limited to no more than 240 hours each calendar year.

(*6*) For the purposes of paragraph (f)(2)(iii)(D) of this section, the Sistersville Plant may use its operating procedures manual, or a plan developed for other reasons, provided that plan meets the requirements of paragraph (f)(2)(iii)(D) of this section for the start-up, shutdown and malfunction plan.

(iii) The Sistersville Plant shall operate the closed-vent system in accordance with the requirements of paragraphs (f)(2)(iii)(A) through (f)(2)(iii)(D) of this section.

(A) Closed-vent system.

(*1*) At all times when the process vent thermal incinerator is operating, the Sistersville Plant shall route the vent streams identified in paragraph (f)(2)(i) of this section from the capper unit to the thermal incinerator through a closed-vent system.

(*2*) The closed-vent system will be designed for and operated with no detectable emissions, as defined in paragraph (f)(6) of this section.

(B) The Sistersville Plant will comply with the performance standards set forth in paragraph (f)(2)(iii)(A)(*1*) of this section on and after the date on which the initial performance test referenced in paragraph (f)(2)(ii)(B) of this section is completed, but no later than sixty (60) days after the initial start-up date.

(C) The Sistersville Plant shall comply with the monitoring requirements of paragraphs (f)(2)(iii)(C)(*1*) through (f)(2)(iii)(C)(*3*) of this section, with respect to the closed-vent system.

(*1*) At the time of the performance test described in paragraph (f)(2)(ii)(B) of this section, the Sistersville Plant shall inspect the closed-vent system as specified in paragraph (f)(5) of this section.

(*2*) At the time of the performance test described in paragraph (f)(2)(ii)(B) of this section, and annually thereafter, the Sistersville Plant shall inspect the closed-vent system for visible, audible, or olfactory indications of leaks.

(*3*) If at any time a defect or leak is detected in the closed-vent system, the Sistersville Plant shall repair the defect or leak in accordance with the requirements of paragraphs (f)(2)(iii)(C)(*3*)(*i*) and (f)(2)(iii)(C)(*3*)(*ii*) of this section.

(*i*) The Sistersville Plant shall make first efforts at repair of the defect no later than five (5) calendar days after detection, and repair shall be completed as soon as possible but no later than forty-five (45) calendar days after detection.

(*ii*) The Sistersville Plant shall maintain a record of the defect repair in accordance with the requirements specified in paragraph (f)(2)(iii)(D) of this section.

(D) The Sistersville Plant shall keep on-site up-to-date, readily accessible records of the inspections and repairs required to be performed by paragraph (f)(2)(iii) of this section.

(iv) The Sistersville Plant shall operate the methanol recovery operation in accordance with paragraphs (f)(2)(iv)(A) through (f)(2)(iv)(C) of this section.

(A) The Sistersville Plant shall operate the condenser associated with the methanol recovery operation at all times during which the capper unit is being operated to manufacture product.

(B) The Sistersville Plant shall comply with the monitoring requirements described in paragraphs (f)(2)(iv)(B)(*1*) through (f)(2)(iv)(B)(*3*) of this section, with respect to the methanol recovery operation.

(*1*) The Sistersville Plant shall perform measurements necessary to determine the information described in paragraphs (f)(2)(iv)(B)(*1*)(*i*) and (f)(2)(iv)(B)(*1*)(*ii*) of this section to demonstrate the percentage recovery by weight of the methanol contained in the influent gas stream to the condenser.

(*i*) Information as is necessary to calculate the annual amount of methanol generated by operating the capper unit.

(*ii*) The annual amount of methanol recovered by the condenser associated with the methanol recovery operation.

(*2*) The Sistersville Plant shall install, calibrate, maintain and operate according to manufacturer specifications, a temperature monitoring device with a continuous recorder for the condenser associated with the methanol recovery operation, as an indicator that the condenser is operating.

(*3*) The Sistersville Plant shall record the dates and times during which the capper unit and the condenser are operating.

(C) The Sistersville Plant shall keep on-site up-to-date, readily-accessible records of the parameters specified to be monitored under paragraph (f)(2)(iv)(B) of this section.

(v) The Sistersville Plant shall comply with the requirements of paragraphs (f)(2)(v)(A) through (f)(2)(v)(C) of this section for the disposition of methanol collected by the methanol recovery operation.

(A) On an annual basis, the Sistersville Plant shall ensure that a minimum of 95% by weight of the methanol collected by the methanol recovery operation (also referred to as the "collected methanol") is utilized for reuse, recovery, or thermal recovery/treatment. The Sistersville Plant may use the methanol on-site, or may transfer or sell the methanol for reuse, recovery, or thermal recovery/treatment at other facilities.

(*1*) Reuse. To the extent reuse of all of the collected methanol destined for reuse, recovery, or thermal recovery is not economically feasible, the Sistersville Plant shall ensure the residual portion is sent for recovery, as defined in paragraph (f)(6) of this section, except as provided in paragraph (f)(2)(v)(A)(*2*) of this section.

(*2*) Recovery. To the extent that reuse or recovery of all the collected methanol destined for reuse, recovery, or thermal recovery is not economically feasible, the Sistersville Plant shall ensure that the residual portion is sent for thermal recovery/treatment, as defined in paragraph (f)(6) of this section.

(*3*) The Sistersville Plant shall ensure that, on an annual basis, no more than 5% of the methanol collected by the methanol recovery operation is subject to bio-treatment.

(*4*) In the event the Sistersville Plant receives written notification of revocation pursuant to paragraph (f)(3)(iv) of this section, the percent limitations set forth under paragraph (f)(2)(v)(A) of this section shall no longer be applicable, beginning on the date of receipt of written notification of revocation.

(B) The Sistersville Plant shall perform such measurements as are necessary to determine the pounds of collected methanol directed to reuse, recovery, thermal recovery/treatment and bio-treatment, respectively, on a monthly basis.

(C) The Sistersville Plant shall keep on-site up-to-date, readily accessible records of the amounts of collected methanol directed to reuse, recovery, thermal recovery/treatment and bio-treatment necessary for the measurements required under paragraph (f)(2)(iv)(B) of this section.

(vi) The Sistersville Plant shall perform a WMPP project in accordance with the requirements and schedules set forth in paragraphs (f)(2)(vi)(A) through (f)(2)(vi)(C) of this section.

(A) In performing the WMPP Project, the Sistersville Plant shall use a Study Team and an Advisory Committee as described in paragraphs (f)(2)(vi)(A)(*1*) through (f)(2)(vi)(A)(*6*) of this section.

(*1*) At a minimum, the multi-functional Study Team shall consist of Sistersville Plant personnel from appropriate plant departments (including both management and employees) and an independent contractor. The Sistersville Plant shall select a contractor that has experience and training in WMPP in the chemical manufacturing industry.

(*2*) The Sistersville Plant shall direct the Study Team such that the team performs the functions described in paragraphs (f)(2)(vi)(A)(2)(*i*) through (f)(2)(vi)(A)(*2*)(*v*) of this section.

(*i*) Review Sistersville Plant operations and waste streams.

(*ii*) Review prior WMPP efforts at the Sistersville Plant.

(*iii*) Develop criteria for the selection of waste streams to be evaluated for the WMPP Project.

(*iv*) Identify and prioritize the waste streams to be evaluated during the study phase of the WMPP Project, based on the criteria described in paragraph (f)(2)(vi)(A)(*2*)(*iii*) of this section.

(*v*) Perform the WMPP Study as required by paragraphs (f)(2)(vi)(A)(*3*) through (f)(2)(vi)(A)(*5*), paragraph (f)(2)(vi)(B), and paragraph (f)(2)(vi)(C) of this section.

(*3*)(*i*) The Sistersville Plant shall establish an Advisory Committee consisting of a representative from EPA, a representative from WVDEP, the Sistersville Plant Manager, the Sistersville Plant

Director of Safety, Health and Environmental Affairs, and a stakeholder representative(s).

(*ii*) The Sistersville Plant shall select the stakeholder representative(s) by mutual agreement of EPA, WVDEP and the Sistersville Plant no later than 20 days after receiving from EPA and WVDEP the names of their respective committee members.

(*4*) The Sistersville Plant shall convene a meeting of the Advisory Committee no later than thirty days after selection of the stakeholder representatives, and shall convene meetings periodically thereafter as necessary for the Advisory Committee to perform its assigned functions. The Sistersville Plant shall direct the Advisory Committee to perform the functions described in paragraphs (f)(2)(vi)(A)(*4*)(*i*) through (f)(2)(vi)(A)(*4*)(*iii*) of this section.

(*i*) Review and comment upon the Study Team's criteria for selection of waste streams, and the Study Team's identification and prioritization of the waste streams to be evaluated during the WMPP Project.

(*ii*) Review and comment upon the Study Team progress reports and the draft WMPP Study Report.

(*iii*) Periodically review the effectiveness of WMPP opportunities implemented as part of the WMPP Project, and, where appropriate, WMPP opportunities previously determined to be infeasible by the Sistersville Plant but which had potential for feasibility in the future.

(*5*) Beginning on January 15, 1998, and every ninety (90) days thereafter until submission of the final WMPP Study Report required by paragraph (f)(2)(vi)(C) of this section, the Sistersville Plant shall direct the Study Team to submit a progress report to the Advisory Committee detailing its efforts during the prior ninety (90) day period.

(B) The Sistersville Plant shall ensure that the WMPP Study and the WMPP Study Report meet the requirements of paragraphs (f)(2)(vi)(B)(*1*) through (f)(2)(vi)(B)(*3*) of this section.

(*1*) The WMPP Study shall consist of a technical, economic, and regulatory assessment of opportunities for source reduction and for environmentally sound recycling for waste streams identified by the Study Team.

(*2*) The WMPP Study shall evaluate the source, nature, and volume of the waste streams; describe all the WMPP opportunities identified by the Study Team; provide a feasibility screening to evaluate the technical and economical feasibility of each of the WMPP opportunities; identify any cross-media impacts or any anticipated transfers of risk associated with each feasible WMPP opportunity; and identify the projected economic savings and projected quantitative waste reduction estimates for each WMPP opportunity identified.

(*3*) No later than October 19, 1998, the Sistersville Plant shall prepare and submit to the members of the Advisory Committee a draft WMPP Study Report which, at a minimum, includes the results of the WMPP Study, identifies WMPP opportunities the Sistersville Plant determines to be feasible, discusses the basis for excluding other opportunities as not feasible, and makes recommendations as to whether the WMPP Study should be continued. The members of the Advisory Committee shall provide any comments to the Sistersville Plant within thirty (30) days of receiving the WMPP Study Report.

(C) Within thirty (30) days after receipt of comments from the members of the Advisory Committee, the Sistersville Plant shall submit to EPA and WVDEP a final WMPP Study Report which identifies those WMPP opportunities the Sistersville Plant determines to be feasible and includes an implementation schedule for each such WMPP opportunity. The Sistersville Plant shall make reasonable efforts to implement all feasible WMPP opportunities in accordance with the priorities identified in the implementation schedule.

(*1*) For purposes of this section, a WMPP opportunity is feasible if the Sistersville Plant considers it to be technically feasible (taking into account engineering and regulatory factors, product line specifications and customer needs) and economically practical (taking into account the full environmental costs and benefits associated with the WMPP opportunity and the company's internal requirements for approval of capital projects). For purposes of the WMPP Project, the Sistersville Plant shall use "An Introduction to Environmental Accounting as a Business Management Tool," (EPA 742/R-95/001) as one tool to identify the full environmental costs and benefits of each WMPP opportunity.

(*2*) In implementing each WMPP opportunity, the Sistersville Plant shall, after consulting with the other members of the Advisory Committee, develop appropriate protocols and methods for determining the information required by paragraphs (f)(2)(vi)(C)(*2*)(*i*) through (f)(2)(vi)(C)(*2*)(*iii*) of this section.

(*i*) The overall volume of wastes reduced.

(*ii*) The quantities of each constituent identified in paragraph (f)(8) of this section reduced in the wastes.

(*iii*) The economic benefits achieved.

(*3*) No requirements of paragraph (f)(2)(vi) of this section are intended to prevent or restrict the Sistersville Plant from evaluating and implementing any WMPP opportunities at the Sistersville Plant in the normal course of its operations or from implementing, prior to the completion of the WMPP Study, any WMPP opportunities identified by the Study Team.

(vii) The Sistersville Plant shall maintain on-site each record required by paragraph (f)(2) of this section, through the MON Compliance Date.

(viii) The Sistersville Plant shall comply with the reporting requirements of paragraphs (f)(2)(viii)(A) through (f)(2)(viii)(G) of this section.

(A) At least sixty days prior to conducting the initial performance test of the thermal incinerator, the Sistersville Plant shall submit to EPA and WVDEP copies of a notification of performance test, as described in 40 CFR 63.7(b). Following the initial performance test of the thermal incinerator, the Sistersville Plant shall submit to EPA and WVDEP copies of the performance test results that include the information relevant to initial performance tests of thermal incinerators contained in 40 CFR 63.7(g)(1), 40 CFR 63.117(a)(4)(i), and 40 CFR 63.117(a)(4)(ii).

(B) Beginning in 1999, on January 31 of each year, the Sistersville Plant shall submit a semiannual written report to the EPA and WVDEP, with respect to the preceding six month period ending on December 31, which contains the information described in paragraphs (f)(2)(viii)(B)(*1*) through (f)(2)(viii)(B)(*10*) of this section.

(*1*) Instances of operating below the minimum operating temperature established for the thermal incinerator under paragraph (f)(2)(ii)(A)(*1*) of this section which were not corrected within 24 hours of onset.

(*2*) Any periods during which the paper unit was being operated to manufacture product while the flow indicator the vent streams to the thermal incinerator showed no flow.

(*3*) Any periods during which the capper unit was being operated to manufacture product while the flow indicator for any bypass device on the closed vent system to the thermal incinerator showed flow.

(*4*) Information required to be reported during that six month period under the preconstruction permit issued under the state permitting program approved under subpart XX of 40 CFR Part 52—Approval and Promulgation of Implementation Plans for West Virginia.

(*5*) Any periods during which the capper unit was being operated to manufacture product while the condenser associated with the methanol recovery operation was not in operation.

(*6*) The amount (in pounds and by month) of methanol collected by the methanol recovery operation during the six month period.

(*7*) The amount (in pounds and by month) of collected methanol utilized for reuse, recovery, thermal recovery/treatment, or bio-treatment, respectively, during the six month period.

(*8*) The calculated amount (in pounds and by month) of methanol generated by operating the capper unit.

(*9*) The status of the WMPP Project, including the status of developing the WMPP Study Report.

(*10*) Beginning in the year after the Sistersville Plant submits the final WMPP Study Report required by paragraph (f)(2)(vi)(C) of this section, and continuing in each subsequent Semiannual Report required by paragraph (f)(2)(viii)(B) of this section, the Sistersville Plant shall report on the progress of the implementation of feasible WMPP opportunities identified in the WMPP Study Report. The Semiannual Report required by paragraph (f)(2)(viii)(B) of this section shall identify any cross-media impacts or impacts to worker safety or community health issues that have occurred as a result of implementation of the feasible WMPP opportunities.

(C) Beginning in 1999, on July 31 of each year, the Sistersville Plant shall provide an Annual Project Report to the EPA and WVDEP Project XL contacts containing the information required by paragraphs (f)(2)(viii)(C)(*1*) through (f)(2)(viii)(C)(*8*) of this section.

(*1*) The categories of information required to be submitted under paragraphs (f)(2)(viii)(B)(*1*) through (f)(2)(viii)(B)(*8*) of this section, for the preceding 12 month period ending on June 30.

(*2*) An updated Emissions Analysis for January through December of the preceding calendar year. The Sistersville Plant shall submit the updated Emissions Analysis in a form substantially equivalent to the previous Emissions Analysis prepared by the Sistersville Plant to support Project XL. The Emissions Analysis shall include a comparison of the volatile organic emissions associated with the capper unit process vents and the wastewater treatment system (using the EPA Water 8 model or other model agreed to by the Sistersville Plant, EPA and WVDEP) under Project XL with the expected emissions from those sources absent Project XL during that period.

(*3*) A discussion of the Sistersville Plant's performance in meeting the requirements of this section, specifically identifying any areas in which the Sistersville Plant either exceeded or failed to achieve any such standard.

(*4*) A description of any unanticipated problems in implementing the XL Project and any steps taken to resolve them.

(*5*) A WMPP Implementation Report that contains the information contained in paragraphs (f)(2)(viii)(C)(*5*)(*i*) through (viii)(C)(*5*)(*vi*) of this section.

(*i*) A summary of the WMPP opportunities selected for implementation.

(*ii*) A description of the WMPP opportunities initiated and/or completed.

(*iii*) Reductions in volume of waste generated and amounts of each constituent reduced in wastes including any constituents identified in paragraph (f)(8) of this section.

(*iv*) An economic benefits analysis.

(*v*) A summary of the results of the Advisory Committee's review of implemented WMPP opportunities.

(*vi*) A reevaluation of WMPP opportunities previously determined to be infeasible by the Sistersville Plant but which had potential for future feasibility.

(*6*) An assessment of the nature of, and the successes or problems associated with, the Sistersville Plant's interaction with the federal and state agencies under the Project.

(*7*) An update on stakeholder involvement efforts.

(*8*) An evaluation of the Project as implemented against the Project XL Criteria and the baseline scenario.

(D) The Sistersville Plant shall submit to the EPA and WVDEP Project XL contacts a written Final Project Report covering the period during which the temporary deferral was effective, as described in paragraph (f)(3) of this section.

(*1*) The Final Project Report shall contain the information required to be submitted for the Semiannual Report required under paragraph (f)(2)(viii)(B) of this section, and the Annual Project Report required under paragraph (f)(2)(viii)(C) of this section.

(*2*) The Sistersville Plant shall submit the Final Project Report to EPA and WVDEP no later than 180 days after the temporary deferral of paragraph (f)(1) of this section is revoked, or 180 days after the MON Compliance Date, whichever occurs first.

(E)(*1*) The Sistersville Plant shall retain on-site a complete copy of each of the report documents to be submitted to EPA and WVDEP in accordance with requirements under paragraph (f)(2) of this section. The Sistersville Plant shall retain this record until 180 days after the MON Compliance Date. The Sistersville Plant shall provide to stakeholders and interested parties a written notice of availability (to be mailed to all persons on the Project mailing list and to be provided to at least one local newspaper of general circulation) of each such document, and provide a copy of each document to any such person upon request, subject to the provisions of 40 CFR part 2.

(*2*) Any reports or other information submitted to EPA or WVDEP may be released to the public pursuant to the Federal Freedom of Information Act (42 U.S.C. 552 *et seq.*), subject to the provisions of 40 CFR part 2.

(F) The Sistersville Plant shall make all supporting monitoring results and records required under paragraph (f)(2) of this section available to EPA and WVDEP within a reasonable amount of time after receipt of a written request from those Agencies, subject to the provisions of 40 CFR part 2.

(G) Each report submitted by the Sistersville Plant under the requirements of paragraph (f)(2) of this section shall be certified by a Responsible Corporate Officer, as defined in 40 CFR 270.11(a)(1).

(H) For each report submitted in accordance with paragraph (f)(2) of this section, the Sistersville Plant shall send one copy each to the addresses in paragraphs (f)(2)(viii)(H)(*1*) through (H)(*3*) of this section.

(*1*) U.S. EPA Region 3, 1650 Arch Street, Philadelphia, PA 19103-2029, Attention Tad Radzinski, Mail Code 3WC11.

(*2*) U.S. EPA, 1200 Pennsylvania Ave., NW, Washington, DC 20460, Attention L. Nancy Birnbaum, Mail Code 2129.

(*3*) West Virginia Division of Environmental Protection, Office of Air Quality, 1558 Washington Street East, Charleston, WV 25311-2599, Attention John H. Johnston.

(3) Effective period and revocation of temporary deferral.

(i) The temporary deferral contained in this section is effective from April 1, 1998, and shall remain effective until the MON Compliance Date. The temporary deferral contained in this section may be revoked prior to the MON Compliance Date, as described in paragraph (f)(3)(iv) of this section.

(ii) On the MON Compliance Date, the temporary deferral contained in this section will no longer be effective.

(iii) The Sistersville Plant shall come into compliance with those requirements deferred by this section no later than the MON Compliance Date. No later than 18 months prior to the MON Compliance Date, the Sistersville Plant shall submit to EPA an implementation schedule that meets the requirements of paragraph (g)(1)(iii) of this section.

(iv) The temporary deferral contained in this section may be revoked for cause, as determined by EPA, prior to the MON Compliance Date. The Sistersville Plant may request EPA to revoke the temporary deferral contained in this section at any time. The revocation shall be effective on the date that the Sistersville Plant receives written notification of revocation from EPA.

(v) Nothing in this section shall affect the provisions of the MON, as applicable to the Sistersville Plant.

(vi) Nothing in paragraph (f) or (g) of this section shall affect any regulatory requirements not referenced in paragraph (f)(1)(iii) or (f)(1)(iv) of this section, as applicable to the Sistersville Plant.

(4) The Sistersville Plant shall conduct the initial performance test required by paragraph (f)(2)(ii)(B) of this section using the procedures in paragraph (f)(4) of this section. The organic concentration and percent reduction shall be measured as TOC minus methane and ethane, according to the procedures specified in paragraph (f)(4) of this section.

(i) Method 1 or 1A of 40 CFR part 60, appendix A, as appropriate, shall be used for selection of the sampling sites.

(A) To determine compliance with the 98 percent reduction of TOC requirement of paragraph (f)(2)(ii)(A)(*1*) of this section, sampling sites shall be located at the inlet of the control device after the final product recovery device, and at the outlet of the control device.

(B) To determine compliance with the 20 parts per million by volume TOC limit in paragraph (f)(2)(ii)(A)(*1*) of this section, the sampling site shall be located at the outlet of the control device.

(ii) The gas volumetric flow rate shall be determined using Method 2, 2A, 2C, or 2D of 40 CFR part 60, appendix A, as appropriate.

(iii) To determine compliance with the 20 parts per million by volume TOC limit in paragraph (f)(2)(ii)(A)(1) of this section, the Sistersville Plant shall use Method 18 of 40 CFR part 60, appendix A to measure TOC minus methane and ethane. Alternatively, any other method or data that has been validated according to the applicable procedures in Method 301 of 40 CFR part 63, appendix A, may be used. The following procedures shall be used to calculate parts per million by volume concentration, corrected to 3 percent oxygen:

(A) The minimum sampling time for each run shall be 1 hour in which either an integrated sample or a minimum of four grab samples shall be taken. If grab sampling is used, then the samples shall be taken at approximately equal intervals in time, such as 15 minute intervals during the run.

(B) The concentration of TOC minus methane and ethane (C_{TOC}) shall be calculated as the sum of the concentrations of the individual components, and shall be computed for each run using the following equation:

$$C_{TOC} = \sum_{i=1}^{x} \frac{\left(\sum_{j=1}^{n} C_{ji}\right)}{x}$$

Where:

C_{TOC} = Concentration of TOC (minus methane and ethane), dry basis, parts per million by volume.

C_{ji} = Concentration of sample components j of sample i, dry basis, parts per million by volume.

n = Number of components in the sample.

x = Number of samples in the sample run.

(C) The concentration of TOC shall be corrected to 3 percent oxygen if a combustion device is the control device.

(*1*) The emission rate correction factor or excess air, integrated sampling and analysis procedures of Method 3B of 40 CFR part 60, appendix A shall be used to determine the oxygen concentration ($\%O_{2d}$). The samples shall be taken during the same time that the TOC (minus methane or ethane) samples are taken.

(*2*) The concentration corrected to 3 percent oxygen (C_c) shall be computed using the following equation:

$$C_c = C_m \left(\frac{17.9}{20.9 \, \%O_{2d}} \right)$$

Where:

C_c = Concentration of TOC corrected to 3 percent oxygen, dry basis, parts per million by volume.

C_m = Concentration of TOC (minus methane and ethane), dry basis, parts per million by volume.

$\%O_{2d}$ = Concentration of oxygen, dry basis, percent by volume.

(iv) To determine compliance with the 98 percent reduction requirement of paragraph (f)(2)(ii)(A)(*1*) of this section, the Sistersville Plant shall use Method 18 of 40 CFR part 60, appendix A; alternatively, any other method or data that has been validated according to the applicable procedures in Method 301 of 40 CFR part 63, appendix A may be used. The following procedures shall be used to calculate percent reduction efficiency:

(A) The minimum sampling time for each run shall be 1 hour in which either an integrated sample or a minimum of four grab samples shall be taken. If grab sampling is used, then the samples shall be taken at approximately equal intervals in time such as 15 minute intervals during the run.

(B) The mass rate of TOC minus methane and ethane (E_i, E_o) shall be computed. All organic compounds (minus methane and ethane) measured by Method 18 of 40 CFR part 60, appendix A are summed using the following equations:

$$E_i = K_2 \left(\sum_{j=1}^{n} C_{ij} M_{ij} \right) Q_i$$

$$E_o = K_2 \left(\sum_{j=1}^{n} C_{oj} M_{oj} \right) Q_o$$

Where:

C_{ij}, C_{oj} = Concentration of sample component j of the gas stream at the inlet and outlet of the control device, respectively, dry basis, parts per million by volume.

E_i, E_o = Mass rate of TOC (minus methane and ethane) at the inlet and outlet of the control device, respectively, dry basis, kilogram per hour.

M_{ij}, M_{oj} = Molecular weight of sample component j of the gas stream at the inlet and outlet of the control device, respectively, gram/gram-mole.

Q_i, Q_o = Flow rate of gas stream at the inlet and outlet of the control device, respectively, dry standard cubic meter per minute.

K_2 = Constant, 2.494×10^{-6} (parts per million)$^{-1}$ (gram-mole per standard cubic meter) (kilogram/gram) (minute/hour), where standard temperature (gram-mole per standard cubic meter) is 20° C.

(C) The percent reduction in TOC (minus methane and ethane) shall be calculated as follows:

$$R = \left(\frac{E_i \, E_o}{E_i} \right) (100)$$

Where:

R = Control efficiency of control device, percent.

E_i = Mass rate of TOC (minus methane and ethane) at the inlet to the control device as calculated under paragraph (f)(4)(iv)(B) of this section, kilograms TOC per hour.

E_o = Mass rate of TOC (minus methane and ethane) at the outlet of the control device, as calculated under paragraph (f)(4)(iv)(B) of this section, kilograms TOC per hour.

(5) At the time of the initial performance test of the process vent thermal incinerator required under paragraph (f)(2)(ii)(B) of this section, the Sistersville Plant shall inspect each closed vent system according to the procedures specified in paragraphs (f)(5)(i) through (f)(5)(vi) of this section.

(i) The initial inspections shall be conducted in accordance with Method 21 of 40 CFR part 60, appendix A.

(ii)(A) Except as provided in paragraph (f)(5)(ii)(B) of this section, the detection instrument shall meet the performance criteria of Method 21 of 40 CFR part 60, appendix A, except the instrument response factor criteria in section 3.1.2(a) of Method 21 of 40 CFR part 60, appendix A shall be for the average composition of the process fluid not each individual volatile organic compound in the stream. For process streams that contain nitrogen, air, or other inerts which are not organic hazardous air pollutants or volatile organic compounds, the average stream response factor shall be calculated on an inert-free basis.

(B) If no instrument is available at the plant site that will meet the performance criteria specified in paragraph (f)(5)(ii)(A) of this section, the instrument readings may be adjusted by multiplying by the average response factor of the process fluid, calculated on an inert-free basis as described in paragraph (f)(5)(ii)(A) of this section.

(iii) The detection instrument shall be calibrated before use on each day of its use by the procedures specified in Method 21 of 40 CFR part 60, appendix A.

(iv) Calibration gases shall be as follows:

(A) Zero air (less than 10 parts per million hydrocarbon in air); and

(B) Mixtures of methane in air at a concentration less than 10,000 parts per million. A calibration gas other than methane in air may be used if the instrument does not respond to methane or if the instrument does not meet the performance criteria specified in paragraph (f)(5)(ii)(A) of this section. In such cases, the calibration gas may be a mixture of one or more of the compounds to be measured in air.

(v) The Sistersville Plant may elect to adjust or not adjust instrument readings for background. If the Sistersville Plant elects to not adjust readings for background, all such instrument readings shall be compared directly to the applicable leak definition to determine whether there is a leak. If the Sistersville Plant elects to adjust instrument readings for background, the Sistersville Plant shall measure background concentration using the procedures in 40 CFR 63.180(b) and (c). The Sistersville Plant shall subtract background reading from the maximum concentration indicated by the instrument.

(vi) The arithmetic difference between the maximum concentration indicated by the instrument and the background level shall be compared with 500 parts per million for determining compliance.

(6) Definitions of terms as used in paragraphs (f) and (g) of this section.

(i) Closed vent system is defined as a system that is not open to the atmosphere and that is composed of piping, connections and, if necessary, flow-inducing devices that transport gas or vapor from the capper unit process vent to the thermal incinerator.

(ii) No detectable emissions means an instrument reading of less than 500 parts per million by volume above background as determined by Method 21 in 40 CFR part 60.

(iii) Reuse includes the substitution of collected methanol (without reclamation subsequent to its collection) for virgin methanol as an ingredient (including uses as an intermediate) or as an effective substitute for a commercial product.

(iv) Recovery includes the substitution of collected methanol for virgin methanol as an ingredient (including uses as an intermediate) or as an effective substitute for a commercial product following reclamation of the methanol subsequent to its collection.

(v) Thermal recovery/treatment includes the use of collected methanol in fuels blending or as a feed to any combustion device to the extent permitted by Federal and state law.

(vi) Bio-treatment includes the treatment of the collected methanol through introduction into a biological treatment system, including the treatment of the collected methanol as a waste stream in an on-site or off-site wastewater treatment system. Introduction of the collected methanol to the on-site wastewater treatment system will be limited to points downstream of the surface impoundments, and will be consistent with the requirements of federal and state law.

(vii) Start-up shall have the meaning set forth at 40 CFR 63.2.

(viii) Flow indicator means a device which indicates whether gas flow is present in the vent stream, and, if required by the permit for the thermal incinerator, which measures the gas flow in that stream.

(ix) Continuous Recorder means a data recording device that records an instantaneous data value at least once every fifteen minutes.

(x) MON means the National Emission Standards for Hazardous Air Pollutants for the source category Miscellaneous Organic Chemical Production and Processes ("MON"), promulgated under the authority of Section 112 of the Clean Air Act.

(xi) MON Compliance Date means the date 3 years after the effective date of the National Emission Standards for Hazardous Air Pollutants for the source category Miscellaneous Organic Chemical Production and Processes ("MON").

(7) OSi Specialties, Incorporated, a subsidiary of Witco Corporation ("OSi"), may seek to transfer its rights and obligations under this section to a future owner of the Sistersville Plant in accordance with the requirements of paragraphs (f)(7)(i) through (f)(7)(iii) of this section.

(i) OSi will provide to EPA a written notice of any proposed transfer at least forty-five days prior to the effective date of any such transfer. The written notice will identify the proposed transferee.

(ii) The proposed transferee will provide to EPA a written request to assume the rights and obligations under this section at least forty-five days prior to the effective date of any such transfer. The written request will describe the transferee's financial and technical capability to assume the obligations under this section, and will include a statement of the transferee's intention to fully comply with the terms of this section and to sign the Final Project Agreement for this XL Project as an additional party.

(iii) Within thirty days of receipt of both the written notice and written request described in paragraphs (f)(7)(i) and (f)(7)(ii) of this section, EPA will determine, based on all relevant information, whether to approve a transfer of rights and obligations under this section from OSi to a different owner.

(8) The constituents to be identified by the Sistersville Plant pursuant to paragraphs (f)(2)(vi)(C)(2)(ii) and (f)(2)(viii)(C)(5)(iii) of this section are: 1 Naphthalenamine; 1,2,4 Trichlorobenzene; 1,1 Dichloroethylene; 1,1,1 Trichloroethane; 1,1,1,2 Tetrachloroethane; 1,1,2 Trichloro 1,2,2 Triflouroethane; 1,1,2 Trichloroethane; 1,1,2,2 Tetrachloroethane; 1,2 Dichlorobenzene; 1,2 Dichloroethane; 1,2 Dichloropropane; 1,2 Dichloropropanone; 1,2 Transdichloroethene; 1,2,Trans-Dichloroethene; 1,2,4,5Tetrachlorobenzine; 1,3 Dichlorobenzene; 1,4 Dichloro 2 butene; 1,4 Di - oxane; 2 Chlorophenol; 2 Cyclohexyl 4,6 dinitrophenol; 2 Methyl Pyridine; 2 Nitropropane; 2, 4-Di-nitrotoluene; Acetone; Acetonitrile; Acrylonitrile; Allyl Alcohol; Aniline; Antimony; Arsenic; Barium; Benzene; Benzotrichloride; Benzyl Chloride; Beryllium; Bis (2 ethyl Hexyl) Phthalate; Butyl Alcohol, n; Butyl Benzyl Phthalate; Cadmium; Carbon Disulfide; Carbon Tetrachloride; Chlorobenzene; Chloroform; Chloromethane; Chromium; Chrysene; Copper; Creosol; Creosol, m-; Creosol, o; Creosol, p; Cyanide; Cyclohexanone; Di-n-octyl phthalate; Dichlorodiflouromethane; Diethyl Phthalate; Dihydrosafrole; Dimethylamine; Ethyl Acetate; Ethyl benzene; Ethyl Ether; Ethylene Glycol Ethyl Ether; Ethylene Oxide; Formaldehyde; Isobutyl Alcohol; Lead; Mercury; Methanol; Methoxychlor; Methyl Chloride; Methyl Chloroformate; Methyl Ethyl Ketone; Methyl Ethyl Ketone Peroxide; Methyl Isobutyl Ketone; Methyl Methacrylate; Methylene Bromide; Methylene Chloride; Naphthalene; Nickel; Nitrobenzene; Nitroglycerine; p-Toluidine; Phenol; Phthalic Anhydride; Polychlorinated Biphenyls; Propargyl Alcohol; Pyridine; Safrole; Selenium; Silver; Styrene; Tetrachloroethylene; Tetrahydrofuran; Thallium; Toluene; Toluene 2,4 Diisocyanate; Trichloroethylene; Trichloroflouromethane; Vanadium; Vinyl Chloride; Warfarin; Xylene; Zinc.

(g) This section applies only to the facility commonly referred to as the OSi Specialties Plant, located on State Route 2, Sistersville, West Virginia ("Sistersville Plant").

(1)(i) No later than 18 months from the date the Sistersville Plant receives written notification of revocation of the temporary deferral for the Sistersville Plant under paragraph (f) of this section, the Sistersville Plant shall, in accordance with the implementation schedule submitted to EPA under paragraph (g)(1)(ii) of this section, either come into compliance with all requirements of this subpart which had been deferred by paragraph (f)(1)(i) of this section, or complete a facility or process modification such that the requirements of §264.1085 are no longer applicable to the two hazardous waste surface impoundments. In any event, the Sistersville Plant must complete the requirements of the previous sentence no later than the MON Compliance Date; if the Sistersville Plant receives written notification of revocation of the temporary deferral after the date 18 months prior to the MON Compliance Date, the date by which the Sistersville Plant must complete the requirements of the previous sentence will be the MON Compliance Date, which would be less than 18 months from the date of notification of revocation.

(ii) Within 30 days from the date the Sistersville Plant receives written notification of revocation under paragraph (f)(3)(iv) of this section, the Sistersville Plant shall enter and maintain in the facility operating record an implementation schedule. The implementation schedule shall demonstrate that within 18 months from the date the Sistersville Plant receives written notification of revocation under paragraph (f)(3)(iv) of this section (but no later than the MON Compliance Date), the Sistersville Plant shall either come into compliance with the regulatory requirements that had been deferred by paragraph (f)(1)(i) of this section, or complete a facility or process modification such that the requirements of §264.1085 are no longer applicable to the two hazardous waste surface impoundments. Within 30 days from the date the Sistersville Plant receives written notification of revocation under paragraph (f)(3)(iv) of this section, the Sistersville Plant shall submit a copy of the implementation schedule to the EPA and WVDEP Project XL contacts identified in paragraph (f)(2)(viii)(H) of this section. The implementation schedule shall reflect the Sistersville Plant's effort to come into compliance as soon as practicable (but no later than 18 months after the date the Sistersville Plant receives written notification of revocation, or the MON Compliance Date, whichever is sooner) with all regulatory requirements that had been deferred under paragraph (f)(1)(i) of this section, or to complete a facility or process modification as soon as practicable (but no later than 18 months after the date the Sistersville Plant receives written notification of revocation, or the MON Compliance Date, whichever is sooner) such that the requirements of §264.1085 are no longer applicable to the two hazardous waste surface impoundments.

(iii) The implementation schedule shall include the information described in either paragraph (g)(1)(iii)(A) or (B) of this section.

(A) Specific calendar dates for: Award of contracts or issuance of purchase orders for the control equipment required by those regulatory requirements that had been deferred by paragraph (f)(1)(i) of this section; initiation of on-site installation of such control equipment; completion of the control equipment installation; performance of any testing to demonstrate that the installed control equipment meets the applicable standards of this subpart; initiation of operation of the control equipment; and compliance with all regulatory requirements that had been deferred by paragraph (f)(1)(i) of this section.

(B) Specific calendar dates for the purchase, installation, performance testing and initiation of operation of equipment to accomplish a facility or process modification such that the requirements of §264.1085 are no longer applicable to the two hazardous waste surface impoundments.

(2) Nothing in paragraphs (f) or (g) of this section shall affect any regulatory requirements not referenced in paragraph (f)(2)(i) or (ii) of this section, as applicable to the Sistersville Plant.

(3) In the event that a notification of revocation is issued pursuant to paragraph (f)(3)(iv) of this section, the requirements referenced in paragraphs (f)(1)(iii) and (f)(1)(iv) of this section are temporarily deferred, with respect to the two hazardous waste surface impoundments, provided that the Sistersville Plant is in compliance with the requirements of paragraphs (f)(2)(ii), (f)(2)(iii), (f)(2)(iv), (f)(2)(v), (f)(2)(vi) and (g) of this section, except as provided under paragraph (g)(4) of this section. The temporary deferral of the previous sentence shall be effective beginning on the date the Sistersville Plant receives written notification of revocation, and subject to paragraph (g)(5) of this section, shall continue to be effective for a maximum period of 18 months from that date, provided that the Sistersville Plant is in compliance with the requirements of paragraphs (f)(2)(ii), (f)(2)(iii), (f)(2)(iv), (f)(2)(v), (f)(2)(vi) and (g) of this section at all times during that 18-month period.

(4) In the event that a notification of revocation is issued pursuant to paragraph (f)(3)(iv) of this section as a result of the permanent removal of the capper unit from methyl capped polyether production service, the requirements referenced in paragraphs (f)(1)(iii) and (f)(1)(iv) of this section are temporarily deferred, with respect to the two hazardous waste surface impoundments, provided that the Sistersville Plant is in compliance with the requirements of paragraphs (f)(2)(vi), and (g) of this section. The temporary deferral of the previous sentence shall be effective beginning on the

date the Sistersville Plant receives written notification of revocation, and subject to paragraph (g)(5) of this section, shall continue to be effective for a maximum period of 18 months from that date, provided that the Sistersville Plant is in compliance with the requirements of paragraphs (f)(2)(vi) and (g) of this section at all times during that 18-month period.

(5) In no event shall the temporary deferral provided under paragraph (g)(3) or (g)(4) of this section be effective after the MON Compliance Date.

[59 FR 62927, Dec. 6, 1994, as amended at 60 FR 26828, May 19, 1995; 60 FR 50428, Sept. 29, 1995; 60 FR 56953, Nov. 13, 1995; 61 FR 28509, June 5, 1996; 61 FR 59952, Nov. 25, 1996; 62 FR 52642, Oct. 8, 1997; 62 FR 64658, Dec. 8, 1997; 63 FR 11131, Mar. 6, 1998; 63 FR 19838, Apr. 22, 1998; 63 FR 49392, Sept. 15, 1998; 63 FR 53847, Oct. 7, 1998; 64 FR 3389, Jan. 21, 1999; 71 FR 40274, July 14, 2006]

§264.1081 Definitions.

As used in this subpart, all terms shall have the meaning given to them in 40 CFR 265.1081, the Act, and parts 260 through 266 of this chapter.

§264.1082 Standards: General.

(a) This section applies to the management of hazardous waste in tanks, surface impoundments, and containers subject to this subpart.

(b) The owner or operator shall control air pollutant emissions from each hazardous waste management unit in accordance with standards specified in §§264.1084 through 264.1087 of this subpart, as applicable to the hazardous waste management unit, except as provided for in paragraph (c) of this section.

(c) A tank, surface impoundment, or container is exempt from standards specified in §264.1084 through §264.1087 of this subpart, as applicable, provided that the waste management unit is one of the following:

(1) A tank, surface impoundment, or container for which all hazardous waste entering the unit has an average VO concentration at the point of waste origination of less than 500 parts per million by weight (ppmw). The average VO concentration shall be determined using the procedures specified in §264.1083(a) of this subpart. The owner or operator shall review and update, as necessary, this determination at least once every 12 months following the date of the initial determination for the hazardous waste streams entering the unit. 📖 15.3.1.3, 15.3.2–3

(2) A tank, surface impoundment, or container for which the organic content of all the hazardous waste entering the waste management unit has been reduced by an organic destruction or removal process that achieves any one of the following conditions: 📖 15.3.3.5

(i) A process that removes or destroys the organics contained in the hazardous waste to a level such that the average VO concentration of the hazardous waste at the point of waste treatment is less than the exit concentration limit (C_t) established for the process. The average VO concentration of the hazardous waste at the point of waste treatment and the exit concentration limit for the process shall be determined using the procedures specified in §264.1083(b) of this subpart.

(ii) A process that removes or destroys the organics contained in the hazardous waste to a level such that the organic reduction efficiency (R) for the process is equal to or greater than 95 percent, and the average VO concentration of the hazardous waste at the point of waste treatment is less than 100 ppmw. The organic reduction efficiency for the process and the average VO concentration of the hazardous waste at the point of waste treatment shall be determined using the procedures specified in §264.1083(b) of this subpart.

(iii) A process that removes or destroys the organics contained in the hazardous waste to a level such that the actual organic mass removal rate (MR) for the process is equal to or greater than the required organic mass removal rate (RMR) established for the process. The required organic mass removal rate and the actual organic mass removal rate for the process shall be determined using the procedures specified in §264.1083(b) of this subpart.

(iv) A biological process that destroys or degrades the organics contained in the hazardous waste, such that either of the following conditions is met:

(A) The organic reduction efficiency (R) for the process is equal to or greater than 95 percent, and the organic biodegradation efficiency (R_{bio}) for the process is equal to or greater than 95 percent. The organic reduction efficiency and the organic biodegradation efficiency for the process shall be determined using the procedures specified in §264.1083(b) of this subpart.

(B) The total actual organic mass biodegradation rate (MR_{bio}) for all hazardous waste treated by the process is equal to or greater than the required organic mass removal rate (RMR). The required organic mass removal rate and the actual organic mass biodegradation rate for the process shall be determined using the procedures specified in §264.1083(b) of this subpart.

(v) A process that removes or destroys the organics contained in the hazardous waste and meets all of the following conditions:

(A) From the point of waste origination through the point where the hazardous waste enters the treatment process, the hazardous waste is managed continuously in waste management units which use air emission controls in accordance with the standards specified in §264.1084 through §264.1087 of this subpart, as applicable to the waste management unit.

(B) From the point of waste origination through the point where the hazardous waste enters the treatment process, any transfer of the hazardous waste is accomplished through continuous hard-piping or other closed system transfer that does not allow exposure of the waste to the atmosphere. The EPA considers a drain system that meets the requirements of 40 CFR part 63, subpart RR—National Emission Standards for Individual Drain Systems to be a closed system.

(C) The average VO concentration of the hazardous waste at the point of waste treatment is less than the lowest average VO concentration at the point of waste origination determined for each of the individual waste streams entering the process or 500 ppmw, whichever value is lower. The average VO concentration of each individual waste stream at the point of waste origination shall be determined using the procedures specified in §264.1083(a) of this subpart. The average VO concentration of the hazardous waste at the point of waste treatment shall be determined using the procedures specified in §264.1083(b) of this subpart.

(vi) A process that removes or destroys the organics contained in the hazardous waste to a level such that the organic reduction efficiency (R) for the process is equal to or greater than 95 percent and the owner or operator certifies that the average VO concentration at the point of waste origination for each of the individual waste streams entering the process is less than 10,000 ppmw. The organic reduction efficiency for the process and the average VO concentration of the hazardous waste at the point of waste origination shall be determined using the procedures specified in §264.1083(b) and §264.1083(a) of this subpart, respectively.

(vii) A hazardous waste incinerator for which the owner or operator has either:

(A) Been issued a final permit under 40 CFR part 270 which implements the requirements of subpart O of this part; or

(B) Has designed and operates the incinerator in accordance with the interim status requirements of 40 CFR part 265, subpart O.

(viii) A boiler or industrial furnace for which the owner or operator has either:

(A) Been issued a final permit under 40 CFR part 270 which implements the requirements of 40 CFR part 266, subpart H, or

(B) Has designed and operates the boiler or industrial furnace in accordance with the interim status requirements of 40 CFR part 266, subpart H.

(ix) For the purpose of determining the performance of an organic destruction or removal process in accordance with the conditions in each of paragraphs (c)(2)(i) through (c)(2)(vi) of this section, the owner or operator shall account for VO concentrations determined to be below the limit of detection of the analytical method by using the following VO concentration:

(A) If Method 25D in 40 CFR part 60, appendix A is used for the analysis, one-half the blank value determined in the method at section 4.4 of Method 25D in 40 CFR part 60, appendix A, or a value of 25 ppmw, whichever is less.

(B) If any other analytical method is used, one-half the sum of the limits of detection established for each organic constituent in the waste that has a Henry's law constant value at least 0.1 mole-fraction-in-the-gas-phase/mole-fraction-in-the-liquid-phase (0.1 Y/X) [which can also be expressed as 1.8×10^{-6} atmospheres/gram-mole/m^3] at 25 degrees Celsius.

(3) A tank or surface impoundment used for biological treatment of hazardous waste in accordance with the requirements of paragraph (c)(2)(iv) of this section.

📖 15.3.1.2.1

(4) A tank, surface impoundment, or container for which all hazardous waste placed in the unit either:

📖 15.3.3.5

(i) Meets the numerical concentration limits for organic hazardous constituents, applicable to the hazardous waste, as specified in 40 CFR part 268—Land Disposal Restrictions under Table "Treatment Standards for Hazardous Waste" in 40 CFR 268.40; or

(ii) The organic hazardous constituents in the waste have been treated by the treatment technology established by the EPA for the waste in 40 CFR 268.42(a), or have been removed or destroyed by an equivalent method of treatment approved by EPA pursuant to 40 CFR 268.42(b).

(5) A tank used for bulk feed of hazardous waste to a waste incinerator and all of the following conditions are met: 15.3.1.2.1

(i) The tank is located inside an enclosure vented to a control device that is designed and operated in accordance with all applicable requirements specified under 40 CFR part 61, subpart FF—National Emission Standards for Benzene Waste Operations for a facility at which the total annual benzene quantity from the facility waste is equal to or greater than 10 megagrams per year;

(ii) The enclosure and control device serving the tank were installed and began operation prior to November 25, 1996 and

(iii) The enclosure is designed and operated in accordance with the criteria for a permanent total enclosure as specified in "Procedure T—Criteria for and Verification of a Permanent or Temporary Total Enclosure" under 40 CFR 52.741, appendix B. The enclosure may have permanent or temporary openings to allow worker access; passage of material into or out of the enclosure by conveyor, vehicles, or other mechanical or electrical equipment; or to direct air flow into the enclosure. The owner or operator shall perform the verification procedure for the enclosure as specified in Section 5.0 to "Procedure T—Criteria for and Verification of a Permanent or Temporary Total Enclosure" annually.

(d) The Regional Administrator may at any time perform or request that the owner or operator perform a waste determination for a hazardous waste managed in a tank, surface impoundment, or container exempted from using air emission controls under the provisions of this section as follows:

(1) The waste determination for average VO concentration of a hazardous waste at the point of waste origination shall be performed using direct measurement in accordance with the applicable requirements of §264.1083(a) of this subpart. The waste determination for a hazardous waste at the point of waste treatment shall be performed in accordance with the applicable requirements of §264.1083(b) of this subpart.

(2) In performing a waste determination pursuant to paragraph (d)(1) of this section, the sample preparation and analysis shall be conducted as follows:

(i) In accordance with the method used by the owner or operator to perform the waste analysis, except in the case specified in paragraph (d)(2)(ii) of this section.

(ii) If the Regional Administrator determines that the method used by the owner or operator was not appropriate for the hazardous waste managed in the tank, surface impoundment, or container, then the Regional Administrator may choose an appropriate method.

(3) In a case when the owner or operator is requested to perform the waste determination, the Regional Administrator may elect to have an authorized representative observe the collection of the hazardous waste samples used for the analysis.

(4) In a case when the results of the waste determination performed or requested by the Regional Administrator do not agree with the results of a waste determination performed by the owner or operator using knowledge of the waste, then the results of the waste determination performed in accordance with the requirements of paragraph (d)(1) of this section shall be used to establish compliance with the requirements of this subpart.

(5) In a case when the owner or operator has used an averaging period greater than 1 hour for determining the average VO concentration of a hazardous waste at the point of waste origination, the Regional Administrator may elect to establish compliance with this subpart by performing or requesting that the owner or operator perform a waste determination using direct measurement based on waste samples collected within a 1-hour period as follows:

(i) The average VO concentration of the hazardous waste at the point of waste origination shall be determined by direct measurement in accordance with the requirements of §264.1083(a) of this subpart.

(ii) Results of the waste determination performed or requested by the Regional Administrator showing that the average VO concentration of the hazardous waste at the point of waste origination is equal to or greater than 500 ppmw shall constitute noncompliance with this subpart except in a case as provided for in paragraph (d)(5)(iii) of this section.

(iii) For the case when the average VO concentration of the hazardous waste at the point of waste origination previously has been determined by the owner or operator using an averaging period greater than 1 hour to be less than 500 ppmw but because of normal operating process variations the VO concentration of the hazardous waste determined by direct measurement for any given 1-hour period may be equal to or greater than 500 ppmw, information that was used by the owner or operator to determine the average VO concentration of the hazardous waste (*e.g.*, test results, measurements, calculations, and other documentation) and recorded in the facility records in accordance with the requirements of §264.1083(a) and §264.1089 of this subpart shall be considered by the Regional Administrator together with the results of the waste determination performed or requested by the Regional Administrator in establishing compliance with this subpart.

[61 FR 59953, Nov. 25, 1996, as amended at 62 FR 64658, Dec. 8, 1997]

§264.1083 Waste determination procedures.

(a) Waste determination procedure to determine average volatile organic (VO) concentration of a hazardous waste at the point of waste origination. 15.3.3.1

(1) An owner or operator shall determine the average VO concentration at the point of waste origination for each hazardous waste placed in a waste management unit exempted under the provisions of §264.1082(c)(1) of this subpart from using air emission controls in accordance with standards specified in §264.1084 through §264.1087 of this subpart, as applicable to the waste management unit.

(i) An initial determination of the average VO concentration of the waste stream shall be made before the first time any portion of the material in the hazardous waste stream is placed in a waste management unit exempted under the provisions of §264.1082(c)(1) of this subpart from using air emission controls, and thereafter an initial determination of the average VO concentration of the waste stream shall be made for each averaging period that a hazardous waste is managed in the unit; and

(ii) Perform a new waste determination whenever changes to the source generating the waste stream are reasonably likely to cause the average VO concentration of the hazardous waste to increase to a level that is equal to or greater than the applicable VO concentration limits specified in §264.1082 of this subpart.

(2) For a waste determination that is required by paragraph (a)(1) of this section, the average VO concentration of a hazardous waste at the point of waste origination shall be determined in accordance with the procedures specified in 40 CFR 265.1084(a)(2) through (a)(4).

(b) Waste determination procedures for treated hazardous waste.

(1) An owner or operator shall perform the applicable waste determinations for each treated hazardous waste placed in waste management units exempted under the provisions of §264.1082(c)(2)(i) through (c)(2)(vi) of this subpart from using air emission controls in accordance with standards specified in §§264.1084 through 264.1087 of this subpart, as applicable to the waste management unit.

(i) An initial determination of the average VO concentration of the waste stream shall be made before the first time any portion of the material in the treated waste stream is placed in the exempt waste management unit, and thereafter update the information used for the waste determination at least once every 12 months following the date of the initial waste determination; and

(ii) Perform a new waste determination whenever changes to the process generating or treating the waste stream are reasonably likely to cause the average VO concentration of the hazardous waste to increase to a level such that the applicable treatment conditions specified in §264.1082 (c)(2) of this subpart are not achieved.

(2) The waste determination for a treated hazardous waste shall be performed in accordance with the procedures specified in 40 CFR 265.1084 (b)(2) through (b)(9), as applicable to the treated hazardous waste.

(c) Procedure to determine the maximum organic vapor pressure of a hazardous waste in a tank.

(1) An owner or operator shall determine the maximum organic vapor pressure for each hazardous waste placed in a tank using Tank Level 1 controls in accordance with standards specified in §264.1084(c) of this subpart.

(2) The maximum organic vapor pressure of the hazardous waste may be determined in accordance with the procedures specified in 40 CFR 265.1084 (c)(2) through (c)(4).

(d) The procedure for determining no detectable organic emissions for the purpose of complying with this subpart shall be conducted in accordance with the procedures specified in 40 CFR 265.1084(d).

[61 FR 59954, Nov. 25, 1996, as amended at 62 FR 64658, Dec. 8, 1997; 64 FR 3389, Jan. 21, 1999]

§264.1084 Standards: Tanks. 15.3.4

(a) The provisions of this section apply to the control of air pollutant emissions from tanks for which §264.1082(b) of this subpart references the use of this section for such air emission control.

(b) The owner or operator shall control air pollutant emissions from each tank subject to this section in accordance with the following requirements as applicable:

(1) For a tank that manages hazardous waste that meets all of the conditions specified in paragraphs (b)(1)(i) through (b)(1)(iii) of this section, the owner or operator shall control air pollutant emissions from the tank in accordance with the Tank Level 1 controls specified in paragraph (c) of this section or the Tank Level 2 controls specified in paragraph (d) of this section. 15.3.4.1.1

(i) The hazardous waste in the tank has a maximum organic vapor pressure which is less than the maximum organic vapor pressure limit for the tank's design capacity category as follows:

(A) For a tank design capacity equal to or greater than 151 m^3, the maximum organic vapor pressure limit for the tank is 5.2 kPa.

(B) For a tank design capacity equal to or greater than 75 m^3 but less than 151 m^3, the maximum organic vapor pressure limit for the tank is 27.6 kPa.

(C) For a tank design capacity less than 75 m^3, the maximum organic vapor pressure limit for the tank is 76.6 kPa.

(ii) The hazardous waste in the tank is not heated by the owner or operator to a temperature that is greater than the temperature at which the maximum organic vapor pressure of the hazardous waste is determined for the purpose of complying with paragraph (b)(1)(i) of this section.

(iii) The hazardous waste in the tank is not treated by the owner or operator using a waste stabilization process, as defined in 40 CFR 265.1081.

(2) For a tank that manages hazardous waste that does not meet all of the conditions specified in paragraphs (b)(1)(i) through (b)(1)(iii) of this section, the owner or operator shall control air pollutant emissions from the tank by using Tank Level 2 controls in accordance with the requirements of paragraph (d) of this section. Examples of tanks required to use Tank Level 2 controls include: A tank used for a waste stabilization process; and a tank for which the hazardous waste in the tank has a maximum organic vapor pressure that is equal to or greater than the maximum organic vapor pressure limit for the tank's design capacity category as specified in paragraph (b)(1)(i) of this section.

(c) Owners and operators controlling air pollutant emissions from a tank using Tank Level 1 controls shall meet the requirements specified in paragraphs (c)(1) through (c)(4) of this section: 15.3.4.1

(1) The owner or operator shall determine the maximum organic vapor pressure for a hazardous waste to be managed in the tank using Tank Level 1 controls before the first time the hazardous waste is placed in the tank. The maximum organic vapor pressure shall be determined using the procedures specified in §264.1083(c) of this subpart. Thereafter, the owner or operator shall perform a new determination whenever changes to the hazardous waste managed in the tank could potentially cause the maximum organic vapor pressure to increase to a level that is equal to or greater than the maximum organic vapor pressure limit for the tank design capacity category specified in paragraph (b)(1)(i) of this section, as applicable to the tank.

(2) The tank shall be equipped with a fixed roof designed to meet the following specifications:

(i) The fixed roof and its closure devices shall be designed to form a continuous barrier over the entire surface area of the hazardous waste in the tank. The fixed roof may be a separate cover installed on the tank (*e.g.*, a removable cover mounted on an open-top tank) or may be an integral part of the tank structural design (*e.g.*, a horizontal cylindrical tank equipped with a hatch).

(ii) The fixed roof shall be installed in a manner such that there are no visible cracks, holes, gaps, or other open spaces between roof section joints or between the interface of the roof edge and the tank wall.

(iii) Each opening in the fixed roof, and any manifold system associated with the fixed roof, shall be either:

(A) Equipped with a closure device designed to operate such that when the closure device is secured in the closed position there are no visible cracks, holes, gaps, or other open spaces in the closure device or between the perimeter of the opening and the closure device; or

(B) Connected by a closed-vent system that is vented to a control device. The control device shall remove or destroy organics in the vent stream, and shall be operating whenever hazardous waste is managed in the tank, except as provided for in paragraphs (c)(2)(iii)(B)(*1*) and (*2*) of this section.

(*1*) During periods when it is necessary to provide access to the tank for performing the activities of paragraph (c)(2)(iii)(B)(*2*) of this section, venting of the vapor headspace underneath the fixed roof to the control device is not required, opening of closure devices is allowed, and removal of the fixed roof is allowed. Following completion of the activity, the owner or operator shall promptly secure the closure device in the closed position or reinstall the cover, as applicable, and resume operation of the control device.

(*2*) During periods of routine inspection, maintenance, or other activities needed for normal operations, and for removal of accumulated sludge or other residues from the bottom of the tank.

(iv) The fixed roof and its closure devices shall be made of suitable materials that will minimize exposure of the hazardous waste to the atmosphere, to the extent practical, and will maintain the integrity of the fixed roof and closure devices throughout their intended service life. Factors to be considered when selecting the materials for and designing the fixed roof and closure devices shall include: Organic vapor permeability, the effects of any contact with the hazardous waste or its vapors managed in the tank; the effects of outdoor exposure to wind, moisture, and sunlight; and the operating practices used for the tank on which the fixed roof is installed.

(3) Whenever a hazardous waste is in the tank, the fixed roof shall be installed with each closure device secured in the closed position except as follows:

(i) Opening of closure devices or removal of the fixed roof is allowed at the following times:

(A) To provide access to the tank for performing routine inspection, maintenance, or other activities needed for normal operations. Examples of such activities include those times when a worker needs to open a port to sample the liquid in the tank, or when a worker needs to open a hatch to maintain or repair equipment. Following completion of the activity, the owner or operator shall promptly secure the closure device in the closed position or reinstall the cover, as applicable, to the tank.

(B) To remove accumulated sludge or other residues from the bottom of tank.

(ii) Opening of a spring-loaded pressure-vacuum relief valve, conservation vent, or similar type of pressure relief device which vents to the atmosphere is allowed during normal operations for the purpose of maintaining the tank internal pressure in accordance with the tank design specifications. The device shall be designed to operate with no detectable organic emissions when the device is secured in the closed position. The settings at which the device opens shall be established such that the device remains in the closed position whenever the tank internal pressure is within the internal pressure operating range determined by the owner or operator based on the tank manufacturer recommendations, applicable regulations, fire protection and prevention codes, standard engineering codes and practices, or other requirements for the safe handling of flammable, ignitable, explosive, reactive, or hazardous materials. Examples of normal operating conditions that may require these devices to open are during those times when the tank internal pressure exceeds the internal pressure operating range for the tank as a result of loading operations or diurnal ambient temperature fluctuations.

(iii) Opening of a safety device, as defined in 40 CFR 265.1081, is allowed at any time conditions require doing so to avoid an unsafe condition.

(4) The owner or operator shall inspect the air emission control equipment in accordance with the following requirements.

(i) The fixed roof and its closure devices shall be visually inspected by the owner or operator to check for defects that could result in air pollutant emissions. Defects include, but are not limited to, visible cracks, holes, or gaps in the roof sections or between the roof and the tank wall; broken, cracked, or otherwise damaged seals or gaskets on closure devices; and broken or missing hatches, access covers, caps, or other closure devices.

(ii) The owner or operator shall perform an initial inspection of the fixed roof and its closure devices on or before the date that the tank becomes subject to this section. Thereafter, the owner or operator shall perform the inspections at least once every year except under the special conditions provided for in paragraph (l) of this section.

(iii) In the event that a defect is detected, the owner or operator shall repair the defect in accordance with the requirements of paragraph (k) of this section.

(iv) The owner or operator shall maintain a record of the inspection in accordance with the requirements specified in §264.1089(b) of this subpart.

(d) Owners and operators controlling air pollutant emissions from a tank using Tank Level 2 controls shall use one of the following tanks: 📖 15.3.4.2

(1) A fixed-roof tank equipped with an internal floating roof in accordance with the requirements specified in paragraph (e) of this section;

(2) A tank equipped with an external floating roof in accordance with the requirements specified in paragraph (f) of this section;

(3) A tank vented through a closed-vent system to a control device in accordance with the requirements specified in paragraph (g) of this section;

(4) A pressure tank designed and operated in accordance with the requirements specified in paragraph (h) of this section; or

(5) A tank located inside an enclosure that is vented through a closed-vent system to an enclosed combustion control device in accordance with the requirements specified in paragraph (i) of this section.

(e) The owner or operator who controls air pollutant emissions from a tank using a fixed roof with an internal floating roof shall meet the requirements specified in paragraphs (e)(1) through (e)(3) of this section.

(1) The tank shall be equipped with a fixed roof and an internal floating roof in accordance with the following requirements:

(i) The internal floating roof shall be designed to float on the liquid surface except when the floating roof must be supported by the leg supports.

(ii) The internal floating roof shall be equipped with a continuous seal between the wall of the tank and the floating roof edge that meets either of the following requirements:

(A) A single continuous seal that is either a liquid-mounted seal or a metallic shoe seal, as defined in 40 CFR 265.1081; or

(B) Two continuous seals mounted one above the other. The lower seal may be a vapor-mounted seal.

(iii) The internal floating roof shall meet the following specifications:

(A) Each opening in a noncontact internal floating roof except for automatic bleeder vents (vacuum breaker vents) and the rim space vents is to provide a projection below the liquid surface.

(B) Each opening in the internal floating roof shall be equipped with a gasketed cover or a gasketed lid except for leg sleeves, automatic bleeder vents, rim space vents, column wells, ladder wells, sample wells, and stub drains.

(C) Each penetration of the internal floating roof for the purpose of sampling shall have a slit fabric cover that covers at least 90 percent of the opening.

(D) Each automatic bleeder vent and rim space vent shall be gasketed.

(E) Each penetration of the internal floating roof that allows for passage of a ladder shall have a gasketed sliding cover.

(F) Each penetration of the internal floating roof that allows for passage of a column supporting the fixed roof shall have a flexible fabric sleeve seal or a gasketed sliding cover.

(2) The owner or operator shall operate the tank in accordance with the following requirements:

(i) When the floating roof is resting on the leg supports, the process of filling, emptying, or refilling shall be continuous and shall be completed as soon as practical.

(ii) Automatic bleeder vents are to be set closed at all times when the roof is floating, except when the roof is being floated off or is being landed on the leg supports.

(iii) Prior to filling the tank, each cover, access hatch, gauge float well or lid on any opening in the internal floating roof shall be bolted or fastened closed (*i.e.*, no visible gaps). Rim space vents are to be set to open only when the internal floating roof is not floating or when the pressure beneath the rim exceeds the manufacturer's recommended setting.

(3) The owner or operator shall inspect the internal floating roof in accordance with the procedures specified as follows:

(i) The floating roof and its closure devices shall be visually inspected by the owner or operator to check for defects that could result in air pollutant emissions. Defects include, but are not limited to: The internal floating roof is not floating on the surface of the liquid inside the tank; liquid has accumulated on top of the internal floating roof; any portion of the roof seals have detached from the roof rim; holes, tears, or other openings are visible in the seal fabric; the gaskets no longer close off the hazardous waste surface from the atmosphere; or the slotted membrane has more than 10 percent open area.

(ii) The owner or operator shall inspect the internal floating roof components as follows except as provided in paragraph (e)(3)(iii) of this section:

(A) Visually inspect the internal floating roof components through openings on the fixed-roof (*e.g.*, manholes and roof hatches) at least once every 12 months after initial fill, and

(B) Visually inspect the internal floating roof, primary seal, secondary seal (if one is in service), gaskets, slotted membranes, and sleeve seals (if any) each time the tank is emptied and degassed and at least every 10 years.

(iii) As an alternative to performing the inspections specified in paragraph (e)(3)(ii) of this section for an internal floating roof equipped with two continuous seals mounted one above the other, the owner or operator may visually inspect the internal floating roof, primary and secondary seals, gaskets, slotted membranes, and sleeve seals (if any) each time the tank is emptied and degassed and at least every 5 years.

(iv) Prior to each inspection required by paragraph (e)(3)(ii) or (e)(3)(iii) of this section, the owner or operator shall notify the Regional Administrator in advance of each inspection to provide the Regional Administrator with the opportunity to have an observer present during the inspection. The owner or operator shall notify the Regional Administrator of the date and location of the inspection as follows:

(A) Prior to each visual inspection of an internal floating roof in a tank that has been emptied and degassed, written notification shall be prepared and sent by the owner or operator so that it is received by the Regional Administrator at least 30 calendar days before refilling the tank except when an inspection is not planned as provided for in paragraph (e)(3)(iv)(B) of this section.

(B) When a visual inspection is not planned and the owner or operator could not have known about the inspection 30 calendar days before refilling the tank, the owner or operator shall notify the Regional Administrator as soon as possible, but no later than 7 calendar days before refilling of the tank. This notification may be made by telephone and immediately followed by a written explanation for why the inspection is unplanned. Alternatively, written notification, including the explanation for the unplanned inspection, may be sent so that it is received by the Regional Administrator at least 7 calendar days before refilling the tank.

(v) In the event that a defect is detected, the owner or operator shall repair the defect in accordance with the requirements of paragraph (k) of this section.

(vi) The owner or operator shall maintain a record of the inspection in accordance with the requirements specified in §264.1089(b) of this subpart.

(4) Safety devices, as defined in 40 CFR 265.1081, may be installed and operated as necessary on any tank complying with the requirements of paragraph (e) of this section.

(f) The owner or operator who controls air pollutant emissions from a tank using an external floating roof shall meet the requirements specified in paragraphs (f)(1) through (f)(3) of this section.

(1) The owner or operator shall design the external floating roof in accordance with the following requirements:

(i) The external floating roof shall be designed to float on the liquid surface except when the floating roof must be supported by the leg supports.

(ii) The floating roof shall be equipped with two continuous seals, one above the other, between the wall of the tank and the roof edge. The lower seal is referred to as the primary seal, and the upper seal is referred to as the secondary seal.

(A) The primary seal shall be a liquid-mounted seal or a metallic shoe seal, as defined in 40 CFR 265.1081. The total area of the gaps between the tank wall and the primary seal shall not exceed 212 square centimeters (cm^2) per meter of tank diameter, and the width of any portion of these gaps shall not exceed 3.8 centimeters (cm). If a metallic shoe seal is used for the primary seal, the metallic shoe seal shall be designed so that one end extends into the liquid in the tank and the other end extends a vertical distance of at least 61 centimeters above the liquid surface.

(B) The secondary seal shall be mounted above the primary seal and cover the annular space between the floating roof and the wall of the tank. The total area of the gaps between the tank wall and the secondary seal shall not exceed 21.2 square centimeters (cm^2) per meter of tank diameter, and the width of any portion of these gaps shall not exceed 1.3 centimeters (cm).

(iii) The external floating roof shall meet the following specifications:

(A) Except for automatic bleeder vents (vacuum breaker vents) and rim space vents, each opening in a noncontact external floating roof shall provide a projection below the liquid surface.

(B) Except for automatic bleeder vents, rim space vents, roof drains, and leg sleeves, each opening in the roof shall be equipped with a gasketed cover, seal, or lid.

(C) Each access hatch and each gauge float well shall be equipped with a cover designed to be bolted or fastened when the cover is secured in the closed position.

(D) Each automatic bleeder vent and each rim space vent shall be equipped with a gasket.

(E) Each roof drain that empties into the liquid managed in the tank shall be equipped with a slotted membrane fabric cover that covers at least 90 percent of the area of the opening.

(F) Each unslotted and slotted guide pole well shall be equipped with a gasketed sliding cover or a flexible fabric sleeve seal.

(G) Each unslotted guide pole shall be equipped with a gasketed cap on the end of the pole.

(H) Each slotted guide pole shall be equipped with a gasketed float or other device which closes off the liquid surface from the atmosphere.

(I) Each gauge hatch and each sample well shall be equipped with a gasketed cover.

(2) The owner or operator shall operate the tank in accordance with the following requirements:

(i) When the floating roof is resting on the leg supports, the process of filling, emptying, or refilling shall be continuous and shall be completed as soon as practical.

(ii) Except for automatic bleeder vents, rim space vents, roof drains, and leg sleeves, each opening in the roof shall be secured and maintained in a closed position at all times except when the closure device must be open for access.

(iii) Covers on each access hatch and each gauge float well shall be bolted or fastened when secured in the closed position.

(iv) Automatic bleeder vents shall be set closed at all times when the roof is floating, except when the roof is being floated off or is being landed on the leg supports.

(v) Rim space vents shall be set to open only at those times that the roof is being floated off the roof leg supports or when the pressure beneath the rim seal exceeds the manufacturer's recommended setting.

(vi) The cap on the end of each unslotted guide pole shall be secured in the closed position at all times except when measuring the level or collecting samples of the liquid in the tank.

(vii) The cover on each gauge hatch or sample well shall be secured in the closed position at all times except when the hatch or well must be opened for access.

(viii) Both the primary seal and the secondary seal shall completely cover the annular space between the external floating roof and the wall of the tank in a continuous fashion except during inspections.

(3) The owner or operator shall inspect the external floating roof in accordance with the procedures specified as follows:

(i) The owner or operator shall measure the external floating roof seal gaps in accordance with the following requirements:

(A) The owner or operator shall perform measurements of gaps between the tank wall and the primary seal within 60 calendar days after initial operation of the tank following installation of the floating roof and, thereafter, at least once every 5 years.

(B) The owner or operator shall perform measurements of gaps between the tank wall and the secondary seal within 60 calendar days after initial operation of the tank following installation of the floating roof and, thereafter, at least once every year.

(C) If a tank ceases to hold hazardous waste for a period of 1 year or more, subsequent introduction of hazardous waste into the tank shall be considered an initial operation for the purposes of paragraphs (f)(3)(i)(A) and (f)(3)(i)(B) of this section.

(D) The owner or operator shall determine the total surface area of gaps in the primary seal and in the secondary seal individually using the following procedure:

(*1*) The seal gap measurements shall be performed at one or more floating roof levels when the roof is floating off the roof supports.

(*2*) Seal gaps, if any, shall be measured around the entire perimeter of the floating roof in each place where a 0.32-centimeter (cm) diameter uniform probe passes freely (without forcing or binding against the seal) between the seal and the wall of the tank and measure the circumferential distance of each such location.

(*3*) For a seal gap measured under paragraph (f)(3) of this section, the gap surface area shall be determined by using probes of various widths to measure accurately the actual distance from the tank wall to the seal and multiplying each such width by its respective circumferential distance.

(*4*) The total gap area shall be calculated by adding the gap surface areas determined for each identified gap location for the primary seal and the secondary seal individually, and then dividing the sum for each seal type by the nominal diameter of the tank. These total gap areas for the primary seal and secondary seal are then compared to the respective standards for the seal type as specified in paragraph (f)(1)(ii) of this section.

(E) In the event that the seal gap measurements do not conform to the specifications in paragraph (f)(1)(ii) of this section, the owner or operator shall repair the defect in accordance with the requirements of paragraph (k) of this section.

(F) The owner or operator shall maintain a record of the inspection in accordance with the requirements specified in §264.1089(b) of this subpart.

(ii) The owner or operator shall visually inspect the external floating roof in accordance with the following requirements:

(A) The floating roof and its closure devices shall be visually inspected by the owner or operator to check for defects that could result in air pollutant emissions. Defects include, but are not limited to: Holes, tears, or other openings in the rim seal or seal fabric of the floating roof; a rim seal detached from the floating roof; all or a portion of the floating roof deck being submerged below the surface of the liquid in the tank; broken, cracked, or otherwise damaged seals or gaskets on closure devices; and broken or missing hatches, access covers, caps, or other closure devices.

(B) The owner or operator shall perform an initial inspection of the external floating roof and its closure devices on or before the date that the tank becomes subject to this section. Thereafter, the owner or operator shall perform the inspections at least once every year except for the special conditions provided for in paragraph (l) of this section.

(C) In the event that a defect is detected, the owner or operator shall repair the defect in accordance with the requirements of paragraph (k) of this section.

(D) The owner or operator shall maintain a record of the inspection in accordance with the requirements specified in §264.1089(b) of this subpart.

(iii) Prior to each inspection required by paragraph (f)(3)(i) or (f)(3)(ii) of this section, the owner or operator shall notify the Regional Administrator in advance of each inspection to provide the Regional Administrator with the opportunity to have an observer present during the inspection. The owner or operator shall notify the Regional Administrator of the date and location of the inspection as follows:

(A) Prior to each inspection to measure external floating roof seal gaps as required under paragraph (f)(3)(i) of this section, written notification shall be prepared and sent by the owner or operator so that it is received by the Regional Administrator at least 30 calendar days before the date the measurements are scheduled to be performed.

(B) Prior to each visual inspection of an external floating roof in a tank that has been emptied and degassed, written notification shall be prepared and sent by the owner or operator so that it is received by the Regional Administrator at least 30 calendar days before refilling the tank except when an inspection is not planned as provided for in paragraph (f)(3)(iii)(C) of this section.

(C) When a visual inspection is not planned and the owner or operator could not have known about the inspection 30 calendar days before refilling the tank, the owner or operator shall notify the Regional Administrator as soon as possible, but no later than 7 calendar days before refilling of the tank. This notification may be made by telephone and immediately followed by a written explanation for why the inspection is unplanned. Alternatively, written notification, including the explanation for the unplanned inspection, may be sent so that it is received by the Regional Administrator at least 7 calendar days before refilling the tank.

(4) Safety devices, as defined in 40 CFR 265.1081, may be installed and operated as necessary on any tank complying with the requirements of paragraph (f) of this section.

(g) The owner or operator who controls air pollutant emissions from a tank by venting the tank to a control device shall meet the requirements specified in paragraphs (g)(1) through (g)(3) of this section. 15.3.4.2.1

(1) The tank shall be covered by a fixed roof and vented directly through a closed-vent system to a control device in accordance with the following requirements:

(i) The fixed roof and its closure devices shall be designed to form a continuous barrier over the entire surface area of the liquid in the tank.

(ii) Each opening in the fixed roof not vented to the control device shall be equipped with a closure device. If the pressure in the vapor headspace underneath the fixed roof is less than atmospheric pressure when the control device is operating, the closure devices shall be designed to operate such that when the closure device is secured in the closed position there are no visible cracks, holes, gaps, or other open spaces in the closure device or between the perimeter of the cover opening and the closure device. If the pressure in the vapor headspace underneath the fixed roof is equal to or greater than atmospheric pressure when the control device is operating, the closure device shall be designed to operate with no detectable organic emissions.

(iii) The fixed roof and its closure devices shall be made of suitable materials that will minimize exposure of the hazardous waste to the atmosphere, to the extent practical, and will maintain the integrity of the fixed roof and closure devices throughout their intended service life. Factors to be considered when selecting the materials for and designing the fixed roof and closure devices shall include: Organic vapor permeability, the effects of any contact with the liquid and its vapor managed in the tank; the effects of outdoor exposure to wind, moisture, and sunlight; and the operating practices used for the tank on which the fixed roof is installed.

(iv) The closed-vent system and control device shall be designed and operated in accordance with the requirements of §264.1087 of this subpart.

(2) Whenever a hazardous waste is in the tank, the fixed roof shall be installed with each closure device secured in the closed position and the vapor headspace underneath the fixed roof vented to the control device except as follows:

(i) Venting to the control device is not required, and opening of closure devices or removal of the fixed roof is allowed at the following times:

(A) To provide access to the tank for performing routine inspection, maintenance, or other activities needed for normal operations. Examples of such activities include those times when a worker needs to open a port to sample liquid in the tank, or when a worker needs to open a hatch to maintain or repair equipment. Following completion of the activity, the owner or operator shall promptly secure the closure device in the closed position or reinstall the cover, as applicable, to the tank.

(B) To remove accumulated sludge or other residues from the bottom of a tank.

(ii) Opening of a safety device, as defined in 40 CFR 265.1081, is allowed at any time conditions require doing so to avoid an unsafe condition.

(3) The owner or operator shall inspect and monitor the air emission control equipment in accordance with the following procedures:

(i) The fixed roof and its closure devices shall be visually inspected by the owner or operator to check for defects that could result in air pollutant emissions. Defects include, but are not limited to, visible cracks, holes, or gaps in the roof sections or between the roof and the tank wall; broken, cracked, or otherwise damaged seals or gaskets on closure devices; and broken or missing hatches, access covers, caps, or other closure devices.

(ii) The closed-vent system and control device shall be inspected and monitored by the owner or operator in accordance with the procedures specified in §264.1087 of this subpart.

(iii) The owner or operator shall perform an initial inspection of the air emission control equipment on or before the date that the tank becomes subject to this section. Thereafter, the owner or operator shall perform the inspections at least once every year except for the special conditions provided for in paragraph (l) of this section.

(iv) In the event that a defect is detected, the owner or operator shall repair the defect in accordance with the requirements of paragraph (k) of this section.

(v) The owner or operator shall maintain a record of the inspection in accordance with the requirements specified in §264.1089(b) of this subpart.

(h) The owner or operator who controls air pollutant emissions by using a pressure tank shall meet the following requirements.

(1) The tank shall be designed not to vent to the atmosphere as a result of compression of the vapor

headspace in the tank during filling of the tank to its design capacity.

(2) All tank openings shall be equipped with closure devices designed to operate with no detectable organic emissions as determined using the procedure specified in §264.1083(d) of this subpart.

(3) Whenever a hazardous waste is in the tank, the tank shall be operated as a closed system that does not vent to the atmosphere except under either or the following conditions as specified in paragraph (h)(3)(i) or (h)(3)(ii) of this section.

(i) At those times when opening of a safety device, as defined in §265.1081 of this subpart, is required to avoid an unsafe condition.

(ii) At those times when purging of inerts from the tank is required and the purge stream is routed to a closed-vent system and control device designed and operated in accordance with the requirements of §264.1087 of this subpart.

(i) The owner or operator who controls air pollutant emissions by using an enclosure vented through a closed-vent system to an enclosed combustion control device shall meet the requirements specified in paragraphs (i)(1) through (i)(4) of this section.

(1) The tank shall be located inside an enclosure. The enclosure shall be designed and operated in accordance with the criteria for a permanent total enclosure as specified in "Procedure T—Criteria for and Verification of a Permanent or Temporary Total Enclosure" under 40 CFR 52.741, appendix B. The enclosure may have permanent or temporary openings to allow worker access; passage of material into or out of the enclosure by conveyor, vehicles, or other mechanical means; entry of permanent mechanical or electrical equipment; or direct airflow into the enclosure. The owner or operator shall perform the verification procedure for the enclosure as specified in Section 5.0 to "Procedure T—Criteria for and Verification of a Permanent or Temporary Total Enclosure" initially when the enclosure is first installed and, thereafter, annually.

(2) The enclosure shall be vented through a closed-vent system to an enclosed combustion control device that is designed and operated in accordance with the standards for either a vapor incinerator, boiler, or process heater specified in §264.1087 of this subpart.

(3) Safety devices, as defined in 40 CFR 265.1081, may be installed and operated as necessary on any enclosure, closed-vent system, or control device used to comply with the requirements of paragraphs (i)(1) and (i)(2) of this section.

(4) The owner or operator shall inspect and monitor the closed-vent system and control device as specified in §264.1087 of this subpart.

(j) The owner or operator shall transfer hazardous waste to a tank subject to this section in accordance with the following requirements:

(1) Transfer of hazardous waste, except as provided in paragraph (j)(2) of this section, to the tank from another tank subject to this section or from a surface impoundment subject to §264.1085 of this subpart shall be conducted using continuous hard-piping or another closed system that does not allow exposure of the hazardous waste to the atmosphere. For the purpose of complying with this provision, an individual drain system is considered to be a closed system when it meets the requirements of 40 CFR part 63, subpart RR—National Emission Standards for Individual Drain Systems.

(2) The requirements of paragraph (j)(1) of this section do not apply when transferring a hazardous waste to the tank under any of the following conditions:

(i) The hazardous waste meets the average VO concentration conditions specified in §264.1082(c)(1) of this subpart at the point of waste origination.

(ii) The hazardous waste has been treated by an organic destruction or removal process to meet the requirements in §264.1082(c)(2) of this subpart.

(iii) The hazardous waste meets the requirements of §264.1082(c)(4) of this subpart.

(k) The owner or operator shall repair each defect detected during an inspection performed in accordance with the requirements of paragraph (c)(4), (e)(3), (f)(3), or (g)(3) of this section as follows:

(1) The owner or operator shall make first efforts at repair of the defect no later than 5 calendar days after detection, and repair shall be completed as soon as possible but no later than 45 calendar days after detection except as provided in paragraph (k)(2) of this section.

(2) Repair of a defect may be delayed beyond 45 calendar days if the owner or operator determines that repair of the defect requires emptying or temporary removal from service of the tank and no alternative tank capacity is available at the site to accept the hazardous waste normally managed in the tank. In this case, the owner or operator shall repair the defect the next time the process or unit that is generating the hazardous

waste managed in the tank stops operation. Repair of the defect shall be completed before the process or unit resumes operation.

(l) Following the initial inspection and monitoring of the cover as required by the applicable provisions of this subpart, subsequent inspection and monitoring may be performed at intervals longer than 1 year under the following special conditions:

(1) In the case when inspecting or monitoring the cover would expose a worker to dangerous, hazardous, or other unsafe conditions, then the owner or operator may designate a cover as an "unsafe to inspect and monitor cover" and comply with all of the following requirements:

(i) Prepare a written explanation for the cover stating the reasons why the cover is unsafe to visually inspect or to monitor, if required.

(ii) Develop and implement a written plan and schedule to inspect and monitor the cover, using the procedures specified in the applicable section of this subpart, as frequently as practicable during those times when a worker can safely access the cover.

(2) In the case when a tank is buried partially or entirely underground, an owner or operator is required to inspect and monitor, as required by the applicable provisions of this section, only those portions of the tank cover and those connections to the tank (*e.g.*, fill ports, access hatches, gauge wells, etc.) that are located on or above the ground surface.

[61 FR 59955, Nov. 25, 1996, as amended at 62 FR 64659, Dec. 8, 1997; 64 FR 3389, Jan. 21, 1999]

§264.1085 Standards: Surface impoundments. 15.3.6

(a) The provisions of this section apply to the control of air pollutant emissions from surface impoundments for which §264.1082(b) of this subpart references the use of this section for such air emission control.

(b) The owner or operator shall control air pollutant emissions from the surface impoundment by installing and operating either of the following:

(1) A floating membrane cover in accordance with the provisions specified in paragraph (c) of this section; or

(2) A cover that is vented through a closed-vent system to a control device in accordance with the provisions specified in paragraph (d) of this section.

(c) The owner or operator who controls air pollutant emissions from a surface impoundment using a floating membrane cover shall meet the requirements specified in paragraphs (c)(1) through (c)(3) of this section.

(1) The surface impoundment shall be equipped with a floating membrane cover designed to meet the following specifications:

(i) The floating membrane cover shall be designed to float on the liquid surface during normal operations and form a continuous barrier over the entire surface area of the liquid.

(ii) The cover shall be fabricated from a synthetic membrane material that is either:

(A) High density polyethylene (HDPE) with a thickness no less than 2.5 millimeters (mm); or

(B) A material or a composite of different materials determined to have both organic permeability properties that are equivalent to those of the material listed in paragraph (c)(1)(ii)(A) of this section and chemical and physical properties that maintain the material integrity for the intended service life of the material.

(iii) The cover shall be installed in a manner such that there are no visible cracks, holes, gaps, or other open spaces between cover section seams or between the interface of the cover edge and its foundation mountings.

(iv) Except as provided for in paragraph (c)(1)(v) of this section, each opening in the floating membrane cover shall be equipped with a closure device designed to operate such that when the closure device is secured in the closed position there are no visible cracks, holes, gaps, or other open spaces in the closure device or between the perimeter of the cover opening and the closure device.

(v) The floating membrane cover may be equipped with one or more emergency cover drains for removal of stormwater. Each emergency cover drain shall be equipped with a slotted membrane fabric cover that covers at least 90 percent of the area of the opening or a flexible fabric sleeve seal.

(vi) The closure devices shall be made of suitable materials that will minimize exposure of the hazardous waste to the atmosphere, to the extent practical, and will maintain the integrity of the closure devices throughout their intended service life. Factors to be considered when selecting the materials of construction and designing the cover and closure devices shall include: Organic vapor permeability; the effects of any contact with the liquid and its vapor managed in the surface impoundment; the effects of outdoor exposure to wind, moisture, and sunlight; and the operating practices used for the surface impoundment on which the floating membrane cover is installed.

(2) Whenever a hazardous waste is in the surface impoundment, the floating membrane cover shall float on the liquid and each closure device shall be secured in the closed position except as follows:

(i) Opening of closure devices or removal of the cover is allowed at the following times:

(A) To provide access to the surface impoundment for performing routine inspection, maintenance, or other activities needed for normal operations. Examples of such activities include those times when a worker needs to open a port to sample the liquid in the surface impoundment, or when a worker needs to open a hatch to maintain or repair equipment. Following completion of the activity, the owner or operator shall promptly replace the cover and secure the closure device in the closed position, as applicable.

(B) To remove accumulated sludge or other residues from the bottom of surface impoundment.

(ii) Opening of a safety device, as defined in 40 CFR 265.1081, is allowed at any time conditions require doing so to avoid an unsafe condition.

(3) The owner or operator shall inspect the floating membrane cover in accordance with the following procedures:

(i) The floating membrane cover and its closure devices shall be visually inspected by the owner or operator to check for defects that could result in air pollutant emissions. Defects include, but are not limited to, visible cracks, holes, or gaps in the cover section seams or between the interface of the cover edge and its foundation mountings; broken, cracked, or otherwise damaged seals or gaskets on closure devices; and broken or missing hatches, access covers, caps, or other closure devices.

(ii) The owner or operator shall perform an initial inspection of the floating membrane cover and its closure devices on or before the date that the surface impoundment becomes subject to this section. Thereafter, the owner or operator shall perform the inspections at least once every year except for the special conditions provided for in paragraph (g) of this section.

(iii) In the event that a defect is detected, the owner or operator shall repair the defect in accordance with the requirements of paragraph (f) of this section.

(iv) The owner or operator shall maintain a record of the inspection in accordance with the requirements specified in §264.1089(c) of this subpart.

(d) The owner or operator who controls air pollutant emissions from a surface impoundment using a cover vented to a control device shall meet the requirements specified in paragraphs (d)(1) through (d)(3) of this section.

(1) The surface impoundment shall be covered by a cover and vented directly through a closed-vent system to a control device in accordance with the following requirements:

(i) The cover and its closure devices shall be designed to form a continuous barrier over the entire surface area of the liquid in the surface impoundment.

(ii) Each opening in the cover not vented to the control device shall be equipped with a closure device. If the pressure in the vapor headspace underneath the cover is less than atmospheric pressure when the control device is operating, the closure devices shall be designed to operate such that when the closure device is secured in the closed position there are no visible cracks, holes, gaps, or other open spaces in the closure device or between the perimeter of the cover opening and the closure device. If the pressure in the vapor headspace underneath the cover is equal to or greater than atmospheric pressure when the control device is operating, the closure device shall be designed to operate with no detectable organic emissions using the procedure specified in §264.1083(d) of this subpart.

(iii) The cover and its closure devices shall be made of suitable materials that will minimize exposure of the hazardous waste to the atmosphere, to the extent practical, and will maintain the integrity of the cover and closure devices throughout their intended service life. Factors to be considered when selecting the materials of construction and designing the cover and closure devices shall include: Organic vapor permeability; the effects of any contact with the liquid or its vapors managed in the surface impoundment; the effects of outdoor exposure to wind, moisture, and sunlight; and the operating practices used for the surface impoundment on which the cover is installed.

(iv) The closed-vent system and control device shall be designed and operated in accordance with the requirements of §264.1087 of this subpart.

(2) Whenever a hazardous waste is in the surface impoundment, the cover shall be installed with each closure device secured in the closed position and the vapor headspace underneath the cover vented to the control device except as follows:

(i) Venting to the control device is not required, and opening of closure devices or removal of the cover is allowed at the following times:

(A) To provide access to the surface impoundment for performing routine inspection, maintenance, or other activities needed for normal operations. Examples of such activities include those times when a worker needs to open a port to sample liquid in the surface impoundment, or when a worker needs to open a hatch to maintain or repair equipment. Following completion of the activity, the owner or operator shall promptly secure the closure device in the closed position or reinstall the cover, as applicable, to the surface impoundment.

(B) To remove accumulated sludge or other residues from the bottom of the surface impoundment.

(ii) Opening of a safety device, as defined in 40 CFR 265.1081, is allowed at any time conditions require doing so to avoid an unsafe condition.

(3) The owner or operator shall inspect and monitor the air emission control equipment in accordance with the following procedures:

(i) The surface impoundment cover and its closure devices shall be visually inspected by the owner or operator to check for defects that could result in air pollutant emissions. Defects include, but are not limited to, visible cracks, holes, or gaps in the cover section seams or between the interface of the cover edge and its foundation mountings; broken, cracked, or otherwise damaged seals or gaskets on closure devices; and broken or missing hatches, access covers, caps, or other closure devices.

(ii) The closed-vent system and control device shall be inspected and monitored by the owner or operator in accordance with the procedures specified in §264.1087 of this subpart.

(iii) The owner or operator shall perform an initial inspection of the air emission control equipment on or before the date that the surface impoundment becomes subject to this section. Thereafter, the owner or operator shall perform the inspections at least once every year except for the special conditions provided for in paragraph (g) of this section.

(iv) In the event that a defect is detected, the owner or operator shall repair the defect in accordance with the requirements of paragraph (f) of this section.

(v) The owner or operator shall maintain a record of the inspection in accordance with the requirements specified in §264.1089(c) of this subpart.

(e) The owner or operator shall transfer hazardous waste to a surface impoundment subject to this section in accordance with the following requirements:

(1) Transfer of hazardous waste, except as provided in paragraph (e)(2) of this section, to the surface impoundment from another surface impoundment subject to this section or from a tank subject to §264.1084 of this subpart shall be conducted using continuous hard-piping or another closed system that does not allow exposure of the waste to the atmosphere. For the purpose of complying with this provision, an individual drain system is considered to be a closed system when it meets the requirements of 40 CFR part 63, subpart RR—National Emission Standards for Individual Drain Systems.

(2) The requirements of paragraph (e)(1) of this section do not apply when transferring a hazardous waste to the surface impoundment under either of the following conditions:

(i) The hazardous waste meets the average VO concentration conditions specified in §264.1082(c)(1) of this subpart at the point of waste origination.

(ii) The hazardous waste has been treated by an organic destruction or removal process to meet the requirements in §264.1082(c)(2) of this subpart.

(iii) The hazardous waste meets the requirements of §264.1082(c)(4) of this subpart.

(f) The owner or operator shall repair each defect detected during an inspection performed in accordance with the requirements of paragraph (c)(3) or (d)(3) of this section as follows:

(1) The owner or operator shall make first efforts at repair of the defect no later than 5 calendar days after detection and repair shall be completed as soon as possible but no later than 45 calendar days after detection except as provided in paragraph (f)(2) of this section.

(2) Repair of a defect may be delayed beyond 45 calendar days if the owner or operator determines that repair of the defect requires emptying or temporary removal from service of the surface impoundment and no alternative capacity is available at the site to accept the hazardous waste normally managed in the surface

impoundment. In this case, the owner or operator shall repair the defect the next time the process or unit that is generating the hazardous waste managed in the surface impoundment stops operation. Repair of the defect shall be completed before the process or unit resumes operation.

(g) Following the initial inspection and monitoring of the cover as required by the applicable provisions of this subpart, subsequent inspection and monitoring may be performed at intervals longer than 1 year in the case when inspecting or monitoring the cover would expose a worker to dangerous, hazardous, or other unsafe conditions. In this case, the owner or operator may designate the cover as an "unsafe to inspect and monitor cover" and comply with all of the following requirements:

(1) Prepare a written explanation for the cover stating the reasons why the cover is unsafe to visually inspect or to monitor, if required.

(2) Develop and implement a written plan and schedule to inspect and monitor the cover using the procedures specified in the applicable section of this subpart as frequently as practicable during those times when a worker can safely access the cover.

[61 FR 59960, Nov. 25, 1996, as amended at 62 FR 64659, Dec. 8, 1997]

§264.1086 Standards: Containers. 📖 15.3.5

(a) The provisions of this section apply to the control of air pollutant emissions from containers for which §264.1082(b) of this subpart references the use of this section for such air emission control.

(b) *General requirements.* (1) The owner or operator shall control air pollutant emissions from each container subject to this section in accordance with the following requirements, as applicable to the container, except when the special provisions for waste stabilization processes specified in paragraph (b)(2) of this section apply to the container.

(i) For a container having a design capacity greater than 0.1 m^3 and less than or equal to 0.46 m^3, the owner or operator shall control air pollutant emissions from the container in accordance with the Container Level 1 standards specified in paragraph (c) of this section. 📖 15.3.5.1

(ii) For a container having a design capacity greater than 0.46 m^3 that is not in light material service, the owner or operator shall control air pollutant emissions from the container in accordance with the Container Level 1 standards specified in paragraph (c) of this section. 📖 15.3.5.1

(iii) For a container having a design capacity greater than 0.46 m^3 that is in light material service, the owner or operator shall control air pollutant emissions from the container in accordance with the Container Level 2 standards specified in paragraph (d) of this section. 📖 15.3.5.2

(2) When a container having a design capacity greater than 0.1 m^3 is used for treatment of a hazardous waste by a waste stabilization process, the owner or operator shall control air pollutant emissions from the container in accordance with the Container Level 3 standards specified in paragraph (e) of this section at those times during the waste stabilization process when the hazardous waste in the container is exposed to the atmosphere. 📖 15.3.5.3

(c) *Container Level 1 standards.* (1) A container using Container Level 1 controls is one of the following: 📖 15.3.5.1.1

(i) A container that meets the applicable U.S. Department of Transportation (DOT) regulations on packaging hazardous materials for transportation as specified in paragraph (f) of this section.

(ii) A container equipped with a cover and closure devices that form a continuous barrier over the container openings such that when the cover and closure devices are secured in the closed position there are no visible holes, gaps, or other open spaces into the interior of the container. The cover may be a separate cover installed on the container (*e.g.,* a lid on a drum or a suitably secured tarp on a roll-off box) or may be an integral part of the container structural design (*e.g.,* a "portable tank" or bulk cargo container equipped with a screw-type cap).

(iii) An open-top container in which an organic-vapor suppressing barrier is placed on or over the hazardous waste in the container such that no hazardous waste is exposed to the atmosphere. One example of such a barrier is application of a suitable organic-vapor suppressing foam.

(2) A container used to meet the requirements of paragraph (c)(1)(ii) or (c)(1)(iii) of this section shall be equipped with covers and closure devices, as applicable to the container, that are composed of suitable materials to minimize exposure of the hazardous waste to the atmosphere and to maintain the equipment integrity, for as long as the container is in service. Factors to be considered in selecting the materials of construction and designing the cover and closure devices shall include: Organic vapor permeability; the

effects of contact with the hazardous waste or its vapor managed in the container; the effects of outdoor exposure of the closure device or cover material to wind, moisture, and sunlight; and the operating practices for which the container is intended to be used.

(3) Whenever a hazardous waste is in a container using Container Level 1 controls, the owner or operator shall install all covers and closure devices for the container, as applicable to the container, and secure and maintain each closure device in the closed position except as follows: 15.3.5.1.2

(i) Opening of a closure device or cover is allowed for the purpose of adding hazardous waste or other material to the container as follows:

(A) In the case when the container is filled to the intended final level in one continuous operation, the owner or operator shall promptly secure the closure devices in the closed position and install the covers, as applicable to the container, upon conclusion of the filling operation.

(B) In the case when discrete quantities or batches of material intermittently are added to the container over a period of time, the owner or operator shall promptly secure the closure devices in the closed position and install covers, as applicable to the container, upon either the container being filled to the intended final level; the completion of a batch loading after which no additional material will be added to the container within 15 minutes; the person performing the loading operation leaving the immediate vicinity of the container; or the shutdown of the process generating the material being added to the container, whichever condition occurs first.

(ii) Opening of a closure device or cover is allowed for the purpose of removing hazardous waste from the container as follows:

(A) For the purpose of meeting the requirements of this section, an empty container as defined in 40 CFR 261.7(b) may be open to the atmosphere at any time (*i.e.*, covers and closure devices are not required to be secured in the closed position on an empty container).

(B) In the case when discrete quantities or batches of material are removed from the container but the container does not meet the conditions to be an empty container as defined in 40 CFR 261.7(b), the owner or operator shall promptly secure the closure devices in the closed position and install covers, as applicable to the container, upon the completion of a batch removal after which no additional material will be removed from the container within 15 minutes or the person performing the unloading operation leaves the immediate vicinity of the container, whichever condition occurs first.

(iii) Opening of a closure device or cover is allowed when access inside the container is needed to perform routine activities other than transfer of hazardous waste. Examples of such activities include those times when a worker needs to open a port to measure the depth of or sample the material in the container, or when a worker needs to open a manhole hatch to access equipment inside the container. Following completion of the activity, the owner or operator shall promptly secure the closure device in the closed position or reinstall the cover, as applicable to the container.

(iv) Opening of a spring-loaded pressure-vacuum relief valve, conservation vent, or similar type of pressure relief device which vents to the atmosphere is allowed during normal operations for the purpose of maintaining the internal pressure of the container in accordance with the container design specifications. The device shall be designed to operate with no detectable organic emissions when the device is secured in the closed position. The settings at which the device opens shall be established such that the device remains in the closed position whenever the internal pressure of the container is within the internal pressure operating range determined by the owner or operator based on container manufacturer recommendations, applicable regulations, fire protection and prevention codes, standard engineering codes and practices, or other requirements for the safe handling of flammable, ignitable, explosive, reactive, or hazardous materials. Examples of normal operating conditions that may require these devices to open are during those times when the internal pressure of the container exceeds the internal pressure operating range for the container as a result of loading operations or diurnal ambient temperature fluctuations.

(v) Opening of a safety device, as defined in 40 CFR 265.1081, is allowed at any time conditions require doing so to avoid an unsafe condition.

(4) The owner or operator of containers using Container Level 1 controls shall inspect the containers and their covers and closure devices as follows: 15.3.5.1.3

(i) In the case when a hazardous waste already is in the container at the time the owner or operator first accepts possession of the container at the facility and the container is not emptied within 24 hours after the container is accepted at the facility (*i.e.*, does not meet the conditions for an empty container as specified in 40 CFR 261.7(b)), the owner or operator shall visually inspect the container and its cover and closure devices to check for visible cracks, holes, gaps, or other open spaces into the interior of the container when the cover and closure devices are secured in the closed position. The container visual inspection shall be conducted on or before the date that the container is accepted at the facility (*i.e.*, the date the container becomes subject to the subpart CC container standards). For purposes of this requirement, the date of acceptance is the date of signature that the facility owner or operator enters on Item 20 of the Uniform Hazardous Waste Manifest in the appendix to 40 CFR part 262 (EPA Forms 8700-22 and 8700-22A), as required under subpart E of this part, at 40 CFR 264.71. If a defect is detected, the owner or operator shall repair the defect in accordance with the requirements of paragraph (c)(4)(iii) of this section.

(ii) In the case when a container used for managing hazardous waste remains at the facility for a period of 1 year or more, the owner or operator shall visually inspect the container and its cover and closure devices initially and thereafter, at least once every 12 months, to check for visible cracks, holes, gaps, or other open spaces into the interior of the container when the cover and closure devices are secured in the closed position. If a defect is detected, the owner or operator shall repair the defect in accordance with the requirements of paragraph (c)(4)(iii) of this section.

(iii) When a defect is detected for the container, cover, or closure devices, the owner or operator shall make first efforts at repair of the defect no later than 24 hours after detection and repair shall be completed as soon as possible but no later than 5 calendar days after detection. If repair of a defect cannot be completed within 5 calendar days, then the hazardous waste shall be removed from the container and the container shall not be used to manage hazardous waste until the defect is repaired.

(5) The owner or operator shall maintain at the facility a copy of the procedure used to determine that containers with capacity of 0.46 m^3 or greater, which do not meet applicable DOT regulations as specified in paragraph (f) of this section, are not managing hazardous waste in light material service.

(d) *Container Level 2 standards.* (1) A container using Container Level 2 controls is one of the following:

15.3.5.2.1

(i) A container that meets the applicable U.S. Department of Transportation (DOT) regulations on packaging hazardous materials for transportation as specified in paragraph (f) of this section.

(ii) A container that operates with no detectable organic emissions as defined in 40 CFR 265.1081 and determined in accordance with the procedure specified in paragraph (g) of this section.

(iii) A container that has been demonstrated within the preceding 12 months to be vapor-tight by using 40 CFR part 60, appendix A, Method 27 in accordance with the procedure specified in paragraph (h) of this section.

(2) Transfer of hazardous waste in or out of a container using Container Level 2 controls shall be conducted in such a manner as to minimize exposure of the hazardous waste to the atmosphere, to the extent practical, considering the physical properties of the hazardous waste and good engineering and safety practices for handling flammable, ignitable, explosive, reactive, or other hazardous materials. Examples of container loading procedures that the EPA considers to meet the requirements of this paragraph include using any one of the following: A submerged-fill pipe or other submerged-fill method to load liquids into the container; a vapor-balancing system or a vapor-recovery system to collect and control the vapors displaced from the container during filling operations; or a fitted opening in the top of a container through which the hazardous waste is filled and subsequently purging the transfer line before removing it from the container opening. 15.3.5.2.2

(3) Whenever a hazardous waste is in a container using Container Level 2 controls, the owner or operator shall install all covers and closure devices for the container, and secure and maintain each closure device in the closed position except as follows: 15.3.5.2.2

(i) Opening of a closure device or cover is allowed for the purpose of adding hazardous waste or other material to the container as follows:

(A) In the case when the container is filled to the intended final level in one continuous operation, the owner or operator shall promptly secure the closure devices in the closed position and install the covers, as applicable to the container, upon conclusion of the filling operation.

(B) In the case when discrete quantities or batches of material intermittently are added to the container over a period of time, the owner or operator shall promptly secure the closure devices in the closed position and install covers, as applicable to the container, upon either the container being filled to the intended final level; the completion of a batch loading after which no additional material will be added to the container within 15 minutes; the person performing the loading operation leaving the immediate vicinity of the container; or the shutdown of the process generating the material being added to the container, whichever condition occurs first.

(ii) Opening of a closure device or cover is allowed for the purpose of removing hazardous waste from the container as follows:

(A) For the purpose of meeting the requirements of this section, an empty container as defined in 40 CFR 261.7(b) may be open to the atmosphere at any time (*i.e.*, covers and closure devices are not required to be secured in the closed position on an empty container).

(B) In the case when discrete quantities or batches of material are removed from the container but the container does not meet the conditions to be an empty container as defined in 40 CFR 261.7(b), the owner or operator shall promptly secure the closure devices in the closed position and install covers, as applicable to the container, upon the completion of a batch removal after which no additional material will be removed from the container within 15 minutes or the person performing the unloading operation leaves the immediate vicinity of the container, whichever condition occurs first.

(iii) Opening of a closure device or cover is allowed when access inside the container is needed to perform routine activities other than transfer of hazardous waste.

Examples of such activities include those times when a worker needs to open a port to measure the depth of or sample the material in the container, or when a worker needs to open a manhole hatch to access equipment inside the container. Following completion of the activity, the owner or operator shall promptly secure the closure device in the closed position or reinstall the cover, as applicable to the container.

(iv) Opening of a spring-loaded, pressure-vacuum relief valve, conservation vent, or similar type of pressure relief device which vents to the atmosphere is allowed during normal operations for the purpose of maintaining the internal pressure of the container in accordance with the container design specifications. The device shall be designed to operate with no detectable organic emission when the device is secured in the closed position. The settings at which the device opens shall be established such that the device remains in the closed position whenever the internal pressure of the container is within the internal pressure operating range determined by the owner or operator based on container manufacturer recommendations, applicable regulations, fire protection and prevention codes, standard engineering codes and practices, or other requirements for the safe handling of flammable, ignitable, explosive, reactive, or hazardous materials. Examples of normal operating conditions that may require these devices to open are during those times when the internal pressure of the container exceeds the internal pressure operating range for the container as a result of loading operations or diurnal ambient temperature fluctuations.

(v) Opening of a safety device, as defined in 40 CFR 265.1081, is allowed at any time conditions require doing so to avoid an unsafe condition.

(4) The owner or operator of containers using Container Level 2 controls shall inspect the containers and their covers and closure devices as follows: 📖 15.3.5.2.3

(i) In the case when a hazardous waste already is in the container at the time the owner or operator first accepts possession of the container at the facility and the container is not emptied within 24 hours after the container is accepted at the facility (*i.e.*, does not meet the conditions for an empty container as specified in 40 CFR 261.7(b)), the owner or operator shall visually inspect the container and its cover and closure devices to check for visible cracks, holes, gaps, or other open spaces into the interior of the container when the cover and closure devices are secured in the closed position. The container visual inspection shall be conducted on or before the date that the container is accepted at the facility (*i.e.*, the date the container becomes subject to the subpart CC container standards). For purposes of this requirement, the date of acceptance is the date of signature that the facility owner or operator enters on Item 20 of the Uniform Hazardous Waste Manifest in the appendix to 40 CFR part 262 (EPA Forms 8700-22 and 8700-22A), as required under subpart E of this part, at 40 CFR 264.71. If a defect is detected, the owner or operator shall repair the defect in accordance with the requirements of paragraph (d)(4)(iii) of this section.

(ii) In the case when a container used for managing hazardous waste remains at the facility for a period of 1 year or more, the owner or operator shall visually inspect the container and its cover and closure devices initially and thereafter, at least once every 12 months, to check for visible cracks, holes, gaps, or other open spaces into the interior of the container when the cover and closure devices are secured in the closed position. If a defect is detected, the owner or operator shall repair the defect in accordance with the requirements of paragraph (d)(4)(iii) of this section.

(iii) When a defect is detected for the container, cover, or closure devices, the owner or operator shall make first efforts at repair of the defect no later than 24 hours after detection, and repair shall be completed as soon as possible but no later than 5 calendar days after detection. If repair of a defect cannot be completed within 5 calendar days, then the hazardous waste shall be removed from the container and the container shall not be used to manage hazardous waste until the defect is repaired.

(e) *Container Level 3 standards.* (1) A container using Container Level 3 controls is one of the following:

📖 **15.3.5.3**

(i) A container that is vented directly through a closed-vent system to a control device in accordance with the requirements of paragraph (e)(2)(ii) of this section.

(ii) A container that is vented inside an enclosure which is exhausted through a closed-vent system to a control device in accordance with the requirements of paragraphs (e)(2)(i) and (e)(2)(ii) of this section.

(2) The owner or operator shall meet the following requirements, as applicable to the type of air emission control equipment selected by the owner or operator:

(i) The container enclosure shall be designed and operated in accordance with the criteria for a permanent total enclosure as specified in "Procedure T—Criteria for and Verification of a Permanent or Temporary Total Enclosure" under 40 CFR 52.741, appendix B. The enclosure may have permanent or temporary openings to allow worker access; passage of containers through the enclosure by conveyor or other mechanical means; entry of permanent mechanical or electrical equipment; or direct airflow into the enclosure. The owner or operator shall perform the verification procedure for the enclosure as specified in Section 5.0 to "Procedure T—Criteria for and Verification of a Permanent or Temporary Total Enclosure" initially when the enclosure is first installed and, thereafter, annually.

(ii) The closed-vent system and control device shall be designed and operated in accordance with the requirements of §264.1087 of this subpart.

(3) Safety devices, as defined in 40 CFR 265.1081, may be installed and operated as necessary on any container, enclosure, closed-vent system, or control device used to comply with the requirements of paragraph (e)(1) of this section.

(4) Owners and operators using Container Level 3 controls in accordance with the provisions of this subpart shall inspect and monitor the closed-vent systems and control devices as specified in §264.1087 of this subpart.

(5) Owners and operators that use Container Level 3 controls in accordance with the provisions of this subpart shall prepare and maintain the records specified in §264.1089(d) of this subpart.

(6) Transfer of hazardous waste in or out of a container using Container Level 3 controls shall be conducted in such a manner as to minimize exposure of the hazardous waste to the atmosphere, to the extent practical, considering the physical properties of the hazardous waste and good engineering and safety practices for handling flammable, ignitable, explosive, reactive, or other hazardous materials. Examples of container loading procedures that the EPA considers to meet the requirements of this paragraph include using any one of the following: A submerged-fill pipe or other submerged-fill method to load liquids into the container; a vapor-balancing system or a vapor-recovery system to collect and control the vapors displaced from the container during filling operations; or a fitted opening in the top of a container through which the hazardous waste is filled and subsequently purging the transfer line before removing it from the container opening.

📖 **15.3.5.3.1**

(f) For the purpose of compliance with paragraph (c)(1)(i) or (d)(1)(i) of this section, containers shall be used that meet the applicable U.S. Department of Transportation (DOT) regulations on packaging hazardous materials for transportation as follows:

(1) The container meets the applicable requirements specified in 49 CFR part 178—Specifications for

Packaging or 49 CFR part 179—Specifications for Tank Cars.

(2) Hazardous waste is managed in the container in accordance with the applicable requirements specified in 49 CFR part 107, subpart B—Exemptions; 49 CFR part 172—Hazardous Materials Table, Special Provisions, Hazardous Materials Communications, Emergency Response Information, and Training Requirements; 49 CFR part 173—Shippers—General Requirements for Shipments and Packages; and 49 CFR part 180—Continuing Qualification and Maintenance of Packagings.

(3) For the purpose of complying with this subpart, no exceptions to the 49 CFR part 178 or part 179 regulations are allowed except as provided for in paragraph (f)(4) of this section.

(4) For a lab pack that is managed in accordance with the requirements of 49 CFR part 178 for the purpose of complying with this subpart, an owner or operator may comply with the exceptions for combination packagings specified in 49 CFR 173.12(b).

(g) To determine compliance with the no detectable organic emissions requirement of paragraph (d)(1)(ii) of this section, the procedure specified in §264.1083(d) of this subpart shall be used.

(1) Each potential leak interface (*i.e.*, a location where organic vapor leakage could occur) on the container, its cover, and associated closure devices, as applicable to the container, shall be checked. Potential leak interfaces that are associated with containers include, but are not limited to: The interface of the cover rim and the container wall; the periphery of any opening on the container or container cover and its associated closure device; and the sealing seat interface on a spring-loaded pressure-relief valve.

(2) The test shall be performed when the container is filled with a material having a volatile organic concentration representative of the range of volatile organic concentrations for the hazardous wastes expected to be managed in this type of container. During the test, the container cover and closure devices shall be secured in the closed position.

(h) Procedure for determining a container to be vapor-tight using Method 27 of 40 CFR part 60, appendix A for the purpose of complying with paragraph (d)(1)(iii) of this section.

(1) The test shall be performed in accordance with Method 27 of 40 CFR part 60, appendix A of this chapter.

(2) A pressure measurement device shall be used that has a precision of ± 2.5 mm water and that is capable of measuring above the pressure at which the container is to be tested for vapor tightness.

(3) If the test results determined by Method 27 indicate that the container sustains a pressure change less than or equal to 750 Pascals within 5 minutes after it is pressurized to a minimum of 4,500 Pascals, then the container is determined to be vapor-tight.

[61 FR 59962, Nov. 25, 1996, as amended at 62 FR 64659, Dec. 8, 1997; 64 FR 3389, Jan. 21, 1999]

§264.1087 Standards: Closed-vent systems and control devices.

(a) This section applies to each closed-vent system and control device installed and operated by the owner or operator to control air emissions in accordance with standards of this subpart.

(b) The closed-vent system shall meet the following requirements:

(1) The closed-vent system shall route the gases, vapors, and fumes emitted from the hazardous waste in the waste management unit to a control device that meets the requirements specified in paragraph (c) of this section.

(2) The closed-vent system shall be designed and operated in accordance with the requirements specified in §264.1033(k) of this part.

(3) In the case when the closed-vent system includes bypass devices that could be used to divert the gas or vapor stream to the atmosphere before entering the control device, each bypass device shall be equipped with either a flow indicator as specified in paragraph (b)(3)(i) of this section or a seal or locking device as specified in paragraph (b)(3)(ii) of this section. For the purpose of complying with this paragraph, low leg drains, high point bleeds, analyzer vents, open-ended valves or lines, spring loaded pressure relief valves, and other fittings used for safety purposes are not considered to be bypass devices.

(i) If a flow indicator is used to comply with paragraph (b)(3) of this section, the indicator shall be installed at the inlet to the bypass line used to divert gases and vapors from the closed-vent system to the atmosphere at a point upstream of the control device inlet. For this paragraph, a flow indicator means a device which indicates the presence of either gas or vapor flow in the bypass line.

(ii) If a seal or locking device is used to comply with paragraph (b)(3) of this section, the device shall be placed on the mechanism by which the bypass device position is controlled (*e.g.*, valve handle, damper lever) when the bypass device is in the closed position such that the bypass device cannot be opened without breaking the seal or removing the lock. Examples of such devices include, but are not limited to, a car-seal or a lock-and-key configuration valve. The owner or operator shall visually inspect the seal or closure mechanism at least once every month to verify that the bypass mechanism is maintained in the closed position.

(4) The closed-vent system shall be inspected and monitored by the owner or operator in accordance with the procedure specified in §264.1033(l).

(c) The control device shall meet the following requirements: 14.5.3.1

(1) The control device shall be one of the following devices:

(i) A control device designed and operated to reduce the total organic content of the inlet vapor stream vented to the control device by at least 95 percent by weight;

(ii) An enclosed combustion device designed and operated in accordance with the requirements of §264.1033(c) of this part; or

(iii) A flare designed and operated in accordance with the requirements of §264.1033(d) of this part.

(2) The owner or operator who elects to use a closed-vent system and control device to comply with the requirements of this section shall comply with the requirements specified in paragraphs (c)(2)(i) through (c)(2)(vi) of this section.

(i) Periods of planned routine maintenance of the control device, during which the control device does not meet the specifications of paragraphs (c)(1)(i), (c)(1)(ii), or (c)(1)(iii) of this section, as applicable, shall not exceed 240 hours per year.

(ii) The specifications and requirements in paragraphs (c)(1)(i), (c)(1)(ii), and (c)(1)(iii) of this section for control devices do not apply during periods of planned routine maintenance.

(iii) The specifications and requirements in paragraphs (c)(1)(i), (c)(1)(ii), and (c)(1)(iii) of this section for control devices do not apply during a control device system malfunction.

(iv) The owner or operator shall demonstrate compliance with the requirements of paragraph (c)(2)(i) of this section (*i.e.*, planned routine maintenance of a control device, during which the control device does not meet the specifications of paragraphs (c)(1)(i), (c)(1)(ii), or (c)(1)(iii) of this section, as applicable, shall not exceed 240 hours per year) by recording the information specified in §264.1089(e)(1)(v) of this subpart.

(v) The owner or operator shall correct control device system malfunctions as soon as practicable after their occurrence in order to minimize excess emissions of air pollutants.

(vi) The owner or operator shall operate the closed-vent system such that gases, vapors, or fumes are not actively vented to the control device during periods of planned maintenance or control device system malfunction (*i.e.*, periods when the control device is not operating or not operating normally) except in cases when it is necessary to vent the gases, vapors, and/or fumes to avoid an unsafe condition or to implement malfunction corrective actions or planned maintenance actions.

(3) The owner or operator using a carbon adsorption system to comply with paragraph (c)(1) of this section shall operate and maintain the control device in accordance with the following requirements:

(i) Following the initial startup of the control device, all activated carbon in the control device shall be replaced with fresh carbon on a regular basis in accordance with the requirements of §264.1033(g) or §264.1033(h) of this part.

(ii) All carbon that is a hazardous waste and that is removed from the control device shall be managed in accordance with the requirements of 40 CFR 264.1033(n), regardless of the average volatile organic concentration of the carbon.

(4) An owner or operator using a control device other than a thermal vapor incinerator, flare, boiler, process heater, condenser, or carbon adsorption system to comply with paragraph (c)(1) of this section shall operate and maintain the control device in accordance with the requirements of §264.1033(j) of this part.

(5) The owner or operator shall demonstrate that a control device achieves the performance requirements of paragraph (c)(1) of this section as follows:

(i) An owner or operator shall demonstrate using either a performance test as specified in paragraph (c)(5)(iii) of this section or a design analysis as specified in paragraph (c)(5)(iv) of this section the performance of each control device except for the following:

(A) A flare;

(B) A boiler or process heater with a design heat input capacity of 44 megawatts or greater;

(C) A boiler or process heater into which the vent stream is introduced with the primary fuel;

(D) A boiler or industrial furnace burning hazardous waste for which the owner or operator has been issued a final permit under 40 CFR part 270 and has designed and operates the unit in accordance with the requirements of 40 CFR part 266, subpart H; or

(E) A boiler or industrial furnace burning hazardous waste for which the owner or operator has designed and operates in accordance with the interim status requirements of 40 CFR part 266, subpart H.

(ii) An owner or operator shall demonstrate the performance of each flare in accordance with the requirements specified in §264.1033(e).

(iii) For a performance test conducted to meet the requirements of paragraph (c)(5)(i) of this section, the owner or operator shall use the test methods and procedures specified in §264.1034(c)(1) through (c)(4).

(iv) For a design analysis conducted to meet the requirements of paragraph (c)(5)(i) of this section, the design analysis shall meet the requirements specified in §264.1035(b)(4)(iii).

(v) The owner or operator shall demonstrate that a carbon adsorption system achieves the performance requirements of paragraph (c)(1) of this section based on the total quantity of organics vented to the atmosphere from all carbon adsorption system equipment that is used for organic adsorption, organic desorption or carbon regeneration, organic recovery, and carbon disposal.

(6) If the owner or operator and the Regional Administrator do not agree on a demonstration of control device performance using a design analysis then the disagreement shall be resolved using the results of a performance test performed by the owner or operator in accordance with the requirements of paragraph (c)(5)(iii) of this section. The Regional Administrator may choose to have an authorized representative observe the performance test.

(7) The closed-vent system and control device shall be inspected and monitored by the owner or operator in accordance with the procedures specified in 40 CFR 264.1033(f)(2) and 40 CFR 264.1033(l). The readings from each monitoring device required by 40 CFR 264.1033(f)(2) shall be inspected at least once each operating day to check control device operation. Any necessary corrective measures shall be immediately implemented to ensure the control device is operated in compliance with the requirements of this section.

[59 FR 62927, Dec. 6, 1994, as amended at 61 FR 4913, Feb. 9, 1996; 61 FR 59965, Nov. 25, 1996; 62 FR 64660, Dec. 8, 1997]

§264.1088 Inspection and monitoring requirements.

(a) The owner or operator shall inspect and monitor air emission control equipment used to comply with this subpart in accordance with the applicable requirements specified in §264.1084 through §264.1087 of this subpart.

(b) The owner or operator shall develop and implement a written plan and schedule to perform the inspections and monitoring required by paragraph (a) of this section. The owner or operator shall incorporate this plan and schedule into the facility inspection plan required under 40 CFR 264.15.

[61 FR 59966, Nov. 25, 1996]

§264.1089 Recordkeeping requirements.

(a) Each owner or operator of a facility subject to requirements of this subpart shall record and maintain the information specified in paragraphs (b) through (j) of this section, as applicable to the facility. Except for air emission control equipment design documentation and information required by paragraphs (i) and (j) of this section, records required by this section shall be maintained in the operating record for a minimum of 3 years. Air emission control equipment design documentation shall be maintained in the operating record until the air emission control equipment is replaced or otherwise no longer in service. Information required by paragraphs (i) and (j) of this section shall be maintained in the operating record for as long as the waste management unit is not using air emission controls specified in §§264.1084 through 264.1087 of this subpart in accordance with the conditions specified in §264.1080(d) or §264.1080(b)(7) of this subpart, respectively.

(b) The owner or operator of a tank using air emission controls in accordance with the requirements of §264.1084 of this subpart shall prepare and maintain records for the tank that include the following information:

(1) For each tank using air emission controls in accordance with the requirements of §264.1084 of this subpart, the owner or operator shall record:

(i) A tank identification number (or other unique identification description as selected by the owner or operator).

(ii) A record for each inspection required by §264.1084 of this subpart that includes the following information: 15.3.4.1.3, 15.3.4.2.3

(A) Date inspection was conducted.

(B) For each defect detected during the inspection: The location of the defect, a description of the defect, the date of detection, and corrective action taken to repair the defect. In the event that repair of the defect is delayed in accordance with the requirements of §264.1084 of this subpart, the owner or operator shall also record the reason for the delay and the date that completion of repair of the defect is expected.

(2) In addition to the information required by paragraph (b)(1) of this section, the owner or operator shall record the following information, as applicable to the tank:

(i) The owner or operator using a fixed roof to comply with the Tank Level 1 control requirements specified in §264.1084(c) of this subpart shall prepare and maintain records for each determination for the maximum organic vapor pressure of the hazardous waste in the tank performed in accordance with the requirements of §264.1084(c) of this subpart. The records shall include the date and time the samples were collected, the analysis method used, and the analysis results. 15.3.4.1.3

(ii) The owner or operator using an internal floating roof to comply with the Tank Level 2 control requirements specified in §264.1084(e) of this subpart shall prepare and maintain documentation describing the floating roof design.

(iii) Owners and operators using an external floating roof to comply with the Tank Level 2 control requirements specified in §264.1084(f) of this subpart shall prepare and maintain the following records:

(A) Documentation describing the floating roof design and the dimensions of the tank.

(B) Records for each seal gap inspection required by §264.1084(f)(3) of this subpart describing the results of the seal gap measurements. The records shall include the date that the measurements were performed, the raw data obtained for the measurements, and the calculations of the total gap surface area. In the event that the seal gap measurements do not conform to the specifications in §264.1084(f)(1) of this subpart, the records shall include a description of the repairs that were made, the date the repairs were made, and the date the tank was emptied, if necessary.

(iv) Each owner or operator using an enclosure to comply with the Tank Level 2 control requirements specified in §264.1084(i) of this subpart shall prepare and maintain the following records:

(A) Records for the most recent set of calculations and measurements performed by the owner or operator to verify that the enclosure meets the criteria of a permanent total enclosure as specified in "Procedure T—Criteria for and Verification of a Permanent or Temporary Total Enclosure" under 40 CFR 52.741, appendix B.

(B) Records required for the closed-vent system and control device in accordance with the requirements of paragraph (e) of this section.

(c) The owner or operator of a surface impoundment using air emission controls in accordance with the requirements of §264.1085 of this subpart shall prepare and maintain records for the surface impoundment that include the following information:

(1) A surface impoundment identification number (or other unique identification description as selected by the owner or operator).

(2) Documentation describing the floating membrane cover or cover design, as applicable to the surface impoundment, that includes information prepared by the owner or operator or provided by the cover manufacturer or vendor describing the cover design, and certification by the owner or operator that the cover meets the specifications listed in §264.1085(c) of this subpart.

(3) A record for each inspection required by §264.1085 of this subpart that includes the following information:

(i) Date inspection was conducted.

(ii) For each defect detected during the inspection the following information: The location of the defect, a description of the defect, the date of detection, and corrective action taken to repair the defect. In the event that repair of the defect is delayed in accordance with the provisions of §264.1085(f) of this subpart, the owner or operator shall also record the reason for the delay and the date that completion of repair of the defect is expected.

(4) For a surface impoundment equipped with a cover and vented through a closed-vent system to a control device, the owner or operator shall prepare

and maintain the records specified in paragraph (e) of this section.

(d) The owner or operator of containers using Container Level 3 air emission controls in accordance with the requirements of §264.1086 of this subpart shall prepare and maintain records that include the following information:

(1) Records for the most recent set of calculations and measurements performed by the owner or operator to verify that the enclosure meets the criteria of a permanent total enclosure as specified in "Procedure T—Criteria for and Verification of a Permanent or Temporary Total Enclosure" under 40 CFR 52.741, appendix B.

(2) Records required for the closed-vent system and control device in accordance with the requirements of paragraph (e) of this section.

(e) The owner or operator using a closed-vent system and control device in accordance with the requirements of §264.1087 of this subpart shall prepare and maintain records that include the following information:

(1) Documentation for the closed-vent system and control device that includes:

(i) Certification that is signed and dated by the owner or operator stating that the control device is designed to operate at the performance level documented by a design analysis as specified in paragraph (e)(1)(ii) of this section or by performance tests as specified in paragraph (e)(1)(iii) of this section when the tank, surface impoundment, or container is or would be operating at capacity or the highest level reasonably expected to occur.

(ii) If a design analysis is used, then design documentation as specified in 40 CFR 264.1035(b)(4). The documentation shall include information prepared by the owner or operator or provided by the control device manufacturer or vendor that describes the control device design in accordance with 40 CFR 264.1035(b)(4)(iii) and certification by the owner or operator that the control equipment meets the applicable specifications.

(iii) If performance tests are used, then a performance test plan as specified in 40 CFR 264.1035(b)(3) and all test results.

(iv) Information as required by 40 CFR 264.1035(c)(1) and 40 CFR 264.1035(c)(2), as applicable.

(v) An owner or operator shall record, on a semiannual basis, the information specified in paragraphs (e)(1)(v)(A) and (e)(1)(v)(B) of this section for those planned routine maintenance operations that would require the control device not to meet the requirements of §264.1087(c)(1)(i), (c)(1)(ii), or (c)(1)(iii) of this subpart, as applicable.

(A) A description of the planned routine maintenance that is anticipated to be performed for the control device during the next 6-month period. This description shall include the type of maintenance necessary, planned frequency of maintenance, and lengths of maintenance periods.

(B) A description of the planned routine maintenance that was performed for the control device during the previous 6-month period. This description shall include the type of maintenance performed and the total number of hours during those 6 months that the control device did not meet the requirements of §264.1087 (c)(1)(i), (c)(1)(ii), or (c)(1)(iii) of this subpart, as applicable, due to planned routine maintenance.

(vi) An owner or operator shall record the information specified in paragraphs (e)(1)(vi)(A) through (e)(1)(vi)(C) of this section for those unexpected control device system malfunctions that would require the control device not to meet the requirements of §264.1087 (c)(1)(i), (c)(1)(ii), or (c)(1)(iii) of this subpart, as applicable.

(A) The occurrence and duration of each malfunction of the control device system.

(B) The duration of each period during a malfunction when gases, vapors, or fumes are vented from the waste management unit through the closed-vent system to the control device while the control device is not properly functioning.

(C) Actions taken during periods of malfunction to restore a malfunctioning control device to its normal or usual manner of operation.

(vii) Records of the management of carbon removed from a carbon adsorption system conducted in accordance with §264.1087(c)(3)(ii) of this subpart.

(f) The owner or operator of a tank, surface impoundment, or container exempted from standards in accordance with the provisions of §264.1082(c) of this subpart shall prepare and maintain the following records, as applicable:

(1) For tanks, surface impoundments, and containers exempted under the hazardous waste organic concentration conditions specified in §264.1082(c)(1) or §§264.1082(c)(2)(i) through (c)(2)(vi) of this subpart,

the owner or operator shall record the information used for each waste determination (*e.g.*, test results, measurements, calculations, and other documentation) in the facility operating log. If analysis results for waste samples are used for the waste determination, then the owner or operator shall record the date, time, and location that each waste sample is collected in accordance with applicable requirements of §264.1083 of this subpart.

(2) For tanks, surface impoundments, or containers exempted under the provisions of §264.1082(c)(2)(vii) or §264.1082(c)(2)(viii) of this subpart, the owner or operator shall record the identification number for the incinerator, boiler, or industrial furnace in which the hazardous waste is treated.

(g) An owner or operator designating a cover as "unsafe to inspect and monitor" pursuant to §264.1084(l) or §264.1085(g) of this subpart shall record in a log that is kept in the facility operating record the following information: The identification numbers for waste management units with covers that are designated as "unsafe to inspect and monitor," the explanation for each cover stating why the cover is unsafe to inspect and monitor, and the plan and schedule for inspecting and monitoring each cover.

(h) The owner or operator of a facility that is subject to this subpart and to the control device standards in 40 CFR part 60, subpart VV, or 40 CFR part 61, subpart V, may elect to demonstrate compliance with the applicable sections of this subpart by documentation either pursuant to this subpart, or pursuant to the provisions of 40 CFR part 60, subpart VV or 40 CFR part 61, subpart V, to the extent that the documentation required by 40 CFR parts 60 or 61 duplicates the documentation required by this section.

(i) For each tank or container not using air emission controls specified in §§264.1084 through 264.1087 of this subpart in accordance with the conditions specified in §264.1080(d) of this subpart, the owner or operator shall record and maintain the following information:

(1) A list of the individual organic peroxide compounds manufactured at the facility that meet the conditions specified in §264.1080(d)(1).

(2) A description of how the hazardous waste containing the organic peroxide compounds identified in paragraph (i)(1) of this section are managed at the facility in tanks and containers. This description shall include:

(i) For the tanks used at the facility to manage this hazardous waste, sufficient information shall be provided to describe for each tank: A facility identification number for the tank; the purpose and placement of this tank in the management train of this hazardous waste; and the procedures used to ultimately dispose of the hazardous waste managed in the tanks.

(ii) For containers used at the facility to manage these hazardous wastes, sufficient information shall be provided to describe: A facility identification number for the container or group of containers; the purpose and placement of this container, or group of containers, in the management train of this hazardous waste; and the procedures used to ultimately dispose of the hazardous waste handled in the containers.

(3) An explanation of why managing the hazardous waste containing the organic peroxide compounds identified in paragraph (i)(1) of this section in the tanks and containers as described in paragraph (i)(2) of this section would create an undue safety hazard if the air emission controls, as required under §§264.1084 through 264.1087 of this subpart, are installed and operated on these waste management units. This explanation shall include the following information:

(i) For tanks used at the facility to manage these hazardous wastes, sufficient information shall be provided to explain: How use of the required air emission controls on the tanks would affect the tank design features and facility operating procedures currently used to prevent an undue safety hazard during the management of this hazardous waste in the tanks; and why installation of safety devices on the required air emission controls, as allowed under this subpart, will not address those situations in which evacuation of tanks equipped with these air emission controls is necessary and consistent with good engineering and safety practices for handling organic peroxides.

(ii) For containers used at the facility to manage these hazardous wastes, sufficient information shall be provided to explain: How use of the required air emission controls on the containers would affect the container design features and handling procedures currently used to prevent an undue safety hazard during the management of this hazardous waste in the containers; and why installation of safety devices on the required air emission controls, as allowed under this subpart, will not address those situations in which evacuation of containers equipped with these air emission controls is necessary and consistent with good engineering and safety practices for handling organic peroxides.

(j) For each hazardous waste management unit not using air emission controls specified in §§264.1084 through 264.1087 of this subpart in accordance with the requirements of §264.1080(b)(7) of this subpart, the owner and operator shall record and maintain the following information:

(1) Certification that the waste management unit is equipped with and operating air emission controls in accordance with the requirements of an applicable Clean Air Act regulation codified under 40 CFR part 60, part 61, or part 63.

(2) Identification of the specific requirements codified under 40 CFR part 60, part 61, or part 63 with which the waste management unit is in compliance.

[61 FR 59966, Nov. 25, 1996, as amended at 62 FR 64660, Dec. 8, 1997]

§264.1090 Reporting requirements.

15.3.7

(a) Each owner or operator managing hazardous waste in a tank, surface impoundment, or container exempted from using air emission controls under the provisions of §264.1082(c) of this subpart shall report to the Regional Administrator each occurrence when hazardous waste is placed in the waste management unit in noncompliance with the conditions specified in §264.1082 (c)(1) or (c)(2) of this subpart, as applicable. Examples of such occurrences include placing in the waste management unit a hazardous waste having an average VO concentration equal to or greater than 500 ppmw at the point of waste origination; or placing in the waste management unit a treated hazardous waste of which the organic content has been reduced by an organic destruction or removal process that fails to achieve the applicable conditions specified in §264.1082 (c)(2)(i) through (c)(2)(vi) of this subpart. The owner or operator shall submit a written report within 15 calendar days of the time that the owner or operator becomes aware of the occurrence. The written report shall contain the EPA identification number, facility name and address, a description of the noncompliance event and the cause, the dates of the noncompliance, and the actions taken to correct the noncompliance and prevent recurrence of the noncompliance. The report shall be signed and dated by an authorized representative of the owner or operator.

(b) Each owner or operator using air emission controls on a tank in accordance with the requirements §264.1084(c) of this subpart shall report to the Regional Administrator each occurrence when hazardous waste is managed in the tank in noncompliance with the conditions specified in §264.1084(b) of this subpart. The owner or operator shall submit a written report within 15 calendar days of the time that the owner or operator becomes aware of the occurrence. The written report shall contain the EPA identification number, facility name and address, a description of the noncompliance event and the cause, the dates of the noncompliance, and the actions taken to correct the noncompliance and prevent recurrence of the noncompliance. The report shall be signed and dated by an authorized representative of the owner or operator.

(c) Each owner or operator using a control device in accordance with the requirements of §264.1087 of this subpart shall submit a semiannual written report to the Regional Administrator excepted as provided for in paragraph (d) of this section. The report shall describe each occurrence during the previous 6-month period when either: (1) A control device is operated continuously for 24 hours or longer in noncompliance with the applicable operating values defined in §264.1035(c)(4); or (2) A flare is operated with visible emissions for 5 minutes or longer in a two-hour period, as defined in §264.1033(d). The written report shall include the EPA identification number, facility name and address, and an explanation why the control device could not be returned to compliance within 24 hours, and actions taken to correct the noncompliance. The report shall be signed and dated by an authorized representative of the owner or operator.

(d) A report to the Regional Administrator in accordance with the requirements of paragraph (c) of this section is not required for a 6-month period during which all control devices subject to this subpart are operated by the owner or operator such that:

(1) During no period of 24 hours or longer did a control device operate continuously in noncompliance with the applicable operating values defined in §264.1035(c)(4); and

(2) No flare was operated with visible emissions for 5 minutes or longer in a two-hour period, as defined in §264.1033(d).

[59 FR 62927, Dec. 6, 1994, as amended at 61 FR 4913, Feb. 9, 1996; 61 FR 59968, Nov. 25, 1996; 71 FR 40274, July 14, 2006]

§264.1091 [Reserved]

Subpart DD—Containment Buildings

📖 10.1.1, 13.8.4.1

Source: 57 FR 37265, Aug. 18, 1992, unless otherwise noted.

§264.1100 Applicability.

The requirements of this subpart apply to owners or operators who store or treat hazardous waste in units designed and operated under §264.1101 of this subpart. The owner or operator is not subject to the definition of land disposal in RCRA section 3004(k) provided that the unit:

(a) Is a completely enclosed, self-supporting structure that is designed and constructed of manmade materials of sufficient strength and thickness to support themselves, the waste contents, and any personnel and heavy equipment that operate within the unit, and to prevent failure due to pressure gradients, settlement, compression, or uplift, physical contact with the hazardous wastes to which they are exposed; climatic conditions; and the stresses of daily operation, including the movement of heavy equipment within the unit and contact of such equipment with containment walls;

(b) Has a primary barrier that is designed to be sufficiently durable to withstand the movement of personnel, wastes, and handling equipment within the unit;

(c) If the unit is used to manage liquids, has:

(1) A primary barrier designed and constructed of materials to prevent migration of hazardous constituents into the barrier;

(2) A liquid collection system designed and constructed of materials to minimize the accumulation of liquid on the primary barrier; and

(3) A secondary containment system designed and constructed of materials to prevent migration of hazardous constituents into the barrier, with a leak detection and liquid collection system capable of detecting, collecting, and removing leaks of hazardous constituents at the earliest practicable time, unless the unit has been granted a variance from the secondary containment system requirements under §264.1101(b)(4);

(d) Has controls sufficient to prevent fugitive dust emissions to meet the no visible emission standard in §264.1101(c)(1)(iv); and

(e) Is designed and operated to ensure containment and prevent the tracking of materials from the unit by personnel or equipment.

[57 FR 37265, Aug. 18, 1992, as amended at 71 FR 16907, Apr. 4, 2006]

§264.1101 Design and operating standards.

(a) All containment buildings must comply with the following design standards:

(1) The containment building must be completely enclosed with a floor, walls, and a roof to prevent exposure to the elements, (*e.g.*, precipitation, wind, run-on), and to assure containment of managed wastes.

(2) The floor and containment walls of the unit, including the secondary containment system if required under paragraph (b) of this section, must be designed and constructed of materials of sufficient strength and thickness to support themselves, the waste contents, and any personnel and heavy equipment that operate within the unit, and to prevent failure due to pressure gradients, settlement, compression, or uplift, physical contact with the hazardous wastes to which they are exposed; climatic conditions; and the stresses of daily operation, including the movement of heavy equipment within the unit and contact of such equipment with containment walls. The unit must be designed so that it has sufficient structural strength to prevent collapse or other failure. All surfaces to be in contact with hazardous wastes must be chemically compatible with those wastes. EPA will consider standards established by professional organizations generally recognized by the industry such as the American Concrete Institute (ACI) and the American Society of Testing Materials (ASTM) in judging the structural integrity requirements of this paragraph. If appropriate to the nature of the waste management operation to take place in the unit, an exception to the structural strength requirement may be made for light-weight doors and windows that meet these criteria:

(i) They provide an effective barrier against fugitive dust emissions under paragraph (c)(1)(iv); and

(ii) The unit is designed and operated in a fashion that assures that wastes will not actually come in contact with these openings.

(3) Incompatible hazardous wastes or treatment reagents must not be placed in the unit or its secondary containment system if they could cause the unit or secondary containment system to leak, corrode, or otherwise fail.

(4) A containment building must have a primary barrier designed to withstand the movement of personnel, waste, and handling equipment in the unit during the operating life of the unit and appropriate for the

physical and chemical characteristics of the waste to be managed.

(b) For a containment building used to manage hazardous wastes containing free liquids or treated with free liquids (the presence of which is determined by the paint filter test, a visual examination, or other appropriate means), the owner or operator must include:

(1) A primary barrier designed and constructed of materials to prevent the migration of hazardous constituents into the barrier (*e.g.*, a geomembrane covered by a concrete wear surface).

(2) A liquid collection and removal system to minimize the accumulation of liquid on the primary barrier of the containment building:

(i) The primary barrier must be sloped to drain liquids to the associated collection system; and

(ii) Liquids and waste must be collected and removed to minimize hydraulic head on the containment system at the earliest practicable time.

(3) A secondary containment system including a secondary barrier designed and constructed to prevent migration of hazardous constituents into the barrier, and a leak detection system that is capable of detecting failure of the primary barrier and collecting accumulated hazardous wastes and liquids at the earliest practicable time.

(i) The requirements of the leak detection component of the secondary containment system are satisfied by installation of a system that is, at a minimum:

(A) Constructed with a bottom slope of 1 percent or more; and

(B) Constructed of a granular drainage material with a hydraulic conductivity of 1×10^{-2} cm/sec or more and a thickness of 12 inches (30.5 cm) or more, or constructed of synthetic or geonet drainage materials with a transmissivity of 3×10^{-5} m^2/sec or more.

(ii) If treatment is to be conducted in the building, an area in which such treatment will be conducted must be designed to prevent the release of liquids, wet materials, or liquid aerosols to other portions of the building.

(iii) The secondary containment system must be constructed of materials that are chemically resistant to the waste and liquids managed in the containment building and of sufficient strength and thickness to prevent collapse under the pressure exerted by overlaying materials and by any equipment used in the containment building. (Containment buildings can serve as secondary containment systems for tanks placed within the building under certain conditions. A containment building can serve as an external liner system for a tank, provided it meets the requirements of §264.193(e)(1). In addition, the containment building must meet the requirements of §264.193(b) and §§264.193(c)(1) and (2) to be considered an acceptable secondary containment system for a tank.)

(4) For existing units other than 90-day generator units, the Regional Administrator may delay the secondary containment requirement for up to two years, based on a demonstration by the owner or operator that the unit substantially meets the standards of this subpart. In making this demonstration, the owner or operator must:

(i) Provide written notice to the Regional Administrator of their request by November 16, 1992. This notification must describe the unit and its operating practices with specific reference to the performance of existing containment systems, and specific plans for retrofitting the unit with secondary containment;

(ii) Respond to any comments from the Regional Administrator on these plans within 30 days; and

(iii) Fulfill the terms of the revised plans, if such plans are approved by the Regional Administrator.

(c) Owners or operators of all containment buildings must:

(1) Use controls and practices to ensure containment of the hazardous waste within the unit; and, at a minimum:

(i) Maintain the primary barrier to be free of significant cracks, gaps, corrosion, or other deterioration that could cause hazardous waste to be released from the primary barrier;

(ii) Maintain the level of the stored/treated hazardous waste within the containment walls of the unit so that the height of any containment wall is not exceeded;

(iii) Take measures to prevent the tracking of hazardous waste out of the unit by personnel or by equipment used in handling the waste. An area must be designated to decontaminate equipment and any rinsate must be collected and properly managed; and

(iv) Take measures to control fugitive dust emissions such that any openings (doors, windows, vents, cracks, etc.) exhibit no visible emissions (see 40 CFR part 60, appendix A, Method 22—Visual Determination of Fugitive Emissions from Material Sources and Smoke Emissions from Flares). In addition, all associated particulate collection devices (*e.g.*, fabric filter, electrostatic precipitator) must be operated and maintained with sound air pollution control practices (see 40 CFR part 60 subpart 292 for guidance). This state of no visible emissions must be maintained effectively at all times during routine operating and maintenance conditions, including when vehicles and personnel are entering and exiting the unit.

(2) Obtain and keep on-site a certification by a qualified Professional Engineer that the containment building design meets the requirements of paragraphs (a), (b), and (c) of this section.

(3) Throughout the active life of the containment building, if the owner or operator detects a condition that could lead to or has caused a release of hazardous waste, the owner or operator must repair the condition promptly, in accordance with the following procedures.

(i) Upon detection of a condition that has led to a release of hazardous waste (*e.g.*, upon detection of leakage from the primary barrier) the owner or operator must:

(A) Enter a record of the discovery in the facility operating record;

(B) Immediately remove the portion of the containment building affected by the condition from service;

(C) Determine what steps must be taken to repair the containment building, remove any leakage from the secondary collection system, and establish a schedule for accomplishing the cleanup and repairs; and

(D) Within 7 days after the discovery of the condition, notify the Regional Administrator of the condition, and within 14 working days, provide a written notice to the Regional Administrator with a description of the steps taken to repair the containment building, and the schedule for accomplishing the work.

(ii) The Regional Administrator will review the information submitted, make a determination regarding whether the containment building must be removed from service completely or partially until repairs and cleanup are complete, and notify the owner or operator of the determination and the underlying rationale in writing.

(iii) Upon completing all repairs and cleanup the owner or operator must notify the Regional Administrator in writing and provide a verification, signed by a qualified, registered professional engineer, that the repairs and cleanup have been completed according to the written plan submitted in accordance with paragraph (c)(3)(i)(D) of this section.

(4) Inspect and record in the facility's operating record, at least once every seven days, except for Performance Track member facilities that must inspect at least once each month, upon approval by the Director, data gathered from monitoring and leak detection equipment as well as the containment building and the area immediately surrounding the containment building to detect signs of releases of hazardous waste. To apply for reduced inspection frequency, the Performance Track member facility must follow the procedures described in §264.15(b)(5).

(d) For a containment building that contains both areas with and without secondary containment, the owner or operator must:

(1) Design and operate each area in accordance with the requirements enumerated in paragraphs (a) through (c) of this section;

(2) Take measures to prevent the release of liquids or wet materials into areas without secondary containment; and

(3) Maintain in the facility's operating log a written description of the operating procedures used to maintain the integrity of areas without secondary containment.

(e) Notwithstanding any other provision of this subpart the Regional Administrator may waive requirements for secondary containment for a permitted containment building where the owner operator demonstrates that the only free liquids in the unit are limited amounts of dust suppression liquids required to meet occupational health and safety requirements, and where containment of managed wastes and liquids can be assured without a secondary containment system.

[57 FR 37265, Aug. 18, 1992, as amended at 71 FR 16907, Apr. 4, 2006; 71 FR 40274, July 14, 2006]

§264.1102 Closure and post-closure care.

(a) At closure of a containment building, the owner or operator must remove or decontaminate all waste residues, contaminated containment system components (liners, etc.) contaminated subsoils, and structures and equipment contaminated with waste and leachate, and manage them as hazardous waste unless §261.3(d) of this chapter applies. The closure plan, closure activities, cost estimates for closure, and financial responsibility for containment buildings must meet all of the requirements specified in subparts G and H of this part.

(b) If, after removing or decontaminating all residues and making all reasonable efforts to effect removal or decontamination of contaminated components, subsoils, structures, and equipment as required in paragraph (a) of this section, the owner or operator finds that not all contaminated subsoils can be practicably removed or decontaminated, he must close the facility and perform post-closure care in accordance with the closure and post-closure requirements that apply to landfills (§264.310). In addition, for the purposes of closure, post-closure, and financial responsibility, such a containment building is then considered to be a landfill, and the owner or operator must meet all of the requirements for landfills specified in subparts G and H of this part.

[57 FR 37265, Aug. 18, 1992, as amended at 71 FR 40274, July 14, 2006]

§§264.1103–264.1110 [Reserved]

Subpart EE—Hazardous Waste Munitions and Explosives Storage

Source: 62 FR 6652, Feb. 12, 1997, unless otherwise noted.

§264.1200 Applicability.

The requirements of this subpart apply to owners or operators who store munitions and explosive hazardous wastes, except as §264.1 provides otherwise. (NOTE: Depending on explosive hazards, hazardous waste munitions and explosives may also be managed in other types of storage units, including containment buildings (40 CFR part 264, subpart DD), tanks (40 CFR part 264, subpart J), or containers (40 CFR part 264, subpart I); See 40 CFR 266.205 for storage of waste military munitions).

§264.1201 Design and operating standards.

(a) Hazardous waste munitions and explosives storage units must be designed and operated with containment systems, controls, and monitoring, that:

(1) Minimize the potential for detonation or other means of release of hazardous waste, hazardous constituents, hazardous decomposition products, or contaminated run-off, to the soil, ground water, surface water, and atmosphere;

(2) Provide a primary barrier, which may be a container (including a shell) or tank, designed to contain the hazardous waste;

(3) For wastes stored outdoors, provide that the waste and containers will not be in standing precipitation;

(4) For liquid wastes, provide a secondary containment system that assures that any released liquids are contained and promptly detected and removed from the waste area, or vapor detection system that assures that any released liquids or vapors are promptly detected and an appropriate response taken (*e.g.*, additional containment, such as overpacking, or removal from the waste area); and

(5) Provide monitoring and inspection procedures that assure the controls and containment systems are working as designed and that releases that may adversely impact human health or the environment are not escaping from the unit.

(b) Hazardous waste munitions and explosives stored under this subpart may be stored in one of the following:

(1) *Earth-covered magazines.* Earth-covered magazines must be:

(i) Constructed of waterproofed, reinforced concrete or structural steel arches, with steel doors that are kept closed when not being accessed;

(ii) Designed and constructed:

(A) To be of sufficient strength and thickness to support the weight of any explosives or munitions stored and any equipment used in the unit;

(B) To provide working space for personnel and equipment in the unit; and

(C) To withstand movement activities that occur in the unit; and

(iii) Located and designed, with walls and earthen covers that direct an explosion in the unit in a safe direction, so as to minimize the propagation of an explosion to adjacent units and to minimize other effects of any explosion.

(2) *Above-ground magazines.* Above-ground magazines must be located and designed so as to minimize the propagation of an explosion to adjacent units and to minimize other effects of any explosion.

(3) *Outdoor or open storage areas.* Outdoor or open storage areas must be located and designed so as to minimize the propagation of an explosion to adjacent units and to minimize other effects of any explosion.

(c) Hazardous waste munitions and explosives must be stored in accordance with a Standard Operating Procedure specifying procedures to ensure safety, security, and environmental protection. If these procedures serve the same purpose as the security and inspection requirements of 40 CFR 264.14, the preparedness and prevention procedures of 40 CFR part 264, subpart C, and the contingency plan and emergency procedures requirements of 40 CFR part 264, subpart D, then these procedures will be used to fulfill those requirements.

(d) Hazardous waste munitions and explosives must be packaged to ensure safety in handling and storage.

(e) Hazardous waste munitions and explosives must be inventoried at least annually.

(f) Hazardous waste munitions and explosives and their storage units must be inspected and monitored as necessary to ensure explosives safety and to ensure that there is no migration of contaminants out of the unit.

§264.1202 Closure and post-closure care.

(a) At closure of a magazine or unit which stored hazardous waste under this subpart, the owner or operator must remove or decontaminate all waste residues, contaminated containment system components, contaminated subsoils, and structures and equipment contaminated with waste, and manage them as hazardous waste unless §261.3(d) of this chapter applies. The closure plan, closure activities, cost estimates for closure, and financial responsibility for magazines or units must meet all of the requirements specified in subparts G and H of this part, except that the owner or operator may defer closure of the unit as long as it remains in service as a munitions or explosives magazine or storage unit.

(b) If, after removing or decontaminating all residues and making all reasonable efforts to effect removal or decontamination of contaminated components, subsoils, structures, and equipment as required in paragraph (a) of this section, the owner or operator finds that not all contaminated subsoils can be practicably removed or decontaminated, he or she must close the facility and perform post-closure care in accordance with the closure and post-closure requirements that apply to landfills (§264.310).

Appendices to Part 264

Appendix I to Part 264—Recordkeeping Instructions

The recordkeeping provisions of §264.73 specify that an owner or operator must keep a written operating record at his facility. This appendix provides additional instructions for keeping *portions* of the operating record. See §264.73(b) for additional recordkeeping requirements.

The following information must be recorded, as it becomes available, and maintained in the operating record until closure of the facility in the following manner:

Records of each hazardous waste received, treated, stored, or disposed of at the facility which include the following:

(1) A description by its common name and the EPA Hazardous Waste Number(s) from part 261 of this chapter which apply to the waste. The waste description also must include the waste's physical form, *i.e.*, liquid, sludge, solid, or contained gas. If the waste is not listed in part 261, subpart D, of this chapter, the description also must include the process that produced it (for example, solid filter cake from production of ____, EPA Hazardous Waste Number W051).

Each hazardous waste listed in part 261, subpart D, of this chapter, and each hazardous waste characteristic defined in part 261, subpart C, of this chapter, has a four-digit EPA Hazardous Waste Number assigned to it. This number must be used for recordkeeping and reporting purposes. Where a hazardous waste contains more than one listed hazardous waste, or where more than one hazardous waste characteristic applies to the waste, the waste description must include all applicable EPA Hazardous Waste Numbers.

(2) The estimated or manifest-reported weight, or volume and density, where applicable, in one of the units of measure specified in Table 1;

Table 1

Unit of measure	Code[1]
Gallons	G
Gallons per Hour	E
Gallons per Day	U
Liters	L
Liters per Hour	H
Liters per Day	V
Short Tons per Hour	D
Metric Tons per Hour	W
Short Tons per Day	N
Metric Tons per Day	S
Pounds per Hour	J
Kilograms per Hour	R
Cubic Yards	Y
Cubic Meters	C
Acres	B
Acre-feet	A
Hectares	Q
Hectare-meter	F
Btu's per Hour	I
Pounds	P
Short tons	T
Kilograms	K
Tons	M

[1]Single digit symbols are used here for data processing purposes.

(3) The method(s) (by handling code(s) as specified in Table 2) and date(s) of treatment, storage, or disposal.

Table 2—Handling Codes for Treatment, Storage and Disposal Methods

Enter the handling code(s) listed below that most closely represents the technique(s) used at the facility to treat, store or dispose of each quantity of hazardous waste received.

1. Storage
   - S01 Container (barrel, drum, etc.)
   - S02 Tank
   - S03 Waste Pile
   - S04 Surface Impoundment
   - S05 Drip Pad
   - S06 Containment Building (Storage)
   - S99 Other Storage (specify)

2. Treatment

(a) Thermal Treatment—
- T06 Liquid injection incinerator
- T07 Rotary kiln incinerator
- T08 Fluidized bed incinerator
- T09 Multiple hearth incinerator
- T10 Infrared furnace incinerator
- T11 Molten salt destructor
- T12 Pyrolysis
- T13 Wet air oxidation
- T14 Calcination
- T15 Microwave discharge
- T18 Other (specify)

(b) Chemical Treatment—
- T19 Absorption mound
- T20 Absorption field
- T21 Chemical fixation
- T22 Chemical oxidation
- T23 Chemical precipitation
- T24 Chemical reduction
- T25 Chlorination
- T26 Chlorinolysis
- T27 Cyanide destruction
- T28 Degradation
- T29 Detoxification
- T30 Ion exchange
- T31 Neutralization
- T32 Ozonation
- T33 Photolysis
- T34 Other (specify)

(c) Physical Treatment—

(1) Separation of components:
- T35 Centrifugation
- T36 Clarification
- T37 Coagulation
- T38 Decanting
- T39 Encapsulation
- T40 Filtration
- T41 Flocculation
- T42 Flotation
- T43 Foaming
- T44 Sedimentation
- T45 Thickening
- T46 Ultrafiltration
- T47 Other (specify)

(2) Removal of Specific Components:
- T48 Absorption-molecular sieve
- T49 Activated carbon
- T50 Blending
- T51 Catalysis
- T52 Crystallization
- T53 Dialysis
- T54 Distillation
- T55 Electrodialysis
- T56 Electrolysis
- T57 Evaporation
- T58 High gradient magnetic separation
- T59 Leaching
- T60 Liquid ion exchange
- T61 Liquid-liquid extraction
- T62 Reverse osmosis
- T63 Solvent recovery
- T64 Stripping
- T65 Sand filter
- T66 Other (specify)

(d) Biological Treatment
- T67 Activated sludge
- T68 Aerobic lagoon
- T69 Aerobic tank
- T70 Anaerobic tank
- T71 Composting
- T72 Septic tank
- T73 Spray irrigation
- T74 Thickening filter
- T75 Trickling filter
- T76 Waste stabilization pond
- T77 Other (specify)
- T78–T79 [Reserved

(e) Boilers and Industrial Furnaces
- T80 Boiler
- T81 Cement Kiln
- T82 Lime Kiln
- T83 Aggregate Kiln
- T84 Phosphate Kiln
- T85 Coke Oven
- T86 Blast Furnace
- T87 Smelting, Melting, or Refining Furnace
- T88 Titanium Dioxide Chloride Process Oxidation Reactor
- T89 Methane Reforming Furnace

T90 Pulping Liquor Recovery Furnace

T91 Combustion Device Used in the Recovery of Sulfur Values from Spent Sulfuric Acid

T92 Halogen Acid Furnaces

T93 Other Industrial Furnaces Listed in 40 CFR 260.10 (specify)

(f) Other Treatment

T94 Containment Building (Treatment)

3. Disposal

D79 Underground Injection

D80 Landfill

D81 Land Treatment

D82 Ocean Disposal

D83 Surface Impoundment (to be closed as a landfill)

D99 Other Disposal (specify)

4. Miscellaneous (Subpart X)

X01 Open Burning/Open Detonation

X02 Mechanical Processing

X03 Thermal Unit

X04 Geologic Repository

X99 Other Subpart X (specify)

[45 FR 33221, May 19, 1980, as amended at 59 FR 13891, Mar. 24, 1994; 71 FR 40274, July 14, 2006]

Appendices II–III to Part 264 [Reserved]

Appendix IV to Part 264—Cochran's Approximation to the Behrens-Fisher Students' t-test

Using all the available background data (n_b readings), calculate the background mean (X_b) and background variance (s_b^2). For the single monitoring well under investigation (n_m reading), calculate the monitoring mean (X_m) and monitoring variance (s_m^2).

For any set of data ($X_1, X_2, \ldots, X_n$) the mean is calculated by:

$$\bar{X} = \frac{X_1 + X_2 \ldots + X_n}{n}$$

and the variance is calculated by:

$$S^2 = \frac{\left(X_1 - \bar{X}\right)^2 + \left(X_2 - \bar{X}\right)^2 \ldots + \left(X_n - \bar{X}\right)^2}{n - 1}$$

where "n" denotes the number of observations in the set of data.

The t-test uses these data summary measures to calculate a t-statistic (t*) and a comparison t-statistic (t_c). The t* value is compared to the t_c value and a conclusion reached as to whether there has been a statistically significant change in any indicator parameter.

The t-statistic for all parameters except pH and similar monitoring parameters is:

$$t^* = \frac{X_m - \bar{X}_s}{\sqrt{\frac{S_m^2}{n_m} + \frac{S_b^2}{n_b}}}$$

If the value of this t-statistic is negative then there is no significant difference between the monitoring data and background data. It should be noted that significantly small negative values may be indicative of a failure of the assumption made for test validity or errors have been made in collecting the background data.

The t-statistic (t_c), against which t* will be compared, necessitates finding t_b and t_m from standard (one-tailed) tables where,

t_b = t-tables with (n_b–1) degrees of freedom, at the 0.05 level of significance.

t_m = t-tables with (n_m–1) degrees of freedom, at the 0.05 level of significance.

Finally, the special weightings W_b and W_m are defined as:

$$W_B = \frac{S_{b^2}}{n_b} \quad \text{and} \quad W_m = \frac{S_{m^2}}{n_m}$$

and so the comparison t-statistic is:

$$t_c = \frac{W_b t_b + W_m t_m}{W_b + W_m}$$

The t-statistic (t*) is now compared with the comparison t-statistic (t_c) using the following decision-rule:

If *t* is equal to or larger than* t_c, then conclude that there most likely *has been a significant increase* in this specific parameter. If *t* is less than* t_c, then conclude that most likely *there has not been a change* in this specific parameter.

The t-statistic for testing pH and similar monitoring parameters is constructed in the same manner as previously described except the negative sign (if any) is discarded and the caveat concerning the negative value is ignored. The standard (two-tailed) tables are used in the construction t_c for pH and similar monitoring parameters.

If t* is equal to or larger than t_c, then conclude that there most likely *has been a significant increase* (if the initial t* had been negative, this would imply a significant decrease). If t* is less than t_c, then conclude that there most likely has been no change.

A further discussion of the test may be found in *Statistical Methods* (6th Edition, Section 4.14) by G. W. Snedecor and W. G. Cochran, or *Principles and Procedures of Statistics* (1st Edition, Section 5.8) by R. G. D. Steel and J. H. Torrie.

Standard T—Tables 0.05 Level of Significance

Degrees of freedom	t-values (one-tail)	t-values (two-tail)
1	6.314	12.706
2	2.920	4.303
3	2.353	3.182
4	2.132	2.776
5	2.015	2.571
6	1.943	2.447
7	1.895	2.365
8	1.860	2.306
9	1.833	2.262
10	1.812	2.228
11	1.796	2.201
12	1.782	2.179
13	1.771	2.160
14	1.761	2.145
15	1.753	2.131
16	1.746	2.120
17	1.740	2.110
18	1.734	2.101

Standard T—Tables 0.05 Level of Significance

Degrees of freedom	t-values (one-tail)	t-values (two-tail)
19	1.729	2.093
20	1.725	2.086
21	1.721	2.080
22	1.717	2.074
23	1.714	2.069
24	1.711	2.064
25	1.708	2.060
30	1.697	2.042
40	1.684	2.021

Adopted from Table III of "Statistical Tables for Biological, Agricultural, and Medical Research" (1947, R. A. Fisher and F. Yates).

[47 FR 32367, July 26, 1982]

Appendix V to Part 264—Examples of Potentially Incompatible Waste

Many hazardous wastes, when mixed with other waste or materials at a hazardous waste facility, can produce effects which are harmful to human health and the environment, such as (1) heat or pressure, (2) fire or explosion, (3) violent reaction, (4) toxic dusts, mists, fumes, or gases, or (5) flammable fumes or gases.

Below are examples of potentially incompatible wastes, waste components, and materials, along with the harmful consequences which result from mixing materials in one group with materials in another group. The list is intended as a guide to owners or operators of treatment, storage, and disposal facilities, and to enforcement and permit granting officials, to indicate the need for special precautions when managing these potentially incompatible waste materials or components.

This list is not intended to be exhaustive. An owner or operator must, as the regulations require, adequately analyze his wastes so that he can avoid creating uncontrolled substances or reactions of the type listed below, whether they are listed below or not.

It is possible for potentially incompatible wastes to be mixed in a way that precludes a reaction (*e.g.*, adding acid to water rather than water to acid) or that neutralizes them (*e.g.*, a strong acid mixed with a strong base), or that controls substances produced (*e.g.*, by generating flammable gases in a closed tank equipped so that ignition cannot occur, and burning the gases in an incinerator).

In the lists below, the mixing of a Group A material with a Group B material may have the potential consequence as noted.

Group 1-A	Group 1-B
Acetylene sludge	Acid sludge
Alkaline caustic liquids	Acid and water
Alkaline cleaner	Battery acid
Alkaline corrosive liquids	Chemical cleaners
Alkaline corrosive battery fluid	Electrolyte, acid
Caustic wastewater	Etching acid liquid or solvent
Lime sludge and other corrosive alkalies	Pickling liquor and other corrosive acids
Lime wastewater	Spent acid
Lime and water	Spent mixed acid
Spent caustic	Spent sulfuric acid

Potential consequences: Heat generation; violent reaction.

Group 2-A	Group 2-B
Aluminum	Any waste in Group 1-A or 1-B
Beryllium	
Calcium	
Lithium	
Magnesium	
Potassium	
Sodium	
Zinc powder	
Other reactive metals and metal hydrides	

Potential consequences: Fire or explosion; generation of flammable hydrogen gas.

Group 3-A	Group 3-B
Alcohols	Any concentrated waste in Groups 1-A or 1-B
Water	Calcium
	Lithium
	Metal hydrides
	Potassium
	$SO_2 Cl_2$, $SOCl_2$, PCl_3, $CH_3 SiCl_3$
	Other water-reactive waste

Potential consequences: Fire, explosion, or heat generation; generation of flammable or toxic gases.

Group 4-A	Group 4-B
Alcohols	Concentrated Group 1-A or 1-B wastes
Aldehydes	Group 2-A wastes
Halogenated hydrocarbons	
Nitrated hydrocarbons	
Unsaturated hydrocarbons	
Other reactive organic compounds and solvents	

Potential consequences: Fire, explosion, or violent reaction.

Group 5-A	Group 5-B
Spent cyanide and sulfide solutions	Group 1-B wastes

Potential consequences: Generation of toxic hydrogen cyanide or hydrogen sulfide gas.

Group 6-A	Group 6-B
Chlorates	Acetic acid and other organic acids
Chlorine	Concentrated mineral acids
Chlorites	Group 2-A wastes
Chromic acid	Group 4-A wastes
Hypochlorites	Other flammable and combustible wastes
Nitrates	
Nitric acid, fuming	
Perchlorates	
Permanganates	
Peroxides	
Other strong oxidizers	

Potential consequences: Fire, explosion, or violent reaction.

Source: "Law, Regulations, and Guidelines for Handling of Hazardous Waste." California Department of Health, February 1975.

[46 FR 2872, Jan. 12, 1981]

Appendix VI to Part 264—Political Jurisdictions[1] in Which Compliance With §264.18(a) Must Be Demonstrated

Alaska	
Aleutian Islands	Kodiak
Anchorage	Lynn Canal-Icy Straits
Bethel	Palmer-Wasilla-Talkeena
Bristol Bay	Seward
Cordova-Valdez	Sitka
Fairbanks-Fort Yukon	Wade Hampton
Juneau	Wrangell Petersburg
Kenai-Cook Inlet	Yukon-Kuskokwim
Ketchikan-Prince of Wales	

Arizona	
Cochise	Greenlee
Graham	Yuma

California
All

Colorado	
Archuleta	Mineral
Conejos	Rio Grande
Hinsdale	Saguache

Hawaii
Hawaii

Idaho	
Bannock	Franklin
Bear Lake	Fremont
Bingham	Jefferson
Bonneville	Madison
Caribou	Oneida
Cassia	Power
Clark	Teton

Montana	
Beaverhead	Meagher
Broadwater	Missoula
Cascade	Park
Deer Lodge	Powell
Flathead	Sanders
Gallatin	Silver Bow
Granite	Stillwater
Jefferson	Sweet Grass
Lake	Teton
Lewis and Clark	Wheatland
Madison	

[1] These include counties, city-county consolidations, and independent cities. In the case of Alaska, the political jurisdictions are election districts, and, in the case of Hawaii, the political jurisdiction listed is the island of Hawaii.

Nevada
All

New Mexico	
Bernalillo	Sante Fe
Catron	Sierra
Grant	Socorro
Hidalgo	Taos
Los Alamos	Torrance
Rio Arriba	Valencia
Sandoval	

Utah	
Beaver	Piute
Box Elder	Rich
Cache	Salt Lake
Carbon	Sanpete
Davis	Sevier
Duchesne	Summit
Emery	Tooele
Garfield	Utah
Iron	Wasatch
Juab	Washington
Millard	Wayne
Morgan	Weber

Washington	
Chelan	Mason
Clallam	Okanogan
Clark	Pacific
Cowlitz	Pierce
Douglas	San Juan Islands
Ferry	Skagit
Grant	Skamania
Grays Harbor	Snohomish
Jefferson	Thurston
King	Wahkiakum
Kitsap	Whatcom
Kittitas	Yakima
Lewis	

Wyoming	
Fremont	Teton
Lincoln	Uinta
Park	Yellowstone National Park
Sublette	

[46 FR 57285, Nov. 23, 1981; 47 FR 953, Jan. 8, 1982]

Appendices VII–VIII to Part 264 [Reserved]

Appendix IX to Part 264—Ground-Water Monitoring List

Ground-Water Monitoring List

Common name[1]	CAS RN[2]	Chemical abstracts service index name[3]
Acenaphthene	83-32-9	Acenaphthylene, 1,2-dihydro-
Acenaphthylene	208-96-8	Acenaphthylene
Acetone	67-64-1	2-Propanone
Acetophenone	98-86-2	Ethanone, 1-phenyl-
Acetonitrile; Methyl cyanide	75-05-8	Acetonitrile
2-Acetylamino-fluorene; 2-AAF	53-96-3	Acetamide, N–9H-fluoren-2-yl-
Acrolein	107-02-8	2-Propenal
Acrylonitrile	107-13-1	2-Propenenitrile
Aldrin	309-00-2	1,4:5,8-Dimethano-naphthalene, 1,2,3,4,10,10-hexachloro-1,4,4a,5,8,8a-hexahydro-(1α,4α, 4aβ, 5α,8α,8aβ)-
Allyl chloride	107-05-1	1-Propene, 3-chloro-
4-Aminobiphenyl	92-67-1	[1,1′-Biphenyl]-4-amine
Aniline	62-53-3	Benzenamine
Anthracene	120-12-7	Anthracene
Antimony	(Total)	Antimony
Aramite	140-57-8	Sulfurous acid, 2-chloroethyl 2-[4-(1,1-dimethylethyl) phenoxy]-1-methylethyl ester
Arsenic	(Total)	Arsenic
Barium	(Total)	Barium
Benzene	71-43-2	Benzene
Benzo[a]anthracene; Benzanthracene	56-55-3	Benz[a]anthracene
Benzo[b]fluor-anthene	205-99-2	Benz[e]acephenanthrylene
Benzo[k]fluor-anthene	207-08-9	Benzo[k]fluoranthene
Benzo[ghi]perylene	191-24-2	Benzo[ghi]perylene
Benzo[a]pyrene	50-32-8	Benzo[a]pyrene
Benzyl alcohol	100-51-6	Benzenemethanol
Beryllium	(Total)	Beryllium
alpha-BHC	319-84-6	Cyclohexane, 1,2,3,4,5,6-hexa-chloro-,(1α, 2α,3β, 4β,5β,6β)-
beta-BHC	319-85-7	Cyclohexane, 1,2,3,4,5,6-hexa-chloro-,(1α,2β, 3α,4β, 5α,6β)-
delta-BHC	319-86-8	Cyclohexane, 1,2,3,4,5,6-hexa-chloro-,(1α,2α, 3α, 4β,5α,6β)-
gamma-BHC; Lindane	58-89-9	Cyclohexane, 1,2,3,4,5,6-hexa-chloro-,(1α, 2α, 3β, 4α,5α,6β)-
Bis(2-chloroethoxy) methane	111-91-1	Ethane, 1,1′-[methylenebis (oxy)]bis [2-chloro-
Bis(2-chloro-ethyl)ether	111-44-4	Ethane, 1,1′-oxybis[2-chloro-
Bis(2-chloro-1-methylethyl) ether; 2,2′-Dichlorodi-isopropyl ether	108-60-1	Propane, 2,2′-oxybis[1-chloro-
Bis(2-ethylhexyl) phthalate	117-81-7	1,2-Benzenedicarboxylic acid, bis(2-ethylhexyl)ester
Bromodichloro-methane	75-27-4	Methane, bromodichloro-
Bromoform; Tribromomethane	75-25-2	Methane, tribromo-
4-Bromophenyl phenyl ether	101-55-3	Benzene, 1-bromo-4-phenoxy-
Butyl benzyl phthalate; Benzyl butyl phthalate	85-68-7	1,2-Benzenedicarboxylic acid, butyl phenylmethyl ester
Cadmium	(Total)	Cadmium
Carbon disulfide	75-15-0	Carbon disulfide
Carbon tetrachloride	56-23-5	Methane, tetrachloro-
Chlordane	57-74-9	4,7-Methano-1H-indene, 1,2,4,5,6,7,8,8- octachloro-2,3,3a, 4,7,7a-hexahydro-
p-Chloroaniline	106-47-8	Benzenamine, 4-chloro-
Chlorobenzene	108-90-7	Benzene, chloro-
Chlorobenzilate	510-15-6	Benzeneacetic acid, 4-chloro-α-(4-chlorophenyl)-α-hydroxy-, ethyl ester
p-Chloro-m-cresol	59-50-7	Phenol, 4-chloro-3-methyl-
Chloroethane; Ethyl chloride	75-00-3	Ethane, chloro-
Chloroform	67-66-3	Methane, trichloro-
2-Chloro-naphthalene	91-58-7	Naphthalene, 2-chloro-
2-Chlorophenol	95-57-8	Phenol, 2-chloro-
4-Chlorophenyl phenyl ether	7005-72-3	Benzene, 1-chloro-4-phenoxy-
Chloroprene	126-99-8	1,3-Butadiene, 2-chloro-
Chromium	(Total)	Chromium
Chrysene	218-01-9	Chrysene
Cobalt	(Total)	Cobalt
Copper	(Total)	Copper
m-Cresol	108-39-4	Phenol, 3-methyl-
o-Cresol	95-48-7	Phenol, 2-methyl-
p-Cresol	106-44-5	Phenol, 4-methyl-
Cyanide	57-12-5	Cyanide
2,4-D; 2,4-Dichloro-phenoxyacetic acid	94-75-7	Acetic acid, (2,4-dichlorophen-oxy)-
4,4′-DDD	72-54-8	Benzene 1,1′-(2,2-dichloro-ethylidene) bis[4-chloro-
4,4′-DDE	72-55-9	Benzene, 1,1′-(dichloro-ethenylidene) bis[4-chloro-
4,4′-DDT	50-29-3	Benzene, 1,1′-(2,2,2-trichloro-ethylidene) bis[4-chloro-
Diallate	2303-16-4	Carbamothioic acid, bis(1-methylethyl)- , S- (2,3-dichloro-2-propenyl) ester
Dibenz[a,h]an-thracene	53-70-3	Dibenz[a,h]anthracene
Dibenzofuran	132-64-9	Dibenzofuran
Dibromo-chloromethane; Chlorodibromo-methane	124-48-1	Methane, dibromochloro-

Ground-Water Monitoring List

Common name[1]	CAS RN[2]	Chemical abstracts service index name[3]
1,2-Dibromo-3-chloropropane; DBCP	96-12-8	Propane, 1,2-dibromo-3-chloro-
1,2-Dibromoethane; Ethylene dibromide	106-93-4	Ethane, 1,2-dibromo-
Di-n-butyl phthalate	84-74-2	1,2-Benzenedicarboxylic acid, dibutyl ester
o-Dichlorobenzene	95-50-1	Benzene, 1,2-dichloro-
m-Dichlorobenzene	541-73-1	Benzene, 1,3-dichloro-
p-Dichlorobenzene	106-46-7	Benzene, 1,4-dichloro-
3,3′-Dichlorobenzidine	91-94-1	[1,1′-Biphenyl]-4,4′-diamine, 3,3′-dichloro-
trans-1,4-Dichloro-2-butene	110-57-6	2-Butene, 1,4-dichloro-, (E)-
Dichlorodifluoromethane	75-71-8	Methane, dichlorodifluoro-
1,1-Dichloroethane	75-34-3	Ethane, 1,1-dichloro-
1,2-Dichloroethane; Ethylene dichloride	107-06-2	Ethane, 1,2-dichloro-
1,1-Dichloroethylene; Vinylidene chloride	75-35-4	Ethene, 1,1-dichloro-
trans-1,2-Dichloroethylene	156-60-5	Ethene, 1,2-dichloro-, (E)-
2,4-Dichlorophenol	120-83-2	Phenol, 2,4-dichloro-
2,6-Dichlorophenol	87-65-0	Phenol, 2,6-dichloro-
1,2-Dichloropropane	78-87-5	Propane, 1,2-dichloro-
cis-1,3-Dichloropropene	10061-01-5	1-Propene, 1,3-dichloro-, (Z)-
trans-1,3-Dichloropropene	10061-02-6	1-Propene, 1,3-dichloro-, (E)-
Dieldrin	60-57-1	2,7:3,6-Dimethanonaphth [2,3-b]oxirene, 3,4,5,6,9,9-hexachloro- 1a,2,2a,3,6,6a,7,7a-octahydro-, (1aα,2β, 2aα, 3β,6β:,6aα,7β,7aα)-
Diethyl phthalate	84-66-2	1,2-Benzenedicarboxylic acid, diethyl ester
O,O-Diethyl O-2-pyrazinyl phosphorothioate; Thionazin	297-97-2	Phosphorothioic acid, O,O-diethyl O-pyrazinyl ester
Dimethoate	60-51-5	Phosphorodithioic acid, O,O-dimethyl S-[2-(methylamino)-2- oxoethyl] ester
p-(Dimethylamino)azobenzene	60-11-7	Benzenamine, N,N-dimethyl-4-(phenylazo)-
7,12-Dimethylbenz[a] anthracene	57-97-6	Benz[a]anthracene, 7,12-dimethyl-
3,3′-Dimethylbenzidine	119-93-7	[1,1′-Biphenyl]-4,4′-diamine, 3,3′-dimethyl-
alpha, alpha-Dimethylphenethylamine	122-09-8	Benzeneethanamine, α,α-dimethyl-
2,4-Dimethylphenol	105-67-9	Phenol, 2,4-dimethyl-
Dimethyl phthalate	131-11-3	1,2-Benzenedicarboxylic acid, dimethyl ester

Ground-Water Monitoring List

Common name[1]	CAS RN[2]	Chemical abstracts service index name[3]
m-Dinitrobenzene	99-65-0	Benzene, 1,3-dinitro-
4,6-Dinitro-o-cresol	534-52-1	Phenol, 2-methyl-4,6-dinitro-
2,4-Dinitrophenol	51-28-5	Phenol, 2,4-dinitro-
2,4-Dinitrotoluene	121-14-2	Benzene, 1-methyl-2,4-dinitro-
2,6-Dinitrotoluene	606-20-2	Benzene, 2-methyl-1,3-dinitro-
Dinoseb; DNBP; 2-sec-Butyl- 4,6-dinitrophenol	88-85-7	Phenol, 2-(1-methylpropyl)-4,6-dinitro-
Di-n-octyl phthalate	117-84-0	1,2-Benzenedicarboxylic acid, dioctyl ester
1,4-Dioxane	123-91-1	1,4-Dioxane
Diphenylamine	122-39-4	Benzenamine, N-phenyl-
Disulfoton	298-04-4	Phosphorodithioic acid, O,O-diethyl S-[2-(ethylthio)ethyl]ester
Endosulfan I	959-98-8	6,9-Methano-2,4,3-benzodioxathiepin, 6,7,8,9,10,10-hexachloro-1,5,5a, 6,9,9a-hexahydro-, 3-oxide,(3α,5aβ,6α,9α,9aβ)-
Endosulfan II	33213-65-9	6,9-Methano-2,4,3-benzodioxathiepin, 6,7,8,9,10,10-hexachloro-1,5,5a, 6,9,9a-hexahydro-, 3-oxide, (3α,5aα,6β,9β,9aα)-
Endosulfan sulfate	1031-07-8	6,9-Methano-2,4,3-benzodioxathiepin, 6,7,8,9,10,10-hexachloro-1,5,5a,6,9,9a-hexahydro-, 3,3-dioxide
Endrin	72-20-8	2,7:3,6-Dimethanonaphth[2,3-b]oxirene, 3,4,5,6,9,9-hexachloro-1a,2,2a,3,6,6a,7,7a- octahydro-, (1aα, 2β,2aβ,3α,6α,6aβ,7β, 7aα)-
Endrin aldehyde	7421-93-4	1,2,4-Methenocyclopenta[cd] pentalene-5-carboxaldehyde, 2,2a,3,3, 4,7- hexachlorodecahydro-, (1α,2β, 2aβ,4β, 4aβ,5β, 6aβ,6bβ,7R*)-
Ethylbenzene	100-41-4	Benzene, ethyl-
Ethyl methacrylate	97-63-2	2-Propenoic acid, 2-methyl-, ethyl ester
Ethyl methanesulfonate	62-50-0	Methanesulfonic acid, ethyl ester
Famphur	52-85-7	Phosphorothioic acid, O-[4-[(dimethylamino)sulfonyl] phenyl]-O,O-dimethyl ester
Fluoranthene	206-44-0	Fluoranthene
Fluorene	86-73-7	9H-Fluorene
Heptachlor	76-44-8	4,7-Methano-1H-indene, 1,4,5,6,7,8,8-heptachloro-3a,4, 7,7a-tetrahydro-
Heptachlor epoxide	1024-57-3	2,5-Methano-2H-indeno[1,2-b]oxirene, 2,3,4,5,6,7,7-heptachloro-1a,1b,5,5a,6,6a,-hexahydro-, (1aα,1bβ,2α,5α,5aβ,6β,6aα)
Hexachlorobenzene	118-74-1	Benzene, hexachloro-

Ground-Water Monitoring List

Common name[1]	CAS RN[2]	Chemical abstracts service index name[3]
Hexachlorobutadiene	87-68-3	1,3-Butadiene, 1,1,2,3,4,4-hexachloro-
Hexachlorocyclopentadiene	77-47-4	1,3-Cyclopentadiene, 1,2,3,4,5,5-hexachloro-
Hexachloroethane	67-72-1	Ethane, hexachloro-
Hexachlorophene	70-30-4	Phenol, 2,2′-methylenebis[3,4,6-trichloro-
Hexachloropropene	1888-71-7	1-Propene, 1,1,2,3,3,3-hexachloro-
2-Hexanone	591-78-6	2-Hexanone
Indeno(1,2,3-cd)pyrene	193-39-5	Indeno[1,2,3-cd]pyrene
Isobutyl alcohol	78-83-1	1-Propanol, 2-methyl-
Isodrin	465-73-6	1,4,5,8-Dimethanonaphthalene, 1,2,3,4,10,10- hexachloro-1,4,4a,5,8,8a hexahydro- (1α, 4α, 4aβ, 5β, 8β, 8aβ)-
Isophorone	78-59-1	2-Cyclohexen-1-one, 3,5,5-trimethyl-
Isosafrole	120-58-1	1,3-Benzodioxole, 5-(1-propenyl)-
Kepone	143-50-0	1,3,4-Metheno-2H-cyclobuta-[cd]pentalen-2-one, 1,1a,3,3a,4,5,5,5a,5b,6-decachlorooctahydro-
Lead	(Total)	Lead
Mercury	(Total)	Mercury
Methacrylonitrile	126-98-7	2-Propenenitrile, 2-methyl-
Methapyrilene	91-80-5	1,2,Ethanediamine, N,N-dimethyl-N′-2-pyridinyl- N′-(2-thienylmethyl)-
Methoxychlor	72-43-5	Benzene, 1,1′-(2,2,2, trichloroethylidene)bis[4-methoxy-
Methyl bromide; Bromomethane	74-83-9	Methane, bromo-
Methyl chloride; Chloromethane	74-87-3	Methane, chloro-
3-Methylcholanthrene	56-49-5	Benz[j]aceanthrylene, 1,2-dihydro-3-methyl-
Methylene bromide; Dibromomethane	74-95-3	Methane, dibromo-
Methylene chloride; Dichloromethane	75-09-2	Methane, dichloro-
Methyl ethyl ketone; MEK	78-93-3	2-Butanone
Methyl iodide; Iodomethane	74-88-4	Methane, iodo-
Methyl methacrylate	80-62-6	2-Propenoic acid, 2-methyl-, methyl ester
Methyl methanesulfonate	66-27-3	Methanesulfonic acid, methyl ester
2-Methylnaphthalene	91-57-6	Naphthalene, 2-methyl-
Methyl parathion; Parathion methyl	298-00-0	Phosphorothioic acid, O,O-dimethyl O-(4-nitrophenyl) ester

Ground-Water Monitoring List

Common name[1]	CAS RN[2]	Chemical abstracts service index name[3]
4-Methyl-2-pentanone; Methyl isobutyl ketone	108-10-1	2-Pentanone, 4-methyl-
Naphthalene	91-20-3	Naphthalene
1,4-Naphthoquinone	130-15-4	1,4-Naphthalenedione
1-Naphthylamine	134-32-7	1-Naphthalenamine
2-Naphthylamine	91-59-8	2-Naphthalenamine
Nickel	(Total)	Nickel
o-Nitroaniline	88-74-4	Benzenamine, 2-nitro-
m-Nitroaniline	99-09-2	Benzenamine, 3-nitro-
p-Nitroaniline	100-01-6	Benzenamine, 4-nitro-
Nitrobenzene	98-95-3	Benzene, nitro-
o-Nitrophenol	88-75-5	Phenol, 2-nitro-
p-Nitrophenol	100-02-7	Phenol, 4-nitro-
4-Nitroquinoline 1-oxide	56-57-5	Quinoline, 4-nitro-, 1-oxide
N-Nitrosodi-n-butylamine	924-16-3	1-Butanamine, N-butyl-N-nitroso-
N-Nitrosodiethylamine	55-18-5	Ethanamine, N-ethyl-N-nitroso-
N-Nitrosodimethylamine	62-75-9	Methanamine, N-methyl-N-nitroso-
N-Nitrosodiphenylamine	86-30-6	Benzenamine, N-nitroso-N-phenyl-
N-Nitrosodipropylamine; Di-n-propylnitrosamine	621-64-7	1-Propanamine, N-nitroso-N-propyl-
N-Nitrosomethylethalamine	10595-95-6	Ethanamine, N-methyl-N-nitroso-
N-Nitrosomorpholine	59-89-2	Morpholine, 4-nitroso-
N-Nitrosopiperidine	100-75-4	Piperidine, 1-nitroso-
N-Nitrosopyrrolidine	930-55-2	Pyrrolidine, 1-nitroso-
5-Nitro-o-toluidine	99-55-8	Benzenamine, 2-methyl-5-nitro-
Parathion	56-38-2	Phosphorothioic acid, O,O-diethyl-O-(4-nitrophenyl) ester
Polychlorinated biphenyls; PCBs	See footnote 4	1,1′-Biphenyl, chloro derivatives
Polychlorinated dibenzo-p-dioxins; PCDDs	See footnote 5	Dibenzo[b,e][1,4]dioxin, chloro derivatives
Polychlorinated dibenzofurans; PCDFs	See footnote 6	Dibenzofuran, chloro derivatives
Pentachlorobenzene	608-93-5	Benzene, pentachloro-
Pentachloroethane	76-01-7	Ethane, pentachloro-
Pentachloronitrobenzene	82-68-8	Benzene, pentachloronitro-
Pentachlorophenol	87-86-5	Phenol, pentachloro-
Phenacetin	62-44-2	Acetamide, N-(4-ethoxyphenyl)
Phenanthrene	85-01-8	Phenanthrene
Phenol	108-95-2	Phenol
p-Phenylenediamine	106-50-3	1,4-Benzenediamine

Ground-Water Monitoring List

Common name[1]	CAS RN[2]	Chemical abstracts service index name[3]
Phorate	298-02-2	Phosphorodithioic acid, O,O-diethyl S- [(ethylthio)methyl] ester
2-Picoline	109-06-8	Pyridine, 2-methyl-
Pronamide	23950-58-5	Benzamide, 3,5-dichloro-N-(1,1-dimethyl-2-propynyl)-
Propionitrile; Ethyl cyanide	107-12-0	Propanenitrile
Pyrene	129-00-0	Pyrene
Pyridine	110-86-1	Pyridine
Safrole	94-59-7	1,3-Benzodioxole, 5-(2-propenyl)-
Selenium	(Total)	Selenium
Silver	(Total)	Silver
Silvex; 2,4,5-TP	93-72-1	Propanoic acid, 2-(2,4,5-trichlorophenoxy)-
Styrene	100-42-5	Benzene, ethenyl-
Sulfide	18496-25-8	Sulfide
2,4,5-T; 2,4,5-Trichlorophenoxyacetic acid	93-76-5	Acetic acid, (2,4,5-trichlorophenoxy)-
2,3,7,8-TCDD; 2,3,7,8-Tetrachlorodibenzo-p-dioxin	1746-01-6	Dibenzo[b,e][1,4]dioxin, 2,3,7,8-tetrachloro-
1,2,4,5-Tetrachlorobenzene	95-94-3	Benzene, 1,2,4,5-tetrachloro-
1,1,1,2-Tetrachloroethane	630-20-6	Ethane, 1,1,1,2-tetrachloro-
1,1,2,2-Tetrachloroethane	79-34-5	Ethane, 1,1,2,2-tetrachloro-
Tetrachloroethylene; Perchloroethylene; Tetrachloroethene	127-18-4	Ethene, tetrachloro-
2,3,4,6-Tetrachlorophenol	58-90-2	Phenol, 2,3,4,6-tetrachloro-
Tetraethyl dithiopyrophosphate; Sulfotepp	3689-24-5	Thiodiphosphoric acid ($[(HO)_2P(S)]_2O$), tetraethyl ester
Thallium	(Total)	Thallium
Tin	(Total)	Tin
Toluene	108-88-3	Benzene, methyl-
o-Toluidine	95-53-4	Benzenamine, 2-methyl-
Toxaphene	8001-35-2	Toxaphene

Ground-Water Monitoring List

Common name[1]	CAS RN[2]	Chemical abstracts service index name[3]
1,2,4-Trichlorobenzene	120-82-1	Benzene, 1,2,4-trichloro-
1,1,1-Trichloroethane; Methylchloroform	71-55-6	Ethane, 1,1,1-trichloro-
1,1,2-Trichloroethane	79-00-5	Ethane, 1,1,2-trichloro-
Trichloroethylene; Trichloroethene	79-01-6	Ethene, trichloro-
Trichlorofluoromethane	75-69-4	Methane, trichlorofluoro-
2,4,5-Trichlorophenol	95-95-4	Phenol, 2,4,5-trichloro-
2,4,6-Trichlorophenol	88-06-2	Phenol, 2,4,6-trichloro-
1,2,3-Trichloropropane	96-18-4	Propane, 1,2,3-trichloro-
O,O,O-Triethyl phosphorothioate	126-68-1	Phosphorothioic acid, O,O,O-triethyl ester
sym-Trinitrobenzene	99-35-4	Benzene, 1,3,5-trinitro-
Vanadium	(Total)	Vanadium
Vinyl acetate	108-05-4	Acetic acid, ethenyl ester
Vinyl chloride	75-01-4	Ethene, chloro-
Xylene (total)	1330-20-7	Benzene, dimethyl-
Zinc	(Total)	Zinc

[1]Common names are those widely used in government regulations, scientific publications, and commerce; synonyms exist for many chemicals.

[2]Chemical Abstracts Service registry number. Where "Total" is entered, all species in the ground water that contain this element are included.

[3]CAS index names are those used in the 9th Cumulative Index.

[4]Polychlorinated biphenyls (CAS RN 1336-36-3); this category contains congener chemicals, including constituents of Aroclor-1016 (CAS RN 12674-11-2), Aroclor-1221 (CAS RN 11104-28-2), Aroclor-1232 (CAS RN 11141-16-5), Aroclor-1242 (CAS RN 53469-21-9), Aroclor-1248 (CAS RN 12672-29-6), Aroclor-1254 (CAS RN 11097-69-1), and Aroclor-1260 (CAS RN 11096-82-5).

[5]This category contains congener chemicals, including tetrachlorodibenzo-p-dioxins (see also 2,3,7,8-TCDD), pentachlorodibenzo-p-dioxins, and hexachlorodibenzo-p-dioxins.

[6]This category contains congener chemicals, including tetrachlorodibenzofurans, pentachlorodibenzofurans, and hexachlorodibenzofurans.

[52 FR 25947, July 9, 1987, as amended at 62 FR 32462, June 13, 1997; 70 FR 34582, June 14, 2005; 70 FR 44151, Aug. 1, 2005]

PART 265—INTERIM STATUS STANDARDS FOR OWNERS AND OPERATORS OF HAZARDOUS WASTE TREATMENT, STORAGE, AND DISPOSAL FACILITIES

Subpart K—Surface Impoundments

Subpart L—Waste Piles

Subpart M—Land Treatment

Subpart N—Landfills

Subpart O—Incinerators

Subpart P—Thermal Treatment

Subpart Q—Chemical, Physical, and Biological Treatment

Authority: 42 U.S.C. 6905, 6906, 6912, 6922, 6923, 6924, 6925, 6935, 6936, and 6937.

Source: 45 FR 33232, May 19, 1980, unless otherwise noted.

Subpart A—General

§265.1 Purpose, scope, and applicability.

(a) The purpose of this part is to establish minimum national standards that define the acceptable management of hazardous waste during the period of interim status and until certification of final closure or, if the facility is subject to post-closure requirements, until post-closure responsibilities are fulfilled.

(b) Except as provided in §265.1080(b), the standards of this part, and of 40 CFR 264.552, 264.553, and 264.554, apply to owners and operators of facilities that treat, store or dispose of hazardous waste who have fully complied with the requirements for interim status under section 3005(e) of RCRA and §270.10 of this chapter until either a permit is issued under section 3005 of RCRA or until applicable part 265 closure and post-closure responsibilities are fulfilled, and to those owners and operators of facilities in existence on November 19, 1980 who have failed to provide timely notification as required by section 3010(a) of RCRA and/or failed to file Part A of the permit application as required by 40 CFR 270.10 (e) and (g). These standards apply to all treatment, storage and disposal of hazardous waste at these facilities after the effective date of these regulations, except as specifically provided otherwise in this part or part 261 of this chapter. 📖 14.2.1

[*Comment:* As stated in section 3005(a) of RCRA, after the effective date of regulations under that section (*i.e.*, parts 270 and 124 of this chapter), the treatment, storage and disposal of hazardous waste is prohibited except in accordance with a permit. Section 3005(e) of RCRA provides for the continued operation of an existing facility that meets certain conditions, until final administrative disposition of the owner's and operator's permit application is made.]

(c) The requirements of this part do not apply to:

(1) A person disposing of hazardous waste by means of ocean disposal subject to a permit issued under the Marine Protection, Research, and Sanctuaries Act;

[*Comment:* These part 265 regulations do apply to the treatment or storage of hazardous waste before it is loaded onto an ocean vessel for incineration or disposal at sea, as provided in paragraph (b) of this section.]

(2) [Reserved]

(3) The owner or operator of a POTW which treats, stores, or disposes of hazardous waste;

[*Comment:* The owner or operator of a facility under paragraphs (c)(1) through (3) of this section is subject to the requirements of part 264 of this chapter to the extent they are included in a permit by rule granted to such a person under part 122 of this chapter, or are required by §144.14 of this chapter.]

(4) A person who treats, stores, or disposes of hazardous waste in a State with a RCRA hazardous waste program authorized under subpart A or B of part 271 of this chapter, except that the requirements of this part will continue to apply:

(i) If the authorized State RCRA program does not cover disposal of hazardous waste by means of underground injection; or

(ii) To a person who treats, stores, or disposes of hazardous waste in a State authorized under subpart A or B of part 271 of this chapter if the State has not been authorized to carry out the requirements and prohibitions applicable to the treatment, storage, or disposal of hazardous waste at his facility which are imposed pursuant to the Hazardous and Solid Waste Act Amendments of 1984. The requirements and prohibitions that are applicable until a State receives authorization to carry them out include all Federal program requirements identified in §271.1(j);

(5) The owner or operator of a facility permitted, licensed, or registered by a State to manage municipal or industrial solid waste, if the only hazardous waste the facility treats, stores, or disposes of is excluded from regulation under this part by §261.5 of this chapter;

(6) The owner or operator of a facility managing recyclable materials described in §261.6 (a)(2), (3), and (4) of this chapter (except to the extent they are referred to in part 279 or subparts C, F, G, or H of part 266 of this chapter). 📖 7.4

(7) A generator accumulating waste on-site in compliance with §262.34 of this chapter, except to the extent the requirements are included in §262.34 of this chapter; 📖 6.3, 7.3

(8) A farmer disposing of waste pesticides from his own use in compliance with §262.70 of this chapter; or

(9) The owner or operator of a totally enclosed treatment facility, as defined in §260.10. 📖 7.5.2

(10) The owner or operator of an elementary neutralization unit or a wastewater treatment unit as defined in §260.10 of this chapter, provided that if the owner or operator is diluting hazardous ignitable (D001) wastes (other than the D001 High TOC Subcategory defined in §268.40 of this chapter, Table Treatment Standards for Hazardous Wastes), or reactive (D003) waste, to remove the characteristic before land disposal, the owner/operator must comply with the requirements set out in §265.17(b). 📖 5.2.3.7, 7.2, 7.5.1

(11)(i) Except as provided in paragraph (c)(11)(ii) of this section, a person engaged in treatment or containment activities during immediate response to any of the following situations: 📖 7.5.4, 10.1.2.4, 10.2.1, 14.4.2.5

(A) A discharge of a hazardous waste;

(B) An imminent and substantial threat of a discharge of a hazardous waste;

(C) A discharge of a material which, when discharged, becomes a hazardous waste.

(D) An immediate threat to human health, public safety, property, or the environment, from the known or suspected presence of military munitions, other explosive material, or an explosive device, as determined by an explosive or munitions emergency response specialist as defined in 40 CFR 260.10.

(ii) An owner or operator of a facility otherwise regulated by this part must comply with all applicable requirements of subparts C and D.

(iii) Any person who is covered by paragraph (c)(11)(i) of this section and who continues or initiates hazardous waste treatment or containment activities after the immediate response is over is subject to all applicable requirements of this part and parts 122 through 124 of this chapter for those activities.

(iv) In the case of an explosives or munitions emergency response, if a Federal, State, Tribal or local official acting within the scope of his or her official responsibilities, or an explosives or munitions emergency response specialist, determines that immediate removal of the material or waste is necessary to protect human health or the environment, that official or specialist may authorize the removal of the material or waste by transporters who do not have EPA identification numbers and without the preparation of a manifest. In the case of emergencies involving military munitions, the responding military emergency response specialist's organizational unit must retain records for three years identifying the dates of the response, the responsible persons responding, the type and description of material addressed, and its disposition.

(12) A transporter storing manifested shipments of hazardous waste in containers meeting the requirements of 40 CFR 262.30 at a transfer facility for a period of ten days or less. 📖 6.6.3.3.1

(13) The addition of absorbent material to waste in a container (as defined in §260.10 of this chapter) or the addition of waste to the absorbent material in a container provided that these actions occur at the time waste is first placed in the containers; and §§265.17(b), 265.171, and 265.172 are complied with. 📖 7.5.3

(14) Universal waste handlers and universal waste transporters (as defined in 40 CFR 260.10) handling the wastes listed below. These handlers are subject to regulation under 40 CFR part 273, when handling the below listed universal wastes. 📖 8.3, 8.4.1

(i) Batteries as described in 40 CFR 273.2;

(ii) Pesticides as described in §273.3 of this chapter;

(iii) Mercury-containing equipment as described in §273.4 of this chapter; and

(iv) Lamps as described in §273.5 of this chapter.

(15) A New York State Utility central collection facility consolidating hazardous waste in accordance with 40 CFR 262.90.

(d) The following hazardous wastes must not be managed at facilities subject to regulation under this part.

(1) EPA Hazardous Waste Nos. F020, F021, F022, F023, F026, or F027 unless:

(i) The wastewater treatment sludge is generated in a surface impoundment as part of the plant's wastewater treatment system;

(ii) The waste is stored in tanks or containers;

(iii) The waste is stored or treated in waste piles that meet the requirements of §264.250(c) as well as all other applicable requirements of subpart L of this part;

(iv) The waste is burned in incinerators that are certified pursuant to the standards and procedures in §265.352; or

(v) The waste is burned in facilities that thermally treat the waste in a device other than an incinerator and that are certified pursuant to the standards and procedures in §265.383.

(e) The requirements of this part apply to owners or operators of all facilities which treat, store or dispose of hazardous waste referred to in 40 CFR part 268, and the 40 CFR part 268 standards are considered material conditions or requirements of the part 265 interim status standards.

(f) Section 266.205 of this chapter identifies when the requirements of this part apply to the storage of military munitions classified as solid waste under §266.202 of this chapter. The treatment and disposal of hazardous waste military munitions are subject to the applicable permitting, procedural, and technical standards in 40 CFR parts 260 through 270.

[45 FR 33232, May 19, 1980, as amended at 45 FR 76075, Nov. 17, 1980; 45 FR 86968, Dec. 31, 1980; 46 FR 27480, May 20, 1981; 47 FR 8306, Feb. 25, 1982; 48 FR 2511, Jan. 19, 1983; 48 FR 14295, Apr. 1, 1983; 49 FR 46095, Nov. 21, 1984; 50 FR 666, Jan. 4, 1985; 50 FR 2005, Jan. 14, 1985; 50 FR 28749, July 15, 1985; 52 FR 21016, June 4, 1987; 52 FR 45798, Dec. 1, 1987; 53 FR 27165, July 19, 1988; 55 FR 22685, June 1, 1990; 57 FR 38564, Aug. 25, 1992; 58 FR 8685, Feb. 16, 1993; 58 FR 26424, May 3, 1993; 58 FR 29884, May 24, 1993; 59 FR 48042, Sept. 19, 1994; 59 FR 62934, Dec. 6, 1994; 60 FR 25542, May 11, 1995; 62 FR 6653, Feb. 12, 1997; 63 FR 65940, Nov. 30, 1998; 64 FR 36488, July 6, 1999; 64 FR 37638, July 12, 1999; 70 FR 45520, Aug. 5, 2005; 71 FR 40274, July 14, 2006]

§§265.2–265.3 [Reserved]

§265.4 Imminent hazard action.

Notwithstanding any other provisions of these regulations, enforcement actions may be brought pursuant to section 7003 of RCRA.

PART 265—Subpart B

Subpart B—General Facility Standards

§265.10 Applicability.

The regulations in this subpart apply to owners and operators of all hazardous waste facilities, except as §265.1 provides otherwise.

§265.11 Identification number.

Every facility owner or operator must apply to EPA for an EPA identification number in accordance with the EPA notification procedures (45 FR 12746).

§265.12 Required notices.

(a)(1) The owner or operator of a facility that has arranged to receive hazardous waste from a foreign source must notify the Regional Administrator in writing at least four weeks in advance of the date the waste is expected to arrive at the facility. Notice of subsequent shipments of the same waste from the same foreign source is not required.

(2) The owner or operator of a recovery facility that has arranged to receive hazardous waste subject to 40 CFR part 262, subpart H must provide a copy of the tracking document bearing all required signatures to the notifier, to the Office of Enforcement and Compliance Assurance, Office of Compliance, Enforcement Planning, Targeting and Data Division (2222A), Environmental Protection Agency, 1200 Pennsylvania Ave., NW., Washington, DC 20460 and to the competent authorities of all other concerned countries within three working days of receipt of the shipment. The original of the signed tracking document must be maintained at the facility for at least three years.

(b) Before transferring ownership or operation of a facility during its operating life, or of a disposal facility during the post-closure care period, the owner or operator must notify the new owner or operator in writing of the requirements of this part and part 270 of this chapter. (Also see §270.72 of this chapter.)

[*Comment:* An owner's or operator's failure to notify the new owner or operator of the requirements of this part in no way relieves the new owner or operator of his obligation to comply with all applicable requirements.]

[45 FR 33232, May 19, 1980, as amended at 48 FR 14295, Apr. 1, 1983; 50 FR 4514, Jan. 31, 1985; 61 FR 16315, Apr. 12, 1996; 71 FR 40274, July 14, 2006]

§265.13 General waste analysis. 18.2.3.2

(a)(1) Before an owner or operator treats, stores, or disposes of any hazardous wastes, or nonhazardous wastes if applicable under §265.113(d), he must obtain a detailed chemical and physical analysis of a representative sample of the wastes. At a minimum, the analysis must contain all the information which must be known to treat, store, or dispose of the waste in accordance with this part and part 268 of this chapter.

(2) The analysis may include data developed under part 261 of this chapter, and existing published or documented data on the hazardous waste or on waste generated from similar processes.

Comment: For example, the facility's records of analyses performed on the waste before the effective date of these regulations, or studies conducted on hazardous waste generated from processes similar to that which generated the waste to be managed at the facility, may be included in the data base required to comply with paragraph (a)(1) of this section. The owner or operator of an off-site facility may arrange for the generator of the hazardous waste to supply part of the information required by paragraph (a)(1) of this section, except as otherwise specified in 40 CFR 268.7 (b) and (c). If the generator does not supply the information, and the owner or operator chooses to accept a hazardous waste, the owner or operator is responsible for obtaining the information required to comply with this section.]

(3) The analysis must be repeated as necessary to ensure that it is accurate and up to date. At a minimum, the analysis must be repeated:

(i) When the owner or operator is notified, or has reason to believe, that the process or operation generating the hazardous wastes or non-hazardous wastes, if applicable, under §265.113(d) has changed; and

(ii) For off-site facilities, when the results of the inspection required in paragraph (a)(4) of this section indicate that the hazardous waste received at the facility does not match the waste designated on the accompanying manifest or shipping paper.

(4) The owner or operator of an off-site facility must inspect and, if necessary, analyze each hazardous waste movement received at the facility to determine whether it matches the identity of the waste specified on the accompanying manifest or shipping paper. 18.2.3.2.1

(b) The owner or operator must develop and follow a written waste analysis plan which describes the procedures which he will carry out to comply with paragraph (a) of this section. He must keep this plan at the facility. At a minimum, the plan must specify:

(1) The parameters for which each hazardous waste, or non-hazardous waste if applicable under §265.113(d), will be analyzed and the rationale for the selection of these parameters (*i.e.*, how analysis for these parameters will provide sufficient information on the waste's properties to comply with paragraph (a) of this section);

(2) The test methods which will be used to test for these parameters;

(3) The sampling method which will be used to obtain a representative sample of the waste to be analyzed. A representative sample may be obtained using either:

(i) One of the sampling methods described in appendix I of part 261 of this chapter; or

(ii) An equivalent sampling method.

[*Comment:* See §260.20(c) of this chapter for related discussion.]

(4) The frequency with which the initial analysis of the waste will be reviewed or repeated to ensure that the analysis is accurate and up to date;

(5) For off-site facilities, the waste analyses that hazardous waste generators have agreed to supply; and

(6) Where applicable, the methods that will be used to meet the additional waste analysis requirements for specific waste management methods as specified in §§265.200, 265.225, 265.252, 265.273, 265.314, 265.341, 265.375, 265.402, 265.1034(d), 265.1063(d), 265.1084, and 268.7 of this chapter.

(7) For surface impoundments exempted from land disposal restrictions under §268.4(a) of this chapter, the procedures and schedule for:

(i) The sampling of impoundment contents;

(ii) The analysis of test data; and,

(iii) The annual removal of residues which are not delisted under §260.22 of this chapter or which exhibit a characteristic of hazardous waste and either:

(A) Do not meet applicable treatment standards of part 268, subpart D; or

(B) Where no treatment standards have been established;

(*1*) Such residues are prohibited from land disposal under §268.32 or RCRA section 3004(d); or

(*2*) Such residues are prohibited from land disposal under §268.33(f).

Publisher's Note: The section referenced above, §268.33(f), is no longer in the RCRA regulations.

(8) For owners and operators seeking an exemption to the air emission standards of Subpart CC of this part in accordance with §265.1083—

(i) If direct measurement is used for the waste determination, the procedures and schedules for waste sampling and analysis, and the results of the analysis of test data to verify the exemption.

(ii) If knowledge of the waste is used for the waste determination, any information prepared by the facility owner or operator or by the generator of the hazardous waste, if the waste is received from off-site, that is used as the basis for knowledge of the waste.

(c) For off-site facilities, the waste analysis plan required in paragraph (b) of this section must also specify the procedures which will be used to inspect and, if necessary, analyze each movement of hazardous waste received at the facility to ensure that it matches the identity of the waste designated on the accompanying manifest or shipping paper. At a minimum, the plan must describe: 📖 18.2.3.2.1

(1) The procedures which will be used to determine the identity of each movement of waste managed at the facility; and

(2) The sampling method which will be used to obtain a representative sample of the waste to be identified, if the identification method includes sampling.

(3) The procedures that the owner or operator of an off-site landfill receiving containerized hazardous waste will use to determine whether a hazardous waste generator or treater has added a biodegradable sorbent to the waste in the container.

[45 FR 33232, May 19, 1980, as amended at 50 FR 4514, Jan. 31, 1985; 50 FR 18374, Apr. 30, 1985; 51 FR 40638, Nov. 7, 1986; 52 FR 25788, July 8, 1987; 54 FR 33396, Aug. 14, 1989; 55 FR 22685, June 1, 1990; 55 FR 25506, June 21, 1990; 56 FR 19290, Apr. 26, 1991; 57 FR 8088, Mar. 6, 1992; 57 FR 54461, Nov. 18, 1992; 59 FR 62935, Dec. 6, 1994; 61 FR 4913, Feb. 9, 1996]

§265.14 Security.

(a) The owner or operator must prevent the unknowing entry, and minimize the possibility for the unauthorized entry, of persons or livestock onto the active portion of his facility, unless:

(1) Physical contact with the waste, structures, or equipment with the active portion of the facility will not injure unknowing or unauthorized persons or livestock which may enter the active portion of a facility, and

(2) Disturbance of the waste or equipment, by the unknowing or unauthorized entry of persons or livestock onto the active portion of a facility, will not cause a violation of the requirements of this part.

(b) Unless exempt under paragraphs (a)(1) and (2) of this section, a facility must have:

(1) A 24-hour surveillance system (*e.g.*, television monitoring or surveillance by guards or facility personnel) which continuously monitors and controls entry onto the active portion of the facility; or

(2)(i) An artificial or natural barrier (*e.g.*, a fence in good repair or a fence combined with a cliff), which completely surrounds the active portion of the facility; and

(ii) A means to control entry, at all times, through the gates or other entrances to the active portion of the facility (*e.g.*, an attendant, television monitors, locked entrance, or controlled roadway access to the facility).

[*Comment:* The requirements of paragraph (b) of this section are satisfied if the facility or plant within which the active portion is located itself has a surveillance system, or a barrier and a means to control entry, which complies with the requirements of paragraph (b)(1) or (2) of this section.]

(c) Unless exempt under paragraphs (a)(1) and (a)(2) of this section, a sign with the legend, "Danger—Unauthorized Personnel Keep Out," must be posted at each entrance to the active portion of a facility, and at other locations, in sufficient numbers to be seen from any approach to this active portion. The legend must be written in English and in any other language predominant in the area surrounding the facility (*e.g.*, facilities in counties bordering the Canadian province of Quebec must post signs in French; facilities in counties bordering Mexico must post signs in Spanish), and must be legible from a distance of at least 25 feet. Existing signs with a legend other than "Danger—Unauthorized Personnel Keep Out" may be used if the legend on the sign indicates that only authorized personnel are allowed to enter the active portion, and that entry onto the active portion can be dangerous.

[*Comment:* See §265.117(b) for discussion of security requirements at disposal facilities during the post-closure care period.]

[45 FR 33232, May 19, 1980, as amended at 71 FR 40274, July 14, 2006]

§265.15 General inspection requirements.

(a) The owner or operator must inspect his facility for malfunctions and deterioration, operator errors, and discharges which may be causing—or may lead to: (1) Release of hazardous waste constituents to the environment or (2) a threat to human health. The owner or operator must conduct these inspections often enough to identify problems in time to correct them before they harm human health or the environment.

(b)(1) The owner or operator must develop and follow a written schedule for inspecting all monitoring equipment, safety and emergency equipment, security devices, and operating and structural equipment (such as dikes and sump pumps) that are important to preventing, detecting, or responding to environmental or human health hazards.

(2) He must keep this schedule at the facility.

(3) The schedule must identify the types of problems (*e.g.*, malfunctions or deterioration) which are to be looked for during the inspection (*e.g.*, inoperative sump pump, leaking fitting, eroding dike, etc.).

(4) The frequency of inspection may vary for the items on the schedule. However, the frequency should be based on the rate of deterioration of the equipment and the probability of an environmental or human health incident if the deterioration, malfunction, or operator error goes undetected between inspections. Areas subject to spills, such as loading and unloading areas, must be inspected daily when in use, except for Performance Track member facilities, that must inspect at least once each month, upon approval by the Director, as described in paragraph (b)(5) of this section. At a minimum, the inspection schedule must include the items and frequencies called for in §§265.174, 265.193, 265.195, 265.226, 265.260, 265.278, 265.304, 265.347, 265.377, 265.403, 265.1033, 265.1052, 265.1053, 265.1058, and 265.1084 through 265.1090, where applicable.

(5) Performance Track member facilities that choose to reduce inspection frequencies must:

(i) Submit an application to the Director. The application must identify the facility as a member of the National Environmental Performance Track Program and identify the management units for reduced inspections and the proposed frequency of inspections. Inspections must be conducted at least once each month.

(ii) Within 60 days, the Director will notify the Performance Track member facility, in writing, if the application is approved, denied, or if an extension to the 60-day deadline is needed. This notice must be placed in the facility's operating record. The Performance Track member facility should consider the application approved if the Director does not: (1) Deny the application; or (2) notify the Performance Track member facility of an extension to the 60-day deadline. In these situations, the Performance Track member facility must adhere to the revised inspection schedule outlined in its application and maintain a copy of the application in the facility's operating record.

(iii) Any Performance Track member facility that discontinues its membership or is terminated from the program must immediately notify the Director of its change in status. The facility must place in its operating record a dated copy of this notification and revert back to the non-Performance Track inspection frequencies within seven calendar days.

(c) The owner or operator must remedy any deterioration or malfunction of equipment or structures which the inspection reveals on a schedule which ensures that the problem does not lead to an environmental or human health hazard. Where a hazard is imminent or has already occurred, remedial action must be taken immediately.

(d) The owner or operator must record inspections in an inspection log or summary. He must keep these records for at least three years from the date of inspection. At a minimum, these records must include the date and time of the inspection, the name of the inspector, a notation of the observations made, and the date and nature of any repairs or other remedial actions. 📖 6.7.5, 9.6, 10.5

[45 FR 33232, May 19, 1980, as amended at 50 FR 4514, Jan. 31, 1985; 57 FR 3491, Jan. 29, 1992; 59 FR 62935, Dec. 6, 1994; 62 FR 64661, Dec. 8, 1997; 71 FR 16908, Apr. 4, 2006]

§265.16 Personnel training. 📖 6.4.1, 6.4.4, 16.1.1

(a)(1) Facility personnel must successfully complete a program of classroom instruction or on-the-job training that teaches them to perform their duties in a way that ensures the facility's compliance with the requirements of this part. The owner or operator must ensure that this program includes all the elements described in the document required under paragraph (d)(3) of this section. 📖 6.4.1.1, 6.5.4

(2) This program must be directed by a person trained in hazardous waste management procedures, and must include instruction which teaches facility personnel hazardous waste management procedures (including contingency plan implementation) relevant to the positions in which they are employed. 📖 6.4.1.3–4

(3) At a minimum, the training program must be designed to ensure that facility personnel are able to respond effectively to emergencies by familiarizing them with emergency procedures, emergency equipment, and emergency systems, including where applicable: 📖 6.4.1.3, 14.4.11.1–2

(i) Procedures for using, inspecting, repairing, and replacing facility emergency and monitoring equipment;

(ii) Key parameters for automatic waste feed cut-off systems;

(iii) Communications or alarm systems;

(iv) Response to fires or explosions;

(v) Response to ground-water contamination incidents; and

(vi) Shutdown of operations.

(4) For facility employees that receive emergency response training pursuant to Occupational Safety and Health Administration (OSHA) regulations 29 CFR 1910.120(p)(8) and 1910.120(q), the facility is not required to provide separate emergency response training pursuant to this section, provided that the overall facility training meets all the requirements of this section.

(b) Facility personnel must successfully complete the program required in paragraph (a) of this section within six months after the effective date of these regulations or six months after the date of their employment or assignment to a facility, or to a new position at a facility, whichever is later. Employees hired after the effective date of these regulations must not work in unsupervised positions until they have completed the training requirements of paragraph (a) of this section. 📖 6.4.1.2

(c) Facility personnel must take part in an annual review of the initial training required in paragraph (a) of this section. 📖 6.4.1.2

(d) The owner or operator must maintain the following documents and records at the facility: 📖 6.4.1.5

(1) The job title for each position at the facility related to hazardous waste management, and the name of the employee filling each job;

(2) A written job description for each position listed under paragraph (d)(1) of this Section. This description may be consistent in its degree of specificity with descriptions for other similar positions in the same company location or bargaining unit, but must include the requisite skill, education, or other qualifications, and duties of facility personnel assigned to each position;

(3) A written description of the type and amount of both introductory and continuing training that will be given to each person filling a position listed under paragraph (d)(1) of this section;

(4) Records that document that the training or job experience required under paragraphs (a), (b), and (c) of this section has been given to, and completed by, facility personnel.

(e) Training records on current personnel must be kept until closure of the facility. Training records on former employees must be kept for at least three years from the date the employee last worked at the facility. Personnel training records may accompany personnel transferred within the same company. 📖 6.4.1.5, 6.7.6

[45 FR 33232, May 19, 1980, as amended at 50 FR 4514, Jan. 31, 1985; 71 FR 16908, Apr. 4, 2006; 71 FR 40274, July 14, 2006]

§265.17 General requirements for ignitable, reactive, or incompatible wastes.

(a) The owner or operator must take precautions to prevent accidental ignition or reaction of ignitable or reactive waste. This waste must be separated and protected from sources of ignition or reaction including but not limited to: Open flames, smoking, cutting and welding, hot surfaces, frictional heat, sparks (static, electrical, or mechanical), spontaneous ignition (*e.g.,* from heat-producing chemical reactions), and radiant heat. While ignitable or reactive waste is being handled, the owner or operator must confine smoking and open flame to specially designated locations. "No Smoking" signs must be conspicuously placed wherever there is a hazard from ignitable or reactive waste.

(b) Where specifically required by other sections of this part, the treatment, storage, or disposal of ignitable or reactive waste, and the mixture or commingling of incompatible wastes, or incompatible wastes and materials, must be conducted so that it does not:

(1) Generate extreme heat or pressure, fire or explosion, or violent reaction;

(2) Produce uncontrolled toxic mists, fumes, dusts, or gases in sufficient quantities to threaten human health;

(3) Produce uncontrolled flammable fumes or gases in sufficient quantities to pose a risk of fire or explosions;

(4) Damage the structural integrity of the device or facility containing the waste; or

(5) Through other like means threaten human health or the environment.

§265.18 Location standards.

The placement of any hazardous waste in a salt dome, salt bed formation, underground mine or cave is prohibited, except for the Department of Energy Waste Isolation Pilot Project in New Mexico.

[50 FR 28749, July 15, 1985]

§265.19 Construction quality assurance program.

(a) *CQA program.* (1) A construction quality assurance (CQA) program is required for all surface impoundment, waste pile, and landfill units that are required to comply with §§265.221(a), 265.254, and 265.301(a). The program must ensure that the constructed unit meets or exceeds all design criteria and specifications in the permit. The program must be developed and implemented under the direction of a CQA officer who is a registered professional engineer.

(2) The CQA program must address the following physical components, where applicable:

(i) Foundations;

(ii) Dikes;

(iii) Low-permeability soil liners;

(iv) Geomembranes (flexible membrane liners);

(v) Leachate collection and removal systems and leak detection systems; and

(vi) Final cover systems.

(b) *Written CQA plan.* Before construction begins on a unit subject to the CQA program under paragraph (a) of this section, the owner or operator must develop a written CQA plan. The plan must identify steps that will be used to monitor and document the quality of materials and the condition and manner of their installation. The CQA plan must include:

(1) Identification of applicable units, and a description of how they will be constructed.

(2) Identification of key personnel in the development and implementation of the CQA plan, and CQA officer qualifications.

(3) A description of inspection and sampling activities for all unit components identified in paragraph (a)(2) of this section, including observations and tests that will be used before, during, and after construction to ensure that the construction materials and the installed unit components meet the design specifications. The description must cover: Sampling size and locations; frequency of testing; data evaluation procedures; acceptance and rejection criteria for construction materials; plans for implementing corrective measures; and data or other information to be recorded and retained in the operating record under §265.73.

(c) *Contents of program.* (1) The CQA program must include observations, inspections, tests, and measurements sufficient to ensure:

(i) Structural stability and integrity of all components of the unit identified in paragraph (a)(2) of this section;

(ii) Proper construction of all components of the liners, leachate collection and removal system, leak detection system, and final cover system, according to permit specifications and good engineering practices, and proper installation of all components (*e.g.,* pipes) according to design specifications;

(iii) Conformity of all materials used with design and other material specifications under §§264.221, 264.251, and 264.301 of this chapter.

(2) The CQA program shall include test fills for compacted soil liners, using the same compaction methods as in the full-scale unit, to ensure that the liners are constructed to meet the hydraulic conductivity requirements of §§264.221(c)(1), 264.251(c)(1), and 264.301(c)(1) of this chapter in the field. Compliance with the hydraulic

conductivity requirements must be verified by using in-situ testing on the constructed test fill. The test fill requirement is waived where data are sufficient to show that a constructed soil liner meets the hydraulic conductivity requirements of §§264.221(c)(1), §264.251(c)(1), and 264.301(c)(1) of this chapter in the field.

(d) *Certification*. The owner or operator of units subject to §265.19 must submit to the Regional Administrator by certified mail or hand delivery, at least 30 days prior to receiving waste, a certification signed by the CQA officer that the CQA plan has been successfully carried out and that the unit meets the requirements of §§265.221(a), 265.254, or 265.301(a). The owner or operator may receive waste in the unit after 30 days from the Regional Administrator's receipt of the CQA certification unless the Regional Administrator determines in writing that the construction is not acceptable, or extends the review period for a maximum of 30 more days, or seeks additional information from the owner or operator during this period. Documentation supporting the CQA officer's certification must be furnished to the Regional Administrator upon request.

[57 FR 3491, Jan. 29, 1992, as amended at 71 FR 40274, July 14, 2006]

Subpart C—Preparedness and Prevention 📖 6.3.7

§265.30 Applicability.

The regulations in this subpart apply to owners and operators of all hazardous waste facilities, except as §265.1 provides otherwise.

§265.31 Maintenance and operation of facility. 📖 6.3.7

Facilities must be maintained and operated to minimize the possibility of a fire, explosion, or any unplanned sudden or non-sudden release of hazardous waste or hazardous waste constituents to air, soil, or surface water which could threaten human health or the environment.

§265.32 Required equipment.

All facilities must be equipped with the following, unless none of the hazards posed by waste handled at the facility could require a particular kind of equipment specified below:

(a) An internal communications or alarm system capable of providing immediate emergency instruction (voice or signal) to facility personnel;

(b) A device, such as a telephone (immediately available at the scene of operations) or a hand-held two-way radio, capable of summoning emergency assistance from local police departments, fire departments, or State or local emergency response teams;

(c) Portable fire extinguishers, fire control equipment (including special extinguishing equipment, such as that using foam, inert gas, or dry chemicals), spill control equipment, and decontamination equipment; and

(d) Water at adequate volume and pressure to supply water hose streams, or foam producing equipment, or automatic sprinklers, or water spray systems.

§265.33 Testing and maintenance of equipment.

All facility communications or alarm systems, fire protection equipment, spill control equipment, and decontamination equipment, where required, must be tested and maintained as necessary to assure its proper operation in time of emergency.

§265.34 Access to communications or alarm system.

(a) Whenever hazardous waste is being poured, mixed, spread, or otherwise handled, all personnel involved in the operation must have immediate access to an internal alarm or emergency communication device, either directly or through visual or voice contact with another employee, unless such a device is not required under §265.32.

(b) If there is ever just one employee on the premises while the facility is operating, he must have immediate access to a device, such as a telephone (immediately available at the scene of operation) or a hand-held two-way radio, capable of summoning external emergency assistance, unless such a device is not required under §265.32.

§265.35 Required aisle space. 📖 6.3.7

The owner or operator must maintain aisle space to allow the unobstructed movement of personnel, fire protection equipment, spill control equipment, and decontamination equipment to any area of facility operation in an emergency, unless aisle space is not needed for any of these purposes.

§265.36 [Reserved]

§265.37 Arrangements with local authorities. 📖 6.3.7, 6.7.7

(a) The owner or operator must attempt to make the following arrangements, as appropriate for the type of waste handled at his facility and the potential need for the services of these organizations:

(1) Arrangements to familiarize police, fire departments, and emergency response teams with the layout of the facility, properties of hazardous waste handled at the facility and associated hazards, places where facility personnel would normally be working, entrances

to roads inside the facility, and possible evacuation routes;

(2) Where more than one police and fire department might respond to an emergency, agreements designating primary emergency authority to a specific police and a specific fire department, and agreements with any others to provide support to the primary emergency authority;

(3) Agreements with State emergency response teams, emergency response contractors, and equipment suppliers; and

(4) Arrangements to familiarize local hospitals with the properties of hazardous waste handled at the facility and the types of injuries or illnesses which could result from fires, explosions, or releases at the facility.

(b) Where State or local authorities decline to enter into such arrangements, the owner or operator must document the refusal in the operating record.

Subpart D—Contingency Plan and Emergency Procedures

§265.50 Applicability.

The regulations in this subpart apply to owners and operators of all hazardous waste facilities, except as §265.1 provides otherwise. 📖 6.3.8, 14.4.2.1–2

§265.51 Purpose and implementation of contingency plan.

(a) Each owner or operator must have a contingency plan for his facility. The contingency plan must be designed to minimize hazards to human health or the environment from fires, explosions, or any unplanned sudden or non-sudden release of hazardous waste or hazardous waste constituents to air, soil, or surface water.

(b) The provisions of the plan must be carried out immediately whenever there is a fire, explosion, or release of hazardous waste or hazardous waste constituents which could threaten human health or the environment.

[45 FR 33232, May 19, 1980, as amended at 50 FR 4514, Jan. 31, 1985]

§265.52 Content of contingency plan. 📖 6.3.8, 6.7.8

(a) The contingency plan must describe the actions facility personnel must take to comply with §§265.51 and 265.56 in response to fires, explosions, or any unplanned sudden or non-sudden release of hazardous waste or hazardous waste constituents to air, soil, or surface water at the facility.

(b) If the owner or operator has already prepared a Spill Prevention, Control, and Countermeasures (SPCC) Plan in accordance with Part 112 of this chapter, or Part 1510 of chapter V, or some other emergency or contingency plan, he need only amend that plan to incorporate hazardous waste management provisions that are sufficient to comply with the requirements of this Part. The owner or operator may develop one contingency plan which meets all regulatory requirements. EPA recommends that the plan be based on the National Response Team's Integrated Contingency Plan Guidance ("One Plan"). When modifications are made to non-RCRA provisions in an integrated contingency plan, the changes do not trigger the need for a RCRA permit modification. 📖 6.7.8

(c) The plan must describe arrangements agreed to by local police departments, fire departments, hospitals, contractors, and State and local emergency response teams to coordinate emergency services, pursuant to §265.37.

(d) The plan must list names, addresses, and phone numbers (office and home) of all persons qualified to act as emergency coordinator (see §265.55), and this list must be kept up to date. Where more than one person is listed, one must be named as primary emergency coordinator and others must be listed in the order in which they will assume responsibility as alternates. 📖 16.1.2

(e) The plan must include a list of all emergency equipment at the facility (such as fire extinguishing systems, spill control equipment, communications and alarm systems (internal and external), and decontamination equipment), where this equipment is required. This list must be kept up to date. In addition, the plan must include the location and a physical description of each item on the list, and a brief outline of its capabilities.

(f) The plan must include an evacuation plan for facility personnel where there is a possibility that evacuation could be necessary. This plan must describe signal(s) to be used to begin evacuation, evacuation routes, and alternate evacuation routes (in cases where the primary routes could be blocked by releases of hazardous waste or fires).

[45 FR 33232, May 19, 1980, as amended at 46 FR 27480, May 20, 1981; 50 FR 4514, Jan. 31, 1985; 71 FR 16908, Apr. 4, 2006]

§265.53 Copies of contingency plan.

A copy of the contingency plan and all revisions to the plan must be:

(a) Maintained at the facility; and

(b) Submitted to all local police departments, fire departments, hospitals, and State and local emergency response teams that may be called upon to provide emergency services.

[45 FR 33232, May 19, 1980, as amended at 50 FR 4514, Jan. 31, 1985]

§265.54 Amendment of contingency plan. 📖 6.7.8

The contingency plan must be reviewed, and immediately amended, if necessary, whenever:

(a) Applicable regulations are revised;

(b) The plan fails in an emergency;

(c) The facility changes—in its design, construction, operation, maintenance, or other circumstances—in a way that materially increases the potential for fires, explosions, or releases of hazardous waste or hazardous waste constituents, or changes the response necessary in an emergency;

(d) The list of emergency coordinators changes; or

(e) The list of emergency equipment changes.

[45 FR 33232, May 19, 1980, as amended at 50 FR 4514, Jan. 31, 1985]

§265.55 Emergency coordinator. 📖 6.3.8

At all times, there must be at least one employee either on the facility premises or on call (*i.e.*, available to respond to an emergency by reaching the facility within a short period of time) with the responsibility for coordinating all emergency response measures. This emergency coordinator must be thoroughly familiar with all aspects of the facility's contingency plan, all operations and activities at the facility, the location and characteristics of waste handled, the location of all records within the facility, and the facility layout. In addition, this person must have the authority to commit the resources needed to carry out the contingency plan.

[*Comment:* The emergency coordinator's responsibilities are more fully spelled out in §265.56. Applicable responsibilities for the emergency coordinator vary, depending on factors such as type and variety of waste(s) handled by the facility, and type and complexity of the facility.]

§265.56 Emergency procedures. 📖 6.3.8

(a) Whenever there is an imminent or actual emergency situation, the emergency coordinator (or his designee when the emergency coordinator is on call) must immediately:

(1) Activate internal facility alarms or communication systems, where applicable, to notify all facility personnel; and

(2) Notify appropriate State or local agencies with designated response roles if their help is needed.

(b) Whenever there is a release, fire, or explosion, the emergency coordinator must immediately identify the character, exact source, amount, and areal extent of any released materials. He may do this by observation or review of facility records or manifests and, if necessary, by chemical analysis.

(c) Concurrently, the emergency coordinator must assess possible hazards to human health or the environment that may result from the release, fire, or explosion. This assessment must consider both direct and indirect effects of the release, fire, or explosion (*e.g.*, the effects of any toxic, irritating, or asphyxiating gases that are generated, or the effects of any hazardous surface water run-offs from water or chemical agents used to control fire and heat-induced explosions).

(d) If the emergency coordinator determines that the facility has had a release, fire, or explosion which could threaten human health, or the environment, outside the facility, he must report his findings as follows: 📖 6.7.8, 14.4.10

(1) If his assessment indicates that evacuation of local areas may be advisable, he must immediately notify appropriate local authorities. He must be available to help appropriate officials decide whether local areas should be evacuated; and

(2) He must immediately notify either the government official designated as the on-scene coordinator for that geographical area (in the applicable regional contingency plan under part 1510 of this title), or the National Response Center (using their 24-hour toll free number 800/424-8802). The report must include:

(i) Name and telephone number of reporter;

(ii) Name and address of facility;

(iii) Time and type of incident (*e.g.*, release, fire);

(iv) Name and quantity of material(s) involved, to the extent known;

(v) The extent of injuries, if any; and

(vi) The possible hazards to human health, or the environment, outside the facility.

(e) During an emergency, the emergency coordinator must take all reasonable measures necessary to ensure that fires, explosions, and releases do not occur, recur, or spread to other hazardous waste at the facility. These measures must include, where applicable, stopping processes and operations, collecting and containing released waste, and removing or isolating containers.

(f) If the facility stops operations in response to a fire, explosion or release, the emergency coordinator must monitor for leaks, pressure buildup, gas generation, or ruptures in valves, pipes, or other equipment, wherever this is appropriate.

(g) Immediately after an emergency, the emergency coordinator must provide for treating, storing, or disposing of recovered waste, contaminated soil or surface water, or any other material that results from a release, fire, or explosion at the facility.

[*Comment:* Unless the owner or operator can demonstrate, in accordance with §261.3(c) or (d) of this chapter, that the recovered material is not a hazardous waste, the owner or operator becomes a generator of hazardous waste and must manage it in accordance with all applicable requirements of parts 262, 263, and 265 of this chapter.]

(h) The emergency coordinator must ensure that, in the affected area(s) of the facility:

(1) No waste that may be incompatible with the released material is treated, stored, or disposed of until cleanup procedures are completed; and

(2) All emergency equipment listed in the contingency plan is cleaned and fit for its intended use before operations are resumed.

(i) The owner or operator must note in the operating record the time, date, and details of any incident that requires implementing the contingency plan. Within 15 days after the incident, he must submit a written report on the incident to the Regional Administrator. The report must include:

(1) Name, address, and telephone number of the owner or operator;

(2) Name, address, and telephone number of the facility;

(3) Date, time, and type of incident (*e.g.*, fire, explosion);

(4) Name and quantity of material(s) involved;

(5) The extent of injuries, if any;

(6) An assessment of actual or potential hazards to human health or the environment, where this is applicable; and

(7) Estimated quantity and disposition of recovered material that resulted from the incident.

[45 FR 33232, May 19, 1980, as amended at 50 FR 4514, Jan. 31, 1985; 71 FR 16908, Apr. 4, 2006; 71 FR 40274, July 14, 2006]

Subpart E—Manifest System, Recordkeeping, and Reporting

§265.70 Applicability.

(a) The regulations in this subpart apply to owners and operators of both on-site and off-site facilities, except as §265.1 provides otherwise. Sections 265.71, 265.72, and 265.76 do not apply to owners and operators of on-site facilities that do not receive any hazardous waste from off-site sources, nor to owners and operators of off-site facilities with respect to waste military munitions exempted from manifest requirements under 40 CFR 266.203(a).

(b) The revised Manifest form and procedures in 40 CFR 260.10, 261.7, 265.70, 265.71. 265.72, and 265.76, shall not apply until September 5, 2006. The Manifest form and procedures in 40 CFR 260.10, 261.7, 265.70, 265.71. 265.72, and 265.76, contained in the 40 CFR, parts 260 to 265, edition revised as of July 1, 2004, shall be applicable until September 5, 2006.

[70 FR 10823, Mar. 4, 2005]

§265.71 Use of manifest system.

📖 6.6

(a)(1) If a facility receives hazardous waste accompanied by a manifest, the owner, operator or his/her agent must sign and date the manifest as indicated in paragraph (a)(2) of this section to certify that the hazardous waste covered by the manifest was received, that the hazardous waste was received except as noted in the discrepancy space of the manifest, or that the hazardous waste was rejected as noted in the manifest discrepancy space.

(2) If a facility receives a hazardous waste shipment accompanied by a manifest, the owner, operator or his/her agent must:

(i) Sign and date, by hand, each copy of the manifest;

(ii) Note any discrepancies (as defined in §265.72(a)) on each copy of the manifest;

(iii) Immediately give the transporter at least one copy of the manifest;

(iv) Within 30 days of delivery, send a copy of the manifest to the generator; and

(v) Retain at the facility a copy of each manifest for at least three years from the date of delivery.

(3) If a facility receives hazardous waste imported from a foreign source, the receiving facility must mail a copy of the manifest to the following address within 30 days of delivery: International Compliance Assurance Division, OFA/OECA (2254A), U.S. Environmental Protection Agency, Ariel Rios Building, 1200 Pennsylvania Avenue, NW., Washington, DC 20460.

(b) If a facility receives, from a rail or water (bulk shipment) transporter, hazardous waste which is accompanied by a shipping paper containing all the information required on the manifest (excluding the EPA identification numbers, generator's certification, and signatures), the owner or operator, or his agent, must:

(1) Sign and date each copy of the manifest or shipping paper (if the manifest has not been received) to certify that the hazardous waste covered by the manifest or shipping paper was received;

(2) Note any significant discrepancies (as defined in §265.72(a)) in the manifest or shipping paper (if the

manifest has not been received) on each copy of the manifest or shipping paper;

[*Comment*: The Agency does not intend that the owner or operator of a facility whose procedures under §265.13(c) include waste analysis must perform that analysis before signing the shipping paper and giving it to the transporter. Section 265.72(b), however, requires reporting an unreconciled discrepancy discovered during later analysis.]

(3) Immediately give the rail or water (bulk shipment) transporter at least one copy of the manifest or shipping paper (if the manifest has not been received);

(4) Within 30 days after the delivery, send a copy of the signed and dated manifest or a signed and dated copy of the shipping paper (if the manifest has not been received within 30 days after delivery) to the generator; and

[*Comment:* Section 262.23(c) of this chapter requires the generator to send three copies of the manifest to the facility when hazardous waste is sent by rail or water (bulk shipment).]

(5) Retain at the facility a copy of the manifest and shipping paper (if signed in lieu of the manifest at the time of delivery) for at least three years from the date of delivery.

(c) Whenever a shipment of hazardous waste is initiated from a facility, the owner or operator of that facility must comply with the requirements of part 262 of this chapter.

[*Comment:* The provisions of §262.34 are applicable to the on-site accumulation of hazardous wastes by generators. Therefore, the provisions of §262.34 only apply to owners or operators who are shipping hazardous waste which they generated at that facility.]

(d) Within three working days of the receipt of a shipment subject to 40 CFR part 262, subpart H, the owner or operator of facility must provide a copy of the tracking document bearing all required signatures to the notifier, to the Office of Enforcement and Compliance Assurance, Office of Compliance, Enforcement Planning, Targeting and Data Division (2222A), Environmental Protection Agency, 1200 Pennsylvania Ave., NW., Washington, DC 20460, and to competent authorities of all other concerned countries. The original copy of the tracking document must be maintained at the facility for at least three years from the date of signature.

(e) A facility must determine whether the consignment state for a shipment regulates any additional wastes (beyond those regulated Federally) as hazardous wastes under its state hazardous waste program. Facilities must also determine whether the consignment state or generator state requires the facility to submit any copies of the manifest to these states.

[45 FR 33232, May 19, 1980, as amended at 45 FR 86970, 86974, Dec. 31, 1980; 50 FR 4514, Jan. 31, 1985; 61 FR 16315, Apr. 12, 1996; 70 FR 10823, Mar. 4, 2005]

§265.72 Manifest discrepancies.

📖 6.6.3.12, 9.5.6.1

(a) Manifest discrepancies are:

(1) Significant differences (as defined by paragraph (b) of this section) between the quantity or type of hazardous waste designated on the manifest or shipping paper, and the quantity and type of hazardous waste a facility actually receives;

(2) Rejected wastes, which may be a full or partial shipment of hazardous waste that the TSDF cannot accept; or

(3) Container residues, which are residues that exceed the quantity limits for "empty" containers set forth in 40 CFR 261.7(b).

(b) Significant differences in quantity are: For bulk waste, variations greater than 10 percent in weight; for batch waste, any variation in piece count, such as a discrepancy of one drum in a truckload. Significant differences in type are obvious differences which can be discovered by inspection or waste analysis, such as waste solvent substituted for waste acid, or toxic constituents not reported on the manifest or shipping paper.

(c) Upon discovering a significant difference in quantity or type, the owner or operator must attempt to reconcile the discrepancy with the waste generator or transporter (*e.g.*, with telephone conversations). If the discrepancy is not resolved within 15 days after receiving the waste, the owner or operator must immediately submit to the Regional Administrator a letter describing the discrepancy and attempts to reconcile it, and a copy of the manifest or shipping paper at issue.

(d)(1) Upon rejecting waste or identifying a container residue that exceeds the quantity limits for "empty" containers set forth in 40 CFR 261.7(b), the facility must consult with the generator prior to forwarding the waste to another facility that can manage the waste. If it is impossible to locate an alternative facility that can receive the waste, the facility may return the rejected waste or residue to the generator. The facility must send the waste to the alternative facility or to the generator within 60 days of the rejection or the container residue identification.

(2) While the facility is making arrangements for forwarding rejected wastes or residues to another facility under this section, it must ensure that either the delivering transporter retains custody of the waste, or the facility must provide for secure, temporary custody of

the waste, pending delivery of the waste to the first transporter designated on the manifest prepared under paragraph (e) or (f) of this section.

(e) Except as provided in paragraph (e)(7) of this section, for full or partial load rejections and residues that are to be sent off-site to an alternate facility, the facility is required to prepare a new manifest in accordance with §262.20(a) of this chapter and the following instructions:

(1) Write the generator's U.S. EPA ID number in Item 1 of the new manifest. Write the generator's name and mailing address in Item 5 of the new manifest. If the mailing address is different from the generator's site address, then write the generator's site address in the designated space in Item 5.

(2) Write the name of the alternate designated facility and the facility's U.S. EPA ID number in the designated facility block (Item 8) of the new manifest.

(3) Copy the manifest tracking number found in Item 4 of the old manifest to the Special Handling and Additional Information Block of the new manifest, and indicate that the shipment is a residue or rejected waste from the previous shipment.

(4) Copy the manifest tracking number found in Item 4 of the new manifest to the manifest reference number line in the Discrepancy Block of the old manifest (Item 18a).

(5) Write the DOT description for the rejected load or the residue in Item 9 (U.S. DOT Description) of the new manifest and write the container types, quantity, and volume(s) of waste.

(6) Sign the Generator's/Offeror's Certification to certify, as the offeror of the shipment, that the waste has been properly packaged, marked and labeled and is in proper condition for transportation.

(7) For full load rejections that are made while the transporter remains present at the facility, the facility may forward the rejected shipment to the alternate facility by completing Item 18b of the original manifest and supplying the information on the next destination facility in the Alternate Facility space. The facility must retain a copy of this manifest for its records, and then give the remaining copies of the manifest to the transporter to accompany the shipment. If the original manifest is not used, then the facility must use a new manifest and comply with paragraphs (e)(1), (2), (3), (4), (5), and (6) of this section.

(f) Except as provided in paragraph (f)(7) of this section, for rejected wastes and residues that must be sent back to the generator, the facility is required to prepare a new manifest in accordance with §262.20(a) of this chapter and the following instructions:

(1) Write the facility's U.S. EPA ID number in Item 1 of the new manifest. Write the generator's name and mailing address in Item 5 of the new manifest. If the mailing address is different from the generator's site address, then write the generator's site address in the designated space for Item 5.

Publisher's Note: EPA's intention is to require the designated facility to enter its own information in Item 5, not the generator's name and mailing address, since the designated facility originates the shipment of rejected wastes. The generator's information should go in Item 8. The agency also intends to make this correction to the regulations in a formal rulemaking but hasn't done so as of the printing of this book. [May 14, 2007 memo from Matt Hale to EPA regional waste directors]

(2) Write the name of the initial generator and the generator's U.S. EPA ID number in the designated facility block (Item 8) of the new manifest.

(3) Copy the manifest tracking number found in Item 4 of the old manifest to the Special Handling and Additional Information Block of the new manifest, and indicate that the shipment is a residue or rejected waste from the previous shipment,

(4) Copy the manifest tracking number found in Item 4 of the new manifest to the manifest reference number line in the Discrepancy Block of the old manifest (Item 18a),

(5) Write the DOT description for the rejected load or the residue in Item 9 (U.S. DOT Description) of the new manifest and write the container types, quantity, and volume(s) of waste.

(6) Sign the Generator's/Offeror's Certification to certify, as offeror of the shipment, that the waste has been properly packaged, marked and labeled and is in proper condition for transportation,

(7) For full load rejections that are made while the transporter remains at the facility, the facility may return the shipment to the generator with the original manifest by completing Item 18b of the manifest and supplying the generator's information in the Alternate Facility space. The facility must retain a copy for its records and then give the remaining copies of the manifest to the transporter to accompany the shipment. If the original manifest is not used, then the facility must use a new manifest and comply with paragraphs (f)(1), (2), (3), (4), (5), and (6) of this section.

(g) If a facility rejects a waste or identifies a container residue that exceeds the quantity limits for "empty" containers set forth in 40 CFR 261.7(b) after it has signed, dated, and returned a copy of the manifest to the delivering transporter or to the generator, the facility must amend its copy of the manifest to indicate the rejected wastes or residues in the discrepancy space of the amended manifest. The facility must also copy the manifest tracking number from Item 4 of the new manifest to the discrepancy space of the amended manifest, and must re-sign and date the manifest to certify to the information as amended. The facility must retain the amended manifest for at least three years from the date of amendment, and must within 30 days, send a copy of the amended manifest to the transporter and generator that received copies prior to their being amended.

[45 FR 33232, May 19, 1980, as amended at 50 FR 4514, Jan. 31, 1985; 70 FR 10823, Mar. 4, 2005; 70 FR 35041, June 16, 2005]

§265.73 Operating record.

(a) The owner or operator must keep a written operating record at his facility.

(b) The following information must be recorded, as it becomes available, and maintained in the operating record for three years unless noted below:

(1) A description and the quantity of each hazardous waste received, and the method(s) and date(s) of its treatment, storage, or disposal at the facility as required by Appendix I to part 265. This information must be maintained in the operating record until closure of the facility;

(2) The location of each hazardous waste within the facility and the quantity at each location. For disposal facilities, the location and quantity of each hazardous waste must be recorded on a map or diagram of each cell or disposal area. For all facilities, this information must include cross-references to manifest document numbers if the waste was accompanied by a manifest. This information must be maintained in the operating record until closure of the facility;

[*Comment:* See §§265.119, 265.279, and 265.309 for related requirements.]

(3) Records and results of waste analysis, waste determinations, and trial tests performed as specified in §§265.13, 265.200, 265.225, 265.252, 265.273, 265.314, 265.341, 265.375, 265.402, 265.1034, 265.1063, 265.1084, 268.4(a), and 268.7 of this chapter.

(4) Summary reports and details of all incidents that require implementing the contingency plan as specified in §265.56(j);

Publisher's Note: The above reference to §265.56(j) is incorrect and should refer to §265.56(i).

(5) Records and results of inspections as required by §265.15(d) (except these data need be kept only three years);

(6) Monitoring, testing or analytical data, and corrective action where required by subpart F of this part and by §§265.19, 265.94, 265.191, 265.193, 265.195, 265.224, 265.226, 265.255, 265.260, 265.276, 265.278, 265.280(d)(1), 265.302, 265.304, 265.347, 265.377, 265.1034(c) through 265.1034(f), 265.1035, 265.1063(d) through 265. 265.1063(i), 265.1064, and 265.1083 through 265.1090. Maintain in the operating record for three years, except for records and results pertaining to ground-water monitoring and cleanup, and response action plans for surface impoundments, waste piles, and landfills, which must be maintained in the operating record until closure of the facility.

[*Comment:* As required by §265.94, monitoring data at disposal facilities must be kept throughout the post-closure period.]

(7) All closure cost estimates under §265.142 and, for disposal facilities, all post-closure cost estimates under §265.144 must be maintained in the operating record until closure of the facility.

(8) Records of the quantities (and date of placement) for each shipment of hazardous waste placed in land disposal units under an extension to the effective date of any land disposal restriction granted pursuant to §268.5 of this chapter, monitoring data required pursuant to a petition under §268.6 of this chapter, or a certification under §268.8 of this chapter, and the applicable notice required by a generator under §268.7(a) of this chapter. All of this information must be maintained in the operating record until closure of the facility.

(9) For an off-site treatment facility, a copy of the notice, and the certification and demonstration if applicable, required by the generator or the owner or operator under §268.7 or §268.8;

(10) For an on-site treatment facility, the information contained in the notice (except the manifest number), and the certification and demonstration if applicable, required by the generator or the owner or operator under §268.7 or §268.8;

(11) For an off-site land disposal facility, a copy of the notice, and the certification and demonstration if applicable, required by the generator or the owner or operator of a treatment facility under §268.7 or §268.8;

(12) For an on-site land disposal facility, the information contained in the notice (except the manifest number), and the certification and demonstration if applicable, required by the generator or the owner or operator of a treatment facility under §268.7 or §268.8.

(13) For an off-site storage facility, a copy of the notice, and the certification and demonstration if applicable, required by the generator or the owner or operator under §268.7 or §268.8; and

(14) For an on-site storage facility, the information contained in the notice (except the manifest number), and the certification and demonstration if applicable, required by the generator or the owner or operator of a treatment facility under §268.7 or §268.8.

(15) Monitoring, testing or analytical data, and corrective action where required by §§265.90, 265.93(d)(2), and 265.93(d)(5), and the certification as required by §265.196(f) must be maintained in the operating record until closure of the facility.

[45 FR 33232, May 19, 1980, as amended at 50 FR 4514, Jan. 31, 1985; 50 FR 18374, Apr. 30, 1985; 51 FR 40638, Nov. 7, 1986; 53 FR 31211, Aug. 17, 1988; 54 FR 26648, June 23, 1989; 55 FR 25507, June 21, 1990; 56 FR 19290, Apr. 26, 1991; 57 FR 3492, Jan. 29, 1992; 59 FR 62935, Dec. 6, 1994; 62 FR 64661, Dec. 8, 1997; 71 FR 16908, Apr. 4, 2006]

§265.74 Availability, retention, and disposition of records.

(a) All records, including plans, required under this part must be furnished upon request, and made available at all reasonable times for inspection, by any officer, employee, or representative of EPA who is duly designated by the Administrator.

(b) The retention period for all records required under this part is extended automatically during the course of any unresolved enforcement action regarding the facility or as requested by the Administrator.

(c) A copy of records of waste disposal locations and quantities under §265.73(b)(2) must be submitted to the Regional Administrator and local land authority upon closure of the facility (see §265.119).

[45 FR 33232, May 19, 1980, as amended at 50 FR 4514, Jan. 31, 1985]

§265.75 Biennial report. 📖 6.8

The owner or operator must prepare and submit a single copy of a biennial report to the Regional Administrator by March 1 of each even numbered year. The biennial report must be submitted on EPA Form 8700-13B. The report must cover facility activities during the previous calendar year and must include the following information:

(a) The EPA identification number, name, and address of the facility;

(b) The calendar year covered by the report;

(c) For off-site facilities, the EPA identification number of each hazardous waste generator from which the facility received a hazardous waste during the year; for imported shipments, the report must give the name and address of the foreign generator;

(d) A description and the quantity of each hazardous waste the facility received during the year. For off-site facilities, this information must be listed by EPA identification number of each generator;

(e) The method of treatment, storage, or disposal for each hazardous waste;

(f) Monitoring data under §265.94(a)(2)(ii) and (iii), and (b)(2), where required;

(g) The most recent closure cost estimate under §265.142, and, for disposal facilities, the most recent post-closure cost estimate under §265.144; and

(h) For generators who treat, store, or dispose of hazardous waste on-site, a description of the efforts undertaken during the year to reduce the volume and toxicity of waste generated.

(i) For generators who treat, store, or dispose of hazardous waste on-site, a description of the changes in volume and toxicity of waste actually achieved during the year in comparison to previous years to the extent such information is available for the years prior to 1984.

(j) The certification signed by the owner or operator of the facility or his authorized representative.

[45 FR 33232, May 19, 1980, as amended at 48 FR 3982, Jan. 28, 1983; 50 FR 4514, Jan. 31, 1985; 51 FR 28556, Aug. 8, 1986]

§265.76 Unmanifested waste report. 📖 6.6

(a) If a facility accepts for treatment, storage, or disposal any hazardous waste from an off-site source without an accompanying manifest, or without an accompanying shipping paper as described by §263.20(e) of this chapter, and if the waste is not excluded from the manifest requirement by this chapter, then the owner or operator must prepare and submit a letter to the Regional Administrator within fifteen days after receiving the waste. The unmanifested waste report must contain the following information:

(1) The EPA identification number, name and address of the facility;

(2) The date the facility received the waste;

(3) The EPA identification number, name and address of the generator and the transporter, if available;

(4) A description and the quantity of each unmanifested hazardous waste the facility received;

(5) The method of treatment, storage, or disposal for each hazardous waste;

(6) The certification signed by the owner or operator of the facility or his authorized representative; and

(7) A brief explanation of why the waste was unmanifested, if known.

(b) [Reserved]

[45 FR 33232, May 19, 1980, as amended at 48 FR 3982, Jan. 28, 1983; 50 FR 4514, Jan. 31, 1985; 70 FR 10824, Mar. 4, 2005]

§265.77 Additional reports.

In addition to submitting the biennial report and unmanifested waste reports described in §§265.75 and 265.76, the owner or operator must also report to the Regional Administrator:

(a) Releases, fires, and explosions as specified in §265.56(j);

Publisher's Note: The above reference to §265.56(j) is incorrect and should refer to §265.56(i).

(b) Ground-water contamination and monitoring data as specified in §§265.93 and 265.94; and

(c) Facility closure as specified in §265.115.

(d) As otherwise required by Subparts AA, BB, and CC of this part.

[45 FR 33232, May 19, 1980, as amended at 48 FR 3982, Jan. 28, 1983; 55 FR 25507, June 21, 1990; 59 FR 62935, Dec. 6, 1994]

Subpart F—Ground-Water Monitoring

§265.90 Applicability.

(a) Within one year after the effective date of these regulations, the owner or operator of a surface impoundment, landfill, or land treatment facility which is used to manage hazardous waste must implement a ground-water monitoring program capable of determining the facility's impact on the quality of ground water in the uppermost aquifer underlying the facility, except as §265.1 and paragraph (c) of this section provide otherwise.

(b) Except as paragraphs (c) and (d) of this section provide otherwise, the owner or operator must install, operate, and maintain a ground-water monitoring system which meets the requirements of §265.91, and must comply with §§265.92 through 265.94. This ground-water monitoring program must be carried out during the active life of the facility, and for disposal facilities, during the post-closure care period as well.

(c) All or part of the ground-water monitoring requirements of this subpart may be waived if the owner or operator can demonstrate that there is a low potential for migration of hazardous waste or hazardous waste constituents from the facility via the uppermost aquifer to water supply wells (domestic, industrial, or agricultural) or to surface water. This demonstration must be in writing, and must be kept at the facility. This demonstration must be certified by a qualified geologist or geotechnical engineer and must establish the following:

(1) The potential for migration of hazardous waste or hazardous waste constituents from the facility to the uppermost aquifer, by an evaluation of:

(i) A water balance of precipitation, evapotranspiration, runoff, and infiltration; and

(ii) Unsaturated zone characteristics (*i.e.*, geologic materials, physical properties, and depth to ground water); and

(2) The potential for hazardous waste or hazardous waste constituents which enter the uppermost aquifer to migrate to a water supply well or surface water, by an evaluation of:

(i) Saturated zone characteristics (*i.e.*, geologic materials, physical properties, and rate of ground-water flow); and

(ii) The proximity of the facility to water supply wells or surface water.

(d) If an owner or operator assumes (or knows) that ground-water monitoring of indicator parameters in accordance with §§265.91 and 265.92 would show statistically significant increases (or decreases in the case of pH) when evaluated under §265.93(b), he may install, operate, and maintain an alternate ground-water monitoring system (other than the one described in §§265.91 and 265.92). If the owner or operator decides to use an alternate ground-water monitoring system he must:

(1) Within one year after the effective date of these regulations, develop a specific plan, certified by a qualified geologist or geotechnical engineer, which satisfies the requirements of §265.93(d)(3), for an alternate ground-water monitoring system. This plan is to be placed in the facility's operating record and maintained until closure of the facility.

(2) Not later than one year after the effective date of these regulations, initiate the determinations specified in §265.93(d)(4);

(3) Prepare a report in accordance with §265.93(d)(5) and place it in the facility's operating record and maintain until closure of the facility.

(4) Continue to make the determinations specified in §265.93(d)(4) on a quarterly basis until final closure of the facility; and

(5) Comply with the recordkeeping and reporting requirements in §265.94(b).

(e) The ground-water monitoring requirements of this subpart may be waived with respect to any surface impoundment that (1) Is used to neutralize wastes which are hazardous solely because they exhibit the corrosivity characteristic under §261.22 of this chapter or are listed as hazardous wastes in subpart D of part 261 of this chapter only for this reason, and (2) contains no other hazardous wastes, if the owner or operator can demonstrate that there is no potential for migration of hazardous wastes from the impoundment. The demonstration must establish, based upon consideration of the characteristics of the wastes and the impoundment, that the corrosive wastes will be neutralized to the extent that they no longer meet the corrosivity characteristic before they can migrate out of the impoundment. The demonstration must be in writing and must be certified by a qualified professional.

(f) The Regional Administrator may replace all or part of the requirements of this subpart applying to a regulated unit (as defined in 40 CFR 264.90), with alternative requirements developed for groundwater monitoring set out in an approved closure or post-closure plan or in an enforceable document (as defined in 40 CFR 270.1(c)(7)), where the Regional Administrator determines that:

(1) A regulated unit is situated among solid waste management units (or areas of concern), a release has occurred, and both the regulated unit and one or more solid waste management unit(s)(or areas of concern) are likely to have contributed to the release; and

(2) It is not necessary to apply the requirements of this subpart because the alternative requirements will protect human health and the environment. The alternative standards for the regulated unit must meet the requirements of 40 CFR 264.101(a).

[45 FR 33232, May 19, 1980, as amended at 47 FR 1255, Jan. 11, 1982; 50 FR 4514, Jan. 31, 1985; 63 FR 56734, Oct. 22, 1998; 71 FR 16909, Apr. 4, 2006; 71 FR 40274, July 14, 2006]

§265.91 Ground-water monitoring system.

(a) A ground-water monitoring system must be capable of yielding ground-water samples for analysis and must consist of:

(1) Monitoring wells (at least one) installed hydraulically upgradient (*i.e.*, in the direction of increasing static head) from the limit of the waste management area. Their number, locations, and depths must be sufficient to yield ground-water samples that are:

(i) Representative of background ground-water quality in the uppermost aquifer near the facility; and

(ii) Not affected by the facility; and

(2) Monitoring wells (at least three) installed hydraulically downgradient (*i.e.*, in the direction of decreasing static head) at the limit of the waste management area. Their number, locations, and depths must ensure that they immediately detect any statistically significant amounts of hazardous waste or hazardous waste constituents that migrate from the waste management area to the uppermost aquifer.

(3) The facility owner or operator may demonstrate that an alternate hydraulically downgradient monitoring well location will meet the criteria outlined below. The demonstration must be in writing and kept at the facility. The demonstration must be certified by a qualified ground-water scientist and establish that:

(i) An existing physical obstacle prevents monitoring well installation at the hydraulically downgradient limit of the waste management area; and

(ii) The selected alternate downgradient location is as close to the limit of the waste management area as practical; and

(iii) The location ensures detection that, given the alternate location, is as early as possible of any statistically significant amounts of hazardous waste or hazardous waste constituents that migrate from the waste management area to the uppermost aquifer.

(iv) Lateral expansion, new, or replacement units are not eligible for an alternate downgradient location under this paragraph.

(b) Separate monitoring systems for each waste management component of a facility are not required provided that provisions for sampling upgradient and downgradient water quality will detect any discharge from the waste management area.

(1) In the case of a facility consisting of only one surface impoundment, landfill, or land treatment area, the waste management area is described by the waste boundary (perimeter).

(2) In the case of a facility consisting of more than one surface impoundment, landfill, or land treatment area, the waste management area is described by an imaginary boundary line which circumscribes the several waste management components.

(c) All monitoring wells must be cased in a manner that maintains the integrity of the monitoring well bore hole. This casing must be screened or perforated, and packed with gravel or sand where necessary, to enable sample collection at depths where appropriate aquifer flow zones exist. The annular space (*i.e.*, the space between the bore hole and well casing) above the sampling depth must be sealed with a suitable material (*e.g.*, cement grout or bentonite slurry) to prevent contamination of samples and the ground water.

[45 FR 33232, May 19, 1980, as amended at 50 FR 4514, Jan. 31, 1985; 56 FR 66369, Dec. 23, 1991]

§265.92 Sampling and analysis.

(a) The owner or operator must obtain and analyze samples from the installed ground-water monitoring system. The owner or operator must develop and follow a ground-water sampling and analysis plan. He must keep this plan at the facility. The plan must include procedures and techniques for:

(1) Sample collection;

(2) Sample preservation and shipment;

(3) Analytical procedures; and

(4) Chain of custody control.

[*Comment:* See "Procedures Manual For Ground-water Monitoring At Solid Waste Disposal Facilities," EPA-530/SW-611, August 1977 and "Methods for Chemical Analysis of Water and Wastes," EPA-600/4-79-020, March 1979 for discussions of sampling and analysis procedures.]

(b) The owner or operator must determine the concentration or value of the following parameters in ground-water samples in accordance with paragraphs (c) and (d) of this section:

(1) Parameters characterizing the suitability of the ground water as a drinking water supply, as specified in appendix III.

(2) Parameters establishing ground-water quality:

(i) Chloride

(ii) Iron

(iii) Manganese

(iv) Phenols

(v) Sodium

(vi) Sulfate

[*Comment:* These parameters are to be used as a basis for comparison in the event a ground-water quality assessment is required under §265.93(d).]

(3) Parameters used as indicators of ground-water contamination:

(i) pH

(ii) Specific Conductance

(iii) Total Organic Carbon

(iv) Total Organic Halogen

(c)(1) For all monitoring wells, the owner or operator must establish initial background concentrations or values of all parameters specified in paragraph (b) of this section. He must do this quarterly for one year.

(2) For each of the indicator parameters specified in paragraph (b)(3) of this section, at least four replicate measurements must be obtained for each sample and the initial background arithmetic mean and variance must be determined by pooling the replicate measurements for the respective parameter concentrations or values in samples obtained from upgradient wells during the first year.

(d) After the first year, all monitoring wells must be sampled and the samples analyzed with the following frequencies:

(1) Samples collected to establish ground-water quality must be obtained and analyzed for the parameters specified in paragraph (b)(2) of this section at least annually.

(2) Samples collected to indicate ground-water contamination must be obtained and analyzed for the parameters specified in paragraph (b)(3) of this section at least semi-annually.

(e) Elevation of the ground-water surface at each monitoring well must be determined each time a sample is obtained.

[45 FR 33232, May 19, 1980, as amended at 50 FR 4514, Jan. 31, 1985]

§265.93 Preparation, evaluation, and response.

(a) Within one year after the effective date of these regulations, the owner or operator must prepare an outline of a ground-water quality assessment program. The outline must describe a more comprehensive groundwater monitoring program (than that described in §§265.91 and 265.92) capable of determining:

(1) Whether hazardous waste or hazardous waste constituents have entered the ground water;

(2) The rate and extent of migration of hazardous waste or hazardous waste constituents in the ground water; and

(3) The concentrations of hazardous waste or hazardous waste constituents in the ground water.

(b) For each indicator parameter specified in §265.92(b)(3), the owner or operator must calculate the arithmetic mean and variance, based on at least four replicate measurements on each sample, for each well monitored in accordance with §265.92(d)(2), and compare these results with its initial background arithmetic mean. The comparison must consider individually each of the wells in the monitoring system, and must use the Student's t-test at the 0.01 level of significance (see appendix IV) to determine statistically significant increases (and decreases, in the case of pH) over initial background.

(c)(1) If the comparisons for the upgradient wells made under paragraph (b) of this section show a significant increase (or pH decrease), the owner or operator must submit this information in accordance with §265.94(a)(2)(ii).

(2) If the comparisons for downgradient wells made under paragraph (b) of this section show a significant increase (or pH decrease), the owner or operator must

then immediately obtain additional ground-water samples from those downgradient wells where a significant difference was detected, split the samples in two, and obtain analyses of all additional samples to determine whether the significant difference was a result of laboratory error.

(d)(1) If the analyses performed under paragraph (c)(2) of this section confirm the significant increase (or pH decrease), the owner or operator must provide written notice to the Regional Administrator—within seven days of the date of such confirmation—that the facility may be affecting ground-water quality.

(2) Within 15 days after the notification under paragraph (d)(1) of this section, the owner or operator must develop a specific plan, based on the outline required under paragraph (a) of this section and certified by a qualified geologist or geotechnical engineer, for a ground-water quality assessment at the facility. This plan must be placed in the facility operating record and be maintained until closure of the facility.

(3) The plan to be submitted under §265.90(d)(1) or paragraph (d)(2) of this section must specify:

(i) The number, location, and depth of wells;

(ii) Sampling and analytical methods for those hazardous wastes or hazardous waste constituents in the facility;

(iii) Evaluation procedures, including any use of previously-gathered ground-water quality information; and

(iv) A schedule of implementation.

(4) The owner or operator must implement the ground-water quality assessment plan which satisfies the requirements of paragraph (d)(3) of this section, and, at a minimum, determine:

(i) The rate and extent of migration of the hazardous waste or hazardous waste constituents in the ground water; and

(ii) The concentrations of the hazardous waste or hazardous waste constituents in the ground water.

(5) The owner or operator must make his first determination under paragraph (d)(4) of this section, as soon as technically feasible, and prepare a report containing an assessment of ground-water quality. This report must be placed in the facility operating record and be maintained until closure of the facility.

(6) If the owner or operator determines, based on the results of the first determination under paragraph (d)(4) of this section, that no hazardous waste or hazardous waste constituents from the facility have entered the ground water, then he may reinstate the indicator evaluation program described in §265.92 and paragraph (b) of this section. If the owner or operator reinstates the indicator evaluation program, he must so notify the Regional Administrator in the report submitted under paragraph (d)(5) of this section.

(7) If the owner or operator determines, based on the first determination under paragraph (d)(4) of this section, that hazardous waste or hazardous waste constituents from the facility have entered the ground water, then he:

(i) Must continue to make the determinations required under paragraph (d)(4) of this section on a quarterly basis until final closure of the facility, if the ground-water quality assessment plan was implemented prior to final closure of the facility; or

(ii) May cease to make the determinations required under paragraph (d)(4) of this section, if the ground-water quality assessment plan was implemented during the post-closure care period.

(e) Notwithstanding any other provision of this subpart, any ground-water quality assessment to satisfy the requirements of §265.93(d)(4) which is initiated prior to final closure of the facility must be completed and reported in accordance with §265.93(d)(5).

(f) Unless the ground water is monitored to satisfy the requirements of §265.93(d)(4), at least annually the owner or operator must evaluate the data on ground-water surface elevations obtained under §265.92(e) to determine whether the requirements under §265.91(a) for locating the monitoring wells continues to be satisfied. If the evaluation shows that §265.91(a) is no longer satisfied, the owner or operator must immediately modify the number, location, or depth of the monitoring wells to bring the ground-water monitoring system into compliance with this requirement.

[45 FR 33232, May 19, 1980, as amended at 50 FR 4514, Jan. 31, 1985; 71 FR 16909, Apr. 4, 2006]

§265.94 Recordkeeping and reporting.

(a) Unless the ground water is monitored to satisfy the requirements of §265.93(d)(4), the owner or operator must:

(1) Keep records of the analyses required in §265.92(c) and (d), the associated ground-water surface elevations required in §265.92(e), and the evaluations required in §265.93(b) throughout the active life of the facility, and, for disposal facilities, throughout the post-closure care period as well; and

(2) Report the following ground-water monitoring information to the Regional Administrator:

(i) During the first year when initial background concentrations are being established for the facility: concentrations or values of the parameters listed in §265.92(b)(1) for each ground-water monitoring well within 15 days after completing each quarterly analysis. The owner or operator must separately identify for each monitoring well any parameters whose concentration or value has been found to exceed the maximum contaminant levels listed in appendix III.

(ii) Annually: Concentrations or values of the parameters listed in §265.92(b)(3) for each groundwater monitoring well, along with the required evaluations for these parameters under §265.93(b). The owner or operator must separately identify any significant differences from initial background found in the upgradient wells, in accordance with §265.93(c)(1). During the active life of the facility, this information must be submitted no later than March 1 following each calendar year.

(iii) No later than March 1 following each calendar year: Results of the evaluations of ground-water surface elevations under §265.93(f), and a description of the response to that evaluation, where applicable.

(b) If the ground water is monitored to satisfy the requirements of §265.93(d)(4), the owner or operator must:

(1) Keep records of the analyses and evaluations specified in the plan, which satisfies the requirements of §265.93(d)(3), throughout the active life of the facility, and, for disposal facilities, throughout the post-closure care period as well; and

(2) Annually, until final closure of the facility, submit to the Regional Administrator a report containing the results of his or her ground-water quality assessment program which includes, but is not limited to, the calculated (or measured) rate of migration of hazardous waste or hazardous waste constituents in the ground water during the reporting period. This information must be submitted no later than March 1 following each calendar year.

[45 FR 33232, May 19, 1980, as amended at 48 FR 3982, Jan. 28, 1983; 50 FR 4514, Jan. 31, 1985]

Subpart G—Closure and Post-Closure

Source: 51 FR 16451, May 2, 1986, unless otherwise noted.

§265.110 Applicability.

Except as §265.1 provides otherwise:

(a) Sections 265.111 through 265.115 (which concern closure) apply to the owners and operators of all hazardous waste management facilities; and

(b) Sections 265.116 through 265.120 (which concern post-closure care) apply to the owners and operators of:

(1) All hazardous waste disposal facilities;

(2) Waste piles and surface impoundments for which the owner or operator intends to remove the wastes at closure to the extent that these sections are made applicable to such facilities in §265.228 or §265.258;

(3) Tank systems that are required under §265.197 to meet requirements for landfills; and

(4) Containment buildings that are required under §265.1102 to meet the requirement for landfills.

(c) Section 265.121 applies to owners and operators of units that are subject to the requirements of 40 CFR 270.1(c)(7) and are regulated under an enforceable document (as defined in 40 CFR 270.1(c)(7)).

(d) The Regional Administrator may replace all or part of the requirements of this subpart (and the unit-specific standards in §265.111(c)) applying to a regulated unit (as defined in 40 CFR 264.90), with alternative requirements for closure set out in an approved closure or post-closure plan, or in an enforceable document (as defined in 40 CFR 270.1(c)(7)), where the Regional Administrator determines that:

(1) A regulated unit is situated among solid waste management units (or areas of concern), a release has occurred, and both the regulated unit and one or more solid waste management unit(s)(or areas of concern) are likely to have contributed to the release, and

(2) It is not necessary to apply the closure requirements of this subpart (and/or those referenced herein) because the alternative requirements will protect human health and the environment, and will satisfy the closure performance standard of §265.111 (a) and (b).

[51 FR 16451, May 2, 1986, as amended at 51 FR 25479, July 14, 1986; 53 FR 34086, Sept. 2, 1988; 57 FR 37267, Aug. 18, 1992; 63 FR 56734, Oct. 22, 1998; 71 FR 40274, July 14, 2006]

§265.111 Closure performance standard.

The owner or operator must close the facility in a manner that:

(a) Minimizes the need for further maintenance, and

(b) Controls, minimizes or eliminates, to the extent necessary to protect human health and the environment, post-closure escape of hazardous waste, hazardous constituents, leachate, contaminated run-off, or hazardous waste decomposition products to the ground or surface waters or to the atmosphere, and

(c) Complies with the closure requirements of this subpart, including, but not limited to, the requirements of

§§265.197, 265.228, 265.258, 265.280, 265.310, 265.351, 265.381, 265.404, and 265.1102.

[51 FR 16451, May 2, 1986, as amended at 57 FR 37267, Aug. 18, 1992; 71 FR 40275, July 14, 2006]

§265.112 Closure plan; amendment of plan.

(a) *Written plan.* By May 19, 1981, or by six months after the effective date of the rule that first subjects a facility to provisions of this section, the owner or operator of a hazardous waste management facility must have a written closure plan. Until final closure is completed and certified in accordance with §265.115, a copy of the most current plan must be furnished to the Regional Administrator upon request, including request by mail. In addition, for facilities without approved plans, it must also be provided during site inspections, on the day of inspection, to any officer, employee, or representative of the Agency who is duly designated by the Administrator.

(b) *Content of plan.* The plan must identify steps necessary to perform partial and/or final closure of the facility at any point during its active life. The closure plan must include, at least:

(1) A description of how each hazardous waste management unit at the facility will be closed in accordance with §265.111; and

(2) A description of how final closure of the facility will be conducted in accordance with §265.111. The description must identify the maximum extent of the operation which will be unclosed during the active life of the facility; and

(3) An estimate of the maximum inventory of hazardous wastes ever on-site over the active life of the facility and a detailed description of the methods to be used during partial and final closure, including, but not limited to methods for removing, transporting, treating, storing or disposing of all hazardous waste, identification of and the type(s) of off-site hazardous waste management unit(s) to be used, if applicable; and

(4) A detailed description of the steps needed to remove or decontaminate all hazardous waste residues and contaminated containment system components, equipment, structures, and soils during partial and final closure including, but not limited to, procedures for cleaning equipment and removing contaminated soils, methods for sampling and testing surrounding soils, and criteria for determining the extent of decontamination necessary to satisfy the closure performance standard; and

(5) A detailed description of other activities necessary during the partial and final closure periods to ensure that all partial closures and final closure satisfy the closure performance standards, including, but not limited to, ground-water monitoring, leachate collection, and run-on and run-off control; and

(6) A schedule for closure of each hazardous waste management unit and for final closure of the facility. The schedule must include, at a minimum, the total time required to close each hazardous waste management unit and the time required for intervening closure activities which will allow tracking of the progress of partial and final closure. (For example, in the case of a landfill unit, estimates of the time required to treat or dispose of all hazardous waste inventory and of the time required to place a final cover must be included.); and

(7) An estimate of the expected year of final closure for facilities that use trust funds to demonstrate financial assurance under §265.143 or §265.145 and whose remaining operating life is less than twenty years, and for facilities without approved closure plans.

(8) For facilities where the Regional Administrator has applied alternative requirements at a regulated unit under §§265.90(f), 265.110(d), and/or 265.140(d), either the alternative requirements applying to the regulated unit, or a reference to the enforceable document containing those alternative requirements.

(c) *Amendment of plan.* The owner or operator may amend the closure plan at any time prior to the notification of partial or final closure of the facility. An owner or operator with an approved closure plan must submit a written request to the Regional Administrator to authorize a change to the approved closure plan. The written request must include a copy of the amended closure plan for approval by the Regional Administrator.

(1) The owner or operator must amend the closure plan whenever:

(i) Changes in operating plans or facility design affect the closure plan, or

(ii) There is a change in the expected year of closure, if applicable, or

(iii) In conducting partial or final closure activities, unexpected events require a modification of the closure plan.

(iv) The owner or operator requests the Regional Administrator to apply alternative requirements to a regulated unit under §§265.90(f), 265.110(d), and/or 265.140(d).

(2) The owner or operator must amend the closure plan at least 60 days prior to the proposed change in facility design or operation, or no later than 60 days after

an unexpected event has occurred which has affected the closure plan. If an unexpected event occurs during the partial or final closure period, the owner or operator must amend the closure plan no later than 30 days after the unexpected event. These provisions also apply to owners or operators of surface impoundments and waste piles who intended to remove all hazardous wastes at closure, but are required to close as landfills in accordance with §265.310.

(3) An owner or operator with an approved closure plan must submit the modified plan to the Regional Administrator at least 60 days prior to the proposed change in facility design or operation, or no more than 60 days after an unexpected event has occurred which has affected the closure plan. If an unexpected event has occurred during the partial or final closure period, the owner or operator must submit the modified plan no more than 30 days after the unexpected event. These provisions also apply to owners or operators of surface impoundments and waste piles who intended to remove all hazardous wastes at closure but are required to close as landfills in accordance with §265.310. If the amendment to the plan is a Class 2 or 3 modification according to the criteria in §270.42, the modification to the plan will be approved according to the procedures in §265.112(d)(4).

(4) The Regional Administrator may request modifications to the plan under the conditions described in paragraph (c)(1) of this section. An owner or operator with an approved closure plan must submit the modified plan within 60 days of the request from the Regional Administrator, or within 30 days if the unexpected event occurs during partial or final closure. If the amendment is considered a Class 2 or 3 modification according to the criteria in §270.42, the modification to the plan will be approved in accordance with the procedures in §265.112(d)(4).

(d) *Notification of partial closure and final closure.* (1) The owner or operator must submit the closure plan to the Regional Administrator at least 180 days prior to the date on which he expects to begin closure of the first surface impoundment, waste pile, land treatment, or landfill unit, or final closure if it involves such a unit, whichever is earlier. The owner or operator must submit the closure plan to the Regional Administrator at least 45 days prior to the date on which he expects to begin partial or final closure of a boiler or industrial furnace. The owner or operator must submit the closure plan to the Regional Administrator at least 45 days prior to the date on which he expects to begin final closure of a facility with only tanks, container storage, or incinerator units. Owners or operators with approved closure plans must notify the Regional Administrator in writing at least 60 days prior to the date on which he expects to begin closure of a surface impoundment, waste pile, landfill, or land treatment unit, or final closure of a facility involving such a unit. Owners or operators with approved closure plans must notify the Regional Administrator in writing at least 45 days prior to the date on which he expects to begin partial or final closure of a boiler or industrial furnace. Owners or operators with approved closure plans must notify the Regional Administrator in writing at least 45 days prior to the date on which he expects to begin final closure of a facility with only tanks, container storage, or incinerator units.

(2) The date when he "expects to begin closure" must be either:

(i) Within 30 days after the date on which any hazardous waste management unit receives the known final volume of hazardous wastes, or, if there is a reasonable possibility that the hazardous waste management unit will receive additional hazardous wastes, no later than one year after the date on which the unit received the most recent volume of hazardous waste. If the owner or operator of a hazardous waste management unit can demonstrate to the Regional Administrator that the hazardous waste management unit or facility has the capacity to receive additional hazardous wastes and he has taken, and will continue to take, all steps to prevent threats to human health and the environment, including compliance with all interim status requirements, the Regional Administrator may approve an extension to this one-year limit; or

(ii) For units meeting the requirements of §265.113(d), no later than 30 days after the date on which the hazardous waste management unit receives the known final volume of nonhazardous wastes, or if there is a reasonable possibility that the hazardous waste management unit will receive additional nonhazardous wastes, no later than one year after the date on which the unit received the most recent volume of nonhazardous wastes. If the owner or operator can demonstrate to the Regional Administrator that the hazardous waste management unit has the capacity to receive additional nonhazardous wastes and he has taken, and will continue to take, all steps to prevent threats to human health and the environment, including compliance with all applicable interim status requirements, the

Regional Administrator may approve an extension to this one-year limit.

(3) The owner or operator must submit his closure plan to the Regional Administrator no later than 15 days after:

(i) Termination of interim status except when a permit is issued simultaneously with termination of interim status; or

(ii) Issuance of a judicial decree or final order under section 3008 of RCRA to cease receiving hazardous wastes or close.

(4) The Regional Administrator will provide the owner or operator and the public, through a newspaper notice, the opportunity to submit written comments on the plan and request modifications to the plan no later than 30 days from the date of the notice. He will also, in response to a request or at his own discretion, hold a public hearing whenever such a hearing might clarify one or more issues concerning a closure plan. The Regional Administrator will give public notice of the hearing at least 30 days before it occurs. (Public notice of the hearing may be given at the same time as notice of the opportunity for the public to submit written comments, and the two notices may be combined.) The Regional Administrator will approve, modify, or disapprove the plan within 90 days of its receipt. If the Regional Administrator does not approve the plan he shall provide the owner or operator with a detailed written statement of reasons for the refusal and the owner or operator must modify the plan or submit a new plan for approval within 30 days after receiving such written statement. The Regional Administrator will approve or modify this plan in writing within 60 days. If the Regional Administrator modifies the plan, this modified plan becomes the approved closure plan. The Regional Administrator must assure that the approved plan is consistent with §§265.111 through 265.115 and the applicable requirements of subpart F of this part, and §§265.197, 265.228, 265.258, 265.280, 265.310, 265.351, 265.381, 265.404, and 265.1102. A copy of the modified plan with a detailed statement of reasons for the modifications must be mailed to the owner or operator.

(e) *Removal of wastes and decontamination or dismantling of equipment.* Nothing in this section shall preclude the owner or operator from removing hazardous wastes and decontaminating or dismantling equipment in accordance with the approved partial or final closure plan at any time before or after notification of partial or final closure.

[51 FR 16451, May 2, 1986, as amended at 54 FR 37935, Sept. 28, 1988; 56 FR 7207, Feb. 21, 1991; 56 FR 42512, Aug. 27, 1991; 57 FR 37267, Aug. 18, 1992; 63 FR 56734, Oct. 22, 1998; 71 FR 40275, July 14, 2006]

§265.113 Closure; time allowed for closure.

(a) Within 90 days after receiving the final volume of hazardous wastes, or the final volume of nonhazardous wastes if the owner or operator complies with all applicable requirements in paragraphs (d) and (e) of this section, at a hazardous waste management unit or facility, or within 90 days after approval of the closure plan, whichever is later, the owner or operator must treat, remove from the unit or facility, or dispose of on-site, all hazardous wastes in accordance with the approved closure plan. The Regional Administrator may approve a longer period if the owner or operator demonstrates that:

(1)(i) The activities required to comply with this paragraph will, of necessity, take longer than 90 days to complete; or

(ii)(A) The hazardous waste management unit or facility has the capacity to receive additional hazardous wastes, or has the capacity to receive non-hazardous wastes if the facility owner or operator complies with paragraphs (d) and (e) of this section; and

(B) There is a reasonable likelihood that he or another person will recommence operation of the hazardous waste management unit or the facility within one year; and

(C) Closure of the hazardous waste management unit or facility would be incompatible with continued operation of the site; and

(2) He has taken and will continue to take all steps to prevent threats to human health and the environment, including compliance with all applicable interim status requirements.

(b) The owner or operator must complete partial and final closure activities in accordance with the approved closure plan and within 180 days after receiving the final volume of hazardous wastes, or the final volume of nonhazardous wastes if the owner or operator complies with all applicable requirements in paragraphs (d) and (e) of this section, at the hazardous waste management unit or facility, or 180 days after approval of the closure plan, if that is later. The Regional Administrator may approve an extension to the closure period if the owner or operator demonstrates that:

(1)(i) The partial or final closure activities will, of necessity, take longer than 180 days to complete; or (ii)(A) The hazardous waste management unit or facility has the capacity to receive additional hazardous wastes, or has the capacity to receive non-hazardous wastes if the facility owner or operator complies with paragraphs (d) and (e) of this section; and

(B) There is reasonable likelihood that he or another person will recommence operation of the hazardous waste management unit or the facility within one year; and

(C) Closure of the hazardous waste management unit or facility would be incompatible with continued operation of the site; and

(2) He has taken and will continue to take all steps to prevent threats to human health and the environment from the unclosed but not operating hazardous waste management unit or facility, including compliance with all applicable interim status requirements.

(c) The demonstrations referred to in paragraphs (a)(1) and (b)(1) of this section must be made as follows:

(1) The demonstrations in paragraph (a)(1) of this section must be made at least 30 days prior to the expiration of the 90-day period in paragraph (a) of this section; and

(2) The demonstration in paragraph (b)(1) of this section must be made at least 30 days prior to the expiration of the 180-day period in paragraph (b) of this section, unless the owner or operator is otherwise subject to the deadlines in paragraph (d) of this section.

(d) The Regional Administrator may allow an owner or operator to receive non-hazardous wastes in a landfill, land treatment, or surface impoundment unit after the final receipt of hazardous wastes at that unit if:

(1) The owner or operator submits an amended part B application, or a part B application, if not previously required, and demonstrates that:

(i) The unit has the existing design capacity as indicated on the part A application to receive non-hazardous wastes; and

(ii) There is a reasonable likelihood that the owner or operator or another person will receive non-hazardous wastes in the unit within one year after the final receipt of hazardous wastes; and

(iii) The non-hazardous wastes will not be incompatible with any remaining wastes in the unit or with the facility design and operating requirements of the unit or facility under this part; and

(iv) Closure of the hazardous waste management unit would be incompatible with continued operation of the unit or facility; and

(v) The owner or operator is operating and will continue to operate in compliance with all applicable interim status requirements; and

(2) The part B application includes an amended waste analysis plan, groundwater monitoring and response program, human exposure assessment required under RCRA section 3019, and closure and post-closure plans, and updated cost estimates and demonstrations of financial assurance for closure and post-closure care as necessary and appropriate to reflect any changes due to the presence of hazardous constituents in the non-hazardous wastes, and changes in closure activities, including the expected year of closure if applicable under §265.112(b)(7), as a result of the receipt of non-hazardous wastes following the final receipt of hazardous wastes; and

(3) The part B application is amended, as necessary and appropriate, to account for the receipt of non-hazardous wastes following receipt of the final volume of hazardous wastes; and

(4) The part B application and the demonstrations referred to in paragraphs (d)(1) and (d)(2) of this section are submitted to the Regional Administrator no later than 180 days prior to the date on which the owner or operator of the facility receives the known final volume of hazardous wastes, or no later than 90 days after the effective date of this rule in the state in which the unit is located, whichever is later.

(e) In addition to the requirements in paragraph (d) of this section, an owner or operator of a hazardous waste surface impoundment that is not in compliance with the liner and leachate collection system requirements in 42 U.S.C. 3004(o)(1) and 3005(j)(1) or 42 U.S.C. 3004(o)(2) or (3) or 3005(j)(2), (3), (4) or (13) must:

(1) Submit with the part B application:

(i) A contingent corrective measures plan; and

(ii) A plan for removing hazardous wastes in compliance with paragraph (e)(2) of this section; and

(2) Remove all hazardous wastes from the unit by removing all hazardous liquids and removing all hazardous sludges to the extent practicable without impairing the integrity of the liner(s), if any.

(3) Removal of hazardous wastes must be completed no later than 90 days after the final receipt of hazardous wastes. The Regional Administrator may approve

an extension to this deadline if the owner or operator demonstrates that the removal of hazardous wastes will, of necessity, take longer than the allotted period to complete and that an extension will not pose a threat to human health and the environment.

(4) If a release that is a statistically significant increase (or decrease in the case of pH) in hazardous constituents over background levels is detected in accordance with the requirements in subpart F of this part, the owner or operator of the unit:

(i) Must implement corrective measures in accordance with the approved contingent corrective measures plan required by paragraph (e)(1) of this section no later than one year after detection of the release, or approval of the contingent corrective measures plan, whichever is later;

(ii) May receive wastes at the unit following detection of the release only if the approved corrective measures plan includes a demonstration that continued receipt of wastes will not impede corrective action; and

(iii) May be required by the Regional Administrator to implement corrective measures in less than one year or to cease receipt of wastes until corrective measures have been implemented if necessary to protect human health and the environment.

(5) During the period of corrective action, the owner or operator shall provide annual reports to the Regional Administrator describing the progress of the corrective action program, compile all ground-water monitoring data, and evaluate the effect of the continued receipt of non-hazardous wastes on the effectiveness of the corrective action.

(6) The Regional Administrator may require the owner or operator to commence closure of the unit if the owner or operator fails to implement corrective action measures in accordance with the approved contingent corrective measures plan within one year as required in paragraph (e)(4) of this section, or fails to make substantial progress in implementing corrective action and achieving the facility's background levels.

(7) If the owner or operator fails to implement corrective measures as required in paragraph (e)(4) of this section, or if the Regional Administrator determines that substantial progress has not been made pursuant to paragraph (e)(6) of this section he shall:

(i) Notify the owner or operator in writing that the owner or operator must begin closure in accordance with the deadline in paragraphs (a) and (b) of this section and provide a detailed statement of reasons for this determination, and

(ii) Provide the owner or operator and the public, through a newspaper notice, the opportunity to submit written comments on the decision no later than 20 days after the date of the notice.

(iii) If the Regional Administrator receives no written comments, the decision will become final five days after the close of the comment period. The Regional Administrator will notify the owner or operator that the decision is final, and that a revised closure plan, if necessary, must be submitted within 15 days of the final notice and that closure must begin in accordance with the deadlines in paragraphs (a) and (b) of this section.

(iv) If the Regional Administrator receives written comments on the decision, he shall make a final decision within 30 days after the end of the comment period, and provide the owner or operator in writing and the public through a newspaper notice, a detailed statement of reasons for the final decision. If the Regional Administrator determines that substantial progress has not been made, closure must be initiated in accordance with the deadlines in paragraphs (a) and (b) of this section.

(v) The final determinations made by the Regional Administrator under paragraphs (e)(7)(iii) and (iv) of this section are not subject to administrative appeal.

[51 FR 16451, May 2, 1986, as amended at 54 FR 33396, Aug. 14, 1989; 56 FR 42512, Aug. 27, 1991; 71 FR 16909, Apr. 4, 2006; 71 FR 40275, July 14, 2006]

§265.114 Disposal or decontamination of equipment, structures and soils.

During the partial and final closure periods, all contaminated equipment, structures and soil must be properly disposed of, or decontaminated unless specified otherwise in §§265.197, 265.228, 265.258, 265.280, or 265.310. By removing all hazardous wastes or hazardous constituents during partial and final closure, the owner or operator may become a generator of hazardous waste and must handle that hazardous waste in accordance with all applicable requirements of part 262 of this chapter.

[51 FR 16451, May 2, 1986, as amended at 53 FR 34086, Sept. 2, 1988]

§265.115 Certification of closure.

Within 60 days of completion of closure of each hazardous waste surface impoundment, waste pile, land treatment, and landfill unit, and within 60 days of completion of final closure, the owner or operator must submit to the Regional Administrator, by registered mail, a certification that the hazardous waste management unit or facility, as applicable, has been closed in accordance with the specifications in the approved closure plan. The certification must be signed by the owner or operator and by a qualified Professional Engineer. Documentation supporting the Professional Engineer's certification must be furnished to the Regional Administrator upon request until he releases the owner or operator from the financial assurance requirements for closure under §265.143(h).

[71 FR 16909, Apr. 4, 2006]

§265.116 Survey plat.

No later than the submission of the certification of closure of each hazardous waste disposal unit, an owner or operator must submit to the local zoning authority, or the authority with jurisdiction over local land use, and to the Regional Administrator, a survey plat indicating the location and dimensions of landfill cells or other hazardous waste disposal units with respect to permanently surveyed benchmarks. This plat must be prepared and certified by a professional land surveyor. The plat filed with the local zoning authority, or the authority with jurisdiction over local land use must contain a note, prominently displayed, which states the owner's or operator's obligation to restrict disturbance of the hazardous waste disposal unit in accordance with the applicable subpart G regulations.

§265.117 Post-closure care and use of property.

(a)(1) Post-closure care for each hazardous waste management unit subject to the requirements of §§265.117 through 265.120 must begin after completion of closure of the unit and continue for 30 years after that date. It must consist of at least the following:

(i) Monitoring and reporting in accordance with the requirements of subparts F, K, L, M, and N of this part; and

(ii) Maintenance and monitoring of waste containment systems in accordance with the requirements of subparts F, K, L, M, and N of this part.

(2) Any time preceding closure of a hazardous waste management unit subject to post-closure care requirements or final closure, or any time during the post-closure period for a particular hazardous waste disposal unit, the Regional Administrator may:

(i) Shorten the post-closure care period applicable to the hazardous waste management unit, or facility, if all disposal units have been closed, if he finds that the reduced period is sufficient to protect human health and the environment (*e.g.*, leachate or groundwater monitoring results, characteristics of the hazardous waste, application of advanced technology, or alternative disposal, treatment, or re-use techniques indicate that the hazardous waste management unit or facility is secure); or

(ii) Extend the post-closure care period applicable to the hazardous waste management unit or facility, if he finds that the extended period is necessary to protect human health and the environment (*e.g.*, leachate or groundwater monitoring results indicate a potential for migration of hazardous wastes at levels which may be harmful to human health and the environment).

(b) The Regional Administrator may require, at partial and final closure, continuation of any of the security requirements of §265.14 during part or all of the post-closure period when:

(1) Hazardous wastes may remain exposed after completion of partial or final closure; or

(2) Access by the public or domestic livestock may pose a hazard to human health.

(c) Post-closure use of property on or in which hazardous wastes remain after partial or final closure must never be allowed to disturb the integrity of the final cover, liner(s), or any other components of the containment system, or the function of the facility's monitoring systems, unless the Regional Administrator finds that the disturbance:

(1) Is necessary to the proposed use of the property, and will not increase the potential hazard to human health or the environment; or

(2) Is necessary to reduce a threat to human health or the environment.

(d) All post-closure care activities must be in accordance with the provisions of the approved post-closure plan as specified in §265.118.

[51 FR 16451, May 2, 1986, as amended at 71 FR 40275, July 14, 2006]

§265.118 Post-closure plan; amendment of plan.

(a) *Written plan.* By May 19, 1981, the owner or operator of a hazardous waste disposal unit must have a written post-closure plan. An owner or operator of a surface impoundment or waste pile that intends to remove all hazardous wastes at closure must prepare a post-closure plan and submit it to the Regional Administrator within 90 days of the date that the owner or operator or Regional Administrator determines that the hazardous waste management unit or facility must be closed as a landfill, subject to the requirements of §§265.117 through 265.120.

(b) Until final closure of the facility, a copy of the most current post-closure plan must be furnished to the Regional Administrator upon request, including request by mail. In addition, for facilities without approved post-closure plans, it must also be provided during site inspections, on the day of inspection, to any officer, employee or representative of the Agency who is duly designated by the Administrator. After final closure has been certified, the person or office specified in §265.118(c)(3) must keep the approved post-closure plan during the post-closure period.

(c) For each hazardous waste management unit subject to the requirements of this section, the post-closure plan must identify the activities that will be carried on after closure of each disposal unit and the frequency of these activities, and include at least:

(1) A description of the planned monitoring activities and frequencies at which they will be performed to comply with subparts F, K, L, M, and N of this part during the post-closure care period; and

(2) A description of the planned maintenance activities, and frequencies at which they will be performed, to ensure:

(i) The integrity of the cap and final cover or other containment systems in accordance with the requirements of subparts K, L, M, and N of this part; and

(ii) The function of the monitoring equipment in accordance with the requirements of subparts F, K, L, M, and N of this part; and

(3) The name, address, and phone number of the person or office to contact about the hazardous waste disposal unit or facility during the post-closure care period.

(4) For facilities subject to §265.121, provisions that satisfy the requirements of §265.121(a)(1) and (3).

(5) For facilities where the Regional Administrator has applied alternative requirements at a regulated unit under §§265.90(f), 265.110(d), and/or 265.140(d), either the alternative requirements that apply to the regulated unit, or a reference to the enforceable document containing those requirements.

(d) *Amendment of plan.* The owner or operator may amend the post-closure plan any time during the active life of the facility or during the post-closure care period. An owner or operator with an approved post-closure plan must submit a written request to the Regional Administrator to authorize a change to the approved plan. The written request must include a copy of the amended post-closure plan for approval by the Regional Administrator.

(1) The owner or operator must amend the post-closure plan whenever:

(i) Changes in operating plans or facility design affect the post-closure plan, or

(ii) Events which occur during the active life of the facility, including partial and final closures, affect the post-closure plan.

(iii) The owner or operator requests the Regional Administrator to apply alternative requirements to a regulated unit under §§265.90(f), 265.110(d), and/or 265.140(d).

(2) The owner or operator must amend the post-closure plan at least 60 days prior to the proposed change in facility design or operation, or no later than 60 days after an unexpected event has occurred which has affected the post-closure plan.

(3) An owner or operator with an approved post-closure plan must submit the modified plan to the Regional Administrator at least 60 days prior to the proposed change in facility design or operation, or no more than 60 days after an unexpected event has occurred which has affected the post-closure plan. If an owner or operator of a surface impoundment or a waste pile who intended to remove all hazardous wastes at closure in accordance with §265.228(b) or §265.258(a) is required to close as a landfill in accordance with §265.310, the owner or operator must submit a post-closure plan within 90 days of the determination by the owner or operator or Regional Administrator that the unit must be closed as a landfill. If the amendment to the post-closure plan is a Class 2 or 3 modification according to the criteria in §270.42, the modification to the plan will be approved according to the procedures in §265.118(f).

(4) The Regional Administrator may request modifications to the plan under the conditions described in paragraph (d)(1) of this section. An owner or operator with an approved post-closure plan must submit the modified plan no later than 60 days of the request from the Regional Administrator. If the amendment to the plan is considered a Class 2 or 3 modification according to the criteria in §270.42, the modifications to the post-closure plan will be approved in accordance with the procedures in §265.118(f). If the Regional Administrator determines that an owner or operator of a surface impoundment or waste pile who intended to remove all hazardous wastes at closure must close the facility as a landfill, the owner or operator must submit a

post-closure plan for approval to the Regional Administrator within 90 days of the determination.

(e) The owner or operator of a facility with hazardous waste management units subject to these requirements must submit his post-closure plan to the Regional Administrator at least 180 days before the date he expects to begin partial or final closure of the first hazardous waste disposal unit. The date he "expects to begin closure" of the first hazardous waste disposal unit must be either within 30 days after the date on which the hazardous waste management unit receives the known final volume of hazardous waste or, if there is a reasonable possibility that the hazardous waste management unit will receive additional hazardous wastes, no later than one year after the date on which the unit received the most recent volume of hazardous wastes. The owner or operator must submit the post-closure plan to the Regional Administrator no later than 15 days after:

(1) Termination of interim status (except when a permit is issued to the facility simultaneously with termination of interim status); or

(2) Issuance of a judicial decree or final orders under section 3008 of RCRA to cease receiving wastes or close.

(f) The Regional Administrator will provide the owner or operator and the public, through a newspaper notice, the opportunity to submit written comments on the post-closure plan and request modifications to the plan no later than 30 days from the date of the notice. He will also, in response to a request or at his own discretion, hold a public hearing whenever such a hearing might clarify one or more issues concerning a post-closure plan. The Regional Administrator will give public notice of the hearing at least 30 days before it occurs. (Public notice of the hearing may be given at the same time as notice of the opportunity for the public to submit written comments, and the two notices may be combined.) The Regional Administrator will approve, modify, or disapprove the plan within 90 days of its receipt. If the Regional Administrator does not approve the plan he shall provide the owner or operator with a detailed written statement of reasons for the refusal and the owner or operator must modify the plan or submit a new plan for approval within 30 days after receiving such written statement. The Regional Administrator will approve or modify this plan in writing within 60 days. If the Regional Administrator modifies the plan, this modified plan becomes the approved post-closure plan. The Regional Administrator must ensure that the approved post-closure plan is consistent with §§265.117 through 265.120. A copy of the modified plan with a detailed statement of reasons for the modifications must be mailed to the owner or operator.

(g) The post-closure plan and length of the post-closure care period may be modified any time prior to the end of the post-closure care period in either of the following two ways:

(1) The owner or operator or any member of the public may petition the Regional Administrator to extend or reduce the post-closure care period applicable to a hazardous waste management unit or facility based on cause, or alter the requirements of the post-closure care period based on cause.

(i) The petition must include evidence demonstrating that:

(A) The secure nature of the hazardous waste management unit or facility makes the post-closure care requirement(s) unnecessary or supports reduction of the post-closure care period specified in the current post-closure plan (*e.g.*, leachate or groundwater monitoring results, characteristics of the wastes, application of advanced technology, or alternative disposal, treatment, or re-use techniques indicate that the facility is secure), or

(B) The requested extension in the post-closure care period or alteration of post-closure care requirements is necessary to prevent threats to human health and the environment (*e.g.*, leachate or groundwater monitoring results indicate a potential for migration of hazardous wastes at levels which may be harmful to human health and the environment).

(ii) These petitions will be considered by the Regional Administrator only when they present new and relevant information not previously considered by the Regional Administrator. Whenever the Regional Administrator is considering a petition, he will provide the owner or operator and the public, through a newspaper notice, the opportunity to submit written comments within 30 days of the date of the notice. He will also, in response to a request or at his own discretion, hold a public hearing whenever a hearing might clarify one or more issues concerning the post-closure plan. The Regional Administrator will give the public notice of the hearing at least 30 days before it occurs. (Public notice of the hearing may be given at the same time as notice of the opportunity for written public comments, and the two notices may be combined.) After considering the comments, he will issue a final determination, based upon the criteria set forth in paragraph (g)(1) of this section.

(iii) If the Regional Administrator denies the petition, he will send the petitioner a brief written response giving a reason for the denial.

(2) The Regional Administrator may tentatively decide to modify the post-closure plan if he deems it necessary to prevent threats to human health and the environment. He may propose to extend or reduce the post-closure care period applicable to a hazardous waste management unit or facility based on cause or alter the requirements of the post-closure care period based on cause.

(i) The Regional Administrator will provide the owner or operator and the affected public, through a newspaper notice, the opportunity to submit written comments within 30 days of the date of the notice and the opportunity for a public hearing as in paragraph (g)(1)(ii) of this section. After considering the comments, he will issue a final determination.

(ii) The Regional Administrator will base his final determination upon the same criteria as required for petitions under paragraph (g)(1)(i) of this section. A modification of the post-closure plan may include, where appropriate, the temporary suspension rather than permanent deletion of one or more post-closure care requirements. At the end of the specified period of suspension, the Regional Administrator would then determine whether the requirement(s) should be permanently discontinued or reinstated to prevent threats to human health and the environment.

[51 FR 16451, May 2, 1986, as amended at 53 FR 37935, Sept. 28, 1988; 63 FR 56734, Oct. 22, 1998]

§265.119 Post-closure notices.

(a) No later than 60 days after certification of closure of each hazardous waste disposal unit, the owner or operator must submit to the local zoning authority, or the authority with jurisdiction over local land use, and to the Regional Administrator, a record of the type, location, and quantity of hazardous wastes disposed of within each cell or other disposal unit of the facility. For hazardous wastes disposed of before January 12, 1981, the owner or operator must identify the type, location and quantity of the hazardous wastes to the best of his knowledge and in accordance with any records he has kept.

(b) Within 60 days of certification of closure of the first hazardous waste disposal unit and within 60 days of certification of closure of the last hazardous waste disposal unit, the owner or operator must:

(1) Record, in accordance with State law, a notation on the deed to the facility property—or on some other instrument which is normally examined during title search—that will in perpetuity notify any potential purchaser of the property that:

(i) The land has been used to manage hazardous wastes; and

(ii) Its use is restricted under 40 CFR part 265, subpart G regulations; and

(iii) The survey plat and record of the type, location, and quantity of hazardous wastes disposed of within each cell or other hazardous waste disposal unit of the facility required by §§265.116 and 265.119(a) have been filed with the local zoning authority or the authority with jurisdiction over local land use and with the Regional Administrator; and

(2) Submit a certification signed by the owner or operator that he has recorded the notation specified in paragraph (b)(1) of this section and a copy of the document in which the notation has been placed, to the Regional Administrator.

(c) If the owner or operator or any subsequent owner of the land upon which a hazardous waste disposal unit was located wishes to remove hazardous wastes and hazardous waste residues, the liner, if any, and all contaminated structures, equipment, and soils, he must request a modification to the approved post-closure plan in accordance with the requirements of §265.118(g). The owner or operator must demonstrate that the removal of hazardous wastes will satisfy the criteria of §265.117(c). By removing hazardous waste, the owner or operator may become a generator of hazardous waste and must manage it in accordance with all applicable requirements of this chapter. If the owner or operator is granted approval to conduct the removal activities, the owner or operator may request that the Regional Administrator approve either:

(1) The removal of the notation on the deed to the facility property or other instrument normally examined during title search, or

(2) The addition of a notation to the deed or instrument indicating the removal of the hazardous waste.

[51 FR 16451, May 2, 1986, as amended at 71 FR 40275, July 14, 2006]

§265.120 Certification of completion of post-closure care.

No later than 60 days after the completion of the established post-closure care period for each hazardous waste disposal unit, the owner or operator must submit to the Regional Administrator, by registered mail, a certification that the post-closure care period for the hazardous waste disposal unit was performed in accordance with the specifications in the approved post-closure plan. The certification must be signed by the owner or operator and a qualified Professional Engineer. Documentation supporting the Professional Engineer's certification must be furnished to the Regional Administrator upon request until he releases the owner or operator from the financial assurance requirements for post-closure care under §265.145(h).

[71 FR 16909, Apr. 4, 2006]

§265.121 Post-closure requirements for facilities that obtain enforceable documents in lieu of post-closure permits.

(a) Owners and operators who are subject to the requirement to obtain a post-closure permit under 40 CFR 270.1(c), but who obtain enforceable documents in lieu of post-closure permits, as provided under 40 CFR 270.1(c)(7), must comply with the following requirements:

(1) The requirements to submit information about the facility in 40 CFR 270.28;

(2) The requirements for facility-wide corrective action in §264.101 of this chapter;

(3) The requirements of 40 CFR 264.91 through 264.100.

(b)(1) The Regional Administrator, in issuing enforceable documents under §265.121 in lieu of permits, will assure a meaningful opportunity for public involvement which, at a minimum, includes public notice and opportunity for public comment:

(i) When the Agency becomes involved in a remediation at the facility as a regulatory or enforcement matter;

(ii) On the proposed preferred remedy and the assumptions upon which the remedy is based, in particular those related to land use and site characterization; and

(iii) At the time of a proposed decision that remedial action is complete at the facility. These requirements must be met before the Regional Administrator may consider that the facility has met the requirements of 40 CFR 270.1(c)(7), unless the facility qualifies for a modification to these public involvement procedures under paragraph (b)(2) or (3) of this section.

(2) If the Regional Administrator determines that even a short delay in the implementation of a remedy would adversely affect human health or the environment, the Regional Administrator may delay compliance with the requirements of paragraph (b)(1) of this section and implement the remedy immediately. However, the Regional Administrator must assure involvement of the public at the earliest opportunity, and, in all cases, upon making the decision that additional remedial action is not needed at the facility.

(3) The Regional Administrator may allow a remediation initiated prior to October 22, 1998 to substitute for corrective action required under a post-closure permit even if the public involvement requirements of paragraph (b)(1) of this section have not been met so long as the Regional Administrator assures that notice and comment on the decision that no further remediation is necessary to protect human health and the environment takes place at the earliest reasonable opportunity after October 22, 1998.

[63 FR 56734, Oct. 22, 1998]

Subpart H—Financial Requirements

Source: 47 FR 15064, Apr. 7, 1982, unless otherwise noted.

§265.140 Applicability.

(a) The requirements of §§265.142, 265.143 and 265.147 through 265.150 apply to owners or operators of all hazardous waste facilities, except as provided otherwise in this section or in §265.1.

(b) The requirements of §§265.144 and 265.145 apply only to owners and operators of:

(1) Disposal facilities;

(2) Tank systems that are required under §265.197 of this chapter to meet the requirements for landfills; and

(3) Containment buildings that are required under §265.1102 to meet the requirements for landfills.

(c) States and the Federal government are exempt from the requirements of this subpart.

(d) The Regional Administrator may replace all or part of the requirements of this subpart applying to a regulated unit with alternative requirements for financial assurance set out in the permit or in an enforceable document (as defined in 40 CFR 270.1(c)(7)), where the Regional Administrator:

(1) Prescribes alternative requirements for the regulated unit under §265.90(f) and/or 265.110(d), and

(2) Determines that it is not necessary to apply the requirements of this subpart because the alternative financial assurance requirements will protect human health and the environment.

[47 FR 15064, Apr. 7, 1982, as amended at 51 FR 16455, May 2, 1986; 51 FR 25479, July 14, 1986; 57 FR 37267, Aug. 18, 1992; 63 FR 56734, Oct. 22, 1998; 71 FR 40275, July 14, 2006]

§265.141 Definitions of terms as used in this subpart.

(a) *Closure plan* means the plan for closure prepared in accordance with the requirements of §265.112.

(b) *Current closure cost estimate* means the most recent of the estimates prepared in accordance with §265.142 (a), (b), and (c).

(c) *Current post-closure cost estimate* means the most recent of the estimates prepared in accordance with §265.144 (a), (b), and (c).

(d) *Parent corporation* means a corporation which directly owns at least 50 percent of the voting stock of the corporation which is the facility owner or operator; the latter corporation is deemed a "subsidiary" of the parent corporation.

(e) *Post-closure plan* means the plan for post-closure care prepared in accordance with the requirements of §§265.117 through 265.120.

(f) The following terms are used in the specifications for the financial tests for closure, post-closure care, and liability coverage. The definitions are intended to assist in the understanding of these regulations and are not intended to limit the meanings of terms in a way that conflicts with generally accepted accounting practices.

Assets means all existing and all probable future economic benefits obtained or controlled by a particular entity.

Current assets means cash or other assets or resources commonly identified as those which are reasonably expected to be realized in cash or sold or consumed during the normal operating cycle of the business.

Current liabilities means obligations whose liquidation is reasonably expected to require the use of existing resources properly classifiable as current assets or the creation of other current liabilities.

Current plugging and abandonment cost estimate means the most recent of the estimates prepared in accordance with §144.62(a), (b), and (c) of this title.

Independently audited refers to an audit performed by an independent certified public accountant in accordance with generally accepted auditing standards.

Liabilities means probable future sacrifices of economic benefits arising from present obligations to transfer assets or provide services to other entities in the future as a result of past transactions or events.

Net working capital means current assets minus current liabilities.

Net worth means total assets minus total liabilities and is equivalent to owner's equity.

Tangible net worth means the tangible assets that remain after deducting liabilities; such assets would not include intangibles such as goodwill and rights to patents or royalties.

(g) In the liability insurance requirements the terms *bodily injury* and *property damage* shall have the meanings given these terms by applicable State law. However, these terms do not include those liabilities which, consistent with standard industry practice, are excluded from coverage in liability policies for bodily injury and property damage. The Agency intends the meanings of other terms used in the liability insurance requirements to be consistent with their common meanings within the insurance industry. The definitions given below of several of the terms are intended to assist in the understanding of these regulations and are not intended to limit their meanings in a way that conflicts with general insurance industry usage.

Accidental occurrence means an accident, including continuous or repeated exposure to conditions, which results in bodily injury or property damage neither expected nor intended from the standpoint of the insured.

Legal defense costs means any expenses that an insurer incurs in defending against claims of third parties brought under the terms and conditions of an insurance policy.

Nonsudden accidental occurrence means an occurrence which takes place over time and involves continuous or repeated exposure.

Sudden accidental occurrence means an occurrence which is not continuous or repeated in nature.

(h) Substantial business relationship means the extent of a business relationship necessary under applicable State law to make a guarantee contract issued incident to that relationship valid and enforceable. A "substantial business relationship" must arise from a pattern of recent or ongoing business transactions, in addition to the guarantee itself, such that a currently existing business relationship between the guarantor and the owner or operator is demonstrated to the satisfaction of the applicable EPA Regional Administrator.

[47 FR 16558, Apr. 16, 1982, as amended at 51 FR 16456, May 2, 1986; 53 FR 33959, Sept. 1, 1988]

§265.142 Cost estimate for closure.

(a) The owner or operator must have a detailed written estimate, in current dollars, of the cost of closing the facility in accordance with the requirements in §§265.111 through 265.115 and applicable closure requirements in

§§265.197, 265.228, 265.258, 265.280, 265.310, 265.351, 265.381, 265.404, and 265.1102.

(1) The estimate must equal the cost of final closure at the point in the facility's active life when the extent and manner of its operation would make closure the most expensive, as indicated by its closure plan (see §265.112(b)); and

(2) The closure cost estimate must be based on the costs to the owner or operator of hiring a third party to close the facility. A third party is a party who is neither a parent nor a subsidiary of the owner or operator. (See definition of parent corporation in §265.141(d).) The owner or operator may use costs for on-site disposal if he can demonstrate that on-site disposal capacity will exist at all times over the life of the facility.

(3) The closure cost estimate may not incorporate any salvage value that may be realized with the sale of hazardous wastes, or non-hazardous wastes if applicable under §265.113(d), facility structures or equipment, land, or other assets associated with the facility at the time of partial or final closure.

(4) The owner or operator may not incorporate a zero cost for hazardous wastes, or non-hazardous wastes if applicable under §265.113(d), that might have economic value.

(b) During the active life of the facility, the owner or operator must adjust the closure cost estimate for inflation within 60 days prior to the anniversary date of the establishment of the financial instrument(s) used to comply with §265.143. For owners and operators using the financial test or corporate guarantee, the closure cost estimate must be updated for inflation within 30 days after the close of the firm's fiscal year and before submission of updated information to the Regional Administrator as specified in §265.143(e)(3). The adjustment may be made by recalculating the closure cost estimate in current dollars, or by using an inflation factor derived from the most recent Implicit Price Deflator for Gross National Product published by the U.S. Department of Commerce in its Survey of Current Business, as specified in paragraphs (b)(1) and (2) of this section. The inflation factor is the result of dividing the latest published annual Deflator by the Deflator for the previous year.

(1) The first adjustment is made by multiplying the closure cost estimate by the inflation factor. The result is the adjusted closure cost estimate.

(2) Subsequent adjustments are made by multiplying the latest adjusted closure cost estimate by the latest inflation factor.

(c) During the active life of the facility, the owner or operator must revise the closure cost estimate no later than 30 days after a revision has been made to the closure plan which increases the cost of closure. If the owner or operator has an approved closure plan, the closure cost estimate must be revised no later than 30 days after the Regional Administrator has approved the request to modify the closure plan, if the change in the closure plan increases the cost of closure. The revised closure cost estimate must be adjusted for inflation as specified in §265.142(b).

(d) The owner or operator must keep the following at the facility during the operating life of the facility: The latest closure cost estimate prepared in accordance with §§265.142 (a) and (c) and, when this estimate has been adjusted in accordance with §265.142(b), the latest adjusted closure cost estimate.

[47 FR 15064, Apr. 7, 1982, as amended at 50 FR 4514, Jan. 31, 1985; 51 FR 16456, May 2, 1986; 54 FR 33397, Aug. 14, 1989; 57 FR 37267, Aug. 18, 1992; 71 FR 40275, July 14, 2006]

§265.143 Financial assurance for closure.

By the effective date of these regulations, an owner or operator of each facility must establish financial assurance for closure of the facility. He must choose from the options as specified in paragraphs (a) through (e) of this section.

(a) *Closure trust fund.* (1) An owner or operator may satisfy the requirements of this section by establishing a closure trust fund which conforms to the requirements of this paragraph and submitting an originally signed duplicate of the trust agreement to the Regional Administrator. The trustee must be an entity which has the authority to act as a trustee and whose trust operations are regulated and examined by a Federal or State agency.

(2) The wording of the trust agreement must be identical to the wording specified in §264.151(a)(1), and the trust agreement must be accompanied by a formal certification of acknowledgment (for example, see §264.151(a)(2)). Schedule A of the trust agreement must be updated within 60 days after a change in the amount of the current closure cost estimate covered by the agreement.

(3) Payments into the trust fund must be made annually by the owner or operator over the 20 years beginning with the effective date of these regulations or over the remaining operating life of the facility as estimated in the closure plan, whichever period is shorter; this period is hereafter referred to as the "pay-in period." The

payments into the closure trust fund must be made as follows:

(i) The first payment must be made by the effective date of these regulations, except as provided in paragraph (a)(5) of this section. The first payment must be at least equal to the current closure cost estimate, except as provided in §265.143(f), divided by the number of years in the pay-in period.

(ii) Subsequent payments must be made no later than 30 days after each anniversary date of the first payment. The amount of each subsequent payment must be determined by this formula:

$$\text{Next payment} = \frac{CE - CV}{Y}$$

where CE is the current closure cost estimate, CV is the current value of the trust fund, and Y is the number of years remaining in the pay-in period.

(4) The owner or operator may accelerate payments into the trust fund or he may deposit the full amount of the current closure cost estimate at the time the fund is established. However, he must maintain the value of the fund at no less than the value that the fund would have if annual payments were made as specified in paragraph (a)(3) of this section.

(5) If the owner or operator establishes a closure trust fund after having used one or more alternate mechanisms specified in this section, his first payment must be in at least the amount that the fund would contain if the trust fund were established initially and annual payments made as specified in paragraph (a)(3) of this section.

(6) After the pay-in period is completed, whenever the current closure cost estimate changes, the owner or operator must compare the new estimate with the trustee's most recent annual valuation of the trust fund. If the value of the fund is less than the amount of the new estimate, the owner or operator, within 60 days after the change in the cost estimate, must either deposit an amount into the fund so that its value after this deposit at least equals the amount of the current closure cost estimate, or obtain other financial assurance as specified in this section to cover the difference.

(7) If the value of the trust fund is greater than the total amount of the current closure cost estimate, the owner or operator may submit a written request to the Regional Administrator for release of the amount in excess of the current closure cost estimate.

(8) If an owner or operator substitutes other financial assurance as specified in this section for all or part of the trust fund, he may submit a written request to the Regional Administrator for release of the amount in excess of the current closure cost estimate covered by the trust fund.

(9) Within 60 days after receiving a request from the owner or operator for release of funds as specified in paragraph (a)(7) or (8) of this section, the Regional Administrator will instruct the trustee to release to the owner or operator such funds as the Regional Administrator specifies in writing.

(10) After beginning partial or final closure, an owner or operator or another person authorized to conduct partial or final closure may request reimbursements for partial or final closure expenditures by submitting itemized bills to the Regional Administrator. The owner or operator may request reimbursements for partial closure only if sufficient funds are remaining in the trust fund to cover the maximum costs of closing the facility over its remaining operating life. No later than 60 days after receiving bills for partial or final closure activities, the Regional Administrator will instruct the trustee to make reimbursements in those amounts as the Regional Administrator specifies in writing, if the Regional Administrator determines that the partial or final closure expenditures are in accordance with the approved closure plan, or otherwise justified. If the Regional Administrator has reason to believe that the maximum cost of closure over the remaining life of the facility will be significantly greater than the value of the trust fund, he may withhold reimbursements of such amounts as he deems prudent until he determines, in accordance with §265.143(h) that the owner or operator is no longer required to maintain financial assurance for final closure of the facility. If the Regional Administrator does not instruct the trustee to make such reimbursements, he will provide to the owner or operator a detailed written statement of reasons.

(11) The Regional Administrator will agree to termination of the trust when:

(i) An owner or operator substitutes alternate financial assurance as specified in this section; or

(ii) The Regional Administrator releases the owner or operator from the requirements of this section in accordance with §265.143(h).

(b) *Surety bond guaranteeing payment into a closure trust fund.* (1) An owner or operator may satisfy the requirements of this section by obtaining a surety bond which conforms to the requirements of this paragraph and submitting the bond to the Regional Administrator. The surety company issuing the bond must, at a minimum, be among those listed as acceptable sureties on Federal bonds in Circular 570 of the U.S. Department of the Treasury.

(2) The wording of the surety bond must be identical to the wording specified in §264.151(b).

(3) The owner or operator who uses a surety bond to satisfy the requirements of this section must also establish a standby trust fund. Under the terms of the bond, all payments made thereunder will be deposited by the surety directly into the standby trust fund in accordance with instructions from the Regional Administrator. This standby trust fund must meet the requirements specified in §265.143(a), except that:

(i) An originally signed duplicate of the trust agreement must be submitted to the Regional Administrator with the surety bond; and

(ii) Until the standby trust fund is funded pursuant to the requirements of this section, the following are not required by these regulations:

(A) Payments into the trust fund as specified in §265.143(a);

(B) Updating of Schedule A of the trust agreement (see §264.151(a)) to show current closure cost estimates;

(C) Annual valuations as required by the trust agreement; and

(D) Notices of nonpayment as required by the trust agreement.

(4) The bond must guarantee that the owner or operator will:

(i) Fund the standby trust fund in an amount equal to the penal sum of the bond before the beginning of final closure of the facility; or

(ii) Fund the standby trust fund in an amount equal to the penal sum within 15 days after an administrative order to begin final closure issued by the Regional Administrator becomes final, or within 15 days after an order to begin final closure is issued by a U.S. district court or other court of competent jurisdiction; or

(iii) Provide alternate financial assurance as specified in this section, and obtain the Regional Administrator's written approval of the assurance provided, within 90 days after receipt by both the owner or operator and the Regional Administrator of a notice of cancellation of the bond from the surety.

(5) Under the terms of the bond, the surety will become liable on the bond obligation when the owner or operator fails to perform as guaranteed by the bond.

(6) The penal sum of the bond must be in an amount at least equal to the current closure cost estimate, except as provided in §265.143(f).

(7) Whenever the current closure cost estimate increases to an amount greater than the penal sum, the owner or operator, within 60 days after the increase, must either cause the penal sum to be increased to an amount at least equal to the current closure cost estimate and submit evidence of such increase to the Regional Administrator, or obtain other financial assurance as specified in this section to cover the increase. Whenever the current closure cost estimate decreases, the penal sum may be reduced to the amount of the current closure cost estimate following written approval by the Regional Administrator.

(8) Under the terms of the bond, the surety may cancel the bond by sending notice of cancellation by certified mail to the owner or operator and to the Regional Administrator. Cancellation may not occur, however, during the 120 days beginning on the date of receipt of the notice of cancellation by both the owner or operator and the Regional Administrator, as evidenced by the return receipts.

(9) The owner or operator may cancel the bond if the Regional Administrator has given prior written consent based on his receipt of evidence of alternate financial assurance as specified in this section.

(c) *Closure letter of credit.* (1) An owner or operator may satisfy the requirements of this section by obtaining an irrevocable standby letter of credit which conforms to the requirements of this paragraph and submitting the letter to the Regional Administrator. The issuing institution must be an entity which has the authority to issue letters of credit and whose letter-of-credit operations are regulated and examined by a Federal or State agency.

(2) The wording of the letter of credit must be identical to the wording specified in §264.151(d).

(3) An owner or operator who uses a letter of credit to satisfy the requirements of this section must also establish a standby trust fund. Under the terms of the letter of credit, all amounts paid pursuant to a draft by the Regional Administrator will be deposited by the issuing institution directly into the standby trust fund in

accordance with instructions from the Regional Administrator. This standby trust fund must meet the requirements of the trust fund specified in §265.143(a), except that:

(i) An originally signed duplicate of the trust agreement must be submitted to the Regional Administrator with the letter of credit; and

(ii) Unless the standby trust fund is funded pursuant to the requirements of this section, the following are not required by these regulations:

(A) Payments into the trust fund as specified in §265.143(a);

(B) Updating of Schedule A of the trust agreement (see §264.151(a)) to show current closure cost estimates;

(C) Annual valuations as required by the trust agreement; and

(D) Notices of nonpayment as required by the trust agreement.

(4) The letter of credit must be accompanied by a letter from the owner or operator referring to the letter of credit by number, issuing institution, and date, and providing the following information: The EPA Identification Number, name, and address of the facility, and the amount of funds assured for closure of the facility by the letter of credit.

(5) The letter of credit must be irrevocable and issued for a period of at least 1 year. The letter of credit must provide that the expiration date will be automatically extended for a period of at least 1 year unless, at least 120 days before the current expiration date, the issuing institution notifies both the owner or operator and the Regional Administrator by certified mail of a decision not to extend the expiration date. Under the terms of the letter of credit, the 120 days will begin on the date when both the owner or operator and the Regional Administrator have received the notice, as evidenced by the return receipts.

(6) The letter of credit must be issued in an amount at least equal to the current closure cost estimate, except as provided in §265.143(f).

(7) Whenever the current closure cost estimate increases to an amount greater than the amount of the credit, the owner or operator, within 60 days after the increase, must either cause the amount of the credit to be increased so that it at least equals the current closure cost estimate and submit evidence of such increase to the Regional Administrator, or obtain other financial assurance as specified in this section to cover the increase. Whenever the current closure cost estimate decreases, the amount of the credit may be reduced to the amount of the current closure cost estimate following written approval by the Regional Administrator.

(8) Following a final administrative determination pursuant to section 3008 of RCRA that the owner or operator has failed to perform final closure in accordance with the approved closure plan when required to do so, the Regional Administrator may draw on the letter of credit.

(9) If the owner or operator does not establish alternate financial assurance as specified in this section and obtain written approval of such alternate assurance from the Regional Administrator within 90 days after receipt by both the owner or operator and the Regional Administrator of a notice from the issuing institution that it has decided not to extend the letter of credit beyond the current expiration date, the Regional Administrator will draw on the letter of credit. The Regional Administrator may delay the drawing if the issuing institution grants an extension of the term of the credit. During the last 30 days of any such extension the Regional Administrator will draw on the letter of credit if the owner or operator has failed to provide alternate financial assurance as specified in this section and obtain written approval of such assurance from the Regional Administrator.

(10) The Regional Administrator will return the letter of credit to the issuing institution for termination when:

(i) An owner or operator substitutes alternate financial assurance as specified in this section; or

(ii) The Regional Administrator releases the owner or operator from the requirements of this section in accordance with §265.143(h).

(d) *Closure insurance.* (1) An owner or operator may satisfy the requirements of this section by obtaining closure insurance which conforms to the requirements of this paragraph and submitting a certificate of such insurance to the Regional Administrator. By the effective date of these regulations the owner or operator must submit to the Regional Administrator a letter from an insurer stating that the insurer is considering issuance of closure insurance conforming to the requirements of this paragraph to the owner or operator. Within 90 days after the effective date of these regulations, the owner or operator must submit the certificate of insurance to the Regional Administrator or establish other financial assurance as specified in this section. At a minimum, the insurer must be licensed to transact the business of insurance, or eligible to provide insurance as an excess or surplus lines insurer, in one or more States.

(2) The wording of the certificate of insurance must be identical to the wording specified in §264.151(e).

(3) The closure insurance policy must be issued for a face amount at least equal to the current closure cost estimate, except as provided in §265.143(f). The term "face amount" means the total amount the insurer is obligated to pay under the policy. Actual payments by the insurer will not change the face amount, although the insurer's future liability will be lowered by the amount of the payments.

(4) The closure insurance policy must guarantee that funds will be available to close the facility whenever final closure occurs. The policy must also guarantee that once final closure begins, the insurer will be responsible for paying out funds, up to an amount equal to the face amount of the policy, upon the direction of the Regional Administrator, to such party or parties as the Regional Administrator specifies.

(5) After beginning partial or final closure, an owner or operator or any other person authorized to conduct closure may request reimbursements for closure expenditures by submitting itemized bills to the Regional Administrator. The owner or operator may request reimbursements for partial closure only if the remaining value of the policy is sufficient to cover the maximum costs of closing the facility over its remaining operating life. Within 60 days after receiving bills for closure activities, the Regional Administrator will instruct the insurer to make reimbursements in such amounts as the Regional Administrator specifies in writing if the Regional Administrator determines that the partial or final closure expenditures are in accordance with the approved closure plan or otherwise justified. If the Regional Administrator has reason to believe that the maximum cost of closure over the remaining life of the facility will be significantly greater than the face amount of the policy, he may withhold reimbursement of such amounts as he deems prudent until he determines, in accordance with §265.143(h), that the owner or operator is no longer required to maintain financial assurance for final closure of the particular facility. If the Regional Administrator does not instruct the insurer to make such reimbursements, he will provide to the owner or operator a detailed written statement of reasons.

(6) The owner or operator must maintain the policy in full force and effect until the Regional Administrator consents to termination of the policy by the owner or operator as specified in paragraph (d)(10) of this section. Failure to pay the premium, without substitution of alternate financial assurance as specified in this section, will constitute a significant violation of these regulations, warranting such remedy as the Regional Administrator deems necessary. Such violation will be deemed to begin upon receipt by the Regional Administrator of a notice of future cancellation, termination, or failure to renew due to nonpayment of the premium, rather than upon the date of expiration.

(7) Each policy must contain a provision allowing assignment of the policy to a successor owner or operator. Such assignment may be conditional upon consent of the insurer, provided such consent is not unreasonably refused.

(8) The policy must provide that the insurer may not cancel, terminate, or fail to renew the policy except for failure to pay the premium. The automatic renewal of the policy must, at a minimum, provide the insured with the option of renewal at the face amount of the expiring policy. If there is a failure to pay the premium, the insurer may elect to cancel, terminate, or fail to renew the policy by sending notice by certified mail to the owner or operator and the Regional Administrator. Cancellation, termination, or failure to renew may not occur, however, during the 120 days beginning with the date of receipt of the notice by both the Regional Administrator and the owner or operator, as evidenced by the return receipts. Cancellation, termination, or failure to renew may not occur and the policy will remain in full force and effect in the event that on or before the date of expiration:

(i) The Regional Administrator deems the facility abandoned; or

(ii) Interim status is terminated or revoked; or

(iii) Closure is ordered by the Regional Administrator or a U.S. district court or other court of competent jurisdiction; or

(iv) The owner or operator is named as debtor in a voluntary or involuntary proceeding under Title 11 (Bankruptcy), U.S. Code; or

(v) The premium due is paid.

(9) Whenever the current closure cost estimate increases to an amount greater than the face amount of the policy, the owner or operator, within 60 days after the increase, must either cause the face amount to be

increased to an amount at least equal to the current closure cost estimate and submit evidence of such increase to the Regional Administrator, or obtain other financial assurance as specified in this section to cover the increase. Whenever the current closure cost estimate decreases, the face amount may be reduced to the amount of the current closure cost estimate following written approval by the Regional Administrator.

(10) The Regional Administrator will give written consent to the owner or operator that he may terminate the insurance policy when:

(i) An owner or operator substitutes alternate financial assurance as specified in this section; or

(ii) The Regional Administrator releases the owner or operator from the requirements of this section in accordance with §265.143(h).

(e) *Financial test and corporate guarantee for closure.* (1) An owner or operator may satisfy the requirements of this section by demonstrating that he passes a financial test as specified in this paragraph. To pass this test the owner or operator must meet the criteria of either paragraph (e)(1)(i) or (ii) of this section:

(i) The owner or operator must have:

(A) Two of the following three ratios: A ratio of total liabilities to net worth less than 2.0; a ratio of the sum of net income plus depreciation, depletion, and amortization to total liabilities greater than 0.1; and a ratio of current assets to current liabilities greater than 1.5; and

(B) Net working capital and tangible net worth each at least six times the sum of the current closure and post-closure cost estimates and the current plugging and abandonment cost estimates; and

(C) Tangible net worth of at least $10 million; and

(D) Assets located in the United States amounting to at least 90 percent of total assets or at least six times the sum of the current closure and post-closure cost estimates and the current plugging and abandonment cost estimates.

(ii) The owner or operator must have:

(A) A current rating for his most recent bond issuance of AAA, AA, A, or BBB as issued by Standard and Poor's or Aaa, Aa, A, or Baa as issued by Moody's; and

(B) Tangible net worth at least six times the sum of the current closure and post-closure cost estimates and the current plugging and abandonment cost estimates; and

(C) Tangible net worth of at least $10 million; and

(D) Assets located in the United States amounting to at least 90 percent of total assets or at least six times the sum of the current closure and post-closure cost estimates and the current plugging and abandonment cost estimates.

(2) The phrase "current closure and post-closure cost estimates" as used in paragraph (e)(1) of this section refers to the cost estimates required to be shown in paragraphs 1-4 of the letter from the owner's or operator's chief financial officer (§264.151(f)). The phrase "current plugging and abandonment cost estimates" as used in paragraph (e)(1) of this section refers to the cost estimates required to be shown in paragraphs 1-4 of the letter from the owner's or operator's chief financial officer (§144.70(f) of this title).

(3) To demonstrate that he meets this test, the owner or operator must submit the following items to the Regional Administrator:

(i) A letter signed by the owner's or operator's chief financial officer and worded as specified in §264.151(f); and

(ii) A copy of the independent certified public accountant's report on examination of the owner's or operator's financial statements for the latest completed fiscal year; and

(iii) A special report from the owner's or operator's independent certified public accountant to the owner or operator stating that:

(A) He has compared the data which the letter from the chief financial officer specifies as having been derived from the independently audited, year-end financial statements for the latest fiscal year with the amounts in such financial statements; and

(B) In connection with that procedure, no matters came to his attention which caused him to believe that the specified data should be adjusted.

(4) The owner or operator may obtain an extension of the time allowed for submission of the documents specified in paragraph (e)(3) of this section if the fiscal year of the owner or operator ends during the 90 days prior to the effective date of these regulations and if the year-end financial statements for that fiscal year will be audited by an independent certified public accountant. The extension will end no later than 90 days after the end of the owner's or operator's fiscal year. To

obtain the extension, the owner's or operator's chief financial officer must send, by the effective date of these regulations, a letter to the Regional Administrator of each Region in which the owner's or operator's facilities to be covered by the financial test are located. This letter from the chief financial officer must:

(i) Request the extension;

(ii) Certify that he has grounds to believe that the owner or operator meets the criteria of the financial test;

(iii) Specify for each facility to be covered by the test the EPA Identification Number, name, address, and current closure and post-closure cost estimates to be covered by the test;

(iv) Specify the date ending the owner's or operator's last complete fiscal year before the effective date of these regulations;

(v) Specify the date, no later than 90 days after the end of such fiscal year, when he will submit the documents specified in paragraph (e)(3) of this section; and

(vi) Certify that the year-end financial statements of the owner or operator for such fiscal year will be audited by an independent certified public accountant.

(5) After the initial submission of items specified in paragraph (e)(3) of this section, the owner or operator must send updated information to the Regional Administrator within 90 days after the close of each succeeding fiscal year. This information must consist of all three items specified in paragraph (e)(3) of this section.

(6) If the owner or operator no longer meets the requirements of paragraph (e)(1) of this section, he must send notice to the Regional Administrator of intent to establish alternate financial assurance as specified in this section. The notice must be sent by certified mail within 90 days after the end of the fiscal year for which the year-end financial data show that the owner or operator no longer meets the requirements. The owner or operator must provide the alternate financial assurance within 120 days after the end of such fiscal year.

(7) The Regional Administrator may, based on a reasonable belief that the owner or operator may no longer meet the requirements of paragraph (e)(1) of this section, require reports of financial condition at any time from the owner or operator in addition to those specified in paragraph (e)(3) of this section. If the Regional Administrator finds, on the basis of such reports or other information, that the owner or operator no longer meets the requirements of paragraph (e)(1) of this section, the owner or operator must provide alternate financial assurance as specified in this section within 30 days after notification of such a finding.

(8) The Regional Administrator may disallow use of this test on the basis of qualifications in the opinion expressed by the independent certified public accountant in his report on examination of the owner's or operator's financial statements (see paragraph (e)(3)(ii) of this section). An adverse opinion or a disclaimer of opinion will be cause for disallowance. The Regional Administrator will evaluate other qualifications on an individual basis. The owner or operator must provide alternate financial assurance as specified in this section within 30 days after notification of the disallowance.

(9) The owner or operator is no longer required to submit the items specified in paragraph (e)(3) of this section when:

(i) An owner or operator substitutes alternate financial assurance as specified in this section; or

(ii) The Regional Administrator releases the owner or operator from the requirements of this section in accordance with §265.143(h).

(10) An owner or operator may meet the requirements of this section by obtaining a written guarantee. The guarantor must be the direct or higher-tier parent corporation of the owner or operator, a firm whose parent corporation is also the parent corporation of the owner or operator, or a firm with a "substantial business relationship" with the owner or operator. The guarantor must meet the requirements for owners or operators in paragraphs (e)(1) through (8) of this section and must comply with the terms of the guarantee. The wording of the guarantee must be identical to the wording specified in §264.151(h). A certified copy of the guarantee must accompany the items sent to the Regional Administrator as specified in paragraph (e)(3) of this section. One of these items must be the letter from the guarantor's chief financial officer. If the guarantor's parent corporation is also the parent corporation of the owner or operator, the letter must describe the value received in consideration of the guarantee. If the guarantor is a firm with a "substantial business relationship" with the owner or operator, this letter must describe this "substantial business relationship" and the value received in consideration of the guarantee. The terms of the guarantee must provide that:

(i) If the owner or operator fails to perform final closure of a facility covered by the corporate guarantee in accordance with the closure plan and other interim status requirements whenever required to do so, the guarantor will do so or establish a trust fund as specified in §265.143(a) in the name of the owner or operator.

(ii) The corporate guarantee will remain in force unless the guarantor sends notice of cancellation by certified mail to the owner or operator and to the Regional Administrator. Cancellation may not occur, however, during the 120 days beginning on the date of receipt of the notice of cancellation by both the owner or operator and the Regional Administrator, as evidenced by the return receipts.

(iii) If the owner or operator fails to provide alternate financial assurance as specified in this section and obtain the written approval of such alternate assurance from the Regional Administrator within 90 days after receipt by both the owner or operator and the Regional Administrator of a notice of cancellation of the corporate guarantee from the guarantor, the guarantor will provide such alternate financial assurance in the name of the owner or operator.

(f) *Use of multiple financial mechanisms.* An owner or operator may satisfy the requirements of this section by establishing more than one financial mechanism per facility. These mechanisms are limited to trust funds, surety bonds, letters of credit, and insurance. The mechanisms must be as specified in paragraphs (a) through (d), respectively, of this section, except that it is the combination of mechanisms, rather than the single mechanism, which must provide financial assurance for an amount at least equal to the current closure cost estimate. If an owner or operator uses a trust fund in combination with a surety bond or a letter of credit, he may use the trust fund as the standby trust fund for the other mechanisms. A single standby trust fund may be established for two or more mechanisms. The Regional Administrator may use any or all of the mechanisms to provide for closure of the facility.

(g) *Use of a financial mechanism for multiple facilities.* An owner or operator may use a financial assurance mechanism specified in this section to meet the requirements of this section for more than one facility. Evidence of financial assurance submitted to the Regional Administrator must include a list showing, for each facility, the EPA Identification Number, name, address, and the amount of funds for closure assured by the mechanism. If the facilities covered by the mechanism are in more than one Region, identical evidence of financial assurance must be submitted to and maintained with the Regional Administrators of all such Regions. The amount of funds available through the mechanism must be no less than the sum of funds that would be available if a separate mechanism had been established and maintained for each facility. In directing funds available through the mechanism for closure of any of the facilities covered by the mechanism, the Regional Administrator may direct only the amount of funds designated for that facility, unless the owner or operator agrees to the use of additional funds available under the mechanism.

(h) *Release of the owner or operator from the requirements of this section.* Within 60 days after receiving certifications from the owner or operator and a qualified Professional Engineer that final closure has been completed in accordance with the approved closure plan, the Regional Administrator will notify the owner or operator in writing that he is no longer required by this section to maintain financial assurance for final closure of the facility, unless the Regional Administrator has reason to believe that final closure has not been in accordance with the approved closure plan. The Regional Administrator shall provide the owner or operator a detailed written statement of any such reason to believe that closure has not been in accordance with the approved closure plan.

[47 FR 15064, Apr. 7, 1982, as amended at 51 FR 16456, May 2, 1986; 57 FR 42843, Sept. 16, 1992; 71 FR 16909, Apr. 4, 2006]

§265.144 Cost estimate for post-closure care.

(a) The owner or operator of a hazardous waste disposal unit must have a detailed written estimate, in current dollars, of the annual cost of post-closure monitoring and maintenance of the facility in accordance with the applicable post-closure regulations in §§265.117 through 265.120, 265.228, 265.258, 265.280, and 265.310.

(1) The post-closure cost estimate must be based on the costs to the owner or operator of hiring a third party to conduct post-closure care activities. A third party is a party who is neither a parent nor subsidiary of the owner or operator. (See definition of parent corporation in §265.141(d).)

(2) The post-closure cost estimate is calculated by multiplying the annual post-closure cost estimate by the number of years of post-closure care required under §265.117.

(b) During the active life of the facility, the owner or operator must adjust the post-closure cost estimate for inflation within 60 days prior to the anniversary date of the establishment of the financial instrument(s) used to comply with §265.145. For owners or operators using the financial test or corporate guarantee, the post-closure care cost estimate must be updated for inflation no later than 30 days after the close of the firm's fiscal year and before submission of updated information to the Regional Administrator as specified in §265.145(d)(5). The adjustment may be made by recalculating the post-closure cost estimate in current dollars or by using an inflation factor derived from the most recent Implicit Price Deflator for Gross National Product published by the U.S. Department of Commerce in its *Survey of Current Business* as specified in §265.145 (b)(1) and (2). The inflation factor is the result of dividing the latest published annual Deflator by the Deflator for the previous year.

(1) The first adjustment is made by multiplying the post-closure cost estimate by the inflation factor. The result is the adjusted post-closure cost estimate.

(2) Subsequent adjustments are made by multiplying the latest adjusted post-closure cost estimate by the latest inflation factor.

(c) During the active life of the facility, the owner or operator must revise the post-closure cost estimate no later than 30 days after a revision to the post-closure plan which increases the cost of post-closure care. If the owner or operator has an approved post-closure plan, the post-closure cost estimate must be revised no later than 30 days after the Regional Administrator has approved the request to modify the plan, if the change in the post-closure plan increases the cost of post-closure care. The revised post-closure cost estimate must be adjusted for inflation as specified in §265.144(b).

(d) The owner or operator must keep the following at the facility during the operating life of the facility: the latest post-closure cost estimate prepared in accordance with §265.144 (a) and (c) and, when this estimate has been adjusted in accordance with §265.144(b), the latest adjusted post-closure cost estimate.

[47 FR 15064, Apr. 7, 1982, as amended at 50 FR 4514, Jan. 31, 1985; 51 FR 16457, May 2, 1986]

§265.145 Financial assurance for post-closure care.

By the effective date of these regulations, an owner or operator of a facility with a hazardous waste disposal unit must establish financial assurance for post-closure care of the disposal unit(s).

(a) *Post-closure trust fund.* (1) An owner or operator may satisfy the requirements of this section by establishing a post-closure trust fund which conforms to the requirements of this paragraph and submitting an originally signed duplicate of the trust agreement to the Regional Administrator. The trustee must be an entity which has the authority to act as a trustee and whose trust operations are regulated and examined by a Federal or State agency.

(2) The wording of the trust agreement must be identical to the wording specified in §264.151(a)(1), and the trust agreement must be accompanied by a formal certification of acknowledgment (for example, see §264.151(a)(2)). Schedule A of the trust agreement must be updated within 60 days after a change in the amount of the current post-closure cost estimate covered by the agreement.

(3) Payments into the trust fund must be made annually by the owner or operator over the 20 years beginning with the effective date of these regulations or over the remaining operating life of the facility as estimated in the closure plan, whichever period is shorter; this period is hereafter referred to as the "pay-in period." The payments into the post-closure trust fund must be made as follows:

(i) The first payment must be made by the effective date of these regulations, except as provided in paragraph (a)(5) of this section. The first payment must be at least equal to the current post-closure cost estimate, except as provided in §265.145(f), divided by the number of years in the pay-in period.

(ii) Subsequent payments must be made no later than 30 days after each anniversary date of the first payment. The amount of each subsequent payment must be determined by this formula:

$$\text{Next payment} = \frac{CE - CV}{Y}$$

where CE is the current post-closure cost estimate, CV is the current value of the trust fund, and Y is the number of years remaining in the pay-in period.

(4) The owner or operator may accelerate payments into the trust fund or he may deposit the full amount of the current post-closure cost estimate at the time the fund is established. However, he must maintain the value of the fund at no less than the value that the fund would have if annual payments were made as specified in paragraph (a)(3) of this section.

(5) If the owner or operator establishes a post-closure trust fund after having used one or more alternate mechanisms specified in this section, his first payment must be in at least the amount that the fund would

contain if the trust fund were established initially and annual payments made as specified in paragraph (a)(3) of this section.

(6) After the pay-in period is completed, whenever the current post-closure cost estimate changes during the operating life of the facility, the owner or operator must compare the new estimate with the trustee's most recent annual valuation of the trust fund. If the value of the fund is less than the amount of the new estimate, the owner or operator, within 60 days after the change in the cost estimate, must either deposit an amount into the fund so that its value after this deposit at least equals the amount of the current post-closure cost estimate, or obtain other financial assurance as specified in this section to cover the difference.

(7) During the operating life of the facility, if the value of the trust fund is greater than the total amount of the current post-closure cost estimate, the owner or operator may submit a written request to the Regional Administrator for release of the amount in excess of the current post-closure cost estimate.

(8) If an owner or operator substitutes other financial assurance as specified in this section for all or part of the trust fund, he may submit a written request to the Regional Administrator for release of the amount in excess of the current post-closure cost estimate covered by the trust fund.

(9) Within 60 days after receiving a request from the owner or operator for release of funds as specified in paragraph (a)(7) or (8) of this section, the Regional Administrator will instruct the trustee to release to the owner or operator such funds as the Regional Administrator specifies in writing.

(10) During the period of post-closure care, the Regional Administrator may approve a release of funds if the owner or operator demonstrates to the Regional Administrator that the value of the trust fund exceeds the remaining cost of post-closure care.

(11) An owner or operator or any other person authorized to conduct post-closure care may request reimbursements for post-closure expenditures by submitting itemized bills to the Regional Administrator. Within 60 days after receiving bills for post-closure care activities, the Regional Administrator will instruct the trustee to make reimbursements in those amounts as the Regional Administrator specifies in writing, if the Regional Administrator determines that the post-closure expenditures are in accordance with the approved post-closure plan or otherwise justified. If the Regional Administrator does not instruct the trustee to make such reimbursements, he will provide the owner or operator with a detailed written statement of reasons.

(12) The Regional Administrator will agree to termination of the trust when:

(i) An owner or operator substitutes alternate financial assurance as specified in this section; or

(ii) The Regional Administrator releases the owner or operator from the requirements of this section in accordance with §265.145(h).

(b) *Surety bond guaranteeing payment into a post-closure trust fund.* (1) An owner or operator may satisfy the requirements of this section by obtaining a surety bond which conforms to the requirements of this paragraph and submitting the bond to the Regional Administrator. The surety company issuing the bond must, at a minimum, be among those listed as acceptable sureties on Federal bonds in Circular 570 of the U.S. Department of the Treasury.

(2) The wording of the surety bond must be identical to the wording specified in §264.151(b).

(3) The owner or operator who uses a surety bond to satisfy the requirements of this section must also establish a standby trust fund. Under the terms of the bond, all payments made thereunder will be deposited by the surety directly into the standby trust fund in accordance with instructions from the Regional Administrator. This standby trust fund must meet the requirements specified in §265.145(a), except that:

(i) An originally signed duplicate of the trust agreement must be submitted to the Regional Administrator with the surety bond; and

(ii) Until the standby trust fund is funded pursuant to the requirements of this section, the following are not required by these regulations:

(A) Payments into the trust fund as specified in §265.145(a);

(B) Updating of Schedule A of the trust agreement (see §264.151(a)) to show current post-closure cost estimates;

(C) Annual valuations as required by the trust agreement; and

(D) Notices of nonpayment as required by the trust agreement.

(4) The bond must guarantee that the owner or operator will:

(i) Fund the standby trust fund in an amount equal to the penal sum of the bond before the beginning of final closure of the facility; or

(ii) Fund the standby trust fund in an amount equal to the penal sum within 15 days after an administrative order to begin final closure issued by the Regional Administrator becomes final, or within 15 days after an order to begin final closure is issued by a U.S. district court or other court of competent jurisdiction; or

(iii) Provide alternate financial assurance as specified in this section, and obtain the Regional Administrator's written approval of the assurance provided, within 90 days after receipt by both the owner or operator and the Regional Administrator of a notice of cancellation of the bond from the surety.

(5) Under the terms of the bond, the surety will become liable on the bond obligation when the owner or operator fails to perform as guaranteed by the bond.

(6) The penal sum of the bond must be in an amount at least equal to the current post-closure cost estimate, except as provided in §265.145(f).

(7) Whenever the current post-closure cost estimate increases to an amount greater than the penal sum, the owner or operator, within 60 days after the increase, must either cause the penal sum to be increased to an amount at least equal to the current post-closure cost estimate and submit evidence of such increase to the Regional Administrator, or obtain other financial assurance as specified in this section to cover the increase. Whenever the current post-closure cost estimate decreases, the penal sum may be reduced to the amount of the current post-closure cost estimate following written approval by the Regional Administrator.

(8) Under the terms of the bond, the surety may cancel the bond by sending notice of cancellation by certified mail to the owner or operator and to the Regional Administrator. Cancellation may not occur, however, during the 120 days beginning on the date of receipt of the notice of cancellation by both the owner or operator and the Regional Administrator, as evidenced by the return receipts.

(9) The owner or operator may cancel the bond if the Regional Administrator has given prior written consent based on his receipt of evidence of alternate financial assurance as specified in this section.

(c) *Post-closure letter of credit.* (1) An owner or operator may satisfy the requirements of this section by obtaining an irrevocable standby letter of credit which conforms to the requirements of this paragraph and submitting the letter to the Regional Administrator. The issuing institution must be an entity which has the authority to issue letters of credit and whose letter-of-credit operations are regulated and examined by a Federal or State agency.

(2) The wording of the letter of credit must be identical to the wording specified in §264.151(d).

(3) An owner or operator who uses a letter of credit to satisfy the requirements of this section must also establish a standby trust fund. Under the terms of the letter of credit, all amounts paid pursuant to a draft by the Regional Administrator will be deposited by the issuing institution directly into the standby trust fund in accordance with instructions from the Regional Administrator. This standby trust fund must meet the requirements of the trust fund specified in §265.145(a), except that:

(i) An originally signed duplicate of the trust agreement must be submitted to the Regional Administrator with the letter of credit; and

(ii) Unless the standby trust fund is funded pursuant to the requirements of this section, the following are not required by these regulations:

(A) Payments into the trust fund as specified in §265.145(a);

(B) Updating of Schedule A of the trust agreement (see §264.151(a)) to show current post-closure cost estimates;

(C) Annual valuations as required by the trust agreement; and

(D) Notices of nonpayment as required by the trust agreement.

(4) The letter of credit must be accompanied by a letter from the owner or operator referring to the letter of credit by number, issuing institution, and date, and providing the following information: The EPA Identification Number, name, and address of the facility, and the amount of funds assured for post-closure care of the facility by the letter of credit.

(5) The letter of credit must be irrevocable and issued for a period of at least 1 year. The letter of credit must provide that the expiration date will be automatically extended for a period of at least 1 year unless, at least 120 days before the current expiration date, the issuing institution notifies both the owner or operator and the Regional Administrator by certified mail of a decision not to extend the expiration date. Under the terms of

the letter of credit, the 120 days will begin on the date when both the owner or operator and the Regional Administrator have received the notice, as evidenced by the return receipts.

(6) The letter of credit must be issued in an amount at least equal to the current post-closure cost estimate, except as provided in §265.145(f).

(7) Whenever the current post-closure cost estimate increases to an amount greater than the amount of the credit during the operating life of the facility, the owner or operator, within 60 days after the increase, must either cause the amount of the credit to be increased so that it at least equals the current post-closure cost estimate and submit evidence of such increase to the Regional Administrator, or obtain other financial assurance as specified in this section to cover the increase. Whenever the current post-closure cost estimate decreases during the operating life of the facility, the amount of the credit may be reduced to the amount of the current post-closure cost estimate following written approval by the Regional Administrator.

(8) During the period of post-closure care, the Regional Administrator may approve a decrease in the amount of the letter of credit if the owner or operator demonstrates to the Regional Administrator that the amount exceeds the remaining cost of post-closure care.

(9) Following a final administrative determination pursuant to section 3008 of RCRA that the owner or operator has failed to perform post-closure care in accordance with the approved post-closure plan and other permit requirements, the Regional Administrator may draw on the letter of credit.

(10) If the owner or operator does not establish alternate financial assurance as specified in this section and obtain written approval of such alternate assurance from the Regional Administrator within 90 days after receipt by both the owner or operator and the Regional Administrator of a notice from the issuing institution that it has decided not to extend the letter of credit beyond the current expiration date, the Regional Administrator will draw on the letter of credit. The Regional Administrator may delay the drawing if the issuing institution grants an extension of the term of the credit. During the last 30 days of any such extension the Regional Administrator will draw on the letter of credit if the owner or operator has failed to provide alternate financial assurance as specified in this section and obtain written approval of such assurance from the Regional Administrator.

(11) The Regional Administrator will return the letter of credit to the issuing institution for termination when:

(i) An owner or operator substitutes alternate financial assurance as specified in this section; or

(ii) The Regional Administrator releases the owner or operator from the requirements of this section in accordance with §265.145(h).

(d) *Post-closure insurance.* (1) An owner or operator may satisfy the requirements of this section by obtaining post-closure insurance which conforms to the requirements of this paragraph and submitting a certificate of such insurance to the Regional Administrator. By the effective date of these regulations the owner or operator must submit to the Regional Administrator a letter from an insurer stating that the insurer is considering issuance of post- closure insurance conforming to the requirements of this paragraph to the owner or operator. Within 90 days after the effective date of these regulations, the owner or operator must submit the certificate of insurance to the Regional Administrator or establish other financial assurance as specified in this section. At a minimum, the insurer must be licensed to transact the business of insurance, or eligible to provide insurance as an excess or surplus lines insurer, in one or more States.

(2) The wording of the certificate of insurance must be identical to the wording specified in §264.151(e).

(3) The post-closure insurance policy must be issued for a face amount at least equal to the current post-closure cost estimate, except as provided in §265.145(f). The term "face amount" means the total amount the insurer is obligated to pay under the policy. Actual payments by the insurer will not change the face amount, although the insurer's future liability will be lowered by the amount of the payments.

(4) The post-closure insurance policy must guarantee that funds will be available to provide post-closure care of the facility whenever the post-closure period begins. The policy must also guarantee that once post-closure care begins the insurer will be responsible for paying out funds, up to an amount equal to the face amount of the policy, upon the direction of the Regional Administrator, to such party or parties as the Regional Administrator specifies.

(5) An owner or operator or any other person authorized to perform post-closure care may request reimbursement for post-closure care expenditures by submitting itemized bills to the Regional Administrator.

Within 60 days after receiving bills for post-closure care activities, the Regional Administrator will instruct the insurer to make reimbursements in those amounts as the Regional Administrator specifies in writing, if the Regional Administrator determines that the post-closure expenditures are in accordance with the approved post-closure plan or otherwise justified. If the Regional Administrator does not instruct the insurer to make such reimbursements, he will provide a detailed written statement of reasons.

(6) The owner or operator must maintain the policy in full force and effect until the Regional Administrator consents to termination of the policy by the owner or operator as specified in paragraph (d)(11) of this section. Failure to pay the premium, without substitution of alternate financial assurance as specified in the section, will constitute a significant violation of these regulations, warranting such remedy as the Regional Administrator deems necessary. Such violation will be deemed to begin upon receipt by the Regional Administrator of a notice of future cancellation, termination, or failure to renew due to nonpayment of the premium, rather than upon the date of expiration.

(7) Each policy most contain a provision allowing assignment of the policy to a successor owner or operator. Such assignment may be conditional upon consent of the insurer, provided such consent is not unreasonably refused.

(8) The policy must provide that the insurer may not cancel, terminate, or fail to renew the policy except for failure to pay the premium. The automatic renewal of the policy must, at a minimum, provide the insured with the option of renewal at the face amount of the expiring policy. If there is a failure to pay the premium, the insurer may elect to cancel, terminate, or fail to renew the policy by sending notice by certified mail to the owner or operator and the Regional Administrator. Cancellation, termination, or failure to renew may not occur, however, during the 120 days beginning with the date of receipt of the notice by both the Regional Administrator and the owner or operator, as evidenced by the return receipts. Cancellation, termination, or failure to renew may not occur and the policy will remain in full force and effect in the event that on or before the date of expiration:

(i) The Regional Administrator deems the facility abandoned; or

(ii) Interim status is terminated or revoked; or

(iii) Closure is ordered by the Regional Administrator or a U.S. district court or other court of competent jurisdiction; or

(iv) The owner or operator is named as debtor in a voluntary or involuntary proceeding under Title 11 (Bankruptcy), U.S. Code; or

(v) The premium due is paid.

(9) Whenever the current post-closure cost estimate increases to an amount greater than the face amount of the policy during the operating life of the facility, the owner or operator, within 60 days after the increase, must either cause the face amount to be increased to an amount at least equal to the current post-closure cost estimate and submit evidence of such increase to the Regional Administrator, or obtain other financial assurance as specified in this section to cover the increase. Whenever the current post-closure cost estimate decreases during the operating life of the facility, the face amount may be reduced to the amount of the current post-closure cost estimate following written approval by the Regional Administrator.

(10) Commencing on the date that liability to make payments pursuant to the policy accrues, the insurer will thereafter annually increase the face amount of the policy. Such increase must be equivalent to the face amounts of the policy, less any payments made, multiplied by an amount equivalent to 85 percent of the most recent investment rate or of the equivalent coupon-issue yield announced by the U.S. Treasury for 26-week Treasury securities.

(11) The Regional Administrator will give written consent to the owner or operator that he may terminate the insurance policy when:

(i) An owner or operator substitutes alternate financial assurance as specified in this section; or

(ii) The Regional Administrator releases the owner or operator from the requirements of this section in accordance with §265.145(h).

(e) *Financial test and corporate guarantee for post-closure care.* (1) An owner or operator may satisfy the requirements of this section by demonstrating that he passes a financial test as specified in this paragraph. To pass this test the owner or operator must meet the criteria either of paragraph (e)(1)(i) or (ii) of this section:

(i) The owner or operator must have:

(A) Two of the following three ratios: a ratio of total liabilities to net worth less than 2.0; a ratio of the sum of net income plus depreciation, depletion, and amortization to total liabilities greater than 0.1; and a ratio of current assets to current liabilities greater than 1.5; and

(B) Net working capital and tangible net worth each at least six times the sum of the current closure and post-closure cost estimates and the current plugging and abandonment cost estimates; and

(C) Tangible net worth of at least $10 million; and

(D) Assets in the United States amounting to at least 90 percent of his total assets or at least six times the sum of the current closure and post-closure cost estimates and the current plugging and abandonment cost estimates.

(ii) The owner or operator must have:

(A) A current rating for his most recent bond issuance of AAA, AA, A, or BBB as issued by Standard and Poor's or Aaa, Aa, A, or Baa as issued by Moody's; and

(B) Tangible net worth at least six times the sum of the current closure and post-closure cost estimates and the current plugging and abandonment cost estimates; and

(C) Tangible net worth of at least $10 million; and

(D) Assets located in the United States amounting to at least 90 percent of his total assets or at least six times the sum of the current closure and post-closure cost estimates and the current plugging and abandonment cost estimates.

(2) The phrase "current closure and post-closure cost estimates" as used in paragraph (e)(1) of this section refers to the cost estimates required to be shown in paragraphs 1-4 of the letter from the owner's or operator's chief financial officer (§264.151(f)). The phrase "current plugging and abandonment cost estimates" as used in paragraph (e)(1) of this section refers to the cost estimates required to be shown in paragraphs 1-4 of the letter from the owner's or operator's chief financial officer (§144.70(f) of this title).

(3) To demonstrate that he meets this test, the owner or operator must submit the following items to the Regional Administrator:

(i) A letter signed by the owner's or operator's chief financial officer and worded as specified in §264.151(f); and

(ii) A copy of the independent certified public accountant's report on examination of the owner's or operator's financial statements for the latest completed fiscal year; and

(iii) A special report from the owner's or operator's independent certified public accountant to the owner or operator stating that:

(A) He has compared the data which the letter from the chief financial officer specifies as having been derived from the independently audited, year-end financial statements for the latest fiscal year with the amounts in such financial statements; and

(B) In connection with that procedure, no matters came to his attention which caused him to believe that the specified data should be adjusted.

(4) The owner or operator may obtain an extension of the time allowed for submission of the documents specified in paragraph (e)(3) of this section if the fiscal year of the owner or operator ends during the 90 days prior to the effective date of these regulations and if the year-end financial statements for that fiscal year will be audited by an independent certified public accountant. The extension will end no later than 90 days after the end of the owner's or operator's fiscal year. To obtain the extension, the owner's or operator's chief financial officer must send, by the effective date of these regulations, a letter to the Regional Administrator of each Region in which the owner's or operator's facilities to be covered by the financial test are located. This letter from the chief financial officer must:

(i) Request the extension;

(ii) Certify that he has grounds to believe that the owner or operator meets the criteria of the financial test;

(iii) Specify for each facility to be covered by the test the EPA Identification Number, name, address, and the current closure and post-closure cost estimates to be covered by the test;

(iv) Specify the date ending the owner's or operator's latest complete fiscal year before the effective date of these regulations;

(v) Specify the date, no later than 90 days after the end of such fiscal year, when he will submit the documents specified in paragraph (e)(3) of this section; and

(vi) Certify that the year-end financial statements of the owner or operator for such fiscal year will be audited by an independent certified public accountant.

(5) After the initial submission of items specified in paragraph (e)(3) of this section, the owner or operator

must send updated information to the Regional Administrator within 90 days after the close of each succeeding fiscal year. This information must consist of all three items specified in paragraph (e)(3) of this section.

(6) If the owner or operator no longer meets the requirements of paragraph (e)(1) of this section, he must send notice to the Regional Administrator of intent to establish alternate financial assurance as specified in this section. The notice must be sent by certified mail within 90 days after the end of the fiscal year for which the year-end financial data show that the owner or operator no longer meets the requirements. The owner or operator must provide the alternate financial assurance within 120 days after the end of such fiscal year.

(7) The Regional Administrator may, based on a reasonable belief that the owner or operator may no longer meet the requirements of paragraph (e)(1) of this section, require reports of financial condition at any time from the owner or operator in addition to those specified in paragraph (e)(3) of this section. If the Regional Administrator finds, on the basis of such reports or other information, that the owner or operator no longer meets the requirements of paragraph (e)(1) of this section, the owner or operator must provide alternate financial assurance as specified in this section within 30 days after notification of such a finding.

(8) The Regional Administrator may disallow use of this test on the basis of qualifications in the opinion expressed by the independent certified public accountant in his report on examination of the owner's or operator's financial statements (see paragraph (e)(3)(ii) of this section). An adverse opinion or a disclaimer of opinion will be cause for disallowance. The Regional Administrator will evaluate other qualifications on an individual basis. The owner or operator must provide alternate financial assurance as specified in this section within 30 days after notification of the disallowance.

(9) During the period of post-closure care, the Regional Administrator may approve a decrease in the current post-closure cost estimate for which this test demonstrates financial assurance if the owner or operator demonstrates to the Regional Administrator that the amount of the cost estimate exceeds the remaining cost of post-closure care.

(10) The owner or operator is no longer required to submit the items specified in paragraph (e)(3) of this section when:

(i) An owner or operator substitutes alternate financial assurance as specified in this section; or

(ii) The Regional Administrator releases the owner or operator from the requirements of this section in accordance with §265.145(h).

(11) An owner or operator may meet the requirements of this section by obtaining a written guarantee. The guarantor must be the direct or higher-tier parent corporation of the owner or operator, a firm whose parent corporation is also the parent corporation of the owner or operator, or a firm with a "substantial business relationship" with the owner or operator. The guarantor must meet the requirements for owners or operators in paragraphs (e)(1) through (9) of this section and must comply with the terms of the guarantee. The wording of the guarantee must be identical to the wording specified in §264.151(h). A certified copy of the guarantee must accompany the items sent to the Regional Administrator as specified in paragraph (e)(3) of this section. One of these items must be the letter from the guarantor's chief financial officer. If the guarantor's parent corporation is also the parent corporation of the owner or operator, the letter must describe the value received in consideration of the guarantee. If the guarantor is a firm with a "substantial business relationship" with the owner or operator, this letter must describe this "substantial business relationship" and the value received in consideration of the guarantee. The terms of the guarantee must provide that:

(i) If the owner or operator fails to perform post-closure care of a facility covered by the corporate guarantee in accordance with the post-closure plan and other interim status requirements whenever required to do so, the guarantor will do so or establish a trust fund as specified in §265.145(a) in the name of the owner or operator.

(ii) The corporate guarantee will remain in force unless the guarantor sends notice of cancellation by certified mail to the owner or operator and to the Regional Administrator. Cancellation may not occur, however, during the 120 days beginning on the date of receipt of the notice of cancellation by both the owner or operator and the Regional Administrator, as evidenced by the return receipts.

(iii) If the owner or operator fails to provide alternate financial assurance as specified in this section and obtain the written approval of such alternate assurance from the Regional Administrator within 90 days after receipt by both the owner or operator and the Regional Administrator of a notice of cancellation of the corporate guarantee from the guarantor, the guarantor will provide such alternate financial assurance in the name of the owner or operator.

(f) *Use of multiple financial mechanisms.* An owner or operator may satisfy the requirements of this section by establishing more than one financial mechanism per facility. These mechanisms are limited to trust funds, surety bonds, letters of credit, and insurance. The mechanisms must be as specified in paragraphs (a) through (d), respectively, of this section, except that it is the combination of mechanisms, rather than the single mechanism, which must provide financial assurance for an amount at least equal to the current post-closure cost estimate. If an owner or operator uses a trust fund in combination with a surety bond or a letter of credit, he may use the trust fund as the standby trust fund for the other mechanisms. A single standby trust fund may be established for two or more mechanisms. The Regional Administrator may use any or all of the mechanisms to provide for post-closure care of the facility.

(g) *Use of a financial mechanism for multiple facilities.* An owner or operator may use a financial assurance mechanism specified in this section to meet the requirements of this section for more than one facility. Evidence of financial assurance submitted to the Regional Administrator must include a list showing, for each facility, the EPA Identification Number, name, address, and the amount of funds for post-closure care assured by the mechanism. If the facilities covered by the mechanism are in more than one Region, identical evidence of financial assurance must be submitted to and maintained with the Regional Administrators of all such Regions. The amount of funds available through the mechanism must be no less than the sum of funds that would be available if a separate mechanism had been established and maintained for each facility. In directing funds available through the mechanism for post-closure care of any of the facilities covered by the mechanism, the Regional Administrator may direct only the amount of funds designated for that facility, unless the owner or operator agrees to the use of additional funds available under the mechanism.

(h) *Release of the owner or operator from the requirements of this section.* Within 60 days after receiving certifications from the owner or operator and a qualified Professional Engineer that the post-closure care period has been completed for a hazardous waste disposal unit in accordance with the approved plan, the Regional Administrator will notify the owner or operator in writing that he is no longer required to maintain financial assurance for post-closure care of that unit, unless the Regional Administrator has reason to believe that post-closure care has not been in accordance with the approved post-closure plan. The Regional Administrator shall provide the owner or operator a detailed written statement of any such reason to believe that post-closure care has not been in accordance with the approved post-closure plan.

[47 FR 15064, Apr. 7, 1982, as amended at 51 FR 16457, May 2, 1986; 57 FR 42843, Sept. 16, 1992; 71 FR 16909, Apr. 4, 2006; 71 FR 40275, July 14, 2006]

§265.146 Use of a mechanism for financial assurance of both closure and post-closure care.

An owner or operator may satisfy the requirements for financial assurance for both closure and post-closure care for one or more facilities by using a trust fund, surety bond, letter of credit, insurance, financial test, or corporate guarantee that meets the specifications for the mechanism in both §§265.143 and 265.145. The amount of funds available through the mechanism must be no less than the sum of funds that would be available if a separate mechanism had been established and maintained for financial assurance of closure and of post-closure care.

§265.147 Liability requirements.

(a) *Coverage for sudden accidental occurrences.* An owner or operator of a hazardous waste treatment, storage, or disposal facility, or a group of such facilities, must demonstrate financial responsibility for bodily injury and property damage to third parties caused by sudden accidental occurrences arising from operations of the facility or group of facilities. The owner or operator must have and maintain liability coverage for sudden accidental occurrences in the amount of at least $1 million per occurrence with an annual aggregate of at least $2 million, exclusive of legal defense costs. This liability coverage may be demonstrated as specified in paragraphs (a)(1), (2), (3), (4), (5), or (6) of this section:

(1) An owner or operator may demonstrate the required liability coverage by having liability insurance as specified in this paragraph.

(i) Each insurance policy must be amended by attachment of the Hazardous Waste Facility Liability Endorsement, or evidenced by a Certificate of Liability Insurance. The wording of the endorsement must be identical to the wording specified in §264.151(i). The wording of the certificate of insurance must be identical to the wording specified in §264.151(j). The owner or operator must submit a signed duplicate original of the endorsement or the certificate of insurance to the Regional Administrator, or Regional Administrators if the facilities are located in more than one Region. If requested by a Regional Administrator, the owner or operator must provide a signed duplicate original of the insurance policy.

(ii) Each insurance policy must be issued by an insurer which, at a minimum, is licensed to transact the business of insurance, or eligible to provide insurance as an excess or surplus lines insurer, in one or more States.

(2) An owner or operator may meet the requirements of this section by passing a financial test or using the guarantee for liability coverage as specified in paragraphs (f) and (g) of this section.

(3) An owner or operator may meet the requirements of this section by obtaining a letter of credit for liability coverage as specified in paragraph (h) of this section.

(4) An owner or operator may meet the requirements of this section by obtaining a surety bond for liability coverage as specified in paragraph (i) of this section.

(5) An owner or operator may meet the requirements of this section by obtaining a trust fund for liability coverage as specified in paragraph (j) of this section.

(6) An owner or operator may demonstrate the required liability coverage through the use of combinations of insurance, financial test, guarantee, letter of credit, surety bond, and trust fund, except that the owner or operator may not combine a financial test covering part of the liability coverage requirement with a guarantee unless the financial statement of the owner or operator is not consolidated with the financial statement of the guarantor. The amounts of coverage demonstrated must total at least the minimum amounts required by this section. If the owner or operator demonstrates the required coverage through the use of a combination of financial assurances under this paragraph, the owner or operator shall specify at least one such assurance as "primary" coverage and shall specify other assurance as "excess" coverage.

(7) An owner or operator shall notify the Regional Administrator in writing within 30 days whenever:

(i) A claim results in a reduction in the amount of financial assurance for liability coverage provided by a financial instrument authorized in paragraphs (a)(1) through (a)(6) of this section; or

(ii) A Certification of Valid Claim for bodily injury or property damages caused by a sudden or non-sudden accidental occurrence arising from the operation of a hazardous waste treatment, storage, or disposal facility is entered between the owner or operator and third-party claimant for liability coverage under paragraphs (a)(1) through (a)(6) of this section; or

(iii) A final court order establishing a judgment for bodily injury or property damage caused by a sudden or non-sudden accidental occurrence arising from the operation of a hazardous waste treatment, storage, or disposal facility is issued against the owner or operator or an instrument that is providing financial assurance for liability coverage under paragraphs (a)(1) through (a)(6) of this section.

(b) *Coverage for nonsudden accidental occurrences.* An owner or operator of a surface impoundment, landfill, or land treatment facility which is used to manage hazardous waste, or a group of such facilities, must demonstrate financial responsibility for bodily injury and property damage to third parties caused by nonsudden accidental occurrences arising from operations of the facility or group of facilities. The owner or operator must have and maintain liability coverage for nonsudden accidental occurrences in the amount of at least $3 million per occurrence with an annual aggregate of at least $6 million, exclusive of legal defense costs. An owner or operator who must meet the requirements of this section may combine the required per-occurrence coverage levels for sudden and nonsudden accidental occurrences into a single per-occurrence level, and combine the required annual aggregate coverage levels for sudden and nonsudden accidental occurrences into a single annual aggregate level. Owners or operators who combine coverage levels for sudden and nonsudden accidental occurrences must maintain liability coverage in the amount of at least $4 million per occurrence and $8 million annual aggregate. This liability coverage may be demonstrated as specified in paragraph (b)(1), (2), (3), (4), (5), or (6) of this section:

(1) An owner or operator may demonstrate the required liability coverage by having liability insurance as specified in this paragraph.

(i) Each insurance policy must be amended by attachment of the Hazardous Waste Facility Liability Endorsement or evidenced by a Certificate of Liability Insurance. The wording of the endorsement must be identical to the wording specified in §264.151(i). The wording of the certificate of insurance must be identical to the wording specified in §264.151(j). The owner or operator must submit a signed duplicate original of the endorsement or the certificate of insurance to the Regional Administrator, or Regional

Administrators if the facilities are located in more than one Region. If requested by a Regional Administrator, the owner or operator must provide a signed duplicate original of the insurance policy.

(ii) Each insurance policy must be issued by an insurer which, at a minimum, is licensed to transact the business of insurance, or eligible to provide insurance as an excess or surplus lines insurer, in one or more States.

(2) An owner or operator may meet the requirements of this section by passing a financial test or using the guarantee for liability coverage as specified in paragraphs (f) and (g) of this section.

(3) An owner or operator may meet the requirements of this section by obtaining a letter of credit for liability coverage as specified in paragraph (h) of this section.

(4) An owner or operator may meet the requirements of this section by obtaining a surety bond for liability coverage as specified in paragraph (i) of this section.

(5) An owner or operator may meet the requirements of this section by obtaining a trust fund for liability coverage as specified in paragraph (j) of this section.

(6) An owner or operator may demonstrate the required liability coverage through the use of combinations of insurance, financial test, guarantee, letter of credit, surety bond, and trust fund, except that the owner or operator may not combine a financial test covering part of the liability coverage requirement with a guarantee unless the financial statement of the owner or operator is not consolidated with the financial statement of the guarantor. The amounts of coverage demonstrated must total at least the minimum amounts required by this section. If the owner or operator demonstrates the required coverage through the use of a combination of financial assurances under this paragraph, the owner or operator shall specify at least one such assurance as "primary" coverage and shall specify other assurance as "excess" coverage.

(7) An owner or operator shall notify the Regional Administrator in writing within 30 days whenever:

(i) A claim results in a reduction in the amount of financial assurance for liability coverage provided by a financial instrument authorized in paragraphs (b)(1) through (b)(6) of this section; or

(ii) A Certification of Valid Claim for bodily injury or property damages caused by a sudden or non-sudden accidental occurrence arising from the operation of a hazardous waste treatment, storage, or disposal facility is entered between the owner or operator and third-party claimant for liability coverage under paragraphs (b)(1) through (b)(6) of this section; or

(iii) A final court order establishing a judgment for bodily injury or property damage caused by a sudden or non-sudden accidental occurrence arising from the operation of a hazardous waste treatment, storage, or disposal facility is issued against the owner or operator or an instrument that is providing financial assurance for liability coverage under paragraphs (b)(1) through (b)(6) of this section.

(c) *Request for variance.* If an owner or operator can demonstrate to the satisfaction of the Regional Administrator that the levels of financial responsibility required by paragraph (a) or (b) of this section are not consistent with the degree and duration of risk associated with treatment, storage, or disposal at the facility or group of facilities, the owner or operator may obtain a variance from the Regional Administrator. The request for a variance must be submitted in writing to the Regional Administrator. If granted, the variance will take the form of an adjusted level of required liability coverage, such level to be based on the Regional Administrator's assessment of the degree and duration of risk associated with the ownership or operation of the facility or group of facilities. The Regional Administrator may require an owner or operator who requests a variance to provide such technical and engineering information as is deemed necessary by the Regional Administrator to determine a level of financial responsibility other than that required by paragraph (a) or (b) of this section. The Regional Administrator will process a variance request as if it were a permit modification request under §270.41(a)(5) of this chapter and subject to the procedures of §124.5 of this chapter. Notwithstanding any other provision, the Regional Administrator may hold a public hearing at his discretion or whenever he finds, on the basis of requests for a public hearing, a significant degree of pubic interest in a tentative decision to grant a variance.

(d) *Adjustments by the Regional Administrator.* If the Regional Administrator determines that the levels of financial responsibility required by paragraph (a) or (b) of this section are not consistent with the degree and duration of risk associated with treatment, storage, or disposal at the facility or group of facilities, the Regional Administrator may adjust the level of financial responsibility required under paragraph (a) or (b) of this section as may be necessary to protect human health and the environment. This adjusted level will be based on the Regional

Administrator's assessment of the degree and duration of risk associated with the ownership or operation of the facility or group of facilities. In addition, if the Regional Administrator determines that there is a significant risk to human health and the environment from nonsudden accidental occurrences resulting from the operations of a facility that is not a surface impoundment, landfill, or land treatment facility, he may require that an owner or operator of the facility comply with paragraph (b) of this section. An owner or operator must furnish to the Regional Administrator, within a reasonable time, any information which the Regional Administrator requests to determine whether cause exists for such adjustments of level or type of coverage. The Regional Administrator will process an adjustment of the level of required coverage as if it were a permit modification under §270.41(a)(5) of this chapter and subject to the procedures of §124.5 of this chapter. Notwithstanding any other provision, the Regional Administrator may hold a public hearing at his discretion or whenever he finds, on the basis of requests for a public hearing, a significant degree of public interest in a tentative decision to adjust the level or type of required coverage.

(e) *Period of coverage.* Within 60 days after receiving certifications from the owner or operator and a qualified Professional Engineer that final closure has been completed in accordance with the approved closure plan, the Regional Administrator will notify the owner or operator in writing that he is no longer required by this section to maintain liability coverage for that facility, unless the Regional Administrator has reason to believe that closure has not been in accordance with the approved closure plan.

(f) *Financial test for liability coverage.* (1) An owner or operator may satisfy the requirements of this section by demonstrating that he passes a financial test as specified in this paragraph. To pass this test the owner or operator must meet the criteria of paragraph (f)(1)(i) or (ii) of this section:

(i) The owner or operator must have:

(A) Net working capital and tangible net worth each at least six times the amount of liability coverage to be demonstrated by this test; and

(B) Tangible net worth of at least $10 million; and

(C) Assets in the United States amounting to either: (1) At least 90 percent of his total assets; or (2) at least six times the amount of liability coverage to be demonstrated by this test.

(ii) The owner or operator must have:

(A) A current rating for his most recent bond issuance of AAA, AA, A, or BBB as issued by Standard and Poor's, or Aaa, Aa, A, or Baa as issued by Moody's; and

(B) Tangible net worth of at least $10 million; and

(C) Tangible net worth at least six times the amount of liability coverage to be demonstrated by this test; and

(D) Assets in the United States amounting to either: (1) At least 90 percent of his total assets; or (2) at least six times the amount of liability coverage to be demonstrated by this test.

(2) The phrase "amount of liability coverage" as used in paragraph (f)(1) of this section refers to the annual aggregate amounts for which coverage is required under paragraphs (a) and (b) of this section.

(3) To demonstrate that he meets this test, the owner or operator must submit the following three items to the Regional Administrator:

(i) A letter signed by the owner's or operator's chief financial officer and worded as specified in §264.151(g). If an owner or operator is using the financial test to demonstrate both assurance for closure or post-closure care, as specified by §§264.143(f), 264.145(f), 265.143(e), and 265.145(e), and liability coverage, he must submit the letter specified in §264.151(g) to cover both forms of financial responsibility; a separate letter as specified in §264.151(f) is not required.

(ii) A copy of the independent certified public accountant's report on examination of the owner's or operator's financial statements for the latest completed fiscal year.

(iii) A special report from the owner's or operator's independent certified public accountant to the owner or operator stating that:

(A) He has compared the data which the letter from the chief financial officer specifies as having been derived from the independently audited, year-end financial statements for the latest fiscal year with the amounts in such financial statements; and

(B) In connection with that procedure, no matters came to his attention which caused him to believe that the specified data should be adjusted.

(4) The owner or operator may obtain a one-time extension of the time allowed for submission of the documents specified in paragraph (f)(3) of this section if the fiscal year of the owner or operator ends during

the 90 days prior to the effective date of these regulations and if the year-end financial statements for that fiscal year will be audited by an independent certified public accountant. The extension will end no later than 90 days after the end of the owner's or operator's fiscal year. To obtain the extension, the owner's or operator's chief financial officer must send, by the effective date of these regulations, a letter to the Regional Administrator of each Region in which the owner's or operator's facilities to be covered by the financial test are located. This letter from the chief financial officer must:

(i) Request the extension;

(ii) Certify that he has grounds to believe that the owner or operator meets the criteria of the financial test;

(iii) Specify for each facility to be covered by the test the EPA Identification Number, name, address, the amount of liability coverage and, when applicable, current closure and post-closure cost estimates to be covered by the test;

(iv) Specify the date ending the owner's or operator's last complete fiscal year before the effective date of these regulations;

(v) Specify the date, no later than 90 days after the end of such fiscal year, when he will submit the documents specified in paragraph (f)(3) of this section; and

(vi) Certify that the year-end financial statements of the owner or operator for such fiscal year will be audited by an independent certified public accountant.

(5) After the initial submission of items specified in paragraph (f)(3) of this section, the owner or operator must send updated information to the Regional Administrator within 90 days after the close of each succeeding fiscal year. This information must consist of all three items specified in paragraph (f)(3) of this section.

(6) If the owner or operator no longer meets the requirements of paragraph (f)(1) of this section, he must obtain insurance, a letter of credit, a surety bond, a trust fund, or a guarantee for the entire amount of required liability coverage as specified in this section. Evidence of liability coverage must be submitted to the Regional Administrator within 90 days after the end of the fiscal year for which the year-end financial data show that the owner or operator no longer meets the test requirements.

(7) The Regional Administrator may disallow use of this test on the basis of qualifications in the opinion expressed by the independent certified public accountant in his report on examination of the owner's or operator's financial statements (see paragraph (f)(3)(ii) of this section). An adverse opinion or a disclaimer of opinion will be cause for disallowance. The Regional Administrator will evaluate other qualifications on an individual basis. The owner or operator must provide evidence of insurance for the entire amount of required liability coverage as specified in this section within 30 days after notification of disallowance.

(g) *Guarantee for liability coverage.* (1) Subject to paragraph (g)(2) of this section, an owner or operator may meet the requirements of this section by obtaining a written guarantee, hereinafter referred to as "guarantee." The guarantor must be the direct or higher-tier parent corporation of the owner or operator, a firm whose parent corporation is also the parent corporation of the owner or operator, or a firm with a "substantial business relationship" with the owner or operator. The guarantor must meet the requirements for owners or operators in paragraphs (f)(1) through (f)(6) of this section. The wording of the guarantee must be identical to the wording specified in §264.151(h)(2) of this chapter. A certified copy of the guarantee must accompany the items sent to the Regional Administrator as specified in paragraph (f)(3) of this section. One of these items must be the letter from the guarantor's chief financial officer. If the guarantor's parent corporation is also the parent corporation of the owner or operator, this letter must describe the value received in consideration of the guarantee. If the guarantor is a firm with a "substantial business relationship" with the owner or operator, this letter must describe this "substantial business relationship" and the value received in consideration of the guarantee.

(i) If the owner or operator fails to satisfy a judgment based on a determination of liability for bodily injury or property damage to third parties caused by sudden or nonsudden accidental occurrences (or both as the case may be), arising from the operation of facilities covered by this corporate guarantee, or fails to pay an amount agreed to in settlement of claims arising from or alleged to arise from such injury or damage, the guarantor will do so up to the limits of coverage.

(ii) [Reserved]

(2)(i) In the case of corporations incorporated in the United States, a guarantee may be used to satisfy the requirements of this section only if the Attorneys General or Insurance Commissioners of (A) the State in which the guarantor is incorporated, and (B) each State in which a facility covered by the guarantee is located have submitted a written statement to EPA that a guarantee executed as described in this section and §264.151(h)(2) is a legally valid and enforceable obligation in that State.

(ii) In the case of corporations incorporated outside the United States, a guarantee may be used to satisfy the requirements of this section only if (A) the non-U.S. corporation has identified a registered agent for service of process in each State in which a facility covered by the guarantee is located and in the State in which it has its principal place of business, and if (B) the Attorney General or Insurance Commissioner of each State in which a facility covered by the guarantee is located and the State in which the guarantor corporation has its principal place of business, has submitted a written statement to EPA that a guarantee executed as described in this section and §264.151(h)(2) is a legally valid and enforceable obligation in that State.

(h) *Letter of credit for liability coverage.* (1) An owner or operator may satisfy the requirements of this section by obtaining an irrevocable standby letter of credit that conforms to the requirements of this paragraph and submitting a copy of the letter of credit to the Regional Administrator.

(2) The financial institution issuing the letter of credit must be an entity that has the authority to issue letters of credit and whose letter of credit operations are regulated and examined by a Federal or State agency.

(3) The wording of the letter of credit must be identical to the wording specified in §264.151(k) of this chapter.

(4) An owner or operator who uses a letter of credit to satisfy the requirements of this section may also establish a standby trust fund. Under the terms of such a letter of credit, all amounts paid pursuant to a draft by the trustee of the standby trust will be deposited by the issuing institution into the standby trust in accordance with instructions from the trustee. The trustee of the standby trust fund must be an entity which has the authority to act as a trustee and whose trust operations are regulated and examined by a Federal or State agency.

(5) The wording of the standby trust fund must be identical to the wording specified in §264.151(n).

(i) *Surety bond for liability coverage.* (1) An owner or operator may satisfy the requirements of this section by obtaining a surety bond that conforms to the requirements of this paragraph and submitting a copy of the bond to the Regional Administrator.

(2) The surety company issuing the bond must be among those listed as acceptable sureties on Federal bonds in the most recent Circular 570 of the U.S. Department of the Treasury.

(3) The wording of the surety bond must be identical to the wording specified in §264.151(l) of this chapter.

(4) A surety bond may be used to satisfy the requirements of this section only if the Attorneys General or Insurance Commissioners of (i) the State in which the surety is incorporated, and (ii) each State in which a facility covered by the surety bond is located have submitted a written statement to EPA that a surety bond executed as described in this section and §264.151(l) of this chapter is a legally valid and enforceable obligation in that State.

(j) *Trust fund for liability coverage.* (1) An owner or operator may satisfy the requirements of this section by establishing a trust fund that conforms to the requirements of this paragraph and submitting an originally signed duplicate of the trust agreement to the Regional Administrator.

(2) The trustee must be an entity which has the authority to act as a trustee and whose trust operations are regulated and examined by a Federal or State agency.

(3) The trust fund for liability coverage must be funded for the full amount of the liability coverage to be provided by the trust fund before it may be relied upon to satisfy the requirements of this section. If at any time after the trust fund is created the amount of funds in the trust fund is reduced below the full amount of the liability coverage to be provided, the owner or operator, by the anniversary date of the establishment of the Fund, must either add sufficient funds to the trust fund to cause its value to equal the full amount of liability coverage to be provided, or obtain other financial assurance as specified in this section to cover the difference. For purposes of this paragraph, "the full amount of the liability coverage to be provided" means the amount of coverage for sudden and/or nonsudden occurrences required to be provided by the owner or operator by this section, less the amount of financial assurance for liability coverage that is being provided by other financial assurance mechanisms being used to demonstrate financial assurance by the owner or operator.

(4) The wording of the trust fund must be identical to the wording specified in §264.151(m) of this part.

(k) Notwithstanding any other provision of this part, an owner or operator using liability insurance to satisfy the requirements of this section may use, until October 16, 1982, a Hazardous Waste Facility Liability Endorsement or Certificate of Liability Insurance that does not certify that the insurer is licensed to transact the business of insurance, or eligible as an excess or surplus lines insurer, in one or more States.

[47 FR 16558, Apr. 16, 1982, as amended at 47 FR 28627, July 1, 1982; 47 FR 30447, July 13, 1982; 48 FR 30115, June 30, 1983; 51 FR 16458, May 2, 1986; 51 FR 25355, July 11, 1986; 52 FR 44321, Nov. 18, 1987; 53 FR 33959, Sept. 1, 1988; 56 FR 30200, July 1, 1991; 56 FR 47912, Sept. 23, 1991; 57 FR 42843, Sept. 16, 1992; 71 FR 16910, Apr. 4, 2006; 71 FR 40275, July 14, 2006]

§265.148 Incapacity of owners or operators, guarantors, or financial institutions.

(a) An owner or operator must notify the Regional Administrator by certified mail of the commencement of a voluntary or involuntary proceeding under Title 11 (Bankruptcy), U.S. Code, naming the owner or operator as debtor, within 10 days after commencement of the proceeding. A guarantor of a corporate guarantee as specified in §§265.143(e) and 265.145(e) must make such a notification if he is named as debtor, as required under the terms of the corporate guarantee (§264.151(h)).

(b) An owner or operator who fulfills the requirements of §265.143, §265.145, or §265.147 by obtaining a trust fund, surety bond, letter of credit, or insurance policy will be deemed to be without the required financial assurance or liability coverage in the event of bankruptcy of the trustee or issuing institution, or a suspension or revocation of the authority of the trustee institution to act as trustee or of the institution issuing the surety bond, letter of credit, or insurance policy to issue such instruments. The owner or operator must establish other financial assurance or liability coverage within 60 days after such an event.

§265.149 Use of State-required mechanisms.

(a) For a facility located in a State where EPA is administering the requirements of this subpart but where the State has hazardous waste regulations that include requirements for financial assurance of closure or post-closure care or liability coverage, an owner or operator may use State-required financial mechanisms to meet the requirements of §265.143, §265.145, or §265.147 if the Regional Administrator determines that the State mechanisms are at least equivalent to the financial mechanisms specified in this subpart. The Regional Administrator will evaluate the equivalency of the mechanisms principally in terms of (1) certainty of the availability of funds for the required closure or post-closure care activities or liability coverage and (2) the amount of funds that will be made available. The Regional Administrator may also consider other factors as he deems appropriate. The owner or operator must submit to the Regional Administrator evidence of the establishment of the mechanism together with a letter requesting that the State-required mechanism be considered acceptable for meeting the requirements of this subpart. The submission must include the following information: The facility's EPA Identification Number, name, and address, and the amount of funds for closure or post-closure care or liability coverage assured by the mechanism. The Regional Administrator will notify the owner or operator of his determination regarding the mechanism's acceptability in lieu of financial mechanisms specified in this subpart. The Regional Administrator may require the owner or operator to submit additional information as is deemed necessary to make this determination. Pending this determination, the owner or operator will be deemed to be in compliance with the requirements of §265.143, §265.145, or §265.147, as applicable.

(b) If a State-required mechanism is found acceptable as specified in paragraph (a) of this section except for the amount of funds available, the owner or operator may satisfy the requirements of this subpart by increasing the funds available through the State-required mechanism or using additional financial mechanisms as specified in this subpart. The amount of funds available through the State and Federal mechanisms must at least equal the amount required by this subpart.

§265.150 State assumption of responsibility.

(a) If a State either assumes legal responsibility for an owner's or operator's compliance with the closure, post-closure care, or liability requirements of this part or assures that funds will be available from State sources to cover those requirements, the owner or operator will be in compliance with the requirements of §265.143, §265.145, or §265.147 if the Regional Administrator determines that the State's assumption of responsibility is at least equivalent to the financial mechanisms specified in this subpart. The Regional Administrator will evaluate the equivalency of State guarantees principally in terms of (1) certainty of the availability of funds for the required closure or post-closure care activities or liability coverage and (2) the amount of funds that will be made available. The Regional Administrator may also consider other factors as he deems appropriate. The owner or operator must submit to the Regional Administrator a letter from the State describing the nature of the State's assumption of responsibility together with a letter from the owner or operator requesting that the State's assumption of responsibility be considered acceptable for meeting the requirements of this subpart. The letter from the State must include, or have attached to it, the following information: The facility's EPA Identification Number, name, and address, and the amount of funds for closure or post-closure care or liability coverage that are guaranteed by the State. The Regional Administrator will notify the owner or operator of his determination regarding the acceptability of the State's guarantee in lieu of financial mechanisms specified in this subpart. The Regional Administrator may require the owner or operator to submit additional information as is deemed necessary to make this determination. Pending this determination, the owner or operator will be deemed to be in compliance with the requirements of §§265.143, §265.145, or §265.147, as applicable.

(b) If a State's assumption of responsibility is found acceptable as specified in paragraph (a) of this section except for the amount of funds available, the owner or operator may satisfy the requirements of this subpart by use of both the State's assurance and additional financial mechanisms as specified in this subpart. The amount of funds available through the State and Federal mechanisms must at least equal the amount required by this subpart.

Subpart I—Use and Management of Containers

§265.170 Applicability. 📖 9.1

The regulations in this subpart apply to owners and operators of all hazardous waste facilities that store containers of hazardous waste, except as §265.1 provides otherwise.

§265.171 Condition of containers.

If a container holding hazardous waste is not in good condition, or if it begins to leak, the owner or operator must transfer the hazardous waste from this container to a container that is in good condition, or manage the waste in some other way that complies with the requirements of this part.

§265.172 Compatibility of waste with container.

The owner or operator must use a container made of or lined with materials which will not react with, and are otherwise compatible with, the hazardous waste to be stored, so that the ability of the container to contain the waste is not impaired.

§265.173 Management of containers.

(a) A container holding hazardous waste must always be closed during storage, except when it is necessary to add or remove waste. 📖 9.2, 16.1.7

(b) A container holding hazardous waste must not be opened, handled, or stored in a manner which may rupture the container or cause it to leak.

[*Comment:* Re-use of containers in transportation is governed by U.S. Department of Transportation regulations, including those set forth in 49 CFR 173.28.]

[45 FR 33232, May 19, 1980, as amended at 45 FR 78529, Nov. 25, 1980]

§265.174 Inspections. 📖 9.6, 16.1.9

At least weekly, the owner or operator must inspect areas where containers are stored, except for Performance Track member facilities, that must conduct inspections at least once each month, upon approval by the Director. To apply for reduced inspection frequency, the Performance Track member facility must follow the procedures described in §265.15(b)(5) of this part. The owner or operator must look for leaking containers and for deterioration of containers caused by corrosion or other factors.

[Comment: See §265.171 for remedial action required if deterioration or leaks are detected.]

[71 FR 16910, Apr. 4, 2006, as amended at 71 FR 40275, July 14, 2006]

§265.175 [Reserved]

§265.176 Special requirements for ignitable or reactive waste.

Containers holding ignitable or reactive waste must be located at least 15 meters (50 feet) from the facility's property line.

[*Comment:* See §265.17(a) for additional requirements.]

§265.177 Special requirements for incompatible wastes.

(a) Incompatible wastes, or incompatible wastes and materials, (see appendix V for examples) must not be placed in the same container, unless §265.17(b) is complied with.

(b) Hazardous waste must not be placed in an unwashed container that previously held an incompatible waste or material (see appendix V for examples), unless §265.17(b) is complied with.

(c) A storage container holding a hazardous waste that is incompatible with any waste or other materials stored nearby in other containers, piles, open tanks, or surface impoundments must be separated from the other materials or protected from them by means of a dike, berm, wall, or other device.

[*Comment:* The purpose of this is to prevent fires, explosions, gaseous emissions, leaching, or other discharge of hazardous waste or hazardous waste constituents which could result from the mixing of incompatible wastes or materials if containers break or leak.]

§265.178 Air emission standards. 15.1–3

The owner or operator shall manage all hazardous waste placed in a container in accordance with the applicable requirements of subparts AA, BB, and CC of this part.

[61 FR 59968, Nov. 25, 1996]

Subpart J—Tank Systems

Source: 51 FR 25479, July 14, 1986, unless otherwise noted.

§265.190 Applicability. 10.1–2

The requirements of this subpart apply to owners and operators of facilities that use tank systems for storing or treating hazardous waste except as otherwise provided in paragraphs (a), (b), and (c) of this section or in §265.1 of this part.

(a) Tank systems that are used to store or treat hazardous waste which contains no free liquids and are situated inside a building with an impermeable floor are exempted from the requirements in §265.193. To demonstrate the absence or presence of free liquids in the stored/ treated waste, the following test must be used: Method 9095B (Paint Filter Liquids Test) as described in "Test Methods for Evaluating Solid Waste, Physical/ Chemical Methods," EPA Publication SW–846, as incorporated by reference in §260.11 of this chapter.

(b) Tank systems, including sumps, as defined in §260.10, that serve as part of a secondary containment system to collect or contain releases of hazardous wastes are exempted from the requirements in §265.193(a).

7.5.4.1.1, 10.2.2

(c) Tanks, sumps, and other collection devices used in conjunction with drip pads, as defined in §260.10 of this chapter and regulated under 40 CFR part 265 subpart W, must meet the requirements of this subpart.

10.1.3.4

[51 FR 25479, July 14, 1986, as amended at 53 FR 34087, Sept. 2, 1988; 55 FR 50486, Dec. 6, 1990; 58 FR 46050, Aug. 31, 1993; 70 FR 34585, June 14, 2005]

§265.191 Assessment of existing tank system's integrity.

10.1.5.1

(a) For each existing tank system that does not have secondary containment meeting the requirements of §265.193, the owner or operator must determine that the tank system is not leaking or is unfit for use. Except as provided in paragraph (c) of this section, the owner or operator must obtain and keep on file at the facility a written assessment reviewed and certified by a qualified Professional Engineer in accordance with §270.11(d) of this chapter, that attests to the tank system's integrity by January 12, 1988.

(b) This assessment must determine that the tank system is adequately designed and has sufficient structural strength and compatibility with the waste(s) to be stored or treated to ensure that it will not collapse, rupture, or fail. At a minimum, this assessment must consider the following:

(1) Design standard(s), if available, according to which the tank and ancillary equipment were constructed;

(2) Hazardous characteristics of the waste(s) that have been or will be handled;

(3) Existing corrosion protection measures;

(4) Documented age of the tank system, if available, (otherwise, an estimate of the age); and

(5) Results of a leak test, internal inspection, or other tank integrity examination such that:

(i) For non-enterable underground tanks, this assessment must consist of a leak test that is capable of taking into account the effects of temperature variations, tank end deflection, vapor pockets, and high water table effects,

(ii) For other than non-enterable underground tanks and for ancillary equipment, this assessment must be either a leak test, as described above, or an internal inspection and/or other tank integrity examination certified by a qualified Professional Engineer in accordance with §270.11(d) of this chapter that addresses cracks, leaks, corrosion, and erosion.

[*Note:* The practices described in the American Petroleum Institute (API) Publication, Guide for Inspection of Refinery Equipment, Chapter XIII, "Atmospheric and Low-Pressure Storage Tanks," 4th edition, 1981, may be used, where applicable, as guidelines in conducting the integrity examination of an other than non-enterable underground tank system.]

(c) Tank systems that store or treat materials that become hazardous wastes subsequent to July 14, 1986 must conduct this assessment within 12 months after the date that the waste becomes a hazardous waste.

(d) If, as a result of the assessment conducted in accordance with paragraph (a) of this section, a tank system is found to be leaking or unfit for use, the owner or operator must comply with the requirements of §265.196.

[51 FR 25479, July 14, 1986, as amended at 71 FR 16910, Apr. 4, 2006]

§265.192 Design and installation of new tank systems or components. 10.1.5.1

(a) Owners or operators of new tank systems or components must ensure that the foundation, structural support, seams, connections, and pressure controls (if applicable) are adequately designed and that the tank system has sufficient structural strength, compatibility with the waste(s) to be stored or treated, and corrosion protection so that it will not collapse, rupture, or fail. The owner or operator must obtain a written assessment reviewed and certified by a qualified Professional Engineer in accordance with §270.11(d) of this chapter attesting that the system has sufficient structural integrity and is acceptable for the storing and treating of hazardous waste. This assessment must include the following information:

(1) Design standard(s) according to which the tank(s) and ancillary equipment is or will be constructed.

(2) Hazardous characteristics of the waste(s) to be handled.

(3) For new tank systems or components in which the external shell of a metal tank or any external metal component of the tank system is or will be in contact with the soil or with water, a determination by a corrosion expert of:

(i) Factors affecting the potential for corrosion, including but not limited to:

(A) Soil moisture content;

(B) Soil pH;

(C) Soil sulfides level;

(D) Soil resistivity;

(E) Structure to soil potential;

(F) Influence of nearby underground metal structures (*e.g.*, piping);

(G) Stray electric current; and,

(H) Existing corrosion-protection measures (*e.g.*, coating, cathodic protection), and

(ii) The type and degree of external corrosion protection that are needed to ensure the integrity of the tank system during the use of the tank system or component, consisting of one or more of the following:

(A) Corrosion-resistant materials of construction such as special alloys or fiberglass-reinforced plastic;

(B) Corrosion-resistant coating (such as epoxy or fiberglass) with cathodic protection (*e.g.*, impressed current or sacrificial anodes); and

(C) Electrical isolation devices such as insulating joints and flanges.

Note: The practices described in the National Association of Corrosion Engineers (NACE) standard, "Recommended Practice (RP-02-85)—Control of External Corrosion on Metallic Buried, Partially Buried, or Submerged Liquid Storage Systems," and the American Petroleum Institute (API) Publication 1632, "Cathodic Protection of Underground Petroleum Storage Tanks and Piping Systems," may be used, where applicable, as guidelines in providing corrosion protection for tank systems.

(4) For underground tank system components that are likely to be affected by vehicular traffic, a determination of design or operational measures that will protect the tank system against potential damage; and

(5) Design considerations to ensure that:

(i) Tank foundations will maintain the load of a full tank;

(ii) Tank systems will be anchored to prevent flotation or dislodgement where the tank system is placed in a saturated zone, or is located within a seismic fault zone; and

(iii) Tank systems will withstand the effects of frost heave.

(b) The owner or operator of a new tank system must ensure that proper handling procedures are adhered to in order to prevent damage to the system during installation. Prior to covering, enclosing, or placing a new tank system or component in use, an independent, qualified installation inspector or a qualified Professional Engineer, either of whom is trained and experienced in the proper installation of tank systems, must inspect the system or component for the presence of any of the following items:

(1) Weld breaks;

(2) Punctures;

(3) Scrapes of protective coatings;

(4) Cracks;

(5) Corrosion;

(6) Other structural damage or inadequate construction or installation.

All discrepancies must be remedied before the tank system is covered, enclosed, or placed in use.

(c) New tank systems or components and piping that are placed underground and that are backfilled must be provided with a backfill material that is a noncorrosive, porous, homogeneous substance and that is carefully installed so that the backfill is placed completely around the tank and compacted to ensure that the tank and piping are fully and uniformly supported.

(d) All new tanks and ancillary equipment must be tested for tightness prior to being covered, enclosed or placed in use. If a tank system is found not to be tight, all repairs necessary to remedy the leak(s) in the system must be performed prior to the tank system being covered, enclosed, or placed in use.

(e) Ancillary equipment must be supported and protected against physical damage and excessive stress due to settlement, vibration, expansion or contraction.

Note: The piping system installation procedures described in American Petroleum Institute (API) Publication 1615 (November 1979), "Installation of Underground Petroleum Storage Systems," or ANSI Standard B31.3, "Petroleum Refinery System," may be used, where applicable, as guidelines for proper installation of piping systems.

(f) The owner or operator must provide the type and degree of corrosion protection necessary, based on the information provided under paragraph (a)(3) of this section, to ensure the integrity of the tank system during use of the tank system. The installation of a corrosion protection system that is field fabricated must be supervised by an independent corrosion expert to ensure proper installation.

(g) The owner or operator must obtain and keep on file at the facility written statements by those persons required to certify the design of the tank system and supervise the installation of the tank system in accordance with the requirements of paragraphs (b) through (f) of this section to attest that the tank system was properly designed and installed and that repairs, pursuant to paragraphs (b) and (d) of this section were performed. These written statements must also include the certification statement as required in §270.11(d) of this chapter.

[51 FR 25479, July 14, 1986; 51 FR 29430, Aug. 15, 1986; 71 FR 16910, Apr. 4, 2006]

§265.193 Containment and detection of releases. 📖 10.3

(a) In order to prevent the release of hazardous waste or hazardous constituents to the environment, secondary containment that meets the requirements of this section must be provided (except as provided in paragraphs (f) and (g) of this section): 📖 10.3.4

(1) For all new and existing tank systems or components, prior to their being put into service.

(2) For tank systems that store or treat materials that become hazardous wastes, within 2 years of the hazardous waste listing, or when the tank system has reached 15 years of age, whichever comes later.

(b) Secondary containment systems must be:

(1) Designed, installed, and operated to prevent any migration of wastes or accumulated liquid out of the system to the soil, ground water, or surface water at any time during the use of the tank system; and

(2) Capable of detecting and collecting releases and accumulated liquids until the collected material is removed.

(c) To meet the requirements of paragraph (b) of this section, secondary containment systems must be at a minimum:

(1) Constructed of or lined with materials that are compatible with the waste(s) to be placed in the tank system and must have sufficient strength and thickness to prevent failure due to pressure gradients (including static head and external hydrological forces), physical contact with the waste to which they are exposed, climatic conditions, the stress of installation, and the stress of daily operation (including stresses from nearby vehicular traffic);

(2) Placed on a foundation or base capable of providing support to the secondary containment system and resistance to pressure gradients above and below the system and capable of preventing failure due to settlement, compression, or uplift;

(3) Provided with a leak detection system that is designed and operated so that it will detect the failure of either the primary and secondary containment structure or any release of hazardous waste or accumulated liquid in the secondary containment system within 24 hours, or at the earliest practicable time if the existing detection technology or site conditions will not allow detection of a release within 24 hours; 📖 10.3.3

(4) Sloped or otherwise designed or operated to drain and remove liquids resulting from leaks, spills, or precipitation. Spilled or leaked waste and accumulated precipitation must be removed from the secondary containment system within 24 hours, or in as timely a manner as is possible to prevent harm to human health or the environment, if removal of the released waste or accumulated precipitation cannot be accomplished within 24 hours.

Note: If the collected material is a hazardous waste under part 261 of this chapter, it is subject to management as a hazardous waste in accordance with all applicable requirements of parts 262 through 265 of this chapter. If the collected material is discharged through a point source to waters of the United States, it is subject to the requirements of sections 301, 304, and 402 of the Clean Water Act, as amended. If discharged to Publicly Owned Treatment Works (POTWs), it is subject to the requirements of section 307 of the Clear Water Act, as amended. If the collected material is released to the environment, it may be subject to the reporting requirements of 40 CFR part 302.

(d) Secondary containment for tanks must include one or more of the following devices:

(1) A liner (external to the tank);

(2) A vault;

(3) A double-walled tank; or

(4) An equivalent device as approved by the Regional Administrator.

(e) In addition to the requirements of paragraphs (b), (c), and (d) of this section, secondary containment systems must satisfy the following requirements:

(1) External liner systems must be:

(i) Designed or operated to contain 100 percent of the capacity of the largest tank within its boundary; 10.3.2.1

(ii) Designed or operated to prevent run-on or infiltration of precipitation into the secondary containment system unless the collection system has sufficient excess capacity to contain run-on or infiltration. Such additional capacity must be sufficient to contain precipitation from a 25-year, 24-hour rainfall event;

(iii) Free of cracks or gaps; and

(iv) Designed and installed to completely surround the tank and to cover all surrounding earth likely to come into contact with the waste if released from the tank(s) (*i.e.*, capable of preventing lateral as well as vertical migration of the waste).

(2) Vault systems must be:

(i) Designed or operated to contain 100 percent of the capacity of the largest tank within its boundary; 10.3.2.1

(ii) Designed or operated to prevent run-on or infiltration of precipitation into the secondary containment system unless the collection system has sufficient excess capacity to contain run-on or infiltration. Such additional capacity must be sufficient to contain precipitation from a 25-year, 24-hour rainfall event;

(iii) Constructed with chemical-resistant water stops in place at all joints (if any);

(iv) Provided with an impermeable interior coating or lining that is compatible with the stored waste and that will prevent migration of waste into the concrete; 10.3.2.2

(v) Provided with a means to protect against the formation of and ignition of vapors within the vault, if the waste being stored or treated:

(A) Meets the definition of ignitable waste under §261.21 of this chapter, or

(B) Meets the definition of reactive waste under §261.23 of this chapter and may form an ignitable or explosive vapor; and

(vi) Provided with an exterior moisture barrier or be otherwise designed or operated to prevent migration of moisture into the vault if the vault is subject to hydraulic pressure.

(3) Double-walled tanks must be:

(i) Designed as an integral structure (*i.e.*, an inner tank within an outer shell) so that any release from the inner tank is contained by the outer shell;

(ii) Protected, if constructed of metal, from both corrosion of the primary tank interior and the external surface of the outer shell; and

(iii) Provided with a built-in, continuous leak detection system capable of detecting a release within 24 hours or at the earliest practicable time, if the owner or operator can demonstrate to the Regional Administrator, and the Regional Administrator concurs, that the existing leak detection technology or site conditions will not allow detection of a release within 24 hours.

Note: The provisions outlined in the Steel Tank Institute's (STI) "Standard for Dual Wall Underground Steel Storage Tank" may be used as guidelines for aspects of the design of underground steel double-walled tanks.

(f) Ancillary equipment must be provided with full secondary containment (*e.g.*, trench, jacketing, double-walled piping) that meets the requirements of paragraphs (b) and (c) of this section except for: 10.3.2.4

(1) Aboveground piping (exclusive of flanges, joints, valves, and connections) that are visually inspected for leaks on a daily basis;

(2) Welded flanges, welded joints, and welded connections that are visually inspected for leaks on a daily basis;

(3) Sealless or magnetic coupling pumps and sealless valves, that are visually inspected for leaks on a daily basis; and

(4) Pressurized aboveground piping systems with automatic shut-off devices (*e.g.*, excess flow check valves, flow metering shutdown devices, loss of pressure actuated shut-off devices) that are visually inspected for leaks on a daily basis.

(g) The owner or operator may obtain a variance from the requirements of this Section if the Regional Administrator finds, as a result of a demonstration by the owner or operator, either: that alternative design and operating practices, together with location characteristics, will prevent the migration of hazardous waste or hazardous constituents into the ground water or surface water at least as effectively as secondary containment during the active life of the tank system or that in the event of a release that does migrate to ground water or surface water, no substantial present or potential hazard will be posed to human health or the environment. New underground tank systems may not, per a demonstration in accordance with paragraph (g)(2) of this section, be exempted from the secondary containment requirements of this section. Application for a variance as allowed in paragraph (g) of this section does not waive compliance with the requirements of this subpart for new tank systems. 10.3.5

(1) In deciding whether to grant a variance based on a demonstration of equivalent protection of ground water and surface water, the Regional Administrator will consider:

(i) The nature and quantity of the waste;

(ii) The proposed alternate design and operation;

(iii) The hydrogeologic setting of the facility, including the thickness of soils between the tank system and ground water; and

(iv) All other factors that would influence the quality and mobility of the hazardous constituents and the potential for them to migrate to ground water or surface water.

(2) In deciding whether to grant a variance, based on a demonstration of no substantial present or potential hazard, the Regional Administrator will consider:

(i) The potential adverse effects on ground water, surface water, and land quality taking into account:

(A) The physical and chemical characteristics of the waste in the tank system, including its potential for migration,

(B) The hydrogeological characteristics of the facility and surrounding land,

(C) The potential for health risks caused by human exposure to waste constituents,

(D) The potential for damage to wildlife, crops, vegetation, and physical structures caused by exposure to waste constituents, and

(E) The persistence and permanence of the potential adverse effects;

(ii) The potential adverse effects of a release on ground-water quality, taking into account:

(A) The quantity and quality of ground water and the direction of ground-water flow,

(B) The proximity and withdrawal rates of water in the area,

(C) The current and future uses of ground water in the area, and

(D) The existing quality of ground water, including other sources of contamination and their cumulative impact on the ground-water quality;

(iii) The potential adverse effects of a release on surface water quality, taking into account:

(A) The quantity and quality of ground water and the direction of ground-water flow,

(B) The patterns of rainfall in the region,

(C) The proximity of the tank system to surface waters,

(D) The current and future uses of surface waters in the area and any water quality standards established for those surface waters, and

(E) The existing quality of surface water, including other sources of contamination and the cumulative impact on surface-water quality; and

(iv) The potential adverse effects of a release on the land surrounding the tank system, taking into account:

(A) The patterns of rainfall in the region, and

(B) The current and future uses of the surrounding land.

(3) The owner or operator of a tank system, for which a variance from secondary containment had been granted in accordance with the requirements of paragraph (g)(1) of this section, at which a release of hazardous waste has occurred from the primary tank system but has not migrated beyond the zone of engineering control (as established in the variance), must:

(i) Comply with the requirements of §265.196, except paragraph (d); and

(ii) Decontaminate or remove contaminated soil to the extent necessary to:

(A) Enable the tank system, for which the variance was granted, to resume operation with the capability for the detection of and response to releases at least equivalent to the capability it had prior to the release, and

(B) Prevent the migration of hazardous waste or hazardous constituents to ground water or surface water; and

(iii) If contaminated soil cannot be removed or decontaminated in accordance with paragraph (g)(3)(ii) of this section, comply with the requirements of §265.197(b);

(4) The owner or operator of a tank system, for which a variance from secondary containment had been granted in accordance with the requirements of paragraph (g)(1) of this section, at which a release of hazardous waste has occurred from the primary tank system and

has migrated beyond the zone of engineering control (as established in the variance), must:

(i) Comply with the requirements of §265.196(a), (b), (c), and (d); and

(ii) Prevent the migration of hazardous waste or hazardous constituents to ground water or surface water, if possible, and decontaminate or remove contaminated soil. If contaminated soil cannot be decontaminated or removed, or if ground water has been contaminated, the owner or operator must comply with the requirements of §265.197(b);

(iii) If repairing, replacing, or reinstalling the tank system, provide secondary containment in accordance with the requirements of paragraphs (a) through (f) of this section or reapply for a variance from secondary containment and meet the requirements for new tank systems in §265.192 if the tank system is replaced. The owner or operator must comply with these requirements even if contaminated soil can be decontaminated or removed, and ground water or surface water has not been contaminated.

(h) The following procedures must be followed in order to request a variance from secondary containment:

(1) The Regional Administrator must be notified in writing by the owner or operator that he intends to conduct and submit a demonstration for a variance from secondary containment as allowed in paragraph (g) of this section according to the following schedule:

(i) For existing tank systems, at least 24 months prior to the date that secondary containment must be provided in accordance with paragraph (a) of this section; and

(ii) For new tank systems, at least 30 days prior to entering into a contract for installation of the tank system.

(2) As part of the notification, the owner or operator must also submit to the Regional Administrator a description of the steps necessary to conduct the demonstration and a timetable for completing each of the steps. The demonstration must address each of the factors listed in paragraph (g)(1) or paragraph (g)(2) of this section.

(3) The demonstration for a variance must be completed and submitted to the Regional Administrator within 180 days after notifying the Regional Administrator of intent to conduct the demonstration.

(4) The Regional Administrator will inform the public, through a newspaper notice, of the availability of the demonstration for a variance. The notice shall be placed in a daily or weekly major local newspaper of general circulation and shall provide at least 30 days from the date of the notice for the public to review and comment on the demonstration for a variance. The Regional Administrator also will hold a public hearing, in response to a request or at his own discretion, whenever such a hearing might clarify one or more issues concerning the demonstration for a variance. Public notice of the hearing will be given at least 30 days prior to the date of the hearing and may be given at the same time as notice of the opportunity for the public to review and comment on the demonstration. These two notices may be combined.

(5) The Regional Administrator will approve or disapprove the request for a variance within 90 days of receipt of the demonstration from the owner or operator and will notify in writing the owner or operator and each person who submitted written comments or requested notice of the variance decision. If the demonstration for a variance is incomplete or does not include sufficient information, the 90-day time period will begin when the Regional Administrator receives a complete demonstration, including all information necessary to make a final determination. If the public comment period in paragraph (h)(4) of this section is extended, the 90-day time period will be similarly extended.

(i) All tank systems, until such time as secondary containment meeting the requirements of this section is provided, must comply with the following: 📖 10.3.4.1

(1) For non-enterable underground tanks, a leak test that meets the requirements of §265.191(b)(5) must be conducted at least annually;

(2) For other than non-enterable underground tanks, and for all ancillary equipment, the owner or operator must either conduct a leak test as in paragraph (i)(1) of this section or an internal inspection or other tank integrity examination by a qualified Professional Engineer that addresses cracks, leaks, and corrosion or erosion at least annually. The owner or operator must remove the stored waste from the tank, if necessary, to allow the condition of all internal tank surfaces to be assessed.

Note: The practices described in the American Petroleum Institute (API) Publication Guide for Inspection of Refining Equipment, Chapter XIII, "Atmospheric and Low Pressure Storage Tanks," 4th edition, 1981, may be used, when applicable, as guidelines for assessing the overall condition of the tank system.

(3) The owner or operator must maintain on file at the facility a record of the results of the assessments conducted in accordance with paragraphs (i)(1) through (i)(3) of this section.

(4) If a tank system or component is found to be leaking or unfit-for-use as a result of the leak test or assessment in paragraphs (i)(1) through (i)(3) of this section, the owner or operator must comply with the requirements of §265.196.

[51 FR 25479, July 14, 1986; 51 FR 29430, Aug. 15, 1986, as amended at 53 FR 34087, Sept. 2, 1988; 71 FR 16910, Apr. 4, 2006; 71 FR 40275, July 14, 2006]

§265.194 General operating requirements. 10.4

(a) Hazardous wastes or treatment reagents must not be placed in a tank system if they could cause the tank, its ancillary equipment, or the secondary containment system to rupture, leak, corrode, or otherwise fail.

(b) The owner or operator must use appropriate controls and practices to prevent spills and overflows from tank or secondary containment systems. These include at a minimum:

(1) Spill prevention controls (*e.g.*, check valves, dry disconnect couplings);

(2) Overfill prevention controls (*e.g.*, level sensing devices, high level alarms, automatic feed cutoff, or bypass to a standby tank); and

(3) Maintenance of sufficient freeboard in uncovered tanks to prevent overtopping by wave or wind action or by precipitation.

(c) The owner or operator must comply with the requirements of §265.196 if a leak or spill occurs in the tank system.

[51 FR 25479, July 14, 1986, as amended at 71 FR 40275, July 14, 2006]

§265.195 Inspections. 10.5

(a) The owner or operator must inspect, where present, at least once each operating day, data gathered from monitoring and leak detection equipment (e.g., pressure or temperature gauges, monitoring wells) to ensure that the tank system is being operated according to its design.

Note: Section 265.15(c) requires the owner or operator to remedy any deterioration or malfunction he finds. Section 265.196 requires the owner or operator to notify the Regional Administrator within 24 hours of confirming a release. Also, 40 CFR part 302 may require the owner or operator to notify the National Response Center of a release.

(b) Except as noted under the paragraph (c) of this section, the owner or operator must inspect at least once each operating day:

(1) Overfill/spill control equipment (e.g., waste-feed cutoff systems, bypass systems, and drainage systems) to ensure that it is in good working order;

(2) Above ground portions of the tank system, if any, to detect corrosion or releases of waste; and

(3) The construction materials and the area immediately surrounding the externally accessible portion of the tank system, including the secondary containment system (e.g., dikes) to detect erosion or signs of releases of hazardous waste (e.g., wet spots, dead vegetation).

(c) Owners or operators of tank systems that either use leak detection equipment to alert facility personnel to leaks, or implement established workplace practices to ensure leaks are promptly identified, must inspect at least weekly those areas described in paragraphs (b)(1) through (3) of this section. Use of the alternate inspection schedule must be documented in the facility's operating record. This documentation must include a description of the established workplace practices at the facility.

(d) Performance Track member facilities may inspect on a less frequent basis, upon approval by the Director, but must inspect at least once each month. To apply for a less than weekly inspection frequency, the Performance Track member facility must follow the procedures described in §265.15(b)(5).

(e) Ancillary equipment that is not provided with secondary containment, as described in §265.193(f)(1) through (4), must be inspected at least once each operating day.

(f) The owner or operator must inspect cathodic protection systems, if present, according to, at a minimum, the following schedule to ensure that they are functioning properly:

(1) The proper operation of the cathodic protection system must be confirmed within six months after initial installation, and annually thereafter; and

(2) All sources of impressed current must be inspected and/or tested, as appropriate, at least bimonthly (*i.e.*, every other month).

Note: The practices described in the National Association of Corrosion Engineers (NACE) standard, "Recommended Practice (RP-02-85)—Control of External Corrosion on Metallic Buried, Partially Buried, or Submerged Liquid Storage Systems," and the American Petroleum Institute (API) Publication 1632, "Cathodic Protection of Underground Petroleum Storage Tanks and Piping Systems," may be used, where applicable, as guidelines in maintaining and inspecting cathodic protection systems.

(g) The owner or operator must document in the operating record of the facility an inspection of those items in paragraphs (a) and (b) of this section.

📖 6.7.5, 10.5

[51 FR 25479, July 14, 1986; 51 FR 29430, Aug. 15, 1986, as amended at 71 FR 16910, Apr. 4, 2006]

§265.196 Response to leaks or spills and disposition of leaking or unfit-for-use tank systems. 📖 10.3.3.1

A tank system or secondary containment system from which there has been a leak or spill, or which is unfit for use, must be removed from service immediately, and the owner or operator must satisfy the following requirements:

(a) *Cessation of use; prevent flow or addition of wastes.* The owner or operator must immediately stop the flow of hazardous waste into the tank system or secondary containment system and inspect the system to determine the cause of the release.

(b) *Removal of waste from tank system or secondary containment system.* (1) If the release was from the tank system, the owner or operator must, within 24 hours after detection of the leak or, if the owner or operator demonstrates that that is not possible, at the earliest practicable time remove as much of the waste as is necessary to prevent further release of hazardous waste to the environment and to allow inspection and repair of the tank system to be performed.

(2) If the release was to a secondary containment system, all released materials must be removed within 24 hours or in as timely a manner as is possible to prevent harm to human health and the environment.

(c) *Containment of visible releases to the environment.* The owner or operator must immediately conduct a visual inspection of the release and, based upon that inspection:

(1) Prevent further migration of the leak or spill to soils or surface water; and

(2) Remove, and properly dispose of, any visible contamination of the soil or surface water.

(d) *Notifications, reports.* (1) Any release to the environment, except as provided in paragraph (d)(2) of this section, must be reported to the Regional Administrator within 24 hours of detection. If the release has been reported pursuant to 40 CFR part 302, that report will satisfy this requirement. 📖 10.3.3.1.1, 14.4.10

(2) A leak or spill of hazardous waste that is:

(i) Less than or equal to a quantity of one (1) pound, and

(ii) Immediately contained and cleaned-up is exempted from the requirements of this paragraph.

(3) Within 30 days of detection of a release to the environment, a report containing the following information must be submitted to the Regional Administrator:

(i) Likely route of migration of the release;

(ii) Characteristics of the surrounding soil (soil composition, geology, hydrogeology, climate);

(iii) Results of any monitoring or sampling conducted in connection with the release, (if available). If sampling or monitoring data relating to the release are not available within 30 days, these data must be submitted to the Regional Administrator as soon as they become available;

(iv) Proximity to downgradient drinking water, surface water, and population areas; and

(v) Description of response actions taken or planned.

(e) *Provision of secondary containment, repair, or closure.* (1) Unless the owner or operator satisfies the requirements of paragraphs (e)(2) through (4) of this section, the tank system must be closed in accordance with §265.197.

(2) If the cause of the release was a spill that has not damaged the integrity of the system, the owner/operator may return the system to service as soon as the released waste is removed and repairs, if necessary, are made.

(3) If the cause of the release was a leak from the primary tank system into the secondary containment system, the system must be repaired prior to returning the tank system to service.

(4) If the source of the release was a leak to the environment from a component of a tank system without secondary containment, the owner/operator must provide the component of the system from which the leak occurred with secondary containment that satisfies the requirements of §265.193 before it can be returned to service, unless the source of the leak is an aboveground portion of a tank system. If the source is an aboveground component that can be inspected visually, the component must be repaired and may be returned to service without secondary containment as long as the requirements of paragraph (f) of this section are satisfied. If a component is replaced to comply with the requirements of this subparagraph, that component must satisfy the requirements for new tank systems or components in

§§265.192 and 265.193. Additionally, if a leak has occurred in any portion of a tank system component that is not readily accessible for visual inspection (*e.g.*, the bottom of an inground or onground tank), the entire component must be provided with secondary containment in accordance with §265.193 prior to being returned to use.

(f) *Certification of major repairs.* If the owner/operator has repaired a tank system in accordance with paragraph (e) of this section, and the repair has been extensive (e.g., installation of an internal liner; repair of a ruptured primary containment or secondary containment vessel), the tank system must not be returned to service unless the owner/operator has obtained a certification by a qualified Professional Engineer in accordance with §270.11(d) that the repaired system is capable of handling hazardous wastes without release for the intended life of the system. This certification is to be placed in the operating record and maintained until closure of the facility.

Note: The Regional Administrator may, on the basis of any information received that there is or has been a release of hazardous waste or hazardous constituents into the environment, issue an order under RCRA section 3004(v), 3008(h), or 7003(a) requiring corrective action or such other response as deemed necessary to protect human health or the environment.

Note: See §265.15(c) for the requirements necessary to remedy a failure. Also, 40 CFR Part 302 requires the owner or operator to notify the National Response Center of a release of any "reportable quantity."

[51 FR 25479, July 14, 1986, as amended at 53 FR 34087, Sept. 2, 1988; 71 FR 16911, Apr. 4, 2006]

PART 265—Subpart J

§265.197 Closure and post-closure care.

(a) At closure of a tank system, the owner or operator must remove or decontaminate all waste residues, contaminated containment system components (liners, etc.), contaminated soils, and structures and equipment contaminated with waste, and manage them as hazardous waste, unless §261.3(d) of this Chapter applies. The closure plan, closure activities, cost estimates for closure, and financial responsibility for tank systems must meet all of the requirements specified in subparts G and H of this part.

(b) If the owner or operator demonstrates that not all contaminated soils can be practicably removed or decontaminated as required in paragraph (a) of this section, then the owner or operator must close the tank system and perform post-closure care in accordance with the closure and post-closure care requirements that apply to landfills (§265.310). In addition, for the purposes of closure, post-closure, and financial responsibility, such a tank system is then considered to be a landfill, and the owner or operator must meet all of the requirements for landfills specified in subparts G and H of this part.

17.6.2

(c) If an owner or operator has a tank system which does not have secondary containment that meets the requirements of §265.193(b) through (f) and which is not exempt from the secondary containment requirements in accordance with §265.193(g), then,

(1) The closure plan for the tank system must include both a plan for complying with paragraph (a) of this section and a contingent plan for complying with paragraph (b) of this section.

(2) A contingent post-closure plan for complying with paragraph (b) of this section must be prepared and submitted as part of the permit application.

(3) The cost estimates calculated for closure and post-closure care must reflect the costs of complying with the contingent closure plan and the contingent post-closure plan, if these costs are greater than the costs of complying with the closure plan prepared for the expected closure under paragraph (a) of this section.

(4) Financial assurance must be based on the cost estimates in paragraph (c)(3) of this section.

(5) For the purposes of the contingent closure and post-closure plans, such a tank system is considered to be a landfill, and the contingent plans must meet all of the closure, post-closure, and financial responsibility requirements for landfills under subparts G and H of this part.

51 FR 25479, July 14, 1986, as amended at 71 FR 40275, July 14, 2006

§265.198 Special requirements for ignitable or reactive wastes.

(a) Ignitable or reactive waste must not be placed in a tank system, unless:

(1) The waste is treated, rendered, or mixed before or immediately after placement in the tank system so that:

(i) The resulting waste, mixture, or dissolved material no longer meets the definition of ignitable or reactive waste under §§261.21 or 261.23 of this chapter; and

(ii) Section 265.17(b) is complied with; or

(2) The waste is stored or treated in such a way that it is protected from any material or conditions that may cause the waste to ignite or react; or

(3) The tank system is used solely for emergencies.

(b) The owner or operator of a facility where ignitable or reactive waste is stored or treated in tanks must comply with the requirements for the maintenance of protective distances between the waste management area and any public ways, streets, alleys, or an adjoining property line that can be built upon as required in Tables 2-1 through 2-6 of the National Fire Protection Association's "Flammable and Combustible Liquids Code," (1977 or 1981), (incorporated by reference, see §260.11).

§265.199 Special requirements for incompatible wastes.

(a) Incompatible wastes, or incompatible waste and materials, must not be placed in the same tank system, unless §265.17(b) is complied with.

(b) Hazardous waste must not be placed in a tank system that has not been decontaminated and that previously held an incompatible waste or material, unless §265.17(b) is complied with.

§265.200 Waste analysis and trial tests.

In addition to performing the waste analysis required by §265.13, the owner or operator must, whenever a tank system is to be used to treat chemically or to store a hazardous waste that is substantially different from waste previously treated or stored in that tank system; or treat chemically a hazardous waste with a substantially different process than any previously used in that tank system:

(a) Conduct waste analyses and trial treatment or storage tests (*e.g.*, bench-scale or pilot-plant scale tests); or

(b) Obtain written, documented information on similar waste under similar operating conditions to show that the proposed treatment or storage will meet the requirements of §265.194(a).

Note: Section 265.13 requires the waste analysis plan to include analyses needed to comply with §§265.198 and 265.199. Section 265.73 requires the owner or operator to place the results from each waste analysis and trial test, or the documented information, in the operating record of the facility.

§265.201 Special requirements for generators of between 100 and 1,000 kg/mo that accumulate hazardous waste in tanks.

(a) The requirements of this section apply to small quantity generators of more than 100 kg but less than 1,000 kg of hazardous waste in a calendar month, that accumulate hazardous waste in tanks for less than 180 days (or 270 days if the generator must ship the waste greater than 200 miles), and do not accumulate over 6,000 kg on-site at any time.

(b) Generators of between 100 and 1,000 kg/mo hazardous waste must comply with the following general operating requirements:

(1) Treatment or storage of hazardous waste in tanks must comply with §265.17(b). 📖 7.3

(2) Hazardous wastes or treatment reagents must not be placed in a tank if they could cause the tank or its inner liner to rupture, leak, corrode, or otherwise fail before the end of its intended life.

(3) Uncovered tanks must be operated to ensure at least 60 centimeters (2 feet) of freeboard, unless the tank is equipped with a containment structure (*e.g.*, dike or trench), a drainage control system, or a diversion structure (*e.g.*, standby tank) with a capacity that equals or exceeds the volume of the top 60 centimeters (2 feet) of the tank.

(4) Where hazardous waste is continuously fed into a tank, the tank must be equipped with a means to stop this inflow (*e.g.*, waste feed cutoff system or by-pass system to a stand-by tank).

Note: These systems are intended to be used in the event of a leak or overflow from the tank due to a system failure (*e.g.*, a malfunction in the treatment process, a crack in the tank, etc.).

(c) Except as noted in paragraph (d) of this section, generators who accumulate between 100 and 1,000 kg/mo of hazardous waste in tanks must inspect, where present:

📖 10.5

(1) Discharge control equipment (*e.g.*, waste feed cutoff systems, by-pass systems, and drainage systems) at least once each operating day, to ensure that it is in good working order;

(2) Data gathered from monitoring equipment (*e.g.*, pressure and temperature gauges) at least once each operating day to ensure that the tank is being operated according to its design;

(3) The level of waste in the tank at least once each operating day to ensure compliance with §265.201(b)(3);

(4) The construction materials of the tank at least weekly to detect corrosion or leaking of fixtures or seams; and

(5) The construction materials of, and the area immediately surrounding, discharge confinement structures (*e.g.*, dikes) at least weekly to detect erosion or obvious signs of leakage (*e.g.*, wet spots or dead vegetation).

Note: As required by §265.15(c), the owner or operator must remedy any deterioration or malfunction he finds.

(d) Generators who accumulate between 100 and 1,000 kg/mo of hazardous waste in tanks or tank systems that have full secondary containment and that either use leak detection equipment to alert facility personnel to leaks, or implement established workplace practices to ensure leaks are promptly identified, must inspect at least weekly, where applicable, the areas identified in paragraphs (c)(1) through (5) of this section. Use of the alternate inspection schedule must be documented in the facility's operating record. This documentation must include a description of the established workplace practices at the facility.

(e) Performance Track member facilities may inspect on a less frequent basis, upon approval by the Director, but must inspect at least once each month. To apply for a less than weekly inspection frequency, the Performance Track member facility must follow the procedures described in §265.15(b)(5).

(f) Generators of between 100 and 1,000 kg/mo accumulating hazardous waste in tanks must, upon closure of the facility, remove all hazardous waste from tanks, discharge control equipment, and discharge confinement structures.

Note: At closure, as throughout the operating period, unless the owner or operator can demonstrate, in accordance with §261.3(c) or (d) of this chapter, that any solid waste removed from his tank is not a hazardous waste, the owner or operator becomes a generator of hazardous waste and must manage it in accordance with all applicable requirements of parts 262, 263, and 265 of this chapter.

(g) Generators of between 100 and 1,000 kg/mo must comply with the following special requirements for ignitable or reactive waste:

(1) Ignitable or reactive waste must not be placed in a tank, unless:

(i) The waste is treated, rendered, or mixed before or immediately after placement in a tank so that (A) the resulting waste, mixture, or dissolution of material no longer meets the definition of ignitable or reactive waste under §261.21 or §261.23 of this chapter, and (B) §265.17(b) is complied with; or

(ii) The waste is stored or treated in such a way that it is protected from any material or conditions that may cause the waste to ignite or react; or

(iii) The tank is used solely for emergencies.

(2) The owner or operator of a facility which treats or stores ignitable or reactive waste in covered tanks must comply with the buffer zone requirements for tanks contained in Tables 2-1 through 2-6 of the National Fire Protection Association's "Flammable and Combustible Liquids Code," (1977 or 1981)(incorporated by reference, see §260.11).

(h) Generators of between 100 and 1,000 kg/mo must comply with the following special requirements for incompatible wastes:

(1) Incompatible wastes, or incompatible wastes and materials, (see appendix V for examples) must not be placed in the same tank, unless §265.17(b) is complied with.

(2) Hazardous waste must not be placed in an unwashed tank which previously held an incompatible waste or material, unless §265.17(b) is complied with.

[51 FR 25479, July 14, 1986, as amended at 53 FR 34087, Sept. 2, 1988; 71 FR 16911, Apr. 4, 2006; 71 FR 40275, July 14, 2006]

§265.202 Air emission standards. 📖 15.1–3

The owner or operator shall manage all hazardous waste placed in a tank in accordance with the applicable requirements of subparts AA, BB, and CC of this part.

[61 FR 59968, Nov. 25, 1996]

Subpart K—Surface Impoundments

§265.220 Applicability. 📖 2.4.4, 10.1.3.2, 14.1.2, 14.2.1.3

The regulations in this subpart apply to owners and operators of facilities that use surface impoundments to treat, store, or dispose of hazardous waste, except as §265.1 provides otherwise.

§265.221 Design and operating requirements.

(a) The owner or operator of each new surface impoundment unit, each lateral expansion of a surface impoundment unit, and each replacement of an existing surface impoundment unit must install two or more liners, and a leachate collection and removal system between the liners, and operate the leachate collection and removal system, in accordance with §264.221(c), unless exempted under §264.221(d), (e), or (f) of this Chapter.

(b) The owner or operator of each unit referred to in paragraph (a) of this section must notify the Regional Administrator at least sixty days prior to receiving waste. The owner or operator of each facility submitting notice must file a part B application within six months of the receipt of such notice.

(c) The owner or operator of any replacement surface impoundment unit is exempt from paragraph (a) of this section if:

(1) The existing unit was constructed in compliance with the design standards of §3004(o)(1)(A)(i) and (o)(5) of the Resource Conservation and Recovery Act; and

(2) There is no reason to believe that the liner is not functioning as designed.

(d) The double liner requirement set forth in paragraph (a) of this section may be waived by the Regional Administrator for any monofill, if:

(1) The monofill contains only hazardous wastes from foundry furnace emission controls or metal casting

molding sand, and such wastes do not contain constituents which would render the wastes hazardous for reasons other than the Toxicity Characteristic in §261.24 of this chapter, with EPA Hazardous Waste Numbers D004 through D017; and

(2)(i)(A) The monofill has at least one liner for which there is no evidence that such liner is leaking. For the purposes of this paragraph the term "liner" means a liner designed, constructed, installed, and operated to prevent hazardous waste from passing into the liner at any time during the active life of the facility, or a liner designed, constructed, installed, and operated to prevent hazardous waste from migrating beyond the liner to adjacent subsurface soil, ground water, or surface water at any time during the active life of the facility. In the case of any surface impoundment which has been exempted from the requirements of paragraph (a) of this section on the basis of a liner designed, constructed, installed, and operated to prevent hazardous waste from passing beyond the liner, at the closure of such impoundment the owner or operator must remove or decontaminate all waste residues, all contaminated liner material, and contaminated soil to the extent practicable. If all contaminated soil is not removed or decontaminated, the owner or operator of such impoundment must comply with appropriate post-closure requirements, including but not limited to ground-water monitoring and corrective action;

(B) The monofill is located more than one-quarter mile from an "underground source of drinking water" (as that term is defined in 40 CFR 270.2); and

(C) The monofill is in compliance with generally applicable ground-water monitoring requirements for facilities with permits under RCRA section 3005(c); or

(ii) The owner or operator demonstrates that the monofill is located, designed and operated so as to assure that there will be no migration of any hazardous constituent into ground water or surface water at any future time.

(e) In the case of any unit in which the liner and leachate collection system has been installed pursuant to the requirements of paragraph (a) of this section and in good faith compliance with paragraph (a) of this section and with guidance documents governing liners and leachate collection systems under paragraph (a) of this section, no liner or leachate collection system which is different from that which was so installed pursuant to paragraph (a) of this section will be required for such unit by the Regional Administrator when issuing the first permit to such facility, except that the Regional Administrator will not be precluded from requiring installation of a new liner when the Regional Administrator has reason to believe that any liner installed pursuant to the requirements of paragraph (a) of this section is leaking.

(f) A surface impoundment must maintain enough freeboard to prevent any overtopping of the dike by overfilling, wave action, or a storm. Except as provided in paragraph (b) of this section, there must be at least 60 centimeters (two feet) of freeboard.

(g) A freeboard level less than 60 centimeters (two feet) may be maintained if the owner or operator obtains certification by a qualified engineer that alternate design features or operating plans will, to the best of his knowledge and opinion, prevent overtopping of the dike. The certification, along with a written identification of alternate design features or operating plans preventing overtopping, must be maintained at the facility.

(h) Surface impoundments that are newly subject to RCRA section 3005(j)(1) due to the promulgation of additional listings or characteristics for the identification of hazardous waste must be in compliance with paragraphs (a), (c) and (d) of this section not later than 48 months after the promulgation of the additional listing or characteristic. This compliance period shall not be cut short as the result of the promulgation of land disposal prohibitions under part 268 of this chapter or the granting of an extension to the effective date of a prohibition pursuant to §268.5 of this chapter, within this 48-month period.

[50 FR 16048, Apr. 23, 1985. Redesignated at 57 FR 3492, Jan. 29, 1992. 50 FR 28749, July 15, 1985, as amended at 55 FR 11876, Mar. 29, 1990; 57 FR 3492, Jan. 29, 1992; 57 FR 37267, Aug. 18, 1992; 71 FR 16911, Apr. 4, 2006; 71 FR 40275, July 14, 2006]

§265.222 Action leakage rate.

(a) The owner or operator of surface impoundment units subject to §265.221(a) must submit a proposed action leakage rate to the Regional Administrator when submitting the notice required under §265.221(b). Within 60 days of receipt of the notification, the Regional Administrator will: Establish an action leakage rate, either as proposed by the owner or operator or modified using the criteria in this section; or extend the review period for up to 30 days. If no action is taken by the Regional Administrator before the original 60 or extended 90 day review periods, the action leakage rate will be approved as proposed by the owner or operator.

(b) The Regional Administrator shall approve an action leakage rate for surface impoundment units subject to §265.221(a). The action leakage rate is the maximum design flow rate that the leak detection system (LDS) can remove without the fluid head on the bottom liner exceeding 1 foot. The action leakage rate must include an adequate safety margin to allow for uncertainties in the design (*e.g.*, slope, hydraulic conductivity, thickness of drainage material), construction, operation, and location of the LDS, waste and leachate characteristics, likelihood and amounts of other sources of liquids in the LDS, and proposed response actions (*e.g.*, the action leakage rate must consider decreases in the flow capacity of the system over time resulting from siltation and clogging, rib layover and creep of synthetic components of the system, overburden pressures, etc.).

(c) To determine if the action leakage rate has been exceeded, the owner or operator must convert the weekly or monthly flow rate from the monitoring data obtained under §265.226(b), to an average daily flow rate (gallons per acre per day) for each sump. Unless the Regional Administrator approves a different calculation, the average daily flow rate for each sump must be calculated weekly during the active life and closure period, and if the unit closes in accordance with §265.228(a)(2), monthly during the post-closure care period when monthly monitoring is required under §265.226(b).

[57 FR 3492, Jan. 29, 1992]

§265.223 Containment system.

All earthen dikes must have a protective cover, such as grass, shale, or rock, to minimize wind and water erosion and to preserve their structural integrity.

§265.224 Response actions.

(a) The owner or operator of surface impoundment units subject to §265.221(a) must develop and keep on site until closure of the facility a response action plan. The response action plan must set forth the actions to be taken if the action leakage rate has been exceeded. At a minimum, the response action plan must describe the actions specified in paragraph (b) of this section.

(b) If the flow rate into the leak detection system exceeds the action leakage rate for any sump, the owner or operator must:

(1) Notify the Regional Administrator in writing of the exceedance within 7 days of the determination;

(2) Submit a preliminary written assessment to the Regional Administrator within 14 days of the determination, as to the amount of liquids, likely sources of liquids, possible location, size, and cause of any leaks, and short-term actions taken and planned;

(3) Determine to the extent practicable the location, size, and cause of any leak;

(4) Determine whether waste receipt should cease or be curtailed, whether any waste should be removed from the unit for inspection, repairs, or controls, and whether or not the unit should be closed;

(5) Determine any other short-term and longer-term actions to be taken to mitigate or stop any leaks; and

(6) Within 30 days after the notification that the action leakage rate has been exceeded, submit to the Regional Administrator the results of the analyses specified in paragraphs (b)(3), (4), and (5) of this section, the results of actions taken, and actions planned. Monthly thereafter, as long as the flow rate in the leak detection system exceeds the action leakage rate, the owner or operator must submit to the Regional Administrator a report summarizing the results of any remedial actions taken and actions planned.

(c) To make the leak and/or remediation determinations in paragraphs (b)(3), (4), and (5) of this section, the owner or operator must:

(1)(i) Assess the source of liquids and amounts of liquids by source,

(ii) Conduct a fingerprint, hazardous constituent, or other analyses of the liquids in the leak detection system to identify the source of liquids and possible location of any leaks, and the hazard and mobility of the liquid; and

(iii) Assess the seriousness of any leaks in terms of potential for escaping into the environment; or

(2) Document why such assessments are not needed.

[57 FR 3492, Jan. 29, 1992. Redesignated and amended at 71 FR 16911, Apr. 4, 2006; 71 FR 40275, July 14, 2006]

§265.225 Waste analysis and trial tests.

(a) In addition to the waste analyses required by §265.13, whenever a surface impoundment is to be used to:

(1) Chemically treat a hazardous waste which is substantially different from waste previously treated in that impoundment; or

(2) Chemically treat hazardous waste with a substantially different process than any previously used in that impoundment; the owner or operator must, before treating the different waste or using the different process:

(i) Conduct waste analyses and trial treatment tests (*e.g.*, bench scale or pilot plant scale tests); or

PART 265—Subpart K

(ii) Obtain written, documented information on similar treatment of similar waste under similar operating conditions; to show that this treatment will comply with §265.17(b).

[*Comment:* As required by §265.13, the waste analysis plan must include analyses needed to comply with §§265.229 and 265.230. As required by §265.73, the owner or operator must place the results from each waste analysis and trial test, or the documented information, in the operating record of the facility.]

(b) [Reserved]

§265.226 Monitoring and inspection.

(a) The owner or operator must inspect:

(1) The freeboard level at least once each operating day to ensure compliance with §265.222, and

(2) The surface impoundment, including dikes and vegetation surrounding the dike, at least once a week to detect any leaks, deterioration, or failures in the impoundment.

(b)(1) An owner or operator required to have a leak detection system under §265.221(a) must record the amount of liquids removed from each leak detection system sump at least once each week during the active life and closure period.

(2) After the final cover is installed, the amount of liquids removed from each leak detection system sump must be recorded at least monthly. If the liquid level in the sump stays below the pump operating level for two consecutive months, the amount of liquids in the sumps must be recorded at least quarterly. If the liquid level in the sump stays below the pump operating level for two consecutive quarters, the amount of liquids in the sumps must be recorded at least semi-annually. If at any time during the post-closure care period the pump operating level is exceeded at units on quarterly or semi-annual recording schedules, the owner or operator must return to monthly recording of amounts of liquids removed from each sump until the liquid level again stays below the pump operating level for two consecutive months.

(3) "Pump operating level" is a liquid level proposed by the owner or operator and approved by the Regional Administrator based on pump activation level, sump dimensions, and level that avoids backup into the drainage layer and minimizes head in the sump. The timing for submission and approval of the proposed "pump operating level" will be in accordance with §265.222(a).

[*Comment:* As required by §265.15(c), the owner or operator must remedy any deterioration or malfunction he finds.]

[45 FR 33232, May 19, 1980, as amended at 57 FR 3493, Jan. 29, 1992]

§265.227 [Reserved]

§265.228 Closure and post-closure care.

(a) At closure, the owner or operator must:

(1) Remove or decontaminate all waste residues, contaminated containment system components (liners, etc.), contaminated subsoils, and structures and equipment contaminated with waste and leachate, and manage them as hazardous waste unless §261.3(d) of this chapter applies; or

(2) Close the impoundment and provide post-closure care for a landfill under subpart G and §265.310, including the following:

(i) Eliminate free liquids by removing liquid wastes or solidifying the remaining wastes and waste residues;

(ii) Stabilize remaining wastes to a bearing capacity sufficient to support the final cover; and

(iii) Cover the surface impoundment with a final cover designed and constructed to:

(A) Provide long-term minimization of the migration of liquids through the closed impoundment;

(B) Function with minimum maintenance;

(C) Promote drainage and minimize erosion or abrasion of the cover;

(D) Accommodate settling and subsidence so that the cover's integrity is maintained; and

(E) Have a permeability less than or equal to the permeability of any bottom liner system or natural subsoils present.

(b) In addition to the requirements of subpart G, and §265.310, during the post-closure care period, the owner or operator of a surface impoundment in which wastes, waste residues, or contaminated materials remain after closure in accordance with the provisions of paragraph (a)(2) of this section must:

(1) Maintain the integrity and effectiveness of the final cover, including making repairs to the cover as necessary to correct the effects of settling, subsidence, erosion, or other events;

(2) Maintain and monitor the leak detection system in accordance with §§264.221(c)(2)(iv) and (3) of this chapter and 265.226(b) and comply with all other applicable leak detection system requirements of this part;

(3) Maintain and monitor the ground-water monitoring system and comply with all other applicable requirements of subpart F of this part; and

(4) Prevent run-on and run-off from eroding or otherwise damaging the final cover.

[52 FR 8708, Mar. 19, 1987, as amended at 57 FR 3493, Jan. 29, 1992; 71 FR 40275, July 14, 2006]

§265.229 Special requirements for ignitable or reactive waste.

Ignitable or reactive waste must not be placed in a surface impoundment, unless the waste and impoundment satisfy all applicable requirements of 40 CFR part 268, and:

(a) The waste is treated, rendered, or mixed before or immediately after placement in the impoundment so that:

(1) The resulting waste, mixture, or dissolution of material no longer meets the definition of ignitable or reactive waste under §261.21 or §261.23 of this chapter; and

(2) Section 265.17(b) is complied with; or

(b)(1) The waste is managed in such a way that it is protected from any material or conditions which may cause it to ignite or react; and

(2) The owner or operator obtains a certification from a qualified chemist or engineer that, to the best of his knowledge and opinion, the design features or operating plans of the facility will prevent ignition or reaction; and

(3) The certification and the basis for it are maintained at the facility; or

(c) The surface impoundment is used solely for emergencies.

[50 FR 16048, Apr. 23, 1985, as amended at 55 FR 22685, June 1, 1990; 57 FR 3493, Jan. 29, 1992; 71 FR 40275, July 14, 2006]

§265.230 Special requirements for incompatible wastes.

Incompatible wastes, or incompatible wastes and materials, (see appendix V for examples) must not be placed in the same surface impoundment, unless §265.17(b) is complied with.

§265.231 Air emission standards. 📖 15.2-3

The owner or operator shall manage all hazardous waste placed in a surface impoundment in accordance with the applicable requirements of subparts BB and CC of this part.

[61 FR 59968, Nov. 25, 1996]

Subpart L—Waste Piles

§265.250 Applicability. 📖 10.1.3.1

The regulations in this subpart apply to owners and operators of facilities that treat or store hazardous waste in piles, except as §265.1 provides otherwise. Alternatively, a pile of hazardous waste may be managed as a landfill under subpart N.

§265.251 Protection from wind.

The owner or operator of a pile containing hazardous waste which could be subject to dispersal by wind must cover or otherwise manage the pile so that wind dispersal is controlled.

§265.252 Waste analysis.

In addition to the waste analyses required by §265.13, the owner or operator must analyze a representative sample of waste from each incoming movement before adding the waste to any existing pile, unless (1) The only wastes the facility receives which are amenable to piling are compatible with each other, or (2) the waste received is compatible with the waste in the pile to which it is to be added. The analysis conducted must be capable of differentiating between the types of hazardous waste the owner or operator places in piles, so that mixing of incompatible waste does not inadvertently occur. The analysis must include a visual comparison of color and texture.

[*Comment:* As required by §265.13, the waste analysis plan must include analyses needed to comply with §§265.256 and 265.257. As required by §265.73, the owner or operator must place the results of this analysis in the operating record of the facility.]

(b) [Reserved]

§265.253 Containment.

If leachate or run-off from a pile is a hazardous waste, then either:

(a)(1) The pile must be placed on an impermeable base that is compatible with the waste under the conditions of treatment or storage;

(2) The owner or operator must design, construct, operate, and maintain a run-on control system capable of preventing flow onto the active portion of the pile during peak discharge from at least a 25-year storm;

(3) The owner or operator must design, construct, operate, and maintain a run-off management system to collect and control at least the water volume resulting from a 24-hour, 25-year storm; and

(4) Collection and holding facilities (*e.g.*, tanks or basins) associated with run-on and run-off control systems must be emptied or otherwise managed expeditiously to maintain design capacity of the system; or

(b)(1) The pile must be protected from precipitation and run-on by some other means; and

(2) No liquids or wastes containing free liquids may be placed in the pile.

[*Comment:* If collected leachate or run-off is discharged through a point source to waters of the United States, it is subject to the requirements of section 402 of the Clean Water Act, as amended.]

[45 FR 33232, May 19, 1980, as amended at 47 FR 32367, July 26, 1982]

§265.254 Design and operating requirements.

The owner or operator of each new waste pile on which construction commences after January 29, 1992, each lateral expansion of a waste pile unit on which construction commences after July 29, 1992, and each such replacement of an existing waste pile unit that is to commence reuse after July 29, 1992 must install two or more liners and a leachate collection and removal system above and between such liners, and operate the leachate collection and removal systems, in accordance with §264.251(c), unless exempted under §264.251(d), (e), or (f), of this chapter; and must comply with the procedures of §265.221(b). "Construction commences" is as defined in §260.10 of this chapter under "existing facility".

[57 FR 3493, Jan. 29, 1992]

§265.255 Action leakage rates.

(a) The owner or operator of waste pile units subject to §265.254 must submit a proposed action leakage rate to the Regional Administrator when submitting the notice required under §265.254. Within 60 days of receipt of the notification, the Regional Administrator will: Establish an action leakage rate, either as proposed by the owner or operator or modified using the criteria in this section; or extend the review period for up to 30 days. If no action is taken by the Regional Administrator before the original 60 or extended 90 day review periods, the action leakage rate will be approved as proposed by the owner or operator.

(b) The Regional Administrator shall approve an action leakage rate for waste pile units subject to §265.254. The action leakage rate is the maximum design flow rate that the leak detection system (LDS) can remove without the fluid head on the bottom liner exceeding 1 foot. The action leakage rate must include an adequate safety margin to allow for uncertainties in the design (*e.g.*, slope, hydraulic conductivity, thickness of drainage material), construction, operation, and location of the LDS, waste and leachate characteristics, likelihood and amounts of other sources of liquids in the LDS, and proposed response actions (*e.g.*, the action leakage rate must consider decreases in the flow capacity of the system over time resulting from siltation and clogging, rib layover and creep of synthetic components of the system, overburden pressures, etc.).

(c) To determine if the action leakage rate has been exceeded, the owner or operator must convert the weekly flow rate from the monitoring data obtained under §265.260, to an average daily flow rate (gallons per acre per day) for each sump. Unless the Regional Administrator approves a different calculation, the average daily flow rate for each sump must be calculated weekly during the active life and closure period.

[57 FR 3493, Jan. 29, 1992; 71 FR 40275, July 14, 2006]

§265.256 Special requirements for ignitable or reactive waste.

(a) Ignitable or reactive waste must not be placed in a pile unless the waste and pile satisfy all applicable requirements of 40 CFR part 268, and:

(1) Addition of the waste to an existing pile (i) results in the waste or mixture no longer meeting the definition of ignitable or reactive waste under §261.21 or §261.23 of this chapter, and (ii) complies with §265.17(b); or

(2) The waste is managed in such a way that it is protected from any material or conditions which may cause it to ignite or react.

(b) [Reserved]

[45 FR 33232, May 19, 1980, as amended at 55 FR 22685, June 1, 1990]

§265.257 Special requirements for incompatible wastes.

(a) Incompatible wastes, or incompatible wastes and materials, (see appendix V for examples) must not be placed in the same pile, unless §265.17(b) is complied with.

(b) A pile of hazardous waste that is incompatible with any waste or other material stored nearby in other containers, piles, open tanks, or surface impoundments must be separated from the other materials, or protected from them by means of a dike, berm, wall, or other device.

[*Comment:* The purpose of this is to prevent fires, explosions, gaseous emissions, leaching, or other discharge of hazardous waste or hazardous waste constituents which could result from the contact or mixing of incompatible wastes or materials.]

(c) Hazardous waste must not be piled on the same area where incompatible wastes or materials were previously piled, unless that area has been decontaminated sufficiently to ensure compliance with §265.17(b).

§265.258 Closure and post-closure care.

(a) At closure, the owner or operator must remove or decontaminate all waste residues, contaminated containment system components (liners, etc.), contaminated subsoils, and structures and equipment contaminated with waste and leachate, and manage them as hazardous waste unless §261.3(d) of this chapter applies; or

(b) If, after removing or decontaminating all residues and making all reasonable efforts to effect removal or decontamination of contaminated components, subsoils, structures, and equipment as required in paragraph (a) of this section, the owner or operator finds that not all contaminated subsoils can be practicably removed or decontaminated, he must close the facility and perform post-closure care in accordance with the closure and post-closure requirements that apply to landfills (§265.310).

[47 FR 32368, July 26, 1982]

§265.259 Response actions.

(a) The owner or operator of waste pile units subject to §265.254 must develop and keep on-site until closure of the facility a response action plan. The response action plan must set forth the actions to be taken if the action leakage rate has been exceeded. At a minimum, the response action plan must describe the actions specified in paragraph (b) of this section.

(b) If the flow rate into the leak determination system exceeds the action leakage rate for any sump, the owner or operator must:

(1) Notify the Regional Administrator in writing of the exceedance within 7 days of the determination;

(2) Submit a preliminary written assessment to the Regional Administrator within 14 days of the determination, as to the amount of liquids, likely sources of liquids, possible location, size, and cause of any leaks, and short-term actions taken and planned;

(3) Determine to the extent practicable the location, size, and cause of any leak;

(4) Determine whether waste receipts should cease or be curtailed, whether any waste should be removed from the unit for inspection, repairs, or controls, and whether or not the unit should be closed;

(5) Determine any other short-term and longer-term actions to be taken to mitigate or stop any leaks; and

(6) Within 30 days after the notification that the action leakage rate has been exceeded, submit to the Regional Administrator the results of the analyses specified in paragraphs (b)(3), (4), and (5) of this section, the results of actions taken, and actions planned. Monthly thereafter, as long as the flow rate in the leak detection system exceeds the action leakage rate, the owner or operator must submit to the Regional Administrator a report summarizing the results of any remedial actions taken and actions planned.

(c) To make the leak and/or remediation determinations in paragraphs (b)(3), (4), and (5) of this section, the owner or operator must:

(1)(i) Assess the source of liquids and amounts of liquids by source,

(ii) Conduct a fingerprint, hazardous constituent, or other analyses of the liquids in the leak detection system to identify the source of liquids and possible location of any leaks, and the hazard and mobility of the liquid; and

(iii) Assess the seriousness of any leaks in terms of potential for escaping into the environment; or

(2) Document why such assessments are not needed.

[57 FR 3494, Jan. 29, 1992, as amended at 71 FR 16911, Apr. 4, 2006; 71 FR 40275, July 14, 2006]

§265.260 Monitoring and inspection.

An owner or operator required to have a leak detection system under §265.254 must record the amount of liquids removed from each leak detection system sump at least once each week during the active life and closure period.

[57 FR 3494, Jan. 29, 1992]

Subpart M—Land Treatment

§265.270 Applicability.

The regulations in this subpart apply to owners and operators of hazardous waste land treatment facilities, except as §265.1 provides otherwise.

§265.271 [Reserved]

§265.272 General operating requirements.

(a) Hazardous waste must not be placed in or on a land treatment facility unless the waste can be made less hazardous or nonhazardous by degradation, transformation, or immobilization processes occurring in or on the soil.

(b) The owner or operator must design, construct, operate, and maintain a run-on control system capable of preventing flow onto the active portions of the facility during peak discharge from at least a 25-year storm.

(c) The owner or operator must design, construct, operate, and maintain a run-off management system capable of collecting and controlling a water volume at least equivalent to a 24-hour, 25-year storm.

(d) Collection and holding facilities (*e.g.*, tanks or basins) associated with run-on and run-off control systems must be emptied or otherwise managed expeditiously after storms to maintain design capacity of the system.

(e) If the treatment zone contains particulate matter which may be subject to wind dispersal, the owner or operator must manage the unit to control wind dispersal.

[45 FR 33232, May 19, 1980, as amended at 47 FR 32368, July 26, 1982; 50 FR 16048, Apr. 23, 1985]

§265.273 Waste analysis.

In addition to the waste analyses required by §265.13, before placing a hazardous waste in or on a land treatment facility, the owner or operator must:

(a) Determine the concentrations in the waste of any substances which equal or exceed the maximum concentrations contained in Table 1 of §261.24 of this chapter that cause a waste to exhibit the Toxicity Characteristic;

(b) For any waste listed in part 261, subpart D, of this chapter, determine the concentrations of any substances which caused the waste to be listed as a hazardous waste; and

(c) If food chain crops are grown, determine the concentrations in the waste of each of the following constituents: arsenic, cadmium, lead, and mercury, unless the owner or operator has written, documented data that show that the constituent is not present.

[*Comment:* Part 261 of this chapter specifies the substances for which a waste is listed as a hazardous waste. As required by §265.13, the waste analysis plan must include analyses needed to comply with §§265.281 and 265.282. As required by §265.73, the owner or operator must place the results from each waste analysis, or the documented information, in the operating record of the facility.]

[45 FR 33232, May 19, 1980, as amended at 55 FR 11876, Mar. 29, 1990]

§§265.274–265.275 [Reserved]

§265.276 Food chain crops.

(a) An owner or operator of a hazardous waste land treatment facility on which food chain crops are being grown, or have been grown and will be grown in the future, must notify the Regional Administrator within 60 days after the effective date of this part.

[*Comment:* The growth of food chain crops at a facility which has never before been used for this purpose is a significant change in process under §122.72(c) of this chapter. Owners or operators of such land treatment facilities who propose to grow food chain crops after the effective date of this part must comply with §122.72(c) of this chapter.]

(b)(1) Food chain crops must not be grown on the treated area of a hazardous waste land treatment facility unless the owner or operator can demonstrate, based on field testing, that any arsenic, lead, mercury, or other constituents identified under §265.273(b):

(i) Will not be transferred to the food portion of the crop by plant uptake or direct contact, and will not otherwise be ingested by food chain animals (*e.g.*, by grazing); or

(ii) Will not occur in greater concentrations in the crops grown on the land treatment facility than in the same crops grown on untreated soils under similar conditions in the same region.

(2) The information necessary to make the demonstration required by paragraph (b)(1) of this section must be kept at the facility and must, at a minimum:

(i) Be based on tests for the specific waste and application rates being used at the facility; and

(ii) Include descriptions of crop and soil characteristics, sample selection criteria, sample size determination, analytical methods, and statistical procedures.

(c) Food chain crops must not be grown on a land treatment facility receiving waste that contains cadmium unless all requirements of paragraphs (c)(1)(i) through (iii) of this section or all requirements of paragraphs (c)(2)(i) through (iv) of this section are met.

(1)(i) The pH of the waste and soil mixture is 6.5 or greater at the time of each waste application, except for waste containing cadmium at concentrations of 2 mg/kg (dry weight) or less;

(ii) The annual application of cadmium from waste does not exceed 0.5 kilograms per hectare (kg/ha) on land used for production of tobacco, leafy vegetables, or root crops grown for human consumption. For other food chain crops, the annual cadmium application rate does not exceed:

Time period	Annual Cd application rate (kg/ha)
Present to June 30, 1984	2.0
July 1, 1984 to December 31, 1986	1.25
Beginning January 1, 1987	0.5

(iii) The cumulative application of cadmium from waste does not exceed the levels in either paragraph (c)(1)(iii)(A) or (B) of this section.

(A)

Soil caption exchange capacity (meq/100g)	Maximum cumulative application (kg/ha)	
	Background soil pH less than 6.5	Background soil pH greater than 6.5
Less than 5	5	5
5 to 15	5	10
Greater than 15	5	20

(B) For soils with a background pH of less than 6.5, the cumulative cadmium application rate does not exceed the levels below: *Provided*, that the pH of the waste and soil mixture is adjusted to and maintained at 6.5 or greater whenever food chain crops are grown.

Soil caption exchange capacity (meq/100g)	Maximum cumulative application (kg/ha)
Less than 5	5
5 to 15	10
Greater than 15	20

(2)(i) The only food chain crop produced is animal feed.

(ii) The pH of the waste and soil mixture is 6.5 or greater at the time of waste application or at the time the crop is planted, whichever occurs later, and this pH level is maintained whenever food chain crops are grown.

(iii) There is a facility operating plan which demonstrates how the animal feed will be distributed to preclude ingestion by humans. The facility operating plan describes the measures to be taken to safeguard against possible health hazards from cadmium entering the food chain, which may result from alternative land uses.

(iv) Future property owners are notified by a stipulation in the land record or property deed which states that the property has received waste at high cadmium application rates and that food chain crops must not be grown except in compliance with paragraph (c)(2) of this section.

[*Comment:* As required by §265.73, if an owner or operator grows food chain crops on his land treatment facility, he must place the information developed in this section in the operating record of the facility.]

[45 FR 33232, May 19, 1980, as amended at 47 FR 32368, July 26, 1982; 48 FR 14295, Apr. 1, 1983]

§265.277 [Reserved]

§265.278 Unsaturated zone (zone of aeration) monitoring.

(a) The owner or operator must have in writing, and must implement, an unsaturated zone monitoring plan which is designed to:

(1) Detect the vertical migration of hazardous waste and hazardous waste constituents under the active portion of the land treatment facility, and

(2) Provide information on the background concentrations of the hazardous waste and hazardous waste constituents in similar but untreated soils nearby; this background monitoring must be conducted before or in conjunction with the monitoring required under paragraph (a)(1) of this section.

(b) The unsaturated zone monitoring plan must include, at a minimum:

(1) Soil monitoring using soil cores, and

(2) Soil-pore water monitoring using devices such as lysimeters.

(c) To comply with paragraph (a)(1) of this section, the owner or operator must demonstrate in his unsaturated zone monitoring plan that:

(1) The depth at which soil and soil-pore water samples are to be taken is below the depth to which the waste is incorporated into the soil;

(2) The number of soil and soil-pore water samples to be taken is based on the variability of:

(i) The hazardous waste constituents (as identified in §265.273(a) and (b)) in the waste and in the soil; and

(ii) The soil type(s); and

(3) The frequency and timing of soil and soil-pore water sampling is based on the frequency, time, and rate of waste application, proximity to ground water, and soil permeability.

(d) The owner or operator must keep at the facility his unsaturated zone monitoring plan, and the rationale used in developing this plan.

(e) The owner or operator must analyze the soil and soil-pore water samples for the hazardous waste constituents that were found in the waste during the waste analysis under §265.273 (a) and (b).

[*Comment:* As required by §265.73, all data and information developed by the owner or operator under this section must be placed in the operating record of the facility.]

§265.279 Recordkeeping.

The owner or operator must include hazardous waste application dates and rates in the operating record required under §265.73.

[47 FR 32368, July 26, 1982]

§265.280 Closure and post-closure.

(a) In the closure plan under §265.112 and the post-closure plan under §265.118, the owner or operator must address the following objectives and indicate how they will be achieved:

(1) Control of the migration of hazardous waste and hazardous waste constituents from the treated area into the ground water;

(2) Control of the release of contaminated run-off from the facility into surface water;

(3) Control of the release of airborne particulate contaminants caused by wind erosion; and

PART 265—Subpart M

(4) Compliance with §265.276 concerning the growth of food-chain crops.

(b) The owner or operator must consider at least the following factors in addressing the closure and post-closure care objectives of paragraph (a) of this section:

(1) Type and amount of hazardous waste and hazardous waste constituents applied to the land treatment facility;

(2) The mobility and the expected rate of migration of the hazardous waste and hazardous waste constituents;

(3) Site location, topography, and surrounding land use, with respect to the potential effects of pollutant migration (*e.g.*, proximity to ground water, surface water and drinking water sources);

(4) Climate, including amount, frequency, and pH of precipitation;

(5) Geological and soil profiles and surface and subsurface hydrology of the site, and soil characteristics, including cation exchange capacity, total organic carbon, and pH;

(6) Unsaturated zone monitoring information obtained under §265.278; and

(7) Type, concentration, and depth of migration of hazardous waste constituents in the soil as compared to their background concentrations.

(c) The owner or operator must consider at least the following methods in addressing the closure and post-closure care objectives of paragraph (a) of this section:

(1) Removal of contaminated soils;

(2) Placement of a final cover, considering:

(i) Functions of the cover (*e.g.*, infiltration control, erosion and run-off control, and wind erosion control); and

(ii) Characteristics of the cover, including material, final surface contours, thickness, porosity and permeability, slope, length of run of slope, and type of vegetation on the cover; and

(3) Monitoring of ground water.

(d) In addition to the requirements of subpart G of this part, during the closure period the owner or operator of a land treatment facility must:

(1) Continue unsaturated zone monitoring in a manner and frequency specified in the closure plan, except that soil pore liquid monitoring may be terminated 90 days after the last application of waste to the treatment zone;

(2) Maintain the run-on control system required under §265.272(b);

(3) Maintain the run-off management system required under §265.272(c); and

(4) Control wind dispersal of particulate matter which may be subject to wind dispersal.

(e) For the purpose of complying with §265.115, when closure is completed the owner or operator may submit to the Regional Administrator certification both by the owner or operator and by an independent, qualified soil scientist, in lieu of a qualified Professional Engineer, that the facility has been closed in accordance with the specifications in the approved closure plan.

(f) In addition to the requirements of §265.117, during the post-closure care period the owner or operator of a land treatment unit must:

(1) Continue soil-core monitoring by collecting and analyzing samples in a manner and frequency specified in the post-closure plan;

(2) Restrict access to the unit as appropriate for its post-closure use;

(3) Assure that growth of food chain crops complies with §265.276; and

(4) Control wind dispersal of hazardous waste.

[45 FR 33232, May 19, 1980, as amended at 47 FR 32368, July 26, 1982; 71 FR 16911, Apr. 4, 2006; 71 FR 40275, July 14, 2006]

§265.281 Special requirements for ignitable or reactive waste.

The owner or operator must not apply ignitable or reactive waste to the treatment zone unless the waste and treatment zone meet all applicable requirements of 40 CFR part 268, and:

(a) The waste is immediately incorporated into the soil so that:

(1) The resulting waste, mixture, or dissolution of material no longer meets the definition of ignitable or reactive waste under §261.21 or §261.23 of this chapter; and

(2) Section 264.17(b) is complied with; or

(b) The waste is managed in such a way that it is protected from any material or conditions which may cause it to ignite or react.

[47 FR 32368, July 26, 1982, as amended at 55 FR 22686, June 1, 1990; 71 FR 40275, July 14, 2006]

§265.282 Special requirements for incompatible wastes.

Incompatible wastes, or incompatible wastes and materials (see appendix V for examples), must not be placed in the same land treatment area, unless §265.17(b) is complied with.

Subpart N—Landfills

§265.300 Applicability.

The regulations in this subpart apply to owners and operators of facilities that dispose of hazardous waste in landfills, except as §265.1 provides otherwise. A waste pile used as a disposal facility is a landfill and is governed by this subpart.

§265.301 Design and operating requirements.

(a) The owner or operator of each new landfill unit, each lateral expansion of a landfill unit, and each replacement of an existing landfill unit must install two or more liners and a leachate collection and removal system above and between such liners, and operate the leachate collection and removal system, in accordance with §264.301(c), unless exempted under §264.301(d), (e), or (f) of this chapter.

(b) The owner or operator of each unit referred to in paragraph (a) of this section must notify the Regional Administrator at least sixty days prior to receiving waste. The owner or operator of each facility submitting notice must file a part B application within six months of the receipt of such notice.

(c) The owner or operator of any replacement landfill unit is exempt from paragraph (a) of this section if:

(1) The existing unit was constructed in compliance with the design standards of section 3004(o)(1)(A)(i) and (o)(5) of the Resource Conservation and Recovery Act; and

(2) There is no reason to believe that the liner is not functioning as designed.

(d) The double liner requirement set forth in paragraph (a) of this section may be waived by the Regional Administrator for any monofill, if:

(1) The monofill contains only hazardous wastes from foundry furnace emission controls or metal casting molding sand, and such wastes do not contain constituents which would render the wastes hazardous for reasons other than the Toxicity Characteristic in §261.24 of this chapter, with EPA Hazardous Waste Numbers D004 through D017; and

(2)(i)(A) The monofill has at least one liner for which there is no evidence that such liner is leaking;

(B) The monofill is located more than one-quarter mile from an "underground source of drinking water" (as that term is defined in 40 CFR 270.2); and

(C) The monofill is in compliance with generally applicable ground-water monitoring requirements for facilities with permits under RCRA section 3005(c); or

(ii) The owner or operator demonstrates that the monofill is located, designed and operated so as to assure that there will be no migration of any hazardous constituent into ground water or surface water at any future time.

(e) In the case of any unit in which the liner and leachate collection system has been installed pursuant to the requirements of paragraph (a) of this section and in good faith compliance with paragraph (a) of this section and with guidance documents governing liners and leachate collection systems under paragraph (a) of this section, no liner or leachate collection system which is different from that which was so installed pursuant to paragraph (a) of this section will be required for such unit by the Regional Administrator when issuing the first permit to such facility, except that the Regional Administrator will not be precluded from requiring installation of a new liner when the Regional Administrator has reason to believe that any liner installed pursuant to the requirements of paragraph (a) of this section is leaking.

(f) The owner or operator must design, construct, operate, and maintain a run-on control system capable of preventing flow onto the active portion of the landfill during peak discharge from at least a 25-year storm.

(g) The owner or operator must design, construct, operate and maintain a run-off management system to collect and control at least the water volume resulting from a 24-hour, 25-year storm.

(h) Collection and holding facilities (*e.g.*, tanks or basins) associated with run-on and run-off control systems must be emptied or otherwise managed expeditiously after storms to maintain design capacity of the system.

(i) The owner or operator of a landfill containing hazardous waste which is subject to dispersal by wind must cover or otherwise manage the landfill so that wind dispersal of the hazardous waste is controlled.

[*Comment:* As required by §265.13, the waste analysis plan must include analyses needed to comply with §§265.312, 265.313, and 265.314. As required by §265.73, the owner or operator must place the results of these analyses in the operating record of the facility.]

[45 FR 33232, May 19, 1980, as amended at 47 FR 32368, July 26, 1982; 50 FR 18374, Apr. 30, 1985. Redesignated from §265.302 at 57 FR 3494, Jan. 29, 1992; 50 FR 28750, July 15, 1985, as amended at 57 FR 3494, Jan. 29, 1992; 57 FR 30658, July 10, 1992; 71 FR 16911, Apr. 4, 2006; 71 FR 40275, July 14, 2006]

§265.302 Action leakage rate.

(a) The owner or operator of landfill units subject to §265.301(a) must submit a proposed action leakage rate to the Regional Administrator when submitting the notice required under §265.301(b). Within 60 days of receipt of the notification, the Regional Administrator will: Establish an action leakage rate, either as proposed by the owner or operator or modified using the criteria in this section; or extend the review period for up to 30 days. If no action is taken by the Regional Administrator before the original 60 or extended 90 day review periods, the action leakage rate will be approved as proposed by the owner or operator.

(b) The Regional Administrator shall approve an action leakage rate for landfill units subject to §265.301(a). The action leakage rate is the maximum design flow rate that the leak detection system (LDS) can remove without the fluid head on the bottom liner exceeding 1 foot. The action leakage rate must include an adequate safety margin to allow for uncertainties in the design (*e.g.*, slope, hydraulic conductivity, thickness of drainage material), construction, operation, and location of the LDS, waste and leachate characteristics, likelihood and amounts of other sources of liquids in the LDS, and proposed response actions (*e.g.*, the action leakage rate must consider decreases in the flow capacity of the system over time resulting from siltation and clogging, rib layover and creep of synthetic components of the system, overburden pressures, etc.).

(c) To determine if the action leakage rate has been exceeded, the owner or operator must convert the weekly or monthly flow rate from the monitoring data obtained under §265.304 to an average daily flow rate (gallons per acre per day) for each sump. Unless the Regional Administrator approves a different calculation, the average daily flow rate for each sump must be calculated weekly during the active life and closure period, and monthly during the post-closure care period when monthly monitoring is required under §265.304(b).

[57 FR 3494, Jan. 29, 1992, as amended at 71 FR 40276, July 14, 2006]

§265.303 Response actions.

(a) The owner or operator of landfill units subject to §265.301(a) must develop and keep on site until closure of the facility a response action plan. The response action plan must set forth the actions to be taken if the action leakage rate has been exceeded. At a minimum, the response action plan must describe the actions specified in paragraph (b) of this section.

(b) If the flow rate into the leak detection system exceeds the action leakage rate for any sump, the owner or operator must:

(1) Notify the Regional Administrator in writing of the exceedance within 7 days of the determination;

(2) Submit a preliminary written assessment to the Regional Administrator within 14 days of the determination, as to the amount of liquids, likely sources of liquids, possible location, size, and cause of any leaks, and short-term actions taken and planned;

(3) Determine to the extent practicable the location, size, and cause of any leak;

(4) Determine whether waste receipt should cease or be curtailed, whether any waste should be removed from the unit for inspection, repairs, or controls, and whether or not the unit should be closed;

(5) Determine any other short-term and longer-term actions to be taken to mitigate or stop any leaks; and

(6) Within 30 days after the notification that the action leakage rate has been exceeded, submit to the Regional Administrator the results of the analyses specified in paragraphs (b)(3), (4), and (5) of this section, the results of actions taken, and actions planned. Monthly thereafter, as long as the flow rate in the leak detection system exceeds the action leakage rate, the owner or operator must submit to the Regional Administrator a report summarizing the results of any remedial actions taken and actions planned.

(c) To make the leak and/or remediation determinations in paragraphs (b)(3), (4), and (5) of this section, the owner or operator must:

(1)(i) Assess the source of liquids and amounts of liquids by source,

(ii) Conduct a fingerprint, hazardous constituent, or other analyses of the liquids in the leak detection system to identify the source of liquids and possible location of any leaks, and the hazard and mobility of the liquid; and

(iii) Assess the seriousness of any leaks in terms of potential for escaping into the environment; or

(2) Document why such assessments are not needed.

[57 FR 3494, Jan. 29, 1992, as amended at 71 FR 16912, Apr. 4, 2006; 71 FR 40276, July 14, 2006]

§265.304 Monitoring and inspection.

(a) An owner or operator required to have a leak detection system under §265.301(a) must record the amount of liquids removed from each leak detection system sump at least once each week during the active life and closure period.

(b) After the final cover is installed, the amount of liquids removed from each leak detection system sump must be recorded at least monthly. If the liquid level in the sump stays below the pump operating level for two consecutive months, the amount of liquids in the sumps must be recorded at least quarterly. If the liquid level in the sump stays below the pump operating level for two consecutive quarters, the amount of liquids in the sumps must be recorded at least semi-annually. If at any time during the post-closure care period the pump operating level is exceeded at units on quarterly or semi-annual recording schedules, the owner or operator must return to monthly recording of amounts of liquids removed from each sump until the liquid level again stays below the pump operating level for two consecutive months.

(c) "Pump operating level" is a liquid level proposed by the owner or operator and approved by the Regional Administrator based on pump activation level, sump dimensions, and level that avoids backup into the drainage layer and minimizes head in the sump. The timing for submission and approval of the proposed "pump operating level" will be in accordance with §265.302(a).

[57 FR 3495, Jan. 29, 1992]

§§265.305–265.308 [Reserved]

§265.309 Surveying and recordkeeping.

The owner or operator of a landfill must maintain the following items in the operating record required in §265.73:

(a) On a map, the exact location and dimensions, including depth, of each cell with respect to permanently surveyed benchmarks; and

(b) The contents of each cell and the approximate location of each hazardous waste type within each cell.

§265.310 Closure and post-closure care.

(a) At final closure of the landfill or upon closure of any cell, the owner or operator must cover the landfill or cell with a final cover designed and constructed to:

(1) Provide long-term minimization of migration of liquids through the closed landfill;

(2) Function with minimum maintenance;

(3) Promote drainage and minimize erosion or abrasion of the cover;

(4) Accommodate settling and subsidence so that the cover's integrity is maintained; and

(5) Have a permeability less than or equal to the permeability of any bottom liner system or natural subsoils present.

(b) After final closure, the owner or operator must comply with all post-closure requirements contained in §§265.117 through 265.120 including maintenance and monitoring throughout the post-closure care period. The owner or operator must:

(1) Maintain the integrity and effectiveness of the final cover, including making repairs to the cover as necessary to correct the effects of settling, subsidence, erosion, or other events;

(2) Maintain and monitor the leak detection system in accordance with §§264.301(c)(3)(iv) and (4) of this chapter and 265.304(b), and comply with all other applicable leak detection system requirements of this part;

(3) Maintain and monitor the ground-water monitoring system and comply with all other applicable requirements of subpart F of this part;

(4) Prevent run-on and run-off from eroding or otherwise damaging the final cover; and

(5) Protect and maintain surveyed benchmarks used in complying with §265.309.

[50 FR 16048, Apr. 23, 1985, as amended at 57 FR 3495, Jan. 29, 1992]

§265.311 [Reserved]

§265.312 Special requirements for ignitable or reactive waste.

(a) Except as provided in paragraph (b) of this section, and in §265.316, ignitable or reactive waste must not be placed in a landfill, unless the waste and landfill meets all applicable requirements of 40 CFR part 268, and:

(1) The resulting waste, mixture, or dissolution of material no longer meets the definition of ignitable or reactive waste under §261.21 or §261.23 of this chapter; and

(2) Section 265.17(b) is complied with.

(b) Except for prohibited wastes which remain subject to treatment standards in subpart D of part 268, ignitable wastes in containers may be landfilled without meeting the requirements of paragraph (a) of this section, provided that the wastes are disposed of in such a way that they are protected from any material or conditions which may cause them to ignite. At a minimum, ignitable wastes must be disposed of in non-leaking containers which are carefully handled and placed so as to avoid heat, sparks, rupture, or any other condition that might cause ignition of the wastes; must be covered daily with soil or other non-combustible material to minimize the potential for ignition of the wastes; and must not be disposed of in cells that contain or will contain other wastes which may generate heat sufficient to cause ignition of the waste.

[47 FR 32368, July 26, 1982, as amended at 55 FR 22686, June 1, 1990; 71 FR 40276, July 14, 2006]

§265.313 Special requirements for incompatible wastes.

Incompatible wastes, or incompatible wastes and materials, (see appendix V for examples) must not be placed in the same landfill cell, unless §265.17(b) is complied with.

§265.314 Special requirements for bulk and containerized liquids.

7.5.3

(a) The placement of bulk or noncontainerized liquid hazardous waste or hazardous waste containing free liquids (whether or not sorbents have been added) in any landfill is prohibited.

(b) Containers holding free liquids must not be placed in a landfill unless: 9.1.2.4

(1) All free-standing liquid,

(i) has been removed by decanting, or other methods,

(ii) has been mixed with sorbent or solidified so that free-standing liquid is no longer observed; or

(iii) had been otherwise eliminated; or

(2) The container is very small, such as an ampule; or

(3) The container is designed to hold free liquids for use other than storage, such as a battery or capacitor; or

(4) The container is a lab pack as defined in §265.316 and is disposed of in accordance with §265.316. 9.7, 13.3.1

(c) To demonstrate the absence or presence of free liquids in either a containerized or a bulk waste, the following test must be used: Method 9095B (Paint Filter Liquids Test) as described in "Test Methods for Evaluating Solid Waste, Physical/Chemical Methods," EPA Publication SW–846, as incorporated by reference in §260.11 of this chapter.

(d) The date for compliance with paragraph (a) of this section is November 19, 1981. The date for compliance with paragraph (c) of this section is March 22, 1982.

(e) Sorbents used to treat free liquids to be disposed of in landfills must be nonbiodegradable. Nonbiodegradable sorbents are: materials listed or described in paragraph (f)(1) of this section; materials that pass one of the tests in paragraph (f)(2) of this section; or materials that are determined by EPA to be nonbiodegradable through the Part 260 petition process.

Publisher's Note: The references to "paragraph (f)(1)" and "paragraph (f)(2)" in the above paragraph are incorrect and should refer to "paragraph (e)(1)" and "paragraph (e)(2)".

(1) Nonbiodegradable sorbents. (i) Inorganic minerals, other inorganic materials, and elemental carbon (*e.g.*, aluminosilicates, clays, smectites, Fuller's earth, bentonite, calcium bentonite, montmorillonite, calcined montmorillonite, kaolinite, micas (illite), vermiculites, zeolites; calcium carbonate (organic free limestone); oxides/hydroxides, alumina, lime, silica (sand), diatomaceous earth; perlite (volcanic glass); expanded volcanic rock; volcanic ash; cement kiln dust; fly ash; rice hull ash; activated charcoal/activated carbon); or

(ii) High molecular weight synthetic polymers (*e.g.*, polyethylene, high density polyethylene (HDPE), polypropylene, polystyrene, polyurethane, polyacrylate, polynorborene, polyisobutylene, ground synthetic rubber, cross-linked allylstyrene and tertiary butyl copolymers). This does not include polymers derived from biological material or polymers specifically designed to be degradable; or

(iii) Mixtures of these nonbiodegradable materials.

(2) Tests for nonbiodegradable sorbents. (i) The sorbent material is determined to be nonbiodegradable under ASTM Method G21-70 (1984a)—Standard Practice for Determining Resistance of Synthetic Polymer Materials to Fungi; or

(ii) The sorbent material is determined to be nonbiodegradable under ASTM Method G22-76 (1984b)—Standard Practice for Determining Resistance of Plastics to Bacteria; or

(iii) The sorbent material is determined to be nonbiodegradable under OECD test 301B: [CO_2 Evolution (Modified Sturm Test)].

(f) The placement of any liquid which is not a hazardous waste in a landfill is prohibited unless the owner or operator of such landfill demonstrates to the Regional Administrator or the Regional Administrator determines that:

(1) The only reasonably available alternative to the placement in such landfill is placement in a landfill or unlined surface impoundment, whether or not permitted or operating under interim status, which contains, or may reasonably be anticipated to contain, hazardous waste; and

(2) Placement in such owner or operator's landfill will not present a risk of contamination of any "underground source of drinking water" (as that term is defined in 40 CFR 270.2).

[45 FR 33232, May 19, 1980, as amended at 47 FR 12318, Mar. 22, 1982; 47 FR 32369, July 26, 1982; 50 FR 18374, Apr. 30, 1985; 50 FR 28750, July 15, 1985; 51 FR 19177, May 28, 1986; 57 FR 54461, Nov. 18, 1992; 58 FR 46050, Aug. 31, 1993; 60 FR 35705, July 11, 1995; 70 FR 34585, June 14, 2005; 71 FR 16912, Apr. 4, 2006; 71 FR 40276, July 14, 2006]

§265.315 Special requirements for containers.

Unless they are very small, such as an ampule, containers must be either:

(a) At least 90 percent full when placed in the landfill; or

(b) Crushed, shredded, or similarly reduced in volume to the maximum practical extent before burial in the landfill.

[50 FR 16048, Apr. 23, 1985]

§265.316 Disposal of small containers of hazardous waste in overpacked drums (lab packs). 📖 9.7

Small containers of hazardous waste in overpacked drums (lab packs) may be placed in a landfill if the following requirements are met:

(a) Hazardous waste must be packaged in non-leaking inside containers. The inside containers must be of a design and constructed of a material that will not react dangerously with, be decomposed by, or be ignited by the waste held therein. Inside containers must be tightly and securely sealed. The inside containers must be of the size and type specified in the Department of Transportation (DOT) hazardous materials regulations (49 CFR parts 173, 178 and 179), if those regulations specify a particular inside container for the waste.

(b) The inside containers must be overpacked in an open head DOT-specification metal shipping container (49 CFR parts 178 and 179) of no more than 416-liter (110 gallon) capacity and surrounded by, at a minimum, a sufficient quantity of sorbent material, determined to be nonbiodegradable in accordance with §265.314(f), to completely sorb all of the liquid contents of the inside containers. The metal outer container must be full after it has been packed with inside containers and sorbent material.

Publisher's Note: The above reference to §265.314(f) is incorrect and should refer to §265.315(e).

(c) The sorbent material used must not be capable of reacting dangerously with, being decomposed by, or being ignited by the contents of the inside containers in accordance with §265.17(b).

(d) Incompatible wastes, as defined in §260.10 of this chapter, must not be placed in the same outside container.

(e) Reactive waste, other than cyanide- or sulfide-bearing waste as defined in §261.23(a)(5) of this chapter, must be treated or rendered non-reactive prior to packaging in accordance with paragraphs (a) through (d) of this section. Cyanide- and sulfide-bearing reactive waste may be packaged in accordance with paragraphs (a) through (d) of this section without first being treated or rendered non-reactive.

(f) Such disposal is in compliance with the requirements of 40 CFR part 268. Persons who incinerate lab packs according to the requirements in 40 CFR 268.42(c)(1) may use fiber drums in place of metal outer containers. Such fiber drums must meet the DOT specifications in 49 CFR 173.12 and be overpacked according to the requirements in paragraph (b) of this section. 📖 13.13.1

[46 FR 56596, Nov. 17, 1981, as amended at 55 FR 22686, June 1, 1990; 57 FR 54461, Nov. 18, 1992; 71 FR 40276, July 14, 2006]

Subpart O—Incinerators

Source: 46 FR 7680, Jan. 23, 1981, unless otherwise noted.

§265.340 Applicability.

(a) The regulations of this subpart apply to owners and operators of hazardous waste incinerators (as defined in §260.10 of this chapter), except as §265.1 provides otherwise.

(b) *Integration of the MACT standards.* (1) Except as provided by paragraphs (b)(2) and (b)(3) of this section, the standards of this part no longer apply when an owner or operator demonstrates compliance with the maximum achievable control technology (MACT) requirements of part 63, subpart EEE, of this chapter by conducting a comprehensive performance test and submitting to the Administrator a Notification of Compliance under §§63.1207(j) and 63.1210(d) of this chapter documenting compliance with the requirements of part 63, subpart EEE, of this chapter.

(2) The following requirements continue to apply even where the owner or operator has demonstrated compliance with the MACT requirements of part 63, subpart EEE of this chapter: §265.351 (closure) and the applicable requirements of subparts A through H, BB and CC of this part.

Publisher's Note: §265.340(b)(2) above is correct and faithful to the September 30, 1999 final rule. [64 FR 53075] However, the current edition of the CFR is incorrect.

(3) Section 265.345 generally prohibiting burning of hazardous waste during startup and shutdown remains in effect if you elect to comply with §270.235(b)(1)(i) of this chapter to minimize emissions of toxic compounds from startup and shutdown.

(c) Owners and operators of incinerators burning hazardous waste are exempt from all of the requirements of this subpart, except §265.351 (Closure), provided that the owner or operator has documented, in writing, that the waste would not reasonably be expected to contain any of the hazardous constituents listed in part 261, appendix VIII, of this chapter, and such documentation is retained at the facility, if the waste to be burned is:

(1) Listed as a hazardous waste in part 261, subpart D, of this chapter solely because it is ignitable (Hazard Code I), corrosive (Hazard Code C), or both; or

(2) Listed as a hazardous waste in part 261, subpart D, of this chapter solely because it is reactive (Hazard Code R) for characteristics other than those listed in §261.23(a)(4) and (5), and will not be burned when other hazardous wastes are present in the combustion zone; or

(3) A hazardous waste solely because it possesses the characteristic of ignitability, corrosivity, or both, as determined by the tests for characteristics of hazardous wastes under part 261, subpart C, of this chapter; or

(4) A hazardous waste solely because it possesses the reactivity characteristics described by §261.23(a)(1), (2), (3), (6), (7), or (8) of this chapter, and will not be burned when other hazardous wastes are present in the combustion zone.

[47 FR 27533, June 24, 1982 and 50 FR 666, Jan. 4, 1985, as amended at 50 FR 49203, Nov. 29, 1985; 56 FR 7208, Feb. 21, 1991; 64 FR 53075, Sept. 30, 1999; 67 FR 6816, Feb. 13, 2002; 70 FR 59575, Oct. 12, 2005]

§265.341 Waste analysis.

In addition to the waste analyses required by §265.13, the owner or operator must sufficiently analyze any waste which he has not previously burned in his incinerator to enable him to establish steady state (normal) operating conditions (including waste and auxiliary fuel feed and air flow) and to determine the type of pollutants which might be emitted. At a minimum, the analysis must determine:

(a) Heating value of the waste;

(b) Halogen content and sulfur content in the waste; and

(c) Concentrations in the waste of lead and mercury, unless the owner or operator has written, documented data that show that the element is not present.

[*Comment:* As required by §265.73, the owner or operator must place the results from each waste analysis, or the documented information, in the operating record of the facility.]

§§265.342–265.344 [Reserved]

§265.345 General operating requirements.

During start-up and shut-down of an incinerator, the owner or operator must not feed hazardous waste unless the incinerator is at steady state (normal) conditions of operation, including steady state operating temperature and air flow.

§265.346 [Reserved]

§265.347 Monitoring and inspections.

The owner or operator must conduct, as a minimum, the following monitoring and inspections when incinerating hazardous waste:

(a) Existing instruments which relate to combustion and emission control must be monitored at least every 15 minutes. Appropriate corrections to maintain steady state combustion conditions must be made immediately either automatically or by the operator. Instruments which relate to combustion and emission control would normally include those measuring waste feed, auxiliary fuel feed, air flow, incinerator temperature, scrubber flow, scrubber pH, and relevant level controls.

(b) The complete incinerator and associated equipment (pumps, valves, conveyors, pipes, etc.) must be inspected at least daily for leaks, spills, and fugitive emissions, and all emergency shutdown controls and system alarms must be checked to assure proper operation.

[46 FR 7678, Jan. 23, 1981, as amended at 47 FR 27533, June 24, 1982]

§§265.348–265.350 [Reserved]

§265.351 Closure.

At closure, the owner or operator must remove all hazardous waste and hazardous waste residues (including but not limited to ash, scrubber waters, and scrubber sludges) from the incinerator.

[*Comment:* At closure, as throughout the operating period, unless the owner or operator can demonstrate, in accordance with §261.3(d) of this chapter, that the residue removed from his incinerator is not a hazardous waste, the owner or operator becomes a generator of hazardous waste and must manage it in accordance with all applicable requirements of parts 262 through 266 of this chapter.]

§265.352 Interim status incinerators burning particular hazardous wastes.

(a) Owners or operators of incinerators subject to this subpart may burn EPA Hazardous Wastes F020, F021, F022, F023, F026, or F027 if they receive a certification from the Assistant Administrator for Solid Waste and Emergency Response that they can meet the performance standards of subpart O of part 264 when they burn these wastes.

(b) The following standards and procedures will be used in determining whether to certify an incinerator:

(1) The owner or operator will submit an application to the Assistant Administrator for Solid Waste and Emergency Response containing applicable information in §§270.19 and 270.62 demonstrating that the incinerator can meet the performance standards in subpart O of part 264 when they burn these wastes.

(2) The Assistant Administrator for Solid Waste and Emergency Response will issue a tentative decision as to whether the incinerator can meet the performance standards in subpart O of part 264. Notification of this tentative decision will be provided by newspaper advertisement and radio broadcast in the jurisdiction where the incinerator is located. The Assistant Administrator for Solid Waste and Emergency Response will accept comment on the tentative decision for 60 days. The Assistant Administrator for Solid Waste and Emergency Response also may hold a public hearing upon request or at his discretion.

(3) After the close of the public comment period, the Assistant Administrator for Solid Waste and Emergency Response will issue a decision whether or not to certify the incinerator.

[50 FR 2005, Jan. 14, 1985]

§§265.353–265.369 [Reserved]

Subpart P—Thermal Treatment

§265.370 Other thermal treatment.

The regulations in this subpart apply to owners or operators of facilities that thermally treat hazardous waste in devices other than enclosed devices using controlled flame combustion, except as §265.1 provides otherwise. Thermal treatment in enclosed devices using controlled flame combustion is subject to the requirements of subpart O if the unit is an incinerator, and subpart H of part 266, if the unit is a boiler or an industrial furnace as defined in §260.10.

[50 FR 666, Jan. 4, 1985, as amended at 56 FR 32692, July 17, 1991]

§§265.371–265.372 [Reserved]

§265.373 General operating requirements.

Before adding hazardous waste, the owner or operator must bring his thermal treatment process to steady state (normal) conditions of operation—including steady state operating temperature—using auxiliary fuel or other means, unless the process is a non-continuous (batch) thermal treatment process which requires a complete thermal cycle to treat a discrete quantity of hazardous waste.

§265.374 [Reserved]

§265.375 Waste analysis.

In addition to the waste analyses required by §265.13, the owner or operator must sufficiently analyze any waste which he has not previously treated in his thermal process to enable him to establish steady state (normal) or other appropriate (for a non-continuous process) operating conditions (including waste and auxiliary fuel feed) and to determine the type of pollutants which might be emitted. At a minimum, the analysis must determine:

(a) Heating value of the waste;

(b) Halogen content and sulfur content in the waste; and

(c) Concentrations in the waste of lead and mercury, unless the owner or operator has written, documented data that show that the element is not present.

[*Comment:* As required by §265.73, the owner or operator must place the results from each waste analysis, or the documented information, in the operating record of the facility.]

§265.376 [Reserved]

§265.377 Monitoring and inspections.

(a) The owner or operator must conduct, as a minimum, the following monitoring and inspections when thermally treating hazardous waste:

(1) Existing instruments which relate to temperature and emission control (if an emission control device is present) must be monitored at least every 15 minutes. Appropriate corrections to maintain steady state or other appropriate thermal treatment conditions must be made immediately either automatically or by the operator. Instruments which relate to temperature and emission control would normally include those measuring waste feed, auxiliary fuel feed, treatment process temperature, and relevant process flow and level controls.

(2) The stack plume (emissions), where present, must be observed visually at least hourly for normal appearance (color and opacity). The operator must immediately make any indicated operating corrections necessary to return any visible emissions to their normal appearance.

(3) The complete thermal treatment process and associated equipment (pumps, valves, conveyors, pipes, etc.) must be inspected at least daily for leaks, spills, and fugitive emissions, and all emergency shutdown controls and system alarms must be checked to assure proper operation.

(b) [Reserved]

§§265.378–265.380 [Reserved]

§265.381 Closure.

At closure, the owner or operator must remove all hazardous waste and hazardous waste residues (including, but not limited to, ash) from the thermal treatment process or equipment.

[*Comment:* At closure, as throughout the operating period, unless the owner or operator can demonstrate, in accordance with §261.3(c) or (d) of this chapter, that any solid waste removed from his thermal treatment process or equipment is not a hazardous waste, the owner or operator becomes a generator of hazardous waste and must manage it in accordance with all applicable requirements of parts 262, 263, and 265 of this chapter.]

§265.382 Open burning; waste explosives. 7.5.4.2

Open burning of hazardous waste is prohibited except for the open burning and detonation of waste explosives. Waste explosives include waste which has the potential to detonate and bulk military propellants which cannot safely be disposed of through other modes of treatment. Detonation is an explosion in which chemical transformation passes through the material faster than the speed of sound (0.33 kilometers/second at sea level). Owners or operators choosing to open burn or detonate waste explosives must do so in accordance with the following table and in a manner that does not threaten human health or the environment.

Pounds of waste explosives or propellants	Minimum distance from open burning or detonation to the property of others
0 to 100	204 meters (670 feet)
101 to 1,000	380 meters (1,250 feet)
1,001 to 10,000	530 meters (1,730 feet)
10,001 to 30,000	690 meters (2,260 feet)

§265.383 Interim status thermal treatment devices burning particular hazardous waste.

(a) Owners or operators of thermal treatment devices subject to this subpart may burn EPA Hazardous Wastes F020, F021, F022, F023, F026, or F027 if they receive a certification from the Assistant Administrator for Solid Waste and Emergency Response that they can meet the performance standards of subpart O of part 264 when they burn these wastes.

(b) The following standards and procedures will be used in determining whether to certify a thermal treatment unit:

(1) The owner or operator will submit an application to the Assistant Administrator for Solid Waste and Emergency Response containing the applicable information in §§270.19 and 270.62 demonstrating that the thermal treatment unit can meet the performance standard in subpart O of part 264 when they burn these wastes.

(2) The Assistant Administrator for Solid Waste and Emergency Response will issue a tentative decision as to whether the thermal treatment unit can meet the performance standards in subpart O of part 264. Notification of this tentative decision will be provided by newspaper advertisement and radio broadcast in the jurisdiction where the thermal treatment device is located. The Assistant Administrator for Solid Waste and Emergency Response will accept comment on the tentative decision for 60 days. The Assistant Administrator for Solid Waste and Emergency Response also may hold a public hearing upon request or at his discretion.

(3) After the close of the public comment period, the Assistant Administrator for Solid Waste and Emergency Response will issue a decision whether or not to certify the thermal treatment unit.

[50 FR 2005, Jan. 14, 1985]

Subpart Q—Chemical, Physical, and Biological Treatment

§265.400 Applicability.

The regulations in this subpart apply to owners and operators of facilities which treat hazardous wastes by chemical, physical, or biological methods in other than tanks, surface impoundments, and land treatment facilities, except as §265.1 provides otherwise. Chemical, physical, and biological treatment of hazardous waste in tanks, surface impoundments, and land treatment facilities must be conducted in accordance with subparts J, K, and M, respectively.

§265.401 General operating requirements.

(a) Chemical, physical, or biological treatment of hazardous waste must comply with §265.17(b).

(b) Hazardous wastes or treatment reagents must not be placed in the treatment process or equipment if they could cause the treatment process or equipment to rupture, leak, corrode, or otherwise fail before the end of its intended life.

(c) Where hazardous waste is continuously fed into a treatment process or equipment, the process or equipment must be equipped with a means to stop this inflow (*e.g.*, a waste feed cut-off system or by-pass system to a standby containment device).

[*Comment:* These systems are intended to be used in the event of a malfunction in the treatment process or equipment.]

§265.402 Waste analysis and trial tests.

(a) In addition to the waste analysis required by §265.13, whenever:

(1) A hazardous waste which is substantially different from waste previously treated in a treatment process or equipment at the facility is to be treated in that process or equipment, or

(2) A substantially different process than any previously used at the facility is to be used to chemically treat hazardous waste; the owner or operator must, before treating the different waste or using the different process or equipment:

(i) Conduct waste analyses and trial treatment tests (*e.g.*, bench scale or pilot plant scale tests); or

(ii) Obtain written, documented information on similar treatment of similar waste under similar operating conditions; to show that this proposed treatment will meet all applicable requirements of §265.401 (a) and (b).

(b) [Reserved]

[*Comment:* As required by §265.13, the waste analysis plan must include analyses needed to comply with §§265.405 and 265.406. As required by §265.73, the owner or operator must place the results from each waste analysis and trial test, or the documented information, in the operating record of the facility.]

§265.403 Inspections.

(a) The owner or operator of a treatment facility must inspect, where present:

(1) Discharge control and safety equipment (*e.g.*, waste feed cut-off systems, by-pass systems, drainage systems, and pressure relief systems) at least once each operating day, to ensure that it is in good working order;

(2) Data gathered from monitoring equipment (*e.g.*, pressure and temperature gauges), at least once each operating day, to ensure that the treatment process or equipment is being operated according to its design;

(3) The construction materials of the treatment process or equipment, at least weekly, to detect corrosion or leaking of fixtures or seams; and

(4) The construction materials of, and the area immediately surrounding, discharge confinement structures (*e.g.*, dikes), at least weekly, to detect erosion or obvious signs of leakage (*e.g.*, wet spots or dead vegetation).

(b) [Reserved]

[*Comment:* As required by §265.15(c), the owner or operator must remedy any deterioration or malfunction he finds.]

§265.404 Closure.

At closure, all hazardous waste and hazardous waste residues must be removed from treatment processes or equipment, discharge control equipment, and discharge confinement structures.

[*Comment:* At closure, as throughout the operating period, unless the owner or operator can demonstrate, in accordance with §261.3 (c) or (d) of this chapter, that any solid waste removed from his treatment process or equipment is not a hazardous waste, the owner or operator becomes a generator of hazardous waste and must manage it in accordance with all applicable requirements of parts 262, 263, and 265 of this chapter.]

§265.405 Special requirements for ignitable or reactive waste.

(a) Ignitable or reactive waste must not be placed in a treatment process or equipment unless:

(1) The waste is treated, rendered, or mixed before or immediately after placement in the treatment process or equipment so that (i) the resulting waste, mixture, or dissolution of material no longer meets the definition of ignitable or reactive waste under §§261.21 or 261.23 of this chapter, and (ii) §265.17(b) is complied with; or

(2) The waste is treated in such a way that it is protected from any material or conditions which may cause the waste to ignite or react.

(b)[Reserved]

[45 FR 33232, May 19, 1980, as amended at 71 FR 40276, July 14, 2006]

§265.406 Special requirements for incompatible wastes.

(a) Incompatible wastes, or incompatible wastes and materials, (see appendix V for examples) must not be placed in the same treatment process or equipment, unless §265.17(b) is complied with.

(b) Hazardous waste must not be placed in unwashed treatment equipment which previously held an incompatible waste or material, unless §265.17(b) is complied with.

Subpart R—Underground Injection

§265.430 Applicability.

Except as §265.1 provides otherwise:

(a) The owner or operator of a facility which disposes of hazardous waste by underground injection is excluded from the requirements of subparts G and H of this part.

(b) The requirements of this subpart apply to owners and operators of wells used to dispose of hazardous waste which are classified as Class I under §144.6(a) of this chapter and which are classified as Class IV under §144.6(d) of this chapter.

[*Comment:* In addition to the requirements of subparts A through E of this part, the owner or operator of a facility which disposes of hazardous waste by underground injection ultimately must comply with the requirements of §§265.431 through 265.437. These sections are reserved at this time. The Agency will propose regulations that would establish those requirements.]

[45 FR 33232, May 19, 1980, as amended at 48 FR 30115, June 30, 1983]

Subparts S–V [Reserved]

Subpart W—Drip Pads

📖 10.1.3.4

Source: 55 FR 50486, Dec. 6, 1990, unless otherwise noted.

§265.440 Applicability.

(a) The requirements of this subpart apply to owners and operators of facilities that use new or existing drip pads to convey treated wood drippage, precipitation, and/or surface water run-off to an associated collection system. Existing drip pads are those constructed before December 6, 1990 and those for which the owner or operator has a design and has entered into binding financial or other agreements for construction prior to December 6, 1990. All other drip pads are new drip pads. The requirement at §265.443(b)(3) to install a leak collection system applies only to those drip pads that are constructed after December 24, 1992 except for those constructed after December 24, 1992 for which the owner or operator has a design and has entered into binding financial or other agreements for construction prior to December 24, 1992.

(b) The owner or operator of any drip pad that is inside or under a structure that provides protection from precipitation so that neither run-off nor run-on is generated is not subject to regulation under §265.443(e) or §265.443(f), as appropriate.

(c) The requirements of this subpart are not applicable to the management of infrequent and incidental drippage in storage yards provided that:

(1) The owner or operator maintains and complies with a written contingency plan that describes how the owner or operator will respond immediately to the discharge of such infrequent and incidental drippage. At a minimum, the contingency plan must describe how the facility will do the following:

(i) Clean up the drippage;

(ii) Document the cleanup of the drippage;

(iii) Retain documents regarding cleanup for three years; and

(iv) Manage the contaminated media in a manner consistent with Federal regulations.

[55 FR 50486, Dec. 6, 1990, as amended by 56 FR 30198, July 1, 1991; 57 FR 61503, Dec. 24, 1992]

§265.441 Assessment of existing drip pad integrity.

(a) For each existing drip pad as defined in §265.440, the owner or operator must evaluate the drip pad and determine that it meets all of the requirements of this subpart, except the requirements for liners and leak detection systems of §265.443(b). No later than the effective date of this rule, the owner or operator must obtain and keep on file at the facility a written assessment of the drip pad, reviewed and certified by a qualified Professional Engineer that attests to the results of the evaluation. The assessment must be reviewed, updated, and re-certified annually until all upgrades, repairs, or modifications necessary to achieve compliance with all the standards of §265.443 are complete. The evaluation must document the extent to which the drip pad meets each of the design and operating standards of §265.443, except the standards for liners and leak detection systems, specified in §265.443(b).

(b) The owner or operator must develop a written plan for upgrading, repairing, and modifying the drip pad to meet the requirements of §265.443(b), and submit the plan to the Regional Administrator no later than 2 years before the date that all repairs, upgrades, and modifications are complete. This written plan must describe all changes to be made to the drip pad in sufficient detail to document compliance with all the requirements of §265.443. The plan must be reviewed and certified by a qualified Professional Engineer.

(c) Upon completion of all repairs and modifications, the owner or operator must submit to the Regional Administrator or State Director, the as-built drawings for the drip pad together with a certification by a qualified Professional Engineer attesting that the drip pad conforms to the drawings.

(d) If the drip pad is found to be leaking or unfit for use, the owner or operator must comply with the provisions of §265.443(m) of this subpart or close the drip pad in accordance with §265.445 of this subpart.

[55 FR 50486, Dec. 6, 1990, as amended at 57 FR 61504, Dec. 24, 1992; 71 FR 16912, Apr. 4, 2006; 71 FR 40276, July 14, 2006]

§265.442 Design and installation of new drip pads.

Owners and operators of new drip pads must ensure that the pads are designed, installed, and operated in accordance with one of the following:

(a) All of the applicable requirements of §§265.443 (except §265.443(a)(4)), 265.444 and 265.445 of this subpart, or

(b) All of the applicable requirements of §§265.443 (except §265.443(b)), 265.444 and 265.445 of this subpart.

[57 FR 61504, Dec. 24, 1992]

§265.443 Design and operating requirements.

(a) Drip pads must:

(1) Be constructed of non-earthen materials, excluding wood and non-structurally supported asphalt;

(2) Be sloped to free-drain treated wood drippage, rain and other waters, or solutions of drippage and water or other wastes to the associated collection system;

(3) Have a curb or berm around the perimeter;

(4)(i) Have a hydraulic conductivity of less than or equal to 1×10^{-7} centimeters per second, *e.g.*, existing concrete drip pads must be sealed, coated, or covered with a surface material with a hydraulic conductivity of less than or equal to 1×10^{-7} centimeters per second such that the entire surface where drippage occurs or may run across is capable of containing such drippage and mixtures of drippage and precipitation, materials, or other wastes while being routed to an associated collection system. This surface material must be maintained free of cracks and gaps that could adversely affect its hydraulic conductivity, and the material must be chemically compatible with the preservatives that contact the drip pad. The requirements of this provision apply only to existing drip pads and those drip pads for which the owner or operator elects to comply with §265.442(b) instead of §265.442(a).

(ii) The owner or operator must obtain and keep on file at the facility a written assessment of the drip pad, reviewed and certified by a qualified Professional Engineer that attests to the results of the evaluation. The assessment must be reviewed, updated and recertified annually. The evaluation must document the extent to which the drip pad meets the design and operating standards of this section, except for paragraph (b) of this section.

(5) Be of sufficient structural strength and thickness to prevent failure due to physical contact, climatic conditions, the stress of installation, and the stress of daily operations, *e.g.*, variable and moving loads such as vehicle traffic, movement of wood, etc.

Note: EPA will generally consider applicable standards established by professional organizations generally recognized by industry such as the American Concrete Institute (ACI) and the American Society of Testing Materials (ASTM) in judging the structural integrity requirement of this paragraph.

(b) If an owner/operator elects to comply with §265.442(a) instead of §265.442(b), the drip pad must have:

(1) A synthetic liner installed below the drip pad that is designed, constructed, and installed to prevent leakage from the drip pad into the adjacent subsurface soil or groundwater or surface water at any time during the active life (including the closure period) of the drip pad. The liner must be constructed of materials that will prevent waste from being absorbed into the liner and prevent releases into the adjacent subsurface soil or ground water or surface water during the active life of the facility. The liner must be:

(i) Constructed of materials that have appropriate chemical properties and sufficient strength and thickness to prevent failure due to pressure gradients (including static head and external hydrogeologic forces), physical contact with the waste or drip pad leakage to which they are exposed, climatic conditions, the stress of installation, and the stress of daily operation (including stresses from vehicular traffic on the drip pad);

(ii) Placed upon a foundation or base capable of providing support to the liner and resistance to pressure gradients above and below the liner to prevent failure of the liner due to settlement, compression or uplift; and

(iii) Installed to cover all surrounding earth that could come in contact with the waste or leakage; and

(2) A leakage detection system immediately above the liner that is designed, constructed, maintained and operated to detect leakage from the drip pad. The leakage detection system must be:

(i) Constructed of materials that are:

(A) Chemically resistant to the waste managed in the drip pad and the leakage that might be generated; and

(B) Of sufficient strength and thickness to prevent collapse under the pressures exerted by overlaying materials and by any equipment used at the drip pad; and

(ii) Designed and operated to function without clogging through the scheduled closure of the drip pad.

(iii) Designed so that it will detect the failure of the drip pad or the presence of a release of hazardous waste or accumulated liquid at the earliest practicable time.

(3) A leakage collection system immediately above the liner that is designed, constructed, maintained and operated to collect leakage from the drip pad such that it can be removed from below the drip pad. The date, time, and quantity of any leakage collected in this system and removed must be documented in the operating log.

(c) Drip pads must be maintained such that they remain free of cracks, gaps, corrosion, or other deterioration that could cause hazardous waste to be released from the drip pad.

Note: See §265.443(m) for remedial action required if deterioration or leakage is detected.

(d) The drip pad and associated collection system must be designed and operated to convey, drain, and collect liquid resulting from drippage or precipitation in order to prevent run-off.

(e) Unless protected by a structure, as described in §265.440(b) of this subpart, the owner or operator must design, construct, operate and maintain a run-on control system capable of preventing flow onto the drip pad during peak discharge from at least a 24-hour, 25-year storm unless the system has sufficient excess capacity to contain any run-on that might enter the system, or the drip pad is protected by a structure or cover, as described in §265.440(b) of this subpart.

(f) Unless protected by a structure or cover, as described in §265.440(b) of this subpart, the owner or operator must design, construct, operate and maintain a run-off management system to collect and control at least the water volume resulting from a 24-hour, 25-year storm.

(g) The drip pad must be evaluated to determine that it meets the requirements of paragraphs (a) through (f) of this section and the owner or operator must obtain a statement from a qualified Professional Engineer certifying that the drip pad design meets the requirements of this section.

(h) Drippage and accumulated precipitation must be removed from the associated collection system as necessary to prevent overflow onto the drip pad.

(i) The drip pad surface must be cleaned thoroughly in a manner and frequency such that accumulated residues of hazardous waste or other materials are removed, with residues being properly managed as hazardous waste, so as to allow weekly inspections of the entire drip pad surface without interference or hindrance from accumulated residues of hazardous waste or other materials on the drip pad. The owner or operator must document the date and time of each cleaning and the cleaning procedure used in the facility's operating log.

(j) Drip pads must be operated and maintained in a manner to minimize tracking of hazardous waste or hazardous waste constituents off the drip pad as a result of activities by personnel or equipment.

(k) After being removed from the treatment vessel, treated wood from pressure and non-pressure processes must be held on the drip pad until drippage has ceased. The owner or operator must maintain records sufficient to document that all treated wood is held on the pad following treatment in accordance with this requirement.

(l) Collection and holding units associated with run-on and run-off control systems must be emptied or otherwise managed as soon as possible after storms to maintain design capacity of the system.

(m) Throughout the active life of the drip pad, if the owner or operator detects a condition that may have caused or has caused a release of hazardous waste, the condition must be repaired within a reasonably prompt period of time following discovery, in accordance with the following procedures:

(1) Upon detection of a condition that may have caused or has caused a release of hazardous waste (*e.g.,* upon detection of leakage by the leak detection system), the owner or operator must:

(i) Enter a record of the discovery in the facility operating log;

(ii) Immediately remove the portion of the drip pad affected by the condition from service;

(iii) Determine what steps must be taken to repair the drip pad, remove any leakage from below the drip pad, and establish a schedule for accomplishing the clean up and repairs;

(iv) Within 24 hours after discovery of the condition, notify the Regional Administrator of the condition and, within 10 working days, provide a written notice to the Regional Administrator with a description of the steps that will be taken to repair the drip pad, and clean up any leakage, and the schedule for accomplishing this work.

(2) The Regional Administrator will review the information submitted, make a determination regarding whether the pad must be removed from service completely or partially until repairs and clean up are complete, and notify the owner or operator of the determination and the underlying rationale in writing.

(3) Upon completing all repairs and clean up, the owner or operator must notify the Regional Administrator in writing and provide a certification, signed by an independent qualified, registered professional engineer, that the repairs and clean up have been completed according to the written plan submitted in accordance with paragraph (m)(1)(iv) of this section.

(n) The owner or operator must maintain, as part of the facility operating log, documentation of past operating and waste handling practices. This must include identification of preservative formulations used in the past, a description of drippage management practices, and a description of treated wood storage and handling practices.

[55 FR 50486, Dec. 6, 1990, as amended at 56 FR 30198, July 1, 1991; 57 FR 5861, Feb. 18, 1992; 57 FR 61504, Dec. 24, 1992; 71 FR 16912, Apr. 4, 2006; 71 FR 40276, July 14, 2006]

§265.444 Inspections.

(a) During construction or installation, liners and cover systems (e.g., membranes, sheets, or coatings) must be inspected for uniformity, damage and imperfections (e.g., holes, cracks, thin spots, or foreign materials). Immediately after construction or installation, liners must be inspected and certified as meeting the requirements of §265.443 by a qualified Professional Engineer. This certification must be maintained at the facility as part of the facility operating record. After installation, liners and covers must be inspected to ensure tight seams and joints and the absence of tears, punctures, or blisters.

(b) While a drip pad is in operation, it must be inspected weekly and after storms to detect evidence of any of the following:

(1) Deterioration, malfunctions or improper operation of run-on and run-off control systems;

(2) The presence of leakage in and proper functioning of leakage detection system.

(3) Deterioration or cracking of the drip pad surface.

Note: See §265.443(m) for remedial action required if deterioration or leakage is detected.

[55 FR 50486, Dec. 6, 1990, as amended at 71 FR 16912, Apr. 4, 2006]

§265.445 Closure.

(a) At closure, the owner or operator must remove or decontaminate all waste residues, contaminated containment system components (pad, liners, etc.), contaminated subsoils, and structures and equipment contaminated with waste and leakage, and manage them as hazardous waste.

(b) If, after removing or decontaminating all residues and making all reasonable efforts to effect removal or decontamination of contaminated components, subsoils, structures, and equipment as required in paragraph (a) of this section, the owner or operator finds that not all contaminated subsoils can be practically removed or decontaminated, he must close the facility and perform post-closure care in accordance with closure and post-closure care requirements that apply to landfills (§265.310). For permitted units, the requirement to have a permit continues throughout the post-closure period.

(c)(1) The owner or operator of an existing drip pad, as defined in §265.440 of this subpart, that does not comply with the liner requirements of §265.443(b)(1) must:

(i) Include in the closure plan for the drip pad under §265.112 both a plan for complying with paragraph (a) of this section and a contingent plan for complying with paragraph (b) of this section in case not all contaminated subsoils can be practicably removed at closure; and

(ii) Prepare a contingent post-closure plan under §265.118 of this part for complying with paragraph (b) of this section in case not all contaminated subsoils can be practicably removed at closure.

(2) The cost estimates calculated under §§265.112 and 265.144 of this part for closure and post-closure care of a drip pad subject to this paragraph must include the cost of complying with the contingent closure plan and the contingent post-closure plan, but are not required to include the cost of expected closure under paragraph (a) of this section.

[71 FR 40276, July 14, 2006]

Subparts X–Z [Reserved]

Subpart AA—Air Emission Standards for Process Vents

Source: 55 FR 25507, June 21, 1990, unless otherwise noted.

§265.1030 Applicability. 15.1.1

(a) The regulations in this subpart apply to owners and operators of facilities that treat, store, or dispose of hazardous wastes (except as provided in §265.1). 15.1.1.1

(b) Except for §§265.1034, paragraphs (d) and (e), this subpart applies to process vents associated with distillation, fractionation, thin-film evaporation, solvent extraction, or air or steam stripping operations that manage hazardous wastes with organic concentrations of at least 10 ppmw, if these operations are conducted in one of the following: 15.1.1.2–5

(1) A unit that is subject to the permitting requirements of 40 CFR part 270, or

(2) A unit (including a hazardous waste recycling unit) that is not exempt from permitting under the provisions of 40 CFR 262.34(a) (*i.e.*, a hazardous waste recycling unit that is not a 90-day tank or container) and that is located at a hazardous waste management facility otherwise subject to the permitting requirements of 40 CFR part 270, or

(3) A unit that is exempt from permitting under the provisions of 40 CFR 262.34(a)(*i.e.*, a "90-day" tank or container) and is not a recycling unit under the requirements of 40 CFR 261.6. 📖 **6.3.11**

Note: The requirements of §§265.1032 through 265.1036 apply to process vents on hazardous waste recycling units previously exempt under paragraph 261.6(c)(1). Other exemptions under §§261.4, and 265.1(c) are not affected by these requirements.]

(c) The requirements of this subpart do not apply to the pharmaceutical manufacturing facility, commonly referred to as the Stonewall Plant, located at Route 340 South, Elkton, Virginia, provided that facility is operated in compliance with the requirements contained in a Clean Air Act permit issued pursuant to 40 CFR 52.2454. The requirements of this subpart shall apply to the facility upon termination of the Clean Air Act permit issued pursuant to 40 CFR 52.2454.

(d) The requirements of this subpart do not apply to the process vents at a facility where the facility owner or operator certifies that all of the process vents that would otherwise be subject to this subpart are equipped with and operating air emission controls in accordance with the process vent requirements of an applicable Clean Air Act regulation codified under 40 CFR part 60, part 61, or part 63. The documentation of compliance under regulations at 40 CFR part 60, part 61, or part 63 shall be kept with, or made readily available with, the facility operating record. 📖 **15.1.1.6**

[55 FR 25507, June 21, 1990, as amended at 56 FR 19290, Apr. 26, 1991; 61 FR 59968, Nov. 25, 1996; 62 FR 52642, Oct. 8, 1997; 62 FR 64661, Dec. 8, 1997]

§265.1031 Definitions.

As used in this subpart, all terms shall have the meaning given them in §264.1031, the Act, and parts 260-266.

§265.1032 Standards: Process vents. 📖 15.1.2.1

(a) The owner or operator of a facility with process vents associated with distillation, fractionation, thin-film evaporation, solvent extraction or air or steam stripping operations managing hazardous wastes with organic concentrations at least 10 ppmw shall either:

(1) Reduce total organic emissions from all affected process vents at the facility below 1.4 kg/h (3 lb/h) and 2.8 Mg/yr (3.1 tons/yr), or

(2) Reduce, by use of a control device, total organic emissions from all affected process vents at the facility by 95 weight percent.

(b) If the owner or operator installs a closed-vent system and control device to comply with the provisions of paragraph (a) of this section, the closed-vent system and control device must meet the requirements of §265.1033.

(c) Determinations of vent emissions and emission reductions or total organic compound concentrations achieved by add-on control devices may be based on engineering calculations or performance tests. If performance tests are used to determine vent emissions, emission reductions, or total organic compound concentrations achieved by add-on control devices, the performance tests must conform with the requirements of §265.1034(c).

(d) When an owner or operator and the Regional Administrator do not agree on determinations of vent emissions and/or emission reductions or total organic compound concentrations achieved by add-on control devices based on engineering calculations, the test methods in §265.1034(c) shall be used to resolve the disagreement.

§265.1033 Standards: Closed-vent systems and control devices. 📖 15.1.2.2

(a)(1) Owners or operators of closed-vent systems and control devices used to comply with provisions of this part shall comply with the provisions of this section.

(2)(i) The owner or operator of an existing facility who cannot install a closed-vent system and control device to comply with the provisions of this subpart on the effective date that the facility becomes subject to the requirements of this subpart must prepare an implementation schedule that includes dates by which the closed-vent system and control device will be installed and in operation. The controls must be installed as soon as possible, but the implementation schedule may allow up to 30 months after the effective date that the facility becomes subject to this subpart for installation and startup.

(ii) Any unit that begins operation after December 21, 1990, and is subject to the requirements of this subpart when operation begins, must comply with the rules immediately (*i.e.*, must have control devices installed and operating on startup of the affected unit); the 30-month implementation schedule does not apply.

(iii) The owner or operator of any facility in existence on the effective date of a statutory or EPA regulatory amendment that renders the facility subject to this subpart shall comply with all requirements of this subpart as soon as practicable but no later than 30 months after the amendment's effective date. When control equipment required by this subpart can not be installed and begin operation by the effective date of the amendment, the facility owner or operator shall prepare an implementation schedule that includes the following information: Specific calendar dates for award of contracts or issuance of purchase orders for the control equipment, initiation of on-site installation of the control equipment, completion of the control equipment installation, and performance of any testing to demonstrate that the installed equipment meets the applicable standards of this subpart. The owner or operator shall enter the implementation schedule in the operating record or in a permanent, readily available file located at the facility.

(iv) Owners and operators of facilities and units that become newly subject to the requirements of this subpart after December 8, 1997, due to an action other than those described in paragraph (a)(2)(iii) of this section must comply with all applicable requirements immediately (*i.e.*, must have control devices installed and operating on the date the facility or unit becomes subject to this subpart; the 30-month implementation schedule does not apply).

(b) A control device involving vapor recovery (*e.g.*, a condenser or adsorber) shall be designed and operated to recover the organic vapors vented to it with an efficiency of 95 weight percent or greater unless the total organic emission limits of §265.1032(a)(1) for all affected process vents can be attained at an efficiency less than 95 weight percent.

(c) An enclosed combustion device (*e.g.*, a vapor incinerator, boiler, or process heater) shall be designed and operated to reduce the organic emissions vented to it by 95 weight percent or greater; to achieve a total organic compound concentration of 20 ppmv, expressed as the sum of the actual compounds, not carbon equivalents, on a dry basis corrected to 3 percent oxygen; or to provide a minimum residence time of 0.50 seconds at a minimum temperature of 760° C. If a boiler or process heater is used as the control device, then the vent stream shall be introduced into the flame combustion zone of the boiler or process heater.

(d)(1) A flare shall be designed for and operated with no visible emissions as determined by the methods specified in paragraph (e)(1) of this section, except for periods not to exceed a total of 5 minutes during any 2 consecutive hours.

(2) A flare shall be operated with a flame present at all times, as determined by the methods specified in paragraph (f)(2)(iii) of this section.

(3) A flare shall be used only if the net heating value of the gas being combusted is 11.2 MJ/scm (300 Btu/scf) or greater, if the flare is steam-assisted or air-assisted; or if the net heating value of the gas being combusted is 7.45 MJ/scm (200 Btu/scf) or greater if the flare is nonassisted. The net heating value of the gas being combusted shall be determined by the methods specified in paragraph (e)(2) of this section.

(4)(i) A steam-assisted or nonassisted flare shall be designed for and operated with an exit velocity, as determined by the methods specified in paragraph (e)(3) of this section, of less than 18.3 m/s (60 ft/s), except as provided in paragraphs (d)(4)(ii) and (iii) of this section.

(ii) A steam-assisted or nonassisted flare designed for and operated with an exit velocity, as determined by the methods specified in paragraph (e)(3) of this section, equal to or greater than 18.3 m/s (60 ft/s) but less than 122 m/s (400 ft/s) is allowed if the net heating value of the gas being combusted is greater than 37.3 MJ/scm (1,000 Btu/scf).

(iii) A steam-assisted or nonassisted flare designed for and operated with an exit velocity, as determined by the methods specified in paragraph (e)(3) of this section, less than the velocity, V_{max}, as determined by the method specified in paragraph (e)(4) of this section, and less than 122 m/s (400 ft/s) is allowed.

(5) An air-assisted flare shall be designed and operated with an exit velocity less than the velocity, V_{max}, as determined by the method specified in paragraph (e)(5) of this section.

(6) A flare used to comply with this section shall be steam-assisted, air-assisted, or nonassisted.

(e)(1) Reference Method 22 in 40 CFR part 60 shall be used to determine the compliance of a flare with the visible emission provisions of this subpart. The observation period is 2 hours and shall be used according to Method 22.

(2) The net heating value of the gas being combusted in a flare shall be calculated using the following equation:

$$H_T = K\left[\sum_{i=1}^{n} C_i H_i\right]$$

where:

H_T = Net heating value of the sample, MJ/scm; where the net enthalpy per mole of offgas is based on combustion at 25° C and 760 mm Hg, but the standard temperature for determining the volume corresponding to 1 mol is 20° C;

K = Constant, 1.74×10^{-7} (1/ppm)(g mol/scm) (MJ/kcal) where standard temperature for (g mol/scm) is 20° C;

C_i = Concentration of sample component i in ppm on a wet basis, as measured for organics by Reference Method 18 in 40 CFR part 60 and measured for hydrogen and carbon monoxide by ASTM D 1946-82 (incorporated by reference as specified in §260.11); and

H_i = Net heat of combustion of sample component i, kcal/g mol at 25° C and 760 mm Hg. The heats of combustion may be determined using ASTM D 2382-83 (incorporated by reference as specified in §260.11) if published values are not available or cannot be calculated.

(3) The actual exit velocity of a flare shall be determined by dividing the volumetric flow rate (in units of standard temperature and pressure), as determined by Reference Methods 2, 2A, 2C, or 2D in 40 CFR part 60 as appropriate, by the unobstructed (free) cross-sectional area of the flare tip.

(4) The maximum allowed velocity in m/s, V_{max}, for a flare complying with paragraph (d)(4)(iii) of this section shall be determined by the following equation:

$$Log_{10}(V_{max}) = (H_T + 28.8) / 31.7$$

where:

H_T = The net heating value as determined in paragraph (e)(2) of this section.

28.8 = Constant,

31.7 = Constant.

(5) The maximum allowed velocity in m/s, V_{max}, for an air-assisted flare shall be determined by the following equation:

$$V_{max} = 8.706 + 0.7084 (H_T)$$

where:

8.706 = Constant.

0.7084 = Constant.

H_T = The net heating value as determined in paragraph (e)(2) of this section.

(f) The owner or operator shall monitor and inspect each control device required to comply with this section to ensure proper operation and maintenance of the control device by implementing the following requirements:

15.1.2.3

(1) Install, calibrate, maintain, and operate according to the manufacturer's specifications a flow indicator that provides a record of vent stream flow from each affected process vent to the control device at least once every hour. The flow indicator sensor shall be installed in the vent stream at the nearest feasible point to the control device inlet, but before being combined with other vent streams.

(2) Install, calibrate, maintain, and operate according to the manufacturer's specifications a device to continuously monitor control device operation as specified below:

(i) For a thermal vapor incinerator, a temperature monitoring device equipped with a continuous recorder. The device shall have an accuracy of ±1 percent of the temperature being monitored in ° C or ±0.5° C, whichever is greater. The temperature sensor shall be installed at a location in the combustion chamber downstream of the combustion zone.

(ii) For a catalytic vapor incinerator, a temperature monitoring device equipped with a continuous recorder. The device shall be capable of monitoring temperature at two locations and have an accuracy of ±1 percent of the temperature being monitored in ° C or ±0.5° C, whichever is greater. One temperature sensor shall be installed in the vent stream at the nearest feasible point to the catalyst bed inlet and a second temperature sensor shall be installed in the vent stream at the nearest feasible point to the catalyst bed outlet.

(iii) For a flare, a heat sensing monitoring device equipped with a continuous recorder that indicates the continuous ignition of the pilot flame.

(iv) For a boiler or process heater having a design heat input capacity less than 44 MW, a temperature monitoring device equipped with a continuous recorder. The device shall have an accuracy of ±1 percent of the temperature being monitored in ° C or ±0.5° C, whichever is greater. The temperature sensor shall be installed at a location in the furnace downstream of the combustion zone.

(v) For a boiler or process heater having a design heat input capacity greater than or equal to 44 MW, a monitoring device equipped with a continuous recorder to measure a parameter(s) that indicates good combustion operating practices are being used.

(vi) For a condenser, either:

(A) A monitoring device equipped with a continuous recorder to measure the concentration level of the organic compounds in the exhaust vent stream from the condenser; or

(B) A temperature monitoring device equipped with a continuous recorder. The device shall be capable of monitoring temperature with an accuracy of ±1 percent of the temperature being monitored in degrees Celsius (° C) or ±0.5° C, whichever is greater. The temperature sensor shall be installed at a location in the exhaust vent stream from the condenser exit (*i.e.*, product side).

(vii) For a carbon adsorption system such as a fixed-bed carbon adsorber that regenerates the carbon bed directly in the control device, either:

(A) A monitoring device equipped with a continuous recorder to measure the concentration level of the organic compounds in the exhaust vent stream from the carbon bed, or

(B) A monitoring device equipped with a continuous recorder to measure a parameter that indicates the carbon bed is regenerated on a regular, predetermined time cycle.

(3) Inspect the readings from each monitoring device required by paragraphs (f)(1) and (2) of this section at least once each operating day to check control device operation and, if necessary, immediately implement the corrective measures necessary to ensure the control device operates in compliance with the requirements of this section.

(g) An owner or operator using a carbon adsorption system such as a fixed-bed carbon adsorber that regenerates the carbon bed directly onsite in the control device, shall replace the existing carbon in the control device with fresh carbon at a regular, predetermined time interval that is no longer than the carbon service life established as a requirement of §265.1035(b)(4)(iii)(F).

(h) An owner or operator using a carbon adsorption system such as a carbon canister that does not regenerate the carbon bed directly onsite in the control device shall replace the existing carbon in the control device with fresh carbon on a regular basis by using one of the following procedures:

(1) Monitor the concentration level of the organic compounds in the exhaust vent stream from the carbon adsorption system on a regular schedule and replace the existing carbon with fresh carbon immediately when carbon breakthrough is indicated. The monitoring frequency shall be daily or at an interval no greater than 20 percent of the time required to consume the total carbon working capacity established as a requirement of §265.1035(b)(4)(iii)(G), whichever is longer.

(2) Replace the existing carbon with fresh carbon at a regular, predetermined time interval that is less than the design carbon replacement interval established as a requirement of §265.1035(b)(4)(iii)(G).

(i) An owner or operator of an affected facility seeking to comply with the provisions of this part by using a control device other than a thermal vapor incinerator, catalytic vapor incinerator, flare, boiler, process heater, condenser, or carbon adsorption system is required to develop documentation including sufficient information to describe the control device operation and identify the process parameter or parameters that indicate proper operation and maintenance of the control device.

(j) A closed-vent system shall meet either of the following design requirements:

(1) A closed-vent system shall be designed to operate with no detectable emissions, as indicated by an instrument reading of less than 500 ppmv above background as determined by the procedure in §265.1034(b) of this subpart, and by visual inspections; or

(2) A closed-vent system shall be designed to operate at a pressure below atmospheric pressure. The system shall be equipped with at least one pressure gauge or other pressure measurement device that can be read from a readily accessible location to verify that negative pressure is being maintained in the closed-vent system when the control device is operating.

(k) The owner or operator shall monitor and inspect each closed-vent system required to comply with this section to ensure proper operation and maintenance of the closed-vent system by implementing the following requirements: 15.1.2.3

(1) Each closed-vent system that is used to comply with paragraph (j)(1) of this section shall be inspected and monitored in accordance with the following requirements:

(i) An initial leak detection monitoring of the closed-vent system shall be conducted by the owner or operator on or before the date that the system becomes subject to this section. The owner or operator shall monitor the closed-vent system components and connections using the procedures specified in §265.1034(b) of this subpart to demonstrate that the closed-vent system operates with no detectable emissions, as indicated by an instrument reading of less than 500 ppmv above background.

(ii) After initial leak detection monitoring required in paragraph (k)(1)(i) of this section, the owner or operator shall inspect and monitor the closed-vent system as follows:

(A) Closed-vent system joints, seams, or other connections that are permanently or semi-permanently sealed (*e.g.,* a welded joint between two sections of hard piping or a bolted and gasketed ducting flange) shall be visually inspected at least once per year to check for defects that could result in air pollutant emissions. The owner or operator shall monitor a component or connection using the procedures specified in §265.1034(b) of this subpart to demonstrate that it operates with no detectable emissions following any time the component is repaired or replaced (*e.g.,* a section of damaged hard piping is replaced with new hard piping) or the connection is unsealed (*e.g.,* a flange is unbolted).

(B) Closed-vent system components or connections other than those specified in paragraph (k)(1)(ii)(A) of this section shall be monitored annually and at other times as requested by the Regional Administrator, except as provided for in paragraph (n) of this section, using the procedures specified in §265.1034(b) of this subpart to demonstrate that the components or connections operate with no detectable emissions.

(iii) In the event that a defect or leak is detected, the owner or operator shall repair the defect or leak in accordance with the requirements of paragraph (k)(3) of this section.

(iv) The owner or operator shall maintain a record of the inspection and monitoring in accordance with the requirements specified in §265.1035 of this subpart.

(2) Each closed-vent system that is used to comply with paragraph (j)(2) of this section shall be inspected and monitored in accordance with the following requirements:

(i) The closed-vent system shall be visually inspected by the owner or operator to check for defects that could result in air pollutant emissions. Defects include, but are not limited to, visible cracks, holes, or gaps in ductwork or piping or loose connections.

(ii) The owner or operator shall perform an initial inspection of the closed-vent system on or before the date that the system becomes subject to this section. Thereafter, the owner or operator shall perform the inspections at least once every year.

(iii) In the event that a defect or leak is detected, the owner or operator shall repair the defect in accordance with the requirements of paragraph (k)(3) of this section.

(iv) The owner or operator shall maintain a record of the inspection and monitoring in accordance with the requirements specified in §265.1035 of this subpart.

(3) The owner or operator shall repair all detected defects as follows:

(i) Detectable emissions, as indicated by visual inspection, or by an instrument reading greater than 500 ppmv above background, shall be controlled as soon as practicable, but not later than 15 calendar days after the emission is detected, except as provided for in paragraph (k)(3)(iii) of this section.

(ii) A first attempt at repair shall be made no later than 5 calendar days after the emission is detected.

(iii) Delay of repair of a closed-vent system for which leaks have been detected is allowed if the repair is technically infeasible without a process unit shutdown, or if the owner or operator determines that emissions resulting from immediate repair would be greater than the fugitive emissions likely to result from delay of repair. Repair of such equipment shall be completed by the end of the next process unit shutdown.

(iv) The owner or operator shall maintain a record of the defect repair in accordance with the requirements specified in §265.1035 of this subpart.

(l) Closed-vent systems and control devices used to comply with provisions of this subpart shall be operated at all times when emissions may be vented to them.

(m) The owner or operator using a carbon adsorption system to control air pollutant emissions shall document that all carbon that is a hazardous waste and that is removed from the control device is managed in one of the following manners, regardless of the average volatile organic concentration of the carbon:

(1) Regenerated or reactivated in a thermal treatment unit that meets one of the following:

(i) The owner or operator of the unit has been issued a final permit under 40 CFR part 270 which implements the requirements of 40 CFR part 264 subpart X; or

(ii) The unit is equipped with and operating air emission controls in accordance with the applicable requirements of subparts AA and CC of either this part or of 40 CFR part 264; or

(iii) The unit is equipped with and operating air emission controls in accordance with a national emission standard for hazardous air pollutants under 40 CFR part 61 or 40 CFR part 63.

(2) Incinerated in a hazardous waste incinerator for which the owner or operator either:

(i) Has been issued a final permit under 40 CFR part 270 which implements the requirements of 40 CFR part 264, subpart O; or

(ii) Has designed and operates the incinerator in accordance with the interim status requirements of subpart O of this part.

(3) Burned in a boiler or industrial furnace for which the owner or operator either:

(i) Has been issued a final permit under 40 CFR part 270 which implements the requirements of 40 CFR part 266, subpart H; or

(ii) Has designed and operates the boiler or industrial furnace in accordance with the interim status requirements of 40 CFR part 266, subpart H.

(n) Any components of a closed-vent system that are designated, as described in §265.1035(c)(9) of this subpart, as unsafe to monitor are exempt from the requirements of paragraph (k)(1)(ii)(B) of this section if:

(1) The owner or operator of the closed-vent system determines that the components of the closed-vent system are unsafe to monitor because monitoring personnel would be exposed to an immediate danger as a consequence of complying with paragraph (k)(1)(ii)(B) of this section; and

(2) The owner or operator of the closed-vent system adheres to a written plan that requires monitoring the closed-vent system components using the procedure specified in paragraph (k)(1)(ii)(B) of this section as frequently as practicable during safe-to-monitor times.

[59 FR 62935, Dec. 6, 1994, as amended at 61 FR 4913, Feb. 9, 1996; 61 FR 59969, Nov. 25, 1996; 62 FR 64661, Dec. 8, 1997; 71 FR 40276, July 14, 2006]

§265.1034 Test methods and procedures.

(a) Each owner or operator subject to the provisions of this subpart shall comply with the test methods and procedures requirements provided in this section.

(b) When a closed-vent system is tested for compliance with no detectable emissions, as required in §265.1033(k) of this subpart, the test shall comply with the following requirements:

(1) Monitoring shall comply with Reference Method 21 in 40 CFR part 60.

(2) The detection instrument shall meet the performance criteria of Reference Method 21.

(3) The instrument shall be calibrated before use on each day of its use by the procedures specified in Reference Method 21.

(4) Calibration gases shall be:

(i) Zero air (less than 10 ppm of hydrocarbon in air).

(ii) A mixture of methane or n-hexane and air at a concentration of approximately, but less than, 10,000 ppm methane or n-hexane.

(5) The background level shall be determined as set forth in Reference Method 21.

(6) The instrument probe shall be traversed around all potential leak interfaces as close to the interface as possible as described in Reference Method 21.

(7) The arithmetic difference between the maximum concentration indicated by the instrument and the background level is compared with 500 ppm for determining compliance.

(c) Performance tests to determine compliance with §265.1032(a) and with the total organic compound concentration limit of §265.1033(c) shall comply with the following:

(1) Performance tests to determine total organic compound concentrations and mass flow rates entering and exiting control devices shall be conducted and data reduced in accordance with the following reference methods and calculation procedures:

(i) Method 2 in 40 CFR part 60 for velocity and volumetric flow rate.

(ii) Method 18 or Method 25A in 40 CFR part 60, appendix A, for organic content. If Method 25A is used, the organic HAP used as the calibration gas must be the single organic HAP representing the largest percent by volume of the emissions. The use of Method 25A is acceptable if the response from the high-level calibration gas is at least 20 times the standard deviation of the response from the zero calibration gas when the instrument is zeroed on the most sensitive scale.

(iii) Each performance test shall consist of three separate runs; each run conducted for at least 1 hour under the conditions that exist when the hazardous waste management unit is operating at the highest load or capacity level reasonably expected to occur. For the purpose of determining total organic compound concentrations and mass flow rates, the average of results of all runs shall apply. The average shall be computed on a time-weighted basis.

(iv) Total organic mass flow rates shall be determined by the following equation:

(A) For sources utilizing Method 18.

$$E_h = Q_{2sd}\left\{\sum_{i=1}^{n} C_i MW_i\right\}[0.0416][10^{-6}]$$

where:

E_h = Total organic mass flow rate, kg/h;

Q_{2sd} = Volumetric flow rate of gases entering or exiting control device, as determined by Method 2, dscm/h;

n = Number of organic compounds in the vent gas;

C_i = Organic concentration in ppm, dry basis, of compound i in the vent gas, as determined by Method 18;

MW_i = Molecular weight of organic compound i in the vent gas, kg/kg-mol;

0.0416 = Conversion factor for molar volume, kg-mol/m^3 (@ 293 K and 760 mm Hg);

10^{-6} = Conversion from ppm

(B) For sources utilizing Method 25A.

$$E_h = (Q)(C)(MW)(0.0416)(10^{-6})$$

where:

E_h = Total organic mass flow rate, kg/h;

Q = Volumetric flow rate of gases entering or exiting control device, as determined by Method 2, dscm/h;

C = Organic concentration in ppm, dry basis, as determined by Method 25A;

MW = Molecular weight of propane, 44;

0.0416 = Conversion factor for molar volume, kg-mol/m^3 (@ 293 K and 760 mm Hg);

10^{-6} = Conversion from ppm.

(v) The annual total organic emission rate shall be determined by the following equation:

$$E_A = (E_h)(H)$$

where:

E_A = Total organic mass emission rate, kg/y;

E_h = Total organic mass flow rate for the process vent, kg/h;

H = Total annual hours of operations for the affected unit, h.

(vi) Total organic emissions from all affected process vents at the facility shall be determined by summing the hourly total organic mass emission rates (E_h, as determined in paragraph (c)(1)(iv) of this section) and by summing the annual total organic mass emission rates (E_A, as determined in paragraph (c)(1)(v) of this section) for all affected process vents at the facility.

(2) The owner or operator shall record such process information as may be necessary to determine the conditions of the performance tests. Operations during periods of startup, shutdown, and malfunction shall not constitute representative conditions for the purpose of a performance test.

(3) The owner or operator of an affected facility shall provide, or cause to be provided, performance testing facilities as follows:

(i) Sampling ports adequate for the test methods specified in paragraph (c)(1) of this section.

(ii) Safe sampling platform(s).

(iii) Safe access to sampling platform(s).

(iv) Utilities for sampling and testing equipment.

(4) For the purpose of making compliance determinations, the time-weighted average of the results of the three runs shall apply. In the event that a sample is accidentally lost or conditions occur in which one of the three runs must be discontinued because of forced shutdown, failure of an irreplaceable portion of the sample train, extreme meteorological conditions, or other circumstances beyond the owner or operator's control, compliance may, upon the Regional Administrator's approval, be determined using the average of the results of the two other runs.

(d) To show that a process vent associated with a hazardous waste distillation, fractionation, thin-film evaporation, solvent extraction, or air or steam stripping operation is not subject to the requirements of this subpart, the owner or operator must make an initial determination that the time-weighted, annual average total organic concentration of the waste managed by the waste management unit is less than 10 ppmw using one of the following two methods:

(1) Direct measurement of the organic concentration of the waste using the following procedures:

(i) The owner or operator must take a minimum of four grab samples of waste for each waste stream managed in the affected unit under process conditions expected to cause the maximum waste organic concentration.

(ii) For waste generated onsite, the grab samples must be collected at a point before the waste is exposed to the atmosphere such as in an enclosed pipe or other closed system that is used to transfer the waste after generation to the first affected distillation fractionation, thin-film evaporation, solvent extraction, or air or steam stripping operation. For waste generated offsite, the grab samples must be collected at the inlet to the first waste management unit that receives the waste provided the waste has been transferred to the facility in a closed system such as a tank truck and the waste is not diluted or mixed with other waste.

(iii) Each sample shall be analyzed and the total organic concentration of the sample shall be computed using Method 9060A (incorporated by reference under §260.11 of this chapter) of "Test Methods for Evaluating Solid Waste, Physical/Chemical Methods," EPA Publication SW–846; or analyzed for its individual organic constituents.

(iv) The arithmetic mean of the results of the analyses of the four samples shall apply for each waste stream managed in the unit in determining the time-weighted, annual average total organic concentration of the waste. The time-weighted average is to be calculated using the annual quantity of each waste stream processed and the mean organic concentration of each waste stream managed in the unit.

(2) Using knowledge of the waste to determine that its total organic concentration is less than 10 ppmw. Documentation of the waste determination is required. Examples of documentation that shall be used to support a determination under this provision include production process information documenting that no organic compounds are used, information that the waste is generated by a process that is identical to a process at the same or another facility that has previously been demonstrated by direct measurement to generate a waste stream having a total organic content less than 10 ppmw, or prior speciation analysis results on the same waste stream where it can also be documented that no process changes have occurred since that analysis that could affect the waste total organic concentration.

(e) The determination that distillation fractionation, thin-film evaporation, solvent extraction, or air or steam stripping operations manage hazardous wastes with time-weighted annual average total organic concentrations less than 10 ppmw shall be made as follows:

(1) By the effective date that the facility becomes subject to the provisions of this subpart or by the date when the waste is first managed in a waste management unit, whichever is later; and

(2) For continuously generated waste, annually; or

(3) Whenever there is a change in the waste being managed or a change in the process that generates or treats the waste.

(f) When an owner or operator and the Regional Administrator do not agree on whether a distillation, fractionation, thin-film evaporation, solvent extraction, or air or steam stripping operation manages a hazardous waste with organic concentrations of at least 10 ppmw based on knowledge of the waste, the dispute may be resolved using direct measurement as specified at paragraph (d)(1) of this section.

[55 FR 25507, June 21, 1990, as amended at 56 FR 19290, Apr. 26, 1991; 61 FR 59970, Nov. 25, 1996; 62 FR 32463, June 13, 1997; 70 FR 34586, June 14, 2005]

§265.1035 Recordkeeping requirements.

📖 15.1.2.4

(a)(1) Each owner or operator subject to the provisions of this subpart shall comply with the recordkeeping requirements of this section.

(2) An owner or operator of more than one hazardous waste management unit subject to the provisions of this subpart may comply with the recordkeeping requirements for these hazardous waste management units in one recordkeeping system if the system identifies each record by each hazardous waste management unit.

(b) Owners and operators must record the following information in the facility operating record:

(1) For facilities that comply with the provisions of §265.1033(a)(2), an implementation schedule that includes dates by which the closed-vent system and control device will be installed and in operation. The schedule must also include a rationale of why the installation cannot be completed at an earlier date. The implementation schedule must be in the facility operating record by the effective date that the facility becomes subject to the provisions of this subpart.

(2) Up-to-date documentation of compliance with the process vent standards in §265.1032, including:

(i) Information and data identifying all affected process vents, annual throughput and operating hours of each affected unit, estimated emission rates for each affected vent and for the overall facility (*i.e.*, the total emissions for all affected vents at the facility), and the approximate location within the facility of each affected unit (*e.g.*, identify the hazardous waste management units on a facility plot plan); and

(ii) Information and data supporting determinations of vent emissions and emission reductions achieved by add-on control devices based on engineering calculations or source tests. For the purpose of determining compliance, determinations of vent emissions and emission reductions must be made using operating parameter values (*e.g.*, temperatures, flow rates or vent stream organic compounds and concentrations) that represent the conditions that result in maximum organic emissions, such as when the waste management unit is operating at the highest load or capacity level reasonably expected to occur. If the owner or operator takes any action (*e.g.*, managing a waste of different composition or increasing operating hours of affected waste management units) that would result in an increase in total organic emissions from affected process vents at the facility, then a new determination is required.

(3) Where an owner or operator chooses to use test data to determine the organic removal efficiency or total organic compound concentration achieved by the control device, a performance test plan. The test plan must include:

(i) A description of how it is determined that the planned test is going to be conducted when the hazardous waste management unit is operating at the highest load or capacity level reasonably expected to occur. This shall include the estimated or design flow rate and organic content of each vent stream and define the acceptable operating ranges of key process and control device parameters during the test program.

(ii) A detailed engineering description of the closed-vent system and control device including:

(A) Manufacturer's name and model number of control device.

(B) Type of control device.

(C) Dimensions of the control device.

(D) Capacity.

(E) Construction materials.

(iii) A detailed description of sampling and monitoring procedures, including sampling and monitoring locations in the system, the equipment to be used, sampling and monitoring frequency, and planned analytical procedures for sample analysis.

(4) Documentation of compliance with §265.1033 shall include the following information:

(i) A list of all information references and sources used in preparing the documentation.

(ii) Records, including the dates, of each compliance test required by §265.1033(j).

(iii) If engineering calculations are used, a design analysis, specifications, drawings, schematics, and piping and instrumentation diagrams based on the appropriate sections of "APTI Course 415: Control of Gaseous Emissions" (incorporated by reference as specified in §260.11) or other engineering texts acceptable to the Regional Administrator that present basic control device design information. Documentation provided by the control device manufacturer or vendor that describes the control device design in accordance with paragraphs (b)(4)(iii)(A) through (b)(4)(iii)(G) of this section may be used to comply with this requirement. The design analysis shall address the vent stream characteristics and control device operation parameters as specified below.

(A) For a thermal vapor incinerator, the design analysis shall consider the vent stream composition, constituent concentrations, and flow rate. The design analysis shall also establish the design minimum and average temperature in the combustion zone and the combustion zone residence time.

(B) For a catalytic vapor incinerator, the design analysis shall consider the vent stream composition, constituent concentrations, and flow rate. The design analysis shall also establish the design minimum and average temperatures across the catalyst bed inlet and outlet.

(C) For a boiler or process heater, the design analysis shall consider the vent stream composition, constituent concentrations, and flow rate. The design analysis shall also establish the design minimum and average flame zone temperatures, combustion zone residence time, and description of method and location where the vent stream is introduced into the combustion zone.

(D) For a flare, the design analysis shall consider the vent stream composition, constituent concentrations, and flow rate. The design analysis shall also consider the requirements specified in §265.1033(d).

(E) For a condenser, the design analysis shall consider the vent stream composition, constituent concentrations, flow rate, relative humidity, and temperature. The design analysis shall also establish the design outlet organic compound concentration level, design average temperature of the condenser exhaust vent stream, and design average temperatures of the coolant fluid at the condenser inlet and outlet.

(F) For a carbon adsorption system such as a fixed-bed adsorber that regenerates the carbon bed directly onsite in the control device, the design analysis shall consider the vent stream composition, constituent concentrations, flow rate, relative humidity, and temperature. The design analysis shall also establish the design exhaust vent stream organic compound concentration level, number and capacity of carbon beds, type and working capacity of activated carbon used for carbon beds, design total steam flow over the period of each complete carbon bed regeneration cycle, duration of the carbon bed steaming and cooling/drying cycles, design carbon bed temperature after regeneration, design carbon bed regeneration time, and design service life of carbon.

(G) For a carbon adsorption system such as a carbon canister that does not regenerate the carbon bed directly onsite in the control device, the design analysis shall consider the vent stream composition, constituent concentrations, flow rate, relative humidity, and temperature. The design analysis shall also establish the design outlet organic concentration level, capacity of carbon bed, type and working capacity of activated carbon used for carbon bed, and design carbon replacement interval based on the total carbon working capacity of the control device and source operating schedule.

(iv) A statement signed and dated by the owner or operator certifying that the operating parameters used in the design analysis reasonably represent the conditions that exist when the hazardous waste management unit is or would be operating at the highest load or capacity level reasonably expected to occur.

(v) A statement signed and dated by the owner or operator certifying that the control device is designed to operate at an efficiency of 95 percent or greater unless the total organic concentration limit of §265.1032(a) is achieved at an efficiency less than 95 weight percent or the total organic emission limits of §265.1032(a) for affected process vents at the facility can be attained by a control device involving vapor recovery at an efficiency less than 95 weight percent. A statement provided by the control device manufacturer or vendor certifying that the control equipment meets the design specifications may be used to comply with this requirement.

(vi) If performance tests are used to demonstrate compliance, all test results.

(c) Design documentation and monitoring, operating, and inspection information for each closed-vent system and control device required to comply with the provisions of this part shall be recorded and kept up-to-date in the facility operating record. The information shall include:

(1) Description and date of each modification that is made to the closed-vent system or control device design.

(2) Identification of operating parameter, description of monitoring device, and diagram of monitoring sensor location or locations used to comply with §265.1033(f)(1) and (f)(2).

(3) Monitoring, operating and inspection information required by paragraphs (f) through (k) of §265.1033 of this subpart.

(4) Date, time, and duration of each period that occurs while the control device is operating when any monitored parameter exceeds the value established in the control device design analysis as specified below:

(i) For a thermal vapor incinerator designed to operate with a minimum residence time of 0.50 seconds at a minimum temperature of 760° C, period when the combustion temperature is below 760° C.

(ii) For a thermal vapor incinerator designed to operate with an organic emission reduction efficiency of 95 percent or greater, period when the combustion zone temperature is more than 28° C below the design average combustion zone temperature established as a requirement of paragraph (b)(4)(iii)(A) of this section.

(iii) For a catalytic vapor incinerator, period when:

(A) Temperature of the vent stream at the catalyst bed inlet is more than 28° C below the average temperature of the inlet vent stream established as a requirement of paragraph (b)(4)(iii)(B) of this section; or

(B) Temperature difference across the catalyst bed is less than 80 percent of the design average temperature difference established as a requirement of paragraph (b)(4)(iii)(B) of this section.

(iv) For a boiler or process heater, period when:

(A) Flame zone temperature is more than 28° C below the design average flame zone temperature established as a requirement of paragraph (b)(4)(iii)(C) of this section; or

(B) Position changes where the vent stream is introduced to the combustion zone from the location established as a requirement of paragraph (b)(4)(iii)(C) of this section.

(v) For a flare, period when the pilot flame is not ignited.

(vi) For a condenser that complies with §265.1033(f)(2)(vi)(A), period when the organic compound concentration level or readings of organic compounds in the exhaust vent stream from the condenser are more than 20 percent greater than the design outlet organic compound concentration level established as a requirement of paragraph (b)(4)(iii)(E) of this section.

(vii) For a condenser that complies with §265.1033(f)(2)(vi)(B), period when:

(A) Temperature of the exhaust vent stream from the condenser is more than 6° C above the design average exhaust vent stream temperature established as a requirement of paragraph (b)(4)(iii)(E) of this section; or

(B) Temperature of the coolant fluid exiting the condenser is more than 6° C above the design average coolant fluid temperature at the condenser outlet established as a requirement of paragraph (b)(4)(iii)(E) of this section.

(viii) For a carbon adsorption system such as a fixed-bed carbon adsorber that regenerates the carbon bed directly onsite in the control device and complies with §265.1033(f)(2)(vii)(A), period when the organic compound concentration level or readings of organic compounds in the exhaust vent stream from the carbon bed are more than 20 percent greater than the design exhaust vent stream organic compound concentration level established as a requirement of paragraph (b)(4)(iii)(F) of this section.

(ix) For a carbon adsorption system such as a fixed-bed carbon adsorber that regenerates the carbon bed directly onsite in the control device and complies with §265.1033(f)(2)(vii)(B), period when the vent stream continues to flow through the control device beyond the predetermined carbon bed regeneration time established as a requirement of paragraph (b)(4)(iii)(F) of this section.

(5) Explanation for each period recorded under paragraph (c)(4) of this section of the cause for control device operating parameter exceeding the design value and the measures implemented to correct the control device operation.

(6) For carbon adsorption systems operated subject to requirements specified in §265.1033(g) or §265.1033(h)(2), date when existing carbon in the control device is replaced with fresh carbon.

(7) For carbon adsorption systems operated subject to requirements specified in §265.1033(h)(1), a log that records:

(i) Date and time when control device is monitored for carbon breakthrough and the monitoring device reading.

(ii) Date when existing carbon in the control device is replaced with fresh carbon.

(8) Date of each control device startup and shutdown.

(9) An owner or operator designating any components of a closed-vent system as unsafe to monitor pursuant to §265.1033(n) of this subpart shall record in a log that is kept in the facility operating record the identification of closed-vent system components that are designated as unsafe to monitor in accordance with the requirements of §265.1033(n) of this subpart, an explanation for each closed-vent system component stating why the closed-vent system component is unsafe to monitor, and the plan for monitoring each closed-vent system component.

(10) When each leak is detected as specified in §265.1033(k) of this subpart, the following information shall be recorded:

(i) The instrument identification number, the closed-vent system component identification number, and the operator name, initials, or identification number.

(ii) The date the leak was detected and the date of first attempt to repair the leak.

(iii) The date of successful repair of the leak.

(iv) Maximum instrument reading measured by Method 21 of 40 CFR part 60, appendix A after it is successfully repaired or determined to be nonrepairable.

(v) "Repair delayed" and the reason for the delay if a leak is not repaired within 15 calendar days after discovery of the leak.

(A) The owner or operator may develop a written procedure that identifies the conditions that justify a delay of repair. In such cases, reasons for delay of repair may be documented by citing the relevant sections of the written procedure.

(B) If delay of repair was caused by depletion of stocked parts, there must be documentation that the spare parts were sufficiently stocked on-site before depletion and the reason for depletion.

(d) Records of the monitoring, operating, and inspection information required by paragraphs (c)(3) through (c)(10) of this section shall be maintained by the owner or operator for at least 3 years following the date of each occurrence, measurement, maintenance, corrective action, or record.

(e) For a control device other than a thermal vapor incinerator, catalytic vapor incinerator, flare, boiler, process heater, condenser, or carbon adsorption system, monitoring and inspection information indicating proper operation and maintenance of the control device must be recorded in the facility operating record.

(f) Up-to-date information and data used to determine whether or not a process vent is subject to the requirements in §265.1032 including supporting documentation as required by §265.1034(d)(2) when application of the knowledge of the nature of the hazardous waste stream or the process by which it was produced is used, shall be recorded in a log that is kept in the facility operating record.

[55 FR 25507, June 21, 1990, as amended at 56 FR 19290, Apr. 26, 1991; 61 FR 59970, Nov. 25, 1996; 71 FR 40276, July 14, 2006]

§§265.1036–265.1049 [Reserved]

Subpart BB—Air Emission Standards for Equipment Leaks

Source: 55 FR 25512, June 21, 1990, unless otherwise noted.

§265.1050 Applicability.
15.2.1

(a) The regulations in this subpart apply to owners and operators of facilities that treat, store, or dispose of hazardous wastes (except as provided in §265.1). 15.2.1.1

(b) Except as provided in §265.1064(k), this subpart applies to equipment that contains or contacts hazardous wastes with organic concentrations of at least 10 percent by weight that are managed in one of the following: 15.2.1.2–5

(1) A unit that is subject to the permitting requirements of 40 CFR part 270, or

(2) A unit (including a hazardous waste recycling unit) that is not exempt from permitting under the provisions of 40 CFR 262.34(a) (*i.e.*, a hazardous waste recycling unit that is not a 90-day tank or container) and that is located at a hazardous waste management facility otherwise subject to the permitting requirements of 40 CFR part 270, or

(3) A unit that is exempt from permitting under the provisions of 40 CFR 262.34(a) (*i.e.*, a "90-day" tank or container) and is not a recycling unit under the provisions of 40 CFR 261.6. 6.3.11

(c) Each piece of equipment to which this subpart applies shall be marked in such a manner that it can be distinguished readily from other pieces of equipment.

(d) Equipment that is in vacuum service is excluded from the requirements of §265.1052 to §265.1060 if it is identified as required in §265.1064(g)(5).

(e) Equipment that contains or contacts hazardous waste with an organic concentration of at least 10 percent by weight for less than 300 hours per calendar year is excluded from the requirements of §§265.1052 through 265.1060 of this subpart if it is identified, as required in §265.1064(g)(6) of this subpart. 15.2.1.4

(f) The requirements of this subpart do not apply to the pharmaceutical manufacturing facility, commonly referred to as the Stonewall Plant, located at Route 340 South, Elkton, Virginia, provided that facility is operated in compliance with the requirements contained in a Clean Air Act permit issued pursuant to 40 CFR 52.2454. The requirements of this subpart shall apply to the facility upon termination of the Clean Air Act permit issued pursuant to 40 CFR 52.2454.

(g) Purged coatings and solvents from surface coating operations subject to the national emission standards for hazardous air pollutants (NESHAP) for the surface coating of automobiles and light-duty trucks at 40 CFR part 63, subpart IIII, are not subject to the requirements of this subpart.

[*Note:* The requirements of §§265.1052 through 265.1064 apply to equipment associated with hazardous waste recycling units previously exempt under paragraph 261.6(c)(1). Other exemptions under §§261.4 and 265.1(c) are not affected by these requirements.]

[55 FR 25512, June 21, 1990, as amended at 61 FR 59970, Nov. 25, 1996; 62 FR 52642, Oct. 8, 1997; 62 FR 64661, Dec. 8, 1997; 69 FR 22661, Apr. 26, 2004]

§265.1051 Definitions.

As used in this subpart, all terms shall have the meaning given them in §264.1031, the Act, and parts 260-266.

§265.1052 Standards: Pumps in light liquid service.
15.2.2.2

(a)(1) Each pump in light liquid service shall be monitored monthly to detect leaks by the methods specified in §265.1063(b), except as provided in paragraphs (d), (e), and (f) of this section.

PART 265—Subpart BB

(2) Each pump in light liquid service shall be checked by visual inspection each calendar week for indications of liquids dripping from the pump seal.

(b)(1) If an instrument reading of 10,000 ppm or greater is measured, a leak is detected.

(2) If there are indications of liquids dripping from the pump seal, a leak is detected.

(c)(1) When a leak is detected, it shall be repaired as soon as practicable, but not later than 15 calendar days after it is detected, except as provided in §265.1059.

(2) A first attempt at repair (*e.g.*, tightening the packing gland) shall be made no later than 5 calendar days after each leak is detected.

(d) Each pump equipped with a dual mechanical seal system that includes a barrier fluid system is exempt from the requirements of paragraph (a), provided the following requirements are met:

(1) Each dual mechanical seal system must be:

(i) Operated with the barrier fluid at a pressure that is at all times greater than the pump stuffing box pressure, or

(ii) Equipped with a barrier fluid degassing reservoir that is connected by a closed-vent system to a control device that complies with the requirements of §265.1060, or

(iii) Equipped with a system that purges the barrier fluid into a hazardous waste stream with no detectable emissions to the atmosphere.

(2) The barrier fluid system must not be a hazardous waste with organic concentrations 10 percent or greater by weight.

(3) Each barrier fluid system must be equipped with a sensor that will detect failure of the seal system, the barrier fluid system or both.

(4) Each pump must be checked by visual inspection, each calendar week, for indications of liquids dripping from the pump seals.

(5)(i) Each sensor as described in paragraph (d)(3) of this section must be checked daily or be equipped with an audible alarm that must be checked monthly to ensure that it is functioning properly.

(ii) The owner or operator must determine, based on design considerations and operating experience, a criterion that indicates failure of the seal system, the barrier fluid system, or both.

(6)(i) If there are indications of liquids dripping from the pump seal or the sensor indicates failure of the seal system, the barrier fluid system, or both based on the criterion determined in paragraph (d)(5)(ii) of this section, a leak is detected.

(ii) When a leak is detected, it shall be repaired as soon as practicable, but not later than 15 calendar days after it is detected, except as provided in §265.1059.

(iii) A first attempt at repair (*e.g.*, relapping the seal) shall be made no later than 5 calendar days after each leak is detected.

(e) Any pump that is designated, as described in §265.1064(g)(2), for no detectable emissions, as indicated by an instrument reading of less than 500 ppm above background, is exempt from the requirements of paragraphs (a), (c), and (d) of this section if the pump meets the following requirements:

(1) Must have no externally actuated shaft penetrating the pump housing.

(2) Must operate with no detectable emissions as indicated by an instrument reading of less than 500 ppm above background as measured by the methods specified in §265.1063(c).

(3) Must be tested for compliance with paragraph (e)(2) of this section initially upon designation, annually, and at other times as requested by the Regional Administrator.

(f) If any pump is equipped with a closed-vent system capable of capturing and transporting any leakage from the seal or seals to a control device that complies with the requirements of §265.1060, it is exempt from the requirements of paragraphs (a) through (e) of this section.

[55 FR 25512, June 21, 1990, as amended at 56 FR 19290, Apr. 26, 1991]

§265.1053 Standards: Compressors.

📖 15.2.2.2

(a) Each compressor shall be equipped with a seal system that includes a barrier fluid system and that prevents leakage of total organic emissions to the atmosphere, except as provided in paragraphs (h) and (i) of this section.

(b) Each compressor seal system as required in paragraph (a) of this section shall be:

(1) Operated with the barrier fluid at a pressure that is at all times greater than the compressor stuffing box pressure, or

(2) Equipped with a barrier fluid system that is connected by a closed-vent system to a control device that complies with the requirements of §265.1060, or

(3) Equipped with a system that purges the barrier fluid into a hazardous waste stream with no detectable emissions to atmosphere.

(c) The barrier fluid must not be a hazardous waste with organic concentrations 10 percent or greater by weight.

(d) Each barrier fluid system as described in paragraphs (a) through (c) of this section shall be equipped with a sensor that will detect failure of the seal system, barrier fluid system, or both.

(e)(1) Each sensor as required in paragraph (d) of this section shall be checked daily or shall be equipped with an audible alarm that must be checked monthly to ensure that it is functioning properly unless the compressor is located within the boundary of an unmanned plant site, in which case the sensor must be checked daily.

(2) The owner or operator shall determine, based on design considerations and operating experience, a criterion that indicates failure of the seal system, the barrier fluid system or both.

(f) If the sensor indicates failure of the seal system, the barrier fluid system, or both based on the criterion determined under paragraph (e)(2) of this section, a leak is detected.

(g)(1) When a leak is detected, it shall be repaired as soon as practicable, but not later than 15 calendar days after it is detected, except as provided in §265.1059.

(2) A first attempt at repair (*e.g.*, tightening the packing gland) shall be made no later than 5 calendar days after each leak is detected.

(h) A compressor is exempt from the requirements of paragraphs (a) and (b) of this section if it is equipped with a closed-vent system capable of capturing and transporting any leakage from the seal to a control device that complies with the requirements of §265.1060, except as provided in paragraph (i) of this section.

(i) Any compressor that is designated, as described in §265.1064(g)(2), for no detectable emission as indicated by an instrument reading of less than 500 ppm above background is exempt from the requirements of paragraphs (a) through (h) of this section if the compressor:

(1) Is determined to be operating with no detectable emissions, as indicated by an instrument reading of less than 500 ppm above background, as measured by the method specified in §265.1063(c).

(2) Is tested for compliance with paragraph (i)(1) of this section initially upon designation, annually, and at other times as requested by the Regional Administrator.

§265.1054 Standards: Pressure relief devices in gas/vapor service. 15.2.2.2

(a) Except during pressure releases, each pressure relief device in gas/vapor service shall be operated with no detectable emissions, as indicated by an instrument reading of less than 500 ppm above background, as measured by the method specified in §265.1063(c).

(b)(1) After each pressure release, the pressure relief device shall be returned to a condition of no detectable emissions, as indicated by an instrument reading of less than 500 ppm above background, as soon as practicable, but no later than 5 calendar days after each pressure release, except as provided in §265.1059.

(2) No later than 5 calendar days after the pressure release, the pressure relief device shall be monitored to confirm the condition of no detectable emissions, as indicated by an instrument reading of less than 500 ppm above background, as measured by the method specified in §265.1063(c).

(c) Any pressure relief device that is equipped with a closed-vent system capable of capturing and transporting leakage from the pressure relief device to a control device as described in §265.1060 is exempt from the requirements of paragraphs (a) and (b) of this section.

§265.1055 Standards: Sampling connection systems. 15.2.2.2

(a) Each sampling connection system shall be equipped with a closed-purge, closed-loop, or closed-vent system. This system shall collect the sample purge for return to the process or for routing to the appropriate treatment system. Gases displaced during filling of the sample container are not required to be collected or captured.

(b) Each closed-purge, closed-loop, or closed-vent system as required in paragraph (a) of this section shall:

(1) Return the purged process fluid directly to the process line; or

(2) Collect and recycle the purged process fluid; or

(3) Be designed and operated to capture and transport all the purged process fluid to a waste management unit that complies with the applicable requirements of §265.1085 through §265.1087 of this subpart or a control device that complies with the requirements of §265.1060 of this subpart.

(c) *In-situ* sampling systems and sampling systems without purges are exempt from the requirements of paragraphs (a) and (b) of this section.

[61 FR 59971, Nov. 25, 1996]

§265.1056 Standards: Open-ended valves or lines. 15.2.2.2

(a)(1) Each open-ended valve or line shall be equipped with a cap, blind flange, plug, or a second valve.

(2) The cap, blind flange, plug, or second valve shall seal the open end at all times except during operations requiring hazardous waste stream flow through the open-ended valve or line.

(b) Each open-ended valve or line equipped with a second valve shall be operated in a manner such that the valve on the hazardous waste stream end is closed before the second valve is closed.

(c) When a double block and bleed system is being used, the bleed valve or line may remain open during operations that require venting the line between the block valves but shall comply with paragraph (a) of this section at all other times.

§265.1057 Standards: Valves in gas/vapor service or in light liquid service. 15.2.2.2

(a) Each valve in gas/vapor or light liquid service shall be monitored monthly to detect leaks by the methods specified in §265.1063(b) and shall comply with paragraphs (b) through (e) of this section, except as provided in paragraphs (f), (g), and (h) of this section' and §§265.1061 and 265.1062.

(b) If an instrument reading of 10,000 ppm or greater is measured, a leak is detected.

(c)(1) Any valve for which a leak is not detected for two successive months may be monitored the first month of every succeeding quarter, beginning with the next quarter, until a leak is detected.

(2) If a leak is detected, the valve shall be monitored monthly until a leak is not detected for 2 successive months.

(d)(1) When a leak is detected, it shall be repaired as soon as practicable, but no later than 15 calendar days after the leak is detected, except as provided in §265.1059.

(2) A first attempt at repair shall be made no later than 5 calendar days after each leak is detected.

(e) First attempts at repair include, but are not limited to, the following best practices where practicable:

(1) Tightening of bonnet bolts.

(2) Replacement of bonnet bolts.

(3) Tightening of packing gland nuts.

(4) Injection of lubricant into lubricated packing.

(f) Any valve that is designated, as described in §265.1064(g)(2), for no detectable emissions, as indicated by an instrument reading of less than 500 ppm above background, is exempt from the requirements of paragraph (a) of this section if the valve:

(1) Has no external actuating mechanism in contact with the hazardous waste stream.

(2) Is operated with emissions less than 500 ppm above background as determined by the method specified in §265.1063(c).

(3) Is tested for compliance with paragraph (f)(2) of this section initially upon designation, annually, and at other times as requested by the Regional Administrator.

(g) Any valve that is designated, as described in §265.1064(h)(1), as an unsafe-to-monitor valve is exempt from the requirements of paragraph (a) of this section if:

(1) The owner or operator of the valve determines that the valve is unsafe to monitor because monitoring personnel would be exposed to an immediate danger as a consequence of complying with paragraph (a) of this section.

(2) The owner or operator of the valve adheres to a written plan that requires monitoring of the valve as frequently as practicable during safe-to-monitor times.

(h) Any valve that is designated, as described in §265.1064(h)(2), as a difficult-to-monitor valve is exempt from the requirements of paragraph (a) of this section if:

(1) The owner or operator of the valve determines that the valve cannot be monitored without elevating the monitoring personnel more than 2 meters above a support surface.

(2) The hazardous waste management unit within which the valve is located was in operation before June 21, 1990.

(3) The owner or operator of the valve follows a written plan that requires monitoring of the valve at least once per calendar year.

§265.1058 Standards: Pumps and valves in heavy liquid service, pressure relief devices in light liquid or heavy liquid service, and flanges and other connectors. 15.2.2.2

(a) Pumps and valves in heavy liquid service, pressure relief devices in light liquid or heavy liquid service, and flanges and other connectors shall be monitored within 5 days by the method specified in §265.1063(b) if evidence of a potential leak is found by visual, audible, olfactory, or any other detection method.

(b) If an instrument reading of 10,000 ppm or greater is measured, a leak is detected.

(c)(1) When a leak is detected, it shall be repaired as soon as practicable, but not later than 15 calendar days after it is detected, except as provided in §265.1059.

(2) The first attempt at repair shall be made no later than 5 calendar days after each leak is detected.

(d) First attempts at repair include, but are not limited to, the best practices described under §265.1057(e).

(e) Any connector that is inaccessible or is ceramic or ceramic-lined (*e.g.*, porcelain, glass, or glass-lined) is exempt from the monitoring requirements of paragraph (a) of this section and from the recordkeeping requirements of §265.1064 of this subpart.

[55 FR 25512, June 21, 1990, as amended at 61 FR 59971, Nov. 25, 1996]

§265.1059 Standards: Delay of repair.

(a) Delay of repair of equipment for which leaks have been detected will be allowed if the repair is technically infeasible without a hazardous waste management unit shutdown. In such a case, repair of this equipment shall occur before the end of the next hazardous waste management unit shutdown.

(b) Delay of repair of equipment for which leaks have been detected will be allowed for equipment that is isolated from the hazardous waste management unit and that does not continue to contain or contact hazardous waste with organic concentrations at least 10 percent by weight.

(c) Delay of repair for valves will be allowed if:

(1) The owner or operator determines that emissions of purged material resulting from immediate repair are greater than the emissions likely to result from delay of repair.

(2) When repair procedures are effected, the purged material is collected and destroyed or recovered in a control device complying with §265.1060.

(d) Delay of repair for pumps will be allowed if:

(1) Repair requires the use of a dual mechanical seal system that includes a barrier fluid system.

(2) Repair is completed as soon as practicable, but not later than 6 months after the leak was detected.

(e) Delay of repair beyond a hazardous waste management unit shutdown will be allowed for a valve if valve assembly replacement is necessary during the hazardous waste management unit shutdown, valve assembly supplies have been depleted, and valve assembly supplies had been sufficiently stocked before the supplies were depleted. Delay of repair beyond the next hazardous waste management unit shutdown will not be allowed unless the next hazardous waste management unit shutdown occurs sooner than 6 months after the first hazardous waste management unit shutdown.

§265.1060 Standards: Closed-vent systems and control devices.

(a) Owners and operators of closed-vent systems and control devices subject to this subpart shall comply with the provisions of §265.1033 of this part.

(b)(1) The owner or operator of an existing facility who can not install a closed-vent system and control device to comply with the provisions of this subpart on the effective date that the facility becomes subject to the provisions of this subpart must prepare an implementation schedule that includes dates by which the closed-vent system and control device will be installed and in operation. The controls must be installed as soon as possible, but the implementation schedule may allow up to 30 months after the effective date that the facility becomes subject to this subpart for installation and startup.

(2) Any units that begin operation after December 21, 1990, and are subject to the provisions of this subpart when operation begins, must comply with the rules immediately (*i.e.*, must have control devices installed and operating on startup of the affected unit); the 30-month implementation schedule does not apply.

(3) The owner or operator of any facility in existence on the effective date of a statutory or EPA regulatory amendment that renders the facility subject to this subpart shall comply with all requirements of this subpart as soon as practicable but no later than 30 months after the amendment's effective date. When control equipment required by this subpart can not be installed and begin operation by the effective date of the amendment, the facility owner or operator shall prepare an implementation schedule that includes the following information: Specific calendar dates for award of contracts or issuance of purchase orders for the control equipment, initiation of on-site installation of the control equipment, completion of the control equipment installation, and performance of any testing to demonstrate that the installed equipment meets the applicable standards of this subpart. The owner or operator shall enter the implementation schedule in the operating record or in a permanent, readily available file located at the facility.

(4) Owners and operators of facilities and units that become newly subject to the requirements of this subpart after December 8, 1997 due to an action other than those described in paragraph (b)(3) of this section must comply with all applicable requirements immediately (*i.e.*, must have control devices installed and

operating on the date the facility or unit becomes subject to this subpart; the 30-month implementation schedule does not apply).

[62 FR 64662, Dec. 8, 1997]

§265.1061 Alternative standards for valves in gas/vapor service or in light liquid service: percentage of valves allowed to leak.

(a) An owner or operator subject to the requirements of §265.1057 may elect to have all valves within a hazardous waste management unit comply with an alternative standard which allows no greater than 2 percent of the valves to leak.

(b) The following requirements shall be met if an owner or operator decides to comply with the alternative standard of allowing 2 percent of valves to leak:

(1) A performance test as specified in paragraph (c) of this section shall be conducted initially upon designation, annually, and at other times requested by the Regional Administrator.

(2) If a valve leak is detected, it shall be repaired in accordance with §265.1057 (d) and (e).

(c) Performance tests shall be conducted in the following manner:

(1) All valves subject to the requirements in §265.1057 within the hazardous waste management unit shall be monitored within 1 week by the methods specified in §265.1063(b).

(2) If an instrument reading of 10,000 ppm or greater is measured, a leak is detected.

(3) The leak percentage shall be determined by dividing the number of valves subject to the requirements in §265.1057 for which leaks are detected by the total number of valves subject to the requirements in §265.1057 within the hazardous waste management unit.

[55 FR 25512, June 21, 1990, as amended at 71 FR 16912, Apr. 4, 2006]

§265.1062 Alternative standards for valves in gas/vapor service or in light liquid service: skip period leak detection and repair.

(a) An owner or operator subject to the requirements of §265.1057 may elect for all valves within a hazardous waste management unit to comply with one of the alternative work practices specified in paragraphs (b)(2) and (3) of this section.

(b)(1) An owner or operator shall comply with the requirements for valves, as described in §265.1057, except as described in paragraphs (b)(2) and (b)(3) of this section.

(2) After two consecutive quarterly leak detection periods with the percentage of valves leaking equal to or less than 2 percent, an owner or operator may begin to skip one of the quarterly leak detection periods (*i.e.*, monitor for leaks once every six months) for the valves subject to the requirements in §265.1057 of this subpart.

(3) After five consecutive quarterly leak detection periods with the percentage of valves leaking equal to or less than 2 percent, an owner or operator may begin to skip three of the quarterly leak detection periods (*i.e.*, monitor for leaks once every year) for the valves subject to the requirements in §265.1057 of this subpart.

(4) If the percentage of valves leaking is greater than 2 percent, the owner or operators shall monitor monthly in compliance with the requirements in §265.1057, but may again elect to use this section after meeting the requirements of §265.1057(c)(1).

[55 FR 25512, June 21, 1990, as amended at 62 FR 64662, Dec. 8, 1997; 71 FR 16912, Apr. 4, 2006]

§265.1063 Test methods and procedures.

(a) Each owner or operator subject to the provisions of this subpart shall comply with the test methods and procedures requirements provided in this section.

(b) Leak detection monitoring, as required in §§265.1052 through 265.1062, shall comply with the following requirements:

(1) Monitoring shall comply with Reference Method 21 in 40 CFR part 60.

(2) The detection instrument shall meet the performance criteria of Reference Method 21.

(3) The instrument shall be calibrated before use on each day of its use by the procedures specified in Reference Method 21.

(4) Calibration gases shall be:

(i) Zero air (less than 10 ppm of hydrocarbon in air).

(ii) A mixture of methane or n-hexane and air at a concentration of approximately, but less than, 10,000 ppm methane or n-hexane.

(5) The instrument probe shall be traversed around all potential leak interfaces as close to the interface as possible as described in Reference Method 21.

(c) When equipment is tested for compliance with no detectable emissions, as required in §§265.1052(e), 265.1053(i), 265.1054, and 265.1057(f), the test shall comply with the following requirements:

(1) The requirements of paragraphs (b)(1) through (4) of this section shall apply.

(2) The background level shall be determined, as set forth in Reference Method 21.

(3) The instrument probe shall be traversed around all potential leak interfaces as close to the interface as possible as described in Reference Method 21.

(4) The arithmetic difference between the maximum concentration indicated by the instrument and the background level is compared with 500 ppm for determining compliance.

(d) In accordance with the waste analysis plan required by §265.13(b), an owner or operator of a facility must determine, for each piece of equipment, whether the equipment contains or contacts a hazardous waste with organic concentration that equals or exceeds 10 percent by weight using the following:

(1) Methods described in ASTM Methods D 2267-88, E 169-87, E 168-88, E 260-85 (incorporated by reference under §260.11);

(2) Method 9060A (incorporated by reference under §260.11 of this chapter) of "Test Methods for Evaluating Solid Waste," EPA Publication SW–846 or analyzed for its individual organic constituents; or

(3) Application of the knowledge of the nature of the hazardous waste stream or the process by which it was produced. Documentation of a waste determination by knowledge is required. Examples of documentation that shall be used to support a determination under this provision include production process information documenting that no organic compounds are used, information that the waste is generated by a process that is identical to a process at the same or another facility that has previously been demonstrated by direct measurement to have a total organic content less than 10 percent, or prior speciation analysis results on the same waste stream where it can also be documented that no process changes have occurred since that analysis that could affect the waste total organic concentration.

(e) If an owner or operator determines that a piece of equipment contains or contacts a hazardous waste with organic concentrations at least 10 percent by weight, the determination can be revised only after following the procedures in paragraph (d)(1) or (d)(2) of this section.

(f) When an owner or operator and the Regional Administrator do not agree on whether a piece of equipment contains or contacts a hazardous waste with organic concentrations at least 10 percent by weight, the procedures in paragraph (d)(1) or (d)(2) of this section can be used to resolve the dispute.

(g) Samples used in determining the percent organic content shall be representative of the highest total organic content hazardous waste that is expected to be contained in or contact the equipment.

(h) To determine if pumps or valves are in light liquid service, the vapor pressures of constituents may be obtained from standard reference texts or may be determined by ASTM D-2879-86 (incorporated by reference under §260.11).

(i) Performance tests to determine if a control device achieves 95 weight percent organic emission reduction shall comply with the procedures of §265.1034 (c)(1) through (c)(4).

[55 FR 25512, June 21, 1990, as amended at 62 FR 32463, June 13, 1997; 70 FR 34586, June 14, 2005; 71 FR 40276, July 14, 2006]

§265.1064 Recordkeeping requirements.

📖 15.2.2.3

(a)(1) Each owner or operator subject to the provisions of this subpart shall comply with the recordkeeping requirements of this section.

(2) An owner or operator of more than one hazardous waste management unit subject to the provisions of this subpart may comply with the recordkeeping requirements for these hazardous waste management units in one recordkeeping system if the system identifies each record by each hazardous waste management unit.

(b) Owners and operators must record the following information in the facility operating record:

(1) For each piece of equipment to which subpart BB of part 265 applies:

(i) Equipment identification number and hazardous waste management unit identification.

(ii) Approximate locations within the facility (*e.g.*, identify the hazardous waste management unit on a facility plot plan).

(iii) Type of equipment (*e.g.*, a pump or pipeline valve).

(iv) Percent-by-weight total organics in the hazardous waste stream at the equipment.

(v) Hazardous waste state at the equipment (*e.g.*, gas/vapor or liquid).

(vi) Method of compliance with the standard (*e.g.*, "monthly leak detection and repair" or "equipped with dual mechanical seals").

(2) For facilities that comply with the provisions of §265.1033(a)(2), an implementation schedule as specified in §265.1033(a)(2).

(3) Where an owner or operator chooses to use test data to demonstrate the organic removal efficiency or total organic compound concentration achieved by the control device, a performance test plan as specified in §265.1035(b)(3).

(4) Documentation of compliance with §265.1060, including the detailed design documentation or performance test results specified in §265.1035(b)(4).

(c) When each leak is detected as specified in §§265.1052, 265.1053, 265.1057, and 265.1058, the following requirements apply:

(1) A weatherproof and readily visible identification, marked with the equipment identification number, the date evidence of a potential leak was found in accordance with §265.1058(a), and the date the leak was detected, shall be attached to the leaking equipment.

(2) The identification on equipment, except on a valve, may be removed after it has been repaired.

(3) The identification on a valve may be removed after it has been monitored for 2 successive months as specified in §265.1057(c) and no leak has been detected during those 2 months.

(d) When each leak is detected as specified in §§265.1052, 265.1053, 265.1057, and 265.1058, the following information shall be recorded in an inspection log and shall be kept in the facility operating record:

(1) The instrument and operator identification numbers and the equipment identification number.

(2) The date evidence of a potential leak was found in accordance with §265.1058(a).

(3) The date the leak was detected and the dates of each attempt to repair the leak.

(4) Repair methods applied in each attempt to repair the leak.

(5) "Above 10,000" if the maximum instrument reading measured by the methods specified in §265.1063(b) after each repair attempt is equal to or greater than 10,000 ppm.

(6) "Repair delayed" and the reason for the delay if a leak is not repaired within 15 calendar days after discovery of the leak.

(7) Documentation supporting the delay of repair of a valve in compliance with §265.1059(c).

(8) The signature of the owner or operator (or designate) whose decision it was that repair could not be effected without a hazardous waste management unit shutdown.

(9) The expected date of successful repair of the leak if a leak is not repaired within 15 calendar days.

(10) The date of successful repair of the leak.

(e) Design documentation and monitoring, operating, and inspection information for each closed-vent system and control device required to comply with the provisions of §265.1060 shall be recorded and kept up-to-date in the facility operating record as specified in §265.1035(c). Design documentation is specified in §265.1035 (c)(1) and (c)(2) and monitoring, operating, and inspection information in §265.1035 (c)(3)–(c)(8).

(f) For a control device other than a thermal vapor incinerator, catalytic vapor incinerator, flare, boiler, process heater, condenser, or carbon adsorption system, monitoring and inspection information indicating proper operation and maintenance of the control device must be recorded in the facility operating record.

(g) The following information pertaining to all equipment subject to the requirements in §§265.1052 through 265.1060 shall be recorded in a log that is kept in the facility operating record:

(1) A list of identification numbers for equipment (except welded fittings) subject to the requirements of this subpart.

(2)(i) A list of identification numbers for equipment that the owner or operator elects to designate for no detectable emissions, as indicated by an instrument reading of less than 500 ppm above background, under the provisions of §§265.1052(e), 265.1053(i), and 265.1057(f).

(ii) The designation of this equipment as subject to the requirements of §§265.1052(e), 265.1053(i), or 265.1057(f) shall be signed by the owner or operator.

(3) A list of equipment identification numbers for pressure relief devices required to comply with §265.1054(a).

(4)(i) The dates of each compliance test required in §§265.1052(e), 265.1053(i), 265.1054, and 265.1057(f).

(ii) The background level measured during each compliance test.

(iii) The maximum instrument reading measured at the equipment during each compliance test.

(5) A list of identification numbers for equipment in vacuum service.

(6) Identification, either by list or location (area or group) of equipment that contains or contacts hazardous waste with an organic concentration of at least 10 percent by weight for less than 300 hours per calendar year.

(h) The following information pertaining to all valves subject to the requirements of §265.1057 (g) and (h) shall be recorded in a log that is kept in the facility operating record:

(1) A list of identification numbers for valves that are designated as unsafe to monitor, an explanation for each valve stating why the valve is unsafe to monitor, and the plan for monitoring each valve.

(2) A list of identification numbers for valves that are designated as difficult to monitor, an explanation for each valve stating why the valve is difficult to monitor, and the planned schedule for monitoring each valve.

(i) The following information shall be recorded in the facility operating record for valves complying with §265.1062:

(1) A schedule of monitoring.

(2) The percent of valves found leaking during each monitoring period.

(j) The following information shall be recorded in a log that is kept in the facility operating record:

(1) Criteria required in §§265.1052 (d)(5)(ii) and 265.1053(e)(2) and an explanation of the criteria.

(2) Any changes to these criteria and the reasons for the changes.

(k) The following information shall be recorded in a log that is kept in the facility operating record for use in determining exemptions as provided in the applicability section of this subpart and other specific subparts:

(1) An analysis determining the design capacity of the hazardous waste management unit.

(2) A statement listing the hazardous waste influent to and effluent from each hazardous waste management unit subject to the requirements in §§265.1052 through 265.1060 and an analysis determining whether these hazardous wastes are heavy liquids.

(3) An up-to-date analysis and the supporting information and data used to determine whether or not equipment is subject to the requirements in §§265.1052 through 265.1060. The record shall include supporting documentation as required by §265.1063(d)(3) when application of the knowledge of the nature of the hazardous waste stream or the process by which it was produced is used. If the owner or operator takes any action (*e.g.*, changing the process that produced the waste) that could result in an increase in the total organic content of the waste contained in or contacted by equipment determined not to be subject to the requirements in §§265.1052 through 265.1060, then a new determination is required.

(l) Records of the equipment leak information required by paragraph (d) of this section and the operating information required by paragraph (e) of this section need be kept only 3 years.

(m) The owner or operator of any facility with equipment that is subject to this subpart and to leak detection, monitoring, and repair requirements under regulations at 40 CFR part 60, part 61, or part 63 may elect to determine compliance with this subpart either by documentation pursuant to §265.1064 of this subpart, or by documentation of compliance with the regulations at 40 CFR part 60, part 61, or part 63 pursuant to the relevant provisions of the regulations at 40 part 60, part 61, or part 63. The documentation of compliance under regulation at 40 CFR part 60, part 61, or part 63 shall be kept with or made readily available with the facility operating record. 📖 15.2.1.6

[55 FR 25512, June 21, 1990, as amended at 56 FR 19290, Apr. 26, 1991; 61 FR 59971, Nov. 25, 1996; 62 FR 64662, Dec. 8, 1997]

§§265.1065–265.1079 [Reserved]

Subpart CC—Air Emission Standards for Tanks, Surface Impoundments, and Containers

Source: 59 FR 62935, Dec. 6, 1994, unless otherwise noted.

§265.1080 Applicability.

📖 15.3.1

(a) The requirements of this subpart apply to owners and operators of all facilities that treat, store, or dispose of hazardous waste in tanks, surface impoundments, or containers subject to either subpart I, J, or K of this part except as §265.1 and paragraph (b) of this section provide otherwise. 📖 15.3.1.1–2

(b) The requirements of this subpart do not apply to the following waste management units at the facility:

📖 15.3.1.2.1

(1) A waste management unit that holds hazardous waste placed in the unit before December 6, 1996, and in which no hazardous waste is added to the unit on or after December 6, 1996.

(2) A container that has a design capacity less than or equal to 0.1 m^3.

(3) A tank in which an owner or operator has stopped adding hazardous waste and the owner or operator

has begun implementing or completed closure pursuant to an approved closure plan.

(4) A surface impoundment in which an owner or operator has stopped adding hazardous waste (except to implement an approved closure plan) and the owner or operator has begun implementing or completed closure pursuant to an approved closure plan.

(5) A waste management unit that is used solely for on-site treatment or storage of hazardous waste that is placed in the unit as a result of implementing remedial activities required under the corrective action authorities of RCRA sections 3004(u), 3004(v), or 3008(h); CERCLA authorities; or similar Federal or State authorities.

(6) A waste management unit that is used solely for the management of radioactive mixed waste in accordance with all applicable regulations under the authority of the Atomic Energy Act and the Nuclear Waste Policy Act.

(7) A hazardous waste management unit that the owner or operator certifies is equipped with and operating air emission controls in accordance with the requirements of an applicable Clean Air Act regulation codified under 40 CFR part 60, part 61, or part 63. For the purpose of complying with this paragraph, a tank for which the air emission control includes an enclosure, as opposed to a cover, must be in compliance with the enclosure and control device requirements of §265.1085(i), except as provided in §265.1083(c)(5).

(8) A tank that has a process vent as defined in 40 CFR 264.1031.

(c) For the owner and operator of a facility subject to this subpart who has received a final permit under RCRA section 3005 prior to December 6, 1996, the following requirements apply:

(1) The requirements of 40 CFR part 264, subpart CC shall be incorporated into the permit when the permit is reissued in accordance with the requirements of 40 CFR 124.15 or reviewed in accordance with the requirements of 40 CFR 270.50(d).

(2) Until the date when the permit is reissued in accordance with the requirements of 40 CFR 124.15 or reviewed in accordance with the requirements of 40 CFR 270.50(d), the owner and operator is subject to the requirements of this subpart.

(d) The requirements of this subpart, except for the recordkeeping requirements specified in §265.1090(i) of this subpart, are administratively stayed for a tank or a container used for the management of hazardous waste generated by organic peroxide manufacturing and its associated laboratory operations when the owner or operator of the unit meets all of the following conditions:

15.3.1.2.1

(1) The owner or operator identifies that the tank or container receives hazardous waste generated by an organic peroxide manufacturing process producing more than one functional family of organic peroxides or multiple organic peroxides within one functional family, that one or more of these organic peroxides could potentially undergo self-accelerating thermal decomposition at or below ambient temperatures, and that organic peroxides are the predominant products manufactured by the process. For the purpose of meeting the conditions of this paragraph, "organic peroxide" means an organic compound that contains the bivalent -O-O- structure and which may be considered to be a structural derivative of hydrogen peroxide where one or both of the hydrogen atoms has been replaced by an organic radical.

(2) The owner or operator prepares documentation, in accordance with the requirements of §265.1090(i) of this subpart, explaining why an undue safety hazard would be created if air emission controls specified in §§265.1085 through 265.1088 of this subpart are installed and operated on the tanks and containers used at the facility to manage the hazardous waste generated by the organic peroxide manufacturing process or processes meeting the conditions of paragraph (d)(1) of this section.

(3) The owner or operator notifies the Regional Administrator in writing that hazardous waste generated by an organic peroxide manufacturing process or processes meeting the conditions of paragraph (d)(1) of this section are managed at the facility in tanks or containers meeting the conditions of paragraph (d)(2) of this section. The notification shall state the name and address of the facility, and be signed and dated by an authorized representative of the facility owner or operator.

(e)(1) Except as provided in paragraph (e)(2) of this section, the requirements of this subpart do not apply to the pharmaceutical manufacturing facility, commonly referred to as the Stonewall Plant, located at Route 340 South, Elkton, Virginia, provided that facility is operated in compliance with the requirements contained in a Clean Air Act permit issued pursuant to 40 CFR 52.2454. The requirements of this subpart shall apply to the facility upon termination of the Clean Air Act permit issued pursuant to 40 CFR 52.2454.

(2) Notwithstanding paragraph (e)(1) of this section, any hazardous waste surface impoundment operated at the Stonewall Plant is subject to the standards in §265.1086 and all requirements related to hazardous waste surface impoundments that are referenced in or by §265.1086, including the closed-vent system and control device requirements of §265.1088 and the recordkeeping requirements of §265.1090(c).

(f) This section applies only to the facility commonly referred to as the OSi Specialties Plant, located on State Route 2, Sistersville, West Virginia ("Sistersville Plant").

(1)(i) Provided that the Sistersville Plant is in compliance with the requirements of paragraph (f)(2) of this section, the requirements referenced in paragraph (f)(1)(iii) of this section are temporarily deferred, as specified in paragraph (f)(3) of this section, with respect to the two hazardous waste surface impoundments at the Sistersville Plant. Beginning on the date that paragraph (f)(1)(ii) of this section is first implemented, the temporary deferral of this paragraph shall no longer be effective.

(ii)(A) In the event that a notice of revocation is issued pursuant to paragraph (f)(3)(iv) of this section, the requirements referenced in paragraph (f)(1)(iii) of this section are temporarily deferred, with respect to the two hazardous waste surface impoundments, provided that the Sistersville Plant is in compliance with the requirements of paragraphs (f)(2)(ii), (f)(2)(iii), (f)(2)(iv), (f)(2)(v), (f)(2)(vi) and (g) of this section, except as provided under paragraph (f)(1)(ii)(B) of this section. The temporary deferral of the previous sentence shall be effective beginning on the date the Sistersville Plant receives written notification of revocation, and continuing for a maximum period of 18 months from that date, provided that the Sistersville Plant is in compliance with the requirements of paragraphs (f)(2)(ii), (f)(2)(iii), (f)(2)(iv), (f)(2)(v), (f)(2)(vi) and (g) of this section at all times during that 18-month period. In no event shall the temporary deferral continue to be effective after the MON Compliance Date.

(B) In the event that a notification of revocation is issued pursuant to paragraph (f)(3)(iv) of this section as a result of the permanent removal of the capper unit from methyl capped polyether production service, the requirements referenced in paragraph (f)(1)(iii) of this section are temporarily deferred, with respect to the two hazardous waste surface impoundments, provided that the Sistersville Plant is in compliance with the requirements of paragraphs (f)(2)(vi), and (g) of this section. The temporary deferral of the previous sentence shall be effective beginning on the date the Sistersville Plant receives written notification of revocation, and continuing for a maximum period of 18 months from that date, provided that the Sistersville Plant is in compliance with the requirements of paragraphs (f)(2)(vi) and (g) of this section at all times during that 18-month period. In no event shall the temporary deferral continue to be effective after the MON Compliance Date.

(iii) The standards in §265.1086 of this part, and all requirements referenced in or by §265.1086 that otherwise would apply to the two hazardous waste surface impoundments, including the closed-vent system and control device requirements of §265.1088 of this part.

(2) Notwithstanding the effective period and revocation provisions in paragraph (f)(3) of this section, the temporary deferral provided in paragraph (f)(1)(i) of this section is effective only if the Sistersville Plant meets the requirements of paragraph (f)(2) of this section.

(i) The Sistersville Plant shall install an air pollution control device on the polyether methyl capper unit ("capper unit"), implement a methanol recovery operation, and implement a waste minimization/pollution prevention ("WMPP") project. The installation and implementation of these requirements shall be conducted according to the schedule described in paragraphs (f)(2)(i) and (f)(2)(vi) of this section.

(A) The Sistersville Plant shall complete the initial start-up of a thermal incinerator on the capper unit's process vents from the first stage vacuum pump, from the flash pot and surge tank, and from the water stripper, no later than April 1, 1998.

(B) The Sistersville Plant shall provide to the EPA and the West Virginia Department of Environmental Protection, written notification of the actual date of initial start-up of the thermal incinerator, and commencement of the methanol recovery operation. The Sistersville Plant shall submit this written notification as soon as practicable, but in no event later than 15 days after such events.

(ii) The Sistersville Plant shall install and operate the capper unit process vent thermal incinerator according to the requirements of paragraphs (f)(2)(ii)(A) through (f)(2)(ii)(D) of this section.

(A) Capper unit process vent thermal incinerator.

(*1*) Except as provided under paragraph (f)(2)(ii)(D) of this section, the Sistersville Plant shall operate the process vent thermal incinerator such that the incinerator reduces the total organic compounds ("TOC") from the process vent streams identified in paragraph (f)(2)(i)(A) of this section, by 98 weight-percent, or to a concentration of 20 parts per million by volume, on a dry basis, corrected to 3 percent oxygen, whichever is less stringent.

(*i*) Prior to conducting the initial performance test required under paragraph (f)(2)(ii)(B) of this section, the Sistersville Plant shall operate the thermal incinerator at or above a minimum temperature of 1600 Fahrenheit.

(*ii*) After the initial performance test required under paragraph (f)(2)(ii)(B) of this section, the Sistersville Plant shall operate the thermal incinerator at or above the minimum temperature established during that initial performance test.

(*iii*) The Sistersville Plant shall operate the process vent thermal incinerator at all times that the capper unit is being operated to manufacture product.

(*2*) The Sistersville Plant shall install, calibrate, and maintain all air pollution control and monitoring equipment described in paragraphs (f)(2)(i)(A) and (f)(2)(ii)(B)(*3*) of this section, according to the manufacturer's specifications, or other written procedures that provide adequate assurance that the equipment can reasonably be expected to control and monitor accurately, and in a manner consistent with good engineering practices during all periods when emissions are routed to the unit.

(B) The Sistersville Plant shall comply with the requirements of paragraphs (f)(2)(ii)(B)(*1*) through (f)(2)(ii)(B)(*3*) of this section for performance testing and monitoring of the capper unit process vent thermal incinerator.

(*1*) Within 120 days after thermal incinerator initial start-up, the Sistersville Plant shall conduct a performance test to determine the minimum temperature at which compliance with the emission reduction requirement specified in paragraph (f)(4) of this section is achieved. This determination shall be made by measuring TOC minus methane and ethane, according to the procedures specified in paragraph (f)(2)(ii)(B) of this section.

(*2*) The Sistersville Plant shall conduct the initial performance test in accordance with the standards set forth in paragraph (f)(4) of this section.

(*3*) Upon initial start-up, the Sistersville Plant shall install, calibrate, maintain and operate, according to manufacturer's specifications and in a manner consistent with good engineering practices, the monitoring equipment described in paragraphs (f)(2)(ii)(B)(*3*)(*i*) through (f)(2)(ii)(B)(*3*)(*iii*) of this section.

(*i*) A temperature monitoring device equipped with a continuous recorder. The temperature monitoring device shall be installed in the firebox or in the duct work immediately downstream of the firebox in a position before any substantial heat exchange is encountered.

(*ii*) A flow indicator that provides a record of vent stream flow to the incinerator at least once every fifteen minutes. The flow indicator shall be installed in the vent stream from the process vent at a point closest to the inlet of the incinerator.

(*iii*) If the closed-vent system includes bypass devices that could be used to divert the gas or vapor stream to the atmosphere before entering the control device, each bypass device shall be equipped with either a bypass flow indicator or a seal or locking device as specified in this paragraph. For the purpose of complying with this paragraph, low leg drains, high point bleeds, analyzer vents, open-ended valves or lines, spring-loaded pressure relief valves, and other fittings used for safety purposes are not considered to be bypass devices. If a bypass flow indicator is used to comply with this paragraph, the bypass flow indicator shall be installed at the inlet to the bypass line used to divert gases and vapors from the closed-vent system to the atmosphere at a point upstream of the control device inlet. If a seal or locking device (*e.g.* car-seal or lock-and-key configuration) is used to comply with this paragraph, the device shall be placed on the mechanism by which the bypass device position is controlled (*e.g.*, valve handle, damper levels) when the bypass device is in the closed position such that the bypass device cannot be opened without breaking the seal or removing the lock. The Sistersville Plant shall visually inspect the seal or locking device at least once every month to verify that the bypass mechanism is maintained in the closed position.

(C) The Sistersville Plant shall keep on-site an up-to-date, readily accessible record of the information described in paragraphs (f)(2)(ii)(C)(*1*) through (f)(2)(ii)(C)(*4*) of this section.

(*1*) Data measured during the initial performance test regarding the firebox temperature of the incinerator and the percent reduction of TOC achieved by the incinerator, and/or such other information required in addition to or in lieu of that information by the WVDEP in its approval of equivalent test methods and procedures.

(*2*) Continuous records of the equipment operating procedures specified to be monitored under paragraph (f)(2)(ii)(B)(*3*) of this section, as well as records of periods of operation during which the firebox temperature falls below the minimum temperature established under paragraph (f)(2)(ii)(A)(*1*) of this section.

(*3*) Records of all periods during which the vent stream has no flow rate to the extent that the capper unit is being operated during such period.

(*4*) Records of all periods during which there is flow through a bypass device.

(D) The Sistersville Plant shall comply with the start-up, shutdown, maintenance and malfunction requirements contained in paragraphs (f)(2)(ii)(D)(*1*) through (f)(2)(ii)(D)(*6*) of this section, with respect to the capper unit process vent incinerator.

(*1*) The Sistersville Plant shall develop and implement a Start-up, Shutdown and Malfunction Plan as required by the provisions set forth in paragraph (f)(2)(ii)(D) of this section. The plan shall describe, in detail, procedures for operating and maintaining the thermal incinerator during periods of start-up, shutdown and malfunction, and a program of corrective action for malfunctions of the thermal incinerator.

(*2*) The plan shall include a detailed description of the actions the Sistersville Plant will take to perform the functions described in paragraphs (f)(2)(ii)(D)(*2*)(*i*) through (f)(2)(ii)(D)(*2*)(*iii*) of this section.

(*i*) Ensure that the thermal incinerator is operated in a manner consistent with good air pollution control practices.

(*ii*) Ensure that the Sistersville Plant is prepared to correct malfunctions as soon as practicable after their occurrence in order to minimize excess emissions.

(*iii*) Reduce the reporting requirements associated with periods of start-up, shutdown and malfunction.

(*3*) During periods of start-up, shutdown and malfunction, the Sistersville Plant shall maintain the process unit and the associated thermal incinerator in accordance with the procedures set forth in the plan.

(*4*) The plan shall contain record keeping requirements relating to periods of start-up, shutdown or malfunction, actions taken during such periods in conformance with the plan, and any failures to act in conformance with the plan during such periods.

(*5*) During periods of maintenance or malfunction of the thermal incinerator, the Sistersville Plant may continue to operate the capper unit, provided that operation of the capper unit without the thermal incinerator shall be limited to no more than 240 hours each calendar year.

(*6*) For the purposes of paragraph (f)(2)(iii)(D) of this section, the Sistersville Plant may use its operating procedures manual, or a plan developed for other reasons, provided that plan meets the requirements of paragraph (f)(2)(iii)(D) of this section for the start-up, shutdown and malfunction plan.

(iii) The Sistersville Plant shall operate the closed-vent system in accordance with the requirements of paragraphs (f)(2)(iii)(A) through (f)(2)(iii)(D) of this section.

(A) Closed-vent system.

(*1*) At all times when the process vent thermal incinerator is operating, the Sistersville Plant shall route the vent streams identified in paragraph (f)(2)(i) of this section from the capper unit to the thermal incinerator through a closed-vent system.

(*2*) The closed-vent system will be designed for and operated with no detectable emissions, as defined in paragraph (f)(6) of this section.

(B) The Sistersville Plant will comply with the performance standards set forth in paragraph (f)(2)(iii)(A)(*1*) of this section on and after the date on which the initial performance test referenced in paragraph (f)(2)(ii)(B) of this section is completed, but no later than sixty (60) days after the initial start-up date.

(C) The Sistersville Plant shall comply with the monitoring requirements of paragraphs (f)(2)(iii)(C)(*1*) through (f)(2)(iii)(C)(*3*) of this section, with respect to the closed-vent system.

(*1*) At the time of the performance test described in paragraph (f)(2)(ii)(B) of this section, the Sistersville Plant shall inspect the closed-vent system as specified in paragraph (f)(5) of this section.

(*2*) At the time of the performance test described in paragraph (f)(2)(ii)(B) of this section, and annually thereafter, the Sistersville Plant shall inspect the closed-vent system for visible, audible, or olfactory indications of leaks.

(*3*) If at any time a defect or leak is detected in the closed-vent system, the Sistersville Plant shall repair the defect or leak in accordance with the requirements of paragraphs (f)(2)(iii)(C)(*3*)(*i*) and (f)(2)(iii)(C)(*3*)(*ii*) of this section.

(*i*) The Sistersville Plant shall make first efforts at repair of the defect no later than five (5) calendar days after detection, and repair shall be completed as soon as possible but no later than forty-five (45) calendar days after detection.

(*ii*) The Sistersville Plant shall maintain a record of the defect repair in accordance with the requirements specified in paragraph (f)(2)(iii)(D) of this section.

(D) The Sistersville Plant shall keep on-site up-to-date, readily accessible records of the inspections and repairs required to be performed by paragraph (f)(2)(iii) of this section.

(iv) The Sistersville Plant shall operate the methanol recovery operation in accordance with paragraphs (f)(2)(iv)(A) through (f)(2)(iv)(C) of this section.

(A) The Sistersville Plant shall operate the condenser associated with the methanol recovery operation at all times during which the capper unit is being operated to manufacture product.

(B) The Sistersville Plant shall comply with the monitoring requirements described in paragraphs (f)(2)(B)(*1*) through (f)(2)(B)(*3*) of this section, with respect to the methanol recovery operation.

(*1*) The Sistersville Plant shall perform measurements necessary to determine the information described in paragraphs (f)(2)(iv)(B)(*1*)(*i*) and (f)(2)(iv)(B)(*1*)(*ii*) of this section to demonstrate the percentage recovery by weight of the methanol contained in the influent gas stream to the condenser.

(*i*) Information as is necessary to calculate the annual amount of methanol generated by operating the capper unit.

(*ii*) The annual amount of methanol recovered by the condenser associated with the methanol recovery operation.

(*2*) The Sistersville Plant shall install, calibrate, maintain and operate according to manufacturer specifications, a temperature monitoring device with a continuous recorder for the condenser associated with the methanol recovery operation, as an indicator that the condenser is operating.

(*3*) The Sistersville Plant shall record the dates and times during which the capper unit and the condenser are operating.

(C) The Sistersville Plant shall keep on-site up-to-date, readily-accessible records of the parameters specified to be monitored under paragraph (f)(2)(iv)(B) of this section.

(v) The Sistersville Plant shall comply with the requirements of paragraphs (f)(2)(v)(A) through (f)(2)(v)(C) of this section for the disposition of methanol collected by the methanol recovery operation.

(A) On an annual basis, the Sistersville Plant shall ensure that a minimum of 95% by weight of the methanol collected by the methanol recovery operation (also referred to as the "collected methanol") is utilized for reuse, recovery, or thermal recovery/treatment. The Sistersville Plant may use the methanol on-site, or may transfer or sell the methanol for reuse, recovery, or thermal recovery/treatment at other facilities.

(*1*) *Reuse.* To the extent reuse of all of the collected methanol destined for reuse, recovery, or thermal recovery is not economically feasible, the Sistersville Plant shall ensure the residual portion is sent for recovery, as defined in paragraph (f)(6) of this section, except as provided in paragraph (f)(2)(v)(A)(*2*) of this section.

(*2*) *Recovery.* To the extent that reuse or recovery of all the collected methanol destined for reuse, recovery, or thermal recovery is not economically feasible, the Sistersville Plant shall ensure that the residual portion is sent for thermal recovery/treatment, as defined in paragraph (f)(6) of this section.

(*3*) The Sistersville Plant shall ensure that, on an annual basis, no more than 5% of the methanol collected by the methanol recovery operation is subject to bio-treatment.

(*4*) In the event the Sistersville Plant receives written notification of revocation pursuant to paragraph (f)(3)(iv) of this section, the percent limitations set forth under paragraph (f)(2)(v)(A) of this section shall no longer be applicable, beginning on the date of receipt of written notification of revocation.

(B) The Sistersville Plant shall perform such measurements as are necessary to determine the pounds of collected methanol directed to reuse, recovery, thermal recovery/treatment and bio-treatment, respectively, on a monthly basis.

(C) The Sistersville Plant shall keep on-site up-to-date, readily accessible records of the amounts of collected methanol directed to reuse, recovery, thermal recovery/treatment and bio-treatment necessary for the measurements required under paragraph (f)(2)(iv)(B) of this section.

(vi) The Sistersville Plant shall perform a WMPP project in accordance with the requirements and schedules set forth in paragraphs (f)(2)(vi)(A) through (f)(2)(vi)(C) of this section.

(A) In performing the WMPP Project, the Sistersville Plant shall use a Study Team and an Advisory Committee as described in paragraphs (f)(2)(vi)(A)(*1*) through (f)(2)(vi)(A)(*6*) of this section.

(*1*) At a minimum, the multi-functional Study Team shall consist of Sistersville Plant personnel from appropriate plant departments (including both management and employees) and an independent contractor. The Sistersville Plant shall select a contractor that has experience and training in WMPP in the chemical manufacturing industry.

(*2*) The Sistersville Plant shall direct the Study Team such that the team performs the functions described in paragraphs (f)(2)(vi)(A)(*2*)(*i*) through (f)(2)(vi)(A)(*2*)(*v*) of this section.

(*i*) Review Sistersville Plant operations and waste streams.

(*ii*) Review prior WMPP efforts at the Sistersville Plant.

(*iii*) Develop criteria for the selection of waste streams to be evaluated for the WMPP Project.

(*iv*) Identify and prioritize the waste streams to be evaluated during the study phase of the WMPP Project, based on the criteria described in paragraph (f)(2)(vi)(A)(*2*)(*iii*) of this section.

(*v*) Perform the WMPP Study as required by paragraphs (f)(2)(vi)(A)(*3*) through (f)(2)(vi)(A)(*5*), paragraph (f)(2)(vi)(B), and paragraph (f)(2)(vi)(C) of this section.

(*3*)(*i*) The Sistersville Plant shall establish an Advisory Committee consisting of a representative from EPA, a representative from WVDEP, the Sistersville Plant Manager, the Sistersville Plant Director of Safety, Health and Environmental Affairs, and a stakeholder representative(s).

(*ii*) The Sistersville Plant shall select the stakeholder representative(s) by mutual agreement of EPA, WVDEP and the Sistersville Plant no later than 20 days after receiving from EPA and WVDEP the names of their respective committee members.

(*4*) The Sistersville Plant shall convene a meeting of the Advisory Committee no later than thirty days after selection of the stakeholder representatives, and shall convene meetings periodically thereafter as necessary for the Advisory Committee to perform its assigned functions. The Sistersville Plant shall direct the Advisory Committee to perform the functions described in paragraphs (f)(2)(vi)(A)(*4*)(*i*) through (f)(2)(vi)(A)(*4*)(*iii*) of this section.

(*i*) Review and comment upon the Study Team's criteria for selection of waste streams, and the Study Team's identification and prioritization of the waste streams to be evaluated during the WMPP Project.

(*ii*) Review and comment upon the Study Team progress reports and the draft WMPP Study Report.

(*iii*) Periodically review the effectiveness of WMPP opportunities implemented as part of the WMPP Project, and, where appropriate, WMPP opportunities previously determined to be infeasible by the Sistersville Plant but which had potential for feasibility in the future.

(*5*) Beginning on January 15, 1998, and every ninety (90) days thereafter until submission of the final WMPP Study Report required by paragraph (f)(2)(vi)(C) of this section, the Sistersville Plant shall direct the Study Team to submit a progress report to the Advisory Committee detailing its efforts during the prior ninety (90) day period.

(B) The Sistersville Plant shall ensure that the WMPP Study and the WMPP Study Report meet the requirements of paragraphs (f)(2)(vi)(B)(*1*) through (f)(2)(vi)(B)(*3*) of this section.

(*1*) The WMPP Study shall consist of a technical, economic, and regulatory assessment of opportunities for source reduction and for environmentally sound recycling for waste streams identified by the Study Team.

(*2*) The WMPP Study shall evaluate the source, nature, and volume of the waste streams; describe all the WMPP opportunities identified by the Study Team; provide a feasibility screening to evaluate the technical and economical feasibility of each of the WMPP opportunities; identify any cross-media impacts or any anticipated transfers of risk associated with each feasible WMPP opportunity; and identify the projected economic savings and projected quantitative waste reduction estimates for each WMPP opportunity identified.

(*3*) No later than October 19, 1998, the Sistersville Plant shall prepare and submit to the members of the Advisory Committee a draft WMPP Study Report which, at a minimum, includes the results of the WMPP Study, identifies WMPP opportunities the Sistersville Plant determines to be feasible, discusses the basis for excluding other opportunities as not feasible, and makes recommendations as to whether the WMPP Study should be continued. The members of the Advisory Committee shall provide any comments to the Sistersville Plant within thirty (30) days of receiving the WMPP Study Report.

(C) Within thirty (30) days after receipt of comments from the members of the Advisory Committee, the Sistersville Plant shall submit to EPA and WVDEP a final WMPP Study Report which identifies those WMPP opportunities the Sistersville Plant determines to be feasible and includes an implementation schedule for each such WMPP opportunity. The Sistersville Plant shall make reasonable efforts to implement all feasible WMPP opportunities in accordance with the priorities identified in the implementation schedule.

(*1*) For purposes of this section, a WMPP opportunity is feasible if the Sistersville Plant considers it to be technically feasible (taking into account engineering and regulatory factors, product line specifications and customer needs) and economically practical (taking into account the full environmental costs and benefits associated with the WMPP opportunity and the company's internal requirements for approval of capital projects). For purposes of the WMPP Project, the Sistersville Plant shall use "An Introduction to Environmental Accounting as a Business Management Tool," (EPA 742/R-95/001) as one tool to identify the full environmental costs and benefits of each WMPP opportunity.

(*2*) In implementing each WMPP opportunity, the Sistersville Plant shall, after consulting with the other members of the Advisory Committee, develop appropriate protocols and methods for determining the information required by paragraphs (f)(2)(vi)(C)(*2*)(*i*) through (f)(2)(vi)(C)(*2*)(*iii*) of this section.

(*i*) The overall volume of wastes reduced.

(*ii*) The quantities of each constituent identified in paragraph (f)(8) of this section reduced in the wastes.

(*iii*) The economic benefits achieved.

(*3*) No requirements of paragraph (f)(2)(vi) of this section are intended to prevent or restrict the Sistersville Plant from evaluating and implementing any WMPP opportunities at the Sistersville Plant in the normal course of its operations or from implementing, prior to the completion of the WMPP Study, any WMPP opportunities identified by the Study Team.

(vii) The Sistersville Plant shall maintain on-site each record required by paragraph (f)(2) of this section, through the MON Compliance Date.

(viii) The Sistersville Plant shall comply with the reporting requirements of paragraphs (f)(2)(viii)(A) through (f)(2)(viii)(G) of this section.

(A) At least sixty days prior to conducting the initial performance test of the thermal incinerator, the Sistersville Plant shall submit to EPA and WVDEP copies of a notification of performance test, as described in 40 CFR 63.7(b). Following the initial performance test of the thermal incinerator, the Sistersville Plant shall submit to EPA and WVDEP copies of the performance test results that include the information relevant to initial performance tests of thermal incinerators contained in 40 CFR 63.7(g)(1), 40 CFR 63.117(a)(4)(i), and 40 CFR 63.117(a)(4)(ii).

(B) Beginning in 1999, on January 31 of each year, the Sistersville Plant shall submit a semiannual written report to the EPA and WVDEP, with respect to the preceding six month period ending on December 31, which contains the information described in paragraphs (f)(2)(viii)(B)(*1*) through (f)(2)(viii)(B)(*10*) of this section.

(*1*) Instances of operating below the minimum operating temperature established for the thermal incinerator under paragraph (f)(2)(ii)(A)(*1*) of this section which were not corrected within 24 hours of onset.

(*2*) Any periods during which the capper unit was being operated to manufacture product while the flow indicator for the vent streams to the thermal incinerator showed no flow.

(*3*) Any periods during which the capper unit was being operated to manufacture product while the flow indicator for any bypass device on the closed vent system to the thermal incinerator showed flow.

(*4*) Information required to be reported during that six month period under the preconstruction permit issued under the state permitting program approved under subpart XX of 40 CFR Part 52—Approval and Promulgation of Implementation Plans for West Virginia.

(*5*) Any periods during which the capper unit was being operated to manufacture product while the condenser associated with the methanol recovery operation was not in operation.

(*6*) The amount (in pounds and by month) of methanol collected by the methanol recovery operation during the six month period.

(*7*) The amount (in pounds and by month) of collected methanol utilized for reuse, recovery, thermal recovery/treatment, or bio-treatment, respectively, during the six month period.

(*8*) The calculated amount (in pounds and by month) of methanol generated by operating the capper unit.

(*9*) The status of the WMPP Project, including the status of developing the WMPP Study Report.

(*10*) Beginning in the year after the Sistersville Plant submits the final WMPP Study Report required by paragraph (f)(2)(vi)(C) of this section, and continuing in each subsequent Semiannual Report required by paragraph (f)(2)(viii)(B) of this section, the Sistersville Plant shall report on the progress of the implementation of feasible WMPP opportunities identified in the WMPP Study Report. The Semiannual Report required by paragraph (f)(2)(viii)(B) of this section shall identify any cross-media impacts or impacts to worker safety or community health issues that have occurred as a result of implementation of the feasible WMPP opportunities.

(C) Beginning in 1999, on July 31 of each year, the Sistersville Plant shall provide an Annual Project Report to the EPA and WVDEP Project XL contacts containing the information required by paragraphs (f)(2)(viii)(C)(*1*) through (f)(2)(viii)(C)(*8*) of this section.

(*1*) The categories of information required to be submitted under paragraphs (f)(2)(viii)(B)(*1*) through (f)(2)(viii)(B)(*8*) of this section, for the preceding 12 month period ending on June 30.

(*2*) An updated Emissions Analysis for January through December of the preceding calendar year. The Sistersville Plant shall submit the updated Emissions Analysis in a form substantially equivalent to the previous Emissions Analysis prepared by the Sistersville Plant to support Project XL. The Emissions Analysis shall include a comparison of the volatile organic emissions associated with the capper unit process vents and the wastewater treatment system (using the EPA Water 8 model or other model agreed to by the Sistersville Plant, EPA and WVDEP) under Project XL with the expected emissions from those sources absent Project XL during that period.

(*3*) A discussion of the Sistersville Plant's performance in meeting the requirements of this section, specifically identifying any areas in which the Sistersville Plant either exceeded or failed to achieve any such standard.

(*4*) A description of any unanticipated problems in implementing the XL Project and any steps taken to resolve them.

(*5*) A WMPP Implementation Report that contains the information contained in paragraphs (f)(2)(viii)(C)(*5*)(*i*) through (viii)(C)(*5*)(*vi*) of this section.

(*i*) A summary of the WMPP opportunities selected for implementation.

(*ii*) A description of the WMPP opportunities initiated and/or completed.

(*iii*) Reductions in volume of waste generated and amounts of each constituent reduced in wastes including any constituents identified in paragraph (f)(8) of this section.

(*iv*) An economic benefits analysis.

(*v*) A summary of the results of the Advisory Committee's review of implemented WMPP opportunities.

(*vi*) A reevaluation of WMPP opportunities previously determined to be infeasible by the Sistersville Plant but which had potential for future feasibility.

(*6*) An assessment of the nature of, and the successes or problems associated with, the Sistersville Plant's interaction with the federal and state agencies under the Project.

(*7*) An update on stakeholder involvement efforts.

(*8*) An evaluation of the Project as implemented against the Project XL Criteria and the baseline scenario.

(D) The Sistersville Plant shall submit to the EPA and WVDEP Project XL contacts a written Final Project Report covering the period during which the temporary deferral was effective, as described in paragraph (f)(3) of this section.

(*1*) The Final Project Report shall contain the information required to be submitted for the Semiannual Report required under paragraph (f)(2)(viii)(B) of this section, and the Annual Project Report required under paragraph (f)(2)(viii)(C) of this section.

(*2*) The Sistersville Plant shall submit the Final Project Report to EPA and WVDEP no later than 180 days after the temporary deferral of paragraph (f)(1) of this section is revoked, or 180 days after the MON Compliance Date, whichever occurs first.

(E)(*1*) The Sistersville Plant shall retain on-site a complete copy of each of the report documents to be submitted to EPA and WVDEP in accordance with requirements under paragraph (f)(2) of this section. The Sistersville Plant shall retain this record until 180 days after the MON Compliance Date. The Sistersville Plant shall provide to stakeholders and interested parties a written notice of availability (to be mailed to all persons on the Project mailing list and to be provided to at least one local newspaper of general circulation) of each such document, and provide a copy of each document to any such person upon request, subject to the provisions of 40 CFR part 2.

(*2*) Any reports or other information submitted to EPA or WVDEP may be released to the public pursuant to the Federal Freedom of Information Act (42 U.S.C. 552 *et seq.*), subject to the provisions of 40 CFR part 2.

(F) The Sistersville Plant shall make all supporting monitoring results and records required under paragraph (f)(2) of this section available to EPA and WVDEP within a reasonable amount of time after receipt of a written request from those Agencies, subject to the provisions of 40 CFR Part 2.

(G) Each report submitted by the Sistersville Plant under the requirements of paragraph (f)(2) of this section shall be certified by a Responsible Corporate Officer, as defined in 40 CFR 270.11(a)(1).

(H) For each report submitted in accordance with paragraph (f)(2) of this section, the Sistersville Plant shall send one copy each to the addresses in paragraphs (f)(2)(viii)(H)(*1*) through (H)(*3*) of this section.

(*1*) U.S. EPA Region 3, 1650 Arch Street, Philadelphia, PA 19103-2029, Attention Tad Radzinski, Mail Code 3WC11.

(*2*) U.S. EPA, 1200 Pennsylvania Ave., NW, Washington, DC 20460, Attention L. Nancy Birnbaum, Mail Code 1812.

(*3*) West Virginia Division of Environmental Protection, Office of Air Quality, 1558 Washington Street East, Charleston, WV 25311-2599, Attention John H. Johnston.

(3) Effective period and revocation of temporary deferral.

(i) The temporary deferral contained in this section is effective from April 1, 1998, and shall remain effective until the MON Compliance Date. The temporary deferral contained in this section may be revoked prior to the MON Compliance Date, as described in paragraph (f)(3)(iv) of this section.

(ii) On the MON Compliance Date, the temporary deferral contained in this section will no longer be effective.

(iii) The Sistersville Plant shall come into compliance with those requirements deferred by this section no later than the MON Compliance Date. No later than 18 months prior to the MON Compliance Date, the Sistersville Plant shall submit to EPA an implementation schedule that meets the requirements of paragraph (g)(1)(iii) of this section.

(iv) The temporary deferral contained in this section may be revoked for cause, as determined by EPA, prior to the MON Compliance Date. The Sistersville Plant may request EPA to revoke the temporary deferral contained in this section at any time. The revocation shall be effective on the date that the Sistersville Plant receives written notification of revocation from EPA.

(v) Nothing in this section shall affect the provisions of the MON, as applicable to the Sistersville Plant.

(vi) Nothing in paragraphs (f) or (g) of this section shall affect any regulatory requirements not referenced in paragraph (f)(1)(iii) of this section, as applicable to the Sistersville Plant.

(4) The Sistersville Plant shall conduct the initial performance test required by paragraph (f)(2)(ii)(B) of this section using the procedures in paragraph (f)(4) of this section. The organic concentration and percent reduction shall be measured as TOC minus methane and ethane, according to the procedures specified in paragraph (f)(4) of this section.

(i) Method 1 or 1A of 40 CFR part 60, appendix A, as appropriate, shall be used for selection of the sampling sites.

(A) To determine compliance with the 98 percent reduction of TOC requirement of paragraph (f)(2)(ii)(A)(*1*) of this section, sampling sites shall be located at the inlet of the control device after the final product recovery device, and at the outlet of the control device.

(B) To determine compliance with the 20 parts per million by volume TOC limit in paragraph (f)(2)(ii)(A)(*1*) of this section, the sampling site shall be located at the outlet of the control device.

(ii) The gas volumetric flow rate shall be determined using Method 2, 2A, 2C, or 2D of 40 CFR part 60, appendix A, as appropriate.

(iii) To determine compliance with the 20 parts per million by volume TOC limit in paragraph (f)(2)(ii)(A)(*1*) of this section, the Sistersville Plant shall use Method 18 of 40 CFR part 60, appendix A to measure TOC minus methane and ethane. Alternatively, any other method or data that has been validated according to the applicable procedures in Method 301 of 40 CFR part 63, appendix A, may be used. The following procedures shall be used to calculate parts per million by volume concentration, corrected to 3 percent oxygen:

(A) The minimum sampling time for each run shall be 1 hour in which either an integrated sample or a minimum of four grab samples shall be taken. If grab sampling is used, then the samples shall be taken at approximately equal intervals in time, such as 15 minute intervals during the run.

(B) The concentration of TOC minus methane and ethane (C_{TOC}) shall be calculated as the sum of the concentrations of the individual components, and shall be computed for each run using the following equation:

$$C_{TOC} = \sum_{i=1}^{x} \frac{\left(\sum_{j=1}^{n} C_{ji}\right)}{x}$$

Where:

C_{TOC} = Concentration of TOC (minus methane and ethane), dry basis, parts per million by volume.

C_{ji} = Concentration of sample components j of sample i, dry basis, parts per million by volume.

n = Number of components in the sample.

x = Number of samples in the sample run.

(C) The concentration of TOC shall be corrected to 3 percent oxygen if a combustion device is the control device.

(*1*) The emission rate correction factor or excess air, integrated sampling and analysis procedures of Method 3B of 40 CFR part 60, appendix A shall be used to determine the oxygen concentration ($\%O_{2d}$). The samples shall be taken during the same time that the TOC (minus methane or ethane) samples are taken.

(*2*) The concentration corrected to 3 percent oxygen (C_c) shall be computed using the following equation:

$$C_c = C_m \left(\frac{17.9}{20.9 \quad \%O_{2d}} \right)$$

Where:

C_c = Concentration of TOC corrected to 3 percent oxygen, dry basis, parts per million by volume.

C_m = Concentration of TOC (minus methane and ethane), dry basis, parts per million by volume.

$\%O_{2d}$ = Concentration of oxygen, dry basis, percent by volume.

(iv) To determine compliance with the 98 percent reduction requirement of paragraph (f)(2)(ii)(A)(*1*) of this section, the Sistersville Plant shall use Method 18 of 40 CFR part 60, appendix A; alternatively, any other method or data that has been validated according to the applicable procedures in Method 301 of 40 CFR part 63, appendix A may be used. The following procedures shall be used to calculate percent reduction efficiency:

(A) The minimum sampling time for each run shall be 1 hour in which either an integrated sample or a minimum of four grab samples shall be taken. If grab sampling is used, then the samples shall be taken at approximately equal intervals in time such as 15 minute intervals during the run.

(B) The mass rate of TOC minus methane and ethane (E_i, E_o) shall be computed. All organic compounds (minus methane and ethane) measured by Method 18 of 40 CFR part 60, Appendix A are summed using the following equations:

$$E_i = K_2\left(\sum_{j=1}^{n} C_{ij}M_{ij}\right)Q_i$$

$$E_o = K_2\left(\sum_{j=1}^{n} C_{oj}M_{oj}\right)Q_o$$

Where:

C_{ij}, C_{oj} = Concentration of sample component j of the gas stream at the inlet and outlet of the control device, respectively, dry basis, parts per million by volume.

E_i, E_o = Mass rate of TOC (minus methane and ethane) at the inlet and outlet of the control device, respectively, dry basis, kilogram per hour.

M_{ij}, M_{oj} = Molecular weight of sample component j of the gas stream at the inlet and outlet of the control device, respectively, gram/gram-mole.

Q_i, Q_o = Flow rate of gas stream at the inlet and outlet of the control device, respectively, dry standard cubic meter per minute.

K_2 = Constant, 2.494×10^{-6} (parts per million)$^{-1}$ (gram-mole per standard cubic meter) (kilogram/gram) (minute/hour), where standard temperature (gram-mole per standard cubic meter) is 20° C.

(C) The percent reduction in TOC (minus methane and ethane) shall be calculated as follows:

$$R = \left(\frac{E_iE_o}{E_i}\right)(100)$$

where:

R = Control efficiency of control device, percent.

E_i = Mass rate of TOC (minus methane and ethane) at the inlet to the control device as calculated under paragraph (f)(4)(iv)(B) of this section, kilograms TOC per hour.

E_o = Mass rate of TOC (minus methane and ethane) at the outlet of the control device, as calculated under paragraph (f)(4)(iv)(B) of this section, kilograms TOC per hour.

(5) At the time of the initial performance test of the process vent thermal incinerator required under paragraph (f)(2)(ii)(B) of this section, the Sistersville Plant shall inspect each closed vent system according to the procedures specified in paragraphs (f)(5)(i) through (f)(5)(vi) of this section.

(i) The initial inspections shall be conducted in accordance with Method 21 of 40 CFR part 60, appendix A.

(ii)(A) Except as provided in paragraph (f)(5)(ii)(B) of this section, the detection instrument shall meet the performance criteria of Method 21 of 40 CFR part 60, appendix A, except the instrument response factor criteria in section 3.1.2(a) of Method 21 of 40 CFR part 60, appendix A shall be for the average composition of the process fluid not each individual volatile organic compound in the stream. For process streams that contain nitrogen, air, or other inerts which are not organic hazardous air pollutants or volatile organic compounds, the average stream response factor shall be calculated on an inert-free basis.

(B) If no instrument is available at the plant site that will meet the performance criteria specified in paragraph (f)(5)(ii)(A) of this section, the instrument readings may be adjusted by multiplying by the average response factor of the process fluid, calculated on an inert-free basis as described in paragraph (f)(5)(ii)(A) of this section.

(iii) The detection instrument shall be calibrated before use on each day of its use by the procedures specified in Method 21 of 40 CFR part 60, appendix A.

(iv) Calibration gases shall be as follows:

(A) Zero air (less than 10 parts per million hydrocarbon in air); and

(B) Mixtures of methane in air at a concentration less than 10,000 parts per million. A calibration gas other than methane in air may be used if the instrument does not respond to methane or if the instrument does not meet the performance criteria specified in paragraph (f)(5)(ii)(A) of this section. In such cases, the calibration gas may be a mixture of one or more of the compounds to be measured in air.

(v) The Sistersville Plant may elect to adjust or not adjust instrument readings for background. If the Sistersville Plant elects to not adjust readings for background, all such instrument readings shall be compared directly to the applicable leak definition to determine whether there is a leak. If the Sistersville Plant elects to adjust instrument readings for background, the Sistersville Plant shall measure background concentration using the procedures in 40 CFR 63.180(b) and (c). The Sistersville Plant shall subtract background reading from the maximum concentration indicated by the instrument.

(vi) The arithmetic difference between the maximum concentration indicated by the instrument and the background level shall be compared with 500 parts per million for determining compliance.

(6) Definitions of terms as used in paragraphs (f) and (g) of this section.

(i) Closed vent system is defined as a system that is not open to the atmosphere and that is composed of piping, connections and, if necessary, flow-inducing devices that transport gas or vapor from the capper unit process vent to the thermal incinerator.

(ii) No detectable emissions means an instrument reading of less than 500 parts per million by volume above background as determined by Method 21 in 40 CFR part 60.

(iii) Reuse includes the substitution of collected methanol (without reclamation subsequent to its collection) for virgin methanol as an ingredient (including uses as an intermediate) or as an effective substitute for a commercial product.

(iv) Recovery includes the substitution of collected methanol for virgin methanol as an ingredient (including uses as an intermediate) or as an effective substitute for a commercial product following reclamation of the methanol subsequent to its collection.

(v) Thermal recovery/treatment includes the use of collected methanol in fuels blending or as a feed to any combustion device to the extent permitted by federal and state law.

(vi) Bio-treatment includes the treatment of the collected methanol through introduction into a biological treatment system, including the treatment of the collected methanol as a waste stream in an on-site or off-site wastewater treatment system. Introduction of the collected methanol to the on-site wastewater treatment system will be limited to points downstream of the surface impoundments, and will be consistent with the requirements of federal and state law.

(vii) Start-up shall have the meaning set forth at 40 CFR 63.2.

(viii) Flow indicator means a device which indicates whether gas flow is present in the vent stream, and, if required by the permit for the thermal incinerator, which measures the gas flow in that stream.

(ix) Continuous Recorder means a data recording device that records an instantaneous data value at least once every fifteen minutes.

(x) MON means the National Emission Standards for Hazardous Air Pollutants for the source category Miscellaneous Organic Chemical Production and Processes ("MON"), promulgated under the authority of Section 112 of the Clean Air Act.

(xi) MON Compliance Date means the date 3 years after the effective date of the National Emission Standards for Hazardous Air Pollutants for the source category Miscellaneous Organic Chemical Production and Processes ("MON").

(7) OSi Specialties, Incorporated, a subsidiary of Witco Corporation ("OSi"), may seek to transfer its rights and obligations under this section to a future owner of the Sistersville Plant in accordance with the requirements of paragraphs (f)(7)(i) through (f)(7)(iii) of this section.

(i) OSi will provide to EPA a written notice of any proposed transfer at least forty-five days prior to the effective date of any such transfer. The written notice will identify the proposed transferee.

(ii) The proposed transferee will provide to EPA a written request to assume the rights and obligations under this section at least forty-five days prior to the effective date of any such transfer. The written request will describe the transferee's financial and technical capability to assume the obligations under this section, and will include a statement of the transferee's intention to fully comply with the terms of this section and to sign the Final Project Agreement for this XL Project as an additional party.

(iii) Within thirty days of receipt of both the written notice and written request described in paragraphs (f)(7)(i) and (f)(7)(ii) of this section, EPA will determine, based on all relevant information, whether to approve a transfer of rights and obligations under this section from OSi to a different owner.

(8) The constituents to be identified by the Sistersville Plant pursuant to paragraphs (f)(2)(vi)(C)(2)(ii) and (f)(2)(viii)(C)(5)(iii) of this section are: 1 Naphthalenamine; 1, 2, 4 Trichlorobenzene; 1,1 Dichloroethylene; 1,1,1 Trichloroethane; 1,1,1,2 Tetrachloroethane; 1,1,2 Trichloro 1,2,2 Triflouroethane; 1,1,2 Trichloroethane; 1,1,2,2 Tetrachloroethane; 1,2 Dichlorobenzene; 1,2 Dichloroethane; 1,2 Dichloropropane; 1,2 Dichloropropanone; 1,2 Transdichloroethene; 1,2, Trans-Dichloroethene; 1,2,4,5 Tetrachlorobenzine; 1,3 Dichlorobenzene; 1,4 Dichloro 2 butene; 1,4 Dioxane; 2 Chlorophenol; 2 Cyclohexyl 4,6 dinitrophenol; 2 Methyl Pyridine; 2 Nitropropane; 2, 4-Di-nitrotoluene; Acetone; Acetonitrile; Acrylonitrile; Allyl Alcohol; Aniline; Antimony; Arsenic; Barium; Benzene; Benzotrichloride; Benzyl Chloride; Beryllium; Bis (2 ethyl Hexyl) Phthalate; Butyl Alcohol, n; Butyl Benzyl Phthalate; Cadmium; Carbon Disulfide; Carbon Tetrachloride; Chlorobenzene; Chloroform; Chloromethane; Chromium; Chrysene; Copper; Creosol; Creosol, m-; Creosol, o; Creosol, p; Cyanide; Cyclohexanone; Di-n-octyl phthalate; Dichlorodiflouromethane; Diethyl Phthalate; Dihydrosafrole; Dimethylamine; Ethyl Acetate; Ethyl benzene; Ethyl Ether; Ethylene Glycol Ethyl Ether; Ethylene Oxide; Formaldehyde; Isobutyl Alcohol; Lead; Mercury; Methanol; Methoxychlor; Methyl Chloride; Methyl Chloroformate; Methyl Ethyl Ketone; Methyl Ethyl Ketone Peroxide; Methyl Isobutyl Ketone; Methyl Methacrylate; Methylene Bromide; Methylene Chloride; Naphthalene; Nickel; Nitrobenzene; Nitroglycerine; p-Toluidine; Phenol; Phthalic Anhydride; Polychlorinated Biphenyls; Propargyl Alcohol; Pyridine; Safrole; Selenium; Silver; Styrene; Tetrachloroethylene; Tetrahydrofuran; Thallium; Toluene; Toluene 2,4 Diisocyanate; Trichloroethylene; Trichloroflouromethane; Vanadium; Vinyl Chloride; Warfarin; Xylene; Zinc.

(g) This section applies only to the facility commonly referred to as the OSi Specialties Plant, located on State Route 2, Sistersville, West Virginia ("Sistersville Plant").

(1)(i) No later than 18 months from the date the Sistersville Plant receives written notification of revocation of the temporary deferral for the Sistersville Plant under paragraph (f) of this section, the Sistersville Plant shall, in accordance with the implementation schedule submitted to EPA under paragraph (g)(1)(ii) of this section, either come into compliance with all requirements of this subpart which had been deferred by paragraph (f)(1)(i) of this section, or complete a facility or process modification such that the requirements of §265.1086 are no longer applicable to the two hazardous waste surface impoundments. In any event, the Sistersville Plant must complete the requirements of the previous sentence no later than the MON Compliance Date; if the Sistersville Plant receives written notification of revocation of the temporary deferral after the date 18 months prior to the MON Compliance Date, the date by which the Sistersville Plant must complete the requirements of the previous sentence will be the MON Compliance Date, which would be less than 18 months from the date of notification of revocation.

(ii) Within 30 days from the date the Sistersville Plant receives written notification of revocation under paragraph (f)(3)(iv) of this section, the Sistersville Plant shall enter and maintain in the facility operating record an implementation schedule. The implementation schedule shall demonstrate that within 18 months from the date the Sistersville Plant receives written notification of revocation under paragraph (f)(3)(iv) of this section (but no later than the MON Compliance Date), the Sistersville Plant shall either come into compliance with the regulatory requirements that had been deferred by paragraph (f)(1)(i) of this section, or complete a facility or process modification such that the requirements of §265.1086 are no longer applicable to the two hazardous waste surface impoundments. Within 30 days from the date the Sistersville Plant receives written notification of revocation under paragraph (f)(3)(iv) of this section, the Sistersville Plant shall submit a copy of the implementation schedule to the EPA and WVDEP Project XL contacts identified in paragraph (f)(2)(viii)(H) of this section. The implementation schedule shall reflect the Sistersville Plant's effort to come into compliance as soon as practicable (but no later than 18 months after the date the Sistersville Plant receives written notification of revocation, or the MON Compliance Date, whichever is sooner) with all regulatory requirements that had been deferred under paragraph (f)(1)(i) of this section, or to complete a facility or process modification as soon as practicable (but no later than 18 months after the date the Sistersville Plant receives written notification of revocation, or the MON Compliance Date, whichever is sooner) such that the requirements of §265.1086 are no longer applicable to the two hazardous waste surface impoundments.

(iii) The implementation schedule shall include the information described in either paragraph (g)(1)(iii)(A) or (B) of this section.

(A) Specific calendar dates for: award of contracts or issuance of purchase orders for the control equipment required by those regulatory requirements that had been deferred by paragraph (f)(1)(i) of this section; initiation of on-site installation of such control equipment; completion of the control equipment installation; performance of any testing to demonstrate that the installed control equipment meets the applicable standards of this subpart; initiation of operation of the control equipment; and compliance with all regulatory requirements that had been deferred by paragraph (f)(1)(i) of this section.

(B) Specific calendar dates for the purchase, installation, performance testing and initiation of operation of equipment to accomplish a facility or process modification such that the requirements of §265.1086 are no longer applicable to the two hazardous waste surface impoundments.

(2) Nothing in paragraphs (f) or (g) of this section shall affect any regulatory requirements not referenced in paragraph (f)(2)(i) or (ii) of this section, as applicable to the Sistersville Plant.

(3) In the event that a notification of revocation is issued pursuant to paragraph (f)(3)(iv) of this section, the requirements referenced in paragraph (f)(1)(iii) of this section are temporarily deferred, with respect to the two hazardous waste surface impoundments, provided that the Sistersville Plant is in compliance with the requirements of paragraphs (f)(2)(ii), (f)(2)(iii), (f)(2)(iv), (f)(2)(v), (f)(2)(vi) and (g) of this section, except as provided under paragraph (g)(4) of this section. The temporary deferral of the previous sentence shall be effective beginning on the date the Sistersville Plant receives written notification of revocation, and subject to paragraph (g)(5) of this section, shall continue to be effective for a maximum period of 18 months from that date, provided that the Sistersville Plant is in compliance with the requirements of paragraphs (f)(2)(ii), (f)(2)(iii), (f)(2)(iv), (f)(2)(v), (f)(2)(vi) and (g) of this section at all times during that 18-month period.

(4) In the event that a notification of revocation is issued pursuant to paragraph (f)(3)(iv) of this section as a result of the permanent removal of the capper unit from methyl capped polyether production service, the requirements referenced in paragraph (f)(1)(iii) of this section are temporarily deferred, with respect to the two hazardous waste surface impoundments, provided that the Sistersville Plant is in compliance with the requirements of paragraphs (f)(2)(vi), and (g) of this section. The temporary deferral of the previous sentence shall be effective beginning on the date the Sistersville Plant receives written notification of revocation, and subject to paragraph (g)(5) of this section, shall continue to be effective for a maximum period of 18 months from that date, provided that the Sistersville Plant is in compliance with the requirements of paragraphs (f)(2)(vi) and (g) of this section at all times during that 18-month period.

(5) In no event shall the temporary deferral provided under paragraph (g)(3) or (g)(4) of this section be effective after the MON Compliance Date.

[59 FR 62935, Dec. 6, 1994, as amended at 60 FR 26829, May 19, 1995; 60 FR 50429, Sept. 29, 1995; 60 FR 56953, Nov. 13, 1995; 61 FR 28510, June 5, 1996; 61 FR 59971, Nov. 25, 1996; 62 FR 52642, Oct. 8, 1997; 62 FR 64662, Dec. 8, 1997; 63 FR 11139, Mar. 6, 1998; 63 FR 19838, Apr. 22, 1998; 63 FR 49399, Sept. 15, 1998; 63 FR 53847, Oct. 7, 1998; 64 FR 3389, Jan. 21, 1999; 65 FR 47325, Aug. 2, 2000; 66 FR 34376, June 28, 2001; 71 FR 40276, July 14, 2006]

§265.1081 Definitions.

As used in this subpart, all terms not defined herein shall have the meaning given to them in the Act and parts 260 through 266 of this chapter.

Average volatile organic concentration or *average VO concentration* means the mass-weighted average volatile organic concentration of a hazardous waste as determined in accordance with the requirements of §265.1084 of this subpart.

Closure device means a cap, hatch, lid, plug, seal, valve, or other type of fitting that blocks an opening in a cover such that when the device is secured in the closed position it prevents or reduces air pollutant emissions to the atmosphere. Closure devices include devices that are detachable from the cover (*e.g.*, a sampling port cap), manually operated (*e.g.*, a hinged access lid or hatch), or automatically operated (*e.g.*, a spring-loaded pressure relief valve).

Continuous seal means a seal that forms a continuous closure that completely covers the space between the edge of the floating roof and the wall of a tank. A continuous seal may be a vapor-mounted seal, liquid-mounted seal, or metallic shoe seal. A continuous seal may be constructed of fastened segments so as to form a continuous seal.

Cover means a device that provides a continuous barrier over the hazardous waste managed in a unit to prevent or reduce air pollutant emissions to the atmosphere. A cover may have openings (such as access hatches, sampling ports, gauge wells) that are necessary for operation, inspection, maintenance, and repair of the unit on which the cover is used. A cover may be a separate piece of equipment which can be detached and removed from the unit or a cover may be formed by structural features permanently integrated into the design of the unit.

Enclosure means a structure that surrounds a tank or container, captures organic vapors emitted from the tank or container, and vents the captured vapors through a closed-vent system to a control device.

External floating roof means a pontoon-type or double-deck type cover that rests on the surface of the material managed in a tank with no fixed roof. 15.3.4.2.1

Fixed roof means a cover that is mounted on a unit in a stationary position and does not move with fluctuations in the level of the material managed in the unit. 15.3.4.2.1

Floating membrane cover means a cover consisting of a synthetic flexible membrane material that rests upon and is supported by the hazardous waste being managed in a surface impoundment.

Floating roof means a cover consisting of a double deck, pontoon single deck, or internal floating cover which rests upon and is supported by the material being contained, and is equipped with a continuous seal.

Hard-piping means pipe or tubing that is manufactured and properly installed in accordance with relevant standards and good engineering practices.

In light material service means the container is used to manage a material for which both of the following conditions apply: The vapor pressure of one or more of the organic constituents in the material is greater than 0.3 kilopascals (kPa) at 20° C; and the total concentration of the pure organic constituents having a vapor pressure greater than 0.3 kPa at 20° C is equal to or greater than 20 percent by weight.

Internal floating roof means a cover that rests or floats on the material surface (but not necessarily in complete contact with it) inside a tank that has a fixed roof. 15.3.4.2.1

Liquid-mounted seal means a foam or liquid-filled primary seal mounted in contact with the hazardous waste between the tank wall and the floating roof continuously around the circumference of the tank.

Malfunction means any sudden, infrequent, and not reasonably preventable failure of air pollution control equipment, process equipment, or a process to operate in a normal or usual manner. Failures that are caused in part by poor maintenance or careless operation are not malfunctions.

Maximum organic vapor pressure means the sum of the individual organic constituent partial pressures exerted by the material contained in a tank, at the maximum vapor pressure-causing conditions (*i.e.*, temperature, agitation, pH effects of combining wastes, etc.) reasonably expected to occur in the tank. For the purpose of this subpart, maximum organic vapor pressure is determined using the procedures specified in §265.1084(c) of this subpart. 15.3.4.1.1

Metallic shoe seal means a continuous seal that is constructed of metal sheets which are held vertically against the wall of the tank by springs, weighted levers, or other mechanisms and is connected to the floating roof by braces or other means. A flexible coated fabric (envelope) spans the annular space between the metal sheet and the floating roof.

No detectable organic emissions means no escape of organics to the atmosphere as determined using the procedure specified in §265.1084(d) of this subpart.

Point of waste origination means as follows: 15.3.1.3.2

(1) When the facility owner or operator is the generator of the hazardous waste, the point of waste origination means the point where a solid waste produced by a system, process, or waste management unit is determined to be a hazardous waste as defined in 40 CFR part 261.

Note: In this case, this term is being used in a manner similar to the use of the term "point of generation" in air standards established for waste management operations under authority of the Clean Air Act in 40 CFR parts 60, 61, and 63.]

(2) When the facility owner and operator are not the generator of the hazardous waste, point of waste origination means the point where the owner or operator accepts delivery or takes possession of the hazardous waste.

Point of waste treatment means the point where a hazardous waste to be treated in accordance with §265.1083(c)(2) of this subpart exits the treatment process. Any waste determination shall be made before the waste is conveyed, handled, or otherwise managed in a manner that allows the waste to volatilize to the atmosphere.

Safety device means a closure device such as a pressure relief valve, frangible disc, fusible plug, or any other type of device which functions exclusively to prevent physical damage or permanent deformation to a unit or its air emission control equipment by venting gases or vapors directly to the atmosphere during unsafe conditions resulting from an unplanned, accidental, or emergency event. For the purpose of this subpart, a safety device is not used for routine venting of gases or vapors from the vapor headspace underneath a cover such as during filling of the unit or to adjust the pressure in this vapor headspace in response to normal daily diurnal ambient temperature fluctuations. A safety device is designed to remain in a closed position during normal operations and open only when the internal pressure, or another relevant parameter, exceeds the device threshold setting applicable to the air emission control equipment as determined by the owner or operator based on manufacturer recommendations, applicable regulations, fire protection and prevention codes, standard engineering codes and practices, or other requirements for the safe handling of flammable, ignitable, explosive, reactive, or hazardous materials.

Single-seal system means a floating roof having one continuous seal. This seal may be vapor-mounted, liquid-mounted, or a metallic shoe seal.

Vapor-mounted seal means a continuous seal that is mounted such that there is a vapor space between the hazardous waste in the unit and the bottom of the seal.

Volatile organic concentration or *VO concentration* means the fraction by weight of the volatile organic compounds contained in a hazardous waste expressed in terms of parts per million (ppmw) as determined by direct measurement or by knowledge of the waste in accordance with the requirements of §265.1084 of this subpart. For the purpose of determining the VO concentration of a hazardous waste, organic compounds with a Henry's law constant value of at least 0.1 mole-fraction-in-the-gas-phase/mole-fraction-in the liquid-phase (0.1 Y/X) (which can also be expressed as 1.8×10^{-6} atmospheres/gram-mole/m^3) at 25 degrees Celsius must be included. Appendix VI of this subpart presents a list of compounds known to have a Henry's law constant value less than the cutoff level. 15.3.1.3.1

Waste determination means performing all applicable procedures in accordance with the requirements of §265.1084 of this subpart to determine whether a hazardous waste meets standards specified in this subpart. Examples of a waste determination include performing the procedures in accordance with the requirements of §265.1084 of this subpart to determine the average VO concentration of a hazardous waste at the point of waste origination; the average VO concentration of a hazardous waste at the point of waste treatment and comparing the results to the exit concentration limit specified for the process used to treat the hazardous waste; the organic reduction efficiency and the organic biodegradation efficiency for a biological process used to treat a hazardous waste and comparing the results to the applicable standards; or the maximum volatile organic vapor pressure for a hazardous waste in a tank and comparing the results to the applicable standards.

Waste stabilization process means any physical or chemical process used to either reduce the mobility of hazardous constituents in a hazardous waste or eliminate free liquids as determined by Test Method 9095B (Paint Filter Liquids Test) in "Test Methods for Evaluating Solid Waste, Physical/Chemical Methods," EPA Publication SW–846, as incorporated by reference in §260.11. A waste stabilization process includes mixing the hazardous waste with binders or other materials, and curing the resulting hazardous waste and binder mixture. Other synonymous terms used to refer to this process are "waste fixation" or "waste solidification." This does not include the adding of absorbent materials to the surface of a waste, without mixing, agitation, or subsequent curing, to absorb free liquid. 15.3.5.3

[59 FR 62935, Dec. 6, 1994, as amended at 61 FR 4914, Feb. 9, 1996; 61 FR 59971, Nov. 25, 1996; 62 FR 64662, Dec. 8, 1997; 70 FR 34586, June 14, 2005]

§265.1082 Schedule for implementation of air emission standards.

(a) Owners or operators of facilities existing on December 6, 1996 and subject to subparts I, J, and K of this part shall meet the following requirements:

(1) Install and begin operation of all control equipment or waste management units required to comply with this subpart and complete modifications of production or treatment processes to satisfy exemption criteria in accordance with §265.1083(c) of this subpart by December 6, 1996, except as provided for in paragraph (a)(2) of this section.

(2) When control equipment or waste management units required to comply with this subpart cannot be installed and in operation or modifications of production or treatment processes to satisfy exemption criteria in accordance with §265.1083(c) of this subpart cannot be completed by December 6, 1996, the owner or operator shall:

(i) Install and begin operation of the control equipment and waste management units, and complete modifications of production or treatment processes as soon as possible but no later than December 8, 1997.

(ii) Prepare an implementation schedule that includes the following information: specific calendar dates for award of contracts or issuance of purchase orders for control equipment, waste management units, and production or treatment process modifications; initiation of on-site installation of control equipment or waste management units, and modifications of production or treatment processes; completion of control equipment or waste management unit installation, and production or treatment process modifications; and performance of testing to demonstrate that the installed equipment or waste management units, and modified production or treatment processes meet the applicable standards of this subpart.

(iii) For facilities subject to the recordkeeping requirements of §265.73 of this part, the owner or operator shall enter the implementation schedule specified in paragraph (a)(2)(ii) of this section in the operating record no later than December 6, 1996.

(iv) For facilities not subject to §265.73 of this part, the owner or operator shall enter the implementation schedule specified in paragraph (a)(2)(ii) of this section in a permanent, readily available file located at the facility no later than December 6, 1996.

(b) Owners or operators of facilities and units in existence on the effective date of a statutory or EPA regulatory amendment that renders the facility subject to subparts I, J, or K of this part shall meet the following requirements:

(1) Install and begin operation of control equipment or waste management units required to comply with this subpart, and complete modifications of production or treatment processes to satisfy exemption criteria of §265.1083(c) of this subpart by the effective date of the amendment, except as provided for in paragraph (b)(2) of this section.

(2) When control equipment or waste management units required to comply with this subpart cannot be installed and begin operation, or when modifications of production or treatment processes to satisfy exemption criteria of §265.1083(c) of this subpart cannot be completed by the effective date of the amendment, the owner or operator shall:

(i) Install and begin operation of the control equipment or waste management unit, and complete modification of production or treatment processes as soon as possible but no later than 30 months after the effective date of the amendment.

(ii) For facilities subject to the recordkeeping requirements of §265.73 of this part, enter and maintain the implementation schedule specified in paragraph (a)(2)(ii) of this section in the operating record no later than the effective date of the amendment, or

(iii) For facilities not subject to §265.73 of this part, the owner or operator shall enter and maintain the implementation schedule specified in paragraph (a)(2)(ii) of this section in a permanent, readily available file located at the facility site no later than the effective date of the amendment.

(c) Owners and operators of facilities and units that become newly subject to the requirements of this subpart after December 8, 1997 due to an action other than those described in paragraph (b) of this section must comply with all applicable requirements immediately (*i.e.*, must have control devices installed and operating on the date the facility or unit becomes subject to this subpart; the 30-month implementation schedule does not apply).

(d) The Regional Administrator may elect to extend the implementation date for control equipment at a facility, on a case by case basis, to a date later than December 8, 1997, when special circumstances that are beyond the facility owner's or operator's control delay installation or operation of control equipment, and the owner or operator has made all reasonable and prudent attempts to comply with the requirements of this subpart.

[62 FR 64662, Dec. 8, 1997]

§265.1083 Standards: General.

(a) This section applies to the management of hazardous waste in tanks, surface impoundments, and containers subject to this subpart.

(b) The owner or operator shall control air pollutant emissions from each hazardous waste management unit in accordance with standards specified in §§265.1085 through 265.1088 of this subpart, as applicable to the hazardous waste management unit, except as provided for in paragraph (c) of this section.

(c) A tank, surface impoundment, or container is exempt from standards specified in §265.1085 through §265.1088 of this subpart, as applicable, provided that the waste management unit is one of the following:

(1) A tank, surface impoundment, or container for which all hazardous waste entering the unit has an average VO concentration at the point of waste origination of less than 500 parts per million by weight (ppmw). The average VO concentration shall be determined using the procedures specified in §265.1084(a) of this subpart. The owner or operator shall review and update, as necessary, this determination at least once every 12 months following the date of the initial determination for the hazardous waste streams entering the unit.

📖 15.3.1.3, 15.3.2–3

(2) A tank, surface impoundment, or container for which the organic content of all the hazardous waste entering the waste management unit has been reduced by an organic destruction or removal process that achieves any one of the following conditions: 15.3.3.5

(i) A process that removes or destroys the organics contained in the hazardous waste to a level such that the average VO concentration of the hazardous waste at the point of waste treatment is less than the exit concentration limit (C_t) established for the process. The average VO concentration of the hazardous waste at the point of waste treatment and the exit concentration limit for the process shall be determined using the procedures specified in §265.1084(b) of this subpart.

(ii) A process that removes or destroys the organics contained in the hazardous waste to a level such that the organic reduction efficiency (R) for the process is equal to or greater than 95 percent, and the average VO concentration of the hazardous waste at the point of waste treatment is less than 100 ppmw. The organic reduction efficiency for the process and the average VO concentration of the hazardous waste at the point of waste treatment shall be determined using the procedures specified in §265.1084(b) of this subpart.

(iii) A process that removes or destroys the organics contained in the hazardous waste to a level such that the actual organic mass removal rate (MR) for the process is equal to or greater than the required organic mass removal rate (RMR) established for the process. The required organic mass removal rate and the actual organic mass removal rate for the process shall be determined using the procedures specified in §265.1084(b) of this subpart.

(iv) A biological process that destroys or degrades the organics contained in the hazardous waste, such that either of the following conditions is met:

(A) The organic reduction efficiency (R) for the process is equal to or greater than 95 percent, and the organic biodegradation efficiency (R_{bio}) for the process is equal to or greater than 95 percent. The organic reduction efficiency and the organic biodegradation efficiency for the process shall be determined using the procedures specified in §265.1084(b) of this subpart.

(B) The total actual organic mass biodegradation rate (MR_{bio}) for all hazardous waste treated by the process is equal to or greater than the required organic mass removal rate (RMR). The required organic mass removal rate and the actual organic mass biodegradation rate for the process shall be determined using the procedures specified in §265.1084(b) of this subpart.

(v) A process that removes or destroys the organics contained in the hazardous waste and meets all of the following conditions:

(A) From the point of waste origination through the point where the hazardous waste enters the treatment process, the hazardous waste is managed continuously in waste management units which use air emission controls in accordance with the standards specified in §265.1085 through §265.1088 of this subpart, as applicable to the waste management unit.

(B) From the point of waste origination through the point where the hazardous waste enters the treatment process, any transfer of the hazardous waste is accomplished through continuous hard-piping or other closed system transfer that does not allow exposure of the waste to the atmosphere. The EPA considers a drain system that meets the requirements of 40 CFR part 63, subpart RR—National Emission Standards for Individual Drain Systems to be a closed system.

(C) The average VO concentration of the hazardous waste at the point of waste treatment is less than the lowest average VO concentration at the point of waste origination determined for each of the individual waste streams entering the process or 500 ppmw, whichever value is lower. The average VO concentration of each individual waste stream at the point of waste origination shall be determined using the procedures specified in §265.1084(a) of this subpart. The average VO concentration of the hazardous waste at the point of waste treatment shall be determined using the procedures specified in §265.1084(b) of this subpart.

(vi) A process that removes or destroys the organics contained in the hazardous waste to a level such that the organic reduction efficiency (R) for the process is equal to or greater than 95 percent and the owner or operator certifies that the average VO concentration at the point of waste origination for each of the individual waste streams entering the process is less than 10,000 ppmw. The organic reduction efficiency for the process and the average VO concentration of the hazardous waste at the point of waste origination shall be determined using the procedures specified in §265.1084(b) and §265.1084(a) of this subpart, respectively.

(vii) A hazardous waste incinerator for which the owner or operator has either:

(A) Been issued a final permit under 40 CFR part 270 which implements the requirements of 40 CFR part 264, subpart O; or

(B) Has designed and operates the incinerator in accordance with the interim status requirements of subpart O of this part.

(viii) A boiler or industrial furnace for which the owner or operator has either:

(A) Been issued a final permit under 40 CFR part 270 which implements the requirements of 40 CFR part 266, subpart H, or

(B) Has designed and operates the boiler or industrial furnace in accordance with the interim status requirements of 40 CFR part 266, subpart H.

(ix) For the purpose of determining the performance of an organic destruction or removal process in accordance with the conditions in each of paragraphs (c)(2)(i) through (c)(2)(vi) of this section, the owner or operator shall account for VO concentrations determined to be below the limit of detection of the analytical method by using the following VO concentration:

(A) If Method 25D in 40 CFR part 60, appendix A is used for the analysis, one-half the blank value determined in the method at section 4.4 of Method 25D in 40 CFR part 60, appendix A, or a value of 25 ppmw, whichever is less.

(B) If any other analytical method is used, one-half the sum of the limits of detection established for each organic constituent in the waste that has a Henry's law constant value at least 0.1 mole-fraction-in-the-gas-phase/mole-fraction-in-the-liquid-phase (0.1 Y/X) [which can also be expressed as 1.8×10^{-6} atmospheres/gram-mole/m^3] at 25 degrees Celsius.

(3) A tank or surface impoundment used for biological treatment of hazardous waste in accordance with the requirements of paragraph (c)(2)(iv) of this section.

📖 15.3.1.2.1

(4) A tank, surface impoundment, or container for which all hazardous waste placed in the unit either:

📖 15.3.3.5

(i) Meets the numerical concentration limits for organic hazardous constituents, applicable to the hazardous waste, as specified in 40 CFR part 268—Land Disposal Restrictions under Table "Treatment Standards for Hazardous Waste" in 40 CFR 268.40; or

(ii) The organic hazardous constituents in the waste have been treated by the treatment technology established by the EPA for the waste in 40 CFR 268.42(a), or have been removed or destroyed by an equivalent method of treatment approved by EPA pursuant to 40 CFR 268.42(b).

(5) A tank used for bulk feed of hazardous waste to a waste incinerator and all of the following conditions are met:

📖 15.3.1.2.1

(i) The tank is located inside an enclosure vented to a control device that is designed and operated in accordance with all applicable requirements specified under 40 CFR part 61, subpart FF—National Emission Standards for Benzene Waste Operations for a facility at which the total annual benzene quantity from the facility waste is equal to or greater than 10 megagrams per year;

(ii) The enclosure and control device serving the tank were installed and began operation prior to November 25, 1996; and

(iii) The enclosure is designed and operated in accordance with the criteria for a permanent total enclosure as specified in "Procedure T—Criteria for and Verification of a Permanent or Temporary Total Enclosure" under 40 CFR 52.741, Appendix B. The enclosure may have permanent or temporary openings to allow worker access; passage of material into or out of the enclosure by conveyor, vehicles, or other mechanical or electrical equipment; or to direct air flow into the enclosure. The owner or operator shall perform the verification procedure for the enclosure as specified in Section 5.0 to "Procedure T—Criteria for and Verification of a Permanent or Temporary Total Enclosure" annually.

(d) The Regional Administrator may at any time perform or request that the owner or operator perform a waste determination for a hazardous waste managed in a tank, surface impoundment, or container exempted from using air emission controls under the provisions of this section as follows:

(1) The waste determination for average VO concentration of a hazardous waste at the point of waste origination shall be performed using direct measurement in accordance with the applicable requirements of §265.1084(a) of this subpart. The waste determination for a hazardous waste at the point of waste treatment shall be performed in accordance with the applicable requirements of §265.1084(b) of this subpart.

(2) In performing a waste determination pursuant to paragraph (d)(1) of this section, the sample preparation and analysis shall be conducted as follows:

(i) In accordance with the method used by the owner or operator to perform the waste analysis, except in the case specified in paragraph (d)(2)(ii) of this section.

(ii) If the Regional Administrator determines that the method used by the owner or operator was not appropriate for the hazardous waste managed in the tank, surface impoundment, or container, then the Regional Administrator may choose an appropriate method.

(3) In a case when the owner or operator is requested to perform the waste determination, the Regional Administrator may elect to have an authorized representative observe the collection of the hazardous waste samples used for the analysis.

(4) In a case when the results of the waste determination performed or requested by the Regional Administrator do not agree with the results of a waste determination performed by the owner or operator using knowledge of the waste, then the results of the waste determination performed in accordance with the requirements of paragraph (d)(1) of this section shall be used to establish compliance with the requirements of this subpart.

(5) In a case when the owner or operator has used an averaging period greater than 1 hour for determining the average VO concentration of a hazardous waste at the point of waste origination, the Regional Administrator may elect to establish compliance with this subpart by performing or requesting that the owner or operator perform a waste determination using direct measurement based on waste samples collected within a 1-hour period as follows:

(i) The average VO concentration of the hazardous waste at the point of waste origination shall be determined by direct measurement in accordance with the requirements of §265.1084(a) of this subpart.

(ii) Results of the waste determination performed or requested by the Regional Administrator showing that the average VO concentration of the hazardous waste at the point of waste origination is equal to or greater than 500 ppmw shall constitute noncompliance with this subpart except in a case as provided for in paragraph (d)(5)(iii) of this section.

(iii) For the case when the average VO concentration of the hazardous waste at the point of waste origination previously has been determined by the owner or operator using an averaging period greater than 1 hour to be less than 500 ppmw but because of normal operating process variations the VO concentration of the hazardous waste determined by direct measurement for any given 1-hour period may be equal to or greater than 500 ppmw, information that was used by the owner or operator to determine the average VO concentration of the hazardous waste (*e.g.*, test results, measurements, calculations, and other documentation) and recorded in the facility records in accordance with the requirements of §265.1084(a) and §265.1090 of this subpart shall be considered by the Regional Administrator together with the results of the waste determination performed or requested by the Regional Administrator in establishing compliance with this subpart.

[61 FR 59972, Nov. 25, 1996, as amended at 62 FR 64663, Dec. 8, 1997]

§265.1084 Waste determination procedures.

(a) Waste determination procedure to determine average volatile organic (VO) concentration of a hazardous waste at the point of waste origination. 📖 15.3.3.1

(1) An owner or operator shall determine the average VO concentration at the point of waste origination for each hazardous waste placed in a waste management unit exempted under the provisions of §265.1083(c)(1) of this subpart from using air emission controls in accordance with standards specified in §265.1085 through §265.1088 of this subpart, as applicable to the waste management unit.

(i) An initial determination of the average VO concentration of the waste stream shall be made before the first time any portion of the material in the hazardous waste stream is placed in a waste management unit exempted under the provisions of §265.1083(c)(1) of this subpart from using air emission controls, and thereafter an initial determination of the average VO concentration of the waste stream shall be made for each averaging period that a hazardous waste is managed in the unit; and

(ii) Perform a new waste determination whenever changes to the source generating the waste stream are reasonably likely to cause the average VO concentration of the hazardous waste to increase to a level that is equal to or greater than the VO concentration limit specified in §265.1083(c)(1) of this subpart.

(2) For a waste determination that is required by paragraph (a)(1) of this section, the average VO concentration of a hazardous waste at the point of waste origination shall be determined using either direct

measurement as specified in paragraph (a)(3) of this section or by knowledge as specified in paragraph (a)(4) of this section.

(3) Direct measurement to determine average VO concentration of a hazardous waste at the point of waste origination.

(i) Identification. The owner or operator shall identify and record the point of waste origination for the hazardous waste.

(ii) Sampling. Samples of the hazardous waste stream shall be collected at the point of waste origination in a manner such that volatilization of organics contained in the waste and in the subsequent sample is minimized and an adequately representative sample is collected and maintained for analysis by the selected method.

(A) The averaging period to be used for determining the average VO concentration for the hazardous waste stream on a mass-weighted average basis shall be designated and recorded. The averaging period can represent any time interval that the owner or operator determines is appropriate for the hazardous waste stream but shall not exceed 1 year.

(B) A sufficient number of samples, but no less than four samples, shall be collected and analyzed for a hazardous waste determination. All of the samples for a given waste determination shall be collected within a one-hour period. The average of the four or more sample results constitutes a waste determination for the waste stream. One or more waste determinations may be required to represent the complete range of waste compositions and quantities that occur during the entire averaging period due to normal variations in the operating conditions for the source or process generating the hazardous waste stream. Examples of such normal variations are seasonal variations in waste quantity or fluctuations in ambient temperature.

(C) All samples shall be collected and handled in accordance with written procedures prepared by the owner or operator and documented in a site sampling plan. This plan shall describe the procedure by which representative samples of the hazardous waste stream are collected such that a minimum loss of organics occurs throughout the sample collection and handling process, and by which sample integrity is maintained. A copy of the written sampling plan shall be maintained onsite in the facility operating records. An example of acceptable sample collection and handling procedures for a total volatile organic constituent concentration may be found in Method 25D in 40 CFR part 60, appendix A.

(D) Sufficient information, as specified in the "site sampling plan" required under paragraph (a)(3)(ii)(C) of this section, shall be prepared and recorded to document the waste quantity represented by the samples and, as applicable, the operating conditions for the source or process generating the hazardous waste represented by the samples.

(iii) *Analysis.* Each collected sample shall be prepared and analyzed in accordance with Method 25D in 40 CFR part 60, appendix A for the total concentration of volatile organic constituents, or using one or more methods when the individual organic compound concentrations are identified and summed and the summed waste concentration accounts for and reflects all organic compounds in the waste with Henry's law constant values at least 0.1 mole-fraction-in-the-gas-phase/mole-fraction-in-the-liquid-phase (0.1 Y/X) [which can also be expressed as 1.8×10^{-6} atmospheres/gram-mole/m^3] at 25 degrees Celsius. At the owner or operator's discretion, the owner or operator may adjust test data obtained by any appropriate method to discount any contribution to the total volatile organic concentration that is a result of including a compound with a Henry's law constant value of less than 0.1 Y/X at 25 degrees Celsius. To adjust these data, the measured concentration of each individual chemical constituent contained in the waste is multiplied by the appropriate constituent-specific adjustment factor (f_{m25D}). If the owner or operator elects to adjust test data, the adjustment must be made to all individual chemical constituents with a Henry's law constant value greater than or equal to 0.1 Y/X at 25 degrees Celsius contained in the waste. Constituent-specific adjustment factors (f_{m25D}) can be obtained by contacting the Waste and Chemical Processes Group, Office of Air Quality Planning and Standards, Research Triangle Park, NC 27711. Other test methods may be used if they meet the requirements in paragraph (a)(3)(iii)(A) or (B) of this section and provided the requirement to reflect all organic compounds in the waste with Henry's law constant values greater than or equal to 0.1 Y/X [which can also be expressed as 1.8×10^{-6} atmospheres/gram-mole/m^3] at 25 degrees Celsius, is met.

(A) Any EPA standard method that has been validated in accordance with "Alternative Validation

Procedure for EPA Waste and Wastewater Methods," 40 CFR part 63, appendix D.

(B) Any other analysis method that has been validated in accordance with the procedures specified in Section 5.1 or Section 5.3, and the corresponding calculations in Section 6.1 or Section 6.3, of Method 301 in 40 CFR part 63, appendix A. The data are acceptable if they meet the criteria specified in Section 6.1.5 or Section 6.3.3 of Method 301. If correction is required under section 6.3.3 of Method 301, the data are acceptable if the correction factor is within the range 0.7 to 1.30. Other sections of Method 301 are not required.

(iv) Calculations.

(A) The average VO concentration ($\overline{C}$) on a mass-weighted basis shall be calculated by using the results for all waste determinations conducted in accordance with paragraphs (a)(3)(ii) and (iii) of this section and the following equation:

$$\overline{C} = \frac{1}{Q_T} \times \sum_{i=1}^{n} (Q_i \times C_i)$$

$\overline{C}$ = Average VO concentration of the hazardous waste at the point of waste origination on a mass-weighted basis, ppmw.

i = Individual waste determination "i" of the hazardous waste.

n = Total number of waste determinations of the hazardous waste conducted for the averaging period (not to exceed 1 year).

Q_i = Mass quantity of hazardous waste stream represented by C_i, kg/hr.

Q_T = Total mass quantity of hazardous waste during the averaging period, kg/hr.

C_i = Measured VO concentration of waste determination "i" as determined in accordance with the requirements of paragraph (a)(3)(iii) of this section (*i.e.* the average of the four or more samples specified in paragraph (a)(3)(ii)(B) of this section), ppmw.

(B) For the purpose of determining C_i, for individual waste samples analyzed in accordance with paragraph (a)(3)(iii) of this section, the owner or operator shall account for VO concentrations determined to be below the limit of detection of the analytical method by using the following VO concentration:

(*1*) If Method 25D in 40 CFR part 60, Appendix A is used for the analysis, one-half the blank value determined in the method at section 4.4 of Method 25D in 40 CFR part 60, appendix A.

(*2*) If any other analytical method is used, one-half the sum of the limits of detection established for each organic constituent in the waste that has a Henry's law constant values at least 0.1 mole-fraction-in-the-gas-phase/mole-fraction-in-the-liquid-phase (0.1 Y/X) [which can also be expressed as 1.8×10^{-6} atmospheres/gram-mole/m^3] at 25 degrees Celsius.

(v) Provided that the test method is appropriate for the waste as required under paragraph (a)(3)(iii) of this section, the EPA will determine compliance based on the test method used by the owner or operator as recorded pursuant to §265.1090(f)(1) of this subpart.

(4) Use of owner or operator knowledge to determine average VO concentration of a hazardous waste at the point of waste origination. 15.3.3.2

(i) Documentation shall be prepared that presents the information used as the basis for the owner's or operator's knowledge of the hazardous waste stream's average VO concentration. Examples of information that may be used as the basis for knowledge include: Material balances for the source or process generating the hazardous waste stream; constituent-specific chemical test data for the hazardous waste stream from previous testing that are still applicable to the current waste stream; previous test data for other locations managing the same type of waste stream; or other knowledge based on information included in manifests, shipping papers, or waste certification notices.

(ii) If test data are used as the basis for knowledge, then the owner or operator shall document the test method, sampling protocol, and the means by which sampling variability and analytical variability are accounted for in the determination of the average VO concentration. For example, an owner or operator may use organic concentration test data for the hazardous waste stream that are validated in accordance with Method 301 in 40 CFR part 63, appendix A as the basis for knowledge of the waste.

(iii) An owner or operator using chemical constituent-specific concentration test data as the basis for knowledge of the hazardous waste may adjust the test data to the corresponding average VO concentration value which would have been obtained had the waste samples been analyzed using Method 25D in 40 CFR part 60, appendix A. To adjust these data, the measured concentration for each individual chemical constituent contained in the waste is multiplied by the appropriate constituent-specific adjustment factor (f_{m25D}).

(iv) In the event that the Regional Administrator and the owner or operator disagree on a determination of the average VO concentration for a hazardous waste stream using knowledge, then the results from a determination of average VO concentration using direct measurement as specified in paragraph (a)(3) of this section shall be used to establish compliance with the applicable requirements of this subpart. The Regional Administrator may perform or request that the owner or operator perform this determination using direct measurement. The owner or operator may choose one or more appropriate methods to analyze each collected sample in accordance with the requirements of paragraph (a)(3)(iii) of this section.

(b) Waste determination procedures for treated hazardous waste.

(1) An owner or operator shall perform the applicable waste determination for each treated hazardous waste placed in a waste management unit exempted under the provisions of §265.1083 (c)(2)(i) through (c)(2)(vi) of this subpart from using air emission controls in accordance with standards specified in §§265.1085 through 265.1088 of this subpart, as applicable to the waste management unit.

(i) An initial determination of the average VO concentration of the waste stream shall be made before the first time any portion of the material in the treated waste stream is placed in a waste management unit exempted under the provisions of §265.1083(c)(2), §265.1083(c)(3), or §265.1083(c)(4) of this subpart from using air emission controls, and thereafter update the information used for the waste determination at least once every 12 months following the date of the initial waste determination; and

(ii) Perform a new waste determination whenever changes to the process generating or treating the waste stream are reasonably likely to cause the average VO concentration of the hazardous waste to increase to a level such that the applicable treatment conditions specified in §265.1083(c)(2), §265.1083(c)(3), or §265.1083(c)(4) of this subpart are not achieved.

(2) The owner or operator shall designate and record the specific provision in §265.1083(c)(2) of this subpart under which the waste determination is being performed. The waste determination for the treated hazardous waste shall be performed using the applicable procedures specified in paragraphs (b)(3) through (b)(9) of this section.

(3) Procedure to determine the average VO concentration of a hazardous waste at the point of waste treatment.

(i) Identification. The owner or operator shall identify and record the point of waste treatment for the hazardous waste.

(ii) Sampling. Samples of the hazardous waste stream shall be collected at the point of waste treatment in a manner such that volatilization of organics contained in the waste and in the subsequent sample is minimized and an adequately representative sample is collected and maintained for analysis by the selected method.

(A) The averaging period to be used for determining the average VO concentration for the hazardous waste stream on a mass-weighted average basis shall be designated and recorded. The averaging period can represent any time interval that the owner or operator determines is appropriate for the hazardous waste stream but shall not exceed 1 year.

(B) A sufficient number of samples, but no less than four samples, shall be collected and analyzed for a hazardous waste determination. All of the samples for a given waste determination shall be collected within a one-hour period. The average of the four or more sample results constitutes a waste determination for the waste stream. One or more waste determinations may be required to represent the complete range of waste compositions and quantities that occur during the entire averaging period due to normal variations in the operating conditions for the process generating or treating the hazardous waste stream. Examples of such normal variations are seasonal variations in waste quantity or fluctuations in ambient temperature.

(C) All samples shall be collected and handled in accordance with written procedures prepared by the owner or operator and documented in a site sampling plan. This plan shall describe the procedure by which representative samples of the hazardous waste stream are collected such that a minimum loss of organics occurs throughout the sample collection and handling process, and by which sample integrity is maintained. A copy of the written sampling plan shall be maintained onsite in the facility operating records. An example of acceptable sample collection and handling procedures for a total volatile organic constituent concentration may be found in Method 25D in 40 CFR part 60, appendix A.

(D) Sufficient information, as specified in the "site sampling plan" required under paragraph (C) of (b)(3)(ii) this section, §265.1084(b)(3)(ii), shall be prepared and recorded to document the waste quantity represented by the samples and, as applicable, the operating conditions for the process treating the hazardous waste represented by the samples.

(iii) *Analysis.* Each collected sample shall be prepared and analyzed in accordance with Method 25D in 40 CFR part 60, appendix A for the total concentration of volatile organic constituents, or using one or more methods when the individual organic compound concentrations are identified and summed and the summed waste concentration accounts for and reflects all organic compounds in the waste with Henry's law constant values at least 0.1 mole-fraction-in-the-gas-phase/mole-fraction-in-the-liquid-phase (0.1 Y/X) [which can also be expressed as 1.8×10^{-6} atmospheres/gram-mole/m^3] at 25 degrees Celsius. When the owner or operator is making a waste determination for a treated hazardous waste that is to be compared to an average VO concentration at the point of waste origination or the point of waste entry to the treatment system to determine if the conditions of §264.1082(c)(2)(i) through (c)(2)(vi) of this chapter, or §265.1083(c)(2)(i) through (c)(2)(vi) of this subpart are met, then the waste samples shall be prepared and analyzed using the same method or methods as were used in making the initial waste determinations at the point of waste origination or at the point of entry to the treatment system. At the owner or operator's discretion, the owner or operator may adjust test data obtained by any appropriate method to discount any contribution to the total volatile organic concentration that is a result of including a compound with a Henry's law constant value less than 0.1 Y/X at 25 degrees Celsius. To adjust these data, the measured concentration of each individual chemical constituent in the waste is multiplied by the appropriate constituent-specific adjustment factor (f_{m25D}). If the owner or operator elects to adjust test data, the adjustment must be made to all individual chemical constituents with a Henry's law constant value greater than or equal to 0.1 Y/X at 25 degrees Celsius contained in the waste. Constituent-specific adjustment factors (f_{m25D}) can be obtained by contacting the Waste and Chemical Processes Group, Office of Air Quality Planning and Standards, Research Triangle Park, NC 27711. Other test methods may be used if they meet the requirements in paragraph (a)(3)(iii)(A) or (B) of this section and provided the requirement to reflect all organic compounds in the waste with Henry's law constant values greater than or equal to 0.1 Y/X [which can also be expressed as 1.8×10^{-6} atmospheres/gram-mole/m^3] at 25 degrees Celsius, is met.

(A) Any EPA standard method that has been validated in accordance with "Alternative Validation Procedure for EPA Waste and Wastewater Methods," 40 CFR part 63, appendix D.

(B) Any other analysis method that has been validated in accordance with the procedures specified in Section 5.1 or Section 5.3, and the corresponding calculations in Section 6.1 or Section 6.3, of Method 301 in 40 CFR part 63, appendix A. The data are acceptable if they meet the criteria specified in Section 6.1.5 or Section 6.3.3 of Method 301. If correction is required under section 6.3.3 of Method 301, the data are acceptable if the correction factor is within the range 0.7 to 1.30. Other sections of Method 301 are not required.

(C) Method 625 in 40 CFR part 136, appendix A. Perform corrections to the compounds for which the analysis is being conducted based on the "accuracy as recovery" using the factors in Table 7 of the method.

(iv) *Calculations.* The average VO concentration ($\overline{C}$) on a mass-weighted basis shall be calculated by using the results for all waste determinations conducted in accordance with paragraphs (b)(3)(ii) and (iii) of this section and the following equation:

$$\overline{C} = \frac{1}{Q_T} \times \sum_{i=1}^{n} (Q_i \times C_i)$$

where:

$\overline{C}$ = Average VO concentration of the hazardous waste at the point of waste treatment on a mass-weighted basis, ppmw.

i = Individual waste determination "i" of the hazardous waste.

n = Total number of waste determinations of the hazardous waste conducted for the averaging period (not to exceed 1 year).

Q_i = Mass quantity of hazardous waste stream represented by C_i, kg/hr.

Q_T = Total mass quantity of hazardous waste during the averaging period, kg/hr.

C_i = Measured VO concentration of waste determination "i" as determined in accordance with the requirements of paragraph (b)(3)(iii) of this section (*i.e.* the average of the four or more samples specified in paragraph (b)(3)(ii)(B) of this section), ppmw.

(v) Provided that the test method is appropriate for the waste as required under paragraph (b)(3)(iii) of this section, compliance shall be determined based on the test method used by the owner or operator as recorded pursuant to §265.1090(f)(1) of this subpart.

(4) Procedure to determine the exit concentration limit (C_t) for a treated hazardous waste. 15.3.3.5

(i) The point of waste origination for each hazardous waste treated by the process at the same time shall be identified.

(ii) If a single hazardous waste stream is identified in paragraph (b)(4)(i) of this section, then the exit concentration limit (C_t) shall be 500 ppmw.

(iii) If more than one hazardous waste stream is identified in paragraph (b)(4)(i) of this section, then the average VO concentration of each hazardous waste stream at the point of waste origination shall be determined in accordance with the requirements of paragraph (a) of this section. The exit concentration limit (C_t) shall be calculated by using the results determined for each individual hazardous waste stream and the following equation:

$$C_t = \frac{\sum_{x=1}^{m}\left(Q_x \times \bar{C}_x\right) + \sum_{y=1}^{n}\left(Q_y \times 500 \text{ ppmw}\right)}{\sum_{x=1}^{m} Q_x + \sum_{y=1}^{n} Q_y}$$

Where:

C_t = Exit concentration limit for treated hazardous waste, ppmw.

x = Individual hazardous waste stream "x" that has an average VO concentration less than 500 ppmw at the point of waste origination as determined in accordance with the requirements of §265.1084(a) of this subpart.

y = Individual hazardous waste stream "y" that has an average VO concentration equal to or greater than 500 ppmw at the point of waste origination as determined in accordance with the requirements of §265.1084(a) of this subpart.

m = Total number of "x" hazardous waste streams treated by process.

n = Total number of "y" hazardous waste streams treated by process.

Q_x = Annual mass quantity of hazardous waste stream "x," kg/yr.

Q_y = Annual mass quantity of hazardous waste stream "y," kg/yr.

$\bar{C}_x$ = Average VO concentration of hazardous waste stream "x" at the point of waste origination as determined in accordance with the requirements of §265.1084(a) of this subpart, ppmw.

(5) Procedure to determine the organic reduction efficiency (R) for a treated hazardous waste. 15.3.3.5

(i) The organic reduction efficiency (R) for a treatment process shall be determined based on results for a minimum of three consecutive runs.

(ii) All hazardous waste streams entering the treatment process and all hazardous waste streams exiting the treatment process shall be identified. The owner or operator shall prepare a sampling plan for measuring these streams that accurately reflects the retention time of the hazardous waste in the process.

(iii) For each run, information shall be determined for each hazardous waste stream identified in paragraph (b)(5)(ii) of this section using the following procedures:

(A) The mass quantity of each hazardous waste stream entering the process (Q_b) and the mass quantity of each hazardous waste stream exiting the process (Q_a) shall be determined.

(B) The average VO concentration at the point of waste origination of each hazardous waste stream entering the process (C_b) during the run shall be determined in accordance with the requirements of paragraph (a)(3) of this section. The average VO concentration at the point of waste treatment of each waste stream exiting the process (C_a) during the run shall be determined in accordance with the requirements of paragraph (b)(3) of this section.

(iv) The waste volatile organic mass flow entering the process (E_b) and the waste volatile organic mass flow exiting the process (E_a) shall be calculated by using the results determined in accordance with paragraph (b)(5)(iii) of this section and the following equations:

$$E_b = \frac{1}{10^6}\sum_{j=1}^{m}\left(Q_{bj} \times \bar{C}_{bj}\right)$$

$$E_a = \frac{1}{10^6}\sum_{j=1}^{m}\left(Q_{aj} \times \bar{C}_{aj}\right)$$

Where:

E_a = Waste volatile organic mass flow exiting process, kg/hr.

E_b = Waste volatile organic mass flow entering process, kg/hr.

m = Total number of runs (at least 3)

j = Individual run "j"

Q_b = Mass quantity of hazardous waste entering process during run "j," kg/hr.

Q_a = Average mass quantity of hazardous waste exiting process during run "j," kg/hr.

$\overline{C}_a$ = Average VO concentration of hazardous waste exiting process during run "j" as determined in accordance with the requirements of §265.1084(b)(3) of this subpart, ppmw.

$\overline{C}_b$ = Average VO concentration of hazardous waste entering process during run "j" as determined in accordance with the requirements of §265.1084(b)(3) of this subpart, ppmw.

(v) The organic reduction efficiency of the process shall be calculated by using the results determined in accordance with paragraph (b)(5)(iv) of this section and the following equation:

$$R = \frac{E_b - E_a}{E_b} \times 100\%$$

Where:

R = Organic reduction efficiency, percent.

E_b = Waste volatile organic mass flow entering process as determined in accordance with the requirements of paragraph (b)(5)(iv) of this section, kg/hr.

E_a = Waste volatile organic mass flow exiting process as determined in accordance with the requirements of paragraph (b)(5)(iv) of this section, kg/hr.

(6) Procedure to determine the organic biodegradation efficiency (R_{bio}) for a treated hazardous waste.

15.3.3.5

(i) The fraction of organics biodegraded (F_{bio}) shall be determined using the procedure specified in 40 CFR part 63, appendix C of this chapter.

(ii) The R_{bio} shall be calculated by using the following equation:

$$R_{bio} = F_{bio} \times 100\%$$

Where:

R_{bio} = Organic biodegradation efficiency, percent.

F_{bio} = Fraction of organic biodegraded as determined in accordance with the requirements of paragraph (b)(6)(i) of this section.

(7) Procedure to determine the required organic mass removal rate (RMR) for a treated hazardous waste.

15.3.3.5

(i) All of the hazardous waste streams entering the treatment process shall be identified.

(ii) The average VO concentration of each hazardous waste stream at the point of waste origination shall be determined in accordance with the requirements of paragraph (a) of this section.

(iii) For each individual hazardous waste stream that has an average VO concentration equal to or greater than 500 ppmw at the point of waste origination, the average volumetric flow rate and the density of the hazardous waste stream at the point of waste origination shall be determined.

(iv) The RMR shall be calculated by using the average VO concentration, average volumetric flow rate, and density determined for each individual hazardous waste stream, and the following equation:

$$RMR = \sum_{y=1}^{n} \left[V_y \times k_y \times \frac{(\overline{C}_y - 500\ \text{ppmw})}{10^6} \right]$$

Where:

RMR = Required organic mass removal rate, kg/hr.

y = Individual hazardous waste stream "y" that has an average VO concentration equal to or greater than 500 ppmw at the point of waste origination as determined in accordance with the requirements of §265.1084(a) of this subpart.

n = Total number of "y" hazardous waste streams treated by process.

V_y = Average volumetric flow rate of hazardous waste stream "y" at the point of waste origination, m^3/hr.

k_y = Density of hazardous waste stream "y," kg/m^3

$\overline{C}_y$ = Average VO concentration of hazardous waste stream "y" at the point of waste origination as determined in accordance with the requirements of §265.1084(a) of this subpart, ppmw.

(8) Procedure to determine the actual organic mass removal rate (MR) for a treated hazardous waste.

15.3.3.5

(i) The MR shall be determined based on results for a minimum of three consecutive runs. The sampling time for each run shall be 1 hour.

(ii) The waste volatile organic mass flow entering the process (E_b) and the waste volatile organic mass flow exiting the process (E_a) shall be determined in accordance with the requirements of paragraph (b)(5)(iv) of this section.

(iii) The MR shall be calculated by using the mass flow rate determined in accordance with the requirements of paragraph (b)(8)(ii) of this section and the following equation:

$$MR = E_b - E_a$$

Where:

MR = Actual organic mass removal rate, kg/hr.

E_b = Waste volatile organic mass flow entering process as determined in accordance with the requirements of paragraph (b)(5)(iv) of this section, kg/hr.

E_a = Waste volatile organic mass flow exiting process as determined in accordance with the requirements of paragraph (b)(5)(iv) of this section, kg/hr.

(9) Procedure to determine the actual organic mass biodegradation rate (MR_{bio}) for a treated hazardous waste. 📖 15.3.3.5

(i) The MR_{bio} shall be determined based on results for a minimum of three consecutive runs. The sampling time for each run shall be 1 hour.

(ii) The waste organic mass flow entering the process (E_b) shall be determined in accordance with the requirements of paragraph (b)(5)(iv) of this section.

(iii) The fraction of organic biodegraded (F_{bio}) shall be determined using the procedure specified in 40 CFR part 63, appendix C of this chapter.

(iv) The MR_{bio} shall be calculated by using the mass flow rates and fraction of organic biodegraded determined in accordance with the requirements of paragraphs (b)(9)(ii) and (b)(9)(iii) of this section, respectively, and the following equation:

$$MR_{bio} = E_b \times F_{bio}$$

Where:

MR_{bio} = Actual organic mass biodegradation rate, kg/hr.

E_b = Waste organic mass flow entering process as determined in accordance with the requirements of paragraph (b)(5)(iv) of this section, kg/hr.

F_{bio} = Fraction of organic biodegraded as determined in accordance with the requirements of paragraph (b)(9)(iii) of this section.

(c) Procedure to determine the maximum organic vapor pressure of a hazardous waste in a tank. 📖 15.3.4.1.1

(1) An owner or operator shall determine the maximum organic vapor pressure for each hazardous waste placed in a tank using Tank Level 1 controls in accordance with the standards specified in §265.1085(c) of this subpart.

(2) An owner or operator shall use either direct measurement as specified in paragraph (c)(3) of this section or knowledge of the waste as specified by paragraph (c)(4) of this section to determine the maximum organic vapor pressure which is representative of the hazardous waste composition stored or treated in the tank.

(3) Direct measurement to determine the maximum organic vapor pressure of a hazardous waste.

(i) Sampling. A sufficient number of samples shall be collected to be representative of the waste contained in the tank. All samples shall be collected and handled in accordance with written procedures prepared by the owner or operator and documented in a site sampling plan. This plan shall describe the procedure by which representative samples of the hazardous waste are collected such that a minimum loss of organics occurs throughout the sample collection and handling process and by which sample integrity is maintained. A copy of the written sampling plan shall be maintained on-site in the facility operating records. An example of acceptable sample collection and handling procedures may be found in Method 25D in 40 CFR part 60, appendix A.

(ii) Analysis. Any appropriate one of the following methods may be used to analyze the samples and compute the maximum organic vapor pressure of the hazardous waste:

(A) Method 25E in 40 CFR part 60 appendix A;

(B) Methods described in American Petroleum Institute Publication 2517, Third Edition, February 1989, "Evaporative Loss from External Floating-Roof Tanks," (incorporated by reference—refer to §260.11 of this chapter);

(C) Methods obtained from standard reference texts;

(D) ASTM Method 2879-92 (incorporated by reference—refer to §260.11 of this chapter); and

(E) Any other method approved by the Regional Administrator.

(4) Use of knowledge to determine the maximum organic vapor pressure of the hazardous waste. Documentation shall be prepared and recorded that presents the information used as the basis for the owner's or operator's knowledge that the maximum organic vapor pressure of the hazardous waste is less than the maximum vapor pressure limit listed in §265.1085(b)(1)(i) of this subpart for the applicable tank design capacity category. An example of information that may be used is documentation that the hazardous waste is generated by a process for which at other locations it previously has

been determined by direct measurement that the waste maximum organic vapor pressure is less than the maximum vapor pressure limit for the appropriate tank design capacity category.

(d) Procedure for determining no detectable organic emissions for the purpose of complying with this subpart:

(1) The test shall be conducted in accordance with the procedures specified in Method 21 of 40 CFR part 60, appendix A. Each potential leak interface (*i.e.*, a location where organic vapor leakage could occur) on the cover and associated closure devices shall be checked. Potential leak interfaces that are associated with covers and closure devices include, but are not limited to: The interface of the cover and its foundation mounting; the periphery of any opening on the cover and its associated closure device; and the sealing seat interface on a spring-loaded pressure relief valve.

(2) The test shall be performed when the unit contains a hazardous waste having an organic concentration representative of the range of concentrations for the hazardous waste expected to be managed in the unit. During the test, the cover and closure devices shall be secured in the closed position.

(3) The detection instrument shall meet the performance criteria of Method 21 of 40 CFR part 60, appendix A, except the instrument response factor criteria in section 3.1.2(a) of Method 21 shall be for the average composition of the organic constituents in the hazardous waste placed in the waste management unit, not for each individual organic constituent.

(4) The detection instrument shall be calibrated before use on each day of its use by the procedures specified in Method 21 of 40 CFR part 60, appendix A.

(5) Calibration gases shall be as follows:

(i) Zero air (less than 10 ppmv hydrocarbon in air), and

(ii) A mixture of methane or n-hexane and air at a concentration of approximately, but less than, 10,000 ppmv methane or n-hexane.

(6) The background level shall be determined according to the procedures in Method 21 of 40 CFR part 60, appendix A.

(7) Each potential leak interface shall be checked by traversing the instrument probe around the potential leak interface as close to the interface as possible, as described in Method 21 of 40 CFR part 60, appendix A. In the case when the configuration of the cover or closure device prevents a complete traverse of the interface, all accessible portions of the interface shall be sampled. In the case when the configuration of the closure device prevents any sampling at the interface and the device is equipped with an enclosed extension or horn (*e.g.*, some pressure relief devices), the instrument probe inlet shall be placed at approximately the center of the exhaust area to the atmosphere.

(8) The arithmetic difference between the maximum organic concentration indicated by the instrument and the background level shall be compared with the value of 500 ppmv except when monitoring a seal around a rotating shaft that passes through a cover opening, in which case the comparison shall be as specified in paragraph (d)(9) of this section. If the difference is less than 500 ppmv, then the potential leak interface is determined to operate with no detectable organic emissions.

(9) For the seals around a rotating shaft that passes through a cover opening, the arithmetic difference between the maximum organic concentration indicated by the instrument and the background level shall be compared with the value of 10,000 ppmw. If the difference is less than 10,000 ppmw, then the potential leak interface is determined to operate with no detectable organic emissions.

[61 FR 59974, Nov. 25, 1996, as amended at 62 FR 64664, Dec. 8, 1997; 64 FR 3390, January 21, 1999; 70 FR 34586, June 14, 2005]

§265.1085 Standards: Tanks.

15.3.4

(a) The provisions of this section apply to the control of air pollutant emissions from tanks for which §265.1083(b) of this subpart references the use of this section for such air emission control.

(b) The owner or operator shall control air pollutant emissions from each tank subject to this section in accordance with the following requirements, as applicable:

(1) For a tank that manages hazardous waste that meets all of the conditions specified in paragraphs (b)(1)(i) through (b)(1)(iii) of this section, the owner or operator shall control air pollutant emissions from the tank in accordance with the Tank Level 1 controls specified in paragraph (c) of this section or the Tank Level 2 controls specified in paragraph (d) of this section. 15.3.4.1.1

(i) The hazardous waste in the tank has a maximum organic vapor pressure which is less than the maximum organic vapor pressure limit for the tank's design capacity category as follows:

(A) For a tank design capacity equal to or greater than 151 m^3, the maximum organic vapor pressure limit for the tank is 5.2 kPa.

(B) For a tank design capacity equal to or greater than 75 m^3 but less than 151 m^3, the maximum organic vapor pressure limit for the tank is 27.6 kPa.

(C) For a tank design capacity less than 75 m^3, the maximum organic vapor pressure limit for the tank is 76.6 kPa.

(ii) The hazardous waste in the tank is not heated by the owner or operator to a temperature that is greater than the temperature at which the maximum organic vapor pressure of the hazardous waste is determined for the purpose of complying with paragraph (b)(1)(i) of this section.

(iii) The hazardous waste in the tank is not treated by the owner or operator using a waste stabilization process, as defined in §265.1081 of this subpart.

(2) For a tank that manages hazardous waste that does not meet all of the conditions specified in paragraphs (b)(1)(i) through (b)(1)(iii) of this section, the owner or operator shall control air pollutant emissions from the tank by using Tank Level 2 controls in accordance with the requirements of paragraph (d) of this section. Examples of tanks required to use Tank Level 2 controls include: A tank used for a waste stabilization process; and a tank for which the hazardous waste in the tank has a maximum organic vapor pressure that is equal to or greater than the maximum organic vapor pressure limit for the tank's design capacity category as specified in paragraph (b)(1)(i) of this section.

(c) Owners and operators controlling air pollutant emissions from a tank using Tank Level 1 controls shall meet the requirements specified in paragraphs (c)(1) through (c)(4) of this section: 15.3.4.1

(1) The owner or operator shall determine the maximum organic vapor pressure for a hazardous waste to be managed in the tank using Tank Level 1 controls before the first time the hazardous waste is placed in the tank. The maximum organic vapor pressure shall be determined using the procedures specified in §265.1084(c) of this subpart. Thereafter, the owner or operator shall perform a new determination whenever changes to the hazardous waste managed in the tank could potentially cause the maximum organic vapor pressure to increase to a level that is equal to or greater than the maximum organic vapor pressure limit for the tank design capacity category specified in paragraph (b)(1)(i) of this section, as applicable to the tank.

(2) The tank shall be equipped with a fixed roof designed to meet the following specifications:

(i) The fixed roof and its closure devices shall be designed to form a continuous barrier over the entire surface area of the hazardous waste in the tank. The fixed roof may be a separate cover installed on the tank (*e.g.*, a removable cover mounted on an open-top tank) or may be an integral part of the tank structural design (*e.g.*, a horizontal cylindrical tank equipped with a hatch).

(ii) The fixed roof shall be installed in a manner such that there are no visible cracks, holes, gaps, or other open spaces between roof section joints or between the interface of the roof edge and the tank wall.

(iii) Each opening in the fixed roof, and any manifold system associated with the fixed roof, shall be either:

(A) Equipped with a closure device designed to operate such that when the closure device is secured in the closed position there are no visible cracks, holes, gaps, or other open spaces in the closure device or between the perimeter of the opening and the closure device; or

(B) Connected by a closed-vent system that is vented to a control device. The control device shall remove or destroy organics in the vent stream, and shall be operating whenever hazardous waste is managed in the tank, except as provided for in paragraphs (c)(2)(iii)(B)(*1*) and (*2*) of this section.

(*1*) During periods it is necessary to provide access to the tank for performing the activities of paragraph (c)(2)(iii)(B)(2) of this section, venting of the vapor headspace underneath the fixed roof to the control device is not required, opening of closure devices is allowed, and removal of the fixed roof is allowed. Following completion of the activity, the owner or operator shall promptly secure the closure device in the closed position or reinstall the cover, as applicable, and resume operation of the control device.

(*2*) During periods of routine inspection, maintenance, or other activities needed for normal operations, and for the removal of accumulated sludge or other residues from the bottom of the tank.

(iv) The fixed roof and its closure devices shall be made of suitable materials that will minimize exposure of the hazardous waste to the atmosphere, to the extent practical, and will maintain the integrity of the fixed roof and closure devices throughout their intended service life. Factors to be considered when selecting the materials for and designing the fixed roof and closure devices shall include: Organic vapor permeability, the effects of any contact with the hazardous waste or its vapors managed in the tank; the effects of outdoor exposure to wind, moisture, and sunlight; and the operating practices used for the tank on which the fixed roof is installed.

(3) Whenever a hazardous waste is in the tank, the fixed roof shall be installed with each closure device secured in the closed position except as follows:

(i) Opening of closure devices or removal of the fixed roof is allowed at the following times:

(A) To provide access to the tank for performing routine inspection, maintenance, or other activities needed for normal operations. Examples of such activities include those times when a worker needs to open a port to sample the liquid in the tank, or when a worker needs to open a hatch to maintain or repair equipment. Following completion of the activity, the owner or operator shall promptly secure the closure device in the closed position or reinstall the cover, as applicable, to the tank.

(B) To remove accumulated sludge or other residues from the bottom of tank.

(ii) Opening of a spring-loaded pressure-vacuum relief valve, conservation vent, or similar type of pressure relief device which vents to the atmosphere is allowed during normal operations for the purpose of maintaining the tank internal pressure in accordance with the tank design specifications. The device shall be designed to operate with no detectable organic emissions when the device is secured in the closed position. The settings at which the device opens shall be established such that the device remains in the closed position whenever the tank internal pressure is within the internal pressure operating range determined by the owner or operator based on the tank manufacturer recommendations, applicable regulations, fire protection and prevention codes, standard engineering codes and practices, or other requirements for the safe handling of flammable, ignitable, explosive, reactive, or hazardous materials. Examples of normal operating conditions that may require these devices to open are during those times when the tank internal pressure exceeds the internal pressure operating range for the tank as a result of loading operations or diurnal ambient temperature fluctuations.

(iii) Opening of a safety device, as defined in §265.1081 of this subpart, is allowed at any time conditions require doing so to avoid an unsafe condition.

(4) The owner or operator shall inspect the air emission control equipment in accordance with the following requirements.

(i) The fixed roof and its closure devices shall be visually inspected by the owner or operator to check for defects that could result in air pollutant emissions. Defects include, but are not limited to, visible cracks, holes, or gaps in the roof sections or between the roof and the tank wall; broken, cracked, or otherwise damaged seals or gaskets on closure devices; and broken or missing hatches, access covers, caps, or other closure devices.

(ii) The owner or operator shall perform an initial inspection of the fixed roof and its closure devices on or before the date that the tank becomes subject to this section. Thereafter, the owner or operator shall perform the inspections at least once every year except under the special conditions provided for in paragraph (l) of this section.

(iii) In the event that a defect is detected, the owner or operator shall repair the defect in accordance with the requirements of paragraph (k) of this section.

(iv) The owner or operator shall maintain a record of the inspection in accordance with the requirements specified in §265.1090(b) of this subpart.

(d) Owners and operators controlling air pollutant emissions from a tank using Tank Level 2 controls shall use one of the following tanks: 15.3.4.2

(1) A fixed-roof tank equipped with an internal floating roof in accordance with the requirements specified in paragraph (e) of this section;

(2) A tank equipped with an external floating roof in accordance with the requirements specified in paragraph (f) of this section;

(3) A tank vented through a closed-vent system to a control device in accordance with the requirements specified in paragraph (g) of this section;

(4) A pressure tank designed and operated in accordance with the requirements specified in paragraph (h) of this section; or

(5) A tank located inside an enclosure that is vented through a closed-vent system to an enclosed combustion control device in accordance with the requirements specified in paragraph (i) of this section.

(e) The owner or operator who controls air pollutant emissions from a tank using a fixed-roof with an internal floating roof shall meet the requirements specified in paragraphs (e)(1) through (e)(3) of this section.

(1) The tank shall be equipped with a fixed roof and an internal floating roof in accordance with the following requirements:

(i) The internal floating roof shall be designed to float on the liquid surface except when the floating roof must be supported by the leg supports.

(ii) The internal floating roof shall be equipped with a continuous seal between the wall of the tank and the floating roof edge that meets either of the following requirements:

(A) A single continuous seal that is either a liquid-mounted seal or a metallic shoe seal, as defined in §265.1081 of this subpart; or

(B) Two continuous seals mounted one above the other. The lower seal may be a vapor-mounted seal.

(iii) The internal floating roof shall meet the following specifications:

(A) Each opening in a noncontact internal floating roof except for automatic bleeder vents (vacuum breaker vents) and the rim space vents is to provide a projection below the liquid surface.

(B) Each opening in the internal floating roof shall be equipped with a gasketed cover or a gasketed lid except for leg sleeves, automatic bleeder vents, rim space vents, column wells, ladder wells, sample wells, and stub drains.

(C) Each penetration of the internal floating roof for the purpose of sampling shall have a slit fabric cover that covers at least 90 percent of the opening.

(D) Each automatic bleeder vent and rim space vent shall be gasketed.

(E) Each penetration of the internal floating roof that allows for passage of a ladder shall have a gasketed sliding cover.

(F) Each penetration of the internal floating roof that allows for passage of a column supporting the fixed roof shall have a flexible fabric sleeve seal or a gasketed sliding cover.

(2) The owner or operator shall operate the tank in accordance with the following requirements:

(i) When the floating roof is resting on the leg supports, the process of filling, emptying, or refilling shall be continuous and shall be completed as soon as practical.

(ii) Automatic bleeder vents are to be set closed at all times when the roof is floating, except when the roof is being floated off or is being landed on the leg supports.

(iii) Prior to filling the tank, each cover, access hatch, gauge float well or lid on any opening in the internal floating roof shall be bolted or fastened closed (*i.e.*, no visible gaps). Rim space vents are to be set to open only when the internal floating roof is not floating or when the pressure beneath the rim exceeds the manufacturer's recommended setting.

(3) The owner or operator shall inspect the internal floating roof in accordance with the procedures specified as follows:

(i) The floating roof and its closure devices shall be visually inspected by the owner or operator to check for defects that could result in air pollutant emissions. Defects include, but are not limited to: The internal floating roof is not floating on the surface of the liquid inside the tank; liquid has accumulated on top of the internal floating roof; any portion of the roof seals have detached from the roof rim; holes, tears, or other openings are visible in the seal fabric; the gaskets no longer close off the hazardous waste surface from the atmosphere; or the slotted membrane has more than 10 percent open area.

(ii) The owner or operator shall inspect the internal floating roof components as follows except as provided in paragraph (e)(3)(iii) of this section:

(A) Visually inspect the internal floating roof components through openings on the fixed-roof (*e.g.*, manholes and roof hatches) at least once every 12 months after initial fill, and

(B) Visually inspect the internal floating roof, primary seal, secondary seal (if one is in service), gaskets, slotted membranes, and sleeve seals (if any) each time the tank is emptied and degassed and at least every 10 years.

(iii) As an alternative to performing the inspections specified in paragraph (e)(3)(ii) of this section for an internal floating roof equipped with two continuous seals mounted one above the other, the owner or operator may visually inspect the internal floating roof, primary and secondary seals, gaskets, slotted membranes, and sleeve seals (if any) each time the tank is emptied and degassed and at least every 5 years.

(iv) Prior to each inspection required by paragraph (e)(3)(ii) or (e)(3)(iii) of this section, the owner or operator shall notify the Regional Administrator in advance of each inspection to provide the Regional Administrator with the opportunity to have an observer present during the inspection. The owner or operator shall notify the Regional Administrator of the date and location of the inspection as follows:

(A) Prior to each visual inspection of an internal floating roof in a tank that has been emptied and degassed, written notification shall be prepared and sent by the owner or operator so that it is received by the Regional Administrator at least 30 calendar days before refilling the tank except when an inspection is not planned as provided for in paragraph (e)(3)(iv)(B) of this section.

(B) When a visual inspection is not planned and the owner or operator could not have known about the inspection 30 calendar days before refilling the tank, the owner or operator shall notify the Regional Administrator as soon as possible, but no later than 7 calendar days before refilling of the tank. This notification may be made by telephone and immediately followed by a written explanation for why the inspection is unplanned. Alternatively, written notification, including the explanation for the unplanned inspection, may be sent so that it is received by the Regional Administrator at least 7 calendar days before refilling the tank.

(v) In the event that a defect is detected, the owner or operator shall repair the defect in accordance with the requirements of paragraph (k) of this section.

(vi) The owner or operator shall maintain a record of the inspection in accordance with the requirements specified in §265.1090(b) of this subpart.

(4) Safety devices, as defined in §265.1081 of this subpart, may be installed and operated as necessary on any tank complying with the requirements of paragraph (e) of this section.

(f) The owner or operator who controls air pollutant emissions from a tank using an external floating roof shall meet the requirements specified in paragraphs (f)(1) through (f)(3) of this section.

(1) The owner or operator shall design the external floating roof in accordance with the following requirements:

(i) The external floating roof shall be designed to float on the liquid surface except when the floating roof must be supported by the leg supports.

(ii) The floating roof shall be equipped with two continuous seals, one above the other, between the wall of the tank and the roof edge. The lower seal is referred to as the primary seal, and the upper seal is referred to as the secondary seal.

(A) The primary seal shall be a liquid-mounted seal or a metallic shoe seal, as defined in §265.1081 of this subpart. The total area of the gaps between the tank wall and the primary seal shall not exceed 212 square centimeters (cm^2) per meter of tank diameter, and the width of any portion of these gaps shall not exceed 3.8 centimeters (cm). If a metallic shoe seal is used for the primary seal, the metallic shoe seal shall be designed so that one end extends into the liquid in the tank and the other end extends a vertical distance of at least 61 centimeters above the liquid surface.

(B) The secondary seal shall be mounted above the primary seal and cover the annular space between the floating roof and the wall of the tank. The total area of the gaps between the tank wall and the secondary seal shall not exceed 21.2 square centimeters (cm^2) per meter of tank diameter, and the width of any portion of these gaps shall not exceed 1.3 centimeters (cm).

(iii) The external floating roof shall meet the following specifications:

(A) Except for automatic bleeder vents (vacuum breaker vents) and rim space vents, each opening in a noncontact external floating roof shall provide a projection below the liquid surface.

(B) Except for automatic bleeder vents, rim space vents, roof drains, and leg sleeves, each opening in the roof shall be equipped with a gasketed cover, seal, or lid.

(C) Each access hatch and each gauge float well shall be equipped with a cover designed to be bolted or fastened when the cover is secured in the closed position.

(D) Each automatic bleeder vent and each rim space vent shall be equipped with a gasket.

(E) Each roof drain that empties into the liquid managed in the tank shall be equipped with a slotted membrane fabric cover that covers at least 90 percent of the area of the opening.

(F) Each unslotted and slotted guide pole well shall be equipped with a gasketed sliding cover or a flexible fabric sleeve seal.

(G) Each unslotted guide pole shall be equipped with a gasketed cap on the end of the pole.

(H) Each slotted guide pole shall be equipped with a gasketed float or other device which closes off the liquid surface from the atmosphere.

(I) Each gauge hatch and each sample well shall be equipped with a gasketed cover.

(2) The owner or operator shall operate the tank in accordance with the following requirements:

(i) When the floating roof is resting on the leg supports, the process of filling, emptying, or refilling shall be continuous and shall be completed as soon as practical.

(ii) Except for automatic bleeder vents, rim space vents, roof drains, and leg sleeves, each opening in the roof shall be secured and maintained in a closed position at all times except when the closure device must be open for access.

(iii) Covers on each access hatch and each gauge float well shall be bolted or fastened when secured in the closed position.

(iv) Automatic bleeder vents shall be set closed at all times when the roof is floating, except when the roof is being floated off or is being landed on the leg supports.

(v) Rim space vents shall be set to open only at those times that the roof is being floated off the roof leg supports or when the pressure beneath the rim seal exceeds the manufacturer's recommended setting.

(vi) The cap on the end of each unslotted guide pole shall be secured in the closed position at all times except when measuring the level or collecting samples of the liquid in the tank.

(vii) The cover on each gauge hatch or sample well shall be secured in the closed position at all times except when the hatch or well must be opened for access.

(viii) Both the primary seal and the secondary seal shall completely cover the annular space between the external floating roof and the wall of the tank in a continuous fashion except during inspections.

(3) The owner or operator shall inspect the external floating roof in accordance with the procedures specified as follows:

(i) The owner or operator shall measure the external floating roof seal gaps in accordance with the following requirements:

(A) The owner or operator shall perform measurements of gaps between the tank wall and the primary seal within 60 calendar days after initial operation of the tank following installation of the floating roof and, thereafter, at least once every 5 years.

(B) The owner or operator shall perform measurements of gaps between the tank wall and the secondary seal within 60 calendar days after initial operation of the tank following installation of the floating roof and, thereafter, at least once every year.

(C) If a tank ceases to hold hazardous waste for a period of 1 year or more, subsequent introduction of hazardous waste into the tank shall be considered an initial operation for the purposes of paragraphs (f)(3)(i)(A) and (f)(3)(i)(B) of this section.

(D) The owner or operator shall determine the total surface area of gaps in the primary seal and in the secondary seal individually using the following procedure:

(*1*) The seal gap measurements shall be performed at one or more floating roof levels when the roof is floating off the roof supports.

(*2*) Seal gaps, if any, shall be measured around the entire perimeter of the floating roof in each place where a 0.32-centimeter (cm) diameter uniform probe passes freely (without forcing or binding against the seal) between the seal and the wall of the tank and measure the circumferential distance of each such location.

(*3*) For a seal gap measured under paragraph (f)(3) of this section, the gap surface area shall be determined by using probes of various widths to measure accurately the actual distance from the tank wall to the seal and multiplying each such width by its respective circumferential distance.

(*4*) The total gap area shall be calculated by adding the gap surface areas determined for each identified gap location for the primary seal and the secondary seal individually, and then dividing the sum for each seal type by the nominal diameter of the tank. These total gap areas for the primary seal and secondary seal are then compared to the respective standards for the seal type as specified in paragraph (f)(1)(ii) of this section.

(E) In the event that the seal gap measurements do not conform to the specifications in paragraph (f)(1)(ii) of this section, the owner or operator shall repair the defect in accordance with the requirements of paragraph (k) of this section.

(F) The owner or operator shall maintain a record of the inspection in accordance with the requirements specified in §265.1090(b) of this subpart.

(ii) The owner or operator shall visually inspect the external floating roof in accordance with the following requirements:

(A) The floating roof and its closure devices shall be visually inspected by the owner or operator to check for defects that could result in air pollutant emissions. Defects include, but are not limited to: Holes, tears, or other openings in the rim seal or seal fabric of the floating roof; a rim seal detached from the floating roof; all or a portion of the floating roof deck being submerged below the surface of the liquid in the tank; broken, cracked, or otherwise damaged seals or gaskets on closure devices; and broken or missing hatches, access covers, caps, or other closure devices.

(B) The owner or operator shall perform an initial inspection of the external floating roof and its closure devices on or before the date that the tank becomes subject to this section. Thereafter, the owner or operator shall perform the inspections at least once every year except for the special conditions provided for in paragraph (l) of this section.

(C) In the event that a defect is detected, the owner or operator shall repair the defect in accordance with the requirements of paragraph (k) of this section.

(D) The owner or operator shall maintain a record of the inspection in accordance with the requirements specified in §265.1090(b) of this subpart.

(iii) Prior to each inspection required by paragraph (f)(3)(i) or (f)(3)(ii) of this section, the owner or operator shall notify the Regional Administrator in advance of each inspection to provide the Regional Administrator with the opportunity to have an observer present during the inspection. The owner or operator shall notify the Regional Administrator of the date and location of the inspection as follows:

(A) Prior to each inspection to measure external floating roof seal gaps as required under paragraph (f)(3)(i) of this section, written notification shall be prepared and sent by the owner or operator so that it is received by the Regional Administrator at least 30 calendar days before the date the measurements are scheduled to be performed.

(B) Prior to each visual inspection of an external floating roof in a tank that has been emptied and degassed, written notification shall be prepared and sent by the owner or operator so that it is received by the Regional Administrator at least 30 calendar days before refilling the tank except when an inspection is not planned as provided for in paragraph (f)(3)(iii)(C) of this section.

(C) When a visual inspection is not planned and the owner or operator could not have known about the inspection 30 calendar days before refilling the tank, the owner or operator shall notify the Regional Administrator as soon as possible, but no later than 7 calendar days before refilling of the tank. This notification may be made by telephone and immediately followed by a written explanation for why the inspection is unplanned. Alternatively, written notification, including the explanation for the unplanned inspection, may be sent so that it is received by the Regional Administrator at least 7 calendar days before refilling the tank.

(4) Safety devices, as defined in 40 CFR 265.1081, may be installed and operated as necessary on any tank complying with the requirements of paragraph (f) of this section.

(g) The owner or operator who controls air pollutant emissions from a tank by venting the tank to a control device shall meet the requirements specified in paragraphs (g)(1) through (g)(3) of this section. 📖 15.3.4.2.1

(1) The tank shall be covered by a fixed roof and vented directly through a closed-vent system to a control device in accordance with the following requirements:

(i) The fixed roof and its closure devices shall be designed to form a continuous barrier over the entire surface area of the liquid in the tank.

(ii) Each opening in the fixed roof not vented to the control device shall be equipped with a closure device. If the pressure in the vapor headspace underneath the fixed roof is less than atmospheric pressure when the control device is operating, the closure devices shall be designed to operate such that when the closure device is secured in the closed position there are no visible cracks, holes, gaps, or other open spaces in the closure device or between the perimeter of the cover opening and the closure device. If the pressure in the vapor headspace underneath the fixed roof is equal to or greater than atmospheric pressure when the control device is operating, the closure device shall be designed to operate with no detectable organic emissions.

(iii) The fixed roof and its closure devices shall be made of suitable materials that will minimize exposure of the hazardous waste to the atmosphere, to the extent practical, and will maintain the integrity of the fixed roof and closure devices throughout their intended service life. Factors to be considered when selecting the materials for and designing the fixed roof and closure devices shall include: Organic vapor permeability, the effects of any contact with the liquid and its vapor managed in the tank; the effects of outdoor exposure to wind, moisture, and sunlight; and the operating practices used for the tank on which the fixed roof is installed.

(iv) The closed-vent system and control device shall be designed and operated in accordance with the requirements of §265.1088 of this subpart.

(2) Whenever a hazardous waste is in the tank, the fixed roof shall be installed with each closure device secured in the closed position and the vapor headspace underneath the fixed roof vented to the control device except as follows:

(i) Venting to the control device is not required, and opening of closure devices or removal of the fixed roof is allowed at the following times:

(A) To provide access to the tank for performing routine inspection, maintenance, or other activities needed for normal operations. Examples of such activities include those times when a worker needs to open a port to sample liquid in the tank, or when a worker needs to open a hatch to maintain or repair equipment. Following completion of the activity, the owner or operator shall promptly secure the closure device in the closed position or reinstall the cover, as applicable, to the tank.

(B) To remove accumulated sludge or other residues from the bottom of a tank.

(ii) Opening of a safety device, as defined in §265.1081 of this subpart, is allowed at any time conditions require doing so to avoid an unsafe condition.

(3) The owner or operator shall inspect and monitor the air emission control equipment in accordance with the following procedures:

(i) The fixed roof and its closure devices shall be visually inspected by the owner or operator to check for defects that could result in air pollutant emissions. Defects include, but are not limited to, visible cracks, holes, or gaps in the roof sections or between the roof and the tank wall; broken, cracked, or otherwise damaged seals or gaskets on closure devices; and broken or missing hatches, access covers, caps, or other closure devices.

(ii) The closed-vent system and control device shall be inspected and monitored by the owner or operator in accordance with the procedures specified in §265.1088 of this subpart.

(iii) The owner or operator shall perform an initial inspection of the air emission control equipment on or before the date that the tank becomes subject to this section. Thereafter, the owner or operator shall perform the inspections at least once every year except for the special conditions provided for in paragraph (l) of this section.

(iv) In the event that a defect is detected, the owner or operator shall repair the defect in accordance with the requirements of paragraph (k) of this section.

(v) The owner or operator shall maintain a record of the inspection in accordance with the requirements specified in §265.1090(b) of this subpart.

(h) The owner or operator who controls air pollutant emissions by using a pressure tank shall meet the following requirements.

(1) The tank shall be designed not to vent to the atmosphere as a result of compression of the vapor headspace in the tank during filling of the tank to its design capacity.

(2) All tank openings shall be equipped with closure devices designed to operate with no detectable organic emissions as determined using the procedure specified in §265.1084(d) of this subpart.

(3) Whenever a hazardous waste is in the tank, the tank shall be operated as a closed system that does not vent to the atmosphere except under either of the following conditions as specified in paragraph (h)(3)(i) or (h)(3)(ii) of this section.

(i) At those times when opening of a safety device, as defined in §265.1081 of this subpart, is required to avoid an unsafe condition.

(ii) At those times when purging of inerts from the tank is required and the purge stream is routed to a closed-vent system and control device designed and operated in accordance with the requirements of §265.1088 of this subpart.

(i) The owner or operator who controls air pollutant emissions by using an enclosure vented through a closed-vent system to an enclosed combustion control device shall meet the requirements specified in paragraphs (i)(1) through (i)(4) of this section.

(1) The tank shall be located inside an enclosure. The enclosure shall be designed and operated in accordance with the criteria for a permanent total enclosure as specified in "Procedure T—Criteria for and Verification of a Permanent or Temporary Total Enclosure" under 40 CFR 52.741, appendix B. The enclosure may have permanent or temporary openings to allow worker access; passage of material into or out of the enclosure by conveyor, vehicles, or other mechanical means; entry of permanent mechanical or electrical equipment; or direct airflow into the enclosure. The owner or operator shall perform the verification procedure for the enclosure as specified in Section 5.0 to "Procedure T—Criteria for and Verification of a Permanent or Temporary Total Enclosure" initially when the enclosure is first installed and, thereafter, annually.

(2) The enclosure shall be vented through a closed-vent system to an enclosed combustion control device that is designed and operated in accordance with the standards for either a vapor incinerator, boiler, or process heater specified in §265.1088 of this subpart.

(3) Safety devices, as defined in §265.1081 of this subpart, may be installed and operated as necessary on any enclosure, closed-vent system, or control device used to comply with the requirements of paragraphs (i)(1) and (i)(2) of this section.

(4) The owner or operator shall inspect and monitor the closed-vent system and control device as specified in §265.1088 of this subpart.

(j) The owner or operator shall transfer hazardous waste to a tank subject to this section in accordance with the following requirements:

(1) Transfer of hazardous waste, except as provided in paragraph (j)(2) of this section, to the tank from another tank subject to this section or from a surface impoundment subject to §265.1086 of this subpart shall be conducted using continuous hard-piping or another closed system that does not allow exposure of the hazardous waste to the atmosphere. For the purpose of complying with this provision, an individual drain system is considered to be a closed system when it meets the requirements of 40 CFR part 63, subpart RR—National Emission Standards for Individual Drain Systems.

(2) The requirements of paragraph (j)(1) of this section do not apply when transferring a hazardous waste to the tank under any of the following conditions:

(i) The hazardous waste meets the average VO concentration conditions specified in §265.1083(c)(1) of this subpart at the point of waste origination.

(ii) The hazardous waste has been treated by an organic destruction or removal process to meet the requirements in §265.1083(c)(2) of this subpart.

(iii) The hazardous waste meets the requirements of §265.1083(c)(4) of this subpart.

(k) The owner or operator shall repair each defect detected during an inspection performed in accordance with the requirements of paragraphs (c)(4), (e)(3), (f)(3), or (g)(3) of this section as follows:

(1) The owner or operator shall make first efforts at repair of the defect no later than 5 calendar days after detection, and repair shall be completed as soon as possible but no later than 45 calendar days after detection except as provided in paragraph (k)(2) of this section.

(2) Repair of a defect may be delayed beyond 45 calendar days if the owner or operator determines that repair of the defect requires emptying or temporary removal from service of the tank and no alternative tank capacity is available at the site to accept the hazardous waste normally managed in the tank. In this case, the owner or operator shall repair the defect the next time the process or unit that is generating the hazardous waste managed in the tank stops operation. Repair of the defect shall be completed before the process or unit resumes operation.

(l) Following the initial inspection and monitoring of the cover as required by the applicable provisions of this subpart, subsequent inspection and monitoring may be performed at intervals longer than 1 year under the following special conditions:

(1) In the case when inspecting or monitoring the cover would expose a worker to dangerous, hazardous, or other unsafe conditions, then the owner or operator may designate a cover as an "unsafe to inspect and monitor cover" and comply with all of the following requirements:

(i) Prepare a written explanation for the cover stating the reasons why the cover is unsafe to visually inspect or to monitor, if required.

(ii) Develop and implement a written plan and schedule to inspect and monitor the cover, using the procedures specified in the applicable section of this subpart, as frequently as practicable during those times when a worker can safely access the cover.

(2) In the case when a tank is buried partially or entirely underground, an owner or operator is required to inspect and monitor, as required by the applicable provisions of this section, only those portions of the tank cover and those connections to the tank (*e.g.*, fill ports, access hatches, gauge wells, etc.) that are located on or above the ground surface.

[61 FR 59979, Nov. 25, 1996, as amended at 62 FR 64666, Dec. 8, 1997; 64 FR 3391, Jan. 21, 1999; 71 FR 40276, July 14, 2006]

§265.1086 Standards: Surface impoundments. 15.3.6

(a) The provisions of this section apply to the control of air pollutant emissions from surface impoundments for which §265.1083(b) of this subpart references the use of this section for such air emission control.

(b) The owner or operator shall control air pollutant emissions from the surface impoundment by installing and operating either of the following:

(1) A floating membrane cover in accordance with the provisions specified in paragraph (c) of this section; or

(2) A cover that is vented through a closed-vent system to a control device in accordance with the requirements specified in paragraph (d) of this section.

(c) The owner or operator who controls air pollutant emissions from a surface impoundment using a floating membrane cover shall meet the requirements specified in paragraphs (c)(1) through (c)(3) of this section.

(1) The surface impoundment shall be equipped with a floating membrane cover designed to meet the following specifications:

(i) The floating membrane cover shall be designed to float on the liquid surface during normal operations and form a continuous barrier over the entire surface area of the liquid.

(ii) The cover shall be fabricated from a synthetic membrane material that is either:

(A) High density polyethylene (HDPE) with a thickness no less than 2.5 millimeters (mm); or

(B) A material or a composite of different materials determined to have both organic permeability properties that are equivalent to those of the material listed in paragraph (c)(1)(ii)(A) of this section and chemical and physical properties that maintain the material integrity for the intended service life of the material.

(iii) The cover shall be installed in a manner such that there are no visible cracks, holes, gaps, or other open spaces between cover section seams or between the interface of the cover edge and its foundation mountings.

(iv) Except as provided for in paragraph (c)(1)(v) of this section, each opening in the floating membrane cover shall be equipped with a closure device designed to operate such that when the closure device is secured in the closed position there are no visible cracks, holes, gaps, or other open spaces in the closure device or between the perimeter of the cover opening and the closure device.

(v) The floating membrane cover may be equipped with one or more emergency cover drains for removal of stormwater. Each emergency cover drain shall be equipped with a slotted membrane fabric cover that covers at least 90 percent of the area of the opening or a flexible fabric sleeve seal.

(vi) The closure devices shall be made of suitable materials that will minimize exposure of the hazardous waste to the atmosphere, to the extent practical, and will maintain the integrity of the closure devices throughout their intended service life. Factors to be considered when selecting the materials of construction and designing the cover and closure devices shall include: Organic vapor permeability; the effects of any contact with the liquid and its vapor managed in the surface impoundment; the effects of outdoor exposure to wind, moisture, and sunlight; and the operating practices used for the surface impoundment on which the floating membrane cover is installed.

(2) Whenever a hazardous waste is in the surface impoundment, the floating membrane cover shall float on the liquid and each closure device shall be secured in the closed position except as follows:

(i) Opening of closure devices or removal of the cover is allowed at the following times:

(A) To provide access to the surface impoundment for performing routine inspection, maintenance, or other activities needed for normal operations. Examples of such activities include those times when a worker needs to open a port to sample the liquid in the surface impoundment, or when a worker needs to open a hatch to maintain or repair equipment. Following completion of the activity, the owner or operator shall promptly replace the cover and secure the closure device in the closed position, as applicable.

(B) To remove accumulated sludge or other residues from the bottom of surface impoundment.

(ii) Opening of a safety device, as defined in §265.1081 of this subpart, is allowed at any time conditions require doing so to avoid an unsafe condition.

(3) The owner or operator shall inspect the floating membrane cover in accordance with the following procedures:

(i) The floating membrane cover and its closure devices shall be visually inspected by the owner or operator to check for defects that could result in air pollutant emissions. Defects include, but are not limited to, visible cracks, holes, or gaps in the cover section seams or between the interface of the cover edge and its foundation mountings; broken, cracked, or otherwise damaged seals or gaskets on closure devices; and broken or missing hatches, access covers, caps, or other closure devices.

(ii) The owner or operator shall perform an initial inspection of the floating membrane cover and its closure devices on or before the date that the surface impoundment becomes subject to this section. Thereafter, the owner or operator shall perform the inspections at least once every year except for the special conditions provided for in paragraph (g) of this section.

(iii) In the event that a defect is detected, the owner or operator shall repair the defect in accordance with the requirements of paragraph (f) of this section.

(iv) The owner or operator shall maintain a record of the inspection in accordance with the requirements specified in §265.1090(c) of this subpart.

(d) The owner or operator who controls air pollutant emissions from a surface impoundment using a cover vented to a control device shall meet the requirements specified in paragraphs (d)(1) through (d)(3) of this section.

(1) The surface impoundment shall be covered by a cover and vented directly through a closed-vent system to a control device in accordance with the following requirements:

(i) The cover and its closure devices shall be designed to form a continuous barrier over the entire surface area of the liquid in the surface impoundment.

(ii) Each opening in the cover not vented to the control device shall be equipped with a closure device. If the pressure in the vapor headspace underneath the cover is less than atmospheric pressure when the control device is operating, the closure devices shall be designed to operate such that when the closure device is secured in the closed position there are no visible cracks, holes, gaps, or other open spaces in the closure device or between the perimeter of the cover opening and the closure device. If the pressure in the vapor headspace underneath the cover is equal to or greater than atmospheric pressure when the control device is operating, the closure device shall be designed to operate with no detectable organic emissions using the procedure specified in §265.1084(d) of this subpart.

(iii) The cover and its closure devices shall be made of suitable materials that will minimize exposure of the hazardous waste to the atmosphere, to the extent practical, and will maintain the integrity of the cover and closure devices throughout their intended service life. Factors to be considered when selecting the materials of construction and designing the cover and closure devices shall include: Organic vapor permeability; the effects of any contact with the liquid or its vapors managed in the surface impoundment; the effects of outdoor exposure to wind, moisture, and sunlight; and the operating practices used for the surface impoundment on which the cover is installed.

(iv) The closed-vent system and control device shall be designed and operated in accordance with the requirements of §265.1088 of this subpart.

(2) Whenever a hazardous waste is in the surface impoundment, the cover shall be installed with each closure device secured in the closed position and the vapor headspace underneath the cover vented to the control device except as follows:

(i) Venting to the control device is not required, and opening of closure devices or removal of the cover is allowed at the following times:

(A) To provide access to the surface impoundment for performing routine inspection, maintenance, or other activities needed for normal operations. Examples of such activities include those times when a worker needs to open a port to sample liquid in the surface impoundment, or when a worker needs to open a hatch to maintain or repair equipment. Following completion of the activity, the owner or operator shall promptly secure the closure device in the closed position or reinstall the cover, as applicable, to the surface impoundment.

(B) To remove accumulated sludge or other residues from the bottom of the surface impoundment.

(ii) Opening of a safety device, as defined in §265.1081 of this subpart, is allowed at any time conditions require doing so to avoid an unsafe condition.

(3) The owner or operator shall inspect and monitor the air emission control equipment in accordance with the following procedures:

(i) The surface impoundment cover and its closure devices shall be visually inspected by the owner or operator to check for defects that could result in air pollutant emissions. Defects include, but are not limited to, visible cracks, holes, or gaps in the cover section seams or between the interface of the cover edge and its foundation mountings; broken, cracked, or otherwise damaged seals or gaskets on closure devices; and broken or missing hatches, access covers, caps, or other closure devices.

(ii) The closed-vent system and control device shall be inspected and monitored by the owner or operator in accordance with the procedures specified in §265.1088 of this subpart.

(iii) The owner or operator shall perform an initial inspection of the air emission control equipment on or before the date that the surface impoundment becomes subject to this section. Thereafter, the owner or operator shall perform the inspections at least once every year except for the special conditions provided for in paragraph (g) of this section.

(iv) In the event that a defect is detected, the owner or operator shall repair the defect in accordance with the requirements of paragraph (f) of this section.

(v) The owner or operator shall maintain a record of the inspection in accordance with the requirements specified in §265.1090(c) of this subpart.

(e) The owner or operator shall transfer hazardous waste to a surface impoundment subject to this section in accordance with the following requirements:

(1) Transfer of hazardous waste, except as provided in paragraph (e)(2) of this section, to the surface impoundment from another surface impoundment subject to this section or from a tank subject to §265.1085 of this subpart shall be conducted using continuous hard-piping or another closed system that does not allow exposure of the waste to the atmosphere. For the purpose of complying with this provision, an individual drain system is considered to be a closed system when it meets the requirements of 40 CFR part 63, subpart RR—National Emission Standards for Individual Drain Systems.

(2) The requirements of paragraph (e)(1) of this section do not apply when transferring a hazardous waste to the surface impoundment under either of the following conditions:

(i) The hazardous waste meets the average VO concentration conditions specified in §265.1083(c)(1) of this subpart at the point of waste origination.

(ii) The hazardous waste has been treated by an organic destruction or removal process to meet the requirements in §265.1083(c)(2) of this subpart.

(iii) The hazardous waste meets the requirements of §265.1083(c)(4) of this subpart.

(f) The owner or operator shall repair each defect detected during an inspection performed in accordance with the requirements of paragraph (c)(3) or (d)(3) of this section as follows:

(1) The owner or operator shall make first efforts at repair of the defect no later than 5 calendar days after detection, and repair shall be completed as soon as possible but no later than 45 calendar days after detection except as provided in paragraph (f)(2) of this section.

(2) Repair of a defect may be delayed beyond 45 calendar days if the owner or operator determines that repair of the defect requires emptying or temporary removal from service of the surface impoundment and no alternative capacity is available at the site to accept the hazardous waste normally managed in the surface impoundment. In this case, the owner or operator shall repair the defect the next time the process or unit that is generating the hazardous waste managed in the tank stops operation. Repair of the defect shall be completed before the process or unit resumes operation.

(g) Following the initial inspection and monitoring of the cover as required by the applicable provisions of this subpart, subsequent inspection and monitoring may be performed at intervals longer than 1 year in the case when inspecting or monitoring the cover would expose a worker to dangerous, hazardous, or other unsafe conditions. In this case, the owner or operator may designate the cover as an "unsafe to inspect and monitor cover" and comply with all of the following requirements:

(1) Prepare a written explanation for the cover stating the reasons why the cover is unsafe to visually inspect or to monitor, if required.

(2) Develop and implement a written plan and schedule to inspect and monitor the cover using the procedures specified in the applicable section of this subpart as frequently as practicable during those times when a worker can safely access the cover.

[61 FR 59984, Nov. 25, 1996, as amended at 62 FR 64666, Dec. 8, 1997]

§265.1087 Standards: Containers. 15.3.5

(a) The provisions of this section apply to the control of air pollutant emissions from containers for which §265.1083(b) of this subpart references the use of this section for such air emission control.

(b) *General requirements.* (1) The owner or operator shall control air pollutant emissions from each container subject to this section in accordance with the following requirements, as applicable to the container, except when the special provisions for waste stabilization processes specified in paragraph (b)(2) of this section apply to the container.

(i) For a container having a design capacity greater than 0.1 m^3 and less than or equal to 0.46 m^3, the owner or operator shall control air pollutant emissions from the container in accordance with the Container Level 1 standards specified in paragraph (c) of this section. 15.3.5.1

(ii) For a container having a design capacity greater than 0.46 m^3 that is not in light material service, the owner or operator shall control air pollutant emissions from the container in accordance with the Container Level 1 standards specified in paragraph (c) of this section. 15.3.5.1

(iii) For a container having a design capacity greater than 0.46 m^3 that is in light material service, the owner or operator shall control air pollutant emissions from the container in accordance with the Container Level 2 standards specified in paragraph (d) of this section. 15.3.5.2

(2) When a container having a design capacity greater than 0.1 m^3 is used for treatment of a hazardous waste by a waste stabilization process, the owner or operator shall control air pollutant emissions from the container in accordance with the Container Level 3 standards specified in paragraph (e) of this section at those times during the waste stabilization process when the hazardous waste in the container is exposed to the atmosphere. 15.3.5.3

(c) *Container Level 1 standards.* (1) A container using Container Level 1 controls is one of the following: 15.3.5.1.1

(i) A container that meets the applicable U.S. Department of Transportation (DOT) regulations on packaging hazardous materials for transportation as specified in paragraph (f) of this section.

(ii) A container equipped with a cover and closure devices that form a continuous barrier over the container openings such that when the cover and closure devices are secured in the closed position there are no visible holes, gaps, or other open spaces into the interior of the container. The cover may be a separate cover installed on the container (*e.g.*, a lid on a drum or a suitably secured tarp on a roll-off box) or may be an integral part of the container structural design (*e.g.*, a "portable tank" or bulk cargo container equipped with a screw-type cap).

(iii) An open-top container in which an organic-vapor suppressing barrier is placed on or over the hazardous waste in the container such that no hazardous waste is exposed to the atmosphere. One example of such a barrier is application of a suitable organic-vapor suppressing foam.

(2) A container used to meet the requirements of paragraph (c)(1)(ii) or (c)(1)(iii) of this section shall be equipped with covers and closure devices, as applicable to the container, that are composed of suitable materials to minimize exposure of the hazardous waste to the atmosphere and to maintain the equipment integrity for as long as it is in service. Factors to be considered in selecting the materials of construction and designing the cover and closure devices shall include: Organic vapor permeability, the effects of contact with the hazardous waste or its vapor managed in the container; the effects of outdoor exposure of the closure device or cover material to wind, moisture, and sunlight; and the operating practices for which the container is intended to be used.

(3) Whenever a hazardous waste is in a container using Container Level 1 controls, the owner or operator shall install all covers and closure devices for the container, as applicable to the container, and secure and maintain each closure device in the closed position except as follows: 15.3.5.1.2

PART 265—Subpart CC

(i) Opening of a closure device or cover is allowed for the purpose of adding hazardous waste or other material to the container as follows:

(A) In the case when the container is filled to the intended final level in one continuous operation, the owner or operator shall promptly secure the closure devices in the closed position and install the covers, as applicable to the container, upon conclusion of the filling operation.

(B) In the case when discrete quantities or batches of material intermittently are added to the container over a period of time, the owner or operator shall promptly secure the closure devices in the closed position and install covers, as applicable to the container, upon either the container being filled to the intended final level; the completion of a batch loading after which no additional material will be added to the container within 15 minutes; the person performing the loading operation leaving the immediate vicinity of the container; or the shutdown of the process generating the material being added to the container, whichever condition occurs first.

(ii) Opening of a closure device or cover is allowed for the purpose of removing hazardous waste from the container as follows:

(A) For the purpose of meeting the requirements of this section, an empty container as defined in 40 CFR 261.7(b) may be open to the atmosphere at any time (*i.e.*, covers and closure devices are not required to be secured in the closed position on an empty container).

(B) In the case when discrete quantities or batches of material are removed from the container but the container does not meet the conditions to be an empty container as defined in 40 CFR 261.7(b), the owner or operator shall promptly secure the closure devices in the closed position and install covers, as applicable to the container, upon the completion of a batch removal after which no additional material will be removed from the container within 15 minutes or the person performing the unloading operation leaves the immediate vicinity of the container, whichever condition occurs first.

(iii) Opening of a closure device or cover is allowed when access inside the container is needed to perform routine activities other than transfer of hazardous waste. Examples of such activities include those times when a worker needs to open a port to measure the depth of or sample the material in the container, or when a worker needs to open a manhole hatch to access equipment inside the container. Following completion of the activity, the owner or operator shall promptly secure the closure device in the closed position or reinstall the cover, as applicable to the container.

(iv) Opening of a spring-loaded, pressure-vacuum relief valve, conservation vent, or similar type of pressure relief device which vents to the atmosphere is allowed during normal operations for the purpose of maintaining the container internal pressure in accordance with the design specifications of the container. The device shall be designed to operate with no detectable organic emissions when the device is secured in the closed position. The settings at which the device opens shall be established such that the device remains in the closed position whenever the internal pressure of the container is within the internal pressure operating range determined by the owner or operator based on container manufacturer recommendations, applicable regulations, fire protection and prevention codes, standard engineering codes and practices, or other requirements for the safe handling of flammable, ignitable, explosive, reactive, or hazardous materials. Examples of normal operating conditions that may require these devices to open are during those times when the internal pressure of the container exceeds the internal pressure operating range for the container as a result of loading operations or diurnal ambient temperature fluctuations.

(v) Opening of a safety device, as defined in §265.1081 of this subpart, is allowed at any time conditions require doing so to avoid an unsafe condition.

(4) The owner or operator of containers using Container Level 1 controls shall inspect the containers and their covers and closure devices as follows: 15.3.5.1.3

(i) In the case when a hazardous waste already is in the container at the time the owner or operator first accepts possession of the container at the facility and the container is not emptied within 24 hours after the container is accepted at the facility (*i.e.*, does not meet the conditions for an empty container as specified in 40 CFR 261.7(b)), the owner or operator shall visually inspect the container and its cover and closure devices to check for visible cracks, holes, gaps, or other open spaces into the interior of the container when the cover and closure devices are secured in the closed position. The container visual inspection shall be conducted on or before the date that the container is accepted at the facility (*i.e.*, the date the container becomes subject to the subpart CC container standards). For purposes of this requirement, the date of acceptance is the date of signature that the facility owner or operator enters on Item 20 of the Uniform Hazardous Waste Manifest in the appendix to 40 CFR part 262 (EPA Forms 8700-22 and 8700-22A), as required under subpart E of this part, at 40 CFR 265.71. If a defect is detected, the owner or operator shall repair the defect in accordance with the requirements of paragraph (c)(4)(iii) of this section.

(ii) In the case when a container used for managing hazardous waste remains at the facility for a period of 1 year or more, the owner or operator shall visually inspect the container and its cover and closure devices initially and thereafter, at least once every 12 months, to check for visible cracks, holes, gaps, or other open spaces into the interior of the container when the cover and closure devices are secured in the closed position. If a defect is detected, the owner or operator shall repair the defect in accordance with the requirements of paragraph (c)(4)(iii) of this section.

(iii) When a defect is detected for the container, cover, or closure devices, the owner or operator shall make first efforts at repair of the defect no later than 24 hours after detection, and repair shall be completed as soon as possible but no later than 5 calendar days after detection. If repair of a defect cannot be completed within 5 calendar days, then the hazardous waste shall be removed from the container and the container shall not be used to manage hazardous waste until the defect is repaired.

(5) The owner or operator shall maintain at the facility a copy of the procedure used to determine that containers with capacity of 0.46 m^3 or greater, which do not meet applicable DOT regulations as specified in paragraph (f) of this section, are not managing hazardous waste in light material service.

(d) *Container Level 2 standards.* (1) A container using Container Level 2 controls is one of the following:

15.3.5.2.1

(i) A container that meets the applicable U.S. Department of Transportation (DOT) regulations on packaging hazardous materials for transportation as specified in paragraph (f) of this section.

(ii) A container that operates with no detectable organic emissions as defined in §265.1081 of this subpart and determined in accordance with the procedure specified in paragraph (g) of this section.

(iii) A container that has been demonstrated within the preceding 12 months to be vapor-tight by using 40 CFR part 60, appendix A, Method 27 in accordance with the procedure specified in paragraph (h) of this section.

(2) Transfer of hazardous waste in or out of a container using Container Level 2 controls shall be conducted in such a manner as to minimize exposure of the hazardous waste to the atmosphere, to the extent practical, considering the physical properties of the hazardous waste and good engineering and safety practices for handling flammable, ignitable, explosive, reactive or other hazardous materials. Examples of container loading procedures that the EPA considers to meet the requirements of this paragraph include using any one of the following: A submerged-fill pipe or other submerged-fill method to load liquids into the container; a vapor-balancing system or a vapor-recovery system to collect and control the vapors displaced from the container during filling operations; or a fitted opening in the top of a container through which the hazardous waste is filled and subsequently purging the transfer line before removing it from the container opening. 15.3.5.2.2

(3) Whenever a hazardous waste is in a container using Container Level 2 controls, the owner or operator shall install all covers and closure devices for the container, and secure and maintain each closure device in the closed position except as follows: 15.3.5.2.2

(i) Opening of a closure device or cover is allowed for the purpose of adding hazardous waste or other material to the container as follows:

(A) In the case when the container is filled to the intended final level in one continuous operation, the owner or operator shall promptly secure the closure devices in the closed position and install the covers, as applicable to the container, upon conclusion of the filling operation.

(B) In the case when discrete quantities or batches of material intermittently are added to the container over a period of time, the owner or operator shall promptly secure the closure devices in the closed position and install covers, as applicable to the container, upon either the container being filled to the intended final level; the completion of a batch loading after which no additional material will be added to the container within 15 minutes; the person performing the loading operation leaving the immediate vicinity of the container; or the shutdown of the process generating the material being added to the container, whichever condition occurs first.

(ii) Opening of a closure device or cover is allowed for the purpose of removing hazardous waste from the container as follows:

(A) For the purpose of meeting the requirements of this section, an empty container as defined in 40 CFR 261.7(b) may be open to the atmosphere at any time (*i.e.*, covers and closure devices are not required to be secured in the closed position on an empty container).

(B) In the case when discrete quantities or batches of material are removed from the container but the container does not meet the conditions to be an empty container as defined in 40 CFR 261.7(b), the owner or operator shall promptly secure the closure devices in the closed position and install covers, as applicable to the container, upon the completion of a batch removal after which no additional material will be removed from the container within 15 minutes or the person performing the unloading operation leaves the immediate vicinity of the container, whichever condition occurs first.

(iii) Opening of a closure device or cover is allowed when access inside the container is needed to perform routine activities other than transfer of hazardous waste. Examples of such activities include those times when a worker needs to open a port to measure the depth of or sample the material in the container, or when a worker needs to open a manhole hatch to access equipment inside the container. Following completion of the activity, the owner or operator shall promptly secure the closure device in the closed position or reinstall the cover, as applicable to the container.

(iv) Opening of a spring-loaded, pressure-vacuum relief valve, conservation vent, or similar type of pressure relief device which vents to the atmosphere is allowed during normal operations for the purpose of maintaining the internal pressure of the container in accordance with the container design specifications. The device shall be designed to operate with no detectable organic emission when the device is secured in the closed position. The settings at which the device opens shall be established such that the device remains in the closed position whenever the internal pressure of the container is within the internal pressure operating range determined by the owner or operator based on container manufacturer recommendations, applicable regulations, fire protection and prevention codes, standard engineering codes and practices, or other requirements for the safe handling of flammable, ignitable, explosive, reactive, or hazardous materials. Examples of normal operating conditions that may require these devices to open are during those times when the internal pressure of the container exceeds the internal pressure operating range for the container as a result of loading operations or diurnal ambient temperature fluctuations.

(v) Opening of a safety device, as defined in §265.1081 of this subpart, is allowed at any time conditions require doing so to avoid an unsafe condition.

(4) The owner or operator of containers using Container Level 2 controls shall inspect the containers and their covers and closure devices as follows: 📖 15.3.5.2.3

(i) In the case when a hazardous waste already is in the container at the time the owner or operator first accepts possession of the container at the facility and the container is not emptied within 24 hours after the container is accepted at the facility (*i.e.*, does not meet the conditions for an empty container as specified in 40 CFR 261.7(b)), the owner or operator shall visually inspect the container and its cover and closure devices to check for visible cracks, holes, gaps, or other open spaces into the interior of the container when the cover and closure devices are secured in the closed position. The container visual inspection shall be conducted on or before the date that the container is accepted at the facility (*i.e.*, the date the container becomes subject to the subpart CC container standards). For purposes of this requirement, the date of acceptance is the date of signature that the facility owner or operator enters on Item 20 of the Uniform Hazardous Waste Manifest in the appendix to 40 CFR part 262 (EPA Forms 8700-22 and 8700-22A), as required under subpart E of this part, at §265.71. If a defect is detected, the owner or operator shall repair the defect in accordance with the requirements of paragraph (d)(4)(iii) of this section.

(ii) In the case when a container used for managing hazardous waste remains at the facility for a period of 1 year or more, the owner or operator shall visually inspect the container and its cover and closure devices initially and thereafter, at least once every 12 months, to check for visible cracks, holes, gaps, or other open spaces into the interior of the container when the cover and closure devices are secured in the closed position. If a defect is detected, the owner or operator shall repair the defect in accordance with the requirements of paragraph (d)(4)(iii) of this section.

(iii) When a defect is detected for the container, cover, or closure devices, the owner or operator shall make first efforts at repair of the defect no later than 24 hours after detection, and repair shall be completed as soon as possible but no later than 5 calendar days after detection. If repair of a defect cannot be completed within 5 calendar days, then the hazardous waste shall be removed from the container and the container shall not be used to manage hazardous waste until the defect is repaired.

(e) *Container Level 3 standards.* (1) A container using Container Level 3 controls is one of the following:

15.3.5.3

(i) A container that is vented directly through a closed-vent system to a control device in accordance with the requirements of paragraph (e)(2)(ii) of this section.

(ii) A container that is vented inside an enclosure which is exhausted through a closed-vent system to a control device in accordance with the requirements of paragraphs (e)(2)(i) and (e)(2)(ii) of this section.

(2) The owner or operator shall meet the following requirements, as applicable to the type of air emission control equipment selected by the owner or operator:

(i) The container enclosure shall be designed and operated in accordance with the criteria for a permanent total enclosure as specified in "Procedure T—Criteria for and Verification of a Permanent or Temporary Total Enclosure" under 40 CFR 52.741, appendix B. The enclosure may have permanent or temporary openings to allow worker access; passage of containers through the enclosure by conveyor or other mechanical means; entry of permanent mechanical or electrical equipment; or direct airflow into the enclosure. The owner or operator shall perform the verification procedure for the enclosure as specified in Section 5.0 to "Procedure T—Criteria for and Verification of a Permanent or Temporary Total Enclosure" initially when the enclosure is first installed and, thereafter, annually.

(ii) The closed-vent system and control device shall be designed and operated in accordance with the requirements of §265.1088 of this subpart.

(3) Safety devices, as defined in §265.1081 of this subpart, may be installed and operated as necessary on any container, enclosure, closed-vent system, or control device used to comply with the requirements of paragraph (e)(1) of this section.

(4) Owners and operators using Container Level 3 controls in accordance with the provisions of this subpart shall inspect and monitor the closed-vent systems and control devices as specified in §265.1088 of this subpart.

(5) Owners and operators that use Container Level 3 controls in accordance with the provisions of this subpart shall prepare and maintain the records specified in §265.1090(d) of this subpart.

(6) Transfer of hazardous waste in or out of a container using Container Level 3 controls shall be conducted in such a manner as to minimize exposure of the hazardous waste to the atmosphere, to the extent practical, considering the physical properties of the hazardous waste and good engineering and safety practices for handling flammable, ignitable, explosive, reactive, or other hazardous materials. Examples of container loading procedures that the EPA considers to meet the requirements of this paragraph include using any one of the following: A submerged-fill pipe or other submerged-fill method to load liquids into the container; a vapor-balancing system or a vapor-recovery system to collect and control the vapors displaced from the container during filling operations; or a fitted opening in the top of a container through which the hazardous waste is filled and subsequently purging the transfer line before removing it from the container opening.

15.3.5.3.1

(f) For the purpose of compliance with paragraph (c)(1)(i) or (d)(1)(i) of this section, containers shall be used that meet the applicable U.S. Department of Transportation (DOT) regulations on packaging hazardous materials for transportation as follows:

(1) The container meets the applicable requirements specified in 49 CFR part 178—Specifications for Packaging or 49 CFR part 179—Specifications for Tank Cars.

(2) Hazardous waste is managed in the container in accordance with the applicable requirements specified in

49 CFR part 107, subpart B—Exemptions; 49 CFR part 172—Hazardous Materials Table, Special Provisions, Hazardous Materials Communications, Emergency Response Information, and Training Requirements; 49 CFR part 173—Shippers—General Requirements for Shipments and Packages; and 49 CFR part 180—Continuing Qualification and Maintenance of Packagings.

(3) For the purpose of complying with this subpart, no exceptions to the 49 CFR part 178 or part 179 regulations are allowed except as provided for in paragraph (f)(4) of this section.

(4) For a lab pack that is managed in accordance with the requirements of 49 CFR part 178 for the purpose of complying with this subpart, an owner or operator may comply with the exceptions for combination packagings specified in 49 CFR 173.12(b).

(g) To determine compliance with the no detectable organic emissions requirements of paragraph (d)(1)(ii) of this section, the procedure specified in §265.1084(d) of this subpart shall be used.

(1) Each potential leak interface (*i.e.*, a location where organic vapor leakage could occur) on the container, its cover, and associated closure devices, as applicable to the container, shall be checked. Potential leak interfaces that are associated with containers include, but are not limited to: The interface of the cover rim and the container wall; the periphery of any opening on the container or container cover and its associated closure device; and the sealing seat interface on a spring-loaded pressure-relief valve.

(2) The test shall be performed when the container is filled with a material having a volatile organic concentration representative of the range of volatile organic concentrations for the hazardous wastes expected to be managed in this type of container. During the test, the container cover and closure devices shall be secured in the closed position.

(h) Procedure for determining a container to be vapor-tight using Method 27 of 40 CFR part 60, appendix A for the purpose of complying with paragraph (d)(1)(iii) of this section.

(1) The test shall be performed in accordance with Method 27 of 40 CFR part 60, appendix A of this chapter.

(2) A pressure measurement device shall be used that has a precision of ±2.5 mm water and that is capable of measuring above the pressure at which the container is to be tested for vapor tightness.

(3) If the test results determined by Method 27 indicate that the container sustains a pressure change less than or equal to 750 Pascals within 5 minutes after it is pressurized to a minimum of 4,500 Pascals, then the container is determined to be vapor-tight.

[61 FR 59986, Nov. 25, 1996, as amended at 62 FR 64666, Dec. 8, 1997; 64 FR 3391, Jan. 21, 1999; 71 FR 40276, July 14, 2006]

§265.1088 Standards: Closed-vent systems and control devices.

(a) This section applies to each closed-vent system and control device installed and operated by the owner or operator to control air emissions in accordance with standards of this subpart.

(b) The closed-vent system shall meet the following requirements:

(1) The closed-vent system shall route the gases, vapors, and fumes emitted from the hazardous waste in the waste management unit to a control device that meets the requirements specified in paragraph (c) of this section.

(2) The closed-vent system shall be designed and operated in accordance with the requirements specified in §265.1033(j) of this part.

(3) In the case when the closed-vent system includes bypass devices that could be used to divert the gas or vapor stream to the atmosphere before entering the control device, each bypass device shall be equipped with either a flow indicator as specified in paragraph (b)(3)(i) of this section or a seal or locking device as specified in paragraph (b)(3)(ii) of this section. For the purpose of complying with this paragraph, low leg drains, high point bleeds, analyzer vents, open-ended valves or lines, spring-loaded pressure relief valves, and other fittings used for safety purposes are not considered to be bypass devices.

(i) If a flow indicator is used to comply with paragraph (b)(3) of this section, the indicator shall be installed at the inlet to the bypass line used to divert gases and vapors from the closed-vent system to the atmosphere at a point upstream of the control device inlet. For this paragraph, a flow indicator means a device which indicates the presence of either gas or vapor flow in the bypass line.

(ii) If a seal or locking device is used to comply with paragraph (b)(3) of this section, the device shall be placed on the mechanism by which the bypass device position is controlled (*e.g.*, valve handle, damper lever) when the bypass device is in the closed position such that the bypass device cannot be opened without breaking the seal or removing the lock. Examples of such devices include, but are not limited to, a car-seal or a lock-and-key configuration valve. The owner or operator shall visually inspect the seal or closure mechanism at least once every month to verify that the bypass mechanism is maintained in the closed position.

(4) The closed-vent system shall be inspected and monitored by the owner or operator in accordance with the procedure specified in 40 CFR 265.1033(k).

(c) The control device shall meet the following requirements: 14.5.3.1

(1) The control device shall be one of the following devices:

(i) A control device designed and operated to reduce the total organic content of the inlet vapor stream vented to the control device by at least 95 percent by weight;

(ii) An enclosed combustion device designed and operated in accordance with the requirements of §265.1033(c); or

(iii) A flare designed and operated in accordance with the requirements of §265.1033(d).

(2) The owner or operator who elects to use a closed-vent system and control device to comply with the requirements of this section shall comply with the requirements specified in paragraphs (c)(2)(i) through (c)(2)(vi) of this section.

(i) Periods of planned routine maintenance of the control device, during which the control device does not meet the specifications of paragraphs (c)(1)(i), (c)(1)(ii), or (c)(1)(iii) of this section, as applicable, shall not exceed 240 hours per year.

(ii) The specifications and requirements in paragraphs (c)(1)(i), (c)(1)(ii), and (c)(1)(iii) of this section for control devices do not apply during periods of planned routine maintenance.

(iii) The specifications and requirements in paragraphs (c)(1)(i), (c)(1)(ii), and (c)(1)(iii) of this section for control devices do not apply during a control device system malfunction.

(iv) The owner or operator shall demonstrate compliance with the requirements of paragraph (c)(2)(i) of this section (*i.e.*, planned routine maintenance of a control device, during which the control device does not meet the specifications of paragraphs (c)(1)(i), (c)(1)(ii), or (c)(1)(iii) of this section, as applicable, shall not exceed 240 hours per year) by recording the information specified in §265.1090(e)(1)(v) of this subpart.

(v) The owner or operator shall correct control device system malfunctions as soon as practicable after their occurrence in order to minimize excess emissions of air pollutants.

(vi) The owner or operator shall operate the closed-vent system such that gases, vapors, and/or fumes are not actively vented to the control device during periods of planned maintenance or control device system malfunction (*i.e.*, periods when the control device is not operating or not operating normally) except in cases when it is necessary to vent the gases, vapors, or fumes to avoid an unsafe condition or to implement malfunction corrective actions or planned maintenance actions.

(3) The owner or operator using a carbon adsorption system to comply with paragraph (c)(1) of this section shall operate and maintain the control device in accordance with the following requirements:

(i) Following the initial startup of the control device, all activated carbon in the control device shall be replaced with fresh carbon on a regular basis in accordance with the requirements of §265.1033(g) or §265.1033(h).

(ii) All carbon that is a hazardous waste and that is removed from the control device shall be managed in accordance with the requirements of 40 CFR 265.1033(m), regardless of the average volatile organic concentration of the carbon.

(4) An owner or operator using a control device other than a thermal vapor incinerator, flare, boiler, process heater, condenser, or carbon adsorption system to comply with paragraph (c)(1) of this section shall operate and maintain the control device in accordance with the requirements of §265.1033(i).

(5) The owner or operator shall demonstrate that a control device achieves the performance requirements of paragraph (c)(1) of this section as follows:

(i) An owner or operator shall demonstrate using either a performance test as specified in paragraph (c)(5)(iii) of this section or a design analysis as specified in paragraph (c)(5)(iv) of this section the performance of each control device except for the following:

(A) A flare;

(B) A boiler or process heater with a design heat input capacity of 44 megawatts or greater;

(C) A boiler or process heater into which the vent stream is introduced with the primary fuel;

(D) A boiler or industrial furnace burning hazardous waste for which the owner or operator has been issued a final permit under 40 CFR part 270 and has designed and operates the unit in accordance with the requirements of 40 CFR part 266, subpart H; or

(E) A boiler or industrial furnace burning hazardous waste for which the owner or operator has designed and operates in accordance with the interim status requirements of 40 CFR part 266, subpart H.

(ii) An owner or operator shall demonstrate the performance of each flare in accordance with the requirements specified in §265.1033(e).

(iii) For a performance test conducted to meet the requirements of paragraph (c)(5)(i) of this section, the owner or operator shall use the test methods and procedures specified in §265.1034(c)(1) through (c)(4).

(iv) For a design analysis conducted to meet the requirements of paragraph (c)(5)(i) of this section, the design analysis shall meet the requirements specified in §265.1035(b)(4)(iii).

(v) The owner or operator shall demonstrate that a carbon adsorption system achieves the performance requirements of paragraph (c)(1) of this section based on the total quantity of organics vented to the atmosphere from all carbon adsorption system equipment that is used for organic adsorption, organic desorption or carbon regeneration, organic recovery, and carbon disposal.

(6) If the owner or operator and the Regional Administrator do not agree on a demonstration of control device performance using a design analysis then the disagreement shall be resolved using the results of a performance test performed by the owner or operator in accordance with the requirements of paragraph (c)(5)(iii) of this section. The Regional Administrator may choose to have an authorized representative observe the performance test.

(7) The closed-vent system and control device shall be inspected and monitored by the owner or operator in accordance with the procedures specified in 40 CFR 265.1033(f)(2) and 40 CFR 265.1033(k). The readings from each monitoring device required by 40 CFR 265.1033(f)(2) shall be inspected at least once each operating day to check control device operation. Any necessary corrective measures shall be immediately implemented to ensure the control device is operated in compliance with the requirements of this section.

[59 FR 62935, Dec. 6, 1994, as amended at 61 FR 4915, Feb. 9, 1996; 61 FR 59989, Nov. 25, 1996; 62 FR 64667, Dec. 8, 1997]

§265.1089 Inspection and monitoring requirements.

(a) The owner or operator shall inspect and monitor air emission control equipment used to comply with this subpart in accordance with the applicable requirements specified in §265.1085 through §265.1088 of this subpart.

(b) The owner or operator shall develop and implement a written plan and schedule to perform the inspections and monitoring required by paragraph (a) of this section. The owner or operator shall incorporate this plan and schedule into the facility inspection plan required under 40 CFR 265.15.

[61 FR 59990, Nov. 25, 1996]

§265.1090 Recordkeeping requirements.

(a) Each owner or operator of a facility subject to requirements in this subpart shall record and maintain the information specified in paragraphs (b) through (j) of this section, as applicable to the facility. Except for air emission control equipment design documentation and information required by paragraphs (i) and (j) of this section, records required by this section shall be maintained in the operating record for a minimum of 3 years. Air emission control equipment design documentation shall be maintained in the operating record until the air emission control equipment is replaced or otherwise no longer in service. Information required by paragraphs (i) and (j) of this section shall be maintained in the operating record for as long as the waste management unit is not using air emission controls specified in §§265.1085 through 265.1088 of this subpart in accordance with the conditions specified in §265.1080(d) or §265.1080(b)(7) of this subpart, respectively.

(b) The owner or operator of a tank using air emission controls in accordance with the requirements of §265.1085 of this subpart shall prepare and maintain records for the tank that include the following information:

(1) For each tank using air emission controls in accordance with the requirements of §265.1085 of this subpart, the owner or operator shall record:

(i) A tank identification number (or other unique identification description as selected by the owner or operator).

(ii) A record for each inspection required by §265.1085 of this subpart that includes the following information: 📖 15.3.4.1.3, 15.3.4.2.3

(A) Date inspection was conducted.

(B) For each defect detected during the inspection: The location of the defect, a description of the defect, the date of detection, and corrective action taken to repair the defect. In the event that repair of the defect is delayed in accordance with the provisions of §265.1085 of this subpart, the owner or operator shall also record the reason for the delay and the date that completion of repair of the defect is expected.

(2) In addition to the information required by paragraph (b)(1) of this section, the owner or operator shall record the following information, as applicable to the tank:

(i) The owner or operator using a fixed roof to comply with the Tank Level 1 control requirements specified in §265.1085(c) of this subpart shall prepare and maintain records for each determination for the maximum organic vapor pressure of the hazardous waste in the tank performed in accordance with the requirements of §265.1085(c) of this subpart. The records shall include the date and time the samples were collected, the analysis method used, and the analysis results. 📖 15.3.4.1.3

(ii) The owner or operator using an internal floating roof to comply with the Tank Level 2 control requirements specified in §265.1085(e) of this subpart shall prepare and maintain documentation describing the floating roof design.

(iii) Owners and operators using an external floating roof to comply with the Tank Level 2 control requirements specified in §265.1085(f) of this subpart shall prepare and maintain the following records:

(A) Documentation describing the floating roof design and the dimensions of the tank.

(B) Records for each seal gap inspection required by §265.1085(f)(3) of this subpart describing the results of the seal gap measurements. The records shall include the date that the measurements were performed, the raw data obtained for the measurements, and the calculations of the total gap surface area. In the event that the seal gap measurements do not conform to the specifications in §265.1085(f)(1) of this subpart, the records shall include a description of the repairs that were made, the date the repairs were made, and the date the tank was emptied, if necessary.

(iv) Each owner or operator using an enclosure to comply with the Tank Level 2 control requirements specified in §265.1085(i) of this subpart shall prepare and maintain the following records:

(A) Records for the most recent set of calculations and measurements performed by the owner or operator to verify that the enclosure meets the criteria of a permanent total enclosure as specified in "Procedure T—Criteria for and Verification of a Permanent or Temporary Total Enclosure" under 40 CFR 52.741, appendix B.

(B) Records required for the closed-vent system and control device in accordance with the requirements of paragraph (e) of this section.

(c) The owner or operator of a surface impoundment using air emission controls in accordance with the requirements of §265.1086 of this subpart shall prepare and maintain records for the surface impoundment that include the following information:

(1) A surface impoundment identification number (or other unique identification description as selected by the owner or operator).

(2) Documentation describing the floating membrane cover or cover design, as applicable to the surface impoundment, that includes information prepared by the owner or operator or provided by the cover manufacturer or vendor describing the cover design, and certification by the owner or operator that the cover meets the specifications listed in §265.1086(c) of this subpart.

(3) A record for each inspection required by §265.1086 of this subpart that includes the following information:

(i) Date inspection was conducted.

(ii) For each defect detected during the inspection the following information: The location of the defect, a description of the defect, the date of detection, and corrective action taken to repair the defect. In the event that repair of the defect is delayed in accordance with the provisions of §265.1086(f) of this subpart, the owner or operator shall also record the reason for the delay and the date that completion of repair of the defect is expected.

(4) For a surface impoundment equipped with a cover and vented through a closed-vent system to a control device, the owner or operator shall prepare

and maintain the records specified in paragraph (e) of this section.

(d) The owner or operator of containers using Container Level 3 air emission controls in accordance with the requirements of §265.1087 of this subpart shall prepare and maintain records that include the following information:

(1) Records for the most recent set of calculations and measurements performed by the owner or operator to verify that the enclosure meets the criteria of a permanent total enclosure as specified in "Procedure T—Criteria for and Verification of a Permanent or Temporary Total Enclosure" under 40 CFR 52.741, appendix B.

(2) Records required for the closed-vent system and control device in accordance with the requirements of paragraph (e) of this section.

(e) The owner or operator using a closed-vent system and control device in accordance with the requirements of §265.1088 of this subpart shall prepare and maintain records that include the following information:

(1) Documentation for the closed-vent system and control device that includes:

(i) Certification that is signed and dated by the owner or operator stating that the control device is designed to operate at the performance level documented by a design analysis as specified in paragraph (e)(1)(ii) of this section or by performance tests as specified in paragraph (e)(1)(iii) of this section when the tank, surface impoundment, or container is or would be operating at capacity or the highest level reasonably expected to occur.

(ii) If a design analysis is used, then design documentation as specified in 40 CFR 265.1035(b)(4). The documentation shall include information prepared by the owner or operator or provided by the control device manufacturer or vendor that describes the control device design in accordance with 40 CFR 265.1035(b)(4)(iii) and certification by the owner or operator that the control equipment meets the applicable specifications.

(iii) If performance tests are used, then a performance test plan as specified in 40 CFR 265.1035(b)(3) and all test results.

(iv) Information as required by 40 CFR 265.1035(c)(1) and 40 CFR 265.1035(c)(2), as applicable.

(v) An owner or operator shall record, on a semiannual basis, the information specified in paragraphs (e)(1)(v)(A) and (e)(1)(v)(B) of this section for those planned routine maintenance operations that would require the control device not to meet the requirements of §265.1088 (c)(1)(i), (c)(1)(ii), or (c)(1)(iii) of this subpart, as applicable.

(A) A description of the planned routine maintenance that is anticipated to be performed for the control device during the next 6-month period. This description shall include the type of maintenance necessary, planned frequency of maintenance, and lengths of maintenance periods.

(B) A description of the planned routine maintenance that was performed for the control device during the previous 6-month period. This description shall include the type of maintenance performed and the total number of hours during those 6 months that the control device did not meet the requirements of §265.1088 (c)(1)(i), (c)(1)(ii), or (c)(1)(iii) of this subpart, as applicable, due to planned routine maintenance.

(vi) An owner or operator shall record the information specified in paragraphs (e)(1)(vi)(A) through (e)(1)(vi)(C) of this section for those unexpected control device system malfunctions that would require the control device not to meet the requirements of §265.1088 (c)(1)(i), (c)(1)(ii), or (c)(1)(iii) of this subpart, as applicable.

(A) The occurrence and duration of each malfunction of the control device system.

(B) The duration of each period during a malfunction when gases, vapors, or fumes are vented from the waste management unit through the closed-vent system to the control device while the control device is not properly functioning.

(C) Actions taken during periods of malfunction to restore a malfunctioning control device to its normal or usual manner of operation.

(vii) Records of the management of carbon removed from a carbon adsorption system conducted in accordance with §265.1088(c)(3)(ii) of this subpart.

(f) The owner or operator of a tank, surface impoundment, or container exempted from standards in accordance with the provisions of §265.1083(c) of this subpart shall prepare and maintain the following records, as applicable:

(1) For tanks, surface impoundments, or containers exempted under the hazardous waste organic concentration conditions specified in §265.1083(c)(1) or §265.1083(c)(2)(i) through (c)(2)(vi) of this subpart,

the owner or operator shall record the information used for each waste determination (*e.g.*, test results, measurements, calculations, and other documentation) in the facility operating log. If analysis results for waste samples are used for the waste determination, then the owner or operator shall record the date, time, and location that each waste sample is collected in accordance with applicable requirements of §265.1084 of this subpart.

(2) For tanks, surface impoundments, or containers exempted under the provisions of §265.1083(c)(2)(vii) or §265.1083(c)(2)(viii) of this subpart, the owner or operator shall record the identification number for the incinerator, boiler, or industrial furnace in which the hazardous waste is treated.

(g) An owner or operator designating a cover as "unsafe to inspect and monitor" pursuant to §265.1085(l) or §265.1086(g) of this subpart shall record in a log that is kept in the facility operating record the following information: The identification numbers for waste management units with covers that are designated as "unsafe to inspect and monitor," the explanation for each cover stating why the cover is unsafe to inspect and monitor, and the plan and schedule for inspecting and monitoring each cover.

(h) The owner or operator of a facility that is subject to this subpart and to the control device standards in 40 CFR part 60, subpart VV, or 40 CFR part 61, subpart V, may elect to demonstrate compliance with the applicable sections of this subpart by documentation either pursuant to this subpart, or pursuant to the provisions of 40 CFR part 60, subpart VV or 40 CFR part 61, subpart V, to the extent that the documentation required by 40 CFR parts 60 or 61 duplicates the documentation required by this section.

(i) For each tank or container not using air emission controls specified in §§265.1085 through 265.1088 of this subpart in accordance with the conditions specified in §265.1080(d) of this subpart, the owner or operator shall record and maintain the following information:

(1) A list of the individual organic peroxide compounds manufactured at the facility that meet the conditions specified in §265.1080(d)(1).

(2) A description of how the hazardous waste containing the organic peroxide compounds identified in paragraph (i)(1) of this section are managed at the facility in tanks and containers. This description shall include the following information:

(i) For the tanks used at the facility to manage this hazardous waste, sufficient information shall be provided to describe for each tank: A facility identification number for the tank; the purpose and placement of this tank in the management train of this hazardous waste; and the procedures used to ultimately dispose of the hazardous waste managed in the tanks.

(ii) For containers used at the facility to manage these hazardous wastes, sufficient information shall be provided to describe: A facility identification number for the container or group of containers; the purpose and placement of this container, or group of containers, in the management train of this hazardous waste; and the procedures used to ultimately dispose of the hazardous waste handled in the containers.

(3) An explanation of why managing the hazardous waste containing the organic peroxide compounds identified in paragraph (i)(1) of this section in the tanks and containers as described in paragraph (i)(2) of this section would create an undue safety hazard if the air emission controls, as required under §§265.1085 through 265.1088 of this subpart, are installed and operated on these waste management units. This explanation shall include the following information:

(i) For tanks used at the facility to manage these hazardous wastes, sufficient information shall be provided to explain: How use of the required air emission controls on the tanks would affect the tank design features and facility operating procedures currently used to prevent an undue safety hazard during the management of this hazardous waste in the tanks; and why installation of safety devices on the required air emission controls, as allowed under this subpart, will not address those situations in which evacuation of tanks equipped with these air emission controls is necessary and consistent with good engineering and safety practices for handling organic peroxides.

(ii) For containers used at the facility to manage these hazardous wastes, sufficient information shall be provided to explain: How use of the required air emission controls on the containers would affect the container design features and handling procedures currently used to prevent an undue safety hazard during the management of this hazardous waste in the containers; and why installation of safety devices on the required air emission controls, as allowed under this subpart, will not address those situations in which evacuation of containers equipped with these air emission controls is necessary and consistent with good engineering and safety practices for handling organic peroxides.

(j) For each hazardous waste management unit not using air emission controls specified in §§265.1085 through 265.1088 of this subpart in accordance with the provisions of §265.1080(b)(7) of this subpart, the owner and operator shall record and maintain the following information:

(1) Certification that the waste management unit is equipped with and operating air emission controls in accordance with the requirements of an applicable Clean Air Act regulation codified under 40 CFR part 60, part 61, or part 63.

(2) Identification of the specific requirements codified under 40 CFR part 60, part 61, or part 63 with which the waste management unit is in compliance.

[61 FR 59990, Nov. 25, 1996, as amended at 62 FR 64667, Dec. 8, 1997; 71 FR 40276, July 14, 2006]

§265.1091 [Reserved]

Subpart DD—Containment Buildings

6.3.4.4, 7.3.2.1, 10.1.1, 13.8.4.1

Source: 57 FR 37268, Aug. 18, 1992, unless otherwise noted.

§265.1100 Applicability.

The requirements of this subpart apply to owners or operators who store or treat hazardous waste in units designed and operated under §265.1101 of this subpart. The owner or operator is not subject to the definition of land disposal in RCRA section 3004(k) provided that the unit:

(a) Is a completely enclosed, self-supporting structure that is designed and constructed of manmade materials of sufficient strength and thickness to support themselves, the waste contents, and any personnel and heavy equipment that operate within the units, and to prevent failure due to pressure gradients, settlement, compression, or uplift, physical contact with the hazardous wastes to which they are exposed; climatic conditions; and the stresses of daily operation, including the movement of heavy equipment within the unit and contact of such equipment with containment walls;

(b) Has a primary barrier that is designed to be sufficiently durable to withstand the movement of personnel and handling equipment within the unit;

(c) If the unit is used to manage liquids, has:

(1) A primary barrier designed and constructed of materials to prevent migration of hazardous constituents into the barrier;

(2) A liquid collection system designed and constructed of materials to minimize the accumulation of liquid on the primary barrier; and

(3) A secondary containment system designed and constructed of materials to prevent migration of hazardous constituents into the barrier, with a leak detection and liquid collection system capable of detecting, collecting, and removing leaks of hazardous constituents at the earliest possible time, unless the unit has been granted a variance from the secondary containment system requirements under §265.1101(b)(4);

(d) Has controls as needed to prevent fugitive dust emissions; and

(e) Is designed and operated to ensure containment and prevent the tracking of materials from the unit by personnel or equipment.

[57 FR 37268, Aug. 18, 1992, as amended at 71 FR 16912, Apr. 4, 2006; 71 FR 40276, July 14, 2006]

§265.1101 Design and operating standards.

(a) All containment buildings must comply with the following design standards:

(1) The containment building must be completely enclosed with a floor, walls, and a roof to prevent exposure to the elements, (*e.g.*, precipitation, wind, run-on), and to assure containment of managed wastes.

(2) The floor and containment walls of the unit, including the secondary containment system if required under paragraph (b) of this section, must be designed and constructed of materials of sufficient strength and thickness to support themselves, the waste contents, and any personnel and heavy equipment that operate within the unit, and to prevent failure due to pressure gradients, settlement, compression, or uplift, physical contact with the hazardous wastes to which they are exposed; climatic conditions; and the stresses of daily operation, including the movement of heavy equipment within the unit and contact of such equipment with containment walls. The unit must be designed so that it has sufficient structural strength to prevent collapse or other failure. All surfaces to be in contact with hazardous wastes must be chemically compatible with those wastes. EPA will consider standards established by professional organizations generally recognized by the industry such as the American Concrete Institute (ACI) and the American Society of Testing Materials

(ASTM) in judging the structural integrity requirements of this paragraph. If appropriate to the nature of the waste management operation to take place in the unit, an exception to the structural strength requirement may be made for light-weight doors and windows that meet these criteria:

(i) They provide an effective barrier against fugitive dust emissions under paragraph (c)(1)(iv); and

(ii) The unit is designed and operated in a fashion that assures that wastes will not actually come in contact with these openings.

(3) Incompatible hazardous wastes or treatment reagents must not be placed in the unit or its secondary containment system if they could cause the unit or secondary containment system to leak, corrode, or otherwise fail.

(4) A containment building must have a primary barrier designed to withstand the movement of personnel, waste, and handling equipment in the unit during the operating life of the unit and appropriate for the physical and chemical characteristics of the waste to be managed.

(b) For a containment building used to manage hazardous wastes containing free liquids or treated with free liquids (the presence of which is determined by the paint filter test, a visual examination, or other appropriate means), the owner or operator must include:

(1) A primary barrier designed and constructed of materials to prevent the migration of hazardous constituents into the barrier (e.g. a geomembrane covered by a concrete wear surface).

(2) A liquid collection and removal system to prevent the accumulation of liquid on the primary barrier of the containment building:

(i) The primary barrier must be sloped to drain liquids to the associated collection system; and

(ii) Liquids and waste must be collected and removed to minimize hydraulic head on the containment system at the earliest practicable time that protects human health and the environment.

(3) A secondary containment system including a secondary barrier designed and constructed to prevent migration of hazardous constituents into the barrier, and a leak detection system that is capable of detecting failure of the primary barrier and collecting accumulated hazardous wastes and liquids at the earliest practicable time.

(i) The requirements of the leak detection component of the secondary containment system are satisfied by installation of a system that is, at a minimum:

(A) Constructed with a bottom slope of 1 percent or more; and

(B) Constructed of a granular drainage material with a hydraulic conductivity of 1×10^{-2} cm/sec or more and a thickness of 12 inches (30.5 cm) or more, or constructed of synthetic or geonet drainage materials with a transmissivity of 3×10^{-5} m^2/sec or more.

(ii) If treatment is to be conducted in the building, an area in which such treatment will be conducted must be designed to prevent the release of liquids, wet materials, or liquid aerosols to other portions of the building.

(iii) The secondary containment system must be constructed of materials that are chemically resistant to the waste and liquids managed in the containment building and of sufficient strength and thickness to prevent collapse under the pressure exerted by overlaying materials and by any equipment used in the containment building. (Containment buildings can serve as secondary containment systems for tanks placed within the building under certain conditions. A containment building can serve as an external liner system for a tank, provided it meets the requirements of §265.193(e)(1). In addition, the containment building must meet the requirements of §265.193 (b) and (c) to be considered an acceptable secondary containment system for a tank.)

(4) For existing units other than 90-day generator units, the Regional Administrator may delay the secondary containment requirement for up to two years, based on a demonstration by the owner or operator that the unit substantially meets the standards of this Subpart. In making this demonstration, the owner or operator must:

(i) Provide written notice to the Regional Administrator of their request by February 18, 1993. This notification must describe the unit and its operating practices with specific reference to the performance of existing containment systems, and specific plans for retrofitting the unit with secondary containment;

(ii) Respond to any comments from the Regional Administrator on these plans within 30 days; and

(iii) Fulfill the terms of the revised plans, if such plans are approved by the Regional Administrator.

(c) Owners or operators of all containment buildings must:

(1) Use controls and practices to ensure containment of the hazardous waste within the unit; and, at a minimum:

(i) Maintain the primary barrier to be free of significant cracks, gaps, corrosion, or other deterioration that could cause hazardous waste to be released from the primary barrier;

(ii) Maintain the level of the stored/treated hazardous waste within the containment walls of the unit so that the height of any containment wall is not exceeded;

(iii) Take measures to prevent the tracking of hazardous waste out of the unit by personnel or by equipment used in handling the waste. An area must be designated to decontaminate equipment and any rinsate must be collected and properly managed; and

(iv) Take measures to control fugitive dust emissions such that any openings (doors, windows, vents, cracks, etc.) exhibit no visible emissions. In addition, all associated particulate collection devices (*e.g.,* fabric filter, electrostatic precipitator) must be operated and maintained with sound air pollution control practices. This state of no visible emissions must be maintained effectively at all times during normal operating conditions, including when vehicles and personnel are entering and exiting the unit.

(2) Obtain and keep on-site a certification by a qualified Professional Engineer that the containment building design meets the requirements of paragraphs (a), (b), and (c) of this section.

(3) Throughout the active life of the containment building, if the owner or operator detects a condition that could lead to or has caused a release of hazardous waste, the owner or operator must repair the condition promptly, in accordance with the following procedures.

(i) Upon detection of a condition that has led to a release of hazardous waste (*e.g.,* upon detection of leakage from the primary barrier) the owner or operator must:

(A) Enter a record of the discovery in the facility operating record;

(B) Immediately remove the portion of the containment building affected by the condition from service;

(C) Determine what steps must be taken to repair the containment building, remove any leakage from the secondary collection system, and establish a schedule for accomplishing the cleanup and repairs; and

(D) Within 7 days after the discovery of the condition, notify the Regional Administrator of the condition, and within 14 working days, provide a written notice to the Regional Administrator with a description of the steps taken to repair the containment building, and the schedule for accomplishing the work.

(ii) The Regional Administrator will review the information submitted, make a determination regarding whether the containment building must be removed from service completely or partially until repairs and cleanup are complete, and notify the owner or operator of the determination and the underlying rationale in writing.

(iii) Upon completing all repairs and cleanup the owner or operator must notify the Regional Administrator in writing and provide a verification, signed by a qualified, registered professional engineer, that the repairs and cleanup have been completed according to the written plan submitted in accordance with paragraph (c)(3)(i)(D) of this section.

(4) Inspect and record in the facility's operating record at least once every seven days, except for Performance Track member facilities, that must inspect up to once each month, upon approval of the director, data gathered from monitoring and leak detection equipment as well as the containment building and the area immediately surrounding the containment building to detect signs of releases of hazardous waste. To apply for reduced inspection frequency, the Performance Track member facility must follow the procedures described in §265.15(b)(5).

(d) For a containment building that contains both areas with and without secondary containment, the owner or operator must:

(1) Design and operate each area in accordance with the requirements enumerated in paragraphs (a) through (c) of this section;

(2) Take measures to prevent the release of liquids or wet materials into areas without secondary containment; and

(3) Maintain in the facility's operating log a written description of the operating procedures used to maintain the integrity of areas without secondary containment.

(e) Notwithstanding any other provision of this subpart, the Regional Administrator may waive requirements for secondary containment for a permitted containment building where the owner or operator demonstrates that the only free liquids in the unit are limited amounts of dust suppression liquids required to meet occupational health and safety requirements, and where containment of managed wastes and liquids can be assured without a secondary containment system.

[57 FR 37268, Aug. 18, 1992, as amended at 71 FR 16912, Apr. 4, 2006; 71 FR 40276, July 14, 2006]

§265.1102 Closure and post-closure care.

(a) At closure of a containment building, the owner or operator must remove or decontaminate all waste residues, contaminated containment system components (liners, etc.), contaminated subsoils, and structures and equipment contaminated with waste and leachate, and manage them as hazardous waste unless §261.3(d) of this chapter applies. The closure plan, closure activities, cost estimates for closure, and financial responsibility for containment buildings must meet all of the requirements specified in subparts G and H of this part.

(b) If, after removing or decontaminating all residues and making all reasonable efforts to effect removal or decontamination of contaminated components, subsoils, structures, and equipment as required in paragraph (a) of this section, the owner or operator finds that not all contaminated subsoils can be practicably removed or decontaminated, he must close the facility and perform post-closure care in accordance with the closure and post-closure requirements that apply to landfills (§265.310). In addition, for the purposes of closure, post-closure, and financial responsibility, such a containment building is then considered to be a landfill, and the owner or operator must meet all of the requirements for landfills specified in subparts G and H of this part.

§§265.1103–265.1110 [Reserved]

Subpart EE—Hazardous Waste Munitions and Explosives Storage

Source: 62 FR 6653, Feb. 12, 1997, unless otherwise noted.

§265.1200 Applicability.

The requirements of this subpart apply to owners or operators who store munitions and explosive hazardous wastes, except as §265.1 provides otherwise. (NOTE: Depending on explosive hazards, hazardous waste munitions and explosives may also be managed in other types of storage units, including containment buildings (40 CFR part 265, subpart DD), tanks (40 CFR part 265, subpart J), or containers (40 CFR part 265, subpart I); See 40 CFR 266.205 for storage of waste military munitions).

§265.1201 Design and operating standards.

(a) Hazardous waste munitions and explosives storage units must be designed and operated with containment systems, controls, and monitoring, that:

(1) Minimize the potential for detonation or other means of release of hazardous waste, hazardous constituents, hazardous decomposition products, or contaminated run-off, to the soil, ground water, surface water, and atmosphere;

(2) Provide a primary barrier, which may be a container (including a shell) or tank, designed to contain the hazardous waste;

(3) For wastes stored outdoors, provide that the waste and containers will not be in standing precipitation;

(4) For liquid wastes, provide a secondary containment system that assures that any released liquids are contained and promptly detected and removed from the waste area, or vapor detection system that assures that any released liquids or vapors are promptly detected and an appropriate response taken (*e.g.*, additional containment, such as overpacking, or removal from the waste area); and

(5) Provide monitoring and inspection procedures that assure the controls and containment systems are working as designed and that releases that may adversely impact human health or the environment are not escaping from the unit.

(b) Hazardous waste munitions and explosives stored under this subpart may be stored in one of the following:

(1) *Earth-covered magazines.* Earth-covered magazines must be:

(i) Constructed of waterproofed, reinforced concrete or structural steel arches, with steel doors that are kept closed when not being accessed;

(ii) Designed and constructed:

(A) To be of sufficient strength and thickness to support the weight of any explosives or munitions stored and any equipment used in the unit;

(B) To provide working space for personnel and equipment in the unit; and

(C) To withstand movement activities that occur in the unit; and

(iii) Located and designed, with walls and earthen covers that direct an explosion in the unit in a safe direction, so as to minimize the propagation of an explosion to adjacent units and to minimize other effects of any explosion.

(2) *Above-ground magazines.* Above-ground magazines must be located and designed so as to minimize the propagation of an explosion to adjacent units and to minimize other effects of any explosion.

(3) *Outdoor or open storage areas.* Outdoor or open storage areas must be located and designed so as to minimize the propagation of an explosion to adjacent units and to minimize other effects of any explosion.

(c) Hazardous waste munitions and explosives must be stored in accordance with a Standard Operating Procedure specifying procedures to ensure safety, security, and environmental protection. If these procedures serve the same purpose as the security and inspection requirements of 40 CFR 265.14, the preparedness and prevention procedures of 40 CFR part 265, subpart C, and the contingency plan and emergency procedures requirements of 40 CFR part 265, subpart D, then these procedures will be used to fulfill those requirements.

(d) Hazardous waste munitions and explosives must be packaged to ensure safety in handling and storage.

(e) Hazardous waste munitions and explosives must be inventoried at least annually.

(f) Hazardous waste munitions and explosives and their storage units must be inspected and monitored as necessary to ensure explosives safety and to ensure that there is no migration of contaminants out of the unit.

§265.1202 Closure and post-closure care.

(a) At closure of a magazine or unit which stored hazardous waste under this subpart, the owner or operator must remove or decontaminate all waste residues, contaminated containment system components, contaminated subsoils, and structures and equipment contaminated with waste, and manage them as hazardous waste unless §261.3(d) of this chapter applies. The closure plan, closure activities, cost estimates for closure, and financial responsibility for magazines or units must meet all of the requirements specified in subparts G and H of this part, except that the owner or operator may defer closure of the unit as long as it remains in service as a munitions or explosives magazine or storage unit.

(b) If, after removing or decontaminating all residues and making all reasonable efforts to effect removal or decontamination of contaminated components, subsoils, structures, and equipment as required in paragraph (a) of this section, the owner or operator finds that not all contaminated subsoils can be practicably removed or decontaminated, he or she must close the facility and perform post-closure care in accordance with the closure and post-closure requirements that apply to landfills (40 CFR 264.310).

Appendices to Part 265

Appendix I to Part 265—Recordkeeping Instructions

The recordkeeping provisions of §265.73 specify that an owner or operator must keep a written operating record at his facility. This appendix provides additional instructions for keeping portions of the operating record. See §265.73(b) for additional recordkeeping requirements.

The following information must be recorded, as it becomes available, and maintained in the operating record until closure of the facility in the following manner:

Records of each hazardous waste received, treated, stored, or disposed of at the facility which include the following:

(1) A description by its common name and the EPA Hazardous Waste Number(s) from part 261 of this chapter which apply to the waste. The waste description also must include the waste's physical form, *i.e.*, liquid, sludge, solid, or contained gas. If the waste is not listed in part 261, subpart D, of this chapter, the description also must include the process that produced it (for example, solid filter cake from production of ______, EPA Hazardous Waste Number W051).

Each hazardous waste listed in part 261, subpart D, of this chapter, and each hazardous waste characteristic defined in part 261, subpart C, of this chapter, has a four-digit EPA Hazardous Waste Number assigned to it. This number must be used for recordkeeping and reporting purposes. Where a hazardous waste contains more than one listed hazardous waste, or where more than one hazardous waste characteristic applies to the waste, the waste description must include all applicable EPA Hazardous Waste Numbers.

(2) The estimated or manifest-reported weight, or volume and density, where applicable, in one of the units of measure specified in Table 1; and

Table 1

Unit of measure	Code[1]	Unit of measure	Code[1]
Gallons	G	Cubic Yards	Y
Gallons per Hour	E	Cubic Meters	C
Gallons per Day	U	Acres	B
Liters	L	Acre-feet	A
Liters Per Hour	H	Hectares	Q
Liters Per Day	V	Hectare-meter	F
Short Tons Per Hour	D	Btu's per Hour	I
Metric Tons Per Hour	W	Pounds	P
Short Tons Per Day	N	Short tons	T
Metric Tons Per Day	S	Kilograms	K
Pounds Per Hour	J	Tons	M
Kilograms Per Hour	R		

[1]Single digit symbols are used here for data processing purposes.

(3) The method(s)(by handling code(s) as specified in Table 2) and date(s) of treatment, storage, or disposal.

Table 2—Handling Codes for Treatment, Storage and Disposal Methods

Enter the handling code(s) listed below that most closely represents the technique(s) used at the facility to treat, store or dispose of each quantity of hazardous waste received.

1. Storage
   - S01 Container (barrel, drum, etc.)
   - S02 Tank
   - S03 Waste Pile
   - S04 Surface Impoundment
   - S05 Drip Pad
   - S06 Containment Building (Storage)
   - S99 Other Storage (specify)
2. Treatment
   - (a) Thermal Treatment—
     - T06 Liquid injection incinerator
     - T07 Rotary kiln incinerator
     - T08 Fluidized bed incinerator
     - T09 Multiple hearth incinerator
     - T10 Infrared furnace incinerator
     - T11 Molten salt destructor
     - T12 Pyrolysis
     - T13 Wet Air oxidation
     - T14 Calcination
     - T15 Microwave discharge
     - T18 Other (specify)
   - (b) Chemical Treatment—
     - T19 Absorption mound
     - T20 Absorption field
     - T21 Chemical fixation
     - T22 Chemical oxidation
     - T23 Chemical precipitation
     - T24 Chemical reduction
     - T25 Chlorination
     - T26 Chlorinolysis
     - T27 Cyanide destruction
     - T28 Degradation
     - T29 Detoxification
     - T30 Ion exchange
     - T31 Neutralization
     - T32 Ozonation
     - T33 Photolysis
     - T34 Other (specify)
   - (c) Physical Treatment—
     - (1) Separation of components
       - T35 Centrifugation
       - T36 Clarification
       - T37 Coagulation
       - T38 Decanting
       - T39 Encapsulation
       - T40 Filtration
       - T41 Flocculation
       - T42 Flotation
       - T43 Foaming
       - T44 Sedimentation
       - T45 Thickening
       - T46 Ultrafiltration
       - T47 Other (specify)
     - (2) Removal of Specific Components
       - T48 Absorption-molecular sieve
       - T49 Activated carbon
       - T50 Blending
       - T51 Catalysis
       - T52 Crystallization
       - T53 Dialysis
       - T54 Distillation
       - T55 Electrodialysis
       - T56 Electrolysis
       - T57 Evaporation
       - T58 High gradient magnetic separation
       - T59 Leaching
       - T60 Liquid ion exchange
       - T61 Liquid-liquid extraction
       - T62 Reverse osmosis
       - T63 Solvent recovery
       - T64 Stripping
       - T65 Sand filter
       - T66 Other (specify)
   - (d) Biological Treatment
     - T67 Activated sludge
     - T68 Aerobic lagoon
     - T69 Aerobic tank
     - T70 Anaerobic tank
     - T71 Composting
     - T72 Septic tank
     - T73 Spray irrigation
     - T74 Thickening filter
     - T75 Trickling filter
     - T76 Waste stabilization pond
     - T77 Other (specify)
     - T78–T79 [Reserved]
   - (e) Boilers and Industrial Furnaces
     - T80 Boiler
     - T81 Cement Kiln
     - T82 Lime Kiln
     - T83 Aggregate Kiln
     - T84 Phosphate Kiln
     - T85 Coke Oven
     - T86 Blast Furnace
     - T87 Smelting, Melting, or Refining Furnace
     - T88 Titanium Dioxide Chloride Process Oxidation Reactor
     - T89 Methane Reforming Furnace
     - T90 Pulping Liquor Recovery Furnace

T91 Combustion Device Used in the Recovery of Sulfur Values From Spent Sulfuric Acid

T92 Halogen Acid Furnaces

T93 Other Industrial Furnaces Listed in 40 CFR 260.10 (specify)

(f) Other Treatment

T94 Containment Building (Treatment)

3. Disposal

D79 Underground Injection

D80 Landfill

D81 Land Treatment

D82 Ocean Disposal

D83 Surface Impoundment (to be closed as a landfill)

D99 Other Disposal (specify)

4. Miscellaneous

X01 Open Burning/Open Detonation

X02 Mechanical Processing

X03 Thermal Unit

X04 Geologic Repository

X99 Other (specify)

[45 FR 33232, May 19, 1980, as amended at 59 FR 13892, Mar. 24, 1994; 71 FR 40276, July 14, 2006]

Appendix II to Part 265 [Reserved]

Appendix III to Part 265—EPA Interim Primary Drinking Water Standards

Parameter	Maximum level (mg/l)
Arsenic	0.05
Barium	1.0
Cadmium	0.01
Chromium	0.05
Fluoride	1.4-2.4
Lead	0.05
Mercury	0.002
Nitrate (as N)	10
Selenium	0.01
Silver	0.05
Endrin	0.0002
Lindane	0.004
Methoxychlor	0.1
Toxaphene	0.005
2,4-D	0.1
2,4,5-TP Silver	0.01
Radium	5 pCi/1
Gross Alpha	15 pCi/1
Gross Beta	4 millirem/yr
Turbidity	1/TU
Coliform Bacteria	1/100 ml

[Comment: Turbidity is applicable only to surface water supplies.]

Appendix IV to Part 265—Tests for Significance

As required in §265.93(b) the owner or operator must use the Student's t-test to determine statistically significant changes in the concentration or value of an indicator parameter in periodic groundwater samples when compared to the initial background concentration or value of that indicator parameter. The comparison must consider individually each of the wells in the monitoring system. For three of the indicator parameters (specific conductance, total organic carbon, and total organic halogen) a single-tailed Student's t-test must be used to test at the 0.01 level of significance for significant increases over background. The difference test for pH must be a two-tailed Student's t-test at the overall 0.01 level of significance.

The student's t-test involves calculation of the value of a t-statistic for each comparison of the mean (average) concentration or value (based on a minimum of four replicate measurements) of an indicator parameter with its initial background concentration or value. The calculated value of the t-statistic must then be compared to the value of the t-statistic found in a table for t-test of significance at the specified level of significance. A calculated value of t which exceeds the value of t found in the table indicates a statistically significant change in the concentration or value of the indicator parameter.

Formulae for calculation of the t-statistic and tables for t-test of significance can be found in most introductory statistics texts.

Appendix V to Part 265—Examples of Potentially Incompatible Waste

Many hazardous wastes, when mixed with other waste or materials at a hazardous waste facility, can produce effects which are harmful to human health and the environment, such as (1) heat or pressure, (2) fire or explosion, (3) violent reaction, (4) toxic dusts, mists, fumes, or gases, or (5) flammable fumes or gases.

Below are examples of potentially incompatible wastes, waste components, and materials, along with the harmful consequences which result from mixing materials in one group with materials in another group. The list is intended as a guide to owners or operators of treatment, storage, and disposal facilities, and to enforcement and permit granting officials, to indicate the need for special precautions when managing these potentially incompatible waste materials or components.

This list is not intended to be exhaustive. An owner or operator must, as the regulations require, adequately analyze his wastes so that he can avoid creating uncontrolled substances or reactions of the type listed below, whether they are listed below or not.

It is possible for potentially incompatible wastes to be mixed in a way that precludes a reaction (*e.g.,* adding acid to water rather than water to acid) or that neutralizes them (*e.g.,* a strong acid mixed with a strong base), or that controls substances produced (*e.g.,* by generating flammable gases in a closed tank equipped so that ignition cannot occur, and burning the gases in an incinerator).

In the lists below, the mixing of a Group A material with a Group B material may have the potential consequence as noted.

Group 1-A	Group 1-B
Acetylene sludge	Acid sludge
Alkaline caustic liquids	Acid and water
Alkaline cleaner	Battery acid
Alkaline corrosive liquids	Chemical cleaners
Alkaline corrosive battery fluid	Electrolyte, acid
Caustic wastewater	Etching acid liquid or solvent
Lime sludge and other corrosive alkalies	Pickling liquor and other corrosive acids
Lime wastewater	Spent acid
Lime and water	Spent mixed acid
Spent caustic	Spent sulfuric acid

Potential consequences: Heat generation; violent reaction.

Group 2-A	Group 2-B
Aluminum Beryllium Calcium Lithium Magnesium Potassium Sodium Zinc powder Other reactive metals and metal hydrides	Any waste in Group 1-A or 1-B

Potential consequences: Fire or explosion; generation of flammable hydrogen gas.

Group 3-A	Group 3-B
Alcohols Water	Any concentrated waste in Groups 1-A or 1-B Calcium Lithium Metal hydrides Potassium SO_2Cl_2, $SOCl_2$, PCl_3, CH_3SiCl_3 Other water-reactive waste

Potential consequences: Fire, explosion, or heat generation; generation of flammable or toxic gases.

Group 4-A	Group 4-B
Alcohols Aldehydes Halogenated hydrocarbons Nitrated hydrocarbons Unsaturated hydrocarbons Other reactive organic compounds and solvents	Concentrated Group 1-A or 1-B wastes Group 2-A wastes

Potential consequences: Fire, explosion, or violent reaction.

Group 5-A	Group 5-B
Spent cyanide and sulfide solutions	Group 1-B wastes

Potential consequences: Generation of toxic hydrogen cyanide or hydrogen sulfide gas.

Group 6-A	Group 6-B
Chlorates Chlorine Chlorites Chromic acid Hyphochlorites Nitrates Nitric acid, fuming Perchlorates Permanganates Peroxides Other strong oxidizers	Acetic acid and other organic acids Concentrated mineral acids Group 2-A wastes Group 4-A wastes Other flammable and combustible wastes

Potential consequences: Fire, explosion, or violent reaction.

Source: "Law, Regulations, and Guidelines for Handling of Hazardous Waste." California Department of Health, February 1975.

[45 FR 33232, May 19, 1980, as amended at 71 FR 40276, July 14, 2006]

Appendix VI to Part 265—Compounds With Henry's Law Constant Less Than 0.1 Y/X

Compound name	CAS No.
Acetaldol	107-89-1
Acetamide	60-35-5
2-Acetylaminofluorene	53-96-3
3-Acetyl-5-hydroxypiperidine	
3-Acetylpiperidine	618-42-8
1-Acetyl-2-thiourea	591-08-2
Acrylamide	79-06-1
Acrylic acid	79-10-7
Adenine	73-24-5
Adipic acid	124-04-9
Adiponitrile	111-69-3
Alachlor	15972-60-8
Aldicarb	116-06-3
Ametryn	834-12-8
4-Aminobiphenyl	92-67-1
4-Aminopyridine	504-24-5
Aniline	62-53-3
o-Anisidine	90-04-0
Anthraquinone	84-65-1
Atrazine	1912-24-9
Benzenearsonic acid	98-05-5
Benzenesulfonic acid	98-11-3
Benzidine	92-87-5
Benzo(a)anthracene	56-55-3
Benzo(k)fluoranthene	207-08-9
Benzoic acid	65-85-0
Benzo(g,h,i)perylene	191-24-2
Benzo(a)pyrene	50-32-8
Benzyl alcohol	100-51-6
gamma-BHC	58-89-9
Bis(2-ethylhexyl)phthalate	117-81-7
Bromochloromethyl acetate	
Bromoxynil	1689-84-5
Butyric acid	107-92-6
Caprolactam (hexahydro-2H-azepin-2-one)	105-60-2
Catechol (o-dihydroxybenzene)	120-80-9
Cellulose	9004-34-6
Cell wall	
Chlorhydrin (3-Chloro-1,2-propanediol)	96-24-2
Chloroacetic acid	79-11-8
2-Chloroacetophenone	93-76-5
p-Chloroaniline	106-47-8
p-Chlorobenzophenone	134-85-0
Chlorobenzilate	510-15-6
p-Chloro-m-cresol (6-chloro-m-cresol)	59-50-7
3-Chloro-2,5-diketo pyrrolidine	

Compound name	CAS No.
Chloro-1,2-ethane diol	
4-Chlorophenol	106-48-9
Chlorophenol polymers (2-chlorophenol & 4-chlorophenol)	95-57-8 & 106-48-9
1-(o-Chlorophenyl)thiourea	5344-82-1
Chrysene	218-01-9
Citric acid	77-92-9
Creosote	8001-58-9
m-Cresol	108-39-4
o-Cresol	95-48-7
p-Cresol	106-44-5
Cresol (mixed isomers)	1319-77-3
4-Cumylphenol	27576-86
Cyanide	57-12-5
4-Cyanomethyl benzoate	
Diazinon	333-41-5
Dibenzo(a,h)anthracene	53-70-3
Dibutylphthalate	84-74-2
2,5-Dichloroaniline (N,N'-dichloroaniline)	95-82-9
2,6-Dichlorobenzonitrile11	1194-65-6
2,6-Dichloro-4-nitroaniline	99-30-9
2,5-Dichlorophenol	333-41-5
3,4-Dichlorotetrahydrofuran	3511-19
Dichlorvos (DDVP)	62-73-7
Diethanolamine	111-42-2
N,N-Diethylaniline	91-66-7
Diethylene glycol	111-46-6
Diethylene glycol dimethyl ether (dimethyl Carbitol)	111-96-6
Diethylene glycol monobutyl ether (butyl Carbitol)	112-34-5
Diethylene glycol monoethyl ether acetate (Carbitol acetate)	112-15-2
Diethylene glycol monoethyl ether (Carbitol Cellosolve)	111-90-0
Diethylene glycol monomethyl ether (methyl Carbitol)	111-77-3
N,N'-Diethylhydrazine	1615-80-1
Diethyl (4-methylumbelliferyl) thionophosphate	299-45-6
Diethyl phosphorothioate	126-75-0
N,N'-Diethylpropionamide	15299-99-7
Dimethoate	60-51-5
2,3-Dimethoxystrychnidin-10-one	357-57-3
4-Dimethylaminoazobenzene	60-11-7
7,12-Dimethylbenz(a)anthracene	57-97-6
3,3-Dimethylbenzidine	119-93-7
Dimethylcarbamoyl chloride	79-44-7
Dimethyldisulfide	624-92-0
Dimethylformamide	68-12-2
1,1-Dimethylhydrazine	57-14-7
Dimethylphthalate	131-11-3
Dimethylsulfone	67-71-0
Dimethylsulfoxide	67-68-5
4,6-Dinitro-o-cresol	534-52-1
1,2-Diphenylhydrazine	122-66-7
Dipropylene glycol (1,1'-oxydi-2-propanol)	110-98-5
Endrin	72-20-8

Compound name	CAS No.
Epinephrine	51-43-4
mono-Ethanolamine	141-43-5
Ethyl carbamate (urethane)	5-17-96
Ethylene glycol	107-21-1
Ethylene glycol monobutyl ether (butyl Cellosolve)	111-76-2
Ethylene glycol monoethyl ether (Cellosolve)	110-80-5
Ethylene glycol monoethyl ether acetate (Cellosolve acetate)	111-15-9
Ethylene glycol monomethyl ether (methyl Cellosolve)	109-86-4
Ethylene glycol monophenyl ether (phenyl Cellosolve)	122-99-6
Ethylene glycol monopropyl ether (propyl Cellosolve)	2807-30-9
Ethylene thiourea (2-imidazolidinethione)	96-45-7
4-Ethylmorpholine	100-74-3
3-Ethylphenol	620-17-7
Fluoroacetic acid, sodium salt	62-74-8
Formaldehyde	50-00-0
Formamide	75-12-7
Formic acid	64-18-6
Fumaric acid	110-17-8
Glutaric acid	110-94-1
Glycerin (Glycerol)	56-81-5
Glycidol	556-52-5
Glycinamide	598-41-4
Glyphosate	1071-83-6
Guthion	86-50-0
Hexamethylene- 1,6-diisocyanate (1,6-diisocyanatohexane)	822-06-0
Hexamethyl phosphoramide	680-31-9
Hexanoic acid	142-62-1
Hydrazine	302-01-2
Hydrocyanic acid	74-90-8
Hydroquinone	123-31-9
Hydroxy-2-propionitrile (hydracrylonitrile)	109-78-4
Indeno (1,2,3-cd) pyrene	193-39-5
Lead acetate	301-04-2
Lead subacetate (lead acetate, monobasic)	1335-32-6
Leucine	61-90-5
Malathion	121-75-5
Maleic acid	110-16-7
Maleic anhydride	108-31-6
Mesityl oxide	141-79-7
Methane sulfonic acid	75-75-2
Methomyl	16752-77-5
p-Methoxyphenol	150-76-5
Methyl acrylate	96-33-3
4,4'-Methylene-bis- (2-chloroaniline)	101-14-4
4,4'-Methylenediphenyl diisocyanate (diphenyl methane diisocyanate)	101-68-8
4,4'-Methylenedianiline	101-77-9
Methylene diphenylamine (MDA)	
5-Methylfurfural	620-02-0
Methylhydrazine	60-34-4
Methyliminoacetic acid	
Methyl methane sulfonate	66-27-3

Compound name	CAS No.
1-Methyl-2-methoxyaziridine	
Methylparathion	298-00-0
Methyl sulfuric acid (sulfuric acid, dimethyl ester)	77-78-1
4-Methylthiophenol	106-45-6
Monomethylformamide (N-methylformamide)	123-39-7
Nabam	142-59-6
alpha-Naphthol	90-15-3
beta-Naphthol	135-19-3
alpha-Naphthylamine	134-32-7
beta-Naphthylamine	91-59-8
Neopentyl glycol (dimethylpropane)	126-30-7
Niacinamide	98-92-0
o-Nitroaniline	88-74-4
Nitroglycerin	55-63-0
2-Nitrophenol	88-75-5
4-Nitrophenol	100-02-7
N-Nitrosodimethylamine	62-75-9
Nitrosoguanidine	674-81-7
N-Nitroso-n-methylurea	684-93-5
N-Nitrosomorpholine (4-nitrosomorpholine)	59-89-2
Oxalic acid	144-62-7
Parathion	56-38-2
Pentaerythritol	115-77-5
Phenacetin	62-44-2
Phenol	108-95-2
Phenylacetic acid	103-82-2
m-Phenylene diamine	108-45-2
o-Phenylene diamine	95-54-5
p-Phenylene diamine	106-50-3
Phenyl mercuric acetate	62-38-4
Phorate	298-02-2
Phthalic anhydride	85-44-9
alpha-Picoline (2-methyl pyridine)	109-06-8
1,3-Propane sultone	1120-71-4
beta-Propiolactone	57-57-8
Proporur (Baygon)	
Propylene glycol	57-55-6
Pyrene	129-00-0
Pyridinium bromide	39416-48-3
Quinoline	91-22-5
Quinone (p-benzoquinone)	106-51-4
Resorcinol	108-46-3
Simazine	122-34-9
Sodium acetate	127-09-3
Sodium formate	141-53-7
Strychnine	57-24-9
Succinic acid	110-15-6
Succinimide	123-56-8
Sulfanilic acid	121-47-1
Terephthalic acid	100-21-0
Tetraethyldithiopyrophosphate	3689-24-5
Tetraethylenepentamine	112-57-2
Thiofanox	39196-18-4
Thiosemicarbazide	79-19-6
2,4-Toluenediamine	95-80-7
2,6-Toluenediamine	823-40-5
3,4-Toluenediamine	496-72-0
2,4-Toluene diisocyanate	584-84-9
p-Toluic acid	99-94-5
m-Toluidine	108-44-1
1,1,2-Trichloro- 1,2,2-trifluoroethane	76-13-1
Triethanolamine	102-71-6
Triethylene glycol dimethyl ether	
Tripropylene glycol	24800-44-0
Warfarin	81-81-2
3,4-Xylenol (3,4-dimethylphenol)	95-65-8

[62 FR 64668, Dec. 8, 1997, as amended at 71 FR 40276, July 14, 2006]

PART 265—Appendices

PART 266—STANDARDS FOR THE MANAGEMENT OF SPECIFIC HAZARDOUS WASTES AND SPECIFIC TYPES OF HAZARDOUS WASTE MANAGEMENT FACILITIES

Authority: 42 U.S.C. 1006, 2002(a), 3001–3009, 3014, 6905, 6906, 6912, 6921, 6922, 6924–6927, 6934, and 6937.

Source: 50 FR 666, Jan. 4, 1985, unless otherwise noted.

Subparts A–B [Reserved]

Subpart C—Recyclable Materials Used in a Manner Constituting Disposal

§266.20 Applicability.

(a) The regulations of this subpart apply to recyclable materials that are applied to or placed on the land:

(1) Without mixing with any other substance(s); or

(2) After mixing or combination with any other substance(s). These materials will be referred to throughout this subpart as "materials used in a manner that constitutes disposal."

(b) Products produced for the general public's use that are used in a manner that constitutes disposal and that contain recyclable materials are not presently subject to regulation if the recyclable materials have undergone a chemical reaction in the course of producing the products so as to become inseparable by physical means and if such products meet the applicable treatment standards in subpart D of part 268 (or applicable prohibition levels in §268.32 or RCRA section 3004(d), where no treatment standards have been established) for each recyclable material (*i.e.*, hazardous waste) that they contain. 📖 **1.2.6.1, 11.4.1.1.1, 13.4.3**

(c) Anti-skid/deicing uses of slags, which are generated from high temperature metals recovery (HTMR) processing of hazardous waste K061, K062, and F006, in a manner constituting disposal are not covered by the exemption in paragraph (b) of this section and remain subject to regulation.

(d) Fertilizers that contain recyclable materials are not subject to regulation provided that: 📖 **1.2.6.1, 11.4.1.1.1**

(1) They are zinc fertilizers excluded from the definition of solid waste according to §261.4(a)(21) of this chapter; or

(2) They meet the applicable treatment standards in subpart D of Part 268 of this chapter for each hazardous waste that they contain. 📖 **13.4.3**

[50 FR 666, Jan. 4, 1985, as amended at 52 FR 21307, June 5, 1987; 54 FR 36970, Sept. 6, 1989; 59 FR 43500, Aug. 24, 1994; 67 FR 48414, July 24, 2002]

§266.21 Standards applicable to generators and transporters of materials used in a manner that constitutes disposal.

Generators and transporters of materials that are used in a manner that constitutes disposal are subject to the applicable requirements of parts 262 and 263 of this chapter, and the notification requirement under section 3010 of RCRA. 📖 **1.2.6.1**

§266.22 Standards applicable to storers of materials that are to be used in a manner that constitutes disposal who are not the ultimate users.

Owners or operators of facilities that store recyclable materials that are to be used in a manner that constitutes disposal, but who are not the ultimate users of the materials, are regulated under all applicable provisions of subparts A through L of parts 264 and 265 and parts 270 and 124 of this chapter and the notification requirement under section 3010 of RCRA. 📖 **1.2.6.1**

§266.23 Standards applicable to users of materials that are used in a manner that constitutes disposal.

(a) Owners or operators of facilities that use recyclable materials in a manner that constitutes disposal are regulated under all applicable provisions of subparts A through N of parts 124, 264, 265, 268, and 270 of this chapter and the notification requirement under section 3010 of RCRA. (These requirements do not apply to products which contain these recyclable materials under the provisions of §266.20(b) of this chapter.) 1.2.6.1

(b) The use of waste or used oil or other material, which is contaminated with dioxin or any other hazardous waste (other than a waste identified solely on the basis of ignitability), for dust suppression or road treatment is prohibited.

[50 FR 666, Jan. 4, 1985, as amended at 50 FR 28750, July 15, 1985; 59 FR 48042, Sept. 19, 1994]

Subparts D–E [Reserved]

Subpart F—Recyclable Materials Utilized for Precious Metal Recovery

§266.70 Applicability and requirements.

(a) The regulations of this subpart apply to recyclable materials that are reclaimed to recover economically significant amounts of gold, silver, platinum, palladium, iridium, osmium, rhodium, ruthenium, or any combination of these.

(b) Persons who generate, transport, or store recyclable materials that are regulated under this subpart are subject to the following requirements:

(1) Notification requirements under section 3010 of RCRA;

(2) Subpart B of part 262 (for generators), §§263.20 and 263.21 (for transporters), and §§265.71 and 265.72 (for persons who store) of this chapter; and

(3) For precious metals exported to or imported from designated OECD member countries for recovery, subpart H of part 262 and §265.12(a)(2) of this chapter. For precious metals exported to or imported from non-OECD countries for recovery, subparts E and F of 40 CFR part 262.

(c) Persons who store recycled materials that are regulated under this subpart must keep the following records to document that they are not accumulating these materials speculatively (as defined in §261.1(c) of this chapter);

(1) Records showing the volume of these materials stored at the beginning of the calendar year;

(2) The amount of these materials generated or received during the calendar year; and

(3) The amount of materials remaining at the end of the calendar year.

(d) Recyclable materials that are regulated under this subpart that are accumulated speculatively (as defined in §261.1(c) of this chapter) are subject to all applicable provisions of parts 262 through 265, 270 and 124 of this chapter.

[50 FR 666, Jan. 4, 1985, as amended at 61 FR 16315, Apr. 12, 1996; 71 FR 40277, July 14, 2006]

Subpart G—Spent Lead-Acid Batteries Being Reclaimed

4.20, 8.1

§266.80 Applicability and requirements.

(a) Are spent lead-acid batteries exempt from hazardous waste management requirements? If you generate, collect, transport, store, or regenerate lead-acid batteries for reclamation purposes, you may be exempt from certain hazardous waste management requirements. Use the following table to determine which requirements apply to you. Alternatively, you may choose to manage your spent lead-acid batteries under the "Universal Waste" rule in 40 CFR part 273. 4.20, 8.1

If your batteries***	And if you***	Then you***	And you***
(1) Will be reclaimed through regeneration (such as by electrolyte replacement).		are exempt from 40 CFR parts 262 (except for §262.11), 263, 264, 265, 266, 268, 270, 124 of this chapter, and the notification requirements at section 3010 of RCRA.	are subject to 40 CFR parts 261 and §262.11 of this chapter.
(2) Will be reclaimed other than through regeneration.	generate, collect, and/or transport these batteries.	are exempt from 40 CFR parts 262 (except for §262.11), 263, 264, 265, 266, 270, 124 of this chapter, and the notification requirements at section 3010 of RCRA.	are subject to 40 CFR parts 261 and §262.11, and applicable provisions under part 268.
(3) Will be reclaimed other than through regeneration.	store these batteries but you aren't the reclaimer.	are exempt from 40 CFR parts 262 (except for §262.11), 263, 264, 265, 266, 270, 124 of this chapter, and the notification requirements at section 3010 of RCRA.	are subject to 40 CFR parts 261, §262.11, and applicable provisions under part 268.
(4) Will be reclaimed other than through regeneration.	store these batteries before you reclaim them.	must comply with 40 CFR 266.80(b) and as appropriate other regulatory provisions described in 266.80(b).	are subject to 40 CFR parts 261, §262.11, and applicable provisions under part 268.
(5) Will be reclaimed other than through regeneration.	don't store these batteries before you reclaim them.	are exempt from 40 CFR parts 262 (except for §262.11), 263, 264, 265, 266, 270, 124 of this chapter, and the notification requirements at section 3010 of RCRA.	are subject to 40 CFR parts 261, §262.11, and applicable provisions under part 268.

(b) If I store spent lead-acid batteries before I reclaim them but not through regeneration, which requirements apply? The requirements of paragraph (b) of this section apply to you if you store spent lead-acid batteries before you reclaim them, but you don't reclaim them through regeneration. The requirements are slightly different depending on your RCRA permit status. 📖 4.20

(1) For Interim Status Facilities, you must comply with:

(i) Notification requirements under section 3010 of RCRA.

(ii) All applicable provisions in subpart A of part 265 of this chapter.

(iii) All applicable provisions in subpart B of part 265 of this chapter except §265.13 (waste analysis).

(iv) All applicable provisions in subparts C and D of part 265 of this chapter.

(v) All applicable provisions in subpart E of part 265 of this chapter except §§265.71 and 265.72 (dealing with the use of the manifest and manifest discrepancies).

(vi) All applicable provisions in subparts F through L of part 265 of this chapter.

(vii) All applicable provisions in parts 270 and 124 of this chapter.

(2) For Permitted Facilities:

(i) Notification requirements under section 3010 of RCRA.

(ii) All applicable provisions in subpart A of part 264 of this chapter.

(iii) All applicable provisions in subpart B of part 264 of this chapter (but not §264.13 (waste analysis).

(iv) All applicable provisions in subparts C and D of part 264 of this chapter.

(v) All applicable provisions in subpart E of part 264 of this chapter (but not §264.71 or §264.72 (dealing with the use of the manifest and manifest discrepancies).

(vi) All applicable provisions in subparts F through L of part 264 of this chapter.

(vii) All applicable provisions in parts 270 and 124 of this chapter.

[63 FR 71229, Dec. 24, 1998; 71 FR 40277, July 14, 2006]

Subpart H—Hazardous Waste Burned in Boilers and Industrial Furnaces

Source: 56 FR 7208, Feb. 21, 1991, unless otherwise noted.

§266.100 Applicability.

(a) The regulations of this subpart apply to hazardous waste burned or processed in a boiler or industrial furnace (as defined in §260.10 of this chapter) irrespective of the purpose of burning or processing, except as provided by paragraphs (b), (c), (d), (g), and (h) of this section. In this subpart, the term "burn" means burning for energy recovery or destruction, or processing for materials recovery or as an ingredient. The emissions standards of §§266.104, 266.105, 266.106, and 266.107 apply to facilities operating under interim status or under a RCRA permit as specified in §§266.102 and 266.103.

(b) *Integration of the MACT standards.* (1) Except as provided by paragraphs (b)(2), (b)(3), and (b)(4) of this section, the standards of this part do not apply to a new hazardous waste boiler or industrial furnace unit that becomes subject to RCRA permit requirements after October 12, 2005; or no longer apply when an owner or operator of an existing hazardous waste boiler or industrial furnace unit demonstrates compliance with the maximum achievable control technology (MACT) requirements of part 63, subpart EEE, of this chapter by conducting a comprehensive performance test and submitting to the Administrator a Notification of Compliance under §§63.1207(j) and 63.1210(d) of this chapter documenting compliance with the requirements of part 63, subpart EEE, of this chapter. Nevertheless, even after this demonstration of compliance with the MACT standards, RCRA permit conditions that were based on the standards of this part will continue to be in effect until they are removed from the permit or the permit is terminated or revoked, unless the permit expressly provides otherwise.

(2) The following standards continue to apply:

(i) If you elect to comply with §270.235(a)(1)(i) of this chapter to minimize emissions of toxic compounds from startup, shutdown, and malfunction events, §266.102(e)(1) requiring operations in accordance with the operating requirements specified in the permit at all times that hazardous waste is in the unit, and §266.102(e)(2)(iii) requiring compliance with the emission standards and operating requirements during startup and shutdown if hazardous waste is in the combustion chamber, except for particular hazardous wastes. These provisions apply only during startup, shutdown, and malfunction events;

(ii) The closure requirements of §§266.102(e)(11) and 266.103(l);

(iii) The standards for direct transfer of §266.111;

(iv) The standards for regulation of residues of §266.112; and

(v) The applicable requirements of subparts A through H, BB and CC of parts 264 and 265 of this chapter.

(3) If you own or operate a boiler or hydrochloric acid production furnace that is an area source under §63.2 of this chapter and you elect not to comply with the emission standards under §§63.1216, 63.1217, and 63.1218 of this chapter for particulate matter, semivolatile and low volatile metals, and total chlorine, you also remain subject to:

(i) Section 266.105—Standards to control particulate matter;

(ii) Section 266.106—Standards to control metals emissions, except for mercury; and

(iii) Section 266.107—Standards to control hydrogen chloride and chlorine gas.

(4) The particulate matter standard of §266.105 remains in effect for boilers that elect to comply with the alternative to the particulate matter standard under §§63.1216(e) and 63.1217(e) of this chapter.

(c) The following hazardous wastes and facilities are not subject to regulation under this subpart:

(1) Used oil burned for energy recovery that is also a hazardous waste solely because it exhibits a characteristic of hazardous waste identified in subpart C of part 261 of this chapter. Such used oil is subject to regulation under part 279 of this chapter;

(2) Gas recovered from hazardous or solid waste landfills when such gas is burned for energy recovery;

(3) Hazardous wastes that are exempt from regulation under §§261.4 and 261.6(a)(3) (iii) and (iv) of this chapter, and hazardous wastes that are subject to the special requirements for conditionally exempt small quantity generators under §261.5 of this chapter; and

(4) Coke ovens, if the only hazardous waste burned is EPA Hazardous Waste No. K087, decanter tank tar sludge from coking operations.

(d) Owners and operators of smelting, melting, and refining furnaces (including pyrometallurgical devices such as cupolas, sintering machines, roasters, and foundry furnaces, but not including cement kilns, aggregate kilns, or halogen acid furnaces burning hazardous waste) that process hazardous waste solely for metal recovery are conditionally exempt from regulation under this subpart, except for §§266.101 and 266.112. 📖 7.4.2.1

(1) To be exempt from §§266.102 through 266.111, an owner or operator of a metal recovery furnace or mercury recovery furnace must comply with the following requirements, except that an owner or operator of a lead or a nickel-chromium recovery furnace, or a metal recovery furnace that burns baghouse bags used to capture metallic dusts emitted by steel manufacturing, must comply with the requirements of paragraph (d)(3) of this section, and owners or operators of lead recovery furnaces that are subject to regulation under the Secondary Lead Smelting NESHAP must comply with the requirements of paragraph (h) of this section.

(i) Provide a one-time written notice to the Director indicating the following:

(A) The owner or operator claims exemption under this paragraph;

(B) The hazardous waste is burned solely for metal recovery consistent with the provisions of paragraph (d)(2) of this section;

(C) The hazardous waste contains recoverable levels of metals; and

(D) The owner or operator will comply with the sampling and analysis and recordkeeping requirements of this paragraph;

(ii) Sample and analyze the hazardous waste and other feedstocks as necessary to comply with the requirements of this paragraph by using appropriate methods; and

(iii) Maintain at the facility for at least three years records to document compliance with the provisions of this paragraph including limits on levels of toxic organic constituents and Btu value of the waste, and levels of recoverable metals in the hazardous waste compared to normal nonhazardous waste feedstocks.

(2) A hazardous waste meeting either of the following criteria is not processed solely for metal recovery:

(i) The hazardous waste has a total concentration of organic compounds listed in part 261, appendix VIII, of this chapter exceeding 500 ppm by weight, as-fired, and so is considered to be burned for destruction. The concentration of organic compounds in a waste as-generated may be reduced to the 500 ppm limit by *bona fide* treatment that removes or destroys organic constituents. Blending for dilution to meet the 500 ppm limit is prohibited and documentation that the waste has not been impermissibly diluted must be retained in the records required by paragraph (d)(1)(iii) of this section; or

(ii) The hazardous waste has a heating value of 5,000 Btu/lb or more, as-fired, and so is considered to be burned as fuel. The heating value of a waste as-generated may be reduced to below the 5,000 Btu/lb limit by *bona fide* treatment that removes or destroys organic constituents. Blending for dilution to meet the 5,000 Btu/lb limit is prohibited and documentation that the waste has not been impermissibly diluted must be retained in the records required by paragraph (d)(1)(iii) of this section.

(3) To be exempt from §§266.102 through 266.111, an owner or operator of a lead or nickel-chromium or mercury recovery furnace (except for owners or operators of lead recovery furnaces subject to regulation under the Secondary Lead Smelting NESHAP) or a metal recovery furnace that burns baghouse bags used to capture metallic dusts emitted by steel manufacturing, must provide a one-time written notice to the Director identifying each hazardous waste burned and specifying whether the owner or operator claims an exemption for each waste under this paragraph or paragraph (d)(1) of this section. The owners or operator must comply with the requirements of paragraph (d)(1) of this section for those wastes claimed to be exempt under that paragraph and must comply with the requirements below for those wastes claimed to be exempt under this paragraph (d)(3).

(i) The hazardous wastes listed in appendices XI, XII, and XIII, part 266, and baghouse bags used to capture metallic dusts emitted by steel manufacturing are exempt from the requirements of paragraph (d)(1) of this section, provided that:

(A) A waste listed in appendix XI of this part must contain recoverable levels of lead, a waste listed in appendix XII of this part must contain recoverable levels of nickel or chromium, a waste listed in appendix XIII of this part must contain recoverable levels of mercury and contain less than 500 ppm of 40 CFR part 261, appendix VIII organic constituents, and baghouse bags used to capture metallic dusts emitted by steel manufacturing must contain recoverable levels of metal; and

(B) The waste does not exhibit the Toxicity Characteristic of §261.24 of this chapter for an organic constituent; and

(C) The waste is not a hazardous waste listed in subpart D of part 261 of this chapter because it is listed for an organic constituent as identified in appendix VII of part 261 of this chapter; and

(D) The owner or operator certifies in the one-time notice that hazardous waste is burned under the provisions of paragraph (d)(3) of this section and that sampling and analysis will be conducted or other information will be obtained as necessary to ensure continued compliance with these requirements. Sampling and analysis shall be conducted according to paragraph (d)(1)(ii) of this section and records to document compliance with paragraph (d)(3) of this section shall be kept for at least three years.

(ii) The Director may decide on a case-by-case basis that the toxic organic constituents in a material listed in appendix XI, XII, or XIII of this part that contains a total concentration of more than 500 ppm toxic organic compounds listed in appendix VIII, part 261 of this chapter, may pose a hazard to human health and the environment when burned in a metal recovery furnace exempt from the requirements of this subpart. In that situation, after adequate notice and opportunity for comment, the metal recovery furnace will become subject to the requirements of this subpart when burning that material. In making the hazard determination, the Director will consider the following factors:

(A) The concentration and toxicity of organic constituents in the material; and

(B) The level of destruction of toxic organic constituents provided by the furnace; and

(C) Whether the acceptable ambient levels established in appendices IV or V of this part may be exceeded for any toxic organic compound that may be emitted based on dispersion modeling to predict the maximum annual average off-site ground level concentration.

(e) The standards for direct transfer operations under §266.111 apply only to facilities subject to the permit standards of §266.102 or the interim status standards of §266.103.

(f) The management standards for residues under §266.112 apply to any boiler or industrial furnace burning hazardous waste.

(g) Owners and operators of smelting, melting, and refining furnaces (including pyrometallurgical devices such as cupolas, sintering machines, roasters, and foundry furnaces) that process hazardous waste for recovery of economically significant amounts of the precious metals gold, silver, platinum, palladium, iridium, osmium, rhodium, or ruthenium, or any combination of these are conditionally exempt from regulation under this subpart, except for §266.112. To be exempt from §§266.101 through 266.111, an owner or operator must: 7.4.2.1

(1) Provide a one-time written notice to the Director indicating the following:

(i) The owner or operator claims exemption under this paragraph;

(ii) The hazardous waste is burned for legitimate recovery of precious metal; and

(iii) The owner or operator will comply with the sampling and analysis and recordkeeping requirements of this paragraph; and

(2) Sample and analyze the hazardous waste as necessary to document that the waste contains economically significant amounts of the metals and that the treatment recovers economically significant amounts of precious metal; and

(3) Maintain at the facility for at least three years records to document that all hazardous wastes burned are burned for recovery of economically significant amounts of precious metal.

(h) Starting June 23, 1997, owners or operators of lead recovery furnaces that process hazardous waste for recovery of lead and that are subject to regulation under the Secondary Lead Smelting NESHAP, are conditionally exempt from regulation under this subpart, except for §266.101. To be exempt, an owner or operator must provide a one-time notice to the Director identifying each hazardous waste burned and specifying that the owner or operator claims an exemption under this paragraph. The notice also must state that the waste burned has a total concentration of non-metal compounds listed in part 261, appendix VIII, of this chapter of less than 500 ppm by weight, as fired and as provided in paragraph (d)(2)(i) of this section, or is listed in appendix XI to this part 266.

[56 FR 7208, Feb. 21, 1991; 56 FR 32688, July 17, 1991, as amended at 56 FR 42513, Aug. 27, 1991; 56 FR 43877, Sept. 5, 1991; 57 FR 27888, June 22, 1992; 57 FR 38564, Aug. 25, 1992; 57 FR 41612, Sept. 10, 1992; 59 FR 38545, July 28, 1994; 59 FR 48042, Sept. 19, 1994; 63 FR 42186, Aug. 6, 1998; 64 FR 53075, Sept. 30, 1999; 67 FR 6816, Feb. 13, 2002; 67 FR 6996, Feb. 14, 2002; 70 FR 34587, June 14, 2005; 70 FR 59576, Oct. 12, 2005; 71 FR 40277, July 14, 2006; 73 FR 18984, Apr. 8, 2008]

§266.101 Management prior to burning.

(a) *Generators.* Generators of hazardous waste that is burned in a boiler or industrial furnace are subject to part 262 of this chapter.

(b) *Transporters.* Transporters of hazardous waste that is burned in a boiler or industrial furnace are subject to part 263 of this chapter.

(c) *Storage and treatment facilities.* (1) Owners and operators of facilities that store or treat hazardous waste that is burned in a boiler or industrial furnace are subject to the applicable provisions of parts 264, 265, and 270 of this chapter, except as provided by paragraph (c)(2) of this section. These standards apply to storage and treatment by the burner as well as to storage and treatment facilities operated by intermediaries (processors, blenders, distributors, etc.) between the generator and the burner. 7.1.2.3

(2) Owners and operators of facilities that burn, in an onsite boiler or industrial furnace exempt from regulation under the small quantity burner provisions of §266.108, hazardous waste that they generate are exempt from the regulations of parts 264, 265, and 270 of this chapter applicable to storage units for those storage units that store mixtures of hazardous waste and the primary fuel to the boiler or industrial furnace in tanks that feed the fuel mixture directly to the burner. Storage of hazardous waste prior to mixing with the primary fuel is subject to regulation as prescribed in paragraph (c)(1) of this section.

[56 FR 7208, Feb. 21, 1991, as amended at 57 FR 38564, Aug. 25, 1992; 64 FR 53075, Sept. 30, 1999]

§266.102 Permit standards for burners.

(a) *Applicability*—(1) *General.* Owners and operators of boilers and industrial furnaces burning hazardous waste and not operating under interim status must comply with the requirements of this section and §§270.22 and 270.66 of this chapter, unless exempt under the small quantity burner exemption of §266.108.

(2) *Applicability of part 264 standards.* Owners and operators of boilers and industrial furnaces that burn hazardous waste are subject to the following provisions of part 264 of this chapter, except as provided otherwise by this subpart:

(i) In subpart A (General), 264.4;

(ii) In subpart B (General facility standards), §§264.11-264.18;

(iii) In subpart C (Preparedness and prevention), §§264.31-264.37;

(iv) In subpart D (Contingency plan and emergency procedures), §§264.51-264.56;

(v) In subpart E (Manifest system, recordkeeping, and reporting), the applicable provisions of §§264.71-264.77;

(vi) In subpart F (Releases from Solid Waste Management Units), §§264.90 and 264.101;

(vii) In subpart G (Closure and post-closure), §§264.111-264.115;

(viii) In subpart H (Financial requirements), §§264.141, 264.142, 264.143, and 264.147-264.151, except that States and the Federal government are exempt from the requirements of subpart H; and

(ix) Subpart BB (Air emission standards for equipment leaks), except §§264.1050(a).

(b) *Hazardous waste analysis.* (1) The owner or operator must provide an analysis of the hazardous waste that quantifies the concentration of any constituent identified in appendix VIII of part 261 of this chapter that may reasonably be expected to be in the waste. Such constituents must be identified and quantified if present, at levels detectable by using appropriate analytical procedures. The appendix VIII, part 261 constituents excluded from this analysis must be identified and the basis for their exclusion explained. This analysis will be used to provide all information required by this subpart and §§270.22 and 270.66 of this chapter and to enable the permit writer to prescribe such permit conditions as necessary to protect human health and the environment. Such analysis must be included as a portion of the part B permit application, or, for facilities operating under the interim status standards of this subpart, as a portion of the trial burn plan that may be submitted before the part B application under provisions of §270.66(g) of this chapter as well as any other analysis required by the permit authority in preparing the permit. Owners and operators of boilers and industrial furnaces not operating under the interim status standards must provide the information required by §§270.22 or 270.66(c) of this chapter in the part B application to the greatest extent possible.

(2) Throughout normal operation, the owner or operator must conduct sampling and analysis as necessary to ensure that the hazardous waste, other fuels, and industrial furnace feedstocks fired into the boiler or industrial furnace are within the physical and chemical composition limits specified in the permit.

(c) *Emissions standards.* Owners and operators must comply with emissions standards provided by §§266.104 through 266.107.

(d) *Permits.* (1) The owner or operator may burn only hazardous wastes specified in the facility permit and only under the operating conditions specified under paragraph (e) of this section, except in approved trial burns under the conditions specified in §270.66 of this chapter.

(2) Hazardous wastes not specified in the permit may not be burned until operating conditions have been specified under a new permit or permit modification, as applicable. Operating requirements for new wastes may be based on either trial burn results or alternative data included with part B of a permit application under §270.22 of this chapter.

(3) Boilers and industrial furnaces operating under the interim status standards of §266.103 are permitted under procedures provided by §270.66(g) of this chapter.

(4) A permit for a new boiler or industrial furnace (those boilers and industrial furnaces not operating under the interim status standards) must establish appropriate conditions for each of the applicable requirements of this section, including but not limited to allowable hazardous waste firing rates and operating conditions necessary to meet the requirements of paragraph (e) of this section, in order to comply with the following standards:

(i) For the period beginning with initial introduction of hazardous waste and ending with initiation of the trial burn, and only for the minimum time required to bring the device to a point of operational readiness to conduct a trial burn, not to exceed a duration of 720 hours operating time when burning hazardous waste, the operating requirements must be those most likely to ensure compliance with the emission standards of §§266.104 through 266.107, based on the Director's engineering judgment. If the applicant is seeking a waiver from a trial burn to demonstrate conformance with a particular emission standard, the operating requirements during this initial period of operation shall include those specified by the applicable provisions of §266.104, §266.105, §266.106, or §266.107. The Director may extend the duration of this period for up to 720 additional hours when good cause for the extension is demonstrated by the applicant.

(ii) For the duration of the trial burn, the operating requirements must be sufficient to demonstrate compliance with the emissions standards of §§266.104 through 266.107 and must be in accordance with the approved trial burn plan;

(iii) For the period immediately following completion of the trial burn, and only for the minimum period sufficient to allow sample analysis, data computation, submission of the trial burn results by the applicant, review of the trial burn results and modification of the facility permit by the Director to reflect the trial burn results, the operating requirements must be those most likely to ensure compliance with the emission standards §§266.104 through 266.107 based on the Director's engineering judgment.

(iv) For the remaining duration of the permit, the operating requirements must be those demonstrated in a trial burn or by alternative data specified in §270.22 of this chapter, as sufficient to ensure compliance with the emissions standards of §§266.104 through 266.107.

(e) *Operating requirements*—(1) *General.* A boiler or industrial furnace burning hazardous waste must be operated in accordance with the operating requirements specified in the permit at all times where there is hazardous waste in the unit.

(2) *Requirements to ensure compliance with the organic emissions standards*—(i) *DRE standard.* Operating conditions will be specified either on a case-by-case basis for each hazardous waste burned as those demonstrated (in a trial burn or by alternative data as specified in §270.22) to be sufficient to comply with the destruction and removal efficiency (DRE) performance standard of §266.104(a) or as those special operating requirements provided by §266.104(a)(4) for the waiver of the DRE trial burn. When the DRE trial burn is not waived under §266.104(a)(4), each set of operating requirements will specify the composition of the hazardous waste (including acceptable variations in the physical and chemical properties of the hazardous waste which will not affect compliance with the DRE performance standard) to which the operating requirements apply. For each such hazardous waste, the permit will specify acceptable operating limits including, but not limited to, the following conditions as appropriate:

(A) Feed rate of hazardous waste and other fuels measured and specified as prescribed in paragraph (e)(6) of this section;

(B) Minimum and maximum device production rate when producing normal product expressed in appropriate units, measured and specified as prescribed in paragraph (e)(6) of this section;

(C) Appropriate controls of the hazardous waste firing system;

(D) Allowable variation in boiler and industrial furnace system design or operating procedures;

(E) Minimum combustion gas temperature measured at a location indicative of combustion chamber temperature, measured and specified as prescribed in paragraph (e)(6) of this section;

(F) An appropriate indicator of combustion gas velocity, measured and specified as prescribed in paragraph (e)(6) of this section, unless documentation is provided under §270.66 of this chapter demonstrating adequate combustion gas residence time; and

(G) Such other operating requirements as are necessary to ensure that the DRE performance standard of §266.104(a) is met.

(ii) *Carbon monoxide and hydrocarbon standards.* The permit must incorporate a carbon monoxide (CO) limit and, as appropriate, a hydrocarbon (HC) limit as provided by paragraphs (b), (c), (d), (e) and (f) of §266.104. The permit limits will be specified as follows:

(A) When complying with the CO standard of §266.104(b)(1), the permit limit is 100 ppmv;

(B) When complying with the alternative CO standard under §266.104(c), the permit limit for CO is based on the trial burn and is established as the average over all valid runs of the highest hourly rolling average CO level of each run, and the permit limit for HC is 20 ppmv (as defined in §266.104(c)(1)), except as provided in §266.104(f).

(C) When complying with the alternative HC limit for industrial furnaces under §266.104(f), the permit limit for HC and CO is the baseline level when hazardous waste is not burned as specified by that paragraph.

(iii) *Start-up and shut-down.* During start-up and shut-down of the boiler or industrial furnace, hazardous waste (except waste fed solely as an ingredient under the Tier I (or adjusted Tier I) feed rate screening limits for metals and chloride/chlorine, and except low risk waste exempt from the trial burn requirements under §§266.104(a)(5), 266.105, 266.106, and 266.107) must not be fed into the device unless the device is operating within the conditions of operation specified in the permit.

(3) *Requirements to ensure conformance with the particulate standard.* (i) Except as provided in paragraphs (e)(3)(ii) and (iii) of this section, the permit shall specify the following operating requirements to ensure conformance with the particulate standard specified in §266.105:

(A) Total ash feed rate to the device from hazardous waste, other fuels, and industrial furnace feedstocks, measured and specified as prescribed in paragraph (e)(6) of this section;

(B) Maximum device production rate when producing normal product expressed in appropriate units, and measured and specified as prescribed in paragraph (e)(6) of this section;

(C) Appropriate controls on operation and maintenance of the hazardous waste firing system and any air pollution control system;

(D) Allowable variation in boiler and industrial furnace system design including any air pollution control system or operating procedures; and

(E) Such other operating requirements as are necessary to ensure that the particulate standard in §266.105(a) is met.

(ii) Permit conditions to ensure conformance with the particulate matter standard shall not be provided for facilities exempt from the particulate matter standard under §266.105(b);

(iii) For cement kilns and light-weight aggregate kilns, permit conditions to ensure compliance with the particulate standard shall not limit the ash content of hazardous waste or other feed materials.

(4) *Requirements to ensure conformance with the metals emissions standard.* (i) For conformance with the Tier I (or adjusted Tier I) metals feed rate screening limits of paragraphs (b) or (e) of §266.106, the permit shall specify the following operating requirements:

(A) Total feed rate of each metal in hazardous waste, other fuels, and industrial furnace feedstocks measured and specified under provisions of paragraph (e)(6) of this section;

(B) Total feed rate of hazardous waste measured and specified as prescribed in paragraph (e)(6) of this section;

(C) A sampling and metals analysis program for the hazardous waste, other fuels, and industrial furnace feedstocks;

(ii) For conformance with the Tier II metals emission rate screening limits under §266.106(c) and the Tier III metals controls under §266.106(d), the permit shall specify the following operating requirements:

(A) Maximum emission rate for each metal specified as the average emission rate during the trial burn;

(B) Feed rate of total hazardous waste and pumpable hazardous waste, each measured and specified as prescribed in paragraph (e)(6)(i) of this section;

(C) Feed rate of each metal in the following feedstreams, measured and specified as prescribed in paragraphs (e)(6) of this section:

(*1*) Total feedstreams;

(*2*) Total hazardous waste feed; and

(*3*) Total pumpable hazardous waste feed;

(D) Total feed rate of chlorine and chloride in total feedstreams measured and specified as prescribed in paragraph (e)(6) of this section;

(E) Maximum combustion gas temperature measured at a location indicative of combustion chamber temperature, and measured and specified as prescribed in paragraph (e)(6) of this section;

(F) Maximum flue gas temperature at the inlet to the particulate matter air pollution control system measured and specified as prescribed in paragraph (e)(6) of this section;

(G) Maximum device production rate when producing normal product expressed in appropriate units and measured and specified as prescribed in paragraph (e)(6) of this section;

(H) Appropriate controls on operation and maintenance of the hazardous waste firing system and any air pollution control system;

(I) Allowable variation in boiler and industrial furnace system design including any air pollution control system or operating procedures; and

(J) Such other operating requirements as are necessary to ensure that the metals standards under §§266.106(c) or 266.106(d) are met.

(iii) For conformance with an alternative implementation approach approved by the Director under §266.106(f), the permit will specify the following operating requirements:

(A) Maximum emission rate for each metal specified as the average emission rate during the trial burn;

(B) Feed rate of total hazardous waste and pumpable hazardous waste, each measured and specified as prescribed in paragraph (e)(6)(i) of this section;

(C) Feed rate of each metal in the following feedstreams, measured and specified as prescribed in paragraph (e)(6) of this section:

(*1*) Total hazardous waste feed; and

(*2*) Total pumpable hazardous waste feed;

(D) Total feed rate of chlorine and chloride in total feedstreams measured and specified prescribed in paragraph (e)(6) of this section;

(E) Maximum combustion gas temperature measured at a location indicative of combustion chamber temperature, and measured and specified as prescribed in paragraph (e)(6) of this section;

(F) Maximum flue gas temperature at the inlet to the particulate matter air pollution control system measured and specified as prescribed in paragraph (e)(6) of this section;

(G) Maximum device production rate when producing normal product expressed in appropriate units and measured and specified as prescribed in paragraph (e)(6) of this section;

(H) Appropriate controls on operation and maintenance of the hazardous waste firing system and any air pollution control system;

(I) Allowable variation in boiler and industrial furnace system design including any air pollution control system or operating procedures; and

(J) Such other operating requirements as are necessary to ensure that the metals standards under §§266.106(c) or 266.106(d) are met.

(5) *Requirements to ensure conformance with the hydrogen chloride and chlorine gas standards.* (i) For conformance with the Tier I total chloride and chlorine feed rate screening limits of §266.107(b)(1), the permit will specify the following operating requirements:

(A) Feed rate of total chloride and chlorine in hazardous waste, other fuels, and industrial furnace feedstocks measured and specified as prescribed in paragraph (e)(6) of this section;

(B) Feed rate of total hazardous waste measured and specified as prescribed in paragraph (e)(6) of this section;

(C) A sampling and analysis program for total chloride and chlorine for the hazardous waste, other fuels, and industrial furnace feedstocks;

(ii) For conformance with the Tier II HCl and Cl_2 emission rate screening limits under §266.107(b)(2) and the Tier III HCl and Cl_2 controls under §266.107(c), the permit will specify the following operating requirements:

(A) Maximum emission rate for HCl and for Cl_2 specified as the average emission rate during the trial burn;

(B) Feed rate of total hazardous waste measured and specified as prescribed in paragraph (e)(6) of this section;

(C) Total feed rate of chlorine and chloride in total feedstreams, measured and specified as prescribed in paragraph (e)(6) of this section;

(D) Maximum device production rate when producing normal product expressed in appropriate units, measured and specified as prescribed in paragraph (e)(6) of this section;

(E) Appropriate controls on operation and maintenance of the hazardous waste firing system and any air pollution control system;

(F) Allowable variation in boiler and industrial furnace system design including any air pollution control system or operating procedures; and

(G) Such other operating requirements as are necessary to ensure that the HCl and Cl_2 standards under §266.107 (b)(2) or (c) are met.

(6) *Measuring parameters and establishing limits based on trial burn data*—(i) *General requirements.* As specified in paragraphs (e)(2) through (e)(5) of this section, each operating parameter shall be measured, and permit limits on the parameter shall be established, according to either of the following procedures:

(A) *Instantaneous limits.* A parameter may be measured and recorded on an instantaneous basis (*i.e.*, the value that occurs at any time) and the permit limit specified as the time-weighted average during all valid runs of the trial burn; or

(B) *Hourly rolling average.* (*1*) The limit for a parameter may be established and continuously monitored on an hourly rolling average basis defined as follows:

(*i*) A continuous monitor is one which continuously samples the regulated parameter without interruption, and evaluates the detector response at least once each 15 seconds, and computes and records the average value at least every 60 seconds.

(ii) An hourly rolling average is the arithmetic mean of the 60 most recent 1-minute average values recorded by the continuous monitoring system.

(*2*) The permit limit for the parameter shall be established based on trial burn data as the average over all valid test runs of the highest hourly rolling average value for each run.

(ii) *Rolling average limits for carcinogenic metals and lead.* Feed rate limits for the carcinogenic metals (*i.e.*, arsenic, beryllium, cadmium and chromium) and lead may be established either on an hourly rolling average basis as prescribed by paragraph (e)(6)(i) of this section or on (up to) a 24 hour rolling average basis. If the owner or operator elects to use an average period from 2 to 24 hours:

(A) The feed rate of each metal shall be limited at any time to ten times the feed rate that would be allowed on an hourly rolling average basis;

(B) The continuous monitor shall meet the following specifications:

(*1*) A continuous monitor is one which continuously samples the regulated parameter without interruption, and evaluates the detector response at least once each 15 seconds, and computes and records the average value at least every 60 seconds.

(*2*) The rolling average for the selected averaging period is defined as the arithmetic mean of one hour block averages for the averaging period. A one hour block average is the arithmetic mean of the one minute averages recorded during the 60-minute period beginning at one minute after the beginning of the preceding clock hour; and

(C) The permit limit for the feed rate of each metal shall be established based on trial burn data as the average over all valid test runs of the highest hourly rolling average feed rate for each run.

(iii) *Feed rate limits for metals, total chloride and chlorine, and ash.* Feed rate limits for metals, total chlorine and chloride, and ash are established and monitored by knowing the concentration of the substance (*i.e.*, metals, chloride/chlorine, and ash) in each feedstream and the flow rate of the feedstream. To monitor the feed rate of these substances, the flow rate of each feedstream must be monitored under the continuous monitoring requirements of paragraphs (e)(6) (i) and (ii) of this section.

(iv) *Conduct of trial burn testing.* (A) If compliance with all applicable emissions standards of §§266.104 through 266.107 is not demonstrated simultaneously during a set of test runs, the operating conditions of additional test runs required to demonstrate compliance with remaining emissions standards must be as close as possible to the original operating conditions.

(B) Prior to obtaining test data for purposes of demonstrating compliance with the emissions standards of §§266.104 through 266.107 or establishing limits on operating parameters under this section, the facility must operate under trial burn conditions for a sufficient period to reach steady-state operations. The Director may determine, however, that industrial furnaces that recycle collected particulate matter back into the furnace and that comply with an alternative implementation approach for metals under §266.106(f) need not reach steady state conditions with respect to the flow of metals in the system prior to beginning compliance testing for metals emissions.

(C) Trial burn data on the level of an operating parameter for which a limit must be established in the permit must be obtained during emissions sampling for the pollutant(s) (*i.e.*, metals, PM, HCl/Cl_2, organic compounds) for which the parameter must be established as specified by paragraph (e) of this section.

(7) *General requirements*—(i) *Fugitive emissions.* Fugitive emissions must be controlled by:

(A) Keeping the combustion zone totally sealed against fugitive emissions; or

(B) Maintaining the combustion zone pressure lower than atmospheric pressure; or

(C) An alternate means of control demonstrated (with part B of the permit application) to provide fugitive emissions control equivalent to maintenance of combustion zone pressure lower than atmospheric pressure.

(ii) *Automatic waste feed cutoff.* A boiler or industrial furnace must be operated with a functioning system that automatically cuts off the hazardous waste feed when operating conditions deviate from those established under this section. The Director may limit the number of cutoffs per an operating period on a case-by-case basis. In addition:

(A) The permit limit for (the indicator of) minimum combustion chamber temperature must be maintained while hazardous waste or hazardous waste residues remain in the combustion chamber,

(B) Exhaust gases must be ducted to the air pollution control system operated in accordance with the permit requirements while hazardous waste or hazardous waste residues remain in the combustion chamber; and

(C) Operating parameters for which permit limits are established must continue to be monitored during the cutoff, and the hazardous waste feed shall not be restarted until the levels of those parameters comply with the permit limits. For parameters that may be monitored on an instantaneous basis, the Director will establish a minimum period of time after a waste feed cutoff during which the parameter must not exceed the permit limit before the hazardous waste feed may be restarted.

(iii) *Changes.* A boiler or industrial furnace must cease burning hazardous waste when changes in combustion properties, or feed rates of the hazardous waste, other fuels, or industrial furnace feedstocks, or changes in the boiler or industrial furnace design or operating conditions deviate from the limits as specified in the permit.

(8) *Monitoring and Inspections.* (i) The owner or operator must monitor and record the following, at a minimum, while burning hazardous waste:

(A) If specified by the permit, feed rates and composition of hazardous waste, other fuels, and industrial furnace feedstocks, and feed rates of ash, metals, and total chloride and chlorine;

(B) If specified by the permit, carbon monoxide (CO), hydrocarbons (HC), and oxygen on a continuous basis at a common point in the boiler or industrial furnace downstream of the combustion zone and prior to release of stack gases to the atmosphere in accordance with operating requirements specified in paragraph (e)(2)(ii) of this section. CO, HC, and oxygen monitors must be installed, operated, and maintained in accordance with methods specified in appendix IX of this part.

(C) Upon the request of the Director, sampling and analysis of the hazardous waste (and other fuels and industrial furnace feedstocks as appropriate), residues, and exhaust emissions must be conducted to verify that the operating requirements established in the permit achieve the applicable standards of §§266.104, 266.105, 266.106, and 266.107.

(ii) All monitors shall record data in units corresponding to the permit limit unless otherwise specified in the permit.

(iii) The boiler or industrial furnace and associated equipment (pumps, valves, pipes, fuel storage tanks, etc.) must be subjected to thorough visual inspection when it contains hazardous waste, at least daily for leaks, spills, fugitive emissions, and signs of tampering.

(iv) The automatic hazardous waste feed cutoff system and associated alarms must be tested at least once every 7 days when hazardous waste is burned to verify operability, unless the applicant demonstrates to the Director that weekly inspections will unduly restrict or upset operations and that less frequent inspections will be adequate. At a minimum, operational testing must be conducted at least once every 30 days.

(v) These monitoring and inspection data must be recorded and the records must be placed in the operating record required by §264.73 of this chapter.

(9) *Direct transfer to the burner.* If hazardous waste is directly transferred from a transport vehicle to a boiler or industrial furnace without the use of a storage unit, the owner and operator must comply with §266.111.

(10) *Recordkeeping.* The owner or operator must maintain in the operating record of the facility all information and data required by this section for five years.

(11) *Closure.* At closure, the owner or operator must remove all hazardous waste and hazardous waste residues (including, but not limited to, ash, scrubber waters, and scrubber sludges) from the boiler or industrial furnace.

[56 FR 7208, Feb. 21, 1991; 56 FR 32688, July 17, 1991, as amended at 56 FR 42512, 42514, Aug. 27, 1991; 70 FR 34588, June 14, 2005; 71 FR 16913, Apr. 4, 2006; 71 FR 40277, July 14, 2006]

§266.103 Interim status standards for burners.

(a) *Purpose, scope, applicability*—(1) *General.* (i) The purpose of this section is to establish minimum national standards for owners and operators of "existing" boilers and industrial furnaces that burn hazardous waste where such standards define the acceptable management of hazardous waste during the period of interim status. The standards of this section apply to owners and operators of existing facilities until either a permit is issued under §266.102(d) or until closure responsibilities identified in this section are fulfilled.

(ii) *Existing* or *in existence* means a boiler or industrial furnace that on or before August 21, 1991 is either in operation burning or processing hazardous waste or for which construction (including the ancillary facilities to burn or to process the hazardous waste) has commenced. A facility has commenced construction if the owner or operator has obtained the Federal, State, and local approvals or permits necessary to begin physical construction; and either:

(A) A continuous on-site, physical construction program has begun; or

(B) The owner or operator has entered into contractual obligations—which cannot be canceled or modified without substantial loss—for physical construction of the facility to be completed within a reasonable time.

(iii) If a boiler or industrial furnace is located at a facility that already has a permit or interim status, then the facility must comply with the applicable regulations dealing with permit modifications in §270.42 or changes in interim status in §270.72 of this chapter.

(2) *Exemptions.* The requirements of this section do not apply to hazardous waste and facilities exempt under §§266.100(b), or 266.108.

(3) *Prohibition on burning dioxin-listed wastes.* The following hazardous waste listed for dioxin and hazardous waste derived from any of these wastes may not be burned in a boiler or industrial furnace operating under interim status: F020, F021, F022, F023, F026, and F027.

(4) *Applicability of part 265 standards.* Owners and operators of boilers and industrial furnaces that burn hazardous waste and are operating under interim status are subject to the following provisions of part 265 of this chapter, except as provided otherwise by this section:

(i) In subpart A (General), §265.4;

(ii) In subpart B (General facility standards), §§265.11-265.17;

(iii) In subpart C (Preparedness and prevention), §§265.31-265.37;

(iv) In subpart D (Contingency plan and emergency procedures), §§265.51-265.56;

(v) In subpart E (Manifest system, recordkeeping, and reporting), §§265.71-265.77, except that §§265.71, 265.72, and 265.76 do not apply to owners and operators of on-site facilities that do not receive any hazardous waste from off-site sources;

(vi) In subpart G (Closure and post-closure), §§265.111-265.115;

(vii) In subpart H (Financial requirements), §§265.141, 265.142, 265.143, and 265.147–265.150, except that States and the Federal government are exempt from the requirements of subpart H; and

(viii) Subpart BB (Air emission standards for equipment leaks), except §265.1050(a).

(5) *Special requirements for furnaces.* The following controls apply during interim status to industrial furnaces (*e.g.*, kilns, cupolas) that feed hazardous waste for a purpose other than solely as an ingredient (see paragraph (a)(5)(ii) of this section) at any location other than the hot end where products are normally discharged or where fuels are normally fired:

(i) *Controls.* (A) The hazardous waste shall be fed at a location where combustion gas temperatures are at least 1800° F;

(B) The owner or operator must determine that adequate oxygen is present in combustion gases to combust organic constituents in the waste and retain documentation of such determination in the facility record;

(C) For cement kiln systems, the hazardous waste shall be fed into the kiln; and

(D) The hydrocarbon controls of §266.104(c) or paragraph (c)(5) of this section apply upon certification of compliance under paragraph (c) of this section irrespective of the CO level achieved during the compliance test.

(ii) *Burning hazardous waste solely as an ingredient.* A hazardous waste is burned for a purpose other than solely as an ingredient if it meets either of these criteria:

(A) The hazardous waste has a total concentration of nonmetal compounds listed in part 261, appendix VIII, of this chapter exceeding 500 ppm by weight, as-fired, and so is considered to be burned for destruction. The concentration of nonmetal compounds in a waste as-generated may be reduced to the 500 ppm limit by *bona fide* treatment that removes or destroys nonmetal constituents. Blending for dilution to meet the 500 ppm limit is prohibited and documentation that the waste has not been impermissibly diluted must be retained in the facility record; or

(B) The hazardous waste has a heating value of 5,000 Btu/lb or more, as-fired, and so is considered to be burned as fuel. The heating value of a waste as-generated may be reduced to below the 5,000 Btu/lb limit by *bona fide* treatment that removes or destroys organic constituents. Blending to augment the heating value to meet the 5,000 Btu/lb limit is prohibited and documentation that the waste has not been impermissibly blended must be retained in the facility record.

(6) *Restrictions on burning hazardous waste that is not a fuel.* Prior to certification of compliance under paragraph (c) of this section, owners and operators shall not feed hazardous waste that has a heating value less than 5,000 Btu/lb, as-generated, (except that the heating value of a waste as-generated may be increased to above the 5,000 Btu/lb limit by *bona fide* treatment; however, blending to augment the heating value to meet the 5,000 Btu/lb limit is prohibited and records must be kept to document that impermissible blending has not occurred) in a boiler or industrial furnace, except that:

(i) Hazardous waste may be burned solely as an ingredient; or

(ii) Hazardous waste may be burned for purposes of compliance testing (or testing prior to compliance testing) for a total period of time not to exceed 720 hours; or

(iii) Such waste may be burned if the Director has documentation to show that, prior to August 21, 1991:

(A) The boiler or industrial furnace is operating under the interim status standards for incinerators provided by subpart O of part 265 of this chapter, or the interim status standards for thermal treatment units provided by subpart P of part 265 of this chapter; and

(B) The boiler or industrial furnace met the interim status eligibility requirements under §270.70 of this chapter for subpart O or subpart P of part 265 of this chapter; and

(C) Hazardous waste with a heating value less than 5,000 Btu/lb was burned prior to that date; or

(iv) Such waste may be burned in a halogen acid furnace if the waste was burned as an excluded ingredient under §261.2(e) of this chapter prior to February 21, 1991 and documentation is kept on file supporting this claim.

(7) *Direct transfer to the burner.* If hazardous waste is directly transferred from a transport vehicle to a boiler or industrial furnace without the use of a storage unit, the owner and operator must comply with §266.111.

(b) *Certification of precompliance*—(1) *General.* The owner or operator must provide complete and accurate information specified in paragraph (b)(2) of this section to the Director on or before August 21, 1991, and must establish limits for the operating parameters specified in paragraph (b)(3) of this section. Such information is termed a "certification of precompliance" and constitutes a certification that the owner or operator has determined that, when the facility is operated within the limits specified in paragraph (b)(3) of this section, the owner or operator believes that, using best engineering judgment, emissions of particulate matter, metals, and HCl and Cl_2 are not likely to exceed the limits provided by §§266.105, 266.106, and 266.107. The facility may burn hazardous waste only under the operating conditions that the owner or operator establishes under paragraph (b)(3) of this section until the owner or operator submits a revised certification of precompliance under paragraph (b)(8) of this section or a certification of compliance under paragraph (c) of this section, or until a permit is issued.

(2) *Information required.* The following information must be submitted with the certification of precompliance to support the determination that the limits established for the operating parameters identified in paragraph (b)(3) of this section are not likely to result in an exceedance of the allowable emission rates for particulate matter, metals, and HCl and Cl_2:

(i) General facility information:

(A) EPA facility ID number;

(B) Facility name, contact person, telephone number, and address;

(C) Description of boilers and industrial furnaces burning hazardous waste, including type and capacity of device;

(D) A scaled plot plan showing the entire facility and location of the boilers and industrial furnaces burning hazardous waste; and

(E) A description of the air pollution control system on each device burning hazardous waste, including the temperature of the flue gas at the inlet to the particulate matter control system.

(ii) Except for facilities complying with the Tier I or Adjusted Tier I feed rate screening limits for metals or total chlorine and chloride provided by §§266.106 (b) or (e) and 266.107 (b)(1) or (e), respectively, the estimated uncontrolled (at the inlet to the air pollution control system) emissions of particulate matter, each metal controlled by §266.106, and hydrogen chloride and chlorine, and the following information to support such determinations:

(A) The feed rate (lb/hr) of ash, chlorine, antimony, arsenic, barium, beryllium, cadmium, chromium, lead, mercury, silver, and thallium in each feedstream (hazardous waste, other fuels, industrial furnace feedstocks);

(B) The estimated partitioning factor to the combustion gas for the materials identified in paragraph (b)(2)(ii)(A) of this section and the basis for the estimate and an estimate of the partitioning to HCl and Cl_2 of total chloride and chlorine in feed materials. To estimate the partitioning factor, the owner or operator must use either best engineering judgment or the procedures specified in appendix IX of this part.

(C) For industrial furnaces that recycle collected particulate matter (PM) back into the furnace and that will certify compliance with the metals emissions standards under paragraph (c)(3)(ii)(A), the estimated enrichment factor for each metal. To estimate the enrichment factor, the owner or operator must use either best engineering judgment or the procedures specified in "Alternative Methodology for Implementing Metals Controls" in appendix IX of this part.

(D) If best engineering judgment is used to estimate partitioning factors or enrichment factors under paragraphs (b)(2)(ii)(B) or (b)(2)(ii)(C) respectively, the basis for the judgment. When best engineering judgment is used to develop or evaluate data or information and make determinations under this section, the determinations must be made by a qualified, registered professional engineer and a certification of his/her determinations in accordance with §270.11(d) of this chapter must be provided in the certification of precompliance.

(iii) For facilities complying with the Tier I or Adjusted Tier I feed rate screening limits for metals or total chlorine and chloride provided by §§266.106 (b) or (e) and 266.107 (b)(1) or (e), the feed rate (lb/hr) of total chloride and chlorine, antimony, arsenic, barium, beryllium, cadmium, chromium, lead, mercury, silver, and thallium in each feed stream (hazardous waste, other fuels, industrial furnace feedstocks).

(iv) For facilities complying with the Tier II or Tier III emission limits for metals or HCl and Cl_2 (under §§266.106 (c) or (d) or 266.107(b)(2) or (c)), the estimated controlled (outlet of the air pollution control system) emissions rates of particulate matter, each metal controlled by §266.106, and HCl and Cl_2, and the following information to support such determinations:

(A) The estimated air pollution control system (APCS) removal efficiency for particulate matter, HCl, Cl_2, antimony, arsenic, barium, beryllium, cadmium, chromium, lead, mercury, silver, and thallium.

(B) To estimate APCS removal efficiency, the owner or operator must use either best engineering judgment or the procedures prescribed in appendix IX of this part.

(C) If best engineering judgment is used to estimate APCS removal efficiency, the basis for the judgment. Use of best engineering judgment must be in conformance with provisions of paragraph (b)(2)(ii)(D) of this section.

(v) Determination of allowable emissions rates for HCl, Cl_2, antimony, arsenic, barium, beryllium, cadmium, chromium, lead, mercury, silver, and thallium, and the following information to support such determinations:

(A) For all facilities:

(*1*) Physical stack height;

(*2*) Good engineering practice stack height as defined by 40 CFR 51.100(ii);

(*3*) Maximum flue gas flow rate;

(*4*) Maximum flue gas temperature;

(*5*) Attach a US Geological Service topographic map (or equivalent) showing the facility location and surrounding land within 5 km of the facility;

(*6*) Identify terrain type: complex or noncomplex; and

(*7*) Identify land use: urban or rural.

(B) For owners and operators using Tier III site specific dispersion modeling to determine allowable levels under §266.106(d) or §266.107(c), or adjusted Tier I feed rate screening limits under §§266.106(e) or 266.107(e):

(*1*) Dispersion model and version used;

(*2*) Source of meteorological data;

(*3*) The dilution factor in micrograms per cubic meter per gram per second of emissions for the maximum annual average off-site (unless on-site is required) ground level concentration (MEI location); and

(*4*) Indicate the MEI location on the map required under paragraph (b)(2)(v)(A)(*5*);

(vi) For facilities complying with the Tier II or III emissions rate controls for metals or HCl and Cl_2, a comparison of the estimated controlled emissions rates determined under paragraph (b)(2)(iv) with the allowable emission rates determined under paragraph (b)(2)(v);

(vii) For facilities complying with the Tier I (or adjusted Tier I) feed rate screening limits for metals or total chloride and chlorine, a comparison of actual feed rates of each metal and total chlorine and chloride determined under paragraph (b)(2)(iii) of this section to the Tier I allowable feed rates; and

(viii) For industrial furnaces that feed hazardous waste for any purpose other than solely as an ingredient (as defined by paragraph (a)(5)(ii) of this section) at any location other than the product discharge end of the device, documentation of compliance with the requirements of paragraphs (a)(5)(i)(A), (B), and (C) of this section.

(ix) For industrial furnaces that recycle collected particulate matter (PM) back into the furnace and that will certify compliance with the metals emissions standards under paragraph (c)(3)(ii)(A) of this section:

(A) The applicable particulate matter standard in lb/hr; and

(B) The precompliance limit on the concentration of each metal in collected PM.

(3) *Limits on operating conditions.* The owner and operator shall establish limits on the following parameters consistent with the determinations made under paragraph (b)(2) of this section and certify (under provisions of paragraph (b)(9) of this section) to the Director that the facility will operate within the limits during interim status when there is hazardous waste in the unit until revised certification of precompliance under paragraph (b)(8) of this section or certification of compliance under paragraph (c) of this section:

(i) Feed rate of total hazardous waste and (unless complying with the Tier I or adjusted Tier I metals feed rate screening limits under §266.106 (b) or (e)) pumpable hazardous waste;

(ii) Feed rate of each metal in the following feed streams:

(A) Total feed streams, except that industrial furnaces that comply with the alternative metals implementation approach under paragraph (b)(4) of this section must specify limits on the concentration of each metal in collected particulate matter in lieu of feed rate limits for total feedstreams;

(B) Total hazardous waste feed, unless complying with the Tier I or Adjusted Tier I metals feed rate screening limits under §266.106 (b) or (e); and

(C) Total pumpable hazardous waste feed, unless complying with the Tier I or adjusted Tier I metals feed rate screening limits under §266.106 (b) or (e);

(iii) Total feed rate of chlorine and chloride in total feed streams;

(iv) Total feed rate of ash in total feed streams, except that the ash feed rate for cement kilns and lightweight aggregate kilns is not limited; and

(v) Maximum production rate of the device in appropriate units when producing normal product, unless complying with the Tier I or Adjusted Tier I feed rate screening limits for chlorine under §266.107 (b)(1) or (e) and for all metals under §266.106 (b) or (e), and the uncontrolled particulate emissions do not exceed the standard under §266.105.

(4) *Operating requirements for furnaces that recycle PM.* Owners and operators of furnaces that recycle collected particulate matter (PM) back into the furnace and that will certify compliance with the metals emissions controls under paragraph (c)(3)(ii)(A) of this section must comply with the special operating requirements provided in "Alternative Methodology for Implementing Metals Controls" in appendix IX of this part.

(5) *Measurement of feed rates and production rate*—(i) *General requirements.* Limits on each of the parameters specified in paragraph (b)(3) of this section (except for limits on metals concentrations in collected particulate matter (PM) for industrial furnaces that recycle collected PM) shall be established and continuously monitored under either of the following methods:

(A) *Instantaneous limits.* A limit for a parameter may be established and continuously monitored and recorded on an instantaneous basis (*i.e.*, the value that occurs at any time) not to be exceeded at any time; or

(B) *Hourly rolling average limits.* A limit for a parameter may be established and continuously monitored on an hourly rolling average basis defined as follows:

(*1*) A continuous monitor is one which continuously samples the regulated parameter without interruption, and evaluates the detector response at least once each 15 seconds, and computes and records the average value at least every 60 seconds.

(*2*) An hourly rolling average is the arithmetic mean of the 60 most recent 1-minute average values recorded by the continuous monitoring system.

(ii) *Rolling average limits for carcinogenic metals and lead.* Feed rate limits for the carcinogenic metals (arsenic, beryllium, cadmium, and chromium) and lead may be established either on an hourly rolling average basis as prescribed by paragraph (b)(5)(i)(B) or on (up to) a 24 hour rolling average basis. If the owner or operator elects to use an averaging period from 2 to 24 hours:

(A) The feed rate of each metal shall be limited at any time to ten times the feed rate that would be allowed on an hourly rolling average basis;

(B) The continuous monitor shall meet the following specifications:

(*1*) A continuous monitor is one which continuously samples the regulated parameter without interruption, and evaluates the detector response at least once each 15 seconds, and computes and records the average value at least every 60 seconds.

(*2*) The rolling average for the selected averaging period is defined as the arithmetic mean of one hour block averages for the averaging period. A one hour block average is the arithmetic mean of the one minute averages recorded during the 60-minute period beginning at one minute after the beginning of preceding clock hour.

(iii) *Feed rate limits for metals, total chloride and chlorine, and ash.* Feed rate limits for metals, total chlorine and chloride, and ash are established and monitored by knowing the concentration of the substance (*i.e.*, metals, chloride/chlorine, and ash) in each feedstream and the flow rate of the feedstream. To monitor the feed rate of these substances, the flow rate of each feedstream must be monitored under the continuous monitoring requirements of paragraphs (b)(5)(i) and (ii) of this section.

(6) *Public notice requirements at precompliance.* On or before August 21, 1991 the owner or operator must submit a notice with the following information for publication in a major local newspaper of general circulation and send a copy of the notice to the appropriate units of State and local government. The owner and operator must provide to the Director with the certification of precompliance evidence of submitting the notice for publication. The notice, which shall be entitled "Notice of Certification of Precompliance with Hazardous Waste Burning Requirements of 40 CFR 266.103(b)", must include:

(i) Name and address of the owner and operator of the facility as well as the location of the device burning hazardous waste;

(ii) Date that the certification of precompliance is submitted to the Director;

(iii) Brief description of the regulatory process required to comply with the interim status requirements of this section including required emissions testing to demonstrate conformance with emissions standards for organic compounds, particulate matter, metals, and HCl and Cl_2;

(iv) Types and quantities of hazardous waste burned including, but not limited to, source, whether solids or liquids, as well as an appropriate description of the waste;

(v) Type of device(s) in which the hazardous waste is burned including a physical description and maximum production rate of each device;

(vi) Types and quantities of other fuels and industrial furnace feedstocks fed to each unit;

(vii) Brief description of the basis for this certification of precompliance as specified in paragraph (b)(2) of this section;

(viii) Locations where the record for the facility can be viewed and copied by interested parties. These records and locations shall at a minimum include:

(A) The administrative record kept by the Agency office where the supporting documentation was submitted or another location designated by the Director; and

(B) The BIF correspondence file kept at the facility site where the device is located. The correspondence file must include all correspondence between the facility and the Director, State and local regulatory officials, including copies of all certifications and notifications, such as the precompliance certification, precompliance public notice, notice of compliance testing, compliance test report, compliance certification, time extension requests and approvals or denials, enforcement notifications of violations, and copies of EPA and State site visit reports submitted to the owner or operator.

(ix) Notification of the establishment of a facility mailing list whereby interested parties shall notify the Agency that they wish to be placed on the mailing list to receive future information and notices about this facility; and

(x) Location (mailing address) of the applicable EPA Regional Office, Hazardous Waste Division, where further information can be obtained on EPA regulation of hazardous waste burning.

(7) *Monitoring other operating parameters.* When the monitoring systems for the operating parameters listed in paragraphs (c)(1) (v through xiii) of this section are installed and operating in conformance with vendor specifications or (for CO, HC, and oxygen) specifications provided by appendix IX of this part, as appropriate, the parameters shall be continuously monitored and records shall be maintained in the operating record.

(8) *Revised certification of precompliance.* The owner or operator may revise at any time the information and operating conditions documented under paragraphs (b)(2) and (b)(3) of this section in the certification of precompliance by submitting a revised certification of precompliance under procedures provided by those paragraphs.

(i) The public notice requirements of paragraph (b)(6) of this section do not apply to recertifications.

(ii) The owner and operator must operate the facility within the limits established for the operating parameters under paragraph (b)(3) of this section until a revised certification is submitted under this paragraph or a certification of compliance is submitted under paragraph (c) of this section.

(9) *Certification of precompliance statement.* The owner or operator must include the following signed statement with the certification of precompliance submitted to the Director:

"I certify under penalty of law that this information was prepared under my direction or supervision in accordance with a system designed to ensure that qualified personnel properly gathered and evaluated the information and supporting documentation. Copies of all emissions tests, dispersion modeling results and other information used to determine conformance with the requirements of §266.103(b) are available at the facility and can be obtained from the facility contact person listed above. Based on my inquiry of the person or persons who manages the facility, or those persons directly responsible for gathering the information, the information submitted is, to the best of my knowledge and belief, true, accurate, and complete. I am aware that there are significant penalties for submitting false information, including the possibility of fine and imprisonment for knowing violations.

I also acknowledge that the operating limits established in this certification pursuant to §266.103(b) (3) and (4) are enforceable limits at which the facility can legally operate during interim status until: (1) A revised certification of precompliance is submitted, (2) a certification of compliance is submitted, or (3) an operating permit is issued."

(c) *Certification of compliance.* The owner or operator shall conduct emissions testing to document compliance with the emissions standards of §§266.104 (b) through (e), 266.105, 266.106, 266.107, and paragraph (a)(5)(i)(D) of this section, under the procedures prescribed by this paragraph, except under extensions of time provided by paragraph (c)(7). Based on the compliance test, the owner or operator shall submit to the Director on or before August 21, 1992 a complete and accurate "certification of compliance" (under paragraph (c)(4) of this section) with those emission standards establishing limits on the operating parameters specified in paragraph (c)(1).

(1) *Limits on operating conditions.* The owner or operator shall establish limits on the following parameters based on operations during the compliance test (under procedures prescribed in paragraph (c)(4)(iv) of this section) or as otherwise specified and include these limits with the certification of compliance. The boiler or industrial furnace must be operated in accordance with these operating limits and the applicable emissions standards of §§266.104(b) through (e), 266.105, 266.106, 266.107, and 266.103(a)(5)(i)(D) at all times when there is hazardous waste in the unit.

(i) Feed rate of total hazardous waste and (unless complying with the Tier I or adjusted Tier I metals feed rate screening limits under §266.106(b) or (e)), pumpable hazardous waste;

(ii) Feed rate of each metal in the following feedstreams:

(A) Total feedstreams, except that:

(*1*) Facilities that comply with Tier I or Adjusted Tier I metals feed rate screening limits may set their operating limits at the metals feed rate screening limits determined under §266.106(b) or (e); and

(*2*) Industrial furnaces that must comply with the alternative metals implementation approach under paragraph (c)(3)(ii) of this section must specify limits on the concentration of each metal in the collected particulate matter in lieu of feed rate limits for total feedstreams;

(B) Total hazardous waste feed (unless complying with the Tier I or Adjusted Tier I metals feed rate screening limits under §266.106(b) or (e)); and

(C) Total pumpable hazardous waste feed (unless complying with the Tier I or Adjusted Tier I metals feed rate screening limits under §266.106(b) or (e));

(iii) Total feed rate of chlorine and chloride in total feed streams, except that facilities that comply with Tier I or Adjusted Tier I feed rate screening limits may set their operating limits at the total chlorine and chloride feed rate screening limits determined under §266.107(b)(1) or (e);

(iv) Total feed rate of ash in total feed streams, except that the ash feed rate for cement kilns and lightweight aggregate kilns is not limited;

(v) Carbon monoxide concentration, and where required, hydrocarbon concentration in stack gas. When complying with the CO controls of §266.104(b), the CO limit is 100 ppmv, and when complying with the HC controls of §266.104(c), the HC limit is 20 ppmv. When complying with the CO controls of §266.104(c), the CO limit is established based on the compliance test;

(vi) Maximum production rate of the device in appropriate units when producing normal product, unless complying with the Tier I or Adjusted Tier I feed rate screening limits for chlorine under §266.107(b)(1) or (e) and for all metals under §266.106(b) or (e), and the uncontrolled particulate emissions do not exceed the standard under §266.105;

(vii) Maximum combustion chamber temperature where the temperature measurement is as close to the combustion zone as possible and is upstream of any quench water injection (unless complying with the Tier I or Adjusted Tier I metals feed rate screening limits under §266.106(b) or (e));

(viii) Maximum flue gas temperature entering a particulate matter control device (unless complying with Tier I or Adjusted Tier I metals feed rate screening limits under §266.106(b) or (e) and the total chlorine and chloride feed rate screening limits under §266.107(b) or (e));

(ix) For systems using wet scrubbers, including wet ionizing scrubbers (unless complying with the Tier I or Adjusted Tier I metals feed rate screening limits under §266.106(b) or (e) and the total chlorine and chloride feed rate screening limits under §266.107(b)(1) or (e)):

(A) Minimum liquid to flue gas ratio;

(B) Minimum scrubber blowdown from the system or maximum suspended solids content of scrubber water; and

(C) Minimum pH level of the scrubber water;

(x) For systems using venturi scrubbers, the minimum differential gas pressure across the venturi (unless complying with the Tier I or Adjusted Tier I metals feed rate screening limits under §266.106(b) or (e) and the total chlorine and chloride feed rate screening limits under §266.107(b)(1) or (e));

(xi) For systems using dry scrubbers (unless complying with the Tier I or Adjusted Tier I metals feed rate screening limits under §266.106(b) or (e) and the total chlorine and chloride feed rate screening limits under §266.107(b)(1) or (e)):

(A) Minimum caustic feed rate; and

(B) Maximum flue gas flow rate;

(xii) For systems using wet ionizing scrubbers or electrostatic precipitators (unless complying with the Tier I or Adjusted Tier I metals feed rate screening limits under §266.106(b) or (e) and the total chlorine and chloride feed rate screening limits under §266.107(b)(1) or (e)):

(A) Minimum electrical power in kilovolt amperes (kVA) to the precipitator plates; and

(B) Maximum flue gas flow rate;

(xiii) For systems using fabric filters (baghouses), the minimum pressure drop (unless complying with the Tier I or Adjusted Tier I metal feed rate screening limits under §266.106(b) or (e) and the total chlorine and chloride feed rate screening limits under §266.107(b)(1) or (e)).

(2) *Prior notice of compliance testing.* At least 30 days prior to the compliance testing required by paragraph (c)(3) of this section, the owner or operator shall notify the Director and submit the following information:

(i) General facility information including:

(A) EPA facility ID number;

(B) Facility name, contact person, telephone number, and address;

(C) Person responsible for conducting compliance test, including company name, address, and telephone number, and a statement of qualifications;

(D) Planned date of the compliance test;

(ii) Specific information on each device to be tested including:

(A) Description of boiler or industrial furnace;

(B) A scaled plot plan showing the entire facility and location of the boiler or industrial furnace;

(C) A description of the air pollution control system;

(D) Identification of the continuous emission monitors that are installed, including:

(*1*) Carbon monoxide monitor;

(*2*) Oxygen monitor;

(*3*) Hydrocarbon monitor, specifying the minimum temperature of the system and, if the temperature is less than 150° C, an explanation of why a heated system is not used (see paragraph (c)(5) of this section) and a brief description of the sample gas conditioning system;

(E) Indication of whether the stack is shared with another device that will be in operation during the compliance test;

(F) Other information useful to an understanding of the system design or operation.

(iii) Information on the testing planned, including a complete copy of the test protocol and Quality Assurance/Quality Control (QA/QC) plan, and a summary description for each test providing the following information at a minimum:

(A) Purpose of the test (*e.g.*, demonstrate compliance with emissions of particulate matter); and

(B) Planned operating conditions, including levels for each pertinent parameter specified in paragraph (c)(1) of this section.

(3) *Compliance testing*—(i) *General.* Compliance testing must be conducted under conditions for which the owner or operator has submitted a certification of precompliance under paragraph (b) of this section and under conditions established in the notification of compliance testing required by paragraph (c)(2) of this section. The owner or operator may seek approval on a case-by-case basis to use compliance test data from one unit in lieu of testing a similar onsite unit. To support the request, the owner or operator must provide a comparison of the hazardous waste burned and other feedstreams, and the design, operation, and maintenance of both the tested unit and the similar unit. The Director shall provide a written approval to use compliance test data in lieu of testing a similar unit if he finds that the hazardous wastes, the devices, and the operating conditions are sufficiently similar, and the data from the other compliance test is adequate to meet the requirements of §266.103(c).

(ii) *Special requirements for industrial furnaces that recycle collected PM.* Owners and operators of industrial furnaces that recycle back into the furnace particulate matter (PM) from the air pollution control system must comply with one of the following procedures for testing to determine compliance with the metals standards of §266.106(c) or (d):

(A) The special testing requirements prescribed in "Alternative Method for Implementing Metals Controls" in appendix IX of this part; or

(B) Stack emissions testing for a minimum of 6 hours each day while hazardous waste is burned during interim status. The testing must be conducted when burning normal hazardous waste for that day at normal feed rates for that day and when the air pollution control system is operated under normal conditions. During interim status, hazardous waste analysis for metals content must be sufficient for the owner or operator to determine if changes in metals content may affect the ability of the facility to meet the metals emissions standards established under §266.106(c) or (d). Under this option, operating limits (under paragraph (c)(1) of this section) must be established during compliance testing under paragraph (c)(3) of this section only on the following parameters;

(*1*) Feed rate of total hazardous waste;

(*2*) Total feed rate of chlorine and chloride in total feed streams;

(*3*) Total feed rate of ash in total feed streams, except that the ash feed rate for cement kilns and lightweight aggregate kilns is not limited;

(*4*) Carbon monoxide concentration, and where required, hydrocarbon concentration in stack gas;

(*5*) Maximum production rate of the device in appropriate units when producing normal product; or

(C) Conduct compliance testing to determine compliance with the metals standards to establish limits on the operating parameters of paragraph (c)(1) of this section only after the kiln system has been conditioned to enable it to reach equilibrium with respect to metals fed into the system and metals emissions. During conditioning, hazardous waste and raw materials having the same metals content as will be fed during the compliance test must be fed at the feed rates that will be fed during the compliance test.

(iii) *Conduct of compliance testing.* (A) If compliance with all applicable emissions standards of §§266.104 through 266.107 is not demonstrated simultaneously during a set of test runs, the operating conditions of additional test runs required to demonstrate compliance with remaining emissions standards must be as close as possible to the original operating conditions.

(B) Prior to obtaining test data for purposes of demonstrating compliance with the applicable emissions standards of §§266.104 through 266.107 or establishing limits on operating parameters under this section, the facility must operate under compliance test conditions for a sufficient period to reach steady-state operations. Industrial furnaces that recycle collected particulate matter back into the furnace and that comply with paragraphs (c)(3)(ii)(A) or (B) of this section, however, need not reach steady state conditions with respect to the flow of metals in the system prior to beginning compliance testing for metals.

(C) Compliance test data on the level of an operating parameter for which a limit must be established in the certification of compliance must be obtained during emissions sampling for the pollutant(s) (*i.e.*, metals, PM, HCl/Cl_2, organic compounds) for which the parameter must be established as specified by paragraph (c)(1) of this section.

(4) *Certification of compliance.* Within 90 days of completing compliance testing, the owner or operator must certify to the Director compliance with the emissions standards of §§266.104 (b), (c), and (e), 266.105, 266.106, 266.107, and paragraph (a)(5)(i)(D) of this section. The certification of compliance must include the following information:

(i) General facility and testing information including:

(A) EPA facility ID number;

(B) Facility name, contact person, telephone number, and address;

(C) Person responsible for conducting compliance testing, including company name, address, and telephone number, and a statement of qualifications;

(D) Date(s) of each compliance test;

(E) Description of boiler or industrial furnace tested;

(F) Person responsible for quality assurance/quality control (QA/QC), title, and telephone number, and statement that procedures prescribed in the QA/QC plan submitted under §266.103(c)(2)(iii) have been followed, or a description of any changes and an explanation of why changes were necessary.

(G) Description of any changes in the unit configuration prior to or during testing that would alter any of the information submitted in the prior notice of compliance testing under paragraph (c)(2) of this section, and an explanation of why the changes were necessary;

(H) Description of any changes in the planned test conditions prior to or during the testing that alter any of the information submitted in the prior notice of compliance testing under paragraph (c)(2) of this section, and an explanation of why the changes were necessary; and

(I) The complete report on results of emissions testing.

(ii) Specific information on each test including:

(A) Purpose(s) of test (*e.g.*, demonstrate conformance with the emissions limits for particulate matter, metals, HCl, Cl_2, and CO)

(B) Summary of test results for each run and for each test including the following information:

(*1*) Date of run;

(*2*) Duration of run;

(*3*) Time-weighted average and highest hourly rolling average CO level for each run and for the test;

(*4*) Highest hourly rolling average HC level, if HC monitoring is required for each run and for the test;

(*5*) If dioxin and furan testing is required under §266.104(e), time-weighted average emissions for each run and for the test of chlorinated dioxin and furan emissions, and the predicted maximum annual average ground level concentration of the toxicity equivalency factor;

(*6*) Time-weighted average particulate matter emissions for each run and for the test;

(*7*) Time-weighted average HCl and Cl_2 emissions for each run and for the test;

(*8*) Time-weighted average emissions for the metals subject to regulation under §266.106 for each run and for the test; and

(*9*) QA/QC results.

(iii) Comparison of the actual emissions during each test with the emissions limits prescribed by §§266.104(b), (c), and (e), 266.105, 266.106, and 266.107 and established for the facility in the certification of precompliance under paragraph (b) of this section.

(iv) Determination of operating limits based on all valid runs of the compliance test for each applicable parameter listed in paragraph (c)(1) of this section using either of the following procedures:

(A) *Instantaneous limits.* A parameter may be measured and recorded on an instantaneous basis (*i.e.*, the value that occurs at any time) and the operating limit specified as the time-weighted average during all runs of the compliance test; or

(B) *Hourly rolling average basis.* (*1*) The limit for a parameter may be established and continuously monitored on an hourly rolling average basis defined as follows:

(*i*) A continuous monitor is one which continuously samples the regulated parameter without interruption, and evaluates the detector response at least once each 15 seconds, and computes and records the average value at least every 60 seconds.

(*ii*) An hourly rolling average is the arithmetic mean of the 60 most recent 1-minute average values recorded by the continuous monitoring system.

(*2*) The operating limit for the parameter shall be established based on compliance test data as the average over all test runs of the highest hourly rolling average value for each run.

(C) *Rolling average limits for carcinogenic metals and lead.* Feed rate limits for the carcinogenic metals (*i.e.*, arsenic, beryllium, cadmium and chromium) and lead may be established either on an hourly rolling average basis as prescribed by paragraph (c)(4)(iv)(B) of this section or on (up to) a 24 hour rolling average basis. If the owner or operator elects to use an averaging period from 2 to 24 hours:

(*1*) The feed rate of each metal shall be limited at any time to ten times the feed rate that would be allowed on an hourly rolling average basis;

(*2*) The continuous monitor shall meet the following specifications:

(*i*) A continuous monitor is one which continuously samples the regulated parameter without interruption, and evaluates the detector response at least once each 15 seconds, and computes and records the average value at least every 60 seconds.

(*ii*) The rolling average for the selected averaging period is defined as arithmetic mean of one hour block averages for the averaging period. A one hour block average is the arithmetic mean of the one minute averages recorded during the 60-minute period beginning at one minute after the beginning of preceding clock hour; and

(*3*) The operating limit for the feed rate of each metal shall be established based on compliance test data as the average over all test runs of the highest hourly rolling average feed rate for each run.

(D) *Feed rate limits for metals, total chloride and chlorine, and ash.* Feed rate limits for metals, total chlorine and chloride, and ash are established and monitored by knowing the concentration of the substance (*i.e.*, metals, chloride/chlorine, and ash) in each feedstream and the flow rate of the feedstream. To monitor the feed rate of these substances, the flow rate of each feedstream must be monitored under the continuous monitoring requirements of paragraphs (c)(4)(iv) (A) through (C) of this section.

(v) *Certification of compliance statement.* The following statement shall accompany the certification of compliance:

"I certify under penalty of law that this information was prepared under my direction or supervision in accordance with a system designed to ensure that qualified personnel properly gathered and evaluated the information and supporting documentation. Copies of all emissions tests, dispersion modeling results and other information used to determine conformance with the requirements of §266.103(c) are available at the facility and can be obtained from the facility contact person listed above. Based on my inquiry of the person or persons who manages the facility, or those persons directly responsible for gathering the information, the information submitted is, to the best of my knowledge and belief, true, accurate, and complete. I am aware that there are significant penalties for submitting false information, including the possibility of fine and imprisonment for knowing violations.

I also acknowledge that the operating conditions established in this certification pursuant to §266.103(c)(4)(iv) are enforceable limits at which the facility can legally operate during interim status until a revised certification of compliance is submitted."

(5) *Special requirements for HC monitoring systems.* When an owner or operator is required to comply with the hydrocarbon (HC) controls provided by §266.104(c) or paragraph (a)(5)(i)(D) of this section, a conditioned gas monitoring system may be used in conformance with specifications provided in appendix IX of this part provided that the owner or operator submits a certification of compliance without using extensions of time provided by paragraph (c)(7) of this section.

(6) *Special operating requirements for industrial furnaces that recycle collected PM.* Owners and operators of industrial furnaces that recycle back into the furnace particulate matter (PM) from the air pollution control system must:

(i) When complying with the requirements of paragraph (c)(3)(ii)(A) of this section, comply with the operating requirements prescribed in "Alternative Method to Implement the Metals Controls" in appendix IX of this part; and

(ii) When complying with the requirements of paragraph (c)(3)(ii)(B) of this section, comply with the operating requirements prescribed by that paragraph.

(7) *Extensions of time.* (i) If the owner or operator does not submit a complete certification of compliance for all of the applicable emissions standards of §§266.104, 266.105, 266.106, and 266.107 by August 21, 1992, he/she must either:

(A) Stop burning hazardous waste and begin closure activities under paragraph (l) of this section for the hazardous waste portion of the facility; or

(B) Limit hazardous waste burning only for purposes of compliance testing (and pretesting to prepare for compliance testing) a total period of 720 hours for the period of time beginning August 21, 1992, submit a notification to the Director by August 21, 1992 stating that the facility is operating under restricted interim status and intends to resume burning hazardous waste, and submit a complete certification of compliance by August 23, 1993; or

(C) Obtain a case-by-case extension of time under paragraph (c)(7)(ii) of this section.

(ii) The owner or operator may request a case-by-case extension of time to extend any time limit provided by paragraph (c) of this section if compliance with the time limit is not practicable for reasons beyond the control of the owner or operator.

(A) In granting an extension, the Director may apply conditions as the facts warrant to ensure timely compliance with the requirements of this section and that the facility operates in a manner that does not pose a hazard to human health and the environment;

(B) When an owner or operator requests an extension of time to enable the facility to comply with the alternative hydrocarbon provisions of §266.104(f) and obtain a RCRA operating permit because the facility cannot meet the HC limit of §266.104(c) of this chapter:

(*1*) The Director shall, in considering whether to grant the extension:

(*i*) Determine whether the owner and operator have submitted in a timely manner a complete part B permit application that includes information required under §270.22(b) of this chapter; and

(*ii*) Consider whether the owner and operator have made a good faith effort to certify compliance with all other emission controls, including the controls on dioxins and furans of §266.104(e) and the controls on PM, metals, and HCl/Cl_2.

(*2*) If an extension is granted, the Director shall, as a condition of the extension, require the facility to operate under flue gas concentration limits on CO and HC that, based on available information, including information in the part B permit application, are baseline CO and HC levels as defined by §266.104(f)(1).

(8) *Revised certification of compliance.* The owner or operator may submit at any time a revised certification of compliance (recertification of compliance) under the following procedures:

(i) Prior to submittal of a revised certification of compliance, hazardous waste may not be burned for more than a total of 720 hours under operating conditions that exceed those established under a current certification of compliance, and such burning may be conducted only for purposes of determining whether the facility can operate under revised conditions and continue to meet the applicable emissions standards of §§266.104, 266.105, 266.106, and 266.107;

(ii) At least 30 days prior to first burning hazardous waste under operating conditions that exceed those established under a current certification of compliance, the owner or operator shall notify the Director and submit the following information:

(A) EPA facility ID number, and facility name, contact person, telephone number, and address;

(B) Operating conditions that the owner or operator is seeking to revise and description of the changes in facility design or operation that prompted the need to seek to revise the operating conditions;

(C) A determination that when operating under the revised operating conditions, the applicable emissions standards of §§266.104, 266.105, 266.106, and 266.107 are not likely to be exceeded. To document this determination, the owner or operator shall submit the applicable information required under paragraph (b)(2) of this section; and

(D) Complete emissions testing protocol for any pretesting and for a new compliance test to determine compliance with the applicable emissions standards of §§266.104, 266.105, 266.106, and 266.107 when operating under revised operating conditions. The protocol shall include a schedule of pre-testing and compliance testing. If the owner and operator revises the scheduled date for the compliance test, he/she shall notify the Director in writing at least 30 days prior to the revised date of the compliance test;

(iii) Conduct a compliance test under the revised operating conditions and the protocol submitted to the Director to determine compliance with the applicable emissions standards of §§266.104, 266.105, 266.106, and 266.107; and

(iv) Submit a revised certification of compliance under paragraph (c)(4) of this section.

(d) *Periodic Recertifications.* The owner or operator must conduct compliance testing and submit to the Director a recertification of compliance under provisions of paragraph (c) of this section within five years from submitting the previous certification or recertification. If the owner or operator seeks to recertify compliance under new operating conditions, he/she must comply with the requirements of paragraph (c)(8) of this section.

(e) *Noncompliance with certification schedule.* If the owner or operator does not comply with the interim status compliance schedule provided by paragraphs (b), (c), and (d) of this section, hazardous waste burning must terminate on the date that the deadline is missed, closure activities must begin under paragraph (l) of this section, and hazardous waste burning may not resume except under an operating permit issued under §270.66 of this chapter. For purposes of compliance with the closure provisions of paragraph (l) of this section and §§265.112(d)(2) and 265.113 of this chapter the boiler or industrial furnace has received "the known final volume of hazardous waste" on the date that the deadline is missed.

(f) *Start-up and shut-down.* Hazardous waste (except waste fed solely as an ingredient under the Tier I (or adjusted Tier I) feed rate screening limits for metals and chloride/chlorine) must not be fed into the device during start-up and shut-down of the boiler or industrial furnace, unless the device is operating within the conditions of operation specified in the certification of compliance.

(g) *Automatic waste feed cutoff.* During the compliance test required by paragraph (c)(3) of this section, and upon certification of compliance under paragraph (c) of this section, a boiler or industrial furnace must be operated with a functioning system that automatically cuts off the hazardous waste feed when the applicable operating conditions specified in paragraphs (c)(1) (i) and (v through xiii) of this section deviate from those established in the certification of compliance. In addition:

(1) To minimize emissions of organic compounds, the minimum combustion chamber temperature (or the indicator of combustion chamber temperature) that occurred during the compliance test must be maintained while hazardous waste or hazardous waste residues remain in the combustion chamber, with the minimum temperature during the compliance test defined as either:

(i) If compliance with the combustion chamber temperature limit is based on an hourly rolling average, the minimum temperature during the compliance test is considered to be the average over all runs of the lowest hourly rolling average for each run; or

(ii) If compliance with the combustion chamber temperature limit is based on an instantaneous temperature measurement, the minimum temperature during the compliance test is considered to be the time-weighted average temperature during all runs of the test; and

(2) Operating parameters limited by the certification of compliance must continue to be monitored during the cutoff, and the hazardous waste feed shall not be restarted until the levels of those parameters comply with the limits established in the certification of compliance.

(h) *Fugitive emissions.* Fugitive emissions must be controlled by:

(1) Keeping the combustion zone totally sealed against fugitive emissions; or

(2) Maintaining the combustion zone pressure lower than atmospheric pressure; or

(3) An alternate means of control that the owner or operator can demonstrate provide fugitive emissions control equivalent to maintenance of combustion zone pressure lower than atmospheric pressure. Support for such demonstration shall be included in the operating record.

(i) *Changes.* A boiler or industrial furnace must cease burning hazardous waste when changes in combustion properties, or feed rates of the hazardous waste, other fuels, or industrial furnace feedstocks, or changes in the boiler or industrial furnace design or operating conditions deviate from the limits specified in the certification of compliance.

(j) *Monitoring and Inspections.* (1) The owner or operator must monitor and record the following, at a minimum, while burning hazardous waste:

(i) Feed rates and composition of hazardous waste, other fuels, and industrial furnace feed stocks, and feed rates of ash, metals, and total chloride and chlorine as necessary to ensure conformance with the certification of precompliance or certification of compliance;

(ii) Carbon monoxide (CO), oxygen, and if applicable, hydrocarbons (HC), on a continuous basis at a common point in the boiler or industrial furnace downstream of the combustion zone and prior to release of stack gases to the atmosphere in accordance with the operating limits specified in the certification of compliance. CO, HC, and oxygen monitors must be installed, operated, and maintained in accordance with methods specified in appendix IX of this part.

(iii) Upon the request of the Director, sampling and analysis of the hazardous waste (and other fuels and industrial furnace feed stocks as appropriate) and the stack gas emissions must be conducted to verify that the operating conditions established in the certification of precompliance or certification of compliance achieve the applicable standards of §§266.104, 266.105, 266.106, and 266.107.

(2) The boiler or industrial furnace and associated equipment (pumps, valves, pipes, fuel storage tanks, etc.) must be subjected to thorough visual inspection when they contain hazardous waste, at least daily for leaks, spills, fugitive emissions, and signs of tampering.

(3) The automatic hazardous waste feed cutoff system and associated alarms must be tested at least once every 7 days when hazardous waste is burned to verify operability, unless the owner or operator can demonstrate that weekly inspections will unduly restrict or upset operations and that less frequent inspections will be adequate. Support for such demonstration shall be included in the operating record. At a minimum, operational testing must be conducted at least once every 30 days.

(4) These monitoring and inspection data must be recorded and the records must be placed in the operating log.

(k) *Recordkeeping.* The owner or operator must keep in the operating record of the facility all information and data required by this section for five years.

(l) *Closure.* At closure, the owner or operator must remove all hazardous waste and hazardous waste residues (including, but not limited to, ash, scrubber waters, and scrubber sludges) from the boiler or industrial furnace and must comply with §§265.111-265.115 of this chapter.

[56 FR 7208, Feb. 21, 1991; 56 FR 32689, July 17, 1991, as amended at 56 FR 42512, 42514, Aug. 27, 1991; 57 FR 38564, Aug. 25, 1992; 57 FR 45000, Sept. 30, 1992; 60 FR 33913, June 29, 1995; 71 FR 16913, Apr. 4, 2006; 71 FR 40277, July 14, 2006]

§266.104 Standards to control organic emissions.

(a) *DRE standard*—(1) *General.* Except as provided in paragraph (a)(3) of this section, a boiler or industrial furnace burning hazardous waste must achieve a destruction and removal efficiency (DRE) of 99.99% for all organic hazardous constituents in the waste feed. To demonstrate conformance with this requirement, 99.99% DRE must be demonstrated during a trial burn for each principal organic hazardous constituent (POHC) designated (under paragraph (a)(2) of this section) in its permit for each waste feed. DRE is determined for each POHC from the following equation:

$$DRE = \left[1 - \frac{W_{out}}{W_{in}}\right] \times 100$$

where:

W_{in} = Mass feed rate of one principal organic hazardous constituent (POHC) in the hazardous waste fired to the boiler or industrial furnace; and

W_{out} = Mass emission rate of the same POHC present in stack gas prior to release to the atmosphere.

(2) *Designation of POHCs.* Principal organic hazardous constituents (POHCs) are those compounds for which compliance with the DRE requirements of this section shall be demonstrated in a trial burn in conformance with procedures prescribed in §270.66 of this chapter. One or more POHCs shall be designated by the Director for each waste feed to be burned. POHCs shall be designated based on the degree of difficulty of destruction of the organic constituents in the waste and on their concentrations or mass in the waste feed considering the results of waste analyses submitted with part B of the permit application. POHCs are most likely to be selected from among those compounds listed in part 261, appendix VIII of this chapter that are also present in the normal waste feed. However, if the applicant demonstrates to the Regional Administrator's satisfaction that a compound not listed in appendix VIII or not present in the normal waste feed is a suitable indicator of compliance with the DRE requirements of this section, that compound may be designated as a POHC. Such POHCs need not be toxic or organic compounds.

(3) *Dioxin-listed waste.* A boiler or industrial furnace burning hazardous waste containing (or derived from) EPA Hazardous Wastes Nos. F020, F021, F022, F023, F026, or F027 must achieve a destruction and removal efficiency (DRE) of 99.9999% for each POHC designated (under paragraph (a)(2) of this section) in its permit. This performance must be demonstrated on POHCs that are more difficult to burn than tetra-, penta-, and hexachlorodibenzo-p-dioxins and dibenzofurans. DRE is determined for each POHC from the equation in paragraph (a)(1) of this section. In addition, the owner or operator of the boiler or industrial furnace must notify the Director of intent to burn EPA Hazardous Waste Nos. F020, F021, F022, F023, F026, or F027.

(4) *Automatic waiver of DRE trial burn.* Owners and operators of boilers operated under the special operating

requirements provided by §266.110 are considered to be in compliance with the DRE standard of paragraph (a)(1) of this section and are exempt from the DRE trial burn.

(5) *Low risk waste.* Owners and operators of boilers or industrial furnaces that burn hazardous waste in compliance with the requirements of §266.109(a) are considered to be in compliance with the DRE standard of paragraph (a)(1) of this section and are exempt from the DRE trial burn.

(b) *Carbon monoxide standard.* (1) Except as provided in paragraph (c) of this section, the stack gas concentration of carbon monoxide (CO) from a boiler or industrial furnace burning hazardous waste cannot exceed 100 ppmv on an hourly rolling average basis (*i.e.*, over any 60 minute period), continuously corrected to 7 percent oxygen, dry gas basis.

(2) CO and oxygen shall be continuously monitored in conformance with "Performance Specifications for Continuous Emission Monitoring of Carbon Monoxide and Oxygen for Incinerators, Boilers, and Industrial Furnaces Burning Hazardous Waste" in appendix IX of this part.

(3) Compliance with the 100 ppmv CO limit must be demonstrated during the trial burn (for new facilities or an interim status facility applying for a permit) or the compliance test (for interim status facilities). To demonstrate compliance, the highest hourly rolling average CO level during any valid run of the trial burn or compliance test must not exceed 100 ppmv.

(c) *Alternative carbon monoxide standard.* (1) The stack gas concentration of carbon monoxide (CO) from a boiler or industrial furnace burning hazardous waste may exceed the 100 ppmv limit provided that stack gas concentrations of hydrocarbons (HC) do not exceed 20 ppmv, except as provided by paragraph (f) of this section for certain industrial furnaces.

(2) HC limits must be established under this section on an hourly rolling average basis (*i.e.*, over any 60 minute period), reported as propane, and continuously corrected to 7 percent oxygen, dry gas basis.

(3) HC shall be continuously monitored in conformance with "Performance Specifications for Continuous Emission Monitoring of Hydrocarbons for Incinerators, Boilers, and Industrial Furnaces Burning Hazardous Waste" in appendix IX of this part. CO and oxygen shall be continuously monitored in conformance with paragraph (b)(2) of this section.

(4) The alternative CO standard is established based on CO data during the trial burn (for a new facility) and the compliance test (for an interim status facility). The alternative CO standard is the average over all valid runs of the highest hourly average CO level for each run. The CO limit is implemented on an hourly rolling average basis, and continuously corrected to 7 percent oxygen, dry gas basis.

(d) *Special requirements for furnaces.* Owners and operators of industrial furnaces (*e.g.*, kilns, cupolas) that feed hazardous waste for a purpose other than solely as an ingredient (see §266.103(a)(5)(ii)) at any location other than the end where products are normally discharged and where fuels are normally fired must comply with the hydrocarbon limits provided by paragraphs (c) or (f) of this section irrespective of whether stack gas CO concentrations meet the 100 ppmv limit of paragraph (b) of this section.

(e) *Controls for dioxins and furans.* Owners and operators of boilers and industrial furnaces that are equipped with a dry particulate matter control device that operates within the temperature range of 450-750° F, and industrial furnaces operating under an alternative hydrocarbon limit established under paragraph (f) of this section must conduct a site-specific risk assessment as follows to demonstrate that emissions of chlorinated dibenzo-p-dioxins and dibenzofurans do not result in an increased lifetime cancer risk to the hypothetical maximum exposed individual (MEI) exceeding 1 in 100,000:

(1) During the trial burn (for new facilities or an interim status facility applying for a permit) or compliance test (for interim status facilities), determine emission rates of the tetra-octa congeners of chlorinated dibenzo-p-dioxins and dibenzofurans (CDDs/CDFs) using Method 0023A, Sampling Method for Polychlorinated Dibenzo-p-Dioxins and Polychlorinated Dibenzofurans Emissions from Stationary Sources, EPA Publication SW-846, as incorporated by reference in §260.11 of this chapter.

(2) Estimate the 2,3,7,8-TCDD toxicity equivalence of the tetra-octa CDDs/CDFs congeners using "Procedures for Estimating the Toxicity Equivalence of Chlorinated Dibenzo-p-Dioxin and Dibenzofuran Congeners" in appendix IX of this part. Multiply the emission rates of CDD/CDF congeners with a toxicity equivalence greater than zero (see the procedure) by the calculated toxicity equivalence factor to estimate the equivalent emission rate of 2,3,7,8-TCDD;

(3) Conduct dispersion modeling using methods recommended in appendix W of part 51 of this chapter

("Guideline on Air Quality Models (Revised)" (1986) and its supplements), the "Hazardous Waste Combustion Air Quality Screening Procedure", provided in appendix IX of this part, or in Screening Procedures for Estimating the Air Quality Impact of Stationary Sources, Revised (incorporated by reference in §260.11) to predict the maximum annual average off-site ground level concentration of 2,3,7,8-TCDD equivalents determined under paragraph (e)(2) of this section. The maximum annual average concentration must be used when a person resides on-site; and

(4) The ratio of the predicted maximum annual average ground level concentration of 2,3,7,8-TCDD equivalents to the risk-specific dose for 2,3,7,8-TCDD provided in appendix V of this part (2.2×10^{-7}) shall not exceed 1.0.

(f) *Monitoring CO and HC in the by-pass duct of a cement kiln.* Cement kilns may comply with the carbon monoxide and hydrocarbon limits provided by paragraphs (b), (c), and (d) of this section by monitoring in the by-pass duct provided that:

(1) Hazardous waste is fired only into the kiln and not at any location downstream from the kiln exit relative to the direction of gas flow; and

(2) The by-pass duct diverts a minimum of 10% of kiln off-gas into the duct.

(g) *Use of emissions test data to demonstrate compliance and establish operating limits.* Compliance with the requirements of this section must be demonstrated simultaneously by emissions testing or during separate runs under identical operating conditions. Further, data to demonstrate compliance with the CO and HC limits of this section or to establish alternative CO or HC limits under this section must be obtained during the time that DRE testing, and where applicable, CDD/CDF testing under paragraph (e) of this section and comprehensive organic emissions testing under paragraph (f) is conducted.

(h) *Enforcement.* For the purposes of permit enforcement, compliance with the operating requirements specified in the permit (under §266.102) will be regarded as compliance with this section. However, evidence that compliance with those permit conditions is insufficient to ensure compliance with the requirements of this section may be "information" justifying modification or revocation and re-issuance of a permit under §270.41 of this chapter.

[56 FR 7208, Feb. 21, 1991; 56 FR 32689, July 17, 1991, as amended at 57 FR 38565, Aug. 25, 1992; 58 FR 38883, July 20, 1993; 60 FR 33914, June 29, 1995; 62 FR 32463, June 13, 1997]

§266.105 Standards to control particulate matter.

(a) A boiler or industrial furnace burning hazardous waste may not emit particulate matter in excess of 180 milligrams per dry standard cubic meter (0.08 grains per dry standard cubic foot) after correction to a stack gas concentration of 7% oxygen, using procedures prescribed in 40 CFR part 60, appendix A, methods 1 through 5, and appendix IX of this part.

(b) An owner or operator meeting the requirements of §266.109(b) for the low risk waste exemption is exempt from the particulate matter standard.

(c) Oxygen correction. (1) Measured pollutant levels must be corrected for the amount of oxygen in the stack gas according to the formula:

$$Pc = Pm \times 14 / (E - Y)$$

Where:

Pc is the corrected concentration of the pollutant in the stack gas,

Pm is the measured concentration of the pollutant in the stack gas,

E is the oxygen concentration on a dry basis in the combustion air fed to the device, and

Y is the measured oxygen concentration on a dry basis in the stack.

(2) For devices that feed normal combustion air, E will equal 21 percent. For devices that feed oxygen-enriched air for combustion (that is, air with an oxygen concentration exceeding 21 percent), the value of E will be the concentration of oxygen in the enriched air.

(3) Compliance with all emission standards provided by this subpart must be based on correcting to 7 percent oxygen using this procedure.

(d) For the purposes of permit enforcement, compliance with the operating requirements specified in the permit (under §266.102) will be regarded as compliance with this section. However, evidence that compliance with those permit conditions is insufficient to ensure compliance with the requirements of this section may be "information" justifying modification or revocation and re-issuance of a permit under §270.41 of this chapter.

[56 FR 7208, Feb. 21, 1991, as amended at 64 FR 53075, Sept. 30, 1999]

§266.106 Standards to control metals emissions.

(a) *General.* The owner or operator must comply with the metals standards provided by paragraphs (b), (c), (d), (e), or (f) of this section for each metal listed in paragraph (b) of this section that is present in the hazardous waste at detectable levels by using appropriate analytical procedures.

(b) *Tier I feed rate screening limits.* Feed rate screening limits for metals are specified in appendix I of this part as a function of terrain-adjusted effective stack height and terrain and land use in the vicinity of the facility. Criteria for facilities that are not eligible to comply with the screening limits are provided in paragraph (b)(7) of this section.

(1) *Noncarcinogenic metals.* The feed rates of antimony, barium, lead, mercury, thallium, and silver in all feed streams, including hazardous waste, fuels, and industrial furnace feed stocks shall not exceed the screening limits specified in appendix I of this part.

(i) The feed rate screening limits for antimony, barium, mercury, thallium, and silver are based on either:

(A) An hourly rolling average as defined in §266.102(e)(6)(i)(B); or

(B) An instantaneous limit not to be exceeded at any time.

(ii) The feed rate screening limit for lead is based on one of the following:

(A) An hourly rolling average as defined in §266.102(e)(6)(i)(B);

(B) An averaging period of 2 to 24 hours as defined in §266.102(e)(6)(ii) with an instantaneous feed rate limit not to exceed 10 times the feed rate that would be allowed on an hourly rolling average basis; or

(C) An instantaneous limit not to be exceeded at any time.

(2) *Carcinogenic metals.* (i) The feed rates of arsenic, cadmium, beryllium, and chromium in all feed streams, including hazardous waste, fuels, and industrial furnace feed stocks shall not exceed values derived from the screening limits specified in appendix I of this part. The feed rate of each of these metals is limited to a level such that the sum of the ratios of the actual feed rate to the feed rate screening limit specified in appendix I shall not exceed 1.0, as provided by the following equation:

$$\sum_{i=1}^{n} \frac{AFR_{(i)}}{FRSL_{(i)}} \leq 1.0$$

where:

n = number of carcinogenic metals

AFR = actual feed rate to the device for metal "i"

FRSL = feed rate screening limit provided by appendix I of this part for metal "i".

(ii) The feed rate screening limits for the carcinogenic metals are based on either:

(A) An hourly rolling average; or

(B) An averaging period of 2 to 24 hours as defined in §266.102(e)(6)(ii) with an instantaneous feed rate limit not to exceed 10 times the feed rate that would be allowed on an hourly rolling average basis.

(3) *TESH.* (i) The terrain-adjusted effective stack height is determined according to the following equation:

$$TESH = Ha + H1 - Tr$$

where:

Ha = Actual physical stack height

H1 = Plume rise as determined from appendix VI of this part as a function of stack flow rate and stack gas exhaust temperature.

Tr = Terrain rise within five kilometers of the stack.

(ii) The stack height (Ha) may not exceed good engineering practice as specified in 40 CFR 51.100(ii).

(iii) If the TESH for a particular facility is not listed in the table in the appendices, the nearest lower TESH listed in the table shall be used. If the TESH is four meters or less, a value of four meters shall be used.

(4) *Terrain type.* The screening limits are a function of whether the facility is located in noncomplex or complex terrain. A device located where any part of the surrounding terrain within 5 kilometers of the stack equals or exceeds the elevation of the physical stack height (Ha) is considered to be in complex terrain and the screening limits for complex terrain apply. Terrain measurements are to be made from U.S. Geological Survey 7.5-minute topographic maps of the area surrounding the facility.

(5) *Land use.* The screening limits are a function of whether the facility is located in an area where the land use is urban or rural. To determine whether land use in the vicinity of the facility is urban or rural, procedures provided in appendices IX or X of this part shall be used.

(6) *Multiple stacks.* Owners and operators of facilities with more than one on-site stack from a boiler, industrial furnace, incinerator, or other thermal treatment unit subject to controls of metals emissions under a RCRA operating permit or interim status controls must comply with the screening limits for all such units assuming all hazardous waste is fed into the device with the worst-case stack based on dispersion characteristics. The worst-case stack is determined from the following equation as applied to each stack:

$$K = HVT$$

Where:

K = a parameter accounting for relative influence of stack height and plume rise;

H = physical stack height (meters);

V = stack gas flow rate (m^3/second); and

T = exhaust temperature (° K).

The stack with the lowest value of K is the worst-case stack.

(7) *Criteria for facilities not eligible for screening limits.* If any criteria below are met, the Tier I and Tier II screening limits do not apply. Owners and operators of such facilities must comply with either the Tier III standards provided by paragraph (d) of this section or with the adjusted Tier I feed rate screening limits provided by paragraph (e) of this section.

(i) The device is located in a narrow valley less than one kilometer wide;

(ii) The device has a stack taller than 20 meters and is located such that the terrain rises to the physical height within one kilometer of the facility;

(iii) The device has a stack taller than 20 meters and is located within five kilometers of a shoreline of a large body of water such as an ocean or large lake;

(iv) The physical stack height of any stack is less than 2.5 times the height of any building within five building heights or five projected building widths of the stack and the distance from the stack to the closest boundary is within five building heights or five projected building widths of the associated building; or

(v) The Director determines that standards based on site-specific dispersion modeling are required.

(8) *Implementation.* The feed rate of metals in each feedstream must be monitored to ensure that the feed rate screening limits are not exceeded.

(c) *Tier II emission rate screening limits.* Emission rate screening limits are specified in appendix I as a function of terrain-adjusted effective stack height and terrain and land use in the vicinity of the facility. Criteria for facilities that are not eligible to comply with the screening limits are provided in paragraph (b)(7) of this section.

(1) *Noncarcinogenic metals.* The emission rates of antimony, barium, lead, mercury, thallium, and silver shall not exceed the screening limits specified in appendix I of this part.

(2) *Carcinogenic metals.* The emission rates of arsenic, cadmium, beryllium, and chromium shall not exceed values derived from the screening limits specified in appendix I of this part. The emission rate of each of these metals is limited to a level such that the sum of the ratios of the actual emission rate to the emission rate screening limit specified in appendix I shall not exceed 1.0, as provided by the following equation:

$$\sum_{i=1}^{n} \frac{AER_{(i)}}{ERSL_{(i)}} \leq 1.0$$

where:

n = number of carcinogenic metals

AER = actual emission rate for metal "i"

ERSL = emission rate screening limit provided by appendix I of this part for metal "i".

(3) *Implementation.* The emission rate limits must be implemented by limiting feed rates of the individual metals to levels during the trial burn (for new facilities or an interim status facility applying for a permit) or the compliance test (for interim status facilities). The feed rate averaging periods are the same as provided by paragraphs (b)(1)(i) and (ii) and (b)(2)(ii) of this section. The feed rate of metals in each feedstream must be monitored to ensure that the feed rate limits for the feedstreams specified under §§266.102 or 266.103 are not exceeded.

(4) *Definitions and limitations.* The definitions and limitations provided by paragraph (b) of this section for the following terms also apply to the Tier II emission rate screening limits provided by paragraph (c) of this section: terrain-adjusted effective stack height, good engineering practice stack height, terrain type, land use, and criteria for facilities not eligible to use the screening limits.

(5) *Multiple stacks.* (i) Owners and operators of facilities with more than one onsite stack from a boiler, industrial furnace, incinerator, or other thermal treatment unit subject to controls on metals emissions under a RCRA operating permit or interim status controls must comply with the emissions screening limits for any such stacks assuming all hazardous waste is fed into the device with the worst-case stack based on dispersion characteristics.

(ii) The worst-case stack is determined by procedures provided in paragraph (b)(6) of this section.

(iii) For each metal, the total emissions of the metal from those stacks shall not exceed the screening limit for the worst-case stack.

(d) *Tier III and Adjusted Tier I site-specific risk assessment.* The requirements of this paragraph apply to facilities complying with either the Tier III or Adjusted Tier I controls, except where specified otherwise.

(1) *General.* Conformance with the Tier III metals controls must be demonstrated by emissions testing to determine the emission rate for each metal. In addition, conformance with either the Tier III or Adjusted Tier I metals controls must be demonstrated by air dispersion modeling to predict the maximum annual average off-site ground level concentration for each metal, and a demonstration that acceptable ambient levels are not exceeded.

(2) *Acceptable ambient levels.* Appendices IV and V of this part list the acceptable ambient levels for purposes of this rule. Reference air concentrations (RACs) are listed for the noncarcinogenic metals and 10^{-5} risk-specific doses (RSDs) are listed for the carcinogenic metals. The RSD for a metal is the acceptable ambient level for that metal provided that only one of the four carcinogenic metals is emitted. If more than one carcinogenic metal is emitted, the acceptable ambient level for the carcinogenic metals is a fraction of the RSD as described in paragraph (d)(3) of this section.

(3) *Carcinogenic metals.* For the carcinogenic metals, arsenic, cadmium, beryllium, and chromium, the sum of the ratios of the predicted maximum annual average off-site ground level concentrations (except that on-site concentrations must be considered if a person resides on site) to the risk-specific dose (RSD) for all carcinogenic metals emitted shall not exceed 1.0 as determined by the following equation:

$$\sum_{i=1}^{n} \frac{\text{Predicted Ambient Concentration}_{(i)}}{\text{Risk-Specific Dose}_{(i)}} \leq 1.0$$

where: n = number of carcinogenic metals

(4) *Noncarcinogenic metals.* For the noncarcinogenic metals, the predicted maximum annual average off-site ground level concentration for each metal shall not exceed the reference air concentration (RAC).

(5) *Multiple stacks.* Owners and operators of facilities with more than one on-site stack from a boiler, industrial furnace, incinerator, or other thermal treatment unit subject to controls on metals emissions under a RCRA operating permit or interim status controls must conduct emissions testing (except that facilities complying with Adjusted Tier I controls need not conduct emissions testing) and dispersion modeling to demonstrate that the aggregate emissions from all such on-site stacks do not result in an exceedance of the acceptable ambient levels.

(6) *Implementation.* Under Tier III, the metals controls must be implemented by limiting feed rates of the individual metals to levels during the trial burn (for new facilities or an interim status facility applying for a permit) or the compliance test (for interim status facilities). The feed rate averaging periods are the same as provided by paragraphs (b)(1) (i) and (ii) and (b)(2)(ii) of this section. The feed rate of metals in each feedstream must be monitored to ensure that the feed rate limits for the feedstreams specified under §§266.102 or 266.103 are not exceeded.

(e) *Adjusted Tier I feed rate screening limits.* The owner or operator may adjust the feed rate screening limits provided by appendix I of this part to account for site-specific dispersion modeling. Under this approach, the adjusted feed rate screening limit for a metal is determined by back-calculating from the acceptable ambient level provided by appendices IV and V of this part using dispersion modeling to determine the maximum allowable emission rate. This emission rate becomes the adjusted Tier I feed rate screening limit. The feed rate screening limits for carcinogenic metals are implemented as prescribed in paragraph (b)(2) of this section.

(f) *Alternative implementation approaches.* (1) The Director may approve on a case-by-case basis approaches to implement the Tier II or Tier III metals emission limits provided by paragraphs (c) or (d) of this section alternative to monitoring the feed rate of metals in each feedstream.

(2) The emission limits provided by paragraph (d) of this section must be determined as follows:

(i) For each noncarcinogenic metal, by back-calculating from the RAC provided in appendix IV of this part to determine the allowable emission rate for each metal using the dilution factor for the maximum annual average ground level concentration predicted by dispersion modeling in conformance with paragraph (h) of this section; and

(ii) For each carcinogenic metal by:

(A) Back-calculating from the RSD provided in appendix V of this part to determine the allowable emission rate for each metal if that metal were the only carcinogenic metal emitted using the dilution factor for the maximum annual average ground level concentration predicted by dispersion modeling in conformance with paragraph (h) of this section; and

(B) If more than one carcinogenic metal is emitted, selecting an emission limit for each carcinogenic metal not to exceed the emission rate determined by paragraph (f)(2)(ii)(A) of this section such that the sum for all carcinogenic metals of the ratios of the selected emission limit to the emission rate determined by that paragraph does not exceed 1.0.

(g) *Emission testing*—(1) *General.* Emission testing for metals shall be conducted using Method 0060, Determinations of Metals in Stack Emissions, EPA Publication SW-846, as incorporated by reference in §260.11 of this chapter.

(2) *Hexavalent chromium.* Emissions of chromium are assumed to be hexavalent chromium unless the owner or operator conducts emissions testing to determine hexavalent chromium emissions using procedures prescribed in Method 0061, Determination of Hexavalent Chromium Emissions from Stationary Sources, EPA Publication SW-846, as incorporated by reference in §260.11 of this chapter.

(h) *Dispersion Modeling.* Dispersion modeling required under this section shall be conducted according to methods recommended in appendix W of part 51 of this chapter ("Guideline on Air Quality Models (Revised)" (1986) and its supplements), the "Hazardous Waste Combustion Air Quality Screening Procedure", provided in appendix IX of this part, or in Screening Procedures for Estimating the Air Quality Impact of Stationary Sources, Revised (incorporated by reference in §260.11) to predict the maximum annual average off-site ground level concentration. However, on-site concentrations must be considered when a person resides on-site.

(i) *Enforcement.* For the purposes of permit enforcement, compliance with the operating requirements specified in the permit (under §266.102) will be regarded as compliance with this section. However, evidence that compliance with those permit conditions is insufficient to ensure compliance with the requirements of this section may be "information" justifying modification or revocation and re-issuance of a permit under §270.41 of this chapter.

[56 FR 7208, Feb. 21, 1991; 56 FR 32689, July 17, 1991; 57 FR 38565, Aug. 25, 1992; 58 FR 38883, July 20, 1993; 62 FR 32463, June 13, 1997; 70 FR 34588, June 14, 2005; 71 FR 40277, July 14, 2006]

§266.107 Standards to control hydrogen chloride (HCl) and chlorine gas (Cl_2) emissions.

(a) *General.* The owner or operator must comply with the hydrogen chloride (HCl) and chlorine (Cl_2) controls provided by paragraph (b), (c), or (e) of this section.

(b) *Screening limits*—(1) *Tier I feed rate screening limits.* Feed rate screening limits are specified for total chlorine in appendix II of this part as a function of terrain-adjusted effective stack height and terrain and land use in the vicinity of the facility. The feed rate of total chlorine and chloride, both organic and inorganic, in all feed streams, including hazardous waste, fuels, and industrial furnace feed stocks shall not exceed the levels specified.

(2) *Tier II emission rate screening limits.* Emission rate screening limits for HCl and Cl_2 are specified in appendix III of this part as a function of terrain-adjusted effective stack height and terrain and land use in the vicinity of the facility. The stack emission rates of HCl and Cl_2 shall not exceed the levels specified.

(3) *Definitions and limitations.* The definitions and limitations provided by §266.106(b) for the following terms also apply to the screening limits provided by this paragraph: terrain-adjusted effective stack height, good engineering practice stack height, terrain type, land use, and criteria for facilities not eligible to use the screening limits.

(4) *Multiple stacks.* Owners and operators of facilities with more than one on-site stack from a boiler, industrial furnace, incinerator, or other thermal treatment unit subject to controls on HCl or Cl_2 emissions under a RCRA operating permit or interim status controls must comply with the Tier I and Tier II screening limits for those stacks assuming all hazardous waste is fed into the device with the worst-case stack based on dispersion characteristics.

(i) The worst-case stack is determined by procedures provided in §266.106(b)(6).

(ii) Under Tier I, the total feed rate of chlorine and chloride to all subject devices shall not exceed the screening limit for the worst-case stack.

(iii) Under Tier II, the total emissions of HCl and Cl_2 from all subject stacks shall not exceed the screening limit for the worst-case stack.

(c) *Tier III site-specific risk assessments*—(1) *General.* Conformance with the Tier III controls must be demonstrated by emissions testing to determine the emission rate for HCl and Cl_2, air dispersion modeling to predict the maximum annual average off-site ground level concentration for each compound, and a demonstration that acceptable ambient levels are not exceeded.

(2) *Acceptable ambient levels.* Appendix IV of this part lists the reference air concentrations (RACs) for

HCl (7 micrograms per cubic meter) and Cl_2 (0.4 micrograms per cubic meter).

(3) *Multiple stacks.* Owners and operators of facilities with more than one on-site stack from a boiler, industrial furnace, incinerator, or other thermal treatment unit subject to controls on HCl or Cl_2 emissions under a RCRA operating permit or interim status controls must conduct emissions testing and dispersion modeling to demonstrate that the aggregate emissions from all such on-site stacks do not result in an exceedance of the acceptable ambient levels for HCl and Cl_2.

(d) *Averaging periods.* The HCl and Cl_2 controls are implemented by limiting the feed rate of total chlorine and chloride in all feedstreams, including hazardous waste, fuels, and industrial furnace feed stocks. Under Tier I, the feed rate of total chloride and chlorine is limited to the Tier I Screening Limits. Under Tier II and Tier III, the feed rate of total chloride and chlorine is limited to the feed rates during the trial burn (for new facilities or an interim status facility applying for a permit) or the compliance test (for interim status facilities). The feed rate limits are based on either:

(1) An hourly rolling average as defined in §266.102(e)(6); or

(2) An instantaneous basis not to be exceeded at any time.

(e) *Adjusted Tier I feed rate screening limits.* The owner or operator may adjust the feed rate screening limit provided by appendix II of this part to account for site-specific dispersion modeling. Under this approach, the adjusted feed rate screening limit is determined by back-calculating from the acceptable ambient level for Cl_2 provided by appendix IV of this part using dispersion modeling to determine the maximum allowable emission rate. This emission rate becomes the adjusted Tier I feed rate screening limit.

(f) *Emissions testing.* Emissions testing for HCl and Cl_2 shall be conducted using the procedures described in Methods 0050 or 0051, EPA Publication SW-846, as incorporated by reference in §260.11 of this chapter.

(g) *Dispersion modeling.* Dispersion modeling shall be conducted according to the provisions of §266.106(h).

(h) *Enforcement.* For the purposes of permit enforcement, compliance with the operating requirements specified in the permit (under §266.102) will be regarded as compliance with this section. However, evidence that compliance with those permit conditions is insufficient to ensure compliance with the requirements of this section may be "information" justifying modification or revocation and re-issuance of a permit under §270.41 of this chapter.

[56 FR 7208, Feb. 21, 1991; 56 FR 32690, July 17, 1991; 57 FR 38566, Aug. 25, 1992; 62 FR 32463, June 13, 1997]

§266.108 Small quantity on-site burner exemption.

(a) *Exempt quantities.* Owners and operators of facilities that burn hazardous waste in an on-site boiler or industrial furnace are exempt from the requirements of this subpart provided that:

(1) The quantity of hazardous waste burned in a device for a calendar month does not exceed the limits provided in the following table based on the terrain-adjusted effective stack height as defined in §266.106(b)(3):

Exempt Quantities for Small Quantity Burner Exemption

Terrain-adjusted effective stack height of device (meters)	Allowable hazardous waste burning rate (gallons/month)	Terrain-adjusted effective stack height of device (meters)	Allowable hazardous waste burning rate (gallons/month)
0 to 3.9	0	40.0 to 44.9	210
4.0 to 5.9	13	45.0 to 49.9	260
6.0 to 7.9	18	50.0 to 54.9	330
8.0 to 9.9	27	55.0 to 59.9	400
10.0 to 11.9	40	60.0 to 64.9	490
12.0 to 13.9	48	65.0 to 69.9	610
14.0 to 15.9	59	70.0 to 74.9	680
16.0 to 17.9	69	75.0 to 79.9	760
18.0 to 19.9	76	80.0 to 84.9	850
20.0 to 21.9	84	85.0 to 89.9	960
22.0 to 23.9	93	90.0 to 94.9	1,100
24.0 to 25.9	100	95.0 to 99.9	1,200
26.0 to 27.9	110	100.0 to 104.9	1,300
28.0 to 29.9	130	105.0 to 109.9	1,500
30.0 to 34.9	140	110.0 to 114.9	1,700
35.0 to 39.9	170	115.0 or greater	1,900

(2) The maximum hazardous waste firing rate does not exceed at any time 1 percent of the total fuel requirements for the device (hazardous waste plus other fuel) on a total heat input or mass input basis, whichever results in the lower mass feed rate of hazardous waste.

(3) The hazardous waste has a minimum heating value of 5,000 Btu/lb, as generated; and

(4) The hazardous waste fuel does not contain (and is not derived from) EPA Hazardous Waste Nos. F020, F021, F022, F023, F026, or F027.

(b) *Mixing with nonhazardous fuels.* If hazardous waste fuel is mixed with a nonhazardous fuel, the quantity of hazardous waste before such mixing is used to comply with paragraph (a).

(c) *Multiple stacks.* If an owner or operator burns hazardous waste in more than one on-site boiler or industrial furnace exempt under this section, the quantity limits provided by paragraph (a)(1) of this section are implemented according to the following equation:

$$\sum_{i=1}^{n} \frac{\text{Actual Quantity Burned}_{(i)}}{\text{Allowable Quantity Burned}_{(i)}} \leq 1.0$$

where:

n means the number of stacks;

Actual Quantity Burned means the waste quantity burned per month in device "i";

Allowable Quantity Burned means the maximum allowable exempt quantity for stack "i" from the table in (a)(1) above.

Note: Hazardous wastes that are subject to the special requirements for small quantity generators under §261.5 of this chapter may be burned in an off-site device under the exemption provided by §266.108, but must be included in the quantity determination for the exemption.

(d) *Notification requirements.* The owner or operator of facilities qualifying for the small quantity burner exemption under this section must provide a one-time signed, written notice to EPA indicating the following:

(1) The combustion unit is operating as a small quantity burner of hazardous waste;

(2) The owner and operator are in compliance with the requirements of this section; and

(3) The maximum quantity of hazardous waste that the facility may burn per month as provided by §266.108(a)(1).

(e) *Recordkeeping requirements.* The owner or operator must maintain at the facility for at least three years sufficient records documenting compliance with the hazardous waste quantity, firing rate, and heating value limits of this section. At a minimum, these records must indicate the quantity of hazardous waste and other fuel burned in each unit per calendar month, and the heating value of the hazardous waste.

[56 FR 7208, Feb. 21, 1991; 56 FR 32690, July 17, 1991, as amended at 56 FR 42515, Aug. 27, 1991; 57 FR 38566, Aug. 25, 1992]

§266.109 Low risk waste exemption.

(a) *Waiver of DRE standard.* The DRE standard of §266.104(a) does not apply if the boiler or industrial furnace is operated in conformance with (a)(1) of this section and the owner or operator demonstrates by procedures prescribed in (a)(2) of this section that the burning will not result in unacceptable adverse health effects.

(1) The device shall be operated as follows:

(i) A minimum of 50 percent of fuel fired to the device shall be fossil fuel, fuels derived from fossil fuel, tall oil, or, if approved by the Director on a case-by-case basis, other nonhazardous fuel with combustion characteristics comparable to fossil fuel. Such fuels are termed "primary fuel" for purposes of this section. (Tall oil is a fuel derived from vegetable and rosin fatty acids.) The 50 percent primary fuel firing rate shall be determined on a total heat or mass input basis, whichever results in the greater mass feed rate of primary fuel fired;

(ii) Primary fuels and hazardous waste fuels shall have a minimum as-fired heating value of 8,000 Btu/lb;

(iii) The hazardous waste is fired directly into the primary fuel flame zone of the combustion chamber; and

(iv) The device operates in conformance with the carbon monoxide controls provided by §266.104(b)(1). Devices subject to the exemption provided by this section are not eligible for the alternative carbon monoxide controls provided by §266.104(c).

(2) Procedures to demonstrate that the hazardous waste burning will not pose unacceptable adverse public health effects are as follows:

(i) Identify and quantify those nonmetal compounds listed in appendix VIII, part 261 of this chapter that could reasonably be expected to be present in the hazardous waste. The constituents excluded from analysis must be identified and the basis for their exclusion explained;

(ii) Calculate reasonable, worst case emission rates for each constituent identified in paragraph (a)(2)(i) of this section by assuming the device achieves 99.9 percent destruction and removal efficiency. That is, assume that 0.1 percent of the mass weight of each constituent fed to the device is emitted.

(iii) For each constituent identified in paragraph (a)(2)(i) of this section, use emissions dispersion modeling to predict the maximum annual average ground level concentration of the constituent.

(A) Dispersion modeling shall be conducted using methods specified in §266.106(h).

(B) Owners and operators of facilities with more than one on-site stack from a boiler or industrial furnace that is exempt under this section must conduct dispersion modeling of emissions from all stacks exempt under this section to predict ambient levels prescribed by this paragraph.

(iv) Ground level concentrations of constituents predicted under paragraph (a)(2)(iii) of this section must not exceed the following levels:

(A) For the noncarcinogenic compounds listed in appendix IV of this part, the levels established in appendix IV;

(B) For the carcinogenic compounds listed in appendix V of this part, the sum for all constituents of the ratios of the actual ground level concentration to the level established in appendix V cannot exceed 1.0; and

(C) For constituents not listed in appendix IV or V, 0.1 micrograms per cubic meter.

(b) *Waiver of particulate matter standard.* The particulate matter standard of §266.105 does not apply if:

(1) The DRE standard is waived under paragraph (a) of this section; and

(2) The owner or operator complies with the Tier I or adjusted Tier I metals feed rate screening limits provided by §266.106 (b) or (e).

[56 FR 7208, Feb. 21, 1991; 56 FR 32690, July 17, 1991, as amended at 56 FR 42515, Aug. 27, 1991; 71 FR 40277, July 14, 2006]

§266.110 Waiver of DRE trial burn for boilers.

Boilers that operate under the special requirements of this section, and that do not burn hazardous waste containing (or derived from) EPA Hazardous Waste Nos. F020, F021, F022, F023, F026, or F027, are considered to be in conformance with the DRE standard of §266.104(a), and a trial burn to demonstrate DRE is waived. When burning hazardous waste:

(a) A minimum of 50 percent of fuel fired to the device shall be fossil fuel, fuels derived from fossil fuel, tall oil, or, if approved by the Director on a case-by-case basis, other nonhazardous fuel with combustion characteristics comparable to fossil fuel. Such fuels are termed "primary fuel" for purposes of this section. (Tall oil is a fuel derived from vegetable and rosin fatty acids.) The 50 percent primary fuel firing rate shall be determined on a total heat or mass input basis, whichever results in the greater mass feed rate of primary fuel fired;

(b) Boiler load shall not be less than 40 percent. Boiler load is the ratio at any time of the total heat input to the maximum design heat input;

(c) Primary fuels and hazardous waste fuels shall have a minimum as-fired heating value of 8,000 Btu/lb, and each material fired in a burner where hazardous waste is fired must have a heating value of at least 8,000 Btu/lb, as-fired;

(d) The device shall operate in conformance with the carbon monoxide standard provided by §266.104(b)(1). Boilers subject to the waiver of the DRE trial burn provided by this section are not eligible for the alternative carbon monoxide standard provided by §266.104(c);

(e) The boiler must be a watertube type boiler that does not feed fuel using a stoker or stoker type mechanism; and

(f) The hazardous waste shall be fired directly into the primary fuel flame zone of the combustion chamber with an air or steam atomization firing system, mechanical atomization system, or a rotary cup atomization system under the following conditions:

(1) *Viscosity.* The viscosity of the hazardous waste fuel as-fired shall not exceed 300 SSU;

(2) *Particle size.* When a high pressure air or steam atomizer, low pressure atomizer, or mechanical atomizer is used, 70% of the hazardous waste fuel must pass through a 200 mesh (74 micron) screen, and when a rotary cup atomizer is used, 70% of the hazardous waste must pass through a 100 mesh (150 micron) screen;

(3) *Mechanical atomization systems.* Fuel pressure within a mechanical atomization system and fuel flow rate shall be maintained within the design range taking into account the viscosity and volatility of the fuel;

(4) *Rotary cup atomization systems.* Fuel flow rate through a rotary cup atomization system must be maintained within the design range taking into account the viscosity and volatility of the fuel.

[56 FR 7208, Feb. 21, 1991; 56 FR 32690, July 17, 1991, as amended at 56 FR 42515, Aug. 27, 1991]

§266.111 Standards for direct transfer.

(a) *Applicability.* The regulations in this section apply to owners and operators of boilers and industrial furnaces subject to §§266.102 or 266.103 if hazardous waste is directly transferred from a transport vehicle to a boiler or industrial furnace without the use of a storage unit.

(b) *Definitions.* (1) When used in this section, the following terms have the meanings given below:

Direct transfer equipment means any device (including but not limited to, such devices as piping, fittings, flanges, valves, and pumps) that is used to distribute, meter, or control the flow of hazardous waste between a container (*i.e.*, transport vehicle) and a boiler or industrial furnace.

Container means any portable device in which hazardous waste is transported, stored, treated, or otherwise handled, and includes transport vehicles that are containers themselves (*e.g.*, tank trucks, tanker-trailers, and rail tank cars), and containers placed on or in a transport vehicle.

(2) This section references several requirements provided in subparts I and J of parts 264 and 265. For purposes of this section, the term "tank systems" in those referenced requirements means direct transfer equipment as defined in paragraph (b)(1) of this section.

(c) *General operating requirements.* (1) No direct transfer of a pumpable hazardous waste shall be conducted from an open-top container to a boiler or industrial furnace.

(2) Direct transfer equipment used for pumpable hazardous waste shall always be closed, except when necessary to add or remove the waste, and shall not be opened, handled, or stored in a manner that may cause any rupture or leak.

(3) The direct transfer of hazardous waste to a boiler or industrial furnace shall be conducted so that it does not:

(i) Generate extreme heat or pressure, fire, explosion, or violent reaction;

(ii) Produce uncontrolled toxic mists, fumes, dusts, or gases in sufficient quantities to threaten human health;

(iii) Produce uncontrolled flammable fumes or gases in sufficient quantities to pose a risk of fire or explosions;

(iv) Damage the structural integrity of the container or direct transfer equipment containing the waste;

(v) Adversely affect the capability of the boiler or industrial furnace to meet the standards provided by §§266.104 through 266.107; or

(vi) Threaten human health or the environment.

(4) Hazardous waste shall not be placed in direct transfer equipment, if it could cause the equipment or its secondary containment system to rupture, leak, corrode, or otherwise fail.

(5) The owner or operator of the facility shall use appropriate controls and practices to prevent spills and overflows from the direct transfer equipment or its secondary containment systems. These include at a minimum:

(i) Spill prevention controls (*e.g.*, check valves, dry discount couplings); and

(ii) Automatic waste feed cutoff to use if a leak or spill occurs from the direct transfer equipment.

(d) *Areas where direct transfer vehicles (containers) are located.* Applying the definition of container under this section, owners and operators must comply with the following requirements:

(1) The containment requirements of §264.175 of this chapter;

(2) The use and management requirements of subpart I, part 265 of this chapter, except for §§265.170 and 265.174, and except that in lieu of the special requirements of §265.176 for ignitable or reactive waste, the owner or operator may comply with the requirements for the maintenance of protective distances between the waste management area and any public ways, streets, alleys, or an adjacent property line that can be built upon as required in Tables 2-1 through 2-6 of the National Fire Protection Association's (NFPA) "Flammable and Combustible Liquids Code," (1977 or 1981), (incorporated by reference, see §260.11). The owner or operator must obtain and keep on file at the facility a written certification by the local Fire Marshall that the installation meets the subject NFPA codes; and

(3) The closure requirements of §264.178 of this chapter.

(e) *Direct transfer equipment.* Direct transfer equipment must meet the following requirements:

(1) *Secondary containment.* Owners and operators shall comply with the secondary containment requirements of §265.193 of this chapter, except for paragraphs 265.193 (a), (d), (e), and (i) as follows:

(i) For all new direct transfer equipment, prior to their being put into service; and

(ii) For existing direct transfer equipment within 2 years after August 21, 1991.

(2) *Requirements prior to meeting secondary containment requirements.* (i) For existing direct transfer equipment that does not have secondary containment, the owner or operator shall determine whether the equipment is leaking or is unfit for use. The owner or operator shall obtain and keep on file at the facility a written assessment reviewed and certified by a qualified, registered professional engineer in accordance with §270.11(d) of this chapter that attests to the equipment's integrity by August 21, 1992.

(ii) This assessment shall determine whether the direct transfer equipment is adequately designed and has sufficient structural strength and compatibility with the waste(s) to be transferred to ensure that it will not collapse, rupture, or fail. At a minimum, this assessment shall consider the following:

(A) Design standard(s), if available, according to which the direct transfer equipment was constructed;

(B) Hazardous characteristics of the waste(s) that have been or will be handled;

(C) Existing corrosion protection measures;

(D) Documented age of the equipment, if available, (otherwise, an estimate of the age); and

(E) Results of a leak test or other integrity examination such that the effects of temperature variations, vapor pockets, cracks, leaks, corrosion, and erosion are accounted for.

(iii) If, as a result of the assessment specified above, the direct transfer equipment is found to be leaking or unfit for use, the owner or operator shall comply with the requirements of §§265.196 (a) and (b) of this chapter.

(3) *Inspections and recordkeeping.* (i) The owner or operator must inspect at least once each operating hour when hazardous waste is being transferred from the transport vehicle (container) to the boiler or industrial furnace:

(A) Overfill/spill control equipment (*e.g.*, waste-feed cutoff systems, bypass systems, and drainage systems) to ensure that it is in good working order;

(B) The above ground portions of the direct transfer equipment to detect corrosion, erosion, or releases of waste (*e.g.*, wet spots, dead vegetation); and

(C) Data gathered from monitoring equipment and leak-detection equipment, (*e.g.*, pressure and temperature gauges) to ensure that the direct transfer equipment is being operated according to its design.

(ii) The owner or operator must inspect cathodic protection systems, if used, to ensure that they are functioning properly according to the schedule provided by §265.195(b) of this chapter:

(iii) Records of inspections made under this paragraph shall be maintained in the operating record at the facility, and available for inspection for at least 3 years from the date of the inspection.

(4) *Design and installation of new ancillary equipment.* Owners and operators must comply with the requirements of §265.192 of this chapter.

(5) *Response to leaks or spills.* Owners and operators must comply with the requirements of §265.196 of this chapter.

(6) *Closure.* Owners and operators must comply with the requirements of §265.197 of this chapter, except for §265.197 (c)(2) through (c)(4).

[50 FR 666, Jan. 4, 1985, as amended at 56 FR 42515, Aug. 27, 1991]

§266.112 Regulation of residues.

📖 5.2.3.5, 13.12.3.1

A residue derived from the burning or processing of hazardous waste in a boiler or industrial furnace is not excluded from the definition of a hazardous waste under §261.4(b) (4), (7), or (8) unless the device and the owner or operator meet the following requirements:

(a) The device meets the following criteria:

(1) *Boilers.* Boilers must burn at least 50% coal on a total heat input or mass input basis, whichever results in the greater mass feed rate of coal; 📖 4.13.4

(2) *Ore or mineral furnaces.* Industrial furnaces subject to §261.4(b)(7) must process at least 50% by weight normal, nonhazardous raw materials; 📖 4.15.3

(3) *Cement kilns.* Cement kilns must process at least 50% by weight normal cement-production raw materials;

(b) The owner or operator demonstrates that the hazardous waste does not significantly affect the residue by demonstrating conformance with either of the following criteria:

(1) *Comparison of waste-derived residue with normal residue.* The waste-derived residue must not contain appendix VIII, part 261 constituents (toxic constituents)

that could reasonably be attributable to the hazardous waste at concentrations significantly higher than in residue generated without burning or processing of hazardous waste, using the following procedure. Toxic compounds that could reasonably be attributable to burning or processing the hazardous waste (constituents of concern) include toxic constituents in the hazardous waste, and the organic compounds listed in appendix VIII of this part that may be generated as products of incomplete combustion. For polychlorinated dibenzo-p-dioxins and polychlorinated dibenzo-furans, analyses must be performed to determine specific congeners and homologues, and the results converted to 2,3,7,8-TCDD equivalent values using the procedure specified in section 4.0 of appendix IX of this part.

(i) *Normal residue.* Concentrations of toxic constituents of concern in normal residue shall be determined based on analyses of a minimum of 10 samples representing a minimum of 10 days of operation. Composite samples may be used to develop a sample for analysis provided that the compositing period does not exceed 24 hours. The upper tolerance limit (at 95% confidence with a 95% proportion of the sample distribution) of the concentration in the normal residue shall be considered the statistically-derived concentration in the normal residue. If changes in raw materials or fuels reduce the statistically-derived concentrations of the toxic constituents of concern in the normal residue, the statistically-derived concentrations must be revised or statistically-derived concentrations of toxic constituents in normal residue must be established for a new mode of operation with the new raw material or fuel. To determine the upper tolerance limit in the normal residue, the owner or operator shall use statistical procedures prescribed in "Statistical Methodology for Bevill Residue Determinations" in appendix IX of this part.

(ii) *Waste-derived residue.* Waste-derived residue shall be sampled and analyzed as often as necessary to determine whether the residue generated during each 24-hour period has concentrations of toxic constituents that are higher than the concentrations established for the normal residue under paragraph (b)(1)(i) of this section. If so, hazardous waste burning has significantly affected the residue and the residue shall not be excluded from the definition of a hazardous waste. Concentrations of toxic constituents of concern in the waste-derived residue shall be determined based on analysis of one or more samples obtained over a 24-hour period. Multiple samples may be analyzed, and multiple samples may be taken to form a composite sample for analysis provided that the sampling period does not exceed 24 hours. If more than one sample is analyzed to characterize waste-derived residues generated over a 24-hour period, the concentration of each toxic constituent shall be the arithmetic mean of the concentrations in the samples. No results may be disregarded; or

(2) *Comparison of waste-derived residue concentrations with health-based limits*—(i) *Nonmetal constituents:* The concentration of each nonmetal toxic constituent of concern (specified in paragraph (b)(1) of this section) in the waste-derived residue must not exceed the health-based level specified in appendix VII of this part, or the level of detection, whichever is higher. If a health-based limit for a constituent of concern is not listed in appendix VII of this part, then a limit of 0.002 micrograms per kilogram or the level of detection (which must be determined by using appropriate analytical procedures), whichever is higher, must be used. The levels specified in appendix VII of this part (and the default level of 0.002 micrograms per kilogram or the level of detection for constituents as identified in Note 1 of appendix VII of this chapter) are administratively stayed under the condition, for those constituents specified in paragraph (b)(1) of this section, that the owner or operator complies with alternative levels defined as the land disposal restriction limits specified in §268.43 of this chapter for F039 nonwastewaters. In complying with those alternative levels, if an owner or operator is unable to detect a constituent despite documenting use of best good-faith efforts as defined by applicable Agency guidance or standards, the owner or operator is deemed to be in compliance for that constituent. Until new guidance or standards are developed, the owner or operator may demonstrate such good-faith efforts by achieving a detection limit for the constituent that does not exceed an order of magnitude above the level provided by §268.43 of this chapter for F039 nonwastewaters. In complying with the §268.43 of this chapter F039 nonwastewater levels for polychlorinated dibenzo-p-dioxins and polychlorinated dibenzo-furans, analyses must be performed for total hexachlorodibenzo-p-dioxins, total hexachlorodibenzofurans, total pentachlorodibenzo-p-dioxins, total pentachlorodibenzofurans, total

tetrachlorodibenzo-p-dioxins, and total tetrachlorodibenzofurans.

Note to this paragraph (b)(2)(i): The administrative stay, under the condition that the owner or operator complies with alternative levels defined as the land disposal restriction limits specified in §268.43 of this chapter for F039 nonwastewaters, remains in effect until further administrative action is taken and notice is published in the *Federal Register* and the *Code of Federal Regulations.*

(ii) *Metal constituents.* The concentration of metals in an extract obtained using the Toxicity Characteristic Leaching Procedure of §261.24 of this chapter must not exceed the levels specified in appendix VII of this part; and

(iii) *Sampling and analysis.* Waste-derived residue shall be sampled and analyzed as often as necessary to determine whether the residue generated during each 24-hour period has concentrations of toxic constituents that are higher than the health-based levels. Concentrations of toxic constituents of concern in the waste-derived residue shall be determined based on analysis of one or more samples obtained over a 24-hour period. Multiple samples may be analyzed, and multiple samples may be taken to form a composite sample for analysis provided that the sampling period does not exceed 24 hours. If more than one sample is analyzed to characterize waste-derived residues generated over a 24-hour period, the concentration of each toxic constituent shall be the arithmetic mean of the concentrations in the samples. No results may be disregarded; and

(c) Records sufficient to document compliance with the provisions of this section shall be retained until closure of the boiler or industrial furnace unit. At a minimum, the following shall be recorded.

(1) Levels of constituents in appendix VIII, part 261, that are present in waste-derived residues;

(2) If the waste-derived residue is compared with normal residue under paragraph (b)(1) of this section:

(i) The levels of constituents in appendix VIII, part 261, that are present in normal residues; and

(ii) Data and information, including analyses of samples as necessary, obtained to determine if changes in raw materials or fuels would reduce the concentration of toxic constituents of concern in the normal residue.

[50 FR 666, Jan. 4, 1985, as amended at 56 FR 42516, Aug. 27, 1991; 57 FR 38566, Aug. 25, 1992; 58 FR 59602, Nov. 9, 1993; 64 FR 53076, Sept. 30, 1999; 70 FR 34588, June 14, 2005]

Subparts I–L [Reserved]

Subpart M—Military Munitions

14.6

Source: 62 FR 6654, Feb. 12, 1997, unless otherwise noted.

§266.200 Applicability.

(a) The regulations in this subpart identify when military munitions become a solid waste, and, if these wastes are also hazardous under this subpart or 40 CFR part 261, the management standards that apply to these wastes.

(b) Unless otherwise specified in this subpart, all applicable requirements in 40 CFR parts 260 through 270 apply to waste military munitions.

§266.201 Definitions.

In addition to the definitions in 40 CFR 260.10, the following definitions apply to this subpart:

Active range means a military range that is currently in service and is being regularly used for range activities.

Chemical agents and munitions are defined as in 50 U.S.C. section 1521(j)(1).

Director is as defined in 40 CFR 270.2.

Explosives or munitions emergency response specialist is as defined in 40 CFR 260.10.

Explosives or munitions emergency is as defined in 40 CFR 260.10.

Explosives or munitions emergency response is as defined in 40 CFR 260.10.

Inactive range means a military range that is not currently being used, but that is still under military control and considered by the military to be a potential range area, and that has not been put to a new use that is incompatible with range activities.

Military means the Department of Defense (DOD), the Armed Services, Coast Guard, National Guard, Department of Energy (DOE), or other parties under contract or acting as an agent for the foregoing, who handle military munitions.

Military munitions is as defined in 40 CFR 260.10.

Military range means designated land and water areas set aside, managed, and used to conduct research on, develop, test, and evaluate military munitions and explosives, other ordnance, or weapon systems, or to train military personnel in their use and handling. Ranges include firing lines and positions, maneuver areas, firing lanes, test pads, detonation pads, impact areas, and buffer zones with restricted access and exclusionary areas.

Unexploded ordnance (UXO) means military munitions that have been primed, fused, armed, or otherwise prepared for action, and have been fired, dropped, launched, projected, or placed in such a manner as to constitute a hazard to operations, installation, personnel, or material and remain unexploded either by malfunction, design, or any other cause.

§266.202 Definition of solid waste.

(a) A military munition is not a solid waste when:

(1) Used for its intended purpose, including: 14.6.2.3

(i) Use in training military personnel or explosives and munitions emergency response specialists (including training in proper destruction of unused propellant or other munitions); or

(ii) Use in research, development, testing, and evaluation of military munitions, weapons, or weapon systems; or

(iii) Recovery, collection, and on-range destruction of unexploded ordnance and munitions fragments during range clearance activities at active or inactive ranges. However, "use for intended purpose" does not include the on-range disposal or burial of unexploded ordnance and contaminants when the burial is not a result of product use. 14.6.2.4

(2) An unused munition, or component thereof, is being repaired, reused, recycled, reclaimed, disassembled, reconfigured, or otherwise subjected to materials recovery activities, unless such activities involve use constituting disposal as defined in 40 CFR 261.2(c)(1), or burning for energy recovery as defined in 40 CFR 261.2(c)(2). 14.6.2.2

(b) An unused military munition is a solid waste when any of the following occurs: 14.6.2.1

(1) The munition is abandoned by being disposed of, burned, detonated (except during intended use as specified in paragraph (a) of this section), incinerated, or treated prior to disposal; or

(2) The munition is removed from storage in a military magazine or other storage area for the purpose of being disposed of, burned, or incinerated, or treated prior to disposal, or

(3) The munition is deteriorated or damaged (*e.g.*, the integrity of the munition is compromised by cracks, leaks, or other damage) to the point that it cannot be put into serviceable condition, and cannot reasonably be recycled or used for other purposes; or

(4) The munition has been declared a solid waste by an authorized military official.

(c) A used or fired military munition is a solid waste: 14.6.2.4

(1) When transported off range or from the site of use, where the site of use is not a range, for the purposes of storage, reclamation, treatment, disposal, or treatment prior to disposal; or

(2) If recovered, collected, and then disposed of by burial, or landfilling either on or off a range.

(d) For purposes of RCRA section 1004(27), a used or fired military munition is a solid waste, and, therefore, is potentially subject to RCRA corrective action authorities under sections 3004(u) and (v), and 3008(h), or imminent and substantial endangerment authorities under section 7003, if the munition lands off-range and is not promptly rendered safe and/or retrieved. Any imminent and substantial threats associated with any remaining material must be addressed. If remedial action is infeasible, the operator of the range must maintain a record of the event for as long as any threat remains. The record must include the type of munition and its location (to the extent the location is known). 14.6.2.4

§266.203 Standards applicable to the transportation of solid waste military munitions.

(a) *Criteria for hazardous waste regulation of waste non-chemical military munitions in transportation.* (1) Waste military munitions that are being transported and that exhibit a hazardous waste characteristic or are listed as hazardous waste under 40 CFR part 261, are listed or identified as a hazardous waste (and thus are subject to regulation under 40 CFR parts 260 through 270), unless all the following conditions are met:

(i) The waste military munitions are not chemical agents or chemical munitions;

(ii) The waste military munitions must be transported in accordance with the Department of Defense shipping controls applicable to the transport of military munitions;

(iii) The waste military munitions must be transported from a military owned or operated installation to a military owned or operated treatment, storage, or disposal facility; and

(iv) The transporter of the waste must provide oral notice to the Director within 24 hours from the time the transporter becomes aware of any loss or theft of the waste military munitions, or any failure to meet a condition of paragraph (a)(1) of this section that may endanger health or the environment. In addition, a written submission describing the circumstances shall be provided within 5 days from the time the transporter becomes aware of any loss or theft of the waste military munitions or any failure to meet a condition of paragraph (a)(1) of this section.

(2) If any waste military munitions shipped under paragraph (a)(1) of this section are not received by the receiving facility within 45 days of the day the waste was shipped, the owner or operator of the receiving facility must report this non-receipt to the Director within 5 days.

(3) The exemption in paragraph (a)(1) of this section from regulation as hazardous waste shall apply only to the transportation of non-chemical waste military munitions. It does not affect the regulatory status of waste military munitions as hazardous wastes with regard to storage, treatment or disposal.

(4) The conditional exemption in paragraph (a)(1) of this section applies only so long as all of the conditions in paragraph (a)(1) of this section are met.

(b) *Reinstatement of exemption.* If any waste military munition loses its exemption under paragraph (a)(1) of this section, an application may be filed with the Director for reinstatement of the exemption from hazardous waste transportation regulation with respect to such munition as soon as the munition is returned to compliance with the conditions of paragraph (a)(1) of this section. If the Director finds that reinstatement of the exemption is appropriate based on factors such as the transporter's provision of a satisfactory explanation of the circumstances of the violation, or a demonstration that the violations are not likely to recur, the Director may reinstate the exemption under paragraph (a)(1) of this section. If the Director does not take action on the reinstatement application within 60 days after receipt of the application, then reinstatement shall be deemed granted, retroactive to the date of the application. However, the Director may terminate a conditional exemption reinstated by default in the preceding sentence if the Director finds that reinstatement is inappropriate based on factors such as the transporter's failure to provide a satisfactory explanation of the circumstances of the violation, or failure to demonstrate that the violations are not likely to recur. In reinstating the exemption under paragraph (a)(1) of this section, the Director may specify additional conditions as are necessary to ensure and document proper transportation to protect human health and the environment.

(c) *Amendments to DOD shipping controls.* The Department of Defense shipping controls applicable to the transport of military munitions referenced in paragraph (a)(1)(ii) of this section are Government Bill of Lading (GBL) (GSA Standard Form 1109), requisition tracking form DD Form 1348, the Signature and Talley Record (DD Form 1907), Special Instructions for Motor Vehicle Drivers (DD Form 836), and the Motor Vehicle Inspection Report (DD Form 626) in effect on November 8, 1995, except as provided in the following sentence. Any amendments to the Department of Defense shipping controls shall become effective for purposes of paragraph (a)(1) of this section on the date the Department of Defense publishes notice in the *Federal Register* that the shipping controls referenced in paragraph (a)(1)(ii) of this section have been amended.

§266.204 Standards applicable to emergency responses.

Explosives and munitions emergencies involving military munitions or explosives are subject to 40 CFR 262.10(i), 263.10(e), 264.1(g)(8), 265.1(c)(11), and 270.1(c)(3), or alternatively to 40 CFR 270.61.

§266.205 Standards applicable to the storage of solid waste military munitions.

(a) *Criteria for hazardous waste regulation of waste non-chemical military munitions in storage.* (1) Waste military munitions in storage that exhibit a hazardous waste characteristic or are listed as hazardous waste under 40 CFR Part 261, are listed or identified as a hazardous waste (and thus are subject to regulation under 40 CFR Parts 260 through 279), unless all the following conditions are met:

(i) The waste military munitions are not chemical agents or chemical munitions.

(ii) The waste military munitions must be subject to the jurisdiction of the Department of Defense Explosives Safety Board (DDESB).

(iii) The waste military munitions must be stored in accordance with the DDESB storage standards applicable to waste military munitions.

(iv) Within 90 days of August 12, 1997 or within 90 days of when a storage unit is first used to store waste military munitions, whichever is later, the owner or operator must notify the Director of the location of any waste storage unit used to store waste military munitions for which the conditional exemption in paragraph (a)(1) is claimed.

(v) The owner or operator must provide oral notice to the Director within 24 hours from the time the owner or operator becomes aware of any loss or theft of the waste military munitions, or any failure to meet a condition of paragraph (a)(1) that may endanger health or the environment. In addition, a written submission describing the circumstances shall be provided within 5 days from the time the owner or operator becomes aware of any loss or theft of the waste military munitions or any failure to meet a condition of paragraph (a)(1) of this section.

(vi) The owner or operator must inventory the waste military munitions at least annually, must inspect the waste military munitions at least quarterly for compliance with the conditions of paragraph (a)(1) of this section, and must maintain records of the findings of these inventories and inspections for at least three years.

(vii) Access to the stored waste military munitions must be limited to appropriately trained and authorized personnel.

(2) The conditional exemption in paragraph (a)(1) of this section from regulation as hazardous waste shall apply only to the storage of non-chemical waste military munitions. It does not affect the regulatory status of waste military munitions as hazardous wastes with regard to transportation, treatment or disposal.

(3) The conditional exemption in paragraph (a)(1) of this section applies only so long as all of the conditions in paragraph (a)(1) of this section are met.

(b) Notice of termination of waste storage. The owner or operator must notify the Director when a storage unit identified in paragraph (a)(1)(iv) of this section will no longer be used to store waste military munitions.

(c) Reinstatement of conditional exemption. If any waste military munition loses its conditional exemption under paragraph (a)(1) of this section, an application may be filed with the Director for reinstatement of the conditional exemption from hazardous waste storage regulation with respect to such munition as soon as the munition is returned to compliance with the conditions of paragraph (a)(1) of this section. If the Director finds that reinstatement of the conditional exemption is appropriate based on factors such as the owner's or operator's provision of a satisfactory explanation of the circumstances of the violation, or a demonstration that the violations are not likely to recur, the Director may reinstate the conditional exemption under paragraph (a)(1) of this section. If the Director does not take action on the reinstatement application within 60 days after receipt of the application, then reinstatement shall be deemed granted, retroactive to the date of the application. However, the Director may terminate a conditional exemption reinstated by default in the preceding sentence if he/she finds that reinstatement is inappropriate based on factors such as the owner's or operator's failure to provide a satisfactory explanation of the circumstances of the violation, or failure to demonstrate that the violations are not likely to recur. In reinstating the conditional exemption under paragraph (a)(1) of this section, the Director may specify additional conditions as are necessary to ensure and document proper storage to protect human health and the environment.

(d) Waste chemical munitions. (1) Waste military munitions that are chemical agents or chemical munitions and that exhibit a hazardous waste characteristic or are listed as hazardous waste under 40 CFR Part 261, are listed or identified as a hazardous waste and shall be subject to the applicable regulatory requirements of RCRA subtitle C.

(2) Waste military munitions that are chemical agents or chemical munitions and that exhibit a hazardous waste characteristic or are listed as hazardous waste under 40 CFR Part 261, are not subject to the storage prohibition in RCRA section 3004(j), codified at 40 CFR 268.50.

(e) Amendments to DDESB storage standards. The DDESB storage standards applicable to waste military munitions, referenced in paragraph (a)(1)(iii) of this section, are DOD 6055.9-STD ("DOD Ammunition and Explosive Safety Standards"), in effect on November 8, 1995, except as provided in the following sentence. Any amendments to the DDESB storage standards shall become effective for purposes of paragraph (a)(1) of this section on the date the Department of Defense publishes notice in the *Federal Register* that the DDESB standards referenced in paragraph (a)(1) of this section have been amended.

§266.206 Standards applicable to the treatment and disposal of waste military munitions.

The treatment and disposal of hazardous waste military munitions are subject to the applicable permitting, procedural, and technical standards in 40 CFR Parts 260 through 270.

Subpart N—Conditional Exemption for Low-Level Mixed Waste Storage, Treatment, Transportation and Disposal. 4.4.4–5

Source: 66 FR 27262, May 16, 2001, unless otherwise noted.

Terms

§266.210 What definitions apply to this subpart?

This subpart uses the following special definitions:

Agreement State means a state that has entered into an agreement with the NRC under subsection 274b of the Atomic Energy Act of 1954, as amended (68 Stat. 919), to assume responsibility for regulating within its borders byproduct, source, or special nuclear material in quantities not sufficient to form a critical mass.

Certified delivery means certified mail with return receipt requested, or equivalent courier service, or other means, that provides the sender with a receipt confirming delivery.

Director refers to the definition in 40 CFR 270.2.

Eligible Naturally Occurring and/or Accelerator-produced Radioactive Material (NARM) is NARM that is eligible for the Transportation and Disposal Conditional Exemption. It is a NARM waste that contains RCRA hazardous waste, meets the waste acceptance criteria of, and is allowed by State NARM regulations to be disposed of at a low-level radioactive waste disposal facility (LLRWDF) licensed in accordance with 10 CFR part 61 or NRC Agreement State equivalent regulations.

Exempted waste means a waste that meets the eligibility criteria in 266.225 and meets all of the conditions in §266.230, or meets the eligibility criteria in 40 CFR 266.310 and complies with all the conditions in §266.315. Such waste is conditionally exempted from the regulatory definition of hazardous waste described in 40 CFR 261.3.

Hazardous Waste means any material which is defined to be hazardous waste in accordance with 40 CFR 261.3, "Definition of Hazardous Waste."

Land Disposal Restriction (LDR) Treatment Standards means treatment standards, under 40 CFR part 268, that a RCRA hazardous waste must meet before it can be disposed of in a RCRA hazardous waste land disposal unit.

License means a license issued by the Nuclear Regulatory Commission, or NRC Agreement State, to users that manage radionuclides regulated by NRC, or NRC Agreement States, under authority of the Atomic Energy Act of 1954, as amended.

Low-Level Mixed Waste (LLMW) is a waste that contains both low-level radioactive waste and RCRA hazardous waste.

Low-Level Radioactive Waste (LLW) is a radioactive waste which contains source, special nuclear, or byproduct material, and which is not classified as high-level radioactive waste, transuranic waste, spent nuclear fuel, or byproduct material as defined in section 11e.(2) of the Atomic Energy Act. (See also NRC definition of "waste" at 10 CFR 61.2)

Mixed Waste means a waste that contains both RCRA hazardous waste and source, special nuclear, or byproduct material subject to the Atomic Energy Act of 1954, as amended. 4.4.2

Naturally Occurring and/or Accelerator-produced Radioactive Material (NARM) means radioactive materials that: 4.4.1.2

(1) Are naturally occurring and are not source, special nuclear, or byproduct materials (as defined by the AEA) or

(2) Are produced by an accelerator. NARM is regulated by the States under State law, or by DOE (as authorized by the AEA) under DOE orders.

NRC means the U. S. Nuclear Regulatory Commission.

We or *us* within this subpart, means the Director as defined in 40 CFR 270.2.

You means a generator, treater, or other handler of low-level mixed waste or eligible NARM.

Storage and Treatment Conditional Exemption and Eligibility 4.4.5.1

§266.220 What does a storage and treatment conditional exemption do?

The storage and treatment conditional exemption exempts your low-level mixed waste from the regulatory definition of hazardous waste in 40 CFR 261.3 if your waste meets the eligibility criteria in §266.225 and you meet the conditions in §266.230.

§266.225 What wastes are eligible for the storage and treatment conditional exemption?

Low-level mixed waste (LLMW), defined in §266.210, is eligible for this conditional exemption if it is generated and managed by you under a single NRC or NRC Agreement State license. (Mixed waste generated at a facility with a different license number and shipped to your facility for storage or treatment requires a permit and is ineligible for this exemption. In addition, NARM waste is ineligible this exemption.)

§266.230 What conditions must you meet for your LLMW to qualify for and maintain a storage and treatment exemption?

(a) For your LLMW to qualify for the exemption you must notify us in writing by certified delivery that you are claiming a conditional exemption for the LLMW stored on your facility. The dated notification must include your name, address, RCRA identification number, NRC or NRC Agreement State license number, the waste code(s) and storage unit(s) for which you are seeking an exemption, and a statement that you meet the conditions of this subpart. Your notification must be signed by your authorized representative who certifies that the information in the notification is true, accurate, and complete. You must notify us of your claim either within 90 days of the effective date of this rule in your State, or within 90 days of when a storage unit is first used to store conditionally exempt LLMW.

(b) To qualify for and maintain an exemption for your LLMW you must:

(1) Store your LLMW waste in tanks or containers in compliance with the requirements of your license that apply to the proper storage of low-level radioactive waste (not including those license requirements that relate solely to recordkeeping);

(2) Store your LLMW in tanks or containers in compliance with chemical compatibility requirements of a tank or container in 40 CFR 264.177, or 264.199 or 40 CFR 265.177, or 265.199;

(3) Certify that facility personnel who manage stored conditionally exempt LLMW are trained in a manner that ensures that the conditionally exempt waste is safely managed and includes training in chemical waste management and hazardous materials incidents response that meets the personnel training standards found in 40 CFR 265.16(a)(3);

(4) Conduct an inventory of your stored conditionally exempt LLMW at least annually and inspect it at least quarterly for compliance with subpart N of this part; and

(5) Maintain an accurate emergency plan and provide it to all local authorities who may have to respond to a fire, explosion, or release of hazardous waste or hazardous constituents. Your plan must describe emergency response arrangements with local authorities; describe evacuation plans; list the names, addresses, and telephone numbers of all facility personnel qualified to work with local authorities as emergency coordinators; and list emergency equipment.

Treatment

§266.235 What waste treatment does the storage and treatment conditional exemption allow?

You may treat your low-level mixed waste at your facility within a tank or container in accordance with the terms of your NRC or NRC Agreement State license. Treatment that cannot be done in a tank or container without a RCRA permit (such as incineration) is not allowed under this exemption.

Loss of Conditional Exemption

§266.240 How could you lose the conditional exemption for your LLMW and what action must you take?

(a) Your LLMW will automatically lose the storage and treatment conditional exemption if you fail to meet any of the conditions specified in §266.230. When your LLMW loses the exemption, you must immediately manage that waste which failed the condition as RCRA hazardous waste, and the storage unit storing the LLMW immediately becomes subject to RCRA hazardous waste container and/or tank storage requirements.

(1) If you fail to meet any of the conditions specified in §266.230 you must report to us and the NRC, or the oversight agency in the NRC Agreement State, in writing by certified delivery within 30 days of learning of the failure. Your report must be signed by your authorized representative certifying that the information provided is true, accurate, and complete. This report must include:

(i) The specific condition(s) you failed to meet;

(ii) A description of the LLMW (including the waste name, hazardous waste codes and quantity) and storage location at the facility; and

(iii) The date(s) on which you failed to meet the condition(s).

(2) If the failure to meet any of the conditions may endanger human health or the environment, you must also immediately notify us orally within 24 hours and follow up with a written notification within five days. Failures that may endanger human health or the environment include, but are not limited to, discharge of a CERCLA reportable quantity

or other leaking or exploding tanks or containers, or detection of radionuclides above background or hazardous constituents in the leachate collection system of a storage area. If the failure may endanger human health or the environment, you must follow the provisions of your emergency plan.

(b) We may terminate your conditional exemption for your LLMW, or require you to meet additional conditions to claim a conditional exemption, for serious or repeated noncompliance with any requirement(s) of subpart N of this part.

§266.245 If you lose the storage and treatment conditional exemption for your LLMW, can the exemption be reclaimed?

(a) You may reclaim the storage and treatment exemption for your LLMW if:

(1) You again meet the conditions specified in §266.230; and

(2) You send us a notice by certified delivery that you are reclaiming the exemption for your LLMW. Your notice must be signed by your authorized representative certifying that the information contained in your notice is true, complete, and accurate. In your notice you must do the following:

(i) Explain the circumstances of each failure.

(ii) Certify that you have corrected each failure that caused you to lose the exemption for your LLMW and that you again meet all the conditions as of the date you specify.

(iii) Describe plans that you have implemented, listing specific steps you have taken, to ensure the conditions will be met in the future.

(iv) Include any other information you want us to consider when we review your notice reclaiming the exemption.

(b) We may terminate a reclaimed conditional exemption if we find that your claim is inappropriate based on factors including, but not limited to, the following: you have failed to correct the problem; you explained the circumstances of the failure unsatisfactorily; or you failed to implement a plan with steps to prevent another failure to meet the conditions of §266.230. In reviewing a reclaimed conditional exemption under this section, we may add conditions to the exemption to ensure that waste management during storage and treatment of the LLMW will protect human health and the environment.

Recordkeeping

§266.250 What records must you keep at your facility and for how long?

(a) In addition to those records required by your NRC or NRC Agreement State license, you must keep records as follows:

(1) Your initial notification records, return receipts, reports to us of failure(s) to meet the exemption conditions, and all records supporting any reclaim of an exemption;

(2) Records of your LLMW annual inventories, and quarterly inspections;

(3) Your certification that facility personnel who manage stored mixed waste are trained in safe management of LLMW including training in chemical waste management and hazardous materials incidents response; and

(4) Your emergency plan as specified in §266.230(b).

(b) You must maintain records concerning notification, personnel trained, and your emergency plan for as long as you claim this exemption and for three years thereafter, or in accordance with NRC regulations under 10 CFR part 20 (or equivalent NRC Agreement State regulations), whichever is longer. You must maintain records concerning your annual inventory and quarterly inspections for three years after the waste is sent for disposal, or in accordance with NRC regulations under 10 CFR part 20 (or equivalent NRC Agreement State regulations), whichever is longer.

Reentry Into RCRA

§266.255 When is your LLMW no longer eligible for the storage and treatment conditional exemption?

(a) When your LLMW has met the requirements of your NRC or NRC Agreement State license for decay-in-storage and can be disposed of as non-radioactive waste, then the conditional exemption for storage no longer applies. On that date your waste is subject to hazardous waste regulation under the relevant sections of 40 CFR parts 260 through 271, and the time period for accumulation of a hazardous waste as specified in 40 CFR 262.34 begins.

(b) When your conditionally exempt LLMW, which has been generated and stored under a single NRC or NRC Agreement State license number, is removed from storage, it is no longer eligible for the storage and treatment exemption. However, your waste may be eligible for the transportation and disposal conditional exemption at §266.305.

Storage Unit Closure

§266.260 Do closure requirements apply to units that stored LLMW prior to the effective date of Subpart N?

Interim status and permitted storage units that have been used to store only LLMW prior to the effective date of subpart N of this part and, after that date, store only LLMW which becomes exempt under this subpart N, are not subject to the closure requirements of 40 CFR parts 264 and 265. Storage units (or portions of units) that have been used to store both LLMW and non-mixed hazardous waste prior to the effective date of subpart N or are used to store both after that date remain subject to closure requirements with respect to the non-mixed hazardous waste.

Transportation and Disposal Conditional Exemption

4.4.5.2

§266.305 What does the transportation and disposal conditional exemption do?

This conditional exemption exempts your waste from the regulatory definition of hazardous waste in 40 CFR 261.3 if your waste meets the eligibility criteria under §266.310, and you meet the conditions in §266.315.

Eligibility

§266.310 What wastes are eligible for the transportation and disposal conditional exemption?

Eligible waste must be:

(a) A low-level mixed waste (LLMW), as defined in §266.210, that meets the waste acceptance criteria of a LLRWDF; and/or

(b) An eligible NARM waste, defined in §266.210.

Conditions

§266.315 What are the conditions you must meet for your waste to qualify for and maintain the transportation and disposal conditional exemption?

You must meet the following conditions for your eligible waste to qualify for and maintain the exemption:

(a) The eligible waste must meet or be treated to meet LDR treatment standards as described in §266.320.

(b) If you are not already subject to NRC, or NRC Agreement State equivalent manifest and transportation regulations for the shipment of your waste, you must manifest and transport your waste according to NRC regulations as described in §266.325.

(c) The exempted waste must be in containers when it is disposed of in the LLRWDF as described in §266.340.

(d) The exempted waste must be disposed of at a designated LLRWDF as described in §266.335.

§266.320 What treatment standards must your eligible waste meet?

Your LLMW or eligible NARM waste must meet Land Disposal Restriction (LDR) treatment standards specified in 40 CFR part 268, subpart D.

§266.325 Are you subject to the manifest and transportation condition in §266.315(b)?

If you are not already subject to NRC, or NRC Agreement State equivalent manifest and transportation regulations for the shipment of your waste, you must meet the manifest requirements under 10 CFR 20.2006 (or NRC Agreement State equivalent regulations), and the transportation requirements under 10 CFR 1.5 (or NRC Agreement State equivalent regulations) to ship the exempted waste.

§266.330 When does the transportation and disposal exemption take effect?

The exemption becomes effective once all the following have occurred:

(a) Your eligible waste meets the applicable LDR treatment standards.

(b) You have received return receipts that you have notified us and the LLRWDF as described in §266.345.

(c) You have completed the packaging and preparation for shipment requirements for your waste according to NRC Packaging and Transportation regulations found under 10 CFR part 71 (or NRC Agreement State equivalent regulations); and you have prepared a manifest for your waste according to NRC manifest regulations found under 10 CFR part 20 (or NRC Agreement State equivalent regulations), and

(d) You have placed your waste on a transportation vehicle destined for a LLRWDF licensed by NRC or an NRC Agreement State.

§266.335 Where must your exempted waste be disposed of?

Your exempted waste must be disposed of in a LLRWDF that is regulated and licensed by NRC under 10 CFR part 61 or by an NRC Agreement State under equivalent State regulations, including State NARM licensing regulations for eligible NARM.

§266.340 What type of container must be used for disposal of exempted waste?

Your exempted waste must be placed in containers before it is disposed. The container must be:

(a) A carbon steel drum; or

(b) An alternative container with equivalent containment performance in the disposal environment as a carbon steel drum; or

(c) A high integrity container as defined by NRC.

Notification

§266.345 Whom must you notify?

(a) You must provide a one time notice to us stating that you are claiming the transportation and disposal conditional exemption prior to the initial shipment of an exempted waste from your facility to a LLRWDF. Your dated written notice must include your facility name, address, phone number, and RCRA ID number, and be sent by certified delivery.

(b) You must notify the LLRWDF receiving your exempted waste by certified delivery before shipment of each exempted waste. You can only ship the exempted waste after you have received the return receipt of your notice to the LLRWDF. This notification must include the following:

(1) A statement that you have claimed the exemption for the waste.

(2) A statement that the eligible waste meets applicable LDR treatment standards.

(3) Your facility's name, address, and RCRA ID number.

(4) The RCRA hazardous waste codes prior to the exemption of the waste streams.

(5) A statement that the exempted waste must be placed in a container according to §266.340 prior to disposal in order for the waste to remain exempt under the transportation and disposal conditional exemption of subpart N of this part.

(6) The manifest number of the shipment that will contain the exempted waste.

(7) A certification that all the information provided is true, complete, and accurate. The statement must be signed by your authorized representative.

Recordkeeping

§266.350 What records must you keep at your facility and for how long?

In addition to those records required by your NRC or NRC Agreement State license, you must keep records as follows:

(a) You must follow the applicable existing recordkeeping requirements under 40 CFR 264.73, 40 CFR 265.73, and 40 CFR 268.7 of this chapter to demonstrate that your waste has met LDR treatment standards prior to your claiming the exemption.

(b) You must keep a copy of all notifications and return receipts required under Secs. 266.355, and 266.360 for three years after the exempted waste is sent for disposal.

(c) You must keep a copy of all notifications and return receipts required under §266.345(a) for three years after the last exempted waste is sent for disposal.

(d) You must keep a copy of the notification and return receipt required under §266.345(b) for three years after the exempted waste is sent for disposal.

(e) If you are not already subject to NRC, or NRC Agreement State equivalent manifest and transportation regulations for the shipment of your waste, you must also keep all other documents related to tracking the exempted waste as required under 10 CFR 20.2006 or NRC Agreement State equivalent regulations, including applicable NARM requirements, in addition to the records specified in §266.350(a) through (d).

Loss of Transportation and Disposal Conditional Exemption

§266.355 How could you lose the transportation and disposal conditional exemption for your waste and what actions must you take?

(a) Any waste will automatically lose the transportation and disposal exemption if you fail to manage it in accordance with all of the conditions specified in §266.315.

(1) When you fail to meet any of the conditions specified in §266.315 for any of your wastes, you must report to us, in writing by certified delivery, within 30 days of learning of the failure. Your report must be signed by your authorized representative certifying that the information provided is true, accurate, and complete. This report must include:

(i) The specific condition(s) that you failed to meet for the waste;

(ii) A description of the waste (including the waste name, hazardous waste codes and quantity) that lost the exemption; and

(iii) The date(s) on which you failed to meet the condition(s) for the waste.

(2) If the failure to meet any of the conditions may endanger human health or the environment, you must also immediately notify us orally within 24 hours and follow up with a written notification within 5 days.

(b) We may terminate your ability to claim a conditional exemption for your waste, or require you to meet additional conditions to claim a conditional exemption, for serious or repeated noncompliance with any requirement(s) of subpart N of this part.

§266.360 If you lose the transportation and disposal conditional exemption for a waste, can the exemption be reclaimed?

(a) You may reclaim the transportation and disposal exemption for a waste after you have received a return receipt confirming that we have received your notification of the loss of the exemption specified in §266.355(a) and if:

(1) You again meet the conditions specified in §266.315 for the waste; and

(2) You send a notice, by certified delivery, to us that you are reclaiming the exemption for the waste. Your notice must be signed by your authorized representative certifying that the information provided is true, accurate, and complete. The notice must:

(i) Explain the circumstances of each failure.

(ii) Certify that each failure that caused you to lose the exemption for the waste has been corrected and that you again meet all conditions for the waste as of the date you specify.

(iii) Describe plans you have implemented, listing the specific steps that you have taken, to ensure that conditions will be met in the future.

(iv) Include any other information you want us to consider when we review your notice reclaiming the exemption.

(b) We may terminate a reclaimed conditional exemption if we find that your claim is inappropriate based on factors including, but not limited to: you have failed to correct the problem; you explained the circumstances of the failure unsatisfactorily; or you failed to implement a plan with steps to prevent another failure to meet the conditions of §266.315. In reviewing a reclaimed conditional exemption under this section, we may add conditions to the exemption to ensure that transportation and disposal activities will protect human health and the environment.

Appendices to Part 266

Appendix I to Part 266—Tier I and Tier II Feed Rate and Emissions Screening Limits for Metals

Table I-A—Tier I and Tier II Feed Rate and Emissions Screening Limits for Noncarcinogenic Metals for Facilities in Noncomplex Terrain

[Values for urban areas]

Terrain adjusted eff. stack ht. (m)	Antimony (g/hr)	Barium (g/hr)	Lead (g/hr)	Mercury (g/hr)	Silver (g/hr)	Thallium (g/hr)
4	6.0E+01	1.0E+04	1.8E+01	6.0E+01	6.0E+02	6.0E+01
6	6.8E+01	1.1E+04	2.0E+01	6.8E+01	6.8E+02	6.8E+01
8	7.6E+01	1.3E+04	2.3E+01	7.6E+01	7.6E+02	7.6E+01
10	8.6E+01	1.4E+04	2.6E+01	8.6E+01	8.6E+02	8.6E+01
12	9.6E+01	1.7E+04	3.0E+01	9.6E+01	9.6E+02	9.6E+01
14	1.1E+02	1.8E+04	3.4E+01	1.1E+02	1.1E+03	1.1E+02
16	1.3E+02	2.1E+04	3.6E+01	1.3E+02	1.3E+03	1.3E+02
18	1.4E+02	2.4E+04	4.3E+01	1.4E+02	1.4E+03	1.4E+02
20	1.6E+02	2.7E+04	4.6E+01	1.6E+02	1.6E+03	1.6E+02
22	1.8E+02	3.0E+04	5.4E+01	1.8E+02	1.8E+03	1.8E+02
24	2.0E+02	3.4E+04	6.0E+01	2.0E+02	2.0E+03	2.0E+02
26	2.3E+02	3.9E+04	6.8E+01	2.3E+02	2.3E+03	2.3E+02
28	2.6E+02	4.3E+04	7.8E+01	2.6E+02	2.6E+03	2.6E+02
30	3.0E+02	5.0E+04	9.0E+01	3.0E+02	3.0E+03	3.0E+02
35	4.0E+02	6.6E+04	1.1E+02	4.0E+02	4.0E+03	4.0E+02
40	4.6E+02	7.8E+04	1.4E+02	4.6E+02	4.6E+03	4.6E+02
45	6.0E+02	1.0E+05	1.8E+02	6.0E+02	6.0E+03	6.0E+02
50	7.8E+02	1.3E+05	2.3E+02	7.8E+02	7.8E+03	7.8E+02
55	9.6E+02	1.7E+05	3.0E+02	9.6E+02	9.6E+03	9.6E+02
60	1.2E+03	2.0E+05	3.6E+02	1.2E+03	1.2E+04	1.2E+03
65	1.5E+03	2.5E+05	4.3E+02	1.5E+03	1.5E+04	1.5E+03
70	1.7E+03	2.8E+05	5.0E+02	1.7E+03	1.7E+04	1.7E+03
75	1.9E+03	3.2E+05	5.8E+02	1.9E+03	1.9E+04	1.9E+03
80	2.2E+03	3.6E+05	6.4E+02	2.2E+03	2.2E+04	2.2E+03
85	2.5E+03	4.0E+05	7.6E+02	2.5E+03	2.5E+04	2.5E+03
90	2.8E+03	4.6E+05	8.2E+02	2.8E+03	2.8E+04	2.8E+03
95	3.2E+03	5.4E+05	9.6E+02	3.2E+03	3.2E+04	3.2E+03
100	3.6E+03	6.0E+05	1.1E+03	3.6E+03	3.6E+04	3.6E+03
105	4.0E+03	6.8E+05	1.2E+03	4.0E+03	4.0E+04	4.0E+03
110	4.6E+03	7.8E+05	1.4E+03	4.6E+03	4.6E+04	4.6E+03
115	5.4E+03	8.6E+05	1.6E+03	5.4E+03	5.4E+04	5.4E+03
120	6.0E+03	1.0E+06	1.8E+03	6.0E+03	6.0E+04	6.0E+03

Table I-B—Tier I and Tier II Feed Rate and Emissions Screening Limits for Noncarcinogenic Metals for Facilities in Noncomplex Terrain

[Values for rural areas]

Terrain adjusted eff. stack ht. (m)	Antimony (g/hr)	Barium (g/hr)	Lead (g/hr)	Mercury (g/hr)	Silver (g/hr)	Thallium (g/hr)
4	3.1E+01	5.2E+03	9.4E+00	3.1E+01	3.1E+02	3.1E+01
6	3.6E+01	6.0E+03	1.1E+01	3.6E+01	3.6E+02	3.6E+01
8	4.0E+01	6.8E+03	1.2E+01	4.0E+01	4.0E+02	4.0E+01
10	4.6E+01	7.8E+03	1.4E+01	4.6E+01	4.6E+02	4.6E+01
12	5.8E+01	9.6E+03	1.7E+01	5.8E+01	5.8E+02	5.8E+01
14	6.8E+01	1.1E+04	2.1E+01	6.8E+01	6.8E+02	6.8E+01
16	8.6E+01	1.4E+04	2.6E+01	8.6E+01	8.6E+02	8.6E+01
18	1.1E+02	1.8E+04	3.2E+01	1.1E+02	1.1E+03	1.1E+02
20	1.3E+02	2.2E+04	4.0E+01	1.3E+02	1.3E+03	1.3E+02
22	1.7E+02	2.8E+04	5.0E+01	1.7E+02	1.7E+03	1.7E+02
24	2.2E+02	3.6E+04	6.4E+01	2.2E+02	2.2E+03	2.2E+02
26	2.8E+02	4.6E+04	8.2E+01	2.8E+02	2.8E+03	2.8E+02
28	3.5E+02	5.8E+04	1.0E+02	3.5E+02	3.5E+03	3.5E+02
30	4.3E+02	7.6E+04	1.3E+02	4.3E+02	4.3E+03	4.3E+02
35	7.2E+02	1.2E+05	2.1E+02	7.2E+02	7.2E+03	7.2E+02
40	1.1E+03	1.8E+05	3.2E+02	1.1E+03	1.1E+04	1.1E+03
45	1.5E+03	2.5E+05	4.6E+02	1.5E+03	1.5E+04	1.5E+03
50	2.0E+03	3.3E+05	6.0E+02	2.0E+03	2.0E+04	2.0E+03
55	2.6E+03	4.4E+05	7.8E+02	2.6E+03	2.6E+04	2.6E+03
60	3.4E+03	5.8E+05	1.0E+03	3.4E+03	3.4E+04	3.4E+03
65	4.6E+03	7.6E+05	1.4E+03	4.6E+03	4.6E+04	4.6E+03
70	5.4E+03	9.0E+05	1.6E+03	5.4E+03	5.4E+04	5.4E+03
75	6.4E+03	1.1E+06	1.9E+03	6.4E+03	6.4E+04	6.4E+03
80	7.6E+03	1.3E+06	2.3E+03	7.6E+03	7.6E+04	7.6E+03
85	9.4E+03	1.5E+06	2.8E+03	9.4E+03	9.4E+04	9.4E+03
90	1.1E+04	1.8E+06	3.3E+03	1.1E+04	1.1E+05	1.1E+04
95	1.3E+04	2.2E+06	3.9E+03	1.3E+04	1.3E+05	1.3E+04
100	1.5E+04	2.6E+06	4.6E+03	1.5E+04	1.5E+05	1.5E+04
105	1.8E+04	3.0E+06	5.4E+03	1.8E+04	1.8E+05	1.8E+04
110	2.2E+04	3.6E+06	6.6E+03	2.2E+04	2.2E+05	2.2E+04
115	2.6E+04	4.4E+06	7.8E+03	2.6E+04	2.6E+05	2.6E+04
120	3.1E+04	5.0E+06	9.2E+03	3.1E+04	3.1E+05	3.1E+04

Table I-C—Tier I and Tier II Feed Rate and Emissions Screening Limits for Noncarcinogenic Metals for Facilities in Complex Terrain

[Values for urban and rural areas]

Terrain adjusted eff. stack ht. (m)	Antimony (g/hr)	Barium (g/hr)	Lead (g/hr)	Mercury (g/hr)	Silver (g/hr)	Thallium (g/hr)
4	1.4E+01	2.4E+03	4.3E+00	1.4E+01	1.4E+02	1.4E+01
6	2.1E+01	3.5E+03	6.2E+00	2.1E+01	2.1E+02	2.1E+01
8	3.0E+01	5.0E+03	9.2E+00	3.0E+01	3.0E+02	3.0E+01
10	4.3E+01	7.6E+03	1.3E+01	4.3E+01	4.3E+02	4.3E+01
12	5.4E+01	9.0E+03	1.7E+01	5.4E+01	5.4E+02	5.4E+01
14	6.8E+01	1.1E+04	2.0E+01	6.8E+01	6.8E+02	6.8E+01
16	7.8E+01	1.3E+04	2.4E+01	7.8E+01	7.8E+02	7.8E+01
18	8.6E+01	1.4E+04	2.6E+01	8.6E+01	8.6E+02	8.6E+01
20	9.6E+01	1.6E+04	2.9E+01	9.6E+01	9.6E+02	9.6E+01
22	1.0E+02	1.8E+04	3.2E+01	1.0E+02	1.0E+03	1.0E+02
24	1.2E+02	1.9E+04	3.5E+01	1.2E+02	1.2E+03	1.2E+02
26	1.3E+02	2.2E+04	3.6E+01	1.3E+02	1.3E+03	1.3E+02
28	1.4E+02	2.4E+04	4.3E+01	1.4E+02	1.4E+03	1.4E+02
30	1.6E+02	2.7E+04	4.6E+01	1.6E+02	1.6E+03	1.6E+02
35	2.0E+02	3.3E+04	5.8E+01	2.0E+02	2.0E+03	2.0E+02
40	2.4E+02	4.0E+04	7.2E+01	2.4E+02	2.4E+03	2.4E+02
45	3.0E+02	5.0E+04	9.0E+01	3.0E+02	3.0E+03	3.0E+02
50	3.6E+02	6.0E+04	1.1E+02	3.6E+02	3.6E+03	3.6E+02
55	4.6E+02	7.6E+04	1.4E+02	4.6E+02	4.6E+03	4.6E+02
60	5.8E+02	9.4E+04	1.7E+02	5.8E+02	5.8E+03	5.8E+02
65	6.8E+02	1.1E+05	2.1E+02	6.8E+02	6.8E+03	6.8E+02
70	7.8E+02	1.3E+05	2.4E+02	7.8E+02	7.8E+03	7.8E+02
75	8.6E+02	1.4E+05	2.6E+02	8.6E+02	8.6E+03	8.6E+02
80	9.6E+02	1.6E+05	2.9E+02	9.6E+02	9.6E+03	9.6E+02
85	1.1E+03	1.8E+05	3.3E+02	1.1E+03	1.1E+04	1.1E+03
90	1.2E+03	2.0E+05	3.6E+02	1.2E+03	1.2E+04	1.2E+03
95	1.4E+03	2.3E+05	4.0E+02	1.4E+03	1.4E+04	1.4E+03
100	1.5E+03	2.6E+05	4.6E+02	1.5E+03	1.5E+04	1.5E+03
105	1.7E+03	2.8E+05	5.0E+02	1.7E+03	1.7E+04	1.7E+03
110	1.9E+03	3.2E+05	5.8E+02	1.9E+03	1.9E+04	1.9E+03
115	2.1E+03	3.6E+05	6.4E+02	2.1E+03	2.1E+04	2.1E+03
120	2.4E+03	4.0E+05	7.2E+02	2.4E+03	2.4E+04	2.4E+03

Table I-D—Tier I and Tier II Feed Rate and Emissions Screening Limits for Carcinogenic Metals for Facilities in Noncomplex Terrain

	Values for use in urban areas				Values for use in rural areas			
Terrain adjusted eff. stack ht. (m)	Arsenic (g/hr)	Cadmium (g/hr)	Chromium (g/hr)	Beryllium (g/hr)	Arsenic (g/hr)	Cadmium (g/hr)	Chromium (g/hr)	Beryllium (g/hr)
4	4.6E-01	1.1E+00	1.7E-01	8.2E-01	2.4E-01	5.8E-01	8.6E-02	4.3E-01
6	5.4E-01	1.3E+00	1.9E-01	9.4E-01	2.8E-01	6.6E-01	1.0E-01	5.0E-01
8	6.0E-01	1.4E+00	2.2E-01	1.1E+00	3.2E-01	7.6E-01	1.1E-01	5.6E-01
10	6.8E-01	1.6E+00	2.4E-01	1.2E+00	3.6E-01	8.6E-01	1.3E-01	6.4E-01
12	7.6E-01	1.8E+00	2.7E-01	1.4E+00	4.3E-01	1.1E+00	1.6E-01	7.8E-01
14	8.6E-01	2.1E+00	3.1E-01	1.5E+00	5.4E-01	1.3E+00	2.0E-01	9.6E-01
16	9.6E-01	2.3E+00	3.5E-01	1.7E+00	6.8E-01	1.6E+00	2.4E-01	1.2E+00
18	1.1E+00	2.6E+00	4.0E-01	2.0E+00	8.2E-01	2.0E+00	3.0E-01	1.5E+00
20	1.2E+00	3.0E+00	4.4E-01	2.2E+00	1.0E+00	2.5E+00	3.7E-01	1.9E+00
22	1.4E+00	3.4E+00	5.0E-01	2.5E+00	1.3E+00	3.2E+00	4.8E-01	2.4E+00
24	1.6E+00	3.9E+00	5.8E-01	2.8E+00	1.7E+00	4.0E+00	6.0E-01	3.0E+00
26	1.8E+00	4.3E+00	6.4E-01	3.2E+00	2.1E+00	5.0E+00	7.6E-01	3.9E+00
28	2.0E+00	4.8E+00	7.2E-01	3.6E+00	2.7E+00	6.4E+00	9.8E-01	5.0E+00
30	2.3E+00	5.4E+00	8.2E-01	4.0E+00	3.5E+00	8.2E+00	1.2E+00	6.2E+00
35	3.0E+00	6.8E+00	1.0E+00	5.4E+00	5.4E+00	1.3E+01	1.9E+00	9.6E+00
40	3.6E+00	9.0E+00	1.3E+00	6.8E+00	8.2E+00	2.0E+01	3.0E+00	1.5E+01
45	4.6E+00	1.1E+01	1.7E+00	8.6E+00	1.1E+01	2.8E+01	4.2E+00	2.1E+01
50	6.0E+00	1.4E+01	2.2E+00	1.1E+01	1.5E+01	3.7E+01	5.4E+00	2.8E+01
55	7.6E+00	1.8E+01	2.7E+00	1.4E+01	2.0E+01	5.0E+01	7.2E+00	3.6E+01
60	9.4E+00	2.2E+01	3.4E+00	1.7E+01	2.7E+01	6.4E+01	9.6E+00	4.8E+01
65	1.1E+01	2.8E+01	4.2E+00	2.1E+01	3.6E+01	8.6E+01	1.3E+01	6.4E+01
70	1.3E+01	3.1E+01	4.6E+00	2.4E+01	4.3E+01	1.0E+02	1.5E+01	7.6E+01
75	1.5E+01	3.6E+01	5.4E+00	2.7E+01	5.0E+01	1.2E+02	1.8E+01	9.0E+01
80	1.7E+01	4.0E+01	6.0E+00	3.0E+01	6.0E+01	1.4E+02	2.2E+01	1.1E+02
85	1.9E+01	4.6E+01	6.8E+00	3.4E+01	7.2E+01	1.7E+02	2.6E+01	1.3E+02
90	2.2E+01	5.0E+01	7.8E+00	3.9E+01	8.6E+01	2.0E+02	3.0E+01	1.5E+02
95	2.5E+01	5.8E+01	9.0E+00	4.4E+01	1.0E+02	2.4E+02	3.6E+01	1.8E+02
100	2.8E+01	6.8E+01	1.0E+01	5.0E+01	1.2E+02	2.9E+02	4.3E+01	2.2E+02
105	3.2E+01	7.6E+01	1.1E+01	5.6E+01	1.4E+02	3.4E+02	5.0E+01	2.6E+02
110	3.6E+01	8.6E+01	1.3E+01	6.4E+01	1.7E+02	4.0E+02	6.0E+01	3.0E+02
115	4.0E+01	9.6E+01	1.5E+01	7.2E+01	2.0E+02	4.8E+02	7.2E+01	3.6E+02
120	4.6E+01	1.1E+02	1.7E+01	8.2E+01	2.4E+02	5.8E+02	8.6E+01	4.3E+02

Table I-E—Tier I and Tier II Feed Rate and Emissions Screening Limits for Carcinogenic Metals for Facilities in Complex Terrain

[Values for use in urban and rural areas]

Terrain adjusted eff. stack ht. (m)	Arsenic (g/hr)	Cadmium (g/hr)	Chromium (g/hr)	Beryllium (g/hr)
4	1.1E-01	2.6E-01	4.0E-02	2.0E-01
6	1.6E-01	3.9E-01	5.8E-02	2.9E-01
8	2.4E-01	5.8E-01	8.6E-02	4.3E-01
10	3.5E-01	8.2E-01	1.3E-01	6.2E-01
12	4.3E-01	1.0E+00	1.5E-01	7.6E-01
14	5.0E-01	1.3E+00	1.9E-01	9.4E-01
16	6.0E-01	1.4E+00	2.2E-01	1.1E+00
18	6.8E-01	1.6E+00	2.4E-01	1.2E+00
20	7.6E-01	1.8E+00	2.7E-01	1.3E+00
22	8.2E-01	1.9E+00	3.0E-01	1.5E+00
24	9.0E-01	2.1E+00	3.3E-01	1.6E+00
26	1.0E+00	2.4E+00	3.6E-01	1.8E+00
28	1.1E+00	2.7E+00	4.0E-01	2.0E+00
30	1.2E+00	3.0E+00	4.4E-01	2.2E+00
35	1.5E+00	3.7E+00	5.4E-01	2.7E+00
40	1.9E+00	4.6E+00	6.8E-01	3.4E+00
45	2.4E+00	5.4E+00	8.4E-01	4.2E+00
50	2.9E+00	6.8E+00	1.0E+00	5.0E+00
55	3.5E+00	8.4E+00	1.3E+00	6.4E+00
60	4.3E+00	1.0E+01	1.5E+00	7.8E+00
65	5.4E+00	1.3E+01	1.9E+00	9.6E+00
70	6.0E+00	1.4E+01	2.2E+00	1.1E+01
75	6.8E+00	1.6E+01	2.4E+00	1.2E+01
80	7.6E+00	1.8E+01	2.7E+00	1.3E+01
85	8.2E+00	2.0E+01	3.0E+00	1.5E+01
90	9.4E+00	2.3E+01	3.4E+00	1.7E+01
95	1.0E+01	2.5E+01	4.0E+00	1.9E+01
100	1.2E+01	2.8E+01	4.3E+00	2.1E+01
105	1.3E+01	3.2E+01	4.8E+00	2.4E+01
110	1.5E+01	3.5E+01	5.4E+00	2.7E+01
115	1.7E+01	4.0E+01	6.0E+00	3.0E+01
120	1.9E+01	4.4E+01	6.4E+00	3.3E+01

[56 FR 7228, Feb. 21, 1991; 56 FR 32690, July 17, 1991]

Appendix II to Part 266—Tier I Feed Rate Screening Limits for Total Chlorine

Terrain-adjusted effective stack height (m)	Noncomplex Terrain		Complex Terrain (g/hr)
	Urban (g/hr)	Rural (g/hr)	
4	8.2E+01	4.2E+01	1.9E+01
6	9.1E+01	4.8E+01	2.8E+01
8	1.0E+02	5.3E+01	4.1E+01
10	1.2E+02	6.2E+01	5.8E+01
12	1.3E+02	7.7E+01	7.2E+01
14	1.5E+02	9.1E+01	9.1E+01
16	1.7E+02	1.2E+02	1.1E+02
18	1.9E+02	1.4E+02	1.2E+02
20	2.1E+02	1.8E+02	1.3E+02
22	2.4E+02	2.3E+02	1.4E+02
24	2.7E+02	2.9E+02	1.6E+02
26	3.1E+02	3.7E+02	1.7E+02
28	3.5E+02	4.7E+02	1.9E+02
30	3.9E+02	5.8E+02	2.1E+02
35	5.3E+02	9.6E+02	2.6E+02
40	6.2E+02	1.4E+03	3.3E+02
45	8.2E+02	2.0E+03	4.0E+02
50	1.1E+03	2.6E+03	4.8E+02
55	1.3E+03	3.5E+03	6.2E+02
60	1.6E+03	4.6E+03	7.7E+02
65	2.0E+03	6.2E+03	9.1E+02
70	2.3E+03	7.2E+03	1.1E+03
75	2.5E+03	8.6E+03	1.2E+03
80	2.9E+03	1.0E+04	1.3E+03
85	3.3E+03	1.2E+04	1.4E+03
90	3.7E+03	1.4E+04	1.6E+03
95	4.2E+03	1.7E+04	1.8E+03
100	4.8E+03	2.1E+04	2.0E+03
105	5.3E+03	2.4E+04	2.3E+03
110	6.2E+03	2.9E+04	2.5E+03
115	7.2E+03	3.5E+04	2.8E+03
120	8.2E+03	4.1E+04	3.2E+03

[56 FR 32690, July 17, 1991]

Appendix III to Part 266—Tier II Emission Rate Screening Limits for Free Chlorine and Hydrogen Chloride

Terrain-adjusted effective stack height (m)	Noncomplex terrain				Complex terrain [Values for use in urban and rural areas]	
	Values for urban areas		Values for rural areas			
	Cl_2 (g/hr)	HCl (g/hr)	Cl_2 (g/hr)	HCl (g/hr)	Cl_2 (g/hr)	HCl (g/hr)
4	8.2E+01	1.4E+03	4.2E+01	7.3E+02	1.9E+01	3.3E+02
6	9.1E+01	1.6E+03	4.8E+01	8.3E+02	2.8E+01	4.9E+02
8	1.0E+02	1.8E+03	5.3E+01	9.2E+02	4.1E+01	7.1E+02
10	1.2E+02	2.0E+03	6.2E+01	1.1E+03	5.8E+01	1.0E+03
12	1.3E+02	2.3E+03	7.7E+01	1.3E+03	7.2E+01	1.3E+03
14	1.5E+02	2.6E+03	9.1E+01	1.6E+03	9.1E+01	1.6E+03
16	1.7E+02	2.9E+03	1.2E+02	2.0E+03	1.1E+02	1.8E+03
18	1.9E+02	3.3E+03	1.4E+02	2.5E+03	1.2E+02	2.0E+03
20	2.1E+02	3.7E+03	1.8E+02	3.1E+03	1.3E+02	2.3E+03
22	2.4E+02	4.2E+03	2.3E+02	3.9E+03	1.4E+02	2.4E+03
24	2.7E+02	4.8E+03	2.9E+02	5.0E+03	1.6E+02	2.8E+03
26	3.1E+02	5.4E+03	3.7E+02	6.5E+03	1.7E+02	3.0E+03
28	3.5E+02	6.0E+03	4.7E+02	8.1E+03	1.9E+02	3.4E+03
30	3.9E+02	6.9E+03	5.8E+02	1.0E+04	2.1E+02	3.7E+03
35	5.3E+02	9.2E+03	9.6E+02	1.7E+04	2.6E+02	4.6E+03
40	6.2E+02	1.1E+04	1.4E+03	2.5E+04	3.3E+02	5.7E+03
45	8.2E+02	1.4E+04	2.0E+03	3.5E+04	4.0E+02	7.0E+03
50	1.1E+03	1.8E+04	2.6E+03	4.6E+04	4.8E+02	8.4E+03
55	1.3E+03	2.3E+04	3.5E+03	6.1E+04	6.2E+02	1.1E+04
60	1.6E+03	2.9E+04	4.6E+03	8.1E+04	7.7E+02	1.3E+04
65	2.0E+03	3.4E+04	6.2E+03	1.1E+05	9.1E+02	1.6E+04
70	2.3E+03	3.9E+04	7.2E+03	1.3E+05	1.1E+03	1.8E+04
75	2.5E+03	4.5E+04	8.6E+03	1.5E+05	1.2E+03	2.0E+04
80	2.9E+03	5.0E+04	1.0E+04	1.8E+05	1.3E+03	2.3E+04
85	3.3E+03	5.8E+04	1.2E+04	2.2E+05	1.4E+03	2.5E+04
90	3.7E+03	6.6E+04	1.4E+04	2.5E+05	1.6E+03	2.9E+04
95	4.2E+03	7.4E+04	1.7E+04	3.0E+05	1.8E+03	3.2E+04
100	4.8E+03	8.4E+04	2.1E+04	3.6E+05	2.0E+03	3.5E+04
105	5.3E+03	9.2E+04	2.4E+04	4.3E+05	2.3E+03	3.9E+04
110	6.2E+03	1.1E+05	2.9E+04	5.1E+05	2.5E+03	4.5E+04
115	7.2E+03	1.3E+05	3.5E+04	6.1E+05	2.8E+03	5.0E+04
120	8.2E+03	1.4E+05	4.1E+04	7.2E+05	3.2E+03	5.6E+04

[56 FR 32691, July 17, 1991, as amended at 71 FR 40277, July 14, 2006]

Appendix IV to Part 266—Reference Air Concentrations*

Constituent	CAS No.	RAC (ug/m^3)
Acetaldehyde	75-07-0	10
Acetonitrile	75-05-8	10
Acetophenone	98-86-2	100
Acrolein	107-02-8	20
Aldicarb	116-06-3	1
Aluminum Phosphide	20859-73-8	0.3
Allyl Alcohol	107-18-6	5
Antimony	7440-36-0	0.3
Barium	7440-39-3	50
Barium Cyanide	542-62-1	50
Bromomethane	74-83-9	0.8
Calcium Cyanide	592-01-8	30
Carbon Disulfide	75-15-0	200
Chloral	75-87-6	2
Chlorine (free)		0.4
2-Chloro-1,3-butadiene	126-99-8	3
Chromium III	16065-83-1	1000
Copper Cyanide	544-92-3	5
Cresols	1319-77-3	50
Cumene	98-82-8	1
Cyanide (free)	57-12-15	20
Cyanogen	460-19-5	30
Cyanogen Bromide	506-68-3	80
Di-n-butyl Phthalate	84-74-2	100
o-Dichlorobenzene	95-50-1	10
p-Dichlorobenzene	106-46-7	10
Dichlorodifluoromethane	75-71-8	200
2,4-Dichlorophenol	120-83-2	3
Diethyl Phthalate	84-66-2	800
Dimethoate	60-51-5	0.8
2,4-Dinitrophenol	51-28-5	2
Dinoseb	88-85-7	0.9
Diphenylamine	122-39-4	20
Endosulfan	115-29-1	0.05
Endrin	72-20-8	0.3
Fluorine	7782-41-4	50
Formic Acid	64-18-6	2000
Glycidyaldehyde	765-34-4	0.3
Hexachlorocyclopentadiene	77-47-4	5
Hexachlorophene	70-30-4	0.3
Hydrocyanic Acid	74-90-8	20

Constituent	CAS No.	RAC (ug/m³)
Hydrogen Chloride	7647-01-1	7
Hydrogen Sulfide	7783-06-4	3
Isobutyl Alcohol	78-83-1	300
Lead	7439-92-1	0.09
Maleic Anhydride	108-31-6	100
Mercury	7439-97-6	0.3
Methacrylonitrile	126-98-7	0.1
Methomyl	16752-77-5	20
Methoxychlor	72-43-5	50
Methyl Chlorocarbonate	79-22-1	1000
Methyl Ethyl Ketone	78-93-3	80
Methyl Parathion	298-00-0	0.3
Nickel Cyanide	557-19-7	20
Nitric Oxide	10102-43-9	100
Nitrobenzene	98-95-3	0.8
Pentachlorobenzene	608-93-5	0.8
Pentachlorophenol	87-86-5	30
Phenol	108-95-2	30
M-Phenylenediamine	108-45-2	5
Phenylmercuric Acetate	62-38-4	0.075
Phosphine	7803-51-2	0.3
Phthalic Anhydride	85-44-9	2000
Potassium Cyanide	151-50-8	50
Potassium Silver Cyanide	506-61-6	200
Pyridine	110-86-1	1
Selenious Acid	7783-60-8	3
Selenourea	630-10-4	5
Silver	7440-22-4	3
Silver Cyanide	506-64-9	100
Sodium Cyanide	143-33-9	30
Strychnine	57-24-9	0.3
1,2,4,5-Tetrachlorobenzene	95-94-3	0.3
2,3,4,6-Tetrachlorophenol	58-90-2	30
Tetraethyl Lead	78-00-2	0.0001
Tetrahydrofuran	109-99-9	10
Thallic Oxide	1314-32-5	0.3
Thallium	7440-28-0	0.5
Thallium (I) Acetate	563-68-8	0.5
Thallium (I) Carbonate	6533-73-9	0.3
Thallium (I) Chloride	7791-12-0	0.3
Thallium (I) Nitrate	10102-45-1	0.5
Thallium Selenite	12039-52-0	0.5
Thallium (I) Sulfate	7446-18-6	0.075
Thiram	137-26-8	5
Toluene	108-88-3	300
1,2,4-Trichlorobenzene	120-82-1	20
Trichloromonofluoromethane	75-69-4	300
2,4,5-Trichlorophenol	95-95-4	100
Vanadium Pentoxide	1314-62-1	20
Warfarin	81-81-2	0.3
Xylenes	1330-20-7	80
Zinc Cyanide	557-21-1	50
Zinc Phosphide	1314-84-7	0.3

*The RAC for other appendix VIII part 261 constituents not listed herein or in appendix V of this part is 0.1 ug/m³.

[56 FR 7232, Feb. 21, 1991; 56 FR 32691, July 17, 1991, as amended at 71 FR 40277, July 14, 2006]

Appendix V to Part 266—Risk Specific Doses (10^{-5})

Constituent	CAS No.	Unit risk (m³/µg)	RsD (µg/m³)
Acrylamide	79-06-1	1.3E–03	7.7E–03
Acrylonitrile	107-13-1	6.8E–05	1.5E–01
Aldrin	309-00-2	4.9E–03	2.0E–03
Aniline	62-53-3	7.4E–06	1.4E+00
Arsenic	7440-38-2	4.3E–03	2.3E–03
Benz(a)anthracene	56-55-3	8.9E–04	1.1E–02
Benzene	71-43-2	8.3E–06	1.2E+00
Benzidine	92-87-5	6.7E–02	1.5E–04
Benzo(a)pyrene	50-32-8	3.3E–03	3.0E–03
Beryllium	7440-41-7	2.4E–03	4.2E–03
Bis(2-chloroethyl)ether	111-44-4	3.3E–04	3.0E–02
Bis(chloromethyl)ether	542-88-1	6.2E–02	1.6E–04
Bis(2-ethylhexyl)-phthalate	117-81-7	2.4E–07	4.2E+01
1,3-Butadiene	106-99-0	2.8E–04	3.6E–02
Cadmium	7440-43-9	1.8E–03	5.6E–03
Carbon Tetrachloride	56-23-5	1.5E–05	6.7E–01
Chlordane	57-74-9	3.7E–04	2.7E–02

Constituent	CAS No.	Unit risk ($m^3/\mu g$)	RsD ($\mu g/m^3$)
Chloroform	67-66-3	2.3E–05	4.3E–01
Chloromethane	74-87-3	3.6E–06	2.8E+00
Chromium VI	7440-47-3	1.2E–02	8.3E–04
DDT	50-29-3	9.7E–05	1.0E–01
Dibenz(a,h)anthracene	53-70-3	1.4E–02	7.1E–04
1,2-Dibromo-3-chloropropane	96-12-8	6.3E–03	1.6E–03
1,2-Dibromoethane	106-93-4	2.2E–04	4.5E–02
1,1-Dichloroethane	75-34-3	2.6E–05	3.8E–01
1,2-Dichloroethane	107-06-2	2.6E–05	3.8E–01
1,1-Dichloroethylene	75-35-4	5.0E–05	2.0E–01
1,3-Dichloropropene	542-75-6	3.5E–01	2.9E–05
Dieldrin	60-57-1	4.6E–03	2.2E–03
Diethylstilbestrol	56-53-1	1.4E–01	7.1E–05
Dimethylnitrosamine	62-75-9	1.4E–02	7.1E–04
2,4-Dinitrotoluene	121-14-2	8.8E–05	1.1E–01
1,2-Diphenylhydrazine	122-66-7	2.2E–04	4.5E–02
1,4-Dioxane	123-91-1	1.4E–06	7.1E+00
Epichlorohydrin	106-89-8	1.2E–06	8.3E+00
Ethylene Oxide	75-21-8	1.0E–04	1.0E–01
Ethylene Dibromide	106-93-4	2.2E–04	4.5E–02
Formaldehyde	50-00-0	1.3E–05	7.7E–01
Heptachlor	76-44-8	1.3E–03	7.7E–03
Heptachlor Epoxide	1024-57-3	2.6E–03	3.8E–03
Hexachlorobenzene	118-74-1	4.9E–04	2.0E–02
Hexachlorobutadiene	87-68-3	2.0E–05	5.0E–01
Alpha-hexachloro-cyclohexane	319-84-6	1.8E–03	5.6E–03
Beta-hexachloro-cyclohexane	319-85-7	5.3E–04	1.9E–02
Gamma-hexachloro-cyclohexane	58-89-9	3.8E–04	2.6E–02
Hexachlorocyclohexane, Technical		5.1E-04	2.0E–02
Hexachlorodibenzo-p-dioxin (1,2 Mixture)		1.3E+0	7.7E–06
Hexachloroethane	67-72-1	4.0E–06	2.5E+00
Hydrazine	302-01-2	2.9E–03	3.4E–03
Hydrazine Sulfate	302-01-2	2.9E–03	3.4E–03
3-Methylcholanthrene	56-49-5	2.7E–03	3.7E–03
Methyl Hydrazine	60-34-4	3.1E–04	3.2E–02
Methylene Chloride	75-09-2	4.1E–06	2.4E+00
4,4′-Methylene-bis-2-chloroaniline	101-14-4	4.7E–05	2.1E–01
Nickel	7440-02-0	2.4E–04	4.2E–02
Nickel Refinery Dust	7440-02-0	2.4E–04	4.2E–02
Nickel Subsulfide	12035-72-2	4.8E–04	2.1E–02
2-Nitropropane	79-46-9	2.7E–02	3.7E–04
N-Nitroso-n-butylamine	924-16-3	1.6E–03	6.3E–03
N-Nitroso-n-methylurea	684-93-5	8.6E–02	1.2E–04
N-Nitrosodiethylamine	55-18-5	4.3E–02	2.3E–04
N-Nitrosopyrrolidine	930-55-2	6.1E–04	1.6E–02
Pentachloronitrobenzene	82-68-8	7.3E–05	1.4E–01
PCBs	1336-36-3	1.2E–03	8.3E–03
Pronamide	23950-58-5	4.6E–06	2.2E+00
Reserpine	50-55-5	3.0E–03	3.3E–03
2,3,7,8-Tetrachloro-dibenzo-p-dioxin	1746-01-6	4.5E+01	2.2E–07
1,1,2,2-Tetrachloroethane	79-34-5	5.8E–05	1.7E–01
Tetrachloroethylene	127-18-4	4.8E–07	2.1E+01
Thiourea	62-56-6	5.5E–04	1.8E–02
1,1,2-Trichloroethane	79-00-5	1.6E–05	6.3E–01
Trichloroethylene	79-01-6	1.3E–06	7.7E+00
2,4,6-Trichlorophenol	88-06-2	5.7E–06	1.8E+00
Toxaphene	8001-35-2	3.2E–04	3.1E–02
Vinyl Chloride	75-01-4	7.1E–06	1.4E+00

[56 FR 7232, Feb. 21, 1991, as amended at 71 FR 40277, July 14, 2006]

Appendix VI to Part 266—Stack Plume Rise

[Estimated Plume Rise (in Meters) Based on Stack Exit Flow Rate and Gas Temperature]

Flow rate (m^3/s)	Exhaust Temperature (° K)										
	< 325	325 – 349	350 – 399	400 – 449	450 – 499	500 – 599	600 – 699	700 – 799	800 – 999	1000 – 1499	> 1499
< 0.5	0	0	0	0	0	0	0	0	0	0	0
0.5 – 0.9	0	0	0	0	0	0	0	0	1	1	1
1.0 – 1.9	0	0	0	0	1	1	2	3	3	3	4
2.0 – 2.9	0	0	1	3	4	4	6	6	7	8	9
3.0 – 3.9	0	1	2	5	6	7	9	10	11	12	13
4.0 – 4.9	1	2	4	6	8	10	12	13	14	15	17
5.0 – 7.4	2	3	5	8	10	12	14	16	17	19	21
7.5 – 9.9	3	5	8	12	15	17	20	22	22	23	24
10.0 – 12.4	4	6	10	15	19	21	23	24	25	26	27
12.5 – 14.9	4	7	12	18	22	23	25	26	27	28	29
15.0 – 19.9	5	8	13	20	23	24	26	27	28	29	31
20.0 – 24.9	6	10	17	23	25	27	29	30	31	32	34
25.0 – 29.9	7	12	20	25	27	29	31	32	33	35	36
30.0 – 34.9	8	14	22	26	29	31	33	35	36	37	39
35.0 – 39.9	9	16	23	28	30	32	35	36	37	39	41
40.0 – 49.9	10	17	24	29	32	34	36	38	39	41	42
50.0 – 59.9	12	21	26	31	34	36	39	41	42	44	46
60.0 – 69.9	14	22	27	33	36	39	42	43	45	47	49
70.0 – 79.9	16	23	29	35	38	41	44	46	47	49	51
80.0 – 89.9	17	25	30	36	40	42	46	48	49	51	54
90.0 – 99.9	19	26	31	38	42	44	48	50	51	53	56
100.0 – 119.9	21	26	32	39	43	46	49	52	53	55	58
120.0 – 139.9	22	28	35	42	46	49	52	55	56	59	61
140.0 – 159.9	23	30	36	44	48	51	55	58	59	62	65
160.0 – 179.9	25	31	38	46	50	54	58	60	62	65	67
180.0 – 199.9	26	32	40	48	52	56	60	63	65	67	70
> 199.9	26	33	41	49	54	58	62	65	67	69	73

[56 FR 7233, Feb. 21, 1991, as amended at 71 FR 40277, July 14, 2006]

Appendix VII to Part 266—Health-Based Limits for Exclusion of Waste-Derived Residues*

Metals—TCLP Extract Concentration Limits

Constituent	CAS No.	Concentration limits (mg/L)
Antimony	7440-36-0	1xE+00
Arsenic	7440-38-2	5xE+00
Barium	7440-39-3	1xE+02
Beryllium	7440-41-7	7xE-03
Cadmium	7440-43-9	1xE+00
Chromium	7440-47-3	5xE+00
Lead	7439-92-1	5xE+00
Mercury	7439-97-6	2xE-01
Nickel	7440-02-0	7xE+01
Selenium	7782-49-2	1xE+00
Silver	7440-22-4	5xE+00
Thallium	7440-28-0	7xE+00

Nonmetals—Residue Concentration Limits

Constituent	CAS No.	Concentration limits for residues (mg/kg)
Acetonitrile	75-05-8	2xE-01
Acetophenone	98-86-2	4xE+00
Acrolein	107-02-8	5xE-01
Acrylamide	79-06-1	2xE-04
Acrylonitrile	107-13-1	7xE-04
Aldrin	309-00-2	2xE-05
Allyl alcohol	107-18-6	2xE-01
Aluminum phosphide	20859-73-8	1xE-02
Aniline	62-53-3	6xE-02
Barium cyanide	542-62-1	1xE+00
Benz(a)anthracene	56-55-3	1xE-04
Benzene	71-43-2	5xE-03
Benzidine	92-87-5	1xE-06
Bis(2-chloroethyl) ether	111-44-4	3xE-04
Bis(chloromethyl) ether	542-88-1	2xE-06
Bis(2-ethylhexyl) phthalate	117-81-7	3xE+01
Bromoform	75-25-2	7xE-01
Calcium cyanide	592-01-8	1xE-06
Carbon disulfide	75-15-0	4xE+00
Carbon tetrachloride	56-23-5	5xE-03
Chlordane	57-74-9	3xE-04
Chlorobenzene	108-90-7	1xE+00
Chloroform	67-66-3	6xE-02
Copper cyanide	544-92-3	2xE-01
Cresols (Cresylic acid)	1319-77-3	2xE+00
Cyanogen	460-19-5	1xE+00
DDT	50-29-3	1xE-03

Nonmetals—Residue Concentration Limits

Constituent	CAS No.	Concentration limits for residues (mg/kg)
Dibenz(a, h)-anthracene	53-70-3	7xE-06
1,2-Dibromo-3-chloropropane	96-12-8	2xE-05
p-Dichlorobenzene	106-46-7	7.5xE-02
Dichlorodifluoromethane	75-71-8	7xE+00
1,1-Dichloroethylene	75-35-4	5xE-03
2,4-Dichlorophenol	120-83-2	1xE-01
1,3-Dichloropropene	542-75-6	1xE-03
Dieldrin	60-57-1	2xE-05
Diethyl phthalate	84-66-2	3xE+01
Diethylstilbesterol	56-53-1	7xE-07
Dimethoate	60-51-5	3xE-02
2,4-Dinitrotoluene	121-14-2	5xE-04
Diphenylamine	122-39-4	9xE-01
1,2-Diphenylhydrazine	122-66-7	5xE-04
Endosulfan	115-29-7	2xE-03
Endrin	72-20-8	2xE-04
Epichlorohydrin	106-89-8	4xE-02
Ethylene dibromide	106-93-4	4xE-07
Ethylene oxide	75-21-8	3xE-04
Fluorine	7782-41-4	4xE+00
Formic acid	64-18-6	7xE+01
Heptachlor	76-44-8	8xE-05
Heptachlor epoxide	1024-57-3	4xE-05
Hexachlorobenzene	118-74-1	2xE-04
Hexachlorobutadiene	87-68-3	5xE-03
Hexachlorocyclopentadiene	77-47-4	2xE-01
Hexachlorodibenzo-p-dioxins	19408-74-3	6xE-08
Hexachloroethane	67-72-1	3xE-02
Hydrazine	302-01-1	1xE-04
Hydrogen cyanide	74-90-8	7xE-05
Hydrogen sulfide	7783-06-4	1xE-06
Isobutyl alcohol	78-83-1	1xE+01
Methomyl	16752-77-5	1xE+00
Methoxychlor	72-43-5	1xE-01
3-Methylcholanthrene	56-49-5	4xE-05
4,4'-Methylenebis (2-chloroaniline)	101-14-4	2xE-03
Methylene chloride	75-09-2	5xE-02
Methyl ethyl ketone (MEK)	78-93-3	2xE+00
Methyl hydrazine	60-34-4	3xE-04
Methyl parathion	298-00-0	2xE-02
Naphthalene	91-20-3	1xE+01
Nickel cyanide	557-19-7	7xE-01
Nitric oxide	10102-43-9	4xE+00
Nitrobenzene	98-95-3	2xE-02
N-Nitrosodi-n-butylamine	924-16-3	6xE-05
N-Nitrosodiethylamine	55-18-5	2xE-06
N-Nitroso-N-methylurea	684-93-5	1xE-07

PART 266—Appendices

Nonmetals—Residue Concentration Limits

Constituent	CAS No.	Concentration limits for residues (mg/kg)
N-Nitrosopyrrolidine	930-55-2	2xE-04
Pentachlorobenzene	608-93-5	3xE-02
Pentachloronitrobenzene (PCNB)	82-68-8	1xE-01
Pentachlorophenol	87-86-5	1xE+00
Phenol	108-95-2	1xE+00
Phenylmercury acetate	62-38-4	3xE-03
Phosphine	7803-51-2	1xE-02
Polychlorinated biphenyls, N.O.S	1336-36-3	5xE-05
Potassium cyanide	151-50-8	2xE+00
Potassium silver cyanide	506-61-6	7xE+00
Pronamide	23950-58-5	3xE+00
Pyridine	110-86-1	4xE-02
Reserpine	50-55-5	3xE-05
Selenourea	630-10-4	2xE-01
Silver cyanide	506-64-9	4xE+00
Sodium cyanide	143-33-9	1xE+00
Strychnine	57-24-9	1xE-02
1,2,4,5-Tetrachlorobenzene	95-94-3	1xE-02
1,1,2,2-tetrachloroethane	79-34-5	2xE-03
Tetrachloroethylene	127-18-4	7xE-01
2,3,4,6-Tetrachlorophenol	58-90-2	1xE-02
Tetraethyl lead	78-00-2	4xE-06
Thiourea	62-56-6	2xE-04
Toluene	108-88-3	1xE+01
Toxaphene	8001-35-2	5xE-03
1,1,2-Trichloroethane	79-00-5	6xE-03
Trichloroethylene	79-01-6	5xE-03
Trichloromonofluoromethane	75-69-4	1xE+01
2,4,5-Trichlorophenol	95-95-4	4xE+00
2,4,6-Trichlorophenol	88-06-2	4xE+00
Vanadium pentoxide	1314-62-1	7xE-01
Vinyl chloride	75-01-4	2xE-03

* *Note 1:* The health-based concentration limits for appendix VIII part 261 constituents for which a health-based concentration is not provided below is 2xE-06 mg/kg.

Note 2: The levels specified in this appendix and the default level of 0.002 micrograms per kilogram or the level of detection for constituents as identified in Note 1 of this appendix are administratively stayed under the condition, for those constituents specified in §266.112(b)(1), that the owner or operator complies with alternative levels defined as the land disposal restriction limits specified in §268.43 of this chapter for F039 nonwastewaters. See §266.112(b)(2)(i).

[56 FR 7234, Feb. 21, 1991; 56 FR 32691, July 17, 1991, as amended at 58 FR 59603, Nov. 9, 1993]

Appendix VIII To Part 266—Organic Compounds for Which Residues Must Be Analyzed

Volatiles	Semivolatiles
Benzene	Bis(2-ethylhexyl)phthalate
Toluene	Naphthalene
Carbon tetrachloride	Phenol
Chloroform	Diethyl phthalate
Methylene chloride	Butyl benzyl phthalate
Trichloroethylene	2,4-Dimethylphenol
Tetra chloroethylene	o-Dichlorobenzene
1,1,1-Trichloroethane	m-Dichlorobenzene
Chlorobenzene	p-Dichlorobenzene
cis-1,4-Dichloro-2-butene	Hexachlorobenzene
Bromochloromethane	2,4,6-Trichlorophenol
Bromodichloromethane	Fluoranthene
Bromoform	o-Nitrophenol
Bromomethane	1,2,4-Trichlorobenzene
Methylene bromide	o-Chlorophenol
Methyl ethyl ketone	Pentachlorophenol
	Pyrene
	Dimethyl phthalate
	Mononitrobenzene
	2,6-Toluene diisocyanate
	Polychlorinated dibenzo-p-dioxins[1]
	Polychlorinated dibenzo-furans[1]

[1] Analyses for polychlorinated dibenzo-p-dioxins and polychlorinated dibenzo-furans are required only for residues collected from areas downstream of the combustion chamber (*e.g.*, ductwork, boiler tubes, heat exchange surfaces, air pollution control devices, etc.).

Note to the table: Analysis is not required for those compounds that do not have an established F039 nonwastewater concentration limit.

[64 FR 53076, Sept. 30, 1999, as amended at 64 FR 63213, Nov. 19, 1999; 71 FR 40277, July 14, 2006]

Appendix IX to Part 266—Methods Manual for Compliance With the BIF Regulations

Burning Hazardous Waste in Boilers and Industrial Furnaces

Table of Contents

Section 1.0 Introduction

This document presents required methods for demonstrating compliance with U.S. Environmental Protection Agency regulations for boilers and industrial furnaces (BIFs) burning hazardous waste (see 40 CFR part 266, subpart H). The methods included in this document are:

1. Performance Specifications for Continuous Emission Monitoring (CEM) of Carbon Monoxide, Oxygen, and Hydrocarbons in Stack Gases.
2. Procedures for Estimating the Toxicity Equivalency of Chlorinated Dibenzo-p-dioxin and Dibenzofuran Congeners.
3. Hazardous Waste Combustion Air Quality Screening Procedures (HWCAQSP).
4. Simplified Land Use Classification Procedure for Compliance vith Tier I and Tier II Limits.
5. Statistical Methodology for Bevill Residue Determinations.
6. Procedures for Determining Default Values for Air Pollution Control System Removal Efficiencies.
7. Procedures for Determining Default Values for Partitioning of Metals, Ash, and Total Chloride/Chlorine.
8. Alternate Methodology for Implementing Metals Controls.

   a. Sampling and analytical methods for multiple metals, hexavalent chromium, HCl and chlorine, polychlorinated dibenzo-p-dioxins and dibenzofurans, and aldehydes and ketones can be found in "Test Methods for Evaluating Solid Wastes, Physical/ Chemical Methods" (EPA Publication SW–846). Additional methods referenced in subpart H of part 266 but not included in this document can be found in 40 CFR parts 60 and 61, and SW–846.

   b. The CEM performance specifications of section 2.0, the relevant sampling Methods 0011, 0023A, 0050, 0051, 0060, and 0061 of SW–846, incorporated by reference in §260.11, and the toxicity equivalency procedure for dioxins and furans of section 4.0 are required procedures for determining compliance with BIF regulations. For the determination of chloride from HCl/Cl_2 emission sampling train, you must use appropriate methods. For the determination of carbonyl compounds by high-performance liquid chromatography, you must use appropriate methods. The CEM performance specifications are interim. The finalized CEM performance specifications will be published in 40 CFR parts 60 and 61.

Section 2.0 Performance Specifications for Continuous Emission Monitoring Systems

2.1 *Performance Specifications for Continuous Emission Monitoring of Carbon Monoxide and Oxygen for Incinerators, Boilers, and Industrial Furnaces Burning Hazardous Waste*

2.1.1 *Applicability and Principle*

2.1.1.1 Applicability. These performance specifications apply to carbon monoxide (CO) and oxygen (O2) continuous emission monitoring systems (CEMSs) installed on incinerators, boilers, and industrial furnaces burning hazardous waste. The specifications include procedures which are intended to be used to evaluate the acceptability of the CEMS at the time of its installation or whenever specified in regulations or permits. The procedures are not designed to evaluate CEMS performance over an extended period of time. The source owner or operator is responsible for the proper calibration, maintenance, and operation of the CEMS at all times.

2.1.1.2 Principle. Installation and measurement location specifications, performance and equipment specifications, test and data reduction procedures, and brief quality assurance guidelines are included in the specifications. Calibration drift, relative accuracy, calibration error, and response time tests are conducted to determine conformance of the CEMS with the specifications.

2.1.2 *Definitions*

2.1.2.1 Continuous Emission Monitoring System (CEMS). A continuous monitor is one in which the sample to be analyzed passes the measurement section of the analyzer without interruption, and which evaluates the detector response to the sample at least once each 15 seconds and computes and records the results at least every 60 seconds. A CEMS consists of all the equipment used to acquire data and includes the sample extraction and transport hardware, the analyzer(s), and the data recording/processing hardware and software.

2.1.2.2 Monitoring System Types. The specifications require CEMSs capable of accepting calibration gases. Alternative system designs may be used if approved by the Regional Administrator. There are two basic types of monitoring systems: extractive and in-situ.

2.1.2.2.1 Extractive. Systems that use a pump or other mechanical, pneumatic, or hydraulic means to draw a sample of the stack or flue gas and convey it to a remotely located analyzer.

2.1.2.2.2 In-situ. Systems that perform an analysis without removing a sample from the stack. Point in-situ analyzers place the sensing or detecting element directly in the flue gas stream. Cross-stack in-situ analyzers measure the parameter of interest by placing a source beam on one side of the stack and the detector (in single-pass instruments) or a retroreflector (in double-pass instruments) on the other side, and measuring the parameter of interest (*e.g.*, CO) by the attenuation of the beam by the gas in its path.

2.1.2.3 Instrument Measurement Range. The difference between the minimum and maximum concentration that can be measured by a specific instrument. The minimum is often stated or assumed to be zero and the range expressed only as the maximum.

2.1.2.4 Span or Span Value. Full scale instrument measurement range.

2.1.2.5 Calibration Drift (CD). The difference in the CEMS output readings from the established reference value after a stated period of operation during which no unscheduled maintenance, repair, or adjustment takes place. A CD test is performed to demonstrate the stability of the CEMS calibration over time.

2.1.2.6 Response Time. The time interval between the start of a step change in the system input (*e.g.*, change of calibration gas) and the time when the data recorder displays 95 percent of the final value.

2.1.2.7 Accuracy. A measure of agreement between a measured value and an accepted or true value, expressed as the percentage difference between the true and measured values relative to the true value. For these performance specifications, accuracy is checked by conducting a calibration error (CE) test and a relative accuracy (RA) test. Certain facilities, such as those using solid waste or batch-fed processes, may observe long periods of almost no CO emissions with brief, high-level CO emission spikes. These facilities, as well as facilities whose CO emissions never exceed 5-10 ppm, may need to be exempted from the RA requirement because the RA test procedure cannot ensure acquisition of meaningful test results under these conditions. An alternative procedure for accuracy determination is described in section 2.1.9.

2.1.2.8 Calibration Error (CE). The difference between the concentration indicated by the CEMS and the known concentration of the cylinder gas. A CE test procedure is performed to document the accuracy and linearity of the monitoring equipment over the entire measurement range.

2.1.2.9 Relative Accuracy (RA). A comparison of the CEMS response to a value measured by a performance test method (PTM). The RA test is used to validate the calibration technique and verify the ability of the CEMS to provide representative and accurate measurements.

2.1.2.10 Performance Test Method (PTM). The sampling and analysis procedure used to obtain reference measurements for comparison to CEMS measurements. The applicable test methods are Method 10, 10A, or 10B (for the determination of CO) and Method 3 or 3A (for the determination of O_2). These methods are found in 40 CFR part 60, appendix A.

2.1.2.11 Performance Specification Test (PST) Period. The period during which CD, CE, response time, and RA tests are conducted.

2.1.2.12 Centroidal Area. A concentric area that is geometrically similar to the stack or duct cross section and is no greater than 1 percent of the stack or duct cross-sectional area.

2.1.3 *Installation and Measurement Location Specifications*

2.1.3.1 CEMS Installation and Measurement Locations. The CEMS shall be installed in a location in which measurements representative of the source's emissions can be obtained. The optimum location of the sample interface for the CEMS is determined by a number of factors, including ease of access for calibration and maintenance, the degree to which sample conditioning will be required, the degree to which it represents total emissions, and the degree to which it represents the combustion situation in the firebox. The location should be as free from in-leakage influences as possible and reasonably free from severe flow disturbances. The sample location should be at least two equivalent duct diameters downstream from the nearest control device, point of pollutant generation, or other point at which a change in the pollutant concentration or emission rate occurs and at least 0.5 diameter upstream from the exhaust or control device. The equivalent duct diameter is calculated as per 40 CFR part 60, appendix A, method 1, section 2.1. If these criteria are not achievable or if the location is otherwise less than optimum, the possibility of stratification should be checked as described in Section 2.1.3.3 to determine whether the location would cause failure of the relative accuracy test.

2.1.3.1.1 For extractive or point in-situ CEMSs, the measurement point should be within or centrally located over the centroidal area of the stack or duct cross section.

2.1.3.1.2 For cross-stack CEMSs, the effective measurement path should (1) have at least 70 percent of the path within the inner 50 percent of the stack or duct cross-sectional area or (2) be centrally located over any part of the centroidal area.

2.1.3.1.3 Both the CO and O_2 monitors should be installed at the same general location. If this is not possible, they may be installed at different locations if the effluent gases at both sample locations are not stratified and there is no in-leakage of air between sampling locations.

2.1.3.2 Performance Test Method (PTM) Measurement Location and Traverse Points.

2.1.3.2.1 Select an accessible PTM measurement point at least two equivalent diameters downstream from the nearest control device, the point of CO generation, or other point at which a change in the CO concentration may occur, and at least a half equivalent diameter upstream from the effluent exhaust or control device. When pollutant concentration changes are due solely to diluent leakage (*e.g.*, air heater leakages) and CO and O_2 are simultaneously measured at the same location, one half diameter may be used in place of two equivalent diameters. The CEMS and PTM locations need not be the same.

2.1.3.2.2 Select traverse points that ensure acquisition of representative samples over the stack or duct cross section. At a minimum, establish a measurement line that passes through the centroidal area in the direction of any expected stratification. If this line interferes with the CEMS measurements, displace the line up to 30 cm (or 5 percent of the equivalent diameter of the cross section, whichever is less) from the centroidal area. Locate three traverse points at 17, 50, and 83 percent of the measurement line. If the measurement line is no longer than 2.4 meters and pollutant stratification is not expected, the tester may choose to locate the three traverse points on the line at 0.4, 1.2, and 2.0 meters from the stack or duct wall. This option must not be used at a site located within eight equivalent diameters downstream of a flow disturbance. The tester may select other traverse points, provided that they can be shown to the satisfaction of the Administrator to provide a representative sample over the stack or duct cross-section. Conduct all necessary PTM tests within 3 cm of the selected traverse points. Sampling must not be performed within 3 cm of the duct or stack inner wall.

2.1.3.3 Stratification Test Procedure. Stratification is defined as a difference in excess of 10 percent between the average concentration in the duct or stack and the concentration at any point more than 1.0 meter from the duct or stack wall. To determine whether effluent stratification exists, a dual probe system should be used to determine the average effluent concentration while measurements at each traverse point are being made. One probe, located at the stack or duct centroid, is used as a stationary reference point to indicate the change in effluent concentration over time. The second probe is used for sampling at the traverse points specified in method 1, appendix A, 40 CFR part 60. The monitoring system samples sequentially at the reference and traverse points throughout the testing period for five minutes at each point.

2.1.4 *CEMS Performance and Equipment Specifications*

Table 2.1-1 summarizes the performance specifications for the CEMSs. Two sets of standards for CO are given; one for low-range and another for high-range measurements. The high-range specifications relate to measurement and quantification of short duration high concentration peaks, while the low-range specifications relate to the overall average operating condition of the burning device. The dual-range specifications can be met by using (1) one analyzer for each range, (2) a dual range unit, or (3) a single measurement range instrument capable of meeting both specifications with a single unit. Adjustments cannot be made to the analyzer between determinations of low- and high-level accuracy within the single measurement range. In the second case, when the concentration exceeds the span of the lower range, the data acquisition system recorder shall switch to the high range automatically.

Table 2.1-1—Performance Specifications of CO and O_2 Monitors

Parameter	CO monitors		O_2 monitors
	Low range	High range	
Calibration drift 24 hours	<6 ppm[1]	<90 ppm	<0.5% O_2
Calibration error	<10 ppm[1]	<150 ppm	<0.5% O_2
Response time	<2 min	<2 min	<2 min
Relative accuracy[2]	(3)	(3)	(incorporated in CO RA calculation)

[1] For Tier II, CD and CE are 3% and 5% or twice the permit limit, respectively.

[2] Expressed as the sum of the mean absolute value plus the 95% confidence interval of a series of measurements.

[3] The greater of 10% of PTM or 10 ppm.

2.1.4.1 CEMS Span Value. In order to measure high and low concentrations with the same or similar degree of accuracy, the maximum ranges (span values) are specified for low and high range analyzers. The span values are listed in Table 2.1-2. Tier I and Tier II format definitions are established in 40 CFR part 266, subpart H.

Table 2.1-2—CEMS Span Values for CO and O_2 Monitors

	CO monitors		O_2 monitor (percent)
	Low range (ppm)	High range (ppm)	
Tier I rolling average format	200	3,000	25
Tier II rolling average format	2 x permit limit	3,000	25

2.1.4.2 Daily Calibration Gas Values. The owner or operator must choose calibration gas concentrations (or calibration filters for in-situ systems) that include zero and high-level calibration values for the daily calibration checks. For a single measurement range monitor, three CO calibration gas concentrations (or calibration filters for in-situ systems) shall be used, *i.e.*, the zero and high-level concentrations of the low-range CO analyzer and the high-level concentration of the high-range CO analyzer.

2.1.4.2.1 The zero level for the CO or O_2 analyzer may be between zero and 20 percent of the span value, *e.g.*, 0-40 ppm for low-range CO analyzer, 0-600 ppm for the high-range CO analyzer, and 0-5 percent for the O_2 analyzer (for Tier I).

2.1.4.2.2 The high-level concentration for the CO or O_2 analyzer shall be between 50 and 90 percent of the span value, *i.e.*, 100-180 ppm for the low-range CO analyzer, 1500-2700 ppm for the high-range CO analyzer, and 12.5-22.5 percent O_2 for the O_2 analyzer.

2.1.4.3 Data Recorder Scale. The strip chart recorder, computer, or digital recorder must be capable of recording all readings within the CEMS's measurement range and shall have a resolution of 0.5 percent of span value, *i.e.*, 1 ppm CO for low-range CO analyzer, 15 ppm CO for high-range CO analyzer, and 0.1 percent O_2 for the O_2 analyzer.

2.1.4.4 Response Time. The response time for the CO or O_2 monitor shall not exceed 2 minutes to achieve 95 percent of the final stable value.

2.1.4.5 Calibration Drift. The CEMS must allow the determination of CD at the zero and high-level values. The CD must be determined separately for CO and O_2 monitors in terms of concentration. The CO CEMS calibration response must not drift or deviate from the reference value of the calibration gas (or calibration filters for in-situ systems) by more than 3 percent of the span value after each 24-hour period of the 7-day test, *i.e.*, 6 ppm CO for the low-range analyzer (Tier I) and 90 ppm for the high-range analyzer, at both zero and high levels. The O_2 monitor calibration response must not drift or deviate from the reference value by more than 0.5 percent O_2 at both zero and high levels.

2.1.4.6 Relative Accuracy. The result of the RA test of the CO CEMS (which incorporates the O_2 monitor) must be no greater than 10 percent of the mean value of the PTM results or must be within 10 ppm CO of the PTM results, whichever is less restrictive. The ppm CO concentration shall be corrected to 7 percent O_2 before calculating the RA.

2.1.4.7 Calibration Error. The mean difference between the CEMS and reference values at all three test points (see Table 2.1-3) must be no greater than 5 percent of span value for CO monitors (*i.e.*, 10 ppm CO for low range Tier I CO analyzers and 150 ppm CO for high range CO analyzers) and 0.5 percent for O_2 analyzers.

Table 2.1-3—Calibration Error Concentration Ranges for Tier I

Measurement point	GAS Concentration Ranges		
	CO, ppm		O_2, percent
	Low range[1]	High range	
1	0-40	0-600	0-2
2	60-80	900-1200	8-10
3	140-160	2100-2400	14-16

[1] For Tier II, the CE specifications for the low-range CO CEMS are 0-20%, 30-40%, and 70-80% of twice the permit limit.

2.1.4.8 Measurement and Recording Frequency. The sample to be analyzed shall pass through the measurement section of the analyzer without interruption. The detector shall measure the sample concentration at least once every 15 seconds. An average emission rate shall be computed and recorded at least once every 60 seconds.

2.1.4.9 Hourly Rolling Average Calculation. The CEMS shall calculate every minute an hourly rolling average, which is the arithmetic mean of the 60 most recent 1-minute average values.

2.1.4.10 Retest. If the CEMS produces results within the specified criteria, the test is successful. If the CEMS does not meet one or more of the criteria, the necessary corrections must be made and the performance tests repeated.

2.1.5 *Test Periods*

2.1.5.1 Pretest Preparation Period. Install the CEMS, prepare the PTM test site according to the specifications in section 2.1.3, and prepare the CEMS for operation and calibration according to the manufacturer's written instructions. A pretest conditioning period similar to that of the 7-day CD test is recommended to verify the operational status of the CEMS.

2.1.5.2 Calibration Drift Test Period. While the facility is operating under normal conditions, determine the CD at 24-hour intervals for seven consecutive days according to the procedure given in section 2.1.6.1. All CD determinations must be made following a 24-hour period during which no unscheduled maintenance, repair, or adjustment takes place. If the combustion unit is taken out of service during the test period, record the onset and duration of the downtime and continue the calibration drift test when the unit resumes operation.

2.1.5.3 Relative Accuracy Test Period. Conduct the RA test according to the procedure in section 2.1.6.4 while the facility is operating under normal conditions. RA testing for CO and O_2 shall be conducted simultaneously so that the results can be calculated for CO corrected to 7 percent O_2. The RA test shall be conducted during the CD test period. It is emphasized that during the CD test period, no adjustments or repairs may be made to the CEMS other than routine calibration adjustments performed immediately following the daily CD determination.

2.1.5.4 Calibration Error Test and Response Time Test Periods. Conduct the CE and response time tests during the CD test period.

2.1.6 *Performance Specification Test Procedures*

2.1.6.1 Calibration Drift Test.

2.1.6.1.1 Sampling Strategy. Conduct the CD test for all monitors at 24-hour intervals for seven consecutive days using calibration gases at the two (or three, if applicable) concentration levels specified in section 2.1.4.2. Introduce the calibration gases into the sampling system as close to the sampling probe outlet as practical. The gas shall pass through all filters, scrubbers, conditioners, and other CEMS components used during normal sampling. If periodic automatic or manual adjustments are made to the CEMS zero and calibration settings, conduct the CD test immediately before these adjustments, or conduct it in such a way that the CD can be determined. Record the CEMS response and subtract this value from the reference (calibration gas) value. To meet the specification, none of the differences shall exceed the limits specified in Table 2.1-1.

2.1.6.1.2 Calculations. Summarize the results on a data sheet. An example is shown in Figure 2.1-1. Calculate the differences between the CEMS responses and the reference values.

2.1.6.2 Response Time. Check the entire CEMS including sample extraction and transport, sample conditioning, gas analyses, and the data recording.

2.1.6.2.1 Introduce zero gas into the system. For extractive systems, introduce the calibration gases at the probe as near to the sample location as possible. For in-situ system, introduce the zero gas at a point such that all components active in the analysis are tested. When the system output has stabilized (no change greater than 1 percent of full scale for 30 seconds), switch to monitor stack effluent and wait for a stable value. Record the

Figure 2.1-1 Calibration Drift Determination

SOURCE:	DATE:
MONITOR:	LOCATION:
SERIAL NUMBER:	SPAN:

LOW RANGE	
HIGH RANGE	

	DAY	DATE	TIME	CALIBRATION VALUE	MONITOR RESPONSE	DIFFERENCE	PERCENT OF SPAN*
ZERO/LOW LEVEL	1						
	2						
	3						
	4						
	5						
	6						
	7						
HIGH LEVEL	1						
	2						
	3						
	4						
	5						
	6						
	7						

*Acceptance Criteria: ≤5% of span each day for seven days.

time (upscale response time) required to reach 95 percent of the final stable value.

2.1.6.2.2 Next, introduce a high-level calibration gas and repeat the above procedure. Repeat the entire procedure three times and determine the mean upscale and downscale response times. The longer of the two means is the system response time.

2.1.6.3 Calibration Error Test Procedure.

2.1.6.3.1 Sampling Strategy. Challenge each monitor (both low- and high-range CO and O_2) with zero gas and EPA Protocol 1 cylinder gases at three measurement points within the ranges specified in Table 2.1-3.

2.1.6.3.1.1 If a single measurement range is used, the calibration gases used in the daily CD checks (if they are Protocol 1 cylinder gases and meet the criteria in section 2.1.6.3.1) may be used for determining CE.

2.1.6.3.1.2 Operate each monitor in its normal sampling mode as nearly as possible. The calibration gas shall be injected into the sample system as close to the sampling probe outlet as practical and should pass through all CEMS components used during normal sampling. Challenge the CEMS three non-consecutive times at each measurement point and record the responses. The duration of each gas injection should be sufficient to ensure that the CEMS surfaces are conditioned.

2.1.6.3.2 Calculations. Summarize the results on a data sheet. An example data sheet is shown in Figure 2.1-2. Average the differences between the instrument response and the certified cylinder gas value for each gas. Calculate three CE results (five CE results for a single-range CO CEMS) according to Equation 5 (section 2.1.7.5). No confidence coefficient is used in CE calculations.

2.1.6.4 Relative Accuracy Test Procedure.

2.1.6.4.1 Sampling Strategy for PTM tests. Conduct the PTM tests in such a way that they will yield measurements representative of the emissions from the source and can be correlated to the CEMS data. Although it is preferable to conduct the CO, diluent, and moisture (if needed) simultaneously, moisture measurements that are taken within a 60-minute period which includes the simultaneous CO and O_2 measurements may be used to calculate the dry CO concentration.

Note: At times, CEMS RA tests may be conducted during incinerator performance tests. In these cases, PTM results obtained during CEMS RA tests may be used to determine compliance with incinerator emissions limits as long as the source and test conditions are consistent with the applicable regulations.

2.1.6.4.2 Performance Test Methods.

2.1.6.4.2.1 Unless otherwise specified in the regulations, method 3 or 3A and method 10, 10A, or 10B (40 CFR part 60, appendix A) are the test methods for O_2 and CO, respectively. Make a sample traverse of at least 21 minutes, sampling for 7 minutes at each of three traverse points (see section 3.2).

2.1.6.4.2.2 When the installed CEMS uses a nondispersive infrared (NDIR) analyzer, method 10 shall use the alternative interference trap specified in section 10.1 of the method. An option, which may be approved by the Administrator in certain cases, would allow the test to be conducted using method 10 without the interference trap. Under this option, a laboratory interference test is performed for the analyzer prior to the field test. The laboratory interference test includes the analysis of SO_2, NO, and CO_2 calibration gases over the range of expected effluent concentrations. Acceptable performance is indicated if the CO analyzer response to each of the gases is less than 1 percent of the applicable measurement range of the analyzer.

2.1.6.4.3 Number of PTM Tests. Conduct a minimum of nine sets of all necessary PTM tests. If more than nine sets are conducted, a maximum of three sets may be rejected at the tester's discretion. The total number of sets used to determine the RA must be greater than or equal to nine. All data, including the rejected data, must be reported.

2.1.6.4.4 Correlation of PTM and CEMS Data. The time and duration of each PTM test run and the CEMS response time should be considered in correlating the data. Use the CEMS final output (the one used for reporting) to determine an

Figure 2.1-2 Calibration Error Determination

SOURCE:	DATE:
MONITOR:	LOCATION:
SERIAL NUMBER:	SPAN:

LOW RANGE	
HIGH RANGE	

RUN NUMBER	CALIBRATION VALUE	MONITOR RESPONSE	DIFFERENCE		
			Zero/Low	Mid	High
1 - Zero					
2 - Mid					
3 - High					
4 - Mid					
5 - Zero					
6 - High					
7 - Zero					
8 - Mid					
9 - High					
		Mean Difference =			
		Calibration Error =	%	%	%

integrated average CO concentration for each PTM test run. Confirm that the pair of results are on a consistent moisture and O_2 concentration basis. Each integrated CEMS value should then be compared against the corresponding average PTM value. If the CO concentration measured by the CEMS is normalized to a specified diluent concentration, the PTM results shall be normalized to the same value.

2.1.6.4.5 Calculations. Summarize the results on a data sheet. Calculate the mean of the PTM values and calculate the arithmetic differences between the PTM and the CEMS data sets. The mean of the differences, standard deviation, confidence coefficient, and CEMS RA should be calculated using Equations 1 through 4.

2.1.7 *Equations*

2.1.7.1 Arithmetic Mean ($\bar{d}$). Calculate d of the difference of a data set using Equation 1.

$$\bar{d} = \frac{1}{n}\sum_{i=1}^{n} d_i \qquad \text{(Eq. 1)}$$

where:

n = Number of data points.

$\sum_{i=1}^{n} d_i$ = Algebraic sum of the individual differences d_i.

When the mean of the differences of pairs of data is calculated, correct the data for moisture, if applicable.

2.1.7.2 Standard Deviation (S_d). Calculate S_d using Equation 2.

$$S_d = \sqrt{\frac{\sum_{i=1}^{n} d_i^2 - \frac{\sum_{i=1}^{n} d_i^2}{n}}{n-1}} \qquad \text{(Eq. 2)}$$

2.1.7.3 Confidence Coefficient (CC). Calculate the 2.5 percent error CC (one-tailed) using Equation 3.

$$CC = t_{0.975}\frac{S_d}{\sqrt{n}} \qquad \text{(Eq. 3)}$$

where:

$t_{0.975}$ = t-value (see Table 2.1-4).

Table 2.1-4—t-Values

n[a]	$t_{0.975}$	n[a]	$t_{0.975}$	n[a]	$t_{0.975}$
2	12.706	7	2.447	12	2.201
3	4.303	8	2.365	13	2.179
4	3.182	9	2.306	14	2.160
5	2.776	10	2.662	15	2.145
6	2.571	11	2.228	16	2.131

[a] The values in this table are already corrected for n-1 degrees of freedom. Use n equal to the number of individual values.

2.1.7.4 Relative Accuracy. Calculate the RA of a set of data using Equation 4.

$$RA = \frac{|\bar{d}| + |CC|}{\overline{PTM}} \times 100 \qquad \text{(Eq. 4)}$$

where:

$|\bar{d}|$ = Absolute value of the mean of the differences (Equation 1).

$|CC|$ = Absolute value of the confidence coefficient (Equation 3).

$\overline{PTM}$ = Average reference value.

2.1.7.5 Calibration Error. Calculate CE using Equation 5.

$$CE = \left|\frac{\bar{d}}{FS}\right| \times 100 \qquad \text{(Eq. 5)}$$

where:

$\bar{d}$ = Mean difference between CEMS response and the known reference concentration.

2.1.8 *Reporting*

At a minimum, summarize in tabular form the results of the CD, RA, response time, and CE test, as appropriate. Include all data sheets, calculations, CEMS data records, and cylinder gas or reference material certifications.

2.1.9 *Alternative Procedure*

2.1.9.1 Alternative RA Procedure Rationale. Under some operating conditions, it may not be possible to obtain meaningful results using the RA test procedure. This includes conditions where consistent, very low CO emissions or low CO emissions interrupted periodically by short duration, high level spikes are observed. It may be appropriate in these circumstances to waive the PTM RA test and substitute the following procedure.

2.1.9.2 Alternative RA Procedure. Conduct a complete CEMS status check following the manufacturer's written instructions. The check should include operation of the light source, signal receiver, timing mechanism functions, data acquisition and data reduction functions, data recorders, mechanically operated functions (mirror movements, calibration gas valve operations, etc.), sample filters, sample line heaters, moisture traps, and other related functions of the CEMS, as applicable. All parts of the CEMS must be functioning properly before the RA requirement can be waived. The instruments must also have successfully passed the CE and CD requirements of the performance specifications. Substitution of the alternative procedure requires approval of the Regional Administrator.

2.1.10 *Quality Assurance (QA)*

Proper calibration, maintenance, and operation of the CEMS is the responsibility of the owner or operator. The owner or operator must establish a QA program to evaluate and monitor CEMS performance. As a minimum, the QA program must include:

2.1.10.1 A daily calibration check for each monitor. The calibration must be adjusted if the check indicates the instrument's CD exceeds the specification established in section 2.1.4.5. The gases shall be injected as close to the probe as possible to provide a check of the entire sampling system. If an alternative calibration procedure is desired (*e.g.*, direct injections or gas cells), subject to Administrator approval, the adequacy of this alternative procedure may be demonstrated during the initial 7-day CD test. Periodic comparisons of the two procedures are suggested.

2.1.10.2 A daily system audit. The audit must include a review of the calibration check data, an inspection of the recording system, an inspection of the control panel warning lights, and an inspection of the sample transport and interface system (*e.g.*, flowmeters, filters), as appropriate.

2.1.10.3 A quarterly calibration error (CE) test. Quarterly RA tests may be substituted for the CE test when approved by the Director on a case-by-case basis.

2.1.10.4 An annual performance specification test.

2.1.11 *References*

1. Jahnke, James A. and G.J. Aldina, "Handbook: Continuous Air Pollution Source Monitoring Systems," U.S. Environmental Protection Agency Technology Transfer, Cincinnati, Ohio 45268, EPA-625/6-79-005, June 1979.

2. "Gaseous Continuous Emissions Monitoring Systems-Performance Specification Guidelines for SO_2, NO_x, CO_2, O_2, and TRS." U.S. Environmental Protection Agency OAQPS, ESED, Research Triangle Park, North Carolina 27711, EPA-450/3-82-026, October 1982.
3. "Quality Assurance Handbook for Air Pollution Measurement Systems: Volume I. Principles." U.S. Environmental Protection Agency ORD/EMSL, Research Triangle Park, North Carolina, 27711, EPA-600/9-76-006, December 1984.
4. Michie, Raymond, M. Jr., et. al., "Performance Test Results and Comparative Data for Designated Reference Methods for Carbon Monoxide," U.S. Environmental Protection Agency ORD/EMSL, Research Triangle Park, North Carolina, 27711, EPA-600/S4-83-013, September 1982.
5. Ferguson, B.B., R.E. Lester, and W.J. Mitchell, "Field Evaluation of Carbon Monoxide and Hydrogen Sulfide Continuous Emission Monitors at an Oil Refinery," U.S. Environmental Protection Agency, Research Triangle Park, North Carolina, 27711, EPA-600/4-82-054, August 1982.

2.2 *Performance Specifications for Continuous Emission Monitoring of Hydrocarbons for Incinerators, Boilers, and Industrial Furnaces Burning Hazardous Waste*

2.2.1 *Applicability and Principle*

2.2.1.1 Applicability. These performance specifications apply to hydrocarbon (HC) continuous emission monitoring systems (CEMSs) installed on incinerators, boilers, and industrial furnaces burning hazardous waste. The specifications include procedures which are intended to be used to evaluate the acceptability of the CEMS at the time of its installation or whenever specified in regulations or permits. The procedures are not designed to evaluate CEMS performance over an extended period of time. The source owner or operator is responsible for the proper calibration, maintenance, and operation of the CEMS at all times.

2.2.1.2 Principle. A gas sample is extracted from the source through a heated sample line and heated filter (except as provided by section 2.2.10) to a flame ionization detector (FID). Results are reported as volume concentration equivalents of propane. Installation and measurement location specifications, performance and equipment specifications, test and data reduction procedures, and brief quality assurance guidelines are included in the specifications. Calibration drift, calibration error, and response time tests are conducted to determine conformance of the CEMS with the specifications.

2.2.2 *Definitions*

2.2.2.1 Continuous Emission Monitoring System (CEMS). The total equipment used to acquire data, which includes sample extraction and transport hardware, analyzer, data recording and processing hardware, and software. The system consists of the following major subsystems:

2.2.2.1.1 Sample Interface. That portion of the system that is used for one or more of the following: Sample acquisition, sample transportation, sample conditioning, or protection of the analyzer from the effects of the stack effluent.

2.2.2.1.2 Organic Analyzer. That portion of the system that senses organic concentration and generates an output proportional to the gas concentration.

2.2.2.1.3 Data Recorder. That portion of the system that records a permanent record of the measurement values. The data recorder may include automatic data reduction capabilities.

2.2.2.2 Instrument Measurement Range. The difference between the minimum and maximum concentration that can be measured by a specific instrument. The minimum is often stated or assumed to be zero and the range expressed only as the maximum.

2.2.2.3 Span or Span Value. Full scale instrument measurement range.

2.2.2.4 Calibration Gas. A known concentration of a gas in an appropriate diluent gas.

2.2.2.5 Calibration Drift (CD). The difference in the CEMS output readings from the established reference value after a stated period of operation during which no unscheduled maintenance, repair, or adjustment takes place. A CD test is performed to demonstrate the stability of the CEMS calibration over time.

2.2.2.6 Response Time. The time interval between the start of a step change in the system input (*e.g.*, change of calibration gas) and the time when the data recorder displays 95 percent of the final value.

2.2.2.7 Accuracy. A measurement of agreement between a measured value and an accepted or true value, expressed as the percentage difference between the true and measured values relative to the true value. For these performance specifications, accuracy is checked by conducting a calibration error (CE) test.

2.2.2.8 Calibration Error (CE). The difference between the concentration indicated by the CEMS and the known concentration of the cylinder gas. A CE test procedure is performed to document the accuracy and linearity of the monitoring equipment over the entire measurement range.

2.2.2.9 Performance Specification Test (PST) Period. The period during which CD, CE, and response time tests are conducted.

2.2.2.10 Centroidal Area. A concentric area that is geometrically similar to the stack or duct cross section and is no greater than 1 percent of the stack or duct cross-sectional area.

2.2.3 *Installation and Measurement Location Specifications*

2.2.3.1 CEMS Installation and Measurement Locations. The CEMS shall be installed in a location in which measurements representative of the source's emissions can be obtained. The optimum location of the sample interface for the CEMS is determined by a number of factors, including ease of access for calibration and maintenance, the degree to which sample conditioning will be required, the degree to which it represents total emissions, and the degree to which it represents the combustion situation in the firebox. The location should be as free from in-leakage influences as possible and reasonably free from severe flow disturbances. The sample location should be at least two equivalent duct diameters downstream from the nearest control device, point of pollutant generation, or other point at which a change in the pollutant concentration or emission rate occurs and at least 0.5 diameter upstream from the exhaust or control device. The equivalent duct diameter is calculated as per 40 CFR part 60, appendix A, method 1, section 2.1. If these criteria are not achievable or if the location is otherwise less than optimum, the possibility of stratification should be investigated as described in section 2.2.3.2. The measurement point shall be within the centroidal area of the stack or duct cross section.

2.2.3.2 Stratification Test Procedure. Stratification is defined as a difference in excess of 10 percent between the average concentration in the duct or stack and the concentration at any point more than 1.0 meter from the duct or stack wall. To determine whether effluent stratification exists, a dual probe system should be used to determine the average effluent concentration while measurements at each traverse point are being made. One probe, located at the stack or duct centroid, is used as a stationary reference point to indicate the change in effluent concentration over time. The second probe is used for sampling at the traverse points specified in 40 CFR part 60 appendix A, method 1. The monitoring system samples sequentially at the reference and traverse points throughout the testing period for five minutes at each point.

2.2.4 *CEMS Performance and Equipment Specifications*

If this method is applied in highly explosive areas, caution and care shall be exercised in choice of equipment and installation.

2.2.4.1 Flame Ionization Detector (FID) Analyzer. A heated FID analyzer capable of meeting or exceeding the requirements of these specifications. Heated systems shall maintain the temperature of the sample gas between 150° C (300° F) and 175° C (350° F) throughout the system. This requires all system components such as the probe, calibration valve, filter, sample lines, pump, and the FID to be kept heated at all times such that no moisture is condensed out of the system.

Note: As specified in the regulations, unheated HC CEMs may be considered an acceptable interim alternative monitoring technique. For additional notes, see section 2.2.10. The essential components of the measurement system are described below:

2.2.4.1.1 Sample Probe. Stainless steel, or equivalent, to collect a gas sample from the centroidal area of the stack cross-section.

2.2.4.1.2 Sample Line. Stainless steel or Teflon tubing to transport the sample to the analyzer.

Note: Mention of trade names or specific products does not constitute endorsement by the Environmental Protection Agency.

2.2.4.1.3 Calibration Valve Assembly. A heated three-way valve assembly to direct the zero and calibration gases to the analyzer is recommended. Other methods, such as quick-connect lines, to route calibration gas to the analyzers are applicable.

2.2.4.1.4 Particulate Filter. An in-stack or out-of-stack sintered stainless steel filter is recommended if exhaust gas particulate loading is significant. An out-of-stack filter must be heated.

2.2.4.1.5 Fuel. The fuel specified by the manufacturer (*e.g.*, 40 percent hydrogen/60 percent helium, 40 percent hydrogen/60 percent nitrogen gas mixtures, or pure hydrogen) should be used.

2.2.4.1.6 Zero Gas. High purity air with less than 0.1 parts per million by volume (ppm) HC as methane or carbon equivalent or less than 0.1 percent of the span value, whichever is greater.

2.2.4.1.7 Calibration Gases. Appropriate concentrations of propane gas (in air or nitrogen). Preparation of the calibration gases should be done according to the procedures in EPA Protocol 1. In addition, the manufacturer of the cylinder gas should provide a recommended shelf life for each calibration gas cylinder over which the concentration does not change by more than ±2 percent from the certified value.

2.2.4.2 CEMS Span Value. 100 ppm propane.

2.2.4.3 Daily Calibration Gas Values. The owner or operator must choose calibration gas concentrations that include zero and high-level calibration values.

2.2.4.3.1 The zero level may be between 0 and 20 ppm (zero and 20 percent of the span value).

2.2.4.3.2 The high-level concentration shall be between 50 and 90 ppm (50 and 90 percent of the span value).

2.2.4.4 Data Recorder Scale. The strip chart recorder, computer, or digital recorder must be capable of recording all readings within the CEMS's measurement range and shall have a resolution of 0.5 ppm (0.5 percent of span value).

2.2.4.5 Response Time. The response time for the CEMS must not exceed 2 minutes to achieve 95 percent of the final stable value.

2.2.4.6 Calibration Drift. The CEMS must allow the determination of CD at the zero and high-level values. The CEMS calibration response must not differ by more than ±3 ppm (±3 percent of the span value) after each 24-hour period of the 7-day test at both zero and high levels.

2.2.4.7 Calibration Error. The mean difference between the CEMS and reference values at all three test points listed below shall be no greater than 5 ppm (±5 percent of the span value).

2.2.4.7.1 Zero Level. Zero to 20 ppm (0 to 20 percent of span value).

2.2.4.7.2 Mid-Level. 30 to 40 ppm (30 to 40 percent of span value).

2.2.4.7.3 High-Level. 70 to 80 ppm (70 to 80 percent of span value).

2.2.4.8 Measurement and Recording Frequency. The sample to be analyzed shall pass through the measurement section of the analyzer without interruption. The detector shall measure the sample concentration at least once every 15 seconds. An average emission rate shall be computed and recorded at least once every 60 seconds.

2.2.4.9 Hourly Rolling Average Calculation. The CEMS shall calculate every minute an hourly rolling average, which is the arithmetic mean of the 60 most recent 1-minute average values.

2.2.4.10 Retest. If the CEMS produces results within the specified criteria, the test is successful. If the CEMS does not meet one or more of the criteria, necessary corrections must be made and the performance tests repeated.

2.2.5 *Performance Specification Test (PST) Periods*

2.2.5.1 Pretest Preparation Period. Install the CEMS, prepare the PTM test site according to the specifications in section 2.2.3, and prepare the CEMS for operation and calibration according to the manufacturer's written instructions. A pretest conditioning period similar to that of the 7-day CD test is recommended to verify the operational status of the CEMS.

2.2.5.2 Calibration Drift Test Period. While the facility is operating under normal conditions, determine the magnitude of the CD at 24-hour intervals for seven consecutive days according to the procedure given in section 2.2.6.1. All CD determinations must be made following a 24-hour period during which no unscheduled maintenance, repair, or adjustment takes place. If the combustion unit is taken out of service during the test period, record the onset and duration of the downtime and continue the CD test when the unit resumes operation.

2.2.5.3 Calibration Error Test and Response Time Test Periods. Conduct the CE and response time tests during the CD test period.

2.2.6 *Performance Specification Test Procedures*

2.2.6.1 Calibration Drift Test.

2.2.6.1.1 Sampling Strategy. Conduct the CD test at 24-hour intervals for seven consecutive days using calibration gases at the two daily concentration levels specified in section 2.2.4.3. Introduce the two calibration gases into the sampling system as close to the sampling probe outlet as practical. The gas shall pass through all CEM components used during normal sampling. If periodic automatic or manual adjustments are made to the CEMS zero and calibration settings, conduct the CD test immediately before these adjustments, or conduct it in such a way that the CD can be determined. Record the CEMS response and subtract this value from the reference (calibration gas) value. To meet the specification, none of the differences shall exceed 3 ppm.

2.2.6.1.2 Calculations. Summarize the results on a data sheet. An example is shown in Figure 2.2-1. Calculate the differences between the CEMS responses and the reference values.

2.2.6.2 Response Time. The entire system including sample extraction and transport, sample conditioning, gas analyses, and the data recording is checked with this procedure.

Figure 2.2-1 Calibration Drift Determination

SOURCE:	DATE:
MONITOR:	LOCATION:
SERIAL NUMBER:	SPAN:

	DAY	DATE	TIME	CALIBRATION VALUE	MONITOR RESPONSE	DIFFERENCE	PERCENT OF SPAN*
ZERO/LOW LEVEL	1						
	2						
	3						
	4						
	5						
	6						
	7						
HIGH LEVEL	1						
	2						
	3						
	4						
	5						
	6						
	7						

*Acceptance Criteria: ≤3% of span each day for seven days.

Figure 2.2-2 Calibration Error Determination

SOURCE:	DATE:
MONITOR:	LOCATION:
SERIAL NUMBER:	SPAN:

RUN NUMBER	CALIBRATION VALUE	MONITOR RESPONSE	DIFFERENCE		
			Zero/Low	Mid	High
1 - Zero					
2 - Mid					
3 - High					
4 - Mid					
5 - Zero					
6 - High					
7 - Zero					
8 - Mid					
9 - High					
		Mean Difference =			
		Calibration Error =	%	%	%

2.2.6.2.1 Introduce the calibration gases at the probe as near to the sample location as possible. Introduce the zero gas into the system. When the system output has stabilized (no change greater than 1 percent of full scale for 30 sec), switch to monitor stack effluent and wait for a stable value. Record the time (upscale response time) required to reach 95 percent of the final stable value.

2.2.6.2.2 Next, introduce a high-level calibration gas and repeat the above procedure. Repeat the entire procedure three times and determine the mean upscale and downscale response times. The longer of the two means is the system response time.

2.2.6.3 Calibration Error Test Procedure.

2.2.6.3.1 Sampling Strategy. Challenge the CEMS with zero gas and EPA Protocol 1 cylinder gases at measurement points within the ranges specified in section 2.2.4.7.

2.2.6.3.1.1 The daily calibration gases, if Protocol 1, may be used for this test.

2.2.6.3.1.2 Operate the CEMS as nearly as possible in its normal sampling mode. The calibration gas should be injected into the sampling system as close to the sampling probe outlet as practical and shall pass through all filters, scrubbers, conditioners, and other monitor components used during normal sampling. Challenge the CEMS three non-consecutive times at each measurement point and record the responses. The duration of each gas injection should be for a sufficient period of time to ensure that the CEMS surfaces are conditioned.

2.2.6.3.2 Calculations. Summarize the results on a data sheet. An example data sheet is shown in Figure 2.2-2. Average the differences between the instrument response and the certified cylinder gas value for each gas. Calculate three CE results according to Equation 1. No confidence coefficient is used in CE calculations.

2.2.7 *Equations*

2.2.7.1 Calibration Error. Calculate CE using Equation 1.

$$CE = \left|\frac{\bar{d}}{FS}\right| \times 100 \qquad \text{(Eq. 1)}$$

where:

$\bar{d}$ = Mean difference between CEMS response and the known reference concentration.

2.2.8 *Reporting*

At a minimum, summarize in tabular form the results of the CD, response time, and CE test, as appropriate. Include all the data sheets, calculations, CEMS data records, and cylinder gas or reference material certifications.

2.2.9 *Quality Assurance (QA)*

Proper calibration, maintenance, and operation of the CEMS is the responsibility of the owner or operator. The owner or operator must establish a QA program to evaluate and monitor CEMS performance. As a minimum, the QA program must include:

2.2.9.1 A daily calibration check for each monitor. The calibration must be adjusted if the check indicates the instrument's CD exceeds 3 ppm. The gases shall be injected as close to the probe as possible to provide a check of the entire sampling system. If an alternative calibration procedure is desired (*e.g.*, direct injections or gas cells), subject to Administrator approval, the adequacy of this alternative procedure may be demonstrated during the initial 7-day CD test. Periodic comparisons of the two procedures are suggested.

2.2.9.2 A daily system audit. The audit must include a review of the calibration check data, an inspection of the recording system, an inspection of the control panel warning lights, and an inspection of the sample transport and interface system (*e.g.*, flowmeters, filters), as appropriate.

2.2.9.3 A quarterly CE test. Quarterly RA tests may be substituted for the CE test when approved by the Director on a case-by-case basis.

2.2.9.4 An annual performance specification test.

2.2.10 *Alternative Measurement Technique*

The regulations allow gas conditioning systems to be used in conjunction with unheated HC CEMs during an interim period. This gas conditioning may include cooling to not less than 40° F and the use of condensate traps to reduce the moisture content of sample gas entering the FID to less than 2 percent. The gas conditioning system, however, must not allow the sample gas to bubble through the condensate as this would remove water soluble organic compounds. All components upstream of the conditioning system should be heated as described in section 2.2.4 to minimize operating and maintenance problems.

2.2.11 *References*

1. Measurement of Volatile Organic Compounds-Guideline Series. U.S. Environmental Protection Agency, Research Triangle Park, North Carolina, 27711, EPA-450/2-78-041, June 1978.
2. Traceability Protocol for Establishing True Concentrations of Gases Used for Calibration and Audits of Continuous Source Emission Monitors (Protocol No. 1). U.S. Environmental Protection Agency ORD/EMSL, Research Triangle Park, North Carolina, 27711, June 1978.
3. Gasoline Vapor Emission Laboratory Evaluation-Part 2. U.S. Environmental Protection Agency, OAQPS, Research Triangle Park, North Carolina, 27711, EMB Report No. 76-GAS-6, August 1975.

Section 3.0 Sampling and Analytical Methods

Note: The sampling and analytical methods to the BIF manual are published in "Test Methods for Evaluating Solid Waste, Physical/Chemical Methods," EPA Publication SW-846.

Section 4.0 Procedure for Estimating the Toxicity Equivalency of Chlorinated Dibenzo-p-Dioxin and Dibenzofuran Congeners

PCDDs and PCDFs must be determined using whichever is the most recent version between of SW–846 Method 0023A (incorporated by reference, in §260.11) as identified, or OAQPS Method 23 of appendix A to part 60. In this method, individual congeners or homologues[1] are measured and then summed to yield a total PCDD/PCDF value. No toxicity factors are specified in the method to compute risks from such emissions.

For the purpose of estimating risks posed by emissions from boilers and industrial furnaces, however, specific congeners and homologues must be measured using the specified method and then multiplied by the assigned toxicity equivalence factors (TEFs), using procedures described in "Interim Procedures for Estimating Risks Associated with Exposures to Mixtures of Chlorinated Dibenzo-p-Dioxins and Dibenzofurans (CDDs and CDFs) and 1989 Update," EPA/625/3-89/016, March 1989. The resulting 2,3,7,8-TCDD equivalents value is used in the subsequent risk calculations and modeling efforts as discussed in the BIF final rule.

The procedure for calculating the 2,3,7,8-TCDD equivalent is as follows:

1. Using method 23, determine the concentrations of 2,7,3,8-congeners of various PCDDs and PCDFs in the sample.
2. Multiply the congener concentrations in the sample by the TEF listed in Table 4.0-1 to express the congener concentrations in terms of 2,3,7,8-TCDD equivalent. Note that congeners not chlorinated at 2,3,7, and 8 positions have a zero toxicity factor in this table.

Table 4.0-1—2,3,7,8-TCDD Toxicity Equivalence Factors (TEFs)[1]

Compound	I-TEFs, 89	Compound	I-TEFs, 89
Mono-, Di-, and TriCDDs	0	2,3,7,8-TCDF	0.1
2,3,7,8-TCDD	1	Other TCDFs	0
Other TCDDs	0	1,2,3,7,8-PeCDF	0.05
2,3,7,8-PeCDD	0.5	2,3,4,7,8-PeCDF	0.5
Other PeCDDs	0	Other PeCDFs	0
2,3,7,8-HxCDD	0.1	2378-HxCDFs	0.1
Other HxCDDs	0	Other HxCDFs	0
2,3,7,8-HpCDD	0.01	2378-HpCDFs	0.01
Other HpCDDs	0	Other HpCDFs	0
OCDD	0.001	OCDF	0.001
Mono-, Di-, and TriCDFs	0		

Reference: Adapted from NATO/CCMS, 1988a.

[1] Interim Procedures for Estimating Risks Associated with Exposures to Mixtures of Chlorinated Dibenzo-p-Dioxins and Dibenzofurans (CDDs and CDFs) 1989 Update EPA/625/3-89/016, March 1989.

3. Add the products obtained in step 2, to obtain the total 2,3,7,8-TCDD equivalent in the sample.

Sample calculations are provided in EPA document No. EPA/625/3-89/016, March 1989, which can be obtained from the EPA, ORD Publications Office, Cincinnati, Ohio (Phone no. 513-569-7562).

[1] The term "congener" refers to any one particular member of the same chemical family; *e.g.*, there are 75 congeners of chlorinated dibenzo-p-dioxins. The term "homologue" refers to a group of structurally related chemicals that have the same degree of chlorination. For example, there are eight homologues of CDs, monochlorinated through octachlorinated. Dibenzo-p-dioxins and dibenzofurans that are chlorinated at the 2,3,7, and 8 positions are denoted as "2378" congeners, except when 2,3,7,8–TCDD is uniquely referred to: *e.g.*, 1,2,3,7,8–PeCDF and 2,3,4,7,8–PeCDF are both referred to as "2378–PeCDFs."

Section 5.0 Hazardous Waste Combustion Air Quality Screening Procedure

The HWCAQSP is a combined calculation/reference table approach for conservatively estimating short-term and annual average facility impacts for stack emissions. The procedure is based on extensive short-term modeling of 11 generic source types and on a set of adjustment factors for estimating annual average concentrations from short-term concentrations. Facility impacts may be determined based on the selected worst-case stack or on multiple stacks, in which the impacts from each stack are estimated separately and then added to produce the total facility impact.

This procedure is most useful for facilities with multiple stacks, large source-to-property boundary distances, and complex terrain between 1 and 5 km from the facility. To ensure a sufficient degree of conservatism, the HWCAQSP may not be used if any of the five screening procedure limitations listed below are true:

- The facility is located in a narrow valley less than 1 km wide;
- The facility has a stack taller than 20 m and is located such that the terrain rises to the stack height within 1 km of the facility;
- The facility has a stack taller than 20 m and is located within 5 km of the shoreline of a large body of water;
- The facility property line is within 200 m of the stack and the physical stack height is less than 10 m; or
- On-site receptors are of concern, and stack height is less than 10 m.

If any of these criteria are met or the Director determines that this procedure is not appropriate, then detailed site-specific modeling or modeling using the "Screening Procedures for Estimating the Air Quality Impact of Stationary Sources," EPA -450/4-88-010, Office of Air Quality Planning and Standards, August 1988, is required. Detailed site-specific dispersion modeling must conform to the EPA "Guidance on Air Quality Models (Revised)", EPA 450/2-78-027R, Office of Air Quality Planning and Standards, Research Triangle Park, North Carolina, July 1986. This document provides guidance on both the proper selection and regulatory application of air quality models.

Introduction

The Hazardous Waste Combustion Air Quality Screening Procedure (HWCAQSP) (also referred to hereafter as "the screening procedure" or "the procedure") provides a quick, easy method for estimating maximum (hourly) and annual average ambient air impacts associated with the combustion of hazardous waste. The methodology is conservative in nature and estimates dispersion coefficients[1] based on facility-specific information.

The screening procedure can be used to determine emissions limits at sites where the nearest meteorological (STAR) station is not representative of the meteorology at the site. If the screen shows that emissions from the site are adequately protective, then the need to collect site-specific meteorological data can be eliminated.

The screening procedure is generally most helpful for facilities meeting one or more of the following conditions:

- Multiple stacks with substantially different release specifications (*e.g.*, stack heights differ by >50 percent, exit temperatures differ by >50° K, or the exit flow rates differ by more than a factor of 2),
- Terrain located between 1 km and 5 km from the site increases in elevation by more than the physical height of the shortest stack (*i.e.*, the facility is located in complex terrain), or
- Significant distance between the facility's stacks and the site boundary [guidance on determining whether a distance is "significant" is provided in Step 6(B) of the procedure].

Steps 1 through 9 of the screening procedure present a simplified method for determining emissions based on the use of the "worst-case" stack. If the simplified method shows that desired feed rates result in emissions that exceed allowable limits for one or more pollutants, a refined analysis to examine the emissions from each stack can be conducted. This multiple-stack method is presented in Step 10.

The steps involved in screening methodology are as follows:

Step 1. Define Source Characteristics

Step 2. Determine the Applicability of the Screening Procedure

Step 3. Select the Worst-Case Stack

Step 4. Verify Good Engineering Practice (GEP) Criteria

Step 5. Determine the Effective Stack Height and Terrain-Adjusted Effective Stack Height

Step 6. Classify the Site as Urban or Rural

Step 7. Determine Maximum Dispersion Coefficients

Step 8. Estimate Maximum Ambient Air Concentrations

Step 9. Determine Compliance With Regulatory Limits

Step 10. Multiple Stack Method

Step 1: Define Source Characteristics

Provide the following source data:[2]

Stack Data:	Stack No. 1	Stack No. 2	Stack No. 3
Physical stack height (m)	______	______	______
Exhaust temperature (° K)	______	______	______
Flow rate (m^3/sec)	______	______	______

Nearby Building Dimensions

Consider all buildings within five building heights or five maximum projected widths of the stack(s). For the building with the greatest height, fill in the spaces below.

Building Height (m)____________________

Maximum projected building width (m)____________________

Nearby Terrain Data

Determine maximum terrain rise for the following three distance ranges from the facility (not required if the highest stack is less than 10 m in height):

________(m)	________(m)	________(m)
0–0.5 km	0–2.5 km	0–5 km

Distance from facility to nearest shoreline (km)____________________

Valley width (km)____________________

1 The term dispersion coefficient refers to the change in ambient air concentration (µg/m³) resulting from a source with an emission rate of 1 g/sec.

2 Worksheet space is provided for three stacks. If the facility has additional stacks, copy the form and revise stack identification numbers for 4, 5, etc.

PART 266—Appendices

Step 2: Determine the Applicability of the Screening Procedure

Fill in the following data:

	Yes	No
Is the facility in a valley < km in width?	______	______
Is the terrain rise within 1 km of the facility greater than the physical stack height of the tallest stack? (Only applies to stacks ≤20 meters in height)	______	______
Is the distance to the nearest shoreline <5 km? (Only applies to facilities with stacks ≤20 meters in height)	______	______
For the building listed in Step 1, is the closest property boundary <5 times the building height or <5 times the maximum projected building width? (Only applies to facilities with a stack height <2.5 times the building height)	______	______

If the answer is "no" to all the preceding questions, then the HWCAQSP is acceptable. If the answer to any question is "yes", the procedure is not acceptable.

Step 3: Select the Worst-Case Stack

If the facility has several stacks, a worst-case stack must be chosen to conservatively represent release conditions at the facility. Follow the steps below to identify the worst-case stack.

Apply the following equation to each stack:

$$K = HVT$$

where:

K = an arbitrary parameter accounting for the relative influence of the stack height and plume rise.

H = Physical stack height (m)

V = Flow rate (m^3/sec)

T = Exhaust temperature (° K)

Complete the following table to compute the "K" value for each stack:

Stack No	Stack height (m)	x	Flow rate (m^3/sec)	x	Exit temp (° K)	=	K
1	________	x	________	x	________	=	________
2	________	x	________	x	________	=	________
3	________	x	________	x	________	=	________

Select the stack with the lowest "K" value. This is the worst-case stack that will be used for Steps 4 through 9.

Worst-Case Stack is identified as Stack No. ______

Step 4: Verify Good Engineering Practice (GEP) Criteria

Confirm that the selected worst-case stack meets Good Engineering Practice (GEP) criteria. The stack height to be used in the subsequent steps of this procedure must not be greater than the maximum GEP. Maximum and minimum GEP stack heights are defined as follows:

$$\text{CEP (minimum)} = H + (1.5 \times L)$$

$$\text{GEP (maximum)} = \text{greater of } 65\text{ m or } H + (1.5 \times L)$$

where:

H = height of the building selected in Step 1 measured from ground level elevation at the base of the stack

L = the lesser dimension of the height or projected width of the building selected in Step 1

Record the following data for the worst-case stack:

Stack height (m) = __________

H(m) = __________

L(m) = __________

Then compute the following:

GEP (minimum) (m) = __________

GEP (maximum) (m) = __________

If the physical height of the worst-case stack exceeds the maximum GEP, then use the maximum GEP stack height for the subsequent steps of this analysis;

If the physical height of the worst-case stack is less than the minimum GEP, then use generic source number 11 as the selected source for further analysis and proceed directly to Step 6;

If the physical height of the worst-case stack is between the minimum and maximum GEP, then use the actual physical stack height for the subsequent steps of this analysis.

Step 5: Determine the Effective Stack Height and the Terrain-Adjusted Effective Stack Height (TAESH)

The effective stack height is an important factor in dispersion modeling. The effective stack height is the physical height of the stack plus plume rise. As specified in Step 4, the stack height used to estimate the effective stack height must not exceed GEP requirements. Plume rise is a function of the stack exit gas temperature and flow rate.

In this analysis, the effective stack height is used to select the generic source that represents the dispersion characteristics of the facility. For facilities located in flat terrain and for all facilities with worst-case stacks less than or equal to 10 meters in height, generic source numbers are selected strictly on the basis of effective stack height. In all other cases, the effective stack height is further adjusted to take into account the terrain rise near the facility. This "terrain-adjusted effective stack height" (TAESH) is then used to select the generic source number that represents the dispersion characteristics of the facility. Follow the steps below to identify the effective stack height, the TAESH (where applicable), and the corresponding generic source number.

(A) Go to Table 5.0-1 and find the plume rise value corresponding to the stack temperature and exit flow rate for the worst-case stack determined in Step 3.

Table 5.0-1—Estimated Plume Rise (in Meters) Based on Stack Exit Flow Rate and Gas Temperature

[Exhaust Temperature (° K)]

Flow rate (m^3/s)	< 325	325 – 349	350 – 399	400 – 449	450 – 499	500 – 599	600 – 699	700 – 799	800 – 999	1000 – 1499	> 1499
<0.5	0	0	0	0	0	0	0	0	0	0	0
0.5 – 0.9	0	0	0	0	0	0	0	0	1	1	1
1.0 – 1.9	0	0	0	0	1	1	2	3	3	3	4
2.0 – 2.9	0	0	1	3	4	4	6	6	7	8	9
3.0 – 3.9	0	1	2	5	6	7	9	10	11	12	13
4.0 – 4.9	1	2	4	6	8	10	12	13	14	15	17
5.0 – 7.4	2	3	5	8	10	12	14	16	17	19	21
7.5 – 9.9	3	5	8	12	15	17	20	22	22	23	24
10.0 – 12.4	4	6	10	15	19	21	23	24	25	26	27

Table 5.0-1—Estimated Plume Rise (in Meters) Based on Stack Exit Flow Rate and Gas Temperature

[Exhaust Temperature (° K)]

Flow rate (m^3/s)	< 325	325 – 349	350 – 399	400 – 449	450 – 499	500 – 599	600 – 699	700 – 799	800 – 999	1000 – 1499	> 1499
12.5 – 14.9	4	7	12	18	22	23	25	26	27	28	29
15.0 – 19.9	5	8	13	20	23	24	26	27	28	29	31
20.0 – 24.9	6	10	17	23	25	27	29	30	31	32	34
25.0 – 29.9	7	12	20	25	27	29	31	32	33	35	36
30.0 – 34.9	8	14	22	26	29	31	33	35	36	37	39
35.0 – 39.9	9	16	23	28	30	32	35	36	37	39	41
40.0 – 49.9	10	17	24	29	32	34	36	38	39	41	42
50.0 – 59.9	12	21	26	31	34	36	39	41	42	44	46
60.0 – 69.9	14	22	27	33	36	39	42	43	45	47	49
70.0 – 79.9	16	23	29	35	38	41	44	46	47	49	51
80.0 – 89.9	17	25	30	36	40	42	46	48	49	51	54
90.0 – 99.9	19	26	31	38	42	44	48	50	51	53	56
100.0 – 119.9	21	26	32	39	43	46	49	52	53	55	58
120.0 – 139.9	22	28	35	42	46	49	52	55	56	59	61
140.0 – 159.9	23	30	36	44	48	51	55	58	59	62	65
160.0 – 179.9	25	31	38	46	50	54	58	60	62	65	67
180.0 – 199.9	26	32	40	48	52	56	60	63	65	67	70
> 199.9	26	33	41	49	54	58	62	65	67	69	73

Plume rise = ________(m)

(B) Add the plume rise to the GEP stack height of the worst-case stack determined in Steps 3 and 4.

GEP stack height (m)	+	Plume rise (m)	=	Effective stack height (m)
________	+	________	=	________

(C) Go to the first column of Table 5.0-2 and identify the range of effective stack heights that includes the effective stack height estimated in Step 5(B). Record the generic source number that corresponds to this range.

Table 5.0-2—Selection of Generic Source Number

Effective stack height (m)	Generic source No.	Effective stack height (m)	Generic source No.
<10.0	1	42.0-52.9	7
10.0-14.9	2	53.0-64.9	8
15.0-19.9	3	65.0-112.9	9
20.0-24.9	4	113.0+	10
25.0-30.9	5	Downwash	11
31.0-41.9	6		

Generic source number = __________

(D) If the source is located in flat terrain[3], or if the generic source number identified in Step 5(C) above is 1 or 11 (regardless of terrain classification), use the generic source number determined in Step 5(C) and proceed directly to Step 6. Otherwise, continue to Step 5(E).

(E) For those situations where the conditions in Step 5(D) do not apply, the effective stack height must be adjusted for terrain. The TAESH for each distance range is computed by subtracting the terrain rise within the distance range from the effective stack height.[4]

Distance range (km)	Effective stack height (m) [see step 5(B)]	–	Maximum terrain rise (m) (see step 1)	=	TAESH (m)
0.0-0.5	________	–	________	=	________
>0.5-2.5	________	–	________	=	________
>2.5-5.0	________	–	________	=	________

If the terrain rise for any of the distance ranges is greater than the effective stack height, set the TAESH equal to zero and use generic source number 1 for that distance range.

Record the generic source numbers from Table 5.0-2 based on each of the TAESH values.

Distance range (km)	Generic source No. (after terrain adjustment)
0.0-0.5	____________
>0.5-2.5	____________
>2.5-5.0	____________

Step 6: Classify the Site as Urban or Rural

(A) Classify the land use near the facility as either urban or rural by determining the percentage of urban land use types (as defined in Table 3; for further guidance see the footnoted references) that fall within 3 km of the facility.[5]

3 The terrain is considered flat and terrain adjustment factors are not used if the maximum terrain rise within 5 km of the facility (see Step 1) is less than 10 percent of the physical stack height of the worst-case stack.

4 Refer to Step 1 for terrain adjustment data. Note that the distance from the source to the outer radii of each range is used. For example, for the range >0.5-2.5 km, the maximum terrain rise in the range 0.0-2.5 km is used.

5 The delineation of urban and rural areas can be difficult for the residential-type areas listed in Table 5.0-3. The degree of resolution in Table 5.0-3 for residential areas often cannot be identified without conducting site area inspections. This process can require extensive analysis, which, for many applications, can be greatly streamlined without sacrificing confidence in selecting the appropriate urban or rural classification. The fundamental simplifying assumption is based on the premise that many applications will have clear-cut urban/rural designations, i.e., most will be in rural settings that can be definitively characterized through a review of aerial photographs, zoning maps, or U.S. Geological Survey topographical maps.

Table 5.0-3—Classification of Land Use Types

Type[1]	Description	Urban or rural designation[2]
I1	Heavy Industrial	Urban
I2	Light/Moderate Industrial	Urban
CI	Commercial	Urban
R1	Common Residential (Normal Easements)	Rural
R2	Compact Residential (Single Family)	Urban
R3	Compact Residential (Multi-Family)	Rural
R4	Estate Residential (Multi- Acre Plots)	Rural
A1	Metropolitan Natural	Rural
A2	Agricultural	Rural
A3	Undeveloped (Grasses/Weeds)	Rural
A4	Undeveloped (Heavily Wooded)	Rural
A5	Water Surfaces	Rural

[1] EPA, Guideline on Air Quality Models (Revised), EPA-450/2-78-027R, Office of Air Quality Planning and Standards, Research Triangle Park, North Carolina, July, 1986.

[2] Auer, August H. Jr., "Correlation of Land Use and Cover with meteorological Anomalies," Journal of Applied Meteorology, pp. 636-643, 1978.

	Visual	Planimeter
Method Used to Estimate Percent Urban Land Use:	______	______

	Urban	Rural
Estimated Percentages	______	______

If the urban land use percentage is less than or equal to 30 percent based on a visual estimate, or 50 percent based on a planimeter, the local land use is considered rural. Otherwise, the local land use is considered urban.

	Urban	Rural
Classification (check applicable space)	______	______

(B) Based on the TAESH and the urban/rural classification of surrounding land use, use the following table to determine the threshold distance between any stack and the nearest facility boundary.

Terrain adjusted effective stack height range (m)	Distance (m)	
	Urban	Rural
1 – 9.9	200	200
10 – 14.9	200	250
15 – 19.9	200	250
20 – 24.9	200	350
25 – 30.9	200	450
31 – 41.9	200	550
42 – 52.9	250	800
53 – 64.9	300	1000
65 – 112.9	400	1200
113+	700	2500

Record the following information:

Threshold distance from the table (m): ____

Minimum distance from any stack to property boundary (m): ____

If the minimum distance between any stack and the nearest facility boundary is greater than the threshold distance, the surrounding buffer distance is considered significant and the facility is likely to benefit from use of the HWCAQSP relative to the Tier I and II limits (see discussion of benefits from using HWCAQSP in Introduction section).

Step 7: Determine Maximum Dispersion Coefficients

(A) Determine maximum average hourly dispersion coefficients. Based on the results of Step 6(A), select either Table 5.0-4 (urban) or Table 5.0-5 (rural) to determine the maximum average hourly dispersion coefficient.[6] For flat terrain [defined in Step 5(D)] and for all sites with generic source numbers 1 or 11, use Step 7(A)(1). For rolling or complex terrain (excluding generic sources numbers 1 and 11), use Step 7(A)(2).

(1) Search down the appropriate generic source number column [based on Step 5(C)], beginning at the minimum fenceline distance listed in Step 6(B).[7] Record the maximum average hourly dispersion coefficient encountered.

Maximum Average Hourly Dispersion Coefficient = ____(μg/m³/g/sec)

(2) For each of the three distance-based generic source numbers listed in Step 5(E), search down the appropriate generic source number columns, beginning at the minimum fenceline distance listed in Step 6(B). Note that different columns may be used for each of the three distance ranges if there is a need for terrain adjustment. Record the maximum dispersion coefficient for each generic source number.

Distance range (km)	Generic source No. [from Step 5(E)]	Maximum dispersion coefficient (μg/m³/m/sec)
0.0-0.5	________	________
>0.5-2.5	________	________
>2.5-5.0	________	________
>5.0-20.0	________	________

(B) Determine annual/hourly ratio for rural analysis. The maximum average annual dispersion coefficient is approximated by multiplying the maximum hourly dispersion coefficient (identified in Step 7(A)) by the appropriate ratio selection from Table 5.0-6. The generic source number(s) [from Steps 5(C) or 5(E)], urban/rural designation (from Step 6), and the terrain type are used to select the appropriate scaling factor. Use the noncomplex terrain designation for all sources located in flat terrain, for all sources where the physical stack height of the worst-case stack is less than or equal to 10 m, for all sources where the worst-case stack is less than the minimum GEP, and for those sources where all of the TAESH values in Step 5(E) are greater than zero. Use the complex terrain designation in all other situations.

6 For the distance range 6 to 20 kilometers, generic source number 1 is used to conservatively represent the maximum dispersion coefficient.

7 Exclude all distances that are closer to the facility than the property boundary. For example, if the actual distance to the nearest property boundary is 265 meters, begin at the 300 meter distance in Tables 5.0-4 and 5.0-5.

Table 5.0-4—ISCST Predicted Maximum Concentrations (µg/m³)[a] for Hazardous Waste Combustors Using Urban Conditions

Distance (KM)	Generic Source #1 (<10M)	Generic Source #2 (10M)	Generic Source #3 (15M)	Generic Source #4 (20M)	Generic Source #5 (25M)	Generic Source #6 (31M)	Generic Source #7 (42M)	Generic Source #8 (53M)	Generic Source #9 (65M)	Generic Source #10 (113M)	Generic Source #11 (Downwash)
0.20	680.1	517.5	368.7	268.7	168.5	129.8	63.4	30.1	18.4	1.6	662.3
0.25	521.9	418.2	303.7	232.6	163.0	124.2	67.6	38.5	19.8	3.2	500.0
0.30	407.7	351.7	256.2	199.0	147.0	118.3	63.5	41.5	25.0	4.2	389.3
0.35	326.2	304.2	221.6	172.7	130.2	107.9	60.0	40.5	27.3	5.4	311.9
0.40	268.5	268.5	195.6	152.5	115.7	97.1	59.6	37.8	27.4	5.8	268.5
0.45	240.8	240.7	175.4	136.7	103.9	87.6	56.6	37.2	26.3	5.8	240.8
0.50	218.5	218.5	159.2	124.1	94.4	79.7	52.9	36.7	24.7	5.8	218.5
0.55	200.3	200.3	145.9	113.8	86.5	73.1	49.2	35.4	24.5	6.6	200.3
0.60	185.1	185.1	134.9	105.1	80.0	67.6	45.8	33.8	24.3	7.1	185.1
0.65	172.2	172.2	125.5	97.8	74.4	62.9	42.7	32.0	23.7	7.4	172.2
0.70	161.2	161.2	117.4	91.6	69.6	58.9	40.1	30.2	22.9	7.5	161.2
0.75	151.6	151.6	110.5	86.1	65.5	55.4	37.7	28.6	22.0	7.5	151.6
0.80	143.2	143.2	104.4	81.4	61.9	52.3	35.6	27.1	21.1	7.4	143.2
0.85	135.8	135.8	99.0	77.2	58.7	49.6	33.8	25.7	20.2	7.2	135.8
0.90	129.2	129.2	94.2	73.4	55.8	47.2	32.1	24.5	19.3	7.0	129.2
0.95	123.3	123.3	89.9	70.1	53.3	45.0	30.7	23.4	18.5	6.8	123.3
1.00	118.0	118.0	86.0	67.0	51.0	43.1	29.4	22.4	17.7	6.5	118.0
1.10	108.8	108.0	79.3	61.8	47.0	39.7	27.1	20.6	16.4	6.5	108.8
1.20	101.1	101.1	73.7	57.4	43.7	36.9	25.2	19.2	15.2	6.4	101.1
1.30	94.6	94.6	68.9	53.7	40.9	34.5	23.5	18.0	14.2	6.3	94.6
1.40	89.0	89.0	64.8	50.6	38.5	32.5	22.1	16.9	13.4	6.1	89.0
1.50	84.1	84.1	61.3	47.8	36.3	30.7	20.9	16.0	12.7	5.9	84.1
1.60	79.8	79.8	58.2	45.4	34.5	29.2	19.9	15.2	12.0	5.6	79.8
1.70	76.0	76.0	55.4	43.2	32.9	27.8	18.9	14.4	11.4	5.4	76.0
1.80	72.7	72.7	53.0	41.3	31.4	26.5	18.1	13.8	10.9	5.2	72.7
1.90	69.6	69.6	50.7	39.6	30.1	25.4	17.3	13.2	10.5	5.0	69.6
2.00	66.9	66.9	48.8	38.0	28.9	24.4	16.7	12.7	10.1	4.8	66.9
2.25	61.1	61.1	44.5	34.7	26.4	22.3	15.2	11.6	9.2	4.4	61.1
2.50	56.4	56.4	41.1	32.1	24.4	20.6	14.0	10.7	8.5	4.1	56.4
2.75	52.6	52.6	38.3	29.9	22.7	19.2	10.0	10.0	7.9	3.8	52.6
3.00	49.3	49.3	35.9	28.0	21.3	18.0	9.4	9.4	7.4	3.6	49.3
4.00	40.2	40.2	29.3	22.8	17.4	14.7	7.6	7.6	6.1	2.9	40.2
5.00	34.5	34.5	25.2	19.6	14.9	12.6	6.6	6.6	5.2	2.5	34.5
6.00	30.7	30.7	30.7	30.7	30.7	30.7	30.7	30.7	30.7	30.7	30.7
7.00	27.8	27.8	27.8	37.8	27.8	27.8	27.8	27.8	27.8	27.8	27.8
8.00	25.5	25.5	25.5	25.5	25.5	25.5	25.5	25.5	25.5	25.5	25.5
9.00	23.8	23.8	23.8	23.8	23.8	23.8	23.8	23.8	23.8	23.8	23.8
10.00	22.3	22.3	22.3	22.3	22.3	22.3	22.3	22.3	22.3	22.3	22.3
15.00	17.6	17.6	17.6	17.6	17.6	17.6	17.6	17.6	17.6	17.6	17.6
20.00	15.0	15.0	15.0	15.0	15.0	15.0	15.0	15.0	15.0	15.01	15.0

[a]Based on a 1 Gram/Second Emission Rate

Table 5.0-5—ISCST Predicted Maximum Concentrations (μg/m^3)[a] for Hazardous Waste Combustors Using Rural Conditions

Distance (KM)	Generic Source #1 (M)	Generic Source #2 (10M)	Generic Source #3 (15M)	Generic Source #4 (20M)	Generic Source #5 (25M)	Generic Source #6 (31M)	Generic Source #7 (42M)	Generic Source #8 (53M)	Generic Source #9 (65M)	Generic Source #10 (113M)	Generic Source #11 (Downwash)
0.20	1771.1	670.3	308.6	176.8	102.8	76.5	28.0	10.1	3.5	0.0	1350.8
0.25	1310.6	678.4	316.9	183.6	104.6	71.8	38.0	17.6	7.9	0.2	1227.3
0.30	1002.3	629.2	303.4	199.1	100.4	75.0	39.7	24.0	12.6	0.8	1119.3
0.35	798.4	569.6	282.3	200.7	117.0	71.1	36.3	25.9	16.8	1.9	1023.8
0.40	656.9	516.5	278.7	194.4	125.2	82.7	25.3	24.6	18.1	3.1	938.9
0.45	621.5	471.1	277.6	184.3	127.5	89.7	35.6	21.7	17.6	4.3	851.8
0.50	633.5	432.4	272.0	172.7	125.7	92.9	34.4	21.6	15.9	5.5	787.8
0.55	630.1	399.2	263.8	168.0	121.6	93.3	38.6	22.1	13.6	6.5	730.6
0.60	616.6	370.4	254.0	169.1	116.2	91.8	42.6	21.7	14.3	6.7	676.4
0.65	596.7	345.4	243.6	168.1	110.3	89.2	45.3	20.9	14.7	6.4	633.4
0.70	573.2	323.4	232.9	165.6	104.5	85.8	47.0	23.3	14.6	5.9	592.0
0.75	546.9	304.0	222.3	162.0	98.8	82.2	47.7	25.5	14.3	5.5	554.6
0.80	520.9	286.8	212.1	157.7	98.8	78.5	47.8	27.1	13.8	5.1	522.1
0.85	495.7	271.5	202.4	153.0	99.0	74.9	47.4	28.3	15.0	4.7	491.8
0.90	471.5	257.8	193.3	148.1	98.6	71.4	46.6	29.1	16.3	4.5	464.2
0.95	448.5	245.4	184.7	143.1	97.6	72.3	45.6	29.6	17.3	4.2	438.9
1.00	426.8	234.2	176.8	138.1	96.3	72.6	44.4	29.8	18.2	4.0	415.8
1.10	387.5	214.7	162.5	128.2	91.9	71.1	41.8	29.5	19.3	3.9	375.0
1.20	353.5	198.4	150.3	119.3	87.4	69.1	39.1	28.6	19.8	4.1	340.3
1.30	323.0	189.6	139.9	111.5	82.9	66.7	36.6	27.5	19.8	4.2	310.4
1.40	296.6	182.2	130.8	104.5	78.7	64.2	34.3	26.2	19.5	4.2	284.6
1.50	273.3	174.6	122.9	98.3	74.7	61.6	32.3	24.9	19.0	4.2	262.0
1.60	252.7	167.0	115.9	92.8	71.0	59.1	31.8	23.6	18.4	4.2	242.2
1.70	234.5	159.6	109.7	87.9	67.6	56.7	31.6	22.5	17.7	4.3	224.7
1.80	218.3	152.4	104.1	83.5	64.4	54.3	31.3	21.4	17.0	4.5	211.9
1.90	203.7	145.6	99.1	79.5	61.5	52.1	30.9	20.4	16.3	4.8	198.4
2.00	190.7	139.1	94.6	75.9	58.8	50.0	30.4	19.5	15.7	5.1	186.3
2.25	164.4	124.5	85.1	68.3	53.0	45.4	28.9	18.1	14.2	5.4	160.8
2.50	143.7	112.1	77.3	62.1	48.2	41.4	27.2	17.9	12.9	5.5	140.7
2.75	127.0	101.5	70.9	56.9	38.1	38.1	25.6	17.5	11.8	5.4	124.5
3.00	113.4	92.4	65.6	52.6	35.2	35.2	24.0	17.0	11.2	5.2	112.5
4.00	78.8	67.3	50.6	40.6	27.2	27.2	29.0	14.3	10.4	4.3	78.3
5.00	59.1	54.6	41.4	33.2	22.2	22.2	15.6	12.0	9.3	3.5	58.8
6.00	56.7	46.7	46.7	46.7	46.7	46.7	46.7	46.7	46.7	46.7	46.7
7.00	40.4	40.4	40.4	40.4	40.4	40.4	40.4	40.4	40.4	40.4	40.4
8.00	35.8	35.8	35.8	35.8	35.8	35.8	35.8	35.8	35.8	35.8	35.8
9.00	32.2	32.2	32.2	32.2	32.2	32.2	32.2	32.2	32.2	32.2	32.2
10.00	29.4	29.4	29.4	29.4	29.4	29.4	29.4	29.4	29.4	29.4	29.4
15.00	20.5	20.5	20.5	20.5	20.5	20.5	20.5	20.5	20.5	20.5	20.5
20.00	15.9	15.9	15.9	15.9	15.9	15.9	15.9	15.9	15.9	15.9	15.9

[a]Based on a 1 Gram/Second Emission Rate

Table 5.0-6—95th Percentile of Annual/Hourly Ratios

Noncomplex Terrain			Complex Terrain		
Source	Urban	Rural	Source	Urban	Rural
1	0.019	0.014	1	0.020	0.053
2	0.033	0.019	2	0.020	0.053
3	0.031	0.018	3	0.030	0.057
4	0.029	0.017	4	0.051	0.047
5	0.028	0.017	5	0.067	0.039
6	0.028	0.017	6	0.059	0.034
7	0.031	0.015	7	0.036	0.031
8	0.030	0.013	8	0.026	0.024
9	0.029	0.011	9	0.026	0.024
10	0.029	0.008	10	0.017	0.013
11	0.018	0.015	11	0.020	0.053

(C) Determine maximum average annual dispersion coefficient. The maximum average annual dispersion coefficient is determined by multiplying the maximum hourly dispersion coefficient (Step 7(A)) by its corresponding annual/hourly ratio (Step 7(B)).

Terrain	Distance from stack (m)	Generic source No.	Maximum hourly dispersion coefficient ($\mu g/m^3$/g/sec)	Annual hourly ratio	Maximum annual dispersion coefficient ($\mu g/m^3$/g/sec)[1]
Flat	0-20.0				
	0-0.5				
	≤0.5-2.5				
Rolling or	≤2.5-5.0				
Complex	≤5.0-20.0				

[1]Maximum hourly dispersion coefficient times annual/hourly ratio.

Step 8: Estimate Maximum Ambient Air Concentrations—see procedures prescribed in subpart H of 40 CFR part 266.

Step 9: Determine Compliance with Regulatory Limits—see procedures prescribed in subpart H of 40 CFR part 266.

Step 10: Multiple Stack Method (Optional)

This option is a special case procedure that may be helpful when (1) the facility exceeded the regulatory limits for one or more pollutants, as detailed in Step 9, and (2) the facility has multiple stacks with substantially different emission rates and effective release heights. Only those pollutants that fail the Step 9 screening limits need to be addressed in this exercise.

This procedure assesses the environmental impacts from each stack and then sums the results to estimate total impacts. This option is conceptually the same as the basic approach (Steps 1 through 9) and does not involve complex calculations. However, it is more time-consuming and is recommended only if the basic approach fails to meet the risk criteria. The procedure is outlined below.

(A) Compute effective stack heights for each stack.[8]

Stack No.	GEP stack height (m)	Flow rate (m^3/sec)	Exit temp (° K)	Plume rise (m)	Effective stack height (m)
1	______	______	______	______	______
2	______	______	______	______	______
3	______	______	______	______	______

Add an additional page if more than three stacks are involved. Circle the maximum and minimum effective stack heights.

(B) Determine if this multiple-stack screening procedure will likely produce less conservative results than the procedure in Steps 1 through 9. To do this, compute the ratio of maximum-to-minimum effective stack height:

$$\frac{\text{Maximum Effective Stack Height}}{\text{Minimum Effective Stack Height}} = \_\_\_\_\_\_$$

If the above ratio is greater than 1.25, proceed with the remaining steps. Otherwise, this option is less likely to significantly reduce the degree of conservatism in the screening method.

(C) Determine if terrain adjustment is needed and select generic source numbers. Select the shortest stack height and maximum terrain rise out to 5 km from Step 1 and determine if the facility is in flat terrain.

Shortest stack height (m) = ______________

Maximum terrain rise in meters out to 5 km = ______________

$$\frac{\text{Terrain Rise (m)}}{\text{Shortest Stack Height (m)}} \times 100 = \_\_\_\_\_\_ \%$$

If the value above is greater than 10 percent, the terrain is considered nonflat; proceed to Step 10(D). If the ratio is less than or equal to 10 percent, the terrain is considered flat. Identify the generic source numbers based on effective stack heights computed in Step 10(A). Refer to Table 5.0-2 provided earlier to identify generic source numbers. Record the generic source numbers identified and proceed to Step 10(F).

	Stack No. 1	Stack No. 2	Stack No. 3
Generic Source Numbers	______	______	______

(D) Compute the TAESH and select generic source numbers (four sources located in nonflat terrain).

1. Compute the TAESH for all remaining stacks using the following equation:

$$HE - TR = TAESH$$

where:

HE = effective stack height (m)
TR = maximum terrain rise for each distance range (m)
TAESH = terrain-adjusted effective stack height (m)

Use the Table Below To Calculate the TAESH for Each Stack[9]

Stack No.	Distance Range (km)								
	0–0.5			>0.5–2.5			>2.5–5.0		
	HE	– TR	= TAESH	HE	– TR	= TAESH	HE	– TR	= TAESH
1	__	– __	= ____	__	– __	= ____	__	– __	= ____
2	__	– __	= ____	__	– __	= ____	__	– __	= ____
3	__	– __	= ____	__	– __	= ____	__	– __	= ____

8 Follow the procedure outlined in Step 4 of the basic screening procedure to determine the GEP for each stack. If a stack's physical height exceeds the maximum GEP, use the maximum GEP values. If a stack's physical height is less than the minimum GEP, use generic source number 11 in the subsequent steps of this analysis. Follow the procedure in Steps 5(A) and 5(B) to determine the effective height of each stack.

9 Refer to Step 1 for terrain adjustment data. Note that the distance from the source to the outer radii of each range is used. For example, for the range >0.5-2.5 km, the maximum terrain rise in the range 0.0-2.5 km is used.

For those stacks where the terrain rise within a distance range is greater than the effective stack height (*i.e.*, HE-TR is less than zero), the TAESH for that distance range is set equal to zero, and generic source number 1 should be used for that distance range for all subsequent distance ranges. Additionally, for all stacks with a physical stack height of less than or equal to 10 meters, use generic source number 1 for all distance ranges.[10] For the remaining stacks, proceed to Step 10(D)(2).

2. For the remaining stacks, refer to Table 5.0-2 and, for each distance range, identify the generic source number that includes the TAESH. Use the values obtained from Steps 10(D)(1) and 10(D)(2) to complete the following summary worksheet;

Generic Source Number After Terrain Adjusted
(if Needed)

Stack No.	0-0.5 km	>0.5-2.5 km	>2.5-5.0 km
1	______	______	______
2	______	______	______
3	______	______	______

(E) Identify maximum average hourly dispersion coefficients. Based on the land use classification of the site (*e.g.*, urban or rural), use either Table 5.0-4 or Table 5.0-5 to determine the appropriate dispersion coefficient for each distance range for each stack. Begin at the minimum fenceline distance indicated in Step 7(B) and record on Worksheet 5.0-1 the dispersion coefficient for each stack/distance range. For stacks located in facilities in flat terrain, the generic source numbers were computed in Step 10(C). For stacks located in facilities in rolling and complex terrain, the generic source numbers were computed in Step 10(D). For flat terrain applications and for stacks with a physical height of less than or equal to 10 meters, only one generic source number is used per stack for all distance ranges. For other situations up to three generic source numbers may be needed per stack (*i.e.*, a unique generic source number per distance range). In Tables 5.0-4 and 5.0-5, the dispersion coefficients for distances of 6 km to 20 km are the same for all generic source numbers in order to conservatively represent terrain beyond 5 km (past the limits of the terrain analysis).

(F) Estimate maximum hourly ambient air concentrations. In this step, pollutant-specific emission rates are multiplied by appropriate dispersion coefficients to estimate ambient air concentrations. For each stack, emissions are multiplied by the dispersion coefficient selected in Step 10(E) and summed across all stacks to estimate ambient air concentrations at various distances from the facility. From these summed concentrations, the maximum hourly ambient air concentration is selected. First, select the maximum emission rate of the pollutant.[11] Record these data in the spaces provided below.[12]

Maximum Annual Emission Rates (g/sec)

Pollutant	Stack 1	Stack 2	Stack 3
______	______	______	______
______	______	______	______

10 This applies to all stacks less than or equal to 10 meters regardless of the terrain classification.

11 Recall that it is recommended that this analysis be performed for only one or two pollutants. The pollutants chosen for this analysis should be those that show the most significant exceedances of the risk threshold.

12 Refer to Step 8 of the basic screening procedure. At this point in the screening procedure, annual emissions are used to represent hourly average emission rates. These values will be adjusted by the annual/hourly ratio to estimate annual average concentrations.

Worksheet 5.0-1 Dispersion Coefficient by Downwind Distance[1]

Distance	Stack 1	Stack 2	Stack 3
0.20			
0.25			
0.30			
0.35			
0.40			
0.45			
0.50			
0.55			
0.60			
0.65			
0.70			
0.75			
0.80			
0.85			
0.90			
0.95			
1.00			
1.10			
1.20			
1.30			
1.40			
1.50			
1.60			
1.70			
1.80			
1.90			
2.00			
2.25			
2.50			
2.75			
3.00			
4.00			
5.00			
6.00			
7.00			
8.00			
9.00			
10.00			
15.00			
20.00			

[1] *Note:* This procedure places all stacks at the same point, but allows for consideration of different effective stack heights. The distance to the closest boundary (extracted from Step 1) should be the closest distance to any stack.

Complete a separate copy of Worksheet 5.0-2 for each pollutant and select the highest hourly concentration from the summation column at the far right of the worksheet. Record the maximum hourly air concentration for each pollutant analyzed (add additional lines if needed):

Pollutant	Maximum hourly air concentration
______	______
______	______

Worksheet 5.0-2 Maximum Hourly Ambient Air Concentration

Pollutant____________________

Total Distance (km)	Stack 1 ER x DC = C	Stack 2 ER x DC = C	Stack 3 ER x DC = C	Summed Concentration from all Stacks
0.20	___ x ___ = ___	___ x ___ = ___	___ x ___ = ___	___
0.25	___ x ___ = ___	___ x ___ = ___	___ x ___ = ___	___
0.30	___ x ___ = ___	___ x ___ = ___	___ x ___ = ___	___
0.35	___ x ___ = ___	___ x ___ = ___	___ x ___ = ___	___
0.40	___ x ___ = ___	___ x ___ = ___	___ x ___ = ___	___
0.45	___ x ___ = ___	___ x ___ = ___	___ x ___ = ___	___
0.50	___ x ___ = ___	___ x ___ = ___	___ x ___ = ___	___
0.55	___ x ___ = ___	___ x ___ = ___	___ x ___ = ___	___
0.60	___ x ___ = ___	___ x ___ = ___	___ x ___ = ___	___
0.65	___ x ___ = ___	___ x ___ = ___	___ x ___ = ___	___
0.70	___ x ___ = ___	___ x ___ = ___	___ x ___ = ___	___
0.75	___ x ___ = ___	___ x ___ = ___	___ x ___ = ___	___
0.80	___ x ___ = ___	___ x ___ = ___	___ x ___ = ___	___
0.85	___ x ___ = ___	___ x ___ = ___	___ x ___ = ___	___
0.90	___ x ___ = ___	___ x ___ = ___	___ x ___ = ___	___
0.95	___ x ___ = ___	___ x ___ = ___	___ x ___ = ___	___
1.00	___ x ___ = ___	___ x ___ = ___	___ x ___ = ___	___
1.10	___ x ___ = ___	___ x ___ = ___	___ x ___ = ___	___
1.20	___ x ___ = ___	___ x ___ = ___	___ x ___ = ___	___
1.30	___ x ___ = ___	___ x ___ = ___	___ x ___ = ___	___
1.40	___ x ___ = ___	___ x ___ = ___	___ x ___ = ___	___
1.50	___ x ___ = ___	___ x ___ = ___	___ x ___ = ___	___
1.60	___ x ___ = ___	___ x ___ = ___	___ x ___ = ___	___
1.70	___ x ___ = ___	___ x ___ = ___	___ x ___ = ___	___
1.80	___ x ___ = ___	___ x ___ = ___	___ x ___ = ___	___
1.90	___ x ___ = ___	___ x ___ = ___	___ x ___ = ___	___
2.00	___ x ___ = ___	___ x ___ = ___	___ x ___ = ___	___
2.25	___ x ___ = ___	___ x ___ = ___	___ x ___ = ___	___
2.50	___ x ___ = ___	___ x ___ = ___	___ x ___ = ___	___
2.75	___ x ___ = ___	___ x ___ = ___	___ x ___ = ___	___
3.00	___ x ___ = ___	___ x ___ = ___	___ x ___ = ___	___
4.00	___ x ___ = ___	___ x ___ = ___	___ x ___ = ___	___
5.00	___ x ___ = ___	___ x ___ = ___	___ x ___ = ___	___
6.00	___ x ___ = ___	___ x ___ = ___	___ x ___ = ___	___
7.00	___ x ___ = ___	___ x ___ = ___	___ x ___ = ___	___
8.00	___ x ___ = ___	___ x ___ = ___	___ x ___ = ___	___
9.00	___ x ___ = ___	___ x ___ = ___	___ x ___ = ___	___
10.00	___ x ___ = ___	___ x ___ = ___	___ x ___ = ___	___
15.00	___ x ___ = ___	___ x ___ = ___	___ x ___ = ___	___
20.00	___ x ___ = ___	___ x ___ = ___	___ x ___ = ___	___

ER = Annual Average Emission Rate

DC = Hourly Dispersion Coefficient (from Worksheet 5.0-1)

C = Estimated Maximum Hourly Ambient Air Concentration

(G) Determine the complex/noncomplex designation for each stack. For each stack, subtract the maximum terrain rise within 5 km of the site from the physical stack height and designate the stack as either complex or noncomplex. If the stack height minus the maximum terrain rise (within 5 km) is greater than zero or if the stack is less than 10 meters in physical height, then assign the stack a noncomplex designation. If the stack height minus the maximum terrain rise (within 5 km) is less than or equal to zero, then assign the stack a complex designation.

Perform the following computation for each stack and record the information in the spaces provided. Check in the spaces provided whether the stack designation is complex or noncomplex.

Stack No.	Stack height (m)		Maximum terrain rise (m)		Complex	Noncomplex
1	______	–	______	=	(m) ______	______
2	______	–	______	=	(m) ______	______
3	______	–	______	=	(m) ______	______

(H) Identify annual/hourly ratios. Extract the annual/hourly ratios for each stack by referring to Table 5.0-6. Generic source numbers (from Steps 10(C) or 10(D), urban/rural designation (from Step 6)), and complex or noncomplex terrain designations (from Step 10(G)) are used to select the appropriate scaling factor needed to convert hourly maximum concentrations to estimates of annual average concentrations.

Complete the following table:[13]

Stack No.	Generic source No. steps 10 (C or D) [Distance ranges (km)]			Annual/hourly ratio (from table 5.0-6) [Distance ranges (km)]		
	0-0.5	>0.5-2.5	>2.5-5.0	0-0.5	>0.5-2.5	>2.5-5.0
1	______	______	______	______	______	______
2	______	______	______	______	______	______
3	______	______	______	______	______	______

(I) Select the highest annual/hourly ratio among all of the stacks,[14] and then estimate the maximum annual average ambient air concentrations for each pollutant by completing the following table,

Pollutant	C_a (μg/m³)	x	R	=	C_a(μg/m³)
______	______	x	______	=	______
______	______	x	______	=	______

where:

C = Maximum total hourly ambient air concentration (μg/m³) for pollutant "N" from Step 10(F),

C_a = Maximum annual average air concentration for pollutant "N" (μg/m³),

R = Annual/hourly ratio.

(J) Use the maximum annual average concentrations from Step 10(I) to determine compliance with regulatory requirements.

13 If any stack (excluding generic stack number 1 and 11) in Step 10(D) shows a negative terrain adjusted stack height, use the complex terrain annual/hourly ratios.

14 As an option, the user can identify the stack with the highest ratio for each distance range (rather than the absolute highest). In this case, extra sheets would be needed to show estimated annual average concentrations from each stack by multiplying emission rate times maximum hourly dispersion coefficient times maximum annual/hourly ratio for applicable distance range. Then sum across all stacks for each downwind distance.

Section 6.0—Simplified Land Use Classification Procedure for Compliance With Tier I and Tier II Limits

6.1 *Introduction*

This section provides a simplified procedure to classify areas in the vicinity of boilers and industrial furnace sites as urban or rural in order to set risk-based emission limits under subpart H of 40 CFR part 266. Urban/rural classification is needed because dispersion rates differ between urban and rural areas and thus, the risk per unit emission rate differs accordingly. The combination of greater surface roughness (more buildings/structures to generate turbulent mixing) and the greater amount of heat released from the surface in an urban area (generates buoyancy-induced mixing) produces greater rates of dispersion. The emission limit tables in the regulation, therefore, distinguish between urban and rural areas.

EPA guidance (EPA 1986)[1] [*Publisher's Note:* The preceding footnote reference refers to footnote number 1 of Table 6.0-1.] provides two alternative procedures to determine whether the character of an area is predominantly urban or rural. One procedure is based on land use typing and the other is based on population density. Both procedures require consideration of characteristics within a 3-km radius from a source, in this case the facility stack(s). The land use typing method is preferred because it more directly relates to the surface characteristics that affect dispersion rates. The remainder of this discussion is, therefore, focused on the land use method.

While the land use method is more direct, it can also be labor-intensive to apply. For this discussion, the land use method has been simplified so that it is consistent with EPA guidance (EPA 1986; Auer 1978), while streamlining the process for the majority of applications so that a clear-cut decision can be made without the need for detailed analysis. Table 6.0-1 summarizes the simplified approach for classifying areas as urban or rural. As shown, the applicant always has the option of applying standard (*i.e.*, more detailed) analyses to more accurately distinguish between urban and rural areas. However, the procedure presented here allows for simplified determinations, where appropriate, to expedite the permitting process.

Table 6.0-1—Classification of Land Use Types

Type[1]	Description	Urban or rural designation[2]
I1	Heavy Industrial	Urban
I2	Light/Moderate Industrial	Urban
C1	Commercial	Urban
R1	Common Residential (Normal Easements)	Rural
R2	Compact Residential (Single Family)	Urban
R3	Compact Residential (Multi-Family)	Urban
R4	Estate Residential (Multi-Acre Plots)	Rural
A1	Metropolitan Natural	Rural
A2	Agricultural	Rural
A3	Undeveloped (Grasses/Weeds)	Rural
A4	Undeveloped (Heavily Wooded)	Rural
A5	Water Surfaces	Rural

[1]EPA, Guideline on Air Quality Models (Revised), EPA-450/2-78-027R, Office of Air Quality Planning and Standards, Research Triangle Park, North Carolina, July, 1986.

[2]Auer, August H. Jr., "Correlation of Land Use and Cover with Meteorological Anomalies," Journal of Applied Meteorology, pp. 636-643, 1978.

6.2 *Simplified Land Use Process*

The land use approach considers four primary land use types: industrial (I), commercial (C), residential (R), and agricultural (A). Within these primary classes, subclasses are identified, as shown in table 6.0-1. The goal is to estimate the percentage of the area within a 3-km radius that is urban type and the percentage that is rural type. Industrial and commercial areas are classified as urban; agricultural areas are classified as rural.

The delineation of urban and rural areas, however, can be more difficult for the residential type areas shown in table 6.0-1. The degree of resolution shown in table 6.0-1 for residential areas often cannot be identified without conducting site area inspections and/or referring to zoning maps. This process can require extensive analysis, which, for many applications, can be greatly streamlined without sacrificing confidence in selecting the appropriate urban or rural classification.

The fundamental simplifying assumption is based on the premise that many applications will have clear-cut urban/rural designations, *i.e.*, most will be in rural settings that can be definitively characterized through a brief review of topographical maps. The color coding on USGS topographical maps provides the most effective means of simplifying the typing scheme. The suggested typing designations for the color codes found on topographical maps are as follows:

Green Wooded areas (rural).

White White areas generally will be treated as rural. This code applies to areas that are unwooded and do not have densely packed structures which would require the pink code (house omission tint). Parks, industrial areas, and unforested rural land will appear as white on the topographical maps. Of these categories, only the industrial areas could potentially be classified as urban based on EPA 1986 or Auer 1978. Industrial areas can be easily identified in most cases by the characteristics shown in Figure 6.0-1. For this simplified procedure, white areas that have an industrial classification will be treated as urban areas.

Section 7.0—Statistical Methodology for Bevill Residue Determinations

This section describes the statistical comparison of waste-derived residue to normal residue for use in determining eligibility for the Bevill exemption under 40 CFR 266.112.

7.1 *Comparison of Waste-Derived Residue to Normal Residue*

To be eligible for the Bevill exclusion from the definition of hazardous waste under 40 CFR 266.112(b)(1), waste-derived residue must not contain Appendix VIII, Part 261, constituents that could reasonably be attributable to the hazardous waste (toxic constituents) at concentrations significantly higher than in residue generated without burning or processing hazardous waste (normal residue). Concentrations of toxic constituents in normal residue are determined based on analysis of a minimum of 10 samples representing a minimum of 10 days of operation. The statistically-derived concentrations in normal residue are determined as the upper tolerance limit (95% confidence with a 95% proportion of the sample distribution) of the normal residue concentrations. The upper tolerance limit is to be determined as described in Section 7.2 below. If changes in raw materials or fuels could lower the statistically-derived concentrations of toxic constituents of concern, the statistically-derived baseline must be re-established for any such mode of operation with the new raw material or fuel.

Concentrations of toxic constituents in waste-derived residue are determined based on the analysis of one or more samples collected over a compositing period of not more than 24 hours. Multiple samples of the waste-derived residue may be analyzed or subsamples may be composited for analysis, provided that the sampling period does not exceed 24 hours. If more than one sample is analyzed to characterize the waste-derived residue generated over a 24-hour period, the arithmetic mean of the concentrations must be used as the waste-derived concentration for each constituent.

The concentration of a toxic constituent in the waste-derived residue is not considered to be significantly higher than in the normal residue (*i.e.*, the residue passes the Bevill test for that constituent) if the concentration in the waste-derived residue does not exceed the statistically-derived concentration.

7.2 *Calculation of the Upper Tolerance Limit*

The 95% confidence with 95% proportion of the sample distribution (upper tolerance limit) is calculated for a set of values assuming that the values are normally distributed. The upper tolerance limit is a one-sided calculation and is an appropriate statistical test for cases in which a single value (the waste-derived residue concentration) is compared to the distribution of a range of values (the minimum of 10 measurements of normal residue concentrations). The upper tolerance limit value is determined as follows:

$$UTL = X + (K)(S)$$

where

X = mean of the normal residue concentrations, $X = X_i/n$,

K = coefficient for sample size n, 95% confidence and 95% proportion,

S = standard deviation of the normal residue concentrations, $S = (\Sigma(X_i - X)^2/(n - 1))^{0.5}$, and

n = sample size.

The values of K at the 95% confidence and 95% proportion, and sample size n are given in Table 7.0-1.

Table 7.0-1—K Values for 95% Confidence and 95% Proportion

Sample size (n)	K	Sample size (n)	K
10	2.911	18	2.458
11	2.815	19	2.423
12	2.736	20	2.396
13	2.670	21	2.371
14	2.614	22	2.350
15	2.566	23	2.329
16	2.523	24	2.303
17	2.486	25	2.292

For example, a normal residue test results in 10 samples with the following analytical results for toxic constituent A:

Sample No.	Concentration of constituent A (ppm)	Sample No.	Concentration of constituent A (ppm)
1	10	6	12
2	10	7	10
3	15	8	16
4	10	9	15
5	7	10	10

The mean and the standard deviation of these measurements, calculated using the above equations, are 11.5 and 2.9, respectively. Assuming that the values are normally distributed, the upper tolerance limit (UTL) is given by:

$$UTL = 11.5 + (2.911)(2.9) = 19.9 \text{ ppm}$$

Thus, if the concentration of constituent A in the waste-derived residue is below 19.9 ppm, then the waste-derived residue is eligible for the Bevill exclusion for constituent A.

Figure 6.0-1
Supplementary Publication Symbols

117 **Single track**
Line weight .005". Tie weight .003", length .04", spaced .20" center to center.

118 **Single track abandoned**
Same as existing track with space .02", dash .18". Label.

119 **Single track under construction**
Same as existing track with space .02", dash .38". Label UNDER CONSTRUCTION.

120 **Multiple main line track**
Overall width .017". Line weight .003". Tie length .052", spaced .20" center to center. If more than two tracks label, with double cross tie at point of change. Double cross tie .017" overall width.

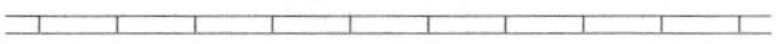

121 **Multiple track abandoned**
Same as existing track with space .02", dash .18". Label ABANDONED.

122 **Multiple track under construction**
Same as existing track with space .02", dash .38". Label UNDER CONSTRUCTION.

123 **Juxtaposition**
Alternate ties, spaced .20" center to center. Minimum space between tracks .011". Line weight for single tracks .005", multiple tracks .003".

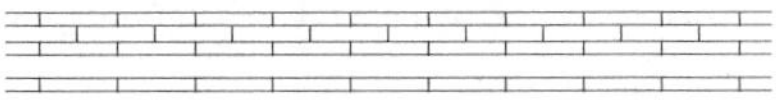

124 **Railroad in street**
Ties spaced .20" center to center. Label if narrow gauge. Tie weight .003".

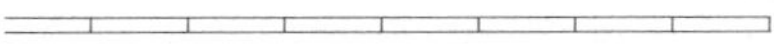

125 **Yards**
Line weight .003". Space between tracks .011". Ties spaced .20" center to center, maximum length to touch 6 tracks.

126 **Sidings**
Line weight .003". Scribe to scale with minimum space between tracks .011". Ties spaced .20" center to center, length .04" for single track.

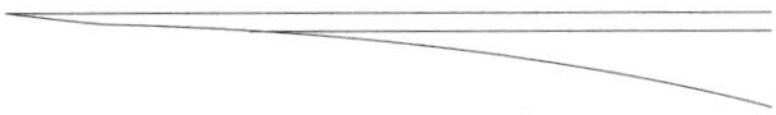

176 **Large buildings**
Outline weight .003". When width exceeds .06", hatch at 45° angle to building in NE direction, lines .002", spaced .02" center to center.

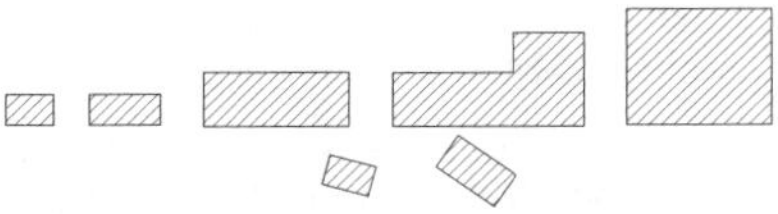

178 **Sewage disposal or filtration plant**
Line weight .003". See symbol 700 for blue hatching. Label.

196 **Tanks: oil, gas, water, etc.**
Circle .03" minimum, 10" maximum. Label as to content.

197 **Tanks: oil, gas, water, etc.**
Exceeding 10" in diameter. Outline weight .003". Hatch SW-NE with .002" lines spaced .02" center to center. Label as to content.

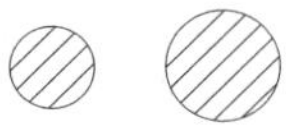

PART 266—Appendices

7.3 *Normal Distribution Assumption*

As noted in Section 7.2 above, this statistical approach (use of the upper tolerance limit) for calculation of the concentration in normal residue is based on the assumption that the concentration data are distributed normally. The Agency is aware that concentration data of this type may not always be distributed normally, particularly when concentrations are near the detection limits. There are a number of procedures that can be used to test the distribution of a data set. For example, the Shapiro-Wilk test, examination of a histogram or plot of the data on normal probability paper, and examination of the coefficient of skewness are methods that may be applicable, depending on the nature of the data (References 1 and 2).

If the concentration data are not adequately represented by a normal distribution, the data may be transformed to attain a near normal distribution. The Agency has found that concentration data, especially when near detection levels, often exhibit a lognormal distribution. The assumption of a lognormal distribution has been used in various programs at EPA, such as in the Office of Resource Conservation and Recovery Land Disposal Restrictions program for determination of BDAT treatment standards. The transformed data may be tested for normality using the procedures identified above. If the transformed data are better represented by a normal distribution than the untransformed data, the transformed data should be used in determining the upper tolerance limit using the procedures in Section 7.2 above.

In all cases where the owner or operator wishes to use other than an assumption of normally distributed data or believes that use of an alternate statistical approach is appropriate to the specific data set, he/she must provide supporting rationale in the operating record that demonstrates that the data treatment is based upon sound statistical practice.

7.4 *Nondetect Values*

The Agency is developing guidance regarding the treatment of nondetect values (data where the concentration of the constituent being measured is below the lowest concentration for which the analytical method is valid) in carrying out the statistical determination described above. Until the guidance information is available, facilities may present their own approach to the handling of nondetect data points, but must provide supporting rationale in the operating record for consideration by the Director.

7.5 *References*

1. Shapiro, S.S. and Wilk, M.B. (1965), "An Analysis of Variance Test for Normality (complete samples)," Biometrika, 52,591-611.
2. Bhattacharyya, G.K. and R.A. Johnson (1977), Statistical Concepts and Methods, John Wiley and Sons, New York.

Section 8.0—Procedures for Determining Default Values for Air Pollution Control System Removal Efficiencies

During interim status, owners or operators of boilers and industrial furnaces burning hazardous waste must submit documentation to EPA that certifies that emissions of HCl, $C1_2$, metals, and particulate matter (PM) are not likely to exceed allowable emission rates. See certification of precompliance under 40 CFR 266.103(b). This documentation also establishes interim status feed rate and operating limits for the facility. For the initial certification, estimates of emissions and system removal efficiencies (SREs) can be made to establish the operating limits. Subsequently, owners or operators must use emissions testing to demonstrate that emissions do not exceed allowable levels, and to establish operating limits. See 40 CFR 266.103(c). However, initial estimates of emissions for certification of precompliance can be based on estimated or established SREs.

The SRE combines the effect of partitioning of the chlorine, metals, or PM and the air pollution control system removal efficiency (APCS RE) for these pollutants. The SRE is defined as:

$$\text{SRE} = (\text{species input} - \text{species emitted}) / \text{species input}$$

The SRE can be calculated from the partitioning factor (PF) and APCS RE by the following formula:

$$\text{SRE} = 1 - \left[(\text{PF} / 100) \times (1 - \text{APCS RE} / 100)\right]$$

where:

PF = percentage of the pollutant partitioned to the combustion gas

Estimates of the PF and/or the APCS RE can be based on either EPA's default values or engineering judgement. EPA's default values for the APCS RE for metals, HCl, Cl_2, and PM are described in this section. EPA's default values for partitioning of these pollutants are described in section 9.0.

Guidelines for the use of engineering judgement to estimate APCS REs or PFs are described in section 9.4.

8.1 *APCS RE Default Values for Metals*

EPA's default assumptions for APCS RE for metals are shown in Table 8.1-1. The default values in the table are conservative estimates of the removal efficiencies for metals in BIFs, depending on the volatility of the metal and the type of APCS.

Table 8.1-1—Air Pollution Control Systems (APCS) and Their Conservatively Estimated Efficiencies for Controlling Toxic Metals (%)

APCS	Metal Volatility		
	Nonvolatile	Volatile	Very Volatile
WS	40	30	20
VS-20	80	75	20
VS-60	87	75	40
ESP-1	90	75	0
ESP-2	92	80	0
ESP-4	95	80	0
WESP	90	85	40
FF	90	80	0
SD/FF	97	90	0
DS/FF	95	90	0
IWS	90	87	75

WS = Wet Scrubber including: Sieve Tray Tower, Packed Tower, Bubble Cap Tower
VS-20 = Venturi Scrubber, ca. 20-30 in W.G. Δ p
VS-60 = Venturi Scrubber, ca. >60 in W.G. Δ p
ESP-1 = Electrostatic Precipitator; 1 stage
ESP-2 = Electrostatic Precipitator; 2 stage
ESP-4 = Electrostatic Precipitator; 4 stage
IWS = Ionizing Wet Scrubber
DS = Dry Scrubber
FF = Fabric Filter (Baghouse)
SD = Spray Dryer (Wet/Dry Scrubber)
WESP = Wet Electrostatic Precipitator

The volatility of a metal depends on the temperature, the thermal input, the chlorine content of the waste, and the identity and concentration of the metal. Metals that do not vaporize at combustion zone temperatures are classified as "nonvolatile". Such metals typically enter the APCS in the form of large particles that are removed relatively easily. Metals that vaporize in the combustion zone and condense before entering the APCS are classified as "volatile". Such metals typically enter the APCS in the form of very fine, submicron particles that are rather inefficiently removed in many APCSs. Metals that vaporize in the combustion zone and do not condense before entering the APCS are classified as "very volatile". Such metals enter the APCS in the form of a vapor that is very inefficiently removed in many APCSs.

Typically, BIFs have combustion zone temperatures high enough to vaporize any hazardous metal at concentrations sufficient to exceed risk-based emission limits. For this reason, the default assumption is that there are no nonvolatile metals. Tables 8.1-2 and 8.1-3 are used to determine whether metals are classified as "volatile" or "very volatile" depending on the temperature entering the APCS, the thermal input, and whether the waste is chlorinated or nonchlorinated.

Table 8.1-2—Temperature (F) Entering APCS Above Which Metals Are Classified as Very Volatile in Combustion of Nonchlorinated Wastes

Metal		Thermal Input (MMBtu/hr)[1]				
Name	**Symbol**	**1**	**10**	**100**	**1000**	**10000**
Arsenic	As	320	280	240	200	160
Cadmium	Cd	1040	940	860	780	720
Chromium	Cr	2000	1760	1580	1420	1380
Beryllium	Be	1680	1440	1240	1080	980
Antimony	Sb	680	600	540	480	420
Barium	Ba	2240	1820	1540	1360	1240
Lead	Pb	1280	1180	1080	1000	920
Mercury	Hg	340	300	260	220	180
Silver	Ag	1820	1640	1480	1340	1220
Thallium	Tl	900	800	700	620	540

[1]Interpolation of thermal input is not allowed. If a BIF fires between two ranges, the APCS temperature under the higher thermal input must be used.

Example: For a BIF firing 10-100 MMBtu/hr, Mercury is considered very volatile at APCS temperatures above 260 F and volatile at APCS temperatures of 260 F and below.

Table 8.1-3—Temperature (F) Entering APCS Above Which Metals Are Classified as Very Volatile In Combustion of Chlorinated Wastes

Metal		Thermal Input (MMBtu/hr)[1]				
Name	**Symbol**	**1**	**10**	**100**	**1000**	**10000**
Arsenic	As	320	280	240	200	160
Cadmium	Cd	1040	940	860	780	720
Chromium	Cr	>140	>140	>140	>140	>140
Beryllium	Be	1680	1440	1240	1080	980
Antimony	Sb	680	600	540	480	420
Barium	Ba	2060	1840	1680	1540	1420
Lead	Pb	>140	>140	>140	>140	>140
Mercury	Hg	340	300	260	220	180
Silver	Ag	1080	940	840	740	660
Thallium	Tl	900	800	700	620	540

[1]Interpolation of thermal input is not allowed. If a BIF fires between two ranges, the APCS temperature under the higher thermal input must be used.

Example: For a BIF firing 10-100 MMBtu/hr, Mercury is considered very volatile at APCS temperatures above 260 F and volatile at APCS temperatures of 260 F and below.

A waste is considered chlorinated if chlorine is present in concentrations greater than 0.1 percent by weight. In the EPA guidance document "Guidance for Metals and Hydrogen Chloride Controls for Hazardous Waste Incinerators, Volume IV of the Hazardous Waste Incineration Guidance Series,"(1) one percent is used for the chlorinated/nonchlorinated cutoff. However, best engineering judgement, based on examination of pilot-scale data reported by Carroll et al. (2) on the effects of waste chlorine content on metals emissions, suggests that the 1 percent cutoff may not be sufficiently conservative.

Tables 8.1-2 and 8.1-3 were compiled based on equilibrium calculations. Metals are classified as very volatile at all temperatures above the temperature at which the vapor pressure of the metal is greater than 10 percent of the vapor pressure that results in emissions exceeding the most conservative risk-based emissions limits.

8.2 *APCS RE Default Values for HCl and Cl_2*

Default assumptions for APCS RE for HCl in BIFs are shown in Table 8.2-1. This table is identical to the column for other BIFs except that cement kilns have a minimum HCl removal efficiency of 83 percent. Because of the alkaline nature of the raw materials in cement kilns, most of the chlorine is converted to chloride salts. Thus, the minimum APCS RE for HCl for cement kilns is independent of the APCS train.

Removal efficiency of Cl_2 for most types of APCS is generally minimal. Therefore, the default assumption for APCS RE for Cl_2 for all APCSs is 0 percent. This is applicable to all BIFs, including cement kilns.

Table 8.2-1—Air Pollution Control Systems (APCS) and Their Conservatively Estimated Efficiencies for Removing Hydrogen Chloride (HCl) and Particulate Matter (PM) (%)

APCD	HCl		
	Cement kilns	**Other BIFs**	**PM**
WS	97	97	40
VS-20	97	97	80
VS-60	98	98	87
ESP-1	83	0	90
ESP-2	83	0	92
ESP-4	83	0	95
WESP	83	70	90
FF	83	0	90
SD/FF	98	98	97
DS/FF	98	98	95
WS/IWS	99	99	95
IWS	99	99	90

WS = Wet Scrubber including: Sieve Tray Tower, Packed Tower, Bubble Cap Tower

PS = Proprietary Wet Scrubber Design (A number of proprietary wet scrubbers have come on the market in recent years that are highly efficient on both particulates and corrosive gases. Two such units are offered by Calvert Environmental Equipment Co. and by Hydro-Sonic Systems, Inc.).

VS-20 = Venturi Scrubber, ca. 20-30 in W.G. Δ p

VS-60 = Venturi Scrubber, ca. >60 in W.G. Δ p

ESP-1 = Electrostatic Precipitator; 1 stage

ESP-2 = Electrostatic Precipitator; 2 stage

ESP-4 = Electrostatic Precipitator; 4 stage

IWS = Ionizing Wet Scrubber

DS = Dry Scrubber

FF = Fabric Filter (Baghouse)

SD = Spray Dryer (Wet/Dry Scrubber)

PART 266—Appendices

8.3 *APCS RE Default Values for Ash*

Default assumptions for APCS RE for PM are also shown in Table 8.1-4. These figures are conservative estimates of PM removal efficiencies for different types of APCSs. They are identical to the figures in the Nonvolatile APCS RE column for hazardous metals presented in Table 8.1-1 because the same collection mechanisms and collection efficiencies that apply to nonvolatile metals also apply to PM.

[*Publisher's Note:* Even though the *Code of Federal Regulations* refers to Table 8.1-4 above, the correct reference is to Table 8.2-1.]

8.4 *References*

1. U.S. Environmental Protection Agency. "Guidance on Metals and Hydrogen Chloride Controls for Hazardous Waste Incinerators," Office of Solid Waste, Washington, DC, August 1989.
2. Carroll, G.J., R.C. Thurnau, R.E. Maurnighan, L.R. Waterland, J.W. Lee, and D.J. Fournier. The Partitioning of Metals in Rotary Kiln Incineration. Proceedings of the Third International Conference on New Frontiers for Hazardous Waste Management. NTIS Document No. EPA/600/9-89/072, p. 555 (1989).

Section 9.0—Procedures for Determining Default Values for Partitioning of Metals, Ash, and Total Chloride/Chlorine

Pollutant partitioning factor estimates can come from two sources: default assumptions or engineering judgement. EPA's default assumptions are discussed below for metals, HCl, Cl_2, and PM. The default assumptions are used to conservatively predict the partitioning factor for several types of BIFs. Engineering judgement-based partitioning factor estimates are discussed in section 9.4.

9.1 *Partitioning Default Value for Metals*

To be conservative, the Agency is assuming that 100 percent of each metal in each feed stream is partitioned to the combustion gas. Owners/operators may use this default value or a supportable, site-specific value developed following the general guidelines provided in section 9.4.

9.2 *Special Procedures for Chlorine, HCl, and Cl_2*

The Agency has established the special procedures presented below for chlorine because the emission limits are based on the pollutants HCl and Cl_2 formed from chlorine fed to the combustor. Therefore, the owner/operator must estimate the controlled emission rate of both HCl and Cl_2 and show that they do not exceed allowable levels.

1. The default partitioning value for the fraction of chlorine in the total feed streams that is partitioned to combustion gas is 100 percent. Owners/operators may use this default value or a supportable, site-specific value developed following the general guidelines provided in section 9.4.
2. To determine the partitioning of chlorine in the combustion gas to HCl versus Cl_2, either use the default values below or use supportable site-specific values developed following the general guidelines provided in section 9.4.
   - For BIFs excluding halogen acid furnaces (HAFs), with a total feed stream chlorine/hydrogen ratio ≤ 0.95, the default partitioning factor is 20 percent Cl_2, 80 percent HCl.
   - For HAFs and for BIFs with a total feed stream chlorine/hydrogen ratio >0.95, the default partitioning factor is 100 percent Cl_2.
3. To determine the uncontrolled (*i.e.*, prior to acid gas APCS) emission rate of HCl and Cl_2, multiply the feed rate of chlorine times the partitioning factor for each pollutant. Then, for HCl, convert the chlorine emission rate to HCl by multiplying it by the ratio of the molecular weight of HCl to the molecular weight of Cl (*i.e.*, 36.5/35.5). No conversion is needed for Cl_2.

9.3 *Special Procedures for Ash*

This section: (1) Explains why ash feed rate limits are not applicable to cement and light-weight aggregate kilns; (2) presents the default partitioning values for ash; and (3) explains how to convert the 0.08 gr/dscf, corrected to 7% O_2, PM emission limit to a PM emission rate.

Waiver for Cement and Light-Weight Aggregate Kilns. For cement kilns and light-weight aggregate kilns, raw material feed streams contain the vast majority of the ash input, and a significant amount of the ash in the feed stream is entrained into the kiln exhaust gas. For these devices, the ash content of the hazardous waste stream is expected to have a negligible effect on total ash emissions. For this reason, there is no ash feed rate compliance limit for cement kilns or light-weight aggregate kilns. Nonetheless, cement kilns and light-weight aggregate kilns are required to initially certify that PM emissions are not likely to exceed the PM limit, and subsequently, certify through compliance testing that the PM limit is not exceeded.

Default Partitioning Value for Ash. The default assumption for partitioning of ash depends on the feed stream firing system. There are two methods by which materials may be fired into BIFs: Suspension-firing and bed-firing.

The suspension category includes atomized and lanced pumpable liquids and suspension-fired pulverized solids. The default partitioning assumption for materials fired by these systems is that 100 percent of the ash partitions to the combustion gas.

The bed-fired category consists principally of stoker boilers and raw materials (and in some cases containerized hazardous waste) fed into cement and light-weight aggregate kilns. The default partitioning assumption for materials fired on a bed is that 5 percent of the ash partitions to the combustion gas.

Converting the PM Concentration-Based Standard to a PM Mass Emission Rate. The emission limit for BIFs is 0.08 gr/dscf, corrected to 7% 0_2, unless a more stringent standard applies [*e.g.*, a New Source Performance Standard (NSPS) or a State standard implemented under the State Implementation Plan (SIP)]. To convert the 0.08 gr/dscf standard to a PM mass emission rate:

1. Determine the flue gas 0_2 concentration (percent by volume, dry) and flue gas flow rate (dry standard cubic feet per minute); and
2. Calculate the allowable PM mass emission rate by multiplying the concentration- based PM emission standard times the flue gas flow rate times a dilution correction factor equal to [(21-0_2 concentration from step 1)/(21-7)].

9.4 *Use of Engineering Judgement To Estimate Partitioning and APCS RE Values*

Engineering judgement may be used in place of EPA's conservative default assumptions to estimate partitioning and APCS RE values provided that the engineering judgement is defensible and properly documented. To properly document engineering judgement, the owner/operator must keep a written record of all assumptions and calculations necessary to justify the APCS RE used. The owner/operator must provide this record to the Director upon request and must be prepared to defend the assumptions and calculations used.

If the engineering judgement is based on emissions testing, the testing will often document the emission rate of a pollutant relative to the feed rate of that pollutant rather than the partitioning factor or APCS RE.

Examples of situations where the use of engineering judgement may be supportable to estimate a partitioning factor, APCS RE, or SRE include:

- Using emissions testing data from the facility to support an SRE, even though the testing may not meet full QA/QC procedures (*e.g.*, triplicate test runs). The closer the test results conform with full QA/QC procedures and the closer the operating conditions during the test conform with the established operating conditions for the facility, the more supportable the engineering judgement will be.
- Applying emissions testing data documenting an SRE for one metal, including nonhazardous surrogate metals to another less volatile metal.
- Applying emissions testing data documenting an SRE from one facility to a similar facility.
- Using APCS vendor guarantees of removal efficiency.

9.5 *Restrictions on Use of Test Data*

The measurement of an SRE or an APCS RE may be limited by the detection limits of the measurement technique. If the emission of a pollutant is undetectable, then the calculation of SRE or APCS RE should be based on the lower limit of detectability. An SRE or APCS RE of 100 percent is not acceptable.

Further, mass balance data of facility inputs, emissions, and products/residues may not be used to support a partitioning factor, given the inherent uncertainties of such procedures. Partitioning factors other than the default values may be supported based on engineering judgement, considering, for example, process chemistry. Emissions test data may be used to support an engineering judgement-based SRE, which includes both partitioning and APCS RE.

9.5 *References*

1. Barton, R.G., W.D. Clark, and W.R. Seeker. (1990) "Fate of Metals in Waste Combustion Systems". Combustion Science and Technology. 74, 1-6, p. 327

Section 10.0—Alternative Methodology for Implementing Metals Controls

10.1 *Applicability*

This method for controlling metals emissions applies to cement kilns and other industrial furnaces operating under interim status that recycle emission control residue back into the furnace.

10.2 *Introduction*

Under this method, cement kilns and other industrial furnaces that recycle emission control residue back into the furnace must comply with a kiln dust concentration limit (*i.e.*, a collected particulate matter (PM) limit) for each metal, as well as limits on the maximum feedrates of each of the metals in: (1) pumpable hazardous waste; and (2) all hazardous waste.

The following subsections describe how this method for controlling metals emissions is to be implemented:

- Subsection 10.3 discusses the basis of the method and the assumptions upon which it is founded;
- Subsection 10.4 provides an overview of the implementation of the method;
- Subsection 10.5 is a step-by-step procedure for implementation of the method;
- Subsection 10.6 describes the compliance procedures for this method; and
- Appendix A describes the statistical calculations and tests to be used in the method.

10.3 *Basis*

The viability of this method depends on three fundamental assumptions:

(1) Variations in the ratio of the metal concentration in the emitted particulate to the metal concentration in the collected kiln dust (referred to as the enrichment factor or EF) for any given metal at any given facility will fall within a normal distribution that can be experimentally determined.

(2) The metal concentrations in the collected kiln dust can be accurately and representatively measured.

(3) The facility will remain in compliance with the applicable particulate matter (PM) emission standard.

Given these assumptions. metal emissions can be related to the measured concentrations in the collected kiln dust by the following equation:

$$ME\left(\frac{\text{lb Emitted Metal}}{\text{hr}}\right) = PME\left(\frac{\text{lb PM}}{\text{hr}}\right) DMC\left(\frac{\text{lb Dust Metal}}{\text{lb Dust}}\right) EF\left(\frac{\text{lb Emitted Metal / lb PM}}{\text{lb Dust Metal / lb Dust}}\right) \quad (1)$$

Where:

ME is the metal emitted;

PME is the particulate matter emitted;

DMC is the metal concentration in the collected kiln dust; and

EF is the enrichment factor, which is the ratio of the metal concentration in the emitted particulate matter to the metal concentration in the collected kiln dust.

This equation can be rearranged to calculate a maximum allowable dust metal concentration limit (DMCL) by assuming worst-case conditions that: metal emissions are at the Tier III (or Tier II) limit (see 40 CFR 266.106), and that particulate emissions are at the particulate matter limit (PML):

$$DMCL\left(\frac{\text{lb Dust Metal}}{\text{lb Dust}}\right) = \frac{\text{Tier III Limit}\left(\frac{\text{lb Emitted Metal}}{\text{hr}}\right)}{PML\left(\frac{\text{lb PM}}{\text{hr}}\right) EF\left(\frac{\text{lb Emitted Metal / lb PM}}{\text{lb Dust Metal / lb Dust}}\right)} \quad (2)$$

The enrichment factor used in the above equation must be determined experimentally from a minimum of 10 tests in which metal concentrations are measured in kiln dust and stack samples taken simultaneously. This approach provides a range of enrichment factors that can be inserted into a statistical distribution (t-distribution) to determine $EF_{95\%}$ and $EF_{99\%}$. $EF_{95\%}$ is the value at which there is a 95% confidence level that the enrichment factor is below this value at any given time. Similarly, $EF_{99\%}$ is the value at which there is a 99% confidence level that the enrichment factor is below this value at any given time. $EF_{95\%}$ is used to calculate the "violation" dust metal concentration limit ($DMCL_v$):

$$DMCL_v\left(\frac{\text{lb Dust Metal}}{\text{lb Dust}}\right) = \frac{\text{Tier III Limit}\left(\frac{\text{lb Emitted Metal}}{\text{hr}}\right)}{PML\left(\frac{\text{lb PM}}{\text{hr}}\right) EF_{95\%}\left(\frac{\text{lb Emitted Metal / lb PM}}{\text{lb Dust Metal / lb Dust}}\right)} \quad (3)$$

If the kiln dust metal concentration is just above this "violation" limit, and the PM emissions are at the PM emissions limit, there is a

5% chance that the metal emissions are above the Tier III limit. In such a case, the facility would be in violation of the metals standard.

To provide a margin of safety, a second, more conservative kiln dust metal concentration limit is also used. This "conservative" dust metal concentration limit ($DMCL_c$) is calculated using a "safe" enrichment factor (SEF). If $EF_{99\%}$ is greater than two times the value of $EF_{95\%}$, the "safe" enrichment factor can be calculated using Equation 4a:

$$SEF \geq 2\,EF_{95\%} \qquad (4a)$$

If $EF_{99\%}$ is not greater than two times the value of $EF_{95\%}$, the "safe" enrichment factor can be calculated using Equation 4b:

$$SEF \geq EF_{99\%} \qquad (4b)$$

In cases where the enrichment factor cannot be determined because the kiln dust metal concentration is nondetectable, the "safe" enrichment factor is as follows:

$$SEF = 100 \qquad (4c)$$

For all cases, the "conservative" dust metal concentration limit is calculated using the following equation:

$$DMCL_c\left(\frac{\text{lb Dust Metal}}{\text{lb Dust}}\right) = \frac{\text{Tier III Limit}\left(\frac{\text{lb Emitted Metal}}{\text{hr}}\right)}{PML\left(\frac{\text{lb PM}}{\text{hr}}\right) SEF\left(\frac{\text{lb Emitted Metal / lb PM}}{\text{lb Dust Metal / lb Dust}}\right)} \qquad (5)$$

If the kiln dust metal concentration at a facility is just above the "conservative" limit based on that "safe" enrichment factor provided in Equation 4a, and the PM emissions are at the PM emissions limit, there is a 5% chance that the metal emissions are above one-half the Tier III limit. If the kiln dust metal concentration at the facility is just above the "conservative" limit based on the "safe" enrichment factor provided in Equation 4b, and the PM emissions are at the PM emissions limit, there is a 1% chance that the metal emissions are above the Tier III limit. In either case, the facility would be unacceptably close to a violation. If this situation occurs more than 5% of the time, the facility would be required to rerun the series of 10 tests to determine the enrichment factor. To avoid this expense, the facility would be advised to reduce its metals feedrates or to take other appropriate measures to maintain its kiln dust metal concentrations in compliance with the "conservative" dust metal concentration limits.

In cases where the enrichment factor cannot be determined because the kiln dust metal concentration is nondetectable, and thus no EF_{95}% exists, the "violation" dust metal concentration limit is set at ten times the "conservative" limit:

$$DMCL_v = 10 \times DMCL_c \qquad (6)$$

10.4 *Overview*

The flowchart for implementing the method is shown in Figure 10.4-1. The general procedure is as follows:

- Follow the certification of precompliance procedures described in subsection 10.6 (to comply with 40 CFR 266.103(b)).
- For each metal of concern, perform a series of tests to establish the relationship (enrichment factor) between the concentration of emitted metal and the metal concentration in the collected kiln dust.
- Use the demonstrated enrichment factor, in combination with the Tier III (or Tier II) metal emission limit and the most stringent applicable particulate emission limit, to calculate the "violation" and "conservative" dust metal concentration limits. Include this information with the certification of compliance under 40 CFR 266.103(c).
- Perform daily and/or weekly monitoring of the cement kiln dust metal concentration to ensure (with appropriate QA/QC) that the metal concentration does not exceed either limit.
  —If the cement kiln dust metal concentration exceeds the "conservative" limit more than 5% of the time (*i.e.*, more than three failures in last 60 tests), the series of tests to determine the enrichment factor must be repeated.
  —If the cement kiln dust metal concentration exceeds the "violation" limit, a violation has occurred.
- Perform quarterly tests to verify that the enrichment factor has not increased significantly. If the enrichment factor has increased, the series of tests to determine the enrichment factor must be repeated.

10.5 *Implementation Procedures*

A step-by-step description for implementing the method is provided below:

(1) Prepare initial limits and test plans.

- Determine the Tier III metal emission limit. The Tier II metal emission limit may also be used (see 40 CFR 266.106).
- Determine the applicable PM emission standard. This standard is the most stringent particulate emission standard that applies to the facility. A facility may elect to restrict itself to an even more stringent self-imposed PM emission standard, particularly if the facility finds that it is easier to control particulate emissions than to reduce the kiln dust concentration of a certain metal (*i.e.*, lead).
- Determine which metals need to be monitored (*i.e.*, all hazardous metals for which Tier III emission limits are lower than PM emission limits—assuming PM is pure metal).
- Follow the compliance procedures described in Subsection 10.6.
- Follow appropriate guidelines for preparing test plans and waste analysis plans for the following tests:
  —Compliance tests to determine limits on metal feedrates in pumpable hazardous wastes and in all hazardous wastes (as well as to determine other compliance parameters);
  —Initial tests to determine enrichment factors;
  —Quarterly tests to verify enrichment factors;
  —Analysis of hazardous waste feedstreams; and
  —Daily and/or weekly monitoring of kiln dust for continuing compliance.

(2) Conduct tests to determine the enrichment factor.

- These tests must be conducted within a 14-day period. No more than two tests may be conducted in any single day. If the tests are not completed within a 14-day period, they must be repeated.
- Simultaneous stack samples and kiln dust samples must be taken.
  —Stack sampling must be conducted with the multiple metals train according to procedures provided in section 10.3 of this Methods Manual.
  —Kiln dust sampling must be conducted as follows:

PART 266—Appendices

Figure 10.4-1
Compliance Implementation Flow Chart

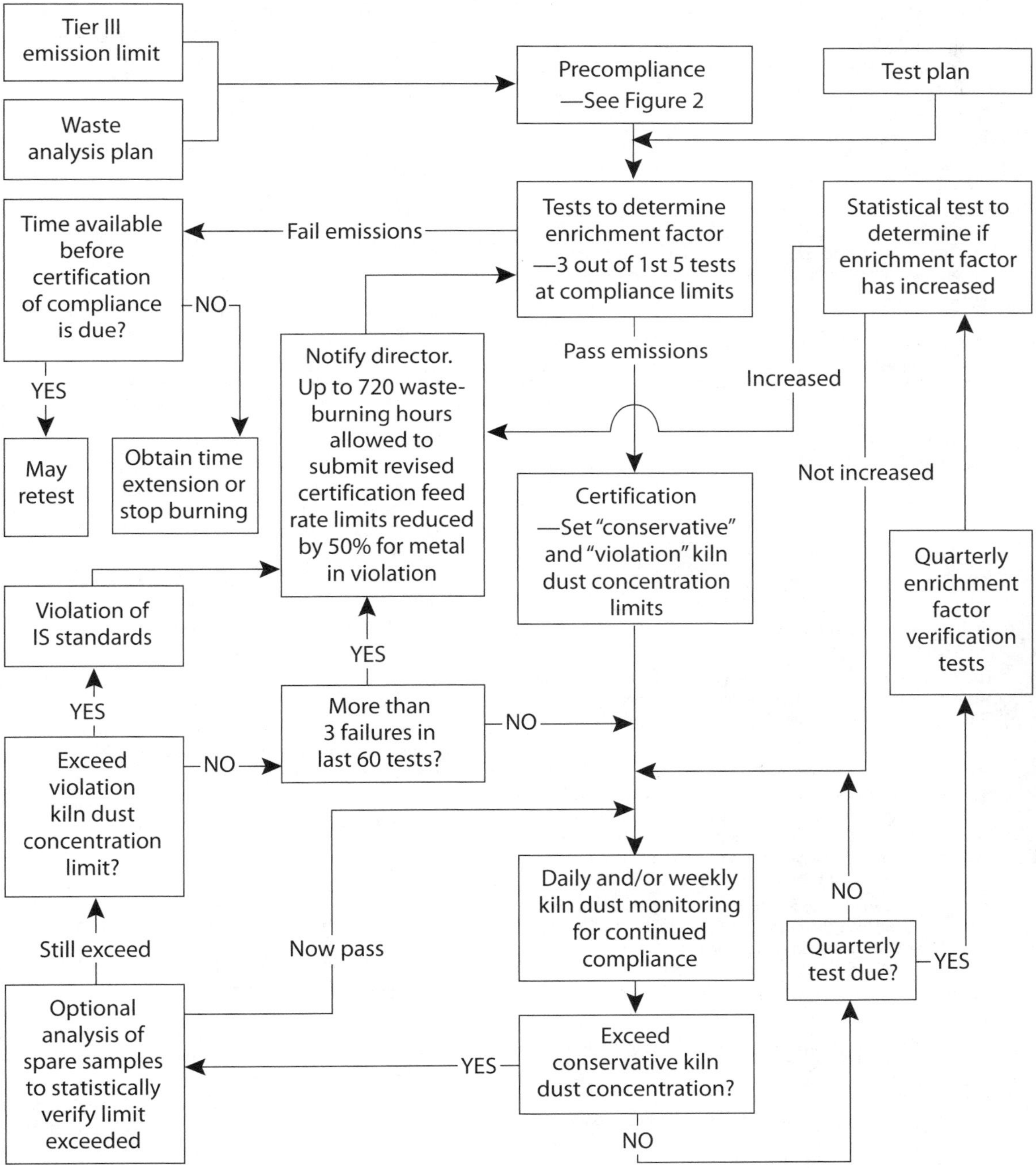

—Follow appropriate sampling and analytical procedures such as those described in the waste analysis plan as they pertain to the condition and accessibility of the dust.

—Samples should be representative of the last ESP or Fabric Filter in the APCS series.

- The feedrates of hazardous metals in all pumpable hazardous waste streams and in all hazardous waste streams must be monitored during these tests. It is recommended (but not required) that the feedrates of hazardous metals in all feedstreams also be monitored.
- At least ten single (noncomposited) runs are required during the tests.

—The facility must follow a normal schedule of kiln dust recharging for all of the tests.

—Three of the first five tests must be compliance tests in conformance with 40 CFR 266.103(c); *i.e.*, they must be used to determine maximum allowable feedrates of metals in pumpable hazardous wastes, and in all hazardous wastes, as well as to determine other compliance limits (see 40 CFR 266.103(c)(1)).

—The remainder of the tests need not be conducted under full compliance test conditions; however, the facility must operate at its compliance test production rate, and it must burn hazardous waste during these tests such that the feedrate of each metal for pumpable and total hazardous wastes is at least 25% of the feedrate during compliance testing. If these criteria, and those discussed below, are not met for any parameter during a test, then either the test is not valid for determining enrichment factors under this method, or the compliance limits for that parameter must be established based on these test conditions rather than on the compliance test conditions.

- Verify that compliance emission limits are not exceeded.

—Metal emissions must not exceed Tier III (or Tier II) limits.

—PM emissions must not exceed the most stringent of applicable PM standards (or an optional self-imposed particulate standard).

- The facility must generate normal, marketable product using normal raw materials and fuels under normal operating conditions (for parameters other than those specified under this method) when these tests are conducted.
- Chromium must be treated as a special case:

—The enrichment factor for total chromium is calculated in the same way as the enrichment factor for other metals (*i.e.*, the enrichment factor is the ratio of the concentration of total chromium in the emitted particulate matter to the concentration of total chromium in the collected kiln dust).

—The enrichment factor for hexavalent chromium (if measured) is defined as the ratio of the concentration of hexavalent chromium in the emitted particulate matter to the concentration of total chromium in the collected kiln dust.

(3) Use the enrichment factors measured in Step 2 to determine $EF_{95\%}$, $EF_{99\%}$, and SEF.

- Calculate $EF_{95\%}$ and $EF_{99\%}$ according to the t-distribution as described in Appendix A
- Calculate SEF by

—Equation 4a if $EF_{95\%}$ is determinable and if $EF_{99\%}$ is greater than two times $EF_{95\%}$,

—Equation 4b if $EF_{95\%}$ is determinable and if $EF_{99\%}$ is not greater than two times $EF_{95\%}$.

—Equation 4c if $EF_{95\%}$ is not determinable.

The facility may choose to set an even more conservative SEF to give itself a larger margin of safety between the point where corrective action is necessary and the point where a violation occurs.

(4) Prepare certification of compliance.

- Calculate the "conservative" dust metal concentration limit ($DMCL_c$) using Equation 5.

—Chromium is treated as a special case. The "conservative" kiln dust chromium concentration limit is set for total chromium, not for hexavalent chromium. The limit for total chromium must be calculated using the Tier III (or Tier II) metal limit for hexavalent chromium.

—If the stack samples described in Step 2 were analyzed for hexavalent chromium, the SEF based on the hexavalent chromium enrichment factors (as defined in Step 2) must be used in this calculation.

—If the stack samples were not analyzed for hexavalent chromium, then the SEF based on the total chromium enrichment factor must be used in this calculation.

- Calculate the "violation" dust metal concentration limit ($DMCL_v$) using Equation 3 if $EF_{95\%}$ is determinable, or using Equation 6 if $EF_{95\%}$ is not determinable.

—Chromium is treated as a special case. The "violation" kiln dust chromium concentration limit is set for total chromium, not for hexavalent chromium. The limit for total chromium must be calculated using the Tier III (or Tier II) metal limit for hexavalent chromium.

—If the stack samples taken in Step 2 were analyzed for hexavalent chromium, the $EF_{95\%}$ based on the hexavalent chromium enrichment factor (as defined in Step 2) should be used in this calculation.

—If the stack samples were not analyzed for hexavalent chromium, the $EF_{95\%}$ based on the total chromium enrichment factor must be used in this calculation.

- Submit certification of compliance.
- Steps 2-4 must be repeated for recertification, which is required once every 3 years (see §266.103(d)).

(5) Monitor metal concentrations in kiln dust for continuing compliance, and maintain compliance with all compliance limits for the duration of interim status.

- Metals to be monitored during compliance testing are classified as either "critical" or "noncritical" metals.

—All metals must initially be classified as "critical" metals and be monitored on a daily basis.

—A "critical" metal may be reclassified as a "noncritical" metal if its concentration in the kiln dust remains below 10% of its "conservative" kiln dust metal concentration limit for 30 consecutive daily samples. "Noncritical" metals must be monitored on a weekly basis.

—A "noncritical" metal must be reclassified as a "critical" metal if its concentration in the kiln dust is above 10% of its "conservative" kiln dust metal concentration limit for any single daily or weekly sample.

- Noncompliance with the sampling and analysis schedule prescribed by this method is a violation of the metals controls under §266.103.
- Follow the sampling, compositing, and analytical procedures described in this method and in other appropriate methods, as they pertain to the condition and accessibility of the kiln dust.

- Follow the same procedures and sample at the same locations as were used for kiln dust samples collected to determine the enrichment factors (as discussed in Step 2).
- Samples must be collected at least once every 8 hours, and a daily composite must be prepared according to appropriate procedures.
  - —At least one composite sample is required. This sample is referred to as the "required" sample.
  - —For QA/QC purposes, a facility may elect to collect two or more additional samples. These samples are referred to as the "spare" samples. These additional samples must be collected over the same time period and according to the same procedures as those used for the "required" sample.
  - —Samples for "critical" metals must be daily composites.
  - —Samples for "noncritical" metals must be weekly composites. These samples can be composites of the original 8-hour samples, or they can be composites of daily composite samples.
- Analyze the "required" sample to determine the concentration of each metal.
  - —This analysis must be completed within 48 hours of the close of the sampling period. Failure to meet this schedule is a violation of the metals standards of §266.103.
- If the "conservative" kiln dust metal concentration limit is exceeded for any metal, refer to Step 8.
- If the "conservative" kiln dust metal concentration limit is not exceeded, continue with the daily or weekly monitoring (Step 5) for the duration of interim status.
- Conduct quarterly enrichment factor verification tests, as described in Step 6.

(6) Conduct quarterly enrichment factor verification tests.

- After certification of compliance with the metals standards, a facility must conduct quarterly enrichment factor verification tests every three months for the duration of interim status. The first quarterly test must be completed within three months of certification (or recertification). Each subsequent quarterly test must be completed within three months of the preceding quarterly test. Failure to meet this schedule is a violation.
- Simultaneous stack samples and kiln dust samples must be collected.
- Follow the same procedures and sample at the same locations as were used for kiln dust samples and stack samples collected to determine the enrichment factors (as discussed in Step 2).
- At least three single (noncomposited) runs are required. These tests need not be conducted under the operating conditions of the initial compliance test; however, the facility must operate under the following conditions:
  - —It must operate at compliance test production rate.
  - —It must burn hazardous waste during the test, and for the 2-day period immediately preceding the test, such that the feedrate of each metal for pumpable and total hazardous wastes consist of at least 25% of the operating limits established during the compliance test.
  - —It must remain in compliance with all compliance parameters (see §266.103(c)(1)).
  - —It must follow a normal schedule of kiln dust recharging.
  - —It must generate normal marketable product from normal raw materials during the tests.

(7) Conduct a statistical test to determine if the enrichment factors measured in the quarterly verification tests have increased significantly from the enrichment factors determined in the tests conducted in Step 2. The enrichment factors have increased significantly if all three of the following criteria are met:

- By applying the t-test described in appendix A, it is determined that the enrichment factors measured in the quarterly tests are not taken from the same population as the enrichment factors measured in the Step 2 tests;
- The $EF_{95\%}$ calculated for the combined data sets (*i.e.*, the quarterly test data and the original Step 2 test data) according to the t-distribution (described in appendix A) is more than 10% higher than the $EF_{95\%}$ based on the enrichment factors previously measured in Step 2; and
- The highest measured kiln dust metal concentration recorded in the previous quarter is more than 10% of the "violation" kiln dust concentration limit that would be calculated from the combined $EF_{95\%}$.

If the enrichment factors have increased significantly, the tests to determine the enrichment factors must be repeated (refer to Step 11). If the enrichment factors have not increased significantly, continue to use the kiln dust metal concentration limits based on the enrichment factors previously measured in Step 2, and continue with the daily and/or weekly monitoring described in Step 5.

(8) If the "conservative" kiln dust metal concentration limit was exceeded for any metal in any single analysis of the "required" kiln dust sample, the "spare" samples corresponding to the same period may be analyzed to determine if the exceedance was due to a sampling or analysis error.

- If no "spare" samples were taken, refer to Step 9.
- If the average of all the samples for a given day (or week, as applicable) (including the "required" sample and the "spare" samples) does not exceed the "conservative" kiln dust metal concentration limit, no corrective measures are necessary; continue with the daily and/or weekly monitoring as described in Step 5.
- If the average of all the samples for a given day (or week, as applicable) exceeds the "conservative" kiln dust metal concentration limit, but the average of the "spare" samples is below the "conservative" kiln dust metal concentration limit, apply the Q-test, described in appendix A, to determine whether the "required" sample concentration can be judged as an outlier.
  - —If the "required" sample concentration is judged an outlier, no corrective measures are necessary; continue with the daily and/or weekly monitoring described in Step 5.
  - —If the "required" sample concentration is not judged an outlier, refer to Step 9.

(9) Determine if the "violation" kiln dust metal concentration has been exceeded based on either the average of all the samples collected during the 24-hour period in question, or if discarding an outlier can be statistically justified by the Q-test described in appendix A, on the average of the remaining samples.

- If the "violation" kiln dust metal concentration limit has been exceeded, a violation of the metals controls under §266.103(c) has occurred. Notify the Director that a violation has occurred. Hazardous waste may be burned for testing purposes for up to 720 operating hours to support a revised certification of compliance. Note that the Director may grant an extension of the hours of hazardous waste burning under §266.103(c)(7) if additional burning time is needed to support a revised certification for reasons beyond the control of the owner or operator. Until a revised certification of compliance is submitted to the Director, the feedrate of the metals in violation in total and pumpable hazardous waste feeds is limited to 50% of the previous compliance test limits.

- If the "violation" kiln dust metal concentration has not been exceeded:
  —If the exceedance occurred in a daily composite sample, refer to Step 10.
  —If the exceedance occurred in a weekly composite sample, refer to Step 11.

(10) Determine if the "conservative" kiln dust metal concentration limit has been exceeded more than three times in the last 60 days.

- If not, log this exceedance and continue with the daily and/or weekly monitoring (Step 5).
- If so, the tests to determine the enrichment factors must be repeated (refer to Step 11).
- This determination is made separately for each metal. For example,
  —Three exceedances for each of the ten hazardous metals are allowed within any 60-day period.
  —Four exceedances of any single metal in any 60-day period is not allowed.
- This determination should be made daily, beginning on the first day of daily monitoring. For example, if four exceedances of any single metal occur in the first four days of daily monitoring, do not wait until the end of the 60-day period; refer immediately to Step 11.

(11) The tests to determine the enrichment factor must be repeated if: (1) More than three exceedances of the "conservative" kiln dust metal concentration limit occur within any 60 consecutive daily samples; (2) an excursion of the "conservative" kiln dust metal concentration limit occurs in any weekly sample; or (3) a quarterly test indicates that the enrichment factors have increased significantly.

- The facility must notify the Director if these tests must be repeated.
- The facility has up to 720 hazardous-waste-burning hours to redetermine the enrichment factors for the metal or metals in question and to recertify (beginning with a return to Step 2). During this period, the facility must reduce the feed rate of the metal in violation by 50%. If the facility has not completed the recertification process within this period, it must stop burning or obtain an extension. Hazardous waste burning may resume only when the recertification process (ending with Step 4) has been completed.
- Meanwhile, the facility must continue with daily kiln dust metals monitoring (Step 5) and must remain in compliance with the "violation" kiln dust metal concentration limits (Step 9).

10.6 *Precompliance Procedures*

Cement kilns and other industrial furnaces that recycle emission control residue back into the furnace must comply with the same certification schedules and procedures (with the few exceptions described below) that apply to other boilers and industrial furnaces. These schedules and procedures, as set forth in §266.103, require no later than the effective date of the rule, each facility submit a certification which establishes precompliance limits for a number of compliance parameters (see §266.103(b)(3)), and that each facility immediately begin to operate under these limits.

These precompliance limits must ensure that interim status emissions limits for hazardous metals, particulate matter, HCl, and Cl_2 are not likely to be exceeded. Determination of the values of the precompliance limits must be made based on either (1) conservative default assumptions provided in this Methods Manual, or (2) engineering judgement.

The flowchart for implementing the precompliance procedures is shown in Figure 10.6-1. The step-by-step precompliance implementation procedure is described below. The precompliance implementation procedures and numbering scheme are similar to those used for the compliance procedures described in Subsection 10.5.

(1) Prepare initial limits and test plans.

- Determine the Tier III metal emission limit. The Tier II metal emission limit may also be used (see 40 CFR 266.106).
- Determine the applicable PM emission standard. This standard is the most stringent particulate emission standard that applies to the facility. A facility may elect to restrict itself to an even more stringent self-imposed PM emission standard, particularly if the facility finds that it is easier to control particulate emissions than to reduce the kiln dust concentration of a certain metal (*i.e.*, lead).
- Determine which metals need to be monitored (*i.e.*, all hazardous metals for which Tier III emission limits are lower than PM emission limits, assuming PM is pure metal).
- Follow appropriate procedures for preparing waste analysis plans for the following tasks:
  —Analysis of hazardous waste feedstreams.
  —Daily and/or weekly monitoring of kiln dust concentrations for continuing compliance.

(2) Determine the "safe" enrichment factor for precompliance. In this context, the "safe" enrichment factor is a conservatively high estimate of the enrichment factor (the ratio of the emitted metal concentration to the metal concentration in the collected kiln dust). The "safe" enrichment factor must be calculated from either conservative default values, or engineering judgement.

- Conservative default values for the "safe" enrichment factor are as follows:
  —SEF=10 for all hazardous metals except mercury.
  —SEF=10 for antimony, arsenic, barium, beryllium, cadmium, chromium, lead, silver, and thallium.
  —SEF=100 for mercury.
- Engineering judgement may be used in place of conservative default assumptions provided that the engineering judgement is defensible and properly documented. The facility must keep a written record of all assumptions and calculations necessary to justify the SEF. The facility must provide this record to EPA upon request and must be prepared to defend these assumptions and calculations.

  Examples of situations where the use of engineering judgement is appropriate include:
  —Use of data from precompliance tests;
  —Use of data from previous compliance tests; and
  —Use of data from similar facilities.

(3) This step does not apply to precompliance procedures.

(4) Prepare certification of precompliance.

- Calculate the "conservative" dust metal concentration limit ($DMCL_c$) using Equation 5.
- Submit certification of precompliance. This certification must include precompliance limits for all compliance parameters that apply to other boilers and industrial furnaces (*i.e.*, those that do not recycle emission control residue back into the furnace) as listed in §266.103(b)(3), except that it is not necessary

PART 266—Appendices

Figure 10.6-1
Precompliance Implementation Flow Chart

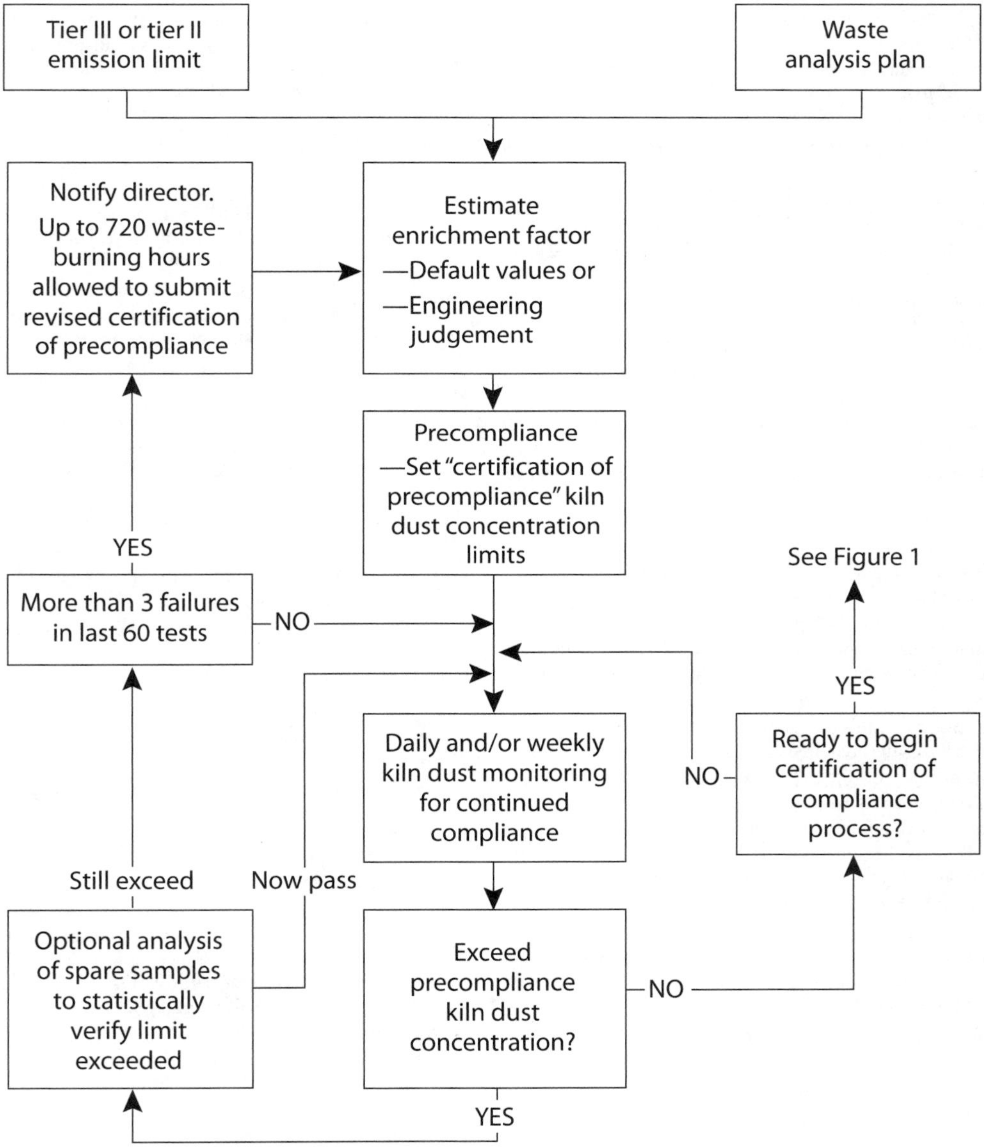

to set precompliance limits on maximum feedrate of each hazardous metal in all combined feedstreams.

- Furnaces that recycle collected PM back into the furnace (and that elect to comply with this method (see §266.103(c)(3)(ii)) are subject to a special precompliance parameter, however. They must establish precompliance limits on the maximum concentration of each hazardous metal in collected kiln dust (which must be set according to the procedures described above).

(5) Monitor metal concentration in kiln dust for continuing compliance, and maintain compliance with all precompliance limits until certification of compliance has been submitted.

- Metals to be monitored during precompliance testing are classified as either "critical" or "noncritical" metals.
  - —All metals must initially be classified as "critical" metals and be monitored on a daily basis.
  - —A "critical" metal may be reclassified as a "noncritical" metal if its concentration in the kiln dust remains below 10% of its "conservative" kiln dust metal concentration limit for 30 consecutive daily samples. "Noncritical" metals must be monitored on a weekly basis, at a minimum.
  - —A "noncritical" metal must be reclassified as a "critical" metal if its concentration in the kiln dust is above 10% of its "conservative" kiln dust metal concentration limit for any single daily or weekly sample.
- It is a violation if the facility fails to analyze the kiln dust for any "critical" metal on any single day or for any "noncritical" metal during any single week, when hazardous waste is burned.
- Follow the sampling, compositing, and analytical procedures described in this method and in other appropriate methods as they pertain to the condition and accessibility of the kiln dust.
- Samples must be collected at least once every 8 hours, and a daily composite must be prepared according to appropriate procedures.
  - —At least one composite sample is required. This sample is referred to as the "required" sample.
  - —For QA/QC purposes, a facility may elect to collect two or more additional samples. These samples are referred to as the "spare" samples. These additional samples must be collected over the same time period and according to the same procedures as those used for the "required" sample.
  - —Samples for "critical" metals must be daily composites.
  - —Samples for "noncritical" metals must be weekly composites, at a minimum. These samples can be composites of the original 8-hour samples, or they can be composites of daily composite samples.
- Analyze the "required" sample to determine the concentration of each metal.
  - —This analysis must be completed within 48 hours of the close of the sampling period. Failure to meet this schedule is a violation.
- If the "conservative" kiln dust metal concentration limit is exceeded for any metal, refer to Step 8.
- If the "conservative" kiln dust metal concentration limit is not exceeded, continue with the daily and/or weekly monitoring (Step 5) for the duration of interim status.

(6) This step does not apply to precompliance procedures.

(7) This step does not apply to precompliance procedures.

(8) If the "conservative" kiln dust metal concentration limit was exceeded for any metal in any single analysis of the "required" kiln dust sample, the "spare" samples corresponding to the same period may be analyzed to determine if the exceedance is due to a sampling or analysis error.

- If no "spare" samples were taken, refer to Step 9.
- If the average of all the samples for a given day (or week, as applicable) (including the "required" sample and the "spare" samples) does not exceed the "conservative" kiln dust metal concentration limit, no corrective measures are necessary; continue with the daily and/or weekly monitoring as described in Step 5.
- If the average of all the samples for a given day (or week, as applicable) exceeds the "conservative" kiln dust metal concentration limit, but the average of the "spare" samples is below the "conservative" kiln dust metal concentration limit, apply the Q-test, described in appendix A, to determine whether the "required" sample concentration can be judged as an outlier.
  - —If the "required" sample concentration is judged an outlier, no corrective measures are necessary; continue with the daily and/or weekly monitoring described in Step 5.
  - —If the "required" sample concentration is not judged an outlier, refer to Step 10.

(9) This step does not apply to precompliance procedures.

(10) Determine if the "conservative" kiln dust metal concentration limit has been exceeded more than three times in the last 60 days.

- If not, log this exceedance and continue with the daily and/or weekly monitoring (Step 5).
- If so, the tests to determine the enrichment factors must be repeated (refer to Step 11).
- This determination is made separately for each metal; for example:
  - —Three exceedances for each of the ten hazardous metals are allowed within any 60-day period.
  - —Four exceedances of any single metal in any 60-day period is not allowed.
- This determination should be made daily, beginning on the first day of daily monitoring. For example, if four exceedances of any single metal occur in the first four days of daily monitoring, do not wait until the end of the 60-day period; refer immediately to Step 11.

(11) A revised certification of precompliance must be submitted to the Director (or certification of compliance must be submitted) if: (1) More than three exceedances of the "conservative" kiln dust metal concentration limit occur within any 60 consecutive daily samples; or (2) an exceedance of the "conservative" kiln dust metal concentration limit occurs in any weekly sample.

- The facility must notify the Director if a revised certification of precompliance must be submitted.
- The facility has up to 720 waste-burning hours to submit a certification of compliance or a revised certification of precompliance. During this period, the feed rate of the metal in violation must be reduced by 50%. In the case of a revised certification of precompliance, engineering judgement must be used to ensure that the "conservative" kiln dust metal concentration will not be exceeded. Examples of how this goal might be accomplished include:
  - —Changing equipment or operating procedures to reduce the kiln dust metal concentration;

—Changing equipment or operating procedures, or using more detailed engineering judgement, to decrease the estimated SEF and thus increase the "conservative" kiln dust metal concentration limit;

—Increasing the "conservative" kiln dust metal concentration limit by imposing a stricter PM emissions standard; or

—Increasing the "conservative" kiln dust metal concentration limit by performing a more detailed risk assessment to increase the metal emission limits.

- Meanwhile, the facility must continue with daily kiln dust metals monitoring (Step 5).

Appendix A to Appendix IX to Part 266—Statistics

A.1 *Determination of Enrichment Factor*

After at least 10 initial emissions tests are performed, an enrichment factor for each metal must be determined. At the 95% confidence level, the enrichment factor, $EF_{95\%}$, is based on the test results and is statistically determined so there is only a 5% chance that the enrichment factor at any given time will be larger than $EF_{95\%}$. Similarly, at the 99% confidence level, the enrichment factor, $EF_{99\%}$, is statistically determined so there is only a 1% chance that the enrichment factor at any given time will be larger than $EF_{99\%}$.

For a large number of samples (n > 30), $EF_{95\%}$ is based on a normal distribution, and is equal to:

$$EF_{95\%} = \overline{EF} + z_c\sigma \qquad (1)$$

where:

$$\overline{EF} = \frac{\sum_{i=1}^{n} EF_i}{n} \qquad (2)$$

$$\sigma = \left[\frac{\sum_{i=1}^{n}\left(EF_i - \overline{EF}\right)^2}{n}\right]^{\frac{1}{2}} \qquad (3)$$

For a 95% confidence level, z_c is equal to 1.645.

For a small number of samples (n<30), $EF_{95\%}$ is based on the t-distribution and is equal to:

$$EF_{95\%} = \overline{EF} + t_c S \qquad (4)$$

where the standard deviation, S, is defined as:

$$S = \left[\frac{\sum_{i=1}^{n}\left(EF_i - \overline{EF}\right)^2}{n-1}\right]^{\frac{1}{2}} \qquad (5)$$

t_c is a function of the number of samples and the confidence level that is desired. It increases in value as the sample size decreases and the confidence level increases. The 95% confidence level is used in this method to calculate the "violation" kiln dust metal concentration limit; and the 99% confidence level is sometimes used to calculate the "conservative" kiln dust metal concentration limit. Values of t_c are shown in table A-1 for various degrees of freedom (degrees of freedom=sample size-1) at the 95% and 99% confidence levels. As the sample size approaches infinity, the normal distribution is approached.

Table A-1—t-Distribution

n−1 or n_1+n_2-2	$t_{.95}$	$t_{.99}$	n−1 or n_1+n_2-2	$t_{.95}$	$t_{.99}$
1	6.31	31.82	14	1.76	2.62
2	2.92	6.96	15	1.75	2.60
3	2.35	4.54	16	1.75	2.58
4	2.13	3.75	17	1.74	2.57
5	2.02	3.36	18	1.73	2.55
6	1.94	3.14	19	1.73	2.54
7	1.90	3.00	20	1.72	2.53
8	1.86	2.90	25	1.71	2.48
9	1.83	2.82	30	1.70	2.46
10	1.81	2.76	40	1.68	2.42
11	1.80	2.72	60	1.67	2.39
12	1.78	2.68	120	1.66	2.36
13	1.77	2.65	∞	1.645	2.33

A.2 *Comparison of Enrichment Factor Groups*

To determine if the enrichment factors measured in the quarterly tests are significantly different from the enrichment factors determined in the initial Step 2 tests, the t-test is used. In this test, the value t_{meas}:

$$t_{meas} = \frac{\overline{EF}_1 - \overline{EF}_2}{\sigma_t\left(\frac{1}{n_1} + \frac{1}{n_2}\right)^{\frac{1}{2}}} \qquad (6)$$

$$\sigma_t = \left(\frac{(n_1 - 1)S_1^2 + (n_2 - 1)S_2^2}{n_1 + n_2 - 2}\right)^{\frac{1}{2}} \qquad (7)$$

is compared to t_{crit} at the desired confidence level. The 95% confidence level is used in this method. Values of t_{crit} are shown in table A-1 for various degrees of freedom (degrees of freedom n_1+n_2-2) at the 95% and 99% confidence levels. If t_{meas} is greater then t_{crit}, it can be concluded with 95% confidence that the two groups are not from the same population.

A.3 *Rejection of Data*

If the concentration of any hazardous metal in the "required" kiln dust sample exceeds the kiln dust metal concentration limit, the "spare" samples are analyzed. If the average of the combined "required" and "spare" values is still above the limit, a statistical test is used to decide if the upper value can be rejected.

The "Q-test" is used to determine if a data point can be rejected. The difference between the questionable result and its neighbor is divided by the spread of the entire data set. The resulting ratio, Q_{meas}, is then compared with rejection values that are critical for a particular degree of confidence, where Q_{meas} is:

$$\sigma^{meas} = \frac{DMC_{highest} - DMC_{next\ highest}}{DMC_{highest} - DMC_{lowest}} \qquad (8)$$

The 90% confidence level for data rejection is used in this method. Table A-2 provides the values of Q_{crit} at the 90% confidence level. If Q_{meas} is larger than Q_{crit}, the data point can be discarded. Only one data point from a sample group can be rejected using this method.

Table A-2—Critical Values for Use in the Q-Test

n	Q_{crit}	n	Q_{crit}
3	0.94	7	0.51
4	0.76	8	0.47
5	0.64	9	0.44
6	0.56	10	0.41

[56 FR 32692, July 17, 1991 as amended 56 FR 42512, 42516, Aug. 27, 1991; 57 FR 38566, Aug. 25, 1992; 57 FR 44999, Sept. 30, 1992; 62 FR 32463, June 13, 1997; 70 FR 34588, June 14, 2005; 71 FR 40277, July 14, 2006; 74 FR 30231, June 25, 2009]

Appendix X to Part 266 [Reserved]

Appendix XI to Part 266—Lead-Bearing Materials That May be Processed in Exempt Lead Smelters

A. *Exempt Lead-Bearing Materials When Generated or Originally Produced By Lead-Associated Industries*[1]

Acid dump/fill solids
Sump mud
Materials from laboratory analyses
Acid filters
Baghouse bags
Clothing (*e.g.*, coveralls, aprons, shoes, hats, gloves)
Sweepings
Air filter bags and cartridges
Respiratory cartridge filters
Shop abrasives
Stacking boards
Waste shipping containers (*e.g.*, cartons, bags, drums, cardboard)
Paper hand towels
Wiping rags and sponges
Contaminated pallets
Water treatment sludges, filter cakes, residues, and solids
Emission control dusts, sludges, filter cakes, residues, and solids from lead-associated industries (*e.g.*, K069 and D008 wastes)
Spent grids, posts, and separators
Spent batteries
Lead oxide and lead oxide residues
Lead plates and groups
Spent battery cases, covers, and vents
Pasting belts
Water filter media
Cheesecloth from pasting rollers
Pasting additive bags
Asphalt paving materials

B. *Exempt Lead-Bearing Materials When Generated or Originally Produced By Any Industry*

Charging jumpers and clips
Platen abrasive
Fluff from lead wire and cable casings
Lead-based pigments and compounding pigment dust

[56 FR 42517, Aug. 27, 1991]

[1] Lead-associated industries are lead smelters, lead-acid battery manufacturing, and lead chemical manufacturing (e.g., manufacturing of lead oxide or other lead compounds).

Appendix XII to Part 266—Nickel or Chromium-Bearing Materials that may be Processed in Exempt Nickel-Chromium Recovery Furnaces

A. *Exempt Nickel or Chromium-Bearing Materials when Generated by Manufacturers or Users of Nickel, Chromium, or Iron*

Baghouse bags
Raney nickel catalyst
Floor sweepings
Air filters
Electroplating bath filters
Wastewater filter media
Wood pallets
Disposable clothing (coveralls, aprons, hats, and gloves)
Laboratory samples and spent chemicals
Shipping containers and plastic liners from containers or vehicles used to transport nickel or chromium-containing wastes
Respirator cartridge filters
Paper hand towels

B. *Exempt Nickel or Chromium-Bearing Materials when Generated by Any Industry*

Electroplating wastewater treatment sludges (F006)
Nickel and/or chromium-containing solutions
Nickel, chromium, and iron catalysts
Nickel-cadmium and nickel-iron batteries
Filter cake from wet scrubber system water treatment plants in the specialty steel industry[1]
Filter cake from nickel-chromium alloy pickling operations[1]

[56 FR 42517, Aug. 27, 1991]

Appendix XIII to Part 266—Mercury Bearing Wastes That May Be Processed in Exempt Mercury Recovery Units

These are exempt mercury-bearing materials with less than 500 ppm of 40 CFR Part 261, appendix VIII organic constituents when generated by manufacturers or users of mercury or mercury products.

1. Activated carbon
2. Decomposer graphite
3. Wood
4. Paper
5. Protective clothing
6. Sweepings
7. Respiratory cartridge filters
8. Cleanup articles
9. Plastic bags and other contaminated containers
10. Laboratory and process control samples
11. K106 and other wastewater treatment plant sludge and filter cake
12. Mercury cell sump and tank sludge
13. Mercury cell process solids
14. Recoverable levels of mercury contained in soil

[59 FR 48042, Sept. 19, 1994, as amended at 71 FR 40278, July 14, 2006]

[1] If a hazardous waste under an authorized State program.

PART 267—STANDARDS FOR OWNERS AND OPERATORS OF HAZARDOUS WASTE FACILITIES OPERATING UNDER A STANDARDIZED PERMIT

Authority: 42 U.S.C. 6902, 6912(a), 6924–6926, and 6930.

Source: 70 FR 53453, Sept. 8, 2005, unless otherwise noted.

Subpart A—General

§267.1 What are the purpose, scope and applicability of this part?

(a) The purpose of this part is to establish minimum national standards which define the acceptable management of hazardous waste under a 40 CFR part 270, subpart J standardized permit.

(b) This part applies to owners and operators of facilities who treat or store hazardous waste under a 40 CFR part 270, subpart J standardized permit, except as provided otherwise in 40 CFR part 261, subpart A, or 40 CFR 264.1(f) and (g).

§267.2 What is the relationship to interim status standards?

If you are a facility owner or operator who has fully complied with the requirements for interim status—as defined in section 3005(e) of RCRA and regulations under 40 CFR 270.70—you must comply with the regulations specified in 40 CFR part 265 instead of the regulations in this part, until final administrative disposition of the standardized permit application is made, except as provided under 40 CFR part 264, subpart S.

§267.3 How does this part affect an imminent hazard action?

Notwithstanding any other provisions of this part, enforcement actions may be brought pursuant to section 7003 of RCRA.

Subpart B—General Facility Standards

§267.10 Does this subpart apply to me?

This subpart applies to you if you own or operate a facility that treats or stores hazardous waste under a 40 CFR part 270, subpart J standardized permit, except as provided in §267.1(b).

§267.11 What must I do to comply with this subpart?

To comply with this subpart, you must obtain an identification number, and follow the requirements below for waste analysis, security, inspections, training, special waste handling, and location standards.

§267.12 How do I obtain an identification number?

You must apply to EPA for an EPA identification number following the EPA notification procedures and using EPA form 8700–12. You may obtain information and required forms from your state hazardous waste regulatory agency or from your EPA regional office.

§267.13 What are my waste analysis requirements?

(a) Before you treat or store any hazardous wastes, you must obtain a detailed chemical and physical analysis of a representative sample of the wastes. At a minimum, the analysis must contain all the information needed to treat or store the waste to comply with this part and 40 CFR part 268.

(1) You may include data in the analysis that was developed under 40 CFR part 261, and published or documented data on the hazardous waste or on hazardous waste generated from similar processes.

(2) You must repeat the analysis as necessary to ensure that it is accurate and up to date. At a minimum, you must repeat the analysis if the process or operation generating the hazardous wastes has changed.

(b) You must develop and follow a written waste analysis plan that describes the procedures you will follow to comply with paragraph (a) of this section. You must keep this plan at the facility. If you receive wastes generated from off-site, and are eligible for a standardized permit, you also must have submitted the waste analysis plan with the Notice of Intent. At a minimum, the plan must specify all of the following:

(1) The hazardous waste parameters that you will analyze and the rationale for selecting these parameters (that is, how analysis for these parameters will provide sufficient information on the waste's properties to comply with paragraph (a) of this section).

(2) The test methods you will use to test for these parameters.

(3) The sampling method you will use to obtain a representative sample of the waste to be analyzed. You may obtain a representative sample using either:

(i) One of the sampling methods described in appendix I of 40 CFR part 261; or

(ii) An equivalent sampling method.

(4) How frequently you will review or repeat the initial analysis of the waste to ensure that the analysis is accurate and up to date.

(5) Where applicable, the methods you will use to meet the additional waste analysis requirements for specific waste management methods as specified in 40 CFR 264.17, 264.1034(d), 264.1063(d), and 264.1083.

§267.14 What are my security requirements?

(a) You must prevent, and minimize the possibility for, livestock and unauthorized people from entering the active portion of your facility.

(b) Your facility must have:

(1) A 24-hour surveillance system (for example, television monitoring or surveillance by guards or facility personnel) that continuously monitors and controls entry onto the active portion of the facility; or

(2) An artificial or natural barrier (for example, a fence in good repair or a fence combined with a cliff) that completely surrounds the active portion of the facility; and

(3) A means to control entry, at all times, through the gates or other entrances to the active portion of the facility (for example, an attendant, television monitors, locked entrance, or controlled roadway access to the facility).

(c) You must post a sign at each entrance to the active portion of a facility, and at other prominent locations, in sufficient numbers to be seen from any approach to this active portion. The sign must bear the legend "Danger—Unauthorized Personnel Keep Out." The legend must be in English and in any other language predominant in the area surrounding the facility (for example, facilities in counties bordering the Canadian province of Quebec must post signs in French, and facilities in counties bordering Mexico must post signs in Spanish), and must be legible from a distance of at least 25 feet. You may use existing signs with a legend other than "Danger—Unauthorized Personnel Keep Out" if the legend on the sign indicates that only authorized personnel are allowed to enter the active portion, and that entry onto the active portion can be dangerous.

§267.15 What are my general inspection requirements?

(a) You must inspect your facility for malfunctions and deterioration, operator errors, and discharges that may be causing, or may lead to:

(1) Release of hazardous waste constituents to the environment; or

(2) A threat to human health. You must conduct these inspections often enough to identify problems in time to correct them before they result in harm to human health or the environment.

(b) You must develop and follow a written schedule for inspecting, monitoring equipment, safety and emergency equipment, security devices, and operating and structural equipment (such as dikes and sump pumps) that are important to preventing, detecting, or responding to environmental or human health hazards.

(1) You must keep this schedule at the facility.

(2) The schedule must identify the equipment and devices you will inspect and what problems you look for, such as malfunctions or deterioration of equipment (for example, inoperative sump pump, leaking fitting, etc.).

(3) The frequency of your inspections may vary for the items on the schedule. However, the frequency should be based on the rate of deterioration of the equipment and the probability of an environmental or human health incident if the deterioration, malfunction, or any operator error goes undetected between inspections. Areas subject to spills, such as loading and unloading areas, must be inspected daily when in use. At a minimum, the inspection schedule must include the items and frequencies required in §§267.174, 267.193, 267.195, 267.1103, and 40 CFR 264.1033, 264.1052, 264.1053, 264.1058, and 264.1083 through 264.1089, where applicable.

(c) You must remedy any deterioration or malfunction of equipment or structures that the inspection reveals in time to prevent any environmental or human health hazard. Where a hazard is imminent or has already occurred, you must take remedial action immediately.

(d) You must record all inspections. You must keep these records for at least three years from the date of inspection. At a minimum, you must include the date and time of the inspection, the name of the inspector, a notation of the observations made, and the date and nature of any repairs or other remedial actions.

§267.16 What training must my employees have?

(a) Your facility personnel must successfully complete a program of classroom instruction or on-the-job training that teaches them to perform their duties in a way that ensures the facility's compliance with the requirements of this part. You must ensure that this program includes all the elements described in the documents that are required under paragraph (d)(3) of this section.

(1) A person trained in hazardous waste management procedures must direct this program, and must teach facility personnel hazardous waste management procedures (including contingency plan implementation) relevant to their employment positions.

(2) At a minimum, the training program must be designed to ensure that facility personnel are able to respond effectively to emergencies by including instruction on emergency procedures, emergency equipment, and emergency systems, including all of the following, where applicable:

(i) Procedures for using, inspecting, repairing, and replacing facility emergency and monitoring equipment

(ii) Key parameters for automatic waste feed cut-off systems.

(iii) Communications or alarm systems.

(iv) Response to fires or explosions.

(v) Response to ground water contamination incidents.

(vi) Shutdown of operations.

(b) Facility personnel must successfully complete the program required in paragraph (a) of this section within six months after the date of their employment or assignment to a facility, or to a new position at a facility, whichever is later. Employees hired after the effective date of your standardized permit must not work in unsupervised positions until they have completed the training requirements of paragraph (a) of this section.

(c) Facility personnel must take part in an annual review of the initial training required in paragraph (a) of this section.

(d) You must maintain the following documents and records at your facility:

(1) The job title for each position at the facility related to hazardous waste management, and the name of the employee filling each job;

(2) A written job description for each position listed under paragraph (d)(1) of this section. This description must include the requisite skill, education, or other qualifications, and duties of employees assigned to each position;

(3) A written description of the type and amount of both introductory and continuing training that will be given to each person filling a position listed under paragraph (d)(1) of this section;

(4) Records that document that facility personnel have received and completed the training or job experience required under paragraphs (a), (b), and (c) of this section.

(e) You must keep training records on current personnel until your facility closes. You must keep training records on former employees for at least three years from the date the employee last worked at your facility. Personnel training records may accompany personnel transferred within your company.

§267.17 What are the requirements for managing ignitable, reactive, or incompatible wastes?

(a) You must take precautions to prevent accidental ignition or reaction of ignitable or reactive waste by following these requirements:

(1) You must separate these wastes and protect them from sources of ignition or reaction such as: open flames, smoking, cutting and welding, hot surfaces, frictional heat, sparks (static, electrical, or mechanical), spontaneous ignition (for example, from heat-producing chemical reactions), and radiant heat.

(2) While ignitable or reactive waste is being handled, you must confine smoking and open flames to specially designated locations.

(3) "No Smoking" signs must be conspicuously placed wherever there is a hazard from ignitable or reactive waste.

(b) If you treat or store ignitable or reactive waste, or mix incompatible waste or incompatible wastes and other materials, you must take precautions to prevent reactions that:

(1) Generate extreme heat or pressure, fire or explosions, or violent reactions.

(2) Produce uncontrolled toxic mists, fumes, dusts, or gases in sufficient quantities to threaten human health or the environment.

(3) Produce uncontrolled flammable fumes or gases in sufficient quantities to pose a risk of fire or explosions.

(4) Damage the structural integrity of the device or facility.

(5) Threaten human health or the environment in any similar way.

(c) You must document compliance with paragraph (a) or (b) of this section. You may base this documentation on references to published scientific or engineering literature, data from trial tests (for example bench scale or pilot scale tests), waste analyses (as specified in §267.13), or the results of the treatment of similar wastes by similar treatment processes and under similar operating conditions.

§267.18 What are the standards for selecting the location of my facility?

(a) You may not locate portions of new facilities where hazardous waste will be treated or stored within 61 meters (200 feet) of a fault that has had displacement in Holocene time.

(1) "Fault" means a fracture along which rocks on one side have been displaced with respect to those on the other side.

(2) "Displacement" means the relative movement of any two sides of a fault measured in any direction.

(3) "Holocene" means the most recent epoch of the Quaternary period, extending from the end of the Pleistocene to the present.

Note to paragraph (a)(3): Procedures for demonstrating compliance with this standard are specified in 40 CFR 270.14(b)(11). Facilities which are located in political jurisdictions other than those listed in appendix VI of 40 CFR part 264, are assumed to be in compliance with this requirement.

(b) If your facility is located in a 100-year flood plain, it must be designed, constructed, operated, and maintained to prevent washout of any hazardous waste by a 100-year flood.

(1) "100-year flood plain" means any land area that is subject to a one percent or greater chance of flooding in any given year from any source.

(2) "Washout" means the movement of hazardous waste from the active portion of the facility as a result of flooding.

(3) "100-year flood" means a flood that has a one percent chance of being equaled or exceeded in any given year.

Subpart C—Preparedness and Prevention

§267.30 Does this subpart apply to me?

This subpart applies to you if you own or operate a facility that treats or stores hazardous waste under a 40 CFR part 270, subpart J standardized permit, except as provided in §267.1(b).

§267.31 What are the general design and operation standards?

You must design, construct, maintain, and operate your facility to minimize the possibility of a fire, explosion, or any unplanned sudden or non-sudden release of hazardous waste or hazardous waste constituents to air, soil, or surface water that could threaten human health or the environment.

§267.32 What equipment am I required to have?

Your facility must be equipped with all of the following, unless none of the hazards posed by waste handled at the facility could require a particular kind of equipment specified below:

(a) An internal communications or alarm system capable of providing immediate emergency instruction (voice or signal) to facility personnel.

(b) A device, such as a telephone (immediately available at the scene of operations) or a hand-held two-way radio, capable of summoning emergency assistance from local police departments, fire departments, or State or local emergency response teams.

(c) Portable fire extinguishers, fire control equipment (including special extinguishing equipment, such as that using foam, inert gas, or dry chemicals), spill control equipment, and decontamination equipment.

(d) Water at adequate volume and pressure to supply water hose streams, or foam-producing equipment, or automatic sprinklers, or water spray systems.

§267.33 What are the testing and maintenance requirements for the equipment?

You must test and maintain all required facility communications or alarm systems, fire protection equipment, spill control equipment, and decontamination equipment, as necessary, to assure its proper operation in time of emergency.

§267.34 When must personnel have access to communication equipment or an alarm system?

(a) Whenever hazardous waste is being poured, mixed, spread, or otherwise handled, all personnel involved in the operation must have immediate access to an internal alarm or emergency communication device, either directly or through visual or voice contact with another employee, unless the device is not required under §267.32.

(b) If just one employee is on the premises while the facility is operating, that person must have immediate access to a device, such as a telephone (immediately available at the scene of operation) or a hand-held two-way radio, capable of summoning external emergency assistance, unless not required under §267.32.

§267.35 How do I ensure access for personnel and equipment during emergencies?

You must maintain enough aisle space to allow the unobstructed movement of personnel, fire protection equipment, spill control equipment, and decontamination equipment to any area of facility operation in an emergency, as appropriate, considering the type of waste being stored or treated.

§267.36 What arrangements must I make with local authorities for emergencies?

(a) You must attempt to make the following arrangements, as appropriate, for the type of waste handled at your facility and the potential need for the services of these organizations:

(1) Arrangements to familiarize police, fire departments, and emergency response teams with the layout of the facility, properties of hazardous waste handled at the facility and associated hazards, places where facility personnel would normally be working, entrances to and roads inside the facility, and possible evacuation routes.

(2) Agreements designating primary emergency authority to a specific police and a specific fire department where more than one police and fire department might respond to an emergency, and agreements with any others to provide support to the primary emergency authority.

(3) Agreements with State emergency response teams, emergency response contractors, and equipment suppliers.

(4) Arrangements to familiarize local hospitals with the properties of hazardous waste handled at the facility and the types of injuries or illnesses that could result from fires, explosions, or releases at the facility.

(b) If State or local authorities decline to enter into such arrangements, you must document the refusal in the operating record.

Subpart D—Contingency Plan and Emergency Procedures

§267.50 Does this subpart apply to me?

This subpart applies to you if you own or operate a facility that treats or stores hazardous waste under a 40 CFR part 270, subpart J standardized permit, except as provided in §267.1(b).

§267.51 What is the purpose of the contingency plan and how do I use it?

(a) You must have a contingency plan for your facility. You must design the plan to minimize hazards to human health or the environment from fires, explosions, or any unplanned sudden or non-sudden release of hazardous waste or hazardous waste constituents to air, soil, or surface water.

(b) You must implement the provisions of the plan immediately whenever there is a fire, explosion, or release of hazardous waste or hazardous waste constituents which could threaten human health or the environment.

§267.52 What must be in the contingency plan?

(a) Your contingency plan must:

(1) Describe the actions facility personnel will take to comply with §§267.51 and 267.56 in response to fires, explosions, or any unplanned sudden or non-sudden release of hazardous waste or hazardous waste constituents to air, soil, or surface water at the facility.

(2) Describe all arrangements agreed upon under §267.36 by local police departments, fire departments, hospitals, contractors, and state and local emergency response teams to coordinate emergency services.

(3) List names, addresses, and phone numbers (office and home) of all persons qualified to act as emergency coordinator (see §267.55), and you must keep the list up to date. Where more than one person is listed, one must be named as primary emergency coordinator and others must be listed in the order in which they will assume responsibility as alternates.

(4) Include a current list of all emergency equipment at the facility (such as fire extinguishing systems, spill control equipment, communications and alarm systems (internal and external), and decontamination equipment), where this equipment is required. In addition, you must include the location and a physical description of each item on the list, and a brief outline of its capabilities.

(5) Include an evacuation plan for facility personnel where there is a possibility that evacuation could be necessary. You must describe signal(s) to be used to begin

evacuation, evacuation routes, and alternate evacuation routes (in cases where the primary routes could be blocked by releases of hazardous waste or fires).

(b) If you have already prepared a Spill Prevention, Control, and Countermeasures (SPCC) Plan under 40 CFR part 112, or some other emergency or contingency plan, you need only amend that plan to incorporate hazardous waste management provisions that will comply with the requirements of this part.

§267.53 Who must have copies of the contingency plan?

(a) You must maintain a copy of the plan with all revisions at the facility; and

(b) You must submit a copy with all revisions to all local police departments, fire departments, hospitals, and state and local emergency response teams that may be called upon to provide emergency services.

§267.54 When must I amend the contingency plan?

You must review, and immediately amend the contingency plan, if necessary, whenever:

(a) The facility permit is revised.

(b) The plan fails in an emergency.

(c) You change the facility (in its design, construction, operation, maintenance, or other circumstances) in a way that materially increases the potential for fires, explosions, or releases of hazardous waste or hazardous waste constituents, or changes the response necessary in an emergency.

(d) You change the list of emergency coordinators.

(e) You change the list of emergency equipment.

§267.55 What is the role of the emergency coordinator?

At least one employee must be either on the facility premises or on call at all times (that is, available to respond to an emergency by reaching the facility within a short period of time) who has the responsibility for coordinating all emergency response measures. This emergency coordinator must be thoroughly familiar with all aspects of the facility's contingency plan, all operations and activities at the facility, the location and characteristics of waste handled, the location of all records within the facility, and the facility layout. In addition, this person must have the authority to commit the resources needed to carry out the contingency plan.

§267.56 What are the required emergency procedures for the emergency coordinator?

(a) Whenever there is an imminent or actual emergency situation, the emergency coordinator (or his designee when the emergency coordinator is on call) must immediately:

(1) Activate internal facility alarm or communication systems, where applicable, to notify all facility personnel, and

(2) Notify appropriate State or local agencies with designated response roles if their help is needed.

(b) Whenever there is a release, fire, or explosion, the emergency coordinator must:

(1) Immediately identify the character, exact source, amount, and areal extent of any released materials. He may do this by observation or review of facility records or manifests, and, if necessary, by chemical analysis.

(2) Assess possible hazards to human health or the environment that may result from the release, fire, or explosion. This assessment must consider both direct and indirect effects of the release, fire, or explosion. For example, the assessment would consider the effects of any toxic, irritating, or asphyxiating gases that are generated, or the effects of any hazardous surface water run-off from water or chemical agents used to control fire and heat-induced explosions.

(c) If the emergency coordinator determines that the facility has had a release, fire, or explosion which could threaten human health, or the environment, outside the facility, he must report his findings as follows:

(1) If his assessment indicates that evacuation of local areas may be advisable, he must immediately notify appropriate local authorities. He must be available to help appropriate officials decide whether local areas should be evacuated; and

(2) He must immediately notify either the government official designated as the on-scene coordinator for that geographical area, or the National Response Center (using their 24-hour toll-free number 800/424–8802). The report must include:

(i) Name and telephone number of the reporter.

(ii) Name and address of facility.

(iii) Time and type of incident (for example, a release or a fire).

(iv) Name and quantity of material(s) involved, to the extent known.

(v) The extent of injuries, if any.

(vi) The possible hazards to human health or the environment outside the facility.

(d) During an emergency, the emergency coordinator must take all reasonable measures necessary to ensure that fires, explosions, and releases do not occur, recur, or spread to other hazardous waste at the facility. These measures must include, where applicable, stopping processes and operations, collecting and containing release waste, and removing or isolating containers.

(e) If the facility stops operations in response to a fire, explosion, or release, the emergency coordinator must monitor for leaks, pressure buildup, gas generation, or ruptures in valves, pipes, or other equipment, when appropriate.

§267.57 What must the emergency coordinator do after an emergency?

(a) Immediately after an emergency, the emergency coordinator must provide for treating, storing, or disposing of recovered waste, contaminated soil or surface water, or any other material that results from a release, fire, or explosion at the facility.

(b) The emergency coordinator must ensure that, in the affected area(s) of the facility:

(1) No waste that may be incompatible with the released material is treated, stored, or disposed of until cleanup procedures are completed.

(2) All emergency equipment listed in the contingency plan is cleaned and fit for its intended use before operations are resumed.

§267.58 What notification and recordkeeping must I do after an emergency?

(a) You must notify the Regional Administrator, and appropriate State and local authorities, that the facility is in compliance with §267.57(b) before operations are resumed in the affected area(s) of the facility.

(b) You must note the time, date, and details of any incident that requires implementing the contingency plan in the operating record. Within 15 days after the incident, you must submit a written report on the incident to the Regional Administrator. You must include the following in the report:

(1) The name, address, and telephone number of the owner or operator.

(2) The name, address, and telephone number of the facility.

(3) The date, time, and type of incident (*e.g.*, fire, explosion).

(4) The name and quantity of material(s) involved.

(5) The extent of injuries, if any.

(6) An assessment of actual or potential hazards to human health or the environment, where this is applicable.

(7) The estimated quantity and disposition of recovered material that resulted from the incident.

Subpart E—Recordkeeping, Reporting, and Notifying

§267.70 Does this subpart apply to me?

This subpart applies to you if you own or operate a facility that stores or non-thermally treats a hazardous waste under a 40 CFR part 270, subpart J standardized permit, except as provided in §267.1(b). In addition, you must comply with the manifest requirements of 40 CFR part 262 whenever a shipment of hazardous waste is initiated from your facility.

§267.71 Use of the manifest system.

(a) If a facility receives hazardous waste accompanied by a manifest, the owner or operator, or his agent, must:

(1) Sign and date each copy of the manifest to certify that the hazardous waste covered by the manifest was received;

(2) Note any significant discrepancies in the manifest (as defined in §267.72(a)) on each copy of the manifest;

(3) Immediately give the transporter at least one copy of the signed manifest;

(4) Within 30 days after the delivery, send a copy of the manifest to the generator; and

(5) Retain at the facility a copy of each manifest for at least three years from the date of delivery.

(b) If a facility receives, from a rail or water (bulk shipment) transporter, hazardous waste which is accompanied by a shipping paper containing all the information required on the manifest (excluding the EPA identification numbers, generator's certification, and signatures), the owner or operator, or his agent, must:

(1) Sign and date each copy of the manifest or shipping paper (if the manifest has not been received) to certify that the hazardous waste covered by the manifest or shipping paper was received;

(2) Note any significant discrepancies (as defined in §267.72(a)) in the manifest or shipping paper (if the manifest has not been received) on each copy of the manifest or shipping paper. Note that the Agency does not intend that the owner or operator of a facility whose procedures under §267.13(c) include waste analysis must perform that analysis before signing the shipping paper and giving it to the transporter. Section

267.72(b), however, requires reporting an unreconciled discrepancy discovered during later analysis.

Publisher's Note: The above reference to §267.13(c) is incorrect and should refer to §267.13(b).

(3) Immediately give the rail or water (bulk shipment) transporter at least one copy of the manifest or shipping paper (if the manifest has not been received);

(4) Within 30 days after the delivery, send a copy of the signed and dated manifest to the generator; however, if the manifest has not been received within 30 days after delivery, the owner or operator, or his agent, must send a copy of the shipping paper signed and dated to the generator. Note that §262.23(c) of this chapter requires the generator to send three copies of the manifest to the facility when hazardous waste is sent by rail or water (bulk shipment); and

(5) Retain at the facility a copy of the manifest and shipping paper (if signed in lieu of the manifest at the time of delivery) for at least three years from the date of delivery.

(c) Whenever a shipment of hazardous waste is initiated from a facility, the owner or operator of that facility must comply with the requirements of part 262 of this chapter. The Agency notes that the provisions of §262.34 are applicable to the on-site accumulation of hazardous wastes by generators. Therefore, the provisions of §262.34 only apply to owners or operators who are shipping hazardous waste which they generated at that facility.

(d) Within three working days of the receipt of a shipment subject to 40 CFR part 262, subpart H, the owner or operator of the facility must provide a copy of the tracking document bearing all required signatures to the notifier, to the Office of Enforcement and Compliance Assurance, Office of Compliance, Enforcement Planning, Targeting and Data Division (2222A), Environmental Protection Agency, 1200 Pennsylvania Ave., NW., Washington, DC 20460, and to competent authorities of all other concerned countries. The original copy of the tracking document must be maintained at the facility for at least three years from the date of signature.

§267.72 Manifest discrepancies.

(a) Manifest discrepancies are differences between the quantity or type of hazardous waste designated on the manifest or shipping paper, and the quantity or type of hazardous waste a facility actually receives. Significant discrepancies in quantity are:

(1) For bulk waste, variations greater than 10 percent in weight; and

(2) For batch waste, any variation in piece count, such as a discrepancy of one drum in a truckload. Significant discrepancies in type are obvious differences which can be discovered by inspection or waste analysis, such as waste solvent substituted for waste acid, or toxic constituents not reported on the manifest or shipping paper.

(b) Upon discovering a significant discrepancy, the owner or operator must attempt to reconcile the discrepancy with the waste generator or transporter (*e.g.*, with telephone conversations). If the discrepancy is not resolved within 15 days after receiving the waste, the owner or operator must immediately submit to the Regional Administrator a letter describing the discrepancy and attempts to reconcile it, and a copy of the manifest or shipping paper at issue.

§267.73 What information must I keep?

(a) You must keep a written operating record at your facility.

(b) You must record the following information, as it becomes available, and maintain the operating record until you close the facility:

(1) A description and the quantity of each type of hazardous waste generated, and the method(s) and date(s) of its storage and/or treatment at the facility as required by Appendix I of 40 CFR part 264;

(2) The location of each hazardous waste within the facility and the quantity at each location;

(3) Records and results of waste analyses and waste determinations you perform as specified in §§267.13, 267.17, and 40 CFR 264.1034, 264.1063, 264.1083, and 268.7;

(4) Summary reports and details of all incidents that require you to implement the contingency plan as specified in §267.58(b));

(5) Records and results of inspections as required by §267.15(d) (except you need to keep these data for only three years);

(6) Monitoring, testing or analytical data, and corrective action when required by subpart F of this part and §§267.191, 267.193, 267.195, and 40 CFR 264.1034(c) through 264.1034(f), 264.1035, 264.1063(d) through 264.1063(i), 264.1064, 264.1088, 264.1089, and 264.1090;

(7) All closure cost estimates under §267.142;

(8) Your certification, at least annually, that you have a program in place to reduce the volume and toxicity of hazardous waste that you generate to the degree that you determine to be economically practicable; and

that the proposed method of treatment or storage is that practicable method currently available to you that minimizes the present and future threat to human health and the environment;

(9) For an on-site treatment facility, the information contained in the notice (except the manifest number), and the certification and demonstration, if applicable, required by you under 40 CFR 268.7; and

(10) For an on-site storage facility, the information in the notice (except the manifest number), and the certification and demonstration, if applicable, required by you under 40 CFR 268.7.

(11) For an off-site treatment facility, a copy of the notice, and the certification and demonstration, if applicable, required by the generator or the owner or operator under §268.7 or §268.8;

(12) For an off-site storage facility, a copy of the notice, and the certification and demonstration, if applicable, required by the generator or the owner or operator under §268.7 or §268.8.

§267.74 Who sees the records?

(a) You must furnish all records, including plans, required under this part upon the request of any officer, employee, or representative of EPA who is duly designated by the Administrator, and make them available at all reasonable times for inspection.

(b) The retention period for all records required under this part is extended automatically during the course of any unresolved enforcement action involving the facility or as requested by the Administrator.

§267.75 What reports must I prepare and to whom do I send them?

You must prepare a biennial report and other reports listed in paragraph (b) of this section.

(a) Biennial report. You must prepare and submit a single copy of a biennial report to the Regional Administrator by March 1 of each even numbered year. The biennial report must be submitted on EPA form 8700–13B. The report must cover facility activities during the previous calendar year and must include:

(1) The EPA identification number, name, and address of the facility;

(2) The calendar year covered by the report;

(3) The method of treatment or storage for each hazardous waste;

(4) The most recent closure cost estimate under §267.142;

(5) A description of the efforts undertaken during the year to reduce the volume and toxicity of generated waste.

(6) A description of the changes in volume and toxicity of waste actually achieved during the year in comparison to previous years to the extent such information is available for the years prior to 1984.

(7) The certification signed by you.

(b) Additional reports. In addition to submitting the biennial reports, you must also report to the Regional Administrator:

(1) Releases, fires, and explosions as specified in §267.58(b);

(2) Facility closures specified in §267.117; and

(3) As otherwise required by subparts I, J, and DD of this part and part 264, subparts AA, BB, CC.

(c) For off-site facilities, the EPA identification number of each hazardous waste generator from which the facility received a hazardous waste during the year; for imported shipments, the report must give the name and address of the foreign generator;

(d) A description and the quantity of each hazardous waste the facility received during the year. For off-site facilities, this information must be listed by EPA identification number of each generator.

§267.76 What notifications must I make?

Before transferring ownership or operation of a facility during its operating life, you must notify the new owner or operator in writing of the requirements of this part and 40 CFR part 270, subpart J.

Subpart F—Releases from Solid Waste Management Units

§267.90 Who must comply with this section?

This subpart applies to you if you own or operate a facility that treats or stores hazardous waste under a 40 CFR part 270, subpart J standardized permit, except as provided in §267.1(b), or unless your facility already has a permit that imposes requirements for corrective action under 40 CFR 264.101.

§§267.91–267.100 [Reserved]

§267.101 What must I do to address corrective action for solid waste management units?

(a) You must institute corrective action as necessary to protect human health and the environment for all releases of hazardous waste or constituents from any solid waste management unit at the facility, regardless of the time at which waste was placed in such unit.

(b) The Regional Administrator will specify corrective action in the supplemental portion of your standardized permit in accordance with this section and 40 CFR part 264, subpart S. The Regional Administrator will include in the supplemental portion of your standardized permit schedules of compliance for corrective action (where corrective action cannot be completed prior to issuance of the permit) and assurances of financial responsibility for completing corrective action.

(c) You must implement corrective action beyond the facility property boundary, where necessary to protect human health and the environment, unless you demonstrate to the satisfaction of the Regional Administrator that, despite your best efforts, you were unable to obtain the necessary permission to undertake such actions. You are not relieved of all responsibility to clean up a release that has migrated beyond the facility boundary where off-site access is denied. On-site measures to address such releases will be determined on a case-by-case basis. You must provide assurances of financial responsibility for such corrective action.

(d) You do not have to comply with this section if you are the owner or operator of a remediation waste site unless your site is part of a facility that is subject to a permit for treating, storing, or disposing of hazardous wastes that are not remediation wastes.

Subpart G—Closure

§267.110 Does this subpart apply to me?

This subpart applies to you if you own or operate a facility that treats or stores hazardous waste under a 40 CFR part 270, subpart J standardized permit, except as provided in §267.1(b).

§267.111 What general standards must I meet when I stop operating the unit?

You must close the storage and treatment units in a manner that:

(a) Minimizes the need for further maintenance; and

(b) Controls, minimizes, or eliminates, to the extent necessary to protect human health and the environment, post-closure escape of hazardous waste, hazardous constituents, leachate, contaminated run-off, or hazardous waste decomposition products to the ground or surface waters or to the atmosphere; and

(c) Meets the closure requirements of this subpart and the requirements of §§267.176, 267.201, and 267.1108. If you determine that, when applicable, the closure requirements of §267.201(tanks) or §267.1108 (containment buildings) cannot be met, then you must close the unit in accordance with the requirements that apply to landfills (§264.310). In addition, for the purposes of post-closure and financial responsibility, such a tank system or containment building is then considered to be a landfill, and you must apply for a post-closure care permit in accordance with 40 CFR part 270.

§267.112 What procedures must I follow?

(a) To close a facility, you must follow your approved closure plan, and follow notification requirements.

(1) Your closure plan must be submitted at the time you submitted your Notice of Intent to operate under a standardized permit. Final issuance of the standardized permit constitutes approval of the closure plan, and the plan becomes a condition of the RCRA standardized permit.

(2) The Director's approval of the plan must ensure that the approved plan is consistent with §§267.111 through 267.115, 267.176, 267.201, and 267.1108.

(b) Satisfy the requirements for content of closure plan. The closure plan must identify steps necessary to perform partial and/or final closure of the facility. The closure plan must include, at least:

(1) A description of how each hazardous waste management unit at the facility subject to this subpart will be closed following §267.111.

(2) A description of how final closure of the facility will be conducted in accordance with §267.111. The description must identify the maximum extent of the operations which will be unclosed during the active life of the facility.

(3) An estimate of the maximum inventory of hazardous wastes ever on site during the active life of the facility and a detailed description of the methods you will use during partial and/or final closure, such as methods for removing, transporting, treating, storing, or disposing of all hazardous wastes, and identification of the type(s) of off-site hazardous waste management units to be used, if applicable.

(4) A detailed description of the steps needed to remove or decontaminate all hazardous waste residues and contaminated containment system components, equipment, structures, and soils during partial or final closure. These might include procedures for cleaning equipment and removing contaminated soils, methods for sampling and testing surrounding soils, and criteria for determining the extent of decontamination required to satisfy the closure performance standard;

(5) A detailed description of other activities necessary during the closure period to ensure that partial or final closure satisfies the closure performance standards.

(6) A schedule for closure of each hazardous waste management unit, and for final closure of the facility. The schedule must include, at a minimum, the total time required to close each hazardous waste management unit and the time required for intervening closure activities that allow tracking of progress of partial or final closure.

(7) For facilities that use trust funds to establish financial assurance under §267.143 and that are expected to close prior to the expiration of the permit, an estimate of the expected year of final closure.

(c) You may submit a written notification to the Director for a permit modification to amend the closure plan at any time prior to the notification of partial or final closure of the facility, following the applicable procedures in 40 CFR 124.211.

(1) Events leading to a change in the closure plan, and therefore requiring a modification, may include:

(i) A change in the operating plan or facility design;

(ii) A change in the expected year of closure, if applicable; or

(iii) In conducting partial or final closure activities, an unexpected event requiring a modification of the approved closure plan.

(2) The written notification or request must include a copy of the amended closure plan for review or approval by the Director. The Director will approve, disapprove, or modify this amended plan in accordance with the procedures in 40 CFR 124.211 and 270.320.

(d) Notification before final closure. (1) You must notify the Director in writing at least 45 days before the date that you expect to begin final closure of a treatment or storage tank, container storage area, or containment building.

(2) The date when you "expect to begin closure" must be no later than 30 days after the date that any hazardous waste management unit receives the known final volume of hazardous wastes.

(3) If your facility's permit is terminated, or if you are otherwise ordered, by judicial decree or final order under section 3008 of RCRA, to cease receiving hazardous wastes or to close, then the requirements of this paragraph (d) do not apply. However, you must close the facility following the deadlines established in §267.115.

§267.113 Will the public have the opportunity to comment on the plan?

(a) The Director will provide you and the public, when the draft standardized permit is public noticed, the opportunity to submit written comments on the plan and to the draft permit as allowed by 40 CFR 124.208. The Director will also, in response to a request or at his/her own discretion, hold a public hearing whenever such a hearing might clarify one or more issues concerning the closure plan, and the permit.

(b) The Director will give public notice of the hearing 30 days before it occurs. Public notice of the hearing may be given at the same time as notice of the opportunity for the public to submit written comments, and the two notices may be combined.

§267.114 [Reserved]

§267.115 After I stop operating, how long until I must close?

(a) Within 90 days after the final volume of hazardous waste is sent to a unit, you must treat or remove from the unit all hazardous wastes following the approved closure plan.

(b) You must complete final closure activities in accordance with the approved closure plan within 180 days after the final volume of hazardous wastes is sent to the unit. The Director may approve an extension of 180 days to the closure period if you comply with all applicable requirements for requesting a modification to the permit and demonstrate that:

(1) The final closure activities will take longer than 180 days to complete due to circumstances beyond your control, excluding ground water contamination; and

(2) You have taken and will continue to take all steps to prevent threats to human health and the environment from the unclosed, but not operating hazardous waste management unit or facility, including compliance with all applicable permit requirements.

(3) The demonstration must be made at least 30 days prior to the expiration of the initial 180-day period.

(c) Nothing in this section precludes you from removing hazardous wastes and decontaminating or dismantling equipment in accordance with the approved final closure plan at any time before or after notification of final closure.

§267.116 What must I do with contaminated equipment, structure, and soils?

You must properly dispose of or decontaminate all contaminated equipment, structures, and soils during the partial and final closure periods. By removing any hazardous wastes or hazardous constituents during partial and final closure, you may become a generator of hazardous waste and must handle that waste following all applicable requirements of 40 CFR part 262.

§267.117 How do I certify closure?

Within 60 days of the completion of final closure of each unit under a part 270 subpart J standardized permit, you must submit to the Director, by registered mail, a certification that each hazardous waste management unit or facility, as applicable, has been closed following the specifications in the closure plan. Both you and an independent registered professional engineer must sign the certification. You must furnish documentation supporting the independent registered professional engineer's certification to the Director upon request until he releases you from the financial assurance requirements for closure under §267.143(i).

Subpart H—Financial Requirements

§267.140 Who must comply with this subpart, and briefly, what do they have to do?

(a) The regulations in this subpart apply to owners and operators who treat or store hazardous waste under a standardized permit, except as provided in §267.1(b), or §267.140(d) below.

(b) The owner or operator must:

(1) Prepare a closure cost estimate as required in §267.142;

(2) Demonstrate financial assurance for closure as required in §267.143; and

(3) Demonstrate financial assurance for liability as required in §267.147.

(c) The owner or operator must notify the Regional Administrator if the owner or operator is named as a debtor in a bankruptcy proceeding under Title 11 (Bankruptcy), U.S. Code (See also §267.148).

(d) States and the Federal government are exempt from the requirements of this subpart.

§267.141 Definitions of terms as used in this subpart.

(a) *Closure plan* means the plan for closure prepared in accordance with the requirements of §267.112.

(b) *Current closure cost estimate* means the most recent of the estimates prepared in accordance with §267.142 (a), (b), and (c).

(c) [Reserved]

(d) *Parent corporation* means a corporation which directly owns at least 50 percent of the voting stock of the corporation which is the facility owner or operator; the latter corporation is deemed a "subsidiary" of the parent corporation.

(e) [Reserved]

(f) The following terms are used in the specifications for the financial tests for closure and liability coverage. The definitions are intended to assist in the understanding of these regulations and are not intended to limit the meanings of terms in a way that conflicts with generally accepted accounting practices:

Assets means all existing and all probable future economic benefits obtained or controlled by a particular entity.

Current plugging and abandonment cost estimate means the most recent of the estimates prepared in accordance with §144.62(a), (b), and (c) of this chapter.

Independently audited refers to an audit performed by an independent certified public accountant in accordance with generally accepted auditing standards.

Liabilities means probable future sacrifices of economic benefits arising from present obligations to transfer assets or provide services to other entities in the future as a result of past transactions or events.

Tangible net worth means the tangible assets that remain after deducting liabilities; such assets would not include intangibles such as goodwill and rights to patents or royalties.

(g) In the liability insurance requirements, the terms *bodily injury and property damage* shall have the meanings given these terms by applicable State law. However, these terms do not include those liabilities which, consistent with standard industry practices, are excluded from coverage in liability policies for bodily injury and property damage. The Agency intends the meanings of other terms used in the liability insurance requirements to be consistent with their common meanings within the insurance industry. The definitions given below of several of the terms are intended to assist in the understanding of these regulations and are not intended to limit their meanings in a way that conflicts with general insurance industry usage.

Accidental occurrence means an accident, including continuous or repeated exposure to conditions, which results in bodily injury or property damage neither expected nor intended from the standpoint of the insured.

Legal defense costs means any expenses that an insurer incurs in defending against claims of third parties brought under the terms and conditions of an insurance policy.

Sudden accidental occurrence means an occurrence which is not continuous or repeated in nature.

(h) *Substantial business relationship* means the extent of a business relationship necessary under applicable State law to make a guarantee contract issued incident to that relationship valid and enforceable. A "substantial business relationship" must arise from a pattern of recent or ongoing business transactions, in addition to the guarantee itself, such that a currently existing business relationship between the guarantor and the owner or operator is demonstrated to the satisfaction of the applicable EPA Regional Administrator.

§267.142 Cost estimate for closure.

(a) The owner or operator must have at the facility a detailed written estimate, in current dollars, of the cost of closing the facility in accordance with the requirements in §§267.111 through 267.115 and applicable closure requirements in §§267.176, 267.201, 267.1108.

(1) The estimate must equal the cost of final closure at the point in the facility's active life when the extent and manner of its operation would make closure the most expensive, as indicated by the closure plan (see §267.112(b)); and

(2) The closure cost estimate must be based on the costs to the owner or operator of hiring a third party to close the facility. A third party is a party who is neither a parent nor a subsidiary of the owner or operator. (See definition of parent corporation in §267.141(d).) The owner or operator may use costs for on-site disposal if he can demonstrate that on-site disposal capacity will exist at all times over the life of the facility.

(3) The closure cost estimate may not incorporate any salvage value that may be realized with the sale of hazardous wastes, or non-hazardous wastes, facility structures or equipment, land, or other assets associated with the facility at the time of partial or final closure.

(4) The owner or operator may not incorporate a zero cost for hazardous wastes, or non-hazardous wastes that might have economic value.

(b) During the active life of the facility, the owner or operator must adjust the closure cost estimate for inflation within 60 days prior to the anniversary date of the establishment of the financial instrument(s) used to comply with §267.143. For owners and operators using the financial test or corporate guarantee, the closure cost estimate must be updated for inflation within 30 days after the close of the firm's fiscal year and before submission of updated information to the Regional Administrator as specified in §267.143(f)(2)(iii). The adjustment may be made by recalculating the maximum costs of closure in current dollars, or by using an inflation factor derived from the most recent Implicit Price Deflator for Gross Domestic Product published by the U.S. Department of Commerce in its Survey of Current Business, as specified in paragraphs (b)(1) and (2) of this section. The inflation factor is the result of dividing the latest published annual Deflator by the Deflator for the previous year.

(1) The first adjustment is made by multiplying the closure cost estimate by the inflation factor. The result is the adjusted closure cost estimate.

(2) Subsequent adjustments are made by multiplying the latest adjusted closure cost estimate by the latest inflation factor.

(c) During the active life of the facility, the owner or operator must revise the closure cost estimate no later than 30 days after the Regional Administrator has approved the request to modify the closure plan, if the change in the closure plan increases the cost of closure. The revised closure cost estimate must be adjusted for inflation as specified in §267.142(b).

(d) The owner or operator must keep the following at the facility during the operating life of the facility: The latest closure cost estimate prepared in accordance with paragraphs (a) and (c) of this section and, when this estimate has been adjusted in accordance with paragraph (b) of this section, the latest adjusted closure cost estimate.

§267.143 Financial assurance for closure.

The owner or operator must establish financial assurance for closure of each storage or treatment unit that he owns or operates. In establishing financial assurance for closure, the owner or operator must choose from the financial assurance mechanisms in paragraphs (a), (b), (c), (d), (e), (f), and (g) of this section. The owner or operator can also use a combination of mechanisms for a single facility if they meet the requirement in paragraph (h) of this section, or may use a single mechanism for multiple facilities as in paragraph (i) of this section. The Regional Administrator will release the owner or operator from the requirements of this section after the owner or operator meets the criteria under paragraph (j) of this section.

(a) *Closure Trust Fund.* Owners and operators can use the "closure trust fund," that is specified in 40 CFR 264.143(a)(1) and (2), and 264.143(a)(6)–(11). For purposes of this paragraph, the following provisions also apply:

(1) Payments into the trust fund for a new facility must be made annually by the owner or operator over the remaining operating life of the facility as estimated

in the closure plan, or over 3 years, whichever period is shorter. This period of time is hereafter referred to as the "pay-in period."

(2) For a new facility, the first payment into the closure trust fund must be made before the facility may accept the initial storage. A receipt from the trustee must be submitted by the owner or operator to the Regional Administrator before this initial storage of waste. The first payment must be at least equal to the current closure cost estimate, divided by the number of years in the pay-in period, except as provided in paragraph (h) of this section for multiple mechanisms. Subsequent payments must be made no later than 30 days after each anniversary date of the first payment. The owner or operator determines the amount of each subsequent payment by subtracting the current value of the trust fund from the current closure cost estimate, and dividing this difference by the number of years remaining in the pay-in period. Mathematically, the formula is

Next Payment = (Current Closure Estimate – Current Value of the Trust Fund) Divided by Years Remaining in the Pay-In Period.

(3) The owner or operator of a facility existing on the effective date of this paragraph can establish a trust fund to meet this paragraph's financial assurance requirements. If the value of the trust fund is less than the current closure cost estimate when a final approval of the permit is granted for the facility, the owner or operator must pay the difference into the trust fund within 60 days.

(4) The owner or operator may accelerate payments into the trust fund or deposit the full amount of the closure cost estimate when establishing the trust fund. However, he must maintain the value of the fund at no less than the value that the fund would have if annual payments were made as specified in paragraph (a)(2) or (a)(3) of this section.

(5) The owner or operator must submit a trust agreement with the wording specified in 40 CFR 264.151(a)(1).

(b) *Surety Bond Guaranteeing Payment into a Closure Trust Fund.* Owners and operators can use the "surety bond guaranteeing payment into a closure trust fund," as specified in 40 CFR 264.143(b), including the use of the surety bond instrument specified at 40 CFR 264.151(b), and the standby trust specified at 40 CFR 264.143(b)(3).

(c) *Surety Bond Guaranteeing Performance of Closure.* Owners and operators can use the "surety bond guaranteeing performance of closure," as specified in 40 CFR 264.143(c), the submission and use of the surety bond instrument specified at 40 CFR 264.151(c), and the standby trust specified at 40 CFR 264.143(c)(3).

(d) *Closure Letter of Credit.* Owners and operators can use the "closure letter of credit" specified in 40 CFR 264.143(d), the submission and use of the irrevocable letter of credit instrument specified in 40 CFR 264.151(d), and the standby trust specified in 40 CFR 264.143(d)(3).

(e) *Closure Insurance.* Owners and operators can use "closure insurance," as specified in 40 CFR 264.143(e), utilizing the certificate of insurance for closure specified at 40 CFR 264.151(e).

(f) *Corporate financial test.* An owner or operator that satisfies the requirements of this paragraph may demonstrate financial assurance up to the amount specified in this paragraph:

(1) *Financial component.*

(i) The owner or operator must satisfy one of the following three conditions:

(A) A current rating for its senior unsecured debt of AAA, AA, A, or BBB as issued by Standard and Poor's or Aaa, Aa, A or Baa as issued by Moody's; or

(B) A ratio of less than 1.5 comparing total liabilities to net worth; or

(C) A ratio of greater than 0.10 comparing the sum of net income plus depreciation, depletion and amortization, minus $10 million, to total liabilities.

(ii) The tangible net worth of the owner or operator must be greater than:

(A) The sum of the current environmental obligations (see paragraph (f)(2)(i)(A)(1) of this section), including guarantees, covered by a financial test plus $10 million, except as provided in paragraph (f)(1)(ii)(B) of this section.

(B) $10 million in tangible net worth plus the amount of any guarantees that have not been recognized as liabilities on the financial statements provided all of the environmental obligations (see paragraph (f)(2)(i)(A)(1) of this section) covered by a financial test are recognized as liabilities on the owner's or operator's audited financial statements, and subject to the approval of the Regional Administrator.

(iii) The owner or operator must have assets located in the United States amounting to at least the sum of environmental obligations covered by a financial test as described in paragraph (f)(2)(i)(A)(1) of this section.

(2) *Recordkeeping and reporting requirements.*

(i) The owner or operator must submit the following items to the Regional Administrator:

(A) A letter signed by the owner's or operator's chief financial officer that:

(*1*) Lists all the applicable current types, amounts, and sums of environmental obligations covered by a financial test. These obligations include both obligations in the programs which EPA directly operates and obligations where EPA has delegated authority to a State or approved a State's program. These obligations include, but are not limited to:

(*i*) Liability, closure, post-closure and corrective action cost estimates required for hazardous waste treatment, storage, and disposal facilities under 40 CFR 264.101, 264.142, 264.144, 264.147, 265.142, 265.144, and 265.147;

(*ii*) Cost estimates required for municipal solid waste management facilities under 40 CFR 258.71, 258.72, and 258.73;

(*iii*) Current plugging cost estimates required for UIC facilities under 40 CFR 144.62;

(*iv*) Cost estimates required for petroleum underground storage tank facilities under 40 CFR 280.93;

(*v*) Cost estimates required for PCB storage facilities under 40 CFR 761.65;

(*vi*) Any financial assurance required under, or as part of an action undertaken under, the Comprehensive Environmental Response, Compensation, and Liability Act; and

(*vii*) Any other environmental obligations that are assured through a financial test.

(*2*) Provides evidence demonstrating that the firm meets the conditions of either paragraph (f)(1)(i)(A) or (f)(1)(i)(B) or (f)(1)(i)(C) of this section and paragraphs (f)(1)(ii) and (f)(1)(iii) of this section.

(B) A copy of the independent certified public accountant's unqualified opinion of the owner's or operator's financial statements for the latest completed fiscal year. To be eligible to use the financial test, the owner's or operator's financial statements must receive an unqualified opinion from the independent certified public accountant. An adverse opinion, disclaimer of opinion, or other qualified opinion will be cause for disallowance, with the potential exception for qualified opinions provided in the next sentence. The Regional Administrator may evaluate qualified opinions on a case-by-case basis and allow use of the financial test in cases where the Regional Administrator deems that the matters which form the basis for the qualification are insufficient to warrant disallowance of the test. If the Regional Administrator does not allow use of the test, the owner or operator must provide alternate financial assurance that meets the requirements of this section within 30 days after the notification of disallowance.

(C) If the chief financial officer's letter providing evidence of financial assurance includes financial data showing that the owner or operator satisfies paragraph (f)(1)(i)(B) or (f)(1)(i)(C) of this section that are different from data in the audited financial statements referred to in paragraph (f)(2)(i)(B) of this section or any other audited financial statement or data filed with the SEC, then a special report from the owner's or operator's independent certified public accountant to the owner or operator is required. The special report shall be based upon an agreed upon procedures engagement in accordance with professional auditing standards and shall describe the procedures performed in comparing the data in the chief financial officer's letter derived from the independently audited, year-end financial statements for the latest fiscal year with the amounts in such financial statements, the findings of that comparison, and the reasons for any differences.

(D) If the chief financial officer's letter provides a demonstration that the firm has assured for environmental obligations as provided in paragraph (f)(1)(ii)(B) of this section, then the letter shall include a report from the independent certified public accountant that verifies that all of the environmental obligations covered by a financial test have been recognized as liabilities on the audited financial statements, how these obligations have been measured and reported, and that the tangible net worth of the firm is at least $10 million plus the amount of any guarantees provided.

(ii) The owner or operator of a new facility must submit the items specified in paragraph (f)(2)(i) of this section to the Regional Administrator at least 60 days before placing waste in the facility.

(iii) After the initial submission of items specified in paragraph (f)(2)(i) of this section, the owner or operator must send updated information to the Regional Administrator within 90 days following the close of the owner or operator's fiscal year. The Regional Administrator may provide up to an additional 45 days for an owner or operator who can demonstrate that 90 days is insufficient time to acquire audited financial statements. The updated information must consist of all items specified in paragraph (f)(2)(i) of this section.

(iv) The owner or operator is no longer required to submit the items specified in this paragraph (f)(2) of this section or comply with the requirements of this paragraph (f) when:

(A) The owner or operator substitutes alternate financial assurance as specified in this section that is not subject to these recordkeeping and reporting requirements; or

(B) The Regional Administrator releases the owner or operator from the requirements of this section in accordance with paragraph (j) of this section.

(v) An owner or operator who no longer meets the requirements of paragraph (f)(1) of this section cannot use the financial test to demonstrate financial assurance. Instead an owner or operator who no longer meets the requirements of paragraph (f)(1) of this section, must:

(A) Send notice to the Regional Administrator of intent to establish alternate financial assurance as specified in this section. The owner or operator must send this notice by certified mail within 90 days following the close the owner or operator's fiscal year for which the year-end financial data show that the owner or operator no longer meets the requirements of this section.

(B) Provide alternative financial assurance within 120 days after the end of such fiscal year.

(vi) The Regional Administrator may, based on a reasonable belief that the owner or operator may no longer meet the requirements of paragraph (f)(1) of this section, require at any time the owner or operator to provide reports of its financial condition in addition to or including current financial test documentation as specified in paragraph (f)(2) of this section. If the Regional Administrator finds that the owner or operator no longer meets the requirements of paragraph (f)(1) of this section, the owner or operator must provide alternate financial assurance that meets the requirements of this section.

(g) *Corporate Guarantee.*

(1) An owner or operator may meet the requirements of this section by obtaining a written guarantee. The guarantor must be the direct or higher-tier parent corporation of the owner or operator, a firm whose parent corporation is also the parent corporation of the owner or operator, or a firm with a "substantial business relationship" with the owner or operator. The guarantor must meet the requirements for owners or operators in paragraph (f) of this section and must comply with the terms of the guarantee. The wording of the guarantee must be identical to the wording in 40 CFR 264.151(h). The certified copy of the guarantee must accompany the letter from the guarantor's chief financial officer and accountants' opinions. If the guarantor's parent corporation is also the parent corporation of the owner or operator, the letter from the guarantor's chief financial officer must describe the value received in consideration of the guarantee. If the guarantor is a firm with a "substantial business relationship" with the owner or operator, this letter must describe this "substantial business relationship" and the value received in consideration of the guarantee.

(2) For a new facility, the guarantee must be effective and the guarantor must submit the items in paragraph (g)(1) of this section and the items specified in paragraph (f)(2)(i) of this section to the Regional Administrator at least 60 days before the owner or operator places waste in the facility.

(3) The terms of the guarantee must provide that:

(i) If the owner or operator fails to perform closure at a facility covered by the guarantee, the guarantor will:

(A) Perform, or pay a third party to perform closure (performance guarantee); or

(B) Establish a fully funded trust fund as specified in paragraph (a) of this section in the name of the owner or operator (payment guarantee).

(ii) The guarantee will remain in force for as long as the owner or operator must comply with the applicable financial assurance requirements of this subpart unless the guarantor sends prior notice of cancellation by certified mail to the owner or operator and to the Regional Administrator. Cancellation may not occur, however, during the 120 days beginning on the date of receipt of the notice of cancellation by both the owner or operator and the Regional Administrator as evidenced by the return receipts.

(iii) If notice of cancellation is given, the owner or operator must, within 90 days following receipt of the cancellation notice by the owner or operator and the Regional Administrator, obtain alternate financial assurance, and submit documentation for that alternate financial assurance to the Regional Administrator. If the owner or operator fails to provide alternate financial assurance and obtain the written approval of such alternative assurance from the Regional Administrator within the 90-day period, the guarantor must provide that alternate assurance in the name of the owner or operator and submit the necessary documentation for the alternative assurance to the Regional Administrator within 120 days of the cancellation notice.

(4) If a corporate guarantor no longer meets the requirements of paragraph (f)(1) of this section, the owner or operator must, within 90 days, obtain alternative assurance, and submit the assurance to the Regional Administrator for approval. If the owner or operator fails to provide alternate financial assurance within the 90-day period, the guarantor must provide that alternate assurance within the next 30 days, and submit it to the Regional Administrator for approval.

(5) The guarantor is no longer required to meet the requirements of this paragraph (g) when:

(i) The owner or operator substitutes alternate financial assurance as specified in this section; or

(ii) The owner or operator is released from the requirements of this section in accordance with paragraph (j) of this section.

(h) *Use of Multiple Financial Mechanisms.* An owner or operator may use more than one mechanism at a particular facility to satisfy the requirements of this section. The acceptable mechanisms are trust funds, surety bonds guaranteeing payment into a trust fund, letters of credit, insurance, the financial test, and the guarantee, except owners or operators cannot combine the financial test with the guarantee. The mechanisms must be as specified in paragraphs (a), (b), (d), (e), (f), and (g) respectively of this section, except it is the combination of mechanisms rather than a single mechanism that must provide assurance for an amount at least equal to the cost estimate. If an owner or operator uses a trust fund in combination with a surety bond or letter of credit, he may use the trust fund as the standby trust for the other mechanisms. A single trust fund can be established for two or more mechanisms. The Regional Administrator may use any or all of the mechanisms to provide for closure of the facility.

(i) *Use of a financial mechanism for multiple facilities.* An owner or operator may use a financial mechanism for multiple facilities, as specified in §264.143(h) of this chapter.

(j) *Release of the owner or operator from the requirements of this section.* Within 60 days after receiving certifications from the owner or operator and an independent registered professional engineer that final closure has been completed in accordance with the approved closure plan, the Regional Administrator will notify the owner or operator in writing that the owner or operator is no longer required by this section to maintain financial assurance for final closure of the facility, unless the Regional Administrator has reason to believe that final closure has not been completed in accordance with the approved closure plan. The Regional Administrator shall provide the owner or operator with a detailed written statement of any such reasons to believe that closure has not been conducted in accordance with the approved closure plan.

§§267.144–267.146 [Reserved]

§267.147 Liability requirements.

(a) *Coverage for sudden accidental occurrences.* An owner or operator of a hazardous waste treatment or storage facility, or a group of such facilities, must demonstrate financial responsibility for bodily injury and property damage to third parties caused by sudden accidental occurrences arising from operations of the facility or group of facilities. The owner or operator must have and maintain liability coverage for sudden accidental occurrences in the amount of at least $1 million per occurrence with an annual aggregate of at least $2 million, exclusive of legal defense costs. This liability coverage may be demonstrated as specified in paragraphs (a)(1) through (a)(7) of this section:

(1) *Trust fund for liability coverage.* An owner or operator may meet the requirements of this section by obtaining a trust fund for liability coverage as specified in 40 CFR 264.147(j).

(2) *Surety bond for liability coverage.* An owner or operator may meet the requirements of this section by obtaining a surety bond for liability coverage as specified in 40 CFR 264.147(i).

(3) *Letter of credit for liability coverage.* An owner or operator may meet the requirements of this section by obtaining a letter of credit for liability coverage as specified in 40 CFR 264.147(h).

(4) *Insurance for liability coverage.* An owner or operator may meet the requirements of this section by obtaining liability insurance as specified in 40 CFR 264.147(a)(1).

(5) *Financial test for liability coverage.* An owner or operator may meet the requirements of this section by passing a financial test as specified in paragraph (f) of this section.

(6) *Guarantee for liability coverage.* An owner or operator may meet the requirements of this section by obtaining a guarantee as specified in paragraph (g) of this section.

(7) *Combination of mechanisms.* An owner or operator may demonstrate the required liability coverage through the use of combinations of mechanisms as allowed by 40 CFR 264.147(a)(6).

(8) An owner or operator shall notify the Regional Administrator in writing within 30 days whenever:

(i) A claim results in a reduction in the amount of financial assurance for liability coverage provided by a financial instrument authorized in paragraphs (a)(1) through (a)(7) of this section; or

(ii) A Certification of Valid Claim for bodily injury or property damages caused by a sudden accidental occurrence arising from the operation of a hazardous waste treatment, storage, or disposal facility is entered between the owner or operator and third-party claimant for liability coverage under paragraphs (a)(1) through (a)(7) of this section; or

(iii) A final court order establishing a judgment for bodily injury or property damage caused by a sudden accidental occurrence arising from the operation of a hazardous waste treatment, storage, or disposal facility is issued against the owner or operator or an instrument that is providing financial assurance for liability coverage under paragraphs (a)(1) through (a)(7) of this section.

(b)–(d) [Reserved]

(e) *Period of coverage.* Within 60 days after receiving certifications from the owner or operator and an independent registered professional engineer that final closure has been completed in accordance with the approved closure plan, the Regional Administrator will notify the owner or operator in writing that he is no longer required by this section to maintain liability coverage from that facility, unless the Regional Administrator has reason to believe that closure has not been in accordance with the approved closure plan.

(f) *Financial test for Liability Coverage.* An owner or operator that satisfies the requirements of this paragraph (f) may demonstrate financial assurance for liability up to the amount specified in this paragraph (f):

(1) *Financial component.*

(i) If using the financial test for only liability coverage, the owner or operator must have tangible net worth greater than the sum of the liability coverage to be demonstrated by this test plus $10 million.

(ii) The owner or operator must have assets located in the United States amounting to at least the amount of liability covered by this financial test.

(iii) An owner or operator who is demonstrating coverage for liability and any other environmental obligations, including closure under §267.143(f), through a financial test must meet the requirements of §267.143(f).

(2) Recordkeeping and reporting requirements.

(i) The owner or operator must submit the following items to the Regional Administrator:

(A) A letter signed by the owner's or operator's chief financial officer that provides evidence demonstrating that the firm meets the conditions of paragraphs (f)(1)(i) and (f)(1)(ii) of this section. If the firm is providing only liability coverage through a financial test for a facility or facilities with a permit under §267, the letter should use the wording in §267.151(b). If the firm is providing only liability coverage through a financial test for facilities regulated under part 267 and also part 264 or part 265, it should use the letter in §264.151(g). If the firm is providing liability coverage through a financial test for a facility or facilities with a permit under §267, and it assures closure costs or any other environmental obligations through a financial test, it must use the letter in §267.151(a) for the facilities issued a permit under §267.

(B) A copy of the independent certified public accountant's unqualified opinion of the owner's or operator's financial statements for the latest completed fiscal year. To be eligible to use the financial test, the owner's or operator's financial statements must receive an unqualified opinion from the independent certified public accountant. An adverse opinion, disclaimer of opinion, or other qualified opinion will be cause for disallowance, with the potential exception for qualified opinions provided in the next sentence. The Regional Administrator may evaluate qualified opinions on a case-by-case basis and allow use of the financial test in cases where the Regional Administrator deems that the matters which form the basis for the qualification are insufficient to warrant disallowance of the test. If the Regional Administrator does not allow use of the test, the owner or operator must provide alternate financial assurance that meets the requirements of this section (§267.147) within 30 days after the notification of disallowance.

(C) If the chief financial officer's letter providing evidence of financial assurance includes financial data showing that the owner or operator satisfies paragraphs (f)(1)(i) and (ii) of this section that are different from data in the audited financial statements referred to in paragraph (f)(2)(i)(B) of this section or any other audited financial statement or data filed with the SEC, then a special report from the owner's or operator's independent certified public accountant to the owner or operator is required. The special report shall be based upon an agreed upon procedures engagement in accordance with professional auditing standards and shall describe the procedures performed in comparing the data in the chief financial officer's letter derived from the independently audited, year-end financial statements for the latest fiscal year with the amounts in such financial statements, the findings of that comparison, and the reasons for any differences.

(ii) The owner or operator of a new facility must submit the items specified in paragraph (f)(2)(i) of this section to the Regional Administrator at least 60 days before placing waste in the facility.

(iii) After the initial submission of items specified in paragraph (f)(2)(i) of this section, the owner or operator must send updated information to the Regional Administrator within 90 days following the close of the owner or operator's fiscal year. The Regional Administrator may provide up to an additional 45 days for an owner or operator who can demonstrate that 90 days is insufficient time to acquire audited financial statements. The updated information must consist of all items specified in paragraph (f)(2)(i) of this section.

(iv) The owner or operator is no longer required to submit the items specified in this paragraph (f)(2) or comply with the requirements of this paragraph (f) when:

(A) The owner or operator substitutes alternate financial assurance as specified in this section that is not subject to these recordkeeping and reporting requirements; or

(B) The Regional Administrator releases the owner or operator from the requirements of this section in accordance with paragraph (j) of this section.

(v) An owner or operator who no longer meets the requirements of paragraph (f)(1) of this section cannot use the financial test to demonstrate financial assurance. An owner or operator who no longer meets the requirements of paragraph (f)(1) of this section, must:

(A) Send notice to the Regional Administrator of intent to establish alternate financial assurance as specified in this section. The owner or operator must send this notice by certified mail within 90 days following the close of the owner or operator's fiscal year for which the year-end financial data show that the owner or operator no longer meets the requirements of this section.

(B) Provide alternative financial assurance within 120 days after the end of such fiscal year.

(vi) The Regional Administrator may, based on a reasonable belief that the owner or operator may no longer meet the requirements of paragraph (f)(1) of this section, require at any time the owner or operator to provide reports of its financial condition in addition to or including current financial test documentation as specified in paragraph (f)(2) of this section. If the Regional Administrator finds that the owner or operator no longer meets the requirements of paragraph (f)(1) of this section, the owner or operator must provide alternate financial assurance that meets the requirements of this section.

(g) *Guarantee for liability coverage.* (1) Subject to paragraph (g)(2) of this section, an owner or operator may meet the requirements of this section by obtaining a written guarantee, hereinafter referred to as "guarantee." The guarantor must be the direct or higher-tier parent corporation of the owner or operator, a firm whose parent corporation is also the parent corporation of the owner or operator, or a firm with a "substantial business relationship" with the owner or operator. The guarantor must meet the requirements for owners or operators in paragraphs (f)(1) through (f)(3) of this section. The wording of the guarantee must be identical to the wording specified in 40 CFR 264.151(h)(2). A certified copy of the guarantee must accompany the items sent to the Regional Administrator as specified in paragraph (f)(2) of this section. One of these items must be the letter from the guarantor's chief financial officer. If the guarantor's parent corporation is also the parent corporation of the owner or operator, this letter must describe the value received in consideration of the guarantee. If the guarantor is a firm with a "substantial business relationship" with the owner or operator, this letter must describe this "substantial business relationship" and the value received in consideration of the guarantee.

(i) If the owner or operator fails to satisfy a judgment based on a determination of liability for bodily injury or property damage to third parties caused by sudden accidental occurrences arising from the operation of facilities covered by this corporate guarantee, or fails to pay an amount agreed to in settlement of claims arising from or alleged to arise from such injury or damage, the guarantor will do so up to the limits of coverage.

(ii) [Reserved]

(2)(i) In the case of corporations incorporated in the United States, a guarantee may be used to satisfy the requirements of this section only if the Attorneys General or Insurance Commissioners of the State in which the guarantor is incorporated, and each State in which a facility covered by the guarantee is located, have submitted a written statement to EPA that a guarantee executed as described in this section and 40 CFR 264.151(h)(2) is a legally valid and enforceable obligation in that State.

(ii) In the case of corporations incorporated outside the United States, a guarantee may be used to satisfy the requirements of this section only if:

(A) The non-U.S. corporation has identified a registered agent for service of process in each State in which a facility covered by the guarantee is located and in the State in which it has its principal place of business; and

(B) The Attorney General or Insurance Commissioner of each State in which a facility covered by the guarantee is located and the State in which the guarantor corporation has its principal place of business, has submitted a written statement to EPA that a guarantee executed as described in this section and 40 CFR 264.151(h)(2) is a legally valid and enforceable obligation in that State.

[70 FR 53453, Sept. 8, 2005, as amended at 71 FR 40278, July 14, 2006]

§267.148 Incapacity of owners or operators, guarantors, or financial institutions.

(a) An owner or operator must notify the Regional Administrator by certified mail of the commencement of a voluntary or involuntary proceeding under Title 11 (Bankruptcy), U.S. Code, naming the owner or operator as debtor, within 10 days after commencement of the proceeding. A guarantor of a corporate guarantee as specified in §§267.143(g) and 267.147 (g) must make such a notification if he is named as debtor, as required under the terms of the corporate guarantee (§264.151(h)).

(b) An owner or operator who fulfills the requirements of §267.143 or §267.147 by obtaining a trust fund, surety bond, letter of credit, or insurance policy will be deemed to be without the required financial assurance or liability coverage in the event of bankruptcy of the trustee or issuing institution, or a suspension or revocation of the authority of the trustee institution to act as trustee or of the institution issuing the surety bond, letter of credit, or insurance policy to issue such instruments. The owner or operator must establish other financial assurance or liability coverage within 60 days after such an event.

§267.149 [Reserved]

§267.150 State assumption of responsibility.

(a) If a State either assumes legal responsibility for an owner's or operator's compliance with the closure care or liability requirements of this part or assures that funds will be available from State sources to cover those requirements, the owner or operator will be in compliance with the requirements of §267.143 or §267.147 if the Regional Administrator determines that the State's assumption of responsibility is at least equivalent to the financial mechanisms specified in this subpart. The Regional Administrator will evaluate the equivalency of State guarantees principally in terms of: Certainty of the availability of funds for the required closure care activities or liability coverage; and the amount of funds that will be made available. The Regional Administrator may also consider other factors as he deems appropriate. The owner or operator must submit to the Regional Administrator a letter from the State describing the nature of the State's assumption of responsibility together with a letter from the owner or operator requesting that the State's assumption of responsibility be considered acceptable for meeting the requirements of this subpart. The letter from the State must include, or have attached to it, the following information: The facility's EPA Identification Number, name, and address, and the amount of funds for closure care or liability coverage that are guaranteed by the State. The Regional Administrator will notify the owner or operator of his determination regarding the acceptability of the State's guarantee in lieu of financial mechanisms specified in this subpart. The Regional Administrator may require the owner or operator to submit additional information as is deemed necessary to make this determination. Pending this determination, the owner or operator will be deemed to be in compliance with the requirements of §267.143 or §267.147, as applicable.

(b) If a State's assumption of responsibility is found acceptable as specified in paragraph (a) of this section except for the amount of funds available, the owner or operator may satisfy the requirements of this subpart by use of both the State's assurance and additional financial mechanisms as specified in this subpart. The amount of funds available through the State and Federal mechanisms must at least equal the amount required by this subpart.

§267.151 Wording of the instruments.

(a) The chief financial officer of an owner or operator of a facility with a standardized permit who uses a financial test to demonstrate financial assurance for that facility must complete a letter as specified in §267.143(f) of this chapter. The letter must be worded as follows, except that instructions in brackets are to be replaced with the relevant information and the brackets deleted:

I am the chief financial officer of [name and address of firm]. This letter is in support of this firm's use of the financial test to demonstrate financial assurance for closure costs, as specified in [insert "subpart H of 40 CFR part 267" or the citation to the corresponding state regulation]. This firm qualifies for the financial test on the basis of having [insert "a current rating for its senior unsecured debt of AAA, AA, A, or BBB as issued by Standard and Poor's or Aaa, Aa, A or Baa as issued by Moody's" or "a ratio of less than 1.50 comparing total liabilities to net worth" or "a ratio of greater than 0.10 comparing the sum of net income plus depreciation, depletion and amortization, minus $10 million, to total liabilities."]

This firm [insert "is required" or "is not required"] to file a Form 10K with the Securities and Exchange Commission (SEC) for the latest fiscal year.

The fiscal year of this firm ends on [month, day]. The figures for the following items marked with an asterisk are derived from this firm's independently audited, year-end financial statements for the latest completed fiscal year, ended [date].

[If this firm qualifies on the basis of its bond rating fill in the requested information: "This firm has a rating of its senior unsecured debt of" [insert the bond rating] "from" [insert "Standard and Poor's" or "Moody's"]. Complete Line 1. Total Liabilities below and then skip the remaining questions in the next section and resume completing the form at the section entitled *Obligations Covered by a Financial Test or Corporate Guarantee.*]

[If this firm qualifies for the financial test on the basis of its ratio of liabilities to net worth, or sum of income, depreciation, depletion, and amortization to net worth, please complete the following section.]

*1. Total Liabilities .... $______

*2. Net Worth .... $______

*3. Net Income .... $______

*4. Depreciation .... $______

*5. Depletion (if applicable) .... $______

*6. Amortization .... $______

*7. Sum of Lines 3, 4, 5 & 6 .... $______

[If the above figures are taken directly from the most recent audited financial statements for this firm insert "The above figures are taken directly from the most recent audited financial statements for this firm." If they are not, insert "The following items are not taken directly from the firms most recent audited financial statements" [insert the numbers of the items and attach an explanation of how they were derived.]

[Complete the following calculations]

8. Line 1 ÷ Line 2 = ... $______

9. Line 7 ÷ Line 1 = ... $______

Is Line 8 less than 1.5? .... ______Yes ______No

Is Line 9 greater than 0.10? .... ______Yes ______No

[If you did not answer Yes to either of these two questions, you cannot use the financial test and need not complete this letter. Instead, you must notify the permitting authority for the facility that you intend to establish alternate financial assurance as specified in 40 CFR 267.143. The owner or operator must send this notice by certified mail within 90 days following the close of the owner or operator's fiscal year for which the year-end financial data show that the owner or operator no longer meets the requirements of this section. The owner or operator must also provide alternative financial assurance within 120 days after the end of such fiscal year.]

Obligations Covered by a Financial Test or Corporate Guarantee

[On the following lines list all obligations that are covered by a financial test or a corporate guarantee extended by your firm. You may add additional lines and leave blank entries that do not apply to your situation.]

Hazardous Waste Facility Name and ID	State	Closure	Post-Closure	Corrective Action
______	______	$______	$______	$______
______	______	______	______	______

Hazardous Waste Third Party Liability .... $______

Municipal Waste Facilities	State	Closure	Post-Closure	Corrective Action
______	______	$______	$______	$______
______	______	______	______	______

Underground Injection Control	State	Plugging Action
	______	$______

Petroleum Underground Storage Tanks .... ______

PCB Storage Facility Name and ID	State	Closure
	______	$______

Any financial assurance required under, or as part of an action undertaken under, the Comprehensive Environmental Response, Compensation, and Liability Act.

Site Name	State	Amount
____________________	________	$________

Any other environmental obligations that are assured through a financial test.

Name	Amount
____________________	$________

*10. Total of all amounts .... $________

*11. Line 10 + $10,000,000 = ... $________

*12. Total Assets .... $________

*13. Intangible Assets .... $________

*14. Tangible Assets (Line 12 – Line 13) .... $________

*15. Tangible Net Worth (Line 14 – Line 1) .... $________

*16. Assets in the United States .... $________

Is Line 15 greater than Line 11? .... ______Yes ______No

Is Line 16 no less than Line 10? .... ______Yes ______No

[You must be able to answer Yes to both these questions to use the financial test for this facility.]

I hereby certify that the wording of this letter is identical to the wording specified in 40 CFR 267.151 as such regulations were constituted on the date shown immediately below.

[Signature] ____________________

[Name] ____________________

[Title] ____________________

[Date] ____________________

[After completion, a signed copy of the form must be sent to the permitting authority of the state or territory where the facility is located. In addition, a signed copy must be sent to every authority who (1) requires a demonstration through a financial test for each of the other obligations in the letter that are assured through a financial test, or (2) accepts a guarantee for an obligation listed in this letter.]

(b) The chief financial officer of an owner or operator of a facility with a standardized permit who use a financial test to demonstrate financial assurance only for third party liability for that (or other standardized permit) facility(ies) must complete a letter as specified in Section 267.147(f) of this chapter. The letter must be worded as follows, except that instructions in brackets are to be replaced with the relevant information and the brackets deleted:

I am the chief financial officer of [name and address of firm]. This letter is in support of this firm's use of the financial test to demonstrate financial assurance for third party liability, as specified in [insert "subpart H of 40 CFR part 267" or the citation to the corresponding state regulation]. This firm qualifies for the financial test on the basis of having tangible net worth of at least $10 million more than the amount of liability coverage and assets in the United States of at least the amount of liability coverage.

This firm [insert "is required" or "is not required"] to file a Form 10K with the Securities and Exchange Commission (SEC) for the latest fiscal year.

The fiscal year of this firm ends on [month, day]. The figures for the following items marked with an asterisk are derived from this firm's independently audited, year-end financial statements for the latest completed fiscal year, ended [date].

[Please complete the following section.]

*1. Total Assets .... $________

*2. Intangible Assets .... $________

*3. Tangible Assets (Line 1 – Line 2) .... $________

*4. Total Liabilities .... $________

5. Tangible Net Worth (Line 3 – Line 4) .... $________

*6. Assets in the United States .... $________

7. Amount of liability coverage .... $________

Is Line 5 at least $10 million greater than Line 7? .... ______Yes ______No

Is Line 6 at least equal to Line 7? .... ______Yes ______No

[You must be able to answer Yes to both these questions to use the financial test for this facility.]

I hereby certify that the wording of this letter is identical to the wording specified in 40 CFR 267.151 as such regulations were constituted on the date shown immediately below.

[Signature] ____________________

[Name] ____________________

[Title] ____________________

[Date] ____________________

[After completion, a signed copy of the form must be sent to the permitting authority of the state or territory where the facility(ies) is(are) located.]

Subpart I—Use and Management of Containers

§267.170 Does this subpart apply to me?

This subpart applies to you if you own or operate a facility that treats or stores hazardous waste in containers under a 40 CFR part 270 subpart J standardized permit, except as provided in §267.1(b).

§267.171 What standards apply to the containers?

Standards apply to the condition of the containers, to the compatibility of waste with the containers, and to the management of the containers.

(a) Condition of containers. If a container holding hazardous waste is not in good condition (for example, it exhibits severe rusting or apparent structural defects) or if it begins to leak, you must either:

(1) Transfer the hazardous waste from this container to a container that is in good condition; or

(2) Manage the waste in some other way that complies with the requirements of this part.

(b) Compatibility of waste with containers. To ensure that the ability of the container to contain the waste is not impaired, you must use a container made of or lined with materials that are compatible and will not react with the hazardous waste to be stored.

(c) Management of containers. (1) You must always keep a container holding hazardous waste closed during storage, except when you add or remove waste.

(2) You must never open, handle, or store a container holding hazardous waste in a manner that may rupture the container or cause it to leak.

§267.172 What are the inspection requirements?

At least weekly, you must inspect areas where you store containers, looking for leaking containers and for deterioration of containers and the containment system caused by corrosion or other factors.

§267.173 What standards apply to the container storage areas?

(a) You must design and operate a containment system for your container storage areas according to the requirements in paragraph (b) of this section, except as otherwise provided by paragraph (c) of this section.

(b) The design and operating requirements for a containment system are:

(1) A base must underlie the containers that is free of cracks or gaps and is sufficiently impervious to contain leaks, spills, and accumulated precipitation until the collected material is detected and removed.

(2) The base must be sloped or the containment system, must be otherwise designed and operated to drain and remove liquids resulting from leaks, spills, or precipitation, unless the containers are elevated or are otherwise protected from contact with accumulated liquids.

(3) The containment system must have sufficient capacity to contain 10% of the volume of containers, or the volume of the largest container, whichever is greater. This requirement does not apply to containers that do not contain free liquids.

(4) You must prevent run-on into the containment system unless the collection system has sufficient excess capacity, in addition to that required in paragraph (b)(3) of this section, to contain the liquid.

(5) You must remove any spilled or leaked waste and accumulated precipitation from the sump or collection area as promptly as is necessary to prevent overflow of the collection system.

(c) Except as provided in paragraph (d) of this section, you do not need a containment system as defined in paragraph (b) of this section for storage areas that store containers holding only wastes with no free liquids, if:

(1) The storage area is sloped or is otherwise designed and operated to drain and remove liquid resulting from precipitation; or

(2) The containers are elevated or are otherwise protected from contact with accumulated liquid.

(d) You must have a containment system defined by paragraph (b) of this section for storage areas that store containers holding F020, F021, F022, F023, F026, and F027 wastes, even if the wastes do not contain free liquids.

§267.174 What special requirements must I meet for ignitable or reactive waste?

You must locate containers holding ignitable or reactive waste at least 15 meters (50 feet) from your facility property line. You must also follow the general requirements for ignitable or reactive wastes that are specified in §267.17(a).

§267.175 What special requirements must I meet for incompatible wastes?

(a) You must not place incompatible wastes, or incompatible wastes and materials (see appendix V to 40 CFR part 264 for examples), in the same container, unless you comply with §267.17(b).

(b) You must not place hazardous waste in an unwashed container that previously held an incompatible waste or material.

(c) You must separate a storage container holding a hazardous waste that is incompatible with any waste or with other materials stored nearby in other containers, piles, open tanks, or surface impoundments from the other materials, or protect the containers by means of a dike, berm, wall, or other device.

§267.176 What must I do when I want to stop using the containers?

You must remove all hazardous waste and hazardous waste residues from the containment system. You must decontaminate or remove remaining containers, liners, bases, and soil containing, or contaminated with, hazardous waste or hazardous waste residues.

§267.177 What air emission standards apply?

You must manage all hazardous waste placed in a container according to the requirements of subparts AA, BB, and CC of 40 CFR part 264. Under a standardized permit, the following control devices are permissible: Thermal vapor incinerator, catalytic vapor incinerator, flame, boiler, process heater, condenser, and carbon absorption unit.

Subpart J—Tank Systems

§267.190 Does this subpart apply to me?

This subpart applies to you if you own or operate a facility that treats or stores hazardous waste in above-ground or on-ground tanks under a 40 CFR part 270 subpart J standardized permit, except as provided in §267.1(b).

(a) You do not have to meet the secondary containment requirements in §267.195 if your tank systems do not contain free liquids and are situated inside a building with an impermeable floor. You must demonstrate the absence or presence of free liquids in the stored/treated waste, using Method 9095B (Paint Filter Liquids Test) as described in "Test Methods for Evaluating Solid Waste, Physical/Chemical Methods," EPA Publication SW–846, as incorporated by reference in 40 CFR 260.11.

(b) You do not have to meet the secondary containment requirements of §267.195(a) if your tank system, including sumps, as defined in 40 CFR 260.10, is part of a secondary containment system to collect or contain releases of hazardous wastes.

§267.191 What are the required design and construction standards for new tank systems or components?

You must ensure that the foundation, structural support, seams, connections, and pressure controls (if applicable) are adequately designed and that the tank system has sufficient structural strength, compatibility with the waste(s) to be stored or treated, and corrosion protection to ensure that it will not collapse, rupture, or fail. You must obtain a written assessment, reviewed and certified by an independent, qualified registered professional engineer, following 40 CFR 270.11(d), attesting that the tank system has sufficient structural integrity and is acceptable for the storing and treating of hazardous waste. This assessment must include, at a minimum, the following information:

(a) Design standard(s) for the construction of tank(s) and/or the ancillary equipment.

(b) Hazardous characteristics of the waste(s) to be handled.

(c) For new tank systems or components in which the external shell of a metal tank or any external metal component of the tank system will be in contact with the soil or with water, a determination by a corrosion expert of:

(1) Factors affecting the potential for corrosion, such as:

(i) Soil moisture content.

(ii) Soil pH.

(iii) Soil sulfides level.

(iv) Soil resistivity.

(v) Structure to soil potential.

(vi) Existence of stray electric current.

(vii) Existing corrosion-protection measures (for example, coating, cathodic protection).

(2) The type and degree of external corrosion protection needed to ensure the integrity of the tank system during the use of the tank system or component, consisting of one or more of the following:

(i) Corrosion-resistant materials of construction such as special alloys, fiberglass reinforced plastic, etc.

(ii) Corrosion-resistant coating (such as epoxy, fiberglass, etc.) with cathodic protection (for example, impressed current or sacrificial anodes) and

(iii) Electrical isolation devices such as insulating joints, flanges, etc.

(d) Design considerations to ensure that:

(1) Tank foundations will maintain the load of a full tank.

(2) Tank systems will be anchored to prevent flotation or dislodgment where the tank system is placed in a saturated zone, or is located within a seismic fault zone subject to the standards of §267.18(a).

(3) Tank systems will withstand the effects of frost heave.

§267.192 What handling and inspection procedures must I follow during installation of new tank systems?

(a) You must ensure that you follow proper handling procedures to prevent damage to a new tank system during installation. Before placing a new tank system or component in use, an independent, qualified installation inspector or an independent, qualified, registered professional engineer, either of whom is trained and experienced in the proper installation of tank systems or components, must inspect the system for the presence of any of the following items:

(1) Weld breaks.

(2) Punctures.

(3) Scrapes of protective coatings.

(4) Cracks.

(5) Corrosion.

(6) Other structural damage or inadequate construction/installation.

(b) You must remedy all discrepancies before the tank system is placed in use.

§267.193 What testing must I do?

You must test all new tanks and ancillary equipment for tightness before you place them in use. If you find a tank system that is not tight, you must perform all repairs necessary to remedy the leak(s) in the system before you cover, enclose, or place the tank system into use.

§267.194 What installation requirements must I follow?

(a) You must support and protect ancillary equipment against physical damage and excessive stress due to settlement, vibration, expansion, or contraction.

(b) You must provide the type and degree of corrosion protection recommended by an independent corrosion expert, based on the information provided under §267.191(c), to ensure the integrity of the tank system during use of the tank system. An independent corrosion expert must supervise the installation of a corrosion protection system that is field fabricated to ensure proper installation.

(c) You must obtain, and keep at the facility, written statements by those persons required to certify the design of the tank system and to supervise the installation of the tank system as required in §§267.192, 267.193, and paragraphs (a) and (b) of this section. The written statement must attest that the tank system was properly designed and installed and that you made repairs under §§267.192 and 267.193. These written statements must also include the certification statement as required in 40 CFR 270.11(d).

§267.195 What are the secondary containment requirements?

To prevent the release of hazardous waste or hazardous constituents to the environment, you must provide secondary containment that meets the requirements of this section for all new and existing tank systems.

(a) Secondary containment systems must be:

(1) Designed, installed, and operated to prevent any migration of wastes or accumulated liquid out of the system to the soil, groundwater, or surface water at any time during the use of the tank system; and

(2) Capable of detecting and collecting releases and accumulated liquids until the collected material is removed.

(b) To meet the requirements of paragraph (a) of this section, secondary containment systems must be, at a minimum:

(1) Constructed of or lined with materials that are compatible with the wastes(s) to be placed in the tank system and must have sufficient strength and thickness to prevent failure owing to pressure gradients (including static head and external hydrological forces), physical contact with the waste to which it is exposed, climatic conditions, and the stress of daily operation (including stresses from nearby vehicular traffic).

(2) Placed on a foundation or base capable of providing support to the secondary containment system, resistance to pressure gradients above and below the system, and capable of preventing failure due to settlement, compression, or uplift.

(3) Provided with a leak-detection system that is designed and operated so that it will detect the failure of either the primary or secondary containment structure or the presence of any release of hazardous waste or accumulated liquid in the secondary containment system within 24 hours.

(4) Sloped or otherwise designed or operated to drain and remove liquids resulting from leaks, spills, or precipitation. You must remove spilled or leaked waste and accumulated precipitation from the secondary containment system within 24 hours, or as promptly as possible, to prevent harm to human health and the environment.

§267.196 What are the required devices for secondary containment and what are their design, operating and installation requirements?

(a) Secondary containment for tanks must include one or more of the following:

(1) A liner (external to the tank).

(2) A double-walled tank.

(3) An equivalent device; you must maintain documentation of equivalency at the facility.

(b) External liner systems must be:

(1) Designed or operated to contain 100 percent of the capacity of the largest tank within its boundary.

(2) Designed or operated to prevent run-on or infiltration of precipitation into the secondary containment system unless the collection system has sufficient excess capacity to contain run-on or infiltration. The additional capacity must be sufficient to contain precipitation from a 25-year, 24-hour rainfall event.

(3) Free of cracks or gaps.

(4) Designed and installed to surround the tank completely and to cover all surrounding earth likely to come into contact with the waste if the waste is released from the tank(s) (that is, capable of preventing lateral as well as vertical migration of the waste).

(c) Double-walled tanks must be:

(1) Designed as an integral structure (that is, an inner tank completely enveloped within an outer shell) so

that any release from the inner tank is contained by the outer shell.

(2) Protected, if constructed of metal, from both corrosion of the primary tank interior and of the external surface of the outer shell.

(3) Provided with a built-in continuous leak detection system capable of detecting a release within 24 hours.

§267.197 What are the requirements for ancillary equipment?

You must provide ancillary equipment with secondary containment (for example, trench, jacketing, double-walled piping) that meets the requirements of §267.195 (a) and (b), except for:

(a) Above ground piping (exclusive of flanges, joints, valves, and other connections) that are visually inspected for leaks on a daily basis;

(b) Welded flanges, welded joints, and welded connections, that are visually inspected for leaks on a daily basis;

(c) Sealless or magnetic coupling pumps and sealless valves, that are visually inspected for leaks on a daily basis; and

(d) Pressurized above ground piping systems with automatic shut-off devices (for example, excess flow check valves, flow metering shutdown devices, loss of pressure actuated shut-off devices) that are visually inspected for leaks on a daily basis.

§267.198 What are the general operating requirements for my tank systems?

(a) You must not place hazardous wastes or treatment reagents in a tank system if they could cause the tank, its ancillary equipment, or the containment system to rupture, leak, corrode, or otherwise fail.

(b) You must use appropriate controls and practices to prevent spills and overflows from tank or containment systems. These include, at a minimum:

(1) Spill prevention controls (for example, check valves, dry disconnect couplings).

(2) Overfill prevention controls (for example, level sensing devices, high level alarms, automatic feed cutoff, or bypass to a standby tank).

(3) Sufficient freeboard in uncovered tanks to prevent overtopping by wave or wind action or by precipitation.

(c) You must comply with the requirements of §267.200 if a leak or spill occurs in the tank system.

§267.199 What inspection requirements must I meet?

You must comply with the following requirements for scheduling, conducting, and documenting inspections.

(a) Develop and follow a schedule and procedure for inspecting overfill controls.

(b) Inspect at least once each operating day:

(1) Aboveground portions of the tank system to detect corrosion or releases of waste.

(2) Data gathered from monitoring and leak detection equipment (for example, pressure or temperature gauges, monitoring wells) to ensure that the tank system is being operated according to its design.

(3) The construction materials and the area immediately surrounding the externally accessible portion of the tank system, including the secondary containment system (for example, dikes) to detect erosion or signs of releases of hazardous waste (for example, wet spots, dead vegetation).

(c) Inspect cathodic protection systems, if present, according to, at a minimum, the following schedule to ensure that they are functioning properly:

(1) Confirm that the cathodic protection system is operating properly within six months after initial installation and annually thereafter.

(2) Inspect and/or test all sources of impressed current, as appropriate, at least every other month.

(d) Document, in the operating record of the facility, an inspection of those items in paragraphs (a) through (c) of this section.

§267.200 What must I do in case of a leak or a spill?

If there has been a leak or a spill from a tank system or secondary containment system, or if either system is unfit for use, you must remove the system from service immediately, and you must satisfy the following requirements:

(a) Immediately stop the flow of hazardous waste into the tank system or secondary containment system and inspect the system to determine the cause of the release.

(b) Remove the waste from the tank system or secondary containment system.

(1) If the release was from the tank system, you must, within 24 hours after detecting the leak, remove as much of the waste as is necessary to prevent further release of hazardous waste to the environment and to allow inspection and repair of the tank system to be performed.

(2) If the material released was to a secondary containment system, you must remove all released materials within 24 hours or as quickly as possible to prevent harm to human health and the environment.

(c) Immediately conduct a visual inspection of the release and, based upon that inspection:

(1) Prevent further migration of the leak or spill to soils or surface water.

(2) Remove, and properly dispose of, any visible contamination of the soil or surface water.

(d) Report any release to the environment, except as provided in paragraph (d)(1) of this section, to the Regional Administrator within 24 hours of its detection. If you have reported the release pursuant to 40 CFR part 302, that report will satisfy this requirement.

(1) You need not report on a leak or spill of hazardous waste if it is:

(i) Less than or equal to a quantity of one (1) pound; and

(ii) Immediately contained and cleaned up.

(2) Within 30 days of detection of a release to the environment, you must submit a report to the Regional Administrator containing the following information:

(i) The likely route of migration of the release.

(ii) The characteristics of the surrounding soil (soil composition, geology, hydrogeology, climate).

(iii) The results of any monitoring or sampling conducted in connection with the release (if available). If sampling or monitoring data relating to the release are not available within 30 days, you must submit these data to the Regional Administrator as soon as they become available.

(iv) The proximity to downgradient drinking water, surface water, and populated areas.

(v) A description of response actions taken or planned.

(e) Either close the system or make necessary repairs.

(1) Unless you satisfy the requirements of paragraphs (e)(2) and (3) of this section, you must close the tank system according to §267.201.

(2) If the cause of the release was a spill that has not damaged the integrity of the system, you may return the system to service as soon as you remove the released waste and make any necessary repairs.

(3) If the cause of the release was a leak from the primary tank system into the secondary containment system, you must repair the system before returning the tank system to service.

(f) If you have made extensive repairs to a tank system in accordance with paragraph (e) of this section (for example, installation of an internal liner; repair of a ruptured primary containment or secondary containment vessel), you may not return the tank system to service unless the repair is certified by an independent, qualified, registered, professional engineer in accordance with 40 CFR 270.11(d).

(1) The engineer must certify that the repaired system is capable of handling hazardous wastes without release for the intended life of the system.

(2) You must submit this certification to the Regional Administrator within seven days after returning the tank system to use.

§267.201 What must I do when I stop operating the tank system?

When you close a tank system, you must remove or decontaminate all waste residues, contaminated containment system components (liners, etc.), contaminated soils, and structures and equipment contaminated with waste, and manage them as hazardous waste, unless 40 CFR 261.3(d) applies. The closure plan, closure activities, cost estimates for closure, and financial responsibility for tank systems must meet all of the requirements specified in subparts G and H of this part.

§267.202 What special requirements must I meet for ignitable or reactive wastes?

(a) You may not place ignitable or reactive waste in tank systems, unless:

(1) You treat, render, or mix the waste before or immediately after placement in the tank system so that:

(i) You comply with §267.17(b); and

(ii) The resulting waste, mixture, or dissolved material no longer meets the definition of ignitable or reactive waste under §261.21 or §261.23 of this chapter; or

(2) You store or treat the waste in such a way that it is protected from any material or conditions that may cause the waste to ignite or react; or

(3) You use the tank system solely for emergencies.

(b) If you store or treat ignitable or reactive waste in a tank, you must comply with the requirements for the maintenance of protective distances between the waste management area and any public ways, streets, alleys, or an adjoining property line that can be built upon as required in Tables 2–1 through 2–6 of the National Fire Protection Association's "Flammable and Combustible Liquids Code," (1977 or 1981), (incorporated by reference, see 40 CFR 260.11).

§267.203 What special requirements must I meet for incompatible wastes?

(a) You may not place incompatible wastes, or incompatible wastes and materials, in the same tank system, unless you comply with §267.17(b).

(b) You may not place hazardous waste in a tank system that has not been decontaminated and that previously held an incompatible waste or material, unless you comply with §267.17(b).

§267.204 What air emission standards apply?

You must manage all hazardous waste placed in a tank following the requirements of subparts AA, BB, and CC of 40 CFR part 264. Under a standardized permit, the following control devices are permissible: Thermal vapor incinerator, catalytic vapor incinerator, flame, boiler, process heater, condenser, and carbon absorption unit.

Subparts K through CC—[Reserved]

Subpart DD—Containment buildings

§267.1100 Does this subpart apply to me?

This subpart applies to you if you own or operate a facility that treats or stores hazardous waste in containment buildings under a 40 CFR part 270 subpart J standardized permit, except as provided in §267.1(b). Storage and/or treatment in your containment building is not land disposal as defined in 40 CFR 268.2 if your unit meets the requirements of §§267.1101, 267.1102, and 267.1103.

§267.1101 What design and operating standards must my containment building meet?

Your containment building must comply with the design and operating standards in this section. EPA will consider standards established by professional organizations generally recognized by the industry such as the American Concrete Institute (ACI) and the American Society of Testing Materials (ASTM) in judging the structural integrity requirements of this section.

(a) The containment building must be completely enclosed with a floor, walls, and a roof to prevent exposure to the elements, (*e.g.*, precipitation, wind, run-on), and to assure containment of managed wastes.

(b) The floor and containment walls of the unit, including the secondary containment system, if required under §267.1103, must be designed and constructed of manmade materials of sufficient strength and thickness to:

(1) Support themselves, the waste contents, and any personnel and heavy equipment that operates within the unit.

(2) Prevent failure due to:

(i) Pressure gradients, settlement, compression, or uplift.

(ii) Physical contact with the hazardous wastes to which they are exposed.

(iii) Climatic conditions.

(iv) Stresses of daily operation, including the movement of heavy equipment within the unit and contact of such equipment with containment walls.

(v) Collapse or other failure.

(c) All surfaces to be in contact with hazardous wastes must be chemically compatible with those wastes.

(d) You must not place incompatible hazardous wastes or treatment reagents in the unit or its secondary containment system if they could cause the unit or secondary containment system to leak, corrode, or otherwise fail.

(e) A containment building must have a primary barrier designed to withstand the movement of personnel, waste, and handling equipment in the unit during the operating life of the unit and appropriate for the physical and chemical characteristics of the waste to be managed.

(f) If appropriate to the nature of the waste management operation to take place in the unit, an exception to the structural strength requirement may be made for lightweight doors and windows that meet these criteria:

(1) They provide an effective barrier against fugitive dust emissions under §267.1102(d).

(2) The unit is designed and operated in a fashion that assures that wastes will not actually come in contact with these openings.

(g) You must inspect and record in the facility's operating record, at least once every seven days, data gathered from monitoring equipment and leak detection equipment, as well as the containment building and the area immediately surrounding the containment building to detect signs of releases of hazardous waste.

(h) You must obtain certification by a qualified registered professional engineer that the containment building design meets the requirements of §§267.1102, 267.1103, and paragraphs (a) through (f) of this section.

§267.1102 What other requirements must I meet to prevent releases?

You must use controls and practices to ensure containment of the hazardous waste within the unit, and must, at a minimum:

(a) Maintain the primary barrier to be free of significant cracks, gaps, corrosion, or other deterioration that could cause hazardous waste to be released from the primary barrier.

(b) Maintain the level of the stored/treated hazardous waste within the containment walls of the unit so that the height of any containment wall is not exceeded.

(c) Take measures to prevent personnel or by equipment used in handling the waste from tracking hazardous waste out of the unit. You must designate an area to decontaminate equipment, and you must collect and properly manage any rinsate.

(d) Take measures to control fugitive dust emissions such that any openings (doors, windows, vents, cracks, etc.) exhibit no visible emissions (see 40 CFR part 60, appendix A, Method 22—Visual Determination of Fugitive Emissions from Material Sources and Smoke Emissions from Flares). In addition, you must operate and maintain all associated particulate collection devices (for example, fabric filter, electrostatic precipitator) with sound air pollution control practices. You must effectively maintain this state of no visible emissions at all times during routine operating and maintenance conditions, including when vehicles and personnel are entering and exiting the unit.

§267.1103 What additional design and operating standards apply if liquids will be in my containment building?

If your containment building will be used to manage hazardous wastes containing free liquids or treated with free liquids, as determined by the paint filter test, by a visual examination, or by other appropriate means, you must include:

(a) A primary barrier designed and constructed of materials to prevent the migration of hazardous constituents into the barrier (for example, a geomembrane covered by a concrete wear surface).

(b) A liquid collection and removal system to minimize the accumulation of liquid on the primary barrier of the containment building.

(1) The primary barrier must be sloped to drain liquids to the associated collection system; and

(2) You must collect and remove liquids and waste to minimize hydraulic head on the containment system at the earliest practicable time.

(c) A secondary containment system, including a secondary barrier designed and constructed to prevent migration of hazardous constituents into the barrier, and a leak detection system capable of detecting failure of the primary barrier and collecting accumulated hazardous wastes and liquids at the earliest practical time.

(1) You may meet the requirements of the leak detection component of the secondary containment system by installing a system that is, at a minimum:

(i) Constructed with a bottom slope of 1 percent or more; and

(ii) Constructed of a granular drainage material with a hydraulic conductivity of 1×10^{-2} cm/sec or more and a thickness of 12 inches (30.5 cm) or more, or constructed of synthetic or geonet drainage materials with a transmissivity of 3×10^{-5} m^2 sec or more.

(2) If you will be conducting treatment in the building, you must design the area in which the treatment will be conducted to prevent the release of liquids, wet materials, or liquid aerosols to other portions of the building.

(3) You must construct the secondary containment system using materials that are chemically resistant to the waste and liquids managed in the containment building and of sufficient strength and thickness to prevent collapse under the pressure exerted by overlaying materials and by any equipment used in the containment building.

§267.1104 How may I obtain a waiver from secondary containment requirements?

Notwithstanding any other provision of this subpart, the Regional Administrator may waive requirements for secondary containment for a permitted containment building where:

(a) You demonstrate that the only free liquids in the unit are limited amounts of dust suppression liquids required to meet occupational health and safety requirements, and

(b) Containment of managed wastes and dust suppression liquids can be assured without a secondary containment system.

§267.1105 What do I do if my containment building contains areas both with and without secondary containment?

For these containment buildings, you must:

(a) Design and operate each area in accordance with the requirements enumerated in §§267.1101 through 267.1103.

(b) Take measures to prevent the release of liquids or wet materials into areas without secondary containment.

(c) Maintain in the facility's operating log a written description of the operating procedures used to maintain the integrity of areas without secondary containment.

§267.1106 What do I do if I detect a release?

Throughout the active life of the containment building, if you detect a condition that could lead to or has caused a release of hazardous waste, you must repair the condition promptly, in accordance with the following procedures.

(a) Upon detection of a condition that has lead to a release of hazardous waste (for example, upon detection of leakage from the primary barrier), you must:

(1) Enter a record of the discovery in the facility operating record;

(2) Immediately remove the portion of the containment building affected by the condition from service;

(3) Determine what steps you must take to repair the containment building, to remove any leakage from the secondary collection system, and to establish a schedule for accomplishing the cleanup and repairs; and

(4) Within 7 days after the discovery of the condition, notify the Regional Administrator of the condition, and within 14 working days, provide a written notice to the Regional Administrator with a description of the steps taken to repair the containment building, and the schedule for accomplishing the work.

(b) The Regional Administrator will review the information submitted, make a determination regarding whether the containment building must be removed from service completely or partially until repairs and cleanup are complete, and notify you of the determination and the underlying rationale in writing.

(c) Upon completing all repairs and cleanup, you must notify the Regional Administrator in writing and provide a verification, signed by a qualified, registered professional engineer, that the repairs and cleanup have been completed according to the written plan submitted in accordance with paragraph (a)(4) of this section.

§267.1107 Can a containment building itself be considered secondary containment?

Containment buildings can serve as secondary containment systems for tanks placed within the building under certain conditions.

(a) A containment building can serve as an external liner system for a tank, provided it meets the requirements of §267.196(a).

(b) The containment building must also meet the requirements of §267.195(a), (b)(1) and (2) to be considered an acceptable secondary containment system for a tank.

§267.1108 What must I do when I stop operating the containment building?

When you close a containment building, you must remove or decontaminate all waste residues, contaminated containment system components (liners, etc.), contaminated subsoils, and structures and equipment contaminated with waste and leachate, and manage them as hazardous waste unless 40 CFR 261.3(d) applies. The closure plan, closure activities, cost estimates for closure, and financial responsibility for containment buildings must meet all of the requirements specified in subparts G and H of this part.

PART 268—LAND DISPOSAL RESTRICTIONS

Authority: 42 U.S.C. 6905, 6912(a), 6921, and 6924.

Subpart A—General

§268.1 Purpose, scope, and applicability. 13.1

(a) This part identifies hazardous wastes that are restricted from land disposal and defines those limited circumstances under which an otherwise prohibited waste may continue to be land disposed.

(b) Except as specifically provided otherwise in this part or part 261 of this chapter, the requirements of this part apply to persons who generate or transport hazardous waste and owners and operators of hazardous waste treatment, storage, and disposal facilities. 13.1.1

(c) Restricted wastes may continue to be land disposed as follows:

(1) Where persons have been granted an extension to the effective date of a prohibition under subpart C of this part or pursuant to §268.5, with respect to those wastes covered by the extension;

(2) Where persons have been granted an exemption from a prohibition pursuant to a petition under §268.6, with respect to those wastes and units covered by the petition;

(3) Wastes that are hazardous only because they exhibit a hazardous characteristic, and which are otherwise prohibited under this part, or part 148 of this chapter, are not prohibited if the wastes: 13.4.1

(i) Are disposed into a nonhazardous or hazardous injection well as defined under 40 CFR 146.6(a); and

(ii) Do not exhibit any prohibited characteristic of hazardous waste identified in 40 CFR part 261, subpart C at the point of injection.

(4) Wastes that are hazardous only because they exhibit a hazardous characteristic, and which are otherwise prohibited under this part, are not prohibited if the wastes meet any of the following criteria, unless the wastes are subject to a specified method of treatment other than DEACT in §268.40, or are D003 reactive cyanide: 13.4.1, 14.1.6.2

(i) The wastes are managed in a treatment system which subsequently discharges to waters of the U.S. pursuant to a permit issued under section 402 of the Clean Water Act; or

(ii) The wastes are treated for purposes of the pretreatment requirements of section 307 of the Clean Water Act; or

(iii) The wastes are managed in a zero discharge system engaged in Clean Water Act-equivalent treatment as defined in §268.37(a); and

(iv) The wastes no longer exhibit a prohibited characteristic at the point of land disposal (*i.e.*, placement in a surface impoundment).

(d) The requirements of this part shall not affect the availability of a waiver under section 121(d)(4) of the Comprehensive Environmental Response, Compensation, and Liability Act of 1980 (CERCLA).

(e) The following hazardous wastes are not subject to any provision of part 268:

(1) Waste generated by small quantity generators of less than 100 kilograms of non-acute hazardous waste or less than 1 kilogram of acute hazardous waste per month, as defined in §261.5 of this chapter; 13.1.1

(2) Waste pesticides that a farmer disposes of pursuant to §262.70;

(3) Wastes identified or listed as hazardous after November 8, 1984 for which EPA has not promulgated land disposal prohibitions or treatment standards;

(4) *De minimis* losses of characteristic wastes to wastewaters are not considered to be prohibited wastes and are defined as losses from normal material handling operations (*e.g.* spills from the unloading or transfer of materials from bins or other containers, leaks from pipes, valves or other devices used to transfer materials); minor leaks of process equipment, storage tanks or containers; leaks from well-maintained pump packings and seals; sample purgings; and relief device discharges; discharges from safety showers and rinsing and cleaning of personal safety equipment; rinsate from empty containers or from containers that are rendered empty by that rinsing; and laboratory wastes not exceeding one per cent of the total flow of wastewater into the facility's headworks on an annual basis, or with a combined annualized average concentration not exceeding one part per million in the headworks of the facility's wastewater treatment or pretreatment facility.

(f) Universal waste handlers and universal waste transporters (as defined in 40 CFR 260.10) are exempt from 40 CFR 268.7 and 268.50 for the hazardous wastes listed below. These handlers are subject to regulation under 40 CFR part 273. 8.1–4, 13.13.3

(1) Batteries as described in 40 CFR 273.2;

(2) Pesticides as described in §273.3 of this chapter;

(3) Mercury-containing equipment as described in §273.4 of this chapter; and

(4) Lamps as described in 40 CFR 273.5.

[51 FR 40638, Nov. 7, 1986; 52 FR 21016, June 4, 1987, as amended at 53 FR 27165, July 19, 1988; 53 FR 31212, Aug. 17, 1988; 54 FR 36970, Sept. 6, 1989; 55 FR 22686, June 1, 1990; 58 FR 29884, May 24, 1993; 59 FR 48043, Sept. 19, 1994; 60 FR 25542, May 11, 1995; 61 FR 15663, Apr. 8, 1996; 61 FR 33682, June 28, 1996; 62 FR 26019, May 12, 1997; 64 FR 36488, July 6, 1999; 70 FR 45520, Aug. 5, 2005]

§268.2 Definitions applicable in this part.

When used in this part the following terms have the meanings given below:

(a) *Halogenated organic compounds* or *HOCs* means those compounds having a carbon-halogen bond which are listed under appendix III to this part.

(b) *Hazardous constituent* or *constituents* means those constituents listed in appendix VIII to part 261 of this chapter.

(c) *Land disposal* means placement in or on the land, except in a corrective action management unit or staging pile, and includes, but is not limited to, placement in a landfill, surface impoundment, waste pile, injection well, land treatment facility, salt dome formation, salt bed formation, underground mine or cave, or placement in a concrete vault, or bunker intended for disposal purposes. 13.1.3

(d) *Nonwastewaters* are wastes that do not meet the criteria for wastewaters in paragraph (f) of this section. 13.1.5.1

(e) *Polychlorinated biphenyls* or *PCBs* are halogenated organic compounds defined in accordance with 40 CFR 761.3.

(f) *Wastewaters* are wastes that contain less than 1% by weight total organic carbon (TOC) and less than 1% by weight total suspended solids (TSS). 13.1.5.1

(g) *Debris* means solid material exceeding a 60 mm particle size that is intended for disposal and that is: a manufactured object; or plant or animal matter; or natural geologic material. However, the following materials are not debris: any material for which a specific treatment standard is provided in Subpart D, Part 268, namely lead acid batteries, cadmium batteries, and radioactive lead solids; process residuals such as smelter slag and residues from the treatment of waste, wastewater, sludges, or air emission residues; and intact containers of hazardous waste that are not ruptured and that retain at least 75% of their original volume. A mixture of debris that has not been treated to the standards provided by §268.45 and other material is subject to regulation as debris if the mixture is comprised primarily of debris, by volume, based on visual inspection. 9.1.1, 13.8

(h) *Hazardous debris* means debris that contains a hazardous waste listed in subpart D of part 261 of this chapter, or that exhibits a characteristic of hazardous waste identified in subpart C of part 261 of this chapter. Any deliberate mixing of prohibited hazardous waste with debris that changes its treatment classification (*i.e.*, from waste to hazardous debris) is not allowed under the dilution prohibition in §268.3. 5.3.2, 13.8

(i) *Underlying hazardous constituent* means any constituent listed in §268.48, Table UTS—Universal Treatment Standards, except fluoride, selenium, sulfides, vanadium, and zinc, which can reasonably be expected to be present at the point of generation of the hazardous waste at a concentration above the constituent-specific UTS treatment standards. 13.3, 13.7.3

(j) *Inorganic metal-bearing waste* is one for which EPA has established treatment standards for metal hazardous constituents, and which does not otherwise contain significant organic or cyanide content as described in §268.3(c)(1), and is specifically listed in appendix XI of this part.

(k) *Soil* means unconsolidated earth material composing the superficial geologic strata (material overlying bedrock), consisting of clay, silt, sand, or gravel size particles as classified by the U.S. Natural Resources Conservation Service, or a mixture of such materials with liquids, sludges or solids which is inseparable by simple mechanical removal processes and is made up primarily of soil by volume based on visual inspection. Any deliberate mixing of prohibited hazardous waste with soil that changes its treatment classification (*i.e.*, from waste to contaminated soil) is not allowed under the dilution prohibition in §268.3. 13.7

[55 FR 22686, June 1, 1990, as amended at 56 FR 3877, Jan. 31, 1991; 57 FR 37270, Aug. 18, 1992; 58 FR 8685, Feb. 16, 1993; 58 FR 29884, May 24, 1993; 59 FR 48043, Sept. 19, 1994; 60 FR 244, Jan. 3, 1995; 61 FR 15597, 15662, Apr. 8, 1996; 61 FR 33682, June 28, 1996; 63 FR 28639, May 26, 1998; 63 FR 65940, Nov. 30, 1998; 64 FR 25414, May 11, 1999; 71 FR 40278, July 14, 2006]

§268.3 Dilution prohibited as a substitute for treatment.

5.1.3.1, 13.11

(a) Except as provided in paragraph (b) of this section, no generator, transporter, handler, or owner or operator of a treatment, storage, or disposal facility shall in any way dilute a restricted waste or the residual from treatment of a restricted waste as a substitute for adequate treatment to achieve compliance with subpart D of this part, to circumvent the effective date of a prohibition in subpart C of this part, to otherwise avoid a prohibition in subpart C of this part, or to circumvent a land disposal prohibition imposed by RCRA section 3004. 13.11

(b) Dilution of wastes that are hazardous only because they exhibit a characteristic in treatment systems which include land-based units which treat wastes subsequently discharged to a water of the United States pursuant to a permit issued under section 402 of the Clean Water Act (CWA), or which treat wastes in a CWA-equivalent treatment system, or which treat wastes for the purposes of pretreatment requirements under section 307 of the CWA is not impermissible dilution for purposes of this section unless a method other than DEACT has been specified in §268.40 as the treatment standard, or unless the waste is a D003 reactive cyanide wastewater or nonwastewater. 13.11

(c) Combustion of the hazardous waste codes listed in Appendix XI of this part is prohibited, unless the waste, at the point of generation, or after any *bona fide* treatment such as cyanide destruction prior to combustion, can be demonstrated to comply with one or more of the following criteria (unless otherwise specifically prohibited from combustion): 13.11

(1) The waste contains hazardous organic constituents or cyanide at levels exceeding the constituent-specific treatment standard found in §268.48;

(2) The waste consists of organic, debris-like materials (*e.g.*, wood, paper, plastic, or cloth) contaminated with an inorganic metal-bearing hazardous waste;

(3) The waste, at point of generation, has reasonable heating value such as greater than or equal to 5000 BTU per pound;

(4) The waste is co-generated with wastes for which combustion is a required method of treatment;

(5) The waste is subject to Federal and/or State requirements necessitating reduction of organics (including biological agents); or

(6) The waste contains greater than 1% Total Organic Carbon (TOC).

(d) It is a form of impermissible dilution, and therefore prohibited, to add iron filings or other metallic forms of iron to lead-containing hazardous wastes in order to achieve any land disposal restriction treatment standard for lead. Lead-containing wastes include D008 wastes (wastes exhibiting a characteristic due to the presence of lead), all characteristic wastes containing lead as an underlying hazardous constituent, listed wastes containing lead as a regulated constituent, and hazardous media containing any of the aforementioned lead-containing wastes. 📖 **2.6.6, 7.1.1.1**

[61 FR 15663, Apr. 8, 1996, as amended at 61 FR 33682, June 28, 1996; 63 FR 28639, May 26, 1998]

§268.4 Treatment surface impoundment exemption.

(a) Wastes which are otherwise prohibited from land disposal under this part may be treated in a surface impoundment or series of impoundments provided that:

(1) Treatment of such wastes occurs in the impoundments;

(2) The following conditions are met:

(i) *Sampling and testing.* For wastes with treatment standards in subpart D of this part and/or prohibition levels in subpart C of this part or RCRA section 3004(d), the residues from treatment are analyzed, as specified in §268.7 or §268.32, to determine if they meet the applicable treatment standards or where no treatment standards have been established for the waste, the applicable prohibition levels. The sampling method, specified in the waste analysis plan under §264.13 or §265.13, must be designed such that representative samples of the sludge and the supernatant are tested separately rather than mixed to form homogeneous samples.

(ii) *Removal.* The following treatment residues (including any liquid waste) must be removed at least annually; residues which do not meet the treatment standards promulgated under subpart D of this part; residues which do not meet the prohibition levels established under subpart C of this part or imposed by statute (where no treatment standards have been established); residues which are from the treatment of wastes prohibited from land disposal under subpart C of this part (where no treatment standards have been established and no prohibition levels apply); or residues from managing listed wastes which are not delisted under §260.22 of this chapter. If the volume of liquid flowing through the impoundment or series of impoundments annually is greater than the volume of the impoundment or impoundments, this flow-through constitutes removal of the supernatant for the purpose of this requirement.

(iii) *Subsequent management.* Treatment residues may not be placed in any other surface impoundment for subsequent management.

(iv) *Recordkeeping.* Sampling and testing and recordkeeping provisions of §§264.13 and 265.13 of this chapter apply.

(3) The impoundment meets the design requirements of §264.221(c) or §265.221(a) of this chapter, regardless that the unit may not be new, expanded, or a replacement, and be in compliance with applicable ground water monitoring requirements of subpart F of part 264 or part 265 of this chapter unless:

(i) Exempted pursuant to §264.221 (d) or (e) of this chapter, or to §265.221 (c) or (d) of this chapter; or,

(ii) Upon application by the owner or operator, the Administrator, after notice and an opportunity to comment, has granted a waiver of the requirements on the basis that the surface impoundment:

(A) Has at least one liner, for which there is no evidence that such liner is leaking;

(B) Is located more than one-quarter mile from an underground source of drinking water; and

(C) Is in compliance with generally applicable ground water monitoring requirements for facilities with permits; or,

(iii) Upon application by the owner or operator, the Administrator, after notice and an opportunity to comment, has granted a modification to the requirements on the basis of a demonstration that the surface impoundment is located, designed, and operated so as to assure that there will be no migration of any hazardous constituent into ground water or surface water at any future time.

(4) The owner or operator submits to the Regional Administrator a written certification that the requirements of §268.4(a)(3) have been met. The following certification is required:

I certify under penalty of law that the requirements of 40 CFR 268.4(a)(3) have been met for all surface impoundments being used to treat restricted wastes. I believe that the submitted information is true, accurate, and complete. I am aware that there are significant penalties for submitting false information, including the possibility of fine and imprisonment.

(b) Evaporation of hazardous constituents as the principal means of treatment is not considered to be treatment for purposes of an exemption under this section.

[51 FR 40638, Nov. 7, 1986; 52 FR 21016, June 4, 1987, as amended at 52 FR 25788, July 8, 1987; 53 FR 31212, Aug. 17, 1988; 62 FR 26019, May 12, 1997; 63 FR 28639, May 26, 1998; 71 FR 40278, July 14, 2006]

§268.5 Procedures for case-by-case extensions to an effective date.

(a) Any person who generates, treats, stores, or disposes of a hazardous waste may submit an application to the Administrator for an extension to the effective date of any applicable restriction established under subpart C of this part. The applicant must demonstrate the following:

(1) He has made a good-faith effort to locate and contract with treatment, recovery, or disposal facilities nationwide to manage his waste in accordance with the effective date of the applicable restriction established under subpart C of this part;

(2) He has entered into a binding contractual commitment to construct or otherwise provide alternative treatment, recovery (*e.g.*, recycling), or disposal capacity that meets the treatment standards specified in subpart D or, where treatment standards have not been specified, such treatment, recovery, or disposal capacity is protective of human health and the environment.

(3) Due to circumstances beyond the applicant's control, such alternative capacity cannot reasonably be made available by the applicable effective date. This demonstration may include a showing that the technical and practical difficulties associated with providing the alternative capacity will result in the capacity not being available by the applicable effective date;

(4) The capacity being constructed or otherwise provided by the applicant will be sufficient to manage the entire quantity of waste that is the subject of the application;

(5) He provides a detailed schedule for obtaining required operating and construction permits or an outline of how and when alternative capacity will be available;

(6) He has arranged for adequate capacity to manage his waste during an extension and has documented in the application the location of all sites at which the waste will be managed; and

(7) Any waste managed in a surface impoundment or landfill during the extension period will meet the requirements of paragraph (h)(2) of this section.

(b) An authorized representative signing an application described under paragraph (a) of this section shall make the following certification:

I certify under penalty of law that I have personally examined and am familiar with the information submitted in this document and all attachments and that, based on my inquiry of those individuals immediately responsible for obtaining the information, I believe that the information is true, accurate, and complete. I am aware that there are significant penalties for submitting false information, including the possibility of fine and imprisonment.

(c) After receiving an application for an extension, the Administrator may request any additional information which he deems as necessary to evaluate the application.

(d) An extension will apply only to the waste generated at the individual facility covered by the application and will not apply to restricted waste from any other facility.

(e) On the basis of the information referred to in paragraph (a) of this section, after notice and opportunity for comment, and after consultation with appropriate State agencies in all affected States, the Administrator may grant an extension of up to 1 year from the effective date. The Administrator may renew this extension for up to 1 additional year upon the request of the applicant if the demonstration required in paragraph (a) of this section can still be made. In no event will an extension extend beyond 24 months from the applicable effective date specified in subpart C of part 268. The length of any extension authorized will be determined by the Administrator based on the time required to construct or obtain the type of capacity needed by the applicant as described in the completion schedule discussed in paragraph (a)(5) of this section. The Administrator will give public notice of the intent to approve or deny a petition and provide an opportunity for public comment. The final decision on a petition will be published in the *Federal Register*.

(f) Any person granted an extension under this section must immediately notify the Administrator as soon as he has knowledge of any change in the conditions certified to in the application.

(g) Any person granted an extension under this section shall submit written progress reports at intervals designated by the Administrator. Such reports must describe the overall progress made toward constructing or otherwise providing alternative treatment, recovery or disposal capacity; must identify any event which may cause or has caused a delay in the development of the capacity; and must summarize the steps taken to mitigate the delay. The Administrator can revoke the extension at any time if the applicant does not demonstrate a good-faith effort to meet the schedule for completion, if the Agency denies or revokes any required permit, if conditions certified in the application change, or for any violation of this chapter.

(h) Whenever the Administrator establishes an extension to an effective date under this section, during the period for which such extension is in effect:

(1) The storage restrictions under §268.50(a) do not apply; and

(2) Such hazardous waste may be disposed in a landfill or surface impoundment only if such unit is in compliance with the technical requirements of the following provisions regardless of whether such unit is existing, new, or a replacement or lateral expansion.

(i) The landfill, if in interim status, is in compliance with the requirements of subpart F of part 265 and §265.301 (a), (c), and (d) of this chapter; or,

(ii) The landfill, if permitted, is in compliance with the requirements of subpart F of part 264 and §264.301 (c), (d) and (e) of this chapter; or

(iii) The surface impoundment, if in interim status, is in compliance with the requirements of subpart F of part 265, §265.221 (a), (c), and (d) of this chapter, and RCRA section 3005(j)(1); or

(iv) The surface impoundment, if permitted, is in compliance with the requirements of subpart F of part 264 and §264.221 (c), (d) and (e) of this chapter; or

(v) The surface impoundment, if newly subject to RCRA section 3005(j)(1) due to the promulgation of additional listings or characteristics for the identification of hazardous waste, is in compliance with the requirements of subpart F of part 265 of this chapter within 12 months after the promulgation of additional listings or characteristics of hazardous waste, and with the requirements of §265.221 (a), (c) and (d) of this chapter within 48 months after the promulgation of additional listings or characteristics of hazardous waste. If a national capacity variance is granted, during the period the variance is in effect, the surface impoundment, if newly subject to RCRA section 3005(j)(1) due to the promulgation of additional listings or characteristics of hazardous waste, is in compliance with the requirements of subpart F of part 265 of this chapter within 12 months after the promulgation of additional listings or characteristics of hazardous waste, and with the requirements of §265.221 (a), (c) and (d) of this chapter within 48 months after the promulgation of additional listings or characteristics of hazardous waste; or

(vi) The landfill, if disposing of containerized liquid hazardous wastes containing PCBs at concentrations greater than or equal to 50 ppm but less than 500 ppm, is also in compliance with the requirements of 40 CFR 761.75 and parts 264 and 265.

(i) Pending a decision on the application the applicant is required to comply with all restrictions on land disposal under this part once the effective date for the waste has been reached.

[51 FR 40638, Nov. 7, 1986; 52 FR 21016, June 4, 1987, as amended at 52 FR 25788, July 8, 1987; 54 FR 36971, Sept. 6, 1989; 55 FR 23935, June 13, 1990; 57 FR 37270, Aug. 18, 1992]

§268.6 Petitions to allow land disposal of a waste prohibited under subpart C of part 268.

(a) Any person seeking an exemption from a prohibition under subpart C of this part for the disposal of a restricted hazardous waste in a particular unit or units must submit a petition to the Administrator demonstrating, to a reasonable degree of certainty, that there will be no migration of hazardous constituents from the disposal unit or injection zone for as long as the wastes remain hazardous. The demonstration must include the following components:

(1) An identification of the specific waste and the specific unit for which the demonstration will be made;

(2) A waste analysis to describe fully the chemical and physical characteristics of the subject waste;

(3) A comprehensive characterization of the disposal unit site including an analysis of background air, soil, and water quality.

(4) A monitoring plan that detects migration at the earliest practicable time;

(5) Sufficient information to assure the Administrator that the owner or operator of a land disposal unit receiving restricted waste(s) will comply with other applicable Federal, State, and local laws.

(b) The demonstration referred to in paragraph (a) of this section must meet the following criteria:

(1) All waste and environmental sampling, test, and analysis data must be accurate and reproducible to the extent that state-of-the-art techniques allow;

(2) All sampling, testing, and estimation techniques for chemical and physical properties of the waste and all environmental parameters must have been approved by the Administrator;

(3) Simulation models must be calibrated for the specific waste and site conditions, and verified for accuracy by comparison with actual measurements;

(4) A quality assurance and quality control plan that addresses all aspects of the demonstration must be approved by the Administrator; and,

(5) An analysis must be performed to identify and quantify any aspects of the demonstration that contribute significantly to uncertainty. This analysis must include an evaluation of the consequences of predictable future events, including, but not limited to, earthquakes, floods, severe storm events, droughts, or other natural phenomena.

(c) Each petition referred to in paragraph (a) of this section must include the following:

(1) A monitoring plan that describes the monitoring program installed at and/or around the unit to verify continued compliance with the conditions of the variance. This monitoring plan must provide information on the monitoring of the unit and/or the environment around the unit. The following specific information must be included in the plan:

(i) The media monitored in the cases where monitoring of the environment around the unit is required;

(ii) The type of monitoring conducted at the unit, in the cases where monitoring of the unit is required;

(iii) The location of the monitoring stations;

(iv) The monitoring interval (frequency of monitoring at each station);

(v) The specific hazardous constituents to be monitored;

(vi) The implementation schedule for the monitoring program;

(vii) The equipment used at the monitoring stations;

(viii) The sampling and analytical techniques employed; and

(ix) The data recording/reporting procedures.

(2) Where applicable, the monitoring program described in paragraph (c)(1) of this section must be in place for a period of time specified by the Administrator, as part of his approval of the petition, prior to receipt of prohibited waste at the unit.

(3) The monitoring data collected according to the monitoring plan specified under paragraph (c)(1) of this section must be sent to the Administrator according to a format and schedule specified and approved in the monitoring plan, and

(4) A copy of the monitoring data collected under the monitoring plan specified under paragraph (c)(1) of this section must be kept on-site at the facility in the operating record.

(5) The monitoring program specified under paragraph (c)(1) of this section meets the following criteria:

(i) All sampling, testing, and analytical data must be approved by the Administrator and must provide data that is accurate and reproducible.

(ii) All estimation and monitoring techniques must be approved by the Administrator.

(iii) A quality assurance and quality control plan addressing all aspects of the monitoring program must be provided to and approved by the Administrator.

(d) Each petition must be submitted to the Administrator.

(e) After a petition has been approved, the owner or operator must report any changes in conditions at the unit and/or the environment around the unit that significantly depart from the conditions described in the variance and affect the potential for migration of hazardous constituents from the units as follows:

(1) If the owner or operator plans to make changes to the unit design, construction, or operation, such a change must be proposed, in writing, and the owner or operator must submit a demonstration to the Administrator at least 30 days prior to making the change. The Administrator will determine whether the proposed change invalidates the terms of the petition and will determine the appropriate response. Any change must be approved by the Administrator prior to being made.

(2) If the owner or operator discovers that a condition at the site which was modeled or predicted in the petition does not occur as predicted, this change must be reported, in writing, to the Administrator within 10 days of discovering the change. The Administrator will determine whether the reported change from the terms of the petition requires further action, which may include termination of waste acceptance and revocation of the petition, petition modifications, or other responses.

(f) If the owner or operator determines that there is migration of hazardous constituent(s) from the unit, the owner or operator must:

(1) Immediately suspend receipt of prohibited waste at the unit, and

(2) Notify the Administrator, in writing, within 10 days of the determination that a release has occurred.

(3) Following receipt of the notification the Administrator will determine, within 60 days of receiving notification, whether the owner or operator can continue to receive prohibited waste in the unit and whether the

variance is to be revoked. The Administrator shall also determine whether further examination of any migration is warranted under applicable provisions of part 264 or part 265.

(g) Each petition must include the following statement signed by the petitioner or an authorized representative:

I certify under penalty of law that I have personally examined and am familiar with the information submitted in this petition and all attached documents, and that, based on my inquiry of those individuals immediately responsible for obtaining the information, I believe that submitted information is true, accurate, and complete. I am aware that there are significant penalties for submitting false information, including the possibility of fine and imprisonment.

(h) After receiving a petition, the Administrator may request any additional information that reasonably may be required to evaluate the demonstration.

(i) If approved, the petition will apply to land disposal of the specific restricted waste at the individual disposal unit described in the demonstration and will not apply to any other restricted waste at that disposal unit, or to that specific restricted waste at any other disposal unit.

(j) The Administrator will give public notice in the *Federal Register* of the intent to approve or deny a petition and provide an opportunity for public comment. The final decision on a petition will be published in the *Federal Register.*

(k) The term of a petition granted under this section shall be no longer than the term of the RCRA permit if the disposal unit is operating under a RCRA permit, or up to a maximum of 10 years from the date of approval provided under paragraph (g) of this section if the unit is operating under interim status. In either case, the term of the granted petition shall expire upon the termination or denial of a RCRA permit, or upon the termination of interim status or when the volume limit of waste to be land disposed during the term of petition is reached.

(l) Prior to the Administrator's decision, the applicant is required to comply with all restrictions on land disposal under this part once the effective date for the waste has been reached.

(m) The petition granted by the Administrator does not relieve the petitioner of his responsibilities in the management of hazardous waste under 40 CFR part 260 through part 271.

(n) Liquid hazardous wastes containing polychlorinated biphenyls at concentrations greater than or equal to 500 ppm are not eligible for an exemption under this section.

[51 FR 40638, Nov. 7, 1986; 52 FR 21016, June 4, 1987, as amended at 52 FR 25789, July 8, 1987; 53 FR 31212, Aug. 17, 1988; 54 FR 36971, Sept. 6, 1989; 71 FR 40278, July 14, 2006]

§268.7 Testing, tracking, and recordkeeping requirements for generators, treaters, and disposal facilities. 13.12, 16.1.6, 18.4.2

(a) *Requirements for generators:* (1) A generator of hazardous waste must determine if the waste has to be treated before it can be land disposed. This is done by determining if the hazardous waste meets the treatment standards in §268.40, 268.45, or §268.49. This determination can be made concurrently with the hazardous waste determination required in §262.11 of this chapter, in either of two ways: testing the waste or using knowledge of the waste. If the generator tests the waste, testing would normally determine the total concentration of hazardous constituents, or the concentration of hazardous constituents in an extract of the waste obtained using test method 1311 in "Test Methods of Evaluating Solid Waste, Physical/Chemical Methods," EPA Publication SW–846, (incorporated by reference, see §260.11 of this chapter), depending on whether the treatment standard for the waste is expressed as a total concentration or concentration of hazardous constituent in the waste's extract. (Alternatively, the generator must send the waste to a RCRA-permitted hazardous waste treatment facility, where the waste treatment facility must comply with the requirements of §264.13 of this chapter and paragraph (b) of this section.) In addition, some hazardous wastes must be treated by particular treatment methods before they can be land disposed and some soils are contaminated by such hazardous wastes. These treatment standards are also found in §268.40, and are described in detail in §268.42, Table 1. These wastes, and soils contaminated with such wastes, do not need to be tested (however, if they are in a waste mixture, other wastes with concentration level treatment standards would have to be tested). If a generator determines they are managing a waste or soil contaminated with a waste, that displays a hazardous characteristic of ignitability, corrosivity, reactivity, or toxicity, they must comply with the special requirements of §268.9 of this part in addition to any applicable requirements in this section. 13.2, 18.1.6, 18.5.1

(2) If the waste or contaminated soil does not meet the treatment standards, or if the generator chooses not to make the determination of whether his waste must be treated, with the initial shipment of waste to each treatment or storage facility, the generator must send a one-time written notice to each treatment or storage facility receiving the waste, and place a copy in the file. The notice must include the information in column "268.7(a)(2)" of the Generator Paperwork Requirements Table in paragraph (a)(4) of this section. (Alternatively, if the

generator chooses not to make the determination of whether the waste must be treated, the notification must include the EPA Hazardous Waste Numbers and Manifest Number of the first shipment and must state "This hazardous waste may or may not be subject to the LDR treatment standards. The treatment facility must make the determination.") No further notification is necessary until such time that the waste or facility change, in which case a new notification must be sent and a copy placed in the generator's file. 📖 **13.12.3.2–4**

(3) If the waste or contaminated soil meets the treatment standard at the original point of generation:

[*Publisher's Note:* When EPA streamlined the LDR notification and certification regulations on May 12, 1997 (62 *FR* 25997), §268.7(a)(3) was rewritten for clarity. At that time, we believe the agency unintentionally changed the meaning of this paragraph by restricting it to "the original point of generation." The result is that some references to §268.7(a)(3) from other places (e.g., §268.7(a)(5)(iii)) appear to be incorrect. Based on the regulatory history, we believe that this paragraph should read: "If the waste or contaminated soil meets the treatment standard:".]

(i) With the initial shipment of waste to each treatment, storage, or disposal facility, the generator must send a one-time written notice to each treatment, storage, or disposal facility receiving the waste, and place a copy in the file. The notice must include the information indicated in column "268.7(a)(3)" of the Generator Paperwork Requirements Table in §268.7(a)(4) and the following certification statement, signed by an authorized representative:

I certify under penalty of law that I personally have examined and am familiar with the waste through analysis and testing or through knowledge of the waste to support this certification that the waste complies with the treatment standards specified in 40 CFR part 268 subpart D. I believe that the information I submitted is true, accurate, and complete. I am aware that there are significant penalties for submitting a false certification, including the possibility of a fine and imprisonment.

(ii) For contaminated soil, with the initial shipment of wastes to each treatment, storage, or disposal facility, the generator must send a one-time written notice to each facility receiving the waste and place a copy in the file. The notice must include the information in column "268.7(a)(3)" of the Generator Paperwork Requirements Table in §268.7(a)(4). 📖 **13.12.3.11**

(iii) If the waste changes, the generator must send a new notice and certification to the receiving facility, and place a copy in their files. Generators of hazardous debris excluded from the definition of hazardous waste under §261.3(f) of this chapter are not subject to these requirements.

(4) For reporting, tracking, and recordkeeping when exceptions allow certain wastes or contaminated soil that do not meet the treatment standards to be land disposed: There are certain exemptions from the requirement that hazardous wastes or contaminated soil meet treatment standards before they can be land disposed. These include, but are not limited to case-by-case extensions under §268.5, disposal in a no-migration unit under §268.6, or a national capacity variance or case-by-case capacity variance under subpart C of this part. If a generator's waste is so exempt, then with the initial shipment of waste, the generator must send a one-time written notice to each land disposal facility receiving the waste. The notice must include the information indicated in column "268.7(a)(4)" of the Generator Paperwork Requirements Table below. If the

Generator Paperwork Requirements Table

📖 **13.12**

Required information	§268.7 (a)(2)	§268.7 (a)(3)	§268.7 (a)(4)	§268.7 (a)(9)
1. EPA Hazardous Waste Numbers and Manifest Number of first shipment	✓	✓	✓	✓
2. Statement: this waste is not prohibited from land disposal			✓	
3. The waste is subject to the LDRs. The constituents of concern for F001-F005, and F039, and underlying hazardous constituents in characteristic wastes, unless the waste will be treated and monitored for all constituents. If all constituents will be treated and monitored, there is no need to put them all on the LDR notice 📖 **13.3, 13.12.3.11**	✓	✓		
4. The notice must include the applicable wastewater/nonwastewater category (see §§268.2(d) and (f)) and subdivisions made within a waste code based on waste-specific criteria (such as D003 reactive cyanide)	✓	✓		
5. Waste analysis data (when available)	✓	✓	✓	
6. Date the waste is subject to the prohibition			✓	
7. For hazardous debris, when treating with the alternative treatment technologies provided by §268.45: the contaminants subject to treatment, as described in §268.45(b); and an indication that these contaminants are being treated to comply with §268.45	✓		✓	
8. For contaminated soil subject to LDRs as provided in §268.49(a), the constituents subject to treatment as described in §268.49(d), and the following statement: This contaminated soil [does/does not] contain listed hazardous waste and [does/does not] exhibit a characteristic of hazardous waste and [is subject to/complies with] the soil treatment standards as provided by §268.49(c) or the universal treatment standards	✓	✓		
9. A certification is needed (see applicable section for exact wording)		✓		✓

waste changes, the generator must send a new notice to the receiving facility, and place a copy in their files.

(5) If a generator is managing and treating prohibited waste or contaminated soil in tanks, containers, or containment buildings regulated under 40 CFR 262.34 to meet applicable LDR treatment standards found at §268.40, the generator must develop and follow a written waste analysis plan which describes the procedures they will carry out to comply with the treatment standards. (Generators treating hazardous debris under the alternative treatment standards of Table 1, §268.45, however, are not subject to these waste analysis requirements.) The plan must be kept on site in the generator's records, and the following requirements must be met: 📖 6.7.4, 7.3.2.5, 18.2.3.1

(i) The waste analysis plan must be based on a detailed chemical and physical analysis of a representative sample of the prohibited waste(s) being treated, and contain all information necessary to treat the waste(s) in accordance with the requirements of this part, including the selected testing frequency.

(ii) Such plan must be kept in the facility's on-site files and made available to inspectors.

(iii) Wastes shipped off-site pursuant to this paragraph must comply with the notification requirements of §268.7(a)(3).

(6) If a generator determines that the waste or contaminated soil is restricted based solely on his knowledge of the waste, all supporting data used to make this determination must be retained on-site in the generator's files. If a generator determines that the waste is restricted based on testing this waste or an extract developed using the test method 1311 in "Test Methods for Evaluating Solid Waste, Physical/Chemical Methods," EPA Publication SW-846, as referenced in §260.11 of this chapter, and all waste analysis data must be retained on-site in the generator's files.

(7) If a generator determines that he is managing a prohibited waste that is excluded from the definition of hazardous or solid waste or is exempted from Subtitle C regulation under 40 CFR 261.2 through 261.6 subsequent to the point of generation (including deactivated characteristic hazardous wastes managed in wastewater treatment systems subject to the Clean Water Act (CWA) as specified at 40 CFR 261.4(a)(2) or that are CWA-equivalent, or are managed in an underground injection well regulated by the SDWA), he must place a one-time notice describing such generation, subsequent exclusion from the definition of hazardous or solid waste or exemption from RCRA Subtitle C regulation, and the disposition of the waste, in the facility's on-site files. 📖 4.1.7, 4.16.6, 7.2.3.4, 13.1.3.1, 13.12.1.1, 13.12.3.1

(8) Generators must retain on-site a copy of all notices, certifications, waste analysis data, and other documentation produced pursuant to this section for at least three years from the date that the waste that is the subject of such documentation was last sent to on-site or off-site treatment, storage, or disposal. The three year record retention period is automatically extended during the course of any unresolved enforcement action regarding the regulated activity or as requested by the Administrator. The requirements of this paragraph apply to solid wastes even when the hazardous characteristic is removed prior to disposal, or when the waste is excluded from the definition of hazardous or solid waste under 40 CFR 261.2 through 261.6, or exempted from Subtitle C regulation, subsequent to the point of generation. 📖 6.7.2, 18.4.5

(9) If a generator is managing a lab pack containing hazardous wastes and wishes to use the alternative treatment standard for lab packs found at §268.42(c): 📖 9.7, 13.13.1

(i) With the initial shipment of waste to a treatment facility, the generator must submit a notice that provides the information in column "§268.7(a)(9)" in the Generator Paperwork Requirements Table of paragraph (a)(4) of this section, and the following certification. The certification, which must be signed by an authorized representative and must be placed in the generator's files, must say the following:

> I certify under penalty of law that I personally have examined and am familiar with the waste and that the lab pack contains only wastes that have not been excluded under appendix IV to 40 CFR part 268 and that this lab pack will be sent to a combustion facility in compliance with the alternative treatment standards for lab packs at 40 CFR 268.42(c). I am aware that there are significant penalties for submitting a false certification, including the possibility of fine or imprisonment.

(ii) No further notification is necessary until such time that the wastes in the lab pack change, or the receiving facility changes, in which case a new notice and certification must be sent and a copy placed in the generator's file.

(iii) If the lab pack contains characteristic hazardous wastes (D001-D043), underlying hazardous constituents (as defined in §268.2(i)) need not be determined.

Publisher's Note: Note that §268.7(a)(9)(iii) refers to D001-D043, but it actually should refer to D001-D008 and D010-D043 because lab packs cannot contain D009 and be incinerated per §268.42(c).

(iv) The generator must also comply with the requirements in paragraphs (a)(6) and (a)(7) of this section.

(10) Small quantity generators with tolling agreements pursuant to 40 CFR 262.20(e) must comply with the applicable notification and certification requirements of paragraph (a) of this section for the initial shipment of the waste subject to the agreement. Such generators must retain on-site a copy of the notification and certification, together with the tolling agreement, for at least three years after termination or expiration of the agreement. The three-year record retention period is automatically extended during the course of any unresolved enforcement action regarding the regulated activity or as requested by the Administrator.

(b) Treatment facilities must test their wastes according to the frequency specified in their waste analysis plans as required by 40 CFR 264.13 (for permitted TSDs) or 40 CFR 265.13 (for interim status facilities). Such testing must be performed as provided in paragraphs (b)(1), (b)(2) and (b)(3) of this section. 📖 13.12, 18.4.3

(1) For wastes or contaminated soil with treatment standards expressed in the waste extract (TCLP), the owner or operator of the treatment facility must test an extract of the treatment residues, using test method 1311 (the Toxicity Characteristic Leaching Procedure, described in "Test Methods for Evaluating Solid Waste, Physical/Chemical Methods," EPA Publication SW-846 as incorporated by reference in §260.11 of this chapter) to assure that the treatment residues extract meet the applicable treatment standards.

(2) For wastes or contaminated soil with treatment standards expressed as concentrations in the waste, the owner or operator of the treatment facility must test the treatment residues (not an extract of such residues) to assure that they meet the applicable treatment standards.

(3) A one-time notice must be sent with the initial shipment of waste or contaminated soil to the land disposal facility. A copy of the notice must be placed in the treatment facility's file.

(i) No further notification is necessary until such time that the waste or receiving facility change, in which case a new notice must be sent and a copy placed in the treatment facility's file.

(ii) The one-time notice must include these requirements:

Treatment Facility Paperwork Requirements Table

Required information	§268.7 (b)
1. EPA Hazardous Waste Numbers and Manifest Number of first shipment	✓
2. The waste is subject to the LDRs. The constituents of concern for F001-F005, and F039, and underlying hazardous constituents in characteristic wastes, unless the waste will be treated and monitored for all constituents. If all constituents will be treated and monitored, there is no need to put them all on the LDR notice 📖 13.3	✓
3. The notice must include the applicable wastewater/ nonwastewater category (see §§268.2(d) and (f)) and subdivisions made within a waste code based on waste-specific criteria (such as D003 reactive cyanide)	✓
4. Waste analysis data (when available)	✓
5. For contaminated soil subject to LDRs as provided in 268.49(a), the constituents subject to treatment as described in 268.49(d) and the following statement, "this contaminated soil [does/does not] exhibit a characteristic of hazardous waste and [is subject to/ complies with] the soil treatment standards as provided by 268.49(c)"	✓
6. A certification is needed (see applicable section for exact wording)	✓

(4) The treatment facility must submit a one-time certification signed by an authorized representative with the initial shipment of waste or treatment residue of a restricted waste to the land disposal facility. The certification must state:

> I certify under penalty of law that I have personally examined and am familiar with the treatment technology and operation of the treatment process used to support this certification. Based on my inquiry of those individuals immediately responsible for obtaining this information, I believe that the treatment process has been operated and maintained properly so as to comply with the treatment standards specified in 40 CFR 268.40 without impermissible dilution of the prohibited waste. I am aware there are significant penalties for submitting a false certification, including the possibility of fine and imprisonment.

A certification is also necessary for contaminated soil and it must state:

> I certify under penalty of law that I have personally examined and am familiar with the treatment technology and operation of the treatment process used to support this certification and believe that it has been maintained and operated properly so as to comply with treatment standards specified in 40 CFR 268.49 without impermissible dilution of the prohibited wastes. I am aware there are significant penalties for submitting a false certification, including the possibility of fine and imprisonment.

(i) A copy of the certification must be placed in the treatment facility's on-site files. If the waste or treatment residue changes, or the receiving facility changes, a new certification must be sent to the receiving facility, and a copy placed in the file.

(ii) Debris excluded from the definition of hazardous waste under §261.3(f) of this chapter (*i.e.*, debris treated by an extraction or destruction technology provided by Table 1, §268.45, and debris that the Director has determined does not contain hazardous waste), however, is subject to the notification and certification requirements of paragraph (d) of this section rather than the certification requirements of this paragraph.

(iii) For wastes with organic constituents having treatment standards expressed as concentration levels, if compliance with the treatment standards is based in whole or in part on the analytical detection limit alternative specified in §268.40(d), the certification, signed by an authorized representative, must state the following:

> I certify under penalty of law that I have personally examined and am familiar with the treatment technology and operation of the treatment process used to support this certification. Based on my inquiry of those individuals immediately responsible for obtaining this information, I believe that the nonwastewater organic constituents have been treated by combustion units as specified in 268.42, Table 1. I have been unable to detect the nonwastewater organic constituents, despite having used best good-faith efforts to analyze for such constituents. I am aware there are significant penalties for submitting a false certification, including the possibility of fine and imprisonment.

(iv) For characteristic wastes that are subject to the treatment standards in §268.40 (other than those expressed as a method of treatment), or §268.49, and that contain underlying hazardous constituents as defined in §268.2(i); if these wastes are treated on-site to remove the hazardous characteristic; and are then sent off-site for treatment of underlying hazardous constituents, the certification must state the following:

> I certify under penalty of law that the waste has been treated in accordance with the requirements of 40 CFR 268.40 or 268.49 to remove the hazardous characteristic. This decharacterized waste contains underlying hazardous constituents that require further treatment to meet treatment standards. I am aware that there are significant penalties for submitting a false certification, including the possibility of fine and imprisonment.

(v) For characteristic wastes that contain underlying hazardous constituents as defined §268.2(i) that are treated on-site to remove the hazardous characteristic to treat underlying hazardous constituents to levels in §268.48 Universal Treatment Standards, the certification must state the following:

> I certify under penalty of law that the waste has been treated in accordance with the requirements of 40 CFR 268.40 to remove the hazardous characteristic and that underlying hazardous constituents, as defined in §268.2(i) have been treated on-site to meet the §268.48 Universal Treatment Standards. I am aware that there are significant penalties for submitting a false certification, including the possibility of fine and imprisonment.

(5) If the waste or treatment residue will be further managed at a different treatment, storage, or disposal facility, the treatment, storage, or disposal facility sending the waste or treatment residue off-site must comply with the notice and certification requirements applicable to generators under this section. 14.1.6.3

(6) Where the wastes are recyclable materials used in a manner constituting disposal subject to the provisions of §266.20(b) of this chapter regarding treatment standards and prohibition levels, the owner or operator of a treatment facility (*i.e.*, the recycler) must, for the initial shipment of waste, prepare a one-time certification described in paragraph (b)(4) of this section, and a one-time notice which includes the information in paragraph (b)(3) of this section (except the manifest number). The certification and notification must be placed in the facility's on-site files. If the waste or the receiving facility changes, a new certification and notification must be prepared and placed in the on site files. In addition, the recycling facility must also keep records of the name and location of each entity receiving the hazardous waste-derived product.

(c) Except where the owner or operator is disposing of any waste that is a recyclable material used in a manner constituting disposal pursuant to 40 CFR 266.20(b), the owner or operator of any land disposal facility disposing any waste subject to restrictions under this part must: 18.4.4

(1) Have copies of the notice and certifications specified in paragraph (a) or (b) of this section.

(2) Test the waste, or an extract of the waste or treatment residue developed using test method 1311 (the Toxicity Characteristic Leaching Procedure, described in "Test Methods for Evaluating Solid Waste, Physical/Chemical Methods," EPA Publication SW-846 as incorporated by reference in §260.11 of this chapter), to assure that the wastes or treatment residues are in compliance with the applicable treatment standards set forth in subpart D of this part. Such testing must be performed according to the frequency specified in the

facility's waste analysis plan as required by §264.13 or §265.13 of this chapter.

(d) Generators or treaters who first claim that hazardous debris is excluded from the definition of hazardous waste under §261.3(f) of this chapter (*i.e.*, debris treated by an extraction or destruction technology provided by Table 1, §268.45, and debris that the EPA Regional Administrator (or his designated representative) or State authorized to implement part 268 requirements has determined does not contain hazardous waste) are subject to the following notification and certification requirements:

(1) A one-time notification, including the following information, must be submitted to the EPA Regional hazardous waste management division director (or his designated representative) or State authorized to implement part 268 requirements:

(i) The name and address of the Subtitle D facility receiving the treated debris;

(ii) A description of the hazardous debris as initially generated, including the applicable EPA Hazardous Waste Number(s); and

(iii) For debris excluded under §261.3(f)(1) of this chapter, the technology from Table 1, §268.45, used to treat the debris.

(2) The notification must be updated if the debris is shipped to a different facility, and, for debris excluded under §261.3(f)(1) of this chapter, if a different type of debris is treated or if a different technology is used to treat the debris.

(3) For debris excluded under §261.3(f)(1) of this chapter, the owner or operator of the treatment facility must document and certify compliance with the treatment standards of Table 1, §268.45, as follows:

(i) Records must be kept of all inspections, evaluations, and analyses of treated debris that are made to determine compliance with the treatment standards;

(ii) Records must be kept of any data or information the treater obtains during treatment of the debris that identifies key operating parameters of the treatment unit; and

(iii) For each shipment of treated debris, a certification of compliance with the treatment standards must be signed by an authorized representative and placed in the facility's files. The certification must state the following: "I certify under penalty of law that the debris has been treated in accordance with the requirements of 40 CFR 268.45. I am aware that there are significant penalties for making a false certification, including the possibility of fine and imprisonment."

(e) Generators and treaters who first receive from EPA or an authorized state a determination that a given contaminated soil subject to LDRs as provided in §268.49(a) no longer contains a listed hazardous waste and generators and treaters who first determine that a contaminated soil subject to LDRs as provided in §268.49(a) no longer exhibits a characteristic of hazardous waste must:

(1) Prepare a one-time only documentation of these determinations including all supporting information; and,

(2) Maintain that information in the facility files and other records for a minimum of three years.

[51 FR 40638, Nov. 7, 1986; 52 FR 21016, June 4, 1987, as amended at 52 FR 25789, July 8, 1987; 53 FR 31213, Aug. 17, 1988; 54 FR 26648, June 23, 1989; 54 FR 36971, Sept. 6, 1989; 55 FR 22687, June 1, 1990; 55 FR 23935, June 13, 1990; 56 FR 3877, Jan. 31, 1991; 57 FR 37270, Aug. 18, 1992; 58 FR 29884, May 24, 1993; 58 FR 46050, Aug. 31, 1993; 59 FR 47980, Sept. 19, 1994; 59 FR 48043, Sept. 19, 1994; 60 FR 244, Jan. 3, 1995; 61 FR 15598, Apr. 8, 1996; 62 FR 26019, May 12, 1997; 63 FR 28639, May 26, 1998; 64 FR 25414, May 11, 1999; 64 FR 56471, Oct. 20, 1999; 71 FR 16913, Apr. 4, 2006; 71 FR 40278, July 14, 2006]

§268.8 [Reserved]

§268.9 Special rules regarding wastes that exhibit a characteristic.

(a) The initial generator of a solid waste must determine each EPA Hazardous Waste Number (waste code) applicable to the waste in order to determine the applicable treatment standards under subpart D of this part. This determination may be made concurrently with the hazardous waste determination required in §262.11 of this chapter. For purposes of part 268, the waste will carry the waste code for any applicable listed waste (40 CFR part 261, subpart D). In addition, where the waste exhibits a characteristic, the waste will carry one or more of the characteristic waste codes (40 CFR part 261, subpart C), except when the treatment standard for the listed waste operates in lieu of the treatment standard for the characteristic waste, as specified in paragraph (b) of this section. If the generator determines that their waste displays a hazardous characteristic (and is not D001 nonwastewaters treated by CMBST, RORGS, OR POLYM of §268.42, Table 1), the generator must determine the underlying hazardous constituents (as defined at §268.2(i)) in the characteristic waste. 13.2–3, 13.6

(b) Where a prohibited waste is both listed under 40 CFR part 261, subpart D and exhibits a characteristic under 40 CFR part 261, subpart C, the treatment standard for the waste code listed in 40 CFR part 261, subpart D will operate in lieu of the standard for the waste code under 40 CFR part 261, subpart C, provided that the treatment standard for the listed waste includes a treatment standard for the constituent that causes the waste to exhibit the characteristic. Otherwise, the waste must meet the treatment standards for all applicable listed and characteristic waste codes. 13.6

(c) In addition to any applicable standards determined from the initial point of generation, no prohibited waste which exhibits a characteristic under 40 CFR part 261, subpart C may be land disposed unless the waste complies with the treatment standards under subpart D of this part.

(d) Wastes that exhibit a characteristic are also subject to §268.7 requirements, except that once the waste is no longer hazardous, a one-time notification and certification must be placed in the generator's or treater's on-site files. The notification and certification must be updated if the process or operation generating the waste changes and/or if the subtitle D facility receiving the waste changes. 13.12.2, 13.12.3.2, 13.12.3.6–7

(1) The notification must include the following information:

(i) Name and address of the RCRA Subtitle D facility receiving the waste shipment; and

(ii) A description of the waste as initially generated, including the applicable EPA hazardous waste code(s), treatability group(s), and underlying hazardous constituents (as defined in §268.2(i)), unless the waste will be treated and monitored for all underlying hazardous constituents. If all underlying hazardous constituents will be treated and monitored, there is no requirement to list any of the underlying hazardous constituents on the notice.

(2) The certification must be signed by an authorized representative and must state the language found in §268.7(b)(4).

(i) If treatment removes the characteristic but does not meet standards applicable to underlying hazardous constituents, then the certification found in §268.7(b)(4)(iv) applies.

(ii) [Reserved]

[55 FR 22688, June 1, 1990, as amended at 56 FR 3878, Jan. 31, 1991; 57 FR 37271, Aug. 18, 1992; 58 FR 29885, May 24, 1993; 59 FR 48045, Sept. 19, 1994; 60 FR 245, Jan. 3, 1995; 61 FR 15599, 15662, Apr. 8, 1996; 62 FR 26022, May 12, 1997; 64 FR 25415, May 11, 1999; 71 FR 16913, Apr. 4, 2006]

Subpart B—Schedule for Land Disposal Prohibition and Establishment of Treatment Standards

Source: 51 FR 19305, May 28, 1986, unless otherwise noted.

§§268.10–268.12 [Reserved]

§268.13 Schedule for wastes identified or listed after November 8, 1984.

In the case of any hazardous waste identified or listed under section 3001 after November 8, 1984, the Administrator shall make a land disposal prohibition determination within 6 months after the date of identification or listing.

§268.14 Surface impoundment exemptions.

(a) This section defines additional circumstances under which an otherwise prohibited waste may continue to be placed in a surface impoundment.

(b) Wastes which are newly identified or listed under section 3001 after November 8, 1984, and stored in a surface impoundment that is newly subject to subtitle C of RCRA as a result of the additional identification or listing, may continue to be stored in the surface impoundment for 48 months after the promulgation of the additional listing or characteristic, notwithstanding that the waste is otherwise prohibited from land disposal, provided that the surface impoundment is in compliance with the requirements of subpart F of part 265 of this chapter within 12 months after promulgation of the new listing or characteristic.

(c) Wastes which are newly identified or listed under section 3001 after November 8, 1984, and treated in a surface impoundment that is newly subject to subtitle C of RCRA as a result of the additional identification or listing, may continue to be treated in that surface impoundment, notwithstanding that the waste is otherwise prohibited from land disposal, provided that surface impoundment is in compliance with the requirements of subpart F of part 265 of this chapter within 12 months after the promulgation of the new listing or characteristic. In addition, if the surface impoundment continues to treat hazardous waste after 48 months from promulgation of the additional listing or characteristic, it must then be in compliance with §268.4.

[57 FR 37271, Aug. 18, 1992, as amended at 71 FR 40278, July 14, 2006]

Subpart C—Prohibitions on Land Disposal

§268.20 Waste specific prohibitions—Dyes and/or pigments production wastes.

(a) Effective August 23, 2005, the waste specified in 40 CFR part 261 as EPA Hazardous Waste Number K181, and soil and debris contaminated with this waste, radioactive wastes mixed with this waste, and soil and debris contaminated with radioactive wastes mixed with this waste are prohibited from land disposal.

(b) The requirements of paragraph (a) of this section do not apply if:

(1) The wastes meet the applicable treatment standards specified in subpart D of this Part;

(2) Persons have been granted an exemption from a prohibition pursuant to a petition under §268.6, with respect to those wastes and units covered by the petition;

(3) The wastes meet the applicable treatment standards established pursuant to a petition granted under §268.44;

(4) Hazardous debris has met the treatment standards in §268.40 or the alternative treatment standards in §268.45; or

(5) Persons have been granted an extension to the effective date of a prohibition pursuant to §268.5, with respect to these wastes covered by the extension.

(c) To determine whether a hazardous waste identified in this section exceeds the applicable treatment standards specified in §268.40, the initial generator must test a sample of the waste extract or the entire waste, depending on whether the treatment standards are expressed as concentrations in the waste extract of the waste, or the generator may use knowledge of the waste. If the waste contains regulated constituents in excess of the applicable subpart D levels, the waste is prohibited from land disposal, and all requirements of part 268 are applicable, except as otherwise specified.

[70 FR 9177, Feb. 24, 2005]

§§268.21–268.29 [Reserved]

§268.30 Waste specific prohibitions—wood preserving wastes.

(a) Effective August 11, 1997, the following wastes are prohibited from land disposal: the wastes specified in 40 CFR part 261 as EPA Hazardous Waste numbers F032, F034, and F035.

(b) Effective May 12, 1999, the following wastes are prohibited from land disposal: soil and debris contaminated with F032, F034, F035; and radioactive wastes mixed with EPA Hazardous waste numbers F032, F034, and F035.

(c) Between May 12, 1997 and May 12, 1999, soil and debris contaminated with F032, F034, F035; and radioactive waste mixed with F032, F034, and F035 may be disposed in a landfill or surface impoundment only if such unit is in compliance with the requirements specified in §268.5(h)(2) of this part.

(d) The requirements of paragraphs (a) and (b) of this section do not apply if:

(1) The wastes meet the applicable treatment standards specified in Subpart D of this part;

(2) Persons have been granted an exemption from a prohibition pursuant to a petition under §268.6, with respect to those wastes and units covered by the petition;

(3) The wastes meet the applicable alternate treatment standards established pursuant to a petition granted under §268.44; or

(4) Persons have been granted an extension to the effective date of a prohibition pursuant to §268.5, with respect to those wastes covered by the extension.

(e) To determine whether a hazardous waste identified in this section exceeds the applicable treatment standards specified in §268.40, the initial generator must test a sample of the waste extract or the entire waste, depending on whether the treatment standards are expressed as concentrations in the waste extract or the waste, or the generator may use knowledge of the waste. If the waste contains constituents in excess of the applicable Universal Treatment Standard levels of §268.48 of this part, the waste is prohibited from land disposal, and all requirements of part 268 are applicable, except as otherwise specified.

[62 FR 26022, May 12, 1997]

§268.31 Waste specific prohibitions—Dioxin-containing wastes.

(a) Effective November 8, 1988, the dioxin-containing wastes specified in 40 CFR 261.31 as EPA Hazardous Waste Nos. F020, F02l, F022, F023, F026, F027, and F028, are prohibited from land disposal unless the following condition applies:

(1) The F020-F023 and F026-F028 dioxin-containing waste is contaminated soil and debris resulting from a response action taken under section 104 or 106 of the Comprehensive Environmental Response, Compensation, and Liability Act of 1980 (CERCLA) or a corrective action taken under subtitle C of the Resource Conservation and Recovery Act (RCRA).

(b) Effective November 8, 1990, the F020-F023 and F026-F028 dioxin-containing wastes listed in paragraph (a)(1) of this section are prohibited from land disposal.

(c) Between November 8, 1988, and November 8, 1990, wastes included in paragraph (a)(1) of this section may be disposed in a landfill or surface impoundment only if such unit is in compliance with the requirements specified in §268.5(h)(2) and all other applicable requirements of parts 264 and 265 of this chapter.

(d) The requirements of paragraphs (a) and (b) of this section do not apply if:

(1) The wastes meet the standards of subpart D of this part; or

(2) Persons have been granted an exemption from a prohibition pursuant to a petition under §268.6, with respect to those wastes and units covered by the petition; or

(3) Persons have been granted an extension to the effective date of a prohibition pursuant to §268.5, with respect to those wastes covered by the extension.

[53 FR 31216, Aug. 17, 1988]

§268.32 Waste specific prohibitions—Soils exhibiting the toxicity characteristic for metals and containing PCBs. 13.7.3

(a) Effective December 26, 2000, the following wastes are prohibited from land disposal: any volumes of soil exhibiting the toxicity characteristic solely because of the presence of metals (D004-D011) and containing PCBs.

(b) The requirements of paragraph (a) of this section do not apply if:

(1)(i) The wastes contain halogenated organic compounds in total concentration less than 1,000 mg/kg; and

(ii) The wastes meet the treatment standards specified in Subpart D of this part for EPA hazardous waste numbers D004-D011, as applicable; or

(2)(i) The wastes contain halogenated organic compounds in total concentration less than 1,000 mg/kg; and

(ii) The wastes meet the alternative treatment standards specified in §268.49 for contaminated soil; or

(3) Persons have been granted an exemption from a prohibition pursuant to a petition under §268.6, with respect to those wastes and units covered by the petition; or

(4) The wastes meet applicable alternative treatment standards established pursuant to a petition granted under §268.44.

[65 FR 81380, Dec. 26, 2000]

§268.33 Waste specific prohibitions—chlorinated aliphatic wastes.

(a) Effective May 8, 2001, the wastes specified in 40 CFR part 261 as EPA Hazardous Wastes Numbers K174, and K175, soil and debris contaminated with these wastes, radioactive wastes mixed with these wastes, and soil and debris contaminated with radioactive wastes mixed with these wastes are prohibited from land disposal.

(b) The requirements of paragraph (a) of this section do not apply if:

(1) The wastes meet the applicable treatment standards specified in subpart D of this part;

(2) Persons have been granted an exemption from a prohibition pursuant to a petition under §268.6, with respect to those wastes and units covered by the petition;

(3) The wastes meet the applicable treatment standards established pursuant to a petition granted under §268.44;

(4) Hazardous debris has met the treatment standards in §268.40 or the alternative treatment standards in §268.45; or

(5) Persons have been granted an extension to the effective date of a prohibition pursuant to §268.5, with respect to these wastes covered by the extension.

(c) To determine whether a hazardous waste identified in this section exceeds the applicable treatment standards specified in §268.40, the initial generator must test a sample of the waste extract or the entire waste, depending on whether the treatment standards are expressed as concentrations in the waste extract or the waste, or the generator may use knowledge of the waste. If the waste contains regulated constituents in excess of the applicable levels of subpart D of this part, the waste is prohibited from land disposal, and all requirements of part 268 are applicable, except as otherwise specified.

(d) Disposal of K175 wastes that have complied with all applicable 40 CFR 268.40 treatment standards must also be macroencapsulated in accordance with 40 CFR 268.45 Table 1 unless the waste is placed in:

(1) A Subtitle C monofill containing only K175 wastes that meet all applicable 40 CFR 268.40 treatment standards; or

(2) A dedicated Subtitle C landfill cell in which all other wastes being co-disposed are at pH ≤ 6.0.

[65 FR 67127, Nov. 8, 2000]

§268.34 Waste specific prohibitions—toxicity characteristic metal wastes.

(a) Effective August 24, 1998, the following wastes are prohibited from land disposal: the wastes specified in 40 CFR Part 261 as EPA Hazardous Waste numbers D004-D011 that are newly identified (*i.e.* wastes, soil, or debris identified as hazardous by the Toxic Characteristic Leaching Procedure but not the Extraction Procedure), and waste, soil, or debris from mineral processing operations that is identified as hazardous by the specifications at 40 CFR Part 261.

(b) Effective November 26, 1998, the following waste is prohibited from land disposal: Slag from secondary lead smelting which exhibits the Toxicity Characteristic due to the presence of one or more metals.

(c) Effective May 26, 2000, the following wastes are prohibited from land disposal: newly identified characteristic wastes from elemental phosphorus processing; radioactive wastes mixed with EPA Hazardous wastes D004-D011 that are newly identified (*i.e.*, wastes, soil, or debris identified as hazardous by the Toxic Characteristic Leaching Procedure but not the Extraction Procedure); or mixed with newly identified characteristic mineral processing wastes, soil, or debris.

(d) Between May 26, 1998 and May 26, 2000, newly identified characteristic wastes from elemental phosphorus processing, radioactive waste mixed with D004-D011 wastes that are newly identified (*i.e.*, wastes, soil, or debris identified as hazardous by the Toxic Characteristic Leaching Procedure but not the Extraction Procedure), or mixed with newly identified characteristic mineral processing wastes, soil, or debris may be disposed in a landfill or surface impoundment only if such unit is in compliance with the requirements specified in §268.5(h) of this part.

(e) The requirements of paragraphs (a) and (b) of this section do not apply if:

(1) The wastes meet the applicable treatment standards specified in subpart D of this part:

(2) Persons have been granted an exemption from a prohibition pursuant to a petition under §268.6, with respect to those wastes and units covered by the petition;

(3) The wastes meet the applicable alternate treatment standards established pursuant to a petition granted under §268.44; or

(4) Persons have been granted an extension to the effective date of a prohibition pursuant to §268.5, with respect to these wastes covered by the extension.

(f) To determine whether a hazardous waste identified in this section exceeds the applicable treatment standards specified in §268.40, the initial generator must test a sample of the waste extract or the entire waste, depending on whether the treatment standards are expressed as concentration in the waste extract or the waste, or the generator may use knowledge of the waste. If the waste contains constituents (including underlying hazardous constituents in characteristic wastes) in excess of the applicable Universal Treatment Standard levels of §268.48 of this part, the waste is prohibited from land disposal, and all requirements of part 268 are applicable, except as otherwise specified.

[63 FR 28641, May 26, 1998, as amended at 63 FR 48127, Sept. 9, 1998]

§268.35 Waste specific prohibitions—petroleum refining wastes.

(a) Effective February 8, 1999, the wastes specified in 40 CFR part 261 as EPA Hazardous Wastes Numbers K169, K170, K171, and K172, soils and debris contaminated with these wastes, radioactive wastes mixed with these hazardous wastes, and soils and debris contaminated with these radioactive mixed wastes, are prohibited from land disposal.

(b) The requirements of paragraph (a) of this section do not apply if:

(1) The wastes meet the applicable treatment standards specified in Subpart D of this part;

(2) Persons have been granted an exemption from a prohibition pursuant to a petition under §268.6, with respect to those wastes and units covered by the petition;

(3) The wastes meet the applicable treatment standards established pursuant to a petition granted under §268.44;

(4) Hazardous debris that have met treatment standards in §268.40 or in the alternative treatment standards in §268.45; or

(5) Persons have been granted an extension to the effective date of a prohibition pursuant to §268.5, with respect to these wastes covered by the extension.

(c) To determine whether a hazardous waste identified in this section exceeds the applicable treatment standards specified in §268.40, the initial generator must test a sample of the waste extract or the entire waste, depending on whether the treatment standards are expressed as concentrations in the waste extract or the waste, or the generator may use knowledge of the waste. If the waste contains constituents in excess of the applicable Universal Treatment Standard levels of §268.48, the waste is prohibited from land disposal, and all requirements of this part are applicable, except as otherwise specified.

[63 FR 42186, Aug. 6, 1998]

§268.36 Waste specific prohibitions—inorganic chemical wastes.

(a) Effective May 20, 2002, the wastes specified in 40 CFR part 261 as EPA Hazardous Wastes Numbers K176, K177, and K178, and soil and debris contaminated with these wastes, radioactive wastes mixed with these wastes, and soil and debris contaminated with radioactive wastes mixed with these wastes are prohibited from land disposal.

(b) The requirements of paragraph (a) of this section do not apply if:

(1) The wastes meet the applicable treatment standards specified in subpart D of this part;

(2) Persons have been granted an exemption from a prohibition pursuant to a petition under §268.6, with respect to those wastes and units covered by the petition;

(3) The wastes meet the applicable treatment standards established pursuant to a petition granted under §268.44;

(4) Hazardous debris has met the treatment standards in §268.40 or the alternative treatment standards in §268.45; or

(5) Persons have been granted an extension to the effective date of a prohibition pursuant to §268.5, with respect to these wastes covered by the extension.

(c) To determine whether a hazardous waste identified in this section exceeds the applicable treatment standards specified in §268.40, the initial generator must test a sample of the waste extract or the entire waste, depending on whether the treatment standards are expressed as concentrations in the waste extract or the waste, or the generator may use knowledge of the waste. If the waste contains regulated constituents in excess of the applicable subpart D levels, the waste is prohibited from land disposal, and all requirements of this part are applicable, except as otherwise specified.

[66 FR 58298, Nov. 20, 2001]

§268.37 Waste specific prohibitions—ignitable and corrosive characteristic wastes whose treatment standards were vacated.

(a) Effective August 9, 1993, the wastes specified in 40 CFR 261.21 as D001 (and is not in the High TOC Ignitable Liquids Subcategory), and specified in §261.22 as D002, that are managed in systems other than those whose discharge is regulated under the Clean Water Act (CWA), or that inject in Class I deep wells regulated under the Safe Drinking Water Act (SDWA), or that are zero dischargers that engage in CWA-equivalent treatment before ultimate land disposal, are prohibited from land disposal. CWA-equivalent treatment means biological treatment for organics, alkaline chlorination or ferrous sulfate precipitation for cyanide, precipitation/sedimentation for metals, reduction of hexavalent chromium, or other treatment technology that can be demonstrated to perform equally or greater than these technologies. 13.3

(b) Effective February 10, 1994, the wastes specified in 40 CFR 261.21 as D001 (and is not in the High TOC Ignitable Liquids Subcategory), and specified in §261.22 as D002, that are managed in systems defined in 40 CFR 144.6(e) and 146.6(e) as Class V injection wells, that do not engage in CWA-equivalent treatment before injection, are prohibited from land disposal.

[58 FR 29885, May 24, 1993]

§268.38 Waste specific prohibitions—newly identified organic toxicity characteristic wastes and newly listed coke by-product and chlorotoluene production wastes.

(a) Effective December 19, 1994, the wastes specified in 40 CFR 261.32 as EPA Hazardous Waste numbers K141, K142, K143, K144, K145, K147, K148, K149, K150, and K151 are prohibited from land disposal. In addition, debris contaminated with EPA Hazardous Waste numbers F037, F038, K107-K112, K117, K118, K123-K126, K131, K132, K136, U328, U353, U359, and soil and debris contaminated with D012-D043, K141-K145, and K147-K151 are prohibited from land disposal. The following wastes that are specified in 40 CFR 261.24, Table 1 as EPA Hazardous Waste numbers: D012, D013, D014, D015, D016, D017, D018, D019, D020, D021, D022, D023, D024, D025, D026, D027, D028, D029, D030, D031, D032, D033, D034, D035, D036, D037, D038, D039, D040, D041, D042, D043 that are not radioactive, or that are managed in systems other than those whose discharge is regulated under the Clean Water Act (CWA), or that are zero dischargers that do not engage in CWA-equivalent treatment before ultimate land disposal, or that are injected in Class I deep wells regulated under the Safe Drinking Water Act (SDWA), are prohibited from land disposal. CWA-equivalent treatment means biological treatment for organics, alkaline chlorination or ferrous sulfate precipitation for cyanide, precipitation/ sedimentation for metals, reduction of hexavalent chromium, or other treatment technology that can be demonstrated to perform equally or better than these technologies.

(b) On September 19, 1996, radioactive wastes that are mixed with D018-D043 that are managed in systems other than those whose discharge is regulated under the Clean Water Act (CWA), or that inject in Class I deep wells regulated under the Safe Drinking Water Act (SDWA), or that are zero dischargers that engage in CWA-equivalent treatment before ultimate land disposal, are prohibited from land disposal. CWA-equivalent treatment means biological treatment for organics, alkaline chlorination or ferrous sulfate precipitation for cyanide, precipitation/sedimentation for metals, reduction of hexavalent chromium, or other treatment technology that can be demonstrated to perform equally or greater than these technologies. Radioactive wastes mixed with K141-K145, and K147-K151 are also prohibited from land disposal. In addition, soil and debris contaminated with these radioactive mixed wastes are prohibited from land disposal.

(c) Between December 19, 1994 and September 19, 1996, the wastes included in paragraphs (b) of this section may be disposed in a landfill or surface impoundment, only if such unit is in compliance with the requirements specified in §268.5(h)(2) of this Part.

(d) The requirements of paragraphs (a), (b), and (c) of this section do not apply if:

(1) The wastes meet the applicable treatment standards specified in Subpart D of this part;

(2) Persons have been granted an exemption from a prohibition pursuant to a petition under §268.6, with respect to those wastes and units covered by the petition;

(3) The wastes meet the applicable alternate treatment standards established pursuant to a petition granted under §268.44;

(4) Persons have been granted an extension to the effective date of a prohibition pursuant to §268.5, with respect to these wastes covered by the extension.

(e) To determine whether a hazardous waste identified in this section exceeds the applicable treatment standards specified in §268.40, the initial generator must test a sample of the waste extract or the entire waste, depending on whether the treatment standards are expressed as concentrations in the waste extract or the waste, or the generator may use knowledge of the waste. If the waste contains constituents in excess of the applicable Subpart D levels, the waste is prohibited from land disposal, and all requirements of part 268 are applicable, except as otherwise specified.

[59 FR 48045, Sept. 19, 1995]

§268.39 Waste specific prohibitions—spent aluminum potliners; reactive; and carbamate wastes.

(a) On July 8, 1996, the wastes specified in 40 CFR 261.32 as EPA Hazardous Waste numbers K156-K159, and K161; and in 40 CFR 261.33 as EPA Hazardous Waste numbers P127, P128, P185, P188-P192, P194, P196-P199, P201-P205, U271, U278-U280, U364, U367, U372, U373, U387, U389, U394, U395, U404, and U409-U411 are prohibited from land disposal. In addition, soil and debris contaminated with these wastes are prohibited from land disposal.

(b) On July 8, 1996, the wastes identified in 40 CFR 261.23 as D003 that are managed in systems other than those whose discharge is regulated under the Clean Water Act (CWA), or that inject in Class I deep wells regulated under the Safe Drinking Water Act (SDWA), or that are zero dischargers that engage in

CWA-equivalent treatment before ultimate land disposal, are prohibited from land disposal. This prohibition does not apply to unexploded ordnance and other explosive devices which have been the subject of an emergency response. (Such D003 wastes are prohibited unless they meet the treatment standard of DEACT before land disposal (see §268.40)).

(c) On September 21, 1998, the wastes specified in 40 CFR 261.32 as EPA Hazardous Waste number K088 are prohibited from land disposal. In addition, soil and debris contaminated with these wastes are prohibited from land disposal.

(d) On April 8, 1998, radioactive wastes mixed with K088, K156-K159, K161, P127, P128, P185, P188-P192, P194, P196-P199, P201-P205, U271, U278-U280, U364, U367, U372, U373, U387, U389, U394, U395, U404, and U409-U411 are prohibited from land disposal. In addition, soil and debris contaminated with these radioactive mixed wastes are prohibited from land disposal.

(e) Between July 8, 1996, and April 8, 1998, the wastes included in paragraphs (a), (c), and (d) of this section may be disposed in a landfill or surface impoundment, only if such unit is in compliance with the requirements specified in §268.5(h)(2).

(f) The requirements of paragraphs (a), (b), (c), and (d) of this section do not apply if:

(1) The wastes meet the applicable treatment standards specified in Subpart D of this part;

(2) Persons have been granted an exemption from a prohibition pursuant to a petition under §268.6, with respect to those wastes and units covered by the petition;

(3) The wastes meet the applicable alternate treatment standards established pursuant to a petition granted under §268.44;

(4) Persons have been granted an extension to the effective date of a prohibition pursuant to §268.5, with respect to these wastes covered by the extension.

(g) To determine whether a hazardous waste identified in this section exceeds the applicable treatment standards specified in §268.40, the initial generator must test a sample of the waste extract or the entire waste, depending on whether the treatment standards are expressed as concentrations in the waste extract or the waste, or the generator may use knowledge of the waste. If the waste contains constituents in excess of the applicable Subpart D levels, the waste is prohibited from land disposal, and all requirements of this part 268 are applicable, except as otherwise specified.

[61 FR 15663, Apr. 8, 1996, as amended at 61 FR 33683, June 28, 1996; 62 FR 1997, Jan. 14, 1997; 62 FR 32979, June 17, 1997; 62 FR 37699, July 14, 1997; 63 FR 51264, Sept. 24, 1998]

Subpart D—Treatment Standards

📖 13.1.5, 13.4–5

§268.40 Applicability of treatment standards.

(a) A prohibited waste identified in the table "Treatment Standards for Hazardous Wastes" may be land disposed only if it meets the requirements found in the table. For each waste, the table identifies one of three types of treatment standard requirements: 📖 13.4

(1) All hazardous constituents in the waste or in the treatment residue must be at or below the values found in the table for that waste ("total waste standards"); or

(2) The hazardous constituents in the extract of the waste or in the extract of the treatment residue must be at or below the values found in the table ("waste extract standards"); or

(3) The waste must be treated using the technology specified in the table ("technology standard"), which are described in detail in §268.42, Table 1—Technology Codes and Description of Technology-Based Standards.

(b) For wastewaters, compliance with concentration level standards is based on maximums for any one day, except for D004 through D011 wastes for which the previously promulgated treatment standards based on grab samples remain in effect. For all nonwastewaters, compliance with concentration level standards is based on grab sampling. For wastes covered by the waste extract standards, the test Method 1311, the Toxicity Characteristic Leaching Procedure found in "Test Methods for Evaluating Solid Waste, Physical/Chemical Methods," EPA Publication SW–846, as incorporated by reference in §260.11, must be used to measure compliance. An exception is made for D004 and D008, for which either of two test methods may be used: Method 1311, or Method 1310B, the Extraction Procedure Toxicity Test. For wastes covered by a technology standard, the wastes may be land disposed after being treated using that specified technology or an equivalent treatment technology approved by the Administrator under the procedures set forth in §268.42(b).

(c) When wastes with differing treatment standards for a constituent of concern are combined for purposes of treatment, the treatment residue must meet the lowest treatment standard for the constituent of concern.

(d) Notwithstanding the prohibitions specified in paragraph (a) of this section, treatment and disposal facilities may demonstrate (and certify pursuant to 40 CFR 268.7(b)(5)) compliance with the treatment standards for organic constituents specified by a footnote in the table "Treatment Standards for Hazardous Wastes" in this section, provided the following conditions are satisfied:

(1) The treatment standards for the organic constituents were established based on incineration in units operated in accordance with the technical requirements of 40 CFR part 264, subpart O, or based on combustion in fuel substitution units operating in accordance with applicable technical requirements;

(2) The treatment or disposal facility has used the methods referenced in paragraph (d)(1) of this section to treat the organic constituents; and

(3) The treatment or disposal facility may demonstrate compliance with organic constituents if good-faith analytical efforts achieve detection limits for the regulated organic constituents that do not exceed the treatment standards specified in this section by an order of magnitude.

(e) For characteristic wastes (D001-D043) that are subject to treatment standards in the following table "Treatment Standards for Hazardous Wastes," and are not managed in a wastewater treatment system that is regulated under the Clean Water Act (CWA), that is CWA-equivalent, or that is injected into a Class I nonhazardous deep injection well, all underlying hazardous constituents (as defined in §268.2(i)) must meet Universal Treatment Standards, found in §268.48, Table Universal Treatment Standards, prior to land disposal as defined in §268.2(c) of this part. 📖 13.3

(f) The treatment standards for F001–F005 nonwastewater constituents carbon disulfide, cyclohexanone, and/or methanol apply to wastes which contain only one, two, or three of these constituents. Compliance is measured for these constituents in the waste extract from test Method 1311, the Toxicity Characteristic Leaching Procedure found in "Test Methods for Evaluating Solid Waste, Physical/Chemical Methods", EPA Publication SW-846, as incorporated by reference in §260.11. If the waste contains any of these three constituents along with any of the other 25 constituents found in F001-F005, then compliance with treatment standards for carbon disulfide, cyclohexanone, and/or methanol are not required.

(g) Between August 26, 1996 and March 4, 1999 the treatment standards for the wastes specified in 40 CFR 261.32 as EPA Hazardous Waste numbers K156-K161; and in 40 CFR 261.33 as EPA Hazardous Waste numbers P127, P128, P185, P188-P192, P194, P196-P199, P201-P205, U271, U277-U280, U364-U367, U372, U373, U375-U379, U381-U387, U389-U396, U400-U404, U407, and U409-U411; and soil contaminated with these wastes; may be satisfied by either meeting the constituent concentrations presented in the table "Treatment Standards for Hazardous Wastes" in this section, or by treating the waste by the following technologies: combustion, as defined by the technology code CMBST at §268.42 Table 1, for nonwastewaters; and, biodegradation as defined by the technology code BIODG, carbon adsorption as defined by the technology code CARBN, chemical oxidation as defined by the technology code CHOXD, or combustion as defined as technology code CMBST at §268.42 Table 1, for wastewaters.

(h) Prohibited D004-D011 mixed radioactive wastes and mixed radioactive listed wastes containing metal constituents, that were previously treated by stabilization to the treatment standards in effect at that time and then put into storage, do not have to be re-treated to meet treatment standards in this section prior to land disposal.

(i) [Reserved]

(j) Effective September 4, 1998, the treatment standards for the wastes specified in 40 CFR 261.33 as EPA Hazardous Waste numbers P185, P191, P192, P197, U364, U394, and U395 may be satisfied by either meeting the constituent concentrations presented in the table "Treatment Standards for Hazardous Wastes" in this section, or by treating the waste by the following technologies: combustion, as defined by the technology code CMBST at §268.42 Table 1 of this Part, for nonwastewaters; and, biodegradation as defined by the technology code BIODG, carbon adsorption as defined by the technology code CARBN, chemical oxidation as defined by the technology code CHOXD, or combustion as defined as technology code CMBST at §268.42 Table 1 of this Part, for wastewaters.

PART 268—Subpart D

Treatment Standards for Hazardous Wastes

13.4.1, 13.5

[*Note:* NA means not applicable]

Waste code	Waste description and treatment/regulatory subcategory[1]	Regulated hazardous constituent		Wastewaters	Nonwastewaters
		Common name	CAS[2] No.	Concentration[3] in mg/L; or technology code[4]	Concentration[5] in mg/kg unless noted as "mg/L TCLP"; or technology code[4]
D001[9]	Ignitable Characteristic Wastes, except for the §261.21(a)(1) High TOC Subcategory 13.4.2, 14.1.6.2	NA	NA	DEACT and meet §268.48 standards[8]; or RORGS; or CMBST	DEACT and meet §268.48 standards[8]; or RORGS; or CMBST
	High TOC Ignitable Characteristic Liquids Subcategory based on 40 CFR 261.21(a)(1)—Greater than or equal to 10% total organic carbon. (Note: This subcategory consists of nonwastewaters only.)	NA	NA	NA	RORGS; CMBST; or POLYM
D002[9]	Corrosive Characteristic Wastes 13.4.3, 14.1.6.2	NA	NA	DEACT and meet §268.48 standards[8]	DEACT and meet §268.48 standards[8]
D002, D004, D005, D006, D007, D008, D009, D010, D011	Radioactive high level wastes generated during the reprocessing of fuel rods. (Note: This subcategory consists of nonwastewaters only.)	Corrosivity (pH)	NA	NA	HLVIT
		Arsenic	7440-38-2	NA	HLVIT
		Barium	7440-39-3	NA	HLVIT
		Cadmium	7440-43-9	NA	HLVIT
		Chromium (Total)	7440-47-3	NA	HLVIT
		Lead	7439-92-1	NA	HLVIT
		Mercury	7439-97-6	NA	HLVIT
		Selenium	7782-49-2	NA	HLVIT
		Silver	7440-22-4	NA	HLVIT
D003[9]	Reactive Sulfides Subcategory based on 261.23(a)(5) 13.4.4	NA	NA	DEACT	DEACT
	Explosives Subcategory based on 261.23(a)(6), (7), and (8)	NA	NA	DEACT and meet §268.48 standards[8]	DEACT and meet §268.48 standards[8]
	Unexploded ordnance and other explosive devices which have been the subject of an emergency response	NA	NA	DEACT	DEACT
	Other Reactives Subcategory based on 261.23(a)(1)	NA	NA	DEACT and meet §268.48 standards[8]	DEACT and meet §268.48 standards[8]
	Water Reactive Subcategory based on 261.23(a)(2),(3), and (4). (*Note:* This subcategory consists of nonwastewaters only.)	NA	NA	NA	DEACT and meet §268.48 standards[8]
	Reactive Cyanides Subcategory based on 261.23(a)(5)	Cyanides (Total)[7]	57-12-5	Reserved	590
		Cyanides (Amenable)[7]	57-12-5	0.86	30
D004[9]	Wastes that exhibit, or are expected to exhibit, the characteristic of toxicity for arsenic based on the toxicity characteristic leaching procedure (TCLP) in SW846	Arsenic	7440-38-2	1.4 and meet §268.48 standards[8]	5.0 mg/L TCLP and meet §268.48 standards[8]
D005[9]	Wastes that exhibit, or are expected to exhibit, the characteristic of toxicity for barium based on the toxicity characteristic leaching procedure (TCLP) in SW846	Barium	7440-39-3	1.2 and meet §268.48 standards[8]	21 mg/L TCLP and meet §268.48 standards[8]
D006[9]	Wastes that exhibit, or are expected to exhibit, the characteristic of toxicity for cadmium based on the toxicity characteristic leaching procedure (TCLP) in SW846.	Cadmium	7440-43-9	0.69 and meet §268.48 standards[8]	0.11 mg/L TCLP and meet §268.48 standards[8]

Treatment Standards for Hazardous Wastes

13.4.1, 13.5

[*Note:* NA means not applicable]

Waste code	Waste description and treatment/regulatory subcategory[1]	Regulated hazardous constituent		Wastewaters	Nonwastewaters
		Common name	CAS[2] No.	Concentration[3] in mg/L; or technology code[4]	Concentration[5] in mg/kg unless noted as "mg/L TCLP"; or technology code[4]
	Cadmium Containing Batteries Subcategory. (Note: This subcategory consists of nonwastewaters only)	Cadmium	7440-43-9	NA	RTHRM
	Radioactively contaminated cadmium containing batteries. (Note: This subcategory consists of nonwastewaters only) 13.9.1–2	Cadmium	7440-43-9	NA	Macroencapsulation in accordance with 40 CFR 268.45
D007[9]	Wastes that exhibit, or are expected to exhibit, the characteristic of toxicity for chromium based on the toxicity characteristic leaching procedure (TCLP) in SW846	Chromium (Total)	7440-47-3	2.77 and meet §268.48 standards[8]	0.60 mg/L TCLP and meet §268.48 standards[8]
D008[9]	Wastes that exhibit, or are expected to exhibit, the characteristic of toxicity for lead based on the toxicity characteristic leaching procedure (TCLP) in SW846 13.4.5	Lead	7439-92-1	0.69 and meet §268.48 standards[8]	0.75 mg/L TCLP and meet §268.48 standards[8]
	Lead Acid Batteries Subcategory (*Note:* This standard only applies to lead acid batteries that are identified as RCRA hazardous wastes and that are not excluded elsewhere from regulation under the land disposal restrictions of 40 CFR 268 or exempted under other EPA regulations (see 40 CFR 266.80). This subcategory consists of nonwastewaters only.) 13.9.2	Lead	7439-92-1	NA	RLEAD
	Radioactive Lead Solids Subcategory (*Note:* these lead solids include, but are not limited to, all forms of lead shielding and other elemental forms of lead. These lead solids do not include treatment residuals such as hydroxide sludges, other wastewater treatment residuals, or incinerator ashes that can undergo conventional pozzolanic stabilization, nor do they include organo-lead materials that can be incinerated and stabilized as ash. This subcategory consists of nonwastewaters only) 13.9.2	Lead	7439-92-1	NA	MACRO
D009[9]	Nonwastewaters that exhibit, or are expected to exhibit, the characteristic of toxicity for mercury based on the toxicity characteristic leaching procedure (TCLP) in SW846; and contain greater than or equal to 260 mg/kg total mercury that also contain organics and are not incinerator residues. (High Mercury-Organic Subcategory.)	Mercury	7439-97-6	NA	IMERC; OR RMERC
	Nonwastewaters that exhibit, or are expected to exhibit, the characteristic of toxicity for mercury based on the toxicity characteristic leaching procedure (TCLP) in SW846; and contain greater than or equal to 260 mg/kg total mercury that are inorganic, including incinerator residues and residues from RMERC. (High Mercury-Inorganic Subcategory.) 13.4.5	Mercury	7439-97-6	NA	RMERC
	Nonwastewaters that exhibit, or are expected to exhibit, the characteristic of toxicity for mercury based on the toxicity characteristic leaching procedure (TCLP) in SW846; and contain less than 260 mg/kg total mercury and that are residues from RMERC only. (Low Mercury Subcategory.)	Mercury	7439-97-6	NA	0.20 mg/L TCLP and meet §268.48 standards[8]
	All other nonwastewaters that exhibit, or are expected to exhibit, the characteristic of toxicity for mercury based on the toxicity characteristic leaching procedure (TCLP) in SW846; and contain less than 260 mg/kg total mercury and that are not residues from RMERC. (Low Mercury Subcategory.)	Mercury	7439-97-6	NA	0.025 mg/L TCLP and meet §268.48 standards[8]
	All D009 wastewaters	Mercury	7439-97-6	0.15 and meet §268.48 standards[8]	NA

PART 268—Subpart D

Treatment Standards for Hazardous Wastes

13.4.1, 13.5

[*Note:* NA means not applicable]

Waste code	Waste description and treatment/regulatory subcategory[1]	Regulated hazardous constituent		Wastewaters	Nonwastewaters
		Common name	CAS[2] No.	Concentration[3] in mg/L; or technology code[4]	Concentration[5] in mg/kg unless noted as "mg/L TCLP"; or technology code[4]
	Elemental mercury contaminated with radioactive materials. (*Note:* This subcategory consists of nonwastewaters only.)	Mercury	7439-97-6	NA	AMLGM
	Hydraulic oil contaminated with Mercury Radioactive Materials Subcategory. (*Note:* This subcategory consists of nonwastewaters only.)	Mercury	7439-97-6	NA	IMERC
	Radioactively contaminated mercury containing batteries. (Note: This subcategory consists of nonwastewaters only) 13.9.1	Mercury	7439-97-6	NA	Macroencapsulation in accordance with 40 CFR 268.45
D010[9]	Wastes that exhibit, or are expected to exhibit, the characteristic of toxicity for selenium based on the toxicity characteristic leaching procedure (TCLP) in SW846	Selenium	7782-49-2	0.82 and meet §268.48 standards[8]	5.7 mg/L TCLP and meet §268.48 standards[8]
D011[9]	Wastes that exhibit, or are expected to exhibit, the characteristic of toxicity for silver based on the toxicity characteristic leaching procedure (TCLP) in SW846.	Silver	7440-22-4	0.43 and meet §268.48 standards[8]	0.14 mg/L TCLP and meet §268.48 standards[8]
	Radioactively contaminated silver containing batteries. (Note: This subcategory consists of nonwastewaters only) 13.9.1	Silver	7440-22-4	NA	Macroencapsulation in accordance with 40 CFR 268.45
D012[9]	Wastes that are TC for Endrin based on the TCLP in SW846 Method 1311	Endrin	72-20-8	BIODG; or CMBST	0.13 and meet §268.48 standards[8]
		Endrin aldehyde	7421-93-4	BIODG; or CMBST	0.13 and meet §268.48 standards[8]
D013[9]	Wastes that are TC for Lindane based on the TCLP in SW846 Method 1311	alpha-BHC	319-84-6	CARBN; or CMBST	0.066 and meet §268.48 standards[8]
		beta-BHC	319-85-7	CARBN; or CMBST	0.066 and meet §268.48 standards[8]
		delta-BHC	319-86-8	CARBN; or CMBST	0.066 and meet §268.48 standards[8]
		gamma-BHC (Lindane)	58-89-9	CARBN; or CMBST	0.066 and meet §268.48 standards[8]
D014[9]	Wastes that are TC for Methoxychlor based on the TCLP in SW846 Method 1311	Methoxychlor	72-43-5	WETOX or CMBST	0.18 and meet §268.48 standards[8]
D015[9]	Wastes that are TC for Toxaphene based on the TCLP in SW846 Method 1311	Toxaphene	8001-35-2	BIODG or CMBST	2.6 and meet §268.48 standards[8]
D016[9]	Wastes that are TC for 2,4-D (2,4-Dichlorophenoxyacetic acid) based on the TCLP in SW846 Method 1311	2,4-D(2,4-Dichlorophenoxyacetic acid)	94-75-7	CHOXD; BIODG; or CMBST	10 and meet §268.48 standards[8]
D017[9]	Wastes that are TC for 2,4,5-TP (Silvex) based on the TCLP in SW846 Method 1311	2,4,5-TP(Silvex)	93-72-1	CHOXD or CMBST	7.9 and meet §268.48 standards[8]
D018[9]	Wastes that are TC for Benzene based on the TCLP in SW846 Method 1311 13.4.5	Benzene	71-43-2	0.14 and meet §268.48 standards[8]	10 and meet §268.48 standards[8]
D019[9]	Wastes that are TC for Carbon tetrachloride based on the TCLP in SW846 Method 1311	Carbon tetrachloride	56-23-5	0.057 and meet §268.48 standards[8]	6.0 and meet §268.48 standards[8]
D020[9]	Wastes that are TC for Chlordane based on the TCLP in SW846 Method 1311	Chlordane (alpha and gamma isomers)	57-74-9	0.0033 and meet §268.48 standards[8]	0.26 and meet §268.48 standards[8]

Treatment Standards for Hazardous Wastes

13.4.1, 13.5

[*Note:* NA means not applicable]

Waste code	Waste description and treatment/regulatory subcategory[1]	Regulated hazardous constituent		Wastewaters	Nonwastewaters
		Common name	CAS[2] No.	Concentration[3] in mg/L; or technology code[4]	Concentration[5] in mg/kg unless noted as "mg/L TCLP"; or technology code[4]
D021[9]	Wastes that are TC for Chlorobenzene based on the TCLP in SW846 Method 1311	Chlorobenzene	108-90-7	0.057 and meet §268.48 standards[8]	6.0 and meet §268.48 standards[8]
D022[9]	Wastes that are TC for Chloroform based on the TCLP in SW846 Method 1311	Chloroform	67-66-3	0.046 and meet §268.48 standards[8]	6.0 and meet §268.48 standards[8]
D023[9]	Wastes that are TC for o-Cresol based on the TCLP in SW846 Method 1311	o-Cresol	95-48-7	0.11 and meet §268.48 standards[8]	5.6 and meet §268.48 standards[8]
D024[9]	Wastes that are TC for m-Cresol based on the TCLP in SW846 Method 1311	m-Cresol (difficult to distinguish from p-cresol)	108-39-4	0.77 and meet §268.48 standards[8]	5.6 and meet §268.48 standards[8]
D025[9]	Wastes that are TC for p-Cresol based on the TCLP in SW846 Method 1311	p-Cresol (difficult to distinguish from m-cresol)	106-44-5	0.77 and meet §268.48 standards[8]	5.6 and meet §268.48 standards[8]
D026[9]	Wastes that are TC for Cresols (Total) based on the TCLP in SW846 Method 1311	Cresol-mixed isomers (Cresylic acid) (sum of o-, m-, and p-cresol concentrations)	1319-77-3	0.88 and meet §268.48 standards[8]	11.2 and meet §268.48 standards[8]
D027[9]	Wastes that are TC for p-Dichlorobenzene based on the TCLP in SW846 Method 1311	p-Dichlorobenzene (1,4-Dichloro-benzene)	106-46-7	0.090 and meet §268.48 standards[8]	6.0 and meet §268.48 standards[8]
D028[9]	Wastes that are TC for 1,2-Dichloroethane based on the TCLP in SW846 Method 1311	1,2-Dichloroethane	107-06-2	0.21 and meet §268.48 standards[8]	6.0 and meet §268.48 standards[8]
D029[9]	Wastes that are TC for 1,1-Dichloroethylene based on the TCLP in SW846 Method 1311	1,1-Dichlorethylene	75-35-4	0.025 and meet §268.48 standards[8]	6.0 and meet §268.48 standards[8]
D030[9]	Wastes that are TC for 2,4-Dinitrotoluene based on the TCLP in SW846 Method 1311	2,4-Dinitrotoluene	121-14-2	0.32 and meet §268.48 standards[8]	140 and meet §268.48 standards[8]
D031[9]	Wastes that are TC for Heptachlor based on the TCLP in SW846 Method 1311	Heptachlor	76-44-8	0.0012 and meet §268.48 standards[8]	0.066 and meet §268.48 standards[8]
		Heptachlor epoxide	1024-57-3	0.016 and meet §268.48 standards[8]	0.066 and meet §268.48 standards[8]
D032[9]	Wastes that are TC for Hexachlorobenzene based on the TCLP in SW846 Method 1311	Hexachlorobenzene	118-74-1	0.055 and meet §268.48 standards[8]	10 and meet §268.48 standards[8]
D033[9]	Wastes that are TC for Hexachlorobutadiene based on the TCLP in SW846 Method 1311	Hexachlorobutadiene	87-68-3	0.055 and meet §268.48 standards[8]	5.6 and meet §268.48 standards[8]
D034[9]	Wastes that are TC for Hexachloroethane based on the TCLP in SW846 Method 1311	Hexachloroethane	67-72-1	0.055 and meet §268.48 standards[8]	30 and meet §268.48 standards[8]
D035[9]	Wastes that are TC for Methyl ethyl ketone based on the TCLP in SW846 Method 1311	Methyl ethyl ketone	78-93-3	0.28 and meet §268.48 standards[8]	36 and meet §268.48 standards[8]

Treatment Standards for Hazardous Wastes

13.4.1, 13.5

[*Note:* NA means not applicable]

Waste code	Waste description and treatment/regulatory subcategory[1]	Regulated hazardous constituent		Wastewaters	Nonwastewaters
		Common name	CAS[2] No.	Concentration[3] in mg/L; or technology code[4]	Concentration[5] in mg/kg unless noted as "mg/L TCLP"; or technology code[4]
D036[9]	Wastes that are TC for Nitrobenzene based on the TCLP in SW846 Method 1311	Nitrobenzene	98-95-3	0.068 and meet §268.48 standards[8]	14 and meet §268.48 standards[8]
D037[9]	Wastes that are TC for Pentachlorophenol based on the TCLP in SW846 Method 1311	Pentachlorophenol	87-86-5	0.089 and meet §268.48 standards[8]	7.4 and meet §268.48 standards[8]
D038[9]	Wastes that are TC for Pyridine based on the TCLP in SW846 Method 1311	Pyridine	110-86-1	0.014 and meet §268.48 standards[8]	16 and meet §268.48 standards[8]
D039[9]	Wastes that are TC for Tetrachloroethylene based on the TCLP in SW846 Method 1311	Tetrachloroethylene	127-18-4	0.056 and meet §268.48 standards[8]	6.0 and meet §268.48 standards[8]
D040[9]	Wastes that are TC for Trichloroethylene based on the TCLP in SW846 Method 1311	Trichloroethylene	79-01-6	0.054 and meet §268.48 standards[8]	6.0 and meet §268.48 standards[8]
D041[9]	Wastes that are TC for 2,4,5-Trichlorophenol based on the TCLP in SW846 Method 1311	2,4,5-Trichlorophenol	95-95-4	0.18 and meet §268.48 standards[8]	7.4 and meet §268.48 standards[8]
D042[9]	Wastes that are TC for 2,4,6-Trichlorophenol based on the TCLP in SW846 Method 1311	2,4,6-Trichlorophenol	88-06-2	0.035 and meet §268.48 standards[8]	7.4 and meet §268.48 standards[8]
D043[9]	Wastes that are TC for Vinyl chloride based on the TCLP in SW846 Method 1311	Vinyl chloride	75-01-4	0.27 and meet §268.48 standards[8]	6.0 and meet §268.48 standards[8]
F001, F002, F003, F004, & F005	F001, F002, F003, F004, and/or F005 solvent wastes that contain any combination of one or more of the following spent solvents: acetone, benzene, n-butyl alcohol, carbon disulfide, carbon tetrachloride, chlorinated fluorocarbons, chlorobenzene, o-cresol, m-cresol, p-cresol, cyclohexanone, o-dichlorobenzene, 2-ethoxyethanol, ethyl acetate, ethyl benzene, ethyl ether, isobutyl alcohol, methanol, methylene chloride, methyl ethyl ketone, methyl isobutyl ketone, nitrobenzene, 2-nitropropane, pyridine, tetrachloroethylene, toluene, 1,1,1-trichloroethane, 1,1,2-trichloroethane, 1,1,2-trichloro-1,2,2-trifluorethane, trichloroethylene, trichloromonofluoromethane, and/or xylenes [except as specifically noted in other subcategories]. See further details of these listings in §261.31 13.5	Acetone	67-64-1	0.28	160
		Benzene	71-42-2	0.14	10
		n-Butyl alcohol	71-36-3	5.6	2.6
		Carbon disulfide	75-15-0	3.8	NA
		Carbon tetrachloride	56-23-5	0.057	6.0
		Chlorobenzene	108-90-7	0.057	6.0
		o-Cresol	95-48-7	0.11	5.6
		m-Cresol (difficult to distinguish from p-cresol)	108-39-4	0.77	5.6
		p-Cresol (difficult to distinguish from m-cresol)	106-44-5	0.77	5.6
		Cresol-mixed isomers (Cresylic acid) (sum of o-,m-, and p-cresol concentrations)	1319-77-3	0.88	11.2
		Cyclohexanone	108-94-1	0.36	NA
		o-Dichlorobenzene	95-50-1	0.088	6.0
		Ethyl acetate	141-78-6	0.34	33
		Ethyl benzene	100-41-4	0.057	10
		Ethyl ether	60-29-7	0.12	160
		Isobutyl alcohol	78-83-1	5.6	170
		Methanol	67-56-1	5.6	NA
		Methylene chloride	75-9-2	0.089	30
		Methyl ethyl ketone	78-93-3	0.28	36

Treatment Standards for Hazardous Wastes

13.4.1, 13.5

[*Note:* NA means not applicable]

Waste code	Waste description and treatment/regulatory subcategory[1]	Regulated hazardous constituent		Wastewaters	Nonwastewaters
		Common name	CAS[2] No.	Concentration[3] in mg/L; or technology code[4]	Concentration[5] in mg/kg unless noted as "mg/L TCLP"; or technology code[4]
		Methyl isobutyl ketone	108-10-1	0.14	33
		Nitrobenzene	98-95-3	0.068	14
		Pyridine	110-86-1	0.014	16
		Tetrachloroethylene	127-18-4	0.056	6.0
		Toluene	108-88-3	0.080	10
		1,1,1-Trichlorethane	71-55-6	0.054	6.0
		1,1,2-Trichloroethane	79-00-5	0.054	6.0
		1,1,2-Trichloro-1,2,2-trifluoroethane	76-13-1	0.057	30
		Trichloroethylene	79-01-6	0.054	6.0
		Trichlorofluoromethane	75-69-4	0.020	30
		Xylenes—mixed isomers (sum of o-, m-, and p- xylene concentrations)	1330-20-7	0.32	30
	F003 and/or F005 solvent wastes that contain any combination of one or more of the following three solvents as the only listed F001–5 solvents: carbon disulfide, cyclohexanone, and/or methanol. (formerly 268.41(c))	Carbon disulfide	75-15-0	3.8	4.8 mg/1 TCLP
		Cyclohexanone	108-94-1	0.36	0.75 mg/L TCLP
		Methanol	67-56-1	5.6	0.75 mg/L TCLP
	F005 solvent waste containing 2-Nitropropane as the only listed F001–5 solvent	2-Nitropropane	79-46-9	(WETOX or CHOXD) fb CARBN; or CMBST	CMBST
	F005 solvent waste containing 2-Ethoxyethanol as the only listed F001–5 solvent	2-Ethoxyethanol	110-80-5	BIODG; or CMBST	CMBST
F006	Wastewater treatment sludges from electroplating operations except from the following processes: (1) Sulfuric acid anodizing of aluminum; (2) tin plating on carbon steel; (3) zinc plating (segregated basis) on carbon steel; (4) aluminum or zinc-aluminum plating on carbon steel; (5) cleaning/stripping associated with tin, zinc and aluminum plating on carbon steel; and (6) chemical etching and milling of aluminum	Cadmium	7440-43-9	0.69	0.11 mg/L TCLP
		Chromium (Total)	7440-47-3	2.77	0.60 mg/L TCLP
		Cyanides (Total)[7]	57-12-5	1.2	590
		Cyanides (Amenable)[7]	57-12-5	0.86	30
		Lead	7439-92-1	0.69	0.75 mg/L TCLP
		Nickel	7440-02-0	3.98	11 mg/L TCLP
		Silver	7440-22-4	NA	0.14 mg/L TCLP
F007	Spent cyanide plating bath solutions from electroplating operations	Cadmium	7440-43-9	NA	0.11 mg/L TCLP
		Chromium (Total)	7440-47-3	2.77	0.60 mg/L TCLP
		Cyanides (Total)[7]	57-12-5	1.2	590
		Cyanides (Amenable)[7]	57-12-5	0.86	30
		Lead	7439-92-1	0.69	0.75 mg/L TCLP
		Nickel	7440-02-0	3.98	11 mg/L TCLP
		Silver	7440-22-4	NA	0.14 mg/L TCLP
F008	Plating bath residues from the bottom of plating baths from electroplating operations where cyanides are used in the process	Cadmium	7440-43-9	NA	0.11 mg/L TCLP
		Chromium (Total)	7440-47-3	2.77	0.60 mg/L TCLP
		Cyanides (Total)[7]	57-12-5	1.2	590
		Cyanides (Amenable)[7]	57-12-5	0.86	30
		Lead	7439-92-1	0.69	0.75 mg/L TCLP
		Nickel	7440-02-0	3.98	11 mg/L TCLP
		Silver	7440-22-4	NA	0.14 mg/L TCLP

Treatment Standards for Hazardous Wastes

13.4.1, 13.5

[*Note:* NA means not applicable]

Waste code	Waste description and treatment/regulatory subcategory[1]	Regulated hazardous constituent		Wastewaters	Nonwastewaters
		Common name	CAS[2] No.	Concentration[3] in mg/L; or technology code[4]	Concentration[5] in mg/kg unless noted as "mg/L TCLP"; or technology code[4]
F009	Spent stripping and cleaning bath solutions from electroplating operations where cyanides are used in the process	Cadmium	7440-43-9	NA	0.11 mg/L TCLP
		Chromium (Total)	7440-47-3	2.77	0.60 mg/L TCLP
		Cyanides (Total)[7]	57-12-5	1.2	590
		Cyanides (Amenable)[7]	57-12-5	0.86	30
		Lead	7439-92-1	0.69	0.75 mg/L TCLP
		Nickel	7440-02-0	3.98	11 mg/L TCLP
		Silver	7440-22-4	NA	0.14 mg/L TCLP
F010	Quenching bath residues from oil baths from metal heat treating operations where cyanides are used in the process.	Cyanides (Total) [7]	57-12-5	1.2	590
		Cyanides (Amenable)[7]	57-12-5	0.86	NA
F011	Spent cyanide solutions from salt bath pot cleaning from metal heat treating operations	Cadmium	7440-43-9	NA	0.11 mg/L TCLP
		Chromium (Total)	7440-47-3	2.77	0.60 mg/L TCLP
		Cyanides (Total)[7]	57-12-5	1.2	590
		Cyanides (Amenable)[7]	57-12-5	0.86	30
		Lead	7439-92-1	0.69	0.75 mg/L TCLP
		Nickel	7440-02-0	3.98	11 mg/L TCLP
		Silver	7440-22-4	NA	0.14 mg/L TCLP
F012	Quenching wastewater treatment sludges from metal heat treating operations where cyanides are used in the process	Cadmium	7440-43-9	NA	0.11 mg/L TCLP
		Chromium (Total)	7440-47-3	2.77	0.60 mg/L TCLP
		Cyanides (Total)[7]	57-12-5	1.2	590
		Cyanides (Amenable)[7]	57-12-5	0.86	30
		Lead	7439-92-1	0.69	0.75 mg/L TCLP
		Nickel	7440-02-0	3.98	11 mg/L TCLP
		Silver	7440-22-4	NA	0.14 mg/L TCLP
F019	Wastewater treatment sludges from the chemical conversion coating of aluminum except from zirconium phosphating in aluminum can washing when such phosphating is an exclusive conversion coating process	Chromium (Total)	7440-47-3	2.77	0.60 mg/L TCLP
		Cyanides (Total)[7]	57-12-5	1.2	590
		Cyanides (Amenable)[7]	57-12-5	0.86	30
F020, F021, F022, F023, F026	Wastes (except wastewater and spent carbon from hydrogen chloride purification) from the production or manufacturing use (as a reactant, chemical intermediate, or component in a formulating process) of: (1) tri- or tetrachlorophenol, or of intermediates used to produce their pesticide derivatives, excluding wastes from the production of Hexachlorophene from highly purified 2,4,5-trichlorophenol (F020); (2) pentachlorophenol, or of intermediates used to produce its derivatives (*i.e.*, F021); (3) tetra-, penta-, or hexachlorobenzenes under alkaline conditions (*i.e.*, F022); and from the production of materials on equipment previously used for the production or manufacturing use (as a reactant, chemical intermediate, or component in a formulating process) of: (1) tri- or tetrachlorophenols, excluding wastes from equipment used only for the production of Hexachlorophene from highly purified 2,4,5-trichlorophenol (F023); (2) tetra-, penta-, or hexachlorobenzenes under alkaline conditions (*i.e.*, F026)	HxCDDs (All Hexachlorodibenzo-p-dioxins)	NA	0.000063	0.001
		HxCDFs (All Hexachlorodibenzofurans)	NA	0.000063	0.001
		PeCDDs (All Pentachlorodibenzo-p-dioxins)	NA	0.000063	0.001
		PeCDFs (All Pentachlorodibenzofurans)	NA	0.000035	0.001
		Pentachlorophenol	87-86-5	0.089	7.4
		TCDDs (All Tetrachlorodibenzo-p-dioxins)	NA	0.000063	0.001
		TCDFs (All Tetrachlorodibenzofurans)	NA	0.000063	0.001
		2,4,5-Trichlorophenol	95-95-4	0.18	7.4
		2,4,6-Trichlorophenol	88-06-2	0.035	7.4
		2,3,4,6-Tetrachlorophenol	58-90-2	0.030	7.4

Treatment Standards for Hazardous Wastes

[*Note:* NA means not applicable]

13.4.1, 13.5

Waste code	Waste description and treatment/regulatory subcategory[1]	Regulated hazardous constituent		Wastewaters	Nonwastewaters
		Common name	CAS[2] No.	Concentration[3] in mg/L; or technology code[4]	Concentration[5] in mg/kg unless noted as "mg/L TCLP"; or technology code[4]
F024	Process wastes, including but not limited to, distillation residues, heavy ends, tars, and reactor clean-out wastes, from the production of certain chlorinated aliphatic hydrocarbons by free radical catalyzed processes. These chlorinated aliphatic hydrocarbons are those having carbon chain lengths ranging from one to and including five, with varying amounts and positions of chlorine substitution. (This listing does not include wastewaters, wastewater treatment sludges, spent catalysts, and wastes listed in §261.31 or §261.32.)	All F024 wastes	NA	CMBST[11]	CMBST[11]
		2-Chloro-1,3-butadiene	126-99-8	0.057	0.28
		3-Chloropropylene	107-05-1	0.036	30
		1,1-Dichloroethane	75-34-3	0.059	6.0
		1,2-Dichloroethane	107-06-2	0.21	6.0
		1,2-Dichloropropane	78-87-5	0.85	18
		cis-1,3-Dichloropropylene	10061-01-5	0.036	18
		trans-1,3-Dichloropropylene	10061-02-6	0.036	18
		bis(2-Ethylhexyl) phthalate	117-81-7	0.28	28
		Hexachloroethane	67-72-1	0.055	30
		Chromium (Total)	7440-47-3	2.77	0.60 mg/L TCLP
		Nickel	7440-02-0	3.98	11 mg/L TCLP
F025	Condensed light ends from the production of certain chlorinated aliphatic hydrocarbons, by free radical catalyzed processes. These chlorinated aliphatic hydrocarbons are those having carbon chain lengths ranging from one to and including five, with varying amounts and positions of chlorine substitution. F025—Light Ends Subcategory	Carbon tetrachloride	56-23-5	0.057	6.0
		Chloroform	67-66-3	0.046	6.0
		1,2-Dichloroethane	107-06-2	0.21	6.0
		1,1-Dichloroethylene	75-35-4	0.025	6.0
		Methylene chloride	75-9-2	0.089	30
		1,1,2-Trichloroethane	79-00-5	0.054	6.0
		Trichloroethylene	79-01-6	0.054	6.0
		Vinyl chloride	75-01-4	0.27	6.0
	Spent filters and filter aids, and spent desiccant wastes from the production of certain chlorinated aliphatic hydrocarbons, by free radical catalyzed processes. These chlorinated aliphatic hydrocarbons are those having carbon chain lengths ranging from one to and including five, with varying amounts and positions of chlorine substitution. F025—Spent Filters/Aids and Desiccants Subcategory	Carbon tetrachloride	56-23-5	0.057	6.0
		Chloroform	67-66-3	0.046	6.0
		Hexachlorobenzene	118-74-1	0.055	10
		Hexachlorobutadiene	87-68-3	0.055	5.6
		Hexachloroethane	67-72-1	0.055	30
		Methylene chloride	75-9-2	0.089	30
		1,1,2-Trichloroethane	79-00-5	0.054	6.0
		Trichloroethylene	79-01-6	0.054	6.0
		Vinyl chloride	75-01-4	0.27	6.0
F027	Discarded unused formulations containing tri-, tetra-, or pentachlorophenol or discarded unused formulations containing compounds derived from these chlorophenols. (This listing does not include formulations containing hexachlorophene synthesized from prepurified 2,4,5-trichlorophenol as the sole component)	HxCDDs (All Hexachlorodibenzo-p-dioxins)	NA	0.000063	0.001
		HxCDFs (All Hexachlorodibenzofurans)	NA	0.000063	0.001
		PeCDDs (All Pentachlorodibenzo-p-dioxins)	NA	0.000063	0.001
		PeCDFs (All Pentachlorodibenzofurans)	NA	0.000035	0.001
		Pentachlorophenol	87-86-5	0.089	7.4

Treatment Standards for Hazardous Wastes

13.4.1, 13.5

[*Note:* NA means not applicable]

Waste code	Waste description and treatment/regulatory subcategory[1]	Regulated hazardous constituent		Wastewaters	Nonwastewaters
		Common name	CAS[2] No.	Concentration[3] in mg/L; or technology code[4]	Concentration[5] in mg/kg unless noted as "mg/L TCLP"; or technology code[4]
		TCDDs (All Tetrachlorodibenzo-p-dioxins)	NA	0.000063	0.001
		TCDFs (All Tetra-chlorodibenzofurans)	NA	0.000063	0.001
		2,4,5-Trichlorophenol	95-95-4	0.018	7.4
		2,4,6-Trichlorophenol	88-06-2	0.035	7.4
		2,3,4,6-Tetrachloro-phenol	58-90-2	0.030	7.4
F028	Residues resulting from the incineration or thermal treatment of soil contaminated with EPA Hazardous Wastes Nos. F020, F021, F023, F026, and F027	HxCDDs (All Hexachlorodibenzo-p-dioxins)	NA	0.000063	0.001
		HxCDFs (All Hexachlorodibenzo-furans)	NA	0.000063	0.001
		PeCDDs (All Pentachlorodibenzo-p-dioxins)	NA	0.000063	0.001
		PeCDFs (All Pentachlorodibenzo-furans)	NA	0.000035	0.001
		Pentachlorophenol	87-86-5	0.089	7.4
		TCDDs (All Tetrachlorodibenzo-p-dioxins)	NA	0.000063	0.001
		TCDFs (All Tetra-chlorodibenzofurans)	NA	0.000063	0.001
		2,4,5-Trichlorophenol	95-95-4	0.18	7.4
		2,4,6-Trichlorophenol	88-06-2	0.035	7.4
		2,3,4,6-Tetrachlorophenol	58-90-2	0.30	7.4
F032	Wastewaters (except those that have not come into contact with process contaminants), process residuals, preservative drippage, and spent formulations from wood preserving processes generated at plants that currently use or have previously used chlorophenolic formulations (except potentially cross-contaminated wastes that have had the F032 waste code deleted in accordance with §261.35 of this chapter or potentially cross-contaminated wastes that are otherwise currently regulated as hazardous wastes (*i.e.*, F034 or F035), and where the generator does not resume or initiate use of chlorophenolic formulations). This listing does not include K001 bottom sediment sludge from the treatment of wastewater from wood preserving processes that use creosote and/or penta-chlorophenol.	Acenaphthene	83-32-9	0.059	3.4
		Anthracene	120-12-7	0.059	3.4
		Benz(a)anthracene	56-55-3	0.059	3.4
		Benzo(b)fluoranthene (difficult to distinguish from benzo(k)fluoranthene)	205-99-2	0.11	6.8
		Benzo(k)fluoranthene (difficult to distinguish from benzo(b)fluoranthene)	207-08-9	0.11	6.8
		Benzo(a)pyrene	50-32-8	0.061	3.4
		Chrysene	218-01-9	0.059	3.4
		Dibenz(a,h) anthracene	53-70-3	0.055	8.2
		2-4-Dimethyl phenol	105-67-9	0.036	14
		Fluorene	86-73-7	0.059	3.4

Treatment Standards for Hazardous Wastes

13.4.1, 13.5

[*Note:* NA means not applicable]

Waste code	Waste description and treatment/regulatory subcategory[1]	Regulated hazardous constituent		Wastewaters	Nonwastewaters
		Common name	CAS[2] No.	Concentration[3] in mg/L; or technology code[4]	Concentration[5] in mg/kg unless noted as "mg/L TCLP"; or technology code[4]
		Hexachlorodibenzo-p-dioxins	NA	0.000063, or CMBST[11]	0.001, or CMBST[11]
		Hexachlorodibenzo-furans	NA	0.000063, or CMBST[11]	0.001, or CMBST[11]
		Indeno (1,2,3-c,d) pyrene	193-39-5	0.0055	3.4
		Naphthalene	91-20-3	0.059	5.6
		Pentachlorodibenzo-p-dioxins	NA	0.000063, or CMBST[11]	0.001, or CMBST[11]
		Pentachlorodibenzo-furans	NA	0.000035, or CMBST[11]	0.001, or CMBST[11]
		Pentachlorophenol	87-86-5	0.089	7.4
		Phenanthrene	85-01-8	0.059	5.6
		Phenol	108-95-2	0.039	6.2
		Pyrene	129-00-0	0.067	8.2
		Tetrachlorodibenzo-p-dioxins	NA	0.000063, or CMBST[11]	0.001, or CMBST[11]
		Tetrachlorodibenzo-furans	NA	0.000063, or CMBST[11]	0.001, or CMBST[11]
		2,3,4,6-Tetrachlorophenol	58-90-2	0.030	7.4
		2,4,6-Trichlorophenol	88-06-2	0.035	7.4
		Arsenic	7440-38-2	1.4	5.0 mg/L TCLP
		Chromium (Total)	7440-47-3	2.77	0.60 mg/L TCLP
F034	Wastewaters (except those that have not come into contact with process contaminants), process residuals, preservative drippage, and spent formulations from wood preserving processes generated at plants that use creosote formulations. This listing does not include K001 bottom sediment sludge from the treatment of wastewater from wood preserving processes that use creosote and/or pentachlorophenol.	Acenaphthene	83-32-9	0.059	3.4
		Anthracene	120-12-7	0.059	3.4
		Benz(a)anthracene	56-55-3	0.059	3.4
		Benzo(b)fluoranthene (difficult to distinguish from benzo(k)fluoranthene)	205-99-2	0.11	6.8
		Benzo(k)fluoranthene (difficult to distinguish from benzo(b)fluoranthene)	207-08-9	0.11	6.8
		Benzo(a)pyrene	50-32-8	0.061	3.4
		Chrysene	218-01-9	0.059	3.4
		Dibenz(a,h) anthracene	53-70-3	0.055	8.2
		Fluorene	86-73-7	0.059	3.4
		Indeno (1,2,3-c,d) pyrene	193-39-5	0.0055	3.4
		Naphthalene	91-20-3	0.059	5.6
		Phenanthrene	85-01-8	0.059	5.6
		Pyrene	129-00-0	0.067	8.2
		Arsenic	7440-38-2	1.4	5.0 mg/L TCLP
		Chromium (Total)	7440-47-3	2.77	0.60 mg/L TCLP

Treatment Standards for Hazardous Wastes

13.4.1, 13.5

[*Note:* NA means not applicable]

Waste code	Waste description and treatment/regulatory subcategory[1]	Regulated hazardous constituent		Wastewaters	Nonwastewaters
		Common name	CAS[2] No.	Concentration[3] in mg/L; or technology code[4]	Concentration[5] in mg/kg unless noted as "mg/L TCLP"; or technology code[4]
F035	Wastewaters (except those that have not come into contact with process contaminants), process residuals, preservative drippage, and spent formulations from wood preserving processes generated at plants that use inorganic preservatives containing arsenic or chromium. This listing does not include K001 bottom sediment sludge from the treatment of wastewater from wood preserving processes that use creosote and/or pentachlorophenol.	Arsenic	7440-38-2	1.4	5.0 mg/L TCLP
		Chromium (Total)	7440-47-3	2.77	0.60 mg/L TCLP
F037	Petroleum refinery primary oil/water/solids separation sludge—Any sludge generated from the gravitational separation of oil/water/solids during the storage or treatment of process wastewaters and oily cooling wastewaters from petroleum refineries. Such sludges include, but are not limited to, those generated in: oil/water/solids separators; tanks and impoundments; ditches and other conveyances; sumps; and stormwater units receiving dry weather flow. Sludge generated in stormwater units that do not receive dry weather flow, sludges generated from non-contact once-through cooling waters segregated for treatment from other process or oily cooling waters, sludges generated in aggressive biological treatment units as defined in §261.31(b)(2) (including sludges generated in one or more additional units after wastewaters have been treated in aggressive biological treatment units) and K051 wastes are not included in this listing.	Acenaphthene	83-32-9	0.059	NA
		Anthracene	120-12-7	0.059	3.4
		Benzene	71-43-2	0.14	10
		Benz(a)anthracene	56-55-3	0.059	3.4
		Benzo(a)pyrene	50-32-8	0.061	3.4
		bis(2-Ethylhexyl) phthalate	117-81-7	0.28	28
		Chrysene	218-01-9	0.059	3.4
		Di-n-butyl phthalate	84-74-2	0.057	28
		Ethylbenzene	100-41-4	0.057	10
		Fluorene	86-73-7	0.059	NA
		Naphthalene	91-20-3	0.059	5.6
		Phenanthrene	85-01-8	0.059	5.6
		Phenol	108-95-2	0.039	6.2
		Pyrene	129-00-0	0.067	8.2
		Toluene	108-88-3	0.080	10
		Xylenes-mixed isomers (sum of o-, m-, and p-xylene concentrations)	1330-20-7	0.32	30
		Chromium (Total)	7440-47-3	2.77	0.60 mg/L TCLP
		Cyanides (Total)[7]	57-12-5	1.2	590
		Lead	7439-92-1	0.69	NA
		Nickel	7440-02-0	NA	11 mg/L TCLP
F038	Petroleum refinery secondary (emulsified) oil/water/solids separation sludge and/or float generated from the physical and/or chemical separation of oil/water/solids in process wastewaters and oily cooling wastewaters from petroleum refineries. Such wastes include, but are not limited to, all sludges and floats generated in: induced air floatation (IAF) units, tanks and impoundments, and all sludges generated in DAF units. Sludges generated in stormwater units that do not receive dry weather flow, sludges generated from non-contact once-through cooling waters segregated for treatment from other process or oily cooling waters, sludges and floats generated in aggressive biological treatment units as defined in §261.31(b)(2) (including sludges and floats generated in one or more additional units after wastewaters have been treated in aggressive biological units) and F037, K048, and K051 are not included in this listing.	Benzene	71-43-2	0.14	10
		Benzo(a)pyrene	50-32-8	0.061	3.4
		bis(2-Ethylhexyl) phthalate	117-81-7	0.28	28
		Chrysene	218-01-9	0.059	3.4
		Di-n-butyl phthalate	84-74-2	0.057	28
		Ethylbenzene	100-41-4	0.057	10
		Fluorene	86-73-7	0.059	NA
		Naphthalene	91-20-3	0.059	5.6
		Phenanthrene	85-01-8	0.059	5.6
		Phenol	108-95-2	0.039	6.2
		Pyrene	129-00-0	0.067	8.2
		Toluene	108-88-3	0.080	10

Treatment Standards for Hazardous Wastes

13.4.1, 13.5

[*Note:* NA means not applicable]

Waste code	Waste description and treatment/regulatory subcategory[1]	Regulated hazardous constituent		Wastewaters	Nonwastewaters
		Common name	CAS[2] No.	Concentration[3] in mg/L; or technology code[4]	Concentration[5] in mg/kg unless noted as "mg/L TCLP"; or technology code[4]
		Xylenes-mixed isomers (sum of o-, m-, and p-xylene concentrations)	1330-20-7	0.32	30
		Chromium (Total)	7440-47-3	2.77	0.60 mg/L TCLP
		Cyanides (Total)[7]	57-12-5	1.2	590
		Lead	7439-92-1	0.69	NA
		Nickel	7440-02-0	NA	11 mg/L TCLP
F039	Leachate (liquids that have percolated through land disposed wastes) resulting from the disposal of more than one restricted waste classified as hazardous under Subpart D of this part. (Leachate resulting from the disposal of one or more of the following EPA Hazardous Wastes and no other Hazardous Wastes retains its EPA Hazardous Waste Number(s): F020, F021, F022, F026, F027, and/or F028.)	Acenaphthylene	208-96-8	0.059	3.4
		Acenaphthene	83-32-9	0.059	3.4
		Acetone	67-64-1	0.28	160
		Acetonitrile	75-05-8	5.6	NA
		Acetophenone	96-86-2	0.010	9.7
		2-Acetylaminofluorene	53-96-3	0.059	140
		Acrolein	107-02-8	0.29	NA
		Acrylonitrile	107-13-1	0.24	84
		Aldrin	309-00-2	0.021	0.066
		4-Aminobiphenyl	92-67-1	0.13	NA
		Aniline	62-53-3	0.81	14
		o-Anisidine (2-methoxyaniline)	90-04-0	0.010	0.66
		Anthracene	120-12-7	0.059	3.4
		Aramite	140-57-8	0.36	NA
		alpha-BHC	319-84-6	0.00014	0.066
		beta-BHC	319-85-7	0.00014	0.066
		delta-BHC	319-86-8	0.023	0.066
		gamma-BHC	58-89-9	0.0017	0.066
		Benzene	71-43-2	0.14	10
		Benz(a)anthracene	56-55-3	0.059	3.4
		Benzo(b)fluoranthene (difficult to distinguish from benzo(k)fluoranthene	205-99-2	0.11	6.8
		Benzo(k)fluoranthene (difficult to distinguish from benzo(b)fluoranthene	207-08-9	0.11	6.8
		Benzo(g,h,i)perylene	191-24-2	0.0055	1.8
		Benzo(a)pyrene	50-32-8	0.061	3.4
		Bromodichloromethane	75-27-4	0.35	15
		Methyl bromide (Bromomethane)	74-83-9	0.11	15
		4-Bromophenyl phenyl ether	101-55-3	0.055	15
		n-Butyl alcohol	71-36-3	5.6	2.6

Treatment Standards for Hazardous Wastes

13.4.1, 13.5

[*Note:* NA means not applicable]

Waste code	Waste description and treatment/regulatory subcategory[1]	Regulated hazardous constituent		Wastewaters	Nonwastewaters
		Common name	CAS[2] No.	Concentration[3] in mg/L; or technology code[4]	Concentration[5] in mg/kg unless noted as "mg/L TCLP"; or technology code[4]
		Butyl benzyl phthalate	85-68-7	0.017	28
		2-sec-Butyl-4,6-dinitrophenol (Dinoseb)	88-85-7	0.066	2.5
		Carbon disulfide	75-15-0	3.8	NA
		Carbon tetrachloride	56-23-5	0.057	6.0
		Chlordane (alpha and gamma isomers)	57-74-9	0.0033	0.26
		p-Chloroaniline	106-47-8	0.46	16
		Chlorobenzene	108-90-7	0.057	6.0
		Chlorobenzilate	510-15-6	0.10	NA
		2-Chloro-1,3-butadiene	126-99-8	0.057	NA
		Chlorodibromomethane	124-48-1	0.057	15
		Chloroethane	75-00-3	0.27	6.0
		bis(2-Chloroethoxy)methane	111-91-1	0.036	7.2
		bis(2-Chloroethyl)ether	111-44-4	0.033	6.0
		Chloroform	67-66-3	0.046	6.0
		bis(2-Chloroisopropyl)ether	39638-32-9	0.055	7.2
		p-Chloro-m-cresol	59-50-7	0.018	14
		Chloromethane (Methyl chlorida)	74-87-3	0.19	30
		2-Chloronaphthalene	91-58-7	0.055	5.6
		2-Chlorophenol	95-57-8	0.044	5.7
		3-Chloropropylene	107-05-1	0.036	30
		Chrysene	218-01-9	0.059	3.4
		p-Cresidine	120-71-8	0.010	0.66
		o-Cresol	95-48-7	0.11	5.6
		m-Cresol (difficult to distinguish from p-cresol)	108-39-4	0.77	5.6
		p-Cresol (difficult to distinguish from m-cresol)	106-44-5	0.77	5.6
		Cyclohexanone	108-94-1	0.36	NA
		1,2-Dibromo-3-chloropropane	96-12-8	0.11	15
		Ethylene dibromide (1,2-Dibromoethane)	106-93-4	0.028	15
		Dibromomethane	74-95-3	0.11	15
		2,4-D (2,4-Dichlorophenoxyacetic acid)	94-75-7	0.72	10

Treatment Standards for Hazardous Wastes

[*Note:* NA means not applicable]

13.4.1, 13.5

Waste code	Waste description and treatment/regulatory subcategory[1]	Regulated hazardous constituent		Wastewaters	Nonwastewaters
		Common name	CAS[2] No.	Concentration[3] in mg/L; or technology code[4]	Concentration[5] in mg/kg unless noted as "mg/L TCLP"; or technology code[4]
		o,p′-DDD	53-19-0	0.023	0.087
		p,p′-DDD	72-54-8	0.023	0.087
		o,p′-DDE	3424-82-6	0.031	0.087
		p,p′-DDE	72-55-9	0.031	0.087
		o,p′-DDT	789-02-6	0.0039	0.087
		p,p′-DDT	50-29-3	0.0039	0.087
		Dibenz(a,h) anthracene	53-70-3	0.055	8.2
		Dibenz(a,e)pyrene	192-65-4	0.061	NA
		m-Dichlorobenzene	541-73-1	0.036	6.0
		o-Dichlorobenzene	95-50-1	0.088	6.0
		p-Dichlorobenzene	106-46-7	0.090	6.0
		Dichlorodifluoro-methane	75-71-8	0.23	7.2
		1,1-Dichloroethane	75-34-3	0.059	6.0
		1,2-Dichloroethane	107-06-2	0.21	6.0
		1,1-Dichloroethylene	75-35-4	0.025	6.0
		trans-1,2-Dichloro-ethylene	156-60-5	0.054	30
		2,4-Dichlorophenol	120-83-2	0.044	14
		2,6-Dichlorophenol	87-65-0	0.044	14
		1,2-Dichloropropane	78-87-5	0.85	18
		cis-1,3-Dichloro-propylene	10061-01-5	0.036	18
		trans-1,3-Dichloro-propylene	10061-02-6	0.036	18
		Dieldrin	60-57-1	0.017	0.13
		Diethyl phthalate	84-66-2	0.20	28
		2,4-Dimethylaniline (2,4-xylidine)	95-68-1	0.010	0.66
		2-4-Dimethyl phenol	105-67-9	0.036	14
		Dimethyl phthalate	131-11-3	0.047	28
		Di-n-butyl phthalate	84-74-2	0.057	28
		1,4-Dinitrobenzene	100-25-4	0.32	2.3
		4,6-Dinitro-o-cresol	534-52-1	0.28	160
		2,4-Dinitrophenol	51-28-5	0.12	160
		2,4-Dinitrotoluene	121-14-2	0.32	140
		2,6-Dinitrotoluene	606-20-2	0.55	28
		Di-n-octyl phthalate	117-84-0	0.017	28
		Di-n-propylnitros-amine	621-64-7	0.40	14
		1,4-Dioxane	123-91-1	12.0	170
		Diphenylamine (difficult to distinguish from diphenyl-nitrosamine)	122-39-4	0.92	NA

Treatment Standards for Hazardous Wastes

13.4.1, 13.5

[*Note:* NA means not applicable]

Waste code	Waste description and treatment/regulatory subcategory[1]	Regulated hazardous constituent		Wastewaters	Nonwastewaters
		Common name	CAS[2] No.	Concentration[3] in mg/L; or technology code[4]	Concentration[5] in mg/kg unless noted as "mg/L TCLP"; or technology code[4]
		Diphenylnitrosamine (difficult to distinguish from diphenylamine)	86-30-6	0.92	NA
		1,2-Diphenyl-hydrazine	122-66-7	0.087	NA
		Disulfoton	298-04-4	0.017	6.2
		Endosulfan I	939-98-8	0.023	0.066
		Endosulfan II	33213-6-5	0.029	0.13
		Endosulfan sulfate	1031-07-8	0.029	0.13
		Endrin	72-20-8	0.0028	0.13
		Endrin aldehyde	7421-93-4	0.025	0.13
		Ethyl acetate	141-78-6	0.34	33
		Ethyl cyanide (Propanenitrile)	107-12-0	0.24	360
		Ethyl benzene	100-41-4	0.057	10
		Ethyl ether	60-29-7	0.12	160
		bis(2-Ethylhexyl) phthalate	117-81-7	0.28	28
		Ethyl methacrylate	97-63-2	0.14	160
		Ethylene oxide	75-21-8	0.12	NA
		Famphur	52-85-7	0.017	15
		Fluoranthene	206-44-0	0.068	3.4
		Fluorene	86-73-7	0.059	3.4
		Heptachlor	76-44-8	0.0012	0.066
		Heptachlor epoxide	1024-57-3	0.016	0.066
		1,2,3,4,6,7,8-Heptachlorodibenzo-*p*-dioxin (1,2,3,4,6,7,8-HpCDD)	35822-46-9	0.000035	0.0025
		1,2,3,4,6,7,8-Heptachlorodibenzo-furan (1,2,3,4,6,7,8-HpCDF)	67562-39-4	0.000035	0.0025
		1,2,3,4,7,8,9-Heptachlorodibenzo-furan (1,2,3,4,7,8,9-HpCDF)	55673-89-7	0.000035	0.0025
		Hexachlorobenzene	118-74-1	0.055	10
		Hexachlorobutadiene	87-68-3	0.055	5.6
		Hexachlorocyclopent adiene	77-47-4	0.057	2.4
		HxCDDs (All Hexachlorodibenzo-p-dioxins)	NA	0.000063	0.001
		HxCDFs (All Hexachlorodibenzo-furans)	NA	0.000063	0.001
		Hexachloroethane	67-72-1	0.055	30

Treatment Standards for Hazardous Wastes

13.4.1, 13.5

[*Note:* NA means not applicable]

Waste code	Waste description and treatment/regulatory subcategory[1]	Regulated hazardous constituent		Wastewaters	Nonwastewaters
		Common name	CAS[2] No.	Concentration[3] in mg/L; or technology code[4]	Concentration[5] in mg/kg unless noted as "mg/L TCLP"; or technology code[4]
		Hexachloropropylene	1888-71-7	0.035	30
		Indeno (1,2,3-c,d) pyrene	193-39-5	0.0055	3.4
		Iodomethane	74-88-4	0.19	65
		Isobutyl alcohol	78-83-1	5.6	170
		Isodrin	465-73-6	0.021	0.066
		Isosafrole	120-58-1	0.081	2.6
		Kepone	143-50-8	0.0011	0.13
		Methacrylonitrile	126-98-7	0.24	84
		Methanol	67-56-1	5.6	NA
		Methapyrilene	91-80-5	0.081	1.5
		Methoxychlor	72-43-5	0.25	0.18
		3-Methylcholanthrene	56-49-5	0.0055	15
		4,4-Methylene bis(2-chloroaniline)	101-14-4	0.50	30
		Methylene chloride	75-09-2	0.089	30
		Methyl ethyl ketone	78-93-3	0.28	36
		Methyl isobutyl ketone	108-10-1	0.14	33
		Methyl methacrylate	80-62-6	0.14	160
		Methyl methansulfonate	66-27-3	0.018	NA
		Methyl parathion	298-00-0	0.014	4.6
		Naphthalene	91-20-3	0.059	5.6
		2-Naphthylamine	91-59-8	0.52	NA
		p-Nitroaniline	100-01-6	0.028	28
		Nitrobenzene	98-95-3	0.068	14
		5-Nitro-o-toluidine	99-55-8	0.32	28
		p-Nitrophenol	100-02-7	0.12	29
		N-Nitrosodiethylamine	55-18-5	0.40	28
		N-Nitrosodi-methylamine	62-75-9	0.40	NA
		N-Nitroso-di-n-butyl-amine	924-16-3	0.40	17
		N-Nitrosomethyl-ethylamine	10595-95-6	0.40	2.3
		N-Nitrosomorpholine	59-89-2	0.40	2.3
		N-Nitrosopiperidine	100-75-4	0.013	35
		N-Nitrosopyrrolidine	930-55-2	0.013	35
		1,2,3,4,6,7,8,9-Octa-chlorodibenzo-*p*-dioxin (OCDD)	3268-87-9	0.000063	0.005*

* [*Publisher's Note:* This nonwastewater treatment standard was promulgated as 0.0025 mg/kg on November 8, 2000 [65 *FR* 67128] and never revised by EPA in a rulemaking. However, when the July 1, 2001 *CFR* was issued, the value had been changed to 0.005 mg/kg (consistent with its universal treatment standard in §268.48). Therefore, we have changed the value to 0.005 mg/kg to be consistent with the *CFR* and §268.48.]

Treatment Standards for Hazardous Wastes

[*Note:* NA means not applicable]

13.4.1, 13.5

Waste code	Waste description and treatment/regulatory subcategory[1]	Regulated hazardous constituent		Wastewaters	Nonwastewaters
		Common name	CAS[2] No.	Concentration[3] in mg/L; or technology code[4]	Concentration[5] in mg/kg unless noted as "mg/L TCLP"; or technology code[4]
		1,2,3,4,6,7,8,9-Octa-chlorodibenzofuran (OCDF)	39001-02-0	0.000063	0.005
		Parathion	56-38-2	0.014	4.6
		Total PCBs (sum of all PCB isomer, or all Aroclors)	1336-36-3	0.10	10
		Pentachlorobenzene	608-93-5	0.055	10
		PeCDDs (All Pentachlorodibenzo-p-dioxins)	NA	0.000063	0.001
		PeCDFs (All Pentachlorodibenzo-furans)	NA	0.000035	0.001
		Pentachloronitro-benzene	82-68-8	0.055	4.8
		Pentachlorophenol	87-86-5	0.089	7.4
		Phenacetin	62-44-2	0.081	16
		Phenanthrene	85-01-8	0.059	5.6
		Phenol	108-95-2	0.039	6.2
		1,3-Phenylene-diamine	108-45-2	0.010	0.66
		Phorate	298-02-2	0.021	4.6
		Phthalic anhydride	85-44-9	0.055	NA
		Pronamide	23950-58-5	0.093	1.5
		Pyrene	129-00-0	0.067	8.2
		Pyridine	110-86-1	0.014	16
		Safrole	94-59-7	0.081	22
		Silvex (2,4,5-TP)	93-72-1	0.72	7.9
		2,4,5-T	93-76-5	0.72	7.9
		1,2,4,5-Tetrachloro-benzene	95-94-3	0.055	14
		TCDDs (All Tetrachlorodibenzo-p-dioxins)	NA	0.000063	0.001
		TCDFs (All Tetra-chlorodibenzofurans)	NA	0.000063	0.001
		1,1,1,2-Tetrachloro-ethane	630-20-6	0.057	6.0
		1,1,2,2-Tetrachloro-ethane	79-34-6	0.057	6.0
		Tetrachloroethylene	127-18-4	0.056	6.0
		2,3,4,6-Tetrachloro-phenol	58-90-2	0.030	7.4
		Toluene	108-88-3	0.080	10
		Toxaphene	8001-35-2	0.0095	2.6
		Bromoform (Tribromomethane)	75-25-2	0.63	15

Treatment Standards for Hazardous Wastes

13.4.1, 13.5

[*Note:* NA means not applicable]

Waste code	Waste description and treatment/regulatory subcategory[1]	Regulated hazardous constituent		Wastewaters	Nonwastewaters
		Common name	CAS[2] No.	Concentration[3] in mg/L; or technology code[4]	Concentration[5] in mg/kg unless noted as "mg/L TCLP"; or technology code[4]
		1,2,4-Trichloro-benzene	120-82-1	0.055	19
		1,1,1-Trichloroethane	71-55-6	0.054	6.0
		1,1,2-Trichloroethane	79-00-5	0.054	6.0
		Trichloroethylene	79-01-6	0.054	6.0
		Trichlorofluoro-methane	75-69-4	0.020	30
		2,4,5-Trichlorophenol	95-95-4	0.18	7.4
		2,4,6-Trichlorophenol	88-06-2	0.035	7.4
		1,2,3-Trichloro-propane	96-18-4	0.85	30
		1,1,2-Trichloro-1,2,2-trifluoroethane	76-13-1	0.057	30
		tris(2,3-Dibromo-propyl) phosphate	126-72-7	0.11	NA
		Vinyl chloride	75-01-4	0.27	6.0
		Xylenes-mixed isomers (sum of o-, m-, and p-xylene concentrations)	1330-20-7	0.32	30
		Antimony	7440-36-0	1.9	1.15 mg/L TCLP
		Arsenic	7440-38-2	1.4	5.0 mg/L TCLP
		Barium	7440-39-3	1.2	21 mg/L TCLP
		Beryllium	7440-41-7	0.82	NA
		Cadmium	7440-43-9	0.69	0.11 mg/L TCLP
		Chromium (Total)	7440-47-3	2.77	0.60 mg/L TCLP
		Cyanides (Total)[7]	57-12-5	1.2	590
		Cyanides (Amenable)[7]	57-12-5	0.86	NA
		Fluoride	16964-48-8	35	NA
		Lead	7439-92-1	0.69	0.75 mg/L TCLP
		Mercury	7439-97-6	0.15	0.025 mg/L TCLP
		Nickel	7440-02-0	3.98	11 mg/L TCLP
		Selenium	7782-49-2	0.82	5.7 mg/L TCLP
		Silver	7440-22-4	0.43	0.14 mg/L TCLP
		Sulfide	8496-25-8	14	NA
		Thallium	7440-28-0	1.4	NA
		Vanadium	7440-62-2	4.3	NA
K001	Bottom sediment sludge from the treatment of wastewaters from wood preserving processes that use creosote and/or pentachlorophenol.	Naphthalene	91-20-3	0.059	5.6
		Pentachlorophenol	87-86-5	0.089	7.4
		Phenanthrene	85-01-8	0.059	5.6
		Pyrene	129-00-0	0.067	8.2
		Toluene	108-88-3	0.080	10

Treatment Standards for Hazardous Wastes

[*Note:* NA means not applicable]

13.4.1, 13.5

Waste code	Waste description and treatment/regulatory subcategory[1]	Regulated hazardous constituent		Wastewaters	Nonwastewaters
		Common name	CAS[2] No.	Concentration[3] in mg/L; or technology code[4]	Concentration[5] in mg/kg unless noted as "mg/L TCLP"; or technology code[4]
		Xylenes-mixed isomers (sum of o-, m-, and p-xylene concentrations)	1330-20-7	0.32	30
		Lead	7439-92-1	0.69	0.75 mg/L TCLP
K002	Wastewater treatment sludge from the production of chrome yellow and orange pigments	Chromium (Total)	7440-47-3	2.77	0.60 mg/L TCLP
		Lead	7439-92-1	0.69	0.75 mg/L TCLP
K003	Wastewater treatment sludge from the production of molybdate orange pigments	Chromium (Total)	7440-47-3	2.77	0.60 mg/L TCLP
		Lead	7439-92-1	0.69	0.75 mg/L TCLP
K004	Wastewater treatment sludge from the production of zinc yellow pigments	Chromium (Total)	7440-47-3	2.77	0.60 mg/L TCLP
		Lead	7439-92-1	0.69	0.75 mg/L TCLP
K005	Wastewater treatment sludge from the production of chrome green pigments	Chromium (Total)	7440-47-3	2.77	0.60 mg/L TCLP
		Lead	7439-92-1	0.69	0.75 mg/L TCLP
		Cyanides (Total)[7]	57-12-5	1.2	590
K006	Wastewater treatment sludge from the production of chrome oxide green pigments (anhydrous)	Chromium (Total)	7440-47-3	2.77	0.60 mg/L TCLP
		Lead	7439-92-1	0.69	0.75 mg/L TCLP
	Wastewater treatment sludge from the production of chrome oxide green pigments (hydrated)	Chromium (Total)	7440-47-3	2.77	0.60 mg/L TCLP
		Lead	7439-92-1	0.69	NA
K007	Wastewater treatment sludge from the production of iron blue pigments	Chromium (Total)	7440-47-3	2.77	0.60 mg/L TCLP
		Lead	7439-92-1	0.69	0.75 mg/L TCLP
		Cyanides (Total)[7]	57-12-5	1.2	590
K008	Oven residue from the production of chrome oxide green pigments.	Chromium (Total)	7440-47-3	2.77	0.60 mg/L TCLP
		Lead	7439-92-1	0.69	0.75 mg/L TCLP
K009	Distillation bottoms from the production of acetaldehyde from ethylene	Chloroform	67-66-3	0.046	6.0
K010	Distillation side cuts from the production of acetaldehyde from ethylene	Chloroform	67-66-3	0.046	6.0
K011	Bottom stream from the wastewater stripper in the production of acrylonitrile	Acetonitrile	75-05-8	5.6	38
		Acrylonitrile	107-13-1	0.24	84
		Acrylamide	79-06-1	19	23
		Benzene	71-43-2	0.14	10
		Cyanide (Total)	57-12-5	1.2	590
K013	Bottom stream from the acetonitrile column in the production of acrylonitrile	Acetonitrile	75-05-8	5.6	38
		Acrylonitrile	107-13-1	0.24	84
		Acrylamide	79-06-1	19	23
		Benzene	71-43-2	0.14	10
		Cyanide (Total)	57-12-5	1.2	590
K014	Bottoms from the acetonitrile purification column in the production of acrylonitrile	Acetonitrile	75-05-8	5.6	38
		Acrylonitrile	107-13-1	0.24	84

Treatment Standards for Hazardous Wastes

📖 13.4.1, 13.5

[*Note:* NA means not applicable]

Waste code	Waste description and treatment/regulatory subcategory[1]	Regulated hazardous constituent		Wastewaters	Nonwastewaters
		Common name	CAS[2] No.	Concentration[3] in mg/L; or technology code[4]	Concentration[5] in mg/kg unless noted as "mg/L TCLP"; or technology code[4]
		Acrylamide	79-06-1	19	23
		Benzene	71-43-2	0.14	10
		Cyanide (Total)	57-12-5	1.2	590
K015	Still bottoms from the distillation of benzyl chloride	Anthracene	120-12-7	0.059	3.4
		Benzal chloride	98-87-3	0.055	6.0
		Benzo(b)fluoranthene (difficult to distinguish from benzo(k)fluoranthene	205-99-2	0.11	6.8
		Benzo(k)fluroanthene (difficult to distinguish from benzo(b)fluoranthene	207-08-9	0.11	6.8
		Phenanthrene	85-01-8	0.059	5.6
		Toluene	108-88-3	0.080	10
		Chromium (Total)	7440-47-3	2.77	0.60 mg/L TCLP
		Nickel	7440-02-0	3.98	11 mg/L TCLP
K016	Heavy ends or distillation residues from the production of carbon tetrachloride	Hexachlorobenzene	118-74-1	0.055	10
		Hexachlorobutadiene	87-68-3	0.055	5.6
		Hexachlorocyclo-pentadiene	77-47-4	0.057	2.4
		Hexachloroethane	67-72-1	0.055	30
		Tetrachloroethylene	127-18-4	0.056	6.0
K017	Heavy ends (still bottoms) from the purification column in the production of epichlorohydrin	bis(2-Chloro-ethyl)ether	111-44-4	0.033	6.0
		1,2-Dichloropropane	78-87-5	0.85	18
		1,2,3-Trichloro-propane	96-18-4	0.85	30
K018	Heavy ends from the fractionation column in ethyl chloride production	Chloroethane	75-00-3	0.27	6.0
		Chloromethane	74-87-3	0.19	NA
		1,1-Dichloroethane	75-34-3	0.059	6.0
		1,2-Dichloroethane	107-06-2	0.21	6.0
		Hexachlorobenzene	118-74-1	0.055	10
		Hexachlorobutadiene	87-68-3	0.055	5.6
		Hexachloroethane	67-72-1	0.055	30
		Pentachloroethane	76-01-7	NA	6.0
		1,1,1-Trichloroethane	71-55-6	0.054	6.0
K019	Heavy ends from the distillation of ethylene dichloride in ethylene dichloride production	bis(2-Chloro-ethyl)ether	111-44-4	0.033	6.0
		Chlorobenzene	108-90-7	0.057	6.0
		Chloroform	67-66-3	0.046	6.0
		p-Dichlorobenzene	106-46-7	0.090	NA
		1,2-Dichloroethane	107-06-2	0.21	6.0
		Fluorene	86-73-7	0.059	NA

PART 268—Subpart D

Treatment Standards for Hazardous Wastes

13.4.1, 13.5

[*Note:* NA means not applicable]

Waste code	Waste description and treatment/regulatory subcategory[1]	Regulated hazardous constituent		Wastewaters	Nonwastewaters
		Common name	CAS[2] No.	Concentration[3] in mg/L; or technology code[4]	Concentration[5] in mg/kg unless noted as "mg/L TCLP"; or technology code[4]
		Hexachloroethane	67-72-1	0.055	30
		Naphthalene	91-20-3	0.059	5.6
		Phenanthrene	85-01-8	0.059	5.6
		1,2,4,5-Tetra-chlorobenzene	95-94-3	0.055	NA
		Tetrachloroethylene	127-18-4	0.056	6.0
		1,2,4-Trichloro-benzene	120-82-1	0.055	19
		1,1,1-Trichloroethane	71-55-6	0.054	6.0
K020	Heavy ends from the distillation of vinyl chloride in vinyl chloride monomer production	1,2-Dichloroethane	107-06-2	0.21	6.0
		1,1,2,2-Tetra-chloroethane	79-34-6	0.057	6.0
		Tetrachloroethylene	127-18-4	0.056	6.0
K021	Aqueous spent antimony catalyst waste from fluoromethanes production 13.1.5.1	Carbon tetrachloride	56-23-5	0.057	6.0
		Chloroform	67-66-3	0.046	6.0
		Antimony	7440-36-0	1.9	1.15 mg/L TCLP
K022	Distillation bottom tars from the production of phenol/acetone from cumene	Toluene	108-88-3	0.080	10
		Acetophenone	96-86-2	0.010	9.7
		Diphenylamine (difficult to distinguish from diphenylnitrosamine)	122-39-4	0.92	13
		Diphenylnitrosamine (difficult to distinguish from diphenylamine)	86-30-6	0.92	13
		Phenol	108-95-2	0.039	6.2
		Chromium (Total)	7440-47-3	2.77	0.60 mg/L TCLP
		Nickel	7440-02-0	3.98	11 mg/L TCLP
K023	Distillation light ends from the production of phthalic anhydride from naphthalene	Phthalic anhydride (measured as Phthalic acid or Terephthalic acid)	100-21-0	0.055	28
		Phthalic anhydride (measured as Phthalic acid or Terephthalic acid)	85-44-9	0.055	28
K024	Distillation bottoms from the production of phthalic anhydride from naphthalene	Phthalic anhydride (measured as Phthalic acid or Terephthalic acid)	100-21-0	0.055	28
		Phthalic anhydride (measured as Phthalic acid or Terephthalic acid)	85-44-9	0.055	28

Treatment Standards for Hazardous Wastes

13.4.1, 13.5

[*Note:* NA means not applicable]

Waste code	Waste description and treatment/regulatory subcategory[1]	Regulated hazardous constituent		Wastewaters	Nonwastewaters
		Common name	CAS[2] No.	Concentration[3] in mg/L; or technology code[4]	Concentration[5] in mg/kg unless noted as "mg/L TCLP"; or technology code[4]
K025	Distillation bottoms from the production of nitrobenzene by the nitration of benzene	NA	NA	LLEXT fb SSTRP fb CARBN; or CMBST	CMBST
K026	Stripping still tails from the production of methyl ethyl pyridines	NA	NA	CMBST	CMBST
K027	Centrifuge and distillation residues from toluene diisocyanate production	NA	NA	CARBN; or CMBST	CMBST
K028	Spent catalyst from the hydrochlorinator reactor in the production of 1,1,1- trichloroethane	1,1-Dichloroethane	75-34-3	0.059	6.0
		trans-1,2-Dichloro-ethylene	156-60-5	0.054	30
		Hexachlorobutadiene	87-68-3	0.055	5.6
		Hexachloroethane	67-72-1	0.055	30
		Pentachloroethane	76-01-7	NA	6.0
		1,1,1,2-Tetrachloro-ethane	630-20-6	0.057	6.0
		1,1,2,2-Tetrachloro-ethane	79-34-6	0.057	6.0
		Tetrachloroethylene	127-18-4	0.056	6.0
		1,1,1-Trichloroethane	71-55-6	0.054	6.0
		1,1,2-Trichloroethane	79-00-5	0.054	6.0
		Cadmium	7440-43-9	0.69	NA
		Chromium (Total)	7440-47-3	2.77	0.60 mg/L TCLP
		Lead	7439-92-1	0.69	0.75 mg/L TCLP
		Nickel	7440-02-0	3.98	11 mg/L TCLP
K029	Waste from the product steam stripper in the production of 1,1,1-trichloroethane	Chloroform	67-66-3	0.046	6.0
		1,2-Dichloroethane	107-06-2	0.21	6.0
		1,1-Dichloroethylene	75-35-4	0.025	6.0
		1,1,1-Trichloroethane	71-55-6	0.054	6.0
		Vinyl chloride	75-01-4	0.27	6.0
K030	Column bodies or heavy ends from the combined production of trichloroethylene and perchloroethylene	o-Dichlorobenzene	95-50-1	0.088	NA
		p-Dichlorobenzene	106-46-7	0.090	NA
		Hexachlorobutadiene	87-68-3	0.055	5.6
		Hexachloroethane	67-72-1	0.055	30
		Hexachloropropylene	1888-71-7	NA	30
		Pentachlorobenzene	608-93-5	NA	10
		Pentachloroethane	76-01-7	NA	6.0
		1,2,4,5-Tetrachloro-benzene	95-94-3	0.055	14
		Tetrachloroethylene	127-18-4	0.056	6.0
		1,2,4-Trichloro-benzene	120-82-1	0.055	19

Treatment Standards for Hazardous Wastes

13.4.1, 13.5

[*Note:* NA means not applicable]

Waste code	Waste description and treatment/regulatory subcategory[1]	Regulated hazardous constituent		Wastewaters	Nonwastewaters
		Common name	CAS[2] No.	Concentration[3] in mg/L; or technology code[4]	Concentration[5] in mg/kg unless noted as "mg/L TCLP"; or technology code[4]
K031	By-product salts generated in the production of MSMA and cacodylic acid	Arsenic	7440-38-2	1.4	5.0 mg/L TCLP
K032	Wastewater treatment sludge from the production of chlordane	Hexachlorocyclo-pentadiene	77-47-4	0.057	2.4
		Chlordane (alpha and gamma isomers)	57-74-9	0.0033	0.26
		Heptachlor	76-44-8	0.0012	0.066
		Heptachlor epoxide	1024-57-3	0.016	0.066
K033	Wastewater and scrub water from the chlorination of cyclopentadiene in the production of chlordane	Hexachlorocyclo-pentadiene	77-47-4	0.057	2.4
K034	Filter solids from the filtration of hexachlorocyclopentadiene in the production of chlordane	Hexachlorocylo-pentadiene	77-47-4	0.057	2.4
K035	Wastewater treatment sludges generated in the production of creosote	Acenaphthene	83-32-9	NA	3.4
		Anthracene	120-12-7	NA	3.4
		Benz(a)anthracene	56-55-3	0.059	3.4
		Benzo(a)pyrene	50-32-8	0.061	3.4
		Chrysene	218-01-9	0.059	3.4
		o-Cresol	95-48-7	0.11	5.6
		m-Cresol (difficult to distinguish from p-cresol)	108-39-4	0.77	5.6
		p-Cresol (difficult to distinguish from m-cresol)	106-44-5	0.77	5.6
		Dibenz(a,h)anthra-cene	53-70-3	NA	8.2
		Fluoranthene	206-44-0	0.068	3.4
		Fluorene	86-73-7	NA	3.4
		Indeno(1,2,3-cd)py-rene	193-39-5	NA	3.4
		Naphthalene	91-20-3	0.059	5.6
		Phenanthrene	85-01-8	0.059	5.6
		Phenol	108-95-2	0.039	6.2
		Pyrene	129-00-0	0.067	8.2
K036	Still bottoms from toluene reclamation distillation in the production of disulfoton	Disulfoton	298-04-4	0.017	6.2
K037	Wastewater treatment sludges from the production of disulfoton	Disulfoton	298-04-4	0.017	6.2
		Toluene	108-88-3	0.080	10
K038	Wastewater from the washing and stripping of phorate production	Phorate	298-02-2	0.021	4.6
K039	Filter cake from the filtration of diethylphosphoro-dithioc acid in the production of phorate	NA	NA	CARBN, or CMBST	CMBST

Treatment Standards for Hazardous Wastes

13.4.1, 13.5

[*Note:* NA means not applicable]

Waste code	Waste description and treatment/regulatory subcategory[1]	Regulated hazardous constituent		Wastewaters	Nonwastewaters
		Common name	CAS[2] No.	Concentration[3] in mg/L; or technology code[4]	Concentration[5] in mg/kg unless noted as "mg/L TCLP"; or technology code[4]
K040	Wastewater treatment sludge from the production of phorate	Phorate	298-02-2	0.021	4.6
K041	Wastewater treatment sludge from the production of toxaphene	Toxaphene	8001-35-2	0.0095	2.6
K042	Heavy ends or distillation residues from the distillation of tetrachlorobenzene in the production of 2,4,5-T	o-Dichlorobenzene	95-50-1	0.088	6.0
		p-Dichlorobenzene	106-46-7	0.090	6.0
		Pentachlorobenzene	608-93-5	0.055	10
		1,2,4,5-Tetrachloro-benzene	95-94-3	0.055	14
		1,2,4-Trichloro-benzene	120-82-1	0.055	19
K043	2,6-Dichlorophenol waste from the production of 2,4-D	2,4-Dichlorophenol	120-83-2	0.044	14
		2,6-Dichlorophenol	187-65-0	0.044	14
		2,4,5-Trichlorophenol	95-95-4	0.18	7.4
		2,4,6-Trichlorophenol	88-06-2	0.035	7.4
		2,3,4,6-Tetrachloro-phenol	58-90-2	0.030	7.4
		Pentachlorophenol	87-86-5	0.089	7.4
		Tetrachloroethylene	127-18-4	0.056	6.0
		HxCDDs (All Hexachlorodibenzo-p-dioxins)	NA	0.000063	0.001
		HxCDFs (All Hexa-chlorodibenzofurans)	NA	0.000063	0.001
		PeCDDs (All Pentachlorodibenzo-p-dioxins)	NA	0.000063	0.001
		PeCDFs (All Penta-chlorodibenzofurans)	NA	0.000035	0.001
		TCDDs (All Tetra-chlorodibenzo-p-dioxins)	NA	0.000063	0.001
		TCDFs (All Tetra-chlorodibenzofurans)	NA	0.000063	0.001
K044	Wastewater treatment sludges from the manufacturing and processing of explosives	NA	NA	DEACT	DEACT
K045	Spent carbon from the treatment of wastewater containing explosives	NA	NA	DEACT	DEACT
K046	Wastewater treatment sludges from the manufacturing, formulation and loading of lead-based initiating compounds	Lead	7439-92-1	0.69	0.75 mg/L TCLP
K047	Pink/red water from TNT operations	NA	NA	DEACT	DEACT
K048	Dissolved air flotation (DAF) float from the petroleum refining industry	Benzene	71-43-2	0.14	10
		Benzo(a)pyrene	50-32-8	0.061	3.4

Treatment Standards for Hazardous Wastes

13.4.1, 13.5

[*Note:* NA means not applicable]

Waste code	Waste description and treatment/regulatory subcategory[1]	Regulated hazardous constituent: Common name	Regulated hazardous constituent: CAS[2] No.	Wastewaters Concentration[3] in mg/L; or technology code[4]	Nonwastewaters Concentration[5] in mg/kg unless noted as "mg/L TCLP"; or technology code[4]
		bis(2-Ethylhexyl) phthalate	117-81-7	0.28	28
		Chrysene	218-01-9	0.059	3.4
		Di-n-butyl phthalate	84-74-2	0.057	28
		Ethylbenzene	100-41-4	0.057	10
		Fluorene	86-73-7	0.059	NA
		Naphthalene	91-20-3	0.059	5.6
		Phenanthrene	85-01-8	0.059	5.6
		Phenol	108-95-2	0.039	6.2
		Pyrene	129-00-0	0.067	8.2
		Toluene	108-88-33	0.080	10
		Xylenes-mixed isomers (sum of o-, m-, and p-xylene concentrations)	1330-20-7	0.32	30
		Chromium (Total)	7440-47-3	2.77	0.60 mg/L TCLP
		Cyanides (Total)[7]	57-12-5	1.2	590
		Lead	7439-92-1	0.69	NA
		Nickel	7440-02-0	NA	11 mg/L TCLP
K049	Slop oil emulsion solids from the petroleum refining industry	Anthracene	120-12-7	0.059	3.4
		Benzene	71-43-2	0.14	10
		Benzo(a)pyrene	50-32-8	0.061	3.4
		bis(2-Ethylhexyl) phthalate	117-81-7	0.28	28
		Carbon disulfide	75-15-0	3.8	NA
		Chrysene	218-01-9	0.059	3.4
		2,4-Dimethylphenol	105-67-9	0.036	NA
		Ethylbenzene	100-41-4	0.057	10
		Naphthalene	91-20-3	0.059	5.6
		Phenanthrene	85-01-8	0.059	5.6
		Phenol	108-95-2	0.039	6.2
		Pyrene	129-00-0	0.067	8.2
		Toluene	108-88-3	0.080	10
		Xylenes-mixed isomers (sum of o-, m-, and p-xylene concentrations)	1330-20-7	0.32	30
		Cyanides (Total)[7]	57-12-5	1.2	590
		Chromium (Total)	7440-47-3	2.77	0.60 mg/L TCLP
		Lead	7439-92-1	0.69	NA
		Nickel	7440-02-0	NA	11 mg/L TCLP

Treatment Standards for Hazardous Wastes

13.4.1, 13.5

[*Note:* NA means not applicable]

Waste code	Waste description and treatment/regulatory subcategory[1]	Regulated hazardous constituent		Wastewaters	Nonwastewaters
		Common name	CAS[2] No.	Concentration[3] in mg/L; or technology code[4]	Concentration[5] in mg/kg unless noted as "mg/L TCLP"; or technology code[4]
K050	Heat exchanger bundle cleaning sludge from the petroleum refining industry	Benzo(a)pyrene	50-32-8	0.061	3.4
		Phenol	108-95-2	0.039	6.2
		Cyanides (Total)[7]	57-12-5	1.2	590
		Chromium (Total)	7440-47-3	2.77	0.60 mg/L TCLP
		Lead	7439-92-1	0.69	NA
		Nickel	7440-02-0	NA	11 mg/L TCLP
K051	API separator sludge from the petroleum refining industry	Acenaphthene	83-32-9	0.059	NA
		Anthracene	120-12-7	0.059	3.4
		Benz(a)anthracene	56-55-3	0.059	3.4
		Benzene	71-43-2	0.14	10
		Benzo(a)pyrene	50-32-8	0.061	3.4
		bis(2-Ethylhexyl) phthalate	117-81-7	0.28	28
		Chrysene	218-01-9	0.059	3.4
		Di-n-butyl phthalate	105-67-9	0.057	28
		Ethylbenzene	100-41-4	0.057	10
		Fluorene	86-73-7	0.059	NA
		Naphthalene	91-20-3	0.059	5.6
		Phenanthrene	85-01-8	0.059	5.6
		Phenol	108-95-2	0.039	6.2
		Pyrene	129-00-0	0.067	8.2
		Toluene	108-88-3	0.08	10
		Xylenes-mixed isomers (sum of o-, m-, and p-xylene concentrations)	1330-20-7	0.32	30
		Cyanides (Total)[7]	57-12-5	1.2	590
		Chromium (Total)	7440-47-3	2.77	0.60 mg/L TCLP
		Lead	7439-92-1	0.69	NA
		Nickel	7440-02-0	NA	11 mg/L TCLP
K052	Tank bottoms (leaded) from the petroleum refining industry	Benzene	71-43-2	0.14	10
		Benzo(a)pyrene	50-32-8	0.061	3.4
		o-Cresol	95-48-7	0.11	5.6
		m-Cresol (difficult to distinguish from p-cresol)	108-39-4	0.77	5.6
		p-Cresol (difficult to distinguish from m-cresol)	106-44-5	0.77	5.6
		2,4-Dimethylphenol	105-67-9	0.036	NA
		Ethylbenzene	100-41-4	0.057	10
		Naphthalene	91-20-3	0.059	5.6
		Phenanthrene	85-01-8	0.059	5.6
		Phenol	108-95-2	0.039	6.2

Treatment Standards for Hazardous Wastes

13.4.1, 13.5

[*Note:* NA means not applicable]

Waste code	Waste description and treatment/regulatory subcategory[1]	Regulated hazardous constituent		Wastewaters Concentration[3] in mg/L; or technology code[4]	Nonwastewaters Concentration[5] in mg/kg unless noted as "mg/L TCLP"; or technology code[4]
		Common name	CAS[2] No.		
		Toluene	108-88-3	0.08	10
		Xylenes-mixed isomers (sum of o-, m-, and p-xylene concentrations)	1330-20-7	0.32	30
		Chromium (Total)	7440-47-3	2.77	0.60 mg/L TCLP
		Cyanides (Total)[7]	57-12-5	1.2	590
		Lead	7439-92-1	0.69	NA
		Nickel	7440-02-0	NA	11 mg/L TCLP
K060	Ammonia still lime sludge from coking operations	Benzene	71-43-2	0.14	10
		Benzo(a)pyrene	50-32-8	0.061	3.4
		Naphthalene	91-20-3	0.059	5.6
		Phenol	108-95-2	0.039	6.2
		Cyanides (Total)[7]	57-12-5	1.2	590
K061	Emission control dust/sludge from the primary production of steel in electric furnaces	Antimony	7440-36-0	NA	1.15 mg/L TCLP
		Arsenic	7440-38-2	NA	5.0 mg/L TCLP
		Barium	7440-39-3	NA	21 mg/L TCLP
		Beryllium	7440-41-7	NA	1.22 mg/L TCLP
		Cadmium	7440-43-9	0.69	0.11 mg/L TCLP
		Chromium (Total)	7440-47-3	2.77	0.60 mg/L TCLP
		Lead	7439-92-1	0.69	0.75 mg/L TCLP
		Mercury	7439-97-6	NA	0.025 mg/L TCLP
		Nickel	7440-02-0	3.98	11 mg/L TCLP
		Selenium	7782-49-2	NA	5.7 mg/L TCLP
		Silver	7440-22-4	NA	0.14 mg/L TCLP
		Thallium	7440-28-0	NA	0.20 mg/L TCLP
		Zinc	7440-66-6	NA	4.3 mg/L TCLP
K062	Spent pickle liquor generated by steel finishing operations of facilities within the iron and steel industry (SIC Codes 331 and 332)	Chromium (Total)	7440-47-3	2.77	0.60 mg/L TCLP
		Lead	7439-92-1	0.69	0.75 mg/L TCLP
		Nickel	7440-02-0	3.98	NA
K069	Emission control dust/sludge from secondary lead smelting—Calcium Sulfate (Low Lead) Subcategory	Cadmium	7440-43-9	0.69	0.11 mg/L TCLP
		Lead	7439-92-1	0.69	0.75 mg/L TCLP
	Emission control dust/sludge from secondary lead smelting—Non-Calcium Sulfate (High Lead) Subcategory	NA	NA	NA	RLEAD
K071	K071 (Brine purification muds from the mercury cell process in chlorine production, where separately prepurified brine is not used) nonwastewaters that are residues from RMERC	Mercury	7439-97-6	NA	0.20 mg/L TCLP
	K071 (Brine purification muds from the mercury cell process in chlorine production, where separately prepurified brine is not used) nonwastewaters that are not residues from RMERC	Mercury	7439-97-6	NA	0.025 mg/L TCLP
	All K071 wastewaters	Mercury	7439-97-6	0.15	NA

Treatment Standards for Hazardous Wastes

13.4.1, 13.5

[*Note:* NA means not applicable]

Waste code	Waste description and treatment/regulatory subcategory[1]	Regulated hazardous constituent		Wastewaters	Nonwastewaters
		Common name	CAS[2] No.	Concentration[3] in mg/L; or technology code[4]	Concentration[5] in mg/kg unless noted as "mg/L TCLP"; or technology code[4]
K073	Chlorinated hydrocarbon waste from the purification step of the diaphragm cell process using graphite anodes in chlorine production	Carbon tetrachloride	56-23-5	0.057	6.0
		Chloroform	67-66-3	0.046	6.0
		Hexachloroethane	67-72-1	0.055	30
		Tetrachloroethylene	127-18-4	0.056	6.0
		1,1,1-Trichloroethane	71-55-6	0.054	6.0
K083	Distillation bottoms from aniline production	Aniline	62-53-3	0.81	14
		Benzene	71-43-2	0.14	10
		Cyclohexanone	108-94-1	0.36	NA
		Diphenylamine (difficult to distinguish from diphenylnitrosamine)	122-39-4	0.92	13
		Diphenylnitrosamine (difficult to distinguish from diphenylamine)	86-30-6	0.92	13
		Nitrobenzene	98-95-3	0.068	14
		Phenol	108-95-2	0.039	6.2
		Nickel	7440-02-0	3.98	11 mg/L TCLP
K084	Wastewater treatment sludges generated during the production of veterinary pharmaceuticals from arsenic or organo-arsenic compounds	Arsenic	7440-38-2	1.4	5.0 mg/L TCLP
K085	Distillation or fractionation column bottoms from the production of chlorobenzenes	Benzene	71-43-2	0.14	10
		Chlorobenzene	108-90-7	0.057	6.0
		m-Dichlorobenzene	541-73-1	0.036	6.0
		o-Dichlorobenzene	95-50-1	0.088	6.0
		p-Dichlorobenzene	106-46-7	0.090	6.0
		Hexachlorobenzene	118-74-1	0.055	10
		Total PCBs (sum of all PCB isomers, or all Aroclors)	1336-36-3	0.10	10
		Pentachlorobenzene	608-93-5	0.055	10
		1,2,4,5-Tetrachloro-benzene	95-94-3	0.055	14
		1,2,4-Trichloro-benzene	120-82-1	0.055	19
K086	Solvent wastes and sludges, caustic washes and sludges, or water washes and sludges from cleaning tubs and equipment used in the formulation of ink from pigments, driers, soaps, and stabilizers containing chromium and lead	Acetone	67-64-1	0.28	160
		Acetophenone	96-86-2	0.010	9.7
		bis(2-Ethylhexyl) phthalate	117-81-7	0.28	28
		n-Butyl alcohol	71-36-3	5.6	2.6
		Butylbenzyl phthalate	85-68-7	0.017	28
		Cyclohexanone	108-94-1	0.36	NA

Treatment Standards for Hazardous Wastes

13.4.1, 13.5

[*Note:* NA means not applicable]

Waste code	Waste description and treatment/regulatory subcategory[1]	Regulated hazardous constituent: Common name	Regulated hazardous constituent: CAS[2] No.	Wastewaters Concentration[3] in mg/L; or technology code[4]	Nonwastewaters Concentration[5] in mg/kg unless noted as "mg/L TCLP"; or technology code[4]
		o-Dichlorobenzene	95-50-1	0.088	6.0
		Diethyl phthalate	84-66-2	0.20	28
		Dimethyl phthalate	131-11-3	0.047	28
		Di-n-butyl phthalate	84-74-2	0.057	28
		Di-n-octyl phthalate	117-84-0	0.017	28
		Ethyl acetate	141-78-6	0.34	33
		Ethylbenzene	100-41-4	0.057	10
		Menthanol	67-56-1	5.6	NA
		Methyl ethyl ketone	78-93-3	0.28	36
		Methyl isobutyl ketone	108-10-1	0.14	33
		Methylene chloride	75-09-2	0.089	30
		Naphthalene	91-20-3	0.059	5.6
		Nitrobenzene	98-95-3	0.068	14
		Toluene	108-88-3	0.080	10
		1,1,1-Trichloroethane	71-55-6	0.054	6.0
		Trichloroethylene	79-01-6	0.054	6.0
		Xylenes-mixed isomers (sum of o-, m-, and p-xylene concentrations)	1330-20-7	0.32	30
		Chromium (Total)	7440-47-3	2.77	0.60 mg/L TCLP
		Cyanides (Total)[7]	57-12-5	1.2	590
		Lead	7439-92-1	0.69	0.75 mg/L TCLP
K087	Decanter tank tar sludge from coking operations	Acenaphthylene	208-96-8	0.059	3.4
		Benzene	71-43-2	0.14	10
		Chrysene	218-01-9	0.059	3.4
		Fluoranthene	206-44-0	0.068	3.4
		Indeno(1,2,3-cd)pyrene	193-39-5	0.0055	3.4
		Naphthalene	91-20-3	0.059	5.6
		Phenanthrene	85-01-8	0.059	5.6
		Toluene	108-88-3	0.080	10
		Xylenes-mixed isomers (sum of o-, m-, and p-xylene concentrations)	1330-20-7	0.32	30
		Lead	7439-92-1	0.69	0.75 mg/L TCLP
K088	Spent potliners from primary aluminum reduction	Acenaphthene	83-32-9	0.059	3.4
		Anthracene	120-12-7	0.059	3.4
		Benz(a)anthracene	56-55-3	0.059	3.4
		Benzo(a)pyrene	50-32-8	0.061	3.4
		Benzo(b)fluoranthene	205-99-2	0.11	6.8
		Benzo(k)fluoranthene	207-08-9	0.11	6.8

Treatment Standards for Hazardous Wastes

13.4.1, 13.5

[*Note:* NA means not applicable]

Waste code	Waste description and treatment/regulatory subcategory[1]	Regulated hazardous constituent		Wastewaters	Nonwastewaters
		Common name	CAS[2] No.	Concentration[3] in mg/L; or technology code[4]	Concentration[5] in mg/kg unless noted as "mg/L TCLP"; or technology code[4]
		Benzo(g,h,i)perylene	191-24-2	0.0055	1.8
		Chrysene	218-01-9	0.059	3.4
		Dibenz(a,h)anthracene	53-70-3	0.055	8.2
		Fluoranthene	206-44-0	0.068	3.4
		Indeno(1,2,3-cd)pyrene	193-39-5	0.0055	3.4
		Phenanthrene	85-01-8	0.059	5.6
		Pyrene	129-00-0	0.067	8.2
		Antimony	7440-36-0	1.9	1.15 mg/L TCLP
		Arsenic	7440-38-2	1.4	26.1
		Barium	7440-39-3	1.2	21 mg/L TCLP
		Beryllium	7440-41-7	0.82	1.22 mg/L TCLP
		Cadmium	7440-43-9	0.69	0.11 mg/L TCLP
		Chromium (Total)	7440-47-3	2.77	0.60 mg/L TCLP
		Lead	7439-92-1	0.69	0.75 mg/L TCLP
		Mercury	7439-97-6	0.15	0.025 mg/L TCLP
		Nickel	7440-02-0	3.98	11 mg/L TCLP
		Selenium	7782-49-2	0.82	5.7 mg/L TCLP
		Silver	7440-22-4	0.43	0.14 mg/L TCLP
		Cyanide (Total)[7]	57-12-5	1.2	590
		Cyanide (Amenable)[7]	57-12-5	0.86	30
		Fluoride	16984-48-8	35	NA
K093	Distillation light ends from the production of phthalic anhydride from ortho-xylene	Phthalic anhydride (measured as Phthalic acid or Terephthalic acid)	100-21-0	0.055	28
		Phthalic anhydride (measured as Phthalic acid or Terephthalic acid)	85-44-9	0.055	28
K094	Distillation bottoms from the production of phthalic anhydride from ortho-xylene	Phthalic anhydride (measured as Phthalic acid or Terephthalic acid)	100-21-0	0.055	28
		Phthalic anhydride (measured as Phthalic acid or Terephthalic acid)	85-44-9	0.055	28
K095	Distillation bottoms from the production of 1,1,1-trichloroethane	Hexachloroethane	67-72-1	0.055	30
		Pentachloroethane	76-01-7	0.055	6.0
		1,1,1,2-Tetrachloroethane	630-20-6	0.057	6.0
		1,1,2,2-Tetrachloroethane	79-34-6	0.057	6.0
		Tetrachloroethylene	127-18-4	0.056	6.0

Treatment Standards for Hazardous Wastes

13.4.1, 13.5

[*Note:* NA means not applicable]

Waste code	Waste description and treatment/regulatory subcategory[1]	Regulated hazardous constituent		Wastewaters	Nonwastewaters
		Common name	CAS[2] No.	Concentration[3] in mg/L; or technology code[4]	Concentration[5] in mg/kg unless noted as "mg/L TCLP"; or technology code[4]
		1,1,2-Trichloroethane	79-00-5	0.054	6.0
		Trichloroethylene	79-01-6	0.054	6.0
K096	Heavy ends from the heavy ends column from the production of 1,1,1-trichloroethane	m-Dichlorobenzene	541-73-1	0.036	6.0
		Pentachloroethane	76-01-7	0.055	6.0
		1,1,1,2-Tetrachloroethane	630-20-6	0.057	6.0
		1,1,2,2-Tetrachloroethane	79-34-6	0.057	6.0
		Tetrachloroethylene	127-18-4	0.056	6.0
		1,2,4-Trichlorobenzene	120-82-1	0.055	19
		1,1,2-Trichloroethane	79-00-5	0.054	6.0
		Trichloroethylene	79-01-6	0.054	6.0
K097	Vacuum stripper discharge from the chlordane chlorinator in the production of chlordane	Chlordane (alpha and gamma isomers)	57-74-9	0.0033	0.26
		Heptachlor	76-44-8	0.0012	0.066
		Heptachlor epoxide	1024-57-3	0.016	0.066
		Hexachlorocyclopentadiene	77-47-4	0.057	2.4
K098	Untreated process wastewater from the production of toxaphene	Toxaphene	8001-35-2	0.0095	2.6
K099	Untreated wastewater from the production of 2,4-D	2,4-Dichlorophenoxyacetic acid	94-75-7	0.72	10
		HxCDDs (All Hexachlorodibenzo-p-dioxins)	NA	0.000063	0.001
		HxCDFs (All Hexachlorodibenzofurans)	NA	0.000063	0.001
		PeCDDs (All Pentachlorodibenzo-p-dioxins)	NA	0.000063	0.001
		PeCDFs (All Pentachlorodibenzofurans)	NA	0.000035	0.001
		TCDDs (All Tetrachlorodibenzo-p-dioxins)	NA	0.000063	0.001
		TCDFs (All Tetrachlorodibenzofurans)	NA	0.000063	0.001
K100	Waste leaching solution from acid leaching of emission control dust/sludge from secondary lead smelting	Cadmium	7440-43-9	0.69	0.11 mg/L TCLP
		Chromium (Total)	7440-47-3	2.77	0.60 mg/L TCLP
		Lead	7439-92-1	0.69	0.75 mg/L TCLP

Treatment Standards for Hazardous Wastes

13.4.1, 13.5

[*Note:* NA means not applicable]

Waste code	Waste description and treatment/regulatory subcategory[1]	Regulated hazardous constituent		Wastewaters Concentration[3] in mg/L; or technology code[4]	Nonwastewaters Concentration[5] in mg/kg unless noted as "mg/L TCLP"; or technology code[4]
		Common name	CAS[2] No.		
K101	Distillation tar residues from the distillation of aniline-based compounds in the production of veterinary pharmaceuticals from arsenic or organo-arsenic compounds	o-Nitroaniline	88-74-4	0.27	14
		Arsenic	7440-38-2	1.4	5.0 mg/L TCLP
		Cadmium	7440-43-9	0.69	NA
		Lead	7439-92-1	0.69	NA
		Mercury	7439-97-6	0.15	NA
K102	Residue from the use of activated carbon for decolorization in the production of veterinary pharmaceuticals from arsenic or organo-arsenic compounds	o-Nitrophenol	88-75-5	0.028	13
		Arsenic	7440-38-2	1.4	5.0 mg/L TCLP
		Cadmium	7440-43-9	0.69	NA
		Lead	7439-92-1	0.69	NA
		Mercury	7439-97-6	0.15	NA
K103	Process residues from aniline extraction from the production of aniline	Aniline	62-53-3	0.81	14
		Benzene	71-43-2	0.14	10
		2,4-Dinitrophenol	51-28-5	0.12	160
		Nitrobenzene	98-95-3	0.068	14
		Phenol	108-95-2	0.039	6.2
K104	Combined wastewater streams generated from nitrobenzene/aniline production	Aniline	62-53-3	0.81	14
		Benzene	71-43-2	0.14	10
		2,4-Dinitrophenol	51-28-5	0.12	160
		Nitrobenzene	98-95-3	0.068	14
		Phenol	108-95-2	0.039	6.2
		Cyanides (Total)[7]	57-12-5	1.2	590
K105	Separated aqueous stream from the reactor product washing step in the production of chlorobenzenes	Benzene	71-43-2	0.14	10
		Chlorobenzene	108-90-7	0.057	6.0
		2-Chlorophenol	95-57-8	0.044	5.7
		o-Dichlorobenzene	95-50-1	0.088	6.0
		p-Dichlorobenzene	106-46-7	0.090	6.0
		Phenol	108-95-2	0.039	6.2
		2,4,5-Trichlorophenol	95-95-4	0.18	7.4
		2,4,6-Trichlorophenol	88-06-2	0.035	7.4
K106	K106 (wastewater treatment sludge from the mercury cell process in chlorine production) nonwastewaters that contain greater than or equal to 260 mg/kg total mercury	Mercury	7439-97-6	NA	RMERC
	K106 (wastewater treatment sludge from the mercury cell process in chlorine production) nonwastewaters that contain less than 260 mg/kg total mercury that are residues from RMERC	Mercury	7439-97-6	NA	0.20 mg/L TCLP
	Other K106 nonwastewaters that contain less than 260 mg/kg total mercury and are not residues from RMERC	Mercury	7439-97-6	NA	0.025 mg/L TCLP
	All K106 wastewaters	Mercury	7439-97-6	0.15	NA

Treatment Standards for Hazardous Wastes

13.4.1, 13.5

[*Note:* NA means not applicable]

Waste code	Waste description and treatment/regulatory subcategory[1]	Regulated hazardous constituent		Wastewaters	Nonwastewaters
		Common name	CAS[2] No.	Concentration[3] in mg/L; or technology code[4]	Concentration[5] in mg/kg unless noted as "mg/L TCLP"; or technology code[4]
K107	Column bottoms from product separation from the production of 1,1-dimethylhydrazine (UDMH) from carboxylic acid hydrazides	NA	NA	CMBST; or CHOXD fb CARBN; or BIODG fb CARBN	CMBST
K108	Condensed column overheads from product separation and condensed reactor vent gases from the production of 1,1-dimethylhydrazide (UDMH) from carboxylic acid hydrazides	NA	NA	CMBST; or CHOXD fb CARBN; or BIODG fb CARBN	CMBST
K109	Spent filter cartridges from product purification from the production of 1,1-dimethyhydrazine (UDMH) from carboxylic acid hydrazides	NA	NA	CMBST; or CHOXD fb CARBN; or BIODG fb CARBN	CMBST
K110	Condensed column overheads from intermediate separation from the production of 1,1-dimethylhydrazine (UDMH) from carboxylic acid hydrazides	NA	NA	CMBST; or CHOXD fb CARBN; or BIODG fb CARBN	CMBST
K111	Product washwaters from the production of dinitrotoluene via nitration of toluene	2,4-Dinitrotoluene	121-14-2	0.32	140
		2,6-Dinitrotoluene	606-20-2	0.55	28
K112	Reaction by-product water from the drying column in the production of toluenediamine via hydrogenation of dinitrotoluene	NA	NA	CMBST; or CHOXD fb CARBN; or BIODG fb CARBN	CMBST
K113	Condensed liquid light ends from the purification of toluenediamine in the production of toluenediamine via hydrogenation of dinitrotoluene	NA	NA	CARBN; or CMBST	CMBST
K114	Vicinals from the purification of toluenediamine in the production of toluenediamine via hydrogenation of dinitrotoluene	NA	NA	CARBN; or CMBST	CMBST
K115	Heavy ends from the purification of toluenediamine in the production of toluenediamine via hydrogenation of dinitrotoluene	Nickel	7440-02-0	3.98	11 mg/L TCLP
		NA	NA	CARBN; or CMBST	CMBST
K116	Organic condensate from the solvent recovery column in the production of toluene diisocyanate via phosgenation of toluenediamine	NA	NA	CARBN; or CMBST	CMBST
K117	Wastewater from the reactor vent gas scrubber in the production of ethylene dibromide via bromination of ethene	Methyl bromide (Bromomethane)	74-83-9	0.11	15
		Chloroform	67-66-3	0.046	6.0
		Ethylene dibromide (1,2-Dibromoethane)	106-93-4	0.028	15

PART 268—Subpart D

Treatment Standards for Hazardous Wastes

13.4.1, 13.5

[*Note:* NA means not applicable]

Waste code	Waste description and treatment/regulatory subcategory[1]	Regulated hazardous constituent		Wastewaters	Nonwastewaters
		Common name	CAS[2] No.	Concentration[3] in mg/L; or technology code[4]	Concentration[5] in mg/kg unless noted as "mg/L TCLP"; or technology code[4]
K118	Spent absorbent solids from purification of ethylene dibromide in the production of ethylene dibromide via bromination of ethene	Methyl bromide (Bromomethane)	74-83-9	0.11	15
		Chloroform	67-66-3	0.046	6.0
		Ethylene dibromide (1,2-Dibromoethane)	106-93-4	0.028	15
K123	Process wastewater (including supernates, filtrates, and washwaters) from the production of ethylenebisdithiocarbamic acid and its salts	NA	NA	CMBST; or CHOXD fb (BIODG or CARBN)	CMBST
K124	Reactor vent scrubber water from the production of ethylenebisdithiocarbamic acid and its salts	NA	NA	CMBST; or CHOXD fb (BIODG or CARBN)	CMBST
K125	Filtration, evaporation, and centrifugation solids from the production of ethylenebisdithiocarbamic acid and its salts	NA	NA	CMBST; or CHOXD fb (BIODG or CARBN)	CMBST
K126	Baghouse dust and floor sweepings in milling and packaging operations from the production or formulation of ethylenebisdithiocarbamic acid and its salts	NA	NA	CMBST; or CHOXD fb (BIODG or CARBN)	CMBST
K131	Wastewater from the reactor and spent sulfuric acid from the acid dryer from the production of methyl bromide	Methyl bromide (Bromomethane)	74-83-9	0.11	15
K132	Spent absorbent and wastewater separator solids from the production of methyl bromide	Methyl bromide (Bromomethane)	74-83-9	0.11	15
K136	Still bottoms from the purification of ethylene dibromide in the production of ethylene dibromide via bromination of ethene	Methyl bromide (Bromomethane)	74-83-9	0.11	15
		Chloroform	67-66-3	0.046	6.0
		Ethylene dibromide (1,2-Dibromoethane)	106-93-4	0.028	15
K141	Process residues from the recovery of coal tar, including, but not limited to, collecting sump residues from the production of coke or the recovery of coke by-products produced from coal. This listing does not include K087 (decanter tank tar sludge from coking operations)	Benzene	71-43-2	0.14	10
		Benz(a)anthracene	56-55-3	0.059	3.4
		Benzo(a)pyrene	50-2-8	0.061	3.4
		Benzo(b)fluoranthene (difficult to distinguish from benzo(k)fluoranthene)	205-99-2	0.11	6.8
		Benzo(k)fluoranthene (difficult to distinguish from benzo(b)fluoranthene)	207-08-9	0.11	6.8
		Chrysene	218-01-9	0.059	3.4
		Dibenz(a,h)anthracene	53-70-3	0.055	8.2

PART 268—Subpart D

Treatment Standards for Hazardous Wastes

13.4.1, 13.5

[*Note:* NA means not applicable]

Waste code	Waste description and treatment/regulatory subcategory[1]	Regulated hazardous constituent: Common name	Regulated hazardous constituent: CAS[2] No.	Wastewaters Concentration[3] in mg/L; or technology code[4]	Nonwastewaters Concentration[5] in mg/kg unless noted as "mg/L TCLP"; or technology code[4]
		Indeno(1,2,3-cd)pyrene	193-39-5	0.0055	3.4
K142	Tar storage tank residues from the production of coke from coal or from the recovery of coke by-products produced from coal	Benzene	71-43-2	0.14	10
		Benz(a)anthracene	56-55-3	0.059	3.4
		Benzo(a)pyrene	50-32-8	0.061	3.4
		Benzo(b)fluoranthene (difficult to distinguish from benzo(k)fluoranthene)	205-99-2	0.11	6.8
		Benzo(k)fluoranthene (difficult to distinguish from benzo(b)fluoranthene)	207-08-9	0.11	6.8
		Chrysene	218-01-9	0.059	3.4
		Dibenz(a,h)anthracene	53-70-3	0.055	8.2
		Indeno(1,2,3-cd)pyrene	193-39-5	0.0055	3.4
K143	Process residues from the recovery of light oil, including, but not limited to, those generated in stills, decanters, and wash oil recovery units from the recovery of coke by-products produced from coal	Benzene	71-43-2	0.14	10
		Benz(a)anthracene	56-55-3	0.059	3.4
		Benzo(a)pyrene	50-32-8	0.061	3.4
		Benzo(b)fluoranthene (difficult to distinguish from benzo(k)fluoranthene)	205-99-2	0.11	6.8
		Benzo(k)fluoranthene (difficult to distinguish from benzo(b)fluoranthene)	207-08-9	0.11	6.8
		Chrysene	218-01-9	0.059	3.4
K144	Wastewater sump residues from light oil refining, including, but not limited to, intercepting or contamination sump sludges from the recovery of coke by-products produced from coal	Benzene	71-43-2	0.14	10
		Benz(a)anthracene	56-55-3	0.059	3.4
		Benzo(a)pyrene	50-32-8	0.061	3.4
		Benzo(b)fluoranthene (difficult to distinguish from benzo(k)fluoranthene)	205-99-2	0.11	6.8
		Benzo(k)fluoranthene (difficult to distinguish from benzo(b)fluoranthene)	207-08-9	0.11	6.8
		Chrysene	218-01-9	0.059	3.4
		Dibenz(a,h)anthracene	53-70-3	0.055	8.2
K145	Residues from naphthalene collection and recovery operations from the recovery of coke by-products produced from coal	Benzene	71-43-2	0.14	10
		Benz(a)anthracene	56-55-3	0.059	3.4
		Benzo(a)pyrene	50-32-8	0.061	3.4

Treatment Standards for Hazardous Wastes

13.4.1, 13.5

[*Note:* NA means not applicable]

Waste code	Waste description and treatment/regulatory subcategory[1]	Regulated hazardous constituent		Wastewaters	Nonwastewaters
		Common name	CAS[2] No.	Concentration[3] in mg/L; or technology code[4]	Concentration[5] in mg/kg unless noted as"mg/L TCLP"; or technology code[4]
		Chrysene	218-01-9	0.059	3.4
		Dibenz(a,h)anthracene	53-70-3	0.055	8.2
		Naphthalene	91-20-3	0.059	5.6
K147	Tar storage tank residues from coal tar refining	Benzene	71-43-2	0.14	10
		Benz(a)anthracene	56-55-3	0.059	3.4
		Benzo(a)pyrene	50-32-8	0.061	3.4
		Benzo(b)fluoranthene (difficult to distinguish from benzo(k)fluoranthene)	205-99-2	0.11	6.8
		Benzo(k)fluoranthene (difficult to distinguish from benzo(b)fluoranthene)	207-08-9	0.11	6.8
		Chrysene	218-01-9	0.059	3.4
		Dibenz(a,h)anthracene	53-70-3	0.055	8.2
		Indeno(1,2,3-cd)pyrene	193-39-5	0.0055	3.4
K148	Residues from coal tar distillation, including, but not limited to, still bottoms	Benz(a)anthracene	56-55-3	0.059	3.4
		Benzo(a)pyrene	50-32-8	0.061	3.4
		Benzo(b)fluoranthene (difficult to distinguish from benzo(k)fluoranthene)	205-99-2	0.11	6.8
		Benzo(k)fluoranthene (difficult to distinguish from benzo(b)fluoranthene)	207-08-9	0.11	6.8
		Chrysene	218-01-9	0.059	3.4
		Dibenz(a,h)anthracene	53-70-3	0.055	8.2
		Indeno(1,2,3-cd)pyrene	193-39-5	0.0055	3.4
K149	Distillation bottoms from the production of alpha- (or methyl-) chlorinated toluenes, ring-chlorinated toluenes, benzoyl chlorides, and compounds with mixtures of these functional groups. (This waste does not include still bottoms from the distillations of benzyl chloride.)	Chlorobenzene	108-90-7	0.057	6.0
		Chloroform	67-66-3	0.046	6.0
		Chloromethane	74-87-3	0.19	30
		p-Dichlorobenzene	106-46-7	0.090	6.0
		Hexachlorobenzene	118-74-1	0.055	10
		Pentachlorobenzene	608-93-5	0.055	10
		1,2,4,5-Tetrachloro-benzene	95-94-3	0.055	14
		Toluene	108-88-3	0.080	10
K150	Organic residuals, excluding spent carbon adsorbent, from the spent chlorine gas and hydrochloric acid recovery processes associated with the production of alpha- (or methyl-) chlorinated toluenes, ring-chlorinated toluenes, benzoyl chlorides, and compounds with mixtures of these functional groups	Carbon tetrachloride	56-23-5	0.057	6.0
		Chloroform	67-66-3	0.046	6.0
		Chloromethane	74-87-3	0.19	30
		p-Dichlorobenzene	106-46-7	0.090	6.0
		Hexachlorobenzene	118-74-1	0.055	10
		Pentachlorobenzene	608-93-5	0.055	10

Treatment Standards for Hazardous Wastes

13.4.1, 13.5

[*Note:* NA means not applicable]

Waste code	Waste description and treatment/regulatory subcategory[1]	Regulated hazardous constituent		Wastewaters	Nonwastewaters
		Common name	CAS[2] No.	Concentration[3] in mg/L; or technology code[4]	Concentration[5] in mg/kg unless noted as "mg/L TCLP"; or technology code[4]
		1,2,4,5-Tetrachlorobenzene	95-94-3	0.055	14
		1,1,2,2-Tetrachloroethane	79-34-5	0.057	6.0
		Tetrachloroethylene	127-18-4	0.056	6.0
		1,2,4-Trichlorobenzene	120-82-1	0.055	19
K151	Wastewater treatment sludges, excluding neutralization and biological sludges, generated during the treatment of wastewaters from the production of alpha- (or methyl-) chlorinated toluenes, ring-chlorinated toluenes, benzoyl chlorides, and compounds with mixtures of these functional groups	Benzene	71-43-2	0.14	10
		Carbon tetrachloride	56-23-5	0.057	6.0
		Chloroform	67-66-3	0.046	6.0
		Hexachlorobenzene	118-74-1	0.055	10
		Pentachlorobenzene	608-93-5	0.055	10
		1,2,4,5-Tetrachlorobenzene	95-94-3	0.055	14
		Tetrachloroethylene	127-18-4	0.056	6.0
		Toluene	108-88-3	0.080	10
K156	Organic waste (including heavy ends, still bottoms, light ends, spent solvents, filtrates, and decantates) from the production of carbamates and carbamoyl oximes	Acetonitrile	75-05-8	5.6	1.8
		Acetophenone	98-86-2	0.010	9.7
		Aniline	62-53-3	0.81	14
		Benomyl	17804-35-2	0.056	1.4
		Benzene	71-43-2	0.14	10
		Carbaryl	63-25-2	0.006	0.14
		Carbenzadim	10605-21-7	0.056	1.4
		Carbofuran	1563-66-2	0.006	0.14
		Carbosulfan	55285-14-8	0.028	1.4
		Chlorobenzene	108-90-7	0.057	6.0
		Chloroform	67-66-3	0.046	6.0
		o-Dichlorobenzene	95-50-1	0.088	6.0
		Methomyl	16752-77-5	0.028	0.14
		Methylene chloride	75-09-2	0.089	30
		Methyl ethyl ketone	78-93-3	0.28	36
		Naphthalene	91-20-3	0.059	5.6
		Phenol	108-95-2	0.039	6.2
		Pyridine	110-86-1	0.014	16
		Toluene	108-88-3	0.080	10
		Triethylamine	121-44-8	0.081	1.5
K157	Wastewaters (including scrubber waters, condenser waters, washwaters, and separation waters) from the production of carbamates and carbamoyl oximes	Carbon tetrachloride	56-23-5	0.057	6.0
		Chloroform	67-66-3	0.046	6.0
		Chloromethane	74-87-3	0.19	30
		Methomyl	16752-77-5	0.028	0.14
		Methylene chloride	75-09-2	0.089	30
		Methyl ethyl ketone	78-93-3	0.28	36
		Pyridine	110-86-1	0.014	16
		Triethylamine	121-44-8	0.081	1.5

Treatment Standards for Hazardous Wastes

13.4.1, 13.5

[*Note:* NA means not applicable]

Waste code	Waste description and treatment/regulatory subcategory[1]	Regulated hazardous constituent		Wastewaters	Nonwastewaters
		Common name	CAS[2] No.	Concentration[3] in mg/L; or technology code[4]	Concentration[5] in mg/kg unless noted as "mg/L TCLP"; or technology code[4]
K158	Bag house dusts and filter/separation solids from the production of carbamates and carbamoyl oximes	Benomyl	17804-35-2	0.056	1.4
		Benzene	71-43-2	0.14	10
		Carbenzadim	10605-21-7	0.056	1.4
		Carbofuran	1563-66-2	0.006	0.14
		Carbosulfan	55285-14-8	0.028	1.4
		Chloroform	67-66-3	0.046	6.0
		Methylene chloride	75-09-2	0.089	30
		Phenol	108-95-2	0.039	6.2
K159	Organics from the treatment of thiocarbamate wastes	Benzene	71-43-2	0.14	10
		Butylate	2008-41-5	0.042	1.4
		EPTC (Eptam)	759-94-4	0.042	1.4
		Molinate	2212-67-1	0.042	1.4
		Pebulate	1114-71-2	0.042	1.4
		Vernolate	1929-77-7	0.042	1.4
K161	Purification solids (including filtration, evaporation, and centrifugation solids), baghouse dust and floor sweepings from the production of dithiocarbamate acids and their salts	Antimony	7440-36-0	1.9	1.15 mg/L TCLP
		Arsenic	7440-38-2	1.4	5.0 mg/L TCLP
		Carbon disulfide	75-15-0	3.8	4.8 mg/L TCLP
		Dithiocarbamates (total)	NA	0.028	28
		Lead	7439-92-1	0.69	0.75 mg/L TCLP
		Nickel	7440-02-0	3.98	11.0 mg/L TCLP
		Selenium	7782-49-2	0.82	5.7 mg/L TCLP
K169	Crude oil tank sediment from petroleum refining operations	Benz(a)anthracene	56-55-3	0.059	3.4
		Benzene	71-43-2	0.14	10
		Benzo(g,h,i)perylene	191-24-2	0.0055	1.8
		Chrysene	218-01-9	0.059	3.4
		Ethyl benzene	100-41-4	0.057	10
		Fluorene	86-73-7	0.059	3.4
		Naphthalene	91-20-3	0.059	5.6
		Phenanthrene	85-01-8	0.059	5.6
		Pyrene	129-00-0	0.067	8.2
		Toluene (Methyl Benzene)	108-88-3	0.080	10
		Xylene(s) (Total)	1330-20-7	0.32	30
K170	Clarified slurry oil sediment from petroleum refining operations	Benz(a)anthracene	56-55-3	0.059	3.4
		Benzene	71-43-2	0.14	10
		Benzo(g,h,i)perylene	191-24-2	0.0055	1.8
		Chrysene	218-01-9	0.059	3.4
		Dibenz(a,h)anthracene	53-70-3	0.055	8.2
		Ethyl benzene	100-41-4	0.057	10
		Fluorene	86-73-7	0.059	3.4
		Indeno(1,2,3,-cd)pyrene	193-39-5	0.0055	3.4

Treatment Standards for Hazardous Wastes

13.4.1, 13.5

[*Note:* NA means not applicable]

Waste code	Waste description and treatment/regulatory subcategory[1]	Regulated hazardous constituent		Wastewaters	Nonwastewaters
		Common name	CAS[2] No.	Concentration[3] in mg/L; or technology code[4]	Concentration[5] in mg/kg unless noted as "mg/L TCLP"; or technology code[4]
		Naphthalene	91-20-3	0.059	5.6
		Phenanthrene	85-01-8	0.059	5.6
		Pyrene	129-00-0	0.067	8.2
		Toluene (Methyl Benzene)	108-88-3	0.080	10
		Xylene(s) (Total)	1330-20-7	0.32	30
K171	Spent hydrotreating catalyst from petroleum refining operations, including guard beds used to desulfurize feeds to other catalytic reactors (this listing does not include inert support media)	Benz(a)anthracene	56-55-3	0.059	3.4
		Benzene	71-43-2	0.14	10
		Chrysene	218-01-9	0.059	3.4
		Ethyl benzene	100-41-4	0.057	10
		Naphthalene	91-20-3	0.059	5.6
		Phenanthrene	85-01-8	0.059	5.6
		Pyrene	129-00-0	0.067	8.2
		Toluene (Methyl Benzene)	108-88-3	0.080	10
		Xylene(s) (Total)	1330-20-7	0.32	30
		Arsenic	7440-38-2	1.4	5 mg/L TCLP
		Nickel	7440-02-0	3.98	11 mg/L TCLP
		Vanadium	7440-62-2	4.3	1.6 mg/L TCLP
		Reactive sulfides	NA	DEACT	DEACT
K172	Spent hydrorefining catalyst from petroleum refining operations, including guard beds used to desulfurize feeds to other catalytic reactors (this listing does not include inert support media)	Benzene	71-43-2	0.14	10
		Ethyl benzene	100-41-4	0.057	10
		Toluene (Methyl Benzene)	108-88-3	0.080	10
		Xylene(s) (Total)	1330-20-7	0.32	30
		Antimony	7740-36-0	1.9	1.15 mg/L TCLP
		Arsenic	7440-38-2	1.4	5 mg/L TCLP
		Nickel	7440-02-0	3.98	11.0 mg/L TCLP
		Vanadium	7440-62-2	4.3	1.6 mg/L TCLP
		Reactive sulfides	NA	DEACT	DEACT
K174	Wastewater treatment sludges from the production of ethylene dichloride or vinyl chloride monomer	1,2,3,4,6,7,8-Heptachlorodibenzo-*p*-dioxin (1,2,3,4,6,7,8-HpCDD)	35822-46-9	0.000035 or CMBST[11]	0.0025 or CMBST[11]
		1,2,3,4,6,7,8-Heptachlorodibenzofuran (1,2,3,4,6,7,8-HpCDF)	67562-39-4	0.000035 or CMBST[11]	0.0025 or CMBST[11]
		1,2,3,4,7,8,9-Heptachlorodibenzofuran (1,2,3,4,7,8,9-HpCDF)	55673-89-7	0.000035 or CMBST[11]	0.0025 or CMBST[11]
		HxCDDs (All Hexachlorodibenzo-*p*-dioxins)	34465-46-8	0.000063 or CMBST[11]	0.001 or CMBST[11]
		HxCDFs (All Hexachlorodibenzofurans)	55684-94-1	0.000063 or CMBST[11]	0.001 or CMBST[11]

Treatment Standards for Hazardous Wastes

13.4.1, 13.5

[*Note:* NA means not applicable]

Waste code	Waste description and treatment/regulatory subcategory[1]	Regulated hazardous constituent: Common name	Regulated hazardous constituent: CAS[2] No.	Wastewaters Concentration[3] in mg/L; or technology code[4]	Nonwastewaters Concentration[5] in mg/kg unless noted as "mg/L TCLP"; or technology code[4]
		1,2,3,4,6,7,8,9-Octa-chlorodibenzo-*p*-dioxin (OCDD)	3268-87-9	0.000063 or CMBST[11]	0.005 or CMBST[11]
		1,2,3,4,6,7,8,9-Octa-chlorodibenzofuran (OCDF)	39001-02-0	0.000063 or CMBST[11]	0.005 or CMBST[11]
		PeCDDs (All Pentachlorodibenzo-*p*-dioxins)	36088-22-9	0.000063 or CMBST[11]	0.001 or CMBST[11]
		PeCDFs (All Penta-chlorodibenzofurans)	30402-15-4	0.000035 or CMBST[11]	0.001 or CMBST[11]
		TCDDs (All Tetrachlorodibenzo-*p*-dioxins)	41903-57-5	0.000063 or CMBST[11]	0.001 or CMBST[11]
		TCDFs (All Tetrachloro-dibenzofurans)	55722-27-5	0.000063 or CMBST[11]	0.001 or CMBST[11]
		Arsenic	7440-36-0	1.4	5.0 mg/L TCLP
K175	Wastewater treatment sludge from the production of vinyl chloride monomer using mercuric chloride catalyst in an acetylene-based process	Mercury[12]	7438-97-6	NA	0.025 mg/L TCLP
		pH[12]		NA	pH≤6.0
	All K175 wastewaters	Mercury	7438-97-6	0.15	NA
K176	Baghouse filters from the production of antimony oxide, including filters from the production of intermediates (e.g., antimony metal or crude antimony oxide)	Antimony	7440-36-0	1.9	1.15 mg/L TCLP
		Arsenic	7440-38-2	1.4	5.0 mg/L TCLP
		Cadmium	7440-43-9	0.69	0.11 mg/L TCLP
		Lead	7439-92-1	0.69	0.75 mg/L TCLP
		Mercury	7439-97-6	0.15	0.025 mg/L TCLP
K177	Slag from the production of antimony oxide that is speculatively accumulated or disposed, including slag from the production of intermediates (e.g., antimony metal or crude antimony oxide)	Antimony	7440-36-0	1.9	1.15 mg/L TCLP
		Arsenic	7440-38-2	1.4	5.0 mg/L TCLP
		Lead	7439-92-1	0.69	0.75 mg/L TCLP
K178	Residues from manufacturing and manufacturing-site storage of ferric chloride from acids formed during the production of titanium dioxide using the chloride-ilmenite process	1,2,3,4,6,7,8-Heptachlorodibenzo-*p*-dioxin (1,2,3,4,6,7,8-HpCDD)	35822-39-4	0.000035 or CMBST[11]	0.0025 or CMBST[11]
		1,2,3,4,6,7,8-Hepta-chlorodibenzofuran (1,2,3,4,6,7,8- HpCDF)	67562-39-4	0.000035 or CMBST[11]	0.0025 or CMBST[11]
		1,2,3,4,7,8,9-Hepta-chlorodibenzofuran (1,2,3,4,7,8,9- HpCDF)	55673-89-7	0.000035 or CMBST[11]	0.0025 or CMBST[11]
		HxCDDs (All Hexachlorodibenzo-*p*-dioxins)	34465-46-8	0.000063 or CMBST[11]	0.001 or CMBST[11]
		HxCDFs (All Hexachlorodibenzo-furans)	55684-94-1	0.000063 or CMBST[11]	0.001 or CMBST[11]
		1,2,3,4,6,7,8,9-Octa-chlorodibenzo-*p*-dioxin (OCDD)	3268-87-9	0.000063 or CMBST[11]	0.005 or CMBST[11]

Treatment Standards for Hazardous Wastes

13.4.1, 13.5

[*Note:* NA means not applicable]

Waste code	Waste description and treatment/regulatory subcategory[1]	Regulated hazardous constituent		Wastewaters	Nonwastewaters
		Common name	CAS[2] No.	Concentration[3] in mg/L; or technology code[4]	Concentration[5] in mg/kg unless noted as "mg/L TCLP"; or technology code[4]
		1,2,3,4,6,7,8,9-Octa-chlorodibenzofuran (OCDF)	39001-02-0	0.000063 or CMBST[11]	0.005 or CMBST[11]
		PeCDDs (All Pentachlorodibenzo-*p*-dioxins)	36088-22-9	0.000063 or CMBST[11]	0.001 or CMBST[11]
		PeCDFs (All Pentachlorodibenzo-furans)	30402-15-4	0.000035 or CMBST[11]	0.001 or CMBST[11]
		TCDDs (All tetrachlorodi-benzo-*p*-dioxins)	41903-57-5	0.000063 or CMBST[11]	0.001 or CMBST[11]
		TCDDFs (All tetrachlorodibenzo-furans)	55722-27-5	0.000063 or CMBST[11]	0.001 or CMBST[11]
		Thallium	7440-28-0	1.4	0.20 mg/L TCLP
K181	Nonwastewaters from the production of dyes and/or pigments (including nonwastewaters commingled at the point of generation with nonwastewaters from other processes) that, at the point of generation, contain mass loadings of any of the constituents identified in paragraph (c) of section 261.32 that are equal to or greater than the corresponding paragraph (c) levels, as determined on a calendar year basis.	Aniline	62-53-3	0.81	14
		o-Anisidine (2-methoxyaniline)	90-04-0	0.010	0.66
		4-Chloroaniline	106-47-8	0.46	16
		p-Cresidine	120-71-8	0.010	0.66
		2,4-Dimethylaniline (2,4-xylidine)	95-68-1	0.010	0.66
		1,2-Phenylene-diamine	95-54-5	CMBST; or CHOXD fb (BIODG or CARBN); or BIODG fb CARBN	CMBST; or CHOXD fb (BIODG or CARBN); or BIODG fb CARBN
		1,3-Phenylene-diamine	108-45-2	0.010	0.66
P001	Warfarin, & salts, when present at concentrations greater than 0.3%	Warfarin	81-81-2	(WETOX or CHOXD) fb CARBN; or CMBST	CMBST
P002	1-Acetyl-2-thiourea	1-Acetyl-2-thiourea	591-08-2	(WETOX or CHOXD) fb CARBN; or CMBST	CMBST
P003	Acrolein	Acrolein	107-02-8	0.29	CMBST
P004	Aldrin	Aldrin	309-00-2	0.021	0.066
P005	Allyl alcohol	Allyl alcohol	107-18-6	(WETOX or CHOXD) fb CARBN; or CMBST	CMBST
P006	Aluminum phosphide	Aluminum phosphide	20859-73-8	CHOXD; CHRED; or CMBST	CHOXD; CHRED; or CMBST

Treatment Standards for Hazardous Wastes

13.4.1, 13.5

[*Note:* NA means not applicable]

Waste code	Waste description and treatment/regulatory subcategory[1]	Regulated hazardous constituent		Wastewaters	Nonwastewaters
		Common name	CAS[2] No.	Concentration[3] in mg/L; or technology code[4]	Concentration[5] in mg/kg unless noted as "mg/L TCLP"; or technology code[4]
P007	5-Aminomethyl 3-isoxazolol	5-Aminomethyl 3-isoxazolol	2763-96-4	(WETOX or CHOXD) fb CARBN; or CMBST	CMBST
P008	4-Aminopyridine	4-Aminopyridine	504-24-5	(WETOX or CHOXD) fb CARBN; or CMBST	CMBST
P009	Ammonium picrate	Ammonium picrate	131-74-8	CHOXD; CHRED; CARBN; BIODG; or CMBST	CHOXD; CHRED; or CMBST
P010	Arsenic acid	Arsenic	7440-38-2	1.4	5.0 mg/L TCLP
P011	Arsenic pentoxide	Arsenic	7440-38-2	1.4	5.0 mg/L TCLP
P012	Arsenic trioxide	Arsenic	7440-38-2	1.4	5.0 mg/L TCLP
P013	Barium cyanide	Barium	7440-39-3	NA	21 mg/L TCLP
		Cyanides (Total)[7]	57-12-5	1.2	590
		Cyanides (Amenable)[7]	57-12-5	0.86	30
P014	Thiophenol (Benzene thiol)	Thiophenol (Benzene thiol)	108-98-5	(WETOX or CHOXD) fb CARBN; or CMBST	CMBST
P015	Beryllium dust	Beryllium	7440-41-7	RMETL, or RTHRM	RMETL; or RTHRM
P016	Dichloromethyl ether (Bis(chloromethyl)ether)	Dichloromethyl ether	542-88-1	(WETOX or CHOXD) fb CARBN; or CMBST	CMBST
P017	Bromoacetone	Bromoacetone	598-31-2	(WETOX or CHOXD) fb CARBN; or CMBST	CMBST
P018	Brucine	Brucine	357-57-3	(WETOX or CHOXD) fb CARBN; or CMBST	CMBST
P020	2-sec-Butyl-4,6-dinitrophenol (Dinoseb)	2-sec-Butyl-4,6-dinitrophenol (Dinoseb)	88-85-7	0.066	2.5
P021	Calcium cyanide	Cyanides (Total)[7]	57-12-5	1.2	590
		Cyanides (Amenable)[7]	57-12-5	0.86	30
P022	Carbon disulfide	Carbon disulfide	75-15-0	3.8	CMBST
		Carbon disulfide; alternate[6] standard for nonwastewaters only	75-15-0	NA	4.8 mg/L TCLP

Treatment Standards for Hazardous Wastes

13.4.1, 13.5

[*Note:* NA means not applicable]

Waste code	Waste description and treatment/regulatory subcategory[1]	Regulated hazardous constituent		Wastewaters Concentration[3] in mg/L; or technology code[4]	Nonwastewaters Concentration[5] in mg/kg unless noted as "mg/L TCLP"; or technology code[4]
		Common name	CAS[2] No.		
P023	Chloroacetaldehyde	Chloroacetaldehyde	107-20-0	(WETOX or CHOXD) fb CARBN; or CMBST	CMBST
P024	p-Chloroaniline	p-Chloroaniline	106-47-8	0.46	16
P026	1-(o-Chlorophenyl)thiourea	1-(o-Chloro-phenyl)thiourea	5344-82-1	(WETOX or CHOXD) fb CARBN; or CMBST	CMBST
P027	3-Chloropropionitrile	3-Chloropropionitrile	542-76-7	(WETOX or CHOXD) fb CARBN; or CMBST	CMBST
P028	Benzyl chloride	Benzyl chloride	100-44-7	(WETOX or CHOXD) fb CARBN; or CMBST	CMBST
P029	Copper cyanide	Cyanides (Total)[7]	57-12-5	1.2	590
		Cyanides (Amenable)[7]	57-12-5	0.86	30
P030	Cyanides (soluble salts and complexes)	Cyanides (Total)[7]	57-12-5	1.2	590
		Cyanides (Amenable)[7]	57-12-5	0.86	30
P031	Cyanogen	Cyanogen	460-19-5	CHOXD; WETOX; or CMBST	CHOXD; WETOX; or CMBST
P033	Cyanogen chloride	Cyanogen chloride	506-77-4	CHOXD; WETOX; or CMBST	CHOXD; WETOX; or CMBST
P034	2-Cyclohexly-4,6-dinitrophenol	2-Cyclohexly-4,6-di-nitrophenol	131-89-5	(WETOX or CHOXD) fb CARBN; or CBMST	CMBST
P036	Dichlorophenylarsine	Arsenic	7440-38-2	1.4	5.0 mg/L TCLP
P037	Dieldrin	Dieldrin	60-57-1	0.017	0.13
P038	Diethylarsine	Arsenic	7440-38-2	1.4	5.0 mg/L TCLP
P039	Disulfoton	Disulfoton	298-04-4	0.017	6.2
P040	0,0-Diethyl O-pyrazinyl phosphorothioate	0,0-Diethyl O-pyrazinyl phosphorothioate	297-97-2	CARBN; or CMBST	CMBST
P041	Diethyl-p-nitrophenyl phosphate	Diethyl-p-nitrophenyl phosphate	311-45-5	CARBN; or CMBST	CMBST
P042	Epinephrine	Epinephrine	51-43-4	(WETOX or CHOXD) fb CARBN; or CMBST	CMBST

Treatment Standards for Hazardous Wastes

13.4.1, 13.5

[*Note:* NA means not applicable]

Waste code	Waste description and treatment/regulatory subcategory[1]	Regulated hazardous constituent		Wastewaters	Nonwastewaters
		Common name	CAS[2] No.	Concentration[3] in mg/L; or technology code[4]	Concentration[5] in mg/kg unless noted as "mg/L TCLP"; or technology code[4]
P043	Diisopropylfluorophosphate (DFP)	Diisopropylfluoro-phosphate (DFP)	55-91-4	CARBN; or CMBST	CMBST
P044	Dimethoate	Dimethoate	60-51-5	CARBN; or CMBST	CMBST
P045	Thiofanox	Thiofanox	39196-18-4	(WETOX or CHOXD) fb CARBN; or CMBST	CMBST
P046	alpha, alpha-Dimethylphenethylamine	alpha, alpha-Dimethyl-phenethylamine	122-09-8	(WETOX or CHOXD) fb CARBN; or CMBST	CMBST
P047	4,6-Dinitro-o-cresol	4,6-Dinitro-o-cresol	543-52-1	0.28	160
	4,6-Dinitro-o-cresol salts	NA	NA	(WETOX or CHOXD) fb CARBN; or CMBST	CMBST
P048	2,4-Dinitrophenol	2,4-Dinitrophenol	51-28-5	0.12	160
P049	Dithiobiuret	Dithiobiuret	541-53-7	(WETOX or CHOXD) fb CARBN; or CMBST	CMBST
P050	Endosulfan	Endosulfan I	939-98-8	0.023	0.066
		Endosulfan II	33213-6-5	0.029	0.13
		Endosulfan sulfate	1031-07-8	0.029	0.13
P051	Endrin	Endrin	72-20-8	0.0028	0.13
		Endrin aldehyde	7421-93-4	0.025	0.13
P054	Aziridine	Aziridine	151-56-4	(WETOX or CHOXD) fb CARBN; or CMBST	CMBST
P056	Fluorine	Fluorine (measured in wastewaters only)	16984-48-8	35	ADGAS fb NEUTR
P057	Fluoroacetamide	Fluoroacetamide	640-19-7	(WETOX or CHOXD) fb CARBN; or CMBST	CMBST
P058	Fluoroacetic acid, sodium salt	Fluoroacetic acid, sodium salt	62-74-8	(WETOX or CHOXD) fb CARBN; or CMBST	CMBST
P059	Heptachlor	Heptachlor	76-44-8	0.0012	0.066
		Heptachlor epoxide	1024-57-3	0.016	0.066
P060	Isodrin	Isodrin	465-73-6	0.021	0.066

Treatment Standards for Hazardous Wastes

[*Note:* NA means not applicable]

13.4.1, 13.5

Waste code	Waste description and treatment/regulatory subcategory[1]	Regulated hazardous constituent		Wastewaters	Nonwastewaters
		Common name	CAS[2] No.	Concentration[3] in mg/L; or technology code[4]	Concentration[5] in mg/kg unless noted as "mg/L TCLP"; or technology code[4]
P062	Hexaethyl tetraphosphate	Hexaethyl tetraphosphate	757-58-4	CARBN; or CMBST	CMBST
P063	Hydrogen cyanide	Cyandies (Total)[7]	57-12-5	1.2	590
		Cyanides (Amenable)[7]	57-12-5	0.86	30
P064	Isocyanic acid, ethyl ester	Isocyanic acid, ethyl ester	624-83-9	(WETOX or CHOXD) fb CARBN; or CMBST	CMBST
P065	Mercury fulminate nonwastewaters, regardless of their total mercury content, that are not incinerator residues or are not residues from RMERC	Mercury	7439-97-6	NA	IMERC
	Mercury fulminate nonwastewaters that are either incinerator residues or are residues from RMERC; and contain greater than or equal to 260 mg/kg total mercury	Mercury	7339-97-6	NA	RMERC
	Mercury fulminate nonwastewaters that are residues from RMERC and contain less than 260 mg/kg total mercury	Mercury	7439-97-6	NA	0.20 mg/L TCLP
	Mercury fulminate nonwastewaters that are incinerator residues and contain less than 260 mg/kg total mercury	Mercury	7439-97-6	NA	0.025 mg/L TCLP
	All mercury fulminate wastewaters	Mercury	7439-97-6	0.15	NA
P066	Methomyl	Methomyl	16752-77-5	(WETOX or CHOXD) fb CARBN; or CMBST	CMBST
P067	2-Methyl-aziridine	2-Methyl-aziridine	75-55-8	(WETOX or CHOXD) fb CARBN; or CMBST	CMBST
P068	Methyl hydrazine	Methyl hydrazine	60-34-4	CHOXD; CHRED; CARBN; BIODG; or CMBST	CHOXD; CHRED; or CMBST
P069	2-Methyllactonitrile	2-Methyllactonitrile	75-86-5	(WETOX or CHOXD) fb CARBN; or CMBST	CMBST
P070	Aldicarb	Aldicarb	116-06-3	(WETOX or CHOXD) fb CARBN; or CMBST	CMBST
P071	Methyl parathion	Methyl parathion	298-00-0	0.014	4.6
P072	1-Naphthyl-2-thiourea	1-Naphthyl-2-thiourea	86-88-4	(WETOX or CHOXD) fb CARBN; or CMBST	CMBST

Treatment Standards for Hazardous Wastes

13.4.1, 13.5

[*Note:* NA means not applicable]

Waste code	Waste description and treatment/regulatory subcategory[1]	Regulated hazardous constituent		Wastewaters	Nonwastewaters
		Common name	CAS[2] No.	Concentration[3] in mg/L; or technology code[4]	Concentration[5] in mg/kg unless noted as "mg/L TCLP"; or technology code[4]
P073	Nickel carbonyl	Nickel	7440-02-0	3.98	11 mg/L TCLP
P074	Nickel cyanide	Cyanides (Total)[7]	57-12-5	1.2	590
		Cyanides (Amenable)[7]	57-12-5	0.86	30
		Nickel	7440-02-0	3.98	11 mg/L TCLP
P075	Nicotine and salts	Nicotine and salts	54-11-5	(WETOX or CHOXD) fb CARBN; or CMBST	CMBST
P076	Nitric oxide	Nitric oxide	10102-43-9	ADGAS	ADGAS
P077	p-Nitroaniline	p-Nitroaniline	100-01-6	0.028	28
P078	Nitrogen dioxide	Nitrogen dioxide	10102-44-0	ADGAS	ADGAS
P081	Nitroglycerin	Nitroglycerin	55-63-0	CHOXD; CHRED; CARBN; BIODG; or CMBST	CHOXD; CHRED; or CMBST
P082	N-Nitrosodimethylamine	N-Nitrosodi-methylamine	62-75-9	0.40	2.3
P084	N-Nitrosomethylvinylamine	N-Nitroso-methylvinylamine	4549-40-0	(WETOX or CHOXD) fb CARBN; or CMBST	CMBST
P085	Octamethylpyrophosphoramide	Octamethylpyrophos phoramide	152-16-9	CARBN; OR CMBST	CMBST
P087	Osmium tetroxide	Osmium tetroxide	20816-12-0	RMETL; or RTHRM	RMETL; or RTHRM
P088	Endothall	Endothall	145-73-3	(WETOX or CHOXD) fb CARBN; or CMBST	CMBST
P089	Parathion	Parathion	56-38-2	0.014	4.6
P092	Phenyl mercuric acetate nonwastewaters, regardless of their total mercury content, that are not incinerator residues or are not residues from RMERC	Mercury	7439-97-6	NA	IMERC; or RMERC
	Phenyl mercuric acetate nonwastewaters that are either incinerator residues or are residues from RMERC; and still contain greater than or equal to 260 mg/kg total mercury	Mercury	7439-97-6	NA	RMERC
	Phenyl mercuric acetate nonwastewaters that are residues from RMERC and contain less than 160 mg/kg total mercury	Mercury	7439-97-6	NA	0.20 mg/L TCLP
	Phenyl mercuric acetate nonwastewaters that are incinerator residues and contain less then 260 mg/kg total mercury	Mercury	7439-97-6	NA	0.025 mg/L TCLP

Treatment Standards for Hazardous Wastes

13.4.1, 13.5

[*Note:* NA means not applicable]

Waste code	Waste description and treatment/regulatory subcategory[1]	Regulated hazardous constituent		Wastewaters	Nonwastewaters
		Common name	CAS[2] No.	Concentration[3] in mg/L; or technology code[4]	Concentration[5] in mg/kg unless noted as "mg/L TCLP"; or technology code[4]
	All phenyl mercuric acetate wastewaters.	Mercury	7439-97-6	0.15	NA
P093	Phenylthiourea	Phenylthiourea	103-85-5	(WETOX or CHOXD) fb CARBN; or CMBST	CMBST
P094	Phorate	Phorate	298-02-2	0.021	4.6
P095	Phosgene	Phosgene	75-44-5	(WETOX or CHOXD) fb CARBN; or CMBST	CMBST
P096	Phosphine	Phosphine	7803-51-2	CHOXD; CHRED; or CMBST	CHOXD; CHRED; or CMBST
P097	Famphur	Famphur	52-85-7	0.017	15
P098	Potassium cyanide	Cyanides (Total)[7]	57-12-5	1.2	590
		Cyanides (Amenable)[7]	57-12-5	.086	30
P099	Potassium silver cyanide	Cyanides (Total)[7]	57-12-5	1.2	590
		Cyanides (Amenable)[7]	57-12-5	0.86	30
		Silver	7440-22-4	0.43	0.14 mg/L TCLP
P101	Ethyl cyanide (Propanenitrile)	Ethyl cyanide (Propanenitrile)	107-12-0	0.24	360
P102	Propargyl alcohol	Propargyl alcohol	107-19-7	(WETOX or CHOXD) fb CARBN; or CMBST	CMBST
P103	Selenourea	Selenium	7782-49-2	0.82	5.7 mg/L TCLP
P104	Silver cyanide	Cyanides (Total)[7]	57-12-5	1.2	590
		Cyanides (Amenable)[7]	57-12-5	0.86	30
		Silver	7440-22-4	0.43	0.14 mg/L TCLP
P105	Sodium azide	Sodium azide	26628-22-8	CHOXD; CHRED; CARBN; BIODG; or CMBST	CHOXD; CHRED; or CMBST
P106	Sodium cyanide	Cyanides (Total)[7]	57-12-5	1.2	590
		Cyanides (Amenable)[7]	57-12-5	0.86	30
P108	Strychnine and salts	Strychnine and salts	57-24-9	(WETOX or CHOXD) fb CARBN; or CMBST	CMBST

Treatment Standards for Hazardous Wastes

13.4.1, 13.5

[*Note:* NA means not applicable]

Waste code	Waste description and treatment/regulatory subcategory[1]	Regulated hazardous constituent		Wastewaters	Nonwastewaters
		Common name	CAS[2] No.	Concentration[3] in mg/L; or technology code[4]	Concentration[5] in mg/kg unless noted as "mg/L TCLP"; or technology code[4]
P109	Tetraethyldithiopyrophosphate	Tetraethyldithio-pyrophosphate	3689-24-5	CARBN; or CMBST	CMBST
P110	Tetraethyl lead	Lead	7439-92-1	0.69	0.75 mg/L TCLP
P111	Tetraethylpyrophosphate	Tetraethylpyro-phosphate	107-49-3	CARBN; or CMBST	CMBST
P112	Tetranitromethane	Tetranitromethane	509-14-8	CHOXD; CHRED; CARBN; BIODG; or CMBST	CHOXD; CHRED; or CMBST
P113	Thallic oxide	Thallium (measured in wastewaters only)	7440-28-0	1.4	RTHRM; or STABL
P114	Thallium selenite	Selenium	7782-49-2	0.82	5.7 mg/L TCLP
P115	Thallium (I) sulfate	Thallium (measured in wastewaters only)	7440-28-0	1.4	RTHRM; or STABL
P116	Thiosemicarbazide	Thiosemicarbazide	79-19-6	(WETOX or CHOXD) fb CARBN; or CMBST	CMBST
P118	Trichloromethanethiol	Trichloro-methanethiol	75-70-7	(WETOX or CHOXD) fb CARBN; or CMBST	CMBST
P119	Ammonium vanadate	Vanadium (measured in wastewaters only)	7440-62-2	4.3	STABL
P120	Vandium pentoxide	Vanadium (measured in wastewaters only)	7440-62-2	4.3	STABL
P121	Zinc cyanide	Cyanides (Total)[7]	57-12-5	1.2	590
		Cyanides (Amenable)7	57-12-5	0.86	30
P122	Zinc phosphide Zn_3P_2, when present at concentrations greater than 10%	Zinc Phosphide	1314-84-7	CHOXD; CHRED; or CMBST	CHOXD; CHRED; or CMBST
P123	Toxaphene	Toxaphene	8001-35-2	0.0095	2.6
P127	Carbofuran	Carbofuran	1563-66-2	0.006	0.14
P128	Mexacarbate	Mexacarbate	315-18-4	0.056	1.4
P185	Tirpate[10]	Tirpate	26419-73-8	0.056	0.28
P188	Physostigmine salicylate	Physostigmine salicylate	57-64-7	0.056	1.4
P189	Carbosulfan	Carbosulfan	55285-14-8	0.028	1.4
P190	Metolcarb	Metolcarb	1129-41-5	0.056	1.4
P191	Dimetilan[10]	Dimetilan	644-64-4	0.056	1.4
P192	Isolan[10]	Isolan	119-38-0	0.056	1.4
P194	Oxamyl	Oxamyl	23135-22-0	0.056	0.28

Treatment Standards for Hazardous Wastes

13.4.1, 13.5

[*Note:* NA means not applicable]

Waste code	Waste description and treatment/regulatory subcategory[1]	Regulated hazardous constituent		Wastewaters	Nonwastewaters
		Common name	CAS[2] No.	Concentration[3] in mg/L; or technology code[4]	Concentration[5] in mg/kg unless noted as "mg/L TCLP"; or technology code[4]
P196	Manganese dimethyldithiocarbamate[10]	Dithiocarbamates (total)	NA	0.028	28
P197	Formparanate[10]	Formparanate	17702-57-7	0.056	1.4
P198	Formetanate hydrochloride	Formetanate hydrochloride	23422-53-9	0.056	1.4
P199	Methiocarb	Methiocarb	2032-65-7	0.056	1.4
P201	Promecarb	Promecarb	2631-37-0	0.056	1.4
P202	m-Cumenyl methylcarbamate	m-Cumenyl methylcarbamate	64-00-6	0.056	1.4
P203	Aldicarb sulfone	Aldicarb sulfone	1646-88-4	0.056	0.28
P204	Physostigmine	Physostigmine	57-47-6	0.056	1.4
P205	Ziram	Dithiocarbamates (total)	NA	0.028	28
U001	Acetaldehyde	Acetaldehyde	75-07-0	(WETOX or CHOXD) fb CARBN; or CMBST	CMBST
U002	Acetone	Acetone	67-64-1	0.28	160
U003	Acetonitrile	Acetonitrile	75-05-8	5.6	CMBST
		Acetonitrile; alternate[6] standard for nonwastewaters only	75-05-8	NA	38
U004	Acetophenone	Acetophenone	98-86-2	0.010	9.7
U005	2-Acetylaminofluorene	2-Acetyl-aminofluorene	53-96-3	0.059	140
U006	Acetyl chloride	Acetyl Chloride	75-36-5	(WETOX or CHOXD) fb CARBN; or CMBST	CMBST
U007	Acrylamide	Acrylamide	79-06-1	(WETOX or CHOXD) fb CARBN; or CMBST	CMBST
U008	Acrylic acid	Acrylic acid	79-10-7	(WETOX or CHOXD) fb CARBN; or CMBST	CMBST
U009	Acrylonitrile	Acrylonitrile	107-13-1	0.24	84
U010	Mitomycin C	Mitomycin C	50-07-7	(WETOX or CHOXD) fb CARBN; or CMBST	CMBST
U011	Amitrole	Amitrole	61-82-5	(WETOX or CHOXD) fb CARBN; or CMBST	CMBST

Treatment Standards for Hazardous Wastes

13.4.1, 13.5

[*Note:* NA means not applicable]

Waste code	Waste description and treatment/regulatory subcategory[1]	Regulated hazardous constituent		Wastewaters Concentration[3] in mg/L; or technology code[4]	Nonwastewaters Concentration[5] in mg/kg unless noted as "mg/L TCLP"; or technology code[4]
		Common name	CAS[2] No.		
U012	Aniline	Aniline	62-53-3	0.81	14
U014	Auramine	Auramine	492-80-8	(WETOX or CHOXD) fb CARBN; or CMBST	CMBST
U015	Azaserine	Azaserine	115-02-6	(WETOX or CHOXD) fb CARBN; or CMBST	CMBST
U016	Benz(c)acridine	Benz(c)acridine	225-51-4	(WETOX or CHOXD) fb CARBN; or CMBST	CMBST
U017	Benzal chloride	Benzal chloride	98-87-3	(WETOX or CHOXD) fb CARBN; or CMBST	CMBST
U018	Benz(a)anthracene	Benz(a)anthracene	56-55-3	0.059	3.4
U019	Benzene	Benzene	71-43-2	0.14	10
U020	Benzenesulfonyl chloride	Benzenesulfonyl chloride	98-09-9	(WETOX or CHOXD) fb CARBN; or CMBST	CMBST
U021	Benzidine	Benzidine	92-87-5	(WETOX or CHOXD) fb CARBN; or CMBST	CMBST
U022	Benzo(a)pyrene	Benzo(a)pyrene	50-32-8	0.061	3.4
U023	Benzotrichloride	Benzotrichloride	98-07-7	CHOXD; CHRED; CARBN; BIODG; or CMBST	CHOXD; CHRED; or CMBST
U024	bis(2-Chloroethoxy)methane	bis(2-Chloro-ethoxy)methane	111-91-1	0.036	7.2
U025	bis(2-Chloroethyl)ether	bis(2-Chloro-ethyl)ether	111-44-4	0.033	6.0
U026	Chlornaphazine	Chlornaphazine	494-03-1	(WETOX or CHOXD) fb CARBN; or CMBST	CMBST
U027	bis(2-Chloroisopropyl)ether	bis(2-Chloro-isopropyl)ether	39638-32-9	0.055	7.2
U028	bis(2-Ethylhexyl) phthalate	bis(2-Ethylhexyl) phthalate	117-81-7	0.28	28
U029	Methyl bromide (Bromomethane)	Methyl bromide (Bromomethane)	74-83-9	0.11	15

Treatment Standards for Hazardous Wastes

13.4.1, 13.5

[*Note:* NA means not applicable]

Waste code	Waste description and treatment/regulatory subcategory[1]	Regulated hazardous constituent		Wastewaters	Nonwastewaters
		Common name	CAS[2] No.	Concentration[3] in mg/L; or technology code[4]	Concentration[5] in mg/kg unless noted as "mg/L TCLP"; or technology code[4]
U030	4-Bromophenyl phenyl ether	4-Bromophenyl phenyl ether	101-55-3	0.055	15
U031	n-Butyl alcohol	n-Butyl alcohol	71-36-3	5.6	2.6
U032	Calcium chromate	Chromium (Total)	7440-47-3	2.77	0.60 mg/L TCLP
U033	Carbon oxyfluoride	Carbon oxyfluoride	353-50-4	(WETOX or CHOXD) fb CARBN; or CMBST	CMBST
U034	Trichloroacetaldehyde (Chloral)	Trichloroacetaldehyde (Chloral)	75-87-6	(WETOX or CHOXD) fb CARBN; or CMBST	CMBST
U035	Chlorambucil	Chlorambucil	305-03-3	(WETOX or CHOXD) fb CARBN; or CMBST	CMBST
U036	Chlordane	Chlordane (alpha and gamma isomers)	57-74-9	0.0033	0.26
U037	Chlorobenzene	Chlorobenzene	108-90-7	0.057	6.0
U038	Chlorobenzilate	Chlorobenzilate	510-15-6	0.10	CMBST
U039	p-Chloro-m-cresol	p-Chloro-m-cresol	59-50-7	0.018	14
U041	Epichlorohydrin (1-Chloro-2,3- epoxypropane)	Epichlorohydrin (1-Chloro-2,3-epoxypropane)	106-89-8	(WETOX or CHOXD) fb CARBN; or CMBST	CMBST
U042	2-Chloroethyl vinyl ether	2-Chloroethyl vinyl ether	110-75-8	0.062	CMBST
U043	Vinyl chloride	Vinyl chloride	75-01-4	0.27	6.0
U044	Chloroform	Chloroform	67-66-3	0.046	6.0
U045	Chloromethane (Methyl chloride)	Chloromethane (Methyl chloride)	74-87-3	0.19	30
U046	Chloromethyl methyl ether	Chloromethyl methyl ether	107-30-2	(WETOX or CHOXD) fb CARBN; or CMBST	CMBST
U047	2-Chloronaphthalene	2-Chloronaphthalene	91-58-7	0.055	5.6
U048	2-Chlorophenol	2-Chlorophenol	95-57-8	0.044	5.7
U049	4-Chloro-o-toluidine hydrochloride	4-Chloro-o-toluidine hydrochloride	3165-93-3	(WETOX or CHOXD) fb CARBN; or CMBST	CMBST
U050	Chrysene	Chrysene	218-01-9	0.059	3.4

Treatment Standards for Hazardous Wastes

13.4.1, 13.5

[*Note:* NA means not applicable]

Waste code	Waste description and treatment/regulatory subcategory[1]	Regulated hazardous constituent		Wastewaters	Nonwastewaters
		Common name	CAS[2] No.	Concentration[3] in mg/L; or technology code[4]	Concentration[5] in mg/kg unless noted as "mg/L TCLP"; or technology code[4]
U051	Creosote	Naphthalene	91-20-3	0.059	5.6
		Pentachlorophenol	87-86-5	0.089	7.4
		Phenanthrene	85-01-8	0.059	5.6
		Pyrene	129-00-0	0.067	8.2
		Toluene	108-88-3	0.080	10
		Xylenes-mixed isomers (sum of o-, m-, and p-xylene concentrations)	1330-20-7	0.32	30
		Lead	7439-92-1	0.69	0.75 mg/L TCLP
U052	Cresols (Cresylic acid)	o-Cresol	95-48-7	0.11	5.6
		m-Cresol (difficult to distinguish from p-cresol)	108-39-4	0.77	5.6
		p-Cresol (difficult to distinguish from m-cresol)	106-44-5	0.77	5.6
		Cresol-mixed isomers (Cresylic acid) (sum of o-, m-, and p-cresol concentrations)	1319-77-3	0.88	11.2
U053	Crotonaldehyde	Crotonaldehyde	4170-30-3	(WETOX or CHOXD) fb CARBN; or CMBST	CMBST
U055	Cumene	Cumene	98-82-8	(WETOX or CHOXD) fb CARBN; or CMBST	CMBST
U056	Cyclohexane	Cyclohexane	110-82-7	(WETOX or CHOXD) fb CARBN; or CMBST	CMBST
U057	Cyclohexanone	Cyclohexanone	108-94-1	0.36	CMBST
		Cyclohexanone; alternate[6] standard for nonwastewaters only	108-94-1	NA	0.75 mg/L TCLP
U058	Cyclophosphamide	Cyclophosphamide	50-18-0	CARBN; or CMBST	CMBST
U059	Daunomycin	Daunomycin	20830-81-3	(WETOX or CHOXD) fb CARBN; or CMBST	CMBST
U060	DDD	o,p´-DDD	53-19-0	0.023	0.087
		p,p´-DDD	72-54-8	0.023	0.087

Treatment Standards for Hazardous Wastes

13.4.1, 13.5

[*Note:* NA means not applicable]

Waste code	Waste description and treatment/regulatory subcategory[1]	Regulated hazardous constituent		Wastewaters	Nonwastewaters
		Common name	CAS[2] No.	Concentration[3] in mg/L; or technology code[4]	Concentration[5] in mg/kg unless noted as "mg/L TCLP"; or technology code[4]
U061	DDT	o,p´-DDT	789-02-6	0.0039	0.087
		p,p´-DDT	50-29-3	0.0039	0.087
		o,p´-DDD	53-19-0	0.023	0.087
		p,p´-DDD	72-54-8	0.023	0.087
		o,p´-DDE	3424-82-6	0.031	0.087
		p,p´-DDE	72-55-9	0.031	0.087
U062	Diallate	Diallate	2303-16-4	(WETOX or CHOXD) fb CARBN; or CMBST	CMBST
U063	Dibenz(a,h)anthracene	Dibenz(a,h)anthracene	53-70-3	0.055	8.2
U064	Dibenz(a,i)pyrene	Dibenz(a,i)pyrene	189-55-9	(WETOX or CHOXD) fb CARBN; or CMBST	CMBST
U066	1,2-Dibromo-3-chloropropane	1,2-Dibromo-3-chloropropane	96-12-8	0.11	15
U067	Ethylene dibromide (1,2- Dibromoethane)	Ethylene dibromide (1,2-Dibromoethane)	106-93-4	0.028	15
U068	Dibromomethane	Dibromomethane	74-95-3	0.11	15
U069	Di-n-butyl phthalate	Di-n-butyl phthalate	84-74-2	0.057	28
U070	o-Dichlorobenzene	o-Dichlorobenzene	95-50-1	0.088	6.0
U071	m-Dichlorobenzene	m-Dichlorobenzene	541-73-1	0.036	6.0
U072	p-Dichlorobenzene	p-Dichlorobenzene	106-46-7	0.090	6.0
U073	3,3´-Dichlorobenzidine	3,3´-Dichlorobenzidine	91-94-1	(WETOX or CHOXD) fb CARBN; or CMBST	CMBST
U074	1,4-Dichloro-2-butene	cis-1,4-Dichloro-2-butene	1476-11-5	(WETOX or CHOXD) fb CARBN; or CMBST	CMBST
		trans-1,4-Dichloro-2-butene	764-41-0	(WETOX or CHOXD) fb CARBN; or CMBST	CMBST
U075	Dichlorodifluoromethane	Dichlorodifluoromethane	75-71-8	0.23	7.2
U076	1,1-Dichloroethane	1,1-Dichloroethane	75-34-3	0.059	6.0
U077	1,2-Dichloroethane	1,2-Dichloroethane	107-06-2	0.21	6.0
U078	1,1-Dichloroethylene	1,1-Dichloroethylene	75-35-4	0.025	6.0
U079	1,2-Dichloroethylene	trans-1,2-Dichloroethylene	156-60-5	0.054	30

Treatment Standards for Hazardous Wastes

13.4.1, 13.5

[*Note:* NA means not applicable]

Waste code	Waste description and treatment/regulatory subcategory[1]	Regulated hazardous constituent		Wastewaters Concentration[3] in mg/L; or technology code[4]	Nonwastewaters Concentration[5] in mg/kg unless noted as"mg/L TCLP"; or technology code[4]
		Common name	CAS[2] No.		
U080	Methylene chloride	Methylene chloride	75-09-2	0.089	30
U081	2,4-Dichlorophenol	2,4-Dichlorophenol	120-83-2	0.044	14
U082	2,6-Dichlorophenol	2,6-Dichlorophenol	87-65-0	0.044	14
U083	1,2-Dichloropropane	1,2-Dichloropropane	78-87-5	0.85	18
U084	1,3-Dichloroproplyene	cis-1,3-Dichloro-proplyene	10061-01-5	0.036	18
		trans-1,3-Dichloro-proplyene	10061-02-6	0.036	18
U085	1,2:3,4-Diepoxybutane	1,2:3,4-Diepoxy-butane	1464-53-5	(WETOX or CHOXD) fb CARBN; or CMBST	CMBST
U086	N,N´-Diethylhydrazine	N,N´-Diethyl-hydrazine	1615-80-1	CHOXD; CHRED; CARBN; BIODG; or CMBST	CHOXD; CHRED; or CMBST
U087	O,O-Diethyl S-methyldithiophosphate	O,O-Diethyl S-methyl-dithiophosphate	3288-58-2	CARBN; CMBST	CMBST
U088	Diethyl phthalate	Diethyl phthalate	84-66-2	0.20	28
U089	Diethyl stilbestrol	Diethyl stilbestrol	56-53-1	(WETOX or CHOXD) fb CARBN; or CMBST	CMBST
U090	Dihydrosafrole	Dihydrosafrole	94-58-6	(WETOX or CHOXD) fb CARBN; or CMBST	CMBST
U091	3,3´-Dimethoxybenzidine	3,3´-Dimethoxy-benzidine	119-90-4	(WETOX or CHOXD) fb CARBN; or CMBST	CMBST
U092	Dimethylamine	Dimethylamine	124-40-3	(WETOX or CHOXD) fb CARBN; or CMBST	CMBST
U093	p-Dimethylaminoazobenzene	p-Dimethyl-aminoazobenzene	60-11-7	0.13	CMBST
U094	7,12-Dimethylibenz(a)anthracene	7,12-Dimethyl-benz(a)anthracene	57-97-6	(WETOX or CHOXD) fb CARBN; or CMBST	CMBST
U095	3,3´-Dimethylbenzidine	3,3´-Dimethyl-benzidine	119-93-7	(WETOX or CHOXD) fb CARBN; or CMBST	CMBST

Treatment Standards for Hazardous Wastes

13.4.1, 13.5

[*Note:* NA means not applicable]

Waste code	Waste description and treatment/regulatory subcategory[1]	Regulated hazardous constituent		Wastewaters	Nonwastewaters
		Common name	CAS[2] No.	Concentration[3] in mg/L; or technology code[4]	Concentration[5] in mg/kg unless noted as "mg/L TCLP"; or technology code[4]
U096	alpha, alpha-Dimethyl benzyl hydroperoxide 13.5	alpha, alpha-Dimethyl benzyl hydroperoxide	80-15-9	CHOXD; CHRED; CARBN; BIODG; or CMBST	CHOXD; CHRED; or CMBST
U097	Dimethylcarbamoyl chloride	Dimethylcarbamoyl chloride	79-44-7	(WETOX or CHOXD) fb CARBN; or CMBST	CMBST
U098	1,1-Dimethylhydrazine	1,1-Dimethyl-hydrazine	57-14-7	CHOXD; CHRED; CARBN; BIODG; or CMBST	CHOXD; CHRED; or CMBST
U099	1,2-Dimethylhydrazine	1,2-Dimethyl-hydrazine	540-73-8	CHOXD; CHRED; CARBN; BIODG; or CMBST	CHOXD; CHRED; or CMBST
U101	2,4-Dimethylphenol	2,4-Dimethylphenol	105-67-9	0.036	14
U102	Dimethyl phthalate	Dimethyl phthalate	131-11-3	0.047	28
U103	Dimethyl sulfate	Dimethyl sulfate	77-78-1	CHOXD; CHRED; CARBN; BIODG; or CMBST	CHOXD; CHRED; or CMBST
U105	2,4-Dinitrotoluene	2,4-Dinitrotoluene	121-14-2	0.32	140
U106	2,6-Dinitrotoluene	2,6-Dinitrotoluene	606-20-2	0.55	28
U107	Di-n-octyl phthalate	Di-n-octyl phthalate	117-84-0	0.017	28
U108	1,4-Dioxane	1,4-Dioxane	123-91-1	(WETOX or CHOXD) fb CARBN; or CMBST	CMBST
		1,4-Dioxane; alternate[6]	123-91-1	12.0	170
U109	1,2-Diphenylhydrazine	1,2-Diphenyl-hydrazine	122-66-7	CHOXD; CHRED; CARBN; BIODG; or CMBST	CHOXD; CHRED; or CMBST
		1,2-Diphenyl-hydrazine; alternate[6] standard for wastewaters only	122-66-7	0.087	NA
U110	Dipropylamine	Dipropylamine	142-84-7	(WETOX or CHOXD) fb CARBN; or CMBST	CMBST
U111	Di-n-propylnitrosamine	Di-n-propyl-nitrosamine	621-64-7	0.40	14

Treatment Standards for Hazardous Wastes

13.4.1, 13.5

[*Note:* NA means not applicable]

Waste code	Waste description and treatment/regulatory subcategory[1]	Regulated hazardous constituent		Wastewaters	Nonwastewaters
		Common name	CAS[2] No.	Concentration[3] in mg/L; or technology code[4]	Concentration[5] in mg/kg unless noted as "mg/L TCLP"; or technology code[4]
U112	Ethyl acetate	Ethyl acetate	141-78-6	0.34	33
U113	Ethyl acrylate	Ethyl acrylate	140-88-5	(WETOX or CHOXD) fb CARBN; or CMBST	CMBST
U114	Ethylenebisdithiocarbamic acid salts and esters	Ethylenebisdithiocarbamic acid	111-54-6	(WETOX or CHOXD) fb CARBN; or CMBST	CMBST
U115	Ethylene oxide	Ethylene oxide	75-21-8	(WETOX or CHOXD) fb CARBN; or CMBST	CHOXD; or CMBST
		Ethylene oxide; alternate[6] standard for wastewaters only	75-21-8	0.12	NA
U116	Ethylene thiourea	Ethylene thiourea	96-45-7	(WETOX or CHOXD) fb CARBN; or CMBST	CMBST
U117	Ethyl ether	Ethyl ether	60-29-7	0.12	160
U118	Ethyl methacrylate	Ethyl methacrylate	97-63-2	0.14	160
U119	Ethyl methane sulfonate	Ethyl methane sulfonate	62-50-0	(WETOX or CHOXD) fb CARBN; or CMBST	CMBST
U120	Fluoranthene	Fluoranthene	206-44-0	0.068	3.4
U121	Trichlorofluoromethane	Trichlorofluoromethane	75-69-4	0.020	30
U122	Formaldehyde	Formaldehyde	50-00-0	(WETOX or CHOXD) fb CARBN; or CMBST	CMBST
U123	Formic acid	Formic acid	64-18-6	(WETOX or CHOXD) fb CARBN; or CMBST	CMBST
U124	Furan	Furan	110-00-9	(WETOX or CHOXD) fb CARBN; or CMBST	CMBST
U125	Furfural	Furfural	98-01-1	(WETOX or CHOXD) fb CARBN; or CMBST	CMBST
U126	Glycidylaldehyde	Glycidylaldehyde	765-34-4	(WETOX or CHOXD) fb CARBN; or CMBST	CMBST

PART 268—Subpart D

Treatment Standards for Hazardous Wastes

13.4.1, 13.5

[*Note:* NA means not applicable]

Waste code	Waste description and treatment/regulatory subcategory[1]	Regulated hazardous constituent		Wastewaters	Nonwastewaters
		Common name	CAS[2] No.	Concentration[3] in mg/L; or technology code[4]	Concentration[5] in mg/kg unless noted as "mg/L TCLP"; or technology code[4]
U127	Hexachlorobenzene	Hexachlorobenzene	118-74-1	0.055	10
U128	Hexachlorobutadiene	Hexachlorobutadiene	87-68-3	0.055	5.6
U129	Lindane	alpha-BHC	319-84-6	0.00014	0.066
		beta-BHC	319-85-7	0.00014	0.066
		delta-BHC	319-86-8	0.023	0.066
		gamma-BHC (Lindane)	58-89-9	0.0017	0.066
U130	Hexachlorocyclopentadiene	Hexachlorocyclo-pentadiene	77-47-4	0.057	2.4
U131	Hexachloroethane	Hexachloroethane	67-72-1	0.055	30
U132	Hexachlorophene	Hexachlorophene	70-30-4	(WETOX or CHOXD) fb CARBN; or CMBST	CMBST
U133	Hydrazine	Hydrazine	302-01-2	CHOXD; CHRED; CARBN; BIODG; or CMBST	CHOXD; CHRED; or CMBST
U134	Hydrogen fluoride	Fluoride (measured in wastewaters only)	7664-39-3	35	ADGAS fb NEUTR; or NEUTR
U135	Hydrogen Sulfide	Hydrogen Sulfide	7783-06-4	CHOXD; CHRED; or CMBST	CHOXD; CHRED; or CMBST
U136	Cacodylic acid	Arsenic	7440-38-2	1.4	5.0 mg/L TCLP
U137	Indeno(1,2,3-cd)pyrene	Indeno(1,2,3-cd)py-rene	193-39-5	0.0055	3.4
U138	Iodomethane	Iodomethane	74-88-4	0.19	65
U140	Isobutyl alcohol	Isobutyl alcohol	78-83-1	5.6	170
U141	Isosafrole	Isosafrole	120-58-1	0.081	2.6
U142	Kepone	Kepone	143-50-8	0.0011	0.13
U143	Lasiocarpine	Lasiocarpine	303-34-4	(WETOX or CHOXD) fb CARBN; or CMBST	CMBST
U144	Lead acetate	Lead	7439-92-1	0.69	0.75 mg/L TCLP
U145	Lead phosphate	Lead	7439-92-1	0.69	0.75 mg/L TCLP
U146	Lead subacetate	Lead	7439-92-1	0.69	0.75 mg/L TCLP
U147	Maleic anhydride	Maleic anhydride	108-31-6	(WETOX or CHOXD) fb CARBN; or CMBST	CMBST

PART 268—Subpart D

Treatment Standards for Hazardous Wastes

[*Note:* NA means not applicable]

13.4.1, 13.5

Waste code	Waste description and treatment/regulatory subcategory[1]	Regulated hazardous constituent		Wastewaters Concentration[3] in mg/L; or technology code[4]	Nonwastewaters Concentration[5] in mg/kg unless noted as "mg/L TCLP"; or technology code[4]
		Common name	CAS[2] No.		
U148	Maleic hydrazide	Maleic hydrazide	123-33-1	(WETOX or CHOXD) fb CARBN; or CMBST	CMBST
U149	Malononitrile	Malononitrile	109-77-3	(WETOX or CHOXD) fb CARBN; or CMBST	CMBST
U150	Melphalan	Melphalan	148-82-3	(WETOX or CHOXD) fb CARBN; or CMBST	CMBST
U151	U151 (mercury) nonwastewaters that contain greater than or equal to 260 mg/kg total mercury	Mercury	7439-97-6	NA	RMERC
	U151 (mercury) nonwastewaters that contain less than 260 mg/kg total mercury and that are residues from RMERC only	Mercury	7439-97-6	NA	0.20 mg/L TCLP
	U151 (mercury) nonwastewaters that contain less than 260 mg/kg total mercury and that are not residues from RMERC	Mercury	7439-97-6	NA	0.025 mg/L TCLP
	All U151 (mercury) wastewaters	Mercury	7439-97-6	0.15	NA
	Elemental Mercury Contaminated with Radioactive materials	Mercury	7439-97-6	NA	AMLGM
U152	Methacrylonitrile	Methacrylonitrile	126-98-7	0.24	84
U153	Methanethiol	Methanethiol	74-93-1	(WETOX or CHOXD) fb CARBN; or CMBST	CMBST
U154	Methanol	Methanol	67-56-1	(WETOX or CHOXD) fb CARBN; or CMBST	CMBST
		Methanol, alternate[6] set of standards for both wastewaters and nonwastewaters	67-56-1	5.6	0.75 mg/L TCLP
U155	Methapyrilene	Methapyrilene	91-80-5	0.081	1.5
U156	Methyl chlorocarbonate	Methyl chlorocarbonate	79-22-1	(WETOX or CHOXD) fb CARBN; or CMBST	CMBST
U157	3-Methylcholanthrene	3-Methylcholanthrene	56-49-5	0.0055	15
U158	4,4´-Methylene bis(2-chloroaniline)	4,4´-Methylene bis(2-chloroaniline)	101-14-4	0.50	30
U159	Methyl ethyl ketone	Methyl ethyl ketone	78-93-3	0.28	36
U160	Methyl ethyl ketone peroxide	Methyl ethyl ketone peroxide	1338-23-4	CHOXD; CHRED; CARBN; BIODG; OR CMBST	CHOXD; CHRED; or CMBST

Treatment Standards for Hazardous Wastes

13.4.1, 13.5

[*Note:* NA means not applicable]

Waste code	Waste description and treatment/regulatory subcategory[1]	Regulated hazardous constituent		Wastewaters	Nonwastewaters
		Common name	CAS[2] No.	Concentration[3] in mg/L; or technology code[4]	Concentration[5] in mg/kg unless noted as "mg/L TCLP"; or technology code[4]
U161	Methyl isobutyl ketone	Methyl isobutyl ketone	108-10-1	0.14	33
U162	Methyl methacrylate	Methyl methacrylate	80-62-6	0.14	160
U163	N-Methyl N′-nitro N-nitrosoguanidine	N-Methyl N′-nitro N-nitrosoguanidine	70-25-7	(WETOX or CHOXD) fb CARBN; or CMBST	CMBST
U164	Methylthiouracil	Methylthiouracil	56-04-2	(WETOX or CHOXD) fb CARBN; or CMBST	CMBST
U165	Naphthalene	Naphthalene	91-20-3	0.059	5.6
U166	1,4-Naphthoquinone	1,4-Naphthoquinone	130-15-4	(WETOX or CHOXD) fb CARBN; or CMBST	CMBST
U167	1-Naphthylamine	1-Naphthylamine	134-32-7	(WETOX or CHOXD) fb CARBN; or CMBST	CMBST
U168	2-Naphthylamine	2-Naphthylamine	91-59-8	0.52	CMBST
U169	Nitrobenzene	Nitrobenzene	98-95-3	0.068	14
U170	p-Nitrophenol	p-Nitrophenol	100-02-7	0.12	29
U171	2-Nitropropane	2-Nitropropane	79-46-9	(WETOX or CHOXD) fb CARBN; or CMBST	CMBST
U172	N-Nitrosodi-n-butylamine	N-Nitrosodi-n-butyl-amine	924-16-3	0.40	17
U173	N-Nitrosodiethanolamine	N-Nitrosodi-ethanolamine	1116-54-7	(WETOX or CHOXD) fb CARBN; or CMBST	CMBST
U174	N-Nitrosodiethylamine	N-Nitrosodi-ethylamine	55-18-5	0.40	28
U176	N-Nitroso-N-ethylurea	N-Nitroso-N-ethylurea	759-73-9	(WETOX or CHOXD) fb CARBN; or CMBST	CMBST
U177	N-Nitroso-N-methylurea	N-Nitroso-N-methylurea	684-93-5	(WETOX or CHOXD) fb CARBN; or CMBST	CMBST
U178	N-Nitroso-N-methylurethane	N-Nitroso-N-methylurethane	615-53-2	(WETOX or CHOXD) fb CARBN; or CMBST	CMBST
U179	N-Nitrosopiperidine	N-Nitrosopiperidine	100-75-4	0.013	35

Treatment Standards for Hazardous Wastes

13.4.1, 13.5

[*Note:* NA means not applicable]

Waste code	Waste description and treatment/regulatory subcategory[1]	Regulated hazardous constituent		Wastewaters	Nonwastewaters
		Common name	CAS[2] No.	Concentration[3] in mg/L; or technology code[4]	Concentration[5] in mg/kg unless noted as "mg/L TCLP"; or technology code[4]
U180	N-Nitrosopyrrolidine	N-Nitrosopyrrolidine	930-55-2	0.013	35
U181	5-Nitro-o-toluidine	5-Nitro-o-toluidine	99-55-8	0.32	28
U182	Paraldehyde	Paraldehyde	123-63-7	(WETOX or CHOXD) fb CARBN; or CMBST	CMBST
U183	Pentachlorobenzene	Pentachlorobenzene	608-93-5	0.055	10
U184	Pentachloroethane	Pentachloroethane	76-01-7	(WETOX or CHOXD) fb CARBN; or CMBST	CMBST
		Pentachloroethane; alternate[6] standards for both wastewaters and nonwastewaters	76-01-7	0.055	6.0
U185	Pentachloronitrobenzene	Pentachloronitro-benzene	82-68-8	0.055	4.8
U186	1,3-Pentadiene	1,3-Pentadiene	504-60-9	(WETOX or CHOXD) fb CARBN; or CMBST	CMBST
U187	Phenacetin	Phenacetin	62-44-2	0.081	16
U188	Phenol	Phenol	108-95-2	0.039	6.2
U189	Phosphorus sulfide	Phosphorus sulfide	1314-80-3	CHOXD, CHRED, or CMBST	CHOXD, CHRED, or CMBST
U190	Phthalic anhydride (measured as Phthalic acid or Terephthalic acid)	Phthalic anhydride (measured as Phthalic acid or Terephthalic acid)	100-21-0	0.055	28
		Phthalic anhydride (measured as Phthalic acid or Terephthalic acid)	85-44-9	0.055	28
U191	2-Picoline	2-Picoline	109-06-8	(WETOX or CHOXD) fb CARBN; or CMBST	CMBST
U192	Pronamide	Pronamide	23950-58-5	0.093	1.5
U193	1,3-Propane sultone	1,3-Propane sultone	1120-71-4	(WETOX or CHOXD) fb CARBN; or CMBST	CMBST
U194	n-Propylamine	n-Propylamine	107-10-8	(WETOX or CHOXD) fb CARBN; or CMBST	CMBST
U196	Pyridine	Pyridine	110-86-1	0.014	16

PART 268—Subpart D

Treatment Standards for Hazardous Wastes

13.4.1, 13.5

[*Note:* NA means not applicable]

Waste code	Waste description and treatment/regulatory subcategory[1]	Regulated hazardous constituent		Wastewaters Concentration[3] in mg/L; or technology code[4]	Nonwastewaters Concentration[5] in mg/kg unless noted as "mg/L TCLP"; or technology code[4]
		Common name	CAS[2] No.		
U197	p-Benzoquinone	p-Benzoquinone	106-51-4	(WETOX or CHOXD) fb CARBN; or CMBST	CMBST
U200	Reserpine	Reserpine	50-55-5	(WETOX or CHOXD) fb CARBN; or CMBST	CMBST
U201	Resorcinol	Resorcinol	108-46-3	(WETOX or CHOXD) fb CARBN; or CMBST	CMBST
U202	Saccharin and salts	Saccharin	81-07-2	(WETOX or CHOXD) fb CARBN; or CMBST	CMBST
U203	Safrole	Safrole	94-59-7	0.081	22
U204	Selenium dioxide	Selenium	7782-49-2	0.82	5.7 mg/L TCLP
U205	Selenium sulfide	Selenium	7782-49-2	0.82	5.7 mg/L TCLP
U206	Streptozotocin	Streptozotocin	18883-66-4	(WETOX or CHOXD) fb CARBN; or CMBST	CMBST
U207	1,2,4,5-Tetrachlorobenzene	1,2,4,5-Tetrachloro-benzene	95-94-3	0.055	14
U208	1,1,1,2-Tetrachloroethane	1,1,1,2-Tetrachloro-ethane	630-20-6	0.057	6.0
U209	1,1,2,2-Tetrachloroethane	1,1,2,2-Tetrachloro-ethane	79-34-5	0.057	6.0
U210	Tetrachloroethylene	Tetrachloroethylene	127-18-4	0.056	6.0
U211	Carbon tetrachloride	Carbon tetrachloride	56-23-5	0.057	6.0
U213	Tetrahydrofuran	Tetrahydrofuran	109-99-9	(WETOX or CHOXD) fb CARBN; or CMBST	CMBST
U214	Thallium (I) acetate	Thallium (measured in wastewaters only)	7440-28-0	1.4	RTHRM; or STABL
U215	Thallium (I) carbonate	Thallium (measured in wastewaters only)	7440-28-0	1.4	RTHRM; or STABL
U216	Thallium (I) chloride	Thallium (measured in wastewaters only)	7440-28-0	1.4	RTHRM; or STABL
U217	Thallium (I) nitrate	Thallium (measured in wastewaters only)	7440-28-0	1.4	RTHRM; or STABL

Treatment Standards for Hazardous Wastes

13.4.1, 13.5

[*Note:* NA means not applicable]

Waste code	Waste description and treatment/regulatory subcategory[1]	Regulated hazardous constituent		Wastewaters	Nonwastewaters
		Common name	CAS[2] No.	Concentration[3] in mg/L; or technology code[4]	Concentration[5] in mg/kg unless noted as"mg/L TCLP"; or technology code[4]
U218	Thioacetamide	Thioacetamide	62-55-5	(WETOX or CHOXD) fb CARBN; or CMBST	CMBST
U219	Thiourea	Thiourea	62-56-6	(WETOX or CHOXD) fb CARBN; or CMBST	CMBST
U220	Toluene	Toluene	108-83-3	0.080	10
U221	Toluenediamine	Toluenediamine	25376-45-8	CARBN; or CMBST	CMBST
U222	o-Toluidine hydrochloride	o-Toluidine hydrochloride	636-21-5	(WETOX or CHOXD) fb CARBN; or CMBST	CMBST
U223	Toluene diisocyanate	Toluene diisocyanate	26471-62-5	CARBN; or CMBST	CMBST
U225	Bromoform (Tribromomethane)	Bromoform (Tribromomethane)	75-25-2	0.63	15
U226	1,1,1-Trichloroethane	1,1,1-Trichloroethane	71-55-6	0.054	6.0
U227	1,1,2-Trichloroethane	1,1,2-Trichloroethane	79-00-5	0.054	6.0
U228	Trichloroethylene	Trichloroethylene	79-01-6	0.054	6.0
U234	1,3,5-Trinitrobenzene	1,3,5-Trinitrobenzene	99-35-4	(WETOX or CHOXD) fb CARBN; or CMBST	CMBST
U235	tris-(2,3-Dibromoprophyl)-phosphate	tris-(2,3-Dibromo-prophyl)-phosphate	126-72-7	0.11	0.10
U236	Trypan Blue	Trypan Blue	72-57-1	(WETOX or CHOXD) fb CARBN; or CMBST	CMBST
U237	Uracil mustard	Uracil mustard	66-75-1	(WETOX or CHOXD) fb CARBN; or CMBST	CMBST
U238	Urethane (Ethyl carbamate)	Urethane (Ethyl carbamate)	51-79-6	(WETOX or CHOXD) fb CARBN; or CMBST	CMBST
U239	Xylenes	Xylenes-mixed isomers (sum of o-, m-, and p-xylene concentrations)	1330-20-7	0.32	30
U240	2,4-D (2,4-Dichlorophenoxyacetic acid)	2,4-D (2,4-Dichloro-phenoxyacetic acid)	94-75-7	0.72	10

Treatment Standards for Hazardous Wastes

13.4.1, 13.5

[*Note:* NA means not applicable]

Waste code	Waste description and treatment/regulatory subcategory[1]	Regulated hazardous constituent		Wastewaters	Nonwastewaters
		Common name	CAS[2] No.	Concentration[3] in mg/L; or technology code[4]	Concentration[5] in mg/kg unless noted as "mg/L TCLP"; or technology code[4]
	2,4-D (2,4-Dichlorophenoxyacetic acid) salts and esters		NA	(WETOX or CHOXD) fb CARBN; or CMBST	CMBST
U243	Hexachloropropylene	Hexachloropropylene	1888-71-7	0.035	30
U244	Thiram	Thiram	137-26-8	(WETOX or CHOXD) fb CARBN; or CMBST	CMBST
U246	Cyanogen bromide	Cyanogen bromide	506-68-3	CHOXD; WETOX; or CMBST	CHOXD; WETOX; or CMBST
U247	Methoxychlor	Methoxychlor	72-43-5	0.25	0.18
U248	Warfarin, & salts, when present at concentrations of 0.3% or less	Warfarin	81-81-2	(WETOX or CHOXD) fb CARBN; or CMBST	CMBST
U249	Zinc phosphide, Zn_3P_2, when present at concentrations of 10% or less	Zinc Phosphide	1314-84-7	CHOXD; CHRED; or CMBST	CHOXD; CHRED; or CMBST
U271	Benomyl	Benomyl	17804-35-2	0.056	1.4
U278	Bendiocarb	Bendiocarb	22781-23-3	0.056	1.4
U279	Carbaryl	Carbaryl	63-25-2	0.006	0.14
U280	Barban	Barban	101-27-9	0.056	1.4
U328	o-Toluidine	o-Toluidine	95-53-4	CMBST; or CHOXD fb (BIODG or CARBN); or BIODG fb CARBN.	CMBST
U353	p-Toluidine	p-Toluidine	106-49-0	CMBST; or CHOXD fb (BIODG or CARBN); or BIODG fb CARBN	CMBST
U359	2-Ethoxyethanol	2-Ethoxyethanol	110-80-5	CMBST; or CHOXD fb (BIODG or CARBN); or BIODG fb CARBN	CMBST
U364	Bendiocarb phenol[10]	Bendiocarb phenol	22961-82-6	0.056	1.4
U367	Carbofuran phenol	Carbofuran phenol	1563-38-8	0.056	1.4
U372	Carbendazim	Carbendazim	10605-21-7	0.056	1.4
U373	Propham	Propham	122-42-9	0.056	1.4
U387	Prosulfocarb	Prosulfocarb	52888-80-9	0.042	1.4

Treatment Standards for Hazardous Wastes

13.4.1, 13.5

[*Note:* NA means not applicable]

Waste code	Waste description and treatment/regulatory subcategory[1]	Regulated hazardous constituent		Wastewaters	Nonwastewaters
		Common name	CAS[2] No.	Concentration[3] in mg/L; or technology code[4]	Concentration[5] in mg/kg unless noted as "mg/L TCLP"; or technology code[4]
U389	Triallate	Triallate	2303-17-5	0.042	1.4
U394	A2213[10]	A2213	30558-43-1	0.042	1.4
U395	Diethylene glycol, dicarbamate[10]	Diethylene glycol, dicarbamate	5952-26-1	0.056	1.4
U404	Triethylamine	Triethylamine	121-44-8	0.081	1.5
U409	Thiophanate-methyl	Thiophanate-methyl	23564-05-8	0.056	1.4
U410	Thiodicarb	Thiodicarb	59669-26-0	0.019	1.4
U411	Propoxur	Propoxur	114-26-1	0.056	1.4

Footnotes to Treatment Standard Table 268.40:

[1]The waste descriptions provided in this table do not replace waste descriptions in 40 CFR Part 261. Descriptions of Treatment/Regulatory Subcategories are provided, as needed, to distinguish between applicability of different standards.

[2]CAS means Chemical Abstract Services. When the waste code and/or regulated constituents are described as a combination of a chemical with its salts and/or esters, the CAS number is given for the parent compound only.

[3]Concentration standards for wastewaters are expressed in mg/L and are based on analysis of composite samples.

[4]All treatment standards expressed as a Technology Code or combination of Technology Codes are explained in detail in 40 CFR 268.42 Table 1—Technology Codes and Descriptions of Technology-Based Standards.

[5]Except for Metals (EP or TCLP) and Cyanides (Total and Amenable) the nonwastewater treatment standards expressed as a concentration were established, in part, based upon incineration in units operated in accordance with the technical requirements of 40 CFR part 264, Subpart O or 40 CFR part 265, Subpart O, or based upon combustion in fuel substitution units operating in accordance with applicable technical requirements. A facility may comply with these treatment standards according to provisions in 40 CFR 268.40(d). All concentration standards for nonwastewaters are based on analysis of grab samples.

[6]Where an alternate treatment standard or set of alternate standards has been indicated, a facility may comply with this alternate standard, but only for the Treatment/Regulatory Subcategory or physical form (*i.e.*, wastewater and/or nonwastewater) specified for that alternate standard.

[7]Both Cyanides (Total) and Cyanides (Amenable) for nonwastewaters are to be analyzed using Method 9010C or 9012B, found in "Test Methods for Evaluating Solid Waste, Physical/Chemical Methods," EPA Publication SW–846, as incorporated by reference in 40 CFR 260.11, with a sample size of 10 grams and a distillation time of one hour and 15 minutes.

[8]These wastes, when rendered nonhazardous and then subsequently managed in CWA or CWA-equivalent systems, are not subject to treatment standards. (See §268.1(c) (3) and (4)).

13.4.1

[9]These wastes, when rendered nonhazardous and then subsequently injected in a Class I SDWA well, are not subject to treatment standards. (See §148.1(d)).

13.4.1

[10]The treatment standard for this waste may be satisfied by either meeting the constituent concentrations in this table or by treating the waste by the specified technologies: combustion, as defined by the technology code CMBST at §268.42 Table 1 of this Part, for nonwastewaters; and, biodegradation as defined by the technology code BIODG, carbon adsorption as defined by the technology code CARBN, chemical oxidation as defined by the technology code CHOXD, or combustion as defined as technology code CMBST at §268.42 Table 1 of this Part, for wastewaters.

[11]For these wastes, the definition of CMBST is limited to: (1) Combustion units operating under 40 CFR 266, (2) combustion units permitted under 40 CFR part 264, Subpart O, or (3) combustion units operating under 40 CFR 265, Subpart O, which have obtained a determination of equivalent treatment under 268.42(b).

[12]Disposal of K175 wastes that have complied with all applicable 40 CFR 268.40 treatment standards must also be macroencapsulated in accordance with 40 CFR 268.45 Table 1 unless the waste is placed in:

(1) A Subtitle C monofill containing only K175 wastes that meet all applicable 40 CFR 268.40 treatment standards; or

(2) A dedicated Subtitle C landfill cell in which all other wastes being co-disposed are at pH≤6.0.

[59 FR 48046, Sept. 19, 1994, as amended by 60 FR 245, Jan. 3, 1995; 61 FR 15600, 15662, 15663, Apr. 8, 1996; 61 FR 33683, June 28, 1996; 61 FR 43927, Aug. 26, 1996; 62 FR 7504, Feb. 19, 1997; 62 FR 26022, May 12, 1997; 62 FR 32979, June 17, 1997; 62 FR 45572, Aug. 28, 1997; 63 FR 24625, May 4, 1998; 63 FR 28641, May 26, 1998; 63 FR 35149, June 29, 1998; 63 FR 42187, Aug. 6, 1998; 63 FR 42582, Aug. 10, 1998; 63 FR 46334, Aug. 31, 1998; 63 FR 47415, Sept. 4, 1998; 63 FR 51265, Sept. 24, 1998; 64 FR 25415, May 11, 1999; 64 FR 56471, Oct. 20, 1999; 65 FR14475, Mar. 17, 2000; 65 FR 67127, Nov. 8, 2000; 66 FR 58298, Nov. 20, 2001; 67 FR 17119, Apr. 9, 2002; 67 FR 48414, July 24, 2002; 67 FR 62624, Oct. 7, 2002; 70 FR 9178, Feb. 24, 2005; 70 FR 34589, June 14, 2005; 71 FR 40278, July 14, 2006]

§268.41 Treatment standards expressed as concentrations in waste extract.

For the requirements previously found in this section and for treatment standards in Table CCWE—Constituent Concentrations in Waste Extracts, refer to §268.40.

[59 FR 48103, Sept. 19, 1994]

§268.42 Treatment standards expressed as specified technologies.

13.1.5

Note: For the requirements previously found in this section in Table 2—Technology-Based Standards By RCRA Waste Code, and Table 3—Technology-Based Standards for Specific Radioactive Hazardous Mixed Waste, refer to §268.40.

(a) The following wastes in the table in §268.40 "Treatment Standards for Hazardous Wastes," for which standards are expressed as a treatment method rather than a concentration level, must be treated using the technology or technologies specified in the table entitled "Technology Codes and Description of Technology-Based Standards" in this section.

Table 1—Technology Codes and Description of Technology-Based Standards

Technology code	Description of technology-based standards
ADGAS:	Venting of compressed gases into an absorbing or reacting media (*i.e.*, solid or liquid)—venting can be accomplished through physical release utilizing valves/piping; physical penetration of the container; and/or penetration through detonation.
AMLGM:	Amalgamation of liquid, elemental mercury contaminated with radioactive materials utilizing inorganic reagents such as copper, zinc, nickel, gold, and sulfur that result in a nonliquid, semi-solid amalgam and thereby reducing potential emissions of elemental mercury vapors to the air.
BIODG:	Biodegradation of organics or non-metallic inorganics (*i.e.*, degradable inorganics that contain the elements of phosphorus, nitrogen, and sulfur) in units operated under either aerobic or anaerobic conditions such that a surrogate compound or indicator parameter has been substantially reduced in concentration in the residuals (*e.g.*, Total Organic Carbon can often be used as an indicator parameter for the biodegradation of many organic constituents that cannot be directly analyzed in wastewater residues).
CARBN:	Carbon adsorption (granulated or powdered) of non-metallic inorganics, organo-metallics, and/or organic constituents, operated such that a surrogate compound or indicator parameter has not undergone breakthrough (*e.g.*, Total Organic Carbon can often be used as an indicator parameter for the adsorption of many organic constituents that cannot be directly analyzed in wastewater residues). Breakthrough occurs when the carbon has become saturated with the constituent (or indicator parameter) and substantial change in adsorption rate associated with that constituent occurs.
CHOXD:	Chemical or electrolytic oxidation utilizing the following oxidation reagents (or waste reagents) or combinations of reagents: (1) Hypochlorite (*e.g.*, bleach); (2) chlorine; (3) chlorine dioxide; (4) ozone or UV (ultraviolet light) assisted ozone; (5) peroxides; (6) persulfates; (7) perchlorates; (8) permanganates; and/or (9) other oxidizing reagents of equivalent efficiency, performed in units operated such that a surrogate compound or indicator parameter has been substantially reduced in concentration in the residuals (*e.g.*, Total Organic Carbon can often be used as an indicator parameter for the oxidation of many organic constituents that cannot be directly analyzed in wastewater residues). Chemical oxidation specifically includes what is commonly referred to as alkaline chlorination.
CHRED:	Chemical reduction utilizing the following reducing reagents (or waste reagents) or combinations of reagents: (1) Sulfur dioxide; (2) sodium, potassium, or alkali salts or sulfites, bisulfites, metabisulfites, and polyethylene glycols (*e.g.*, NaPEG and KPEG); (3) sodium hydrosulfide; (4) ferrous salts; and/or (5) other reducing reagents of equivalent efficiency, performed in units operated such that a surrogate compound or indicator parameter has been substantially reduced in concentration in the residuals *e.g.*, Total Organic Halogens can often be used as an indicator parameter for the reduction of many halogenated organic constituents that cannot be directly (analyzed in wastewater residues). Chemical reduction is commonly used for the reduction of hexavalent chromium to the trivalent state.
CMBST:	High temperature organic destruction technologies, such as combustion in incinerators, boilers, or industrial furnaces operated in accordance with the applicable requirements of 40 CFR part 264, subpart O, or 40 CFR part 265, subpart O, or 40 CFR part 266, subpart H, and in other units operated in accordance with applicable technical operating requirements; and certain non-combustive technologies, such as the Catalytic Extraction Process. 13.4.2
DEACT:	Deactivation to remove the hazardous characteristics of a waste due to its ignitability, corrosivity, and/or reactivity.
FSUBS:	Fuel substitution in units operated in accordance with applicable technical operating requirements.
HLVIT:	Vitrification of high level mixed radioactive wastes in units in compliance with all applicable radioactive protection requirements under control of the Nuclear Regulatory Commission.

Table 1—Technology Codes and Description of Technology-Based Standards

Technology code	Description of technology-based standards
IMERC:	Incineration of wastes containing organics and mercury in units operated in accordance with the technical operating requirements of 40 CFR part 264 subpart 0 and part 265 subpart 0. All wastewater and nonwastewater residues derived from this process must then comply with the corresponding treatment standards per waste code with consideration of any applicable subcategories (*e.g.*, High or Low Mercury Subcategories).
INCIN:	Incineration in units operated in accordance with the technical operating requirements of 40 CFR part 264 subpart 0 and part 265 subpart 0.
LLEXT:	Liquid-liquid extraction (often referred to as solvent extraction) of organics from liquid wastes into an immiscible solvent for which the hazardous constituents have a greater solvent affinity, resulting in an extract high in organics that must undergo either incineration, reuse as a fuel, or other recovery/reuse and a raffinate (extracted liquid waste) proportionately low in organics that must undergo further treatment as specified in the standard.
MACRO:	Macroencapsulation with surface coating materials such as polymeric organics (*e.g.*, resins and plastics) or with a jacket of inert inorganic materials to substantially reduce surface exposure to potential leaching media. Macroencapsulation specifically does not include any material that would be classified as a tank or container according to 40 CFR 260.10. 📖 **13.8.5**
NEUTR:	Neutralization with the following reagents (or waste reagents) or combinations of reagents: (1) Acids; (2) bases; or (3) water (including wastewaters) resulting in a pH greater than 2 but less than 12.5 as measured in the aqueous residuals.
NLDBR:	No land disposal based on recycling.
POLYM:	Formation of complex high-molecular weight solids through polymerization of monomers in high-TOC D001 non-wastewaters which are chemical components in the manufacture of plastics.
PRECP:	Chemical precipitation of metals and other inorganics as insoluble precipitates of oxides, hydroxides, carbonates, sulfides, sulfates, chlorides, flourides, or phosphates. The following reagents (or waste reagents) are typically used alone or in combination: (1) Lime (*i.e.*, containing oxides and/or hydroxides of calcium and/or magnesium; (2) caustic (*i.e.*, sodium and/or potassium hydroxides; (3) soda ash (*i.e.*, sodium carbonate); (4) sodium sulfide; (5) ferric sulfate or ferric chloride; (6) alum; or (7) sodium sulfate. Additional floculating, coagulation or similar reagents/ processes that enhance sludge dewatering characteristics are not precluded from use.
RBERY:	Thermal recovery of Beryllium.
RCGAS:	Recovery/reuse of compressed gases including techniques such as reprocessing of the gases for reuse/ resale; filtering/adsorption of impurities; remixing for direct reuse or resale; and use of the gas as a fuel source.

Table 1—Technology Codes and Description of Technology-Based Standards

Technology code	Description of technology-based standards
RCORR:	Recovery of acids or bases utilizing one or more of the following recovery technologies: (1) Distillation (*i.e.*, thermal concentration); (2) ion exchange; (3) resin or solid adsorption; (4) reverse osmosis; and/ or (5) incineration for the recovery of acid—Note: this does not preclude the use of other physical phase separation or concentration techniques such as decantation, filtration (including ultrafiltration), and centrifugation, when used in conjunction with the above listed recovery technologies.
RLEAD:	Thermal recovery of lead in secondary lead smelters.
RMERC:	Retorting or roasting in a thermal processing unit capable of volatilizing mercury and subsequently condensing the volatilized mercury for recovery. The retorting or roasting unit (or facility) must be subject to one or more of the following: (a) a National Emissions Standard for Hazardous Air Pollutants (NESHAP) for mercury; (b) a Best Available Control Technology (BACT) or a Lowest Achievable Emission Rate (LAER) standard for mercury imposed pursuant to a Prevention of Significant Deterioration (PSD) permit; or (c) a state permit that establishes emission limitations (within meaning of section 302 of the Clean Air Act) for mercury. All wastewater and nonwastewater residues derived from this process must then comply with the corresponding treatment standards per waste code with consideration of any applicable subcategories (*e.g.*, High or Low Mercury Subcategories).
RMETL:	Recovery of metals or inorganics utilizing one or more of the following direct physical/ removal technologies: (1) Ion exchange; (2) resin or solid (*i.e.*, zeolites) adsorption; (3) reverse osmosis; (4) chelation/solvent extraction; (5) freeze crystalization; (6) ultrafiltration and/or (7) simple precipitation (*i.e.*, crystalization)—Note: This does not preclude the use of other physical phase separation or concentration techniques such as decantation, filtration (including ultrafiltration), and centrifugation, when used in conjunction with the above listed recovery technologies.
RORGS:	Recovery of organics utilizing one or more of the following technologies: (1) Distillation; (2) thin film evaporation; (3) steam stripping; (4) carbon adsorption; (5) critical fluid extraction; (6) liquid-liquid extraction; (7) precipitation/crystalization (including freeze crystallization); or (8) chemical phase separation techniques (*i.e.*, addition of acids, bases, demulsifiers, or similar chemicals);— Note: this does not preclude the use of other physical phase separation techniques such as a decantation, filtration (including ultrafiltration), and centrifugation, when used in conjunction with the above listed recovery technologies.
RTHRM:	Thermal recovery of metals or inorganics from nonwastewaters in units identified as industrial furnaces according to 40 CFR 260.10 (1), (6), (7), (11), and (12) under the definition of "industrial furnaces".
RZINC:	Resmelting in high temperature metal recovery units for the purpose of recovery of zinc.

Table 1—Technology Codes and Description of Technology-Based Standards

Technology code	Description of technology-based standards
STABL:	Stabilization with the following reagents (or waste reagents) or combinations of reagents: (1) Portland cement; or (2) lime/pozzolans (*e.g.*, fly ash and cement kiln dust)—this does not preclude the addition of reagents (*e.g.*, iron salts, silicates, and clays) designed to enhance the set/cure time and/or compressive strength, or to overall reduce the leachability of the metal or inorganic.
SSTRP:	Steam stripping of organics from liquid wastes utilizing direct application of steam to the wastes operated such that liquid and vapor flow rates, as well as temperature and pressure ranges, have been optimized, monitored, and maintained. These operating parameters are dependent upon the design parameters of the unit, such as the number of separation stages and the internal column design, thus resulting in a condensed extract high in organics that must undergo either incineration, reuse as a fuel, or other recovery/reuse and an extracted wastewater that must undergo further treatment as specified in the standard.
VTD	Vacuum thermal desorption of low-level radioactive hazardous mixed waste in units in compliance with all applicable radioactive protection requirements under control of the Nuclear Regulatory Commission.
WETOX:	Wet air oxidation performed in units operated such that a surrogate compound or indicator parameter has been substantially reduced in concentration in the residuals (*e.g.*, Total Organic Carbon can often be used as an indicator parameter for the oxidation of many organic constituents that cannot be directly analyzed in wastewater residues).
WTRRX:	Controlled reaction with water for highly reactive inorganic or organic chemicals with precautionary controls for protection of workers from potential violent reactions as well as precautionary controls for potential emissions of toxic/ignitable levels of gases released during the reaction.

Note 1: When a combination of these technologies (*i.e.*, a treatment train) is specified as a single treatment standard, the order of application is specified in §268.42, Table 2 by indicating the five letter technology code that must be applied first, then the designation "fb." (an abbreviation for "followed by"), then the five letter technology code for the technology that must be applied next, and so on.

Note 2: When more than one technology (or treatment train) are specified as alternative treatment standards, the five letter technology codes (or the treatment trains) are separated by a semicolon (;) with the last technology preceded by the word "OR". This indicates that any one of these BDAT technologies or treatment trains can be used for compliance with the standard.

(b) Any person may submit an application to the Administrator demonstrating that an alternative treatment method can achieve a measure of performance equivalent to that achieved by methods specified in paragraphs (a), (c), and (d) of this section for wastes or specified in Table 1 of §268.45 for hazardous debris. The applicant must submit information demonstrating that his treatment method is in compliance with federal, state, and local requirements and is protective of human health and the environment. On the basis of such information and any other available information, the Administrator may approve the use of the alternative treatment method if he finds that the alternative treatment method provides a measure of performance equivalent to that achieved by methods specified in paragraphs (a), (c), and (d) of this section for wastes or in Table 1 of §268.45 for hazardous debris. Any approval must be stated in writing and may contain such provisions and conditions as the Administrator deems appropriate. The person to whom such approval is issued must comply with all limitations contained in such a determination.

(c) As an alternative to the otherwise applicable subpart D treatment standards, lab packs are eligible for land disposal provided the following requirements are met: 📖 **9.7, 13.13.1**

(1) The lab packs comply with the applicable provisions of 40 CFR 264.316 and 40 CFR 265.316;

(2) The lab pack does not contain any of the wastes listed in Appendix IV to part 268;

(3) The lab packs are incinerated in accordance with the requirements of 40 CFR part 264, subpart O or 40 CFR part 265, subpart O; and

(4) Any incinerator residues from lab packs containing D004, D005, D006, D007, D008, D010, and D011 are treated in compliance with the applicable treatment standards specified for such wastes in subpart D of this part.

(d) Radioactive hazardous mixed wastes are subject to the treatment standards in §268.40. Where treatment standards are specified for radioactive mixed wastes in the Table of Treatment Standards, those treatment standards will govern. Where there is no specific treatment standard for radioactive mixed waste, the treatment standard for the hazardous waste (as designated by EPA waste code) applies. Hazardous debris containing radioactive waste is subject to the treatment standards specified in §268.45. 📖 **4.4.4.3, 13.9**

[51 FR 40642, Nov. 7, 1986, as amended at 52 FR 25790, July 8, 1987; 55 FR 22692, June 1, 1990; 56 FR 3884, Jan. 31, 1991; 57 FR 8089, Mar. 6, 1992; 57 FR 37273, Aug. 18, 1992; 58 FR 29885, May 24, 1993; 59 FR 31552, June 20, 1994; 59 FR 48103, Sept. 19, 1994; 60 FR 302, Jan. 3, 1995; 61 FR 15654, Apr. 8, 1996; 62 FR 26025, May 12, 1997; 63 FR 28738, May 26, 1998; 71 FR 40278, July 14, 2006; 73 FR 27767, May 14, 2008]

§268.43 Treatment standards expressed as waste concentrations.

For the requirements previously found in this section and for treatment standards in Table CCW—Constituent Concentrations in Wastes, refer to §268.40.

[59 FR 48103, Sept. 19, 1994]

§268.44 Variance from a treatment standard.

(a) Based on a petition filed by a generator or treater of hazardous waste, the Administrator may approve a variance from an applicable treatment standard if:

(1) It is not physically possible to treat the waste to the level specified in the treatment standard, or by the method specified as the treatment standard. To show that this is the case, the petitioner must demonstrate that because the physical or chemical properties of the waste differ significantly from waste analyzed in developing the treatment standard, the waste cannot be treated to the specified level or by the specified method; or

(2) It is inappropriate to require the waste to be treated to the level specified in the treatment standard or by the method specified as the treatment standard, even though such treatment is technically possible. To show that this is the case, the petitioner must either demonstrate that:

(i) Treatment to the specified level or by the specified method is technically inappropriate (for example, resulting in combustion of large amounts of mildly contaminated environmental media); or

(ii) For remediation waste only, treatment to the specified level or by the specified method is environmentally inappropriate because it would likely discourage aggressive remediation.

(b) Each petition must be submitted in accordance with the procedures in §260.20.

(c) Each petition must include the following statement signed by the petitioner or an authorized representative:

I certify under penalty of law that I have personally examined and am familiar with the information submitted in this petition and all attached documents, and that, based on my inquiry of those individuals immediately responsible for obtaining the information, I believe that the submitted information is true, accurate, and complete. I am aware that there are significant penalties for submitting false information, including the possibility of fine and imprisonment.

(d) After receiving a petition for variance from a treatment standard, the Administrator may request any additional information or samples which he may require to evaluate the petition. Additional copies of the complete petition may be requested as needed to send to affected states and Regional Offices.

(e) The Administrator will give public notice in the *Federal Register* of the intent to approve or deny a petition and provide an opportunity for public comment. The final decision on a variance from a treatment standard will be published in the *Federal Register.*

(f) A generator, treatment facility, or disposal facility that is managing a waste covered by a variance from the treatment standards must comply with the waste analysis requirements for restricted wastes found under §268.7.

(g) During the petition review process, the applicant is required to comply with all restrictions on land disposal under this part once the effective date for the waste has been reached.

(h) Based on a petition filed by a generator or treater of hazardous waste, the Administrator or his or her delegated representative may approve a site-specific variance from an applicable treatment standard if:

(1) It is not physically possible to treat the waste to the level specified in the treatment standard, or by the method specified as the treatment standard. To show that this is the case, the petitioner must demonstrate that because the physical or chemical properties of the waste differ significantly from waste analyzed in developing the treatment standard, the waste cannot be treated to the specified level or by the specified method; or

(2) It is inappropriate to require the waste to be treated to the level specified in the treatment standard or by the method specified as the treatment standard, even though such treatment is technically possible. To show that this is the case, the petitioner must either demonstrate that:

(i) Treatment to the specified level or by the specified method is technically inappropriate (for example, resulting in combustion of large amounts of mildly contaminated environmental media where the treatment standard is not based on combustion of such media); or

(ii) For remediation waste only, treatment to the specified level or by the specified method is environmentally inappropriate because it would likely discourage aggressive remediation.

(3) For contaminated soil only, treatment to the level or by the method specified in the soil treatment standards would result in concentrations of hazardous constituents that are below (*i.e.,* lower than) the concentrations necessary to minimize short- and long-term threats to human health and the environment. Treatment variances approved under this paragraph must:

(i) At a minimum, impose alternative land disposal restriction treatment standards that, using a reasonable maximum exposure scenario:

(A) For carcinogens, achieve constituent concentrations that result in the total excess risk to an individual exposed over a lifetime generally falling within a range from 10^{-4} to 10^{-6}; and

(B) For constituents with non-carcinogenic effects, achieve constituent concentrations that an individual could be exposed to on a daily basis without appreciable risk of deleterious effect during a lifetime.

(ii) Not consider post-land-disposal controls.

(4) For contaminated soil only, treatment to the level or by the method specified in the soil treatment standards would result in concentrations of hazardous constituents that are below (*i.e.*, lower than) natural background concentrations at the site where the contaminated soil will land disposed.

(5) Public notice and a reasonable opportunity for public comment must be provided before granting or denying a petition.

(i) Each application for a site-specific variance from a treatment standard must include the information in §260.20(b)(1)-(4);

(j) After receiving an application for a site-specific variance from a treatment standard, the Assistant Administrator, or his delegated representative, may request any additional information or samples which may be required to evaluate the application.

(k) A generator, treatment facility, or disposal facility that is managing a waste covered by a site-specific variance from a treatment standard must comply with the waste analysis requirements for restricted wastes found under §268.7.

(l) During the application review process, the applicant for a site-specific variance must comply with all restrictions on land disposal under this part once the effective date for the waste has been reached.

(m) For all variances, the petitioner must also demonstrate that compliance with any given treatment variance is sufficient to minimize threats to human health and the environment posed by land disposal of the waste. In evaluating this demonstration, EPA may take into account whether a treatment variance should be approved if the subject waste is to be used in a manner constituting disposal pursuant to 40 CFR 266.20 through 266.23.

(n) [Reserved]

(o) The following facilities are excluded from the treatment standards under §268.40, and are subject to the following constituent concentrations:

Table—Wastes Excluded From the Treatment Standards Under §268.40

Facility name[1] and address	Waste code	See also	Regulated hazardous constituent	Wastewaters		Nonwastewaters	
				Concentration (mg/l)	Notes	Concentration (mg/kg)	Notes
Craftsman Plating and Tinning, Corp., Chicago, IL	F006	Table CCWE in 268.40	Cyanides (Total) Cyanides (Amenable) Cadmium Chromium Lead Nickel	1.2 .86 1.6 .32 .040 .44	[2] [2] and [3]	1800 30 NA NA NA NA	[4] [4]
CWM Chemical Services, LLC, Model City, New York	K088[9]	Standards under §268.40	Arsenic	1.4	NA	5.0 mg/L TCLP	NA
DuPont Environmental Treatment Chambers Works, Deepwater, NJ	F039	Standards under §268.40	1,3-phenylenediamine 1,3-PDA	NA	NA	CMBST; CHOXD fb BIODG or CARBN; or BIODG fb CARBN	[13]
Dupont Environmental Treatment—Chambers Works Wastewater Treatment Plant, Deepwater, NJ[8]	K088	Standards under §268.40	Arsenic	1.4	NA	5.0 mg/L TCLP	NA
Energy*Solutions* LLC, Clive, UT[14]	P- and U-listed hazardous waste requiring CMBST	Standards under §268.40	NA	NA	NA	CMBST or VTD	NA
Guardian Industries Jefferson Hills, PA [6, 11, and 12]	D010	Standards under §268.40	Selenium	NA	NA	11 mg/L TCLP	NA
Owens Brockway Glass Container Company, Vernon, CA [6, 7]	D010	Standards under §268.40	Selenium	NA	NA	51 mg/L TCLP	NA

Table—Wastes Excluded From the Treatment Standards Under §268.40

Facility name[1] and address	Waste code	See also	Regulated hazardous constituent	Wastewaters Concentration (mg/l)	Wastewaters Notes	Nonwastewaters Concentration (mg/kg)	Nonwastewaters Notes
Northwestern Plating Works, Inc., Chicago, IL	F006	Table CCWE in 268.40	Cyanides (Total)	1.2	2 and 3	970	4
			Cyanides (Amenable)	.86	2	30	4
			Cadmium	1.6		NA	
			Chromium	.32		NA	
			Lead	.040		NA	
			Nickel	.44		NA	
St. Gobain Containers, El Monte, CA[5, 7]	D010	Standards under §268.40	Selenium	NA	NA	25 mg/L TCLP	NA
U.S. Ecology Idaho, Incorporated, Grandview, Idaho	K088[10]	Standards under §268.40	Arsenic	1.4	NA	5.0 mg/L TCLP	NA

[1] A facility may certify compliance with these treatment standards according to provisions in 40 CFR 268.7.

[2] Cyanide Wastewater Standards for F006 are based on analysis of composite samples.

[3] These facilities must comply with 0.86 mg/l for amenable cyanides in the wastewater exiting the alkaline chlorination system. These facilities must also comply with 40 CFR §268.7.a.4 for appropriate monitoring frequency consistent with the facilities' waste analysis plan.

[4] Cyanide nonwastewaters are analyzed using SW–846 Method 9010C or 9012B, as incorporated by reference in §260.11 of this chapter, sample size 10 grams, distillation time, 1 hour and 15 minutes.

[5] Alternative D010 selenium standard only applies to dry scrubber solid from glass manufacturing wastes.

[6] Alternative D010 selenium standard only applies to electrostatic precipitator dust generated during glass manufacturing operations.

[7] D010 wastes generated by these two facilities must be treated by Chemical Waste Management, Inc. at their Kettleman Hills facility in Kettleman City, California.

[8] Dupont Environmental Treatment—Chambers Works must dispose of this waste in their on-site Subtitle C hazardous waste landfill.

[9] This treatment standard applies only to K088-derived bag house dust, incinerator ash, and filtercake at this facility.

[10] This treatment standard applies only to K088-derived air emission control dust generated by this facility.

[11] D010 wastes generated by this facility may be treated by Heritage Environmental Services, LLC at their RCRA permitted treatment facility in Indianapolis, Indiana or by Chemical Waste Management, Chemical Services Inc. at their RCRA permitted treatment facility in Model City, New York.

[12] D010 waste generated by this facility may be treated by Chemical Waste Management, Chemical Services, LLC. at their treatment facility in Model City, New York.

[13] This treatment standard applies to 1,3-PDA in biosludge from treatment of F039.

[14] This site-specific treatment variance applies only to solid treatment residue resulting from the vacuum thermal desorption (VTD) of P- and U-listed hazardous waste containing radioactive contamination ("mixed waste") at the Energy*Solutions*' LLC facility in Clive, Utah that otherwise requires CMBST as the LDR treatment standard. Once the P- and U-listed mixed waste are treated using VTD, the solid treatment residue can be land disposed at Energy*Solutions*' onsite RCRA permitted mixed waste landfill without further treatment. This treatment variance is conditioned on Energy*Solutions* complying with a Waste Family Demonstration Testing Plan specifically addressing the treatment of these P- and U-listed wastes, with this plan being implemented through a RCRA Part B permit modification for the VTD unit.

Note: NA means Not Applicable.

[51 FR 40642, Nov. 7, 1986, as amended at 52 FR 21017, June 4, 1987; 53 FR 31221, Aug. 17, 1988; 54 FR 36972, Sept. 6, 1989; 56 FR 12355, Mar. 25, 1991; 61 FR 55727, Oct. 28, 1996; 62 FR 26025, May 12, 1997; 62 FR 64509, Dec. 5, 1997; 63 FR 28738, May 26, 1998; 64 FR 28391, May 26, 1999; 66 FR 33890, June 26, 2001; 67 FR 35928, May 22, 2002; 67 FR 36818, May 28, 2002; 68 FR 4392, Jan. 29, 2003; 69 FR 6574, Feb. 11, 2004; 70 FR 34589, June 14, 2005; 70 FR 44511, Aug. 3, 2005; 71 FR 6212, Feb. 7, 2006; 71 FR 40279, July 14, 2006; 73 FR 27767, May 14, 2008]

§268.45 Treatment standards for hazardous debris.

13.8

(a) *Treatment standards.* Hazardous debris must be treated prior to land disposal as follows unless EPA determines under §261.3(f)(2) of this chapter that the debris is no longer contaminated with hazardous waste or the debris is treated to the waste-specific treatment standard provided in this subpart for the waste contaminating the debris:

(1) *General.* Hazardous debris must be treated for each "contaminant subject to treatment" defined by paragraph (b) of this section using the technology or technologies identified in Table 1 of this section.

(2) *Characteristic debris.* Hazardous debris that exhibits the characteristic of ignitability, corrosivity, or reactivity identified under §§261.21, 261.22, and 261.23 of this chapter, respectively, must be deactivated by treatment using one of the technologies identified in Table 1 of this section.

(3) *Mixtures of debris types.* The treatment standards of Table 1 in this section must be achieved for each type of debris contained in a mixture of debris types. If an immobilization technology is used in a treatment train, it must be the last treatment technology used.

(4) *Mixtures of contaminant types.* Debris that is contaminated with two or more contaminants subject to treatment identified under paragraph (b) of this section must be treated for each contaminant using one or more treatment technologies identified in Table 1 of this section. If an immobilization technology is used in a treatment train, it must be the last treatment technology used.

(5) *Waste PCBs.* Hazardous debris that is also a waste PCB under 40 CFR part 761 is subject to the requirements of either 40 CFR part 761 or the requirements of this section, whichever are more stringent.

(b) *Contaminants subject to treatment.* Hazardous debris must be treated for each "contaminant subject to treatment." The contaminants subject to treatment must be determined as follows: 13.8.3

(1) *Toxicity characteristic debris.* The contaminants subject to treatment for debris that exhibits the Toxicity Characteristic (TC) by §261.24 of this chapter are those EP constituents for which the debris exhibits the TC toxicity characteristic.

(2) *Debris contaminated with listed waste.* The contaminants subject to treatment for debris that is contaminated with a prohibited listed hazardous waste are those constituents or wastes for which treatment standards are established for the waste under §268.40.

(3) *Cyanide reactive debris.* Hazardous debris that is reactive because of cyanide must be treated for cyanide.

(c) *Conditioned exclusion of treated debris.* Hazardous debris that has been treated using one of the specified extraction or destruction technologies in Table 1 of this section and that does not exhibit a characteristic of hazardous waste identified under subpart C, part 261, of this chapter after treatment is not a hazardous waste and need not be managed in a subtitle C facility. Hazardous debris contaminated with a listed waste that is treated by an immobilization technology specified in Table 1 is a hazardous waste and must be managed in a subtitle C facility.

(d) *Treatment residuals*—(1) *General requirements.* Except as provided by paragraphs (d)(2) and (d)(4) of this section:

(i) Residue from the treatment of hazardous debris must be separated from the treated debris using simple physical or mechanical means; and

(ii) Residue from the treatment of hazardous debris is subject to the waste-specific treatment standards provided by subpart D of this part for the waste contaminating the debris.

(2) *Nontoxic debris.* Residue from the deactivation of ignitable, corrosive, or reactive characteristic hazardous debris (other than cyanide-reactive) that is not contaminated with a contaminant subject to treatment defined by paragraph (b) of this section, must be deactivated prior to land disposal and is not subject to the waste-specific treatment standards of subpart D of this part.

(3) *Cyanide-reactive debris.* Residue from the treatment of debris that is reactive because of cyanide must meet the treatment standards for D003 in "Treatment Standards for Hazardous Wastes" at §268.40.

(4) *Ignitable nonwastewater residue.* Ignitable nonwastewater residue containing equal to or greater than 10% total organic carbon is subject to the technology specified in the treatment standard for D001: Ignitable Liquids.

(5) *Residue from spalling.* Layers of debris removed by spalling are hazardous debris that remain subject to the treatment standards of this section.

Table 1—Alternative Treatment Standards For Hazardous Debris[1]

13.8.2

Technology description	Performance and/or design and operating standard	Contaminant restrictions[2]
A. Extraction Technologies:		
1. Physical Extraction		
a. *Abrasive Blasting:* Removal of contaminated debris surface layers using water and/or air pressure to propel a solid media (*e.g.*, steel shot, aluminum oxide grit, plastic beads)	*Glass, Metal, Plastic, Rubber:* Treatment to a clean debris surface[3] *Brick, Cloth, Concrete, Paper, Pavement, Rock, Wood:* Removal of at least 0.6 cm of the surface layer; treatment to a clean debris surface[3]	All Debris: None
b. *Scarification, Grinding, and Planing:* Process utilizing striking piston heads, saws, or rotating grinding wheels such that contaminated debris surface layers are removed	Same as above	Same as above

Table 1—Alternative Treatment Standards For Hazardous Debris[1]

13.8.2

Technology description	Performance and/or design and operating standard	Contaminant restrictions[2]
c. *Spalling:* Drilling or chipping holes at appropriate locations and depth in the contaminated debris surface and applying a tool which exerts a force on the sides of those holes such that the surface layer is removed. The surface layer removed remains hazardous debris subject to the debris treatment standards.	Same as above	Same as above
d. *Vibratory Finishing:* Process utilizing scrubbing media, flushing fluid, and oscillating energy such that hazardous contaminants or contaminated debris surface layers are removed[4]	Same as above	Same as above
e. *High Pressure Steam and Water Sprays:* Application of water or steam sprays of sufficient temperature, pressure, residence time, agitation, surfactants, and detergents to remove hazardous contaminants from debris surfaces or to remove contaminated debris surface layers	Same as above	Same as above
2. Chemical Extraction		
a. *Water Washing and Spraying:* Application of water sprays or water baths of sufficient temperature, pressure, residence time, agitation, surfactants, acids, bases, and detergents to remove hazardous contaminants from debris surfaces and surface pores or to remove contaminated debris surface layers	*All Debris:* Treatment to a clean debris surface[3]; *Brick, Cloth, Concrete, Paper, Pavement, Rock, Wood:* Debris must be no more than 1.2 cm (½-inch) in one dimension (*i.e.*, thickness limit,[5] except that this thickness limit may be waived under an "Equivalent Technology" approval under §268.42(b)[8] debris surfaces must be in contact with water solution for at least 15 minutes	*Brick, Cloth, Concrete, Paper, Pavement, Rock, Wood:* Contaminant must be soluble to at least 5% by weight in water solution or 5% by weight in emulsion; if debris is contaminated with a dioxin-listed waste,[6] an "Equivalent Technology" approval under §268.42(b) must be obtained[8]
b. *Liquid Phase Solvent Extraction:* Removal of hazardous contaminants from debris surfaces and surface pores by applying a nonaqueous liquid or liquid solution which causes the hazardous contaminants to enter the liquid phase and be flushed away from the debris along with the liquid or liquid solution while using appropriate agitation, temperature, and residence time[4]	Same as above	*Brick, Cloth, Concrete, Paper, Pavement, Rock, Wood:* Same as above, except that contaminant must be soluble to at least 5% by weight in the solvent
c. *Vapor Phase Solvent Extraction:* Application of an organic vapor using sufficient agitation, residence time, and temperature to cause hazardous contaminants on contaminated debris surfaces and surface pores to enter the vapor phase and be flushed away with the organic vapor[4]	Same as above, except that brick, cloth, concrete, paper, pavement, rock and wood surfaces must be in contact with the organic vapor for at least 60 minutes	Same as above
3. Thermal Extraction		
a. *High Temperature Metals Recovery:* Application of sufficient heat, residence time, mixing, fluxing agents, and/or carbon in a smelting, melting, or refining furnace to separate metals from debris	For refining furnaces, treated debris must be separated from treatment residuals using simple physical or mechanical means,[9] and, prior to further treatment, such residuals must meet the waste-specific treatment standards for organic compounds in the waste contaminating the debris	*Debris contaminated with a dioxin-listed waste:*[5] Obtain an "Equivalent Technology" approval under §268.42(b)[8]
b. *Thermal Desorption:* Heating in an enclosed chamber under either oxidizing or nonoxidizing atmospheres at sufficient temperature and residence time to vaporize hazardous contaminants from contaminated surfaces and surface pores and to remove the contaminants from the heating chamber in a gaseous exhaust gas[7]	*All Debris:* Obtain an "Equivalent Technology" approval under §268.42(b);[8] treated debris must be separated from treatment residuals using simple physical or mechanical means,[9] and, prior to further treatment, such residue must meet the waste-specific treatment standards for organic compounds in the waste contaminating the debris *Brick, Cloth, Concrete, Paper, Pavement, Rock, Wood:* Debris must be no more than 10 cm (4 inches) in one dimension (*i.e.*, thickness limit),[5] except that this thickness limit may be waived under the "Equivalent Technology" approval	*All Debris:* Metals other than mercury

Table 1—Alternative Treatment Standards For Hazardous Debris[1]

13.8.2

Technology description	Performance and/or design and operating standard	Contaminant restrictions[2]
B. Destruction Technologies:		
1. *Biological Destruction (Biodegradation):* Removal of hazardous contaminants from debris surfaces and surface pores in an aqueous solution and biodegradation of organic or nonmetallic inorganic compounds (*i.e.*, inorganics that contain phosphorus, nitrogen, or sulfur) in units operated under either aerobic or anaerobic conditions.	*All Debris:* Obtain an "Equivalent Technology" approval under §268.42(b);[8] treated debris must be separated from treatment residuals using simple physical or mechanical means,[9] and, prior to further treatment, such residue must meet the waste-specific treatment standards for organic compounds in the waste contaminating the debris. *Brick, Cloth, Concrete, Paper, Pavement, Rock, Wood:* Debris must be no more than 1.2 cm (½-inch) in one dimension (*i.e.*, thickness limit),[5] except that this thickness limit may be waived under the "Equivalent Technology" approval.	*All Debris:* Metal contaminants
2. Chemical Destruction		
a. *Chemical Oxidation:* Chemical or electrolytic oxidation utilizing the following oxidation reagents (or waste reagents) or combination of reagents—(1) hypochlorite (e.g., bleach); (2) chlorine; (3) chlorine dioxide; (4) ozone or UV (ultraviolet light) assisted ozone; (5) peroxides; (6) persulfates; (7) perchlorates; (8) permanganates; and/or (9) other oxidizing reagents of equivalent destruction efficiency.[4] Chemical oxidation specifically includes what is referred to as alkaline chlorination.	*All Debris:* Obtain an "Equivalent Technology" approval under §268.42(b);[8] treated debris must be separated from treatment residuals using simple physical or mechanical means,[9] and, prior to further treatment, such residue must meet the waste-specific treatment standards for organic compounds in the waste contaminating the debris. *Brick, Cloth, Concrete, Paper, Pavement, Rock, Wood:* Debris must be no more than 1.2 cm (½-inch) in one dimension (*i.e.*, thickness limit),[5] except that this thickness limit may be waived under the "Equivalent Technology" approval.	*All Debris:* Metal contaminants
b. *Chemical Reduction:* Chemical reaction utilizing the following reducing reagents (or waste reagents) or combination of reagents: (1) sulfur dioxide; (2) sodium, potassium, or alkali salts of sulfites, bisulfites, and metabisulfites, and polyethylene glycols (*e.g.*, NaPEG and KPEG); (3) sodium hydrosulfide; (4) ferrous salts; and/or (5) other reducing reagents of equivalent efficiency.[4]	Same as above	Same as above
3. *Thermal Destruction:* Treatment in an incinerator operating in accordance with Subpart O of Parts 264 or 265 of this chapter; a boiler or industrial furnace operating in accordance with Subpart H of Part 266 of this chapter, or other thermal treatment unit operated in accordance with Subpart X, Part 264 of this chapter, or Subpart P, Part 265 of this chapter, but excluding for purposes of these debris treatment standards Thermal Desorption units.	Treated debris must be separated from treatment residuals using simple physical or mechanical means,[9] and, prior to further treatment, such residue must meet the waste-specific treatment standards for organic compounds in the waste contaminating the debris.	*Brick, Concrete, Glass, Metal, Pavement, Rock, Metal:* Metals other than mercury, except that there are no metal restrictions for vitrification *Debris contaminated with a dioxin-listed waste.*[6] Obtain an "Equivalent Technology" approval under §268.42(b),[8] except that this requirement does not apply to vitrification
C. Immobilization Technologies:		
1. *Macroencapsulation:* Application of surface coating materials such as polymeric organics (*e.g.*, resins and plastics) or use of a jacket of inert inorganic materials to substantially reduce surface exposure to potential leaching media 13.8.5	Encapsulating material must completely encapsulate debris and be resistant to degradation by the debris and its contaminants and materials into which it may come into contact after placement (leachate, other waste, microbes).	None

Table 1—Alternative Treatment Standards For Hazardous Debris[1]

13.8.2

Technology description	Performance and/or design and operating standard	Contaminant restrictions[2]
2. *Microencapsulation:* Stabilization of the debris with the following reagents (or waste reagents) such that the leachability of the hazardous contaminants is reduced: (1) Portland cement; or (2) lime/pozzolans (*e.g.*, fly ash and cement kiln dust). Reagents (*e.g.*, iron salts, silicates, and clays) may be added to enhance the set/cure time and/or compressive strength, or to reduce the leachability of the hazardous constituents.[5]	Leachability of the hazardous contaminants must be reduced. 13.8.5	None
3. *Sealing:* Application of an appropriate material which adheres tightly to the debris surface to avoid exposure of the surface to potential leaching media. When necessary to effectively seal the surface, sealing entails pretreatment of the debris surface to remove foreign matter and to clean and roughen the surface. Sealing materials include epoxy, silicone, and urethane compounds, but paint may not be used as a sealant.	Sealing must avoid exposure of the debris surface to potential leaching media and sealant must be resistant to degradation by the debris and its contaminants and materials into which it may come into contact after placement (leachate, other waste, microbes).	None

[1] Hazardous debris must be treated by either these standards or the waste-specific treatment standards for the waste contaminating the debris. The treatment standards must be met for each type of debris contained in a mixture of debris types, unless the debris is converted into treatment residue as a result of the treatment process. Debris treatment residuals are subject to the waste-specific treatment standards for the waste contaminating the debris.

[2] Contaminant restriction means that the technology is not BDAT for that contaminant. If debris containing a restricted contaminant is treated by the technology, the contaminant must be subsequently treated by a technology for which it is not restricted in order to be land disposed (and excluded from Subtitle C regulation).

[3] "Clean debris surface" means the surface, when viewed without magnification, shall be free of all visible contaminated soil and hazardous waste except that residual staining from soil and waste consisting of light shadows, slight streaks, or minor discolorations, and soil and waste in cracks, crevices, and pits may be present provided that such staining and waste and soil in cracks, crevices, and pits shall be limited to no more than 5% of each square inch of surface area.

[4] Acids, solvents, and chemical reagents may react with some debris and contaminants to form hazardous compounds. For example, acid washing of cyanide-contaminated debris could result in the formation of hydrogen cyanide. Some acids may also react violently with some debris and contaminants, depending on the concentration of the acid and the type of debris and contaminants. Debris treaters should refer to the safety precautions specified in Material Safety Data Sheets for various acids to avoid applying an incompatible acid to a particular debris/contaminant combination. For example, concentrated sulfuric acid may react violently with certain organic compounds, such as acrylonitrile.

[5] If reducing the particle size of debris to meet the treatment standards results in material that no longer meets the 60 mm minimum particle size limit for debris, such material is subject to the waste- specific treatment standards for the waste contaminating the material, unless the debris has been cleaned and separated from contaminated soil and waste prior to size reduction. At a minimum, simple physical or mechanical means must be used to provide such cleaning and separation of nondebris materials to ensure that the debris surface is free of caked soil, waste, or other nondebris material.

[6] Dioxin-listed wastes are EPA Hazardous Waste numbers FO20, FO21, FO22, FO23, FO26, and FO27.

[7] Thermal desorption is distinguished from Thermal Destruction in that the primary purpose of Thermal Desorption is to volatilize contaminants and to remove them from the treatment chamber for subsequent destruction or other treatment.

[8] The demonstration "Equivalent Technology" under §268.42(b) must document that the technology treats contaminants subject to treatment to a level equivalent to that required by the performance and design and operating standards for other technologies in this table such that residual levels of hazardous contaminants will not pose a hazard to human health and the environment absent management controls.

[9] Any soil, waste, and other nondebris material that remains on the debris surface (or remains mixed with the debris) after treatment is considered a treatment residual that must be separated from the debris using, at a minimum, simple physical or mechanical means. Examples of simple physical or mechanical means are vibratory or trommel screening or water washing. The debris surface need not be cleaned to a "clean debris surface" as defined in note 3 when separating treated debris from residue; rather, the surface must be free of caked soil, waste, or other nondebris material. Treatment residuals are subject to the waste-specific treatment standards for the waste contaminating the debris.

[57 FR 37277, Aug. 18, 1992, as amended at 59 FR 48103, Sept. 19, 1994; 63 FR 28738, May 26, 1998; 71 FR 40279, July 14, 2006]

§268.46 Alternative treatment standards based on HTMR.

For the treatment standards previously found in this section, refer to §268.40.

[59 FR 48103, Sept. 19, 1994]

§268.48 Universal treatment standards.

13.3

(a) Table UTS identifies the hazardous constituents, along with the nonwastewater and wastewater treatment standard levels, that are used to regulate most prohibited hazardous wastes with numerical limits. For determining compliance with treatment standards for underlying hazardous constituents as defined in §268.2(i), these treatment standards may not be exceeded. Compliance with these treatment standards is measured by an analysis of grab samples, unless otherwise noted in the following Table UTS.

Universal Treatment Standards

[Note: NA means not applicable]

Regulated constituent common name	CAS[1] Number	Wastewater standard Concentration[2] in mg/L	Nonwastewater standard Concentration[3] in mg/kg unless noted as "mg/L TCLP"
Organic constituents:			
Acenaphthene	83-32-9	0.059	3.4
Acenaphthylene	208-96-8	0.059	3.4
Acetone	67-64-1	0.28	160
Acetonitrile	75-05-8	5.6	38
Acetophenone	96-86-2	0.010	9.7
2-Acetylaminofluorene	53-96-3	0.059	140
Acrolein	107-02-8	0.29	NA
Acrylamide	79-06-1	19	23
Acrylonitrile	107-13-1	0.24	84
Aldicarb sulfone[6]	1646-88-4	0.056	0.28
Aldrin	309-00-2	0.021	0.066
4-Aminobiphenyl	92-67-1	0.13	NA
Aniline	62-53-3	0.81	14
o-Anisidine (2-methoxyaniline)	90–04–0	0.010	0.66
Anthracene	120-12-7	0.059	3.4
Aramite	140-57-8	0.36	NA
alpha-BHC	319-84-6	0.00014	0.066
beta-BHC	319-85-7	0.00014	0.066
delta-BHC	319-86-8	0.023	0.066
gamma-BHC	58-89-9	0.0017	0.066
Barban[6]	101-27-9	0.056	1.4
Bendiocarb[6]	22781-23-3	0.056	1.4
Benomyl[6]	17804-35-2	0.056	1.4
Benzene	71-43-2	0.14	10
Benz(a)anthracene	56-55-3	0.059	3.4
Benzal chloride	98-87-3	0.055	6.0
Benzo(b)fluoranthene (difficult to distinguish from benzo(k)fluoranthene)	205-99-2	0.11	6.8
Benzo(k)fluoranthene (difficult to distinguish from benzo(b)fluoranthene)	207-08-9	0.11	6.8
Benzo(g,h,i)perylene	191-24-2	0.0055	1.8
Benzo(a)pyrene	50-32-8	0.061	3.4
Bromodichloromethane	75-27-4	0.35	15
Bromomethane/Methyl bromide	74-83-9	0.11	15
4-Bromophenyl phenyl ether	101-55-3	0.055	15
n-Butyl alcohol	71-36-3	5.6	2.6
Butylate[6]	2008-41-5	0.042	1.4
Butyl benzyl phthalate	85-68-7	0.017	28
2-sec-Butyl-4,6-dinitrophenol/Dinoseb	88-85-7	0.066	2.5
Carbaryl[6]	63-25-2	0.006	0.14
Carbenzadim[6]	10605-21-7	0.056	1.4
Carbofuran[6]	1563-66-2	0.006	0.14
Carbofuran phenol[6]	1563-38-8	0.056	1.4
Carbon disulfide	75-15-0	3.8	4.8 mg/L TCLP

Universal Treatment Standards

[Note: NA means not applicable]

Regulated constituent common name	CAS[1] Number	Wastewater standard Concentration[2] in mg/L	Nonwastewater standard Concentration[3] in mg/kg unless noted as "mg/L TCLP"
Carbon tetrachloride	56-23-5	0.057	6.0
Carbosulfan[6]	55285-14-8	0.028	1.4
Chlordane (alpha and gamma isomers)	57-74-9	0.0033	0.26
p-Chloroaniline	106-47-8	0.46	16
Chlorobenzene	108-90-7	0.057	6.0
Chlorobenzilate	510-15-6	0.10	NA
2-Chloro-1,3-butadiene	126-99-8	0.057	0.28
Chlorodibromomethane	124-48-1	0.057	15
Chloroethane	75-00-3	0.27	6.0
bis(2-Chloroethoxy)methane	111-91-1	0.036	7.2
bis(2-Chloroethyl)ether	111-44-4	0.033	6.0
Chloroform	67-66-3	0.046	6.0
bis(2-Chloro-isopropyl)ether	39638-32-9	0.055	7.2
p-Chloro-m-cresol	59-50-7	0.018	14
2-Chloroethyl vinyl ether	110-75-8	0.062	NA
Chloromethane/Methyl chloride	74-87-3	0.19	30
2-Chloronaphthalene	91-58-7	0.055	5.6
2-Chlorophenol	95-57-8	0.044	5.7
3-Chloropropylene	107-05-1	0.036	30
Chrysene	218-01-9	0.059	3.4
p-Cresidine	120–71–8	0.010	0.66
o-Cresol	95-48-7	0.11	5.6
m-Cresol (difficult to distinguish from p-cresol)	108-39-4	0.77	5.6
p-Cresol (difficult to distinguish from m-cresol)	106-44-5	0.77	5.6
m-Cumenyl methylcarbamate[6]	64-00-6	0.056	1.4
Cyclohexanone	108-94-1	0.36	0.75 mg/L TCLP
o,p'-DDD	53-19-0	0.023	0.087
p,p'-DDD	72-54-8	0.023	0.087
o,p'-DDE	3424-82-6	0.031	0.087
p,p'-DDE	72-55-9	0.031	0.087
o,p'-DDT	789-02-6	0.0039	0.087
p,p'-DDT	50-29-3	0.0039	0.087
Dibenz(a,h)anthracene	53-70-3	0.055	8.2
Dibenz(a,e)pyrene	192-65-4	0.061	NA
1,2-Dibromo-3-chloro-propane	96-12-8	0.11	15
1,2-Dibromoethane/Ethylene dibromide	106-93-4	0.028	15
Dibromomethane	74-95-3	0.11	15
m-Dichlorobenzene	541-73-1	0.036	6.0
o-Dichlorobenzene	95-50-1	0.088	6.0
p-Dichlorobenzene	106-46-7	0.090	6.0
Dichlorodifluoromethane	75-71-8	0.23	7.2
1,1-Dichloroethane	75-34-3	0.059	6.0
1,2-Dichloroethane	107-06-2	0.21	6.0

Universal Treatment Standards

[Note: NA means not applicable]

Regulated constituent common name	CAS[1] Number	Wastewater standard Concentration[2] in mg/L	Nonwastewater standard Concentration[3] in mg/kg unless noted as "mg/L TCLP"
1,1-Dichloroethylene	75-35-4	0.025	6.0
trans-1,2-Dichloroethylene	156-60-5	0.054	30
2,4-Dichlorophenol	120-83-2	0.044	14
2,6-Dichlorophenol	87-65-0	0.044	14
2,4-Dichlorophenoxyacetic acid/2,4-D	94-75-7	0.72	10
1,2-Dichloropropane	78-87-5	0.85	18
cis-1,3-Dichloropropylene	10061-01-5	0.036	18
trans-1,3-Dichloropropylene	10061-02-6	0.036	18
Dieldrin	60-57-1	0.017	0.13
Diethyl phthalate	84-66-2	0.20	28
p-Dimethylaminoazobenzene	60-11-7	0.13	NA
2,4-Dimethylaniline (2,4-xylidine)	95–68–1	0.010	0.66
2-4-Dimethyl phenol	105-67-9	0.036	14
Dimethyl phthalate	131-11-3	0.047	28
Di-n-butyl phthalate	84-74-2	0.057	28
1,4-Dinitrobenzene	100-25-4	0.32	2.3
4,6-Dinitro-o-cresol	534-52.1	0.28	160
2,4-Dinitrophenol	51-28-5	0.12	160
2,4-Dinitrotoluene	121-14-2	0.32	140
2,6-Dinitrotoluene	606-20-2	0.55	28
Di-n-octyl phthalate	117-84-0	0.017	28
Di-n-propylnitrosamine	621-64-7	0.40	14
1,4-Dioxane	123-91-1	12.0	170
Diphenylamine (difficult to distinguish from diphenylitrosamine)	122-39-4	0.92	13
Diphenylnitrosamine (difficult to distinguish from diphenylamine)	86-30-6	0.92	13
1,2-Diphenylhydrazine	122-66-7	0.087	NA
Disulfoton	298-04-3	0.017	6.2
Dithiocarbamates (total)[6]	NA	0.028	28
Endosulfan I	959-98-8	0.023	0.066
Endosulfan II	33213-65-9	0.029	0.13
Endosulfan sulfate	1031-07-8	0.029	0.13
Endrin	72-20-8	0.0028	0.13
Endrin aldehyde	7421-93-4	0.025	0.13
EPTC[6]	759-94-4	0.042	1.4
Ethyl acetate	141-78-6	0.34	33
Ethyl benzene	100-41-4	0.057	10
Ethyl cyanide/ Propanenitrile	107-12-0	0.24	360
Ethyl ether	60-29-7	0.12	160
*bis(2-Ethylhexyl) phthalate	117-81-7	0.28	28
Ethyl methacrylate	97-63-2	0.14	160
Ethylene oxide	75-21-8	0.12	NA
Famphur	52-85-7	0.017	15

Universal Treatment Standards

[Note: NA means not applicable]

Regulated constituent common name	CAS[1] Number	Wastewater standard Concentration[2] in mg/L	Nonwastewater standard Concentration[3] in mg/kg unless noted as "mg/L TCLP"
Fluoranthene	206-44-0	0.068	3.4
Fluorene	86-73-7	0.059	3.4
Formetanate hydrochloride[6]	23422-53-9	0.056	1.4
Heptachlor	76-44-8	0.0012	0.066
Heptachlor epoxide	1024-57-3	0.016	0.066
1,2,3,4,6,7,8-Heptachlorodibenzo-p-dioxin (1,2,3,4,6,7,8-HpCDD)	35822-46-9	0.000035	0.0025
1,2,3,4,6,7,8-Heptachlorodibenzofuran (1,2,3,4,6,7,8-HpCDF)	67562-39-4	0.000035	0.0025
1,2,3,4,7,8,9-Heptachlorodibenzofuran (1,2,3,4,7,8,9-HpCDF)	55673-89-7	0.000035	0.0025
Hexachlorobenzene	118-74-1	0.055	10
Hexachlorobutadiene	87-68-3	0.055	5.6
Hexachlorocyclopentadiene	77-47-4	0.057	2.4
HxCDDs (All Hexachlorodibenzo-p-dioxins)	NA	0.000063	0.001
HxCDFs (All Hexachlorodibenzofurans)	NA	0.000063	0.001
Hexachloroethane	67-72-1	0.055	30
*Hexachloropropylene	1888-71-7	0.035	30
Indeno (1,2,3-c,d) pyrene	193-39-5	0.0055	3.4
Iodomethane	74-88-4	0.19	65
Isobutyl alcohol	78-83-1	5.6	170
Isodrin	465-73-6	0.021	0.066
Isosafrole	120-58-1	0.081	2.6
Kepone	143-50-0	0.0011	0.13
Methacrylonitrile	126-98-7	0.24	84
Methanol	67-56-1	5.6	0.75 mg/L TCLP
Methapyrilene	91-80-5	0.081	1.5
Methiocarb[6]	2032-65-7	0.056	1.4
Methomyl[6]	16752-77-5	0.028	0.14
Methoxychlor	72-43-5	0.25	0.18
3-Methylchlolanthrene	56-49-5	0.0055	15
4,4-Methylene bis(2-chloroaniline	101-14-4	0.50	30
Methylene chloride	75-09-2	0.089	30
Methyl ethyl ketone	78-93-3	0.28	36
Methyl isobutyl ketone	108-10-1	0.14	33
Methyl methacrylate	80-62-6	0.14	160
Methyl methanesulfonate	66-27-3	0.018	NA
Methyl parathion	298-00-0	0.014	4.6
Metolcarb[6]	1129-41-5	0.056	1.4
Mexacarbate[6]	315-18-4	0.056	1.4
Molinate[6]	2212-67-1	0.042	1.4

**Publisher's Note:* These two constituents were added to the §268.48 table on May 26, 1998 [63 FR 28744]. However, they have been inadvertently dropped from the CFR.

Universal Treatment Standards

[Note: NA means not applicable]

Regulated constituent common name	CAS[1] Number	Wastewater standard Concentration[2] in mg/L	Nonwastewater standard Concentration[3] in mg/kg unless noted as "mg/L TCLP"
Naphthalene	91-20-3	0.059	5.6
2-Naphthylamine	91-59-8	0.52	NA
o-Nitroaniline	88-74-4	0.27	14
p-Nitroaniline	100-01-6	0.028	28
Nitrobenzene	98-95-3	0.068	14
5-Nitro-o-toluidine	99-55-8	0.32	28
o-Nitrophenol	88-75-5	0.028	13
p-Nitrophenol	100-02-7	0.12	29
N-Nitrosodiethylamine	55-18-5	0.40	28
N-Nitrosodimethylamine	62-75-9	0.40	2.3
N-Nitroso-di-n-butylamine	924-16-3	0.40	17
N-Nitrosomethylethylamine	10595-95-6	0.40	2.3
N-Nitrosomorpholine	59-89-2	0.40	2.3
N-Nitrosopiperidine	100-75-4	0.013	35
N-Nitrosopyrrolidine	930-55-2	0.013	35
1,2,3,4,6,7,8,9-Octachlorodibenzo-p-dioxin (OCDD)	3268-87-9	0.000063	0.005
1,2,3,4,6,7,8,9-Octachlorodibenzofuran (OCDF)	39001-02-0	0.000063	0.005
Oxamyl[6]	23135-22-0	0.056	0.28
Parathion	56-38-2	0.014	4.6
Total PCBs (sum of all PCB isomers, or all Aroclors)[8]	1336-36-3	0.10	10
Pebulate[6]	1114-71-2	0.042	1.4
Pentachlorobenzene	608-93-5	0.055	10
PeCDDs (All Pentachlorodibenzo-p-dioxins)	NA	0.000063	0.001
PeCDFs (All Pentachlorodibenzofurans)	NA	0.000035	0.001
Pentachloroethane	76-01-7	0.055	6.0
Pentachloronitrobenzene	82-68-8	0.055	4.8
Pentachlorophenol	87-86-5	0.089	7.4
Phenacetin	62-44-2	0.081	16
Phenanthrene	85-01-8	0.059	5.6
Phenol	108-95-2	0.039	6.2
1,3-Phenylenediamine	108–45–2	0.010	0.66
Phorate	298-02-2	0.021	4.6
Phthalic acid	100-21-0	0.055	28
Phthalic anhydride	85-44-9	0.055	28
Physostigmine[6]	57-47-6	0.056	1.4
Physostigmine salicylate[6]	57-64-7	0.056	1.4
Promecarb[6]	2631-37-0	0.056	1.4
Pronamide	23950-58-5	0.093	1.5
Propham[6]	122-42-9	0.056	1.4
Propoxur[6]	114-26-1	0.056	1.4
Prosulfocarb[6]	52888-80-9	0.042	1.4
Pyrene	129-00-0	0.067	8.2
Pyridine	110-86-1	0.014	16
Safrole	94-59-7	0.081	22
Silvex/2,4,5-TP	93-72-1	0.72	7.9
1,2,4,5-Tetrachlorobenzene	95-94-3	0.055	14

Universal Treatment Standards

[Note: NA means not applicable]

Regulated constituent common name	CAS[1] Number	Wastewater standard Concentration[2] in mg/L	Nonwastewater standard Concentration[3] in mg/kg unless noted as "mg/L TCLP"
TCDDs (All Tetrachlorodibenzo-p-dioxins)	NA	0.000063	0.001
TCDFs (All Tetrachlorodibenzofurans)	NA	0.000063	0.001
1,1,1,2-Tetrachloroethane	630-20-6	0.057	6.0
1,1,2,2-Tetrachloroethane	79-34-5	0.057	6.0
Tetrachloroethylene	127-18-4	0.056	6.0
2,3,4,6-Tetrachlorophenol	58-90-2	0.030	7.4
Thiodicarb[6]	59669-26-0	0.019	1.4
Thiophanate-methyl[6]	23564-05-8	0.056	1.4
Toluene	108-88-3	0.080	10
Toxaphene	8001-35-2	0.0095	2.6
Triallate[6]	2303-17-5	0.042	1.4
Tribromomethane/Bromoform	75-25-2	0.63	15
1, 2, 4-Trichlorobenzene	120-82-1	0.055	19
1,1,1-Trichloroethane	71-55-6	0.054	6.0
1,1,2-Trichloroethane	79-00-5	0.054	6.0
Trichloroethylene	79-01-6	0.054	6.0
Trichloromonofluoromethane	75-69-4	0.020	30
2,4,5-Trichlorophenol	95-95-4	0.18	7.4
2,4,6-Trichlorophenol	88-06-2	0.035	7.4
2,4,5-Trichlorophenoxyacetic acid/2,4,5-T	93-.76-5	0.72	7.9
1,2,3-Trichloropropane	96-18-4	0.85	30
1,1,2-Trichloro-1,2,2-trifluoroethane	76-13-1	0.057	30
Triethylamine[6]	121-44-8	0.081	1.5
tris-(2,3-Dibromopropyl) phosphate	126-72-7	0.11	0.10
Vernolate[6]	1929-77-7	0.042	1.4
Vinyl chloride	75-01-4	0.27	6.0
Xylenes-mixed isomers (sum of o-, m-, and p-xylene concentrations)	1330-20-7	0.32	30
Inorganic Constituents:			
Antimony	7440-36-0	1.9	1.15 mg/L TCLP
Arsenic	7440-38-2	1.4	5.0 mg/L TCLP
Barium	7440-39-3	1.2	21 mg/L TCLP
Beryllium	7440-41-7	0.82	1.22 mg/L TCLP
Cadmium	7440-43-9	0.69	0.11 mg/L TCLP
Chromium (Total)	7440-47-3	2.77	0.60 mg/L TCLP
Cyanides (Total)[4]	57-12-5	1.2	590
Cyanides (Amenable)[4]	57-12-5	0.86	30
Fluoride[5]	16984-48-8	35	NA

Universal Treatment Standards

[Note: NA means not applicable]

Regulated constituent common name	CAS[1] Number	Wastewater standard Concentration[2] in mg/L	Nonwastewater standard Concentration[3] in mg/kg unless noted as "mg/L TCLP"
Lead	7439-92-1	0.69	0.75 mg/L TCLP
Mercury—Nonwastewater from Retort	7439-97-6	NA	0.20 mg/L TCLP
Mercury—All Others	7439-97-6	0.15	0.025 mg/L TCLP
Nickel	7440-02-0	3.98	11 mg/L TCLP
Selenium[7]	7782-49-2	0.82	5.7 mg/L TCLP
Silver	7440-22-4	0.43	0.14 mg/L TCLP
Sulfide[5]	18496-25-8	14	NA
Thallium	7440-28-0	1.4	0.20 mg/L TCLP
Vanadium[5]	7440-62-2	4.3	1.6 mg/L TCLP
Zinc[5]	7440-66-6	2.61	4.3 mg/L TCLP

Footnotes to Table UTS

[1] CAS means Chemical Abstract Services. When the waste code and/or regulated constituents are described as a combination of a chemical with its salts and/or esters, the CAS number is given for the parent compound only.

[2] Concentration standards for wastewaters are expressed in mg/L and are based on analysis of composite samples.

[3] Except for Metals (EP or TCLP) and Cyanides (Total and Amenable) the nonwastewater treatment standards expressed as a concentration were established, in part, based upon incineration in units operated in accordance with the technical requirements of 40 CFR Part 264, Subpart O or 40 CFR Part 265, Subpart O, or based upon combustion in fuel substitution units operating in accordance with applicable technical requirements. A facility may comply with these treatment standards according to provisions in 40 CFR 268.40(d). All concentration standards for nonwastewaters are based on analysis of grab samples.

[4] Both Cyanides (Total) and Cyanides (Amenable) for nonwastewaters are to be analyzed using Method 9010C or 9012B, found in "Test Methods for Evaluating Solid Waste, Physical/Chemical Methods," EPA Publication SW–846, as incorporated by reference in 40 CFR 260.11, with a sample size of 10 grams and a distillation time of one hour and 15 minutes.

[5] These constituents are not "underlying hazardous constituents" in characteristic wastes, according to the definition at §268.2(i).

[6] Between August 26, 1996 and August 26, 1997, these constituents are not underlying hazardous constituents as defined at §268.2(i).

[7] This constituent is not an underlying hazardous constituent as defined at §268.2(i) of this Part because UTS level is greater than its TC level, thus a treated selenium waste would always be characteristically hazardous, unless it is treated to below its characteristic level.

[8] This standard is temporarily deferred for soil exhibiting a hazardous characteristic due to D004-D011 only. 📖 13.7.3

[59 FR 48103, Sept. 19, 1994, as amended by 60 FR 302, Jan. 3, 1995; 61 FR 15654, Apr. 8 1996; 61 FR 33690, June 28, 1996; 62 FR 7596, Feb. 19, 1997; 63 FR 24626, May 4, 1998; 63 FR 28739, May 26, 1998; 63 FR 47417, Sept. 4, 1998; 64 FR 25417, May 11, 1999; 65 FR 14475, Mar. 17, 2000; 65 FR 67131, Nov. 8, 2000; 65 FR 81381, Dec. 26, 2000; 70 FR 9178, Feb. 24, 2005; 70 FR 34590, June 14, 2005; 71 FR 40279, July 14, 2006]

§268.49 Alternative LDR treatment standards for contaminated soil.

📖 13.7

(a) *Applicability.* You must comply with LDRs prior to placing soil that exhibits a characteristic of hazardous waste, or exhibited a characteristic of hazardous waste at the time it was generated, into a land disposal unit. The following chart describes whether you must comply with LDRs prior to placing soil contaminated by listed hazardous waste into a land disposal unit: 📖 13.1.3.1, 13.2, 13.7.2, 14.1.5

If LDRs	And if LDRs	And if	Then you
Applied to the listed waste when it contaminated the soil*	Apply to the listed waste now		Must comply with LDRs
Didn't apply to the listed waste when it contaminated the soil*	Apply to the listed waste now	The soil is determined to contain the listed waste when the soil is first generated	Must comply with LDRs
Didn't apply to the listed waste when it contaminated the soil*	Apply to the listed waste now	The soil is determined not to contain the listed waste when the soil is first generated	Needn't comply with LDRs
Didn't apply to the listed waste when it contaminated the soil*	Don't apply to the listed waste now		Needn't comply with LDRs

* For dates of LDR applicability, see 40 CFR Part 268 Appendix VII. To determine the date any given listed hazardous waste contaminated any give volume of soil, use the last date any given listed hazardous waste was placed into any given land disposal unit or, in the case of an accidental spill, the date of the spill.

(b) Prior to land disposal, contaminated soil identified by paragraph (a) of this section as needing to comply with LDRs must be treated according to the applicable treatment standards specified in paragraph (c) of this section or according to the Universal Treatment Standards specified in 40 CFR 268.48 applicable to the contaminating listed hazardous waste and/or the applicable characteristic of hazardous waste if the soil is characteristic. The treatment standards specified in paragraph (c) of this section and the Universal Treatment Standards may be modified through a treatment variance approved in accordance with 40 CFR 268.44.

(c) *Treatment standards for contaminated soils.* Prior to land disposal, contaminated soil identified by paragraph (a) of this section as needing to comply with LDRs must be treated according to all the standards specified in this paragraph or according to the Universal Treatment Standards specified in 40 CFR 268.48.

(1) *All soils.* Prior to land disposal, all constituents subject to treatment must be treated as follows: 📖 13.7

(A) For non-metals except carbon disulfide, cyclohexanone, and methanol, treatment must achieve

90 percent reduction in total constituent concentrations, except as provided by paragraph (c)(1)(C) of this section.

(B) For metals and carbon disulfide, cyclohexanone, and methanol, treatment must achieve 90 percent reduction in constituent concentrations as measured in leachate from the treated media (tested according to the TCLP) or 90 percent reduction in total constituent concentrations (when a metal removal treatment technology is used), except as provided by paragraph (c)(1)(C)of this section.

(C) When treatment of any constituent subject to treatment to a 90 percent reduction standard would result in a concentration less than 10 times the Universal Treatment Standard for that constituent, treatment to achieve constituent concentrations less than 10 times the universal treatment standard is not required. Universal Treatment Standards are identified in 40 CFR 268.48 Table UTS.

(2) *Soils that exhibit the characteristic of ignitability, corrosivity or reactivity.* In addition to the treatment required by paragraph (c)(1) of this section, prior to land disposal, soils that exhibit the characteristic of ignitability, corrosivity, or reactivity must be treated to eliminate these characteristics. 13.7.1

(3) *Soils that contain nonanalyzable constituents.* In addition to the treatment requirements of paragraphs (c)(1) and (2) of this section, prior to land disposal, the following treatment is required for soils that contain nonanalyzable constituents: 13.7.2

(A) For soil that contains only analyzable and nonanalyzable organic constituents, treatment of the analyzable organic constituents to the levels specified in paragraphs (c)(1) and (2) of this section; or,

(B) For soil that contains only nonanalyzable constituents, treatment by the method(s) specified in §268.42 for the waste contained in the soil.

(d) *Constituents subject to treatment.* When applying the soil treatment standards in paragraph (c) of this section, constituents subject to treatment are any constituents listed in §268.48 Table UTS—Universal Treatment Standards that are reasonably expected to be present in any given volume of contaminated soil, except fluoride, selenium, sulfides, vanadium, zinc, and that are present at concentrations greater than ten times the universal treatment standard. PCBs are not constituent subject to treatment in any given volume of soil which exhibits the toxicity characteristic solely because of the presence of metals. 13.7.3

(e) *Management of treatment residuals.* Treatment residuals from treating contaminated soil identified by paragraph (a) of this section as needing to comply with LDRs must be managed as follows: 13.7.3

(1) Soil residuals are subject to the treatment standards of this section;

(2) Non-soil residuals are subject to:

(A) For soils contaminated by listed hazardous waste, the RCRA Subtitle C standards applicable to the listed hazardous waste; and

(B) For soils that exhibit a characteristic of hazardous waste, if the non-soil residual also exhibits a characteristic of hazardous waste, the treatment standards applicable to the characteristic hazardous waste.

[63 FR 28751, May 26, 1998, as amended at 64 FR 25417, May 11, 1999; 64 FR 56472, Oct. 20, 1999; 65 FR 81381, Dec. 26, 2000; 71 FR 40279, July 14, 2006]

Subpart E—Prohibitions on Storage

§268.50 Prohibitions on storage of restricted wastes. 4.4.4.3.1, 13.9.2, 13.10

(a) Except as provided in this section, the storage of hazardous wastes restricted from land disposal under subpart C of this part of RCRA section 3004 is prohibited, unless the following conditions are met:

(1) A generator stores such wastes in tanks, containers, or containment buildings on-site solely for the purpose of the accumulation of such quantities of hazardous waste as necessary to facilitate proper recovery, treatment, or disposal and the generator complies with the requirements in §262.34 and parts 264 and 265 of this chapter.

(2) An owner/operator of a hazardous waste treatment, storage, or disposal facility stores such wastes in tanks, containers, or containment buildings solely for the purpose of the accumulation of such quantities of hazardous waste as necessary to facilitate proper recovery, treatment, or disposal and: 13.10

(i) Each container is clearly marked to identify its contents and the date each period of accumulation begins;

(ii) Each tank is clearly marked with a description of its contents, the quantity of each hazardous waste received, and the date each period of accumulation begins, or such information for each tank is recorded and maintained in the operating record at that facility. Regardless of whether the tank itself is marked, an owner/operator must comply with the operating record requirements specified in §264.73 or §265.73.

(3) A transporter stores manifested shipments of such wastes at a transfer facility for 10 days or less.

(b) An owner/operator of a treatment, storage or disposal facility may store such wastes for up to one year unless the Agency can demonstrate that such storage was not solely for the purpose of accumulation of such quantities of hazardous waste as are necessary to facilitate proper recovery, treatment, or disposal.

(c) An owner/operator of a treatment, storage or disposal facility may store such wastes beyond one year; however, the owner/operator bears the burden of proving that such storage was solely for the purpose of accumulation of such quantities of hazardous waste as are necessary to facilitate proper recovery, treatment, or disposal.

(d) If a generator's waste is exempt from a prohibition on the type of land disposal utilized for the waste (for example, because of an approved case-by-case extension under §268.5, an approved §268.6 petition, or a national capacity variance under subpart C), the prohibition in paragraph (a) of this section does not apply during the period of such exemption.

(e) The prohibition in paragraph (a) of this section does not apply to hazardous wastes that meet the treatment standards specified under §§268.41, 268.42, and 268.43 or the treatment standards specified under the variance in §268.44, or, where treatment standards have not been specified, is in compliance with the applicable prohibitions specified in §268.32 or RCRA section 3004.

(f) Liquid hazardous wastes containing polychlorinated biphenyls (PCBs) at concentrations greater than or equal to 50 ppm must be stored at a facility that meets the requirements of 40 CFR 761.65(b) and must be removed from storage and treated or disposed as required by this part within one year of the date when such wastes are first placed into storage. The provisions of paragraph (c) of this section do not apply to such PCB wastes prohibited under §268.32 of this part.

(g) The prohibition and requirements in this section do not apply to hazardous remediation wastes stored in a staging pile approved pursuant to §264.554 of this chapter.

[51 FR 40642, Nov. 7, 1986; 52 FR 21017, June 4, 1987, as amended at 52 FR 25791, July 8, 1987; 54 FR 36972, Sept. 6, 1989; 57 FR 37281, Aug. 18, 1992; 63 FR 65940, Nov. 30, 1998; 71 FR 40279, July 14, 2006]

Appendices to Part 268

Appendix I–II to Part 268 [Reserved]

Appendix III to Part 268—List of Halogenated Organic Compounds Regulated Under §268.32

In determining the concentration of HOCs in a hazardous waste for purposes of the §268.32 land disposal prohibition, EPA has defined the HOCs that must be included in a calculation as any compounds having a carbon-halogen bond which are listed in this Appendix (see §268.2). Appendix III to Part 268 consists of the following compounds:

I. Volatiles

1. Bromodichloromethane
2. Bromomethane
3. Carbon Tetrachloride
4. Chlorobenzene
5. 2-Chloro-1,3-butadiene
6. Chlorodibromomethane
7. Chloroethane
8. 2-Chloroethyl vinyl ether
9. Chloroform
10. Chloromethane
11. 3-Chloropropene
12. 1,2-Dibromo-3-chloropropane
13. 1,2-Dibromomethane
14. Dibromomethane
15. Trans-1,4-Dichloro-2-butene
16. Dichlorodifluoromethane
17. 1,1-Dichloroethane
18. 1,2-Dichloroethane
19. 1,1-Dichloroethylene
20. Trans-1,2-Dichloroethene
21. 1,2-Dichloropropane
22. Trans-1,3-Dichloropropene
23. cis-1,3-Dichloropropene
24. Iodomethane
25. Methylene chloride
26. 1,1,1,2-Tetrachloroethane
27. 1,1,2,2-Tetrachloroethane
28. Tetrachloroethene
29. Tribromomethane
30. 1,1,1-Trichloroethane
31. 1,1,2-Trichloroethane
32. Trichlorothene
33. Trichloromonofluoromethane
34. 1,2,3-Thrichloropropane
35. Vinyl Chloride

II. Semivolatiles

1. Bis(2-chloroethoxy)ethane
2. Bis(2-chloroethyl)ether
3. Bis(2-chloroisopropyl)ether
4. p-Chloroaniline
5. Chlorobenzilate
6. p-Chloro-m-cresol
7. 2-Chloronaphthalene
8. 2-Chlorphenol
9. 3-Chloropropionitrile
10. m-Dichlorobenzene
11. o-Dichlorobenzene
12. p-Dichlorobenzene

13. 3.3'-Dichlorobenzidine
14. 2,4-Dichlorophenol
15. 2,6-Dichlorophenol
16. Hexachlorobenzene
17. Hexachlorobutadiene
18. Hexachlorocyclopentadiene
19. Hexachloroethane
20. Hexachloroprophene
21. Hexachlorpropene
22. 4,4'-Methylenebis(2-chloroanaline)
23. Pentachlorobenzene
24. Pentachloroethane
25. Pentachloronitrobenzene
26. Pentachlorophenol
27. Pronamide
28. 1,2,4,5-Tetrachlorobenzene
29. 2,3,4,6-Tetrachlorophenol
30. 1,2,4-Trichlorobenzene
31. 2,4,5-Trichlorophenol
32. 2,4,6-Trichlorophenol
33. Tris(2,3-dibromopropyl)phosphate

III. Organochlorine Pesticides

1. Aldrin
2. alpha-BHC
3. beta-BHC
4. delta-BHC
5. gamma-BHC
6. Chlorodane
7. DDD
8. DDE
9. DDT
10. Dieldrin
11. Endosulfan I
12. Endosulfan II
13. Endrin
14. Endrin aldehyde
15. Heptachlor
16. Heptachlor epoxide
17. Isodrin
18. Kepone
19. Methoxyclor
20. Toxaphene

IV. Phenoxyacetic Acid Herbicides

1. 2,4-Dichlorophenoxyacetic acid
2. Silvex
3. 2,4,5-T

V. PCBs

1. Aroclor 1016
2. Aroclor 1221
3. Aroclor 1232
4. Aroclor 1242
5. Aroclor 1248
6. Aroclor 1254
7. Aroclor 1260
8. PCBs not otherwise specified

VI. Dioxins and Furans

1. Hexachlorodibenzo-p-dioxins
2. Hexachlorodibenzofuran
3. Pentachlorodibenzo-p-dioxins
4. Pentachlorodibenzofuran
5. Tetrachlorodibenzo-p-dioxins
6. Tetrachlorodibenzofuran
7. 2,3,7,8-Tetrachlorodibenzo-p-dioxin

[65 FR 81380, Dec. 26, 2000]

Appendix IV to Part 268—Wastes Excluded From Lab Packs Under the Alternative Treatment Standards of §268.42(c)

13.13.1

Hazardous waste with the following EPA Hazardous Waste Codes may not be placed in lab packs under the alternative lab pack treatment standards of §268.42(c): D009, F019, K003, K004, K005, K006, K062, K071, K100, K106, P010, P011, P012, P076, P078, U134, U151.

[59 FR 48107 Sept. 19, 1994]

Appendix V to Part 268 [Reserved]

Appendix VI to Part 268—Recommended Technologies to Achieve Deactivation of Characteristics in Section 268.42

13.3–4

The treatment standard for many characteristic wastes is stated in the §268.40 Table of Treatment Standards as "Deactivation and meet UTS." EPA has determined that many technologies, when used alone or in combination, can achieve the deactivation portion of the treatment standard. Characteristic wastes that are not managed in a facility regulated by the Clean Water Act (CWA) or in a CWA-equivalent facility, and that also contain underlying hazardous constituents (see §268.2(i)) must be treated not only by a "deactivating" technology to remove the characteristic, but also to achieve the universal treatment standards (UTS) for underlying hazardous constituents. The following appendix presents a partial list of technologies, utilizing the five letter technology codes established in 40 CFR 268.42 Table 1, that may be useful in meeting the treatment standard. Use of these specific technologies is not mandatory and does not preclude direct reuse, recovery, and/or the use of other pretreatment technologies, provided deactivation is achieved and underlying hazardous constituents are treated to achieve the UTS.

Waste code/subcategory	Nonwastewaters	Wastewaters
D001 Ignitable Liquids based on 261.21(a)(1)—Low TOC Nonwastewater Subcategory (containing 1% to <10% TOC)	RORGS INCIN WETOX CHOXD BIODG	n.a.
D001 Ignitable Liquids based on 261.21(a)(1)—Ignitable Wastewater Subcategory (containing <1% TOC)	n.a	RORGS INCIN WETOX CHOXD BIODG
D001 Compressed Gases based on 261.21(A)(3)	RCGAS INCIN FSUBS ADGAS fb INCIN ADGAS fb (CHOXD; or CHRED)	n.a.

Waste code/subcategory	Nonwastewaters	Wastewaters
D001 Ignitable Reactives based on 261.21(a)(2)	WTRRX CHOXD CHRED STABL INCIN	n.a.
D001 Ignitable Oxidizers based on 261.21(a)(4)	CHRED INCIN	CHRED INCIN
D002 Acid Subcategory based on 261.22(a)(1) with pH less than or equal to 2	RCORR NEUTR INCIN	NEUTR INCIN
D002 Alkaline Subcategory based on 261.22(a)(1) with pH greater than or equal to 12.5.	NEUTR INCIN	NEUTR INCIN
D002 Other Corrosives based on 261.22(a)(2)	CHOXD CHRED INCIN STABL	CHOXD CHRED INCIN
D003 Water Reactives based on 261.23(a) (2), (3), and (4)	INCIN WTRRX CHOXD CHRED	n.a.
D003 Reactive Sulfides based on 261.23(a)(5)	CHOXD CHRED INCIN STABL	CHOXD CHRED BIODG INCIN
D003 Explosives based on 261.23(a) (6), (7), and (8)	INCIN CHOXD CHRED	INCIN CHOXD CHRED BIODG CARBN
D003 Other Reactives based on 261.23(a)(1)	INCIN CHOXD CHRED	INCIN CHOXD CHRED BIODG CARBN
K044 Wastewater treatment sludges from the manufacturing and processing of explosives	CHOXD CHRED INCIN	CHOXD CHRED BIODG CARBN INCIN
K045 Spent carbon from the treatment of wastewaters containing explosives	CHOXD CHRED INCIN	CHOXD CHRED BIODG CARBN INCIN
K047 Pink/red water from TNT operations	CHOXD CHRED INCIN	CHOXD CHRED BIODG CARBN INCIN

Note: "n.a." stands for "not applicable"; "fb." stands for "followed by".

[55 FR 22714, June 1, 1990, as amended at 62 FR 26025, May 12, 1997]

Appendix VII to Part 268—LDR Effective Dates of Surface Disposed Prohibited Hazardous Wastes

13.1.5

Table 1—Effective Dates of Surface Disposed Wastes (Non-Soil and Debris) Regulated in the LDRS[a]—Comprehensive List

Waste code	Waste category	Effective date
D001[c]	All (except High TOC Ignitable Liquids)	Aug. 9, 1993
D001	High TOC Ignitable Liquids	Aug. 8, 1990
D002[c]	All	Aug. 9, 1993
D003	Newly identified surface—disposed elemental phosphorus processing wastes	May 26, 2000
D004	Newly identified D004 and mineral processing wastes	Aug. 24, 1998
D004	Mixed radioactive/newly identified D004 or mineral processing wastes	May 26, 2000
D005	Newly identified D005 and mineral processing wastes	Aug. 24, 1998
D005	Mixed radioactive/newly identified D005 or mineral processing wastes	May 26, 2000
D006	Newly identified D006 and mineral processing wastes	Aug. 24, 1998
D006	Mixed radioactive/newly identified D006 or mineral processing wastes	May 26, 2000
D007	Newly identified D007 and mineral processing wastes	Aug. 24, 1998
D007	Mixed radioactive/newly identified D007 or mineral processing wastes	May 26, 2000
D008	Newly identified D008 and mineral processing waste	Aug. 24, 1998
D008	Mixed radioactive/newly identified D008 or mineral processing wastes	May 26, 2000
D009	Newly identified D009 and mineral processing waste	Aug. 24, 1998
D009	Mixed radioactive/newly identified D009 or mineral processing wastes	May 26, 2000
D010	Newly identified D010 and mineral processing wastes	Aug. 24, 1998
D010	Mixed radioactive/newly identified D010 or mineral processing wastes	May 26, 2000
D011	Newly identified D011 and mineral processing wastes	Aug. 24, 1998
D011	Mixed radioactive/newly identified D011 or mineral processing wastes	May 26, 2000
D012 (that exhibit the toxicity characteristic based on the TCLP)[d]	All	Dec. 14, 1994

Table 1—Effective Dates of Surface Disposed Wastes (Non-Soil and Debris) Regulated in the LDRS[a]—Comprehensive List

Waste code	Waste category	Effective date
D013 (that exhibit the toxicity characteristic based on the TCLP)[d]	All	Dec. 14, 1994
D014 (that exhibit the toxicity characteristic based on the TCLP)[d]	All	Dec. 14, 1994
D015 (that exhibit the toxicity characteristic based on the TCLP)[d]	All	Dec. 14, 1994
D016 (that exhibit the toxicity characteristic based on the TCLP)[d]	All	Dec. 14, 1994
D017 (that exhibit the toxicity characteristic based on the TCLP)[d]	All	Dec. 14, 1994
D018	Mixed with radioactive wastes	Sept. 19, 1996
D018	All others	Dec. 19, 1994
D019	Mixed with radioactive wastes	Sept. 19, 1996
D019	All others	Dec. 19, 1994
D020	Mixed with radioactive wastes	Sept. 19, 1996
D020	All others	Dec. 19, 1994
D021	Mixed with radioactive wastes	Sept. 19, 1996
D021	All others	Dec. 19, 1994
D022	Mixed with radioactive wastes	Sept. 19, 1996
D022	All others	Dec. 19, 1994
D023	Mixed with radioactive wastes	Sept. 19, 1996
D023	All others	Dec. 19, 1994
D024	Mixed with radioactive wastes	Sept. 19, 1996
D024	All others	Dec. 19, 1994
D025	Mixed with radioactive wastes	Sept. 19, 1996
D025	All others	Dec. 19, 1994
D026	Mixed with radioactive wastes	Sept. 19, 1996
D026	All others	Dec. 19, 1994
D027	Mixed with radioactive wastes	Sept. 19, 1996
D027	All others	Dec. 19, 1994
D028	Mixed with radioactive wastes	Sept. 19, 1996
D028	All others	Dec. 19, 1994
D029	Mixed with radioactive wastes	Sept. 19, 1996
D029	All others	Dec. 19, 1994
D030	Mixed with radioactive wastes	Sept. 19 1996
D030	All others	Dec. 19, 1994
D031	Mixed with radioactive wastes	Sept. 19, 1996
D031	All others	Dec. 19, 1994

Table 1—Effective Dates of Surface Disposed Wastes (Non-Soil and Debris) Regulated in the LDRS[a]—Comprehensive List

Waste code	Waste category	Effective date
D032	Mixed with radioactive wastes	Sept. 19, 1996
D032	All others	Dec. 19, 1994
D033	Mixed with radioactive wastes	Sept. 19, 1996
D033	All others	Dec. 19, 1994
D034	Mixed with radioactive wastes	Sept. 19, 1996
D034	All others	Dec. 19, 1994
D035	Mixed with radioactive wastes	Sept. 19, 1996
D035	All others	Dec. 19, 1994
D036	Mixed with radioactive wastes	Sept. 19, 1996
D036	All others	Dec. 19, 1994
D037	Mixed with radioactive wastes	Sept. 19, 1996
D037	All others	Dec. 19, 1994
D038	Mixed with radioactive wastes	Sept. 19, 1996
D038	All others	Dec. 19, 1994
D039	Mixed with radioactive wastes	Sept. 19, 1996
D039	All others	Dec. 19, 1994
D040	Mixed with radioactive wastes	Sept. 19, 1996
D040	All others	Dec. 19, 1994
D041	Mixed with radioactive wastes	Sept. 19, 1996
D041	All others	Dec. 19, 1994
D042	Mixed with radioactive wastes	Sept. 19, 1996
D042	All others	Dec. 19, 1994
D043	Mixed with radioactive wastes	Sept. 19, 1996
D043	All others	Dec. 19, 1994
F001	Small quantity generators, CERCLA response/RCRA corrective action, initial generator's solvent-water mixtures, solvent-containing sludges and solids	Nov. 8, 1988
F001	All others	Nov. 8, 1986
F002 (1,1,2-trichloroethane)	Wastewater and Nonwastewater	Aug. 8, 1990
F002	Small quantity generators, CERCLA response/RCRA corrective action, initial generator's solvent-water mixtures, solvent-containing sludges and solids	Nov. 8, 1988
F002	All others	Nov. 8, 1986
F003	Small quantity generators, CERCLA response/RCRA corrective action, initial generator's solvent-water mixtures, solvent-containing sludges and solids	Nov. 8, 1988
F003	All others	Nov. 8, 1986
F004	Small quantity generators, CERCLA response/RCRA corrective action, initial generator's solvent-water mixtures, solvent-containing sludges and solids	Nov. 8, 1988
F004	All others	Nov. 8, 1986
F005 (benzene, 2-ethoxy ethanol, 2-nitropropane)	Wastewater and Nonwastewater	Aug. 8, 1990

Table 1—Effective Dates of Surface Disposed Wastes (Non-Soil and Debris) Regulated in the LDRS[a]—Comprehensive List

Waste code	Waste category	Effective date
F005	Small quantity generators, CERCLA response/RCRA corrective action, initial generator's solvent-water mixtures, solvent-containing sludges and solids	Nov. 8, 1988
F005	All others	Nov. 8, 1986
F006	Wastewater	Aug. 8, 1990
F006	Nonwastewater	Aug. 8, 1988
F006 (cyanides)	Nonwastewater	July 8, 1989
F007	All	July 8, 1989
F008	All	July 8, 1989
F009	All	July 8, 1989
F010	All	June 8, 1989
F011 (cyanides)	Nonwastewater	Dec. 8, 1989
F011	All others	July 8, 1989
F012 (cyanides)	Nonwastewater	Dec. 8, 1989
F012	All others	July 8, 1989
F019	All	Aug. 8, 1990
F020	All	Nov. 8, 1988
F021	All	Nov. 8, 1988
F025	All	Aug. 8, 1990
F026	All	Nov. 8, 1988
F027	All	Nov. 8, 1988
F028	All	Nov. 8, 1988
F032	Mixed with radioactive wastes	May 12, 1999
F032	All others	Aug. 12, 1997
F034	Mixed with radioactive wastes	May 12, 1999
F034	All others	Aug. 12, 1997
F035	Mixed with radioactive wastes	May 12, 1999
F035	All others	Aug. 12, 1997
F037	Not generated from surface impoundment cleanouts or closures	June 30, 1993
F037	Generated from surface impoundment cleanouts or closures	June 30, 1994
F037	Mixed with radioactive wastes	June 30, 1994
F038	Not generated from surface impoundment cleanouts or closures	June 30, 1993
F038	Generated from surface impoundment cleanouts or closures	June 30, 1994
F038	Mixed with radioactive wastes	June 30, 1994
F039	Wastewater	Aug. 8, 1990
F039	Nonwastewater	May 8, 1992
K001 (organics)[b]	All	Aug. 8, 1988
K001	All others	Aug. 8, 1988
K002	All	Aug. 8, 1990
K003	All	Aug. 8, 1990
K004	Wastewater	Aug. 8, 1990
K004	Nonwastewater	Aug. 8, 1988
K005	Wastewater	Aug. 8, 1990
K005	Nonwastewater	June 8, 1989

Table 1—Effective Dates of Surface Disposed Wastes (Non-Soil and Debris) Regulated in the LDRS[a]—Comprehensive List

Waste code	Waste category	Effective date
K006	All	Aug. 8, 1990
K007	Wastewater	Aug. 8, 1990
K007	Nonwastewater	June 8, 1989
K008	Wastewater	Aug. 8, 1990
K008	Nonwastewater	Aug. 8, 1988
K009	All	June 8, 1989
K010	All	June 8, 1989
K011	Wastewater	Aug. 8, 1990
K011	Nonwastewater	June 8, 1989
K013	Wastewater	Aug. 8, 1990
K013	Nonwastewater	June 8, 1989
K014	Wastewater	Aug. 8, 1990
K014	Nonwastewater	June 8, 1989
K015	Wastewater	Aug. 8, 1988
K015	Nonwastewater	Aug. 8, 1990
K016	All	Aug. 8, 1988
K017	All	Aug. 8, 1990
K018	All	Aug. 8, 1988
K019	All	Aug. 8, 1988
K020	All	Aug. 8, 1988
K021	Wastewater	Aug. 8, 1990
K021	Nonwastewater	Aug. 8, 1988
K022	Wastewater	Aug. 8, 1990
K022	Nonwastewater	Aug. 8, 1988
K023	All	June 8, 1989
K024	All	Aug. 8, 1988
K025	Wastewater	Aug. 8, 1990
K025	Nonwastewater	Aug. 8, 1988
K026	All	Aug. 8, 1990
K027	All	June 8, 1989
K028 (metals)	Nonwastewater	Aug. 8, 1990
K028	All others	June 8, 1989
K029	Wastewater	Aug. 8, 1990
K029	Nonwastewater	June 8, 1989
K030	All	Aug. 8, 1988
K031	Wastewater	Aug. 8, 1990
K031	Nonwastewater	May 8, 1992
K032	All	Aug. 8, 1990
K033	All	Aug. 8, 1990
K034	All	Aug. 8, 1990
K035	All	Aug. 8, 1990
K036	Wastewater	June 8, 1989
K036	Nonwastewater	Aug. 8, 1988
K037[b]	Wastewater	Aug. 8, 1988
K037	Nonwastewater	Aug. 8, 1988
K038	All	June 8, 1989
K039	All	June 8, 1989
K040	All	June 8, 1989
K041	All	Aug. 8, 1990
K042	All	Aug. 8, 1990
K043	All	June 8, 1989
K044	All	Aug. 8, 1988
K045	All	Aug. 8, 1988
K046 (Nonreactive)	Nonwastewater	Aug. 8, 1988
K046	All others	Aug. 8, 1990

Table 1—Effective Dates of Surface Disposed Wastes (Non-Soil and Debris) Regulated in the LDRS[a]—Comprehensive List

Waste code	Waste category	Effective date
K047	All	Aug. 8, 1988
K048	Wastewater	Aug. 8, 1990
K048	Nonwastewater	Nov. 8, 1990
K049	Wastewater	Aug. 8, 1990
K049	Nonwastewater	Nov. 8, 1990
K050	Wastewater	Aug. 8, 1990
K050	Nonwastewater	Nov. 8, 1990
K051	Wastewater	Aug. 8, 1990
K051	Nonwastewater	Nov. 8, 1990
K052	Wastewater	Aug. 8, 1990
K052	Nonwastewater	Nov. 8, 1990
K060	Wastewater	Aug. 8, 1990
K060	Nonwastewater	Aug. 8, 1988
K061	Wastewater	Aug. 8, 1990
K061	Nonwastewater	June 30, 1992
K062	All	Aug. 8, 1988
K069 (Non-Calcium Sulfate)	Nonwastewater	Aug. 8, 1988
K069	All others	Aug. 8, 1990
K071	All	Aug. 8, 1990
K073	All	Aug. 8, 1990
K083	All	Aug. 8, 1990
K084	Wastewater	Aug. 8, 1990
K084	Nonwastewater	May 8, 1992
K085	All	Aug. 8, 1990
K086 (organics)[b]	All	Aug. 8, 1988
K086	All others	Aug. 8, 1988
K087	All	Aug. 8, 1988
K088	All others	Oct. 8, 1997
K088	All others	Jan. 8, 1997
K093	All	June 8, 1989
K094	All	June 8, 1989
K095	Wastewater	Aug. 8, 1990
K095	Nonwastewater	June 8, 1989
K096	Wastewater	Aug. 8, 1990
K096	Nonwastewater	June 8, 1989
K097	All	Aug. 8, 1990
K098	All	Aug. 8, 1990
K099	All	Aug. 8, 1988
K100	Wastewater	Aug. 8, 1990
K100	Nonwastewater	Aug. 8, 1988
K101 (organics)	Wastewater	Aug. 8, 1988
K101 (metals)	Wastewater	Aug. 8, 1990
K101 (organics)	Nonwastewater	Aug. 8, 1988
K101 (metals)	Nonwastewater	May 8, 1992
K102 (organics)	Wastewater	Aug. 8, 1988
K102 (metals)	Wastewater	Aug. 8, 1990
K102 (organics)	Nonwastewater	Aug. 8, 1988
K102 (metals)	Nonwastewater	May 8, 1992
K103	All	Aug. 8, 1988
K104	All	Aug. 8, 1988
K105	All	Aug. 8, 1990
K106	Wastewater	Aug. 8, 1990
K106	Nonwastewater	May 8, 1992
K107	Mixed with radioactive wastes	June 30, 1994
K107	All others	Nov. 9, 1992
K108	Mixed with radioactive wastes	June 30, 1994
K108	All others	Nov. 9, 1992
K109	Mixed with radioactive wastes	June 30, 1994
K109	All others	Nov. 9, 1992
K110	Mixed with radioactive wastes	June 30, 1994
K110	All others	Nov. 9, 1992
K111	Mixed with radioactive wastes	June 30, 1994
K111	All others	Nov. 9, 1992
K112	Mixed with radioactive wastes	June 30, 1994
K112	All others	Nov. 9, 1992
K113	All	June 8, 1989
K114	All	June 8, 1989
K115	All	June 8, 1989
K116	All	June 8, 1989
K117	Mixed with radioactive wastes	June 30, 1994
K117	All others	Nov. 9, 1992
K118	Mixed with radioactive wastes	June 30, 1994
K118	All others	Nov. 9, 1992
K123	Mixed with radioactive wastes	June 30, 1994
K123	All others	Nov. 9, 1992
K124	Mixed with radioactive wastes	June 30, 1994
K124	All others	Nov. 9, 1992
K125	Mixed with radioactive wastes	June 30, 1994
K125	All others	Nov. 9, 1992
K126	Mixed with radioactive wastes	June 30, 1994
K126	All others	Nov. 9, 1992
K131	Mixed with radioactive wastes	June 30, 1994
K131	All others	Nov. 9, 1992
K132	Mixed with radioactive wastes	June 30, 1994
K132	All others	Nov. 9, 1992
K136	Mixed with radioactive wastes	June 30, 1994
K136	All others	Nov. 9, 1992
K141	Mixed with radioactive wastes	Sep. 19, 1996
K141	All others	Dec. 19, 1994
K142	Mixed with radioactive wastes	Sep. 19, 1996
K142	All others	Dec. 19, 1994
K143	Mixed with radioactive wastes	Sep. 19, 1996
K143	All others	Dec. 19, 1994
K144	Mixed with radioactive wastes	Sep. 19, 1996
K144	All others	Dec. 19, 1994
K145	Mixed with radioactive wastes	Sep. 19, 1996
K145	All others	Dec. 19, 1994
K147	Mixed with radioactive wastes	Sep. 19, 1996
K147	All others	Dec. 19, 1994
K148	Mixed with radioactive wastes	Sep. 19, 1996
K148	All others	Dec. 19, 1994
K149	Mixed with radioactive wastes	Sep. 19, 1996

Table 1—Effective Dates of Surface Disposed Wastes (Non-Soil and Debris) Regulated in the LDRS[a]—Comprehensive List

Waste code	Waste category	Effective date
K149	All others	Dec. 19, 1994
K150	Mixed with radioactive wastes	Sep. 19, 1996
K150	All others	Dec. 19, 1994
K151	Mixed with radioactive wastes	Sep. 19, 1996
K151	All others	Dec. 19, 1994
K156	Mixed with radioactive wastes	Apr. 8, 1998
K156	All others	July 8, 1996
K157	Mixed with radioactive wastes	Apr. 8, 1998
K157	All others	July 8, 1996
K158	Mixed with radioactive wastes	Apr. 8, 1998
K158	All others	July 8, 1996
K159	Mixed with radioactive wastes	Apr. 8, 1998
K159	All others	July 8, 1996
K160	Mixed with radioactive wastes	Apr. 8, 1998
K160	All others	July 8, 1996
K161	Mixed with radioactive wastes	Apr. 8, 1998
K161	All others	July 8, 1996
P001	All	Aug. 8, 1990
P002	All	Aug. 8, 1990
P003	All	Aug. 8, 1990
P004	All	Aug. 8, 1990
P005	All	Aug. 8, 1990
P006	All	Aug. 8, 1990
P007	All	Aug. 8, 1990
P008	All	Aug. 8, 1990
P009	All	Aug. 8, 1990
P010	Wastewater	Aug. 8, 1990
P010	Nonwastewater	May 8, 1992
P011	Wastewater	Aug. 8, 1990
P011	Nonwastewater	May 8, 1992
P012	Wastewater	Aug. 8, 1990
P012	Nonwastewater	May 8, 1992
P013 (barium)	Nonwastewater	Aug. 8, 1990
P013	All others	June 8, 1989
P014	All	Aug. 8, 1990
P015	All	Aug. 8, 1990
P016	All	Aug. 8, 1990
P017	All	Aug. 8, 1990
P018	All	Aug. 8, 1990
P020	All	Aug. 8, 1990
P021	All	June 8, 1989
P022	All	Aug. 8, 1990
P023	All	Aug. 8, 1990
P024	All	Aug. 8, 1990
P026	All	Aug. 8, 1990
P027	All	Aug. 8, 1990
P028	All	Aug. 8, 1990
P029	All	June 8, 1989
P030	All	June 8, 1989
P031	All	Aug. 8, 1990
P033	All	Aug. 8, 1990
P034	All	Aug. 8, 1990
P036	Wastewater	Aug. 8, 1990
P036	Nonwastewater	May 8, 1992
P037	All	Aug. 8, 1990
P038	Wastewater	Aug. 8, 1990
P038	Nonwastewater	May 8, 1992
P039	All	June 8, 1989
P040	All	June 8, 1989
P041	All	June 8, 1989
P042	All	Aug. 8, 1990
P043	All	June 8, 1989
P044	All	June 8, 1989
P045	All	Aug. 8, 1990
P046	All	Aug. 8, 1990
P047	All	Aug. 8, 1990
P048	All	Aug. 8, 1990
P049	All	Aug. 8, 1990
P050	All	Aug. 8, 1990
P051	All	Aug. 8, 1990
P054	All	Aug. 8, 1990
P056	All	Aug. 8, 1990
P057	All	Aug. 8, 1990
P058	All	Aug. 8, 1990
P059	All	Aug. 8, 1990
P060	All	Aug. 8, 1990
P062	All	June 8, 1989
P063	All	June 8, 1989
P064	All	Aug. 8, 1990
P065	Wastewater	Aug. 8, 1990
P065	Nonwastewater	May 8, 1992
P066	All	Aug. 8, 1990
P067	All	Aug. 8, 1990
P068	All	Aug. 8, 1990
P069	All	Aug. 8, 1990
P070	All	Aug. 8, 1990
P071	All	June 8, 1989
P072	All	Aug. 8, 1990
P073	All	Aug. 8, 1990
P074	All	June 8, 1989
P075	All	Aug. 8, 1990
P076	All	Aug. 8, 1990
P077	All	Aug. 8, 1990
P078	All	Aug. 8, 1990
P081	All	Aug. 8, 1990
P082	All	Aug. 8, 1990
P084	All	Aug. 8, 1990
P085	All	June 8, 1989
P087	All	May 8, 1992
P088	All	Aug. 8, 1990
P089	All	June 8, 1989
P092	Wastewater	Aug. 8, 1990
P092	Nonwastewater	May 8, 1992
P093	All	Aug. 8, 1990
P094	All	June 8, 1989
P095	All	Aug. 8, 1990
P096	All	Aug. 8, 1990
P097	All	June 8, 1989
P098	All	June 8, 1989
P099 (silver)	Wastewater	Aug. 8, 1990
P099	All others	June 8, 1989

Table 1—Effective Dates of Surface Disposed Wastes (Non-Soil and Debris) Regulated in the LDRS[a]—Comprehensive List

Waste code	Waste category	Effective date
P101	All	Aug. 8, 1990
P102	All	Aug. 8, 1990
P103	All	Aug. 8, 1990
P104 (silver)	Wastewater	Aug. 8, 1990
P104	All others	June 8, 1989
P105	All	Aug. 8, 1990
P106	All	June 8, 1989
P108	All	Aug. 8, 1990
P109	All	June 8, 1989
P110	All	Aug. 8, 1990
P111	All	June 8, 1989
P112	All	Aug. 8, 1990
P113	All	Aug. 8, 1990
P114	All	Aug. 8, 1990
P115	All	Aug. 8, 1990
P116	All	Aug. 8, 1990
P118	All	Aug. 8, 1990
P119	All	Aug. 8, 1990
P120	All	Aug. 8, 1990
P121	All	June 8, 1989
P122	All	Aug. 8, 1990
P123	All	Aug. 8, 1990
P127	Mixed with radioactive wastes	Apr. 8, 1998
P127	All others	July 8, 1996
P128	Mixed with radioactive wastes	Apr. 8, 1998
P128	All others	July 8, 1996
P185	Mixed with radioactive wastes	Apr. 8, 1998
P185	All others	July 8, 1996
P188	Mixed with radioactive wastes	Apr. 8, 1998
P188	All others	July 8, 1996
P189	Mixed with radioactive wastes	Apr. 8, 1998
P189	All others	July 8, 1996
P190	Mixed with radioactive wastes	Apr. 8, 1998
P190	All others	July 8, 1996
P191	Mixed with radioactive wastes	Apr. 8, 1998
P191	All others	July 8, 1996
P192	Mixed with radioactive wastes	Apr. 8, 1998
P192	All others	July 8, 1996
P194	Mixed with radioactive wastes	Apr. 8, 1998
P194	All others	July 8, 1996
P196	Mixed with radioactive wastes	Apr. 8, 1998
P196	All others	July 8, 1996
P197	Mixed with radioactive wastes	Apr. 8, 1998
P197	All others	July 8, 1996
P198	Mixed with radioactive wastes	Apr. 8, 1998
P198	All others	July 8, 1996
P199	Mixed with radioactive wastes	Apr. 8, 1998
P199	All others	July 8, 1996
P201	Mixed with radioactive wastes	Apr. 8, 1998
P201	All others	July 8, 1996
P202	Mixed with radioactive wastes	Apr. 8, 1998
P202	All others	July 8, 1996
P203	Mixed with radioactive wastes	Apr. 8, 1998
P203	All others	July 8, 1996
P204	Mixed with radioactive wastes	Apr. 8, 1998
P204	All others	July 8, 1996

Table 1—Effective Dates of Surface Disposed Wastes (Non-Soil and Debris) Regulated in the LDRS[a]—Comprehensive List

Waste code	Waste category	Effective date
P205	Mixed with radioactive wastes	Apr. 8, 1998
P205	All others	July 8, 1996
U001	All	Aug. 8, 1990
U002	All	Aug. 8, 1990
U003	All	Aug. 8, 1990
U004	All	Aug. 8, 1990
U005	All	Aug. 8, 1990
U006	All	Aug. 8, 1990
U007	All	Aug. 8, 1990
U008	All	Aug. 8, 1990
U009	All	Aug. 8, 1990
U010	All	Aug. 8, 1990
U011	All	Aug. 8, 1990
U012	All	Aug. 8, 1990
U014	All	Aug. 8, 1990
U015	All	Aug. 8, 1990
U016	All	Aug. 8, 1990
U017	All	Aug. 8, 1990
U018	All	Aug. 8, 1990
U019	All	Aug. 8, 1990
U020	All	Aug. 8, 1990
U021	All	Aug. 8, 1990
U022	All	Aug. 8, 1990
U023	All	Aug. 8, 1990
U024	All	Aug. 8, 1990
U025	All	Aug. 8, 1990
U026	All	Aug. 8, 1990
U027	All	Aug. 8, 1990
U028	All	June 8, 1989
U029	All	Aug. 8, 1990
U030	All	Aug. 8, 1990
U031	All	Aug. 8, 1990
U032	All	Aug. 8, 1990
U033	All	Aug. 8, 1990
U034	All	Aug. 8, 1990
U035	All	Aug. 8, 1990
U036	All	Aug. 8, 1990
U037	All	Aug. 8, 1990
U038	All	Aug. 8, 1990
U039	All	Aug. 8, 1990
U041	All	Aug. 8, 1990
U042	All	Aug. 8, 1990
U043	All	Aug. 8, 1990
U044	All	Aug. 8, 1990
U045	All	Aug. 8, 1990
U046	All	Aug. 8, 1990
U047	All	Aug. 8, 1990
U049	All	Aug. 8, 1990
U048	All	Aug. 8, 1990
U050	All	Aug. 8, 1990
U051	All	Aug. 8, 1990
U052	All	Aug. 8, 1990
U053	All	Aug. 8, 1990
U055	All	Aug. 8, 1990
U056	All	Aug. 8, 1990
U057	All	Aug. 8, 1990

Table 1—Effective Dates of Surface Disposed Wastes (Non-Soil and Debris) Regulated in the LDRS[a]—Comprehensive List

Waste code	Waste category	Effective date
U058	All	June 8, 1989
U059	All	Aug. 8, 1990
U060	All	Aug. 8, 1990
U061	All	Aug. 8, 1990
U062	All	Aug. 8, 1990
U063	All	Aug. 8, 1990
U064	All	Aug. 8, 1990
U066	All	Aug. 8, 1990
U067	All	Aug. 8, 1990
U068	All	Aug. 8, 1990
U069	All	June 30, 1992
U070	All	Aug. 8, 1990
U071	All	Aug. 8, 1990
U072	All	Aug. 8, 1990
U073	All	Aug. 8, 1990
U074	All	Aug. 8, 1990
U075	All	Aug. 8, 1990
U076	All	Aug. 8, 1990
U077	All	Aug. 8, 1990
U078	All	Aug. 8, 1990
U079	All	Aug. 8, 1990
U080	All	Aug. 8, 1990
U081	All	Aug. 8, 1990
U082	All	Aug. 8, 1990
U083	All	Aug. 8, 1990
U084	All	Aug. 8, 1990
U085	All	Aug. 8, 1990
U086	All	Aug. 8, 1990
U087	All	June 8, 1989
U088	All	June 8, 1989
U089	All	Aug. 8, 1990
U090	All	Aug. 8, 1990
U091	All	Aug. 8, 1990
U092	All	Aug. 8, 1990
U093	All	Aug. 8, 1990
U094	All	Aug. 8, 1990
U095	All	Aug. 8, 1990
U096	All	Aug. 8, 1990
U097	All	Aug. 8, 1990
U098	All	Aug. 8, 1990
U099	All	Aug. 8, 1990
U101	All	Aug. 8, 1990
U102	All	June 8, 1989
U103	All	Aug. 8, 1990
U105	All	Aug. 8, 1990
U106	All	Aug. 8, 1990
U107	All	June 8, 1989
U108	All	Aug. 8, 1990
U109	All	Aug. 8, 1990
U110	All	Aug. 8, 1990
U111	All	Aug. 8, 1990
U112	All	Aug. 8, 1990
U113	All	Aug. 8, 1990
U114	All	Aug. 8, 1990
U115	All	Aug. 8, 1990
U116	All	Aug. 8, 1990

Table 1—Effective Dates of Surface Disposed Wastes (Non-Soil and Debris) Regulated in the LDRS[a]—Comprehensive List

Waste code	Waste category	Effective date
U117	All	Aug. 8, 1990
U118	All	Aug. 8, 1990
U119	All	Aug. 8, 1990
U120	All	Aug. 8, 1990
U121	All	Aug. 8, 1990
U122	All	Aug. 8, 1990
U123	All	Aug. 8, 1990
U124	All	Aug. 8, 1990
U125	All	Aug. 8, 1990
U126	All	Aug. 8, 1990
U127	All	Aug. 8, 1990
U128	All	Aug. 8, 1990
U129	All	Aug. 8, 1990
U130	All	Aug. 8, 1990
U131	All	Aug. 8, 1990
U132	All	Aug. 8, 1990
U133	All	Aug. 8, 1990
U134	All	Aug. 8, 1990
U135	All	Aug. 8, 1990
U136	Wastewater	Aug. 8, 1990
U136	Nonwastewater	May 8, 1992
U137	All	Aug. 8, 1990
U138	All	Aug. 8, 1990
U140	All	Aug. 8, 1990
U141	All	Aug. 8, 1990
U142	All	Aug. 8, 1990
U143	All	Aug. 8, 1990
U144	All	Aug. 8, 1990
U145	All	Aug. 8, 1990
U146	All	Aug. 8, 1990
U147	All	Aug. 8, 1990
U148	All	Aug. 8, 1990
U149	All	Aug. 8, 1990
U150	All	Aug. 8, 1990
U151	Wastewater	Aug. 8, 1990
U151	Nonwastewater	May 8, 1992
U152	All	Aug. 8, 1990
U153	All	Aug. 8, 1990
U154	All	Aug. 8, 1990
U155	All	Aug. 8, 1990
U156	All	Aug. 8, 1990
U157	All	Aug. 8, 1990
U158	All	Aug. 8, 1990
U159	All	Aug. 8, 1990
U160	All	Aug. 8, 1990
U161	All	Aug. 8, 1990
U162	All	Aug. 8, 1990
U163	All	Aug. 8, 1990
U164	All	Aug. 8, 1990
U165	All	Aug. 8, 1990
U166	All	Aug. 8, 1990
U167	All	Aug. 8, 1990
U168	All	Aug. 8, 1990
U169	All	Aug. 8, 1990
U170	All	Aug. 8, 1990
U171	All	Aug. 8, 1990

Table 1—Effective Dates of Surface Disposed Wastes (Non-Soil and Debris) Regulated in the LDRS[a]—Comprehensive List

Waste code	Waste category	Effective date
U172	All	Aug. 8, 1990
U173	All	Aug. 8, 1990
U174	All	Aug. 8, 1990
U176	All	Aug. 8, 1990
U177	All	Aug. 8, 1990
U178	All	Aug. 8, 1990
U179	All	Aug. 8, 1990
U180	All	Aug. 8, 1990
U181	All	Aug. 8, 1990
U182	All	Aug. 8, 1990
U183	All	Aug. 8, 1990
U184	All	Aug. 8, 1990
U185	All	Aug. 8, 1990
U186	All	Aug. 8, 1990
U187	All	Aug. 8, 1990
U188	All	Aug. 8, 1990
U189	All	Aug. 8, 1990
U190	All	June 8, 1989
U191	All	Aug. 8, 1990
U192	All	Aug. 8, 1990
U193	All	Aug. 8, 1990
U194	All	June 8, 1989
U196	All	Aug. 8, 1990
U197	All	Aug. 8, 1990
U200	All	Aug. 8, 1990
U201	All	Aug. 8, 1990
U202	All	Aug. 8, 1990
U203	All	Aug. 8, 1990
U204	All	Aug. 8, 1990
U205	All	Aug. 8, 1990
U206	All	Aug. 8, 1990
U207	All	Aug. 8, 1990
U208	All	Aug. 8, 1990
U209	All	Aug. 8, 1990
U210	All	Aug. 8, 1990
U211	All	Aug. 8, 1990
U213	All	Aug. 8, 1990
U214	All	Aug. 8, 1990
U215	All	Aug. 8, 1990
U216	All	Aug. 8, 1990
U217	All	Aug. 8, 1990
U218	All	Aug. 8, 1990
U219	All	Aug. 8, 1990
U220	All	Aug. 8, 1990
U221	All	June 8, 1989
U222	All	Aug. 8, 1990
U223	All	June 8, 1989
U225	All	Aug. 8, 1990
U226	All	Aug. 8, 1990
U227	All	Aug. 8, 1990
U228	All	Aug. 8, 1990
U234	All	Aug. 8, 1990
U235	All	June 8, 1989
U236	All	Aug. 8, 1990
U237	All	Aug. 8, 1990
U238	All	Aug. 8, 1990

Table 1—Effective Dates of Surface Disposed Wastes (Non-Soil and Debris) Regulated in the LDRS[a]—Comprehensive List

Waste code	Waste category	Effective date
U239	All	Aug. 8, 1990
U240	All	Aug. 8, 1990
U243	All	Aug. 8, 1990
U244	All	Aug. 8, 1990
U246	All	Aug. 8, 1990
U247	All	Aug. 8, 1990
U248	All	Aug. 8, 1990
U249	All	Aug. 8, 1990
U271	Mixed with radioactive wastes	Apr. 8, 1998
U271	All others	July 8, 1996
U277	Mixed with radioactive wastes	Apr. 8, 1998
U277	All others	July 8, 1996
U278	Mixed with radioactive wastes	Apr. 8, 1998
U278	All others	July 8, 1996
U279	Mixed with radioactive wastes	Apr. 8, 1998
U279	All others	July 8, 1996
U280	Mixed with radioactive wastes	Apr. 8, 1998
U280	All others	July 8, 1996
U328	Mixed with radioactive wastes	June 30, 1994
U328	All others	Nov. 9, 1992
U353	Mixed with radioactive wastes	June 30, 1994
U353	All others	Nov. 9, 1992
U359	Mixed with radioactive wastes	June 30, 1994
U359	All others	Nov. 9, 1992
U364	Mixed with radioactive wastes	Apr. 8, 1998
U364	All others	July 8, 1996
U365	Mixed with radioactive wastes	Apr. 8, 1998
U365	All others	July 8, 1996
U366	Mixed with radioactive wastes	Apr. 8, 1998
U366	All others	July 8, 1996
U367	Mixed with radioactive wastes	Apr. 8, 1998
U367	All others	July 8, 1996
U372	Mixed with radioactive wastes	Apr. 8, 1998
U372	All others	July 8, 1996
U373	Mixed with radioactive wastes	Apr. 8, 1998
U373	All others	July 8, 1996
U375	Mixed with radioactive wastes	Apr. 8, 1998
U375	All others	July 8, 1996
U376	Mixed with radioactive wastes	Apr. 8, 1998
U376	All others	July 8, 1996
U377	Mixed with radioactive wastes	Apr. 8, 1998
U377	All others	July 8, 1996
U378	Mixed with radioactive wastes	Apr. 8, 1998
U378	All others	July 8, 1996
U379	Mixed with radioactive wastes	Apr. 8, 1998
U379	All others	July 8, 1996
U381	Mixed with radioactive wastes	Apr. 8, 1998
U381	All others	July 8, 1996
U382	Mixed with radioactive wastes	Apr. 8, 1998
U382	All others	July 8, 1996
U383	Mixed with radioactive wastes	Apr. 8, 1998
U383	All others	July 8, 1996
U384	Mixed with radioactive wastes	Apr. 8, 1998
U384	All others	July 8, 1996
U385	Mixed with radioactive wastes	Apr. 8, 1998
U385	All others	July 8, 1996

Table 1—Effective Dates of Surface Disposed Wastes (Non-Soil and Debris) Regulated in the LDRS[a]—Comprehensive List

Waste code	Waste category	Effective date
U386	Mixed with radioactive wastes	Apr. 8, 1998
U386	All others	July 8, 1996
U387	Mixed with radioactive wastes	Apr. 8, 1998
U387	All others	July 8, 1996
U389	Mixed with radioactive wastes	Apr. 8, 1998
U389	All others	July 8, 1996
U390	Mixed with radioactive wastes	Apr. 8, 1998
U390	All others	July 8, 1996
U391	Mixed with radioactive wastes	Apr. 8, 1998
U391	All others	July 8, 1996
U392	Mixed with radioactive wastes	Apr. 8, 1998
U392	All others	July 8, 1996
U393	Mixed with radioactive wastes	Apr. 8, 1998
U393	All others	July 8, 1996
U394	Mixed with radioactive wastes	Apr. 8, 1998
U394	All others	July 8, 1996
U395	Mixed with radioactive wastes	Apr. 8, 1998
U395	All others	July 8, 1996
U396	Mixed with radioactive wastes	Apr. 8, 1998
U396	All others	July 8, 1996
U400	Mixed with radioactive wastes	Apr. 8, 1998
U400	All others	July 8, 1996
U401	Mixed with radioactive wastes	Apr. 8, 1998
U401	All others	July 8, 1996
U402	Mixed with radioactive wastes	Apr. 8, 1998
U402	All others	July 8, 1996
U403	Mixed with radioactive wastes	Apr. 8, 1998
U403	All others	July 8, 1996
U404	Mixed with radioactive wastes	Apr. 8, 1998
U404	All others	July 8, 1996
U407	Mixed with radioactive wastes	Apr. 8, 1998
U407	All others	July 8, 1996
U409	Mixed with radioactive wastes	Apr. 8, 1998
U409	All others	July 8, 1996
U410	Mixed with radioactive wastes	Apr. 8, 1998
U410	All others	July 8, 1996
U411	Mixed with radioactive wastes	Apr. 8, 1998
U411	All others	July 8, 1996

[a] This table does not include mixed radioactive wastes (from the First, Second, and Third Third rules) which received national capacity variance until May 8, 1992 This table also does not include contaminated soil and debris wastes.

[b] The standard was revised in the Third Third Final Rule (55 FR 22520, June 1, 1990).

[c] The standard was revised in the Third Third Emergency Rule (58 FR 29860, May 24, 1993); the original effective date was August 8, 1990.

[d] The standard was revised in the Phase II Final Rule (59 FR 47982, Sept. 19, 1994); the original effective date was August 8, 1990.

[e] The standards for selected reactive wastes was revised in the Phase III Final Rule (61 FR 15566, Apr. 8, 1996); the original effective date was August 8, 1990.

Table 2—Summary of Effective Dates of Land Disposal Restrictions for Contaminated Soil and Debris (CSD)

Restricted hazardous waste in CSD	Effective date
1. Solvent-(F001-F005) and dioxin-(F020-F023 and F026-F028) containing soil and debris from CERCLA response or RCRA corrective actions	Nov. 8, 1990
2. Soil and debris not from CERCLA response or RCRA corrective actions contaminated with less than 1% total solvents (F001-F005) or dioxins (F020-F023 and F026-F028)	Nov. 8, 1988
3. All soil and debris contaminated with First Third wastes for which treatment standards are based on incineration	Aug. 8, 1990
4. All soil and debris contaminated with Second Third wastes for which treatment standards are based on incineration	June 8, 1991
5. All soil and debris contaminated with Third Third wastes or, First or Second Third "soft hammer" wastes which had treatment standards promulgated in the Third Third rule, for which treatment standards are based on incineration, vitrification, or mercury retorting, acid leaching followed by chemical precipitation, or thermal recovery of metals; as well as all inorganic solids debris contaminated with D004-D011 wastes, and all soil and debris contaminated with mixed RCRA/radioactive wastes	May 8, 1992
6. Soil and debris contaminated with D012-D043, K141-K145, and K147-151 wastes	Dec. 19, 1994
7. Debris (only) contaminated with F037, F038, K107-K112, K117, K118, K123-K126, K131, K132, K136, U328, U353, U359	Dec. 19, 1994
8. Soil and debris contaminated with K156-K161, P127, P128, P188-P192, P194, P196-P199, P201-P205, U271, U277-U280, U364-U367, U372, U373, U375-U379, U381-U387, U389-U396, U400-U404, U407, and U409-U411 wastes	July 8, 1996
9. Soil and debris contaminated with K088 wastes	Oct. 8, 1997
10. Soil and debris contaminated with radioactive wastes mixed with K088, K156-K161, P127, P128, P188-P192, P194, P196-P199, P201-P205, U271, U277-U280, U364-U367, U372, U373, U375-U379, U381-U387, U389-U396, U400-U404, U407, and U409-U411 wastes	April 8, 1998
11. Soil and debris contaminated with F032, F034, and F035	May 12, 1997
12. Soil and debris contaminated with newly identified D004-D011 toxicity characteristic wastes and mineral processing wastes	Aug. 24, 1998
13. Soil and debris contaminated with mixed radioactive newly identified D004-D011 characteristic wastes and mineral processing wastes	May 26, 2000

Note: Appendix VII is provided for the convenience of the reader.

[62 FR 26025, May 12, 1997, as amended at 63 FR 28751, May 26, 1998; 65 FR 36367, June 8, 2000; 66 FR 27297, May 16, 2001]

Appendix VIII to Part 268—LDR Effective Dates of Injected Prohibited Hazardous Wastes

13.1.5

National Capacity LDR Variances for UIC Wastes[a]

Waste code	Waste category	Effective date
F001-F005	All spent F001-F005 solvent containing less than 1 percent total F001-F005 solvent constituents	Aug. 8, 1990
D001 (except High TOC Ignitable Liquids Subcategory)[c]	All	Feb. 10, 1994
D001 (High TOC Ignitable Characteristic Liquids Subcategory)	Nonwastewater	Sept. 19, 1995
D002[b]	All	May 8, 1992
D002[c]	All	Feb. 10, 1994
D003 (cyanides)	All	May 8, 1992
D003 (sulfides)	All	May 8, 1992
D003 (explosives, reactives)	All	May 8, 1992
D007	All	May 8, 1992
D009	Nonwastewater	May 8, 1992
D012	All	Sept. 19, 1995
D013	All	Sept. 19, 1995
D014	All	Sept. 19, 1995
D015	All	Sept. 19, 1995
D016	All	Sept. 19, 1995
D017	All	Sept. 19, 1995
D018	All, including mixed with radioactive wastes	Apr. 8, 1998
D019	All, including mixed with radioactive wastes	Apr. 8, 1998
D020	All, including mixed with radioactive wastes	Apr. 8, 1998
D021	All, including mixed with radioactive wastes	Apr. 8, 1998
D022	All, including mixed with radioactive wastes	Apr. 8, 1998
D023	All, including mixed radioactive wastes	Apr. 8, 1998
D024	All, including mixed radioactive wastes	Apr. 8, 1998
D025	All, including mixed radioactive wastes	Apr. 8, 1998
D026	All, including mixed radioactive wastes	Apr. 8, 1998
D027	All, including mixed radioactive wastes	Apr. 8, 1998
D028	All, including mixed radioactive wastes	Apr. 8, 1998

National Capacity LDR Variances for UIC Wastes[a]

Waste code	Waste category	Effective date
D029	All, including mixed radioactive wastes	Apr. 8, 1998
D030	All, including mixed radioactive wastes	Apr. 8, 1998
D031	All, including mixed radioactive wastes	Apr. 8, 1998
D032	All, including mixed radioactive wastes	Apr. 8, 1998
D033	All, including mixed radioactive wastes	Apr. 8, 1998
D034	All, including mixed radioactive wastes	Apr. 8, 1998
D035	All, including mixed radioactive wastes	Apr. 8, 1998
D036	All, including mixed radioactive wastes	Apr. 8, 1998
D037	All, including mixed radioactive wastes	Apr. 8, 1998
D038	All, including mixed radioactive wastes	Apr. 8, 1998
D039	All, including mixed radioactive wastes	Apr. 8, 1998
D040	All, including mixed radioactive wastes	Apr. 8, 1998
D041	All, including mixed radioactive wastes	Apr. 8, 1998
D042	All, including mixed radioactive wastes	Apr. 8, 1998
D043	All, including mixed radioactive wastes	Apr. 8, 1998
F007	All	June 8, 1991
F032	All, including mixed radioactive wastes	May 12, 1999
F034	All, including mixed radioactive wastes	May 12, 1999
F035	All, including mixed radioactive wastes	May 12, 1999
F037	All	Nov. 8, 1992
F038	All	Nov. 8, 1992
F039	Wastewater	May 8, 1992
K009	Wastewater	June 8, 1991
K011	Nonwastewater	June 8, 1991
K011	Wastewater	May 8, 1992
K013	Nonwastewater	June 8, 1991
K013	Wastewater	May 8, 1992
K014	All	May 8, 1992
K016 (dilute)	All	June 8, 1991
K049	All	Aug. 8, 1990
K050	All	Aug. 8, 1990
K051	All	Aug. 8, 1990
K052	All	Aug. 8, 1990
K062	All	Aug. 8, 1990
K071	All	Aug. 8, 1990
K088	All	Jan. 8, 1997
K104	All	Aug. 8, 1990
K107	All	Nov. 8, 1992
K108	All	Nov. 9, 1992
K109	All	Nov. 9, 1992
K110	All	Nov. 9, 1992
K111	All	Nov. 9, 1992
K112	All	Nov. 9, 1992
K117	All	June 30, 1995
K118	All	June 30, 1995
K123	All	Nov. 9, 1992
K124	All	Nov. 9, 1992

National Capacity LDR Variances for UIC Wastes[a]

Waste code	Waste category	Effective date
K125	All	Nov. 9, 1992
K126	All	Nov. 9, 1992
K131	All	June 30, 1995
K132	All	June 30, 1995
K136	All	Nov. 9, 1992
K141	All	Dec. 19, 1994
K142	All	Dec. 19, 1994
K143	All	Dec. 19, 1994
K144	All	Dec. 19, 1994
K145	All	Dec. 19, 1994
K147	All	Dec. 19, 1994
K148	All	Dec. 19, 1994
K149	All	Dec. 19, 1994
K150	All	Dec. 19, 1994
K151	All	Dec. 19, 1994
K156	All	July 8, 1996
K157	All	July 8, 1996
K158	All	July 8, 1996
K159	All	July 8, 1996
K160	All	July 8, 1996
K161	All	July 8, 1996
NA	Newly identified mineral processing wastes from titanium dioxide production and mixed radioactive/ newly identified D004-D011 characteristic wastes and mineral processing wastes	May 26, 2000
P127	All	July 8, 1996
P128	All	July 8, 1996
P185	All	July 8, 1996
P188	All	July 8, 1996
P189	All	July 8, 1996
P190	All	July 8, 1996
P191	All	July 8, 1996
P192	All	July 8, 1996
P194	All	July 8, 1996
P196	All	July 8, 1996
P197	All	July 8, 1996
P198	All	July 8, 1996
P199	All	July 8, 1996
P201	All	July 8, 1996
P202	All	July 8, 1996
P203	All	July 8, 1996
P204	All	July 8, 1996
P205	All	July 8, 1996
U271	All	July 8, 1996
U277	All	July 8, 1996
U278	All	July 8, 1996
U279	All	July 8, 1996
U280	All	July 8, 1996
U328	All	Nov. 9, 1992
U353	All	Nov. 9, 1992
U359	All	Nov. 9, 1992
U364	All	July 8, 1996
U365	All	July 8, 1996
U366	All	July 8, 1996
U367	All	July 8, 1996
U372	All	July 8, 1996
U373	All	July 8, 1996
U375	All	July 8, 1996
U376	All	July 8, 1996
U377	All	July 8, 1996
U378	All	July 8, 1996
U379	All	July 8, 1996
U381	All	July 8, 1996
U382	All	July 8, 1996
U383	All	July 8, 1996
U384	All	July 8, 1996
U385	All	July 8, 1996
U386	All	July 8, 1996
U387	All	July 8, 1996
U389	All	July 8, 1996
U390	All	July 8, 1996
U391	All	July 8, 1996
U392	All	July 8, 1996
U395	All	July 8, 1996
U396	All	July 8, 1996
U400	All	July 8, 1996
U401	All	July 8, 1996
U402	All	July 8, 1996
U403	All	July 8, 1996
U404	All	July 8, 1996
U407	All	July 8, 1996
U409	All	July 8, 1996
U410	All	July 8, 1996
U411	All	July 8, 1996

[a] Wastes that are deep well disposed on-site receive a six-month variance, with restrictions effective in November 1990.

[b] Deepwell injected D002 liquids with a pH less than 2 must meet the California List treatment standards on August 8, 1990.

[c] Managed in systems defined in 40 CFR 144.6(e) and 14.6(e) as Class V injection wells, that do not engage in CWA-equivalent treatment before injection.

Note: This table is provided for the convenience of the reader.

[62 FR 26037, May 12, 1997, as amended at 63 FR 28752, May 26, 1998; 71 FR 40279, July 14, 2006]

Appendix IX to Part 268—Extraction Procedure (EP) Toxicity Test Method and Structural Integrity Test (Method 1310B)

Note: The EP (Method 1310B) is published in "Test Methods for Evaluating Solid Waste, Physical/Chemical Methods," EPA Publication SW–846, as incorporated by reference in §260.11 of this chapter.

[58 FR 46051, Aug. 31, 1993; 70 FR 34590, June 14, 2005]

Appendix X to Part 268 [Reserved]

Appendix XI to Part 268—Metal Bearing Wastes Prohibited From Dilution in a Combustion Unit According to 40 CFR 268.3(c)[1]

13.11.3

Waste code	Waste description
D004	Toxicity Characteristic for Arsenic
D005	Toxicity Characteristic for Barium
D006	Toxicity Characteristic for Cadmium
D007	Toxicity Characteristic for Chromium
D008	Toxicity Characteristic for Lead
D009	Toxicity Characteristic for Mercury
D010	Toxicity Characteristic for Selenium
D011	Toxicity Characteristic for Silver
F006	Wastewater treatment sludges from electroplating operations except from the following processes: (1) sulfuric acid anodizing of aluminum; (2) tin plating carbon steel; (3) zinc plating (segregated basis) on carbon steel; (4) aluminum or zinc-plating on carbon steel; (5) cleaning/stripping associated with tin, zinc and aluminum plating on carbon steel; and (6) chemical etching and milling of aluminum
F007	Spent cyanide plating bath solutions from electroplating operations
F008	Plating bath residues from the bottom of plating baths from electroplating operations where cyanides are used in the process
F009	Spent stripping and cleaning bath solutions from electroplating operations where cyanides are used in the process
F010	Quenching bath residues from oil baths from metal treating operations where cyanides are used in the process
F011	Spent cyanide solutions from salt bath pot cleaning from metal heat treating operations
F012	Quenching waste water treatment sludges from metal heat treating operations where cyanides are used in the process
F019	Wastewater treatment sludges from the chemical conversion coating of aluminum except from zirconium phosphating in aluminum car washing when such phosphating is an exclusive conversion coating process
K002	Wastewater treatment sludge from the production of chrome yellow and orange pigments
K003	Wastewater treatment sludge from the production of molybdate orange pigments
K004	Wastewater treatment sludge from the production of zinc yellow pigments
K005	Wastewater treatment sludge from the production of chrome green pigments
K006	Wastewater treatment sludge from the production of chrome oxide green pigments (anhydrous and hydrated)
K007	Wastewater treatment sludge from the production of iron blue pigments
K008	Oven residue from the production of chrome oxide green pigments
K061	Emission control dust/sludge from the primary production of steel in electric furnaces
K069	Emission control dust/sludge from secondary lead smelting
K071	Brine purification muds from the mercury cell processes in chlorine production, where separately prepurified brine is not used
K100	Waste leaching solution from acid leaching of emission control dust/sludge from secondary lead smelting
K106	Sludges from the mercury cell processes for making chlorine
P010	Arsenic acid H_3AsO_4
P011	Arsenic oxide As_2O_5
P012	Arsenic trioxide
P013	Barium cyanide
P015	Beryllium
P029	Copper cyanide Cu(CN)
P074	Nickel cyanide $Ni(CN)_2$
P087	Osmium tetroxide
P099	Potassium silver cyanide
P104	Silver cyanide
P113	Thallic oxide
P114	Thallium (I) selenite
P115	Thallium (I) sulfate
P119	Ammonium vanadate
P120	Vanadium oxide V_2O_5
P121	Zinc cyanide
U032	Calcium chromate
U145	Lead phosphate
U151	Mercury
U204	Selenious acid
U205	Selenium disulfide
U216	Thallium (I) chloride
U217	Thallium (I) nitrate

[1] A combustion unit is defined as any thermal technology subject to 40 CFR part 264, subpart O; Part 265, subpart O; and/or 266, subpart H.

[61 FR 15658, Apr. 8, 1996]

PART 270—EPA ADMINISTERED PERMIT PROGRAMS: THE HAZARDOUS WASTE PERMIT PROGRAM

Authority: 42 U.S.C. 6905, 6912, 6924, 6925, 6927, 6939 and 6974.

Source: 48 FR 14228, Apr. 1, 1983, unless otherwise noted.

Subpart A—General Information

§270.1 Purpose and scope of these regulations.

(a) *Coverage.* (1) These permit regulations establish provisions for the Hazardous Waste Permit Program under Subtitle C of the Solid Waste Disposal Act, as amended by the Resource Conservation and Recovery Act of 1976, as amended (RCRA), (Pub. L. 94-580, as amended by Pub. L. 95-609 and by Pub. L. 96-482; 42 U.S.C. 6091 *et seq.*). They apply to EPA and to approved States to the extent provided in part 271.

(2) The regulations in this part cover basic EPA permitting requirements, such as application requirements, standard permit conditions, and monitoring and reporting requirements. These regulations are part of a regulatory scheme implementing RCRA set forth in different parts of the *Code of Federal Regulations.* The following chart indicates where the regulations implementing RCRA appear in the *Code of Federal Regulations.*

Section of RCRA	Coverage	Final regulation
Subtitle C	Overview and definitions	40 CFR part 260
3001	Identification and listing of hazardous waste	40 CFR part 261
3002	Generators of hazardous waste	40 CFR part 262
3003	Transporters of hazardous waste	40 CFR part 263
3004	Standards for HWM facilities	40 CFR parts 264, 265, 266, and 267
3005	Permit requirements for HWM facilities	40 CFR parts 270 and 124
3006	Guidelines for State programs	40 CFR part 271
3010	Preliminary notification of HWM activity	(public notice) 45 FR 12746 February 26, 1980

(3) *Technical regulations.* The RCRA permit program has separate additional Regulations that contain technical requirements. These separate regulations are used by permit issuing authorities to determine what requirements must be placed in permits if they are issued. These separate regulations are located in 40 CFR parts 264, 266, and 267.

(b) *Overview of the RCRA Permit Program.* Not later than 90 days after the promulgation or revision of regulations in 40 CFR part 261 (identifying and listing hazardous wastes) generators and transporters of hazardous waste, and owners or operators of hazardous waste treatment, storage, or disposal facilities may be required to file a notification of that activity under section 3010. Six months after the initial promulgation of the part 261 regulations, treatment, storage, or disposal of hazardous waste by any person who has not applied for or received a RCRA permit is prohibited. Treatment, storage, and disposal facilities (TSDs) that are otherwise subject to permitting under RCRA and that meet the criteria in paragraph (b)(1), or paragraph (b)(2) of this section, may be eligible for a standardized permit under subpart J of this part. A RCRA permit application consists of two parts, part A (see §270.13) and part B (see §270.14 and applicable sections in §§270.15 through 270.29). For "existing HWM facilities," the requirement to submit an application is satisfied by submitting only part A of the permit application until the date the Director sets for submitting part B of the application. (Part A consists of Forms 1 and 3 of the Consolidated Permit Application Forms.) Timely submission of both notification under section 3010 and part A qualifies owners and operators of existing HWM facilities (who are required to have a permit) for interim status under section 3005(e) of RCRA. Facility owners and operators with interim status are treated as having been issued a permit until EPA or a State with interim authorization for Phase II or final authorization under part 271 makes a final determination on the permit application. Facility owners and operators with interim status must comply with interim status standards set forth at 40 CFR part 265 and 266 or with the analogous provisions of a State program which has received interim or final authorization under part 271. Facility owners and operators with interim status are not relieved from complying with other State requirements. For existing HWM facilities, the Director shall set a date, giving at least six months notice, for submission of part B of the application. There is no form for part B of the application; rather, part B must be submitted in narrative form and contain the information set forth in the applicable sections of §§270.14 through 270.29. Owners or operators of new HWM facilities must submit parts A and B of the permit application at least 180 days before physical construction is expected to commence.

(1) The facility generates hazardous waste and then non-thermally treats or stores hazardous waste on-site in tanks, containers, or containment buildings; or

(2) The facility receives hazardous waste generated offsite by a generator under the same ownership as the receiving facility, and then stores or non-thermally treats the hazardous waste in containers, tanks, or containment buildings.

(c) *Scope of the RCRA permit requirement.* RCRA requires a permit for the "treatment," "storage," and "disposal" of any "hazardous waste" as identified or listed in 40 CFR part 261. The terms "treatment," "storage," "disposal," and "hazardous waste" are defined in §270.2. Owners and operators of hazardous waste management units must have permits during the active life (including the closure period) of the unit. Owners and operators of surface impoundments, landfills, land treatment units, and waste pile units that received waste after July 26, 1982, or that certified closure (according to §265.115 of this chapter) after January 26, 1983, must have post-closure permits, unless they demonstrate closure by removal or decontamination as provided under §270.1(c)(5) and (6), or obtain an enforceable document in lieu of a post-closure permit, as provided under paragraph (c)(7) of this section. If a post-closure permit is required, the permit must address applicable 40 CFR part 264 groundwater monitoring, unsaturated zone monitoring, corrective action, and post-closure care requirements of this chapter. The denial of a permit for the active life of a hazardous waste management facility or unit does not affect the requirement to obtain a post-closure permit under this section.

(1) *Specific inclusions.* Owners and operators of certain facilities require RCRA permits as well as permits under other programs for certain aspects of the facility operation. RCRA permits are required for:

(i) Injection wells that dispose of hazardous waste, and associated surface facilities that treat, store or dispose of hazardous waste, (See §270.64). However, the owner and operator with a UIC permit in a State with an approved or promulgated UIC program, will be deemed to have a RCRA permit for the injection well itself if they comply with the requirements of §270.60(b) (permit-by-rule for injection wells).

(ii) Treatment, storage, or disposal of hazardous waste at facilities requiring an NPDES permit. However, the owner and operator of a publicly owned treatment works receiving hazardous waste will be deemed to have a RCRA permit for that waste if they comply with the requirements of §270.60(c) (permit-by-rule for POTWs).

(iii) Barges or vessels that dispose of hazardous waste by ocean disposal and onshore hazardous waste treatment or storage facilities associated with an ocean disposal operation. However, the owner and operator will be deemed to have a RCRA permit for ocean disposal from the barge or vessel itself if they comply with the requirements of §270.60(a) (permit-by-rule for ocean disposal barges and vessels).

(2) *Specific exclusions.* The following persons are among those who are not required to obtain a RCRA permit:

(i) Generators who accumulate hazardous waste onsite for less than the time periods provided in 40 CFR 262.34. 📖 6.3, 7.3

(ii) Farmers who dispose of hazardous waste pesticides from their own use as provided in §262.70 of this chapter;

(iii) Persons who own or operate facilities solely for the treatment, storage or disposal of hazardous waste excluded from regulations under this part by 40 CFR 261.4 or 261.5 (small generator exemption).

(iv) Owners or operators of totally enclosed treatment facilities as defined in 40 CFR 260.10. 📖 7.5.2

(v) Owners and operators of elementary neutralization units or wastewater treatment units as defined in 40 CFR 260.10. 📖 7.2, 7.5.1

(vi) Transporters storing manifested shipments of hazardous waste in containers meeting the requirements of 40 CFR 262.30 at a transfer facility for a period of ten days or less.

(vii) Persons adding absorbent material to waste in a container (as defined in §260.10 of this chapter) and persons adding waste to absorbent material in a container, provided that these actions occur at the time waste is first placed in the container; and §§264.17(b), 264.171, and 264.172 of this chapter are complied with. 📖 7.5.3

(viii) Universal waste handlers and universal waste transporters (as defined in 40 CFR 260.10) managing the wastes listed below. These handlers are subject to regulation under 40 part CFR 273. 📖 8.3–5

(A) Batteries as described in 40 CFR 273.2;

(B) Pesticides as described in §273.3 of this chapter;

(C) Mercury-containing equipment as described in §273.4 of this chapter; and

(D) Lamps as described in §273.5 of this chapter.

(ix) A New York State Utility central collection facility consolidating hazardous waste in accordance with 40 CFR 262.90.

(3) *Further exclusions.* (i) A person is not required to obtain a RCRA permit for treatment or containment activities taken during immediate response to any of the following situations: 📖 2.4.3.3, 7.5.4, 14.4.2.5

(A) A discharge of a hazardous waste;

(B) An imminent and substantial threat of a discharge of hazardous waste;

(C) A discharge of a material which, when discharged, becomes a hazardous waste.

(D) An immediate threat to human health, public safety, property, or the environment from the known or suspected presence of military munitions, other explosive material, or an explosive device, as determined by an explosive or munitions emergency response specialist as defined in 40 CFR 260.10.

(ii) Any person who continues or initiates hazardous waste treatment or containment activities after the immediate response is over is subject to all applicable requirements of this part for those activities.

(iii) In the case of emergency responses involving military munitions, the responding military emergency response specialist's organizational unit must retain records for three years identifying the dates of the response, the responsible persons responding, the type and description of material addressed, and its disposition.

(4) *Permits for less than an entire facility.* EPA may issue or deny a permit for one or more units at a facility without simultaneously issuing or denying a permit to all of the units at the facility. The interim status of any unit for which a permit has not been issued or denied is not affected by the issuance or denial of a permit to any other unit at the facility.

(5) *Closure by removal.* Owners/operators of surface impoundments, land treatment units, and waste piles closing by removal or decontamination under part 265 standards must obtain a post-closure permit unless they can demonstrate to the Regional Administrator that the closure met the standards for closure by removal or decontamination in §264.228, §264.280(e), or §264.258, respectively. The demonstration may be made in the following ways:

(i) If the owner/operator has submitted a part B application for a post-closure permit, the owner/operator may request a determination, based on information contained in the application, that section 264 closure by removal standards were met. If the Regional Administrator believes that §264 standards were met, he/she will notify the public of this proposed decision, allow for public comment, and reach a final determination according to the procedures in paragraph (c)(6) of this section.

(ii) If the owner/operator has not submitted a part B application for a post-closure permit, the owner/operator may petition the Regional Administrator for a determination that a post-closure permit is not required because the closure met the applicable part 264 closure standards.

(A) The petition must include data demonstrating that closure by removal or decontamination standards were met, or it must demonstrate that the unit closed under State requirements that met or exceeded the applicable 264 closure-by-removal standard.

(B) The Regional Administrator shall approve or deny the petition according to the procedures outlined in paragraph (c)(6) of this section.

(6) *Procedures for closure equivalency determination.* (i) If a facility owner/operator seeks an equivalency demonstration under §270.1(c)(5), the Regional Administrator will provide the public, through a newspaper notice, the opportunity to submit written comments on the information submitted by the owner/operator within 30 days from the date of the notice. The Regional Administrator will also, in response to a request or at his/her own discretion, hold a public hearing whenever such a hearing might clarify one or more issues concerning the equivalence of the part 265 closure to a part 264 closure. The Regional Administrator will give public notice of the hearing at least 30 days before it occurs. (Public notice of the hearing may be given at the same time as notice of the opportunity for the public to submit written comments, and the two notices may be combined.)

(ii) The Regional Administrator will determine whether the part 265 closure met 264 closure by removal or decontamination requirements within 90 days of its receipt. If the Regional Administrator finds that the closure did not meet the applicable part 264 standards, he/she will provide the owner/operator with a written statement of the reasons why the closure failed to meet part 264 standards. The owner/operator may submit additional information in support of an equivalency demonstration within 30 days after receiving such written statement. The Regional Administrator will review any additional information submitted and make a final determination within 60 days.

(iii) If the Regional Administrator determines that the facility did not close in accordance with part 264 closure by removal standards, the facility is subject to post-closure permitting requirements.

(7) *Enforceable documents for post-closure care.* At the discretion of the Regional Administrator, an owner or operator may obtain, in lieu of a post-closure permit, an enforceable document imposing the requirements of 40 CFR 265.121. "Enforceable document" means an order, a plan, or other document issued by EPA or by an authorized State under an authority that meets the requirements of 40 CFR 271.16(e) including, but not limited to, a corrective action order issued by EPA under section 3008(h), a CERCLA remedial action, or a closure or post-closure plan.

[48 FR 14228, Apr. 1, 1983, as amended at 48 FR 30113, June 30, 1983; 51 FR 10176, Mar. 24, 1986; 52 FR 45798, Dec. 1, 1987; 53 FR 27165, July 19, 1988; 54 FR 9607, Mar. 7, 1989; 56 FR 32692, July 17, 1991; 60 FR 25542, May 11, 1995; 62 FR 6656, Feb. 12, 1996; 63 FR 56735, Oct. 22, 1998; 64 FR 36488, July 6, 1999; 64 FR 37638, July 12, 1999; 70 FR 45520, Aug. 5, 2005; 70 FR 53474, Sept. 8, 2005; 71 FR 40279, July 14, 2006]

§270.2 Definitions.

The following definitions apply to parts 270, 271 and 124. Terms not defined in this section have the meaning given by RCRA.

Administrator means the Administrator of the United States Environmental Protection Agency, or an authorized representative.

Application means the EPA standard national forms for applying for a permit, including any additions, revisions or modifications to the forms; or forms approved by EPA for use in approved States, including any approved modifications or revisions. Application also includes the information required by the Director under §§270.14 through 270.29 (contents of part B of the RCRA application).

Approved program or approved State means a State which has been approved or authorized by EPA under part 271.

Aquifer means a geological formation, group of formations, or part of a formation that is capable of yielding a significant amount of water to a well or spring.

Closure means the act of securing a Hazardous Waste Management facility pursuant to the requirements of 40 CFR part 264.

Component means any constituent part of a unit or any group of constituent parts of a unit which are assembled to perform a specific function (*e.g.*, a pump seal, pump, kiln liner, kiln thermocouple).

Corrective Action Management Unit or *CAMU* means an area within a facility that is designated by the Regional Administrator under part 264 subpart S, for the purpose of implementing corrective action requirements under §264.101 and RCRA section 3008(h). A CAMU shall only be used for the management of remediation wastes pursuant to implementing such corrective action requirements at the facility. 📖 17.11

CWA means the Clean Water Act (formerly referred to as the Federal Water Pollution Control Act or Federal Water Pollution Control Act amendments of 1972) Pub. L. 92-500, as amended by Pub. L. 92-217 and Pub. L. 95-576; 33 U.S.C. 1251 *et seq.*

Director means the Regional Administrator or the State Director, as the context requires, or an authorized representative. When there is no approved State program, and there is an EPA administered program, Director means the Regional Administrator. When there is an approved State program, Director normally means the State Director. In some circumstances, however, EPA retains the authority to take certain actions even when there is an approved State program. In such cases, the term Director means the Regional Administrator and not the State Director.

Disposal means the discharge, deposit, injection, dumping, spilling, leaking, or placing of any hazardous waste into or on any land or water so that such hazardous waste or any constituent thereof may enter the environment or be emitted into the air or discharged into any waters, including ground water.

Disposal facility means a facility or part of a facility at which hazardous waste is intentionally placed into or on the land or water, and at which hazardous waste will remain after closure. The term disposal facility does not include a corrective action management unit into which remediation wastes are placed.

Draft permit means a document prepared under §124.6 indicating the Director's tentative decision to issue or deny, modify, revoke and reissue, terminate, or reissue a permit. A notice of intent to terminate a permit, and a notice of intent to deny a permit, as discussed in §124.5, are types of draft permits. A denial of a request for modification, revocation and reissuance, or termination, as discussed in §124.5 is not a "draft permit." A proposed permit is not a draft permit.

Elementary neutralization unit means a device which: 📖 7.5.1

(a) Is used for neutralizing wastes only because they exhibit the corrosivity characteristic defined in §261.22 of this chapter, or are listed in subpart D of part 261 of this chapter only for this reason; and

(b) Meets the definition of tank, tank system, container, transport vehicle, or vessel in §260.10 of this chapter. 📖 7.5.1.1.2, 10.1

Emergency permit means a RCRA permit issued in accordance with §270.61.

Environmental Protection Agency (EPA) means the United States Environmental Protection Agency.

EPA means the United States Environmental Protection Agency.

Existing hazardous waste management (HWM) facility or existing facility means a facility which was in operation or for which construction commenced on or before November 19, 1980. A facility has commenced construction if:

(a) The owner or operator has obtained the Federal, State and local approvals or permits necessary to begin physical construction; and either

(b)(1) A continuous on-site, physical construction program has begun; or

(2) The owner or operator has entered into contractual obligations which cannot be cancelled or modified without substantial loss—for physical construction of the facility to be completed within a reasonable time.

Facility mailing list means the mailing list for a facility maintained by EPA in accordance with 40 CFR 124.10(c)(1)(ix).

Facility or activity means any HWM facility or any other facility or activity (including land or appurtenances thereto) that is subject to regulation under the RCRA program.

Federal, State and local approvals or permits necessary to begin physical construction means permits and approvals required under Federal, State or local hazardous waste control statutes, regulations or ordinances.

Final authorization means approval by EPA of a State program which has met the requirements of section 3006(b) of RCRA and the applicable requirements of part 271, subpart A.

Functionally equivalent component means a component which performs the same function or measurement and which meets or exceeds the performance specifications of another component.

Generator means any person, by site location, whose act, or process produces "hazardous waste" identified or listed in 40 CFR part 261.

Ground water means water below the land surface in a zone of saturation.

Hazardous waste means a hazardous waste as defined in 40 CFR 261.3.

Hazardous Waste Management facility (HWM facility) means all contiguous land, and structures, other appurtenances, and improvements on the land, used for treating, storing, or disposing of hazardous waste. A facility may consist of several treatment, storage, or disposal operational units (for example, one or more landfills, surface impoundments, or combinations of them).

HWM facility means Hazardous Waste Management facility.

Injection well means a well into which fluids are being injected.

In operation means a facility which is treating, storing, or disposing of hazardous waste.

Interim authorization means approval by EPA of a State hazardous waste program which has met the requirements of section 3006(g)(2) of RCRA and applicable requirements of part 271, subpart B.

Major facility means any facility or activity classified as such by the Regional Administrator, or, in the case of approved State programs, the Regional Administrator in conjunction with the State Director.

Manifest means the shipping document originated and signed by the generator which contains the information required by subpart B of 40 CFR part 262. 📖 6.6

National Pollutant Discharge Elimination System means the national program for issuing, modifying, revoking and reissuing, terminating, monitoring and enforcing permits, and imposing and enforcing pretreatment requirements, under sections 307, 402, 318, and 405 of the CWA. The term includes an approved program. 📖 4.2

NPDES means National Pollutant Discharge Elimination System. 📖 4.2

New HWM facility means a Hazardous Waste Management facility which began operation or for which construction commenced after November 19, 1980.

Off-site means any site which is not on-site.

On-site means on the same or geographically contiguous property which may be divided by public or private right(s)-of-way, provided the entrance and exit between the properties is at a cross-roads intersection, and access is by crossing as opposed to going along, the right(s)-of-way. Non-contiguous properties owned by the same person but connected by a right-of-way which the person controls and to which the public does not have access, is also considered on-site property.

Owner or operator means the owner or operator of any facility or activity subject to regulation under RCRA.

Permit means an authorization, license, or equivalent control document issued by EPA or an approved State to implement the requirements of this part and parts 271 and 124 of this chapter. Permit includes permit by rule (§270.60), emergency permit (§270.61) and standardized permit (subpart J of this part). Permit does not include RCRA interim status (subpart G of this part), or any permit which has not been the subject of final agency action, such as a draft permit or a proposed permit.

Permit-by-rule means a provision of these regulations stating that a facility or activity is deemed to have a RCRA permit if it meets the requirements of the provision.

Person means an individual, association, partnership, corporation, municipality, State or Federal agency, or an agent or employee thereof.

Physical construction means excavation, movement of earth, erection of forms or structures, or similar activity to prepare an HWM facility to accept hazardous waste.

POTW means publicly owned treatment works. 📖 4.1

Publicly owned treatment works (POTW) means any device or system used in the treatment (including recycling and reclamation) of municipal sewage or industrial wastes of a liquid nature which is owned by a State or municipality. This definition includes sewers, pipes, or other conveyances only if they convey wastewater to a POTW providing treatment. 📖 4.1

RCRA means the Solid Waste Disposal Act as amended by the Resource Conservation and Recovery Act of 1976 (Pub. L. 94-580, as amended by Pub. L. 95-609 and Pub. L. 96-482, 42 U.S.C. 6901 *et seq.*)

Regional Administrator means the Regional Administrator of the appropriate Regional Office of the Environmental Protection Agency or the authorized representative of the Regional Administrator.

Remedial Action Plan (RAP) means a special form of RCRA permit that a facility owner or operator may obtain instead of a permit issued under §§270.3 through 270.66, to authorize the treatment, storage or disposal of hazardous remediation waste (as defined in §260.10 of this chapter) at a remediation waste management site. 📖 17.15

Schedule of compliance means a schedule of remedial measures included in a permit, including an enforceable sequence of interim requirements (for example, actions, operations, or milestone events) leading to compliance with the Act and regulations.

SDWA means the Safe Drinking Water Act (Pub. L. 95-523, as amended by Pub. L. 95-1900; 42 U.S.C. 3001 *et seq.*).

Site means the land or water area where any facility or activity is physically located or conducted, including adjacent land used in connection with the facility or activity.

Standardized permit means a RCRA permit issued under part 124, subpart G of this chapter and subpart J of this part authorizing the facility owner or operator to manage hazardous waste. The standardized permit may have two parts: A uniform portion issued in all cases and a supplemental portion issued at the Director's discretion.

State means any of the 50 States, the District of Columbia, Guam, the Commonwealth of Puerto Rico, the Virgin Islands, American Samoa, and the Commonwealth of the Northern Mariana Islands.

State Director means the chief administrative officer of any State agency operating an approved program, or the delegated representative of the State Director. If responsibility is divided among two or more State agencies, State Director means the chief administrative officer of the State agency authorized to perform the particular procedure or function to which reference is made.

State/EPA Agreement means an agreement between the Regional Administrator and the State which coordinates EPA and State activities, responsibilities and programs.

Storage means the holding of hazardous waste for a temporary period, at the end of which the hazardous waste is treated, disposed, or stored elsewhere.

Transfer facility means any transportation-related facility including loading docks, parking areas, storage areas and other similar areas where shipments of hazardous waste are held during the normal course of transportation.

Transporter means a person engaged in the off-site transportation of hazardous waste by air, rail, highway or water.

Treatment means any method, technique, or process, including neutralization, designed to change the physical, chemical, or biological character or composition of any hazardous waste so as to neutralize such wastes, or so as to recover energy or material resources from the waste, or so as to render such waste non-hazardous, or less hazardous; safer to transport, store, or dispose of; or amenable for recovery, amenable for storage, or reduced in volume. 📖 5.1.4, 7.1

UIC means the Underground Injection Control Program under part C of the Safe Drinking Water Act, including an approved program.

Underground injection means a well injection.

Underground source of drinking water (USDW) means an aquifer or its portion:

(a)(1) Which supplies any public water system; or

(2) Which contains a sufficient quantity of ground water to supply a public water system; and

(i) Currently supplies drinking water for human consumption; or

(ii) Contains fewer than 10,000 mg/l total dissolved solids; and

(b) Which is not an exempted aquifer.

USDW means underground source of drinking water.

Wastewater treatment unit means a device which: 📖 7.2

(a) Is part of a wastewater treatment facility which is subject to regulation under either section 402 or 307(b) of the Clean Water Act; and 📖 7.2.1.1

(b) Receives and treats or stores an influent wastewater which is a hazardous waste as defined in §261.3 of this chapter, or generates and accumulates a wastewater treatment sludge which is a hazardous waste as defined in §261.3 of this chapter, or treats or stores a wastewater treatment sludge which is a hazardous waste as defined in §261.3 of this chapter; and 📖 7.2.1.2

(c) Meets the definition of tank or tank system in §260.10 of this chapter. 📖 7.2.1.3

[48 FR 14228, Apr. 1, 1983, as amended at 48 FR 30113, June 30, 1983; 53 FR 34087, Sept. 2, 1988; 53 FR 37935, Sept. 28, 1988; 58 FR 8685, Feb. 16, 1993; 60 FR 33914, June 29, 1995; 60 FR 63433, Dec. 11, 1995; 63 FR 65941, Nov. 30, 1998; 70 FR 53474, Sept. 8, 2005; 71 FR 40279, July 14, 2006]

§270.3 Considerations under Federal law.

The following is a list of Federal laws that may apply to the issuance of permits under these rules. When any of these laws is applicable, its procedures must be followed. When the applicable law requires consideration or adoption of particular permit conditions or requires the denial of a permit, those requirements also must be followed.

(a) *The Wild and Scenic Rivers Act.* 16 U.S.C. 1273 *et seq.* Section 7 of the Act prohibits the Regional Administrator from assisting by license or otherwise the construction of any water resources project that would have a direct, adverse effect on the values for which a national wild and scenic river was established.

(b) *The National Historic Preservation Act of 1966.* 16 U.S.C. 470 *et seq.* Section 106 of the Act and implementing regulations (36 CFR part 800) require the Regional Administrator, before issuing a license, to adopt measures when feasible to mitigate potential adverse effects of the licensed activity and properties listed or eligible for listing in the National Register of Historic Places. The Act's requirements are to be implemented in cooperation with State Historic Preservation Officers and upon notice to, and when appropriate, in consultation with the Advisory Council on Historic Preservation.

(c) *The Endangered Species Act.* 16 U.S.C. 1531 *et seq.* Section 7 of the Act and implementing regulations (50 CFR part 402) require the Regional Administrator to ensure, in consultation with the Secretary of the Interior or Commerce, that any action authorized by EPA is not likely to jeopardize the continued existence of any endangered or threatened species or adversely affect its critical habitat.

(d) *The Coastal Zone Management Act.* 16 U.S.C. 1451 *et seq.* Section 307(c) of the Act and implementing regulations (15 CFR part 930) prohibit EPA from issuing a permit for an activity affecting land or water use in the coastal zone until the applicant certifies that the proposed activity complies with the State Coastal Zone Management program, and the State or its designated agency concurs with the certification (or the Secretary of Commerce overrides the State's nonconcurrence).

(e) *The Fish and Wildlife Coordination Act.* 16 U.S.C. 661 *et seq.* requires that the Regional Administrator, before issuing a permit proposing or authorizing the impoundment (with certain exemptions), diversion, or other control or modification of any body of water, consult with the appropriate State agency exercising jurisdiction over wildlife resources to conserve those resources.

(f) *Executive orders.* [Reserved]

(Clean Water Act (33 U.S.C. 1251 *et seq.*), Safe Drinking Water Act (42 U.S.C. 300f *et seq.*), Clean Air Act (42 U.S.C. 7401 *et seq.*), Resource Conservation and Recovery Act (42 U.S.C. 6901 *et seq.*))

[48 FR 14228, Apr 1, 1983, as amended at 48 FR 39622, Sept. 1, 1983]

§270.4 Effect of a permit.

(a) Compliance with a RCRA permit during its term constitutes compliance, for purposes of enforcement, with subtitle C of RCRA except for those requirements not included in the permit which:

(1) Become effective by statute;

(2) Are promulgated under part 268 of this chapter restricting the placement of hazardous wastes in or on the land; 13.1.2

(3) Are promulgated under part 264 of this chapter regarding leak detection systems for new and replacement surface impoundment, waste pile, and landfill units, and lateral expansions of surface impoundment, waste pile, and landfill units. The leak detection system requirements include double liners, CQA programs, monitoring, action leakage rates, and response action plans, and will be implemented through the procedures of §270.42 Class 1 permit modifications; or

(4) Are promulgated under subparts AA, BB, or CC of part 265 of this chapter limiting air emissions.

(b) The issuance of a permit does not convey any property rights of any sort, or any exclusive privilege.

(c) The issuance of a permit does not authorize any injury to persons or property or invasion of other private rights, or any infringement of State or local law or regulations.

[48 FR 14228, Apr. 1, 1983, as amended at 57 FR 3495, Jan. 29, 1992; 59 FR 62952, Dec. 6, 1994]

§270.5 Noncompliance and program reporting by the Director.

The Director shall prepare quarterly and annual reports as detailed below. When the State is the permit-issuing authority, the State Director shall submit any reports required under this section to the Regional Administrator. When EPA is the permit-issuing authority, the Regional Administrator shall submit any report required under this section to EPA Headquarters. For purposes of this section only, RCRA permittees shall include RCRA interim status facilities, when appropriate.

(a) *Quarterly reports.* The Director shall submit quarterly narrative reports for major facilities as follows:

(1) *Format.* The report shall use the following format:

(i) Information on noncompliance for each facility;

(ii) Alphabetize by permittee name. When two or more permittees have the same name, the lowest permit number shall be entered first; and

(iii) For each entry on the list, include the following information in the following order:

(A) Name, location, and permit number of the noncomplying permittee.

(B) A brief description and date of each instance of noncompliance for that permittee. Instances of noncompliance may include one or more of the kinds set forth in paragraph (a)(2) of this section.

When a permittee has noncompliance of more than one kind, combine the information into a single entry for each such permittee.

(C) The date(s) and a brief description of the action(s) taken by the Director to ensure compliance.

(D) Status of the instance(s) of noncompliance with the date of the review of the status or the date of resolution.

(E) Any details which tend to explain or mitigate the instance(s) of noncompliance.

(2) *Instances of noncompliance to be reported.* Any instances of noncompliance within the following categories shall be reported in successive reports until the noncompliance is reported as resolved. Once noncompliance is reported as resolved it need not appear in subsequent reports.

(i) *Failure to complete construction elements.* When the permittee has failed to complete, by the date specified in the permit, an element of a compliance schedule involving either planning for construction (for example, award of a contract, preliminary plans), or a construction step (for example, begin construction, attain operation level); and the permittee has not returned to compliance by accomplishing the required element of the schedule within 30 days from the date a compliance schedule report is due under the permit.

(ii) *Modifications to schedules of compliance.* When a schedule of compliance in the permit has been modified under §270.41 or §270.42 because of the permittee's noncompliance.

(iii) *Failure to complete or provide compliance schedule or monitoring reports.* When the permittee has failed to complete or provide a report required in a permit compliance schedule (for example, progress report or notice of noncompliance or compliance) or a monitoring report; and the permittee has not submitted the complete report within 30 days from the date it is due under the permit for compliance schedules, or from the date specified in the permit for monitoring reports.

(iv) *Deficient reports.* When the required reports provided by the permittee are so deficient as to cause misunderstanding by the Director and thus impede the review of the status of compliance.

(v) *Noncompliance with other permit requirements.* Noncompliance shall be reported in the following circumstances:

(A) Whenever the permittee has violated a permit requirement (other than reported under paragraph (a)(2)(i) or (ii) of this section), and has not returned to compliance within 45 days from the date reporting of noncompliance was due under the permit; or

(B) When the Director determines that a pattern of noncompliance exists for a major facility permittee over the most recent four consecutive reporting periods. This pattern includes any violation of the same requirement in two consecutive reporting periods, and any violation of one or more requirements in each of four consecutive reporting periods; or

(C) When the Director determines significant permit non-compliance or other significant event has occurred such as a fire or explosion or migration of fluids into a USDW.

(vi) *All other.* Statistical information shall be reported quarterly on all other instances of noncompliance by major facilities with permit requirements not otherwise reported under paragraph (a) of this section.

(b) *Annual reports*—(1) *Annual noncompliance report.* Statistical reports shall be submitted by the Director on nonmajor RCRA permittees indicating the total number reviewed, the number of noncomplying nonmajor permittees, the number of enforcement actions, and number of permit modifications extending compliance deadlines. The statistical information shall be organized to follow the types of noncompliance listed in paragraph (a) of this section.

(2) In addition to the annual noncompliance report, the Director shall prepare a "program report" which contains information (in a manner and form prescribed by the Administrator) on generators and transporters and the permit status of regulated facilities. The Director shall also include, on a biennial basis, summary information on the quantities and types of hazardous wastes generated, transported, treated, stored and disposed during the preceding odd-numbered year. This summary information shall be reported in a manner and form prescribed by the Administrator and shall be reported according to EPA characteristics and lists of hazardous wastes at 40 CFR part 261.

(c) *Schedule.* (1) For all quarterly reports. On the last working day of May, August, November, and February, the State Director shall submit to the Regional Administrator information concerning noncompliance with RCRA permit requirements by major facilities in the State in accordance with the following schedule. The

Regional Administrator shall prepare and submit information for EPA-issued permits to EPA Headquarters in accordance with the same schedule.

Quarters Covered by Reports on Noncompliance by Major Dischargers
[Date for completion of reports]

January, February, and March	[1]May 31
April, May, and June	[1]August 31
July, August, and September	[1]November 30
October, November, and December	[1]February 28

[1]Reports must be made available to the public for inspection and copying on this date.

[48 FR 14228, Apr. 1, 1983, as amended at 48 FR 30113, June 30, 1983]

§270.6 References.

(a) When used in part 270 of this chapter, the following publications are incorporated by reference. These incorporations by reference were approved by the Director of the Federal Register pursuant to 5 U.S.C. 552(a) and 1 CFR part 51. These materials are incorporated as they exist on the date of approval and a notice of any change in these materials will be published in the *Federal Register*. Copies may be inspected at the Library, U.S. Environmental Protection Agency, 1200 Pennsylvania Ave., NW., (3403T), Washington, DC 20460, *libraryhq@epa.gov*; or at the National Archives and Records Administration (NARA). For information on the availability of this material at NARA, call 202-741-6030, or go to: *http://www.archives.gov/federal_register/code_of_federal_regulations/ibr_locations.html*.

(b) The following materials are available for purchase from the National Technical Information Service (NTIS), 5285 Port Royal Road, Springfield, VA 22161, (703) 605-6000 or (800) 553-6847; or for purchase from the Superintendent of Documents, U.S. Government Printing Office, Washington, DC 20402, (202) 512-1800:

(1) "APTI Course 415: Control of Gaseous Emissions," EPA Publication EPA–450/2–81–005, December 1981, IBR approved for §§270.24 and 270.25.

(2) [Reserved].

[48 FR 14228, Apr. 1, 1983, as amended at 48 FR 30113, June 30, 1983; 52 FR 8073, Mar. 16, 1987; 58 FR 46051, Aug. 31, 1993; 70 FR 59576, Oct. 12, 2005]

Subpart B—Permit Application

§270.10 General application requirements.

(a) Applying for a permit. Below is information on how to obtain a permit and where to find requirements for specific permits: 📖 17.6

(1) If you are covered by RCRA permits by rule (§270.60), you need not apply.

(2) If you currently have interim status, you must apply for permits when required by the Director.

(3) If you are required to have a permit (including new applicants and permittees with expiring permits), you must complete, sign, and submit an application to the Director, as described in this section and §§270.70 through 270.73.

(4) If you are seeking an emergency permit, the procedures for application, issuance, and administration are found exclusively in §270.61.

(5) If you are seeking a research, development, and demonstration permit, the procedures for application, issuance, and administration are found exclusively in §270.65.

(6) If you are seeking a standardized permit, the procedures for application and issuance are found in part 124, subpart G of this chapter and subpart J of this part.

(b) *Who applies?* When a facility or activity is owned by one person but is operated by another person, it is the operator's duty to obtain a permit, except that the owner must also sign the permit application.

(c) *Completeness.* The Director shall not issue a permit before receiving a complete application for a permit except for permits by rule, or emergency permits. An application for a permit is complete when the Director receives an application form and any supplemental information which are completed to his satisfaction. An application for a permit is complete notwithstanding the failure of the owner or operator to submit the exposure information described in paragraph (j) of this section. The Director may deny a permit for the active life of a hazardous waste management facility or unit before receiving a complete application for a permit.

(d) *Information requirements.* All applicants for RCRA permits shall provide information set forth in §270.13 and applicable sections in §§270.14 through 270.29 to the Director, using the application form provided by the Director.

(e) *Existing HWM facilities and interim status qualifications.* (1) Owners and operators of existing hazardous waste management facilities or of hazardous waste management facilities in existence on the effective date of statutory or regulatory amendments under the act that render the facility subject to the requirement to have a RCRA permit must submit part A of their permit application no later than: 📖 17.6.1

(i) Six months after the date of publication of regulations which first require them to comply with the standards set forth in 40 CFR part 265 or 266, or

(ii) Thirty days after the date they first become subject to the standards set forth in 40 CFR part 265 or 266, whichever first occurs.

(iii) For generators generating greater than 100 kilograms but less than 1000 kilograms of hazardous waste in a calendar month and treats, stores, or disposes of these wastes on-site, by March 24, 1987.

Note: For facilities which must comply with part 265 because they handle a waste listed in EPA's May 19, 1980, part 261 regulations (45 FR 33006 *et seq.*), the deadline for submitting an application is November 19, 1980. Where other existing facilities must begin in complying with part 265 or 266 at a later date because of revisions to part 260, 261, 265, or 266, the Administrator will specify in the preamble to those revisions when those facilities must submit a permit application.

(2) The Administrator may by publication in the *Federal Register* extend the date by which owners and operators of specified classes of existing hazardous waste management facilities must submit part A of their permit application if he finds that (i) there has been substantial confusion as to whether the owners and operators of such facilities were required to file a permit application and (ii) such confusion is attributed to ambiguities in EPA's parts 260, 261, 265, or 266 regulations.

(3) The Administrator may by compliance order issued under section 3008 of RCRA extend the date by which the owner and operator of an existing hazardous waste management facility must submit part A of their permit application.

(4) The owner or operator of an existing hazardous waste management facility may be required to submit part B of their permit application. The State Director may require submission of part B (or equivalent completion of the State RCRA application process) if the State in which the facility is located has received interim or final authorization; if not, the Regional Administrator may require submission of Part B. Any owner or operator shall be allowed at least six months from the date of request to submit part B of the application. Any owner or operator of an existing hazardous waste management facility may voluntarily submit part B of the application at any time. Notwithstanding the above, any owner or operator of an existing hazardous waste management facility must submit a part B permit application in accordance with the dates specified in §270.73. Any owner or operator of a land disposal facility in existence on the effective date of statutory or regulatory amendments under this Act that render the facility subject to the requirement to have a RCRA permit must submit a part B application in accordance with the dates specified in §270.73.

(5) Failure to furnish a requested part B application on time, or to furnish in full the information required by the part B application, is grounds for termination of interim status under part 124.

(f) *New HWM facilities.* (1) Except as provided in paragraph (f)(3) of this section, no person shall begin physical construction of a new HWM facility without having submitted parts A and B of the permit application and having received a finally effective RCRA permit.

(2) An application for a permit for a new hazardous waste management facility (including both Parts A and B) may be filed any time after promulgation of those standards in part 264, subpart I *et seq.* applicable to such facility. The application shall be filed with the Regional Administrator if at the time of application the State in which the new hazardous waste management facility is proposed to be located has not received interim or final authorization for permitting such facility; otherwise it shall be filed with the State Director. Except as provided in paragraph (f)(3) of this section, all applications must be submitted at least 180 days before physical construction is expected to commence.

(3) Notwithstanding paragraph (f)(1) of this section, a person may construct a facility for the incineration of polychlorinated biphenyls pursuant to an approval issued by the Administrator under section (6)(e) of the Toxic Substances Control Act and any person owning or operating such a facility may, at any time after construction or operation of such facility has begun, file an application for a RCRA permit to incinerate hazardous waste authorizing such facility to incinerate waste identified or listed under Subtitle C of RCRA.

(g) *Updating permit applications.* (1) If any owner or operator of a hazardous waste management facility has filed Part A of a permit application and has not yet filed part B, the owner or operator shall file an amended part A application:

(i) With the Regional Administrator if the facility is located in a State which has not obtained interim authorization or final authorization, within six months after the promulgation of revised regulations under part 261 listing or identifying additional hazardous wastes, if the facility is treating, storing or disposing of any of those newly listed or identified wastes.

(ii) With the State Director, if the facility is located in a State which has obtained interim authorization or final authorization, no later than the effective date of regulatory provisions listing or designating wastes as hazardous in that State in addition to those listed or designated under the previously approved State program, if the facility is treating, storing or disposing of any of those newly listed or designated wastes; or

(iii) As necessary to comply with provisions of §270.72 for changes during interim status or with the analogous provisions of a State program approved for final authorization or interim authorization. Revised Part A applications necessary to comply with the provisions of §270.72 shall be filed with the Regional Administrator if the State in which the facility in question is located does not have interim authorization or final authorization; otherwise it shall be filed with the State Director (if the State has an analogous provision).

(2) The owner or operator of a facility who fails to comply with the updating requirements of paragraph (g)(1) of this section does not receive interim status as to the wastes not covered by duly filed part A applications.

(h) Reapplying for a permit. If you have an effective permit and you want to reapply for a new one, you have two options:

(1) You may submit a new application at least 180 days before the expiration date of the effective permit, unless the Director allows a later date; or

(2) If you intend to be covered by a standardized permit, you may submit a Notice of Intent as described in §270.51(e)(1) at least 180 days before the expiration date of the effective permit, unless the Director allows a later date. The Director may not allow you to submit applications or Notices of Intent later than the expiration date of the existing permit, except as allowed by §270.51(e)(2).

(i) *Recordkeeping.* Applicants shall keep records of all data used to complete permit applications and any supplemental information submitted under §§270.10(d), 270.13, 270.14 through 270.21 for a period of at least 3 years from the date the application is signed.

(j) *Exposure information.* (1) After August 8, 1985, any part B permit application submitted by an owner or operator of a facility that stores, treats, or disposes hazardous waste in a surface impoundment or a landfill must be accompanied by information, reasonably ascertainable by the owner or operator, on the potential for the public to be exposed to hazardous wastes or hazardous constituents through releases related to the unit. At a minimum, such information must address:

(i) Reasonably foreseeable potential releases from both normal operations and accidents at the unit, including releases associated with transportation to or from the unit;

(ii) The potential pathways of human exposure to hazardous wastes or constituents resulting from the releases described under paragraph (j)(1)(i) of this section; and

(iii) The potential magnitude and nature of the human exposure resulting from such releases.

(2) By August 8, 1985, owners and operators of a landfill or a surface impoundment who have already submitted a part B application must submit the exposure information required in paragraph (j)(1) of this section.

(k) The Director may require a permittee or an applicant to submit information in order to establish permit conditions under §§270.32(b)(2) and 270.50(d) of this chapter.

(l) If the Director concludes, based on one or more of the factors listed in paragraph (l)(1) of this section that compliance with the standards of 40 CFR part 63, subpart EEE alone may not be protective of human health or the environment, the Director shall require the additional information or assessment(s) necessary to determine whether additional controls are necessary to ensure protection of human health and the environment. This includes information necessary to evaluate the potential risk to human health and/or the environment resulting from both direct and indirect exposure pathways. The Director may also require a permittee or applicant to provide information necessary to determine whether such an assessment(s) should be required.

(1) The Director shall base the evaluation of whether compliance with the standards of 40 CFR part 63, subpart EEE alone is protective of human health or the environment on factors relevant to the potential risk from a hazardous waste combustion unit, including, as appropriate, any of the following factors:

(i) Particular site-specific considerations such as proximity to receptors (such as schools, hospitals, nursing homes, day care centers, parks, community activity centers, or other potentially sensitive receptors), unique dispersion patterns, etc.;

(ii) Identities and quantities of emissions of persistent, bioaccumulative or toxic pollutants considering enforceable controls in place to limit those pollutants;

(iii) Identities and quantities of nondioxin products of incomplete combustion most likely to be emitted and to pose significant risk based on known toxicities (confirmation of which should be made through emissions testing);

(iv) Identities and quantities of other off-site sources of pollutants in proximity of the facility that significantly influence interpretation of a facility-specific risk assessment;

(v) Presence of significant ecological considerations, such as the proximity of a particularly sensitive ecological area;

(vi) Volume and types of wastes, for example wastes containing highly toxic constituents;

(vii) Other on-site sources of hazardous air pollutants that significantly influence interpretation of the risk posed by the operation of the source in question;

(viii) Adequacy of any previously conducted risk assessment, given any subsequent changes in conditions likely to affect risk; and

(ix) Such other factors as may be appropriate.

(2) [Reserved].

[48 FR 14228, Apr. 1, 1983; 48 FR 30114, June 30, 1983, as amended at 50 FR 28751, July 15, 1985; 51 FR 10176, Mar. 24, 1986; 52 FR 45799, Dec. 1, 1987; 54 FR 9607, Mar. 7, 1989; 60 FR 33914, June 29, 1995; 70 FR 53474, Sept. 8, 2005; 70 FR 59576, Oct. 12, 2005; 71 FR 40279, July 14, 2006]

§270.11 Signatories to permit applications and reports.

(a) *Applications.* All permit applications shall be signed as follows:

(1) *For a corporation:* By a responsible corporate officer. For the purpose of this section, a responsible corporate officer means (i) A president, secretary, treasurer, or vice-president of the corporation in charge of a principal business function, or any other person who performs similar policy- or decision-making functions for the corporation, or (ii) the manager of one or more manufacturing, production or operating facilities employing more than 250 persons or having gross annual sales or expenditures exceeding $25 million (in second-quarter 1980 dollars), if authority to sign documents has been assigned or delegated to the manager in accordance with corporate procedures.

Note: EPA does not require specific assignments or delegations of authority to responsible corporate officers identified in §270.11(a)(1)(i). The Agency will presume that these responsible corporate officers have the requisite authority to sign permit applications unless the corporation has notified the Director to the contrary. Corporate procedures governing authority to sign permit applications may provide for assignment or delegation to applicable corporate positions under §270.11(a)(1)(ii) rather than to specific individuals.

(2) *For a partnership or sole proprietorship;* by a general partner or the proprietor, respectively; or

(3) *For a municipality, State, Federal, or other public agency:* by either a principal executive officer or ranking elected official. For purposes of this section, a principal executive officer of a Federal agency includes: (i) The chief executive officer of the agency, or (ii) a senior executive officer having responsibility for the overall operations of a principal geographic unit of the agency (*e.g.*, Regional Administrators of EPA).

(b) *Reports.* All reports required by permits and other information requested by the Director shall be signed by a person described in paragraph (a) of this section, or by a duly authorized representative of that person. A person is a duly authorized representative only if:

(1) The authorization is made in writing by a person described in paragraph (a) of this section;

(2) The authorization specifies either an individual or a position having responsibility for overall operation of the regulated facility or activity such as the position of plant manager, operator of a well or a well field, superintendent, or position of equivalent responsibility. (A duly authorized representative may thus be either a named individual or any individual occupying a named position); and

(3) The written authorization is submitted to the Director.

(c) *Changes to authorization.* If an authorization under paragraph (b) of this section is no longer accurate because a different individual or position has responsibility for the overall operation of the facility, a new authorization satisfying the requirements of paragraph (b) of this section must be submitted to the Director prior to or together with any reports, information, or applications to be signed by an authorized representative.

(d)(1) Any person signing a document under paragraph (a) or (b) of this section must make the following certification:

I certify under penalty of law that this document and all attachments were prepared under my direction or supervision according to a system designed to assure that qualified personnel properly gather and evaluate the information submitted. Based on my inquiry of the person or persons who manage the system, or those persons directly responsible for gathering the information, the information submitted is, to the best of my knowledge and belief, true, accurate, and complete. I am aware that there are significant penalties for submitting false information, including the possibility of fine and imprisonment for knowing violations.

(2) For remedial action plans (RAPs) under subpart H of this part, if the operator certifies according to paragraph (d)(1) of this section, then the owner may choose to make the following certification instead of the certification in paragraph (d)(1) of this section:

> Based on my knowledge of the conditions of the property described in the RAP and my inquiry of the person or persons who manage the system referenced in the operator's certification, or those persons directly responsible for gathering the information, the information submitted is, to the best of my knowledge and belief, true, accurate, and complete. I am aware that there are significant penalties for submitting false information, including the possibility of fine and imprisonment for knowing violations.

(Clean Water Act (33 U.S.C. 1251 *et seq.*), Safe Drinking Water Act (42 U.S.C. 300f *et seq.*), Clean Air Act (42 U.S.C. 7401 *et seq.*), Resource Conservation and Recovery Act (42 U.S.C. 6901 *et seq.*))

[48 FR 14228, Apr. 1, 1983, as amended at 48 FR 39622, Sept. 1, 1983; 63 FR 65941, Nov. 30, 1998; 71 FR 40279, July 14, 2006]

§270.12 Confidentiality of information.

(a) In accordance with 40 CFR part 2, any information submitted to EPA pursuant to these regulations may be claimed as confidential by the submitter. Any such claim must be asserted at the time of submission in the manner prescribed on the application form or instructions or, in the case of other submissions, by stamping the words "confidential business information" on each page containing such information. If no claim is made at the time of submission, EPA may make the information available to the public without further notice. If a claim is asserted, the information will be treated in accordance with the procedures in 40 CFR part 2 (Public Information).

(b) Claims of confidentiality for the name and address of any permit applicant or permittee will be denied.

§270.13 Contents of part A of the permit application.

Part A of the RCRA application shall include the following information:

(a) The activities conducted by the applicant which require it to obtain a permit under RCRA.

(b) Name, mailing address, and location, including latitude and longitude of the facility for which the application is submitted.

(c) Up to four SIC codes which best reflect the principal products or services provided by the facility.

(d) The operator's name, address, telephone number, ownership status, and status as Federal, State, private, public, or other entity.

(e) The name, address, and phone number of the owner of the facility.

(f) Whether the facility is located on Indian lands.

(g) An indication of whether the facility is new or existing and whether it is a first or revised application.

(h) For existing facilities, (1) a scale drawing of the facility showing the location of all past, present, and future treatment, storage, and disposal areas; and (2) photographs of the facility clearly delineating all existing structures; existing treatment, storage, and disposal areas; and sites of future treatment, storage, and disposal areas.

(i) A description of the processes to be used for treating, storing, and disposing of hazardous waste, and the design capacity of these items.

(j) A specification of the hazardous wastes listed or designated under 40 CFR part 261 to be treated, stored, or disposed of at the facility, an estimate of the quantity of such wastes to be treated, stored, or disposed annually, and a general description of the processes to be used for such wastes.

(k) A listing of all permits or construction approvals received or applied for under any of the following programs:

(1) Hazardous Waste Management program under RCRA.

(2) UIC program under the SWDA.

(3) NPDES program under the CWA.

(4) Prevention of Significant Deterioration (PSD) program under the Clean Air Act.

(5) Nonattainment program under the Clean Air Act.

(6) National Emission Standards for Hazardous Pollutants (NESHAPS) preconstruction approval under the Clean Air Act.

(7) Ocean dumping permits under the Marine Protection Research and Sanctuaries Act.

(8) Dredge or fill permits under section 404 of the CWA.

(9) Other relevant environmental permits, including State permits.

(l) A topographic map (or other map if a topographic map is unavailable) extending one mile beyond the property boundaries of the source, depicting the facility and each of its intake and discharge structures; each of its hazardous waste treatment, storage, or disposal facilities; each well where fluids from the facility are injected underground; and those wells, springs, other surface water bodies, and drinking water wells listed in public records or otherwise known to the applicant within mile of the facility property boundary.

(m) A brief description of the nature of the business.

(n) For hazardous debris, a description of the debris category(ies) and contaminant category(ies) to be treated, stored, or disposed of at the facility.

[48 FR 14228, Apr. 1, 1983, as amended at 57 FR 37281, Aug. 18, 1992; 71 FR 40279, July 14, 2006]

§270.14 Contents of part B: General requirements.

(a) Part B of the permit application consists of the general information requirements of this section, and the specific information requirements in §§0.14 through 270.29 applicable to the facility. The part B information requirements presented in §§270.14 through 270.29 reflect the standards promulgated in 40 CFR part 264. These information requirements are necessary in order for EPA to determine compliance with the part 264 standards. If owners and operators of HWM facilities can demonstrate that the information prescribed in part B can not be provided to the extent required, the Director may make allowance for submission of such information on a case-by-case basis. Information required in part B shall be submitted to the Director and signed in accordance with the requirements in §270.11. Certain technical data, such as design drawings and specifications, and engineering studies shall be certified by a qualified Professional Engineer. For post-closure permits, only the information specified in §270.28 is required in part B of the permit application.

Publisher's Note: The above reference to "§§0.14 through 270.29" should be §§270.14 through 270.29.

(b) *General information requirements.* The following information is required for all HWM facilities, except as §264.1 provides otherwise:

(1) A general description of the facility.

(2) Chemical and physical analyses of the hazardous waste and hazardous debris to be handled at the facility. At a minimum, these analyses shall contain all the information which must be known to treat, store, or dispose of the wastes properly in accordance with part 264 of this chapter.

(3) A copy of the waste analysis plan required by §264.13(b) and, if applicable §264.13(c).

(4) A description of the security procedures and equipment required by §264.14, or a justification demonstrating the reasons for requesting a waiver of this requirement.

(5) A copy of the general inspection schedule required by §264.15(b) of this part. Include where applicable, as part of the inspection schedule, specific requirements in §§264.174, 264.193(i), 264.195, 264.226, 264.254, 264.273, 264.303, 264.602, 264.1033, 264.1052, 264.1053, 264.1058, 264.1084, 264.1085, 264.1086, and 264.1088 of this part.

(6) A justification of any request for a waiver(s) of the preparedness and prevention requirements of part 264, subpart C.

(7) A copy of the contingency plan required by part 264, subpart D. Note: Include, where applicable, as part of the contingency plan, specific requirements in §§264.227, 264.255, and 264.200.

(8) A description of procedures, structures, or equipment used at the facility to:

(i) Prevent hazards in unloading operations (for example, ramps, special forklifts);

(ii) Prevent runoff from hazardous waste handling areas to other areas of the facility or environment, or to prevent flooding (for example, berms, dikes, trenches);

(iii) Prevent contamination of water supplies;

(iv) Mitigate effects of equipment failure and power outages;

(v) Prevent undue exposure of personnel to hazardous waste (for example, protective clothing); and

(vi) Prevent releases to atmosphere.

(9) A description of precautions to prevent accidental ignition or reaction of ignitable, reactive, or incompatible wastes as required to demonstrate compliance with §264.17 including documentation demonstrating compliance with §264.17(c).

(10) Traffic pattern, estimated volume (number, types of vehicles) and control (for example, show turns across traffic lanes, and stacking lanes (if appropriate); describe access road surfacing and load bearing capacity; show traffic control signals).

(11) Facility location information;

(i) In order to determine the applicability of the seismic standard [§264.18(a)] the owner or operator of a new facility must identify the political jurisdiction (*e.g.*, county, township, or election district) in which the facility is proposed to be located.

[*Comment:* If the county or election district is not listed in appendix VI of part 264, no further information is required to demonstrate compliance with §264.18(a).]

(ii) If the facility is proposed to be located in an area listed in appendix VI of part 264, the owner or operator shall demonstrate compliance with the seismic standard. This demonstration may be made using either published geologic data or data obtained from field investigations carried out by the applicant. The information provided must be of such quality to be acceptable to geologists experienced in identifying and evaluating seismic activity. The information submitted must show that either:

(A) No faults which have had displacement in Holocene time are present, or no lineations which suggest the presence of a fault (which have displacement in Holocene time) within 3,000 feet of a facility are present, based on data from:

(*1*) Published geologic studies,

(*2*) Aerial reconnaissance of the area within a five-mile radius from the facility.

(*3*) An analysis of aerial photographs covering a 3,000 foot radius of the facility, and

(*4*) If needed to clarify the above data, a reconnaissance based on walking portions of the area within 3,000 feet of the facility, or

(B) If faults (to include lineations) which have had displacement in Holocene time are present within 3,000 feet of a facility, no faults pass within 200 feet of the portions of the facility where treatment, storage, or disposal of hazardous waste will be conducted, based on data from a comprehensive geologic analysis of the site. Unless a site analysis is otherwise conclusive concerning the absence of faults within 200 feet of such portions of the facility data shall be obtained from a subsurface exploration (trenching) of the area within a distance no less than 200 feet from portions of the facility where treatment, storage, or disposal of hazardous waste will be conducted. Such trenching shall be performed in a direction that is perpendicular to known faults (which have had displacement in Holocene time) passing within 3,000 feet of the portions of the facility where treatment, storage, or disposal of hazardous waste will be conducted. Such investigation shall document with supporting maps and other analyses, the location of faults found.

[*Comment:* The Guidance Manual for the Location Standards provides greater detail on the content of each type of seismic investigation and the appropriate conditions under which each approach or a combination of approaches would be used.]

(iii) Owners and operators of all facilities shall provide an identification of whether the facility is located within a 100-year floodplain. This identification must indicate the source of data for such determination and include a copy of the relevant Federal Insurance Administration (FIA) flood map, if used, or the calculations and maps used where an FIA map is not available. Information shall also be provided identifying the 100-year flood level and any other special flooding factors (*e.g.*, wave action) which must be considered in designing, constructing, operating, or maintaining the facility to withstand washout from a 100-year flood.

[*Comment:* Where maps for the National Flood Insurance Program produced by the Federal Insurance Administration (FIA) of the Federal Emergency Management Agency are available, they will normally be determinative of whether a facility is located within or outside of the 100-year floodplain. However, where the FIA map excludes an area (usually areas of the floodplain less than 200 feet in width), these areas must be considered and a determination made as to whether they are in the 100-year floodplain. Where FIA maps are not available for a proposed facility location, the owner or operator must use equivalent mapping techniques to determine whether the facility is within the 100-year floodplain, and if so located, what the 100-year flood elevation would be.]

(iv) Owners and operators of facilities located in the 100-year floodplain must provide the following information:

(A) Engineering analysis to indicate the various hydrodynamic and hydrostatic forces expected to result at the site as consequence of a 100-year flood.

(B) Structural or other engineering studies showing the design of operational units (*e.g.*, tanks, incinerators) and flood protection devices (*e.g.*, floodwalls, dikes) at the facility and how these will prevent washout.

(C) If applicable, and in lieu of paragraphs (b)(11)(iv)(A) and (B) of this section, a detailed description of procedures to be followed to remove hazardous waste to safety before the facility is flooded, including:

(*1*) Timing of such movement relative to flood levels, including estimated time to move the waste, to show that such movement can be completed before floodwaters reach the facility.

(*2*) A description of the location(s) to which the waste will be moved and demonstration that those facilities will be eligible to receive hazardous waste in accordance with the regulations under parts 270, 271, 124, and 264 through 266 of this chapter.

(*3*) The planned procedures, equipment, and personnel to be used and the means to ensure that such resources will be available in time for use.

(*4*) The potential for accidental discharges of the waste during movement.

(v) Existing facilities NOT in compliance with §264.18(b) shall provide a plan showing how the facility will be brought into compliance and a schedule for compliance.

(12) An outline of both the introductory and continuing training programs by owners or operators to prepare persons to operate or maintain the HWM facility in a safe manner as required to demonstrate compliance with §264.16. A brief description of how training will be designed to meet actual job tasks in accordance with requirements in §264.16(a)(3).

(13) A copy of the closure plan and, where applicable, the post-closure plan required by §§264.112, 264.118, and 264.197. Include, where applicable, as part of the plans, specific requirements in §§264.178, 264.197, 264.228, 264.258, 264.280, 264.310, 264.351, 264.601, and 264.603.

(14) For hazardous waste disposal units that have been closed, documentation that notices required under §264.119 have been filed.

(15) The most recent closure cost estimate for the facility prepared in accordance with §264.142 and a copy of the documentation required to demonstrate financial assurance under §264.143. For a new facility, a copy of the required documentation may be submitted 60 days prior to the initial receipt of hazardous wastes, if that is later than the submission of the part B.

(16) Where applicable, the most recent post-closure cost estimate for the facility prepared in accordance with §264.144 plus a copy of the documentation required to demonstrate financial assurance under §264.145. For a new facility, a copy of the required documentation may be submitted 60 days prior to the initial receipt of hazardous wastes, if that is later than the submission of the part B.

(17) Where applicable, a copy of the insurance policy or other documentation which comprises compliance with the requirements of §264.147. For a new facility, documentation showing the amount of insurance meeting the specification of §264.147(a) and, if applicable, §264.147(b), that the owner or operator plans to have in effect before initial receipt of hazardous waste for treatment, storage, or disposal. A request for a variance in the amount of required coverage, for a new or existing facility, may be submitted as specified in §264.147(c).

(18) Where appropriate, proof of coverage by a State financial mechanism in compliance with §264.149 or §264.150.

(19) A topographic map showing a distance of 1,000 feet around the facility at a scale of 2.5 centimeters (1 inch) equal to not more than 61.0 meters (200 feet). Contours must be shown on the map. The contour interval must be sufficient to clearly show the pattern of surface water flow in the vicinity of and from each operational unit of the facility. For example, contours with an interval of 1.5 meters (5 feet), if relief is greater than 6.1 meters (20 feet), or an interval of 0.6 meters (2 feet), if relief is less than 6.1 meters (20 feet). Owners and operators of HWM facilities located in mountainous areas should use large contour intervals to adequately show topographic profiles of facilities. The map shall clearly show the following:

(i) Map scale and date.

(ii) 100-year floodplain area.

(iii) Surface waters including intermittent streams.

(iv) Surrounding land uses (residential, commercial, agricultural, recreational).

(v) A wind rose (*i.e.*, prevailing wind-speed and direction).

(vi) Orientation of the map (north arrow).

(vii) Legal boundaries of the HWM facility site.

(viii) Access control (fences, gates).

(ix) Injection and withdrawal wells both on-site and off-site.

(x) Buildings; treatment, storage, or disposal operations; or other structure (recreation areas, runoff control systems, access and internal roads, storm, sanitary, and process sewerage systems, loading and unloading areas, fire control facilities, etc.)

(xi) Barriers for drainage or flood control.

(xii) Location of operational units within the HWM facility site, where hazardous waste is (or will be) treated, stored, or disposed (include equipment cleanup areas).

Note: For large HWM facilities the Agency will allow the use of other scales on a case-by-case basis.

(20) Applicants may be required to submit such information as may be necessary to enable the Regional Administrator to carry out his duties under other Federal laws as required in §270.3 of this part.

(21) For land disposal facilities, if a case-by-case extension has been approved under §268.5 or a petition has been approved under §268.6, a copy of the notice of approval for the extension or petition is required.

(22) A summary of the pre-application meeting, along with a list of attendees and their addresses, and copies of any written comments or materials submitted at the meeting, as required under §124.31(c).

(c) *Additional information requirements.* The following additional information regarding protection of groundwater is required from owners or operators of hazardous waste facilities containing a regulated unit except as provided in §264.90(b) of this chapter:

(1) A summary of the ground-water monitoring data obtained during the interim status period under §§265.90 through 265.94, where applicable.

(2) Identification of the uppermost aquifer and aquifers hydraulically interconnected beneath the facility property, including ground-water flow direction and rate, and the basis for such identification (*i.e.*, the information obtained from hydrogeologic investigations of the facility area).

(3) On the topographic map required under paragraph (b)(19) of this section, a delineation of the waste management area, the property boundary, the proposed "point of compliance" as defined under §264.95, the proposed location of groundwater monitoring wells as required under §264.97, and, to the extent possible, the information required in paragraph (c)(2) of this section.

(4) A description of any plume of contamination that has entered the ground water from a regulated unit at the time that the application was submitted that:

(i) Delineates the extent of the plume on the topographic map required under paragraph (b)(19) of this section;

(ii) Identifies the concentration of each appendix IX, of part 264 of this chapter, constituent throughout the plume or identifies the maximum concentrations of each appendix IX constituent in the plume.

(5) Detailed plans and an engineering report describing the proposed ground water monitoring program to be implemented to meet the requirements of §264.97.

(6) If the presence of hazardous constituents has *not* been detected in the ground water at the time of permit application, the owner or operator must submit sufficient information, supporting data, and analyses to establish a detection monitoring program which meets the requirements of §264.98. This submission must address the following items specified under §264.98:

(i) A proposed list of indicator parameters, waste constituents, or reaction products that can provide a reliable indication of the presence of hazardous constituents in the ground water;

(ii) A proposed ground-water monitoring system;

(iii) Background values for each proposed monitoring parameter or constituent, or procedures to calculate such values; and

(iv) A description of proposed sampling, analysis and statistical comparison procedures to be utilized in evaluating ground-water monitoring data.

(7) If the presence of hazardous constituents has been detected in the ground water at the point of compliance at the time of the permit application, the owner or operator must submit sufficient information, supporting data, and analyses to establish a compliance monitoring program which meets the requirements of §264.99. Except as provided in §264.98(h)(5), the owner or operator must also submit an engineering feasibility plan for a corrective action program necessary to meet the requirements of §264.100, unless the owner or operator obtains written authorization in advance from the Regional Administrator to submit a proposed permit schedule for submittal of such a plan. To demonstrate compliance with §264.99, the owner or operator must address the following items:

Publisher's Note: The section referenced above, §264.98(h)(5), should be §264.98(g)(5).

(i) A description of the wastes previously handled at the facility;

(ii) A characterization of the contaminated ground water, including concentrations of hazardous constituents;

(iii) A list of hazardous constituents for which compliance monitoring will be undertaken in accordance with §§264.97 and 264.99;

(iv) Proposed concentration limits for each hazardous constituent, based on the criteria set forth in §264.94(a), including a justification for establishing any alternate concentration limits;

(v) Detailed plans and an engineering report describing the proposed ground-water monitoring system, in accordance with the requirements of §264.97; and

(vi) A description of proposed sampling, analysis and statistical comparison procedures to be utilized in evaluating ground-water monitoring data.

(8) If hazardous constituents have been measured in the ground water which exceed the concentration limits established under §264.94 Table 1, or if ground water monitoring conducted at the time of permit application under §§265.90 through 265.94 at the waste boundary indicates the presence of hazardous constituents from the facility in ground water over background concentrations, the owner or operator must submit sufficient information, supporting data, and analyses to

establish a corrective action program which meets the requirements of §264.100. However, an owner or operator is not required to submit information to establish a corrective action program if he demonstrates to the Regional Administrator that alternate concentration limits will protect human health and the environment after considering the criteria listed in §264.94(b). An owner or operator who is not required to establish a corrective action program for this reason must instead submit sufficient information to establish a compliance monitoring program which meets the requirements of §264.99 and paragraph (c)(6) of this section. To demonstrate compliance with §264.100, the owner or operator must address, at a minimum, the following items:

(i) A characterization of the contaminated ground water, including concentrations of hazardous constituents;

(ii) The concentration limit for each hazardous constituent found in the ground water as set forth in §264.94;

(iii) Detailed plans and an engineering report describing the corrective action to be taken; and

(iv) A description of how the ground-water monitoring program will demonstrate the adequacy of the corrective action.

(v) The permit may contain a schedule for submittal of the information required in paragraphs (c)(8)(iii) and (iv) provided the owner or operator obtains written authorization from the Regional Administrator prior to submittal of the complete permit application.

(d) *Information requirements for solid waste management units.* (1) The following information is required for each solid waste management unit at a facility seeking a permit: 17.8.1

(i) The location of the unit on the topographic map required under paragraph (b)(19) of this section.

(ii) Designation of type of unit.

(iii) General dimensions and structural description (supply any available drawings).

(iv) When the unit was operated.

(v) Specification of all wastes that have been managed at the unit, to the extent available.

(2) The owner or operator of any facility containing one or more solid waste management units must submit all available information pertaining to any release of hazardous wastes or hazardous constituents from such unit or units.

(3) The owner/operator must conduct and provide the results of sampling and analysis of groundwater, landsurface, and subsurface strata, surface water, or air, which may include the installation of wells, where the Director ascertains it is necessary to complete a RCRA Facility Assessment that will determine if a more complete investigation is necessary.

[48 FR 14228, Apr. 1, 1983; 48 FR 30114, June 30, 1983, as amended at 50 FR 2006, Jan. 14, 1985; 51 FR 16458, May 2, 1986; 51 FR 40653, Nov. 7, 1986; 52 FR 23450, July 9, 1987; 52 FR 25953, July 9, 1987; 52 FR 33936, Sept. 9, 1987; 52 FR 45799, Dec. 1, 1987; 52 FR 46965, Dec. 10, 1987; 54 FR 617, Jan. 9, 1989; 55 FR 25517, June 21, 1990; 57 FR 37281, Aug. 18, 1992; 59 FR 62952, Dec. 6, 1994; 60 FR 63433, Dec. 11, 1995; 61 FR 59996, Nov. 25, 1996; 62 FR 64671, Dec. 8, 1997; 63 FR 56735, Oct. 22, 1998; 71 FR 16914, Apr. 4, 2006; 71 FR 40279, July 14, 2006]

§270.15 Specific part B information requirements for containers.

Except as otherwise provided in §264.170, owners or operators of facilities that store containers of hazardous waste must provide the following additional information:

(a) A description of the containment system to demonstrate compliance with §264.175. Show at least the following:

(1) Basic design parameters, dimensions, and materials of construction.

(2) How the design promotes drainage or how containers are kept from contact with standing liquids in the containment system.

(3) Capacity of the containment system relative to the number and volume of containers to be stored.

(4) Provisions for preventing or managing run-on.

(5) How accumulated liquids can be analyzed and removed to prevent overflow.

(b) For storage areas that store containers holding wastes that do not contain free liquids, a demonstration of compliance with §264.175(c), including:

(1) Test procedures and results or other documentation or information to show that the wastes do not contain free liquids; and

(2) A description of how the storage area is designed or operated to drain and remove liquids or how containers are kept from contact with standing liquids.

(c) Sketches, drawings, or data demonstrating compliance with §264.176 (location of buffer zone and containers holding ignitable or reactive wastes) and §264.177(c) (location of incompatible wastes), where applicable.

(d) Where incompatible wastes are stored or otherwise managed in containers, a description of the procedures used to ensure compliance with §§264.177 (a) and (b), and 264.17 (b) and (c).

(e) Information on air emission control equipment as required in §270.27.

[48 FR 14228, Apr. 1, 1983; 48 FR 30114, June 30, 1983; 59 FR 62952, Dec. 6, 1994]

§270.16 Specific part B information requirements for tank systems.

Except as otherwise provided in §264.190, owners and operators of facilities that use tanks to store or treat hazardous waste must provide the following additional information:

(a) A written assessment that is reviewed and certified by a qualified Professional Engineer as to the structural integrity and suitability for handling hazardous waste of each tank system, as required under §§264.191 and 264.192 of this chapter;

(b) Dimensions and capacity of each tank;

(c) Description of feed systems, safety cutoff, bypass systems, and pressure controls (*e.g.*, vents);

(d) A diagram of piping, instrumentation, and process flow for each tank system;

(e) A description of materials and equipment used to provide external corrosion protection, as required under §264.192(a)(3)(ii);

(f) For new tank systems, a detailed description of how the tank system(s) will be installed in compliance with §264.192 (b), (c), (d), and (e);

(g) Detailed plans and description of how the secondary containment system for each tank system is or will be designed, constructed, and operated to meet the requirements of §264.193 (a), (b), (c), (d), (e), and (f);

(h) For tank systems for which a variance from the requirements of §264.193 is sought (as provided by §§264.193(g)):

(1) Detailed plans and engineering and hydrogeologic reports, as appropriate, describing alternate design and operating practices that will, in conjunction with location aspects, prevent the migration of any hazardous waste or hazardous constituents into the ground water or surface water during the life of the facility, or

(2) A detailed assessment of the substantial present or potential hazards posed to human health or the environment should a release enter the environment.

(i) Description of controls and practices to prevent spills and overflows, as required under §264.194(b); and

(j) For tank systems in which ignitable, reactive, or incompatible wastes are to be stored or treated, a description of how operating procedures and tank system and facility design will achieve compliance with the requirements of §§264.198 and 264.199.

(k) Information on air emission control equipment as required in §270.27.

[51 FR 25486, July 14, 1986; 51 FR 29431, Aug. 15, 1986; 59 FR 62952, Dec. 6, 1994; 71 FR 16914, Apr. 4, 2006]

§270.17 Specific part B information requirements for surface impoundments.

Except as otherwise provided in §264.1, owners and operators of facilities that store, treat or dispose of hazardous waste in surface impoundments must provide the following additional information:

(a) A list of the hazardous wastes placed or to be placed in each surface impoundment;

(b) Detailed plans and an engineering report describing how the surface impoundment is designed and is or will be constructed, operated, and maintained to meet the requirements of §§264.19, 264.221, 264.222, and 264.223 of this chapter, addressing the following items:

(1) The liner system (except for an existing portion of a surface impoundment). If an exemption from the requirement for a liner is sought as provided by §264.221(b), submit detailed plans and engineering and hydrogeologic reports, as appropriate, describing alternate design and operating practices that will, in conjunction with location aspects, prevent the migration of any hazardous constituents into the ground water or surface water at any future time;

(2) The double liner and leak (leachate) detection, collection, and removal system, if the surface impoundment must meet the requirements of §264.221(c) of this chapter. If an exemption from the requirements for double liners and a leak detection, collection, and removal system or alternative design is sought as provided by §264.221 (d), (e), or (f) of this chapter, submit appropriate information;

(3) If the leak detection system is located in a saturated zone, submit detailed plans and an engineering report explaining the leak detection system design and operation, and the location of the saturated zone in relation to the leak detection system;

(4) The construction quality assurance (CQA) plan if required under §264.19 of this chapter;

(5) Proposed action leakage rate, with rationale, if required under §264.222 of this chapter, and response action plan, if required under §264.223 of this chapter;

(6) Prevention of overtopping; and

(7) Structural integrity of dikes;

(c) A description of how each surface impoundment, including the double liner system, leak detection system, cover system, and appurtenances for control of overtopping, will be inspected in order to meet the requirements of §264.226(a), (b), and (d) of this chapter. This information must be included in the inspection plan submitted under §270.14(b)(5);

(d) A certification by a qualified engineer which attests to the structural integrity of each dike, as required under §264.226(c). For new units, the owner or operator must submit a statement by a qualified engineer that he will provide such a certification upon completion of construction in accordance with the plans and specifications;

(e) A description of the procedure to be used for removing a surface impoundment from service, as required under §264.227(b) and (c). This information should be included in the contingency plan submitted under §270.14(b)(7);

(f) A description of how hazardous waste residues and contaminated materials will be removed from the unit at closure, as required under §264.228(a)(1). For any wastes not to be removed from the unit upon closure, the owner or operator must submit detailed plans and an engineering report describing how §264.228(a)(2) and (b) will be complied with. This information should be included in the closure plan and, where applicable, the post-closure plan submitted under §270.14(b)(13);

(g) If ignitable or reactive wastes are to be placed in a surface impoundment, an explanation of how §264.229 will be complied with;

(h) If incompatible wastes, or incompatible wastes and materials will be placed in a surface impoundment, an explanation of how §264.230 will be complied with.

(i) A waste management plan for EPA Hazardous Waste Nos. F020, F021, F022, F023, F026, and F027 describing how the surface impoundment is or will be designed, constructed, operated, and maintained to meet the requirements of §264.231. This submission must address the following items as specified in §264.231:

(1) The volume, physical, and chemical characteristics of the wastes, including their potential to migrate through soil or to volatilize or escape into the atmosphere;

(2) The attenuative properties of underlying and surrounding soils or other materials;

(3) The mobilizing properties of other materials codisposed with these wastes; and

(4) The effectiveness of additional treatment, design, or monitoring techniques.

(j) Information on air emission control equipment as required in §270.27.

[48 FR 14228, Apr. 1, 1983, as amended at 50 FR 2006, Jan. 14, 1985; 50 FR 28752, July 15, 1985; 57 FR 3495, Jan. 29, 1992; 59 FR 62952, Dec. 6, 1994; 71 FR 40279, July 14, 2006]

§270.18 Specific part B information requirements for waste piles.

Except as otherwise provided in §264.1, owners and operators of facilities that store or treat hazardous waste in waste piles must provide the following additional information:

(a) A list of hazardous wastes placed or to be placed in each waste pile;

(b) If an exemption is sought to §264.251 and subpart F of part 264 as provided by §264.250(c) or §264.90(b)(2), an explanation of how the standards of §264.250(c) will be complied with or detailed plans and an engineering report describing how the requirements of §264.90(b)(2) will be met.

(c) Detailed plans and an engineering report describing how the waste pile is designed and is or will be constructed, operated, and maintained to meet the requirements of §§264.19, 264.251, 264.252, and 264.253 of this chapter, addressing the following items:

(1)(i) The liner system (except for an existing portion of a waste pile), if the waste pile must meet the requirements of §264.251(a) of this chapter. If an exemption from the requirement for a liner is sought as provided by §264.251(b) of this chapter, submit detailed plans, and engineering and hydrogeological reports, as appropriate, describing alternate designs and operating practices that will, in conjunction with location aspects, prevent the migration of any hazardous constituents into the ground water or surface water at any future time;

(ii) The double liner and leak (leachate) detection, collection, and removal system, if the waste pile must meet the requirements of §264.251(c) of this chapter. If an exemption from the requirements for double liners and a leak detection, collection, and removal system or alternative design is sought as provided by §264.251(d), (e), or (f) of this chapter, submit appropriate information;

(iii) If the leak detection system is located in a saturated zone, submit detailed plans and an engineering report explaining the leak detection system design and operation, and the location of the saturated zone in relation to the leak detection system;

(iv) The construction quality assurance (CQA) plan if required under §264.19 of this chapter;

(v) Proposed action leakage rate, with rationale, if required under §264.252 of this chapter, and response action plan, if required under §264.253 of this chapter;

(2) Control of run-on;

(3) Control of run-off;

(4) Management of collection and holding units associated with run-on and run-off control systems; and

(5) Control of wind dispersal of particulate matter, where applicable;

(d) A description of how each waste pile, including the double liner system, leachate collection and removal system, leak detection system, cover system, and appurtenances for control of run-on and run-off, will be inspected in order to meet the requirements of §264.254(a), (b), and (c) of this chapter. This information must be included in the inspection plan submitted under §270.14(b)(5);

(e) If treatment is carried out on or in the pile, details of the process and equipment used, and the nature and quality of the residuals;

(f) If ignitable or reactive wastes are to be placed in a waste pile, an explanation of how the requirements of §264.256 will be complied with;

(g) If incompatible wastes, or incompatible wastes and materials will be placed in a waste pile, an explanation of how §264.257 will be complied with;

(h) A description of how hazardous waste residues and contaminated materials will be removed from the waste pile at closure, as required under §264.258(a). For any waste not to be removed from the waste pile upon closure, the owner or operator must submit detailed plans and an engineering report describing how §264.310 (a) and (b) will be complied with. This information should be included in the closure plan and, where applicable, the post-closure plan submitted under §270.14(b)(13).

(i) A waste management plan for EPA Hazardous Waste Nos. F020, F021, F022, F023, F026, and F027 describing how a waste pile that is not enclosed (as defined in §264.250(c)) is or will be designed, constructed, operated, and maintained to meet the requirements of §264.259. This submission must address the following items as specified in §264.259:

(1) The volume, physical, and chemical characteristics of the wastes to be disposed in the waste pile, including their potential to migrate through soil or to volatilize or escape into the atmosphere;

(2) The attenuative properties of underlying and surrounding soils or other materials;

(3) The mobilizing properties of other materials co-disposed with these wastes; and

(4) The effectiveness of additional treatment, design, or monitoring techniques.

[48 FR 14228, Apr. 1, 1983, as amended at 50 FR 2006, Jan. 14, 1985; 50 FR 28752, July 15, 1985; 57 FR 3496, Jan. 29, 1992; 71 FR 40279, July 14, 2006]

§270.19 Specific part B information requirements for incinerators.

Except as §264.340 of this Chapter and §270.19(e) provide otherwise, owners and operators of facilities that incinerate hazardous waste must fulfill the requirements of paragraphs (a), (b), or (c) of this section.

(a) When seeking an exemption under §264.340 (b) or (c) of this chapter (Ignitable, corrosive, or reactive wastes only):

(1) Documentation that the waste is listed as a hazardous waste in part 261, subpart D of this chapter, solely because it is ignitable (Hazard Code I) or corrosive (Hazard Code C) or both; or

(2) Documentation that the waste is listed as a hazardous waste in part 261, subpart D of this chapter, solely because it is reactive (Hazard Code R) for characteristics other than those listed in §261.23(a) (4) and (5) of this chapter, and will not be burned when other hazardous wastes are present in the combustion zone; or

(3) Documentation that the waste is a hazardous waste solely because it possesses the characteristic of ignitability, corrosivity, or both, as determined by the tests for characteristics of hazardous waste under part 261, subpart C of this chapter; or

(4) Documentation that the waste is a hazardous waste solely because it possesses the reactivity characteristics listed in §261.23(a) (1), (2), (3), (6), (7), or (8) of this chapter, and that it will not be burned when other hazardous wastes are present in the combustion zone; or

(b) Submit a trial burn plan or the results of a trial burn, including all required determinations, in accordance with §270.62; or

(c) In lieu of a trial burn, the applicant may submit the following information:

(1) An analysis of each waste or mixture of wastes to be burned including:

(i) Heat value of the waste in the form and composition in which it will be burned.

(ii) Viscosity (if applicable), or description of physical form of the waste.

(iii) An identification of any hazardous organic constituents listed in part 261, appendix VIII, of this chapter, which are present in the waste to be burned, except that the applicant need not analyze for constituents listed in part 261, appendix VIII, of this chapter which would reasonably not be expected to be found in the waste. The constituents excluded from analysis must be identified and the basis for their exclusion stated. The waste analysis must rely on appropriate analytical techniques.

(iv) An approximate quantification of the hazardous constituents identified in the waste, within the precision produced by appropriate analytical methods.

(v) A quantification of those hazardous constituents in the waste which may be designated as POHC's based on data submitted from other trial or operational burns which demonstrate compliance with the performance standards in §264.343 of this chapter.

(2) A detailed engineering description of the incinerator, including:

(i) Manufacturer's name and model number of incinerator.

(ii) Type of incinerator.

(iii) Linear dimension of incinerator unit including cross sectional area of combustion chamber.

(iv) Description of auxiliary fuel system (type/feed).

(v) Capacity of prime mover.

(vi) Description of automatic waste feed cutoff system(s).

(vii) Stack gas monitoring and pollution control monitoring system.

(viii) Nozzle and burner design.

(ix) Construction materials.

(x) Location and description of temperature, pressure, and flow indicating devices and control devices.

(3) A description and analysis of the waste to be burned compared with the waste for which data from operational or trial burns are provided to support the contention that a trial burn is not needed. The data should include those items listed in paragraph (c)(1) of this section. This analysis should specify the POHC's which the applicant has identified in the waste for which a permit is sought, and any differences from the POHC's in the waste for which burn data are provided.

(4) The design and operating conditions of the incinerator unit to be used, compared with that for which comparative burn data are available.

(5) A description of the results submitted from any previously conducted trial burn(s) including:

(i) Sampling and analysis techniques used to calculate performance standards in §264.343 of this chapter,

(ii) Methods and results of monitoring temperatures, waste feed rates, carbon monoxide, and an appropriate indicator of combustion gas velocity (including a statement concerning the precision and accuracy of this measurement),

(6) The expected incinerator operation information to demonstrate compliance with §§264.343 and 264.345 of this chapter including:

(i) Expected carbon monoxide (CO) level in the stack exhaust gas.

(ii) Waste feed rate.

(iii) Combustion zone temperature.

(iv) Indication of combustion gas velocity.

(v) Expected stack gas volume, flow rate, and temperature.

(vi) Computed residence time for waste in the combustion zone.

(vii) Expected hydrochloric acid removal efficiency.

(viii) Expected fugitive emissions and their control procedures.

(ix) Proposed waste feed cut-off limits based on the identified significant operating parameters.

(7) Such supplemental information as the Director finds necessary to achieve the purposes of this paragraph.

(8) Waste analysis data, including that submitted in paragraph (c)(1) of this section, sufficient to allow the Director to specify as permit Principal Organic Hazardous Constituents (permit POHC's) those constituents for which destruction and removal efficiencies will be required.

(d) The Director shall approve a permit application without a trial burn if he finds that:

(1) The wastes are sufficiently similar; and

(2) The incinerator units are sufficiently similar, and the data from other trial burns are adequate to specify (under §264.345 of this chapter) operating conditions that will ensure that the performance standards in §264.343 of this chapter will be met by the incinerator.

(e) When an owner or operator of a hazardous waste incineration unit becomes subject to RCRA permit requirements after October 12, 2005, or when an owner or operator of an existing hazardous waste incineration unit demonstrates compliance with the air emission standards and limitations in part 63, subpart EEE, of this chapter (*i.e.*, by conducting a comprehensive performance test and submitting a Notification of Compliance under §§63.1207(j) and 63.1210(d) of this chapter documenting compliance with all applicable requirements of part 63, subpart EEE, of this chapter), the requirements of this section do not apply, except those provisions the Director determines are necessary to ensure compliance with §§264.345(a) and 264.345(c) of this chapter if you elect to comply with §270.235(a)(1)(i) to minimize emissions of toxic compounds from startup, shutdown, and malfunction events. Nevertheless, the Director may apply the provisions of this section, on a case-by-case basis, for purposes of information collection in accordance with §§270.10(k), 270.10(l), 270.32(b)(2), and 270.32(b)(3).

[48 FR 14228, Apr. 1, 1983, as amended at 58 FR 46051, Aug. 31, 1993; 64 FR 53076, Sept. 30, 1999; 67 FR 6816, Feb. 13, 2002; 67 FR 77692, Dec. 19, 2002; 70 FR 34590, June 14, 2005; 70 FR 59577, Oct. 12, 2005]

§270.20 Specific part B information requirements for land treatment facilities.

Except as otherwise provided in §264.1, owners and operators of facilities that use land treatment to dispose of hazardous waste must provide the following additional information:

(a) A description of plans to conduct a treatment demonstration as required under §264.272. The description must include the following information;

(1) The wastes for which the demonstration will be made and the potential hazardous constituents in the waste;

(2) The data sources to be used to make the demonstration (*e.g.*, literature, laboratory data, field data, or operating data);

(3) Any specific laboratory or field test that will be conducted, including:

(i) The type of test (*e.g.*, column leaching, degradation);

(ii) Materials and methods, including analytical procedures;

(iii) Expected time for completion;

(iv) Characteristics of the unit that will be simulated in the demonstration, including treatment zone characteristics, climatic conditions, and operating practices.

(b) A description of a land treatment program, as required under §264.271. This information must be submitted with the plans for the treatment demonstration, and updated following the treatment demonstration. The land treatment program must address the following items:

(1) The wastes to be land treated;

(2) Design measures and operating practices necessary to maximize treatment in accordance with §264.273(a) including:

(i) Waste application method and rate;

(ii) Measures to control soil pH;

(iii) Enhancement of microbial or chemical reactions;

(iv) Control of moisture content;

(3) Provisions for unsaturated zone monitoring, including:

(i) Sampling equipment, procedures, and frequency;

(ii) Procedures for selecting sampling locations;

(iii) Analytical procedures;

(iv) Chain of custody control;

(v) Procedures for establishing background values;

(vi) Statistical methods for interpreting results;

(vii) The justification for any hazardous constituents recommended for selection as principal hazardous constituents, in accordance with the criteria for such selection in §264.278(a);

(4) A list of hazardous constituents reasonably expected to be in, or derived from, the wastes to be land treated based on waste analysis performed pursuant to §264.13;

(5) The proposed dimensions of the treatment zone;

(c) A description of how the unit is or will be designed, constructed, operated, and maintained in order to meet the requirements of §264.273. This submission must address the following items:

(1) Control of run-on;

(2) Collection and control of run-off;

(3) Minimization of run-off of hazardous constituents from the treatment zone;

(4) Management of collection and holding facilities associated with run-on and run-off control systems;

(5) Periodic inspection of the unit. This information should be included in the inspection plan submitted under §270.14(b)(5);

(6) Control of wind dispersal of particulate matter, if applicable;

(d) If food-chain crops are to be grown in or on the treatment zone of the land treatment unit, a description of how the demonstration required under §264.276(a) will be conducted including:

(1) Characteristics of the food-chain crop for which the demonstration will be made.

(2) Characteristics of the waste, treatment zone, and waste application method and rate to be used in the demonstration;

(3) Procedures for crop growth, sample collection, sample analysis, and data evaluation;

(4) Characteristics of the comparison crop including the location and conditions under which it was or will be grown;

(e) If food-chain crops are to be grown, and cadmium is present in the land-treated waste, a description of how the requirements of §264.276(b) will be complied with;

(f) A description of the vegetative cover to be applied to closed portions of the facility, and a plan for maintaining such cover during the post-closure care period, as required under §§264.280(a)(8) and 264.280(c)(2). This information should be included in the closure plan and, where applicable, the post-closure care plan submitted under §270.14(b)(13);

(g) If ignitable or reactive wastes will be placed in or on the treatment zone, an explanation of how the requirements of §264.281 will be complied with;

(h) If incompatible wastes, or incompatible wastes and materials, will be placed in or on the same treatment zone, an explanation of how §264.282 will be complied with.

(i) A waste management plan for EPA Hazardous Waste Nos. F020, F021, F022, F023, F026, and F027 describing how a land treatment facility is or will be designed, constructed, operated, and maintained to meet the requirements of §264.283. This submission must address the following items as specified in §264.283:

(1) The volume, physical, and chemical characteristics of the wastes, including their potential to migrate through soil or to volatilize or escape into the atmosphere;

(2) The attenuative properties of underlying and surrounding soils or other materials;

(3) The mobilizing properties of other materials co-disposed with these wastes; and

(4) The effectiveness of additional treatment, design, or monitoring techniques.

[48 FR 14228, Apr. 1, 1983; 48 FR 30114, June 30, 1983, as amended at 50 FR 2006, Jan. 14, 1985; 71 FR 40279, July 14, 2006]

§270.21 Specific part B information requirements for landfills.

Except as otherwise provided in §264.1, owners and operators of facilities that dispose of hazardous waste in landfills must provide the following additional information:

(a) A list of the hazardous wastes placed or to be placed in each landfill or landfill cell;

(b) Detailed plans and an engineering report describing how the landfill is designed and is or will be constructed, operated, and maintained to meet the requirements of §§264.19, 264.301, 264.302, and 264.303 of this chapter, addressing the following items:

(1)(i) The liner system (except for an existing portion of a landfill), if the landfill must meet the requirements of §264.301(a) of this chapter. If an exemption from the requirement for a liner is sought as provided by §264.301(b) of this chapter, submit detailed plans, and engineering and hydrogeological reports, as appropriate, describing alternate designs and operating practices that will, in conjunction with location aspects, prevent the migration of any hazardous constituents into the ground water or surface water at any future time;

(ii) The double liner and leak (leachate) detection, collection, and removal system, if the landfill must meet the requirements of §264.301(c) of this chapter. If an exemption from the requirements for double liners and a leak detection, collection, and removal system or alternative design is sought as provided by §264.301(d), (e), or (f) of this chapter, submit appropriate information;

(iii) If the leak detection system is located in a saturated zone, submit detailed plans and an engineering report explaining the leak detection system design and operation, and the location of the saturated zone in relation to the leak detection system;

(iv) The construction quality assurance (CQA) plan if required under §264.19 of this chapter;

(v) Proposed action leakage rate, with rationale, if required under §264.302 of this chapter, and response action plan, if required under §264.303 of this chapter;

(2) Control of run-on;

(3) Control of run-off;

(4) Management of collection and holding facilities associated with run-on and run-off control systems; and

(5) Control of wind dispersal of particulate matter, where applicable;

(c) A description of how each landfill, including the double liner system, leachate collection and removal system, leak detection system, cover system, and appurtenances for control of run-on and run-off, will be inspected in order to meet the requirements of §264.303(a), (b), and (c) of this chapter. This information must be included in the inspection plan submitted under §270.14(b)(5);

(d) A description of how each landfill, including the liner and cover systems, will be inspected in order to meet the requirements of §264.303 (a) and (b). This information should be included in the inspection plan submitted under §270.14(b)(5).

(e) Detailed plans and an engineering report describing the final cover which will be applied to each landfill or landfill cell at closure in accordance with §264.310(a), and a description of how each landfill will be maintained and monitored after closure in accordance with §264.310(b). This information should be included in the closure and post-closure plans submitted under §270.14(b)(13).

(f) If ignitable or reactive wastes will be landfilled, an explanation of how the standards of §264.312 will be complied with;

(g) If incompatible wastes, or incompatible wastes and materials will be landfilled, an explanation of how §264.313 will be complied with;

(h) If bulk or non-containerized liquid waste or wastes containing free liquids is to be landfilled prior to May 8, 1985, an explanation of how the requirements of §264.314(a) will be complied with;

(i) If containers of hazardous waste are to be landfilled, an explanation of how the requirements of §264.315 or §264.316, as applicable, will be complied with.

(j) A waste management plan for EPA Hazardous Waste Nos. F020, F021, F022, F023, F026, and F027 describing how a landfill is or will be designed, constructed, operated, and maintained to meet the requirements of §264.317. This submission must address the following items as specified in §264.317:

(1) The volume, physical, and chemical characteristics of the wastes, including their potential to migrate through soil or to volatilize or escape into the atmosphere;

(2) The attenuative properties of underlying and surrounding soils or other materials;

(3) The mobilizing properties of other materials co-disposed with these wastes; and

(4) The effectiveness of additional treatment, design, or monitoring techniques.

[48 FR 14228, Apr. 1, 1983; 48 FR 30114, June 30, 1983, as amended at 50 FR 2006, Jan. 14, 1985; 50 FR 28752, July 15, 1985; 57 FR 3496, Jan. 29, 1992]

§270.22 Specific part B information requirements for boilers and industrial furnaces burning hazardous waste.

When an owner or operator of a cement kiln, lightweight aggregate kiln, solid fuel boiler, liquid fuel boiler, or hydrochloric acid production furnace becomes subject to RCRA permit requirements after October 12, 2005, or when an owner or operator of an existing cement kiln, lightweight aggregate kiln, solid fuel boiler, liquid fuel boiler, or hydrochloric acid production furnace demonstrates compliance with the air emission standards and limitations in part 63, subpart EEE, of this chapter (*i.e.*, by conducting a comprehensive performance test and submitting a Notification of Compliance under §§63.1207(j) and 63.1210(d) of this chapter documenting compliance with all applicable requirements of part 63, subpart EEE, of this chapter), the requirements of this section do not apply. The requirements of this section do apply, however, if the Director determines certain provisions are necessary to ensure compliance with §§266.102(e)(1) and 266.102(e)(2)(iii) of this chapter if you elect to comply with §270.235(a)(1)(i) to minimize emissions of toxic compounds from startup, shutdown, and malfunction events; or if you are an area source and elect to comply with the §§266.105, 266.106, and 266.107 standards and associated requirements for particulate matter, hydrogen chloride and chlorine gas, and non-mercury metals; or the Director determines certain provisions apply, on a case-by-case basis, for purposes of information collection in accordance with §§270.10(k), 270.10(l), 270.32(b)(2), and 270.32(b)(3).

(a) *Trial burns*—(1) *General.* Except as provided below, owners and operators that are subject to the standards to control organic emissions provided by §266.104 of this chapter, standards to control particulate matter provided by §266.105 of this chapter, standards to control metals emissions provided by §266.106 of this chapter, or standards to control hydrogen chloride or chlorine gas emissions provided by §266.107 of this chapter must conduct a trial burn to demonstrate conformance with those standards and must submit a trial burn plan or the results of a trial burn, including all required determinations, in accordance with §270.66.

(i) A trial burn to demonstrate conformance with a particular emission standard may be waived under provisions of §§266.104 through 266.107 of this chapter and paragraphs (a)(2) through (a)(5) of this section; and

(ii) The owner or operator may submit data in lieu of a trial burn, as prescribed in paragraph (a)(6) of this section.

(2) *Waiver of trial burn for DRE*—(i) *Boilers operated under special operating requirements.* When seeking to be permitted under §§266.104(a)(4) and 266.110 of this chapter that automatically waive the DRE trial burn, the owner or operator of a boiler must submit documentation that the boiler operates under the special operating requirements provided by §266.110 of this chapter.

(ii) *Boilers and industrial furnaces burning low risk waste.* When seeking to be permitted under the provisions for low risk waste provided by §§266.104(a)(5) and 266.109(a) of this chapter that waive the DRE trial burn, the owner or operator must submit:

(A) Documentation that the device is operated in conformance with the requirements of §266.109(a)(1) of this chapter.

(B) Results of analyses of each waste to be burned, documenting the concentrations of nonmetal compounds listed in appendix VIII of part 261 of this chapter, except for those constituents that would reasonably not be expected to be in the waste. The constituents excluded from analysis must be identified and the basis for their exclusion explained. The analysis must rely on appropriate analytical techniques.

(C) Documentation of hazardous waste firing rates and calculations of reasonable, worst-case emission rates of each constituent identified in paragraph (a)(2)(ii)(B) of this section using procedures provided by §266.109(a)(2)(ii) of this chapter.

(D) Results of emissions dispersion modeling for emissions identified in paragraphs (a)(2)(ii)(C) of this section using modeling procedures prescribed by §266.106(h) of this chapter. The Director will review the emission modeling conducted by the applicant to determine conformance with these procedures. The Director will either approve the modeling or determine that alternate or supplementary modeling is appropriate.

(E) Documentation that the maximum annual average ground level concentration of each constituent identified in paragraph (a)(2)(ii)(B) of this section quantified in conformance with paragraph (a)(2)(ii)(D) of this section does not exceed the allowable ambient level established in appendices IV or V of part 266. The acceptable ambient concentration for emitted constituents for which a specific Reference Air Concentration has not been established in appendix IV or Risk-Specific Dose has not been established in appendix V is 0.1 micrograms per cubic meter, as noted in the footnote to appendix IV.

(3) *Waiver of trial burn for metals.* When seeking to be permitted under the Tier I (or adjusted Tier I) metals feed rate screening limits provided by §266.106 (b) and (e) of this chapter that control metals emissions without requiring a trial burn, the owner or operator must submit:

(i) Documentation of the feed rate of hazardous waste, other fuels, and industrial furnace feed stocks;

(ii) Documentation of the concentration of each metal controlled by §266.106 (b) or (e) of this chapter in the hazardous waste, other fuels, and industrial furnace feedstocks, and calculations of the total feed rate of each metal;

(iii) Documentation of how the applicant will ensure that the Tier I feed rate screening limits provided by §266.106 (b) or (e) of this chapter will not be exceeded during the averaging period provided by that paragraph;

(iv) Documentation to support the determination of the terrain-adjusted effective stack height, good engineering practice stack height, terrain type, and land use as provided by §266.106 (b)(3) through (b)(5) of this chapter;

(v) Documentation of compliance with the provisions of §266.106(b)(6), if applicable, for facilities with multiple stacks;

(vi) Documentation that the facility does not fail the criteria provided by §266.106(b)(7) for eligibility to comply with the screening limits; and

(vii) Proposed sampling and metals analysis plan for the hazardous waste, other fuels, and industrial furnace feed stocks.

(4) *Waiver of trial burn for particulate matter.* When seeking to be permitted under the low risk waste provisions of §266.109(b) which waives the particulate standard (and trial burn to demonstrate conformance with the particulate standard), applicants must submit documentation supporting conformance with paragraphs (a)(2)(ii) and (a)(3) of this section.

(5) *Waiver of trial burn for HCl and Cl_2.* When seeking to be permitted under the Tier I (or adjusted Tier I) feed rate screening limits for total chloride and chlorine provided by §266.107 (b)(1) and (e) of this chapter that control emissions of hydrogen chloride (HCl)

and chlorine gas (Cl_2) without requiring a trial burn, the owner or operator must submit:

(i) Documentation of the feed rate of hazardous waste, other fuels, and industrial furnace feed stocks;

(ii) Documentation of the levels of total chloride and chlorine in the hazardous waste, other fuels, and industrial furnace feedstocks, and calculations of the total feed rate of total chloride and chlorine;

(iii) Documentation of how the applicant will ensure that the Tier I (or adjusted Tier I) feed rate screening limits provided by §266.107 (b)(1) or (e) of this chapter will not be exceeded during the averaging period provided by that paragraph;

(iv) Documentation to support the determination of the terrain-adjusted effective stack height, good engineering practice stack height, terrain type, and land use as provided by §266.107(b)(3) of this chapter;

(v) Documentation of compliance with the provisions of §266.107(b)(4), if applicable, for facilities with multiple stacks;

(vi) Documentation that the facility does not fail the criteria provided by §266.107(b)(3) for eligibility to comply with the screening limits; and

(vii) Proposed sampling and analysis plan for total chloride and chlorine for the hazardous waste, other fuels, and industrial furnace feedstocks.

(6) *Data in lieu of trial burn.* The owner or operator may seek an exemption from the trial burn requirements to demonstrate conformance with §§266.104 through 266.107 of this chapter and §270.66 by providing the information required by §270.66 from previous compliance testing of the device in conformance with §266.103 of this chapter, or from compliance testing or trial or operational burns of similar boilers or industrial furnaces burning similar hazardous wastes under similar conditions. If data from a similar device is used to support a trial burn waiver, the design and operating information required by §270.66 must be provided for both the similar device and the device to which the data is to be applied, and a comparison of the design and operating information must be provided. The Director shall approve a permit application without a trial burn if he finds that the hazardous wastes are sufficiently similar, the devices are sufficiently similar, the operating conditions are sufficiently similar, and the data from other compliance tests, trial burns, or operational burns are adequate to specify (under §266.102 of this chapter) operating conditions that will ensure conformance with §266.102(c) of this chapter. In addition, the following information shall be submitted:

(i) For a waiver from any trial burn:

(A) A description and analysis of the hazardous waste to be burned compared with the hazardous waste for which data from compliance testing, or operational or trial burns are provided to support the contention that a trial burn is not needed;

(B) The design and operating conditions of the boiler or industrial furnace to be used, compared with that for which comparative burn data are available; and

(C) Such supplemental information as the Director finds necessary to achieve the purposes of this paragraph.

(ii) For a waiver of the DRE trial burn, the basis for selection of POHCs used in the other trial or operational burns which demonstrate compliance with the DRE performance standard in §266.104(a) of this chapter. This analysis should specify the constituents in appendix VIII, part 261 of this chapter, that the applicant has identified in the hazardous waste for which a permit is sought, and any differences from the POHCs in the hazardous waste for which burn data are provided.

(b) *Alternative HC limit for industrial furnaces with organic matter in raw materials.* Owners and operators of industrial furnaces requesting an alternative HC limit under §266.104(f) of this chapter shall submit the following information at a minimum:

(1) Documentation that the furnace is designed and operated to minimize HC emissions from fuels and raw materials;

(2) Documentation of the proposed baseline flue gas HC (and CO) concentration, including data on HC (and CO) levels during tests when the facility produced normal products under normal operating conditions from normal raw materials while burning normal fuels and when not burning hazardous waste;

(3) Test burn protocol to confirm the baseline HC (and CO) level including information on the type and flow rate of all feedstreams, point of introduction of all feedstreams, total organic carbon content (or other appropriate measure of organic content) of all nonfuel feedstreams, and operating conditions that affect combustion of fuel(s) and destruction of hydrocarbon emissions from nonfuel sources;

(4) Trial burn plan to:

(i) Demonstrate that flue gas HC (and CO) concentrations when burning hazardous waste do not exceed the baseline HC (and CO) level; and

(ii) Identify the types and concentrations of organic compounds listed in appendix VIII, part 261 of this chapter, that are emitted when burning hazardous waste in conformance with procedures prescribed by the Director;

(5) Implementation plan to monitor over time changes in the operation of the facility that could reduce the baseline HC level and procedures to periodically confirm the baseline HC level; and

(6) Such other information as the Director finds necessary to achieve the purposes of this paragraph.

(c) *Alternative metals implementation approach.* When seeking to be permitted under an alternative metals implementation approach under §266.106(f) of this chapter, the owner or operator must submit documentation specifying how the approach ensures compliance with the metals emissions standards of §266.106(c) or (d) and how the approach can be effectively implemented and monitored. Further, the owner or operator shall provide such other information that the Director finds necessary to achieve the purposes of this paragraph.

(d) *Automatic waste feed cutoff system.* Owners and operators shall submit information describing the automatic waste feed cutoff system, including any pre-alarm systems that may be used.

(e) *Direct transfer.* Owners and operators that use direct transfer operations to feed hazardous waste from transport vehicles (containers, as defined in §266.111 of this chapter) directly to the boiler or industrial furnace shall submit information supporting conformance with the standards for direct transfer provided by §266.111 of this chapter.

(f) *Residues.* Owners and operators that claim that their residues are excluded from regulation under the provisions of §266.112 of this chapter must submit information adequate to demonstrate conformance with those provisions.

[56 FR 7235, Feb. 21, 1991; 56 FR 32691, July 17, 1991, as amended at 64 FR 53077, Sept. 30, 1999; 67 FR 6816, Feb. 13, 2002; 67 FR 77692, Dec. 19, 2002; 70 FR 34590, June 14, 2005; 70 FR 59577, Oct. 12, 2005]

§270.23 Specific part B information requirements for miscellaneous units.

Except as otherwise provided in §264.600, owners and operators of facilities that treat, store, or dispose of hazardous waste in miscellaneous units must provide the following additional information:

(a) A detailed description of the unit being used or proposed for use, including the following:

(1) Physical characteristics, materials of construction, and dimensions of the unit;

(2) Detailed plans and engineering reports describing how the unit will be located, designed, constructed, operated, maintained, monitored, inspected, and closed to comply with the requirements of §§264.601 and 264.602; and

(3) For disposal units, a detailed description of the plans to comply with the post-closure requirements of §264.603.

(b) Detailed hydrologic, geologic, and meteorologic assessments and land-use maps for the region surrounding the site that address and ensure compliance of the unit with each factor in the environmental performance standards of §264.601. If the applicant can demonstrate that he does not violate the environmental performance standards of §264.601 and the Director agrees with such demonstration, preliminary hydrologic, geologic, and meteorologic assessments will suffice.

(c) Information on the potential pathways of exposure of humans or environmental receptors to hazardous waste or hazardous constituents and on the potential magnitude and nature of such exposures.

(d) For any treatment unit, a report on a demonstration of the effectiveness of the treatment based on laboratory or field data.

(e) Any additional information determined by the Director to be necessary for evaluation of compliance of the unit with the environmental performance standards of §264.601.

§270.24 Specific part B information requirements for process vents.

Except as otherwise provided in §264.1, owners and operators of facilities that have process vents to which subpart AA of part 264 applies must provide the following additional information:

(a) For facilities that cannot install a closed-vent system and control device to comply with the provisions of 40 CFR 264 subpart AA on the effective date that the facility becomes subject to the provisions of 40 CFR 264 or 265 subpart AA, an implementation schedule as specified in §264.1033(a)(2).

(b) Documentation of compliance with the process vent standards in §264.1032, including:

(1) Information and data identifying all affected process vents, annual throughput and operating hours of each affected unit, estimated emission rates for each affected vent and for the overall facility (*i.e.*, the total emissions for all affected vents at the facility), and the approximate location within the facility of each affected unit (*e.g.*, identify the hazardous waste management units on a facility plot plan).

(2) Information and data supporting estimates of vent emissions and emission reduction achieved by add-on control devices based on engineering calculations or source tests. For the purpose of determining compliance, estimates of vent emissions and emission reductions must be made using operating parameter values (*e.g.*, temperatures, flow rates, or concentrations) that represent the conditions that exist when the waste management unit is operating at the highest load or capacity level reasonably expected to occur.

(3) Information and data used to determine whether or not a process vent is subject to the requirements of §264.1032.

(c) Where an owner or operator applies for permission to use a control device other than a thermal vapor incinerator, catalytic vapor incinerator, flare, boiler, process heater, condenser, or carbon adsorption system to comply with the requirements of §264.1032, and chooses to use test data to determine the organic removal efficiency or the total organic compound concentration achieved by the control device, a performance test plan as specified in §264.1035(b)(3).

(d) Documentation of compliance with §264.1033, including:

(1) A list of all information references and sources used in preparing the documentation.

(2) Records, including the dates, of each compliance test required by §264.1033(k).

(3) A design analysis, specifications, drawings, schematics, and piping and instrumentation diagrams based on the appropriate sections of "APTI Course 415: Control of Gaseous Emissions" (incorporated by reference as specified in §270.6) or other engineering texts acceptable to the Regional Administrator that present basic control device information. The design analysis shall address the vent stream characteristics and control device operation parameters as specified in §264.1035(b)(4)(iii).

(4) A statement signed and dated by the owner or operator certifying that the operating parameters used in the design analysis reasonably represent the conditions that exist when the hazardous waste management unit is or would be operating at the highest load or capacity level reasonably expected to occur.

(5) A statement signed and dated by the owner or operator certifying that the control device is designed to operate at an efficiency of 95 weight percent or greater unless the total organic emission limits of §264.1032(a) for affected process vents at the facility can be attained by a control device involving vapor recovery at an efficiency less than 95 weight percent.

[55 FR 25518, June 21, 1990, as amended at 56 FR 19290, Apr. 26, 1991; 70 FR 59577, Oct. 12, 2005]

§270.25 Specific part B information requirements for equipment.

Except as otherwise provided in §264.1, owners and operators of facilities that have equipment to which subpart BB of part 264 applies must provide the following additional information:

(a) For each piece of equipment to which subpart BB of part 264 applies:

(1) Equipment identification number and hazardous waste management unit identification.

(2) Approximate locations within the facility (*e.g.*, identify the hazardous waste management unit on a facility plot plan).

(3) Type of equipment (*e.g.*, a pump or pipeline valve).

(4) Percent by weight total organics in the hazardous waste stream at the equipment.

(5) Hazardous waste state at the equipment (*e.g.*, gas/vapor or liquid).

(6) Method of compliance with the standard (*e.g.*, "monthly leak detection and repair" or "equipped with dual mechanical seals").

(b) For facilities that cannot install a closed-vent system and control device to comply with the provisions of 40 CFR 264 subpart BB on the effective date that the facility becomes subject to the provisions of 40 CFR 264 or 265 subpart BB, an implementation schedule as specified in §264.1033(a)(2).

(c) Where an owner or operator applies for permission to use a control device other than a thermal vapor incinerator, catalytic vapor incinerator, flare, boiler, process heater, condenser, or carbon adsorption system and chooses to use test data to determine the organic removal efficiency or the total organic compound concentration achieved by the control device, a performance test plan as specified in §264.1035(b)(3).

(d) Documentation that demonstrates compliance with the equipment standards in §§264.1052 to 264.1059. This documentation shall contain the records required under §264.1064. The Regional Administrator may request further documentation before deciding if compliance has been demonstrated.

(e) Documentation to demonstrate compliance with §264.1060 shall include the following information:

(1) A list of all information references and sources used in preparing the documentation.

(2) Records, including the dates, of each compliance test required by §264.1033(j).

(3) A design analysis, specifications, drawings, schematics, and piping and instrumentation diagrams based on the appropriate sections of "APTI Course 415: Control of Gaseous Emissions" (incorporated by reference as specified in §270.6) or other engineering texts acceptable to the Regional Administrator that present basic control device information. The design analysis shall address the vent stream characteristics and control device operation parameters as specified in §264.1035(b)(4)(iii).

(4) A statement signed and dated by the owner or operator certifying that the operating parameters used in the design analysis reasonably represent the conditions that exist when the hazardous waste management unit is operating at the highest load or capacity level reasonably expected to occur.

(5) A statement signed and dated by the owner or operator certifying that the control device is designed to operate at an efficiency of 95 weight percent or greater.

[55 FR 25518, June 21, 1990, as amended at 56 FR 19290, Apr. 26, 1991; 70 FR 59577, Oct. 12, 2005]

§270.26 Special part B information requirements for drip pads.

Except as otherwise provided by §264.1 of this chapter, owners and operators of hazardous waste treatment, storage, or disposal facilities that collect, store, or treat hazardous waste on drip pads must provide the following additional information:

(a) A list of hazardous wastes placed or to be placed on each drip pad.

(b) If an exemption is sought to subpart F of part 264 of this chapter, as provided by §264.90 of this chapter, detailed plans and an engineering report describing how the requirements of §264.90(b)(2) of this chapter will be met.

(c) Detailed plans and an engineering report describing how the drip pad is or will be designed, constructed, operated and maintained to meet the requirements of §264.573 of this chapter, including the as-built drawings and specifications. This submission must address the following items as specified in §264.571 of this chapter:

(1) The design characteristics of the drip pad;

(2) The liner system;

(3) The leakage detection system, including the leak detection system and how it is designed to detect the failure of the drip pad or the presence of any releases of hazardous waste or accumulated liquid at the earliest practicable time;

(4) Practices designed to maintain drip pads;

(5) The associated collection system;

(6) Control of run-on to the drip pad;

(7) Control of run-off from the drip pad;

(8) The interval at which drippage and other materials will be removed from the associated collection system and a statement demonstrating that the interval will be sufficient to prevent overflow onto the drip pad;

(9) Procedures for cleaning the drip pad at least once every seven days to ensure the removal of any accumulated residues of waste or other materials, including but not limited to rinsing, washing with detergents or other appropriate solvents, or steam cleaning and provisions for documenting the date, time, and cleaning procedure used each time the pad is cleaned.

(10) Operating practices and procedures that will be followed to ensure that tracking of hazardous waste or waste constituents off the drip pad due to activities by personnel or equipment is minimized;

(11) Procedures for ensuring that, after removal from the treatment vessel, treated wood from pressure and non-pressure processes is held on the drip pad until drippage has ceased, including recordkeeping practices;

(12) Provisions for ensuring that collection and holding units associated with the run-on and run-off control systems are emptied or otherwise managed as soon as possible after storms to maintain design capacity of the system;

(13) If treatment is carried out on the drip pad, details of the process equipment used, and the nature and quality of the residuals.

(14) A description of how each drip pad, including appurtenances for control of run-on and run-off, will be inspected in order to meet the requirements of §264.573 of this chapter. This information should

be included in the inspection plan submitted under §270.14(b)(5) of this part.

(15) A certification signed by a qualified Professional Engineer, stating that the drip pad design meets the requirements of paragraphs (a) through (f) of §264.573 of this chapter.

(16) A description of how hazardous waste residues and contaminated materials will be removed from the drip pad at closure, as required under §264.575(a) of this chapter. For any waste not to be removed from the drip pad upon closure, the owner or operator must submit detailed plans and an engineering report describing how §264.310 (a) and (b) of this chapter will be complied with. This information should be included in the closure plan and, where applicable, the post-closure plan submitted under §270.14(b)(13).

[55 FR 50489, Dec. 6, 1990. Redesignated and amended at 56 FR 30198, July 1, 1991; 71 FR 16914, Apr. 4, 2006; 71 FR 40279, July 14, 2006]

§270.27 Specific Part B information requirements for air emission controls for tanks, surface impoundments, and containers.

(a) Except as otherwise provided in 40 CFR 264.1, owners and operators of tanks, surface impoundments, or containers that use air emission controls in accordance with the requirements of 40 CFR part 264, subpart CC shall provide the following additional information:

(1) Documentation for each floating roof cover installed on a tank subject to 40 CFR 264.1084(d)(1) or 40 CFR 264.1084(d)(2) that includes information prepared by the owner or operator or provided by the cover manufacturer or vendor describing the cover design, and certification by the owner or operator that the cover meets the applicable design specifications as listed in 40 CFR 264.1084(e)(1) or 40 CFR 264.1084(f)(1).

(2) Identification of each container area subject to the requirements of 40 CFR part 264, subpart CC and certification by the owner or operator that the requirements of this subpart are met.

(3) Documentation for each enclosure used to control air pollutant emissions from tanks or containers in accordance with the requirements of 40 CFR 264.1084(d)(5) or 40 CFR 264.1086(e)(1)(ii) that includes records for the most recent set of calculations and measurements performed by the owner or operator to verify that the enclosure meets the criteria of a permanent total enclosure as specified in "Procedure T—Criteria for and Verification of a Permanent or Temporary Total Enclosure" under 40 CFR 52.741, appendix B.

(4) Documentation for each floating membrane cover installed on a surface impoundment in accordance with the requirements of 40 CFR 264.1085(c) that includes information prepared by the owner or operator or provided by the cover manufacturer or vendor describing the cover design, and certification by the owner or operator that the cover meets the specifications listed in 40 CFR 264.1085(c)(1).

(5) Documentation for each closed-vent system and control device installed in accordance with the requirements of 40 CFR 264.1087 that includes design and performance information as specified in §270.24 (c) and (d) of this part.

(6) An emission monitoring plan for both Method 21 in 40 CFR part 60, appendix A and control device monitoring methods. This plan shall include the following information: monitoring point(s), monitoring methods for control devices, monitoring frequency, procedures for documenting exceedances, and procedures for mitigating noncompliances.

(7) When an owner or operator of a facility subject to 40 CFR part 265, subpart CC cannot comply with 40 CFR part 264, subpart CC by the date of permit issuance, the schedule of implementation required under 40 CFR 265.1082.

[61 FR 59996, Nov. 25, 1996]

§270.28 Part B information requirements for post-closure permits.

📖 6.4.4.1, 17.6

For post-closure permits, the owner or operator is required to submit only the information specified in §§270.14(b)(1), (4), (5), (6), (11), (13), (14), (16), (18) and (19), (c), and (d), unless the Regional Administrator determines that additional information from §§270.14, 270.16, 270.17, 270.18, 270.20, or 270.21 is necessary. The owner or operator is required to submit the same information when an alternative authority is used in lieu of a post-closure permit as provided in §270.1(c)(7).

[63 FR 56735, Oct. 22, 1998]

§270.29 Permit denial.

The Director may, pursuant to the procedures in part 124, deny the permit application either in its entirety or as to the active life of a hazardous waste management facility or unit only.

[54 FR 9607, Mar. 7, 1989]

Subpart C—Permit Conditions

§270.30 Conditions applicable to all permits.

The following conditions apply to all RCRA permits, and shall be incorporated into the permits either expressly or by reference. If incorporated by reference, a specific citation to these regulations (or the corresponding approved State regulations) must be given in the permit.

(a) *Duty to comply.* The permittee must comply with all conditions of this permit, except that the permittee need not comply with the conditions of this permit to the extent and for the duration such noncompliance is authorized in an emergency permit. (See §270.61). Any permit noncompliance, except under the terms of an emergency permit, constitutes a violation of the appropriate Act and is grounds for enforcement action; for permit termination, revocation and reissuance, or modification; or for denial of a permit renewal application.

(b) *Duty to reapply.* If the permittee wishes to continue an activity regulated by this permit after the expiration date of this permit, the permittee must apply for and obtain a new permit.

(c) *Need to halt or reduce activity not a defense.* It shall not be a defense for a permittee in an enforcement action that it would have been necessary to halt or reduce the permitted activity in order to maintain compliance with the conditions of this permit.

(d) In the event of noncompliance with the permit, the permittee shall take all reasonable steps to minimize releases to the environment, and shall carry out such measures as are reasonable to prevent significant adverse impacts on human health or the environment.

(e) *Proper operation and maintenance.* The permittee shall at all times properly operate and maintain all facilities and systems of treatment and control (and related appurtenances) which are installed or used by the permittee to achieve compliance with the conditions of this permit. Proper operation and maintenance includes effective performance, adequate funding, adequate operator staffing and training, and adequate laboratory and process controls, including appropriate quality assurance procedures. This provision requires the operation of back-up or auxiliary facilities or similar systems only when necessary to achieve compliance with the conditions of the permit.

(f) *Permit actions.* This permit may be modified, revoked and reissued, or terminated for cause. The filing of a request by the permittee for a permit modification, revocation and reissuance, or termination, or a notification of planned changes or anticipated noncompliance, does not stay any permit condition.

(g) *Property rights.* The permit does not convey any property rights of any sort, or any exclusive privilege.

(h) *Duty to provide information.* The permittee shall furnish to the Director, within a reasonable time, any relevant information which the Director may request to determine whether cause exists for modifying, revoking and reissuing, or terminating this permit, or to determine compliance with this permit. The permittee shall also furnish to the Director, upon request, copies of records required to be kept by this permit.

(i) *Inspection and entry.* The permittee shall allow the Director, or an authorized representative, upon the presentation of credentials and other documents as may be required by law to:

(1) Enter at reasonable times upon the permittee's premises where a regulated facility or activity is located or conducted, or where records must be kept under the conditions of this permit;

(2) Have access to and copy, at reasonable times, any records that must be kept under the conditions of this permit;

(3) Inspect at reasonable times any facilities, equipment (including monitoring and control equipment), practices, or operations regulated or required under this permit; and

(4) Sample or monitor at reasonable times, for the purposes of assuring permit compliance or as otherwise authorized by RCRA, any substances or parameters at any location.

(j) *Monitoring and records.* (1) Samples and measurements taken for the purpose of monitoring shall be representative of the monitored activity.

(2) The permittee shall retain records of all monitoring information, including all calibration and maintenance records and all original strip chart recordings for continuous monitoring instrumentation, copies of all reports required by this permit, the certification required by §264.73(b)(9) of this chapter, and records of all data used to complete the application for this permit, for a period of at least 3 years from the date of the sample, measurement, report, certification, or application. This period may be extended by request of the Director at any time. The permittee shall maintain records from all ground-water monitoring wells and associated ground-water surface elevations, for the active life of the facility, and for disposal facilities for the post-closure care period as well.

(3) Records for monitoring information shall include:

(i) The date, exact place, and time of sampling or measurements;

(ii) The individual(s) who performed the sampling or measurements;

(iii) The date(s) analyses were performed;

(iv) The individual(s) who performed the analyses;

(v) The analytical techniques or methods used; and

(vi) The results of such analyses.

(k) *Signatory requirements.* All applications, reports, or information submitted to the Director shall be signed and certified (See §270.11.)

(l) *Reporting requirements*—(1) *Planned changes.* The permittee shall give notice to the Director as soon as possible of any planned physical alterations or additions to the permitted facility.

(2) *Anticipated noncompliance.* The permittee shall give advance notice to the Director of any planned changes in the permitted facility or activity which may result in noncompliance with permit requirements. For a new facility, the permittee may not treat, store, or dispose of hazardous waste; and for a facility being modified, the permittee may not treat, store, or dispose of hazardous waste in the modified portion of the facility except as provided in §270.42, until:

(i) The permittee has submitted to the Director by certified mail or hand delivery a letter signed by the permittee and a registered professional engineer stating that the facility has been constructed or modified in compliance with the permit; and

(ii)(A) The Director has inspected the modified or newly constructed facility and finds it is in compliance with the conditions of the permit; or

(B) Within 15 days of the date of submission of the letter in paragraph (l)(2)(i) of this section, the permittee has not received notice from the Director of his or her intent to inspect, prior inspection is waived and the permittee may commence treatment, storage, or disposal of hazardous waste.

(3) *Transfers.* This permit is not transferable to any person except after notice to the Director. The Director may require modification or revocation and reissuance of the permit to change the name of the permittee and incorporate such other requirements as may be necessary under RCRA. (See §270.40)

(4) *Monitoring reports.* Monitoring results shall be reported at the intervals specified elsewhere in this permit.

(5) *Compliance schedules.* Reports of compliance or noncompliance with, or any progress reports on, interim and final requirements contained in any compliance schedule of this permit shall be submitted no later than 14 days following each schedule date.

(6) *Twenty-four hour reporting.* (i) The permittee shall report any noncompliance which may endanger health or the environment orally within 24 hours from the time the permittee becomes aware of the circumstances, including:

(A) Information concerning release of any hazardous waste that may cause an endangerment to public drinking water supplies.

(B) Any information of a release or discharge of hazardous waste or of a fire or explosion from the HWM facility, which could threaten the environment or human health outside the facility.

(ii) The description of the occurrence and its cause shall include:

(A) Name, address, and telephone number of the owner or operator;

(B) Name, address, and telephone number of the facility;

(C) Date, time, and type of incident;

(D) Name and quantity of material(s) involved;

(E) The extent of injuries, if any;

(F) An assessment of actual or potential hazards to the environment and human health outside the facility, where this is applicable; and

(G) Estimated quantity and disposition of recovered material that resulted from the incident.

(iii) A written submission shall also be provided within 5 days of the time the permittee becomes aware of the circumstances. The written submission shall contain a description of the noncompliance and its cause; the period of noncompliance including exact dates and times, and if the noncompliance has not been corrected, the anticipated time it is expected to continue; and steps taken or planned to reduce, eliminate, and prevent reoccurrence of the noncompliance. The Director may waive the five day written notice requirement in favor of a written report within fifteen days.

(7) *Manifest discrepancy report:* If a significant discrepancy in a manifest is discovered, the permittee must attempt to reconcile the discrepancy. If not resolved within fifteen days, the permittee must submit a letter

report, including a copy of the manifest, to the Director. (See 40 CFR 264.72.)

(8) *Unmanifested waste report:* This report must be submitted to the Director within 15 days of receipt of unmanifested waste. (See 40 CFR 264.76)

(9) *Biennial report:* A biennial report must be submitted covering facility activities during odd numbered calendar years. (See 40 CFR 264.75.)

(10) *Other noncompliance.* The permittee shall report all instances of noncompliance not reported under paragraphs (l)(4), (5), and (6) of this section, at the time monitoring reports are submitted. The reports shall contain the information listed in paragraph (l)(6) of this section.

(11) *Other information.* Where the permittee becomes aware that it failed to submit any relevant facts in a permit application, or submitted incorrect information in a permit application or in any report to the Director, it shall promptly submit such facts or information.

(m) *Information repository.* The Director may require the permittee to establish and maintain an information repository at any time, based on the factors set forth in 40 CFR 124.33(b). The information repository will be governed by the provisions in 40 CFR 124.33(c) through (f).

(Clean Water Act (33 U.S.C. 1251 *et seq.*), Safe Drinking Water Act (42 U.S.C. 300f *et seq.*), Clean Air Act (42 U.S.C. 7401 *et seq.*), Resource Conservation and Recovery Act (42 U.S.C. 6901 *et seq.*))

[48 FR 14228, Apr. 1, 1983, as amended at 48 FR 30114, June 30, 1983; 48 FR 39622, Sept. 1, 1983; 50 FR 28752, July 15, 1985; 53 FR 37935, Sept. 28, 1988; 60 FR 63433, Dec. 11, 1995]

§270.31 Requirements for recording and reporting of monitoring results.

All permits shall specify:

(a) Requirements concerning the proper use, maintenance, and installation, when appropriate, of monitoring equipment or methods (including biological monitoring methods when appropriate);

(b) Required monitoring including type, intervals, and frequency sufficient to yield data which are representative of the monitored activity including, when appropriate, continuous monitoring;

(c) Applicable reporting requirements based upon the impact of the regulated activity and as specified in parts 264, 266 and 267. Reporting shall be no less frequent than specified in the above regulations.

§270.32 Establishing permit conditions.

(a) In addition to conditions required in all permits (§270.30), the Director shall establish conditions, as required on a case-by-case basis, in permits under §§270.50 (duration of permits), 270.33(a) (schedules of compliance), 270.31 (monitoring), and for EPA issued permits only, 270.33(b) (alternate schedules of compliance) and 270.3 (considerations under Federal law).

(b)(1) Each RCRA permit shall include permit conditions necessary to achieve compliance with the Act and regulations, including each of the applicable requirements specified in parts 264 and 266 through 268 of this chapter. In satisfying this provision, the Administrator may incorporate applicable requirements of parts 264 and 266 through 268 of this chapter directly into the permit or establish other permit conditions that are based on these parts.

(2) Each permit issued under section 3005 of this act shall contain terms and conditions as the Administrator or State Director determines necessary to protect human health and the environment.

(3) If, as the result of an assessment(s) or other information, the Administrator or Director determines that conditions are necessary in addition to those required under 40 CFR parts 63, subpart EEE, 264 or 266 to ensure protection of human health and the environment, he shall include those terms and conditions in a RCRA permit for a hazardous waste combustion unit.

(c) For a State issued permit, an applicable requirement is a State statutory or regulatory requirement which takes effect prior to final administrative disposition of a permit. For a permit issued by EPA, an applicable requirement is a statutory or regulatory requirement (including any interim final regulation) which takes effect prior to the issuance of the permit. Section 124.14 (reopening of comment period) provides a means for reopening EPA permit proceedings at the discretion of the Director where new requirements become effective during the permitting process and are of sufficient magnitude to make additional proceedings desirable. For State and EPA administered programs, an applicable requirement is also any requirement which takes effect prior to the modification or revocation and reissuance of a permit, to the extent allowed in §270.41.

(d) New or reissued permits, and to the extent allowed under §270.41, modified or revoked and reissued permits, shall incorporate each of the applicable requirements referenced in this section and in 40 CFR 270.31.

(e) *Incorporation.* All permit conditions shall be incorporated either expressly or by reference. If incorporated by reference, a specific citation to the applicable regulations or requirements must be given in the permit.

[48 FR 14228, Apr. 1, 1983, as amended at 50 FR 28752, July 15, 1985; 51 FR 40653, Nov. 7, 1986; 65 FR 30913, May 15, 2000; 70 FR 59577, Oct. 12, 2005]

§270.33 Schedules of compliance.

(a) The permit may, when appropriate, specify a schedule of compliance leading to compliance with the Act and regulations.

(1) *Time for compliance.* Any schedules of compliance under this section shall require compliance as soon as possible.

(2) *Interim dates.* Except as provided in paragraph (b)(1)(ii) of this section, if a permit establishes a schedule of compliance which exceeds 1 year from the date of permit issuance, the schedule shall set forth interim requirements and the dates for their achievement.

(i) The time between interim dates shall not exceed 1 year.

(ii) If the time necessary for completion of any interim requirement is more than 1 year and is not readily divisible into stages for completion, the permit shall specify interim dates for the submission of reports of progress toward completion of the interim requirements and indicate a projected completion date.

(3) *Reporting.* The permit shall be written to require that no later than 14 days following each interim date and the final date of compliance, the permittee shall notify the Director in writing, of its compliance or noncompliance with the interim or final requirements.

(b) *Alternative schedules of compliance.* A RCRA permit applicant or permittee may cease conducting regulated activities (by receiving a terminal volume of hazardous waste and, for treatment and storage HWM facilities, closing pursuant to applicable requirements; and, for disposal HWM facilities, closing and conducting post-closure care pursuant to applicable requirements) rather than continue to operate and meet permit requirements as follows:

(1) If the permittee decides to cease conducting regulated activities at a given time within the term of a permit which has already been issued:

(i) The permit may be modified to contain a new or additional schedule leading to timely cessation of activities; or

(ii) The permittee shall cease conducting permitted activities before noncompliance with any interim or final compliance schedule requirement already specified in the permit.

(2) If the decision to cease conducting regulated activities is made before issuance of a permit whose term will include the termination date, the permit shall contain a schedule leading to termination which will ensure timely compliance with applicable requirements.

(3) If the permittee is undecided whether to cease conducting regulated activities, the Director may issue or modify a permit to contain two schedules as follows:

(i) Both schedules shall contain an identical interim deadline requiring a final decision on whether to cease conducting regulated activities no later than a date which ensures sufficient time to comply with applicable requirements in a timely manner if the decision is to continue conducting regulated activities;

(ii) One schedule shall lead to timely compliance with applicable requirements;

(iii) The second schedule shall lead to cessation of regulated activities by a date which will ensure timely compliance with applicable requirements;

(iv) Each permit containing two schedules shall include a requirement that after the permittee has made a final decision under paragraph (b)(3)(i) of this section it shall follow the schedule leading to compliance if the decision is to continue conducting regulated activities, and follow the schedule leading to termination if the decision is to cease conducting regulated activities.

(4) The applicant's or permittee's decision to cease conducting regulated activities shall be evidenced by a firm public commitment satisfactory to the Director, such as resolution of the board of directors of a corporation.

[48 FR 14228, Apr. 1, 1983, as amended at 48 FR 30114, June 30, 1983; 71 FR 40279, July 14, 2006]

Subpart D—Changes to Permit

§270.40 Transfer of permits.

(a) A permit may be transferred by the permittee to a new owner or operator only if the permit has been modified or revoked and reissued (under §270.40(b) or §270.41(b)(2)) to identify the new permittee and incorporate such other requirements as may be necessary under the appropriate Act.

(b) Changes in the ownership or operational control of a facility may be made as a Class 1 modification with prior written approval of the Director in accordance with §270.42 or as a routine change with prior approval under 40 CFR 124.213. The new owner or operator must submit a revised permit application no later than 90 days prior to the scheduled change. A written agreement containing a specific date for transfer of permit responsibility between the current and new permittees must also be submitted to the Director. When a transfer of ownership or operational control occurs, the old owner or operator shall comply with the requirements of 40 CFR part 264, subpart H (Financial Requirements) until the new owner or operator has demonstrated that he or she is complying with the requirements of that subpart. The new owner or operator must demonstrate compliance with subpart H requirements within six months of the date of the change of ownership or operational control of the facility. Upon demonstration to the Director by the new owner or operator of compliance with subpart H, the Director shall notify the old owner or operator that he or she no longer needs to comply with subpart H as of the date of demonstration.

[53 FR 37935, Sept. 28, 1988; 70 FR 53475, Sept. 8, 2005]

§270.41 Modification or revocation and reissuance of permits.

When the Director receives any information (for example, inspects the facility, receives information submitted by the permittee as required in the permit (see §270.30), receives a request for revocation and reissuance under §124.5 or conducts a review of the permit file), he or she may determine whether one or more of the causes listed in paragraphs (a) and (b) of this section for modification, or revocation and reissuance or both exist. If cause exists, the Director may modify or revoke and reissue the permit accordingly, subject to the limitations of paragraph (c) of this section, and may request an updated application if necessary. When a permit is modified, only the conditions subject to modification are reopened. If a permit is revoked and reissued, the entire permit is reopened and subject to revision and the permit is reissued for a new term. (See 40 CFR 124.5(c)(2).) If cause does not exist under this section, the Director shall not modify or revoke and reissue the permit, except on request of the permittee. If a permit modification is requested by the permittee, the Director shall approve or deny the request according to the procedures of 40 CFR 270.42, or §270.320 and 40 CFR part 124, subpart G. Otherwise, a draft permit must be prepared and other procedures in part 124 (or procedures of an authorized State program) followed.

(a) *Causes for modification.* The following are causes for modification, but not revocation and reissuance, of permits; the following may be causes for revocation and reissuance, as well as modification, when the permittee requests or agrees.

(1) *Alterations.* There are material and substantial alterations or additions to the permitted facility or activity which occurred after permit issuance which justify the application of permit conditions that are different or absent in the existing permit.

(2) *Information.* The Director has received information. Permits may be modified during their terms for this cause only if the information was not available at the time of permit issuance (other than revised regulations, guidance, or test methods) and would have justified the application of different permit conditions at the time of issuance.

(3) *New statutory requirements or regulations.* The standards or regulations on which the permit was based have been changed by statute, through promulgation of new or amended standards or regulations, or by judicial decision after the permit was issued.

(4) *Compliance schedules.* The Director determines good cause exists for modification of a compliance schedule, such as an act of God, strike, flood, or materials shortage or other events over which the permittee has little or no control and for which there is no reasonably available remedy.

(5) Notwithstanding any other provision in this section, when a permit for a land disposal facility is reviewed by the Director under §270.50(d), the Director shall modify the permit as necessary to assure that the facility continues to comply with the currently applicable requirements in parts 124, 260 through 266, and 270.

(b) *Causes for modification or revocation and reissuance.* The following are causes to modify or, alternatively, revoke and reissue a permit:

(1) Cause exists for termination under §270.43, and the Director determines that modification or revocation and reissuance is appropriate.

(2) The Director has received notification (as required in the permit, see §270.30(l)(3)) of a proposed transfer of the permit.

(3) The Director has received notification under 40 CFR 124.202(b) of a facility owner or operator's intent to be covered by a standardized permit.

(c) *Facility siting.* Suitability of the facility location will not be considered at the time of permit modification or revocation and reissuance unless new information or standards indicate that a threat to human health or the environment exists which was unknown at the time of permit issuance.

[48 FR 14228, Apr. 1, 1983, as amended at 48 FR 30114, June 30, 1983; 50 FR 28752, July 15, 1985; 52 FR 45799, Dec. 1, 1987; 53 FR 37936, Sept. 28, 1988; 70 FR 53475, Sept. 8, 2005; 71 FR 40279, July 14, 2006]

§270.42 Permit modification at the request of the permittee.

(a) *Class 1 modifications.* (1) Except as provided in paragraph (a)(2) of this section, the permittee may put into effect Class 1 modifications listed in appendix I of this section under the following conditions:

(i) The permittee must notify the Director concerning the modification by certified mail or other means that establish proof of delivery within 7 calendar days after the change is put into effect. This notice must specify the changes being made to permit conditions or supporting documents referenced by the permit and must explain why they are necessary. Along with the notice, the permittee must provide the applicable information required by §§270.13 through 270.21, 270.62, and 270.63.

(ii) The permittee must send a notice of the modification to all persons on the facility mailing list, maintained by the Director in accordance with 40 CFR 124.10(c)(viii), and the appropriate units of State and local government, as specified in 40 CFR 124.10(c)(ix). This notification must be made within 90 calendar days after the change is put into effect. For the Class I modifications that require prior Director approval, the notification must be made within 90 calendar days after the Director approves the request.

(iii) Any person may request the Director to review, and the Director may for cause reject, any Class 1 modification. The Director must inform the permittee by certified mail that a Class 1 modification has been rejected, explaining the reasons for the rejection. If a Class 1 modification has been rejected, the permittee must comply with the original permit conditions.

(2) Class 1 permit modifications identified in appendix I by an asterisk may be made only with the prior written approval of the Director.

(3) For a Class 1 permit modification, the permittee may elect to follow the procedures in §270.42(b) for Class 2 modifications instead of the Class 1 procedures. The permittee must inform the Director of this decision in the notice required in §270.42(b)(1).

(b) *Class 2 modifications.* (1) For Class 2 modifications, listed in appendix I of this section, the permittee must submit a modification request to the Director that:

(i) Describes the exact change to be made to the permit conditions and supporting documents referenced by the permit;

(ii) Identifies that the modification is a Class 2 modification;

(iii) Explains why the modification is needed; and

(iv) Provides the applicable information required by §§270.13 through 270.21, 270.62, and 270.63.

(2) The permittee must send a notice of the modification request to all persons on the facility mailing list maintained by the Director and to the appropriate units of State and local government as specified in 40 CFR 124.10(c)(ix) and must publish this notice in a major local newspaper of general circulation. This notice must be mailed and published within 7 days before or after the date of submission of the modification request, and the permittee must provide to the Director evidence of the mailing and publication. The notice must include:

(i) Announcement of a 60-day comment period, in accordance with §270.42(b)(5), and the name and address of an Agency contact to whom comments must be sent;

(ii) Announcement of the date, time, and place for a public meeting held in accordance with §270.42(b)(4);

(iii) Name and telephone number of the permittee's contact person;

(iv) Name and telephone number of an Agency contact person;

(v) Location where copies of the modification request and any supporting documents can be viewed and copied; and

(vi) The following statement: "The permittee's compliance history during the life of the permit being modified is available from the Agency contact person."

(3) The permittee must place a copy of the permit modification request and supporting documents in a location accessible to the public in the vicinity of the permitted facility.

(4) The permittee must hold a public meeting no earlier than 15 days after the publication of the notice required in paragraph (b)(2) of this section and no later than 15 days before the close of the 60-day comment period. The meeting must be held to the extent practicable in the vicinity of the permitted facility.

(5) The public shall be provided 60 days to comment on the modification request. The comment period will begin on the date the permittee publishes the notice in the local newspaper. Comments should be submitted to the Agency contact identified in the public notice.

(6)(i) No later than 90 days after receipt of the notification request, the Director must:

(A) Approve the modification request, with or without changes, and modify the permit accordingly;

(B) Deny the request;

(C) Determine that the modification request must follow the procedures in §270.42(c) for Class 3 modifications for the following reasons:

(*1*) There is significant public concern about the proposed modification; or

(*2*) The complex nature of the change requires the more extensive procedures of Class 3.

(D) Approve the request, with or without changes, as a temporary authorization having a term of up to 180 days, or

(E) Notify the permittee that he or she will decide on the request within the next 30 days.

(ii) If the Director notifies the permittee of a 30-day extension for a decision, the Director must, no later than 120 days after receipt of the modification request:

(A) Approve the modification request, with or without changes, and modify the permit accordingly;

(B) Deny the request; or

(C) Determine that the modification request must follow the procedures in §270.42(c) for Class 3 modifications for the following reasons:

(*1*) There is significant public concern about the proposed modification; or

(*2*) The complex nature of the change requires the more extensive procedures of Class 3.

(D) Approve the request, with or without changes, as a temporary authorization having a term of up to 180 days.

(iii) If the Director fails to make one of the decisions specified in paragraph (b)(6)(ii) of this section by the 120th day after receipt of the modification request, the permittee is automatically authorized to conduct the activities described in the modification request for up to 180 days, without formal Agency action. The authorized activities must be conducted as described in the permit modification request and must be in compliance with all appropriate standards of 40 CFR part 265. If the Director approves, with or without changes, or denies the modification request during the term of the temporary or automatic authorization provided for in paragraphs (b)(6) (i), (ii), or (iii) of this section, such action cancels the temporary or automatic authorization.

(iv)(A) In the case of an automatic authorization under paragraph (b)(6)(iii) of this section, or a temporary authorization under paragraph (b)(6) (i)(D) or (ii)(D) of this section, if the Director has not made a final approval or denial of the modification request by the date 50 days prior to the end of the temporary or automatic authorization, the permittee must within seven days of that time send a notification to persons on the facility mailing list, and make a reasonable effort to notify other persons who submitted written comments on the modification request, that:

(*1*) The permittee has been authorized temporarily to conduct the activities described in the permit modification request, and

(*2*) Unless the Director acts to give final approval or denial of the request by the end of the authorization period, the permittee will receive authorization to conduct such activities for the life of the permit.

(B) If the owner/operator fails to notify the public by the date specified in paragraph (b)(6)(iv)(A) of this section, the effective date of the permanent authorization will be deferred until 50 days after the owner/operator notifies the public.

(v) Except as provided in paragraph (b)(6)(vii) of this section, if the Director does not finally approve or deny a modification request before the end of the automatic or temporary authorization period or reclassify the modification as a Class 3, the permittee is authorized to conduct the activities described in the permit modification request for the life of the permit unless modified later under §270.41 or §270.42. The activities authorized under this paragraph must be conducted as described in the permit modification request and must be in compliance with all appropriate standards of 40 CFR part 265.

(vi) In making a decision to approve or deny a modification request, including a decision to issue a temporary authorization or to reclassify a modification as a Class 3, the Director must consider all written comments submitted to the Agency during the public comment period and must respond in writing to all significant comments in his or her decision.

(vii) With the written consent of the permittee, the Director may extend indefinitely or for a specified period the time periods for final approval or denial of a modification request or for reclassifying a modification as a Class 3.

(7) The Director may deny or change the terms of a Class 2 permit modification request under paragraphs (b)(6) (i) through (iii) of this section for the following reasons:

(i) The modification request is incomplete;

(ii) The requested modification does not comply with the appropriate requirements of 40 CFR part 264 or other applicable requirements; or

(iii) The conditions of the modification fail to protect human health and the environment.

(8) The permittee may perform any construction associated with a Class 2 permit modification request beginning 60 days after the submission of the request unless the Director establishes a later date for commencing construction and informs the permittee in writing before day 60.

(c) *Class 3 modifications.* (1) For Class 3 modifications listed in appendix I of this section, the permittee must submit a modification request to the Director that:

(i) Describes the exact change to be made to the permit conditions and supporting documents referenced by the permit;

(ii) Identifies that the modification is a Class 3 modification;

(iii) Explains why the modification is needed; and

(iv) Provides the applicable information required by 40 CFR 270.13 through 270.22, 270.62, 270.63, and 270.66.

(2) The permittee must send a notice of the modification request to all persons on the facility mailing list maintained by the Director and to the appropriate units of State and local government as specified in 40 CFR 124.10(c)(ix) and must publish this notice in a major local newspaper of general circulation. This notice must be mailed and published within seven days before or after the date of submission of the modification request, and the permittee must provide to the Director evidence of the mailing and publication. The notice must include:

(i) Announcement of a 60-day comment period, and a name and address of an Agency contact to whom comments must be sent;

(ii) Announcement of the date, time, and place for a public meeting on the modification request, in accordance with §270.42(c)(4);

(iii) Name and telephone number of the permittee's contact person;

(iv) Name and telephone number of an Agency contact person;

(v) Location where copies of the modification request and any supporting documents can be viewed and copied; and

(vi) The following statement: "The permittee's compliance history during the life of the permit being modified is available from the Agency contact person."

(3) The permittee must place a copy of the permit modification request and supporting documents in a location accessible to the public in the vicinity of the permitted facility.

(4) The permittee must hold a public meeting no earlier than 15 days after the publication of the notice required in paragraph (c)(2) of this section and no later than 15 days before the close of the 60-day comment period. The meeting must be held to the extent practicable in the vicinity of the permitted facility.

(5) The public shall be provided at least 60 days to comment on the modification request. The comment period will begin on the date the permittee publishes the notice in the local newspaper. Comments should be submitted to the Agency contact identified in the notice.

(6) After the conclusion of the 60-day comment period, the Director must grant or deny the permit modification request according to the permit modification procedures of 40 CFR part 124. In addition, the Director must consider and respond to all significant written comments received during the 60-day comment period.

(d) *Other modifications.* (1) In the case of modifications not explicitly listed in appendix I of this section, the permittee may submit a Class 3 modification request to the Agency, or he or she may request a determination by the Director that the modification should be reviewed and approved as a Class 1 or Class 2 modification. If the permittee requests that the modification be classified as a Class 1 or 2 modification, he or she must provide the Agency with the necessary information to support the requested classification.

(2) The Director shall make the determination described in paragraph (d)(1) of this section as promptly as practicable. In determining the appropriate class for a specific modification, the Director shall consider the similarity of the modification to other modifications codified in appendix I and the following criteria:

(i) Class 1 modifications apply to minor changes that keep the permit current with routine changes to the facility or its operation. These changes do not substantially alter the permit conditions or reduce the capacity of the facility to protect human health or the environment. In the case of Class 1 modifications, the Director may require prior approval.

(ii) Class 2 modifications apply to changes that are necessary to enable a permittee to respond, in a timely manner, to,

(A) Common variations in the types and quantities of the wastes managed under the facility permit,

(B) Technological advancements, and

(C) Changes necessary to comply with new regulations, where these changes can be implemented without substantially changing design specifications or management practices in the permit.

(iii) Class 3 modifications substantially alter the facility or its operation.

(e) *Temporary authorizations.* (1) Upon request of the permittee, the Director may, without prior public notice and comment, grant the permittee a temporary authorization in accordance with this subsection. Temporary authorizations must have a term of not more than 180 days.

(2)(i) The permittee may request a temporary authorization for:

(A) Any Class 2 modification meeting the criteria in paragraph (e)(3)(ii) of this section, and

(B) Any Class 3 modification that meets the criteria in paragraph (3)(ii) (A) or (B) of this section; or that meets the criteria in paragraphs (3)(ii) (C) through (E) of this section and provides improved management or treatment of a hazardous waste already listed in the facility permit.

(ii) The temporary authorization request must include:

(A) A description of the activities to be conducted under the temporary authorization;

(B) An explanation of why the temporary authorization is necessary; and

(C) Sufficient information to ensure compliance with 40 CFR part 264 standards.

(iii) The permittee must send a notice about the temporary authorization request to all persons on the facility mailing list maintained by the Director and to appropriate units of State and local governments as specified in 40 CFR 124.10(c)(ix). This notification must be made within seven days of submission of the authorization request.

(3) The Director shall approve or deny the temporary authorization as quickly as practical. To issue a temporary authorization, the Director must find:

(i) The authorized activities are in compliance with the standards of 40 CFR part 264.

(ii) The temporary authorization is necessary to achieve one of the following objectives before action is likely to be taken on a modification request:

(A) To facilitate timely implementation of closure or corrective action activities;

(B) To allow treatment or storage in tanks or containers, or in containment buildings in accordance with 40 CFR part 268;

(C) To prevent disruption of ongoing waste management activities;

(D) To enable the permittee to respond to sudden changes in the types or quantities of the wastes managed under the facility permit; or

(E) To facilitate other changes to protect human health and the environment.

(4) A temporary authorization may be reissued for one additional term of up to 180 days provided that the permittee has requested a Class 2 or 3 permit modification for the activity covered in the temporary authorization, and:

(i) The reissued temporary authorization constitutes the Director's decision on a Class 2 permit modification in accordance with paragraph (b)(6)(i)(D) or (ii)(D) of this section, or

(ii) The Director determines that the reissued temporary authorization involving a Class 3 permit modification request is warranted to allow the authorized activities to continue while the modification procedures of paragraph (c) of this section are conducted.

(f) *Public notice and appeals of permit modification decisions.* (1) The Director shall notify persons on the facility mailing list and appropriate units of State and local government within 10 days of any decision under this section to grant or deny a Class 2 or 3 permit modification request. The Director shall also notify such persons within 10 days after an automatic authorization for a Class 2 modification goes into effect under §270.42(b)(6) (iii) or (v).

(2) The Director's decision to grant or deny a Class 2 or 3 permit modification request under this section may be appealed under the permit appeal procedures of 40 CFR 124.19.

(3) An automatic authorization that goes into effect under §270.42(b)(6) (iii) or (v) may be appealed under the permit appeal procedures of 40 CFR 124.19; however, the permittee may continue to conduct the activities pursuant to the automatic authorization until the appeal has been granted pursuant to §124.19(c), notwithstanding the provisions of §124.15(b).

(g) *Newly regulated wastes and units.* (1) The permittee is authorized to continue to manage wastes listed or identified as hazardous under part 261 of this chapter, or to continue to manage hazardous waste in units newly regulated as hazardous waste management units, if:

(i) The unit was in existence as a hazardous waste facility with respect to the newly listed or characterized waste or newly regulated waste management unit on the effective date of the final rule listing or identifying the waste, or regulating the unit;

(ii) The permittee submits a Class 1 modification request on or before the date on which the waste or unit becomes subject to the new requirements;

(iii) The permittee is in compliance with the applicable standards of 40 CFR parts 265 and 266 of this chapter;

(iv) The permittee also submits a complete Class 2 or 3 modification request within 180 days of the effective date of the rule listing or identifying the waste, or subjecting the unit to RCRA Subtitle C management standards;

(v) In the case of land disposal units, the permittee certifies that each such unit is in compliance with all applicable requirements of part 265 of this chapter for groundwater monitoring and financial responsibility on the date 12 months after the effective date of the rule identifying or listing the waste as hazardous, or regulating the unit as a hazardous waste management unit. If the owner or operator fails to certify compliance with all these requirements, he or she will lose authority to operate under this section.

(2) New wastes or units added to a facility's permit under this subsection do not constitute expansions for the purpose of the 25 percent capacity expansion limit for Class 2 modifications.

(h) *Military hazardous waste munitions treatment and disposal.* The permittee is authorized to continue to accept waste military munitions notwithstanding any permit conditions barring the permittee from accepting off-site wastes, if:

(1) The facility was in existence as a hazardous waste facility, and the facility was already permitted to handle the waste military munitions, on the date when the waste military munitions became subject to hazardous waste regulatory requirements;

(2) On or before the date when the waste military munitions become subject to hazardous waste regulatory requirements, the permittee submits a Class 1 modification request to remove or amend the permit provision restricting the receipt of off-site waste munitions; and

(3) The permittee submits a complete Class 2 modification request within 180 days of the date when the waste military munitions became subject to hazardous waste regulatory requirements.

(i) *Permit modification list.* The Director must maintain a list of all approved permit modifications and must publish a notice once a year in a State-wide newspaper that an updated list is available for review.

(j) *Combustion facility changes to meet part 63 MACT standards.* The following procedures apply to hazardous waste combustion facility permit modifications requested under Appendix I of this section, section L(9).

(1) Facility owners or operators must have complied with the Notification of Intent to Comply (NIC) requirements of 40 CFR 63.1210 that were in effect prior to October 11, 2000, (See 40 CFR part 63 §§63.1200–63.1499 revised as of July 1, 2000) in order to request a permit modification under this section for the purpose of technology changes needed to meet the standards under 40 CFR 63.1203, 63.1204, and 63.1205.

(2) Facility owners or operators must comply with the Notification of Intent to Comply (NIC) requirements of 40 CFR 63.1210(b) and 63.1212(a) before a permit modification can be requested under this section for the purpose of technology changes needed to meet the 40 CFR 63.1215, 63.1216, 63.1217, 63.1218, 63.1219, 63.1220, and 63.1221 standards promulgated on October 12, 2005.

(3) If the Director does not approve or deny the request within 90 days of receiving it, the request shall be

deemed approved. The Director may, at his or her discretion, extend this 90 day deadline one time for up to 30 days by notifying the facility owner or operator.

(k) *Waiver of RCRA permit conditions in support of transition to the part 63 MACT standards.* (1) You may request to have specific RCRA operating and emissions limits waived by submitting a Class 1 permit modification request under Appendix I of this section, section L(10). You must:

(i) Identify the specific RCRA permit operating and emissions limits which you are requesting to waive;

(ii) Provide an explanation of why the changes are necessary in order to minimize or eliminate conflicts between the RCRA permit and MACT compliance; and

(iii) Discuss how the revised provisions will be sufficiently protective.

(iv) The Director shall approve or deny the request within 30 days of receipt of the request. The Director may, as his or her discretion, extend this 30 day deadline one time for up to 30 days by notifying the facility owner or operator.

(2) To request this modification in conjunction with MACT performance testing where permit limits may only be waived during actual test events and pretesting, as defined under 40 CFR 63.1207(h)(2)(i) and (ii), for an aggregate time not to exceed 720 hours of operation (renewable at the discretion of the Administrator) you must:

(i) Submit your modification request to the Director at the same time you submit your test plans to the Administrator; and

(ii) The Director may elect to approve or deny the request contingent upon approval of the test plans.

(l) *Performance Track member facilities.* The following procedures apply to Performance Track member facilities that request a permit modification under Appendix I of this section, section O(1).

(1) Performance Track member facilities must have complied with the requirements of §264.15(b)(5) in order to request a permit modification under this section.

(2) The Performance Track member facility should consider the application approved if the Director does not: deny the application, in writing; or notify the Performance Track member facility, in writing, of an extension to the 60-day deadline within 60 days of receiving the request. In these situations, the Performance Track member facility must adhere to the revised inspection schedule outlined in its application and maintain a copy of the application in the facility's operating record.

[48 FR 14228, Apr. 1, 1983 as amended at 65 FR 42302, July 10, 2000; 66 FR 24270, May 14, 2001; 67 FR 6996, Feb. 14, 2002; 70 FR 59577, Oct. 12, 2005; 71 FR 16914, Apr. 4, 2006; 71 FR 40279, July 14, 2006]

Appendix I to §270.42—Classification of Permit Modification

Modifications	Class
A. *General Permit Provisions*	
1. Administrative and informational changes	1
2. Correction of typographical errors	1
3. Equipment replacement or upgrading with functionally equivalent components (*e.g.*, pipes, valves, pumps, conveyors, controls)	1
4. Changes in the frequency of or procedures for monitoring, reporting, sampling, or maintenance activities by the permittee:	
a. To provide for more frequent monitoring, reporting, sampling, or maintenance	1
b. Other changes	2
5. Schedule of compliance:	
a. Changes in interim compliance dates, with prior approval of the Director	[1]1
b. Extension of final compliance date	3
6. Changes in expiration date of permit to allow earlier permit termination, with prior approval of the Director	[1]1
7. Changes in ownership or operational control of a facility, provided the procedures of §270.40(b) are followed	[1]1
8. Changes to remove permit conditions that are no longer applicable (*i.e.*, because the standards upon which they are based are no longer applicable to the facility)	[1]1
9. Changes to remove permit conditions applicable to a unit excluded under the provisions of §261.4.	[1]1
10. Changes in the expiration date of a permit issued to a facility at which all units are excluded under the provisions of §261.4.	[1]1
B. *General Facility Standards*	
1. Changes to waste sampling or analysis methods:	
a. To conform with agency guidance or regulations	1
b. To incorporate changes associated with F039 (multi-source leachate) sampling or analysis methods	1
c. To incorporate changes associated with underlying hazardous constituents in ignitable or corrosive wastes	[1]1
d. Other changes	2
2. Changes to analytical quality assurance/control plan:	
a. To conform with agency guidance or regulations	1
b. Other changes	2
3. Changes in procedures for maintaining the operating record	1
4. Changes in frequency or content of inspection schedules	2
5. Changes in the training plan:	
a. That affect the type or decrease the amount of training given to employees	2
b. Other changes	1
6. Contingency plan:	
a. Changes in emergency procedures (*i.e.*, spill or release response procedures)	2
b. Replacement with functionally equivalent equipment, upgrade, or relocate emergency equipment listed	1
c. Removal of equipment from emergency equipment list	2

Modifications	Class
d. Changes in name, address, or phone number of coordinators or other persons or agencies identified in the plan	1
7. Construction quality assurance plan:	
a. Changes that the CQA officer certifies in the operating record will provide equivalent or better certainty that the unit components meet the design specifications	1
b. Other changes.	2
Note: When a permit modification (such as introduction of a new unit) requires a change in facility plans or other general facility standards, that change shall be reviewed under the same procedures as the permit modification	
C. *Ground-Water Protection*	
1. Changes to wells:	
a. Changes in the number, location, depth, or design of upgradient or downgradient wells of permitted ground-water monitoring system	2
b. Replacement of an existing well that has been damaged or rendered inoperable, without change to location, design, or depth of the well	1
2. Changes in ground-water sampling or analysis procedures or monitoring schedule, with prior approval of the Director	[1]1
3. Changes in statistical procedure for determining whether a statistically significant change in ground-water quality between upgradient and downgradient wells has occurred, with prior approval of the Director	[1]1
4. Changes in point of compliance	2
5. Changes in indicator parameters, hazardous constituents, or concentration limits (including ACLs):	
a. As specified in the groundwater protection standard	3
b. As specified in the detection monitoring program	2
6. Changes to a detection monitoring program as required by §264.98(h), unless otherwise specified in this appendix	2
7. Compliance monitoring program:	
a. Addition of compliance monitoring program as required by §§264.98(g)(4) and 264.99	3
b. Changes to a compliance monitoring program as required by §264.99(j), unless otherwise specified in this appendix	2
8. Corrective action program:	
a. Addition of a corrective action program as required by §§264.99(h)(2) and 264.100	3
b. Changes to a corrective action program as required by §264.100(h), unless otherwise specified in this appendix	2
D. *Closure*	
1. Changes to the closure plan:	
a. Changes in estimate of maximum extent of operations or maximum inventory of waste on-site at any time during the active life of the facility, with prior approval of the Director	[1]1
b. Changes in the closure schedule for any unit, changes in the final closure schedule for the facility, or extension of the closure period, with prior approval of the Director	[1]1
c. Changes in the expected year of final closure, where other permit conditions are not changed, with prior approval of the Director	[1]1

Modifications	Class
d. Changes in procedures for decontamination of facility equipment or structures, with prior approval of the Director	[1]1
e. Changes in approved closure plan resulting from unexpected events occurring during partial or final closure, unless otherwise specified in this appendix	2
f. Extension of the closure period to allow a landfill, surface impoundment or land treatment unit to receive non-hazardous wastes after final receipt of hazardous wastes under §264.113 (d) and (e)	2
2. Creation of a new landfill unit as part of closure	3
3. Addition of the following new units to be used temporarily for closure activities:	
a. Surface impoundments	3
b. Incinerators	3
c. Waste piles that do not comply with §264.250(c)	3
d. Waste piles that comply with §264.250(c)	2
e. Tanks or containers (other than specified below)	2
f. Tanks used for neutralization, dewatering, phase separation, or component separation, with prior approval of the Director	[1]1
g. Staging piles	2
E. *Post-Closure*	
1. Changes in name, address, or phone number of contact in post-closure plan	1
2. Extension of post-closure care period	2
3. Reduction in the post-closure care period	3
4. Changes to the expected year of final closure, where other permit conditions are not changed	1
5. Changes in post-closure plan necessitated by events occurring during the active life of the facility, including partial and final closure	2
F. *Containers*	
1. Modification or addition of container units:	
a. Resulting in greater than 25% increase in the facility's container storage capacity, except as provided in F(1)(c) and F(4)(a) below	3
b. Resulting in up to 25% increase in the facility's container storage capacity, except as provided in F(1)(c) and F(4)(a) below.	2
c. Or treatment processes necessary to treat wastes that are restricted from land disposal to meet some or all of the applicable treatment standards or to treat wastes to satisfy (in whole or in part) the standard of "use of practically available technology that yields the greatest environmental benefit" contained in 268.8(a)(2)(ii), with prior approval of the Director. This modification may also involve addition of new waste codes or narrative descriptions of wastes. It is not applicable to dioxin-containing wastes (F020, 021, 022, 023, 026, 027, and 028)	[1]1
Publisher's Note: The section referenced above, §268.8(a)(2)(ii), is no longer in the RCRA regulations. It was removed on April 8, 1996 [61 FR 15599].	
2.	
a. Modification of a container unit without increasing the capacity of the unit	2
b. Addition of a roof to a container unit without alteration of the containment system	1
3. Storage of different wastes in containers, except as provided in (F)(4) below:	
a. That require additional or different management practices from those authorized in the permit	3

Modifications	Class
b. That do not require additional or different management practices from those authorized in the permit.	2
Note: See §270.42(g) for modification procedures to be used for the management of newly listed or identified wastes	
4. Storage or treatment of different wastes in containers:	
a. That require addition of units or change in treatment process or management standards, provided that the wastes are restricted from land disposal and are to be treated to meet some or all of the applicable treatment standards, or that are to be treated to satisfy (in whole or in part) the standard of "use of practically available technology that yields the greatest environmental benefit" contained in §268.8(a)(2)(ii). This modification is not applicable to dioxin-containing wastes (F020, 021, 022, 023, 026, 027, and 028)	[1]1
Publisher's Note: The section referenced above, §268.8(a)(2)(ii), is no longer in the RCRA regulations. It was removed on April 8, 1996 [61 FR 15599].	
b. That do not require the addition of units or a change in the treatment process or management standards, and provided that the units have previously received wastes of the same type (*e.g.*, incinerator scrubber water). This modification is not applicable to dioxin-containing wastes (F020, 021, 022, 023, 026, 027, and 028)	[1]1
G. *Tanks*	
1.	
a. Modification or addition of tank units resulting in greater than 25% increase in the facility's tank capacity, except as provided in G(1)(c), G(1)(d), and G(1)(e) below	3
b. Modification or addition of tank units resulting in up to 25% increase in the facility's tank capacity, except as provided in G(1)(d) and G(1)(e) below	2
c. Addition of a new tank that will operate for more than 90 days using any of the following physical or chemical treatment technologies: neutralization, dewatering, phase separation, or component separation	2
d. After prior approval of the Director, addition of a new tank that will operate for up to 90 days using any of the following physical or chemical treatment technologies: neutralization, dewatering, phase separation, or component separation	[1]1
e. Modification or addition of tank units or treatment processes necessary to treat wastes that are restricted from land disposal to meet some or all of the applicable treatment standards or to treat wastes to satisfy (in whole or in part) the standard of "use of practically available technology that yields the greatest environmental benefit" contained in §268.8(a)(2)(ii), with prior approval of the Director. This modification may also involve addition of new waste codes. It is not applicable to dioxin-containing wastes (F020, 021, 022, 023, 026, 027, and 028)	[1]1
Publisher's Note: The section referenced above, §268.8(a)(2)(ii), is no longer in the RCRA regulations. It was removed on April 8, 1996 [61 FR 15599].	
2. Modification of a tank unit or secondary containment system without increasing the capacity of the unit	2
3. Replacement of a tank with a tank that meets the same design standards and has a capacity within ±10% of the replaced tank provided	1
—The capacity difference is no more than 1500 gallons,	
—The facility's permitted tank capacity is not increased, and	
—The replacement tank meets the same conditions in the permit	
4. Modification of a tank management practice	2
5. Management of different wastes in tanks:	
a. That require additional or different management practices, tank design, different fire protection specifications, or significantly different tank treatment process from that authorized in the permit, except as provided in (G)(5)(c) below	3
b. That do not require additional or different management practices, tank design, different fire protection specifications, or significantly different tank treatment process than authorized in the permit, except as provided in (G)(5)(d)	2
c. That require addition of units or change in treatment processes or management standards, provided that the wastes are restricted from land disposal and are to be treated to meet some or all of the applicable treatment standards or that are to be treated to satisfy (in whole or in part) the standard of "use of practically available technology that yields the greatest environmental benefit" contained in §268.8(a)(2)(ii). The modification is not applicable to dioxin-containing wastes (F020, 021, 022, 023, 026, 027, and 028)	[1]1
Publisher's Note: The section referenced above, §268.8(a)(2)(ii), is no longer in the RCRA regulations. It was removed on April 8, 1996 [61 FR 15599].	
d. That do not require the addition of units or a change in the treatment process or management standards, and provided that the units have previously received wastes of the same type (*e.g.*, incinerator scrubber water). This modification is not applicable to dioxin-containing wastes (F020, 021, 022, 023, 026, 027, and 028)	1
Note: See §270.42(g) for modification procedures to be used for the management of newly listed or identified wastes	
H. *Surface Impoundments*	
1. Modification or addition of surface impoundment units that result in increasing the facility's surface impoundment storage or treatment capacity	3
2. Replacement of a surface impoundment unit	3
3. Modification of a surface impoundment unit without increasing the facility's surface impoundment storage or treatment capacity and without modifying the unit's liner, leak detection system, or leachate collection system	2
4. Modification of a surface impoundment management practice	2
5. Treatment, storage, or disposal of different wastes in surface impoundments:	
a. That require additional or different management practices or different design of the liner or leak detection system than authorized in the permit	3

Modifications	Class
b. That do not require additional or different management practices or different design of the liner or leak detection system than authorized in the permit	2
c. That are wastes restricted from land disposal that meet the applicable treatment standards or that are treated to satisfy the standard of "use of practically available technology that yields the greatest environmental benefit" contained in §269.8(a)(2)(ii), and provided that the unit meets the minimum technological requirements stated in §268.5(h)(2). This modification is not applicable to dioxin-containing wastes (F020, 021, 022, 023, 026, 027, and 028)	1
Publisher's Note: The section referenced above, §269.8(a)(2)(ii), which was supposed to be §268.8(a)(2)(ii), is no longer in the RCRA regulations. It was removed on April 8, 1996 [61 FR 15599].	
d. That are residues from wastewater treatment or incineration, provided that disposal occurs in a unit that meets the minimum technological requirements stated in §268.5(h)(2), and provided further that the surface impoundment has previously received wastes of the same type (for example, incinerator scrubber water). This modification is not applicable to dioxin-containing wastes (F020, 021, 022, 023, 026, 027, and 028)	1
6. Modifications of unconstructed units to comply with §§264.221(c), 264.222, 264.223, and 264.226(d)	[1]1
7. Changes in response action plan:	
a. Increase in action leakage rate	3
b. Change in a specific response reducing its frequency or effectiveness	3
c. Other changes.	2
Note: See §270.42(g) for modification procedures to be used for the management of newly listed or identified wastes	
I. *Enclosed Waste Piles.* For all waste piles except those complying with §264.250(c), modifications are treated the same as for a landfill. The following modifications are applicable only to waste piles complying with 264.250(c)	
1. Modification or addition of waste pile units:	
a. Resulting in greater than 25% increase in the facility's waste pile storage or treatment capacity	3
b. Resulting in up to 25% increase in the facility's waste pile storage or treatment capacity	2
2. Modification of waste pile unit without increasing the capacity of the unit	2
3. Replacement of a waste pile unit with another waste pile unit of the same design and capacity and meeting all waste pile conditions in the permit	1
4. Modification of a waste pile management practice	2
5. Storage or treatment of different wastes in waste piles:	
a. That require additional or different management practices or different design of the unit	3
b. That do not require additional or different management practices or different design of the unit	2
6. Conversion of an enclosed waste pile to a containment building unit 13.8.4.1.3	2
Note: See §270.42(g) for modification procedures to be used for the management of newly listed or identified wastes	
J. *Landfills and Unenclosed Waste Piles*	
1. Modification or addition of landfill units that result in increasing the facility's disposal capacity.	3
2. Replacement of a landfill	3
3. Addition or modification of a liner, leachate collection system, leachate detection system, run-off control, or final cover system	3
4. Modification of a landfill unit without changing a liner, leachate collection system, leachate detection system, run-off control, or final cover system	2
5. Modification of a landfill management practice	2
6. Landfill different wastes:	
a. That require additional or different management practices, different design of the liner, leachate collection system, or leachate detection system	3
b. That do not require additional or different management practices, different design of the liner, leachate collection system, or leachate detection system	2
c. That are wastes restricted from land disposal that meet the applicable treatment standards or that are treated to satisfy the standard of "use of practically available technology that yields the greatest environmental benefit" contained in §268.8(a)(2)(ii), and provided that the landfill unit meets the minimum technological requirements stated in §268.5(h)(2). This modification is not applicable to dioxin-containing wastes (F020, 021, 022, 023, 026, 027, and 028)	1
Publisher's Note: The section referenced above, §268.8(a)(2)(ii), is no longer in the RCRA regulations. It was removed on April 8, 1996 [61 FR 15599].	
d. That are residues from wastewater treatment or incineration, provided that disposal occurs in a landfill unit that meets the minimum technological requirements stated in §268.5(h)(2), and provided further that the landfill has previously received wastes of the same type (for example, incinerator ash). This modification is not applicable to dioxin-containing wastes (F020, 021, 022, 023, 026, 027, and 028)	1
7. Modifications of unconstructed units to comply with §§264.251(c), 264.252, 264.253, 264.254(c), 264.301(c), 264.302, 264.303(c), and 264.304	[1]1
8. Changes in response action plan:	
a. Increase in action leakage rate	3
b. Change in a specific response reducing its frequency or effectiveness	3
c. Other changes	2
Note: See §270.42(g) for modification procedures to be used for the management of newly listed or identified wastes	
K. *Land Treatment*	
1. Lateral expansion of or other modification of a land treatment unit to increase areal extent	3
2. Modification of run-on control system	2
3. Modify run-off control system	3
4. Other modifications of land treatment unit component specifications or standards required in permit	2
5. Management of different wastes in land treatment units:	

Modifications	Class
a. That require a change in permit operating conditions or unit design specifications	3
b. That do not require a change in permit operating conditions or unit design specifications	2
Note: See §270.42(g) for modification procedures to be used for the management of newly listed or identified wastes	
6. Modification of a land treatment unit management practice to:	
a. Increase rate or change method of waste application	3
b. Decrease rate of waste application	1
7. Modification of a land treatment unit management practice to change measures of pH or moisture content, or to enhance microbial or chemical reactions	2
8. Modification of a land treatment unit management practice to grow food chain crops, to add to or replace existing permitted crops with different food chain crops, or to modify operating plans for distribution of animal feeds resulting from such crops	3
9. Modification of operating practice due to detection of releases from the land treatment unit pursuant to 264.278(g)(2)	3
10. Changes in the unsaturated zone monitoring system, resulting in a change to the location, depth, number of sampling points, or replace unsaturated zone monitoring devices or components of devices with devices or components that have specifications different from permit requirements	3
11. Changes in the unsaturated zone monitoring system that do not result in a change to the location, depth, number of sampling points, or that replace unsaturated zone monitoring devices or components of devices with devices or components having specifications different from permit requirements	2
12. Changes in background values for hazardous constituents in soil and soil-pore liquid	2
13. Changes in sampling, analysis, or statistical procedure	2
14. Changes in land treatment demonstration program prior to or during the demonstration	2
15. Changes in any condition specified in the permit for a land treatment unit to reflect results of the land treatment demonstration, provided performance standards are met, and the Director's prior approval has been received	[1]1
16. Changes to allow a second land treatment demonstration to be conducted when the results of the first demonstration have not shown the conditions under which the wastes can be treated completely, provided the conditions for the second demonstration are substantially the same as the conditions for the first demonstration and have received the prior approval of the Director	[1]1
17. Changes to allow a second land treatment demonstration to be conducted when the results of the first demonstration have not shown the conditions under which the wastes can be treated completely, where the conditions for the second demonstration are not substantially the same as the conditions for the first demonstration	3
18. Changes in vegetative cover requirements for closure	2
L. Incinerators, Boilers, and Industrial Furnaces:	
1. Changes to increase by more than 25% any of the following limits authorized in the permit: A thermal feed rate limit, a feedstream feed rate limit, a chlorine/chloride feed rate limit, a metal feed rate limit, or an ash feed rate limit. The Director will require a new trial burn to substantiate compliance with the regulatory performance standards unless this demonstration can be made through other means	3
2. Changes to increase by up to 25% any of the following limits authorized in the permit: A thermal feed rate limit, a feedstream feed rate limit, a chlorine/chloride feed rate limit, a metal feed rate limit, or an ash feed rate limit. The Director will require a new trial burn to substantiate compliance with the regulatory performance standards unless this demonstration can be made through other means	2
3. Modification of an incinerator, boiler, or industrial furnace unit by changing the internal size or geometry of the primary or secondary combustion units, by adding a primary or secondary combustion unit, by substantially changing the design of any component used to remove HCl/Cl_2, metals, or particulate from the combustion gases, or by changing other features of the incinerator, boiler, or industrial furnace that could affect its capability to meet the regulatory performance standards. The Director will require a new trial burn to substantiate compliance with the regulatory performance standards unless this demonstration can be made through other means	3
4. Modification of an incinerator, boiler, or industrial furnace unit in a manner that would not likely affect the capability of the unit to meet the regulatory performance standards but which would change the operating conditions or monitoring requirements specified in the permit. The Director may require a new trial burn to demonstrate compliance with the regulatory performance standards	2
5. Operating requirements:	
a. Modification of the limits specified in the permit for minimum or maximum combustion gas temperature, minimum combustion gas residence time, oxygen concentration in the secondary combustion chamber, flue gas carbon monoxide and hydrocarbon concentration, maximum temperature at the inlet to the particulate matter emission control system, or operating parameters for the air pollution control system. The Director will require a new trial burn to substantiate compliance with the regulatory performance standards unless this demonstration can be made through other means	3
b. Modification of any stack gas emission limits specified in the permit, or modification of any conditions in the permit concerning emergency shutdown or automatic waste feed cutoff procedures or controls	3
c. Modification of any other operating condition or any inspection or recordkeeping requirement specified in the permit	2
6. Burning different wastes:	
a. If the waste contains a POHC that is more difficult to burn than authorized by the permit or if burning of the waste requires compliance with different regulatory performance standards than specified in the permit. The Director will require a new trial burn to substantiate compliance with the regulatory performance standards unless this demonstration can be made through other means	3

Modifications	Class
b. If the waste does not contain a POHC that is more difficult to burn than authorized by the permit and if burning of the waste does not require compliance with different regulatory performance standards than specified in the permit	2
Note: See §270.42(g) for modification procedures to be used for the management of newly listed or identified wastes	
7. Shakedown and trial burn:	
a. Modification of the trial burn plan or any of the permit conditions applicable during the shakedown period for determining operational readiness after construction, the trial burn period, or the period immediately following the trial burn	2
b. Authorization of up to an additional 720 hours of waste burning during the shakedown period for determining operational readiness after construction, with the prior approval of the Director	[1]1
c. Changes in the operating requirements set in the permit for conducting a trial burn, provided the change is minor and has received the prior approval of the Director	[1]1
d. Changes in the ranges of the operating requirements set in the permit to reflect the results of the trial burn, provided the change is minor and has received the prior approval of the Director	[1]1
8. Substitution of an alternative type of nonhazardous waste fuel that is not specified in the permit	1
9. Technology changes needed to meet standards under 40 CFR part 63 (Subpart EEE—National Emission Standards for Hazardous Air Pollutants From Hazardous Waste Combustors), provided the procedures of §270.42(j) are followed	[1]1
10. Changes to RCRA permit provisions needed to support transition to 40 CFR part 63 (Subpart EEE—National Emission Standards for Hazardous Air Pollutants From Hazardous Waste Combustors), provided the procedures of §270.42(k) are followed	[1]1
M. Containment Buildings	
1. Modification or addition of containment building units:	
a. Resulting in greater than 25% increase in the facility's containment building storage or treatment capacity	3
b. Resulting in up to 25% increase in the facility's containment building storage or treatment capacity	2
2. Modification of a containment building unit or secondary containment system without increasing the capacity of the unit	2
3. Replacement of a containment building with a containment building that meets the same design standards provided:	
a. The unit capacity is not increased	1
b. The replacement containment building meets the same conditions in the permit	1
4. Modification of a containment building management practice	2
5. Storage or treatment of different wastes in containment buildings:	
a. That require additional or different management practices	3
b. That do not require additional or different management practices	2

Modifications	Class
N. Corrective Action:	
1. Approval of a corrective action management unit pursuant to §264.552 (📖 17.11.3)	3
2. Approval of a temporary unit or time extension for a temporary unit pursuant to §264.553 (📖 17.12)	2
3. Approval of a staging pile or staging pile operating term extension pursuant to §264.554 (📖 17.13)	2
O. Burden Reduction	
1. Approval of reduced inspection frequency for Performance Track member facilities for:	
a. Tanks systems pursuant to §264.195	[1]1
b. Containers pursuant to §264.174	[1]1
c. Containment buildings pursuant to §264.1101(c)(4)	[1]1
d. Areas subject to spills pursuant to §264.15(b)(4)	[1]1
2. Development of one contingency plan based on Integrated Contingency Plan Guidance pursuant to §264.52(b)	1
3. Changes to recordkeeping and reporting requirements pursuant to: §§264.56(i), 264.343(a)(2), 264.1061(b)(1), (d), 264.1062(a)(2), 264.196(f), 264.100(g), and 264.113(e)(5)	1
4. Changes to inspection frequency for tank systems pursuant to §264.195(b)	1
5. Changes to detection and compliance monitoring program pursuant to §§264.98(d), (g)(2), and (g)(3), 264.99(f), and (g)	1

[1]Class 1 modifications requiring prior Agency approval.

[53 FR 37936, Sept. 28, 1988, as amended at 53 FR 41649, Oct. 24, 1988; 54 FR 9607, Mar. 7, 1989; 54 FR 33398, Aug. 14, 1989; 55 FR 22719, June 1, 1990; 56 FR 3928, Jan. 31, 1991; 56 FR 32692, July 17, 1991; 56 FR 7237, Feb. 21, 1991; 56 FR 32692, July 17, 1991; 57 FR 3496, Jan. 29, 1992; 57 FR 37281, Aug. 18, 1992; 58 FR 8685, Feb. 16, 1993; 58 FR 29886, May 24, 1993; 62 FR 6656, Feb. 12, 1997; 63 FR 33829, June 19, 1998; 63 FR 65941, Nov. 30, 1998; 64 FR 53077, Sept. 30, 1999; 70 FR 59577, Oct. 12, 2005; 71 FR 16914, Apr. 4, 2006; 71 FR 40279, July 14, 2006; 73 FR 64788, Oct. 30, 2008]

§270.43 Termination of permits.

(a) The following are causes for terminating a permit during its term, or for denying a permit renewal application:

(1) Noncompliance by the permittee with any condition of the permit;

(2) The permittee's failure in the application or during the permit issuance process to disclose fully all relevant facts, or the permittee's misrepresentation of any relevant facts at any time; or

(3) A determination that the permitted activity endangers human health or the environment and can only be regulated to acceptable levels by permit modification or termination.

(b) The Director shall follow the applicable procedures in part 124 or part 22, as appropriate or State procedures in terminating any permit under this section.

[48 FR 14228, Apr. 1, 1983, as amended at 65 FR 30913, May 15, 2000]

Subpart E—Expiration and Continuation of Permits

§270.50 Duration of permits.

(a) RCRA permits shall be effective for a fixed term not to exceed 10 years.

(b) Except as provided in §270.51, the term of a permit shall not be extended by modification beyond the maximum duration specified in this section.

(c) The Director may issue any permit for a duration that is less than the full allowable term under this section.

(d) Each permit for a land disposal facility shall be reviewed by the Director five years after the date of permit issuance or reissuance and shall be modified as necessary, as provided in §270.41.

[48 FR 14228, Apr. 1, 1983, as amended at 50 FR 28752, July 15, 1985]

§270.51 Continuation of expiring permits.

(a) *EPA permits.* When EPA is the permit-issuing authority, the conditions of an expired permit continue in force under 5 U.S.C. 558(c) until the effective date of a new permit (see §124.15) if:

(1) The permittee has submitted a timely application under §270.14 and the applicable sections in §§270.15 through 270.29 which is a complete (under §270.10(c)) application for a new permit; and

(2) The Regional Administrator through no fault of the permittee, does not issue a new permit with an effective date under §124.15 on or before the expiration date of the previous permit (for example, when issuance is impracticable due to time or resource constraints).

(b) *Effect.* Permits continued under this section remain fully effective and enforceable.

(c) *Enforcement.* When the permittee is not in compliance with the conditions of the expiring or expired permit, the Regional Administrator may choose to do any or all of the following:

(1) Initiate enforcement action based upon the permit which has been continued;

(2) Issue a notice of intent to deny the new permit under §124.6. If the permit is denied, the owner or operator would then be required to cease the activities authorized by the continued permit or be subject to enforcement action for operating without a permit;

(3) Issue a new permit under part 124 with appropriate conditions; or

(4) Take other actions authorized by these regulations.

(d) *State continuation.* In a State with an hazardous waste program authorized under 40 CFR part 271, if a permittee has submitted a timely and complete application under applicable State law and regulations, the terms and conditions of an EPA-issued RCRA permit continue in force beyond the expiration date of the permit, but only until the effective date of the State's issuance or denial of a State RCRA permit.

(e) Standardized permits.

(1) The conditions of your expired standardized permit continue until the effective date of your new permit (see 40 CFR 124.15) if all of the following are true:

(i) If EPA is the permit-issuing authority.

(ii) If you submit a timely and complete Notice of Intent under 40 CFR 124.202(b) requesting coverage under a RCRA standardized permit; and

(iii) If the Director, through no fault on your part, does not issue your permit before your previous permit expires (for example, where it is impractical to make the permit effective by that date because of time or resource constraints).

(2) In some cases, the Director may notify you that you are not eligible for a standardized permit (see 40 CFR 124.206). In those cases, the conditions of your expired permit will continue if you submit the information specified in paragraph (a)(1) of this section (that is, a complete application for a new permit) within 60 days after you receive our notification that you are not eligible for a standardized permit.

(Clean Water Act (33 U.S.C. 1251 *et seq.*), Safe Drinking Water Act (42 U.S.C. 300f *et seq.*), Clean Air Act (42 U.S.C. 7401 *et seq.*), Resource Conservation and Recovery Act (42 U.S.C. 6901 *et seq.*))

[48 FR 14228, Apr. 1, 1983, as amended at 48 FR 39622, Sept. 1, 1983; 70 FR 53475, Sept. 8, 2005]

Subpart F—Special Forms of Permits

§270.60 Permits by rule.

Notwithstanding any other provision of this part or part 124, the following shall be deemed to have a RCRA permit if the conditions listed are met:

(a) *Ocean disposal barges or vessels.* The owner or operator of a barge or other vessel which accepts hazardous waste for ocean disposal, if the owner or operator: 📖 17.6

(1) Has a permit for ocean dumping issued under 40 CFR part 220 (Ocean Dumping, authorized by the Marine Protection, Research, and Sanctuaries Act, as amended, 33 U.S.C. 1420 *et seq.*);

(2) Complies with the conditions of that permit; and

(3) Complies with the following hazardous waste regulations:

(i) 40 CFR 264.11, Identification number;

(ii) 40 CFR 264.71, Use of manifest system;

(iii) 40 CFR 264.72, Manifest discrepancies;

(iv) 40 CFR 264.73(a) and (b)(1), Operating record;

(v) 40 CFR 264.75, Biennial report; and

(vi) 40 CFR 264.76, Unmanifested waste report.

(b) *Injection wells.* The owner or operator of an injection well disposing of hazardous waste, if the owner or operator:

(1) Has a permit for underground injection issued under part 144 or 145; and

(2) Complies with the conditions of that permit and the requirements of §144.14 (requirements for wells managing hazardous waste).

(3) For UIC permits issued after November 8, 1984:

(i) Complies with 40 CFR 264.101; and

(ii) Where the UIC well is the only unit at a facility which requires a RCRA permit, complies with 40 CFR 270.14(d).

(c) *Publicly owned treatment works.* The owner or operator of a POTW which accepts for treatment hazardous waste, if the owner or operator:

(1) Has an NPDES permit;

(2) Complies with the conditions of that permit; and

(3) Complies with the following regulations:

(i) 40 CFR 264.11, Identification number;

(ii) 40 CFR 264.71, Use of manifest system;

(iii) 40 CFR 264.72, Manifest discrepancies;

(iv) 40 CFR 264.73(a) and (b)(1), Operating record;

(v) 40 CFR 264.75, Biennial report;

(vi) 40 CFR 264.76, Unmanifested waste report; and

(vii) For NPDES permits issued after November 8, 1984, 40 CFR 264.101.

(4) If the waste meets all Federal, State, and local pretreatment requirements which would be applicable to the waste if it were being discharged into the POTW through a sewer, pipe, or similar conveyance.

[48 FR 14228, Apr. 1, 1983, as amended at 50 FR 28752, July 15, 1985; 52 FR 45799, Dec. 1, 1987]

§270.61 Emergency permits.

📖 17.6

(a) Notwithstanding any other provision of this part or part 124, in the event the Director finds an imminent and substantial endangerment to human health or the environment the Director may issue a temporary emergency permit: (1) To a non-permitted facility to allow treatment, storage, or disposal of hazardous waste or (2) to a permitted facility to allow treatment, storage, or disposal of a hazardous waste not covered by an effective permit.

(b) This emergency permit:

(1) May be oral or written. If oral, it shall be followed in five days by a written emergency permit;

(2) Shall not exceed 90 days in duration;

(3) Shall clearly specify the hazardous wastes to be received, and the manner and location of their treatment, storage, or disposal;

(4) May be terminated by the Director at any time without process if he or she determines that termination is appropriate to protect human health and the environment;

(5) Shall be accompanied by a public notice published under §124.10(b) including:

(i) Name and address of the office granting the emergency authorization;

(ii) Name and location of the permitted HWM facility;

(iii) A brief description of the wastes involved;

(iv) A brief description of the action authorized and reasons for authorizing it; and

(v) Duration of the emergency permit; and

(6) Shall incorporate, to the extent possible and not inconsistent with the emergency situation, all applicable requirements of this part and 40 CFR parts 264 and 266.

[48 FR 14228, Apr. 1, 1983, as amended at 48 FR 30114, June 30, 1983; 60 FR 63433, Dec. 11, 1996]

§270.62 Hazardous waste incinerator permits.

When an owner or operator of a hazardous waste incineration unit becomes subject to RCRA permit requirements after October 12, 2005, or when an owner or operator of an existing hazardous waste incineration unit demonstrates compliance with the air emission standards and limitations in part 63, subpart EEE, of this chapter (*i.e.*, by conducting a comprehensive performance test and submitting a Notification of Compliance under §§63.1207(j) and 63.1210(d) of this chapter documenting compliance with all applicable requirements of part 63, subpart EEE, of this chapter), the requirements of this section do not apply, except those provisions the Director determines are necessary to ensure compliance with §§264.345(a) and 264.345(c) of this chapter if you elect to comply with

§270.235(a)(1)(i) to minimize emissions of toxic compounds from startup, shutdown, and malfunction events. Nevertheless, the Director may apply the provisions of this section, on a case-by-case basis, for purposes of information collection in accordance with §§270.10(k), 270.10(l), 270.32(b)(2), and 270.32(b)(3).

(a) For the purposes of determining operational readiness following completion of physical construction, the Director must establish permit conditions, including but not limited to allowable waste feeds and operating conditions, in the permit to a new hazardous waste incinerator. These permit conditions will be effective for the minimum time required to bring the incinerator to a point of operational readiness to conduct a trial burn, not to exceed 720 hours operating time for treatment of hazardous waste. The Director may extend the duration of this operational period once, for up to 720 additional hours, at the request of the applicant when good cause is shown. The permit may be modified to reflect the extension according to §270.42 of this chapter.

(1) Applicants must submit a statement, with part B of the permit application, which suggests the conditions necessary to operate in compliance with the performance standards of §264.343 of this chapter during this period. This statement should include, at a minimum, restrictions on waste constituents, waste feed rates and the operating parameters identified in §264.345 of this chapter.

(2) The Director will review this statement and any other relevant information submitted with part B of the permit application and specify requirements for this period sufficient to meet the performance standards of §264.343 of this chapter based on his engineering judgment.

(b) For the purposes of determining feasibility of compliance with the performance standards of §264.343 of this chapter and of determining adequate operating conditions under §264.345 of this chapter, the Director must establish conditions in the permit for a new hazardous waste incinerator to be effective during the trial burn.

(1) Applicants must propose a trial burn plan, prepared under paragraph (b)(2) of this section with a part B of the permit application.

(2) The trial burn plan must include the following information:

(i) An analysis of each waste or mixture of wastes to be burned which includes:

(A) Heat value of the waste in the form and composition in which it will be burned.

(B) Viscosity (if applicable), or description of the physical form of the waste.

(C) An identification of any hazardous organic constituents listed in part 261, appendix VIII of this chapter, which are present in the waste to be burned, except that the applicant need not analyze for constituents listed in part 261, appendix VIII, of this chapter which would reasonably not be expected to be found in the waste. The constituents excluded from analysis must be identified, and the basis for the exclusion stated. The waste analysis must rely on appropriate analytical techniques.

(D) An approximate quantification of the hazardous constituents identified in the waste, within the precision produced by appropriate analytical methods.

(ii) A detailed engineering description of the incinerator for which the permit is sought including:

(A) Manufacturer's name and model number of incinerator (if available).

(B) Type of incinerator.

(C) Linear dimensions of the incinerator unit including the cross sectional area of combustion chamber.

(D) Description of the auxiliary fuel system (type/feed).

(E) Capacity of prime mover.

(F) Description of automatic waste feed cut-off system(s).

(G) Stack gas monitoring and pollution control equipment.

(H) Nozzle and burner design.

(I) Construction materials.

(J) Location and description of temperature, pressure, and flow indicating and control devices.

(iii) A detailed description of sampling and monitoring procedures, including sampling and monitoring locations in the system, the equipment to be used, sampling and monitoring frequency, and planned analytical procedures for sample analysis.

(iv) A detailed test schedule for each waste for which the trial burn is planned including date(s), duration, quantity of waste to be burned, and other factors relevant to the Director's decision under paragraph (b)(5) of this section.

(v) A detailed test protocol, including, for each waste identified, the ranges of temperature, waste feed rate, combustion gas velocity, use of auxiliary fuel, and any other relevant parameters that will be varied to affect the destruction and removal efficiency of the incinerator.

(vi) A description of, and planned operating conditions for, any emission control equipment which will be used.

(vii) Procedures for rapidly stopping waste feed, shutting down the incinerator, and controlling emissions in the event of an equipment malfunction.

(viii) Such other information as the Director reasonably finds necessary to determine whether to approve the trial burn plan in light of the purposes of this paragraph and the criteria in paragraph (b)(5) of this section.

(3) The Director, in reviewing the trial burn plan, shall evaluate the sufficiency of the information provided and may require the applicant to supplement this information, if necessary, to achieve the purposes of this paragraph.

(4) Based on the waste analysis data in the trial burn plan, the Director will specify as trial Principal Organic Hazardous Constituents (POHCs), those constituents for which destruction and removal efficiencies must be calculated during the trial burn. These trial POHCs will be specified by the Director based on his estimate of the difficulty of incineration of the constituents identified in the waste analysis, their concentration or mass in the waste feed, and, for wastes listed in part 261, subpart D, of this chapter, the hazardous waste organic constituent or constituents identified in appendix VII of that part as the basis for listing.

(5) The Director shall approve a trial burn plan if he finds that:

(i) The trial burn is likely to determine whether the incinerator performance standard required by §264.343 of this chapter can be met;

(ii) The trial burn itself will not present an imminent hazard to human health or the environment;

(iii) The trial burn will help the Director to determine operating requirements to be specified under §264.345 of this chapter; and

(iv) The information sought in paragraphs (b)(5) (i) and (ii) of this section cannot reasonably be developed through other means.

(6) The Director must send a notice to all persons on the facility mailing list as set forth in 40 CFR 124.10(c)(1)(ix) and to the appropriate units of State and local government as set forth in 40 CFR 124.10(c)(1)(x) announcing the scheduled commencement and completion dates for the trial burn. The applicant may not commence the trial burn until after the Director has issued such notice.

(i) This notice must be mailed within a reasonable time period before the scheduled trial burn. An additional notice is not required if the trial burn is delayed due to circumstances beyond the control of the facility or the permitting agency.

(ii) This notice must contain:

(A) The name and telephone number of the applicant's contact person;

(B) The name and telephone number of the permitting agency's contact office;

(C) The location where the approved trial burn plan and any supporting documents can be reviewed and copied; and

(D) An expected time period for commencement and completion of the trial burn.

(7) During each approved trial burn (or as soon after the burn as is practicable), the applicant must make the following determinations:

(i) A quantitative analysis of the trial POHCs in the waste feed to the incinerator.

(ii) A quantitative analysis of the exhaust gas for the concentration and mass emissions of the trial POHCs, oxygen (O_2) and hydrogen chloride (HCl).

(iii) A quantitative analysis of the scrubber water (if any), ash residues, and other residues, for the purpose of estimating the fate of the trial POHCs.

(iv) A computation of destruction and removal efficiency (DRE), in accordance with the DRE formula specified in §264.343(a) of this chapter.

(v) If the HCl emission rate exceeds 1.8 kilograms of HCl per hour (4 pounds per hour), a computation of HCl removal efficiency in accordance with §264.343(b) of this chapter.

(vi) A computation of particulate emissions, in accordance with §264.343(c) of this chapter.

(vii) An identification of sources of fugitive emissions and their means of control.

(viii) A measurement of average, maximum, and minimum temperatures and combustion gas velocity.

(ix) A continuous measurement of carbon monoxide (CO) in the exhaust gas.

(x) Such other information as the Director may specify as necessary to ensure that the trial burn will determine compliance with the performance standards in §264.343 of this chapter and to establish the operating conditions required by §264.345 of this chapter as necessary to meet that performance standard.

(8) The applicant must submit to the Director a certification that the trial burn has been carried out in accordance with the approved trial burn plan, and must submit the results of all the determinations required in paragraph (b)(6) of this section. This submission shall be made within 90 days of completion of the trial burn, or later if approved by the Director.

(9) All data collected during any trial burn must be submitted to the Director following the completion of the trial burn.

(10) All submissions required by this paragraph must be certified on behalf of the applicant by the signature of a person authorized to sign a permit application or a report under §270.11.

(11) Based on the results of the trial burn, the Director shall set the operating requirements in the final permit according to §264.345 of this chapter. The permit modification shall proceed according to §270.42.

(c) For the purposes of allowing operation of a new hazardous waste incinerator following completion of the trial burn and prior to final modification of the permit conditions to reflect the trial burn results, the Director may establish permit conditions, including but not limited to allowable waste feeds and operating conditions sufficient to meet the requirements of §264.345 of this chapter, in the permit to a new hazardous waste incinerator. These permit conditions will be effective for the minimum time required to complete sample analysis, data computation and submission of the trial burn results by the applicant, and modification of the facility permit by the Director.

(1) Applicants must submit a statement, with part B of the permit application, which identifies the conditions necessary to operate in compliance with the performance standards of §264.343 of this chapter, during this period. This statement should include, at a minimum, restrictions on waste constituents, waste feed rates, and the operating parameters in §264.345 of this chapter.

(2) The Director will review this statement and any other relevant information submitted with part B of the permit application and specify those requirements for this period most likely to meet the performance standards of §264.343 of this chapter based on his engineering judgment.

(d) For the purpose of determining feasibility of compliance with the performance standards of §264.343 of this chapter and of determining adequate operating conditions under §264.345 of this chapter, the applicant for a permit for an existing hazardous waste incinerator must prepare and submit a trial burn plan and perform a trial burn in accordance with §270.19(b) and paragraphs (b)(2) through (b)(5) and (b)(7) through (b)(10) of this section or, instead, submit other information as specified in §270.19(c). The Director must announce his or her intention to approve the trial burn plan in accordance with the timing and distribution requirements of paragraph (b)(6) of this section. The contents of the notice must include: the name and telephone number of a contact person at the facility; the name and telephone number of a contact office at the permitting agency; the location where the trial burn plan and any supporting documents can be reviewed and copied; and a schedule of the activities that are required prior to permit issuance, including the anticipated time schedule for agency approval of the plan and the time period during which the trial burn would be conducted. Applicants submitting information under §270.19(a) are exempt from compliance with 40 CFR 264.343 and 264.345 and, therefore, are exempt from the requirement to conduct a trial burn. Applicants who submit trial burn plans and receive approval before submission of a permit application must complete the trial burn and submit the results, specified in paragraph (b)(7) of this section, with part B of the permit application. If completion of this process conflicts with the date set for submission of the part B application, the applicant must contact the Director to establish a later date for submission of the part B application or the trial burn results. Trial burn results must be submitted prior to issuance of the permit. When the applicant submits a trial burn plan with part B of the permit application, the Director will specify a time period prior to permit issuance in which the trial burn must be conducted and the results submitted.

[48 FR 14228, Apr. 1, 1983, as amended at 53 FR 37939, Sept. 28, 1988; 58 FR 46051, Aug. 31, 1993; 60 FR 63433, Dec. 11, 1995; 64 FR 53077, Sept. 30, 1999; 67 FR 6816, Feb. 13, 2002; 67 FR 77692, Dec. 19, 2002; 70 FR 34590, June 14, 2005; 70 FR 59578, Oct. 12, 2005]

§270.63 Permits for land treatment demonstrations using field test or laboratory analyses. 17.6

(a) For the purpose of allowing an owner or operator to meet the treatment demonstration requirements of §264.272 of this chapter, the Director may issue a treatment demonstration permit. The permit must contain only those requirements necessary to meet the standards in §264.272(c). The permit may be issued either as a treatment or disposal permit covering only the field test or laboratory analyses, or as a two-phase facility permit covering the field tests, or laboratory analyses, and design, construction operation and maintenance of the land treatment unit.

(1) The Director may issue a two-phase facility permit if he finds that, based on information submitted in part B of the application, substantial, although incomplete or inconclusive, information already exists upon which to base the issuance of a facility permit.

(2) If the Director finds that not enough information exists upon which he can establish permit conditions to attempt to provide for compliance with all of the requirements of subpart M, he must issue a treatment demonstration permit covering only the field test or laboratory analyses.

(b) If the Director finds that a phased permit may be issued, he will establish, as requirements in the first phase of the facility permit, conditions for conducting the field tests or laboratory analyses. These permit conditions will include design and operating parameters (including the duration of the tests or analyses and, in the case of field tests, the horizontal and vertical dimensions of the treatment zone), monitoring procedures, post-demonstration clean-up activities, and any other conditions which the Director finds may be necessary under §264.272(c). The Director will include conditions in the second phase of the facility permit to attempt to meet all subpart M requirements pertaining to unit design, construction, operation, and maintenance. The Director will establish these conditions in the second phase of the permit based upon the substantial but incomplete or inconclusive information contained in the part B application.

(1) The first phase of the permit will be effective as provided in §124.15(b) of this chapter.

(2) The second phase of the permit will be effective as provided in paragraph (d) of this section.

(c) When the owner or operator who has been issued a two-phase permit has completed the treatment demonstration, he must submit to the Director a certification, signed by a person authorized to sign a permit application or report under §270.11, that the field tests or laboratory analyses have been carried out in accordance with the conditions specified in phase one of the permit for conducting such tests or analyses. The owner or operator must also submit all data collected during the field tests or laboratory analyses within 90 days of completion of those tests or analyses unless the Director approves a later date.

(d) If the Director determines that the results of the field tests or laboratory analyses meet the requirements of §264.272 of this chapter, he will modify the second phase of the permit to incorporate any requirements necessary for operation of the facility in compliance with part 264, subpart M, of this chapter, based upon the results of the field tests or laboratory analyses.

(1) This permit modification may proceed under §270.42, or otherwise will proceed as a modification under §270.41(a)(2). If such modifications are necessary, the second phase of the permit will become effective only after those modifications have been made.

(2) If no modifications of the second phase of the permit are necessary, the Director will give notice of his final decision to the permit applicant and to each person who submitted written comments on the phased permit or who requested notice of the final decision on the second phase of the permit. The second phase of the permit then will become effective as specified in §124.15(b).

[48 FR 14228, Apr. 1, 1983, as amended at 53 FR 37939, Sept. 28, 1988]

§270.64 Interim permits for UIC wells.

The Director may issue a permit under this part to any Class I UIC well (see §144.6) injecting hazardous wastes within a State in which no UIC program has been approved or promulgated. Any such permit shall apply and insure compliance with all applicable requirements of 40 CFR part 264, subpart R (RCRA standards for wells), and shall be for a term not to exceed two years. No such permit shall be issued after approval or promulgation of a UIC program in the State. Any permit under this section shall contain a condition providing that it will terminate upon final action by the Director under a UIC program to issue or deny a UIC permit for the facility.

[48 FR 14228, Apr. 1, 1983; 48 FR 30114, June 30, 1983]

§270.65 Research, development, and demonstration permits.

17.6

(a) The Administrator may issue a research, development, and demonstration permit for any hazardous waste treatment facility which proposes to utilize an innovative and experimental hazardous waste treatment technology or process for which permit standards for such experimental activity have not been promulgated under part 264 or 266. Any such permit shall include such terms and conditions as will assure protection of human health and the environment. Such permits:

(1) Shall provide for the construction of such facilities as necessary, and for operation of the facility for not longer than one year unless renewed as provided in paragraph (d) of this section, and

(2) Shall provide for the receipt and treatment by the facility of only those types and quantities of hazardous waste which the Administrator deems necessary for purposes of determining the efficacy and performance capabilities of the technology or process and the effects of such technology or process on human health and the environment, and

(3) Shall include such requirements as the Administrator deems necessary to protect human health and the environment (including, but not limited to, requirements regarding monitoring, operation, financial responsibility, closure, and remedial action), and such requirements as the Administrator deems necessary regarding testing and providing of information to the Administrator with respect to the operation of the facility.

(b) For the purpose of expediting review and issuance of permits under this section, the Administrator may, consistent with the protection of human health and the environment, modify or waive permit application and permit issuance requirements in parts 124 and 270 except that there may be no modification or waiver of regulations regarding financial responsibility (including insurance) or of procedures regarding public participation.

(c) The Administrator may order an immediate termination of all operations at the facility at any time he determines that termination is necessary to protect human health and the environment.

(d) Any permit issued under this section may be renewed not more than three times. Each such renewal shall be for a period of not more than 1 year.

[50 FR 28752, July 15, 1985]

§270.66 Permits for boilers and industrial furnaces burning hazardous waste.

When an owner or operator of a cement kiln, lightweight aggregate kiln, solid fuel boiler, liquid fuel boiler, or hydrochloric acid production furnace becomes subject to RCRA permit requirements after October 12, 2005 or when an owner or operator of an existing cement kiln, lightweight aggregate kiln, solid fuel boiler, liquid fuel boiler, or hydrochloric acid production furnace demonstrates compliance with the air emission standards and limitations in part 63, subpart EEE, of this chapter (*i.e.*, by conducting a comprehensive performance test and submitting a Notification of Compliance under §§63.1207(j) and 63.1210(d) of this chapter documenting compliance with all applicable requirements of part 63, subpart EEE, of this chapter), the requirements of this section do not apply. The requirements of this section do apply, however, if the Director determines certain provisions are necessary to ensure compliance with §§266.102(e)(1) and 266.102(e)(2)(iii) of this chapter if you elect to comply with §270.235(a)(1)(i) to minimize emissions of toxic compounds from startup, shutdown, and malfunction events; or if you are an area source and elect to comply with the §§266.105, 266.106, and 266.107 standards and associated requirements for particulate matter, hydrogen chloride and chlorine gas, and non-mercury metals; or the Director determines certain provisions apply, on a case-by-case basis, for purposes of information collection in accordance with §§270.10(k), 270.10(l), 270.32(b)(2), and 270.32(b)(3).

(a) *General.* Owners and operators of new boilers and industrial furnaces (those not operating under the interim status standards of §266.103 of this chapter) are subject to paragraphs (b) through (f) of this section. Boilers and industrial furnaces operating under the interim status standards of §266.103 of this chapter are subject to paragraph (g) of this section.

(b) *Permit operating periods for new boilers and industrial furnaces.* A permit for a new boiler or industrial furnace shall specify appropriate conditions for the following operating periods:

(1) *Pretrial burn period.* For the period beginning with initial introduction of hazardous waste and ending with initiation of the trial burn, and only for the minimum time required to bring the boiler or industrial furnace to a point of operational readiness to conduct a trial burn, not to exceed 720 hours operating time when burning hazardous waste, the Director must establish in the Pretrial Burn Period of the permit conditions, including but not limited to, allowable hazardous waste feed rates and operating conditions. The Director may extend the duration of this operational period once, for up to 720 additional hours, at the request of the applicant when good cause is shown. The permit may be modified to reflect the extension according to §270.42.

(i) Applicants must submit a statement, with part B of the permit application, that suggests the conditions necessary to operate in compliance with the standards of §§266.104 through 266.107 of this chapter during this period. This statement should include, at a minimum, restrictions on the applicable operating requirements identified in §266.102(e) of this chapter.

(ii) The Director will review this statement and any other relevant information submitted with part B of the permit application and specify requirements for this period sufficient to meet the performance standards of §§266.104 through 266.107 of this chapter based on his/her engineering judgment.

(2) *Trial burn period.* For the duration of the trial burn, the Director must establish conditions in the permit for the purposes of determining feasibility of compliance with the performance standards of §§266.104 through 266.107 of this chapter and determining adequate operating conditions under §266.102(e) of this chapter. Applicants must propose a trial burn plan, prepared under paragraph (c) of this section, to be submitted with part B of the permit application.

(3) *Post-trial burn period.* (i) For the period immediately following completion of the trial burn, and only for the minimum period sufficient to allow sample analysis, data computation, and submission of the trial burn results by the applicant, and review of the trial burn results and modification of the facility permit by the Director to reflect the trial burn results, the Director will establish the operating requirements most likely to ensure compliance with the performance standards of §§266.104 through 266.107 of this chapter based on his engineering judgment.

(ii) Applicants must submit a statement, with part B of the application, that identifies the conditions necessary to operate during this period in compliance with the performance standards of §§266.104 through 266.107 of this chapter. This statement should include, at a minimum, restrictions on the operating requirements provided by §266.102(e) of this chapter.

(iii) The Director will review this statement and any other relevant information submitted with part B of the permit application and specify requirements for this period sufficient to meet the performance standards of §§266.104 through 266.107 of this chapter based on his/her engineering judgment.

(4) *Final permit period.* For the final period of operation, the Director will develop operating requirements in conformance with §266.102(e) of this chapter that reflect conditions in the trial burn plan and are likely to ensure compliance with the performance standards of §§266.104 through 266.107 of this chapter. Based on the trial burn results, the Director shall make any necessary modifications to the operating requirements to ensure compliance with the performance standards. The permit modification shall proceed according to §270.42.

(c) *Requirements for trial burn plans.* The trial burn plan must include the following information. The Director, in reviewing the trial burn plan, shall evaluate the sufficiency of the information provided and may require the applicant to supplement this information, if necessary, to achieve the purposes of this paragraph:

(1) An analysis of each feed stream, including hazardous waste, other fuels, and industrial furnace feed stocks, as fired, that includes:

(i) Heating value, levels of antimony, arsenic, barium, beryllium, cadmium, chromium, lead, mercury, silver, thallium, total chlorine/chloride, and ash;

(ii) Viscosity or description of the physical form of the feed stream;

(2) An analysis of each hazardous waste, as fired, including:

(i) An identification of any hazardous organic constituents listed in appendix VIII, part 261, of this chapter that are present in the feed stream, except that the applicant need not analyze for constituents listed in appendix VIII that would reasonably not be expected to be found in the hazardous waste. The constituents excluded from analysis must be identified and the basis for this exclusion explained. The waste analysis must be conducted in accordance with appropriate analytical techniques.

(ii) An approximate quantification of the hazardous constituents identified in the hazardous waste, within the precision produced by appropriate analytical methods.

(iii) A description of blending procedures, if applicable, prior to firing the hazardous waste, including a detailed analysis of the hazardous waste prior to blending, an analysis of the material with which the hazardous waste is blended, and blending ratios.

(3) A detailed engineering description of the boiler or industrial furnace, including:

(i) Manufacturer's name and model number of the boiler or industrial furnace;

(ii) Type of boiler or industrial furnace;

(iii) Maximum design capacity in appropriate units;

(iv) Description of the feed system for the hazardous waste, and, as appropriate, other fuels and industrial furnace feedstocks;

(v) Capacity of hazardous waste feed system;

(vi) Description of automatic hazardous waste feed cutoff system(s);

(vii) Description of any air pollution control system; and

(viii) Description of stack gas monitoring and any pollution control monitoring systems.

(4) A detailed description of sampling and monitoring procedures including sampling and monitoring locations in the system, the equipment to be used, sampling and monitoring frequency, and planned analytical procedures for sample analysis.

(5) A detailed test schedule for each hazardous waste for which the trial burn is planned, including date(s), duration, quantity of hazardous waste to be burned, and other factors relevant to the Director's decision under paragraph (b)(2) of this section.

(6) A detailed test protocol, including, for each hazardous waste identified, the ranges of hazardous waste feed rate, and, as appropriate, the feed rates of other fuels and industrial furnace feedstocks, and any other relevant parameters that may affect the ability of the boiler or industrial furnace to meet the performance standards in §§266.104 through 266.107 of this chapter.

(7) A description of, and planned operating conditions for, any emission control equipment that will be used.

(8) Procedures for rapidly stopping the hazardous waste feed and controlling emissions in the event of an equipment malfunction.

(9) Such other information as the Director reasonably finds necessary to determine whether to approve the trial burn plan in light of the purposes of this paragraph and the criteria in paragraph (b)(2) of this section.

(d) *Trial burn procedures.* (1) A trial burn must be conducted to demonstrate conformance with the standards of §§266.104 through 266.107 of this chapter under an approved trial burn plan.

(2) The Director shall approve a trial burn plan if he/she finds that:

(i) The trial burn is likely to determine whether the boiler or industrial furnace can meet the performance standards of §§266.104 through 266.107 of this chapter;

(ii) The trial burn itself will not present an imminent hazard to human health and the environment;

(iii) The trial burn will help the Director to determine operating requirements to be specified under §266.102(e) of this chapter; and

(iv) The information sought in the trial burn cannot reasonably be developed through other means.

(3) The Director must send a notice to all persons on the facility mailing list as set forth in 40 CFR 124.10(c)(1)(ix) and to the appropriate units of State and local government as set forth in 40 CFR 124.10(c)(1)(x) announcing the scheduled commencement and completion dates for the trial burn. The applicant may not commence the trial burn until after the Director has issued such notice.

(i) This notice must be mailed within a reasonable time period before the trial burn. An additional notice is not required if the trial burn is delayed due to circumstances beyond the control of the facility or the permitting agency.

(ii) This notice must contain:

(A) The name and telephone number of applicant's contact person;

(B) The name and telephone number of the permitting agency contact office;

(C) The location where the approved trial burn plan and any supporting documents can be reviewed and copied; and

(D) An expected time period for commencement and completion of the trial burn.

(4) The applicant must submit to the Director a certification that the trial burn has been carried out in accordance with the approved trial burn plan, and must submit the results of all the determinations required in paragraph (c) of this section. This submission shall be made within 90 days of completion of the trial burn, or later if approved by the Director.

(5) All data collected during any trial burn must be submitted to the Director following completion of the trial burn.

(6) All submissions required by this paragraph must be certified on behalf of the applicant by the signature of a person authorized to sign a permit application or a report under §270.11.

(e) *Special procedures for DRE trial burns.* When a DRE trial burn is required under §266.104(a) of this chapter, the Director will specify (based on the hazardous waste analysis data and other information in the trial burn plan) as trial Principal Organic Hazardous Constituents (POHCs) those compounds for which destruction and removal efficiencies must be calculated during the trial burn. These trial POHCs will be specified by the Director based on information including his/her estimate of the difficulty of destroying the constituents identified in the hazardous waste analysis, their concentrations or mass in the hazardous waste feed, and, for hazardous waste containing or derived from wastes listed in part 261, subpart D of this chapter, the hazardous waste organic constituent(s) identified in Appendix VII of that part as the basis for listing.

(f) *Determinations based on trial burn.* During each approved trial burn (or as soon after the burn as is practicable), the applicant must make the following determinations:

(1) A quantitative analysis of the levels of antimony, arsenic, barium, beryllium, cadmium, chromium, lead, mercury, thallium, silver, and chlorine/chloride, in the feed streams (hazardous waste, other fuels, and industrial furnace feedstocks);

(2) When a DRE trial burn is required under §266.104(a) of this chapter:

(i) A quantitative analysis of the trial POHCs in the hazardous waste feed;

(ii) A quantitative analysis of the stack gas for the concentration and mass emissions of the trial POHCs; and

(iii) A computation of destruction and removal efficiency (DRE), in accordance with the DRE formula specified in §266.104(a) of this chapter;

(3) When a trial burn for chlorinated dioxins and furans is required under §266.104(e) of this chapter, a quantitative analysis of the stack gas for the concentration and mass emission rate of the 2,3,7,8-chlorinated tetra-octa congeners of chlorinated dibenzo-p-dioxins and furans, and a computation showing conformance with the emission standard;

(4) When a trial burn for particulate matter, metals, or HCl/Cl_2 is required under §§266.105, 266.106 (c) or (d), or 266.107 (b)(2) or (c) of this chapter, a quantitative analysis of the stack gas for the concentrations and mass emissions of particulate matter, metals, or hydrogen chloride (HCl) and chlorine (Cl_2), and computations showing conformance with the applicable emission performance standards;

(5) When a trial burn for DRE, metals, or HCl/Cl_2 is required under §§266.104(a), 266.106 (c) or (d), or 266.107 (b)(2) or (c) of this chapter, a quantitative analysis of the scrubber water (if any), ash residues, other residues, and products for the purpose of estimating the fate of the trial POHCs, metals, and chlorine/chloride;

(6) An identification of sources of fugitive emissions and their means of control;

(7) A continuous measurement of carbon monoxide (CO), oxygen, and where required, hydrocarbons (HC), in the stack gas; and

(8) Such other information as the Director may specify as necessary to ensure that the trial burn will determine compliance with the performance standards in §§266.104 through 266.107 of this chapter and to establish the operating conditions required by §266.102(e) of this chapter as necessary to meet those performance standards.

(g) *Interim status boilers and industrial furnaces.* For the purpose of determining feasibility of compliance with the performance standards of §266.104 through 266.107 of this chapter and of determining adequate operating conditions under §266.103 of this chapter, applicants owning or operating existing boilers or industrial furnaces operated under the interim status standards of §266.103 of this chapter must either prepare and submit a trial burn plan and perform a trial burn in accordance with the requirements of this section or submit other information as specified in §270.22(a)(6). The Director must announce his or her intention to approve of the trial burn plan in accordance with the timing and distribution requirements of paragraph (d)(3) of this section. The contents of the notice must include: the name and telephone number of a contact person at the facility; the name and telephone number of a contact office at the permitting agency; the location where the trial burn plan and any supporting documents can be reviewed and copied; and a schedule of the activities that are required prior to permit issuance, including the anticipated time schedule for agency approval of the plan and the time periods during which the trial burn would be conducted. Applicants who submit a trial burn plan and receive approval before submission of the part B permit application must complete the trial burn and submit the results specified in paragraph (f) of this section with the part B permit application. If completion of this process conflicts with the date set for submission of the part B application, the applicant must contact the Director to establish a later date for submission of the part B application or the trial burn results. If the applicant submits a trial burn plan with part B of the permit application, the trial burn must be conducted and the results submitted within a time period prior to permit issuance to be specified by the Director.

[56 FR 7239, Feb. 21, 1991; 56 FR 32692, July 17, 1991, as amended at 58 FR 46051, Aug. 31, 1993; 60 FR 63433, Dec. 11, 1995; 64 FR 53077, Sept. 30, 1999; 67 FR 6817, Feb. 13, 2002; 67 FR 77692, Dec. 19, 2002; 70 FR 34590, June 14, 2005; 70 FR 59578, Oct. 12, 2005]

§270.67 RCRA standardized permits for storage and treatment units.

RCRA standardized permits are special forms of permits for TSD owners or operators that:

(a) Generate hazardous waste and then non-thermally treat or store the hazardous waste on-site in tanks, containers, or containment buildings; or

(b) Receive hazardous waste generated off-site by a generator under the same ownership as the receiving facility, and then store or non-thermally treat the hazardous waste in containers, tanks, or containment buildings. Standardized permit facility owners or operators are regulated under subpart J of this part, part 124 subpart G of this chapter, and part 267 of this chapter.

[70 FR 53475, Sept. 8, 2005]

§270.68 Remedial Action Plans (RAPs).

Remedial Action Plans (RAPs) are special forms of permits that are regulated under subpart H of this part.

[63 FR 65941, Nov. 30, 1998]

Subpart G—Interim Status

§270.70 Qualifying for interim status.

(a) Any person who owns or operates an "existing HWM facility" or a facility in existence on the effective date of statutory or regulatory amendments under the Act that render the facility subject to the requirement to have a RCRA permit shall have interim status and shall be treated as having been issued a permit to the extent he or she has:

(1) Complied with the requirements of section 3010(a) of RCRA pertaining to notification of hazardous waste activity.

[*Comment:* Some existing facilities may not be required to file a notification under section 3010(a) of RCRA. These facilities may qualify for interim status by meeting paragraph (a)(2) of this section.]

(2) Complied with the requirements of §270.10 governing submission of part A applications;

(b) Failure to qualify for interim status. If EPA has reason to believe upon examination of a part A application that it fails to meet the requirements of §270.13, it shall notify the owner or operator in writing of the apparent deficiency. Such notice shall specify the grounds for EPA's belief that the application is deficient. The owner or operator shall have 30 days from receipt to respond to such a notification and to explain or cure the alleged deficiency in his part A application. If, after such notification and opportunity for response, EPA determines that the application is deficient it may take appropriate enforcement action.

(c) Paragraph (a) of this section shall not apply to any facility which has been previously denied a RCRA permit or if authority to operate the facility under RCRA has been previously terminated.

[48 FR 14228, Apr. 1, 1983, as amended at 49 FR 17718, Apr. 24, 1984; 50 FR 28753, July 15, 1985; 71 FR 40279, July 14, 2006]

§270.71 Operation during interim status.

(a) During the interim status period the facility shall not:

(1) Treat, store, or dispose of hazardous waste not specified in part A of the permit application;

(2) Employ processes not specified in part A of the permit application; or

(3) Exceed the design capacities specified in part A of the permit application.

(b) Interim status standards. During interim status, owners or operators shall comply with the interim status standards at 40 CFR part 265.

§270.72 Changes during interim status. 13.8.4.1.2

(a) Except as provided in paragraph (b), the owner or operator of an interim status facility may make the following changes at the facility:

(1) Treatment, storage, or disposal of new hazardous wastes not previously identified in part A of the permit application (and, in the case of newly listed or identified wastes, addition of the units being used to treat, store, or dispose of the hazardous wastes on the effective date of the listing or identification) if the owner or operator submits a revised part A permit application prior to such treatment, storage, or disposal;

(2) Increases in the design capacity of processes used at the facility if the owner or operator submits a revised part A permit application prior to such a change (along with a justification explaining the need for the change) and the Director approves the changes because:

(i) There is a lack of available treatment, storage, or disposal capacity at other hazardous waste management facilities, or

(ii) The change is necessary to comply with a Federal, State, or local requirement.

(3) Changes in the processes for the treatment, storage, or disposal of hazardous waste or addition of processes if the owner or operator submits a revised part A permit application prior to such change (along with a justification explaining the need for the change) and the Director approves the change because:

(i) The change is necessary to prevent a threat to human health and the environment because of an emergency situation, or

(ii) The change is necessary to comply with a Federal, State, or local requirement.

(4) Changes in the ownership or operational control of a facility if the new owner or operator submits a revised part A permit application no later than 90 days prior to the scheduled change. When a transfer of operational control of a facility occurs, the old owner or operator shall comply with the requirements of 40 CFR part 265, subpart H (Financial Requirements), until the new owner or operator has demonstrated to the Director that he is complying with the requirements of that subpart. The new owner or operator must demonstrate compliance with subpart H requirements within six months of the date of the change in ownership or operational control of the facility. Upon demonstration to the Director by the new owner or operator of compliance with subpart H, the Director shall notify the old owner or operator in writing that he no longer needs to comply with subpart H as of the date of demonstration. All other interim status duties are transferred effective immediately upon the date of the change in ownership or operational control of the facility.

(5) Changes made in accordance with an interim status corrective action order issued by EPA under section 3008(h) or other Federal authority, by an authorized State under comparable State authority, or by a court in a judicial action brought by EPA or by an authorized State. Changes under this paragraph are limited to the treatment, storage, or disposal of solid waste from releases that originate within the boundary of the facility.

(6) Addition of newly regulated units for the treatment, storage, or disposal of hazardous waste if the owner or operator submits a revised part A permit application on or before the date on which the unit becomes subject to the new requirements.

(b) Except as specifically allowed under this paragraph, changes listed under paragraph (a) of this section may not be made if they amount to reconstruction of the hazardous waste management facility. Reconstruction occurs when the capital investment in the changes to the facility exceeds 50 percent of the capital cost of a comparable entirely new hazardous waste management facility. If all other requirements are met, the following changes may be made even if they amount to a reconstruction:

(1) Changes made solely for the purposes of complying with the requirements of 40 CFR 265.193 for tanks and ancillary equipment.

(2) If necessary to comply with Federal, State, or local requirements, changes to an existing unit, changes solely involving tanks or containers, or addition of replacement surface impoundments that satisfy the standards of section 3004(o).

(3) Changes that are necessary to allow owners or operators to continue handling newly listed or identified hazardous wastes that have been treated, stored, or disposed of at the facility prior to the effective date of the rule establishing the new listing or identification.

(4) Changes during closure of a facility or of a unit within a facility made in accordance with an approved closure plan.

(5) Changes necessary to comply with an interim status corrective action order issued by EPA under section 3008(h) or other Federal authority, by an authorized State under comparable State authority, or by a court in a judicial proceeding brought by EPA or an authorized State, provided that such changes are limited to the treatment, storage, or disposal of solid waste from releases that originate within the boundary of the facility.

(6) Changes to treat or store, in tanks, containers, or containment buildings, hazardous wastes subject to land disposal restrictions imposed by part 268 of this chapter or RCRA section 3004, provided that such changes are made solely for the purpose of complying with part 268 of this chapter or RCRA section 3004.

(7) Addition of newly regulated units under paragraph (a)(6) of this section.

(8) Changes necessary to comply with standards under 40 CFR part 63, Subpart EEE—National Emission Standards for Hazardous Air Pollutants From Hazardous Waste Combustors.

[54 FR 9608, Mar. 7, 1989, as amended at 56 FR 7239, Feb. 21, 1991; 57 FR 37282, Aug. 18, 1992; 63 FR 33829, June 19, 1998; 71 FR 40279, July 14, 2006]

§270.73 Termination of interim status.

Interim status terminates when:

(a) Final administrative disposition of a permit application, except an application for a remedial action plan (RAP) under subpart H of this part, is made. 17.9

(b) Interim status is terminated as provided in §270.10(e)(5).

(c) For owners or operators of each land disposal facility which has been granted interim status prior to November 8, 1984, on November 8, 1985, unless:

(1) The owner or operator submits a part B application for a permit for such facility prior to that date; and

(2) The owner or operator certifies that such facility is in compliance with all applicable ground-water monitoring and financial responsibility requirements.

(d) For owners or operators of each land disposal facility which is in existence on the effective date of statutory or regulatory amendments under the Act that render the facility subject to the requirement to have a RCRA permit and which is granted interim status, twelve months after the date on which the facility first becomes subject to such permit requirement unless the owner or operator of such facility:

(1) Submits a part B application for a RCRA permit for such facility before the date 12 months after the date on which the facility first becomes subject to such permit requirement; and

(2) Certifies that such facility is in compliance with all applicable ground water monitoring and financial responsibility requirements.

(e) For owners or operators of any land disposal unit that is granted authority to operate under §270.72(a)(1), (2) or (3), on the date 12 months after the effective date of such requirement, unless the owner or operator certifies that such unit is in compliance with all applicable ground-water monitoring and financial responsibility requirements.

(f) For owners and operators of each incinerator facility which has achieved interim status prior to November 8, 1984, interim status terminates on November 8, 1989, unless the owner or operator of the facility submits a part B application for a RCRA permit for an incinerator facility by November 8, 1986.

(g) For owners or operators of any facility (other than a land disposal or an incinerator facility) which has achieved interim status prior to November 8, 1984, interim status terminates on November 8, 1992, unless the owner or operator of the facility submits a part B application for a RCRA permit for the facility by November 8, 1988.

[48 FR 14228, Apr. 1, 1983, as amended at 50 FR 28753, July 15, 1985; 54 FR 9609, Mar. 7, 1989; 56 FR 7239, Feb. 21, 1991; 56 FR 32692, July 17, 1991; 63 FR 65941, Nov. 30, 1998]

Subpart H—Remedial Action Plans (RAPs) 17.15

Source: 63 FR 65941, Nov. 30, 1998, unless otherwise noted.

§270.79 Why is this subpart written in a special format?

This subpart is written in a special format to make it easier to understand the regulatory requirements. Like other Environmental Protection Agency (EPA) regulations, this establishes enforceable legal requirements. For this subpart, "I" and "you" refer to the owner/operator.

General Information

§270.80 What is a RAP?

(a) A RAP is a special form of RCRA permit that you, as an owner or operator, may obtain, instead of a permit issued under §§270.3 through 270.66, to authorize you to treat, store, or dispose of hazardous remediation waste (as defined in §260.10 of this chapter) at a remediation waste management site. A RAP may only be issued for the area of contamination where the remediation wastes to be managed under the RAP originated, or areas in close proximity to the contaminated area, except as allowed in limited circumstances under §270.230.

(b) The requirements in §§270.3 through 270.66 do not apply to RAPs unless those requirements for traditional RCRA permits are specifically required under §§270.80 through 270.230. The definitions in §270.2 apply to RAPs.

(c) Notwithstanding any other provision of this part or part 124 of this chapter, any document that meets the requirements in this section constitutes a RCRA permit under RCRA section 3005(c).

(d) A RAP may be:

(1) A stand-alone document that includes only the information and conditions required by this subpart; or

(2) Part (or parts) of another document that includes information and/or conditions for other activities at the remediation waste management site, in addition to the information and conditions required by this subpart.

(e) If you are treating, storing, or disposing of hazardous remediation wastes as part of a cleanup compelled by Federal or State cleanup authorities, your RAP does not affect your obligations under those authorities in any way.

(f) If you receive a RAP at a facility operating under interim status, the RAP does not terminate your interim status.

§270.85 When do I need a RAP?

(a) Whenever you treat, store, or dispose of hazardous remediation wastes in a manner that requires a RCRA permit under §270.1, you must either obtain:

(1) A RCRA permit according to §§270.3 through 270.66; or

(2) A RAP according to this subpart.

(b) Treatment units that use combustion of hazardous remediation wastes at a remediation waste management site are not eligible for RAPs under this subpart.

(c) You may obtain a RAP for managing hazardous remediation waste at an already permitted RCRA facility. You must have these RAPs approved as a modification to your existing permit according to the requirements of §270.41 or §270.42 instead of the requirements in this subpart. When you submit an application for such a modification, however, the information requirements in §270.42(a)(1)(i), (b)(1)(iv), and (c)(1)(iv) do not apply; instead, you must submit the information required under §270.110. When your permit is modified the RAP becomes part of the RCRA permit. Therefore when your permit (including the RAP portion) is modified, revoked and reissued, terminated or when it expires, it will be modified according to the applicable requirements in §§270.40 through 270.42, revoked and reissued according to the applicable requirements in §§270.41 and 270.43, terminated according to the applicable requirements in §270.43, and expire according to the applicable requirements in §§270.50 and 270.51.

§270.90 Does my RAP grant me any rights or relieve me of any obligations?

The provisions of §270.4 apply to RAPs. (Note: The provisions of §270.4(a) provide you assurance that, as long as you comply with your RAP, EPA will consider you in compliance with Subtitle C of RCRA, and will not take enforcement actions against you. However, you should be aware of four exceptions to this provision that are listed in §270.4.)

Applying for a RAP

§270.95 How do I apply for a RAP?

To apply for a RAP, you must complete an application, sign it, and submit it to the Director according to the requirements in this subpart.

§270.100 Who must obtain a RAP?

When a facility or remediation waste management site is owned by one person, but the treatment, storage or disposal activities are operated by another person, it is the operator's duty to obtain a RAP, except that the owner must also sign the RAP application.

§270.105 Who must sign the application and any required reports for a RAP?

Both the owner and the operator must sign the RAP application and any required reports according to §270.11(a), (b), and (c). In the application, both the owner and the operator must also make the certification required under §270.11(d)(1). However, the owner may choose the alternative certification under §270.11(d)(2) if the operator certifies under §270.11(d)(1).

§270.110 What must I include in my application for a RAP?

You must include the following information in your application for a RAP:

(a) The name, address, and EPA identification number of the remediation waste management site;

(b) The name, address, and telephone number of the owner and operator;

(c) The latitude and longitude of the site;

(d) The United States Geological Survey (USGS) or county map showing the location of the remediation waste management site;

(e) A scaled drawing of the remediation waste management site showing:

(1) The remediation waste management site boundaries;

(2) Any significant physical structures; and

(3) The boundary of all areas on-site where remediation waste is to be treated, stored or disposed;

(f) A specification of the hazardous remediation waste to be treated, stored or disposed of at the facility or remediation waste management site. This must include information on:

(1) Constituent concentrations and other properties of the hazardous remediation wastes that may affect how such materials should be treated and/or otherwise managed;

(2) An estimate of the quantity of these wastes; and

(3) A description of the processes you will use to treat, store, or dispose of this waste including technologies, handling systems, design and operating parameters you will use to treat hazardous remediation wastes before disposing of them according to the LDR standards of part 268 of this chapter, as applicable;

(g) Enough information to demonstrate that operations that follow the provisions in your RAP application will ensure compliance with applicable requirements of parts 264, 266, and 268 of this chapter;

(h) Such information as may be necessary to enable the Regional Administrator to carry out his duties under other Federal laws as is required for traditional RCRA permits under §270.14(b)(20);

(i) Any other information the Director decides is necessary for demonstrating compliance with this subpart or for determining any additional RAP conditions that are necessary to protect human health and the environment.

§270.115 What if I want to keep this information confidential?

Part 2 (Public Information) of this chapter allows you to claim as confidential any or all of the information you submit to EPA under this subpart. You must assert any such claim at the time that you submit your RAP application or other submissions by stamping the words "confidential business information" on each page containing such information. If you do assert a claim at the time you submit the information, EPA will treat the information according to the procedures in part 2 of this chapter. If you do not assert a claim at the time you submit the information, EPA may make the information available to the public without further notice to you. EPA will deny any requests for confidentiality of your name and/or address.

§270.120 To whom must I submit my RAP application?

You must submit your application for a RAP to the Director for approval.

§270.125 If I submit my RAP application as part of another document, what must I do?

If you submit your application for a RAP as a part of another document, you must clearly identify the components of that document that constitute your RAP application.

Getting a RAP Approved

§270.130 What is the process for approving or denying my application for a RAP?

(a) If the Director tentatively finds that your RAP application includes all of the information required by §270.110 and that your proposed remediation waste management activities meet the regulatory standards, the Director will make a tentative decision to approve your RAP application. The Director will then prepare a draft RAP and provide an opportunity for public comment before making a final decision on your RAP application, according to this subpart.

(b) If the Director tentatively finds that your RAP application does not include all of the information required by §270.110 or that your proposed remediation waste management activities do not meet the regulatory standards, the Director may request additional information from you or ask you to correct deficiencies in your application. If you fail or refuse to provide any additional information the Director requests, or to correct any deficiencies in your RAP application, the Director may make a tentative decision to deny your RAP application. After making this tentative decision, the Director will prepare a notice of intent to deny your RAP application ("notice of intent to deny") and provide an opportunity for public comment before making a final decision on your RAP application, according to the requirements in this Subpart. The Director may deny the RAP application either in its entirety or in part.

§270.135 What must the Director include in a draft RAP?

If the Director prepares a draft RAP, it must include the:

(a) Information required under §270.110(a) through (f);

(b) The following terms and conditions:

(1) Terms and conditions necessary to ensure that the operating requirements specified in your RAP comply with applicable requirements of parts 264, 266, and 268 of this chapter (including any recordkeeping and reporting requirements). In satisfying this provision, the Director may incorporate, expressly or by reference, applicable requirements of parts 264, 266, and 268 of this chapter into the RAP or establish site-specific conditions as required or allowed by parts 264, 266, and 268 of this chapter;

(2) Terms and conditions in §270.30;

(3) Terms and conditions for modifying, revoking and reissuing, and terminating your RAP, as provided in §270.170; and

(4) Any additional terms or conditions that the Director determines are necessary to protect human health and the environment, including any terms and conditions necessary to respond to spills and leaks during use of any units permitted under the RAP; and

(c) If the draft RAP is part of another document, as described in §270.80(d)(2), the Director must clearly identify the components of that document that constitute the draft RAP.

§270.140 What else must the Director prepare in addition to the draft RAP or notice of intent to deny?

Once the Director has prepared the draft RAP or notice of intent to deny, he must then:

(a) Prepare a statement of basis that briefly describes the derivation of the conditions of the draft RAP and the reasons for them, or the rationale for the notice of intent to deny;

(b) Compile an administrative record, including:

(1) The RAP application, and any supporting data furnished by the applicant;

(2) The draft RAP or notice of intent to deny;

(3) The statement of basis and all documents cited therein (material readily available at the issuing Regional office or published material that is generally available need not be physically included with the rest of the record, as long as it is specifically referred to in the statement of basis); and

(4) Any other documents that support the decision to approve or deny the RAP; and

(c) Make information contained in the administrative record available for review by the public upon request.

§270.145 What are the procedures for public comment on the draft RAP or notice of intent to deny?

(a) The Director must:

(1) Send notice to you of his intention to approve or deny your RAP application, and send you a copy of the statement of basis;

(2) Publish a notice of his intention to approve or deny your RAP application in a major local newspaper of general circulation;

(3) Broadcast his intention to approve or deny your RAP application over a local radio station; and

(4) Send a notice of his intention to approve or deny your RAP application to each unit of local government having jurisdiction over the area in which your site is located, and to each State agency having any authority under State law with respect to any construction or operations at the site.

(b) The notice required by paragraph (a) of this section must provide an opportunity for the public to submit written comments on the draft RAP or notice of intent to deny within at least 45 days.

(c) The notice required by paragraph (a) of this section must include:

(1) The name and address of the office processing the RAP application;

(2) The name and address of the RAP applicant, and if different, the remediation waste management site or activity the RAP will regulate;

(3) A brief description of the activity the RAP will regulate;

(4) The name, address and telephone number of a person from whom interested persons may obtain further information, including copies of the draft RAP or notice of intent to deny, statement of basis, and the RAP application;

(5) A brief description of the comment procedures in this section, and any other procedures by which the public may participate in the RAP decision;

(6) If a hearing is scheduled, the date, time, location and purpose of the hearing;

(7) If a hearing is not scheduled, a statement of procedures to request a hearing;

(8) The location of the administrative record, and times when it will be open for public inspection; and

(9) Any additional information the Director considers necessary or proper.

(d) If, within the comment period, the Director receives written notice of opposition to his intention to approve or deny your RAP application and a request for a hearing, the Director must hold an informal public hearing to discuss issues relating to the approval or denial of your RAP application. The Director may also determine on his own initiative that an informal hearing is appropriate. The hearing must include an opportunity for any person to present written or oral comments. Whenever possible, the Director must schedule this hearing at a location convenient to the nearest population center to the remediation waste management site and give notice according to the requirements in paragraph (a) of this section. This notice must, at a minimum, include the information required by paragraph (c) of this section and:

(1) Reference to the date of any previous public notices relating to the RAP application;

(2) The date, time and place of the hearing; and

(3) A brief description of the nature and purpose of the hearing, including the applicable rules and procedures.

§270.150 How will the Director make a final decision on my RAP application?

(a) The Director must consider and respond to any significant comments raised during the public comment period, or during any hearing on the draft RAP or notice of intent to deny, and revise your draft RAP based on those comments, as appropriate.

(b) If the Director determines that your RAP includes the information and terms and conditions required in §270.135, then he will issue a final decision approving your RAP and, in writing, notify you and all commenters on your draft RAP that your RAP application has been approved.

(c) If the Director determines that your RAP does not include the information required in §270.135, then he will issue a final decision denying your RAP and, in writing, notify you and all commenters on your draft RAP that your RAP application has been denied.

(d) If the Director's final decision is that the tentative decision to deny the RAP application was incorrect, he will withdraw the notice of intent to deny and proceed to prepare a draft RAP, according to the requirements in this subpart.

(e) When the Director issues his final RAP decision, he must refer to the procedures for appealing the decision under §270.155.

(f) Before issuing the final RAP decision, the Director must compile an administrative record. Material readily available at the issuing Regional office or published materials which are generally available and which are included in the administrative record need not be physically included with the rest of the record as long as it is specifically referred to in the statement of basis or the response to comments. The administrative record for the final RAP must include information in the administrative record for the draft RAP (see §270.140(b)) and:

(1) All comments received during the public comment period;

(2) Tapes or transcripts of any hearings;

(3) Any written materials submitted at these hearings;

(4) The responses to comments;

(5) Any new material placed in the record since the draft RAP was issued;

(6) Any other documents supporting the RAP; and

(7) A copy of the final RAP.

(g) The Director must make information contained in the administrative record available for review by the public upon request.

§270.155 May the decision to approve or deny my RAP application be administratively appealed?

(a) Any commenter on the draft RAP or notice of intent to deny, or any participant in any public hearing(s) on the draft RAP, may appeal the Director's decision to approve or deny your RAP application to EPA's Environmental Appeals Board under §124.19 of this chapter. Any person who did not file comments, or did not participate in any public hearing(s) on the draft RAP, may petition for administrative review only to the extent of the changes from the draft to the final RAP decision. Appeals of RAPs may be made to the same extent as for final permit decisions under §124.15 of this chapter (or a decision under §270.29 to deny a permit for the active life of a RCRA hazardous waste management facility or unit). Instead of the notice required under §§124.19(c) and 124.10 of this chapter, the Director will give public notice of any grant of review of RAPs by the Environmental Appeals Board through the same means used to provide notice under §270.145. The notice will include:

(1) The briefing schedule for the appeal as provided by the Board;

(2) A statement that any interested person may file an amicus brief with the Board; and

(3) The information specified in §270.145(c), as appropriate.

(b) This appeal is a prerequisite to seeking judicial review of these EPA actions.

§270.160 When does my RAP become effective?

Your RAP becomes effective 30 days after the Director notifies you and all commenters that your RAP is approved unless:

(a) The Director specifies a later effective date in his decision;

(b) You or another person has appealed your RAP under §270.155 (if your RAP is appealed, and the request for review is granted under §270.155, conditions of your RAP are stayed according to §124.16 of this chapter); or

(c) No commenters requested a change in the draft RAP, in which case the RAP becomes effective immediately when it is issued.

§270.165 When may I begin physical construction of new units permitted under the RAP?

You must not begin physical construction of new units permitted under the RAP for treating, storing or disposing of hazardous remediation waste before receiving a finally effective RAP.

How May My RAP Be Modified, Revoked and Reissued, or Terminated?

§270.170 After my RAP is issued, how may it be modified, revoked and reissued, or terminated?

In your RAP, the Director must specify, either directly or by reference, procedures for future modifications, revocations and reissuance, or terminations of your RAP. These procedures must provide adequate opportunities for public review and comment on any modification, revocation and reissuance, or termination that would significantly change your management of your remediation waste, or that otherwise merits public review and comment. If your RAP has been incorporated into a traditional RCRA permit, as allowed under §270.85(c), then the RAP will be modified according to the applicable requirements in §§270.40 through 270.42, revoked and reissued according to the applicable requirements in §§270.41 and 270.43, or terminated according to the applicable requirements of §270.43.

§270.175 For what reasons may the Director choose to modify my final RAP?

(a) The Director may modify your final RAP on his own initiative only if one or more of the following reasons listed in this section exist(s). If one or more of these reasons do not exist, then the Director will not modify your final RAP, except at your request. Reasons for modification are:

(1) You made material and substantial alterations or additions to the activity that justify applying different conditions;

(2) The Director finds new information that was not available at the time of RAP issuance and would have justified applying different RAP conditions at the time of issuance;

(3) The standards or regulations on which the RAP was based have changed because of new or amended statutes, standards or regulations, or by judicial decision after the RAP was issued;

(4) If your RAP includes any schedules of compliance, the Director may find reasons to modify your compliance schedule, such as an act of God, strike, flood, or materials shortage or other events over which you as the owner/operator have little or no control and for which there is no reasonably available remedy;

(5) You are not in compliance with conditions of your RAP;

(6) You failed in the application or during the RAP issuance process to disclose fully all relevant facts, or you misrepresented any relevant facts at the time;

(7) The Director has determined that the activity authorized by your RAP endangers human health or the environment and can only be remedied by modifying; or

(8) You have notified the Director (as required in the RAP under §270.30(l)(3)) of a proposed transfer of a RAP.

(b) Notwithstanding any other provision in this section, when the Director reviews a RAP for a land disposal facility under §270.195, he may modify the permit as necessary to assure that the facility continues to comply with the currently applicable requirements in parts 124, 260 through 266 and 270 of this chapter.

(c) The Director will not reevaluate the suitability of the facility location at the time of RAP modification unless new information or standards indicate that a threat to human health or the environment exists that was unknown when the RAP was issued.

§270.180 For what reasons may the Director choose to revoke and reissue my final RAP?

(a) The Director may revoke and reissue your final RAP on his own initiative only if one or more reasons for revocation and reissuance exist(s). If one or more reasons do not exist, then the Director will not modify or revoke and reissue your final RAP, except at your request. Reasons for modification or revocation and reissuance are the same as the reasons listed for RAP modifications in §270.175(a)(5) through (8) if the Director determines that revocation and reissuance of your RAP is appropriate.

(b) The Director will not reevaluate the suitability of the facility location at the time of RAP revocation and reissuance, unless new information or standards indicate that a threat to human health or the environment exists that was unknown when the RAP was issued.

§270.185 For what reasons may the Director choose to terminate my final RAP, or deny my renewal application?

The Director may terminate your final RAP on his own initiative, or deny your renewal application for the same reasons as those listed for RAP modifications in §270.175(a)(5) through (7) if the Director determines that termination of your RAP or denial of your RAP renewal application is appropriate.

§270.190 May the decision to approve or deny a modification, revocation and reissuance, or termination of my RAP be administratively appealed?

(a) Any commenter on the modification, revocation and reissuance or termination, or any person who participated in any hearing(s) on these actions, may appeal the Director's decision to approve a modification, revocation and reissuance, or termination of your RAP, according to §270.155. Any person who did not file comments or did not participate in any public hearing(s) on the modification, revocation and reissuance or termination, may petition for administrative review only of the changes from the draft to the final RAP decision.

(b) Any commenter on the modification, revocation and reissuance or termination, or any person who participated in any hearing(s) on these actions, may informally appeal the Director's decision to deny a request for modification, revocation and reissuance, or termination to EPA's Environmental Appeals Board. Any person who did not file comments, or did not participate in any public hearing(s) on the modification, revocation and reissuance or termination may petition for administrative review only of the changes from the draft to the final RAP decision.

(c) The process for informal appeals of RAPs is as follows:

(1) The person appealing the decision must send a letter to the Environmental Appeals Board. The letter must briefly set forth the relevant facts.

(2) The Environmental Appeals Board has 60 days after receiving the letter to act on it.

(3) If the Environmental Appeals Board does not take action on the letter within 60 days after receiving it, the appeal shall be considered denied.

(d) This informal appeal is a prerequisite to seeking judicial review of these EPA actions.

§270.195 When will my RAP expire?

RAPs must be issued for a fixed term, not to exceed 10 years, although they may be renewed upon approval by the Director in fixed increments of no more than ten years. In addition, the Director must review any RAP for hazardous waste land disposal five years after the date of issuance or reissuance and you or the Director must follow the requirements for modifying your RAP as necessary to assure that you continue to comply with currently applicable requirements in RCRA sections 3004 and 3005.

§270.200 How may I renew my RAP if it is expiring?

If you wish to renew your expiring RAP, you must follow the process for application for and issuance of RAPs in this subpart.

§270.205 What happens if I have applied correctly for a RAP renewal but have not received approval by the time my old RAP expires?

If you have submitted a timely and complete application for a RAP renewal, but the Director, through no fault of yours, has not issued a new RAP with an effective date on or before the expiration date of your previous RAP, your previous RAP conditions continue in force until the effective date of your new RAP or RAP denial.

Operating Under Your RAP

§270.210 What records must I maintain concerning my RAP?

You are required to keep records of:

(a) All data used to complete RAP applications and any supplemental information that you submit for a period of at least 3 years from the date the application is signed; and

(b) Any operating and/or other records the Director requires you to maintain as a condition of your RAP.

§270.215 How are time periods in the requirements in this subpart and my RAP computed?

(a) Any time period scheduled to begin on the occurrence of an act or event must begin on the day after the act or event. (For example, if your RAP specifies that you must close a staging pile within 180 days after the operating term for that staging pile expires, and the operating term expires on June 1, then June 2 counts as day one of your 180 days, and you would have to complete closure by November 28.)

(b) Any time period scheduled to begin before the occurrence of an act or event must be computed so that the period ends on the day before the act or event. (For example, if you are transferring ownership or operational control of your site, and wish to transfer your RAP, the new owner or operator must submit a revised RAP application no later than 90 days before the scheduled change. Therefore, if you plan to change ownership on January 1, the new owner/operator must submit the revised RAP application no later than October 3, so that the 90th day would be December 31.)

(c) If the final day of any time period falls on a weekend or legal holiday, the time period must be extended to the next working day. (For example, if you wish to appeal the Director's decision to modify your RAP, then you must petition the Environmental Appeals Board within 30 days after the Director has issued the final RAP decision. If the 30th day falls on Sunday, then you may submit your appeal by the Monday after. If the 30th day falls on July 4th, then you may submit your appeal by July 5th.)

(d) Whenever a party or interested person has the right to or is required to act within a prescribed period after the service of notice or other paper upon him by mail, 3 days must be added to the prescribed term. (For example, if you wish to appeal the Director's decision to modify your RAP, then you must petition the Environmental Appeals Board within 30 days after the Director has issued the final RAP decision. However, if the Director notifies you of his decision by mail, then you may have 33 days to petition the Environmental Appeals Board.)

§270.220 How may I transfer my RAP to a new owner or operator?

(a) If you wish to transfer your RAP to a new owner or operator, you must follow the requirements specified in your RAP for RAP modification to identify the new owner or operator, and incorporate any other necessary requirements. These modifications do not constitute "significant" modifications for purposes of §270.170. The new owner/operator must submit a revised RAP application no later than 90 days before the scheduled change along with a written agreement containing a specific date for transfer of RAP responsibility between you and the new permittees.

(b) When a transfer of ownership or operational control occurs, you as the old owner or operator must comply with the applicable requirements in part 264, subpart H (Financial Requirements), of this chapter until the new owner or operator has demonstrated that he is complying with the requirements in that subpart. The new owner or operator must demonstrate compliance with part 264, subpart H, of this chapter within six months of the date of the change in ownership or operational control of the facility or remediation waste management site. When the new owner/operator demonstrates compliance with part 264, subpart H, of this chapter to the Director, the Director will notify you that you no longer need to comply with part 264, subpart H, of this chapter as of the date of demonstration.

§270.225 What must the State or EPA Region report about noncompliance with RAPs?

The State or EPA Region must report noncompliance with RAPs according to the provisions of §270.5.

Obtaining a RAP for an Off-Site Location

§270.230 May I perform remediation waste management activities under a RAP at a location removed from the area where the remediation wastes originated?

(a) You may request a RAP for remediation waste management activities at a location removed from the area where the remediation wastes originated if you believe such a location would be more protective than the contaminated area or areas in close proximity.

(b) If the Director determines that an alternative location, removed from the area where the remediation waste originated, is more protective than managing remediation waste at the area of contamination or areas in close proximity, then the Director may approve a RAP for this alternative location.

(c) You must request the RAP, and the Director will approve or deny the RAP, according to the procedures and requirements in this subpart.

(d) A RAP for an alternative location must also meet the following requirements, which the Director must include in the RAP for such locations:

(1) The RAP for the alternative location must be issued to the person responsible for the cleanup from which the remediation wastes originated;

(2) The RAP is subject to the expanded public participation requirements in §§124.31, 124.32, and 124.33 of this chapter;

(3) The RAP is subject to the public notice requirements in §124.10(c) of this chapter;

(4) The site permitted in the RAP may not be located within 61 meters or 200 feet of a fault which has had displacement in the Holocene time (you must demonstrate compliance with this standard through the requirements in §270.14(b)(11)) (See definitions of terms in §264.18(a) of this chapter);

Note to paragraph (d)(4): Sites located in political jurisdictions other than those listed in Appendix VI of part 264 of this chapter, are assumed to be in compliance with this requirement.

(e) These alternative locations are remediation waste management sites, and retain the following benefits of remediation waste management sites:

(1) Exclusion from facility-wide corrective action under §264.101 of this chapter; and

(2) Application of §264.1(j) of this chapter in lieu of part 264, subparts B, C, and D, of this chapter.

Subpart I—Integration with Maximum Achievable Control Technology (MACT) Standards

§270.235 Options for incinerators, cement kilns, lightweight aggregate kilns, solid fuel boilers, liquid fuel boilers and hydrochloric acid production furnaces to minimize emissions from startup, shutdown, and malfunction events.

(a) *Facilities with existing permits.* (1) *Revisions to permit conditions after documenting compliance with MACT.* The owner or operator of a RCRA-permitted incinerator, cement kiln, lightweight aggregate kiln, solid fuel boiler, liquid fuel boiler, or hydrochloric acid production furnace may request that the Director address permit conditions that minimize emissions from startup, shutdown, and malfunction events under any of the following options when requesting removal of permit conditions that are no longer applicable according to §§264.340(b) and 266.100(b) of this chapter:

(i) *Retain relevant permit conditions.* Under this option, the Director will:

(A) Retain permit conditions that address releases during startup, shutdown, and malfunction events, including releases from emergency safety vents, as these events are defined in the facility's startup, shutdown, and malfunction plan required under §63.1206(c)(2) of this chapter; and

(B) Limit applicability of those permit conditions only to when the facility is operating under its startup, shutdown, and malfunction plan.

(ii) *Revise relevant permit conditions.* (A) Under this option, the Director will:

(*1*) Identify a subset of relevant existing permit requirements, or develop alternative permit requirements, that ensure emissions of toxic compounds are minimized from startup, shutdown, and malfunction events, including releases from emergency safety vents, based on review of information including the source's startup, shutdown, and malfunction plan, design, and operating history.

(*2*) Retain or add these permit requirements to the permit to apply only when the facility is operating under its startup, shutdown, and malfunction plan.

(B) *Changes that may significantly increase emissions.* (*1*) You must notify the Director in writing of changes to the startup, shutdown, and malfunction plan or changes to the design of the source that may significantly increase emissions of toxic compounds from startup, shutdown, or malfunction events, including releases from emergency safety vents. You must notify the Director of such changes within five days of making such changes. You must identify in the notification recommended revisions to permit conditions necessary as a result of the changes to ensure that emissions of toxic compounds are minimized during these events.

(*2*) The Director may revise permit conditions as a result of these changes to ensure that emissions of toxic compounds are minimized during startup, shutdown, or malfunction events, including releases from emergency safety vents either:

(*i*) Upon permit renewal, or, if warranted;

(*ii*) By modifying the permit under §§270.41(a) or 270.42.

(iii) *Remove permit conditions.* Under this option:

(A) The owner or operator must document that the startup, shutdown, and malfunction plan required under §63.1206(c)(2) of this chapter has been approved by the Administrator under §63.1206(c)(2)(ii)(B) of this chapter; and

(B) The Director will remove permit conditions that are no longer applicable according to §§264.340(b) and 266.100(b) of this chapter.

(2) *Addressing permit conditions upon permit reissuance.* The owner or operator of an incinerator, cement kiln, lightweight aggregate kiln, solid fuel boiler, liquid fuel boiler, or hydrochloric acid production furnace that has conducted a comprehensive performance test and submitted to the Administrator a Notification of Compliance documenting compliance with the standards of part 63, subpart EEE, of this chapter may request in the application to reissue the permit for the combustion unit that the Director control emissions from startup, shutdown, and malfunction events under any of the following options:

(i) *RCRA option A.* (A) Under this option, the Director will:

(*1*) Include, in the permit, conditions that ensure compliance with §§264.345(a) and 264.345(c) or §§266.102(e)(1) and 266.102(e)(2)(iii) of this chapter to minimize emissions of toxic compounds from startup, shutdown, and malfunction events, including releases from emergency safety vents; and

(*2*) Specify that these permit requirements apply only when the facility is operating under its startup, shutdown, and malfunction plan.; or

(ii) *RCRA option B.* (A) Under this option, the Director will:

(*1*) Include, in the permit conditions, that ensure emissions of toxic compounds are minimized from startup, shutdown, and malfunction events, including releases from emergency safety vents, based on review of information including the source's startup, shutdown, and malfunction plan, design, and operating history; and

(*2*) Specify that these permit requirements apply only when the facility is operating under its startup, shutdown, and malfunction plan.

(B) *Changes that may significantly increase emissions.* (*1*) You must notify the Director in writing of changes to the startup, shutdown, and malfunction plan or changes to the design of the source that may significantly increase emissions of toxic compounds from startup, shutdown, or malfunction events, including releases from emergency safety vents. You must notify the Director of such changes within five days of making such changes. You must identify in the notification recommended revisions to permit conditions necessary as a result of the changes to ensure that emissions of toxic compounds are minimized during these events.

(*2*) The Director may revise permit conditions as a result of these changes to ensure that emissions of toxic compounds are minimized during startup, shutdown, or malfunction events, including releases from emergency safety vents either:

(*i*) Upon permit renewal, or, if warranted;

(*ii*) By modifying the permit under §§270.41(a) or 270.42; or

(iii) *CAA option.* Under this option:

(A) The owner or operator must document that the startup, shutdown, and malfunction plan required under §63.1206(c)(2) of this chapter has been approved by the Administrator under §63.1206(c)(2)(ii)(B) of this chapter; and

(B) The Director will omit from the permit conditions that are not applicable under §§264.340(b) and 266.100(b) of this chapter.

(b) *Interim status facilities.* (1) *Interim status operations.* In compliance with §§265.340 and 266.100(b), the owner or operator of an incinerator, cement kiln, lightweight aggregate kiln, solid fuel boiler, liquid fuel boiler, or hydrochloric acid production furnace that is operating under the interim status standards of part 265 or 266 of this chapter may control emissions of toxic compounds during startup, shutdown, and malfunction events under either of the following options after conducting a comprehensive performance test and submitting to the Administrator a Notification of Compliance documenting compliance with the standards of part 63, subpart EEE, of this chapter.

(i) *RCRA option.* Under this option, the owner or operator continues to comply with the interim status emission standards and operating requirements of part 265 or 266 of this chapter relevant to control of emissions from startup, shutdown, and malfunction events. Those standards and requirements apply only during startup, shutdown, and malfunction events; or

(ii) *CAA option.* Under this option, the owner or operator is exempt from the interim status standards of part 265 or 266 of this chapter relevant to control of emissions of toxic compounds during startup, shutdown, and malfunction events upon submission of written notification and documentation to the Director that the startup, shutdown, and malfunction plan required under §63.1206(c)(2) of this chapter has been approved by the Administrator under §63.1206(c)(2)(ii)(B) of this chapter.

(2) *Operations under a subsequent RCRA permit.* When an owner or operator of an incinerator, cement kiln, lightweight aggregate kiln, solid fuel boiler, liquid fuel boiler, or hydrochloric acid production furnace that is operating under the interim status standards of parts 265 or 266 of this chapter submits a RCRA permit application, the owner or operator may request that the Director control emissions from startup, shutdown, and malfunction events under any of the options provided by paragraphs (a)(2)(i), (a)(2)(ii), or (a)(2)(iii) of this section.

(c) *New units.* Hazardous waste incinerator, cement kiln, lightweight aggregate kiln, solid fuel boiler, liquid fuel boiler, or hydrochloric acid production furnace units that become subject to RCRA permit requirements after October 12, 2005 must control emissions of toxic compounds during startup, shutdown, and malfunction events under either of the following options:

(1) Comply with the requirements specified in §63.1206(c)(2) of this chapter; or

(2) Request to include in the RCRA permit, conditions that ensure emissions of toxic compounds are minimized from startup, shutdown, and malfunction events, including releases from emergency safety vents, based on review of information including the source's startup, shutdown, and malfunction plan and design. The director will specify that these permit conditions apply only when the facility is operating under its startup, shutdown, and malfunction plan.

[67 FR 6817, Feb. 13, 2002; 70 FR 59578, Oct. 12, 2005]

Subpart J—RCRA Standardized Permits for Storage and Treatment Units

Source: 70 FR 53475, Sept. 8, 2005, unless otherwise noted.

General Information About Standardized Permits

§270.250 What is a RCRA standardized permit?

A RCRA standardized permit (RCRA) is a special type of permit that authorizes you to manage hazardous waste. It is issued under 40 CFR part 124, subpart G and subpart J of this part.

§270.255 Who is eligible for a standardized permit?

(a) You may be eligible for a standardized permit if:

(1) You generate hazardous waste and then store or non-thermally treat the hazardous waste on-site in containers, tanks, or containment buildings; or

(2) You receive hazardous waste generated off-site by a generator under the same ownership as the receiving facility, and then store or non-thermally treat the hazardous waste in containers, tanks, or containment buildings.

(3) We will inform you of your eligibility when we make a decision on your permit application.

(b) [Reserved]

§270.260 What requirements of part 270 apply to a standardized permit?

The following subparts and sections of this part 270 apply to a standardized permit:

(a) Subpart A—General Information: All sections.

(b) Subpart B—Permit Application: §§270.10, 270.11, 270.12, 270.13 and 270.29.

(c) Subpart C—Permit Conditions: All sections.

(d) Subpart D—Changes to Permit: §§270.40, 270.41, and 270.43.

(e) Subpart E—Expiration and Continuation of Permits: All sections.

(f) Subpart F—Special Forms of Permits: §270.67.

(g) Subpart G—Interim Status: All sections.

(h) Subpart H—Remedial Action Plans: Does not apply.

(i) Subpart J—Standardized Permits: All sections.

Applying for a Standardized Permit

§270.270 How do I apply for a standardized permit?

You apply for a standardized permit by following the procedures in 40 CFR part 124, subpart G and this subpart.

§270.275 What information must I submit to the permitting agency to support my standardized permit application?

The information in paragraphs (a) through (j) of this section will be the basis of your standardized permit application. You must submit it to the Director when you submit your Notice of Intent under 40 CFR 124.202(b) requesting coverage under a RCRA standardized permit:

(a) The Part A information described in §270.13.

(b) A meeting summary and other materials required by 40 CFR 124.31.

(c) Documentation of compliance with the location standards of 40 CFR 267.18 and §270.14(b)(11).

(d) Information that allows the Director to carry out our obligations under other Federal laws required in §270.3.

(e) Solid waste management unit information required by §270.14(d).

(f) A certification meeting the requirements of §270.280, and an audit of the facility's compliance status with 40 CFR part 267 as required by §270.280.

(g) A closure plan prepared in accordance with part 267, subpart G.

(h) The most recent closure cost estimate for your facility prepared under §267.142 and a copy of the documentation required to demonstrate financial assurance under §267.143. For a new facility, you may gather the required documentation 60 days before the initial receipt of hazardous wastes.

(i) If you manage wastes generated offsite, the waste analysis plan.

(j) If you manage waste generated from off-site, documentation showing that the waste generator and the off-site facility are under the same ownership.

§270.280 What are the certification requirements?

You must submit a signed certification based on your audit of your facility's compliance with 40 CFR part 267.

(a) Your certification must read: I certify under penalty of law that:

(1) I have personally examined and am familiar with the report containing the results of an audit conducted of my facility's compliance status with 40 CFR part 267, which supports this certification. Based on my inquiry of those individuals immediately responsible for conducting the audit and preparing the report, I believe that my (include paragraph (a)(1)(i) and (ii) this section, whichever applies):

(i) My existing facility complies with all applicable requirements of 40 CFR part 267 and will continue to comply until the expiration of the permit; or

(ii) My facility has been designed, and will be constructed and operated to comply with all applicable requirements of 40 CFR part 267, and will continue to comply until expiration of the permit.

(2) I will make all information that I am required to maintain at my facility by §§270.290 through 277.315

readily available for review by the permitting agency and the public; and,

Publisher's Note: The section referenced above, §277.315, should be §270.315.

(3) I will continue to make all information required by §§270.290 through 277.315 available until the permit expires. I am aware that there are significant penalties for submitting false information, including the possibility of fine and imprisonment for knowing violation.

Publisher's Note: The section referenced above, §277.315, should be §270.315.

(b) You must sign this certification following the requirements of §270.11(a)(1) through (3).

(c) This certification must be based upon an audit that you conduct of your facility's compliance status with 40 CFR part 267. A written audit report, signed and certified as accurate by the auditor, must be submitted to the Director with the 40 CFR 124.202(b) Notice of Intent.

Information That Must Be Kept at Your Facility

§270.290 What general types of information must I keep at my facility?

You must keep the following information at your facility:

(a) A general description of the facility.

(b) Chemical and physical analyses of the hazardous waste and hazardous debris handled at the facility. At a minimum, these analyses must contain all the information you must know to treat or store the wastes properly under the requirements of 40 CFR part 267.

(c) A copy of the waste analysis plan required by 40 CFR 267.13(b).

(d) A description of the security procedures and equipment required by 40 CFR 267.14.

(e) A copy of the general inspection schedule required by 40 CFR 267.15(b). You must include in the inspection schedule applicable requirements of 40 CFR 267.174, 267.193, 267.195, 264.1033, 264.1052, 264.1053, 264.1058, and 264.1088.

(f) A justification of any modification of the preparedness and prevention requirements of 40 CFR part 267, subpart C (§§267.30 to 267.35).

(g) A copy of the contingency plan required by 40 CFR part 267, subpart D.

(h) A description of procedures, structures, or equipment used at the facility to:

(1) Prevent hazards in unloading operations (for example, use ramps, special forklifts),

(2) Prevent runoff from hazardous waste handling areas to other areas of the facility or environment, or to prevent flooding (for example, with berms, dikes, trenches),

(3) Prevent contamination of water supplies,

(4) Mitigate effects of equipment failure and power outages,

(5) Prevent undue exposure of personnel to hazardous waste (for example, requiring protective clothing), and

(6) Prevent releases to atmosphere,

(i) A description of precautions to prevent accidental ignition or reaction of ignitable, reactive, or incompatible wastes as required by 40 CFR 267.17.

(j) Traffic pattern, estimated volume (number, types of vehicles) and control (for example, show turns across traffic lanes, and stacking lanes; describe access road surfacing and load bearing capacity; show traffic control signals).

(k) [Reserved]

(l) An outline of both the introductory and continuing training programs you will use to prepare employees to operate or maintain your facility safely as required by 40 CFR 267.16. A brief description of how training will be designed to meet actual job tasks under 40 CFR 267.16(a)(3) requirements.

Publisher's Note: The above reference to 40 CFR 267.16(a)(3) is incorrect and should refer to 40 CFR 267.16(d)(3).

(m) A copy of the closure plan required by 40 CFR 267.112. Include, where applicable, as part of the plans, specific requirements in 40 CFR 267.176, 267.201, and 267.1108.

(n) [Reserved]

(o) The most recent closure cost estimate for your facility prepared under 40 CFR 267.142 and a copy of the documentation required to demonstrate financial assurance under 40 CFR 267.143. For a new facility, you may gather the required documentation 60 days before the initial receipt of hazardous wastes.

(p) [Reserved]

(q) Where applicable, a copy of the insurance policy or other documentation that complies with the liability requirements of 40 CFR 267.147. For a new facility, documentation showing the amount of insurance meeting the specification of 40 CFR 267.147(a) that you plan to have in effect before initial receipt of hazardous waste for treatment or storage.

(r) Where appropriate, proof of coverage by a State financial mechanism, as required by 40 CFR 267.149 or 267.150.

(s) A topographic map showing a distance of 1,000 feet around your facility at a scale of 2.5 centimeters (1 inch) equal to not more than 61.0 meters (200 feet). The map must show elevation contours. The contour interval must show the pattern of surface water flow in the vicinity of and from each operational unit of the facility. For example, contours with an interval of 1.5 meters (5 feet), if relief is greater than 6.1 meters (20 feet), or an interval of 0.6 meters (2 feet), if relief is less than 6.1 meters (20 feet). If your facility is in a mountainous area, you should use large contour intervals to adequately show topographic profiles of facilities. The map must clearly show the following:

(1) Map scale and date.

(2) 100-year flood plain area.

(3) Surface waters including intermittent streams.

(4) Surrounding land uses (residential, commercial, agricultural, recreational).

(5) A wind rose (*i.e.*, prevailing windspeed and direction).

(6) Orientation of the map (north arrow).

(7) Legal boundaries of your facility site.

(8) Access control (fences, gates).

(9) Injection and withdrawal wells both on-site and off-site.

(10) Buildings; treatment, storage, or disposal operations; or other structure (recreation areas, runoff control systems, access and internal roads, storm, sanitary, and process sewerage systems, loading and unloading areas, fire control facilities, etc.)

(11) Barriers for drainage or flood control.

(12) Location of operational units within your facility, where hazardous waste is (or will be) treated or stored. (Include equipment cleanup areas.)

§270.300 What container information must I keep at my facility?

If you store or treat hazardous waste in containers, you must keep the following information at your facility:

(a) A description of the containment system to demonstrate compliance with the container storage area provisions of 40 CFR 267.173. This description must show the following:

(1) Basic design parameters, dimensions, and materials of construction.

(2) How the design promotes drainage or how containers are kept from contact with standing liquids in the containment system.

(3) Capacity of the containment system relative to the number and volume of containers to be stored.

(4) Provisions for preventing or managing run-on.

(5) How accumulated liquids can be analyzed and removed to prevent overflow.

(b) For storage areas that store containers holding wastes that do not contain free liquids, a demonstration of compliance with 40 CFR 267.173(c), including:

(1) Test procedures and results or other documentation or information to show that the wastes do not contain free liquids.

(2) A description of how the storage area is designed or operated to drain and remove liquids or how containers are kept from contact with standing liquids.

(c) Sketches, drawings, or data demonstrating compliance with 40 CFR 267.174 (location of buffer zone (15m or 50ft) and containers holding ignitable or reactive wastes) and 40 CFR 267.175(c) (location of incompatible wastes in relation to each other), where applicable.

(d) Where incompatible wastes are stored or otherwise managed in containers, a description of the procedures used to ensure compliance with 40 CFR 267.175(a) and (b), and 267.17(b) and (c).

(e) Information on air emission control equipment as required by §270.315.

§270.305 What tank information must I keep at my facility?

If you use tanks to store or treat hazardous waste, you must keep the following information at your facility:

(a) A written assessment that is reviewed and certified by an independent, qualified, registered professional engineer on the structural integrity and suitability for handling hazardous waste of each tank system, as required under 40 CFR 267.191 and 267.192.

(b) Dimensions and capacity of each tank.

(c) Description of feed systems, safety cutoff, bypass systems, and pressure controls (*e.g.*, vents).

(d) A diagram of piping, instrumentation, and process flow for each tank system.

(e) A description of materials and equipment used to provide external corrosion protection, as required under 40 CFR 267.191.

(f) For new tank systems, a detailed description of how the tank system(s) will be installed in compliance with 40 CFR 267.192 and 267.194.

(g) Detailed plans and description of how the secondary containment system for each tank system is or will be designed, constructed, and operated to meet the requirements of 40 CFR 267.195 and 267.196.

(h) [Reserved].

(i) Description of controls and practices to prevent spills and overflows, as required under 40 CFR 267.198.

(j) For tank systems in which ignitable, reactive, or incompatible wastes are to be stored or treated, a description of how operating procedures and tank system and facility design will achieve compliance with the requirements of 40 CFR 267.202 and 267.203.

(k) Information on air emission control equipment as required by §270.315.

§270.310 What equipment information must I keep at my facility?

If your facility has equipment to which 40 CFR part 264, subpart BB applies, you must keep the following information at your facility:

(a) For each piece of equipment to which 40 CFR part 264 subpart BB applies:

(1) Equipment identification number and hazardous waste management unit identification.

(2) Approximate locations within the facility (e.g., identify the hazardous waste management unit on a facility plot plan).

(3) Type of equipment (e.g., a pump or a pipeline valve).

(4) Percent by weight of total organics in the hazardous waste stream at the equipment.

(5) Hazardous waste state at the equipment (e.g., gas/vapor or liquid).

(6) Method of compliance with the standard (e.g., monthly leak detection and repair, or equipped with dual mechanical seals).

(b) For facilities that cannot install a closed-vent system and control device to comply with 40 CFR part 264, subpart BB on the effective date that the facility becomes subject to the subpart BB provisions, an implementation schedule as specified in 40 CFR 264.1033(a)(2).

(c) Documentation that demonstrates compliance with the equipment standards in 40 CFR 264.1052 and 264.1059. This documentation must contain the records required under 40 CFR 264.1064.

(d) Documentation to demonstrate compliance with 40 CFR 264.1060 must include the following information:

(1) A list of all information references and sources used in preparing the documentation.

(2) Records, including the dates, of each compliance test required by 40 CFR 264.1033(j).

(3) A design analysis, specifications, drawings, schematics, and piping and instrumentation diagrams based on the appropriate sections of "Course 415: Control of Gaseous Emissions" (incorporated by reference as specified in 40 CFR 260.11) or other engineering texts acceptable to the Director that present basic control device design information. The design analysis must address the vent stream characteristics and control device operation parameters as specified in 40 CFR 264.1035(b)(4)(iii).

(4) A statement you signed and dated certifying that the operating parameters used in the design analysis reasonably represent the conditions that exist when the hazardous waste management unit is operating at the highest load or capacity level reasonable expected to occur.

(5) A statement you signed and dated certifying that the control device is designed to operate at an efficiency of 95 weight percent or greater.

§270.315 What air emissions control information must I keep at my facility?

If you have air emission control equipment subject to 40 CFR part 264, subpart CC, you must keep the following information at your facility:

(a) Documentation for each floating roof cover installed on a tank subject to 40 CFR 264.1084(d)(1) or (d)(2) that includes information you prepared or the cover manufacturer/vendor provided describing the cover design, and your certification that the cover meets applicable design specifications listed in 40 CFR 264.1084(e)(1) or (f)(1).

(b) Identification of each container area subject to the requirements of 40 CFR part 264, subpart CC and your certification that the requirements of this subpart are met.

(c) Documentation for each enclosure used to control air pollutant emissions from tanks or containers under requirements of 40 CFR 264.1084(d)(5) or 264.1086(e)(1)(ii). You must include records for the most recent set of calculations and measurements you performed to verify that the enclosure meets the criteria of a permanent total enclosure as specified in "Procedure T—Criteria for and Verification of a Permanent or Temporary Total Enclosure" under 40 CFR 52.741, appendix B.

(d) [Reserved]

(e) Documentation for each closed-vent system and control device installed under requirements of 40 CFR 264.1087 that includes design and performance information as specified in §270.24(c) and (d).

(f) An emission monitoring plan for both Method 21 in 40 CFR part 60, appendix A and control device monitoring methods. This plan must include the following information: monitoring point(s), Monitoring methods for control devices, monitoring frequency, procedures for documenting exceedances, and procedures for mitigating noncompliances.

Modifying a Standardized Permit

§270.320 How do I modify my RCRA standardized permit?

You can modify your RCRA standardized permit by following the procedures found in 40 CFR 124.211 through 124.214.

PART 271—REQUIREMENTS FOR AUTHORIZATION OF STATE HAZARDOUS WASTE PROGRAMS

Subpart A—Requirements for Final Authorization

Sec.

Subpart B [Reserved]

Authority: 42 U.S.C. 6905, 6912(a), and 6926.

Source: 48 FR 14248, Apr. 1, 1983, unless otherwise noted.

Subpart A—Requirements for Final Authorization

§271.1 Purpose and scope.

(a) This subpart specifies the procedures EPA will follow in approving, revising, and withdrawing approval of State programs and the requirements State programs must meet to be approved by the Administrator under sections 3006(b), (f) and (h) of RCRA.

(b) State submissions for program approval must be made in accordance with the procedures set out in this subpart.

(c) The substantive provisions which must be included in State programs for them to be approved include requirements for permitting, compliance evaluation, enforcement, public participation, and sharing of information. Many of the requirements for State programs are made applicable to States by cross-referencing other EPA regulations. In particular, many of the provisions of parts 270 and 124 are made applicable to States by the references contained in §271.14.

(d) Upon receipt of a complete submission, EPA will conduct a public hearing, if interest is shown, and determine whether to approve or disapprove the program taking into consideration the requirements of this subpart, the Act and any comments received.

(e) The Administrator shall approve State programs which conform to the applicable requirements of this subpart.

(f) Except as provided in §271.3(a)(3), upon approval of a State permitting program, the Administrator shall suspend the issuance of Federal permits for those activities subject to the approved State program.

Publisher's Note: The section referenced above, §271.3(a)(3), should be §271.3(b)(3).

(g) Any State program approved by the Administrator shall at all times be conducted in accordance with the requirements of this subpart.

(h) Partial State programs are not allowed for programs operating under RCRA final authorization. However, in many cases States will lack authority to regulate activities on Indian lands. This lack of authority does not impair a State's ability to obtain full program approval in accordance with this subpart, *i.e.*, inability of a State to regulate activities on Indian lands does not constitute a partial program. EPA will administer the program on Indian lands if the State does not seek this authority.

Note: States are advised to contact the United States Department of the Interior, Bureau of Indian Affairs, concerning authority over Indian lands.

(i) Except as provided in §271.4, nothing in this subpart precludes a State from:

(1) Adopting or enforcing requirements which are more stringent or more extensive than those required under this subpart;

(2) Operating a program with a greater scope of coverage than that required under this subpart. Where an approved State program has a greater scope of coverage than required by Federal law, the additional coverage is not part of the Federally approved program.

(j) Requirements and prohibitions which are applicable to the generation, transportation, treatment, storage, or disposal of hazardous waste and which are imposed pursuant to the Hazardous and Solid Waste Amendments of 1984 (HSWA) include any requirement or prohibition which has taken effect under HSWA, such as:

(1) All regulations specified in Table 1, and

(2) The self-implementing statutory provisions specified in Table 2 that have taken effect.

Note: See §§264.1(f)(3), 265.1(c)(4)(ii), 271.3(b), 271.21(e)(2) and 271.121(c)(3) for applicability.

Publisher's Note: The section referenced above, §271.121(c)(3), is not in the RCRA regulations.

Table 1—Regulations Implementing the Hazardous and Solid Waste Amendments of 1984

Promulgation date	Title of regulation	Federal Register reference	Effective date
Jan. 14, 1985	Dioxin-containing wastes.	50 FR 1978-2006	July 15, 1985
Apr. 30, 1985	Paint filter liquids test.	50 FR 18370-5	June 14, 1985
July 15, 1985	Codification rule [as corrected in 51 FR 2702, 1/21/86].	50 FR 28702-55	July 15, 1985
Oct. 23, 1985	Listing wastes from the production of dinitrotoluene, toluenediamine, and toluene diisocyanate.	50 FR 42936-43	Oct. 23, 1985
Nov. 29, 1985	Standards for the management of the burning of specific wastes in specific types of facilities.	50 FR 49164-212	Dec. 9, 1985 Mar. 31, 1986 May 29, 1986
Dec. 31, 1985	Amendment of spent solvent listings to include solvent mixtures [as corrected in 51 FR 19176, 5/28/86].	50 FR 53315-20	Jan. 30, 1986
Feb. 13, 1986	Listing wastes from the production of ethylene dibromide (EDB).	51FR 5327-31	Aug. 13, 1986
Feb. 25, 1986	Listing of four spent solvents and the still bottoms from their recovery.	51 FR 6537-42	Aug. 25, 1986
Mar. 24, 1986	Regulations for generators of 100-1000 kg/mo of hazardous waste.	51 FR 10146-76	Sept. 22, 1986
July 14, 1986	Hazardous Waste Tank Regulations:[1] 260.10; 262.34(a)(1); 264.110; 264.140; 264.190-264.199; 265.110; 265.140; 265.190-265.200; 270.14(b); 270.16; and 270.72(e). *Publisher's Note:* The section referenced above, §270.72(e), should be §270.72(b)(1).	51 FR 25422-86	Jan. 12, 1987 Mar. 24, 1987
Aug. 8, 1986	Exports of hazardous waste.	51 FR 28664-86	Nov. 8, 1986
Oct. 24, 1986	Listing Wastes from the Production and Formulation of Ethylenebisdithiocarbamic Acid (EBDC) and its Salts.	51 FR 37725	Apr. 24, 1987
Nov. 7, 1986	Land disposal restrictions for solvents and dioxins.	51 FR 40572	Nov. 8, 1986
July 8, 1987	Land disposal restrictions for California list wastes.	52 FR 25760	July 8, 1987
Sept. 23, 1987	Exception Reporting for Small Quantity Generators of Hazardous Waste.	52 FR 35899	Mar. 23, 1988
Dec. 1, 1987	Codification rule for the 1984 RCRA Amendments.	52 FR 45799	Dec. 31, 1987
Aug. 17, 1988	Land disposal restrictions for First Third wastes.	53 FR 31138-222	Aug. 8, 1988
June 23, 1989	Land Disposal Restrictions for Second Third wastes.	54 FR 26594-652	June 8, 1989
Oct. 6, 1989	Listing Wastes from the Production of Methyl Bromide.	54 FR 41402-408	Apr. 6, 1990
Dec. 11, 1989	Listing Certain Hydrocarbons Produced by Free Radical Catalyzed Processes.	54 FR 50968-978	June 11, 1990
Mar. 29, 1990	Toxicity characteristic.	55 FR 11798-877	Sept. 25, 1990
May 1, 1990	Listing Wastes from the Production of UDMH from Carboxylic Acid Hydrazides.	55 FR 18496-506	Nov. 2, 1990
June 1, 1990	Land Disposal Restrictions for Third Third wastes.	55 FR 22520-720	May 8, 1990
June 21, 1990	Process Vent and Equipment Leak Organic Air Emission Standards for Owners and Operators of Hazardous Waste Treatment, Storage, and Disposal Facilities.	55 FR 25454-519	Dec. 21, 1990

Table 1—Regulations Implementing the Hazardous and Solid Waste Amendments of 1984

Promulgation date	Title of regulation	Federal Register reference	Effective date
Nov. 2, 1990	Petroleum refinery primary and secondary oil/water/solids separation sludge listings.	55 FR 46354-397	May 2, 1991
Dec. 6, 1990	The listing of wastes from wood preserving processes.[2]	55 FR 50450-490	June 6, 1991
Dec. 31, 1990	Burning of Hazardous Waste in Boilers and Industrial Furnaces.	56 FR 7134-7240	Aug. 21, 1991
May 13, 1991	Petroleum refinery primary and secondary oil/water/solids separation sludge listings.	56 FR 21959	May 2, 1991
Aug. 19, 1991	Land disposal restrictions & generic exclusion for K061 nonwastewaters & conditional exclusion for K061 HTMR splash condenser dross residue.	56 FR 41178	Aug. 8, 1991
Jan. 29, 1992	Liners and Leak Detection for Hazardous Waste Land Disposal Units [3].	57 FR 3497	July 29, 1992
June 22, 1992	Exclusion from the definition of solid waste for the recycling of hazardous wastes in the coke by-products industry.	57 FR 27888	June 22, 1992
Aug. 18, 1992	Land disposal restrictions for newly listed wastes in §268.36 (b)-(g).	57 FR 37282	June 30, 1992
Do	Land disposal restrictions for newly listed wastes in §268.36(a), hazardous debris, and generic exclusion for K062 and F006 nonwaste-waters.	Do	Nov. 9, 1992
Aug. 18, 1992	The listing of wastes from the production, recovery, and refining of coke by-products produced from coal.	57 FR 37306	Feb. 18, 1993
Oct. 15, 1992	Listing Wastes from the Production of Chlorinated Toluenes.	57 FR 47386	Apr. 15, 1993
Nov. 18, 1992	Containerized Liquids in Landfills.	57 FR 54461	May 18, 1992
Nov. 24, 1992	Toxicity Characteristic Revision.	57 FR 55117	Nov. 24, 1992
Feb. 16, 1993	Corrective Action Management Units and Temporary Units; Corrective Action Provisions under Subtitle C.	58 FR 8685	Apr. 19, 1993
May 24, 1993	Land disposal restrictions for characteristic wastes whose treatment standards were vacated.	58 FR 29887	Aug. 9, 1993
Nov. 9, 1993	Burning of hazardous waste in boilers and industrial furnaces.	58 FR 59603	Oct. 15, 1993
Sept. 19, 1994	Land Disposal Restrictions Phase II—Universal Treatment Standards, and Treatment Standards for Organic Toxicity Characteristic Wastes and Newly Listed Wastes[4] in §268.38.	47982-48110	Dec. 19, 1994
Dec. 6, 1994	Air Emission Standards for Tanks, Surface Impoundments, and Containers.	59 FR 62896-62953	Dec. 6, 1996
Feb. 9, 1995	Listing Wastes from the Production of Carbamates.	60 FR 7856	Aug. 9, 1995
July 11, 1995	Containerized Liquids in Landfills.	60 FR 35706	Sept. 11, 1995
Apr. 8, 1996	Land Disposal Restrictions Phase III—Decharacterized Wastewaters, Carbamate Wastes, and Spent Aluminum Potliners in §268.39.	61 FR 15660	July 8, 1996
July 1, 1996	Revisions to Criteria applicable to solid waste facilities that may accept CESQG hazardous wastes, excluding MSWLF's.	61 FR 34278	Jan. 1, 1998
Aug. 26, 1996	Emergency Revision of the Land Disposal Restrictions (LDR) Phase III Treatment Standards for Listed Hazardous Wastes from Carbamate Production.	61 FR 43931	Aug. 26, 1996 until Aug. 26, 1997
May 12, 1997	Land Disposal Restrictions for Wood Preserving Wastes and Paperwork Reductions.	62 FR 26040	Aug. 11, 1997
June 17, 1997	Vacated Carbamate wastes.	62 FR 32979	Aug. 9, 1995
Aug. 28, 1997	Second Emergency Revision of the Land Disposal Restrictions (LDR) Phase III Treatment Standards for Listed Hazardous Wastes from Carbamate Production.	62 FR 45572	Aug. 26, 1997 until Aug. 26, 1998
May 4, 1998	Listing of Organobromine Production Wastes.	63 FR 24627	Nov. 4, 1998
May 26, 1998	Land Disposal Restrictions Phase IV Final Rule.	63 FR 28753	Aug. 24, 1998
Aug. 6, 1998	Petroleum Refining Process Wastes.	63 FR 42188	Feb. 8, 1999

Table 1—Regulations Implementing the Hazardous and Solid Waste Amendments of 1984

Promulgation date	Title of regulation	Federal Register reference	Effective date
Sept. 4, 1998	Emergency Revision of the Land Disposal Restrictions (LDR) Phase III Treatment Standards for Listed Hazardous Wastes from Carbamate Production.	63 FR 47418	Sept. 4, 1998
Sept. 21, 1998	Treatment Standards for Hazardous Waste K088.	63 FR 51267	Sept. 21, 1998
Nov. 30, 1998	Hazardous Remediation Waste Management Requirements [5].	63 FR 65947	June 1, 1999
Sept. 30, 1999	Standards for Hazardous Air Pollutants for Hazardous Waste Combustors.	64 FR 53077	Sept. 30, 1999
Mar. 17, 2000	Vacated Organobromine wastes.	65 FR 14475	Nov. 4, 1998
Sept. 29, 2000	Listing of Hazardous Wastes K174 and K175.	65 FR 67132	May 7, 2001
Oct. 31, 2001	Listing of Inorganic Chemical Manufacturing Wastes.	66 FR 58299	May 20, 2002
Jan. 22, 2002	Corrective Action Management Unit Standards Amendments.	67 FR 3029	Apr. 22, 2002
Feb. 13, 2002	Interim Standards for Hazardous Air Pollutants for Hazardous Waste Combustors.	67 FR 6818	Feb. 13, 2002
July 15, 2002	Elimination of LDR Treatment Standards Exemption for K061-Derived Fertilizers.	67 FR 48414	Jan. 24, 2003
Sept. 30, 2002	Land Disposal Restrictions: National Treatment Variance to Designate New Treatment Subcategories for Radioactively Contaminated Cadmium-, Mercury-, and Silver-Containing Batteries.	67 FR 62624	Nov. 21, 2002
Feb. 15, 2005	Listing of Hazards Waste K181.	70 FR 9179	Aug. 23, 2005
Mar. 4, 2005	Waste Minimization Certification in the Revised Manifest Rule.	70 FR 10825	Sept. 6, 2005
July 14, 2005	Process Vent and Equipment Leak Organic Air Emission Standards for Owners and of Operators of Hazardous Waste Treatment, Storage, and Disposal Facilities.	70 FR 34590	July 14, 2005
July 14, 2005	Burning of Hazardous Waste in Boilers and Industrial Furnaces.	70 FR 34590	July 14, 2005
July 14, 2005	Air Emission Standards Tanks, Surface Impoundments, Containers.	70 FR 34590	July 14, 2005
Oct. 12, 2005	Standards for Hazardous Air Pollutants for Hazardous Waste Combustors.	70 FR 59579	Oct. 12, 2005
May 4, 2006	Office of Resource Conservation and Recovery Burden Reduction Project.	71 FR 16862–16915	May 4, 2006
July 28, 2006	Final Rule for Cathode Ray Tubes.	71 FR 42949	Jan. 29, 2007

[1]These regulations implement HSWA only to the extent that they apply to tank systems owned or operated by small quantity generators, establish leak detection requirements for all new underground tank systems, and establish permitting standards for underground tank systems that cannot be entered for inspection.

[2]These regulations, including test methods for benzo(k)fluoranthene and technical standards for drip pads, implement HSWA only to the extent that they apply to the listing of Hazardous Waste No. F032, and wastes that are hazardous because they exhibit the Toxicity Characteristic. These regulations, including test methods for benzo(k)fluoranthene and technical standards for drip pads, do not implement HSWA to the extent that they apply to the listings of Hazardous Waste Nos. F034 and F035.

[3]The following portions of this rule are not HSWA regulations: §§264.19 and 265.19 for final covers.

[4]The following portions of this rule are not HSWA regulations: §§260.30, 260.31, 261.2.

[5]These regulations implement HSWA only to the extent that they apply to the standards for staging piles and to §§264.1(j) and 264.101(d) of this chapter.

Table 2—Self-Implementing Provisions of the Hazardous and Solid Waste Amendments of 1984

Effective date	Self-implementing provision	RCRA citation	Federal Register reference
Nov. 8, 1984	Delisting procedures.	3001(f)	July 15, 1985, 50 FR 28702-55
Do	Waste disposal for small quantity generators prior to March 31, 1986.	3001(d)(5)	Do
Do	Prohibition of disposal in salt domes, salt beds and underground mines and caves.	3004(b)	Do
Do	Land disposal prohibition not applicable to contaminated soil or debris from a CERCLA response action or a RCRA corrective action prior to November 8, 1988.	3004(d)(3)	Do
Do	Loss of interim status.	3005(c)(2)(C) & (e)(2)-(3)	Do

Table 2—Self-Implementing Provisions of the Hazardous and Solid Waste Amendments of 1984

Effective date	Self-implementing provision	RCRA citation	Federal Register reference
Do	Storage of wastes prohibited from land disposal.	3004(j) & 3005(j)(11)	Do
Do	Prohibition of waste and used oil as dust suppressant.	3004(l)	Do
Do	Minimum technological requirements for new and expanding surface impoundments, landfills and incinerators.	3004(o)	Do
Do	Ground water monitoring.	3004(p)	Do
Do	Prohibition for burning fuels containing hazardous waste in any cement kilns.	3004(q)(2)(C)	Do
Do	Financial responsibility for liability of guarantor when owner/operator is in bankruptcy.	3004(t)(2)-(3)	Do
Do	Corrective action.	3004(u)	Do
Do	Review of land disposal permits every 5 years.	3005(c)(3)	Do
Do	Permit terms and conditions necessary to protect human health and the environment.	3005(c)(3)	Do
Do	Research, development, and demonstration permits.	3005(g)	Do
Do	Interim status facilities receiving waste after July 26, 1982.	3005(i)	Do
Do	Deadline for surface impoundment retrofit exemption application.	3005(j)(5)	Do
Feb. 7, 1985	Fuel labeling requirements.	3004(r)	Do
May 8, 1985	Prohibition of liquids in landfills.	3004(c)(1)	Do
Do	Expansions during interim status for waste piles.	3015(a)	Do
Do	Expansions during interim status for landfills and surface impoundments.	3015(b)	Do
Do	Interim control of hazardous waste disposed of by underground injection.	7010(a)	Do
Aug. 5, 1985	Small quantity generator manifest requirements.	3001(d)(3)	Do
Aug. 8, 1985	Exposure assessments to accompany landfill and surface impoundment permit applications.	3019(a)	Do
Sept. 1, 1985	Waste minimization certification on manifest.	3002(b)	Do
Do	Waste minimization permit condition.	3005(h)	Do
Nov. 8, 1985	Prohibition of non-hazardous liquids in landfills.	3004(c)(3)	Do
Do	Notification of hazardous waste export.	3017(c)	Do
Feb. 8, 1986[1]	Notification requirements for producers, burners, blenders, distributors and marketers of waste derived fuel.	3010(a)	Nov. 29, 1985, 50 FR 49164-211
Mar. 31, 1986[2]	Small quantity generator requirements.	3001(d)(8)	Mar. 24, 1986, 51 FR 10146-78
Nov. 8, 1986	Land disposal prohibitions on dioxins and F001-F005 solvents.	3004(e)	Nov. 7, 1986, 51 FR 40572
Do	Temporary granting of exclusion petitions ceases.	3001(f)(2)(B)	
Do	Export of hazardous waste.	3017(a)	Aug. 8, 1986, 51 FR 28664-86
July 8, 1987	Land disposal restrictions for California list wastes.	3004(d)	July 8, 1987, 52 FR 25760
Sept. 23, 1987	Exception reporting for small quantity generators of hazardous waste.	52 FR 35899	Mar. 23, 1988
Aug. 8, 1988	Prohibition on California wastes, dioxins, and solvents in deep injection wells.	3004(f)(3)	
Do	Land disposal restrictions of 1/3 of listed wastes.	3004(g)(6)(A)	Aug. 17, 1988, 53 FR 31138-222
Nov. 8, 1988	Prohibition on wastes in existing surface impoundments unless double lined.	3005(j)	
June 8, 1989	Prohibition on land disposal of 2/3 of listed wastes.	3004(g)(6)(B)	June 23, 1989, 54 FR 26594-652
May 8, 1990	Prohibition on land disposal of 3/3 of listed wastes.	3004(g)(6)(C)	June 1, 1990, 55 FR 22520-720
Aug. 8, 1991	Prohibition on land disposal of K061 high zinc nonwastewaters.	3004(g)(6)(A)	Aug. 19, 1991, 56 FR 41178

Table 2—Self-Implementing Provisions of the Hazardous and Solid Waste Amendments of 1984

Effective date	Self-implementing provision	RCRA citation	Federal Register reference
June 30, 1992	Surface Impoundment Retrofit.	37282	Aug. 18, 1992, 57 FR 37282
Nov. 9, 1992	Prohibition on land disposal of hazardous debris and newly listed wastes.	Do	Aug. 18, 1992, 57 FR 37282
Feb. 18, 1993	Containment buildings.	Do	Aug. 18, 1992, 57 FR 37282
Aug. 9, 1993	Prohibition on land disposal of characteristic wastes whose treatment standards were vacated.	3004(g)(6)(c)	May 24, 1993, 58 FR 29887
Dec. 19, 1994	Prohibition on land disposal of newly listed and identified wastes.	3004(g)(4)(C) and 3004(m)	Sept. 19, 1994, 59 FR 47982-48110
Sept. 19, 1995	Establishment of treatment standards for D001 and D012-D017 wastes injected into nonhazardous deep wells.	3004(m)	Do
Apr. 8, 1996	Prohibition on land disposal of K088 wastes.	3004(m)	Apr. 8, 1996, 61 FR 15660
July 8, 1996	Prohibition on land disposal of carbamate wastes.	3004(m)	Apr. 8, 1996, 61 FR 15660
July 8, 1996	Prohibition on land disposal of carbamate wastes (Vacated wastes).	3004(m)	June 17, 1997, 62 FR 32979
Sept. 6, 1996	Prohibition on land disposal of radioactive waste mixed with the newly listed or identified wastes, including soil and debris.	3004(g)(4)(C) and 3004(m)	Sept. 19, 1994, 59 FR 47982-48110
Oct. 8, 1996	Prohibition on land disposal of K088 wastes.	3004(m)	Apr. 8, 1998, 61 FR 15660
Dec. 6, 1996	Air Emission Standards for Tanks, Surface Impoundments, and Containers.	3004(n)	Dec. 6, 1994, 59 FR 62896-62953
Aug. 11, 1997	Prohibition on land disposal of wood preserving wastes.	3004(g)(4)(c) and 3004 (m)	May 12, 1997, 62 FR 26040
Apr. 8, 1998	Prohibition on disposal of radioactive waste mixed with newly listed or identified wastes, including soil and debris (Vacated carbamate wastes).	3304(g)(4)(c) and 3004(m)	June 17, 1997, 62 FR 32979
Aug. 24, 1998	Prohibition on land disposal of newly identified wastes, including TC metal wastes and characteristic mineral processing wastes; treatment standards for contaminated soil.	3004(m)	May 26, 1998, 63 FR 28753
Sept. 4, 1998	Emergency Revision of the Land Disposal Restrictions (LDR) Phase III Treatment Standards for Listed Hazardous Wastes from Carbamate Production.	3004(m)	Sept. 4, 1998, 63 FR 47418
Sept. 21, 1998	Prohibition on land disposal of K088 wastes, and prohibition on land disposal of radioactive waste mixed with K088 wastes, including soil and debris.	3004(g)(4)(C) and 3004(m)	Sept. 24, 1998, 63 FR 51267
Nov. 4, 1998	Prohibition on land disposal of newly listed and identified wastes.	3004(g)(4)(C) and 3004(m)	May 4, 1998, 63 FR 24596
Nov. 4, 1998	Prohibition on land disposal of radioactive waste mixed with the newly listed and identified wastes, including soil and debris.	3004(m) 3004(g)(4)(C) and 3004(m)	May 4, 1998, 63 FR 24596
Nov. 4, 1998	Prohibition on land disposal of organobromine waste (Vacated wastes).	3004(g)(4)(c) and 3004(m)	Mar. 17, 2000, 65 FR 14475
Nov. 4, 1998	Prohibition on land disposal of radioactive waste mixed with the newly listed and identified wastes, including soil and debris (Vacated organobromine wastes).	3004(m) and 3004(g)(4)(c)	Mar. 17, 2000, 65 FR 14475
Feb. 8, 1999	Prohibition on land disposal of newly listed and identified wastes; and prohibition on land disposal of radioactive waste mixed with the newly listed or identified wastes, including soil and debris.	3004(g)(4)(C) and 3004(m)	Aug. 6, 1998, 63 FR 42188
May 12, 1999	Prohibition on land disposal of radioactive waste and soil and debris mixed with wood preserving wastes.	3004(m)	May 12, 1997, 62 FR 26040

Table 2—Self-Implementing Provisions of the Hazardous and Solid Waste Amendments of 1984

Effective date	Self-implementing provision	RCRA citation	Federal Register reference
May 26, 2000	Prohibition on land disposal of newly identified wastes from elemental phosphorus processing and mixed radioactive and newly identified TC metal/mineral processing wastes (including soil and debris).		
	Prohibition on underground injection of newly identified mineral processing wastes from titanium dioxide production.	3004(m)	May 26, 1998, 63 FR 28753
May 7, 2001	Prohibition on land disposal of K174 and prohibition on land disposal of radioactive waste mixed with K174 and K175 wastes, and K175 wastes, including soil and debris.	3004(g)(4)(C) and 3004(m)	Nov. 8, 2000, 65 FR 67132
May 20, 2002	Prohibition on land disposal of K176, K177, and K178 wastes, and prohibition on land disposal of radioactive waste mixed with K176, K177, and K178 wastes, including soil and debris.	3004(g)(4)(C) and 3004(m)	Nov. 20, 2001, 66 FR 58300
Jan. 24, 2003	Elimination of LDR Treatment Standards Exemption for K061-Derived Fertilizers.	3004(g)(6)	July 24, 2002, 67 FR 48414
Aug. 23, 2005	Prohibition on land disposal of K181 waste, and prohibition on land disposal of radioactive waste mixed with K181 wastes, including soil and debris.	3004(g)(4)(C) and 3004(m)	Feb. 24, 2005, 70 FR 9179

[1]Note that the effective date was changed to Jan. 29, 1986 by the Nov. 29, 1985 rule.
[2]Note that the effective date was changed to Sept. 22, 1986 by the Mar. 24, 1986 rule.

[48 FR 14248, Apr. 1, 1983 as amended at 50 FR 28753, July 15, 1985; 50 FR 42943, Oct. 23, 1985; 50 FR 49207, Nov. 29, 1985; 50 FR 53320, Dec. 31, 1985; 51 FR 5331, Feb. 13, 1986; 51 FR 6542, Feb. 25, 1986; 51 FR 10176, Mar. 24, 1986; 51 FR 25486, July 14, 1986; 51 FR 28685, Aug. 8, 1986; 51 FR 29431, Aug. 15, 1986; 51 FR 33720, Sept. 22, 1986; 51 FR 36013, Oct. 8, 1986; 51 FR 37729, Oct. 24, 1986; 51 FR 40653, Nov. 7, 1986; 52 FR 21018, June 4, 1987; 52 FR 25792, July 8, 1987; 52 FR 35899, Sept. 23, 1987; 52 Fr 45799, Dec. 1, 1987; 53 Fr 31221, Aug. 17, 1988; 54 FR 26652, June 23, 1989; 54 FR 41407, Oct. 6, 1989; 54 FR 50978, Dec. 11, 1989; 55 FR 11876, Mar. 29, 1990; 55 FR 18505, May 2, 1990; 55 FR 22719, June 1, 1990; 55 FR 25519, June 21, 1990; 55 FR 26987, June 29, 1990; 55 FR 31388, Aug. 2, 1990; 55 FR 46396, Nov. 2, 1990; 55 FR 50489, Dec. 6, 1990; 56 FR 7240, Feb. 21, 1991; 56 FR 21959, May 13, 1991; 56 FR 32692, July 17, 1991; 56 FR 41177, Aug. 19, 1991; 57 FR 3497, Jan. 29, 1992; 57 FR 27888, June 22, 1992; 57 FR 37282, Aug. 18, 1992; 57 FR 37306, Aug. 18, 1992; 57 FR 41612, Sept. 10, 1992; 57 FR 47385, Oct. 15, 1992; 57 FR 54461, Nov. 18, 1992; 57 FR 55117, Nov. 24, 1992; 57 FR 61504, Dec. 24, 1992; 58 FR 6854, Feb. 2, 1993; 58 FR 8685, Feb. 16, 1993; 58 FR 29887, May 24, 1993; 58 FR 59603, Nov. 9, 1993; 59 FR 48109, Sept. 19, 1994; 59 FR 62952, Dec. 6, 1994; 60 FR 7856, Feb. 9, 1995; 60 FR 26829, May 19, 1995; 60 FR 35706, July 11, 1995; 60 FR 56954, Nov. 13, 1995; 61 FR 15659, Apr. 8, 1996; 61 FR 28510, June 5, 1996; 61 Fr 34278, July 1, 1996; 61 FR 43931, Aug. 26, 1996; 61 FR 59996, Nov. 25, 1996; 62 FR 26040, May 12, 1997; 62 FR 32979, June 17, 1997; 62 FR 45572, Aug. 28, 1997; 63 FR 24627, May 4, 1998; 63 FR 28753, May 26, 1998; 63 FR 35150, June 29, 1998; 63 FR 42188, Aug. 6, 1998; 63 FR 47418, Sept. 4, 1998; 63 FR 51267, Sept. 24, 1998; 63 FR 65947, Nov. 30, 1998; 64 FR 53077, Sept. 30, 1999; 65 FR 14475, Mar. 17, 2000; 65 FR 67131, Nov. 8, 2000; 66 FR 58299, Nov. 20, 2001; 67 FR 3029, Jan. 22, 2002; 67 FR 6818, Feb. 13, 2002; 67 FR 48414, July 24, 2002; 67 FR 62624, Oct. 7, 2002; 70 FR 9179, Feb. 24, 2005; 70 FR 10825, Mar. 4, 2005; 70 FR 34590, June 14, 2005; 71 FR 16915, Apr. 4, 2006; 71 FR 40280, July 14, 2006; 71 FR 42949, July 28, 2006; 74 FR 30231, June 25, 2009]

§271.2 Definitions.

The definitions in part 270 apply to all subparts of this part.

§271.3 Availability of final authorization.

(a) Where a State program meets the requirements of section 3006 of RCRA and this subpart it may receive authorization for any provision of its program corresponding to a Federal provision in effect on the date of the State's authorization.

(b) States approved under this subpart are authorized to administer and enforce their hazardous waste program in lieu of the Federal program, except as provided below:

(1) Any requirement or prohibition which is applicable to the generation, transportation, treatment, storage, or disposal of hazardous waste and which is imposed pursuant to the Hazardous and Solid Waste Amendments of 1984 takes effect in each State having a finally authorized State program on the same date as such requirement takes effect in other States. These requirements and prohibitions are identified in §271.1(j).

(2) The requirements and prohibitions in §271.1(j) supersede any less stringent provision of a State program. The Administrator is authorized to carry out each such Federal requirement and prohibition in an authorized State except where, pursuant to section 3006(b) or 3006(g)(2) of RCRA, the State has received final or interim authorization to carry out the particular requirement or prohibition. Violations of Federal requirements and prohibitions effective in authorized States are enforceable under sections 3008, 3013 and 7003 of RCRA.

(3) Until an authorized State program is revised to reflect the amendments made by the Hazardous and Solid Waste Amendments of 1984 and such program revisions receive final or interim authorization pursuant to section 3006(b) or 3006(g)(2) of RCRA, the Administrator shall have the authority in such State to issue or deny permits or those portions of permits affected by the requirements and prohibitions established by the Hazardous and Solid Waste Amendments of 1984.

(c) Official State applications for final authorization may be reviewed on the basis of Federal self-implementing statutory provisions that were in effect 12 months prior to the State's submission of its official application (if no implementing regulations have previously been promulgated) and the regulations in 40 CFR parts 124, 260-266, 268, 270 and 271 that were in effect 12 months prior to the State's submission of its official application. To meet this requirement the State may demonstrate that its program qualifies for final authorization pursuant to this subpart or interim authorization under §271.24. States are not precluded from seeking authorization for requirements taking effect less than 12 months prior to the State's submittal of its final application.

[48 FR 14248, Apr. 1, 1983, as amended at 50 FR 28753, July 15, 1985; 51 FR 33721, Sept. 22, 1986; 60 FR 33914, June 29, 1995]

§271.4 Consistency.

To obtain approval, a State program must be consistent with the Federal program and State programs applicable in other States and in particular must comply with the provisions below. For purposes of this section the phrase "State programs applicable in other States" refers only to those State hazardous waste programs which have received final authorization under this part.

(a) Any aspect of the State program which unreasonably restricts, impedes, or operates as a ban on the free movement across the State border of hazardous wastes from or to other States for treatment, storage, or disposal at facilities authorized to operate under the Federal or an approved State program shall be deemed inconsistent.

(b) Any aspect of State law or of the State program which has no basis in human health or environmental protection and which acts as a prohibition on the treatment, storage or disposal of hazardous waste in the State may be deemed inconsistent.

(c) If the State manifest system does not meet the requirements of this part, the State program shall be deemed inconsistent.

[48 FR 14248, Apr. 1, 1983; 48 FR 30114, June 30, 1983]

§271.5 Elements of a program submission.

(a) Any State that seeks to administer a program under this part shall submit to the Administrator at least three copies of a program submission. The submission shall contain the following:

(1) A letter from the Governor of the State requesting program approval;

(2) A complete program description, as required by §271.6 describing how the State intends to carry out its responsibilities under this subpart;

(3) An Attorney General's statement as required by §271.7;

(4) A Memorandum of Agreement with the Regional Administrator as required by §271.8;

(5) Copies of all applicable State statutes and regulations, including those governing State administrative procedures; and

(6) The showing required by §271.20(c) of the State's public participation activities prior to program submission.

(b) Within 30 days of receipt by EPA of a State program submission, EPA will notify the State whether its submission is complete. If EPA finds that a State's submission is complete, the statutory review period (*i.e.*, the period of time allotted for formal EPA review of a proposed State program under section 3006(b) of the Act) shall be deemed to have begun on the date of receipt of the State's submission. If EPA finds that a State's submission is incomplete, the review period shall not begin until all necessary information is received by EPA.

(c) If the State's submission is materially changed during the review period, the review period shall begin again upon receipt of the revised submission.

(d) The State and EPA may extend the review period by agreement.

§271.6 Program description.

Any State that seeks to administer a program under this subpart shall submit a description of the program it proposes to administer in lieu of the Federal program under State law or under an interstate compact. The program description shall include:

(a) A description in narrative form of the scope, structure, coverage and processes of the State program.

(b) A description (including organization charts) of the organization and structure of the State agency or agencies which will have responsibility for administering the program, including the information listed below. If more than one agency is responsible for administration of a program, each agency must have statewide jurisdiction over a class of activities. The responsibilities of each agency must be delineated, their procedures for coordination set forth, and an agency must be designated as a "lead agency" to facilitate communications between EPA and the State agencies having program responsibilities. When the State proposes to administer a program of greater scope of coverage than is required by Federal law, the information provided under this paragraph shall indicate the resources dedicated to administering the Federally required portion of the program.

(1) A description of the State agency staff who will carry out the State program, including the number, occupations, and general duties of the employees. The State need not submit complete job descriptions for every employee carrying out the State program.

(2) An itemization of the estimated costs of establishing and administering the program, including cost of the personnel listed in paragraph (b)(1) of this section, cost of administrative support, and cost of technical support. This estimate must cover the first two years after program approval.

(3) An itemization of the sources and amounts of funding, including an estimate of Federal grant money, available to the State Director to meet the costs listed in paragraph (b)(2) of this section, identifying any restrictions or limitations upon this funding. This estimate must cover the first two years after program approval.

(c) A description of applicable State procedures, including permitting procedures and any State administrative or judicial review procedures.

(d) Copies of the permit form(s), application form(s), and reporting form(s) the State intends to employ in its program. Forms used by the State for hazardous waste management need not be identical to the forms used by EPA but should require the same basic information, except that the State RCRA program must require the use of EPA Manifest Forms 8700-22 and 8700-22A. Where the State preprints information on the Manifest forms, such forms must be submitted with the State's application for approval. Restrictions on preprinting by the States are identified in 40 CFR 271.10(h). Otherwise, the State need not provide copies of uniform national forms it intends to use but should note its intention to use such forms.

(e) A complete description of the State's compliance tracking and enforcement program.

(f) A description of the State manifest tracking system, and of the procedures the State will use to coordinate information with other approved State programs and the Federal program regarding interstate and international shipments.

(g) An estimate of the number of the following:

(1) Generators;

(2) Transporters; and

(3) On- and off-site storage, treatment and disposal facilities, and a brief description of the types of facilities and an indication of the permit status of these facilities.

(h) If available, an estimate of the annual quantities of hazardous wastes generated within the State; transported into and out of the State; and stored, treated, or disposed of within the State: On-site; and Off-site.

[48 FR 14248, Apr. 1, 1983, as amended at 49 FR 10506, Mar. 20, 1984]

§271.7 Attorney General's statement.

(a) Any State that seeks to administer a program under this subpart shall submit a statement from the State Attorney General (or the attorney for those State agencies which have independent legal counsel) that the laws of the State provide adequate authority to carry out the program described under §271.6 and to meet the requirements of this subpart. This statement shall include citations to the specific statutes, administrative regulations and, where appropriate, judicial decisions which demonstrate adequate authority. State statutes and regulations cited by the State Attorney General or independent legal counsel shall be in the form of lawfully adopted State statues and regulations at the time the statement is signed and shall be fully effective by the time the program is approved. To qualify as "independent legal counsel" the attorney signing the statement required by this section must have full authority to independently represent the State agency in court on all matters pertaining to the State program.

Note: EPA will supply States with an Attorney General's statement format on request.

(b) When a State seeks authority over activities on Indian lands, the statement shall contain an appropriate analysis of the State's authority.

§271.8 Memorandum of Agreement with the Regional Administrator.

(a) Any State that seeks to administer a program under this subpart shall submit a Memorandum of Agreement (MOA). The Memorandum of Agreement shall be executed by the State Director and the Regional Administrator and shall become effective when approved by the Administrator. In addition to meeting the requirements of paragraph (b) of this section, the Memorandum of

Agreement may include other terms, conditions, or agreements consistent with this subpart and relevant to the administration and enforcement of the State's regulatory program. The Administrator shall not approve any Memorandum of Agreement which contains provisions which restrict EPA's statutory oversight responsibility.

(b) All Memoranda of Agreement shall include the following:

(1) Provisions for the Regional Administrator to promptly forward to the State Director information obtained prior to program approval in notifications provided under section 3010(a) of RCRA. The Regional Administrator and the State Director shall agree on procedures for the assignment of EPA identification numbers for new generators, transporters, treatment, storage, and disposal facilities.

(2) Provisions specifying the frequency and content of reports, documents and other information which the State is required to submit to EPA. The State shall allow EPA to routinely review State records, reports, and files relevant to the administration and enforcement of the approved program. State reports may be combined with grant reports where appropriate.

(3) Provisions on the State's compliance monitoring and enforcement program, including:

(i) Provisions for coordination of compliance monitoring activities by the State and by EPA. These may specify the basis on which the Regional Administrator will select facilities or activities within the State for EPA inspection. The Regional Administrator will normally notify the State at least 7 days before any such inspection; and

(ii) Procedures to assure coordination of enforcement activities.

(4) Provisions allowing EPA to conduct compliance inspections of all generators, transporters, and HWM facilities in each year for which the State is operating under final authorization. The Regional Administrator and the State Director may agree to limitations on compliance inspections of generators, transporters, and non-major HWM facilities.

(5) No limitations on EPA compliance inspections of generators, transporters, or non-major HWM facilities under paragraph (b)(4) of this section shall restrict EPA's right to inspect any generator, transporter, or HWM facility which it has cause to believe is not in compliance with RCRA; however, before conducting such an inspection, EPA will normally allow the State a reasonable opportunity to conduct a compliance evaluation inspection.

(6) Provisions for the prompt transfer from EPA to the State of pending permit applications and any other information relevant to program operation not already in the possession of the State Director (*e.g.*, support files for permit issuance, compliance reports, etc.). When existing permits are transferred from EPA to the State for administration, the Memorandum of Agreement shall contain provisions specifying a procedure for transferring the administration of these permits. If a State lacks the authority to directly administer permits issued by the Federal government, a procedure may be established to transfer responsibility for these permits.

Note: For example, EPA and the State and the permittee could agree that the State would issue a permit(s) identical to the outstanding Federal permit which would simultaneously be terminated.

(7) Provisions specifying classes and categories of permit applications, draft permits, and proposed permits that the State will send to the Regional Administrator for review, comment and, where applicable, objection.

(8) When appropriate, provisions for joint processing of permits by the State and EPA, for facilities or activities which require permits from both EPA and the State under different programs. See §124.4

Note: To promote efficiency and to avoid duplication and inconsistency, States are encouraged to enter into joint processing agreements with EPA for permit issuance.

(9) Provisions for the State Director to promptly forward to EPA copies of draft permits and permit applications for all major HWM facilities for review and comment. The Regional Administrator and the State Director may agree to limitations regarding review of and comment on draft permits and/or permit applications for non-major HWM facilities. The State Director shall supply EPA copies of final permits for all major HWM facilities.

(10) Provisions for the State Director to review all permits issued under State law prior to the date of program approval and modify or revoke and reissue them to require compliance with the requirements of this subpart. The Regional Administrator and the State Director shall establish a time within which this review must take place.

(11) Provisions for modification of the Memorandum of Agreement in accordance with this subpart.

(c) The Memorandum of Agreement, the annual program grant and the State/EPA Agreement should be consistent. If the State/EPA Agreement indicates that a change is needed in the Memorandum of Agreement, the Memorandum of Agreement may be amended through the procedures set forth in this subpart. The State/EPA Agreement may not override the Memorandum of Agreement.

Note: Detailed program priorities and specific arrangements for EPA support of the State program will change and are therefore more appropriately negotiated in the context of annual agreements rather than in the MOA. However, it may still be appropriate to specify in the MOA the basis for such detailed agreements, *e.g.*, a provision in the MOA specifying that EPA will select facilities in the State for inspection annually as part of the State/EPA agreement.

§271.9 Requirements for identification and listing of hazardous wastes.

(a) The State program must control all the hazardous wastes controlled under 40 CFR part 261 and must adopt a list of hazardous wastes and set of characteristics for identifying hazardous wastes equivalent to those under 40 CFR part 261.

(b) The State is not required to have a delisting mechanism. A State may receive authorization for delisting if the State regulations for delisting decisions are equivalent to §260.20(b) and §260.22, and the State provides public notice and opportunity for comment before granting or denying delisting requests.

[51 FR 33721, Sept. 22, 1986]

§271.10 Requirements for generators of hazardous wastes.

(a) The State program must cover all generators covered by 40 CFR part 262. States must require new generators to contact the State and obtain an EPA identification number before they perform any activity subject to regulation under the approved State hazardous waste program.

(b) The State shall have authority to require and shall require all generators to comply with reporting and recordkeeping requirements equivalent to those under 40 CFR 262.40 and 262.41. States must require that generators keep these records at least 3 years. States that choose to receive electronic documents must include the requirements of 40 CFR Part 3—(Electronic reporting) in their Program (except that states that choose to receive electronic manifests and/or permit the use of electronic manifests must comply with any applicable requirements for e-manifest in this section of this section).

(c) The State program must require that generators who accumulate hazardous wastes for short periods of time comply with requirements that are equivalent to the requirements for accumulating hazardous wastes for short periods of time under 40 CFR 262.34.

(d) The State program must require that generators comply with requirements that are equivalent to the requirements for the packaging, labeling, marking, and placarding of hazardous waste under 40 CFR 262.30 to 262.33, and are consistent with relevant DOT regulations under 49 CFR parts 172, 173, 178 and 179.

(e) The State program shall provide requirements respecting international shipments which are equivalent to those at 40 CFR part 262 subparts E and F, except that:

(1) Advance notification, annual reports and exception reports in accordance with 40 CFR 262.53, 262.55 and 262.56 shall be filed with the Administrator; States may require that copies of the documents referenced also be filed with the State Director; and

(2) The Administrator will notify foreign countries of intended exports in conjunction with the Department of State and primary exporters of foreign countries' responses in accordance with 40 CFR 262.53.

Note: Such notices shall be mailed to the Office of Waste Programs Enforcement, RCRA Enforcement Division (OS-520), Environmental Protection Agency, 1200 Pennsylvania Ave., NW., Washington, DC 20460.

(f) The State must require that all generators of hazardous waste who transport (or offer for transport) such hazardous waste off-site:

(1) Use a manifest system that ensures that interstate and intrastate shipments of hazardous waste are designated for delivery and, in the case of intrastate shipments, are delivered to facilities that are authorized to operate under an approved State program or the federal program. The manifest system must require the use of the manifest format as required by §262.20(a). No other manifest form, shipping document, or information, other than that required by federal law, may be required by the State to travel with the shipment.

(2) Initiate the manifest and designate on the manifest the treatment, storage or disposal facility to which the waste is to be shipped.

(3) Ensure that all wastes offered for transportation are accompanied by a manifest, except:

(i) Shipments subject to 40 CFR 262.20(e) or (f);

(ii) Shipments by rail or water, as specified in 40 CFR 262.23(c) and (d).

(4) Investigate instances where manifests have not been returned by the owner or operator of the designated facility and report such instances to the State in which the shipment originated.

(g) In the case of interstate shipments for which the manifest has not been returned, the State program must provide for notification to the State in which the facility designated on the manifest is located and to the State in which the shipment may have been delivered (or to EPA in the case of unauthorized States).

(h) The State must follow the Federal manifest format for the form and instructions (40 CFR 262.20 and the appendix to part 262).

(1) A state may require the entry of waste codes associated with particular wastes that are regulated as hazardous wastes by the state, if the state codes are not redundant with a federally required code for the same waste. No state, however, may impose enforcement sanctions on a transporter during transportation of the shipment for failure of the form to include a state-required waste code.

(2) Either the State to which a shipment is manifested (consignment State) or the State in which the generator is located (generator State), or both, may require that copies of the manifest form be submitted to the State.

(3) No State, however, may impose enforcement sanctions on a transporter during transportation of the shipment for failure of the form to include preprinted information or optional State information items.

(i) Unless otherwise provided in part 271, the State program shall have standards for generators which are at least as stringent as any amendment to 40 CFR Part 262 which is promulgated after July 1, 1984.

[48 FR 14248, Apr. 1, 1983, as amended at 48 FR 30114, June 30, 1983; 49 FR 10506, Mar. 20, 1984; 49 FR 11180, Mar. 26, 1984; 51 FR 28685, Aug. 8, 1986; 51 FR 33722, Sept. 22, 1986; 56 FR 43705, Sept. 4, 1991; 70 FR 10825, Mar. 4, 2005; 70 FR 59888, Oct. 13, 2005]

§271.11 Requirements for transporters of hazardous wastes.

(a) The State program must cover all transporters covered by 40 CFR part 263. New transporters must be required to contact the State and obtain an EPA identification number from the State before they accept hazardous waste for transport.

(b) The State shall have authority to require and shall require all transporters to comply with reporting and recordkeeping requirements equivalent to those under 40 CFR 263.22. States must require that transporters keep these records at least 3 years. States that choose to receive electronic documents must include the requirements of 40 CFR Part 3—(Electronic reporting) in their Program (except that states that choose to receive electronic manifests and/or permit the use of electronic manifests must comply with any applicable requirements for e-manifest in this section of this section).

(c)(1) The State must require transporters to carry the manifest during transport, except in the case of shipments by rail or water, transporters may carry a shipping paper, as specified in 40 CFR 263.20(e) and (f);

(2) The State must require the transporter to deliver waste only to the facility designated on the manifest, which in the case of return shipments of rejected wastes or regulated container residues, may also include the original generator of the waste shipment.

(3) The State program must provide requirements for shipments by rail or water equivalent to those under 40 CFR 263.20(e) and (f).

(4) For exports of hazardous waste, the state must require the transporter to refuse to accept hazardous waste for export if the transporter knows the shipment does not conform to the EPA Acknowledgment of Consent, to carry an EPA Acknowledgment of Consent to the shipment, to sign and date the International Shipments Block of the manifest to indicate the date the shipment leaves the U.S., and to provide a copy of the manifest to the U.S. Customs official at the point the waste leaves the United States.

(d) For hazardous wastes that are discharged in transit, the State program must require that transporters notify appropriate State, local, and Federal agencies of such discharges, and clean up such wastes, or take action so that such wastes do not present a hazard to human health or the environment. These requirements shall be equivalent to those found at 40 CFR 263.30 and 263.31.

(e) Unless otherwise provided in part 271, the State program shall have standards for transporters which are at least as stringent as any amendment to 40 CFR Part 263 which is promulgated after July 1, 1984.

[48 FR 14248, Apr. 1, 1983, as amended at 51 FR 28686, Aug. 8, 1986; 51 FR 33722, Sept. 22, 1986; 70 FR 10825, Mar. 4, 2005; 70 FR 59888, Oct. 13, 2005]

§271.12 Requirements for hazardous waste management facilities.

The State shall have standards for hazardous waste management facilities which are equivalent to 40 CFR parts 264 and 266. These standards shall include:

(a) Technical standards for tanks, containers, waste piles, incineration, chemical, physical and biological treatment facilities, surface impoundments, landfills, and land treatment facilities;

(b) Financial responsibility during facility operation;

(c) Preparedness for and prevention of discharges or releases of hazardous waste; contingency plans and emergency procedures to be followed in the event of a discharge or release of hazardous waste;

(d) Closure and post-closure requirements including financial requirements to ensure that money will be available for closure and post-closure monitoring and maintenance;

(e) Groundwater monitoring;

(f) Security to prevent unauthorized access to the facility;

(g) Facility personnel training;

(h) Inspections, monitoring, recordkeeping, and reporting. States that choose to receive electronic documents must include the requirements of 40 CFR Part 3—(Electronic reporting) in their Program (except that states that choose to receive electronic manifests and/or permit the use of electronic manifests must comply with paragraph (i) of this section);

(i) Compliance with the manifest system including the requirement that facility owners or operators return a signed copy of the manifest:

(1) To the generator to certify delivery of the hazardous waste shipment or to identify discrepancies; and

(2) To EPA's International Compliance Assurance Division program, at the address referenced in 40 CFR 264.71(a)(3) and 265.71(a)(3), to indicate the receipt of a shipment of hazardous waste imported into the U.S. from a foreign source.

(j) Other requirements to the extent that they are included in 40 CFR parts 264 and 266.

[48 FR 14248, Apr. 1, 1983, as amended at 70 FR 10825, Mar. 4, 2005; 70 FR 59889, Oct. 13, 2005]

§271.13 Requirements with respect to permits and permit applications.

(a) State law must require permits for owners and operators of all hazardous waste management facilities required to obtain a permit under 40 CFR part 270 and prohibit the operation of any hazardous waste management facility without such a permit, except that States may, if adequate legal authority exists, authorize owners and operators of any facility which would qualify for interim status under the Federal program to remain in operation until a final decision is made on the permit application, or until interim status terminates pursuant to 40 CFR 270.73 (b) through (f). When State law authorizes such continued operation it shall require compliance by owners and operators of such facilities with standards at least as stringent as EPA's interim status standards at 40 CFR part 265.

(b) The State must require all new HWM facilities to contact the State and obtain an EPA identification number before commencing treatment, storage, or disposal of hazardous waste.

(c) All permits issued by the State shall require compliance with the standards adopted by the State under §271.12.

(d) All permits issued under State law prior to the date of approval of final authorization shall be reviewed by the State Director and modified or revoked and reissued to require compliance with the requirements of this part.

[48 FR 14248, Apr. 1, 1983, as amended at 51 FR 33722, Sept. 22, 1986]

§271.14 Requirements for permitting.

All State programs under this subpart must have legal authority to implement each of the following provisions and must be administered in conformance with each; except that States are not precluded from omitting or modifying any provisions to impose more stringent requirements:

(a) Section 270.1(c)(1)—(Specific inclusions);

(b) Section 270.4—(Effect of permit);

(c) Section 270.5—(Noncompliance reporting);

(d) Section 270.10—(Application for a permit);

(e) Section 270.11—(Signatories);

(f) Section 270.12—(Confidential information);

(g) Section 270.13—(Contents of part A);

(h) Sections 270.14 through 270.29—(Contents of part B);

Note: States need not use a two part permit application process. The State application process must, however, require information in sufficient detail to satisfy the requirements of §§270.13 through 270.29.

(i) Section 270.30—(Applicable permit conditions);

(j) Section 270.31—(Monitoring requirements);

(k) Section 270.32—(Establishing permit conditions);

(l) Section 270.33—(Schedule of compliance);

(m) Section 270.40—(Permit transfer);

(n) Section 270.41—(Permit modification);

(o) Section 270.43—(Permit termination);

(p) Section 270.50—(Duration);

(q) Section 270.60—(Permit by rule);

(r) Section 270.61—(Emergency permits);

(s) Section 270.64—(Interim permits for UIC wells);

(t) Section 124.3(a)—(Application for a permit);

(u) Section 124.5 (a), (c), (d)—(Modification of permits);

(v) Section 124.6 (a), (d), and (e)—(Draft permit);

(w) Section 124.8—(Fact sheets);

(x) Section 124.10 (a)(1)(ii), (a)(1)(iii), (a)(1)(v), (b), (c), (d), and (e)—(Public notice);

(y) Section 124.11—(Public comments and requests for hearings);

(z) Section 124.12(a)—(Public hearings); and

(aa) Section 124.17 (a) and (c)—(Response to comments).

Note: States need not implement provisions identical to the above listed provisions. Implemented provisions must, however, establish requirements at least as stringent as the corresponding listed provisions. While States may impose more stringent requirements, they may not make one requirement more lenient as a tradeoff for making another requirement more stringent; for example, by requiring that public hearings be held prior to issuing any permit while reducing the amount of advance notice of such a hearing.

[48 FR 14248, Apr. 1, 1983; 48 FR 30115, June 30, 1983]

§271.15 Requirements for compliance evaluation programs.

(a) State programs shall have procedures for receipt, evaluation, retention and investigation for possible enforcement of all notices and reports required of permittees and other regulated persons (and for investigation for possible enforcement of failure to submit these notices and reports).

(b) State programs shall have inspection and surveillance procedures to determine, independent of information supplied by regulated persons, compliance or noncompliance with applicable program requirements. The State shall maintain:

(1) A program which is capable of making comprehensive surveys of all facilities and activities subject to the State Director's authority to identify persons subject to regulation who have failed to comply with permit application or other program requirements. Any compilation, index, or inventory of such facilities and activities shall be made available to the Regional Administrator upon request;

(2) A program for periodic inspections of the facilities and activities subject to regulation. These inspections shall be conducted in a manner designed to:

(i) Determine compliance or noncompliance with issued permit conditions and other program requirements;

(ii) Verify the accuracy of information submitted by permittees and other regulated persons in reporting forms and other forms supplying monitoring data; and

(iii) Verify the adequacy of sampling, monitoring, and other methods used by permittees and other regulated persons to develop that information;

(3) A program for investigating information obtained regarding violations of applicable program and permit requirements; and

(4) Procedures for receiving and ensuring proper consideration of information submitted by the public about violations. Public effort in reporting violations shall be encouraged, and the State Director shall make available information on reporting procedures.

(c) The State Director and State officers engaged in compliance evaluation shall have authority to enter any site or premises subject to regulation or in which records relevant to program operation are kept in order to copy any records, inspect, monitor or otherwise investigate compliance with the State program including compliance with permit conditions and other program requirements. States whose law requires a search warrant before entry conform with this requirement.

(d) Investigatory inspections shall be conducted, samples shall be taken and other information shall be gathered in a manner (*e.g.*, using proper "chain of custody" procedures) that will produce evidence admissible in an enforcement proceeding or in court.

§271.16 Requirements for enforcement authority.

(a) Any State agency administering a program shall have available the following remedies for violations of State program requirements:

(1) To restrain immediately and effectively any person by order or by suit in State court from engaging in any unauthorized activity which is endangering or causing damage to public health or the environment.

Note: This paragraph requires that States have a mechanism (*e.g.*, an administrative cease and desist order or the ability to seek a temporary restraining order) to stop any unauthorized activity endangering public health or the environment.

(2) To sue in courts of competent jurisdiction to enjoin any threatened or continuing violation of any program requirement, including permit conditions, without the necessity of a prior revocation of the permit;

(3) To access or sue to recover in court civil penalties and to seek criminal remedies, including fines, as follows:

(i) Civil penalties shall be recoverable for any program violation in at least the amount of $10,000 per day.

(ii) Criminal remedies shall be obtainable against any person who knowingly transports any hazardous waste to an unpermitted facility; who treats, stores, or disposes of hazardous waste without a permit; who knowingly transports, treats, stores, disposes, recycles, causes to be transported, or otherwise handles any used oil regulated by EPA under section 3014 of RCRA that is not listed or identified as a hazardous waste under the state's hazardous waste program in violation of standards or regulations for management of such used oil; or who makes any false statement, or representation in any application, label, manifest, record, report, permit or other document filed, maintained, or used for purposes of program compliance (including compliance with any standards or regulations for used oil regulated by EPA under section 3014 of RCRA that is not listed or identified as hazardous waste). Criminal fines shall be recoverable in at least the amount of $10,000 per day for each violation, and imprisonment for at least six months shall be available.

(b)(1) The maximum civil penalty or criminal fines (as provided in paragraph (a)(3) of this section) shall be assessable for each instance of violation and, if the violation is continuous, shall be assessable up to the maximum amount for each day of violation.

(2) The burden of proof and degree of knowledge or intent required under State law for establishing violations under paragraph (a)(3) of this section, shall be no greater than the burden of proof or degree of knowledge or intent EPA must provide when it brings an action under the Act.

Note: For example, this requirement is not met if State law includes mental state as an element of proof for civil violations.

(c) A civil penalty assessed, sought, or agreed upon by the State Director under paragraph (a)(3) of this section shall be appropriate to the violation.

Note: To the extent the State judgments or settlements provide penalties in amounts which EPA believes to be substantially inadequate in comparison to the amounts which EPA would require under similar facts, EPA, when authorized by the applicable statute, may commence separate actions for penalties.

In addition to the requirements of this paragraph, the State may have other enforcement remedies. The following enforcement options, while not mandatory, are highly recommended:

Procedures for assessment by the State of the costs of investigations, inspections, or monitoring surveys which lead to the establishment of violations;

Procedures which enable the State to assess or to sue any persons responsible for unauthorized activities for any expenses incurred by the State in removing, correcting, or terminating any adverse effects upon human health and the environment resulting from the unauthorized activity, whether or not accidental;

Procedures which enable the State to sue for compensation for any loss or destruction of wildlife, fish or aquatic life, or their habitat, and for any other damages caused by unauthorized activity, either to the State or to any residents of the State who are directly aggrieved by the unauthorized activity, or both; and

Procedures for the administrative assessment of penalties by the Director.

(d) Any State administering a program under this subpart shall provide for public participation in the State enforcement process by providing either:

(1) Authority which allows intervention as of right in any civil action to obtain the remedies specified in paragraph (a) (2) or (3) of this section by any citizen having an interest which is or may be adversely affected; or

(2)(i) Assurance by the appropriate State agency that it will investigate and provide written responses to all citizen complaints submitted pursuant to the procedures specified in §271.15(b)(4);

(ii) Assurance by the appropriate State enforcement authority that it will not oppose intervention by any citizen when permissive intervention is authorized by statute, rule, or regulation; and

(iii) Assurance by the appropriate State enforcement authority that it will publish notice of and provide at least 30 days for public comment on all proposed settlements of civil enforcement actions, except in cases where a settlement requires some immediate action (*e.g.*, cleanup) which if otherwise delayed could result in substantial damage to either public health or the environment.

(e) Any State authority used to issue an enforceable document either in lieu of a post-closure permit as provided in 40 CFR 270.1(c)(7), or as a source of alternative requirements for regulated units, as provided under 40 CFR 264.90(f), 264.110(c), 264.140(d), 265.90(d), 265.110(d), and 265.140(d), shall have available the following remedies:

(1) Authority to sue in courts of competent jurisdiction to enjoin any threatened or continuing violation of the requirements of such documents, as well as authority to compel compliance with requirements for corrective action or other emergency response measures deemed necessary to protect human health and the environment; and

(2) Authority to access or sue to recover in court civil penalties, including fines, for violations of requirements in such documents.

(Clean Water Act (33 U.S.C. 1251 *et seq.*), Safe Drinking Water Act (42 U.S.C. 300f *et seq.*), Clean Air Act (42 U.S.C. 7401 *et seq.*), Resource Conservation and Recovery Act (42 U.S.C. 6901 *et seq.*); §§1006, 2002(a), 3006 and 7004 of the Solid Waste Disposal Act, as amended by the Resource Conservation and Recovery Act of 1976 (RCRA), as amended, (42 U.S.C. 6905, 6912(a), 6926 and 6974))

[48 FR 14248, Apr. 1, 1983, as amended at 48 FR 39622, Sept. 1, 1983; 49 FR 7372, Feb. 29, 1984; 58 FR 26424, May 3, 1993; 59 FR 10559, Mar. 4, 1994; 63 FR 56735, Oct. 22, 1998]

§271.17 Sharing of information.

(a) Any information obtained or used in the administration of a State program shall be available to EPA upon request without restriction. If the information has been submitted to the State under a claim of confidentiality, the State must submit that claim to EPA when providing information under this subpart. Any information obtained from a State and subject to a claim of confidentiality will be treated in accordance with the regulations in 40 CFR part 2. If EPA obtains from a State information that is not claimed to be confidential, EPA may make that information available to the public without further notice.

(b) EPA shall furnish to States with approved programs the information in its files not submitted under a claim of confidentiality which the State needs to implement its approved program. EPA shall furnish to States with approved programs information submitted to EPA under a claim of confidentiality, which the State needs to implement its approved program, subject to the conditions in 40 CFR part 2.

(c)(1) The State program must provide for the public availability of information obtained by the State regarding facilities and sites for the treatment, storage, and disposal of hazardous waste. Such information must be made available to the public in substantially the same manner, and to the same degree, as would be the case if the Administrator was carrying out the provisions of Subtitle C of RCRA in the State.

(2) A State must revise its program to comply with this section in accordance with §271.21(e)(2)(ii). Interim authorization under §271.24 is not available to demonstrate compliance with this section.

[48 FR 14248, Apr. 1, 1983, as amended at 50 FR 28754, July 15, 1985; 51 FR 33722, Sept. 22, 1986]

§271.18 Coordination with other programs.

(a) Issuance of State permits under this subpart may be coordinated, as provided in part 124, with issuance of UIC, NPDES, and 404 permits whether they are controlled by the State, EPA, or the Corps of Engineers. See §124.4.

(b) The State Director of any approved program which may affect the planning for and development of hazardous waste management facilities and practices shall consult and coordinate with agencies designated under section 4006(b) of RCRA (40 CFR part 255) as responsible for the development and implementation of State solid waste management plans under section 4002(b) of RCRA (40 CFR part 256).

§271.19 EPA review of State permits.

(a) The Regional Administrator may comment on permit applications and draft permits as provided in the Memorandum of Agreement under §271.8.

(b) Where EPA indicates, in a comment, that issuance of the permit would be inconsistent with the approved State program, EPA shall include in the comment:

(1) A statement of the reasons for the comment (including the section of RCRA or regulations promulgated thereunder that support the comment); and

(2) The actions that should be taken by the State Director in order to address the comments (including the conditions which the permit would include if it were issued by the Regional Administrator).

(c) A copy of any comment shall be sent to the permit applicant by the Regional Administrator.

(d) The Regional Administrator shall withdraw such a comment when satisfied that the State has met or refuted his or her concerns.

(e) Under section 3008(a)(3) of RCRA, EPA may terminate a State-issued permit or bring an enforcement action in accordance with the procedures of 40 CFR part 22 in the case of a violation of a State program requirement. In exercising these authorities, EPA will observe the following conditions:

(1) The Regional Administrator may take action under section 3008(a)(3) of RCRA against a holder of a State-issued permit at any time on the ground that the permittee is not complying with a condition of that permit.

(2) The Regional Administrator may take action under section 3008(a)(3) of RCRA against a holder of a State-issued permit at any time on the ground that the permittee is not complying with a condition that the Regional Administrator in commenting on the permit application or draft permit stated was necessary to implement approved State program requirements, whether or not that condition was included in the final permit.

(3) The Regional Administrator may not take action under section 3008(a)(3) of RCRA against a holder of a State-issued permit on the ground that the permittee is not complying with a condition necessary to implement approved State program requirements unless the Regional Administrator stated in commenting on the permit application or draft permit that the condition was necessary.

(4) The Regional Administrator may take action under section 7003 of RCRA against a permit holder at any time whether or not the permit holder is complying with permit conditions.

(f) Notwithstanding the above provisions, EPA shall issue permits, or portions of permits, to facilities in authorized

States as necessary to implement the Hazardous and Solid Waste Amendments of 1984.

[48 FR 14248, Apr. 1, 1983, as amended at 50 FR 28754, July 15, 1985; 65 FR 30913, May 15, 2000]

§271.20 Approval process.

(a) Prior to submitting an application to EPA for approval of a State program, the State shall issue public notice of its intent to seek program approval from EPA. This public notice shall:

(1) Be circulated in a manner calculated to attract the attention of interested persons including:

(i) Publication in enough of the largest newspapers in the State to attract statewide attention; and

(ii) Mailing to persons on the State agency mailing list and to any other persons whom the agency has reason to believe are interested;

(2) Indicate when and where the State's proposed submission may be reviewed by the public;

(3) Indicate the cost of obtaining a copy of the submission;

(4) Provide for a comment period of not less than 30 days during which time interested members of the public may express their views on the proposed program;

(5) Provide that a public hearing will be held by the State or EPA if sufficient public interest is shown or, alternatively, schedule such a public hearing. Any public hearing to be held by the State on its application for authorization shall be scheduled no earlier than 30 days after the notice of hearing is published;

(6) Briefly outline the fundamental aspects of the State program; and

(7) Identify a person that an interested member of the public may contact with any questions.

(b) If the proposed State program is substantially modified after the public comment period provided in paragraph (a)(4) of this section, the State shall, prior to submitting its program to the Administrator, provide an opportunity for further public comment in accordance with the procedures of paragraph (a) of this section. Provided, that the opportunity for further public comment may be limited to those portions of the State's application which have been changed since the prior public notice.

(c) After complying with the requirements of paragraphs (a) and (b) of this section, the State may submit, in accordance with §271.5, a proposed program to EPA for approval. Such formal submission may only be made after the date of promulgation of the last component of Phase II. The program submission shall include copies of all written comments received by the State, a transcript, recording, or summary of any public hearing which was held by the State, and a responsiveness summary which identifies the public participation activities conducted, describes the matters presented to the public, summarizes significant comments received and responds to these comments.

(d) Within 90 days from the date of receipt of a complete program submission for final authorization, the Administrator shall make a tentative determination as to whether or not he expects to grant authorization to the State program. If the Administrator indicates that he may not approve the State program he shall include a general statement of his areas of concern. The Administrator shall give notice of this tentative determination in the *Federal Register* and in accordance with paragraph (a)(1) of this section. Notice of the tentative determination of authorization shall also:

(1) Indicate that a public hearing will be held by EPA no earlier than 30 days after notice of the tentative determination of authorization. The notice may require persons wishing to present testimony to file a request with the Regional Administrator, who may cancel the public hearing if sufficient public interest in a hearing is not expressed.

(2) Afford the public 30 days after the notice to comment on the State's submission and the tentative determination; and

(3) Note the availability of the State submission for inspection and copying by the public.

(e) Within 90 days of the notice given pursuant to paragraph (d) of this section, the Administrator shall make a final determination whether or not to approve the State's program, taking into account any comments submitted. The Administrator shall give notice of this final determination in the *Federal Register* and in accordance with paragraph (a)(1) of this section. The notification shall include a concise statement of the reasons for this determination, and a response to significant comments received.

[48 FR 14248, Apr. 1, 1983; 48 FR 30115, June 30, 1983, as amended at 60 FR 33914, June 29, 1994]

§271.21 Procedures for revision of State programs.

(a) Either EPA or the approved State may initiate program revision. Program revision may be necessary when the controlling Federal or State statutory or regulatory authority is modified or supplemented. The State shall keep EPA fully informed of any proposed modifications to its basic statutory or regulatory authority, its forms, procedures, or priorities.

(b) Revision of a State program shall be accomplished as follows:

(1) The State shall submit a modified program description, Attorney General's statement, Memorandum of Agreement, or such other documents as EPA determines to be necessary under the circumstances.

(2) The Administrator shall approve or disapprove program revisions based on the requirements of this part and of the Act. In approving or disapproving program revisions, the Administrator shall follow the procedures of paragraph (b)(3) or (4) of this section.

(3) The procedures for an immediate final publication of the Administrator's decision are as follows:

(i) The Administrator shall issue public notice of his approval or disapproval of a State program revision:

(A) In the *Federal Register*;

(B) In enough of the largest newspapers in the State to attract Statewide attention; and

(C) By mailing to persons on the State agency mailing list and to any other persons whom the agency has reason to believe are interested.

(ii) The public notice shall summarize the State program revision, indicate whether EPA intends to approve or disapprove the revision and provide for an opportunity to comment for a period of 30 days.

(iii) Approval or disapproval of a State program revision shall become effective 60 days after the date of publication in the *Federal Register* in accordance with paragraph (b)(3)(i) of this section, unless an adverse comment pertaining to the State revision discussed in the notice is received by the end of the comment period. If an adverse comment is received the Administrator shall so notify the State and shall, within 60 days after the date of publication, publish in the *Federal Register* either:

(A) A withdrawal of the immediate final decision; or

(B) A notice containing a response to comments and which either affirms that the immediate final decision takes effect or reverses the decision.

(4) The procedures for proposed and final publication of the Administrator's decision are as follows:

(i) The Administrator shall issue public notice of his proposed approval or disapproval of a State program revision:

(A) In the *Federal Register*;

(B) In enough of the largest newspapers in the State to attract Statewide attention; and

(C) By mailing to persons on the State agency mailing list and to any other persons whom the agency has reason to believe are interested.

(ii) The public notice shall summarize the State program revision, indicate whether EPA intends to approve or disapprove the revision and provide for an opportunity to comment for a period of at least 30 days.

(iii) A State program revision shall become effective when the Administrator's final approval is published in the *Federal Register*.

(c) States with approved programs shall notify EPA whenever they propose to transfer all or part of any program from the approved State agency to any other State agency, and shall identify any new division of responsibilities among the agencies involved. The new agency is not authorized to administer the program until approved by the Administrator under paragraph (b) of this section. Organizational charts required under §271.6(b) shall be revised and resubmitted.

(d) Whenever the Administrator has reason to believe that circumstances have changed with respect to a State program, he may request, and the State shall provide, a supplemental Attorney General's statement, program description, or such other documents or information as are necessary.

(e)(1) As the Federal program changes, authorized State programs must be revised to remain in compliance with this subpart.

(2) Federal program changes are defined for purposes of this section as promulgated amendments to 40 CFR parts 124, 270, 260-266, or 268 and any self-implementing statutory provisions (*i.e.*, those taking effect without prior implementing regulations) which are listed as State program requirements in this subpart. States must modify their programs to reflect Federal program changes and must subsequently submit the modifications to EPA for approval.

(i) For Federal program changes occurring before July 1, 1984, the State program must be modified within one year of the date of the Federal program change.

(ii) Except as provided in paragraphs (e) (iii) and (iv) of this section, for Federal program changes occurring on or after July 1, 1984, the State program must be modified by July 1 of each year to reflect all changes to the Federal program occurring during the 12 months preceding the previous July 1. (For example, States must modify their programs by July 1, 1986 to reflect all changes from July 1, 1984 to June 30, 1985.)

(iii) For Federal program changes identified in §271.1(j) that occur between November 8, 1984 and June 30, 1987 (inclusive), the State program must be modified by July 1, 1989.

(iv) For Federal program changes identified in §271.1(j) that occur between July 1, 1987 and June 30, 1990 (inclusive), the State program must be modified by July 1, 1991.

(v) States may have an additional year to modify their programs for those changes to the Federal program identified in paragraphs (e) (i), (ii), (iii), and (iv) of this section which necessitate a State statutory amendment.

(3) The deadlines in paragraphs (e)(2)(i) through (v) may be extended by the Regional Administrator upon an adequate demonstration by a State that it has made a good faith effort to meet these deadlines and that its legislative or rulemaking procedures render the State unable to do so. No such extension shall exceed six months.

(4)(i) Within 30 days of the completion of the State program modification the State must submit to EPA a copy of the program change and a schedule indicating when the State intends to seek approval of the change. Such schedule shall not exceed the dates provided for in paragraph (e)(4)(ii).

(ii) Within 60 days of the appropriate deadline in paragraphs (e), (f), and (g) of this section, the State must submit to EPA the documentation described in paragraph (b) of this section to revise its program.

(f) A State must modify its program to comply with any Federal program changes which occur prior to the day that final authorization is received, except for those changes that the State has already received authorization for pursuant to §271.3(f). Such State program modifications must be completed and submitted by the deadlines specified in paragraph (e) of this section or by the date of final authorization, whichever is later.

Publisher's Note: The section referenced above, §271.3(f), is not in the RCRA regulations.

(g)(1) States that are unable to modify their programs by the deadlines in paragraph (e) may be placed on a schedule of compliance to adopt the program revision(s) provided that:

(i) The State has received an extension of the program modification deadline under paragraph (e)(3) and has made diligent efforts to revise its program during that period of time,

(ii) The State has made progress in adopting the program modifications,

(iii) The State submits a proposed timetable for the requisite regulatory and/or statutory revisions by the deadline granted under paragraph (e)(3),

(iv) The schedule of compliance for program revisions does not exceed one year from the extended program modification deadline under paragraph (e)(3), and

(v) The schedule of compliance is published in the *Federal Register.*

(2) If a State fails to comply with the schedule of compliance, the Administrator may initiate program withdrawal procedures pursuant to §§271.22 and 271.23.

(h) *Abbreviated authorization revisions.* This abbreviated procedure applies to State Program revisions for the Federal rulemakings listed in Table 1 of this section. The abbreviated procedures are as follows:

(1) An application for a revision of a State's program for the rulemakings listed in Table 1 of this section shall consist of:

(i) A statement from the State that its laws and regulations provide authority that is equivalent to, and no less stringent than, the designated minor rules or parts of rules specified in Table 1 of this section, and which includes references to the specific statutes, administrative regulations and where appropriate, judicial decisions. State statutes and regulations cited in the statement shall be lawfully adopted at the time the statement is signed and fully effective by the time the program revisions are approved; and

(ii) Copies of all applicable State statutes and regulations.

(2) Within 30 days of receipt by EPA of a State's application for final authorization to implement a rule specified in Table 1 of this section, if the Administrator determines that the application is not complete or contains errors, the Administrator shall notify the State. This notice will include a concise statement of the deficiencies which form the basis for this determination. The State will address all deficiencies and resubmit the application to EPA for review.

(3) For purposes of this section an application is considered incomplete when:

(i) Copies of applicable statutes or regulations were not included;

(ii) The statutes or regulations relied on by the State to implement the program revisions are not lawfully adopted at the time the statement is signed or fully effective by the time the program revisions are approved;

(iii) In the statement, the citations to the specific statutes, administrative regulations and where appropriate, judicial decisions are not included or incomplete; or

(iv) The State is not authorized to implement the prerequisite RCRA rules as specified in paragraph (h)(5) of this section.

(4) Within 60 days after receipt of a complete final application from a State for final authorization to implement a rule or rules specified in Table 1 of this section, the Administrator shall publish a notice of the decision to grant final authorization in accordance with the procedures for immediate final publication in paragraph (b)(3) of this section.

(5) To be eligible to use the procedure in this paragraph (h), a State must be authorized for the provisions which the rule listed in Table 1 to this section amends.

Table 1 to §271.21

Title of regulation	Promulgation date	Federal Register reference
Land Disposal Restrictions Phase II—the Universal Treatment Standards in §§268.40 and 268.48 of this chapter only.	Sept. 19, 1994	59 FR 47982
Office of Resource Conservation and Recovery Testing and Monitoring Activities, Methods Innovation Rule.	July 14, 2005	70 FR 34538, June 14, 2005
Process Vent and Equipment Leak Organic Air Emission Standards for Owners and Operators of Hazardous Waste Treatment, Storage, and Disposal Facilities.	July 14, 2005	70 FR 34538, June 14, 2005
Burning of hazardous waste in boilers and industrial furnaces.	July 14, 2005	70 FR 34538, June 14, 2005
Air Emissions Standards for Tanks, Surface Impoundments, and Containers.	July 14, 2005	70 FR 34538, June 14, 2005

[48 FR 14248, Apr. 1, 1983, as amended at 51 FR 7542, Mar. 4, 1986; 51 FR 33722, Sept. 22, 1986; 63 FR 65947, Nov. 30, 1998; 70 FR 34591, June 14, 2005; 71 FR 40280, July 14, 2006; 74 FR 30231, June 25, 2009]

§271.22 Criteria for withdrawing approval of State programs.

(a) The Administrator may withdraw program approval when a State program no longer complies with the requirements of this subpart, and the State fails to take corrective action. Such circumstances include the following:

(1) When the State's legal authority no longer meets the requirements of this part, including:

(i) Failure of the State to promulgate or enact new authorities when necessary; or

(ii) Action by a State legislature or court striking down or limiting State authorities.

(2) When the operation of the State program fails to comply with the requirements of this part, including:

(i) Failure to exercise control over activities required to be regulated under this part, including failure to issue permits;

(ii) Repeated issuance of permits which do not conform to the requirements of this part; or

(iii) Failure to comply with the public participation requirements of this part.

(3) When the State's enforcement program fails to comply with the requirements of this part, including:

(i) Failure to act on violations of permits or other program requirements;

(ii) Failure to seek adequate enforcement penalties or to collect administrative fines when imposed; or

(iii) Failure to inspect and monitor activities subject to regulation.

(4) When the State program fails to comply with the terms of the Memorandum of Agreement required under §271.8.

§271.23 Procedures for withdrawing approval of State programs.

(a) A State with a program approved under this part may voluntarily transfer program responsibilities required by Federal law to EPA by taking the following actions, or in such other manner as may be agreed upon with the Administrator.

(1) The State shall give the Administrator 180 days notice of the proposed transfer and shall submit a plan for the orderly transfer of all relevant program information not in the possession of EPA (such as permits, permit files, compliance files, reports, permit applications) which are necessary for EPA to administer the program.

(2) Within 60 days of receiving the notice and transfer plan, the Administrator shall evaluate the State's transfer plan and shall identify any additional information

needed by the Federal government for program administration and/or identify any other deficiencies in the plan.

(3) At least 30 days before the transfer is to occur the Administrator shall publish notice of the transfer in the *Federal Register* and in enough of the largest newspapers in the State to provide Statewide coverage, and shall mail notice to all permit holders, permit applicants, other regulated persons and other interested persons on appropriate EPA and State mailing lists.

(b) The following procedures apply when the Administrator orders the commencement of proceedings to determine whether to withdraw approval of a State program.

(1) *Order.* The Administrator may order the commencement of withdrawal proceedings on his or her own initiative or in response to a petition from an interested person alleging failure of the State to comply with the requirements of this part as set forth in §271.22. The Administrator shall respond in writing to any petition to commence withdrawal proceedings. He may conduct an informal investigation of the allegations in the petition to determine whether cause exists to commence proceedings under this paragraph. The Administrator's order commencing proceedings under this paragraph shall fix a time and place for the commencement of the hearing and shall specify the allegations against the State which are to be considered at the hearing. Within 30 days the State shall admit or deny these allegations in a written answer. The party seeking withdrawal of the State's program shall have the burden of coming forward with the evidence in a hearing under this paragraph.

(2) *Definitions.* For purposes of this paragraph the definitions of *Act, Administrative Law Judge, Hearing, Hearing Clerk,* and *Presiding Officer* in 40 CFR 22.03 apply in addition to the following:

(i) *Party* means the petitioner, the State, the Agency and any other person whose request to participate as a party is granted.

(ii) *Person* means the Agency, the State and any individual or organization having an interest in the subject matter of the proceeding.

(iii) *Petitioner* means any person whose petition for commencement of withdrawal proceedings has been granted by the Administrator.

(3) *Procedures.* The following provisions of 40 CFR part 22 (Consolidated Rules of Practice) are applicable to proceedings under this paragraph:

(i) Section 22.02—(use of number/gender);

(ii) Section 22.04(c)—(authorities of Presiding Officer);

(iii) Section 22.06—(filing/service of rulings and orders);

(iv) Section 22.07 (a) and (b)—except that, the time for commencement of the hearing shall not be extended beyond the date set in the Administrator's order without approval of the Administrator (computation/extension of time);

(v) Section 22.08—however, substitute "order commencing proceedings" for "complaint"—(*Ex Parte* contacts);

(vi) Section 22.09—(examination of filed documents);

(vii) Section 22.11 (a), (c) and (d), however, motions to intervene must be filed 15 days from the date the notice of the Administrator's order is first published—(intervention);

(viii) Section 22.16 except that, service shall be in accordance with paragraph (b)(4) of this section, the first sentence in §22.16(c) shall be deleted, and, the word "recommended" shall be substituted for the word "initial" in §22.16(c)—(motions);

(ix) Section 22.19 (a), (b) and (c)—(prehearing conference);

(x) Section 22.22—(evidence);

(xi) Section 22.23—(objections/offers of proof);

(xii) Section 22.25—(filing the transcript); and

(xiii) Section 22.26—(findings/conclusions).

(4) *Record of proceedings.* (i) The hearing shall be either stenographically reported verbatim or tape recorded, and thereupon transcribed by an official reporter designated by the Presiding Officer;

(ii) All orders issued by the Presiding Officer, transcripts of testimony, written statements of position, stipulations, exhibits, motions, briefs, and other written material of any kind submitted in the hearing shall be a part of the record and shall be available for inspection or copying in the Office of the Hearing Clerk, 1200 Pennsylvania Ave., NW., Washington, DC 20460;

(iii) Upon notice to all parties the Presiding Officer may authorize corrections to the transcript which involve matters of substance;

(iv) An original and two (2) copies of all written submissions to the hearing shall be filed with the Hearing Clerk;

(v) A copy of each such submission shall be served by the person making the submission upon the Presiding

Officer and each party of record. Service under this paragraph shall take place by mail or personal delivery;

(vi) Every submission shall be accompanied by an acknowledgement of service by the person served or proof of service in the form of a statement of the date, time, and manner of service and the names of the persons served, certified by the person who made service; and

(vii) The Hearing Clerk shall maintain and furnish to any person upon request, a list containing the name, service address, and telephone number of all parties and their attorneys or duly authorized representatives.

(5) *Participation by a person not a party.* A person who is not a party may, at the discretion of the Presiding Officer, be permitted to make a limited appearance by making an oral or written statement of his/her position on the issues within such limits and on such conditions as may be fixed by the Presiding Officer, but he/she may not otherwise participate in the proceeding.

(6) *Rights of parties.* All parties to the proceeding may;

(i) Appear by counsel or other representative in all hearing and pre-hearing proceedings;

(ii) Agree to stipulations of facts which shall be made a part of the record.

(7) *Recommended decision.* (i) Within 30 days after the filing of proposed findings and conclusions, and reply briefs, the Presiding Officer shall evaluate the record before him/her, the proposed findings and conclusions and any briefs filed by the parties and shall prepare a recommended decision, and shall certify the entire record, including the recommended decision, to the Administrator.

(ii) Copies of the recommended decision shall be served upon all parties.

(iii) Within 20 days after the certification and filing of the record and recommended decision, all parties may file with the Administrator exceptions to the recommended decision and a supporting brief.

(8) *Decision by Administrator.* (i) Within 60 days after the certification of the record and filing of the Presiding Officer's recommended decision, the Administrator shall review the record before him and issue his own decision.

(ii) If the Administrator concludes that the State has administered the program in conformity with the Act and regulations his decision shall constitute "final agency action" within the meaning of 5 U.S.C. 704.

(iii) If the Administrator concludes that the State has not administered the program in conformity with the Act and regulations he shall list the deficiencies in the program and provide the State a reasonable time, not to exceed 90 days, to take such appropriate corrective action as the Administrator determines necessary.

(iv) Within the time prescribed by the Administrator the State shall take such appropriate corrective action as required by the Administrator and shall file with the Administrator and all parties a statement certified by the State Director that appropriate corrective action has been taken.

(v) The Administrator may require a further showing in addition to the certified statement that corrective action has been taken.

(vi) If the State fails to take appropriate corrective action and file a certified statement thereof within the time prescribed by the Administrator, the Administrator shall issue a supplementary order withdrawing approval of the State program. If the State takes appropriate corrective action, the Administrator shall issue a supplementary order stating that approval of authority is not withdrawn.

(vii) The Administrator's supplementary order shall constitute final Agency action within the meaning of 5 U.S.C. 704.

(c) Withdrawal of authorization under this section and the Act does not relieve any person from complying with the requirements of State law, nor does it affect the validity of actions by the State prior to withdrawal.

[48 FR 14248, Apr. 1, 1983, as amended at 71 FR 40280, July 14, 2006]

§271.24 Interim authorization under section 3006(g) of RCRA.

(a) Any State which is applying for or has been granted final authorization pursuant to section 3006(b) of RCRA may submit to the Administrator evidence that its program contains (or has been amended to include) any requirement which is substantially equivalent to a requirement identified in §271.1(j) of this part. Such a State may request interim authorization under section 3006(g) of RCRA to carry out the State requirement in lieu of the Administrator carrying out the Federal requirement.

(b) The applications shall be governed by the procedures for program revisions in §271.21(b) of this part.

(c) Interim authorization pursuant to this section expires on January 1, 2003, except that interim authorization for the revised Corrective Action Management Unit rule (except 40 CFR 264.555) promulgated on January 22, 2002 and cited in Table 1 in §271.1 expires on August 30, 2004 if the State has not submitted an application for final authorization.

[57 FR 60132, Dec. 18, 1992; 67 FR 3029, Jan. 22, 2002]

§271.25 HSWA requirements.

Unless otherwise provided in part 271, the State program shall have standards at least as stringent as the requirements and prohibitions that have taken effect under the Hazardous and Solid Waste Amendments of 1984 (HSWA).

[51 FR 33723, Sept. 22, 1986]

§271.26 Requirements for used oil management.

The State shall have standards for used oil management which are equivalent to 40 CFR part 279. These standards shall include:

(a) Standards for used oil generators which are equivalent to those under subpart C of part 279 of this chapter;

(b) Standards for used oil collection centers and aggregation points which are equivalent to those under subpart D of part 279 of this chapter;

(c) Standards for used oil transporters and transfer facilities which are equivalent to those under subpart E of part 279 of this chapter;

(d) Standards for used oil processors and re-refiners which are equivalent to those under subpart F of part 279 of this chapter;

(e) Standards for used oil burners who burn off-specification used oil for energy recovery which are equivalent to those under subpart G of part 279 of this chapter;

(f) Standards for used oil fuel marketers which are equivalent to those under subpart H of part 279 of this chapter; and

(g) Standards for use as a dust suppressant and disposal of used oil which are equivalent to those under subpart I of part 279 of this chapter. A State may petition (*e.g.*, as part of its authorization petition submitted to EPA under §271.5) EPA to allow the use of used oil (that is not mixed with hazardous waste and does not exhibit a characteristic other than ignitability) as a dust suppressant. The State must show that it has a program in place to prevent the use of used oil/hazardous waste mixtures or used oil exhibiting a characteristic other than ignitability as a dust suppressant. In addition, such programs must minimize the impacts of use as a dust suppressant on the environment.

(h)(1) Unless otherwise provided in part 271, state programs shall have standards for the marketing and burning of used oil for energy recovery that are at least as stringent as the requirements and prohibitions that EPA adopted on November 29, in 40 CFR part 266, subpart E of this chapter. The part 279 of this chapter requirements specified in Table 1 (except those provisions identified in footnotes 1 and 2 of Table 1) are Federally enforceable in those states that have not adopted state requirements equivalent to 40 CFR part 279, subparts G and H of this chapter requirements and have not been authorized to enforce the state requirements.

Table 1—Regulations Adopted November 29, 1985 Regarding the Burning of Used Oil for Energy Recovery

[These part 279 provisions will continue to be enforced by EPA]

Former provisions of 40 CFR part 266, subpart E (1992)	Recodified provisions within 40 CFR part 279
§266.40(a)	§279.60(a)
§266.40(b)	§279.1[1]
§266.40(c) [rebuttable presumption]	§279.63(a), (b) and (c)[2]
§266.40(d)(1) and (2)	§279.10(b)(2) and (3)
§266.40(e)	§279.11, §279.60(c)
§266.41(a)(1) and (2)	§279.71
266.41(b)(1) and (2)	§279.61(a), 279.23(a)
§266.42(a)	§279.60(a)
§266.42(b)	§279.70(a)
§266.42(c)	§279.60(a)
§266.43(a)(1)	§279.70(a) and (b)(1)
§266.43(a)(2)	§279.70(b)(2)
§266.43(b)(1)	§279.72(a)
§266.43(b)(2)	§279.71
§266.43(b)(3)	§279.73(a)
§266.43(b)(4)(i-v)	§279.74(a)
§266.43(b)(4)(vi)	not included
§266.43(b)(5)(i) and (ii)	§279.75(a)
§266.43(b)(6)(i)	§279.74(b) and (c), 279.72(b)
§266.43(b)(6)(ii)	§279.74(a), §279.75(b)
§266.44(a)	§279.61(a), §279.23(a)
§266.44(b)	§279.62(a)
§266.44(c)	§279.66(a)
§266.44(d)	§279.72(a)
§266.44(e)	§279.65(a) and (b), §279.66(b), §279.72(b)

[1] Contains additional new definitions that were not included in the 1985 rule.

[2] Paragraphs (c)(1) and (2) of § 279.63 contain new exemptions from the rebuttable presumption that were not part of the 1985 rule.

(2) In states that have not been authorized for the RCRA base program, all requirements of Part 279 will be Federally enforceable effective March 8, 1993.

[57 FR 41612, Sept. 10, 1992, as amended at 58 FR 26424, May 3, 1993]

§271.27 Interim authorization-by-rule for the revised Corrective Action Management Unit rule.

(a) States shall be deemed to have interim authorization pursuant to section 3006(g) of RCRA for the revised Corrective Action Management Unit rule if:

(1) The State has been granted final authorization pursuant to section 3006(b) of RCRA for the regulation entitled "Corrective Action Management Units and Temporary Units," February 16, 1993 and cited in Table 1 in §271.1; and

(2) The State notifies the Regional Administrator by March 25, 2002 that the State intends to and is able to use the revised Corrective Action Management Unit Standards rule as guidance.

(b) Interim authorization pursuant to this section expires on August 30, 2004 if the State has not submitted an application for final authorization.

[67 FR 3029, Jan. 22, 2002]

Subpart B [Reserved]

PART 272—APPROVED STATE HAZARDOUS WASTE MANAGEMENT PROGRAMS

Authority: Sections 2002(a), 3006, and 7004(b) of the Solid Waste Disposal Act, as amended by the Resource Conservation and Recovery Act, as amended, 42 U.S.C. 6912(a), 6926, and 6974(b).

Source: 51 FR 3955, Jan. 31, 1986, unless otherwise noted.

Subpart A—General Provisions

§272.1 Purpose and scope.

This part sets forth the applicable State hazardous waste management programs under section 3006(b) of the Resource Conservation and Recovery Act (RCRA), 42 U.S.C. 6926, and 40 CFR 260.10. "State" is defined in 42 U.S.C. 1004(31) as "any of the several States, the District of Columbia, the Commonwealth of Puerto Rico, the Virgin Islands, Guam, American Samoa, and the Commonwealth of the Northern Mariana Islands."

[58 FR 3500, Jan. 11, 1993]

§272.2 Incorporation by reference.

Material listed as incorporated by reference in part 272 was approved for incorporation by reference by the Director of the *Federal Register* in accordance with 5 U.S.C.

552(a) and 1 CFR part 51. Material is incorporated as it exists on the date of the approval, and notice of any change in the material will be published in the *Federal Register.* Copies may be obtained or inspected at EPA Resource and Conservation Recovery Act (RCRA) Docket Information Center (5305G), 1200 Pennsylvania Ave., NW., Washington, DC 20460 and at the appropriate EPA Regional Office. Copies may be inspected at the Office of the *Federal Register,* 800 North Capitol Street, NW., suite 700, Washington, DC. For an informational listing of the State and local requirements incorporated in part 272, see appendix A to this part.

[58 FR 3500, Jan. 11, 1993]

§§272.3–272.49 [Reserved]

Subpart B—Alabama

§§272.50–272.99 [Reserved]

Subpart C—Alaska

§§272.100–272.149 [Reserved]

Subpart D—Arizona

§272.150 [Reserved]

§272.151 Arizona State-administered program: Final authorization.

(a) Pursuant to section 3006(b) of RCRA, 42 U.S.C. 6926(b), Arizona has final authorization for the following elements as submitted to EPA in Arizona's base program application for final authorization which was approved by EPA effective on December 4, 1985. Subsequent program revision applications were approved effective on October 7, 1991, September 11, 1992, January 22, 1993, December 27, 1993, and June 12, 1995.

(b) *State Statutes and Regulations.*

(1) The Arizona statutes and regulations cited in this paragraph are incorporated by reference as part of the hazardous waste management program under Subtitle C of RCRA, 42 U.S.C. 6921 *et seq.*

(i) EPA Approved Arizona Statutory Requirements Applicable to the Hazardous Waste Management Program, June 1995.

(ii) EPA Approved Arizona Regulatory Requirements Applicable to the Hazardous Waste Management Program, June 1995.

(2) The following statutes and regulations concerning State enforcement, although not incorporated by reference, are part of the authorized State program:

(i) *Arizona Laws Relating to Environmental Quality,* 1993 edition, reprinted from *Arizona Revised Statutes,* Title 49, Sections 49-141 through 49-144; 49-261 through 49-265; 49-287; 49-923 through 49-926; 49-928; and 49-943.

(ii) *Arizona Administrative Code,* Title 18, Chapter 8, December 31, 1994, Sections R18-8-260.D; R18-8-271.F through R18-8-271.Q; and R-18-8-280.

(3) The following statutory and regulatory provisions are broader in scope than the Federal program, are not part of the authorized program, and are not incorporated by reference:

(i) *Arizona Laws Relating to Environmental Quality,* 1993 edition, reprinted from *Arizona Revised Statutes,* Title 49, Sections 49-901 through 49-905; 49-922.01; 49-927; 49-929 through 49-942; and 49-944.

(ii) *Arizona Administrative Code,* Title 18, Chapter 8, December 31, 1994, Sections R18-8-261.J; R18-8-261.L; R18-8-269; and R18-8-270.G.

(4) *Memorandum of Agreement.* The Memorandum of Agreement between EPA Region IX and the Arizona Department of Environmental Quality, signed by the EPA Regional Administrator on June 20, 1991, is referenced as part of the authorized hazardous waste management program under Subtitle C of RCRA, 42 U.S.C. 6921 *et seq.*

(5) *Statement of Legal Authority.* "Attorney General's Statement for Final Authorization", signed by the Attorney General of Arizona on September 13, 1984, and revisions, supplements and addenda to that Statement dated November 22, 1989, October 31, 1990, August 23, 1993 (two documents), and February 3, 1995, are referenced as part of the authorized hazardous waste management program under Subtitle C of RCRA, 42 U.S.C. 6921 *et seq.*

(6) *Program Description.* The Program Description and any other materials submitted as part of the original application or as supplements thereto are referenced as part of the authorized hazardous waste management program under Subtitle C of RCRA, 42 U.S.C. 6921 *et seq.*

[60 FR 44279, Aug. 25, 1995]

§§272.152–272.199 [Reserved]

Subpart E—Arkansas

§272.200 [Reserved]

§272.201 Arkansas State-administered program: Final authorization.

(a) Pursuant to Section 3006(b) of RCRA, 42 U.S.C. 6926(b), Arkansas has final authorization for the following elements as submitted to EPA in Arkansas' base program application for final authorization which was approved by EPA effective on January 25, 1985. Subsequent program revision applications were approved effective on August 23, 1985, May 29, 1990, November 18, 1991, December 4, 1992 and December 21, 1994.

(b) *State Statutes and Regulations.* (1) The Arkansas statutes and regulations cited in this paragraph are incorporated by reference as part of the hazardous waste management program under Subtitle C of RCRA, 42 U.S.C. 6921 *et. seq.*

(i) EPA Approved Arkansas Statutory Requirements Applicable to the Hazardous Waste Management Program, dated March, 1995.

(ii) EPA Approved Arkansas Regulatory Requirements Applicable to the Hazardous Waste Management Program, dated March, 1995.

(2) The following statutes and regulations concerning State enforcement, although not incorporated by reference, are part of the authorized State program:

(i) Arkansas Hazardous Waste Management Act of 1979, as amended, Arkansas Code of 1987 Annotated (A.C.A.), 1993 Replacement, Sections 8-7-204 (except 8-7-204(e)(3)(B)), 8-7-205 through 8-7-214, 8-7-217, 8-7-218, 8-7-220, 8-7-222, 8-7-224 and 8-7-225(b) through 8-7-225(d).

(ii) Arkansas Resource Reclamation Act of 1979, as amended, Arkansas Code of 1987 Annotated (A.C.A.), 1993 Replacement, Sections 8-7-302(3), 8-7-303, 8-7-308(1), and 8-7-308(4).

(iii) Arkansas Department of Pollution Control and Ecology (ADPC&E) Regulation No. 23, Hazardous Waste Management, as amended August 27, 1993, effective September 21, 1993, chapter two, sections 3a(11), 3b, 3c, 4, 6a, 6d through 6m, 7, 8, 12b(7), 12c (except 12(c)(10) and 12(c)(11)), 12d, 12e, 14a, 17; chapter three, sections 19 and 20; chapter five, section 26.

(iv) Arkansas Department of Pollution Control and Ecology, Regulation No. 7, Civil Penalties, May 25, 1984.

(v) Arkansas Department of Pollution Control and Ecology, Regulation No. 8, Administrative Procedures, July 6, 1984.

(3) The following statutory and regulatory provisions are broader in scope than the Federal program, are not part of the authorized program, and are not incorporated by reference:

(i) Arkansas Hazardous Waste Management Act, as amended, Arkansas Code of 1987 Annotated (A.C.A.), 1993 Replacement, Section 8-7-226.

(ii) Arkansas Department of Pollution Control and Ecology Regulation No. 23, Hazardous Waste Management, as amended as amended August 27, 1993, effective September 21, 1993, chapter two, sections 2a(5) (only the second sentence), 2b(11), 3a(10), 11, 16a, and portions of sections 16c and 16d that refer to PCBs; and chapter four, section 23.

(4) *Unauthorized State Provisions:* Arkansas has adopted but is not authorized for the September 1, 1988 (53 FR 33938) and the July 1, 1991 (56 FR 30200) amendments to Parts 264 and 265 addressing liability requirements. Thus, the portions of the Arkansas Hazardous Waste Management code, chapter 2, sections 3a(5) and 3a(6) adopting the September 1, 1988 and the July 1, 1991 amendments are not part of the State's authorized program and are not Federally enforceable.

(5) *Memorandum of Agreement.* The Memorandum of Agreement between EPA Region 6 and the State of Arkansas signed by the EPA Regional Administrator on November 3, 1994 is referenced as part of the authorized hazardous waste management program under Subtitle C of RCRA, 42 U.S.C. 6921 *et seq.*

(6) *Statement of Legal Authority.* "Attorney General's Statement for Final Authorization", signed by the Attorney General of Arkansas on July 9, 1984 and revisions, supplements and addenda to that Statement dated September 24, 1987, February 24, 1989, December 11, 1990, May 7, 1992, and by the Independent Legal Counsel on May 10, 1994 are referenced as part of the authorized hazardous waste management program under Subtitle C of RCRA, 42 U.S.C. 6921 *et seq.*

(7) *Program Description.* The Program Description and any other materials submitted as part of the original application or as supplements thereto are referenced as part of the authorized hazardous waste management program under Subtitle C of RCRA, 42 U.S.C. 6921 *et seq.*

[60 FR 32112, June 20, 1995]

§§272.202–272.249 [Reserved]

Subpart F—California

§§272.250–272.299 [Reserved]

Subpart G—Colorado

§§272.300–272.349 [Reserved]

Subpart H—Connecticut

§§272.350–272.399 [Reserved]

Subpart I—Delaware

§272.400 State authorization.

(a) The State of Delaware is authorized to administer and enforce a hazardous waste management program in lieu of the Federal program under Subtitle C of the Resource Conservation and Recovery Act (RCRA), 42 U.S.C. 6921 *et seq.*, subject to the Hazardous and Solid Waste Act Amendments of 1984 (HSWA) (Pub. L. 98-616, November 8, 1984), 42 U.S.C. 6926 (c) and (g). The Federal program for which a State may receive authorization is defined in 40 CFR 271.9 through 271.17 and 271.21. The State's program, as administered by the Delaware Department of Natural Resources and Environmental Control, was approved by EPA pursuant to 42 U.S.C. 6926(b) and part 271 of this chapter. EPA's approval was effective on June 22, 1984, 48 FR 23837.

(b) Delaware is not authorized to implement any HSWA requirement in lieu of EPA unless EPA has explicitly indicated its intent to do so in a *Federal Register* notice granting Delaware authorization.

(c) Delaware has primary responsibility for enforcing its hazardous waste program. However, EPA retains the authority to exercise its enforcement authorities, including conducting inspections under section 3007, 42 U.S.C. 6927, and taking enforcement actions under sections 3008, 3013, and 7003, 42 U.S.C. 6928, 6934 and 6973, as well as under other Federal laws and regulations.

(d) Delaware must revise its approved program to adopt new changes to the Federal Subtitle C program in accordance with section 3006(b) of RCRA and 40 CFR part 271, subpart A. Delaware must seek final authorization for all program revisions pursuant to section 3006(b) of RCRA, but, on a temporary basis, may seek interim authorization for revisions required by HSWA pursuant to section 3006(g) of RCRA, 42 U.S.C. 6926(g). If Delaware obtains final authorization for the revised requirements pursuant to section 3006(b) of RCRA, the newly authorized provisions will be listed in §272.401. If Delaware obtains interim authorization for the revised requirements pursuant to section 3006(g), the newly authorized provisions will be listed in §272.402.

§272.401 State-administered program: Final authorization.

Pursuant to section 3006(b) of RCRA, 42 U.S.C. 6926(b), Delaware has final authorization for the following elements as submitted to EPA in Delaware's program application and approved by EPA.

(a) *State Statutes and Regulations.* (1) The requirements in the Delaware statutes and regulations cited in this paragraph are incorporated by reference and made a part of the hazardous waste management program under Subtitle C of RCRA, 42 U.S.C. 6921 *et seq.* This incorporation by reference was approved by the Director of the *Federal Register* January 31, 1986.

(i) 7 Delaware Code Annotated sections 6301 through 6307 and 6310 through 6317 (1983 Replacement Volume).

(ii) Delaware Department of Natural Resources and Environmental Control Regulations Governing Hazardous Waste, Parts 260 through 265, 122 and 124, Order Number 83-SW-1, July 28, 1983. (Copies are available from the Delaware Department of Natural Resources and Environmental Control, PO Box 1401, Dover, Delaware 19901.)

(2) The following statutes and regulations, although not incorporated by reference, are part of the authorized State program.

(i) 7 Delaware Code Annotated sections 6308 and 6309 (1974 and Supp. 1983).

(ii) Delaware Administrative Procedures Act, 7 Delaware Code Annotated sections 10101 through 10161 (1974 and Supp. 1983).

(b) *Memorandum of Agreement.* The Memorandum of Agreement between EPA Region III and the Delaware Department of Natural Resources and Environmental Control, signed by the EPA Regional Administrator on December 14, 1983.

(c) *Statement of Legal Authority.* (1) "Attorney General's Statement for Final Authorization", signed by the Attorney General of Delaware of July 26, 1983.

(2) Letter from the Attorney General of Delaware to EPA, April 2, 1984.

(d) *Program Description.* The Program Description and any other materials submitted as part of the original application or as supplements thereto.

§§272.402–272.449 [Reserved]

Subpart J—District of Columbia

§§272.450–272.499 [Reserved]

Subpart K—Florida

§272.500 [Reserved]

§272.501 Florida State-administered program: Final authorization.

(a) Pursuant to section 3006(b) of RCRA, 42 U.S.C. 6926(b), Florida has final authorization for the following elements as submitted to EPA in Florida's base program application for final authorizations which was approved by EPA effective on February 12, 1985. Subsequent program revision applications were approved and effective January 30, 1988; October 30, 1988; January 3, 1989; February 12, 1991; April 6, 1992; April 7, 1992; July 20, 1992; January 10, 1994; September 9, 1994; October 17, 1994; December 27, 1994; and June 2, 1997.

(b) *State Statutes and Regulations.* (1) The Florida statutes and regulations cited in this paragraph are incorporated by reference as part of the hazardous waste management program under Subtitle C of RCRA, 42 U.S.C. 6921 *et seq.*

(i) EPA Approved Florida's Statutory Requirements Applicable to the Hazardous Waste Management Program, dated December 1997.

(ii) EPA Approved Florida's Regulatory Requirements Applicable to the Hazardous Waste Management Program, dated December 1997.

(2) The following statutes and regulations concerning State procedures and enforcement, although not incorporated by reference, are part of the authorized State program:

(i) Florida Statutes, 1993, Chapter 119: 119.01; 119.011; 119.0115 through 119.031; 119.041; 119.05; 119.06; 119.07(1), (2), (3)(a)-(j), (3)(k)(1) first sentence, (3)(l)-(u), (4), (5), and (8); 119.072; 119.08(1)(a), (2) and (3); 119.085; 119.09; 119.092; 119.10; and 119.11 through 119.14.

(ii) Florida Statutes, 1993, Chapter 120: 120.53; 120.57; 120.59; 120.68; and 120.69.

(iii) Florida Statutes, 1993, Chapter 403: 403.021(1)-(9); 403.051(1) and (2); 403.061(21); 403.087(1) second and third sentences, (2)-(4), and (8); 403.0875; 403.091; 403.121; 403.131; 403.141(1) and (2); 403.151; 403.161; 403.201(1)-(3); 403.412; 403.702; 403.703(1); 403.704 (except (8), (11), (20)-(23), (25), and (31)); 403.721(1); 403.721(2)-(4) (except (4)(a)); 403.721(5); 403.721(6)(a)-(g), (j), (k); 403.721(7); 403.722(7) and (9)-(11); 403.7222(3); 403.724(3)-(6); 403.726 (except 403.726(3)); 403.73; 403.7545; 403.8055; and 403.814.

(iv) Florida Statutes, 1994 Supplement to 1993, Chapter 403: 403.061(14); 403.088; 403.707; 403.722(12); 403.7222(3); and 403.727.

(v) Florida Administrative Code, Chapter 62-4, effective July 4, 1995: 62-4.050(1)-(3); 62-4.070(4); and 62-4.070(5).

(vi) Florida Administrative Code, Chapter 62-103, effective October 20, 1996: 62-103.150; and 62-103.155.

(vii) Florida Administrative Code, Chapter 62-730, effective September 7, 1995: 62-730.020(2); 62-730.184; 62-730.200(3); 62-730.220(4); 62-730.220(9); 62-730.231(10); 62-730.240(3); and 62-730.310.

(3) The following statutory and regulatory provisions are broader in scope than the Federal program, are not part of the authorized program, and are not codified herein for enforcement purposes.

(i) Florida Statutes, 1993, Chapter 403: 403.087(5); 403.201(4) (only the phrase "may require by rule a processing fee for and"); 403.704(8); 403.721(4)(a); 403.7215(1)-(4); 403.722(8); 403.723; 403.724(7); 403.754(1)-(7); 403.767(1)-(3)(c); 403.78 through 403.7893; and 403.7895.

(ii) Florida Administrative Code, Chapter 62-4, effective July 4, 1995: 17-4.050(4)(k), (n)-(p), (r) and (s)-(x); 62-4.050(5)-(7).

(iii) Florida Administrative Code, Chapter 62-730, effective September 7, 1995: 62-730.170(2) and (3); 62-730.180(10); 62-730.290 (only the phrase "and submittal of the appropriate permit modification fee").

(4) Unauthorized State Provisions. The State's adoption of the following Federal rules is not approved by EPA and are, therefore, not enforceable:

Federal requirement	Federal Register reference	Publication date
HSWA Codification Rule: Corrective Action (Checklist 17 L)	50 FR 28702	7/15/85
HSWA Codification Rule 2: Corrective Action Beyond Facility Boundary (Checklist 44 B); Corrective Action for Injection Wells (Checklist 44 C); and Permit Modification (Checklist 44 D)	52 FR 45788	12/1/87
Burning of Hazardous Waste in Boilers and Industrial Furnaces (Checklist 85)	56 FR 7134	2/12/91
Burning of Hazardous Waste in Boilers and Industrial Furnaces; Corrections and Technical Amendments I (Checklist 94)	56 FR 32688	7/1/91
Burning of Hazardous Waste in Boilers and Industrial Furnaces; Technical Amendments II (Checklist 96)	56 FR 42504	8/27/91
Coke Ovens Administrative Stay (Checklist 98)	56 FR 43874	9/5/91
Recycled Coke By-Product Exclusion (Checklist 105)	57 FR 27880	6/22/92
Burning Hazardous Waste in Boilers and Industrial Furnaces; Technical Amendment III (Checklist 111)	57 FR 38558	8/25/92
Recycled Used Oil Management Standards (Checklist 112)	57 FR 41566: Amendments to 40 CFR Parts 260, 261, and 266	9/10/92
Burning of Hazardous Waste in Boilers and Industrial Furnaces; Technical Amendment IV (Checklist 114)	57 FR 44999	9/30/92
Corrective Action Management Units and Temporary Units (Checklist 121)	58 FR 8658	2/16/93
Recycled Used Oil Management Standards; Technical Amendments and Corrections I (Checklist 122)	58 FR 26420: Amendments to 40 CFR Parts 261, 264, and 265	5/3/93

(5) Memorandum of Agreement. The Memorandum of Agreement between EPA Region IV and the Florida Department of Environmental Protection, signed by the EPA Regional Administrator on October 23, 1993, as amended on November 28, 1994, and on December 9, 1994, is referenced as part of the authorized hazardous waste management program under Subtitle C of RCRA, 42 U.S.C. 6921 *et seq.*

(6) Statement of Legal Authority. "Attorney General's Statement for Final Authorization" certifications signed by the General Counsel of Florida on June 21, 1984; March 12, 1987; June 16, 1988; February 21, 1989; May 30, 1989; June 13, 1990; May 28, 1991; October 9, 1991; July 14, 1992; September 24, 1993; December 20, 1993; February 27, 1994; January 25, 1996; and May 20, 1996, is referenced as part of the authorized hazardous waste management program under Subtitle C of RCRA, 42 U.S.C. 6921.

(7) Program Description. The Program Description and any other materials submitted as part of the original application, or as supplements thereto, are referenced as part of the authorized hazardous waste management program under Subtitle C of RCRA, 42 U.S.C. 6921 *et seq.*

[63 FR 2898, Jan. 20, 1998]

§§272.502–272.549 [Reserved]

Subpart L—Georgia

§§272.550–272.599 [Reserved]

Subpart M—Hawaii

§§272.600–272.649 [Reserved]

Subpart N—Idaho

Source: 55 FR 50328, Dec. 6, 1990, unless otherwise noted.

§272.651 Idaho State-Administered Program: Final authorization.

(a) Pursuant to section 3006(b) of RCRA, 42 U.S.C. 6926(b), Idaho has final authorization for the following elements as submitted to EPA in Idaho's base program application for final authorization which was approved by EPA effective on April 9, 1990. Subsequent program revision applications were approved effective on June 5, 1992, August 10, 1992, June 11, 1995, January 19, 1999, July 1, 2002, March 10, 2004, and July 22, 2005.

(b) The State of Idaho has primary responsibility for enforcing its hazardous waste management program. However, EPA retains the authority to exercise its inspection and enforcement authorities in accordance with sections 3007, 3008, 3013, 7003 of RCRA, 42 U.S.C. 6927, 6928, 6934, 6973, and any other applicable statutory and regulatory provisions, regardless of whether the State has taken its own actions, as well as in accordance with other statutory and regulatory provisions.

(c) State Statutes and Regulations.

(1) The Idaho statutes and regulations cited in this paragraph are incorporated by reference as part of the hazardous waste management program under subtitle C of RCRA, 42 U.S.C. 6921 *et seq.*

(i) The EPA-Approved Idaho Statutory and Regulatory Requirements Applicable to the Hazardous Waste Management Program, July 2005.

(ii) [Reserved]

(2) EPA considered the following statutes and regulations in evaluating the State program but is not incorporating them herein for enforcement purposes:

(i) Idaho Code (I.C.) containing the General Laws of Idaho Annotated, Title 39, Chapter 44, "Hazardous Waste Management", published in 2002 by the Michie Company, Law Publishers: sections 39–4404; 39–4405 (except 39–4405(8)); 39–4406; 39–4407; 39–4408(4); 39–4409(2) (except first sentence); 39–4409(3); 39–4409(4) (first sentence); 39–4410; 39–4411(1); 39–4411(3); 39–4411(6); 39–4412 through 39–4416; 39–4418; 39–4419; 39–4421; 39–4422; and 39–4423(3) (a) & (b).

(ii) Idaho Code (I.C.) containing the General Laws of Idaho Annotated, Title 39, Chapter 58, "Hazardous Waste Facility Siting Act", published in 2002 by the Michie Company, Law Publishers: sections 39–5804; 39–5809; 39–5810; 39–5813(2); 39–5814; 39–5816; 39–5817; and 39–5818(1).

(iii) Idaho Code (I.C.) containing the General Laws of Idaho Annotated, Volume 2, Title 9, Chapter 3, "Public Writings", published in 1990 by the Michie Company, Law Publishers, Charlottesville, Virginia: sections 9–337(10); 9–337(11); 9–338; 9–339; and 9–344(2).

(iv) 2002 Cumulative Pocket Supplement to the Idaho Code (I.C.), Volume 2, Title 9, Chapter 3, "Public Writing", published in 2002 by the Michie Company, Law Publishers, Charlottesville, Virginia: sections 9–340A, 9–340B, and 9–343.

(v) Idaho Department of Environmental Quality Rules and Regulations, Idaho Administrative Code, IDAPA 58, Title 1, Chapter 5, "Rules and Standards for Hazardous Waste", as published July 2004: sections

58.01.05.000; 58.01.05.356.02 through 58.01.05.356.05; 58.01.05.800; 58.01.05.850; 58.01.05.996; 58.01.05.997; and 58.01.05.999.

(3) The following statutory and regulatory provisions are broader in scope than the Federal program, are not part of the authorized program, are not incorporated by reference, and are not federally enforceable:

(i) Idaho Code containing the General Laws of Idaho Annotated, Title 39, Chapter 44, "Hazardous Waste Management", published in 2002 by the Michie Company, Law Publishers: sections 39–4403(6) & (14); 39–4427; 39–4428 and 39–4429.

(ii) Idaho Code containing the General Laws of Idaho Annotated, Title 39, Chapter 58, "Hazardous Waste Siting Act", published in 2002 by the Michie Company, Law Publishers: section 39–5813(3).

(iii) Idaho Department of Environmental Quality Rules and Regulations, Idaho Administrative Code, IDAPA 58, Title 1, Chapter 5, "Rules and Standards for Hazardous Waste", as published July 2004: sections 58.01.05.355; and 58.01.05.500.

(4) Memorandum of Agreement. The Memorandum of Agreement between EPA Region 10 and the State of Idaho (IDEQ), signed by the EPA Regional Administrator on August 1, 2001, although not incorporated by reference, is referenced as part of the authorized hazardous waste management program under subtitle C of RCRA, 42 U.S.C. 6921, *et seq.*

(5) Statement of Legal Authority. The "Attorney General's Statement for Final Authorization," signed by the Attorney General of Idaho on July 5, 1988 and revisions, supplements and addenda to that Statement, dated July 3, 1989, February 13, 1992, December 29, 1994, September 16, 1996, October 3, 1997, April 6, 2001, September 11, 2002, and September 22, 2004, although not incorporated by reference, are referenced as part of the authorized hazardous waste management program under subtitle C of RCRA, 42 U.S.C. 6921, *et seq.*

(6) Program Description. The Program Description, and any other materials submitted as part of the original application or as supplements thereto, although not incorporated by reference, are referenced as part of the authorized hazardous waste management program under subtitle C of RCRA, 42 U.S.C. 6921 *et seq.*

[64 FR 34136, June 25, 1999; 70 FR 11134, Mar. 8, 2005; 71 FR 20345, Apr. 20, 2006]

§§272.652–272.699 [Reserved]

Subpart O—Illinois

§272.700 State authorization.

(a) The State of Illinois is authorized to administer and enforce a hazardous waste management program in lieu of the Federal program under subtitle C of the Resource Conservation and Recovery Act of 1976 (RCRA), 42 U.S.C. 6921 *et. seq.* subject to the Hazardous and Solid Waste Amendments of 1984 (HSWA), (Public Law 98-616, November 8, 1984), 42 U.S.C. 6926 (c) and (g). The Federal program for which a State may receive authorization is defined in 40 CFR part 271. The State's base program and revisions to that program, as administered by the Illinois Environmental Protection Agency, were approved by EPA pursuant to 42 U.S.C. 6926(b) and 40 CFR part 271. EPA's approval of Illinois' base program was effective on January 31, 1986. EPA's approval of revisions to Illinois' base program were effective on March 5, 1988, April 30, 1990 and June 3, 1991.

(b) Illinois is authorized to implement only those HSWA requirements addressed in 40 CFR 272.701 and codified herein.

(c) Illinois has primary responsibility for enforcing its hazardous waste program. However, EPA retains the authority to exercise its enforcement authorities under Sections 3007, 3008, 3013, and 7003 of RCRA, 42 U.S.C. 6927, 6928, 6934, and 6973, as well as under other Federal laws and regulations.

(d) Illinois must revise its approved program to adopt new changes to the Federal Subtitle C program in accordance with Section 3006(b) of RCRA and 40 CFR part 271, subpart A. Illinois must seek final authorization for all program revisions pursuant to Section 30069b) of RCRA but, on a temporary basis, may seek interim authorization for revisions required by HSWA pursuant to section 3006(g) of RCRA, 42 U.S.C. 6926(g). If Illinois obtains final authorization for the revised requirements pursuant to Section 3006(g), the newly authorized provisions will be listed in §272.701 of this subpart. If Illinois obtains interim authorization for the revised requirements pursuant to Section 3006(g), the newly authorized provisions will be listed in §272.702.

[54 FR 37651, Sept. 12, 1989, as amended at 57 FR 3723, Jan. 31, 1992; 57 FR 45576, Oct. 2, 1992]

§272.701 State-administered program: Final authorization.

Pursuant to section 3006(b) of RCRA, 42 U.S.C. 6926(b), Illinois has final authorization for the following elements submitted to EPA in Illinois; base program and program revision applications for final authorization and approved by EPA effective on January 31, 1986, March 5, 1988, April 30, 1990 and June 3, 1991.

(a) *State Statutes and Regulations.*

(1) The following Illinois regulations and statutes are incorporated by reference with the approval of the Director of the *Federal Register* in accordance with 5 U.S.C. 552(a) and 1 CFR part 51 as part of the hazardous waste management program under Subtitle C of RCRA, 42 U.S.C. 6921 *et seq.*

(i) Illinois Administrative Code, Title 35, Part 702, Sections 702.101-702.104, 702.110-702.187; Part 703, Sections 703.100-703.126, 703.140-703.246; Part 709, Sections 709.102-709.105, 709.201, 709.301, 709.302, 709.401, 709.501-709.603; Part 720, Sections 720.101-720.122, Part 720 Appendix A; Part 721, Sections 721.101-721.133, Part 721 Appendices A, B, C, G, H, I, J, Z; Part 722, Sections 722.110-722.151, Part 722 Appendix A; Part 723, Sections 723.110-723.131; Part 724, Sections 724.101-724.321, 724.326-724.351, 724.354-724.451, Part 724 Appendices A, D, E; Part 725, Sections 725.101-725.248, 725.270-725.530, Part 725 Appendices, A, C, D, E; Part 726, Sections 726.120-726.180; Part 728; and Part 729, Sections 729.100-729.321; (Illinois Administrative Code, January 1, 1985, as amended January 1, 1986, January 1, 1987, and January 1, 1988).

Copies of the Illinois regulations that are incorporated by reference in this paragraph are available from the Secretary of State, Administrative Code Division, 288 Centennial Building, Springfield, Illinois 62756. Copies may be inspected at U.S. EPA headquarters, 1200 Pennsylvania Ave., NW., Washington, DC, or at the Office of *Federal Register*, 800 North Capital Street, NW., suite 700, Washington, DC.

(ii) [Reserved]

(2) The following statutes and regulations concerning State enforcement and procedures, although not codified herein, are part of the authorized State program:

(i) Illinois Revised Statutes, chapter 111, sections 1001 through 1003.52; sections 1003.54 through 1005.1; sections 1007 through 1007.1; section 1020(c); sections 1020.1 through 1022.3; sections 1022.5 through 1022.6; sections 1030 through 1034; and section 1039 parts a, d, g, k.

(ii) Illinois Administrative Code, Title 35 Part 700, Sections 700.101-700.504; Part 702 Sections 702.105-702.109; Part 705, Section 705.101-705.212; Part 720, Sections 720.140-720.141; and Title 2, Part 1826, Sections 1826.101-1826.503, Section 1826 Appendices A and B. (Illinois Administrative Code, January 1, 1985, as amended January 1, 1986, January 1, 1987, and January 1, 1988).

(b) *Memorandum of Agreement.* The Memorandum of Agreement between EPA-Region V and the Illinois Environmental Protection Agency, signed by the EPA Regional Administrator on January 26, 1990, is part of the authorized hazardous waste management program under Subtitle C of RCRA, 42 U.S.C. 6921 *et seq.*

(c) *Statement of Legal Authority.* The Illinois Attorney General's Statements for final authorization signed by the Attorney General of Illinois on June 4, 1985, July 15, 1986, May 26, 1988, and February 23, 1990 are part of the authorized hazardous waste management program under Subtitle C of RCRA, 42 U.S.C. 6921 *et seq.*

(d) *Program Description.* Program Descriptions dated July 26, 1985, August 7, 1986, November 29, 1988, and May 18, 1990, and any other materials submitted as part of, or as supplements to, the original application or revision applications are codified as part of the authorized hazardous waste management program under Subtitle C of RCRA, 42 U.S.C. 6921 *et seq.*

[54 FR 37651, Sept. 12, 1989, as amended at 57 FR 3723, Jan. 31, 1992; 57 FR 45576, Oct. 2, 1992]

§§272.702–272.750 [Reserved]

Subpart P—Indiana

§272.750 [Reserved]

§272.751 Indiana state-administered program: Final authorization.

(a) Pursuant to section 3006(b) of RCRA, 42 U.S.C. 6926(b), Indiana has final authorization for the following elements as submitted to EPA in Indiana's base program application for final authorization which was approved by EPA effective on January 31, 1986. Subsequent program revision applications were approved effective on December 31, 1986, January 19, 1988, September 11, 1989, September 23, 1991 (two separate revisions), September 27, 1991, September 30, 1991, October 21, 1996, November 30, 1999, and January 4, 2001.

(b) *State statutes and regulations.* (1) The Indiana statutes and regulations cited in this paragraph are incorporated by reference as part of the hazardous waste management program under subtitle C of RCRA, 42 U.S.C. 6921 *et seq.* This incorporation by reference was approved by the Director of the Federal Register in accordance with 5 U.S.C. 552(a). Copies of the Indiana regulations that are incorporated by reference in this paragraph are available from the Indiana Legislative Services Agency, Administrative Code and Register Division, 302 State House, Indianapolis, Indiana 46204.

(i) The EPA approved Authorized Indiana Statutory Requirements Applicable to the Hazardous Waste Management Program, dated March 2001.

(ii) The EPA approved Indiana Regulatory Requirements Applicable to the Hazardous Waste Management Program, dated March 2001.

(2) The following statutes and regulations concerning State procedures and enforcement, although not incorporated by reference, are part of the authorized State program:

(i) Annotated Indiana Code, 1998 edition, Title 13, Article 4-21.5, 5-14-3-2, 13-11-2, 13-14-2-2, 13-14-9, 13-14-10, 13-15-2, 13-19-1, 13-19-2, 13-20, 13-22-1, 13-22-3, 13-22-5 through 13-22-14, 13-23, 13-30, and 23-1-16.

(ii) Indiana Administrative Code, as amended, 1996 edition, certified October 24, 1995, 2000 cumulative supplement, certified November 30, 1999, sections 329 IAC 3.1-1-1 through 3.1-1-6; 3.1-1-8 through 3.1-1-14; 3.1-2-1 through 3.1-2-16; 3.1-3-1 through 3.1-3-9; 3.1-4-2 through 3.1-4-26; 3.1-13-5; 3.1-13-8 through 3.1-13-17; 3.1-14-2; 3.1-14-3; and 13-1-3 through 13-1-6.

(3) The following statutory and regulatory provisions are broader in scope than the Federal program, are not part of the authorized program, and are not incorporated by reference: Indiana Administrative Code as amended, 1996 edition, certified October 24, 1995, 2000 cumulative supplement, certified November 30, 1999, sections 329 IAC 3.1-6-3; and 3.1-8-4.

(4) *Unauthorized State provisions:* Although the Federal rules listed in the following table have been adopted by the State and have been included in the materials incorporated by reference in paragraph (b)(1) of this section, EPA has not authorized the State for these rules at this time. While they may be enforceable under State law, they are not enforceable under RCRA:

Federal requirement	Federal Register reference	Publication date
1. Hazardous Waste Management System; Testing and Monitoring Activities (Checklist 158)	62 FR 32452	June 13, 1997
2. Kraft Mill Stream Stripper Condensate Exclusion (Checklist 164)	63 FR 18504	April 15, 1998
3. Recycled Used Oil Management Standards; Technical Correction and Clarification (Checklist 166) as amended (Checklist 166.1)	63 FR 24963	May 6, 1998
4. Bevill Exclusion Revisions and Clarification (Checklist 167E)	63 FR 37780	July 14, 1998
5. Exclusion of Recycled Wood Preserving Wastewaters (Checklist 167F)	63 FR 28556	May 26, 1998
6. Hazardous Waste Combustors Revised Standards (Checklist 168)	63 FR 33782	June 19, 1998
7. Universal Waste Rule; Technical Amendment (Checklist 176)	63 FR 71225	December 24, 1998

(i) Additionally Indiana has adopted but is not authorized to implement the HSWA rules that are listed the following table. EPA will continue to implement the Federal HSWA requirements for which Indiana is not authorized until the State receives specific authorization for those requirements:

Federal requirement	Federal Register reference	Publication date
1. HSWA Codification Rule 2; Corrective Action for Injection Wells (Checklist 44C)	52 FR 45788	December 1, 1987
2. Burning of Hazardous Waste in Boilers and Industrial Furnaces (Checklist 85)	56 FR 7134	February 21, 1991
3. Burning of Hazardous Waste in Boilers and Industrial Furnaces; Corrections and Technical Amendments (Checklist 94)	56 FR 32688	July 17, 1991
4. Burning of Hazardous Waste in Boilers and Industrial Furnaces; Technical Amendments II (Checklist 96)	56 FR 42504	August 27, 1991
5. Burning of Hazardous Waste in Boilers and Industrial Furnaces; Technical Amendment III (Checklist 111)	57 FR 38558	August 25, 1992
6. Burning of Hazardous Waste in Boilers and Industrial Furnaces; Technical Amendment IV (Checklist 114)	57 FR 44999	September 30, 1992
7. Requirements for Preparation, Adoption, and Submittal of Implementation Plans (Checklist 125)	58 FR 38816	July 20, 1993
8. Burning of Hazardous Waste in Boilers and Industrial Furnaces (Checklist 127)	58 FR 59598	November 9, 1993
9. Land Disposal Restrictions-Phase IV: Treatment Standards for Wood Preserving Wastes, Paperwork Reduction and Streamlining, Exemptions from RCRA for Certain Processed Materials; and Miscellaneous Hazardous Waste Provisions (Checklist 157)	62 FR 25998	May 12, 1997
10. Hazardous Waste Management System; Carbamate Production, Identification and Listing of Hazardous Waste; Land Disposal Restrictions (Checklist 159)	62 FR 32974	June 17, 1997
11. Land Disposal Restrictions-Phase III—Emergency Extension of the K088 National Capacity Variance (Checklist 160)	62 FR 37694	July 14, 1997
12. Second Emergency Revision of the Land Disposal Restrictions (LDR) Treatment Standards for Listed Hazardous Wastes from Carbamate Production (Checklist 161)	62 FR 45568	August 28, 1997
13. Organic Air Emission Standards for Tanks, Surface Impoundments, and Containers; Clarification and Technical Amendment (Checklist 163)	62 FR 64636	December 8, 1997
14. Land Disposal Restrictions-Phase IV: Treatment Standards for Metal Wastes and Mineral Processing Wastes (Checklist 167A), Hazardous Soils Treatment Standards and Exclusions (Checklist 167B), and Corrections (Checklist 167C) as amended (Checklist 167C.1)	63 FR 28556 63 FR 31266	May 26, 1998 June 8, 1998

Federal requirement	Federal Register reference	Publication date
15. Petroleum Refining Process (Checklist 169) as amended (Checklist 169.1)	63 FR 42110	August 6, 1998
	63 FR 54356	October 9, 1998
16. Land Disposal Restrictions-Phase IV (Checklist 170)	63 FR 46332	August 31, 1998
17. Emergency Revisions of the Land Disposal Restrictions Treatment Standards (Checklist 171)	63 FR 47409	September 4, 1998
18. Emergency Revision of the Land Disposal Restrictions Treatment Standards (Checklist 172)	63 FR 48124	September 9, 1998
19. Land Disposal Restrictions Treatment Standards (Spent Potliners) (Checklist 173)	63 FR 51254	September 24, 1998

(ii) Some regulations listed in the table in paragraph (b)(4)(i) of this section are predominantly HSWA authority but contain provisions that are not HSWA authority. EPA will not enforce these non-HSWA provisions. The affected rules are as follows:

(A) Burning of Hazardous Waste in Boilers and Industrial Furnaces (BIF), including BIF (February 21, 1991);

(B) Corrections and Technical Amendments I (July 17, 1991);

(C) Technical Amendments II (August 27, 1991);

(D) Technical Amendments III (August 25, 1992);

(E) Amendment IV (September 30, 1992);

(F) Requirements for Preparation, Adoption, and Submittal of Implementation Plans (July 20, 1993); and

(G) BIF (November 9, 1993).

(iii) EPA will not enforce BIF rules for Sludge Dryers, Infrared Incinerators, Plasma Arc Incinerators, and Carbon Regeneration Units, until Indiana is authorized for these rules. Petroleum Refining Process (August 6, 1998, as amended October 9, 1998) 40 CFR 261.3, 261.4, and 261.6 are non-HSWA provisions. Standards Applicable to Owners and Operators of Closed/Closing Facilities (October 22, 1998) 40 CFR 264.90(e), 265.110(c), 265.118(c)(4), 265.121 (except §265.121(a)(2)), 270.1, 270.14(a), and 270.28 are non-HSWA provisions. Hazardous Remediation Waste Management Requirements (HWIR Media) (November 30, 1998) 40 CFR 261.4(g), 264.1(j)(1-13), 264.73(b)(17), 270.2, 270.11(d), 270.68, 270.73(a), and 270.79 through 270.230 (40 CFR part 270, subpart H) except §270.230(e)(1) are non-HSWA provisions. Until Indiana becomes authorized for these rules, EPA will not enforce the non-HSWA provisions.

(5) *Memorandum of Agreement.* The Memorandum of Agreement between EPA Region 5 and the Indiana Department of Environmental Management, signed by the Commissioner of the IDEM on February 14, 1996 and acknowledged by the EPA Regional Administrator in the *Federal Register* noticed signed on July 29, 1996, August 2, 1999, and December 14, 2000, is referenced as part of the authorized hazardous waste management program under subtitle C of RCRA, 42 U.S.C. 6921 *et seq.*

(6) *Statement of legal authority.* "Attorney General's Statement for Final Authorization", signed by the Attorney General of Indiana on June 28, 1985 and revisions, supplements and addenda to that Statement dated August 26, 1986, June 1, 1987, December 15, 1987, March 25, 1988, July 22, 1988, December 15, 1989, May 29, 1996, March 24, 1997, and January 31, 2000 are referenced as part of the authorized hazardous waste management program under subtitle C of RCRA, 42 U.S.C. 6921 *et seq.*

(7) *Program description.* The Program Description and any other materials submitted as part of the original application or as supplements thereto are referenced as part of the authorized hazardous waste management program under subtitle C of RCRA, 42 U.S.C. 6921 *et seq.*

[54 FR 34990, Aug. 23, 1989; 66 FR 53728, Oct. 24, 2001]

§§272.752–272.799 [Reserved]

Subpart Q—Iowa

§§272.800–272.849 [Reserved]

Subpart R—Kansas

§§272.850–272.899 [Reserved]

Subpart S—Kentucky

§§272.900–272.949 [Reserved]

Subpart T—Louisiana

§272.950 [Reserved]

§272.951 Louisiana State-administered program: Final authorization.

(a) Pursuant to section 3006(b) of RCRA, 42 U.S.C. 6926(b), Louisiana has final authorization for the following elements as submitted to EPA in Louisiana's base program application for final authorizations which was approved by EPA effective on February 7, 1985. Subsequent program revision applications were approved effective on January 29, 1990, October 25, 1991, January 23, 1995, March 8, 1995, January 2, 1996, June 11, 1996 and March 16, 1998.

State Statutes and Regulations

(1) The Louisiana statutes and regulations cited in this paragraph are incorporated by reference as part of the hazardous waste management program under Subtitle C of RCRA, 42 U.S.C. 6921 *et seq.*

(i) EPA Approved Louisiana Statutory Requirements Applicable to the Hazardous Waste Management Program, dated June, 1997.

(ii) EPA Approved Louisiana Regulatory Requirements Applicable to the Hazardous Waste Management Program, dated June, 1997.

(2) The following statutes and regulations concerning State procedures and enforcement, although not incorporated by reference, are part of the authorized State program:

(i) Louisiana Statutes Annotated, Revised Statutes, 1989, Volume 17B, Subtitle II of Title 30, Louisiana Environmental Quality Act, 1989: Chapter 2, Sections 2011.A(1)&(2), 2011.B, 2011.C (except 2011.C(1)(a)), 2011.D (introductory paragraph), 2011.D(1)-(3), 2011.D(5)-(9), 2011.D(13)-(15), 2011.D(17)&(18), 2011.D(21) (except 2011.D(21)(e)), 2011.D(22), 2011.E-.G, 2012 (except 2012.F(4) and 2012.G), 2013, 2014.A, 2019.A&.B, 2020 through 2021, 2023, 2024.B-.C, 2025.A-.D, 2025.E(2)-(5), 2025.F (introductory paragraph), 2025.F(1)-(4), 2025.G-.I, 2026, 2027.C, 2028, 2029, 2033, 2037; Chapter 3, Sections 2054.B(1), 2054.B(2)(a); Chapter 9, sections 2174, 2175, 2180.A (introductory paragraph), 2180.A(2)-(8), 2180.B-.C, 2181-2182, 2183.C, 2183.F, 2183.G (except 2183.G(3)), 2183.H, 2186, 2187, 2188.A, 2188.C, 2189, 2190.A-.D, 2191.A-.C, 2192.A, 2192.B (except 2192.B(4)), 2192.C, 2196, 2199 through 2200, 2203.B-.C, 2204.A(2), and 2204.B.

(ii) Louisiana Statutes Annotated, Revised Statutes, 1992 Cumulative Annual Pocket Part, Volume 17B, Subtitle II of Title 30, Louisiana Environmental Quality Act: Chapter 2, section 2011.C(1)(a), 2011.D(21)(e), 2012.F(4), 2012.G, 2018, 2019.C, 2022 (except the first sentence of 2022.A), 2024.A&.D, 2025.E(1), 2025.J, 2027.A&.B; Chapter 9, sections 2180.A(1), 2183.G(3), 2192.B(4).

(iii) Louisiana Administrative Code, Title 33, Part V, Hazardous Waste and Hazardous Materials, Amendments through June 1995: Chapter 1, sections 101, 107.A-.C; Chapter 3, Sections 301.A&.B, 311.A, 311.C, 315 (introductory paragraph), 323.B.3; Chapter 5, Section 503; Chapter 7, Sections 703, 705 and 707 through 721.

(iv) Louisiana Administrative Code, Title 33, Part V, Hazardous Waste and Hazardous Materials, Amendments for July 1995–March 1996: Chapter 3, Section 323.B.4.d. & e.

(3) The following statutory and regulatory provisions are broader in scope than the Federal program, are not part of the authorized program, and are not incorporated by reference:

(i) Louisiana Statutes Annotated, Revised Statutes, 1989, Volume 17B, Subtitle II of Title 30, Louisiana Environmental Quality Act, 1989: Chapter 2, sections 2014.B.-D.

(ii) Louisiana Statutes Annotated, Revised Statutes, 1992 Cumulative Annual Pocket Part, Volume 17B, Subtitle II of Title 30, Louisiana Environmental Quality Act: Sections 2178 and 2197.

(iii) Louisiana Administrative Code, Title 33, Part V, Hazardous Waste and Hazardous Materials, Amendments through June 1995: 327, 1313, and Chapter 51.

(4) Unauthorized State Amendments. The following authorized provisions of the Louisiana regulations include amendments published in the Louisiana Register that are not approved by EPA. Such unauthorized amendments are not part of the State's authorized program and are, therefore, not Federally enforceable. Thus, notwithstanding the language in the Louisiana hazardous waste regulations incorporated by reference at §272.951(b)(1), EPA will only enforce the authorized State provisions with the effective dates indicated in the table below. The actual State regulatory text authorized by EPA for the listed provisions are available as a separate document, Addendum to the EPA-Approved Louisiana Regulatory and Statutory Requirements Applicable to the Hazardous Waste Management Program, June, 1997. Copies of the document can be obtained from EPA Region 6, 1445 Ross Avenue, Dallas, Texas 75202-2733, Phone number: (214) 665-8533.

(5) Memorandum of Agreement. The Memorandum of Agreement between EPA Region 6 and the Louisiana Department of Environmental Quality—Hazardous Waste Division, signed by the EPA Regional Administrator on December 18, 1995, is referenced as part of the authorized hazardous waste management program under Subtitle C of RCRA, 42 U.S.C. 6921 *et seq.*

State provision	Effective date of authorized provision	Unauthorized state amendments	
		State reference	Effective date
LAC §109 "Industrial furnace" introductory paragraph	November 20, 1988	LR 18:1375	December 20, 1992
LAC §303.K.1 (previously LHWR §3.2(k)(1))	July 20, 1984	LR 14:790	November 20, 1988
LAC §901 (LHWR §6.1)	March 20, 1984	LR 20:1000	September 20, 1994
LAC §1111.B.1.c (previously LHWR §7.6(b)(1))	March 20, 1984	LR 16:220	March 20, 1990
LAC §1113 (previously LHWR §7.7)	March 20, 1984	LR 16:220	March 20, 1990
		LR 20:1000	September 20, 1994
		LR 20:1109	October 20, 1994
LAC §2511.B (previously LHWR §14.6(b))	March 20, 1984	LR 16:1057	December 20, 1990
LAC §3105.A	November 21, 1988	LR 18:1256	November 20, 1992
		LR 18:1375	December 20, 1992
		LR 20:1000	September 20, 1994
LAC §3309 (previously LHWR §18.5)	July 20, 1984	LR 16:614	July 20, 1990
LAC §3707.F.1 (previously LHWR 20.4(f)(1))	August 20, 1987	LR 18:723	July 20, 1992
LAC §3707.F.2 (previously LHWR 20.4(f)(2))	August 20, 1987	LR 18:723	July 20, 1992
LAC §3711.F.1	November 21, 1988	LR 18:723	July 20, 1992
LAC §3711.F.2	November 21, 1988	LR 18:723	July 20, 1992
LAC §3711.G (previously LHWR 20.4(g))	March 20, 1984	LR 18:723	July 20, 1992
LAC §3715.F.1 (previously LHWR §20.8(f)(1))	March 20, 1984	LR 18:723	July 20, 1992
LAC §4141	March 20, 1992	LR 18:1375	December 20, 1992
LAC §4307 (previously LHWR §23.4)	March 20, 1984	LR 21:944	September 20, 1995
LAC §4397.B	August 20, 1987	LR 21:266	March 20, 1995
LAC §4403.E.1	March 20, 1990	LR 18:723	July 20, 1992
LAC §4403.E.2	November 21, 1988	LR 18:723	July 20, 1992
LAC §4403.F (previously LHWR §23.52(f))	March 20, 1984	LR 18:723	July 20, 1992
LAC §4407.A.12 (previously LHWR §23.54(a)(12))	March 20, 1984	LR 13:433	August 20, 1987
		LR 18:723	July 20, 1992
LAC §4407.E.1&.2	August 20, 1987	LR 18:723	July 20, 1992
LAC §4407.F (previously LHWR §23.54(f))	March 20, 1984	LR 18:723	July 20, 1992
LAC §4503.B introductory paragraph (previously LHWR §23.102(b))	March 20, 1984	LR 16:1057	December 20, 1990
LAC §4513.A	March 20, 1990	LR 18:1375	December 20, 1992
		LR 20:1000	September 20, 1994
LAC §4901.D.3	September 20, 1994	LR 21:266	March 20, 1995

(6) Statement of Legal Authority. "Attorney General's Statement for Final Authorization", signed by the Attorney General of Louisiana on May 10, 1989 and revisions, supplements and addenda to that Statement dated May 13, 1991, May 3, 1994, December 2, 1994, May 31, 1995, July 24, 1995, and November 30, 1995, are referenced as part of the authorized hazardous waste management program under Subtitle C of RCRA, 42 U.S.C. 6921 *et seq.*

(7) Program Description. The Program Description and any other materials submitted as part of the original application or as supplements thereto are referenced as part of the authorized hazardous waste management program under Subtitle C of RCRA, 42 U.S.C. 6921 *et seq.*

[62 FR 67583, Dec. 29, 1997]

§§272.952–272.999 [Reserved]

Subpart U—Maine

§§272.1000–272.1049 [Reserved]

Subpart V—Maryland

§§272.1050–272.1099 [Reserved]

Subpart W—Massachusetts

§§272.1100–272.1149 [Reserved]

Subpart X—Michigan

§272.1150 State authorization.

(a) The State of Michigan is authorized to administer and enforce a hazardous waste management program in lieu of the Federal program under subtitle C of the Resource Conservation and Recovery Act of 1976 (RCRA),

42 U.S.C. 6921 *et seq.* subject to the Hazardous and Solid Waste Amendments of 1984 (HSWA) (Public Law 98-616, November 8, 1984), 42 U.S.C. 6926 (c) and (g). The Federal program for which a State may receive authorization is defined in 40 CFR part 271. The State's program, as administered by the Michigan Department of Natural Resources, was approved by EPA pursuant to 42 U.S.C. 6926(b) and part 271 of this chapter. EPA's approval of Michigan's base program was effective on October 30, 1986 (see 51 FR 36804). EPA's approval of the revisions to Michigan's base program was effective on January 23, 1990 (see 54 FR 48608) and RCRA Cluster III authorization effective June 24, 1991 (see 56 FR 18517).

(b) Michigan is authorized to implement certain HSWA requirements in lieu of EPA. EPA has explicitly indicated its intent to allow such action in a *Federal Register* notice granting Michigan authorization and RCRA Cluster III authorization effective June 24, 1991 (see 56 FR 18517).

(c) Michigan has primary responsibility for enforcing its hazardous waste program. However, EPA retains the authority to exercise its enforcement authorities under sections 3007, 3008, 3013, and 7003 of RCRA, 42 U.S.C. 6927, 6928, 6934, and 6973, as well as under other Federal laws and regulations.

(d) Michigan must revise its approved program to adopt new changes to the Federal Subtitle C program in accordance with section 3006(b) of RCRA and 40 CFR part 271, subpart A. Michigan must seek final authorization for all program revisions, pursuant to section 3006(b) of RCRA but, on a temporary basis, may seek interim authorization for revisions required by HSWA, pursuant to section 3006(g) of RCRA, 42 U.S.C. 6926(g). If Michigan obtains final authorization for the revised requirements pursuant to section 3006(g), the newly authorized provisions will be listed in §272.1151 of this subpart. If Michigan obtains interim authorization for the revised requirements pursuant to section 3006(g), the newly authorized provisions will be listed in §272.1152.

[54 FR 7421, Feb. 21, 1989, as amended at 55 FR 18112, May 1, 1990; 57 FR 3724, Jan. 31, 1992]

§272.1151 State-administered program: Final authorization. Pursuant to section 3006(b) of RCRA, 42 U.S.C. 6926(b), Michigan has final authorization for the following elements submitted to EPA in Michigan's base program and program revision applications for final authorization and approved by EPA effective on October 30, 1986 (see 51 FR 36804), January 23, 1990 (see 54 FR 46808), and RCRA Cluster III authorization effective June 24, 1991 (see 56 FR 18517).

(a) State Statutes and Regulations. (1) The requirements in the Michigan statutes and regulations cited in this paragraph are incorporated by reference and codified as part of the hazardous waste management program under Subtitle C of RCRA, 42 U.S.C. 6921 *et seq.* This incorporation, by reference, was approved by the Director of the *Federal Register* in accordance with 5 U.S.C. 552(a).

(i) Michigan Compiled Laws Annotated, §§299.501-506, 299.521-522, 299.532-535, 299.537, and 299.539-541 (P.A. 64 of 1979 as amended by P.A. 486 of 1982, effective March 30, 1983). Copies of the State laws incorporated by reference in this paragraph are available from West Publishing Co., 50 West Kellogg Boulevard, P.O. Box 64526, St. Paul, Minnesota 55164-0526.

(ii) Michigan Administrative Code, Rules 299.9101-9206(3)(g), 299.9206(4)-9208(1), 299.9208(3)-9209(1), 9209(4)-(9209(6), 299.9210(2)-9211(1)(a), 299.9211(1)(c)-9212(4), 299.9212(6)-9212(7), 299.9212(8)(b)-9213(1)(a), 299.9213(1)(c), 299.9213(2)-9214(6)(b), 299.9215-9217, 299.9220, 299.9222, 299.9224-9225, 299.9301-9304(1)(b), 299.9304(1)(d)-299.9401(5), 299.9402, 299.9404(1) introductory text, 299.9404(1)(b)-9405, 299.9407-9408(1), 299.9409-9410, 299.9501-9504(1) introductory text, 299.9504(1)(b)-9506, 299.9508-9508(1)(g), 299.9508(1)(i)-9521(1)(b), 299.9521(2)-9522, 299.9601-9611(2)(a), 299.9611(3)-9623(1)(b), 299.9623(3)-9710, 299.9801-9804, 299.11001-11008 (1985 Annual Michigan Administrative Code Supplement, as supplemented by the April 1988 Michigan Register, pages 3-107, and the January 1989 Michigan Register, pages 1-27). Copies of the Michigan regulations that are incorporated by reference in this paragraph are available from the Department of Management and Budget's Publication Office, 7461 Crowner Drive, Lansing, Michigan 48913, Phone: (517) 322-1897. Copies may be inspected at: U.S. EPA Headquarters Library, PM 211A, 401 M St., SW, Washington, DC 20460. Phone: (202) 382-5926; U.S. EPA, Region V, Waste, Pesticides and Toxics Division, Program Management Branch, 7th floor, 77 West Jackson Boulevard, Chicago, IL. Phone: Ms. Judy Feigler, (312) 886-4179; and at the Office of the Federal Register, 800 North Capitol Street, NW., room 700, Washington, DC.

(2) The following statutes and regulations, although not codified herein for enforcement purposes, are part of the authorized State program.

(i) Michigan Compiled Laws Annotated, §24.201-328 (P.A. 306 of 1969, effective July 1, 1970), §§299.507, 299.514-520, 299.523-528, 299.544, and 299.546-548

(P.A. 64 of 1979 as amended by P.A. 486 of 1982, effective March 30, 1983).

(ii) Michigan Administrative Code Rules 299.9521(1)(c), 299.11101-11107 (1985 Annual *Michigan Administrative Code Supplement*, as supplemented by the April, 1988 *Michigan Register*, pages 3-107).

(3) The following statutory and regulatory provisions are broader in scope than the Federal program, are not part of the authorized program, and are not codified herein for enforcement purposes.

(i) Michigan Compiled Laws Annotated, §§299.508-513, 299.529, 299.531, and 299.542-543 (P.A. 64 of 1979 as amended by P.A. 486 of 1982).

(ii) Michigan Administrative Code Rules 299.9208(2), 299.9209 (2) and (3), 299.9210(1), 299.9211(1)(b), 299.9212 (5) and (8)(a), 299.9213(1) (b) and (d), 299.9214(6)(c), 299.9218-9219, 299.9221, 299.9223, 299.9226, 299.9304(1)(c), 299.9401(6), 299.9403, 299.9404(1)(a), 299.9406, 299.9408 (2) and (3), 299.9411-9412, 299.9504(1)(a), 299.9507, 299.9508(1)(h), 299.9523, 299.9611(2) (b) and (c), 299.9623(2), 299.9711, 299.9901-9906 (1985 Michigan Administrative Code Annual Supplement, as supplemented by the April 1988 Michigan Register, pages 3-107, and the January 1989 Michigan Register, pages 1-27).

(b) *Memorandum of Agreement.* The Memorandum of Agreement between EPA—Region V and the Michigan Department of Natural Resources, signed by the EPA Regional Administrator on February 7, 1991, is codified as part of the authorized hazardous waste management program under Subtitle C of RCRA, 42 U.S.C. 6921 *et seq.*

(c) *Statement of Legal Authority.* The Michigan Attorney General's Statements for final authorization signed by the Attorney General of Michigan on October 25, 1985, and supplements to that Statement dated June 3, 1986, September 19, 1986, September 7, 1988, and July 31, 1990, are codified as part of the authorized hazardous waste management program under Subtitle C of RCRA, 42 U.S.C. 6921 *et seq.*

(d) *Program Description.* The Program Description dated June 30, 1984, and the supplements thereto dated June 30, 1986, September 12, 1988, and July 31, 1990, are codified as part of the authorized hazardous waste management program under subtitle C of RCRA, U.S.C. 6921 *et seq.*

[54 FR 7421, Feb. 21, 1989, as amended at 55 FR 18113, May 1, 1990; 57 FR 3725, Jan. 31, 1992; 62 FR 1834, Jan. 14, 1997]

§§272.1152–272.1199 [Reserved]

Subpart Y—Minnesota

§272.1200 [Reserved]

§272.1201 Minnesota State-administered program; Final authorization.

Pursuant to section 3006(b) of RCRA, 42 U.S.C. 6926(b), Minnesota has final authorization for the following elements as submitted to EPA in Minnesota's base program and revision application for final authorization as approved by EPA effective on February 11, 1985. Subsequent program revision applications were approved effective on September 18, 1987, June 23, 1989, August 14, 1990, August 23, 1991, May 18, 1992, May 17, 1993, and March 21, 1994.

(a) *State statutes and regulations.* (1) The Minnesota statutes and regulations cited in appendix A are incorporated by reference as part of the hazardous waste management program under subtitle C of RCRA, 42 U.S.C. 6921 *et seq.*

(i) EPA Approved Minnesota Statutory Requirements Applicable to the Hazardous Waste Management Program, dated April 5, 1994.

(ii) EPA Approved Minnesota Regulatory Requirements Applicable to the Hazardous Waste Management Program, dated April 5, 1994.

(2) The following statutes and regulations concerning State enforcement, although not incorporated by reference for enforcement purposes, are part of the authorized State program: Minnesota Statutes, Chapters 14.02-14.56; 115.07 Subdivisions 1 and 3; 115.071, 116.091; 116.11, and 116B.09 (June 1992 edition).

(b) [Reserved]

[59 FR 45987, Sept. 6, 1994]

§§272.1202–272.1249 [Reserved]

Subpart Z—Mississippi

§§272.1250–272.1299 [Reserved]

Subpart AA—Missouri

§272.1300 State authorization.

(a) The State of Missouri is authorized to administer and enforce a hazardous waste management program in lieu of the Federal program under Subtitle C of the Resource Conservation and Recovery Act of 1976 (RCRA), 42 U.S.C. 6921 *et seq.*, subject to the Hazardous and Solid Waste Amendments of 1984 (HSWA), (Pub. L. 98-616, Nov. 8, 1984), 42 U.S.C. 6926 (c) and (g)). The Federal program for which a State may receive authorization is defined in 40 CFR part 271. The State's program, as administered by the Missouri Department of Natural Resources was approved by EPA pursuant to 42 U.S.C. 6926(b) and part 271 of this Chapter. EPA's approval was effective on December 4, 1985 (50 FR 47740, November 20, 1985).

(b) Missouri is not authorized to implement any HSWA requirements in lieu of EPA unless EPA has explicitly indicated its intent to allow such action in a *Federal Register* notice granting Missouri authorization.

(c) Missouri has primary responsibility for enforcing its hazardous waste program. However, EPA retains the authority to exercise its enforcement authorities under sections 3007, 3008, 3013, and 7003 of RCRA, 42 U.S.C. 6927, 6928, 6934, and 6973, as well as under other Federal laws and regulations.

(d) Missouri must revise its approved program to adopt new changes to the Federal Subtitle C program in accordance with section 3006(b) of RCRA and 40 CFR part 271, subpart A. Missouri must seek final authorization for all program revisions pursuant to section 3006(b) of RCRA, but, on a temporary basis, may seek interim authorization for revisions required by HSWA pursuant to section 3006(g) of RCRA, 42 U.S.C. 6926(g). If Missouri obtains final authorization for the revised requirements pursuant to section 3006(g), the newly authorized provisions will be listed in §272.1301 of this subpart. If Missouri obtains interim authorization for the revised requirements pursuant to section 3006(g), the newly authorized provision will be listed in §227.1302.

[54 FR 8193, Feb. 27, 1989]

§272.1301 State-administered program; Final authorization.

Pursuant to section 3006(b) of RCRA, 42 U.S.C. 6926(b), Missouri has final authorization for the following elements as submitted to EPA in Missouri's program application for final authorization which was approved on November 20, 1985. Subsequent program revision applications were approved on February 27, 1989, and March 12, 1992. Copies may be obtained from the Hazardous Waste Program, Missouri Department of Natural Resources, P.O. Box 176, Jefferson City, Missouri 65102.

(a) *State statutes and regulations.* (1) The Missouri statutes and regulations cited in this paragraph are incorporated by reference as part of the hazardous waste management program under subtitle C of RCRA, 42 U.S.C. 6921 *et seq.*

(i) Missouri Statutory Requirements Applicable to the Hazardous Waste Management Program, 1990.

(ii) Missouri Regulatory Requirements Applicable to the Hazardous Waste Management Program, December 31, 1990.

(2) The following statutes and regulations, although not incorporated by reference for enforcement purposes, are part of the authorized State program. The statutory provisions include: 260.360(4), 260.360(20)-260.377, 260.393-260.394, 260.400, 260.410-260.420, 260.425-260.430. The regulatory provisions include 3.260(1)(A)24-3.260(1)(A)25, 3.260(1)(B)-3.260(1)(D), 4.261(2)(D)3, 5.262(2)(B)2, 5.262(2)(C)2, 5.262(2)(D)1, 6.263(2)(A)10.D-6.263(2)(A)10.I, 6.263(2)(D)3, 7.264(2)(B)1, 7.265(2)(B), 7.266(2)(E)-7.266(2)(E)3, 7.268(2)(A)1, 7.268(2)(A)3, 7.268(2)(E), 7.270(2)(B)12-7.270(2)(B)13, 7.270(2)(B)18, 7.270(2)(C)1.D, 7.270(2)(C)3, 7.270(2)(D)4.

(3) The following statutory and regulatory provisions are broader in scope than the Federal program, and are not part of the authorized State program. The statutory provisions include: 260.360(13), 260.379, 260.380-1.(10), 260.385(1), 260.390(8), 260.391, 260.395-1-260.295-5, 260.395-7.(5)-260.395-7.(6), 260.396, 260.405, 260.423-260.424, 260.431-260.434. The regulatory provisions include: 3.260(1)(A)21, 4.261(2)(A)6-4.261(2)(D)2, 5.262(2)(I), 6.263(2)(A)3-6.263(2)(A)4, 7.264(2)(P), 7.266(2)(C)-7.266(2)(D), 7.266(2)(E)4-7.266(2)(G), 7.270(2)(B)7-7.270(2)(B)8, 7.270(2)(B)10, 7.270(2)(C)1.A, 7.270(2)(H).

(b) *Memorandum of Agreement.* The Memorandum of Agreement between EPA Region VII and the Missouri Department of Natural Resources, signed by the EPA Regional Administrator on August 30, 1988, and the subsequent Agreement signed on August 31, 1992 are referenced as part of the authorized hazardous waste management program under subtitle C of RCRA, 42 U.S.C. 6921 *et seq.*

(c) *Statement of Legal Authority.* (1) "Attorney General's Statement for Final Authorization," signed by the Attorney General of Missouri on June 27, 1985, is codified as part of the authorized hazardous waste management program under Subtitle C of RCRA, 42 U.S.C. 6921 *et seq.*

(2) "Attorney General's Statement for Final Authorization of Changes to the Federal RCRA Program," signed by the delegated Assistant Attorney General of Missouri on December 1, 1987, and the subsequent Statement signed on February 28, 1992, are referenced as part of the authorized hazardous waste management program under subtitle C of RCRA; 42 U.S.C. 6921 *et seq.*

(d) *Program Description.* The Program Description and any other materials submitted as part of the original application or as supplements thereto are codified as part of the authorized hazardous waste management program under Subtitle C of RCRA, 42 U.S.C. 6921 *et seq.*

[54 FR 8193, Feb. 27, 1989, as amended at 58 FR 3500, Jan. 11, 1993]

§§272.1302–272.1349 [Reserved]

Subpart BB—Montana

§272.1350 [Reserved]

§272.1351 Montana State-Administered program: Final Authorization.

(a) Pursuant to section 3006(b) of RCRA, 42 U.S.C. 6926(b), Montana has final authorization for the following elements as submitted to EPA in Montana's base program application for final authorization which was approved by EPA effective on July 25, 1984. Subsequent program revision applications were approved effective on, March 21, 1994, December 24, 1996, December 26, 2000 and November 29, 2005.

(b) The State of Montana has primary responsibility for enforcing its hazardous waste management program. However, EPA retains the authority to exercise its inspection and enforcement authorities in accordance with sections 3007, 3008, 3013, 7003 of RCRA, 42 U.S.C. 6927, 6928, 6934, 6973, and any other applicable statutory and regulatory provisions, regardless of whether the State has taken its own actions, as well as in accordance with other statutory and regulatory provisions.

(c) *State Statutes and Regulations.* (1) The Montana regulations cited in paragraph (c)(1)(i) of this section are incorporated by reference as part of the hazardous waste management program under subtitle C of RCRA, 42 U.S.C. 6921 *et seq.* This incorporation by reference is approved by the Director of the Federal Register in accordance with 5 U.S.C. 552(a) and 1 CFR part 51. Copies of the Montana regulations that are incorporated by reference in this paragraph are available from the Montana Secretary of State, Administrative Rules Bureau, P.O. Box 202801, Helena, MT 59620–2801 (Phone: 406–444–2055). You may inspect a copy at EPA Region 8, from 7 a.m. to 4 p.m., 999 18th Street, Suite 300, Denver, Colorado 80202–2466, or at the National Archives and Records Administration (NARA). For information on the availability of this material at NARA, call 202–741–6030, or go to: *http://www.archives.gov/federal-register/cfr/ibr-locations.html.*

(i) The Binder entitled "EPA Approved Montana Regulatory Requirements Applicable to the Hazardous Waste Management Program", dated November 2005.

(ii) [Reserved]

(2) EPA considered the following statutes and regulations in evaluating the State program but is not incorporating them herein for enforcement purposes:

(i) Montana Code Annotated (MCA) 2005, Title 2, "Government Structure and Administration": Chapter 3, "Public Participation in Governmental Operations", sections 2–3–102 introductory paragraph through 2–3–102(2), 2–3–103(1), 2–3–104, 2–3–105, 2–3–111, 2–3–112, 2–3–221, 2–3–301; Chapter 4, "Administrative Procedure Act", sections 2–4–103, 2–4–315; Chapter 6, "Public Records", sections 2–6–101 *et seq.*; Chapter 15, "Executive Branch Officers and Agencies", sections 2–15–3501 and 2–15–3502.

(ii) Montana Code Annotated (MCA) 2005, Title 25, "Civil Procedure": Chapter 20, "Rules of Civil Procedure", Rule 24(a).

(iii) Montana Code Annotated (MCA) 2005, Title 27, "Civil Liability, Remedies, and Limitations": Chapter 30, "Nuisances", section 27–30–204.

(iv) Montana Code Annotated (MCA) 2005, Title 30, "Trade and Commerce": Chapter 14, "Unfair Trade Practices and Consumer Protection", sections 30–14–402 *et seq.*

(v) Montana Code Annotated (MCA) 2005, Title 75, "Environmental Protection": Chapter 10, "Waste and Litter Control", sections 75–10–107, 75–10–402(3), 75–10–403, 75–10–404(1) introductory paragraph and (1)(a), 75–10–404(1)(e), 75–10–404(2), 75–10–405 (except 75–10–405(1)(i), (1)(j) and (2)(a)), 75–10–406, 75–10–408, 75–10–409, 75–10–410, 75–10–411, 75–10–413, 75–10–414, 75–10–415, 75–10–416, 75–10–417, 75–10–418, 75–10–419, 75–10–420, 75–10–421, 75–10–422, 75–10–424, 75–10–425, 75–10–426, 75–10–427, 75–10–441 and 75–10–442; Chapter 20, "Major Facility Siting".

(vi) Administrative Rules of Montana (ARM), effective April 1, 2005, Title 17, "Environmental Quality": Chapter 53, Hazardous Waste, sections 17.53.104, 17.53.201, 17.53.202, 17.53.206, 17.53.207, 17.53.208, 17.53.212, 17.53.213, 17.53.214, 17.53.215, 17.53.1202(5)(m), 17.53.1202(6).

(3) The following statutory and regulatory provisions are broader in scope than the Federal program, are not part of the authorized program, are not incorporated by reference and are not federally enforceable:

(i) Montana Code Annotated (MCA) 2005, Title 75, "Environmental Protection": Chapter 10, "Waste and

Litter Control", sections 75–10–405(1)(i) & (j), 75–10–405(2)(a), 75–10–431, 75–10–432, 75–10–433, 75–10–434.

(ii) Administrative Rules of Montana (ARM), effective April 1, 2005, Title 17, "Environmental Quality", Chapter 53, Hazardous Waste, sections 17.53.112, 17.53.113, 17.53.703, and 17.53.1202(5)(l), and (17).

(4) *Memorandum of Agreement and Enforcement Agreement.* The Memorandum of Agreement between EPA Region 8 and the State of Montana, signed by the State of Montana Department of Environmental Quality on November 30, 1993, and by the EPA Regional Administrator on December 25, 1993, and the Enforcement Agreement between EPA Region 8 and the State of Montana, signed by the State of Montana Department of Environmental Quality on September 1, 2000, and by the EPA Regional Administrator on September 11, 2000, although not incorporated by reference, are referenced as part of the authorized hazardous waste management program under subtitle C of RCRA, 42 U.S.C. 6921 *et seq.*

(5) *Statement of Legal Authority.* "Independent Legal Counsel Statement", accompanied by an Attorney General concurrence letter signed by the Attorney General of Montana on December 27, 1983 as amended June 7, 1984 and revisions, supplements and addenda to that Statement accompanied by Attorney General concurrence letters dated September 23, 1993, March 28, 1995, June 29, 1995, and April 4, 2005 although not incorporated by reference, are referenced as part of the authorized hazardous waste management program under subtitle C of RCRA, 42 U.S.C. 6921 *et seq.*

(6) *Program Description.* The Program Description and any other materials submitted as supplements thereto, although not incorporated by reference, are referenced as part of the authorized hazardous waste management program under subtitle C of RCRA, 42 U.S.C. 6921 *et seq.*

[71 FR 11538, Mar. 8, 2006]

§§272.1352–272.1399 [Reserved]

Subpart CC—Nebraska

§§272.1400–272.1449 [Reserved]

Subpart DD—Nevada

§§272.1450–272.1499 [Reserved]

Subpart EE—New Hampshire

§§272.1500–272.1549 [Reserved]

Subpart FF—New Jersey

§§272.1550–272.1599 [Reserved]

Subpart GG—New Mexico

§272.1600 [Reserved]

§272.1601 New Mexico State-Administered Program: Final Authorization.

(a) Pursuant to section 3006(b) of RCRA, 42 U.S.C. 6926(b), the EPA granted New Mexico final authorization for the following elements as submitted to EPA in New Mexico's base program application for final authorization which was approved by EPA effective on January 25, 1985. Subsequent program revision applications were approved effective on April 10, 1990, July 25, 1990, December 4, 1992, August 23, 1994, December 21, 1994, July 10, 1995, January 2, 1996, March 10, 1997, October 9, 2001, and October 16, 2007.

(b) The State of New Mexico has primary responsibility for enforcing its hazardous waste management program. However, EPA retains the authority to exercise its inspection and enforcement authorities in accordance with sections 3007, 3008, 3013, 7003 of RCRA, 42 U.S.C. 6927, 6928, 6934, 6973, and any other applicable statutory and regulatory provisions, regardless of whether the State has taken its own actions, as well as in accordance with other statutory and regulatory provisions.

(c) *State Statutes and Regulations.* (1) The New Mexico statutes and regulations cited in paragraph (c)(1)(i) of this section are incorporated by reference as part of the hazardous waste management program under subtitle C of RCRA, 42 U.S.C. 6921 *et seq.* The Director of the Federal Register approves this incorporation by reference in accordance with 5 U.S.C. 552(a) and 1 CFR part 51. You may obtain copies of the New Mexico regulations that are incorporated by reference in this paragraph from the New Mexico Commission of Public Records, State Records Center and Archives, Administrative Law Division, 1205 Camino Carlos Rey, Santa Fe, NM 87507; Phone number (505) 476–7907; Web site: http://www.nmcpr.state.nm.us/. The statutes are available from ConwayGreene Company, 1400 East 30th Street, Suite #402, Cleveland, OH 44114; Phone number (216) 619–8091; Web site: *http://www.conwaygreene.com.* You may inspect a copy at EPA Region 6, 1445 Ross Avenue, Dallas, Texas 75202 (Phone number (214) 665–8533), or at the National Archives and Records Administration (NARA). For information on the availability of this material at NARA, call 202–741–6030, or go to: *http://www.archives.gov/federal-register/cfr/ibr-locations.html.*

(i) The binder entitled "EPA Approved New Mexico Statutory and Regulatory Requirements Applicable to the Hazardous Waste Management Program", dated October 2007.

(ii) [Reserved]

(2) The following provisions provide the legal basis for the State's implementation of the hazardous waste management program, but they are not being incorporated by reference and do not replace Federal authorities:

(i) New Mexico Rules Annotated, Rules of Civil Procedure for the District Courts, Article 4, (1995), Section 1–024.

(ii) New Mexico Statutes 1978 Annotated, Inspection of Public Records Act, Chapter 14, Article 2, (2003 Replacement Pamphlet), Sections 14–2–1 *et seq.*

(iii) New Mexico Statutes 1978 Annotated, Hazardous Waste Act, Chapter 74, Article 4, (2000 Replacement Pamphlet), Sections 74–4–4.1, 74–4–4.2.C through 74–4–4.2.F, 74–4–4.2.G(1), 74–4–4.2.H, 74–4–4.2.I, 74–4–4.7.B and .C, 74–4–5, 74–4–7, 74–4–10.1 (except 74–4–10.1.C), and 74–4–14.

(iv) New Mexico Statutes 1978 Annotated, Hazardous Waste Act, Chapter 74, Article 4, (2002 Cumulative Supplement), Sections 74–4–4 (except 74–4–4E), 74–4–4.3 (except 74–4–4.3.A(2) and 74–4–4.3.F), 74–4–10, 74–4–11 through 74–4–13.

(v) Title 20, Chapter 4, Part 1, New Mexico Administrative Code, effective October 1, 2003, unless otherwise indicated: Sections 20.4.1.901 (except 20.4.1.901.B.1 through 20.4.1.901.B.6, and 20.4.1.901.E), 20.4.1.1100 (June 14, 2000), 20.4.1.1104 (June 14, 2000), 20.4.1.1105 (June 14, 2000), and 20.4.1.1107.

(3)(i) The following statutory provisions are broader in scope than the Federal program, are not part of the authorized program, and are not incorporated by reference:

(ii) New Mexico Statutes 1978 Annotated, Hazardous Waste Act, Chapter 74, Article 4, (2000 Replacement Pamphlet), Sections 74–4–3.3 and 74–4–4.2.J.

(4) *Unauthorized State Amendments.* The State's adoption of the Federal rules listed in the following table is not approved by the EPA and are, therefore, not enforceable:

Federal requirement	Federal Register reference	Publication date
Biennial Report	48 FR 3977	01/28/83
Permit Rules; Settlement Agreement	48 FR 39611	09/01/83
Interim Status Standards; Applicability	48 FR 52718	11/22/83
Chlorinated Aliphatic Hydrocarbon Listing (F024)	49 FR 5308	02/10/84
National Uniform Manifest	49 FR 10490	03/20/84
Recycled Used Oil Management Standards	57 FR 41566: Amendments to 40 CFR Parts 260, 261 and 266	09/10/92
	58 FR 26420: Amendments to 40 CFR Parts 261, 264 and 265	05/03/93
	58 FR 33341: Amendments to 40 CFR Parts 261, 264 and 265	06/17/93
	63 FR 24963: Amendments to 40 CFR Part 261	05/06/98
Mineral Processing Secondary Materials	63 FR 28556; Amendments to 40 CFR Part 261	05/26/98

(5) *Memorandum of Agreement.* The Memorandum of Agreement between EPA Region 6 and the State of New Mexico, signed by the EPA Regional Administrator on July 25, 2007, is referenced as part of the authorized hazardous waste management program under subtitle C of RCRA, 42 U.S.C. 6921 *et seq.*

(6) *Statement of Legal Authority.* "Attorney General's Statement for Final Authorization", signed by the Attorney General of New Mexico January 1985, and revisions, supplements and addenda to that Statement dated April 13, 1988; September 14, 1988; July 19, 1989; July 23, 1992; February 14, 1994; July 18, 1994; July 20, 1994; August 11, 1994; November 28, 1994; August 24, 1995; January 12, 1996; June 14, 2000, and August 3, 2006, are referenced as part of the authorized hazardous waste management program under subtitle C of RCRA, 42 U.S.C. 6921 *et seq.*

(7) *Program Description.* The Program Description and any other materials submitted as supplements thereto are referenced as part of the authorized hazardous waste management program under subtitle C of RCRA, 42 U.S.C. 6921 *et seq.*

[63 FR 23224, Apr. 28, 1998; 68 FR 51487, Aug. 27, 2003; 73 FR 63900, Oct. 28, 2008]

§§272.1602–272.1649 [Reserved]

Subpart HH—New York

§272.1650 [Reserved]

§272.1651 New York State-Administered Program: final authorization.

(a) Pursuant to section 3006(b) of RCRA, 42 U.S.C. 6926(b), New York has final authorization for the following elements as submitted to EPA in New York's base program application for final authorization which was approved by EPA effective on May 29, 1986. Subsequent program revision applications were approved effective on July 3, 1989, May 7, 1990, October 29, 1991, May 22, 1992, August 28, 1995, October 14, 1997, January 15, 2002 and March 14, 2005.

(b) The State of New York has primary responsibility for enforcing its hazardous waste management program. However, EPA retains the authority to exercise its inspection and enforcement authorities in accordance with sections 3007, 3008, 3013, 7003 of RCRA, 42 U.S.C. 6927, 6928, 6934, 6973, and any other applicable statutory and regulatory provisions, regardless of whether the State has taken its own actions, as well as in accordance with other statutory and regulatory provisions.

(c) *State Statutes and Regulations.* (1) The New York regulations cited in paragraph (c)(1)(i) of this section are incorporated by reference as part of the hazardous waste management program under subtitle C of RCRA, 42 U.S.C. 6921 *et seq.* The Director of *Federal Register* approves this incorporation by reference in accordance with 5 U.S.C. 552(a) and 1 CFR part 51. You may obtain copies of the New York regulations that are incorporated by reference in this paragraph from West Group, 610 Opperman Drive, Eagan, MN 55123, ATTENTION: D3-10 (Phone #: 1-800-328-9352). You may inspect a copy at EPA Region 2 Library, 290 Broadway, 16th Floor, New York, NY 10007 (Phone number: (212) 637-3185), or at the National Archives and Records Administration (NARA). For information on the availability of this material at NARA, call 202-741-6030, or go to: http://www.archives.gov/federal-register/cfr/ibr-locations.html.

(i) The Binder entitled "EPA Approved New York Regulatory Requirements Applicable to the Hazardous Waste Management Program", dated March 2005.

(ii) [Reserved]

(2) EPA considered the following statutes and regulations in evaluating the State program but is not incorporating them herein for enforcement purposes:

(i) Environmental Conservation Laws (ECL), 1997 Replacement Volume, as revised by the 2004 Cumulative Pocket Part: sections 1–0303(18), 3–0301(1) (introductory paragraph); 3–0301(1)(a) and (b); 3–0301(1)(m); 3–0301(1)(o); 3–0301(1)(w); 3–0301(1)(x); 3–0301(1)(cc); 3–0301(2) introductory paragraph; 3–0301(2)(a), (b), (d) through (j), (l), (m) and (q); 3–0301(2)(z); 3–0301(4); 19–0301(1) (except 19–0301(c), (e) and (f)); 19–0303(1) through (3); 19–0304; 27–0105; 27–0701; 27–0703; 27–0705; 27–0707 (except 27–0707(2-c)); 27–0711; 27–0900 through 27–0908; 27–0909 (except 27–0909(5)); 27–0910 through 27–0922; 27–1105; 70–0101; 70–0103; 70–0105 (except 70–0105(3) and 70–0105(6)); 70–0107(1) and (2); 70–0107(3) (except 70–0107(3)(a) through (k), (m) and (n)); 70–0109; 70–0113; 70–0115 (except (2)(c) and (d)); 70–0117; 70–0119; 70–0121; 71–0301; 71–1719; 71–2705; 71–2707; 71–2709 through 71–2715; 71–2717; 71–2720; and 71–2727.

(iii) McKinney's Consolidated Laws of New York, Book 1, Executive Law (EL), Article 6: section 102.

(iv) McKinney's Consolidated Laws of New York, Book 46, Public Officers Law (POL), as amended through 2004: sections 87 and 89 (except the phrase "and one-a" at 89(5)(a)(3), and 89(5)(a)(1–a)).

(v) McKinney's Consolidated Laws of New York, Book 7B, Civil Practice Law and Rules (CPLR), as amended through 2004: sections 1013, 6301; 6311; and 6313.

(vi) Title 6, New York Codes, Rules and Regulations (6 NYCRR), Volume A–2A, Hazardous Waste Management System, as amended through April 10, 2004: sections 372.1(f); 373–1.1(f) and (g); 373–1.4(b); 373–1.4(d) through (f); 373–1.6(c); 621.1 through 621.4; 621.5 (except (d)(5), (d)(6)(i), (d)(7)(i)(a), (d)(7)(i)(c) and (d)(9)); 621.6 (except (b), (d)(4) and (d)(5)); 621.7; 621.8; 621.9 (except (a)(5), (c)(2) and (e)(2)); 621.10; 621.11 (except (d)); 621.12 through 621.15; and 621.16 (except (b), (d) and (e)).

(3) The following statutory and regulatory provisions are broader in scope than the Federal program, are not part of the authorized program, are not incorporated by reference and are not federally enforceable:

(i) Environmental Conservation Laws (ECL), 1997 Replacement Volume, as revised by the 2004 Cumulative Pocket Part: sections 27–0301; 27–0303; 27–0305; 27–0307; 27–0909(5); 27–0923; 27–0925 and 27–0926.

(ii) Title 6, New York Codes, Rules and Regulations (6 NYCRR), Volume A–2A, Hazardous Waste Management System, as amended through April 10, 2004:

Section 371.4(e); 372.3(a)(1); 372.3(a)(4); 372.3(b)(6)(iv); 372.3(d)(3); 373–1.1(d)(1)(x); 373–1.4(c); 373–2.15(a)(2); and 374–3.4(a)(2).

(iii) Throughout New York's hazardous waste regulations, the State cross-references Part 364, which sets forth additional transporter requirements including permit and liability requirements (for examples, see 6 NYCRR sections 372.2(b)(8), 373–1.7(h)(3), 374–3.3(i)(1) and (2), 374–3.4(a) and 374–3.6(a)(1)). The transporter permit and liability requirements are broader in scope than the Federal program.

(iv) New York did not adopt an analog to 40 CFR 261.4(g) that excludes certain dredged materials from the State definition of hazardous waste. Instead, the State subjects these materials to full regulation as hazardous wastes.

(v) New York State regulations do not incorporate the Mineral Processing Secondary Materials Exclusion at 40 CFR 261.4(a)(17) and the related changes affecting 40 CFR 261.2(c)(3) and (c)(4)/Table, and 40 CFR 261.2(e)(1)(iii). Since New York did not adopt the exclusion at 40 CFR 261.4(a)(17) the State has a broader in scope program because the effect is to include materials that are not considered solid waste by EPA.

(4) *Unauthorized State Amendments.* (i) The authorized provisions at sections 371.1(c)(7), 373-1.3(d)(3), and 373-2.8(a)(3) of 6 NYCRR, as amended through April 10, 2004, include amendments that are not approved by EPA. Such unauthorized amendments are not part of the State's authorized program and are, therefore, not Federally enforceable. Thus, notwithstanding the language in the New York hazardous waste regulations incorporated by reference at paragraph (b)(1)(i) of this section, EPA will enforce the State regulations that are actually authorized by EPA. The effective dates of the State's authorized provisions are listed in the following Table:

Title 6—New York Codes, Rules and Regulations (6 NYCRR)

State citation	Description	Effective date
371.1(c)(7)	Definition of Solid Waste. Documentation of claims for exemption	
373-2.8(a)(3)	Submission of applications	
373-1.3(d)(3)	Financial Requirements. States and Federal government are exempt from the requirements of this section	

(ii) The actual State regulatory text authorized by EPA (*i.e.*, without the unauthorized amendments) is available as a separate document, *Addendum to the EPA Approved New York Regulatory Requirements Applicable to the Hazardous Waste Management Program, March 2005.* This document is available from EPA Region 2, EPA Region 2 Library, 290 Broadway, 16th Floor, New York, New York 10007, Phone number: (212) 637–3185.

(5) *Memorandum of Agreement.* The Memorandum of Agreement between EPA Region 2 and the State of New York, signed by the Commissioner of the State of New York Department of Environmental Conservation on July 20, 2001, and by the EPA Regional Administrator on January 16, 2002, although not incorporated by reference, is referenced as part of the authorized hazardous waste management program under subtitle C of RCRA, 42 U.S.C. 6921 *et seq.*

(6) *Statement of Legal Authority.* "Attorney General's Statement for Final Authorization", signed by the Attorney General of New York in 1985 and revisions, supplements and addenda to that Statement dated August 18, 1988, July 26, 1989, August 15, 1991, October 11, 1991, July 28, 1994, May 30, 1997, February 5, 2001, and April 2, 2004, although not incorporated by reference, are referenced as part of the authorized hazardous waste management program under subtitle C of RCRA, 42 U.S.C. 6921 *et seq.*

(7) *Program Description.* The Program Description and any other materials submitted as supplements thereto, although not incorporated by reference, are referenced as part of the authorized hazardous waste management program under subtitle C of RCRA, 42 U.S.C. 6921 *et seq.*

[72 FR 14047, Mar. 26, 2007]

§§272.1652–272.1699 [Reserved]

Subpart II—North Carolina

§§272.1700–272.1749 [Reserved]

Subpart JJ—North Dakota

§272.1750 [Reserved]

§272.1751 North Dakota State-administered program: Final authorization.

(a) Pursuant to section 3006(b) of RCRA, 42 U.S.C. 6926(b), North Dakota has final authorization for the following elements as submitted to EPA in North Dakota's base program application for final authorization which was approved by EPA effective on October 19,

1984. Subsequent program revision applications were approved effective on August 24, 1990, July 6, 1992, June 6, 1994, March 20, 2000, November 25, 2005, and April 14, 2008.

(b) The State of North Dakota has primary responsibility for enforcing its hazardous waste management program. However, EPA retains the authority to exercise its inspection and enforcement authorities in accordance with sections 3007, 3008, 3013, 7003 of RCRA, 42 U.S.C. 6927, 6928, 6934, 6973, and any other applicable statutory and regulatory provisions, regardless of whether the State has taken its own actions, as well as in accordance with other statutory and regulatory provisions.

(c) *State Statutes and Regulations.*

(1) The North Dakota statutes and regulations cited in paragraph (c)(1)(i) of this section are incorporated by reference as part of the hazardous waste management program under subtitle C of RCRA, 42 U.S.C. 6921, *et seq.* The Director of the Federal Register approves this incorporation by reference in accordance with 5 U.S.C. 552(a) and 1 CFR part 51. You may obtain copies of the North Dakota statutes that are incorporated by reference from the Matthew Bender & Company Inc., P. O. Box 7587, Charlottesville, VA, 22906-7587, phone number: (800) 833-9844. You may obtain copies of the North Dakota regulations that are incorporated by reference in this paragraph from the North Dakota Legislative Counsel, Second Floor, State Capitol, 600 E Boulevard, Bismarck ND 58505, phone: (701) 328-2916. You may inspect a copy at EPA Region 8, from 7 a.m. to 4 p.m., 1595 Wynkoop Street, Denver, CO, 80202, or at the National Archives and Records Administration (NARA). For information on the availability of this material at NARA, call 202-741-6030, or go to: *http://www.archives.gov/federal-register/cfr/ibr-locations.html.*

(i) The Binder entitled "EPA Approved North Dakota Statutory and Regulatory Requirements Applicable to the Hazardous Waste Management Program", dated July 2006.

(ii) [Reserved]

(2) EPA considered the following statutes and regulations in evaluating the State program but is not incorporating them herein for enforcement purposes:

(i) North Dakota Century Code, 1998 Replacement, Volume 13A, North Dakota Constitution, Article XI: Sections 5 and 6.

(ii) North Dakota Century Code, 2002 Replacement, Volume 4A, Chapter 23–01 "Department of Health" Section 23–01–04.1, (except (6)).

(iii) North Dakota Century Code, Volume 4A, 2002 Replacement, as amended by the 2005 Pocket Supplement. Chapter 23–20.3 "Hazardous Waste": Sections 23–20.3–01, (except (5) and (6)); 23–20.3–02, (except (1), (9), (11), (12), and (17)); 23–20.3–03; 23–20.3–04; 23–20.3–05(3), (5), (6), and (8); 23–20.3–06; 23–20.3–07; 23–20.3–08; 23–20.3–09; and 23–20.3–10.

(iv) North Dakota Century Code, Volume 4A, 2002 Replacement. Chapter 23–29 "Solid Waste Management": Section 23–29–04.

(v) North Dakota Century Code, Volume 5, 1991 Replacement. Chapter 28–32 "Administrative Agencies Practice Act": Section 28–32–21.1.

(vi) North Dakota Century Code, Volume 6, 1996 Replacement. Chapter 32–40 "Environmental Law Enforcement": Sections 32–40–03; 32–40–04; 32–40–05; 32–40–06; 32–40–07; 32–40–08; 32–40–09; 32–40–10; and 32–40–11.

(vii) North Dakota Century Code, Volume 9A, 2001 Replacement, as amended by the 2003 Pocket Supplement. Chapter 44–04 "Duties, Records, and Meetings": Sections 44–04–18; 44–04–18.1; 44–04–18.2; 44–04–18.3; 44–04–18.4; 44–04–18.5; 44–04–18.6; 44–04–18.7; 44–04–18.8; 44–04–19; and 44–04–19.1.

(viii) North Dakota Administrative Code (NDAC), Article 33–24, Hazardous Waste Management, as amended through December 1, 2003: sections 33–24–01–15; 33–24–01–16; 33–24–06–05, (except .1.c); 33–24–06–06.2 and .3; 33–24–06–09; 33–24–06–15, (except introductory paragraph through .1.a); 33–24–07–03.4; 33–24–07–04 through 33–24–07–14; and 33–24–07–25 through 33–24–07–27.

(3) The following statutory and regulatory provisions are broader in scope than the federal program, are not part of the authorized program, are not incorporated by reference and are not federally enforceable:

(i) North Dakota Century Code, 2002 Replacement, Volume 4A, Chapter 23– 01: "Department of Health", "Rulemaking Authority and Procedure" Section 23–01–04.1(6).

(ii) North Dakota Century Code, Volume 4A, 2002 Replacement, as amended by the 2005 Pocket Supplement. Chapter 23–20.3 "Hazardous Waste": Sections 23–20.3–02 (1); 23–20.3–05.1; 23–20.3–05.2; and 23–20.3–05.3.

(iii) North Dakota Administrative Code (NDAC), Article 33–24, "Hazardous Waste Management", as amended through December 1, 2003, sections 33–24–04–02.3, 33–24–06–14.3.a(4) and 33–24–06–21.

(iv) North Dakota's hazardous waste regulations set forth additional transporter requirements including permit requirements at 33–24–04–02. The transporter permit requirements are broader in scope than the federal program.

(4) *Unauthorized State Amendments.* (i) The authorized provisions at sections of the NDAC Article 33:24, as amended through December 1, 2003 include amendments that are not approved by EPA. Such unauthorized amendments are not part of the State's authorized program and are, therefore, not federally enforceable. Thus, notwithstanding the language in the North Dakota hazardous waste regulations incorporated by reference at paragraph (c)(1)(i) of this section, EPA will enforce the State regulations that are actually authorized by EPA. The effective dates of the State's authorized provisions are listed in the following table.

North Dakota Administrative Code (NDAC), Article 33–24

State citation	Description	Effective date
33–24–02–07.4 introductory paragraph	Residues of Hazardous Waste in Empty Containers	10/1/86
33–24–03–12.2	Accumulation Time	1/1/84
33–24–05–421	Applicability of Definitions	12/1/91
33–24–06–17.2.y(8)	Contents of Permit Application	1/1/84

(ii) The actual State regulatory text authorized by EPA (i.e., without the unauthorized amendments) is available as a separate document, *Addendum to the EPA Approved North Dakota Statutory and Regulatory Requirements Applicable to the Hazardous Waste Management Program, July 2006.* This document is available from EPA Region 8, from 9 a.m. to 4 p.m., 1595 Wynkoop Street, Denver, Colorado 80202.

(5) *Memorandum of Agreement.* The Memorandum of Agreement between EPA Region 8 and the State of North Dakota, signed by the State of North Dakota State Department of Health on June 6, 2003, and by the EPA Regional Administrator on August 29, 2003, although not incorporated by reference, is referenced as part of the authorized hazardous waste management program under subtitle C of RCRA, 42 U.S.C. 6921, *et seq.*

(6) *Statement of Legal Authority.* "Attorney General's Statement: Hazardous Waste Management Program" signed by the Attorney General of North Dakota on June 8, 1984, and revisions, supplements, and addenda to that Statement dated February 22, 1989, February 11, 1994, October 13, 1999, April 23, 2004, and August 19, 2004, although not incorporated by reference, are referenced as part of the authorized hazardous waste management program under subtitle C of RCRA, 42 U.S.C. 6921, *et seq.*

(7) *Program Description.* The Program Description and any other materials submitted as supplements thereto, although not incorporated by reference, are referenced as part of the authorized hazardous waste management program under subtitle C of RCRA, 42 U.S.C. 6921, *et seq.*

[73 FR 8615, Feb. 14, 2008]

§§272.1752–272.1799 [Reserved]

Subpart KK—Ohio

§272.1800 State authorization.

(a) The State of Ohio is authorized to administer and enforce a hazardous waste management program in lieu of the Federal program under subtitle C of the Resource Conservation and Recovery Act of 1976 (RCRA), 42 U.S.C. 6291 *et seq.*, subject to the Hazardous and Solid Waste Amendments of 1984 (HSWA) (Pub. L. 98-616, November 8, 1984), 42 U.S.C. 6926 (c) and (g). The Federal program for which a State may receive authorization is defined in 40 CFR part 271. The State's program, as administered by the Ohio Environmental Protection Agency, was approved by EPA pursuant to 42 U.S.C. 6926(b) and part 271 of this chapter. EPA's approval of Ohio's base RCRA program was effective on June 30, 1989 (see 54 FR 27173). EPA's approval of revisions to Ohio's base program was effective on June 7, 1991 (see 56 FR 14203) and August 19, 1991 (see 56 FR 28088).

(b) Ohio is authorized to implement certain HSWA requirements in lieu of EPA. EPA has explicitly indicated its intent to allow much action in a *Federal Register* notice granting Ohio authorization on June 7, 1991 (see 56 FR 14203) and August 19, 1991 (see 56 FR 28088).

(c) Ohio has primary responsibility for enforcing its hazardous waste program. However, EPA retains the authority to exercise its enforcement authorities under Section 3007, 3008, 3013, and 7003 of RCRA, 42 U.S.C. 6927,

6928, 6934, and 6973, as well as under other Federal laws and regulations.

(d) Ohio must revise its approved program to adopt new changes to the Federal Subtitle C program, in accordance with section 3006(b) of RCRA and 40 CFR part 271, subpart A. Ohio must seek final authorization for all program revisions pursuant to section 3006(b) of RCRA but, on a temporary basis, may seek interim authorization for revisions required by HSWA pursuant to section 3006(b) of RCRA, 42 U.S.C. 6926(g). If Ohio obtains final authorization for the revised requirements pursuant to section 3006(b), the newly authorized provisions will be listed in 272.1801 of this subpart. If Ohio in the future obtains interim authorization for the revised requirements pursuant to section 3006(g), the newly authorized provisions will be listed in §272.1802.

[54 FR 27173, June 28, 1989, as amended at 57 FR 4162, Feb. 4, 1992]

§272.1801 State-administered program: Final authorization.

Pursuant to section 3006(b) of RCRA, 42 U.S.C. 6926(b): Ohio has final authorization for the following elements submitted to EPA in Ohio's program application for final authorization and approved by EPA effective on June 30, 1989 (see 54 FR 27173), June 7, 1991 (see 56 FR 14203) and August 19, 1991 (see 56 FR 28088).

(a) *State Statutes and Regulations.* (1) The following Ohio regulations are incorporated by reference and codified as part of the hazardous waste management program under subtitle C of RCRA, 42 U.S.C. 6921 *et seq.* This incorporation by reference was approved by the Director of the *Federal Register* in accordance with 5 U.S.C. 552(a). Ohio Administrative Code, volume 4, chapter 3745, rules: 49-031; 50-01; 50-03; 50-10; 50-11; 50-31 through 50-32; 50-40 through 50-44(C)(3)(j); 50-44(C)(4) through 50-44(C)(4)(k); 50-44(C)(5) through 50-44(C)(5)(i); 50-44(C)(6) through 50-44(C)(7)(j); 50-44(C)(8) through 51-03(C)(2)(b)(ii); 51-03 (D) and (E); 51-04 through 51-05; 51-06(A)(1) through 51-06(A)(3)(g); 51-06(B) through 52-20(F); 52-20 Appendix I through 52-34(F); 52-40 through 52-44; 52-50 through 53-10; 53-11(D) through 53-20(H); 53-21 through 54-99; 55-02 through 55-99; 56-20 through 56-31; 56-33 (A) and (B); 56-50 through 56-60; 56-70 through 56-83; 57-01 through 57-14(B); 57-14(E); 57-15 through 57-18; 57-40 through 58-40; 58-42; 58-43 through 58-44; 58-45(A) through 58-45(E); 58-45(G); 58-46; 58-50 through 58-54; 58-60 through 65-01(C); 65-01(E); 65-10 through 68-14(C); 68-14(F); 68-15 through 68-52; 68-70 through 68-83; 68-011(A) through 68-011(E); 69-01 through 69-30 (OAC June 30, 1990, as supplemented by 1990-1991 Ohio Monthly Record, pages 70-80 (July 1990)). Copies of the Ohio regulations that are incorporated by reference in this paragraph are available from Banks-Baldwin Law Publishing Company, P.O. Box 1974, University Center, Cleveland, Ohio 44106-8697. Customer Service Department.

(2) The following statutory provisions and regulations concerning State enforcement, although not codified herein for enforcement purposes, are part of the authorized State program:

(i) Ohio Revised Code, title 1, chapter 119, sections: 01 through 06.1, and 07 through 13; Ohio Revised Code, title 1, chapter 149, sections 011, 43, and 44 (Banks-Baldwin, 1990); Ohio Revised Code, title 37, chapter 3734, sections: 01 through 05, 07, 09 through 14.1, 16 through 17, 20 through 22, and 31 through 99 (Banks-Baldwin, 1990).

(ii) Ohio Administrative Code, volume 4, chapter 3745, rules: 49-031, 50-21 through 50-30, and 51-03(F) (OAC June 30, 1990, as supplemented by 1990-1991 Ohio Monthly Record, pages 70-80 (July, 1990)).

(3) The following statutory and regulatory provisions are broader in scope than the Federal program, are not part of the authorized program, and are not codified for enforcement purposes.

(i) Ohio Revised Code, Title 37, Chapter 3734, Sections: 06, 08, 18 through 19, and 23 through 30 (Page, 1987).

(ii) Ohio Administrative Code, Volume 4, Chapter 3745, Rules: 50-33 through 50-37, and 53-11(A) through 53-11(C) (OAC June 30, 1988).

(b) *Memorandum of Agreement.* The Memorandum of Agreement between EPA Region V and the Ohio Environmental Protection Agency signed by the EPA Regional Administrator on March 6, 1989, is codified as part of the authorized hazardous waste management program under Subtitle C of RCRA. 42 U.S.C. 6921 *et seq.*

(c) *Statement of Legal Authority.* (1) "Attorney General's Statement for Final Authorization," signed by the Attorney General of Ohio on July 1, 1985, and supplements to that Statement dated June 13, 1990, and October 15, 1990, are codified as part of the authorized hazardous waste management program under subtitle C of RCRA, 42 U.S.C. 6921 *et seq.*

(2) Supplemental "Attorney General's Statements for Final Authorization," and addenda to such Statements signed by the Attorney General of Ohio on December

30, 1988, and February 24, 1989, are codified as part of the authorized hazardous waste management program under Subtitle C of RCRA, 42 U.S.C. 6921 *et seq.*

(d) *Program Description.* The Program Description and any other materials submitted as part of the original application or as supplements thereto dated November 8, 1990, and December 11, 1990, are codified as part of the authorized hazardous waste management program under subtitle C of RCRA, 42 U.S.C. 6921 *et seq.*

[54 FR 27173, June 28, 1989, as amended at 57 FR 4162, Feb. 4, 1992]

§§272.1802–272.1849 [Reserved]

Subpart LL—Oklahoma

§272.1850 [Reserved]

§272.1851 Oklahoma State-administered program: Final authorization.

(a) Pursuant to section 3006(b) of RCRA, 42 U.S.C. 6926(b), Oklahoma has final authorization for the following elements as submitted to EPA in Oklahoma's base program application for final authorization which was approved by EPA effective on January 10, 1985. Subsequent program revision applications were approved effective on June 18, 1990, November 27, 1990, June 3, 1991, November 19, 1991, November 29, 1993, December 21, 1994, April 27, 1995, March 14, 1997, July 14, 1998, November 23, 1998, February 8, 1999, May 30, 2000, July 10, 2000 and March 5, 2001.

(b) State Statutes and Regulations.

(1) The Oklahoma statutes and regulations cited in paragraph (b)(1)(i) of this section are incorporated by reference as part of the hazardous waste management program under subtitle C of RCRA, 42 U.S.C. 6921 *et seq.* (*See §272.2*).

(i) The Binder entitled "EPA Approved Oklahoma Statutory and Regulatory Requirements Applicable to the Hazardous Waste Management Program", dated March, 2001.

(ii) [Reserved]

(2) The following provisions provide the legal basis for the State's implementation of the hazardous waste management program, but they are not being incorporated by reference and do not replace Federal authorities:

(i) Oklahoma Hazardous Waste Management Act, as amended, 27A Oklahoma Statute (O.S.) 1997 Edition (unless otherwise specified), Sections 2-2-104, 2-7-102, 2-7-104, 2-7-105 (except 2-7-105(27), 2-7-105(29) and 2-7-105(34)), 2-7-106, 2-7-107, 2-7-108(B)(2), 2-7-110(A), 2-7-113.1, 2-7-115, 2-7-116(A), 2-7-116(G), 2-7-116(H)(1), 2-7-123, 2-7-126 (1999 Supplement), 2-7-129, 2-7-130, 2-7-131 and 2-7-133.

(ii) The Oklahoma Administrative Code, Title 252, Chapter 205, Hazardous Waste Management, effective June 12, 2000: Subchapter 1, Sections 252:205-1-1(b), 252:205-1-3(a) and (b), 252:205-1-4(a)-(d); Subchapter 3, Sections 252:205-3-2 introductory paragraph, and 252:205-3-2(a)(1).

(3) The following statutory and regulatory provisions are broader in scope than the Federal program, are not part of the authorized program, and are not incorporated by reference:

(i) Oklahoma Hazardous Waste Management Act, as amended, 27A Oklahoma Statute 1997 Edition, Sections 2-7-119, 2-7-121 and 2-7-134.

(ii) The Oklahoma Administrative Code, Title 252, Chapter 205, effective June 12, 2000: Subchapter 1, Section 252:205-1-1(c)(2)-(4), 252:205-1-2 "RRSIA". 252:205-1-2 "Reuse", 252:205-1-2 "Speculative accumulation", 252:205-1-2 "Transfer facility", 252:205-1-2 "Transfer station", 252:205-1-4(e) and (f); Subchapter 5, Sections 252:205-5-1(4), Subchapter 15; Subchapter 17; Subchapter 21; and 252:205 Appendices A, B, and C.

(4) *Unauthorized State Amendments:* The State's adoption of the Federal rules listed below is not yet approved by EPA and is, therefore, not enforceable:

Federal requirement	Federal Register reference	Publication date
Delisting	50 FR 28702	07/15/85
	50 FR 27114	06/27/89
	Amendments to 260.22(a) through 260.22(e)	
Toxicity Characteristics; Hydrocarbon Recovery Operations	55 FR 40834 56 FR 3978 56 FR 13406	10/05/90 02/01/91 04/02/92
Toxicity Characteristics; Chlorofluorocarbon Refrigerants	56 FR 5910	02/13/91
Administrative Stay for K069 Listing	56 FR 19951	05/01/91
Amendments to Interim Status Standards for Downgradient Ground-water Monitoring Well Locations	56 FR 66365	12/23/91
Removal of Legally Obsolete Rules	60 FR 33912	06/29/95
Mineral Processing Secondary Materials Exclusion	63 FR 28556	05/26/98

(5) *Memorandum of Agreement.* The Memorandum of Agreement between EPA Region 6 and the State of Oklahoma (ODEQ), signed by the EPA Regional Administrator on March 1, 2000, is referenced as part of the authorized hazardous waste management program under subtitle C of RCRA, 42 U.S.C. 6921 *et seq.*

(6) *Statement of Legal Authority.* "Attorney General's Statement for Final Authorization", signed by the Attorney General of Oklahoma on January 20, 1984 and revisions, supplements and addenda to that Statement dated January 14, 1988 (as amended July 20, 1989); December 22, 1988 (as amended June 7, 1989 and August 13, 1990); November 20, 1989; November 16, 1990; November 6, 1992; June 24, 1994; December 8, 1994; March 4, 1996; April 15, 1997; February 6, 1998, December 2, 1998, October 15, 1999 and May 31, 2000, are referenced as part of the authorized hazardous waste management program under subtitle C of RCRA, 42 U.S.C. 6921 *et seq.*

(7) *Program Description.* The Program Description and any other materials submitted as supplements thereto are referenced as part of the authorized hazardous waste management program under subtitle C of RCRA, 42 U.S.C. 6921 *et seq.*

[64 FR 46570, Aug. 26, 1999; 68 FR 51491, Aug. 27, 2003]

§§272.1852–272.1899 [Reserved]

Subpart MM—Oregon

§§272.1900–272.1949 [Reserved]

Subpart NN—Pennsylvania

§§272.1950–272.1999 [Reserved]

Subpart OO—Rhode Island

§§272.2000–272.2049 [Reserved]

Subpart PP—South Carolina

§§272.2050–272.2099 [Reserved]

Subpart QQ—South Dakota

§272.2100 [Reserved]

§272.2101 South Dakota State-Administered Program: Final Authorization.

(a) Pursuant to section 3006(b) of RCRA, 42 U.S.C. 6926(b), South Dakota has final authorization for the following elements as submitted to EPA in South Dakota's base program application for final authorization which was approved by EPA effective on November 2, 1984. Subsequent program revision applications were approved effective on June 17, 1991, November 8, 1993, March 11, 1994, September 23, 1996, June 8, 2000, May 24, 2004 and March 8, 2006.

(b) The State of South Dakota has primary responsibility for enforcing its hazardous waste management program. However, EPA retains the authority to exercise its inspection and enforcement authorities in accordance with sections 3007, 3008, 3013, 7003 of RCRA, 42 U.S.C. 6927, 6928, 6934, 6973, and any other applicable statutory and regulatory provisions, regardless of whether the State has taken its own actions, as well as in accordance with other statutory and regulatory provisions.

(c) *State Statutes and Regulations.* (1) The South Dakota regulations cited in paragraph (c)(1)(i) of this section are incorporated by reference as part of the hazardous waste management program under subtitle C of RCRA, 42 U.S.C. 6921 *et seq.* This incorporation by reference is approved by the Director of the Federal Register in accordance with 5 U.S.C. 552(a) and 1 CFR part 51. Copies of the South Dakota regulations that are incorporated by reference in this paragraph are available from the South Dakota Legislative Research Council, 3rd Floor, State Capitol, 500 East Capitol Avenue, Pierre, SD 57501, (Phone: 605–773–3251).

(i) The Binder entitled "EPA Approved South Dakota Regulatory Requirements Applicable to the Hazardous Waste Management Program", dated December, 2005.

(ii) [Reserved]

(2) EPA considered the following statutes and regulations in evaluating the State program but is not incorporating them herein for enforcement purposes:

(i) South Dakota Codified Laws (SDCL), as amended, effective July 1, 2004, Title 1, State Affairs and Government: Chapter 1–26, Administrative Procedures and Rules, sections 1–26–1(1), 1–26–1(4), 1–26–1(8) introductory paragraph, 1–26–1(8)(a), 1–26–2, 1–26–6.6, 1–26–16 through 1–26–19, 1–26–19.1, 1–26–19.2, 1–26–27, 1–26–29, 1–26–30, 1–26–30.1, 1–26–30.2, 1–26–30.4, 1–26–31, 1–26–31.1, 1–26–31.2, 1–26–31.4, 1–26–35 and 1–26–36; Chapter 1–27, Public Records and Files, sections 1–27–1, first sentence, 1–27–3, 1–27–9(2) and 1–27–28(2); Chapter 1–32, Executive Reorganization, section 1–32–1(1); Chapter 1–40, Department of Natural Resources, sections 1–40–4.1, 1–40–24, 1–40–31 and 1–40–34.

(ii) SDCL, as amended, effective July 1, 2004, Title 15, Civil Procedure: Chapter 15–6, Rules of Procedure in Circuit Courts, section 15–6–24(a)–(c).

(iii) SDCL, as amended, effective July 1, 2004, Title 19, Evidence: Chapter 19–13, Privileges, sections 19–13–2(1), 19–13–2(5), 19–13–3, 19–13–20 and 19–13–22.

(iv) SDCL, as amended, effective July 1, 2004, Title 21, Judicial Remedies: Chapter 21–8, Injunction, section 21–8–1.

(v) SDCL, as amended, effective July 1, 2004, Title 22, Crimes: Chapter 22–6, Authorized Punishments, sections 22–6–1 introductory paragraph and 22–6–1(6).

(vi) SDCL, as amended, effective July 1, 2004, Title 23, Law Enforcement: Chapter 23–5, Criminal Identification, sections 23–5–1, 23–5–10(1), 23–5–10(3), 23–5–10(4) and 23–5–11 first sentence; Chapter 23–6, Criminal Statistics, section 23–6–4.

(vii) SDCL, as amended, effective July 1, 2004, Title 34, Public Health and Safety: Chapter 34–21, Radiation and Uranium Resources Exposure Control, section 34–21–2(7).

(viii) SDCL, as amended, effective July 1, 2004, Title 34A, Environmental Protection: Chapter 34A–6, Solid Waste Disposal, section 34A–6–1.3(17); Chapter 34A–10, Remedies for Protection of Environment, sections 34A–10–1, 34A–10–2, 34A–10–5, 34A–10–11, 34A–10–14 and 34A–10–16, Chapter 34A–11, Hazardous Waste Management, sections 34A–11–1 through 34A–11–4, 34A–11–5, 34A–11–8 through 34A–11–12, 34A–11–13 through 34A–11–16, 34A–11–17 through 34A–11–19, 34A–11–21 and 34A–11–22.

(ix) SDCL, as amended, effective July 1, 2004, Title 37, Trade Regulation, Chapter 37–29, Uniform Trade Secrets Act, section 37–29–1(4).

(x) Administrative Rules of South Dakota (ARSD), Article 74:08, Administrative Fees, effective August 29, 2004: Chapter 74:08:01, Fees for Records Reproduction, sections 74:08:01:01 through 74:08:01:07.

(3) The following statutory provisions are broader in scope than the Federal program, are not part of the authorized program, are not incorporated by reference and are not federally enforceable:

(i) SDCL, as amended, effective July 1, 2004, Title 34A, Environmental Protection, Chapter 34A–11, Hazardous Waste Management, sections 34A–11–12.1, 34A–11–16.1, 34A–11–25 and 34A–11–26.

(ii) [Reserved]

(4) *Unauthorized State Amendments.* South Dakota has adopted but is not authorized for the following Federal final rules: (1) Removal of Legally Obsolete Rules (HSWA/non-HSWA) [60 FR 33912, 06/29/95]; (2) Imports and Exports of Hazardous Waste: Implementation of OECD Council Division (HSWA—Not delegable to States) [61 FR 16290, 04/12/96]; (3) Clarification of Standards for Hazard Waste Land Disposal Restriction Treatment Variances (HSWA) [62 FR 64504, 12/05/97]; and (4) Vacatur of Organobromide Production Waste Listings (HSWA) [65 FR 14472, 03/17/00]. Those Federal rules written under RCRA provisions that predate HSWA (non-HSWA) which the State has adopted, but for which it is not authorized, are not Federally enforceable. In contrast, EPA will continue to enforce the Federal HSWA standards for which South Dakota is not authorized until the State receives specific authorization from EPA.

(5) *Memorandum of Agreement.* The Memorandum of Agreement between EPA Region 8 and the State of South Dakota, signed by the State of South Dakota Department of Natural Resources on June 6, 1996, and by the EPA Regional Administrator on June 25, 1996, although not incorporated by reference, is referenced as part of the authorized hazardous waste management program under subtitle C of RCRA, 42 U.S.C. 6921 *et seq.*

(6) *Statement of Legal Authority.* "Attorney General's Statement for Final Authorization", signed by the Attorney General of South Dakota on May 24, 1984, and revisions, supplements and addenda to that Statement dated January 14, 1991, September 11, 1992, September 25, 1992, April 1, 1993, September 24, 1993, August 23, 1994, December 29, 1994, September 5, 1995, October 23, 1997, October 27, 1997, October 28, 1997, November 5, 1999, June 26, 2000, June 18, 2002 and October 19, 2004, although not incorporated by reference, are referenced as part of the authorized hazardous waste management program under subtitle C of RCRA, 42 U.S.C. 6921 *et seq.*

(7) *Program Description.* The Program Description and any other materials submitted as supplements thereto, although not incorporated by reference, are referenced as part of the authorized hazardous waste management program under subtitle C of RCRA, 42 U.S.C. 6921 *et seq.*

[71 FR 11534, Mar. 8, 2006]

§§272.2102–272.2149 [Reserved]

Subpart RR—Tennessee

§§272.2150–272.2199 [Reserved]

Subpart SS—Texas

§272.2200 [Reserved]

§272.2201 Texas State-Administered Program: Final Authorization.

(a) Pursuant to section 3006(b) of RCRA, 42 U.S.C. 6926(b), the EPA granted Texas final authorization for the following elements as submitted to EPA in Texas' Base program application for final authorization which was approved by EPA effective on December 26, 1984. Subsequent program revision applications were approved effective on October 4, 1985, February 17, 1987, March 15, 1990, July 23, 1990, October 21, 1991, December 4, 1992, June 27, 1994, November 26, 1997, December 3, 1997, October 18, 1999, November 15, 1999, September 11, 2000, June 14, 2005, and December 29, 2008.

(b) The State of Texas has primary responsibility for enforcing its hazardous waste management program. However, EPA retains the authority to exercise its inspection and enforcement authorities in accordance with sections 3007, 3008, 3013, 7003 of RCRA, 42 U.S.C. 6927, 6928, 6934, 6973, and any other applicable statutory and regulatory provisions, regardless of whether the State has taken its own actions, as well as in accordance with other statutory and regulatory provisions.

(c) *State Statutes and Regulations.* (1) The Texas statutes and regulations cited in paragraph (c)(1)(i) of this section are incorporated by reference as part of the hazardous waste management program under Subtitle C of RCRA, 42 U.S.C. 6921 *et seq.* This incorporation by reference is approved by the Director of the Federal Register in accordance with 5 U.S.C. 552(a) and 1 CFR part 51. Copies of the Texas regulations that are incorporated by reference in this paragraph are available from West Publishing Company, 620 Opperman Drive, P.O. Box 64526, Saint Paul, MN 55164–0526; Phone: 1–800–328–4880; Web site: *http://west.thomson.com.*

(i) The Binder entitled "EPA Approved Texas Statutory and Regulatory Requirements Applicable to the Hazardous Waste Management Program", dated June 2005

(ii) [Reserved]

(2) The following provisions provide the legal basis for the State's implementation of the hazardous waste management program, but they are not being incorporated by reference and do not replace Federal authorities:

(i) Texas Health and Safety Code (THSC) Annotated, (Vernon, 2001); Chapter 361, The Texas Solid Waste Disposal Act, sections 361.002, 361.016, 361.017, 361.018, 361.024(e), 361.032, 361.033, 361.036, 361.037(a), 361.061, 361.063, 361.064, 361.066(b), 361.067, 361.068(a), 361.069 first two sentences, 361.078, 361.079, 361.080(a), 361.082(b), 381.082(c) (except second sentence), 361.082(e), 361.083, 361.084 (except 361.084(a) and (c)), 361.084(c) (except the phrase ", or evidence of *** waste management"), 361.085, 361.088(a) and (b), 361.088(c) (except the phrase "Except as provided by Subsection (e)", 361.089, 361.090, 361.095(b)–(f), 361.096, 361.097, 361.098(a) (except the phrase "Except as provided in Subsections (b) and (c),"), 361.099(a), 361.100, 361.101, 361.102(a) (except the phrase "Except as provided by Subsections (b) and (c)"), 361.103 through 361.108, 361.109(a), 361.301, 361.321(a) and (b), 361.321(c) (except the phrase "Except as provided by Section 361.322(a)"), 361.321(d), and 361.321(e) (except the phrase "Except as provided by Section 361.322(e)"); Chapter 371, Texas Oil Collection, Management, and Recycling Act, sections 371.0025(b) and (c), 371.024(a), 371.024(c) and (d), 371.026(a) and (b), 371.028, and 371.043(b).

(ii) Texas Health and Safety Code (THSC) Annotated, (Vernon, 2002 Supplement), effective September 1, 2001: Chapter 361, The Texas Solid Waste Disposal Act, sections 361.082(h), 361.084(a), 361.088(g), and 361.114.

(iii) Texas Water Code (TWC), Texas Codes Annotated (Vernon, 2000), effective September 1, 1999, as amended: Chapter 5, sections 5.102 through 5.105, 5.112, 5.351, and 5.501; Chapter 7, sections 7.051(a), 7.053 through 7.062, 7.064 through 7.069, 7.075, 7.101, 7.102, 7.104, 7.107, 7.110, 7.162, 7.163, 7.176, 7.187, 7.189, 7.190, 7.252(1), 7.351, 7.353; Chapter 26, section 26.011; and Chapter 27, sections 27.018 and 27.019.

(iv) Texas Water Code (TWC), Texas Codes Annotated (Vernon, 2002), effective September 1, 2001, as amended: Chapter 5, section 5.177; Chapter 7, sections 7.031, 7.052(a), and 7.102.

(v) Texas Government Code (Vernon, 1998), section 311.027, effective May 11, 1993.

(vi) Texas Administrative Code (TAC), Title 30, Environmental Quality, 1994, as amended, effective through January 1, 1994: Chapter 305, sections 305.91 through 305.93, 305.98, and 305.99.

(vii) Texas Administrative Code (TAC), Title 30, Environmental Quality, 1997, as amended, effective through January 1, 1997: Chapter 281, sections 281.17(d)–(f); Chapter 305, sections 305.29(b)–(d), 305.94 and 305.95, 305.97, 305.100, 305.101 (except 305.101(c)), 305.102, 305.103, and 305.105.

(viii) Texas Administrative Code (TAC), Title 30, Environmental Quality, 2002, as amended, effective through December 31, 2001: Chapter 39, sections 39.13 (except (10)), 39.413 (except (10)); Chapter 50, sections 50.13, 50.19, 50.39, 50.113, 50.119, and 50.139; Chapter 55, sections 55.27 (except (b)), 55.201 (except as applicable to contested case hearings), and 55.211 (except as applicable to contested case hearings); Chapter 70, section 70.10; Chapter 281, sections 281.1 (except the clause "except as provided by *** Prioritization Process)"), 281.2 introductory paragraph, 281.2(4), 281.3(a) and (b), 281.5 (except the clause "Except as provided by *** Discharge Permits)" and the phrase "radioactive material"), 281.18(a) (except for the sentence "For applications for radioactive *** within 30 days.", 281.19(a) (except the last sentence), 281.19(b) (except the phrase "Except as provided in subsection (c) of this section,"), 281.20, 281.21(a) (except the phrase "and the Texas Radiation Control Act *** Chapter 401."), 281.21(b), 281.21(c) (except the phrase "radioactive materials," in 281.21(c)(2)), 281.21(d) introductory paragraph (except the phrase "and the Texas Radiation Control Act *** Chapter 401." and the phrase "For applications for minor amendments *** summary is not necessary."), 281.21(d)(1)–(6) (except the phrase "and, for radioactive *** radiation safety" in 281.21(d)(3)), 281.22(a) (except the phrase "For applications for radioactive *** to deny the license."), 281.22(b) (except the phrase "or an injection well," in the first sentence and the phrase "For underground injection wells *** the same facility or activity."), 281.23(a), 281.24; Chapter 305, sections, 305.64(d) and (f), 305.66(c), 305.66(e) (except for the last sentence), 305.66(f)–(l), 305.123 (except the phrase "and 401 *** regulation)", 305.125(1) and (3), 305.125(20), 305.127(1)(B)(i), 305.127(4)(A) and (C), 305.127(6), 305.401(a), 305.401(b) (except the text "§39.3 of this title (relating to Purpose) *** §55.21 of this title (relating to Requests for Contested Case Hearings, Public Comment"), 305.401(d)–(h); and Chapter 335, sections 335.2(b), 335.43(b), 335.206, 335.391 through 335.393.

(3) The following statutory and regulatory provisions are broader in scope than the Federal program, are not part of the authorized program, and are not incorporated by reference:

(i) Texas Health and Safety Code (THSC) Annotated, (Vernon 2001): Chapter 361, The Texas Solid Waste Disposal Act, sections 361.131 through 140; Chapter 371, Texas Oil Collection, Management, and Recycling Act, sections 371.021, 371.022, 371.024(e), 371.0245, 371.0246, 371.025, and 371.026(c).

(ii) Texas Administrative Code (TAC), Title 30, Environmental Quality, 2002, as amended, effective through December 31, 2001: Chapter 305, sections 305.53, 305.64(b)(4), 305.127(1)(G); Chapter 335, sections 335.321 through 335.332, and Appendices I and II.

(4)(i) *Unauthorized State Amendments.* The following authorized provisions of the Texas regulations include amendments published in the Texas Register that are not approved by EPA. Such unauthorized amendments are not part of the State's authorized program and are, therefore, not Federally enforceable. Thus, notwithstanding the language in the Texas hazardous waste regulations incorporated by reference at paragraph (c)(1)(i) of this section, EPA will enforce the State provisions that are actually authorized by EPA. The effective dates of the State's authorized provisions are listed in the following Table.

State provision	Effective date of authorized provision	Unauthorized state amendments	
		Texas Register reference	Effective date
335.2(c)	11/7/91	18 TexReg 2799	5/12/93
		18 TexReg 8218	11/23/93
35.6(a)	7/29/92	18 TexReg 2799	5/12/93
		22 TexReg 12060	12/15/97
		23 TexReg 10878	10/19/98
335.6(c) introductory paragraph	7/29/92	17 TexReg 8010	
		20 TexReg 2709	11/27/92
		20 TexReg 3722	4/24/95
		21 TexReg 1425	5/30/95
		21 TexReg 2400	3/01/96
		22 TexReg 12060	3/06/96
		23 TexReg 10878	12/15/97
			10/19/98
335.6(g)	7/29/92	18 TexReg 3814	6/28/93
		22 TexReg 12060	12/15/97
		23 TexReg 10878	10/19/98
335.10(b)(22)	7/27/88	17 TexReg 8010	11/27/92
335.24(b) introductory paragraph	3/1/96	21 TexReg 10983	11/20/96
		23 TexReg 10878	10/19/98
335.24(c) introductory paragraph	3/1/96	21 TexReg 10983	11/20/96
		23 TexReg 10878	10/19/98
335.41(c)	9/1/86	18 TexReg 8218	11/23/93
335.45(b)	9/1/86	17 TexReg 5017	7/29/92
335.204(a)(1)	5/28/86	16 TexReg 6065	11/07/91
335.204(b)(1)	5/28/86	16 TexReg 6065	11/07/91
335.204(b)(6)	5/28/86	16 TexReg 6065	11/07/91
335.204(c)(1)	5/28/86	16 TexReg 6065	11/07/91
335.204(d)(1)	5/28/86	16 TexReg 6065	11/07/91
335.204(e)(6)	5/28/86	16 TexReg 6065	11/07/91

(ii) The actual State regulatory text authorized by EPA (i.e., without the unauthorized amendments) is available as a separate document, *Addendum to the EPA-Approved Texas Regulatory and Statutory Requirements Applicable to the Hazardous Waste Management Program, June, 2005.* Copies of the document can be obtained from U.S. EPA Region 6, 1445 Ross Avenue, Suite 1200, Dallas, TX 75202.

(5) *Memorandum of Agreement.* The Memorandum of Agreement between EPA Region VI and the State of Texas, signed by the Executive Director of the Texas Natural Resource Conservation Commission (TNRCC) on April 26, 2000, and by the EPA Regional Administrator on June 14, 2000, is referenced as part of the authorized hazardous waste management program under subtitle C of RCRA, 42 U.S.C. 6921 *et seq.*

(6) *Statement of Legal Authority.* "Attorney General's Statement for Final Authorization", signed by the Attorney General of Texas on May 22, 1984 and revisions, supplements, and addenda to that Statement dated November 21, 1986, July 21, 1988, December 4, 1989, April 11, 1990, July 31, 1991, February 25, 1992, November 30, 1992, March 8, 1993, January 7, 1994, August 9, 1996, October 16, 1996, as amended February 7, 1997, March 11, 1997, January 5, 1999, November 2, 1999, and March 1, 2002 are referenced as part of the authorized hazardous waste management program under Subtitle C of RCRA, 42 U.S.C. 6921 *et seq.*

(7) *Program Description.* The Program Description and any other materials submitted as part of the original application or as supplements thereto are referenced as part of the authorized hazardous waste management program under subtitle C of RCRA, 42 U.S.C. 6921 *et seq.*

[64 FR 49680, Sept. 14, 1999; 73 FR 64257, Oct. 29, 2008]

§§272.2202–272.2249 [Reserved]

Subpart TT—Utah

§272.2250 [Reserved]

§272.2251 Utah State-Administered program: Final authorization

(a) Pursuant to section 3006(b) of RCRA, 42 U.S.C. 6926(b), Utah has Final authorization for the following elements as submitted to EPA in Utah's base program application for Final authorization which was approved by EPA effective on October 24, 1984. Subsequent program revision applications were approved effective on March 7, 1989; July 22, 1991; July 14, 1992; April 13, 1993; December 13, 1994; July 21, 1997; and March 15, 1999.

(b) *State statutes and regulations.* (1) The Utah regulations cited in this paragraph are incorporated by reference as part of the hazardous waste management program under subtitle C of RCRA, 42 U.S.C. 6921 *et seq.* This incorporation by reference was approved by the Director of the Federal Register in accordance with 5 U.S.C. 552(a) and 1 CFR Part 51. Copies of the Utah regulations that are incorporated by reference in this paragraph are available from the Utah Department of Environmental Quality, 288 North 1460 West, Salt Lake City, Utah 84114- 4880, Phone (801) 538-6776.

(i) The EPA Approved Utah Regulatory Requirements Applicable to the Hazardous Waste Management Program, dated March 1999.

(ii) [Reserved]

(2) The following statutes and regulations concerning State procedures and enforcement, although not incorporated by reference, are part of the authorized State program:

(i) Utah Code Annotated, Volume 3A, 1998 Replacement and 1999 Supplement, Title 19: Sections 19-1-306(2), 19-1-306(3), 19-6-102 introductory paragraph, 19-6-102(1) & (2), 19-6-102(6)-(9), 19-6- 102(11), 19-6-102(13)-(21), 19-6-102.1, 19-6-103, 19-6-104(1) except (1)(j), 19-6-105(1) introductory paragraph, 19-6-105(1)(a)-(f), 19-6- 105(1)(i) & (j), 19-6-105(2), 19-6-106, 19-6-107, 19-6-109, 19-6-111, 19-6-112, 19-6-113(1) through (4), 19-6-113(6), 19-6-114, 19-6-115, and 19-6-116.

(ii) Utah Code Annotated, Volume 6D, 1997 Replacement and 1999 Supplement, Title 63: Sections 63-2-103 through 63-2-105, 63-2-201 through 63-2-203 (except 63-2-203(10)), 63-2-204, 63-2-205, 63-2-301 through 63-2-308, 63-2-401 through 63-2-405, and 63-2-802.

(iii) Utah Code Annotated, Volume 3, 1953 as amended 1987, Title 26, Chapter 14: Section 26-14-8.

(iv) Utah Administrative Code revised as of January 3, 1989: R450- 3.1.1(b) & (c) and R450-3-2.4(b).

(v) Utah Administrative Code revised as of February 15, 1996: Sections R315-2-14, R315-3-3(i)(1)&(3), R315-3-11(a), (b) & (f), R315-3-16(b), R315-3-23(b)(1) & (2), R315-3-23(c) & (d), R315-3-24(a) through R315-3-29, and R315-3-34.

(vi) Utah Administrative Code revised as of May 15, 1996: Section R315-15-1.1(j) & (k).

(3) The following statutory and regulatory provisions are broader-in-scope than the Federal program, are

not part of the authorized program, and are not incorporated by reference:

(i) Utah Code Annotated, Volume 3A, 1998 Replacement and 1999 Supplement, Title 19: Sections 19-6-105(3), 19-6-113(5), 19-6-118, 19-6-120, and 19-6-121.

(ii) Utah Administrative Code revised as of February 15, 1996. EPA considers Utah's listing of all P999 and some F999 wastes (specifically: nerve, military, and chemical agents) as more stringent than the Federal rule. To the extent that unused chemical agents, as produced, exhibit a hazardous waste reactivity characteristic, they are considered hazardous waste and, thus, are regulated under Federal rule. Utah's listing of these wastes enhances the degree of regulatory control regarding these wastes. EPA also considers Utah's rule as broader-in-scope than the federal rule for those F999 process wastes which do not exhibit a characteristic for hazardous waste and would not be regulated under Federal rule. R315-2-10(e)(1), 315-2-11(e) introductory paragraph and R315-2-11(e)(1) are broader-in-scope regarding these wastes.

(iii) Utah Administrative Code, as of May 15, 1996: R315-15-7.1(d), R315-15-10, R315-15-11 with respect to used oil transfer and off-specification used oil burning facilities, and R315-15-12 through R315-15-15 except R315-15-13.5(d).

(4) *Unauthorized State provisions:* (i) Although the Federal rules listed in the following table have been adopted by the State and have been included in the materials incorporated by reference in paragraph (b)(1) of this Section, EPA has not authorized the State for these rules at this time. While they may be enforceable under State law, they are not enforceable under RCRA:

Federal Requirement	Federal Register reference	Publication date
Standards for Generators of Hazardous Waste; Manifest Renewal (Revision Checklist 58)	53 FR 45089	11/08/88
Removal of Legally Obsolete Rules (Non-HSWA provisions) (Revision Checklist 144)	60 FR 33912	06/29/95
Testing and Monitoring Activities Amendment III (Revision Checklist 158)	62 FR 32452	06/13/97

(ii) Additionally Utah has adopted but is not authorized to implement the HSWA rules that are listed below in lieu of EPA. EPA will continue to implement the Federal HSWA requirements for which Utah is not authorized until the State receives specific authorization for those requirements.

Federal Requirement	Federal Register reference	Publication date
Removal of Legally Obsolete Rules (HSWA provisions) (Revision Checklist 144)	60 FR 33912	6/29/95
Land Disposal Restrictions Phase III—Decharacterized Wastewaters, Carbamate Wastes, and Spent Potliners (Revision Checklist 151)	61 FR 15566; 61 FR 15660; 61 FR 19117; 61 FR 33680; 61 FR 36419; 61 FR 43924; 62 FR 7502	4/8/96; 4/8/96; 4/30/96; 6/28/96; 7/10/96; 8/26/96; 2/19/97
Organic Air Emission Standards for Tanks, Surface Impoundments, and Containers—formerly Revision Checklist 138 (Rule 154.1)	59 FR 62896	12/6/94
Land Disposal Restrictions Phase III—Emergency Extension of the K088 Capacity Variance (Revision Checklist 155)	62 FR 1992	1/14/97
Land Disposal Restrictions—Phase IV (Revision Checklist 157)	62 FR 25998	5/12/97
Carbamate Production, Identification and Listing of Hazardous Waste; Land Disposal Restrictions (Conformance With the Carbamate Vacatur) (Revision Checklist 159)	62 FR 32974	6/17/97

(5) *Unauthorized State amendments.* The following authorized provisions of the Utah regulations include amendments published in the *Utah State Bulletin* that are not approved by EPA. Such unauthorized amendments are not part of the State's authorized program and are, therefore, not Federally enforceable. Thus, notwithstanding the language in the Utah hazardous waste regulations incorporated by reference at §272.2251(b)(1), EPA will only enforce the authorized State provisions with the effective dates indicated in the table below. The actual State regulatory text authorized by EPA for the listed provisions is available as a separate document, Addendum to the EPA-Approved Utah Regulatory Requirements Applicable to the Hazardous Waste Management Program, March 1999. Copies of the document can be obtained from U.S. EPA Region VIII, 999 18th St., Suite 500, Denver, Colorado 80202-2466, phone (303) 312-6139.

State provision	State reference	Unauthorized State amendments	
		State reference	Effective date
R315-2-1(b)(2)(ii)	9/24/86	DAR 12647	5/29/92
R315-7-11.3(b)	1/3/89	DAR 12652	5/29/92
R315-7-12.6(g)	Base	DAR 09632	1/3/89

At R315-3-23(f)(3)(iv), Utah's analog to 40 CFR 270.33(b)(3)(iv), the State has a printing error in its regulations. The State will fix this error in its next rule making. For the codification, the authorized version of the provision will also be included in the Addendum to the EPA-Approved Utah Regulatory Requirements Applicable to the Hazardous Waste Management Program, March 1999.

(6) *Memorandum of Agreement.* The Memorandum of Agreement between EPA Region VIII and the Utah Department of Environmental Quality, signed by the EPA Regional Administrator on October 4, 1994, is referenced as part of the authorized hazardous waste management program under subtitle C of RCRA, 42 U.S.C. 6921 *et seq.*

(7) *Statement of legal authority.* "Attorney General's Statement for Final Authorization", signed by the Attorney General of Utah on January 16, 1984, and revisions, supplements and addenda to that Statement dated October 29, 1986, March 6, 1991, September 17, 1991, September 223, 1992, November 19, 1993, March 16, 1994, March 20, 1995, November 13, 1997, and March 2, 1999, are referenced as part of the authorized hazardous waste management program under subtitle C of RCRA, 42 U.S.C. 6921 *et seq.*

(8) *Program description.* The Program description and any other materials submitted as part of the original application or as supplements thereto are referenced as part of the authorized hazardous waste management program under subtitle C of RCRA, 42 U.S.C. 6921 *et seq.*

[66 FR 58971, Nov. 26, 2001]

§§272.2252–272.2299 [Reserved]

Subpart UU—Vermont

§§272.2300–272.2349 [Reserved]

Subpart VV—Virginia

§§272.2350–272.2399 [Reserved]

Subpart WW—Washington

§§272.2400–272.2449 [Reserved]

Subpart XX—West Virginia

§§272.2450–272.2499 [Reserved]

Subpart YY—Wisconsin

§272.2500 [Reserved]

§272.2501 Wisconsin State-administered program; final authorization.

Pursuant to section 3006(b) of RCRA, 42 U.S.C. 6926(b): Wisconsin has final authorization for the following elements as submitted to EPA in Wisconsin's base program application for final authorization which was approved by EPA effective on January 31, 1986. Subsequent program revision applications were approved effective on June 6, 1989, January 22, 1990, and April 24, 1992.

State Statutes and Regulations

(a) The Wisconsin statutes and regulations cited in this paragraph are incorporated by reference as part of the hazardous waste management program under subtitle C of RCRA, 42 U.S.C. 6921 *et seq.*

(1) EPA Approved Wisconsin Statutory Requirements Applicable to the Hazardous Waste Management Program, (dated August 9, 1993).

(2) EPA Approved Wisconsin Regulatory Requirements Applicable to the Hazardous Waste Management Program (dated August 9, 1993).

(b) The following statutes and regulations concerning State enforcement, although not incorporated by reference for enforcement purposes, are part of the authorized State program:

(1) Wisconsin Statutes, Volume 1, §§19.21; 19.31; 19.32(2) and (5); 19.35(3) and (4); 19.36; 19.37(1) and (2); Wisconsin Statutes, Volume 3, §§144.69-144.72; 144.73-144.74; 144.76(2) and (3); Wisconsin Statutes Volume 4, §§227.07; 227.09; 227.14; 227.51; and Wisconsin Statutes, Volume 5, §803.09 (1985-86).

(2) Wisconsin Administrative Code, Volume 1, §NR: 2.19; 2.195(1); and 2.195(5) (effective April 1, 1984); Wisconsin Administrative Code, Volume 12, §NR: 680.06(12) (effective March 1, 1991).

[58 FR 49200, Sept. 22, 1993]

§§272.2502–272.2549 [Reserved]

Subpart ZZ—Wyoming

§§272.2550–272.2599 [Reserved]

Subpart AAA—Guam

§§272.2600–272.2649 [Reserved]

Subpart BBB—Puerto Rico

§§272.2650–272.2699 [Reserved]

Subpart CCC—Virgin Islands

§§272.2700–272.2749 [Reserved]

Subpart DDD—American Samoa

§§272.2750–272.2799 [Reserved]

Subpart EEE—Commonwealth of the Northern Mariana Islands

§§272.2800–272.2849 [Reserved]

Appendix to Part 272

Appendix A to Part 272—State Requirements

The following is an informational listing of the State and local requirements incorporated in part 272 of the *Code of Federal Regulations*:

Arizona

The statutory provisions include:

Arizona Laws Relating to Environmental Quality, 1993 edition, reprinted from *Arizona Revised Statutes*, Title 49, Sections 49-921 and 49-922. Copies of the Arizona statutes can be obtained from the State Bar of Arizona, 111 West Munroe, Suite 1800, Phoenix, Arizona 85003-1742.

The regulatory provisions include:

Arizona Administrative Code, Title 18, Chapter 8, December 31, 1994, Sections R18-8-260.A through R18-8-260.C, R18-8-260.E through R18-8-260.H; R18-8-261.A through R18-8-261.I; R18-8-261.K; R18-8-262; R18-8-263; R18-8-264; R18-8-265; R18-8-266; R18-8-268; R18-8-270.A through R18-8-270.F; R18-8-270.H through R18-8-270.Q; and R18-8-271.A through R18-8-271.E. Copies of the Arizona regulations can be obtained from the Arizona Secretary of State, Publications, Notary, Charitable Solicitation & Telemarketing Division, 1700 West Washington, 7th Floor, Phoenix, Arizona 85007-2808.

Arkansas

The statutory provisions include:

Arkansas Hazardous Waste Management Act, as amended, Arkansas Code of 1987 Annotated (A.C.A.), 1993 Replacement, Sections 8-7-202, 8-7-203, 8-7-215, 8-7-216, 8-7-219, 8-7-221, 8-7-223 and 8-7-225(a), as published by The Michie Company, Law Publishers, 1 Town Hall Square, Charlottesville, Virginia 22906-7587.

The regulatory provisions include:

Arkansas Department of Pollution Control and Ecology Regulation No. 23, Hazardous Waste Management, as amended August 27, 1993, effective September 21, 1993, chapter one; chapter two, sections 2a (except the second sentence of 2a(5)), 2b (except 2b(11)), 2c, 3a (except 3a(10), 3a(11) and 3a(13)), 5, 6 introductory paragraph, 6b, 6c, 9, 10, 12 introductory paragraph, 12a, 12b (except 12b(7) and 12b(8)), 12c(10), 12c(11), 13a introductory paragraph, 13a(1) through 13a(7), 13a(11), 14 introductory paragraph, 14b, 15, 16 introductory paragraph, 16b, 16c introductory paragraph, 16c(1) (except the phrase 'or the letters "PCB" for PCB shipments' in 16c(1)(e)), 16c(2) through 16c(6), 16c(7) (except the second and third sentences), 16c(8) through 16c(12), 16d(1) (except the phrase "(including PCBs and PCB contaminated wastes)" in the first sentence), 16d(1)(a) through 16d(1)(d), 16d(1)(e) (except the phrase 'or "PCBs" ' in the first sentence), and 16d(1)(f) through 16e. Copies of the Arkansas regulations can be obtained from the Arkansas Register, Secretary of State, State Capitol Building, Little Rock, Arkansas 72201.

Florida

The statutory provisions include:

Florida Statutes, 1991, Chapter 1: 1.01 (1) and (2).

Florida Statutes, 1993, Chapter 403: 403.031 introductory paragraph; 403.031 (2)-(7); 403.087(1) first sentence, and (6); 403.201(4) (except the phrase "may require by rule a processing fee for and"); 403.703 introductory paragraph; 403.703 (2)-(6), (8)-(28), (30)-(34), (36), and (40), (42)-(44); 403.7045(1) introductory paragraph, (1) (a), (b) and (d); 403.7045(2) introductory paragraph; 403.7045(2) (a)-(c); 403.7045(3) introductory paragraph; 403.7045(3) (a)-(c); 403.72(2); 403.721(1); 403.722 (1)-(6); 403.7221; 403.724(1) (except the phrase "or corrective action"); 403.724(2); 403.728; 403.74 (1), (3)-(5); 403.751(1) (except (d) & (e); and (2).

Florida Statutes, 1994 Supplement to 1993, Chapter 403: 403.031(1); 403.703(1); 403.7222 (1) and (2); 403.74(2).

Florida Statutes, 1993, Chapter 404: 404.031(13).

Copies of the Florida Statutes that are incorporated by reference are available from the Florida Department of State, Division of Elections, Bureau of Administrative Code, Weekly and Laws, The Elliot Building, 401 South Monroe Street, Tallahassee, Florida 32399-0250.

The regulatory provisions include:

The Florida Administrative Code, Chapter 62-4, effective July 4, 1995: 62-4.070(2); 62-4.080; and 62-4.100.

The Florida Administrative Code, Chapter 62-730, effective September 7, 1995: 62-730.001; 62-730.020 (1), (3), and (4); 62-730.021; 62-730.030; 62-730.140; 62-730.150; 62-730.160; 62-730.161; 62-730.170(1); 62-730.171; 62-730.180 (1)-(5), (7), and (8); 62-730.181; 62-730.183; 62-730.185; 62-730.200 (except (3)); 62-730.210; 62-730.220 (1), (2), (3), (5)-(8), (10), and (11); 62-730.231 (except (10)); 62-730.240 (1) and (2); 62-730.250; 62-730.260; 62-730.270(1) (except (1)(b)(4) and (1)(c)(3)), (2), and (3); 62-730.280; 62-730.290 (except the phrase "and submittal of the appropriate permit modification fee" at subparagraph (3)); 62-730.300; 62-730.320; 62-730.330; and 62-730.900.

Copies of the Florida Administrative Code are available from the Florida Department of State, Division of Elections, Bureau of Administrative Code, Weekly and Laws, The Elliot Building, 401 South Monroe Street, Tallahassee, Florida 32399-0250.

Idaho

(a) The statutory provisions include:

Idaho Code containing the General Laws of Idaho Annotated, Title 39, Chapter 44, "Hazardous Waste Management", 2002: sections 39–4402; 39–4403 (except 39–4403(6) & (14)); 39–4408(1)–(3); 39–4409(1) (except fourth and fifth sentences); 39–4409(2) (first sentence); 39–4409(4) (except first sentence); 39–4409(5); 39–4409(6); 39–4409(7); 39–4409(8); 39–4411(2); 39–4411(4); 39–4411(5); 39–4423 (except 39–4423(3) (a) & (b)); and 39–4424.

Idaho Code containing the General Laws of Idaho Annotated, Title 39, Chapter 58, "Hazardous Waste Facility Siting Act", published in 2002 by the Michie Company, Law Publishers: sections 39–5802; 39–5803; 39–5808; 39–5811; 39–5813(1); and 39–5818(2).

Copies of the Idaho statutes that are incorporated by reference are available from Michie Company, Law Publishers, 1 Town Hall Square, Charlottesville, VA 22906–7587.

(b) The regulatory provisions include:

Idaho Department of Environmental Quality Rules and Regulations, Idaho Administrative Code, IDAPA 58, Title 1, Chapter 5, "Rules and Standards for Hazardous Waste", as published on July 2004: sections 58.01.05.001; 58.01.05.002; 58.01.05.003; 58.01.05.004; 58.01.05.005; 58.01.05.006; 58.01.05.007; 58.01.05.008; 58.01.05.009; 58.01.05.010; 58.01.05.011; 58.01.05.012; 58.01.05.013; 58.01.05.014; 58.01.05.015; 58.01.05.016; 58.01.05.356.01; and 58.01.05.998.

Indiana

The statutory provisions include:

Annotated Indiana Code, 1998 edition, Title 13, Sections 13-14-1, 13-14-7, 13-14-8, 13-19-3, 13-22-2, and 13-22-4.

Copies of the Indiana statutes that are incorporated by reference are available from West Publishing Company, 610 Opperman Drive, P.O. Box 64526, St. Paul, Minnesota 55164-0526.

The regulatory provisions include:

Indiana Administrative Code, 1996 edition, 2000 cumulative supplement, Title 329, Article 3.1, Sections 3.1-1-7, 3.1-4-1, 3.1-5-1, 3.1-5-2, 3.1-5-3, 3.1-5-4, 3.1-5-5, 3.1-5-6, 3.1-6-1, 3.1-6-2, 3.1-7-1, 3.1-7-2,

3.1-7-3, 3.1-7-4, 3.1-7-5, 3.1-7-6, 3.1-7-7, 3.1-7-8, 3.1-7-9, 3.1-7-10, 3.1-7-11, 3.1-7-12, 3.1-7-13, 3.1-7-14, 3.1-7-15, 3.1-7-16, 3.1-8-1, 3.1-9-1, 3.1-9-2, 3.1-9-3, 3.1-10-1, 3.1-10-2(1 through 3), 3.1-10-2(5 through 22), 3.1-11-1, 3.1-11-2, 3.1-12-1, 3.1-13-1, 3.1-13-2(1 through 3), 3.1-13-2(5 through 15), 3.1-13-3, 3.1-13-4, 3.1-13-5, 3.1-13-6, 3.1-13-7, 3.1-13-8, 3.1-13-9, 3.1-13-10, 3.1-13-11, 3.1-13-12, 3.1-13-13, 3.1-13-14, 3.1-13-15, 3.1-13-16, 3.1-13-17, 3.1-14-1, 3.1-14-2, 3.1-14-3, 3.1-14-4, 3.1-14-5, 3.1-14-6, 3.1-14-7, 3.1-14-8, 3.1-14-9, 3.1-14-10, 3.1-14-11, 3.1-14-12, 3.1-14-13, 3.1-14-14, 3.1-14-15, 3.1-14-16, 3.1-14-17, 3.1-14-18, 3.1-14-19, 3.1-14-20, 3.1-14-21, 3.1-14-22, 3.1-14-23, 3.1-14-24, 3.1-14-25, 3.1-14-26, 3.1-14-27, 3.1-14-28, 3.1-14-29, 3.1-14-30, 3.1-14-31, 3.1-14-32, 3.1-14-33, 3.1-14-34, 3.1-14-35, 3.1-14-36, 3.1-14-37, 3.1-14-38, 3.1-14-39, 3.1-14-40, 3.1-15-1, 3.1-15-2, 3.1-15-3, 3.1-15-4, 3.1-15-5, 3.1-15-6, 3.1-15-7, 3.1-15-8, 3.1-15-9, 3.1-15-10, 3.1-16-1, 13-1-1, 13-1-2, 13-2-1, 13-2-2, 13-2-3, 13-2-4, 13-2-5, 13-2-6, 13-2-7, 13-2-8, 13-2-9, 13-2-10, 13-2-11, 13-2-12, 13-2-13, 13-2-14, 13-2-15, 13-2-16, 13-2-17, 13-2-18, 13-2-19, 13-2-20, 13-2-21, 13-2-22, 13-2-23, 13-2-24, 13-2-25, 13-2-26, 13-2-27, 13-3-1, 13-3-2, 13-3-3, 13-4-1, 13-4-2, 13-4-3, 13-4-4, 13-4-5, 13-5-1, 13-5-2, 13-5-3, 13-6-1, 13-6-2, 13-6-3, 13-6-4, 13-6-5, 13-6-6, 13-6-7, 13-6-8, 13-7-1, 13-7-2, 13-7-3, 13-7-4, 13-7-5, 13-7-6, 13-7-7, 13-7-8, 13-7-9, 13-7-10, 13-8-1, 13-8-2, 13-8-3, 13-8-4, 13-8-5, 13-8-6, 13-8-7, 13-8-8, 13-9-1, 13-9-2, 13-9-3, 13-9-4, 13-9-5, 13-9-6, 13-10-1, 13-10-2, 13-10-3.

Copies of the Indiana regulations that are incorporated by reference are available from Indiana Legislative Services Agency, Administrative Code and Register Division, Legislative Information Center, 302 State House, Indianapolis, Indiana 46204.

Louisiana

The statutory provisions include:

Louisiana Statutes Annotated, Revised Statutes, 1989, Volume 17B, Subtitle II of Title 30, Louisiana Environmental Quality Act, 1989: Chapter 1, sections 2002, 2003, 2004 introductory paragraph, 2004(1)-(8), 2004(10), 2004(13), 2004(14) introductory paragraph, 2004(14)(a)&(e), 2004(15); Chapter 9, sections 2172, 2173 (except 2173(2), 2173(9) and 2173(11) introductory paragraph), 2183.A,B,D&E, 2183.I, 2188.B, 2201, 2202, 2203.A, 2204.A(1) and 2204.C.

Louisiana Statutes Annotated, Revised Statutes, 1992 Cumulative Annual Pocket Part, Volume 17B, Subtitle II of Title 30, Louisiana Environmental Quality Act: Chapter 1, Section 2004(9); Chapter 2, Section 2022.A first sentence, Chapter 8, Section 2153(1); Chapter 9, Sections 2173(2) and 2173(11); Chapter 18, Section 2417.E(5).

Copies of the Louisiana statutes that are incorporated by reference are available from West Publishing Company, 610 Opperman Drive, P.O. Box 64526, St. Paul, Minnesota 55164-0526.

The regulatory provisions include:

Louisiana Administrative Code, Title 33, Part V, Hazardous Waste and Hazardous Materials, Amendments through June 1995: Chapter 1, Sections 103, 105 introductory paragraph, 105.A-C, 105.D.2-.12, 105.D.13 (except the phrase "except as *** process hazardous waste"), 105.D.14-.17, 105.D.18 (except the phrase "except as *** process hazardous waste"), 105.D.19-.32, 105.D.33 (except 105.D.33.c), 105.D.34, 105.D.35, 105.D.37-.42, 105.D.43 (except 105.D.43.f), 105.D.45-.47, 105.E through 105.I, 105.J.1, 105.K, 105.L; 109 Definitions (except for "Carbon Regeneration Unit", "Commercial Boiler", "Commercial Industrial Furnace", "Consignee", "Containment Building", "Designated Facility", "EPA Acknowledgement of Consent", Item 7 of "Hazardous Waste", Item 2 of "Incinerator", Item 12 of "Industrial Furnace", "Infrared Incinerator", the phrase "containment building" in "Miscellaneous Unit", "Partial Closure", the phrase "and that is not a containment building" in "Pile", "Plasma Arc Incinerator", "Primary Exporter", "Receiving Country", "Sludge Dryer", "Solid Waste", "Transit Country" and "Waste Reduction"), 111; Chapter 3, Sections 303, 305.B-.E, 307, 309 (except 309.L.3.b), 311.B&.E, 313, 315.A-.D, 317, 319, 321 (except 321.C.2.i), 322, 323.A , 323.B introductory paragraph, 323.B.1, 323.B.2 (except 323.B.2.e), 323.B.4, 325 and 329; Chapter 5, Sections 501, 505, 507 through 513, 515 (except for 515.25), 516, 517 (except 517.V), 519, 520, 521 through 532, 533 (except 533.B), 534 and 536; Chapter 7, Section 701; Chapter 9, Sections 901 through 923; Chapter 11, Sections 1101 (except 1101.B&.F), 1103 introductory paragraph, 1103.B (except the phrase "For the purposes of compliance with LAC 33:V.Chapter 22, or"), 1105, 1107 (except 1107.A.4 and 1107.D.5), 1108, 1109 (except 1109.E.1.d, E.8 and E.9), 1111.A, 1111.B.1 introductory paragraph (except the phrase "to a treatment, storage, or disposal facility within the United States"), 1111.B.1.a-.c, 1111.B.1.d (except the phrase "within the United States"), 1111.B.1.e (except the phrase "within the United States"), 1111.B.1.f, 1111.B.2 (except the phrase "for a period of at least three years from the date of the report" and the third and fourth sentences), 1111.C-.D, 1113, 1115 through 1121; Chapter 13, Sections 1301 through 1305, 1307.A introductory paragraph (except last sentence), 1307.B, 1307.C (except last sentence), 1307.D, 1307.E (except the phrase "and, for exports, an EPA Acknowledgement of Consent" at 1307.E.2), 1307.F (except the phrase "and, for exports, an EPA Acknowledgement of Consent" at 1307.F.2), 1307.G (except 1307.G.4), 1307.H, 1309, 1311, 1315 through 1323; Chapter 15, Sections 1501 through 1517, 1519 (except 1519.B.8 and 1519.D), 1521 through 1527, 1529 (except 1529.B.12-.19), 1531; Chapter 17, Sections 1701 through 1745; Chapter 19, Sections 1901 (except 1901.C&.D), 1903, 1905.A-.G, 1907, 1909.A-.C, 1911, 1913, 1915.A-.C, 1917 and 1919; Chapter 21, Sections 2101 (except 2101.D), 2103 through 2117; Chapter 23, Sections 2301, 2303 (except 2303.K), 2304 through 2309, 2311 (except the phrase "the waste and the pile satisfy all applicable requirements of LAC 33:V.Chapter 22, and" at 2311.A), 2313, 2315 and 2317; Chapter 25, Sections 2501, 2503.A through 2503.J, 2503.K (except 2503.K.1.o), 2503.L-.N, 2504 through 2509, 2511.A introductory paragraph (except the phrase "the waste and landfill meet all applicable requirements of LAC 33:V.Chapter 22, and"), 2511.A.2 (except the phrase "or LAC 33:V.4321 for interim status facilities"), 2511.B, 2513 through 2517, 2519 (except 2519.F), 2521 (except 2521.B.2) and 2523; Chapter 26, Sections 2601, 2602 and 2603 (except 2603.F.1); Chapter 27, Sections 2701, 2703 (except for 2703.I&.J), 2705 through 2713, 2715 introductory paragraph (except the phrase "the waste and the treatment zone meet all applicable requirements of LAC 33:V.Chapter 22, and"), 2715.A&.B, 2717 through 2723; Chapter 29, Sections 2901, 2903 (except 2903.I), 2904 through 2911, 2913 introductory paragraph (except the phrase "the waste and impoundment satisfy all applicable requirements of LAC 33:V.Chapter 22, and"), 2913.A.1, 2913.A.2 (except the phrase "or for interim status facilities;"), 2915 and 2917; Chapter 31, Sections 3101, 3103, 3105 (except 3105.D), 3107 through 3121; Chapter 32, sections 3201 through 3207; Chapter 33, Sections 3301, 3303 (except 3303.C&.D), 3305 through 3313, 3315 (except for 3315.K), 3317 through 3322, 3323 (except the phrase "or its successor agency" at 3323.D) and 3325; Chapter 35, Sections 3501 through 3505, 3507 (except the phrase "1803, 1911" at 3507.C), 3509 through 3527; Chapter 37, Sections 3701, 3703, 3705 (except the last sentence of 3705.D), 3707.A-.F, 3707.G (except the phrase "and financial test and guarantee, except that the financial test and guarantee may not be combined" in the second sentence), 3707.H, 3707.I (except the phrase ", and for facilities subject to LAC 33:V.3525 *** LAC 33:V.3525.B.2", and the two occurrences of the phrase "or that the owner or operator has failed *** LAC 33:V.3525"), 3709 through 3713, 3715 (except 3715.F.8), 3717 through 3719; Chapter 40, Sections 4001 through 4025, 4027 (except 4027.C), 4029 through 4093; Chapter 41, Sections 4101, 4103, 4105 introductory paragraph, 4105.A, 4105.B (introductory paragraph), 4105.B.1 introductory paragraph (except the phrase "except that"), 4105.B.1 (except

4105.B.1.a&b), 4105.B.2, 4105.B.4-.14, 4105.C, 4105.E, 4107 through 4113, 4115.A (except the reference "22,"), 4115.B, 4137, 4139.A.1, 4139.A.2 (except 4139.A.2.b&.c), 4139.B.1, 4139.B.4, 4143, 4145; Chapter 43, Sections 4301 (except the last sentence of 4301.E), 4302, 4303 through 4305, 4307 through 4335, 4337 through 4349, 4351 through 4355, 4357 (except 4357.B.8-.14), 4359 through 4365, 4367 through 4375, 4377 (except 4377.B.4), 4379 (except the phrase "and LAC 33:V.4705" at 4379.C), 4381 through 4395, 4397, 4399 (except 4399.A.6.i), 4401, 4403 (except for the phrase "and after receiving the certification required under LAC 33:V.4393.B.2 for facilities subject to LAC 33:V.4393" and the two occurrences of the phrase "or that the owner or operator has failed *** LAC 33:4393" in 4403.H), 4405 through 4411, 4413, 4417 through 4429, 4431 through 4445, 4447 through 4455, 4457.A, 4457.B (except the first occurrence of 4457.B.2), 4459 (except the phrase "the waste and impoundment satisfy all applicable requirements of LAC 33:V.Chapter 22." at 4459.A), 4461, 4462 (except 4462.H), 4463 through 4470, 4471 (except the phrase "the waste and pile satisfy all applicable requirements of LAC 33:V.Chapter 22 and"), 4472 through 4476, 4477 through 4493, 4495 through 4499, 4501 (except 4501.D.3), 4502, 4503 (except the phrase "and landfill meet all applicable requirements of LAC 33:V.Chapter 22, and the waste" at 4503.A introductory paragraph), 4505 through 4509, 4511 introductory paragraph, 4511.A-.D, 4511.E (except the two occurrences of the reference "and F"), 4512, 4513 through 4522, 4523 (except the phrase "and LAC 33:V.Chapter 30 *** LAC 33:V.109" at the end of the paragraph), 4525 through 4534, 4535 through 4547, 4549 through 4559, 4561 through 4589, 4591 through 4601; Chapter 49, Sections 4901.A through 4901.F, 4901.G (except the entries for EPA Hazardous Waste Numbers K042 and 151 in Table 6), 4903 through 4907, Appendices A through D.

Louisiana Administrative Code, Title 33, Part V, Hazardous Waste and Hazardous Materials, Amendments for July 1995–March 1996: Chapter 1, Sections 109 "Designated facility", 109 "Partial Closure", 109 "Solid Waste"; Chapter 3, Sections 305.A, 309.L.3.b, 321.C.2.i, 323.B.2.e, 323.B.4.c, Chapter 5, Section 533.B; Chapter 7, Section 706; Chapter 11, Section 1101.B; Chapter 25, Section 2521.B.2; Chapter 26, Section 2603.F.1; Chapter 28, Sections 2801 through 2809; Chapter 41, Sections 4115.C, 4139.B.2&.3; Chapter 49, Sections 4901.G Table 6 (entries for EPA Hazardous Waste Numbers K042 and 151 only), Appendix A (entry for 2,6-Toluenedine only) and Appendix B (paragraphs 8.2 and 8.2.5 through 8.2.5.4).

Copies of the Louisiana regulations that are incorporated by reference are available from Office of the State Register, P.O. Box 94095, Baton Rouge, LA 70804-9095.

Minnesota

The statutory provisions include: Minnesota Statutes, June 1992 edition, Chapters 13.03; 13.05 Subdivision 9; 13.08; 13.37; 15.17; 15.171; 115.061; 115A.03; 116.06; 116.07 Subdivisions 4, 4a, 4b, 5 and 8; 116.075; 116.081 Subdivisions 1 and 3; and 116.14.

The regulatory provisions include: Minnesota Rules, June 1992 edition, 7001.0010; 7001.0020(B); 7001.0030-7001.0150(3)(C); 7001.0150(3)(E)-7001.0200; 7001.0500-7001.0730(2); 7001.0730(4); 7045.0020-7045.0143; 7045.0205-7045.0270(6); 7045.0275-7045.0310; 7045.0351-7045.0685; 7045.0692-7045.0695; 7045.1300-7045.1380 (June 1992 edition).

Missouri

The statutory provisions include: 260.350-260.360(3), 260.360(5)-260.360(12), 260.360(14)-260.360(19), 260.380-1.-260.380-1.(9), 260.380-2., 260.385(2)-260.390(7), 260.390(9), 260.395-6.-260.395-7.(4), 260.395-7.(7)-260.395-18.

The regulatory provisions include: 3.260-3.260(1)(A)20, 3.260(1)(A)22-3.260(1)(A)23, 3.260(2), 4.261-4.261(2)(A)5, 5.262-5.262(2)(B)1., 5.262(2)(B)3.-5.262(2)(C)1., 5.262(2)(C)2.A.-5.262(2)(D), 5.262(2)(D)2.-5.262(2)(H), 6.263-6.263(2)(A)2., 6.263(2)(A)5.-6.263(2)(A)10.C, 6.263(2)(B)-6.263(2)(D)2., 7.264-7.264(2)(A)2., 7.264(2)(B)2.-7.264(2)(O), 7.264(2)(X), 7.265-7.265(2)(A), 7.265(2)(E)-7.265(2)(K), 7.266-7.266(2), 7.268-7.268(2), 7.268(2)(A)., 7.268(2)(A)4.-7.268(2)(C), 7.270-7.270(2)(B)6., 7.270(2)(B)9., 7.270(2)(B)11., 7.270(2)(B)14.-7.270(2)(B)17., 7.270(2)(C)-7.270(2)(C)1., 7.270(2)(C)1.B.-7.270(2)(C)1.C., 7.270(2)(C)2.-7.270(2)(C)2.C., 7.270(2)(C)2.E., 7.270(2)(D)-7.270(2)(D)3., 7.270(2)(E)-7.270(2)(G).

Montana

The regulatory provisions include:

Administrative Rules of Montana, Title 17, Environmental Quality, Chapter 53, Hazardous Waste, effective April 1, 2005, sections 17.53.101, 17.53.102, 17.53.105, 17.53.107, 17.53.111(1), 17.53.111(2), (except the phrase "or to pay the fee required by ARM 17.53.111" in the introductory paragraph), 17.53.111(3) (except the phrase "and the generator fee required by ARM 17.53.113" at 17.53.111(3)(a)), 17.53.301 (except the phrase "and for which a registration fee is assessed" at 17.53.301(2)(q)), 17.53.401, 17.53.402, 17.53.403, 17.53.501, 17.53.502, 17.53.601, 17.53.602, 17.53.603, 17.53.604, 17.53.701, 17.53.702, 17.53.704, 17.53.706, 17.53.707, 17.53.708, 17.53.801, 17.53.802, 17.53.803, 17.53.901, 17.53.902, 17.53.903, 17.53.1001, 17.53.1002, 17.53.1003, 17.53.1004, 17.53.1101, 17.53.1102, 17.53.1201, 17.53.1202 (except 17.53.1202(5)(l), (5)(m), (6) and (17)), 17.53.1203, 17.53.1301, 17.53.1302, 17.53.1303, 17.53.1401, and 17.53.1402.

Copies of the Montana regulations that are incorporated by reference are available from the Montana Secretary of State, Administrative Rules Bureau, P.O. Box 202801, Helena, MT 59620–2801 (Phone: 406–444–2055).

New Mexico

The statutory provisions include:

New Mexico Statutes 1978 Annotated, Hazardous Waste Act, Chapter 74, Article 4 (2000 Replacement Pamphlet). Please note that for a few provisions the version found in the 2002 Cumulative Supplement to NMSA 74–4 is the approved version of the statutes.

Chapter 74, Article 4, Sections 74–4–2, 74– 4–3 (except 74–4–3.A, 74–4–3.N, 74–4–3.R, and 74–4–3.V) (2002 Cumulative Supplement), 74–4–3.1, 74–4–4.2.A, 74–4– 4.2.B, 74–4–4.2.G introductory paragraph, 74–4–4.2.G(2), 74–4–4.3.F (2002 Cumulative Supplement), 74–4–4.7 (except 74–4–4.7.B and 74–4–4.7.C), 74–4–9, and 74–4–10.1.C, as published by ConwayGreene Company, 1400 East 30th Street, Suite #402, Cleveland, OH 44114; Phone number (216) 619–8091; Web site: *http://www.conwaygreene.com.*

The regulatory provisions include:

Title 20, Chapter 4, Part 1, New Mexico Annotated Code, effective October 1, 2003, unless otherwise indicated, Sections 20.4.100, 20.4.1.101, 20.4.1.200, 20.4.1.300, 20.4.1.400, 20.4.1.401, 20.4.1.500, 20.4.1.501, 20.4.1.600, 20.4.1.601, 20.4.1.700, 20.4.1.800, 20.4.801, 20.4.1.900, 20.4.1.901.B.1 through 20.4.1.901.B.6, 20.4.1.901.E, 20.4.1.1000, 20.4.1.1001 (June 14, 2000), 20.4.1.1102 (June 14, 2000), and 20.4.1103. Copies of the New Mexico regulations can be obtained from the New Mexico Commission of Public Records, State Records Center and Archives, Administrative Law Division, 1205 Camino Carlos Rey, Santa Fe, NM 87507; Phone number (505) 476–7907; Web site: *http://www.nmcpr.state.nm.us/.*

New York

The regulatory provisions include:

Title 6, New York Codes, Rules and Regulations (6 NYCRR), Volume A–2A, Hazardous Waste Management System, as amended through April 10, 2004.

Please note the following:

(1) The State's official regulations, as amended through April 10, 2004, contain typographical and printing errors that were not in the State's regulations submitted for authorization. New York subsequently corrected these errors in its official "Supplement", dated July 15, 2005, filed with the New York Secretary of State. EPA recognizes the corrected provisions as part of the authorized program. The authorized provisions for which typographical and printing errors in the April 10, 2004 regulations have been corrected are noted below by inclusion in parentheses of July 15, 2005 after the regulatory citation.

(2) For a few regulations, the authorized regulation is an earlier version of the New York State regulation. For these regulations, EPA authorized the version of the regulations that appear in the Official Compilation of Code, Rules and Regulations dated January 31, 1992 or January 1, 1999. New York State made later changes to these regulations but these changes have not been authorized by EPA. The regulations where the authorized regulation is an earlier version of the regulation are noted below by inclusion in parentheses of January 31, 1992 or January 1, 1999 after the regulatory citations.

Part 370—Hazardous Waste Management System—General: Sections 370.1(a) (except (a)(3)); 370.1(b) through (d); 370.1(e) (except (e)(1)(xv), (e)(1)(xvi) and (e)(6)(ii) through (iii)); 370.2(a); 370.2(b)(1) through (b)(15) "battery"; 370.2(b)(15) "bedrock" (January 31, 1992); 370.2(b)(17)–(b)(54); 370.2(b)(56) through (b)(71); 370.2(b)(72) (July 15, 2005); 370.2(b)(73) through (b)(91); 370.2(b)(94) through (b)(104); 370.2(b)(106) through (b)(122); 370.2(b)(123) and (124) (July 15, 2005); 370.2(b)(126) through (b)(187); 370.2(b)(188) (July 15, 2005); 370.2(b)(189) through (b)(212); 370(b)(214) and (b)(215); 370.2(b)(216) (except the last sentence); 370.2(b)(217) through (b)(220); 370.3 (except 370.3(c)); 370.4 (except 370.4(a)(1)(i) through (v)); 370.4(a)(1)(i) through (v) (July 15, 2005); 370.5 (except (b)).

Part 371—Identification and Listing of Hazardous Waste: Sections 371.1(a) through (c); 371.1(d) (except (d)(1)(ii)(e)); 371.1(e) (except 371.1(e)(2)(vi)('b')(21); 371.1(f)(1) through (7); 371.1(f)(8) (except the phrase "or such mixing occurs at a facility regulated under Subpart 373–4 or permitted under Part 373 of this Title"); 371.1(f)(9) and (f)(10); 371.1(g)(1)(i); 371.1(g)(1)(ii) (except (g)(1)(ii)(c)); 371.1(g)(1)(iii) (except (g)(1)(iii)(a)); 371.1(g)(1)(iii)(a) (except the phrase "as defined in section 372.5 of this Title, and provide a copy of") (January 1, 1999); 371.1(g)(2) through (4); 371.1(h) through (j); 371.2; 371.3; and 371.4(a) and (b); 371.4(c) (except K171 and K172 entries); 371.4(c), K171 and K172 entries (July 15, 2005); 371.4(d), (f) and (i).

Part 372—Hazardous Waste Manifest System and Related Standards for Generators, Transporters and Facilities: Sections 372.1(a) through (d); 372.1(e)(2)(ii)(c) (January 31, 1992); 372.1(e)(2)(iii)(c) (January 31, 1992); 372.1(e)(3) through (e)(8); 372.1(g) and (h); 372.2 (except (a)(8)(vi)); 372.3 (except (a)(1), (a)(4), (a)(7)(i), (a)(8), (b)(1)(ii), (b)(5)(ii), (b)(6)(iv), (c)(4) and (d)(3)); 372.5 (except (h) and (i); 372.6; 372.7(a) and (b); 372.7(c) (except (c)(1)(ii)); and 372.7(d) (except (d)(4)); 372.7(d)(4) (January 31, 1992).

Part 373, Subpart 373–1—Hazardous Waste Treatment, Storage and Disposal Facility Permitting Requirements: Sections 373–1.1(a) through (c), 373–1.1(d) (except (d)(1)(iii)(b), (d)(1)(iii)(c)(6), (d)(1)(iii)(d), (d)(1)(iv)(a) and (b), (d)(1)(x), (d)(1)(xvi) and (xviii)); 373–1.1(e); 373–1.1(h) and (i); 373–1.2; 373–1.3; 373–1.4(a); 373–1.4(g) and (h); 373–1.5(a)(1); 373–1.5(a)(2) (except (a)(2)(xviii)); 373–1.5(a)(3) and (4); 373–1.5(b) and (c); 373–1.5(d) (except (d)(3)); 373–1.5(e) through (p) (except reserved paragraphs); 373–1.6 (except (c)); 373–1.7 through 373–1.9; 373–1.10 (except (a)(1)); 373–1.10(a)(1) (January 1, 1999); and 373–1.11.

Part 373, Subpart 373–2—Final Status Standards for Owners and Operators of Hazardous Waste Treatment, Storage and Disposal Facilities: Sections 373–2.1 through 373–2.4; 373–2.5(a); 373–2.5(b) (except the last sentence in (b)(1)(i)(b) and the entire provision at (b)(1)(vii)); 373–2.5(c) through (g); 373–2.6 through 373–2.9; 373–2.10 (except last sentence in (g)(4)(i)); 373–2.11; 373–2.12 (except 373–2.12(a)(1), (d) and (g)(2)); 373–2.12(a)(1) (January 31, 1992); 373–2.12(g)(2) (January 31, 1992); 373–2.13; 373–2.14; 373–2.15 (except (a)(2)); 373–2.19; 373–2.23; 373–2.24; 373–2.27; 373–2.28; 373–2.29; 373–2.30; and 373–2.31.

Part 373, Subpart 373–3—Interim Status Standards Regulations for Owners and Operators of Hazardous Waste Facilities: Sections 373–3.1 (except 373–3.1(a)(4) and the phrase "or Subpart 374–2 of this Title" in 373–3.1(a)(6)); 373–3.2 through 373–3.4; 373–3.5 (except last sentence in 373–3.5(b)(1)(i)(b) and (b)(1)(vii)); 373–3.6 through 373–3.9; 373–3.10 (except last sentence in (g)(4)(i)); 373–3.11 through 373–3.14; 373–3.15 (except (a)(2)); 373–3.16 through 373–3.18; 373–3.23; and 373–3.27 through 373–3.31.

Part 374, Subpart 374–1—Standards for the Management of Specific Hazardous Wastes and Specific Types of Hazardous Waste Management Facilities: Sections 374–1.1; 374–1.3; 374–1.6 (except (a)(2)(iii)); 374–1.7; 374–1.8(a)(1); 374–1.8(a)(2) (except the second sentence "Such used oil * * * of this Title" in (a)(2)(i)); 374–1.8(a)(3) through (a)(6); 374–1.8(b) through (m); and 374–1.13.

Part 374, Subpart 374–3—Standards for Universal Waste: Sections 374–3.1 (except (f) and (g)); 374–3.2; 374–3.3; 374–3.4 (except (a)(2)); 374–3.5; 374–3.6; and 374–3.7.

Part 376—Land Disposal Restrictions: Sections 376.1 (except (a)(5), (a)(9), (b)(1)(xi), (e) and (f)); 376.2; 376.3 (except (b)(4), (c) and (d)(2)); 376.4 (except (c)(2) and (e)(1) through (7)); and 376.5.

Appendices: Appendices 19 through 25; Appendices 27 through 30; Appendix 33; Appendix 38; Appendices 40 through 49 and Appendices 51 through 55.

Copies of the New York regulations that are incorporated by reference are available from West Group, 610 Opperman Drive, Eagan, MN 55123, ATTENTION: D3–10 (Phone #: 1–800–328–9352).

North Dakota

(a) The statutory provisions include: North Dakota Century Code, Volume 4A, 2002 Replacement. Chapter 23–20.3 "Hazardous Waste": Sections 23–20.3–05(1), (2), (4), (7), and (9). Copies of the North Dakota statutes that are incorporated by reference are available from the Matthew Bender & Company Inc., P.O. Box 7587, Charlottesville, VA 22906–7587, phone number: (800) 833–9844.

(b) The regulatory provisions include: North Dakota Administrative Code (NDAC), Article 33–24, Hazardous Waste Management, as amended through December 1, 2003.

Please note the following:

For a few regulations, the authorized regulation is an earlier version of the North Dakota State regulation. For these regulations, EPA authorized the version of the regulations that appear in the North Dakota Administrative Code dated July 1, 1997. North Dakota made later changes to these regulations, but these changes have not been authorized by EPA. The regulations where the authorized regulation is an earlier version of the regulation are noted below by inclusion in parentheses of July 1, 1997 after the regulatory citations.

Chapter 33–24–01—General Provisions: Sections 33–24–01–01 through 33–24–01–14.

Chapter 33–24–02—Identification and Listing of Hazardous Waste; 33–24–02–01; 33–24–02–02; 33–24–02–03 except .1.b(3) and (6); 33–24–02–04 through 33–24–02–06; 33–24–02–07; 33–24–02–08 through 33–24–02–19; 33–24–02–22; and Appendices I through V.

Chapter 33–24–03—Standards for Generators: Sections 33–24–03–01; 33–24–03–02; 33–24–03–03.1 and .2; 33–24–03– 03.3, (except the phrases "and a transporter permit" and "and applied for a permit"); 33–24–03–03.4; 33–24–03–04 through 33–24–03–12; 33–24–03–13, (except the phrase "March first of each even-numbered year" in .2); 33–24–03–14 through 33–24–03–24; 33–24–03–30; 33–24–03–40; and Appendix I.

Chapter 33–24–04—Standards for Transporters: Sections 33–24–04–01, (except .4); 33–24–04–02.1, (except the phrase ", a transporter permit, and a registration certificate"); 33–24–04–02.2, (except the phrases "and a registration certificate, or a transporter permit," and "and issue a registration certificate"); and 33–24–04–03 through 33–24–04–08.

Chapter 33–24–05—Standards for Treatment, Storage, and Disposal Facilities and for the Management of Specific Hazardous Wastes and Specific Types of Hazardous Waste Management Facilities: Sections 33–24–05–01; 33–24–05–02, (except the second sentence); 33–24–05–03 through 33–24–05–10; 33–24–05–15 through 33–24–05–20; 33–24–05–26 through 33–24–05–31; 33–24–05–37 through 33–24–05–44; 33–24–05–47 through 33–24–05–50; 33–24–05–51, (except Table 1); 33–24–05–51, Table 1 (July 1, 1997); 33–24–05–52 through 33–24–05–55; 33–24–05–56, (except .11); 33–24–05–57 through 33–24–05–69; 33–24–05–74 through 33–24–05–81; 33–24–05–89 through 33–24–05–93; 33–24–05–94, (except .4.b); 33–24–05–95 through 33–24–05–98; 33–24–05–103 through 33–24–05–115; 33–24–05–118 through 33–24–05–128; 33–24–05–130 through 33–24–05–138; 33–24–05–144 through 33–24–05–151; 33–24–05–160 through 33–24–05–170; 33–24–05–176 through 33–24–05–188; 33–24–05–201 through 33–24–05–204; 33–24–05–230; 33–24–05–235; 33–24–05–250 through 33–24–05–252; 33–24–05–253, (except .3); 33–24–05–256, (except .1.b(2)); 33–24–05–258, (except .4.b(2)); 33–24–05–265; 33–24–05–270 through 33–24–05–279; 33–24–05–280, (except .9); 33–24–05–281; 33–24–05–282, (except .2); 33–24–05–283; 33–24–05–284.8 through .13; 33–24–05–285; 33–24–05–286; 33–24–05–288 through 33–24–05–290; 33–24–05–300 through 33–24–05–303; 33–24–05–400, (except .4); 33–24–05–401 through 33–24–05–406; 33–24–05–420 through 33–24–05–435; 33–24–05–450 through 33–24–05–460; 33–24–05–475 through 33–24–05– 477; 33–24–05–501 through 33–24–05–506; 33–24–05–525 through 33–24–05–537; 33–24–05–550 through 33–24–05–553; 33–24–05–554, (except .1.b); 33–24–05–555; 33–24–05–600; 33–24–05–610 through 33–24–05–612; 33–24–05–620 through 33–24–05–624; 33–24–05–630 through 33–24–05–632; 33–24–05–640 through 33–24–05–647; 33–24–05–650 through 33–24–05–667; 33–24–05–670 through 33–24–05–675; 33–24–05–680; 33–24–05–681; 33–24–05–701 through 33–24–05–705; 33–24–05–708 through 33–24–05–720; 33–24–05–730 through 33–24–05–740; 33–24–05–750 through 33–24–05–756; 33–24–05–760 through 33–24–05–762; 33–24–05–770; 33–24–05–780; 33–24–05–781; 33–24–05–800 through 33–24–05–802; 33–24–05–820 through 33–24–05–826; 33–24–05–850; 33–24–05–855 through 33–24–05–857; 33–24–05–860; 33–24–05–865; 33–24–05–866; 33–24–05–870; 33–24–05–875; 33– 24–05–880; 33–24–05–885; 33–24–05–890; 33–24–05–895 through 33–24–05–900; 33–24–05–905; 33–24–05–910; 33–24–05–915; 33–24–05–916; and Appendices I through VIII, X through XIII, XVI through XXIV; and XXVI through XXIX.

Chapter 33–24–06—Permits: Sections 33–24–06–01, (except .2.a); 33–24–06–01.2.a (July 1, 1997); 33–24–06–02 through 33–24–06–04; 33–24–06–05.1.c; 33–24–06–06, (except .2 and .3); 33–24–06–07; 33–24–06–08; 33–24–06–10 through 33–24–06–13; 33–24–06–14, (except .3.a(4)); 33–24–06–14, Appendix I; 33–24–06–15 introductory paragraph through .1.a; 33–24–06–16.5 through .7; 33–24–06–17, (except .2.k and .2.z); 33–24–06–18 through 33–24–06–20; 33–24–06–30 through 33–24–06–35; and 33–24–06–100.

Chapter 33–24–07—Permitting Procedures: Sections 33–24–07–01; 33–24–07–02; and 33–24–07–03, (except .4).

Copies of the North Dakota regulations that are incorporated by reference are available from North Dakota Legislative Counsel, Second Floor, State Capitol, 600 E Boulevard, Bismarck, ND 58505, phone number: (701) 328–2916.

Oklahoma

The statutory provisions include:

Oklahoma Hazardous Waste Management Act, as amended, 27A Oklahoma Statute 1997 Edition, Sections 2-7-103, 2-7-108(A), 2-7-108(B)(1), 2-7-108(B)(3), 2-7-108(C), 2-7-110(B), 2-7-110(C), 2-7-111(A), 2-7-111(B) (except the last sentence and the phrase, "recycling" in the first sentence), 2-7-111(C)(2)(a) (except the phrase "Except as provided in subparagraph b of this paragraph" and the word "recycling" in the first sentence), 2-7-111(D), 2-7-111(E) (except the word "recycling" in the first sentence), 2-7-112, 2-7-116(B) through 2-7-116(F), 2-7-116(H)(2), 2-7-118(A), 2-7-124, 2-7-125, 2-7-127 and 2-10-301(G).

Copies of the Oklahoma statutes that are incorporated by reference are available from West Publishing Company, 610 Opperman Drive, P. O. Box 64526, St. Paul, Minnesota 55164-0526.

The regulatory provisions include:

The Oklahoma Administrative Code, Title 252, Chapter 205, effective June 12, 2000: Subchapter 1, Sections 252:205-1-1(a), 252:205-1-1(c) introductory paragraph, 252:205-1-1(c)(1), 252:205-1-2 introductory paragraph, 252:205-1-2 "OHWMA", 252:205-1-2 "Post-closure permit", 252:205-1-3(c); Subchapter 3, Sections 252:205-3-1, 252:205-3-2(a)(2), 252:205-3-2(b)-(m), 252:205-3-4, 252:205-3-5 and 252:205-3-6; Subchapter 5, Sections 252:205-5-1 (except 252:205-5-1(4)), 252:205-5-2 through 252:205-5-5; Subchapter 7, Sections 252:205-7-1 through 252:205-7-3 and 252:205-7-4 (except the phrase "or in accordance with 252:205-15-1(d)); Subchapter 9 (except 252:205-9-5 and 252:205-9-6); Subchapter 11, 252:205-11-1(a) (except the word "recycling"), 252:205-11-1(b) through 252:205-11-1(e) and 252:205-11-2; and Subchapter 13, Sections 252:205-13-1(a)-(e).

Copies of the Oklahoma regulations that are incorporated by reference can be obtained from The Oklahoma Register, Office of Administrative Rules, Secretary of State, 101 State Capitol, Oklahoma City, Oklahoma 73105.

South Dakota

The regulatory provisions include:

Administrative Rules of South Dakota, Article 74:28, Hazardous Waste, effective August 29, 2004, sections 74:28:21:01, 74:28:21:02, 74:28:21:03, 74:28:22:01, 74:28:23:01, 74:28:24:01, 74:28:25:01 through 74:28:25:05, 74:28:26:01, 74:28:27:01, 74:28:28:01 through 74:28:28:05, 74:28:29:01, 74:28:30:01 and 74:28:33:01; Article 74:36, Air Pollution Control Program, effective January 2, 2005, section 74:36:11:01.

Copies of the South Dakota regulations that are incorporated by reference are available from the South Dakota Legislative Research Council, 3rd Floor, State Capitol, 500 East Capitol Avenue, Pierre, SD 57501, (Phone: 605–773–3251).

Texas

The statutory provisions include:

Texas Health and Safety Code (THSC) Annotated, (Vernon 2001): Chapter 361, The Texas Solid Waste Disposal Act, sections 361.003 (except (3), (4), (19), (27), (35), and (39)), 361.066(a), 361.082(a), 361.082(f), 361.086, 361.087, 361.093, 361.094, 361.095(a), 361.099(b), and 361.110; Chapter 371, The Texas Oil Collection, Management, and Recycling Act, sections 371.003, 371.024(b), 371.026(d), and 371.041.

Copies of the Texas statutes that are incorporated by reference are available from West Publishing Company, 620 Opperman Drive, P. O. Box 64526, St. Paul, Minnesota 55164–0526; Phone: 1–800–328–4880; Web site: http://west.thomson.com.

The regulatory provisions include: Texas Administrative Code (TAC), Title 30, Environmental Quality, 2002, as amended, effective through December 31, 2001. Please note that the 2002 TAC, Title 30 is the most recent version of the Texas authorized hazardous waste regulations. For a few provisions, the authorized version is found in the TAC, Title 30, Environmental Quality dated January 1, 1994, January 1, 1997, or December 31, 1999. Texas made subsequent changes to these provisions but these changes have not been authorized by EPA. The provisions from earlier sets of regulations are noted in the table below.

Chapter 20, Section 20.15; Chapter 35, Section 35.402(e); Chapter 39, Sections 39.5(g), 39.11, 39.103(a)(2), (b), (d)(4), and (g), 39.405(f)(1), 39.411 (except (b)(4)(B), (b)(10), (11), and (13)), 39.503(d); Chapter 55, Sections 55.25(b)(1)–(3), 55.152(b), 55.154, and 55.156(b)(1); Chapter 281, Section 281.3(c);

Chapter 305—Sections 305.1(a) (except the reference to Chapter 401, relative to Radioactive Materials); 305.2 introductory paragraph (except the references to Chapter 401, relative to Radioactive Materials), 305.2(1), (6), (12), (13), (16), (17), (21), (25), (27)–(29), (32), and (41)–(43); 305.29(a), (January 1, 1997); 305.30; 305.41 (except the reference to Chapter 401, relative to Radioactive Materials); 305.42(a), (b), and (d); 305.43(b); 305.44 (except (d)); 305.45(a) (except (a)(7)(I) and the phrase "§305.54 of this title *** Content of Applications)," in 305.45(a)(8)(C)); 305.45(b); 305.47; 305.50 introductory paragraph–(3) (except the last two sentences in 305.50(2)); 305.50(4) introductory paragraph and (A); 305.50(4)(B)–(D), (January 1, 1994); 305.50(4)(G); 305.50(5)–(8), (13) and (14); 305.51; 305.61; 305.62(a) (except the phrase in the first sentence "§305.70 of this title *** Solid Waste Class I Modifications" and the phrase in the fifth sentence "If the permittee requests a modification of a municipal solid waste permit *** §305.70 of this title."); 305.62(b); 305.62(c), (January 1, 1997); 305.62(d) (except (d)(6)); 305.62(e)–(h); 305.63(a) introductory paragraph (except first sentence); 305.63(a)(1) and (2); 305.63(a)(3) (except last sentence); 305.63(a)(4)–(6); 305.64(a), 305.64(b) (except (4) and (5)); 305.64(c); 305.64(e); 305.64(g), (December 31, 1999); 305.66(a) (except (7)–(9)); 305.66(d); 305.67 (except (c)); 305.69(a)–(h), (January 1, 1997); 305.69(i)–(k) (except (k) A.8–A.10); 305.121 (except the phrase "radioactive material disposal"); 305.122(a)–(c); 305.124; 305.125 (except (1), (3), the last two sentences in (5), (6), (9)(C), the phrase "as otherwise required by Chapter 336 of this title" relative to Radioactive Substances in (11)(B), (20), and (22)); 305.125(6), (January 1, 1997); 305.127 introductory paragraph; 305.127(1)(B)(iii), (E) and (F); 305.127(2); 305.127(3)(A) (except the last two sentences); 305.127(3)(B) and (C); 305.127(4)(B) and (5)(C); 305.128; 305.141 through 305.145; 305.146 introductory paragraph and (1), (January 1, 1997); 305.150; 305.171 through 305.175; 305.181 through 305.184; 305.191 through 305.194; 305.401(c); 305.571 through 305.573;

Chapter 324—Used Oil—Sections 324.1 through 324.2(6); 324.2(7)–(9), (January 1, 1997); 324.3; 324.4, (January 1, 1997); 324.6; 324.7, (January 1, 1997); 324.11 through 324.14; 324.15, (January 1, 1997); 324.16; 324.21, (January 1, 1997);

Chapter 335, Subchapter A—Industrial Solid Waste and Municipal Hazardous Waste in General—Sections 335.1 introductory paragraph—(4), (6)–(13), (17), (18), (20)–(24), (27), (29), (30), (32)–(39), (40) (except for the phrase "or is used for neutralizing the pH of non-hazardous industrial solid waste"), (41)–(43), (45)–(50), (52)–(58), (61)–(70), (72)–(79), (80)–(85) (except the phrase "solid waste or" in each subsection), (86)–(89), (90) (except the phrase "solid waste or"), (91)–(105), (107) (except the phrase "solid waste"), (108), (112), (113) (except the phrase "solid waste"), (114)–(117); 335.1(119) (December 31, 1999); 335.1(121)–(125), (127), (128), (129)(A)–(G) (except the phrase "Except for materials described in subparagraph (H) of this paragraph.", at (129)(D) and (G) introductory paragraphs, (129)(I) and (J), (130), (132)–(141) (except the phrase "solid waste or" at (134), (137) and (139)), (142) (except the phrase "or industrial solid"), (143), (144), (145) (except the phrase "or industrial solid"), (146) (except the phrase "or industrial solid"), (148)–(150), (151) (except the phrase "solid waste or"), (152)–(157), (158) (except the phrase "or industrial solid"), (159)–(160), (161) (except the phrase "solid waste or"); 335.2(a) and (c); 335.2(d), (January 1, 1997); 335.2(e)–(g); 335.2(i), (j) and (l); 335.4; 335.5; 335.6(a); 335.6(b), (January 1, 1997); 335.6(c); 335.6(d) and (e), (January 1, 1994); 335.6(f)–(j); 335.7, (December 31, 1999); 335.8(a)(1) and (2); 335.9(a) (except (a)(2) and (3)); 335.9(a)(2) and (3), (January 1, 1997); 335.9(b), (January 1, 1994); 335.10(a) introductory paragraph and (a)(1), (January 1, 1994); 335.10(a)(3) (except the phrase, "unless the generator is identified in paragraph (2) of this section"); 335.10(a)(4); 335.10(a)(6); 335.10(b) (except 335.10(b)(5), (8), and (18)); 335.10(b)(5), (8), and (18), (January 1, 1994); 335.10(c) (except the phrase "the United States customs official,"); 335.10(d)–(f); 335.11 (except 11(d)); 335.12 (except 335.12(a)(5) and (d)); 335.13(a), (January 1, 1997); 335.13(c) and (d), (January 1, 1994); 335.13(e) and (f), (January 1, 1997); 335.13(g), (January 1, 1994); 335.14; 335.15 introductory paragraph, (January 1, 1994); 335.15(1); 335.17(a); 335.18 (except 335.18(b)); 335.19 (except 335.19(d)); 335.20 through 335.22; 335.23 (except 335.23(2)); 335.23(2), (January 1, 1994); 335.24(a)–(f); 335.24(j) and (k); 335.29 through 335.31;

Chapter 335, Subchapter B—Hazardous Waste Management General Provisions—335.41(a)–(h); 335.41(j); 335.43 and 335.44, (December 31, 1999); 335.45; 335.47 (except 335.47(b) and the second sentence in 335.47(c)(3)); 335.47(b), (December 31, 1999);

Chapter 335, Subchapter C—Standards Applicable to Generators of Hazardous Waste—335.61 (except (f)); 335.62; 335.63; 335.65 through 335.69 (except 335.69(i)); 335.70; 335.71, (January 1, 1994); 335.73; 335.74; 335.76 (except 335.76(a), (b)(1), (f) and (h)); 335.76(a), (b)(1), and (f), (January 1, 1997); 335.77; 335.78 (except (b), (d)(2), (e) introductory paragraph, (f)(2), and (g)(2)); 335.78(b), (e) introductory paragraph, (f)(2), and (g)(2), (January 1, 1997);

Chapter 335, Subchapter D—Standards Applicable to Transporters of Hazardous Waste—335.91 (except 335.91(e)); 335.92; 335.93 (except 335.93(e)); 335.93(e), (December 31, 1999); 335.94 (except the phrase "owned or operated by a registered transporter" in (a) introductory paragraph);

Chapter 335, Subchapter E—Interim Standards for Owners and Operators of Hazardous Waste Storage, Processing, or Disposal Facilities—335.111; 335.112 (except (a)(7), (a)(17), (b)(4)(I) and (J), and (b)(7)); 335.112(a)(7), (January 1, 1997); 335.113; 335.114, (January 1, 1997); 335.115 introductory paragraph, (January 1, 1997); 335.115 (1)–(4); 335.116; 335.117 (except (a)(2)(B), (a)(2)(C), and (b)(2)); 335.117(a)(2)(B), (a)(2)(C), and (b)(2) (January 1, 1997); 335.118 through 335.127;

Chapter 335, Subchapter F—Permitting Standards for Owners and Operators of Hazardous Waste Storage, Processing, or Disposal Facilities—335.151; 335.152 (except (a)(4), (a)(6), and (c)(5)–(7)); 335.152(a)(4), (a)(6), (January 1, 1997); 335.153; 335.154, (January 1, 1997); 335.155 introductory paragraph, (January 1, 1997); 335.155 (1)–(3); 335.156 through 335.166; 335.167(a); 335.167(b) and (c), (December 31, 1999); 335.168 through 335.178;

Chapter 335, Subchapter G—Location Standards for Hazardous Waste Storage, Processing, or Disposal—335.201 (a) (except (a)(3)); 335.201(c); 335.202 introductory paragraph, (2), (4), (9)–(11), (13), (15)–(18); 335.203; 335.204(a) introductory paragraph—(5); 335.204(b)(1)–(6); 335.204(c)(1)–(5); 335.204(d)(1)–(5); 335.204(e) introductory paragraph; 335.204(e)(1) introductory paragraph (except the phrase "Except as *** (B) of this paragraph," and the word "event" at the end of the paragraph); 335.204(e)(2)–(7); 335.204(f); 335.205(a) introductory paragraph—(2) and (e);

Chapter 335, Subchapter H—Standards for the Management of Specific Wastes and Specific Types of Facilities—335.211; 335.212; 335.213, (January 1, 1997); 335.214; 335.221 (except (a)(1)(B)); 335.222 through 335.225; 335.241 (except (b)(4) and (d)); 335.241(d), (January 1, 1997); 335.251; 335.261 (except (e)); 335.271; 335.272;

Chapter 335, Subchapter O—Land Disposal Restrictions—335.431;

Chapter 335, Subchapter R—Waste Classification—335.504 introductory paragraph—(2); 335.504(3) and (4), (December 31, 1999).

Copies of the Texas regulations that are incorporated by reference are available from West Publishing Company, 620 Opperman Drive, P.O. Box 64526, St. Paul, Minnesota 55164–0526; Phone: 1–800–328–4880; Web site: http://west.thomson.com.

Utah

The regulatory provisions include:

Utah Administrative Code effective February 15, 1996: Sections R315-1 except R315-1-1(a), R315-1-1(f)&(h) and R315-1-2(a); R315-2 except R315-2-3(d)(2), R315-2-5, R315-2-6, R315-2-10(e)&(f), R315-2-11(e)&(f), R315-2-17, and R315-2-25(d); R315-3 except R315-3-1(b)&(c), R315-3-3(b)(3), R315-3-3(i)(1)-(3), R315-3-3(n)(8)(iv), R315-3-11(a)&(b), R315-3-11(f), R315-3-13(a)(4), R315-3-16(b), R315-3-23(b)(1)&(2), R315-3-23(c)&(d), R315-3-24 through R315-3-29, R315-3-34 and R315-3-36; R315-4 through R315-7, except R315-7-8.1(c)(12)(iv), R315-7-18.9(d)(2)(i)(A) phrase "given the specific site conditions and the nature and extent of contamination"; R315-8 except R315-8-1(e)(10)(iv), R315-8-6.1(a)(3), R315-8-6.12(b), R315-8-11.2(e) phrase "given the specific site conditions and the nature and extent of contamination", R315-8-14.10(b); R315-9; R315-14 except R315-14-3, R315-14-4, and R315-14-7; R315-16 except R315-16-1.1(a)(4), R315-16-1.6, R 315-16-1.7(c), R315-16-1.7(g), R315-16-1.7(l)(4), R315-16-2.4(d), R315-16-2.5(e), R315-16-2.12, R315-16-3.4(d), R351-16-3.5(e), R315-16-3.6(c)(2) word "lamp", R315-16-3.10(a)(2) word "lamp", R315-16-3.10(b)(2) word "lamp", R315-16-3.12, R315-16-5.1(a); R315-50 except R315-50-9, R315-50-10, R315-50-12, and R315-50-13.

Utah Administrative Code revised as of May 15, 1996: Section R315-15, except R315-15-1.1(j)&(k), R315-15-1.3(b), R315-15-2.1(a)(1) & (4), R315-15-2.3(c)(1), R315-15.2.3(d), R315-15-2.4(a), R315-15-2.4(d)&(e), R315-15-3.1(b), R315-15-3.2(a), R315-15-4.6(f), R315-15-5.1(c), R315-15-5.5(e), R315-15-6.5(e), R315-15-7.1(d), R315-15-8.3, R315-15-9, R315-15-10, R315-15-11 with respect to used oil transfer and off-specification used oil burning facilities, R315-15-12, R315-15-13.5(a)-(c) &(e), R315-15-14, and R315-15-15.

Utah Administrative Code revised as of October 16, 1997: R315-2-3(d)(2), R315-2-10(e), R315-8-6.12(b), R315-8-14.10(b), R315-15-1.3(b), R315-15-2.1(a)(1)&(4), R315-15-2.3(c)(1), R315-15.2.3(d), R315-15-2.4(a), R315-15-2.4(d)&(e), R315-15-3.1(b), R315-15-3.2(a), R315-15-4.6(f), R315-15-5.5(e), R315-15-6.5(e), R315-15-8.3, and R315-15-9.

Utah Administrative Code revised as of February 20, 1998: R315-1-1(a), R315-1-2(a), R315-2-5, R315-2-6, R315-2-10(f), R315-2-11(e), R315-2-11(f), R315-2-17, R315-3-3(b)(3), R315-13-1, R315-14-7, R315-16-5.1(a), R315-50-9, R315-50-10, and R315-50-12.

Copies of the Utah regulations that are incorporated by reference are available from the Utah Department of Environmental Quality, 288 North 1460 West, Salt Lake City, Utah 84114-4880, Phone (801) 538-6776.

Wisconsin

The statutory provisions include: Wisconsin Statutes, Volume 3, Sections: 144.01; 144.43-433; 144.44 (except 144.44(4)(a)); 144.441(1)-(2); 144.441(3) (b), (f), and (g); 144.441(4) (a) and (c)-(g); 144.441(6); 144.442(1), (4)-(11); 144.443; 144.444; 144.60-144.63; and 144.64 (2)-(3) (except for 144.64(2)(e)(1)).

The regulatory provisions include: Wisconsin Administrative Code, Volume 12, §NR 600.01-600.04(2); 600.06; 600.3-600.11; 605.02; 605.04-605.11; Appendix II, III, IV and V; 610.01-610.09(2); 615.01-615.13(2)(b); 620.01; 620.04-620.10(3); 620.14; 625.04(4); 625.05(1)-625.07(7)(c)12; 625.12(1) and (2); 630.02; 630.04-630.40(3)(c); 635.02; 635.05-635.16(17)(d); 635.17(1), (2) and (3); 640.02; 640.06(2)(b); 640.09-640.22(22); 645.04-645.14; 645.17(1)(a)(1)-645.17(1)(a)3.e; 650; 655.02; 655.05-655.13(13); 660.02; 660.08-660.20(2); 665.02; 665.05(1)-665.10(2); 670.06-670.11(2)(d)3; 675.01-675.30(6); 680.01-680.51(5); 685.02; 685.05-685.08(13)(b).

[58 FR 3500, Jan. 11, 1993, as amended at 58 FR 49200, Sept. 22, 1993; 58 FR 52676, 52679, 52682, Oct. 12, 1993; 59 FR 45987, Sept. 6, 1994; 59 FR 52920, Oct. 20, 1994; 60 FR 32112, June 20, 1994; 60 FR 32115, June 20, 1995; 60 FR 44280, Aug. 25, 1995; 61 FR 49269, Sept. 19, 1996; 62 FR 49170, Sept. 19, 1997; 62 FR 67584, Dec. 29, 1997; 63 FR 2899, Jan. 20, 1998; 63 FR 23225, Apr. 28, 1998; 63 FR 23677, Apr. 30, 1998; 64 FR 34137, June 25, 1999; 64 FR 46571, Aug. 26, 1999; 64 FR 49682, Sept. 14, 1999; 66 FR 53730, Oct. 24, 2001; 66 FR 58972, Nov. 26, 2001; 67 FR 49868, August 1, 2002; 70 FR 11135, Mar. 8, 2005; 71 FR 11535, Mar. 8, 2006; 71 FR 11539, Mar. 8, 2006; 71 FR 20345, Apr. 20, 2006; 72 FR 14048, Mar. 26, 2007; 73 FR 8616, Feb. 14, 2008; 73 FR 63901, Oct. 28, 2008; 73 FR 64259, Oct. 29, 2008]

PART 273—STANDARDS FOR UNIVERSAL WASTE MANAGEMENT

Authority: 42 U.S.C. 6922, 6923, 6924, 6925, 6930, and 6937.

Source: 60 FR 25542, May 11, 1995, unless otherwise noted.

Subpart A—General

§273.1 Scope.

(a) This part establishes requirements for managing the following: 📖 8.1

(1) Batteries as described in 40 CFR 273.2;

(2) Pesticides as described in §273.3;

(3) Mercury-containing equipment as described in §273.4; and

(4) Lamps as described in §273.5.

(b) This part provides an alternative set of management standards in lieu of regulation under 40 CFR parts 260 through 272. 📖 8.2

[60 FR 25542, May 11, 1995, as amended at 64 FR 36488, July 6, 1999; 70 FR 45520, Aug. 5, 2005]

§273.2 Applicability—batteries. 📖 8.1

(a) *Batteries covered under 40 CFR part 273.* (1) The requirements of this part apply to persons managing batteries, as described in §273.9, except those listed in paragraph (b) of this section.

(2) Spent lead-acid batteries which are not managed under 40 CFR part 266, subpart G, are subject to management under this part. 📖 4.20

(b) *Batteries not covered under 40 CFR part 273.* The requirements of this part do not apply to persons managing the following batteries:

(1) Spent lead-acid batteries that are managed under 40 CFR part 266, subpart G. 📖 4.20

(2) Batteries, as described in §273.9, that are not yet wastes under part 261 of this chapter, including those that do not meet the criteria for waste generation in paragraph (c) of this section.

(3) Batteries, as described in §273.9, that are not hazardous waste. A battery is a hazardous waste if it exhibits one or more of the characteristics identified in part 261, subpart C of this chapter.

(c) *Generation of waste batteries.* (1) A used battery becomes a waste on the date it is discarded (*e.g.*, when sent for reclamation).

(2) An unused battery becomes a waste on the date the handler decides to discard it.

[60 FR 25542, May 11, 1995, as amended at 64 FR 36488, July 6, 1999]

§273.3 Applicability—pesticides. 8.1

(a) *Pesticides covered under this part 273.* The requirements of this part apply to persons managing pesticides, as described in §273.9, meeting the following conditions, except those listed in paragraph (b) of this section:

(1) Recalled pesticides that are:

(i) Stocks of a suspended and canceled pesticide that are part of a voluntary or mandatory recall under FIFRA Section 19(b), including, but not limited to those owned by the registrant responsible for conducting the recall; or

(ii) Stocks of a suspended or cancelled pesticide, or a pesticide that is not in compliance with FIFRA, that are part of a voluntary recall by the registrant.

(2) Stocks of other unused pesticide products that are collected and managed as part of a waste pesticide collection program.

(b) *Pesticides not covered under 40 CFR part 273.* The requirements of this part do not apply to persons managing the following pesticides:

(1) Recalled pesticides described in paragraph (a)(1) of this section, and unused pesticide products described in paragraph (a)(2) of this section, that are managed by farmers in compliance with 40 CFR 262.70. (40 CFR 262.70 addresses pesticides disposed of on the farmer's own farm in a manner consistent with the disposal instructions on the pesticide label, providing the container is triple rinsed in accordance with 40 CFR 261.7(b)(3));

(2) Pesticides not meeting the conditions set forth in paragraph (a) of this section. These pesticides must be managed in compliance with the hazardous waste regulations in 40 CFR parts 260 through 272;

(3) Pesticides that are not wastes under part 261 of this chapter, including those that do not meet the criteria for waste generation in paragraph (c) of this section or those that are not wastes as described in paragraph (d) of this section; and

(4) Pesticides that are not hazardous waste. A pesticide is a hazardous waste if it is listed in 40 CFR part 261, subpart D or if it exhibits one or more of the characteristics identified in 40 CFR part 261, subpart C.

(c) *When a pesticide becomes a waste.* (1) A recalled pesticide described in paragraph (a)(1) of this section becomes a waste on the first date on which both of the following conditions apply:

(i) The generator of the recalled pesticide agrees to participate in the recall; and

(ii) The person conducting the recall decides to discard (*e.g.*, burn the pesticide for energy recovery).

(2) An unused pesticide product described in paragraph (a)(2) of this section becomes a waste on the date the generator decides to discard it.

(d) *Pesticides that are not wastes.* The following pesticides are not wastes:

(1) Recalled pesticides described in paragraph (a)(1) of this section, provided that the person conducting the recall:

(i) Has not made a decision to discard (*e.g.*, burn for energy recovery) the pesticide. Until such a decision is made, the pesticide does not meet the definition of "solid waste" under 40 CFR 261.2; thus the pesticide is not a hazardous waste and is not subject to hazardous waste requirements, including this part 273. This pesticide remains subject to the requirements of FIFRA; or

(ii) Has made a decision to use a management option that, under 40 CFR 261.2, does not cause the pesticide to be a solid waste (*i.e.*, the selected option is use (other than use constituting disposal) or reuse (other than burning for energy recovery), or reclamation). Such a pesticide is not a solid waste and therefore is not a hazardous waste, and is not subject to the hazardous waste requirements including this part 273. This pesticide, including a recalled pesticide that is exported to a foreign destination for use or reuse, remains subject to the requirements of FIFRA.

(2) Unused pesticide products described in paragraph (a)(2) of this section, if the generator of the unused pesticide product has not decided to discard (*e.g.*, burn for energy recovery) them. These pesticides remain subject to the requirements of FIFRA.

[60 FR 25542, May 11, 1995, as amended at 64 FR 36488, July 6, 1999]

§273.4 Applicability—mercury-containing equipment. 8.1

(a) *Mercury-containing equipment covered under this part 273.* The requirements of this part apply to persons managing mercury-containing equipment, as described in §273.9, except those listed in paragraph (b) of this section.

(b) *Mercury-containing equipment not covered under this part 273.* The requirements of this part do not apply to persons managing the following mercury-containing equipment:

(1) Mercury-containing equipment that is not yet a waste under part 261 of this chapter. Paragraph (c) of this section describes when mercury-containing equipment becomes a waste;

(2) Mercury-containing equipment that is not a hazardous waste. Mercury-containing equipment is a hazardous waste if it exhibits one or more of the characteristics identified in part 261, subpart C of this chapter or is listed in part 261, subpart D of this chapter; and

(3) Equipment and devices from which the mercury-containing components have been removed.

(c) *Generation of waste mercury-containing equipment.* (1) Used mercury-containing equipment becomes a waste on the date it is discarded.

(2) Unused mercury-containing equipment becomes a waste on the date the handler decides to discard it.

[60 FR 25542, May 11, 1995, as amended at 64 FR 36488, July 6, 1999; 70 FR 45520, Aug. 5, 2005]

§273.5 Applicability—lamps.

2.8.1, 8.1

(a) *Lamps covered under this part 273.* The requirements of this part apply to persons managing lamps as described in §273.9, except those listed in paragraph (b) of this section.

(b) *Lamps not covered under this part 273.* The requirements of this part do not apply to persons managing the following lamps:

(1) Lamps that are not yet wastes under part 261 of this chapter as provided in paragraph (c) of this section.

(2) Lamps that are not hazardous waste. A lamp is a hazardous waste if it exhibits one or more of the characteristics identified in part 261, subpart C of this chapter.

(c) *Generation of waste lamps.* (1) A used lamp becomes a waste on the date it is discarded.

(2) An unused lamp becomes a waste on the date the handler decides to discard it.

[64 FR 36488, July 6, 1999]

§§273.6–273.7 [Reserved]

§273.8 Applicability—household and conditionally exempt small quantity generator waste.

(a) Persons managing the wastes listed below may, at their option, manage them under the requirements of this part:

(1) Household wastes that are exempt under §261.4(b)(1) of this chapter and are also of the same type as the universal wastes defined at §273.9; and/or

(2) Conditionally exempt small quantity generator wastes that are exempt under §261.5 of this chapter and are also of the same type as the universal wastes defined at §273.9. 8.3

(b) Persons who commingle the wastes described in paragraphs (a)(1) and (a)(2) of this section together with universal waste regulated under this part must manage the commingled waste under the requirements of this part.

[64 FR 36488, July 6, 1999]

§273.9 Definitions.

Ampule means an airtight vial made of glass, plastic, metal, or any combination of these materials.

Battery means a device consisting of one or more electrically connected electrochemical cells which is designed to receive, store, and deliver electric energy. An electrochemical cell is a system consisting of an anode, cathode, and an electrolyte, plus such connections (electrical and mechanical) as may be needed to allow the cell to deliver or receive electrical energy. The term battery also includes an intact, unbroken battery from which the electrolyte has been removed. 8.1

Destination facility means a facility that treats, disposes of, or recycles a particular category of universal waste, except those management activities described in §273.13 (a) and (c) and §273.33 (a) and (c). A facility at which a particular category of universal waste is only accumulated, is not a destination facility for purposes of managing that category of universal waste. 8.4.2

FIFRA means the Federal Insecticide, Fungicide, and Rodenticide Act (7 U.S.C. 136-136y).

Generator means any person, by site, whose act or process produces hazardous waste identified or listed in part 261 of this chapter or whose act first causes a hazardous waste to become subject to regulation.

Lamp, also referred to as "universal waste lamp" is defined as the bulb or tube portion of an electric lighting device. A lamp is specifically designed to produce radiant energy, most often in the ultraviolet, visible, and infra-red regions of the electromagnetic spectrum.

Examples of common universal waste electric lamps include, but are not limited to, fluorescent, high intensity discharge, neon, mercury vapor, high pressure sodium, and metal halide lamps. 📖 8.1

Large Quantity Handler of Universal Waste means a universal waste handler (as defined in this section) who accumulates 5,000 kilograms or more total of universal waste (batteries, pesticides, mercury-containing equipment, or lamps, calculated collectively) at any time. This designation as a large quantity handler of universal waste is retained through the end of the calendar year in which the 5,000 kilogram limit is met or exceeded. 📖 8.3

Mercury-containing equipment means a device or part of a device (including thermostats, but excluding batteries and lamps) that contains elemental mercury integral to its function. 📖 8.1

On-site means the same or geographically contiguous property which may be divided by public or private right-of-way, provided that the entrance and exit between the properties is at a cross-roads intersection, and access is by crossing as opposed to going along the right of way. Non-contiguous properties owned by the same person but connected by a right-of-way which he controls and to which the public does not have access, are also considered on-site property.

Pesticide means any substance or mixture of substances intended for preventing, destroying, repelling, or mitigating any pest, or intended for use as a plant regulator, defoliant, or desiccant, other than any article that: 📖 8.1

(a) Is a new animal drug under FFDCA section 201(w), or

(b) Is an animal drug that has been determined by regulation of the Secretary of Health and Human Services not to be a new animal drug, or

(c) Is an animal feed under FFDCA section 201(x) that bears or contains any substances described by paragraph (a) or (b) of this section.

Small Quantity Handler of Universal Waste means a universal waste handler (as defined in this section) who does not accumulate 5,000 kilograms or more of universal waste (batteries, pesticides, mercury-containing equipment, or lamps, calculated collectively) at any time. 📖 8.3

Thermostat means a temperature control device that contains metallic mercury in an ampule attached to a bimetal sensing element, and mercury-containing ampules that have been removed from these temperature control devices in compliance with the requirements of 40 CFR 273.13(c)(2) or 273.33(c)(2).

Universal Waste means any of the following hazardous wastes that are subject to the universal waste requirements of this part 273: 📖 8.1

(1) Batteries as described in §273.2;

(2) Pesticides as described in §273.3;

(3) Mercury-containing equipment as described in §273.4; and

(4) Lamps as described in §273.5.

Universal Waste Handler: 📖 8.3

(a) Means:

(1) A generator (as defined in this section) of universal waste; or

(2) The owner or operator of a facility, including all contiguous property, that receives universal waste from other universal waste handlers, accumulates universal waste, and sends universal waste to another universal waste handler, to a destination facility, or to a foreign destination.

(b) Does not mean:

(1) A person who treats (except under the provisions of 40 CFR 273.13 (a) or (c), or 273.33 (a) or (c)), disposes of, or recycles universal waste; or

(2) A person engaged in the off-site transportation of universal waste by air, rail, highway, or water, including a universal waste transfer facility.

Universal Waste Transfer Facility means any transportation-related facility including loading docks, parking areas, storage areas and other similar areas where shipments of universal waste are held during the normal course of transportation for ten days or less.

Universal Waste Transporter means a person engaged in the off-site transportation of universal waste by air, rail, highway, or water. 📖 8.4.1

[60 FR 25542, May 11, 1995, as amended at 63 FR 71230, Dec. 24, 1998. Redesignated and amended at 64 FR 36488, 36489, July 6, 1999; 70 FR 45521, Aug. 5, 2005; 71 FR 40280, July 14, 2006; 72 FR 35666, June 29, 2007]

Subpart B—Standards for Small Quantity Handlers of Universal Waste 📖 8.3

§273.10 Applicability.

This subpart applies to small quantity handlers of universal waste (as defined in 40 CFR 273.9).

[64 FR 36489, July 6, 1999]

§273.11 Prohibitions.

A small quantity handler of universal waste is:

(a) Prohibited from disposing of universal waste; and

(b) Prohibited from diluting or treating universal waste, except by responding to releases as provided in 40 CFR 273.17; or by managing specific wastes as provided in 40 CFR 273.13. 📖 8.3.1.2

§273.12 Notification.

A small quantity handler of universal waste is not required to notify EPA of universal waste handling activities.

§273.13 Waste management. 📖 8.3.1.1

(a) *Universal waste batteries.* A small quantity handler of universal waste must manage universal waste batteries in a way that prevents releases of any universal waste or component of a universal waste to the environment, as follows: 📖 8.3.1.3

(1) A small quantity handler of universal waste must contain any universal waste battery that shows evidence of leakage, spillage, or damage that could cause leakage under reasonably foreseeable conditions in a container. The container must be closed, structurally sound, compatible with the contents of the battery, and must lack evidence of leakage, spillage, or damage that could cause leakage under reasonably foreseeable conditions.

(2) A small quantity handler of universal waste may conduct the following activities as long as the casing of each individual battery cell is not breached and remains intact and closed (except that cells may be opened to remove electrolyte but must be immediately closed after removal):

(i) Sorting batteries by type;

(ii) Mixing battery types in one container;

(iii) Discharging batteries so as to remove the electric charge;

(iv) Regenerating used batteries;

(v) Disassembling batteries or battery packs into individual batteries or cells;

(vi) Removing batteries from consumer products; or

(vii) Removing electrolyte from batteries.

(3) A small quantity handler of universal waste who removes electrolyte from batteries, or who generates other solid waste (*e.g.*, battery pack materials, discarded consumer products) as a result of the activities listed above, must determine whether the electrolyte and/or other solid waste exhibit a characteristic of hazardous waste identified in 40 CFR part 261, subpart C.

(i) If the electrolyte and/or other solid waste exhibit a characteristic of hazardous waste, it is subject to all applicable requirements of 40 CFR parts 260 through 272. The handler is considered the generator of the hazardous electrolyte and/or other waste and is subject to 40 CFR part 262.

(ii) If the electrolyte or other solid waste is not hazardous, the handler may manage the waste in any way that is in compliance with applicable federal, state or local solid waste regulations.

(b) *Universal waste pesticides.* A small quantity handler of universal waste must manage universal waste pesticides in a way that prevents releases of any universal waste or component of a universal waste to the environment. The universal waste pesticides must be contained in one or more of the following:

(1) A container that remains closed, structurally sound, compatible with the pesticide, and that lacks evidence of leakage, spillage, or damage that could cause leakage under reasonably foreseeable conditions; or

(2) A container that does not meet the requirements of paragraph (b)(1) of this Section, provided that the unacceptable container is overpacked in a container that does meet the requirements of paragraph (b)(1) of this Section; or

(3) A tank that meets the requirements of 40 CFR part 265 subpart J, except for 40 CFR 265.197(c), 265.200, and 265.201; or

(4) A transport vehicle or vessel that is closed, structurally sound, compatible with the pesticide, and that lacks evidence of leakage, spillage, or damage that could cause leakage under reasonably foreseeable conditions.

(c) *Mercury-containing equipment.* A small quantity handler of universal waste must manage universal waste mercury-containing equipment in a way that prevents releases of any universal waste or component of a universal waste to the environment, as follows:

(1) A small quantity handler of universal waste must place in a container any universal waste mercury-containing equipment with noncontained elemental mercury or that shows evidence of leakage, spillage, or damage that could cause leakage under reasonably foreseeable conditions. The container must be closed, structurally sound, compatible with the contents of the device, must lack evidence of leakage, spillage, or damage that could cause leakage under reasonably foreseeable conditions, and must be reasonably designed to prevent the escape of mercury into the environment by volatilization or any other means.

(2) A small quantity handler of universal waste may remove mercury-containing ampules from universal

waste mercury-containing equipment provided the handler:

(i) Removes and manages the ampules in a manner designed to prevent breakage of the ampules;

(ii) Removes the ampules only over or in a containment device (*e.g.*, tray or pan sufficient to collect and contain any mercury released from an ampule in case of breakage);

(iii) Ensures that a mercury clean-up system is readily available to immediately transfer any mercury resulting from spills or leaks from broken ampules from that containment device to a container that meets the requirements of 40 CFR 262.34;

(iv) Immediately transfers any mercury resulting from spills or leaks from broken ampules from the containment device to a container that meets the requirements of 40 CFR 262.34;

(v) Ensures that the area in which ampules are removed is well ventilated and monitored to ensure compliance with applicable OSHA exposure levels for mercury;

(vi) Ensures that employees removing ampules are thoroughly familiar with proper waste mercury handling and emergency procedures, including transfer of mercury from containment devices to appropriate containers;

(vii) Stores removed ampules in closed, non-leaking containers that are in good condition;

(viii) Packs removed ampules in the container with packing materials adequate to prevent breakage during storage, handling, and transportation;

(3) A small quantity handler of universal waste mercury-containing equipment that does not contain an ampule may remove the open original housing holding the mercury from universal waste mercury-containing equipment provided the handler:

(i) Immediately seals the original housing holding the mercury with an air-tight seal to prevent the release of any mercury to the environment; and

(ii) Follows all requirements for removing ampules and managing removed ampules under paragraph (c)(2) of this section; and

(4) (i) A small quantity handler of universal waste who removes mercury-containing ampules from mercury-containing equipment or seals mercury from mercury-containing equipment in its original housing must determine whether the following exhibit a characteristic of hazardous waste identified in 40 CFR part 261, subpart C:

(A) Mercury or clean-up residues resulting from spills or leaks and/or

(B) Other solid waste generated as a result of the removal of mercury-containing ampules or housings (*e.g.*, the remaining mercury-containing device).

(ii) If the mercury, residues, and/or other solid waste exhibits a characteristic of hazardous waste, it must be managed in compliance with all applicable requirements of 40 CFR parts 260 through 272. The handler is considered the generator of the mercury, residues, and/or other waste and must manage it in compliance with 40 CFR part 262.

(iii) If the mercury, residues, and/or other solid waste is not hazardous, the handler may manage the waste in any way that is in compliance with applicable federal, state or local solid waste regulations.

(d) *Lamps.* A small quantity handler of universal waste must manage lamps in a way that prevents releases of any universal waste or component of a universal waste to the environment, as follows: 8.3.1.2

(1) A small quantity handler of universal waste must contain any lamp in containers or packages that are structurally sound, adequate to prevent breakage, and compatible with the contents of the lamps. Such containers and packages must remain closed and must lack evidence of leakage, spillage or damage that could cause leakage under reasonably foreseeable conditions.

(2) A small quantity handler of universal waste must immediately clean up and place in a container any lamp that is broken and must place in a container any lamp that shows evidence of breakage, leakage, or damage that could cause the release of mercury or other hazardous constituents to the environment. Containers must be closed, structurally sound, compatible with the contents of the lamps and must lack evidence of leakage, spillage or damage that could cause leakage or releases of mercury or other hazardous constituents to the environment under reasonably foreseeable conditions.

[60 FR 25542, May 11, 1995, as amended at 64 FR 36489, July 6, 1999; 70 FR 45521, Aug. 5, 2005; 71 FR 40280, July 14, 2006]

§273.14 Labeling/marking.

A small quantity handler of universal waste must label or mark the universal waste to identify the type of universal waste as specified below:

(a) Universal waste batteries (*i.e.*, each battery), or a container in which the batteries are contained, must be labeled or marked clearly with any one of the following phrases: "Universal Waste—Battery(ies)," or "Waste Battery(ies)," or "Used Battery(ies);"

(b) A container, (or multiple container package unit), tank, transport vehicle or vessel in which recalled universal waste pesticides as described in 40 CFR 273.3(a)(1) are contained must be labeled or marked clearly with:

(1) The label that was on or accompanied the product as sold or distributed; and

(2) The words "Universal Waste—Pesticide(s)" or "Waste—Pesticide(s);"

(c) A container, tank, or transport vehicle or vessel in which unused pesticide products as described in 40 CFR 273.3(a)(2) are contained must be labeled or marked clearly with:

(1)(i) The label that was on the product when purchased, if still legible;

(ii) If using the labels described in paragraph (c)(1)(i) of this section is not feasible, the appropriate label as required under the Department of Transportation regulation 49 CFR part 172;

(iii) If using the labels described in paragraphs (c)(1)(i) and (ii) of this section is not feasible, another label prescribed or designated by the waste pesticide collection program administered or recognized by a state; and

(2) The words "Universal Waste—Pesticide(s)" or "Waste—Pesticide(s)."

(d)(1) Universal waste mercury-containing equipment (*i.e.*, each device), or a container in which the equipment is contained, must be labeled or marked clearly with any of the following phrases: "Universal Waste—Mercury Containing Equipment," "Waste Mercury-Containing Equipment," or "Used Mercury-Containing Equipment."

(2) A universal waste mercury-containing thermostat or container containing only universal waste mercury-containing thermostats may be labeled or marked clearly with any of the following phrases: "Universal Waste—Mercury Thermostat(s)," "Waste Mercury Thermostat(s)," or "Used Mercury Thermostat(s)."

(e) Each lamp or a container or package in which such lamps are contained must be labeled or marked clearly with one of the following phrases: "Universal Waste—Lamp(s)," or "Waste Lamp(s)," or "Used Lamp(s)".

[60 FR 25542, May 11, 1995, as amended at 64 FR 36489, July 6, 1999; 70 FR 45521, Aug. 5, 2005; 71 FR 40280, July 14, 2006]

§273.15 Accumulation time limits.

(a) A small quantity handler of universal waste may accumulate universal waste for no longer than one year from the date the universal waste is generated, or received from another handler, unless the requirements of paragraph (b) of this section are met.

(b) A small quantity handler of universal waste may accumulate universal waste for longer than one year from the date the universal waste is generated, or received from another handler, if such activity is solely for the purpose of accumulation of such quantities of universal waste as necessary to facilitate proper recovery, treatment, or disposal. However, the handler bears the burden of proving that such activity is solely for the purpose of accumulation of such quantities of universal waste as necessary to facilitate proper recovery, treatment, or disposal.

(c) A small quantity handler of universal waste who accumulates universal waste must be able to demonstrate the length of time that the universal waste has been accumulated from the date it becomes a waste or is received. The handler may make this demonstration by:

(1) Placing the universal waste in a container and marking or labeling the container with the earliest date that any universal waste in the container became a waste or was received;

(2) Marking or labeling each individual item of universal waste (*e.g.*, each battery or thermostat) with the date it became a waste or was received;

(3) Maintaining an inventory system on-site that identifies the date each universal waste became a waste or was received;

(4) Maintaining an inventory system on-site that identifies the earliest date that any universal waste in a group of universal waste items or a group of containers of universal waste became a waste or was received;

(5) Placing the universal waste in a specific accumulation area and identifying the earliest date that any universal waste in the area became a waste or was received; or

(6) Any other method which clearly demonstrates the length of time that the universal waste has been accumulated from the date it becomes a waste or is received.

§273.16 Employee training.

📖 6.4.5

A small quantity handler of universal waste must inform all employees who handle or have responsibility for managing universal waste. The information must describe proper handling and emergency procedures appropriate to the type(s) of universal waste handled at the facility.

§273.17 Response to releases.

(a) A small quantity handler of universal waste must immediately contain all releases of universal wastes and other residues from universal wastes.

(b) A small quantity handler of universal waste must determine whether any material resulting from the release is hazardous waste, and if so, must manage the hazardous waste in compliance with all applicable requirements of 40 CFR parts 260 through 272. The handler is considered the generator of the material resulting from the release, and must manage it in compliance with 40 CFR part 262.

§273.18 Off-site shipments. 📖 6.6.7

(a) A small quantity handler of universal waste is prohibited from sending or taking universal waste to a place other than another universal waste handler, a destination facility, or a foreign destination.

(b) If a small quantity handler of universal waste self-transports universal waste off-site, the handler becomes a universal waste transporter for those self-transportation activities and must comply with the transporter requirements of subpart D of this part while transporting the universal waste.

(c) If a universal waste being offered for off-site transportation meets the definition of hazardous materials under 49 CFR parts 171 through 180, a small quantity handler of universal waste must package, label, mark and placard the shipment, and prepare the proper shipping papers in accordance with the applicable Department of Transportation regulations under 49 CFR parts 172 through 180;

(d) Prior to sending a shipment of universal waste to another universal waste handler, the originating handler must ensure that the receiving handler agrees to receive the shipment.

(e) If a small quantity handler of universal waste sends a shipment of universal waste to another handler or to a destination facility and the shipment is rejected by the receiving handler or destination facility, the originating handler must either:

(1) Receive the waste back when notified that the shipment has been rejected, or

(2) Agree with the receiving handler on a destination facility to which the shipment will be sent.

(f) A small quantity handler of universal waste may reject a shipment containing universal waste, or a portion of a shipment containing universal waste that he has received from another handler. If a handler rejects a shipment or a portion of a shipment, he must contact the originating handler to notify him of the rejection and to discuss reshipment of the load. The handler must:

(1) Send the shipment back to the originating handler, or

(2) If agreed to by both the originating and receiving handler, send the shipment to a destination facility.

(g) If a small quantity handler of universal waste receives a shipment containing hazardous waste that is not a universal waste, the handler must immediately notify the appropriate regional EPA office of the illegal shipment, and provide the name, address, and phone number of the originating shipper. The EPA regional office will provide instructions for managing the hazardous waste.

(h) If a small quantity handler of universal waste receives a shipment of non-hazardous, non-universal waste, the handler may manage the waste in any way that is in compliance with applicable federal, state or local solid waste regulations.

§273.19 Tracking universal waste shipments.

A small quantity handler of universal waste is not required to keep records of shipments of universal waste.

§273.20 Exports.

A small quantity handler of universal waste who sends universal waste to a foreign destination other than to those OECD countries specified in 40 CFR 262.58(a)(1) (in which case the handler is subject to the requirements of 40 CFR part 262, subpart H) must:

(a) Comply with the requirements applicable to a primary exporter in 40 CFR 262.53, 262.56(a)(1) through (4), (6), and (b) and 262.57;

(b) Export such universal waste only upon consent of the receiving country and in conformance with the EPA Acknowledgement of Consent as defined in subpart E of part 262 of this chapter; and

(c) Provide a copy of the EPA Acknowledgment of Consent for the shipment to the transporter transporting the shipment for export.

[60 FR 25542, May 11, 1995, as amended at 61 FR 16315, Apr. 12, 1996]

Subpart C—Standards for Large Quantity Handlers of Universal Waste 📖 8.3

§273.30 Applicability.

This subpart applies to large quantity handlers of universal waste (as defined in §273.9).

[64 FR 36489, July 6, 1999]

§273.31 Prohibitions.

A large quantity handler of universal waste is:

(a) Prohibited from disposing of universal waste; and

(b) Prohibited from diluting or treating universal waste, except by responding to releases as provided in 40 CFR 273.37; or by managing specific wastes as provided in 40 CFR 273.33. 8.3.1.2

§273.32 Notification.

(a)(1) Except as provided in paragraphs (a)(2) and (3) of this section, a large quantity handler of universal waste must have sent written notification of universal waste management to the Regional Administrator, and received an EPA Identification Number, before meeting or exceeding the 5,000 kilogram storage limit.

(2) A large quantity handler of universal waste who has already notified EPA of his hazardous waste management activities and has received an EPA Identification Number is not required to renotify under this section.

(3) A large quantity handler of universal waste who manages recalled universal waste pesticides as described in 40 CFR 273.3(a)(1) and who has sent notification to EPA as required by 40 CFR part 165 is not required to notify for those recalled universal waste pesticides under this section.

(b) This notification must include:

(1) The universal waste handler's name and mailing address;

(2) The name and business telephone number of the person at the universal waste handler's site who should be contacted regarding universal waste management activities;

(3) The address or physical location of the universal waste management activities;

(4) A list of all the types of universal waste managed by the handler (*e.g.*, batteries, pesticides, mercury-containing equipment, and lamps); and

(5) A statement indicating that the handler is accumulating more than 5,000 kilograms of universal waste at one time.

[60 FR 25542, May 11, 1995, as amended at 64 FR 36489, July 6, 1999; 70 FR 45522, Aug. 5, 2005]

§273.33 Waste management. 8.3.1.1

(a) *Universal waste batteries.* A large quantity handler of universal waste must manage universal waste batteries in a way that prevents releases of any universal waste or component of a universal waste to the environment, as follows: 8.3.1.3

(1) A large quantity handler of universal waste must contain any universal waste battery that shows evidence of leakage, spillage, or damage that could cause leakage under reasonably foreseeable conditions in a container. The container must be closed, structurally sound, compatible with the contents of the battery, and must lack evidence of leakage, spillage, or damage that could cause leakage under reasonably foreseeable conditions.

(2) A large quantity handler of universal waste may conduct the following activities as long as the casing of each individual battery cell is not breached and remains intact and closed (except that cells may be opened to remove electrolyte but must be immediately closed after removal):

(i) Sorting batteries by type;

(ii) Mixing battery types in one container;

(iii) Discharging batteries so as to remove the electric charge;

(iv) Regenerating used batteries;

(v) Disassembling batteries or battery packs into individual batteries or cells;

(vi) Removing batteries from consumer products; or

(vii) Removing electrolyte from batteries.

(3) A large quantity handler of universal waste who removes electrolyte from batteries, or who generates other solid waste (*e.g.*, battery pack materials, discarded consumer products) as a result of the activities listed above, must determine whether the electrolyte and/or other solid waste exhibit a characteristic of hazardous waste identified in 40 CFR part 261, subpart C.

(i) If the electrolyte and/or other solid waste exhibit a characteristic of hazardous waste, it must be managed in compliance with all applicable requirements of 40 CFR parts 260 through 272. The handler is considered the generator of the hazardous electrolyte and/or other waste and is subject to 40 CFR part 262.

(ii) If the electrolyte or other solid waste is not hazardous, the handler may manage the waste in any way that is in compliance with applicable federal, state or local solid waste regulations.

(b) *Universal waste pesticides.* A large quantity handler of universal waste must manage universal waste pesticides in a way that prevents releases of any universal waste or component of a universal waste to the environment.

The universal waste pesticides must be contained in one or more of the following:

(1) A container that remains closed, structurally sound, compatible with the pesticide, and that lacks evidence of leakage, spillage, or damage that could cause leakage under reasonably foreseeable conditions; or

(2) A container that does not meet the requirements of paragraph (b)(1) of this section, provided that the unacceptable container is overpacked in a container that does meet the requirements of paragraph (b)(1) of this section; or

(3) A tank that meets the requirements of 40 CFR part 265 subpart J, except for 40 CFR 265.197(c), 265.200, and 265.201; or

(4) A transport vehicle or vessel that is closed, structurally sound, compatible with the pesticide, and that lacks evidence of leakage, spillage, or damage that could cause leakage under reasonably foreseeable conditions.

(c) *Mercury-containing equipment.* A large quantity handler of universal waste must manage universal waste mercury-containing equipment in a way that prevents releases of any universal waste or component of a universal waste to the environment, as follows:

(1) A large quantity handler of universal waste must place in a container any universal waste mercury-containing equipment with noncontained elemental mercury or that shows evidence of leakage, spillage, or damage that could cause leakage under reasonably foreseeable conditions. The container must be closed, structurally sound, compatible with the contents of the device, must lack evidence of leakage, spillage, or damage that could cause leakage under reasonably foreseeable conditions, and must be reasonably designed to prevent the escape of mercury into the environment by volatilization or any other means.

(2) A large quantity handler of universal waste may remove mercury-containing ampules from universal waste mercury-containing equipment provided the handler:

(i) Removes and manages the ampules in a manner designed to prevent breakage of the ampules;

(ii) Removes the ampules only over or in a containment device (*e.g.*, tray or pan sufficient to collect and contain any mercury released from an ampule in case of breakage);

(iii) Ensures that a mercury clean-up system is readily available to immediately transfer any mercury resulting from spills or leaks of broken ampules from that containment device to a container that meets the requirements of 40 CFR 262.34;

(iv) Immediately transfers any mercury resulting from spills or leaks from broken ampules from the containment device to a container that meets the requirements of 40 CFR 262.34;

(v) Ensures that the area in which ampules are removed is well ventilated and monitored to ensure compliance with applicable OSHA exposure levels for mercury;

(vi) Ensures that employees removing ampules are thoroughly familiar with proper waste mercury handling and emergency procedures, including transfer of mercury from containment devices to appropriate containers;

(vii) Stores removed ampules in closed, non-leaking containers that are in good condition;

(viii) Packs removed ampules in the container with packing materials adequate to prevent breakage during storage, handling, and transportation;

(3) A large quantity handler of universal waste mercury-containing equipment that does not contain an ampule may remove the open original housing holding the mercury from universal waste mercury-containing equipment provided the handler:

(i) Immediately seals the original housing holding the mercury with an air-tight seal to prevent the release of any mercury to the environment; and

(ii) Follows all requirements for removing ampules and managing removed ampules under paragraph (c)(2) of this section; and

(4)(i) A large quantity handler of universal waste who removes mercury-containing ampules from mercury-containing equipment or seals mercury from mercury-containing equipment in its original housing must determine whether the following exhibit a characteristic of hazardous waste identified in 40 CFR part 261, subpart C:

(A) Mercury or clean-up residues resulting from spills or leaks and/or

(B) Other solid waste generated as a result of the removal of mercury-containing ampules or housings (*e.g.*, the remaining mercury-containing device).

(ii) If the mercury, residues, and/or other solid waste exhibits a characteristic of hazardous waste, it must be managed in compliance with all applicable requirements of 40 CFR parts 260 through 272. The handler is considered the generator of the mercury, residues, and/or other waste and must manage it in compliance with 40 CFR part 262.

(iii) If the mercury, residues, and/or other solid waste is not hazardous, the handler may manage the waste in any way that is in compliance with applicable federal, state or local solid waste regulations.

(d) *Lamps.* A large quantity handler of universal waste must manage lamps in a way that prevents releases of any universal waste or component of a universal waste to the environment, as follows: 📖 8.3.1.2

(1) A large quantity handler of universal waste must contain any lamp in containers or packages that are structurally sound, adequate to prevent breakage, and compatible with the contents of the lamps. Such containers and packages must remain closed and must lack evidence of leakage, spillage or damage that could cause leakage under reasonably foreseeable conditions.

(2) A large quantity handler of universal waste must immediately clean up and place in a container any lamp that is broken and must place in a container any lamp that shows evidence of breakage, leakage, or damage that could cause the release of mercury or other hazardous constituents to the environment. Containers must be closed, structurally sound, compatible with the contents of the lamps and must lack evidence of leakage, spillage or damage that could cause leakage or releases of mercury or other hazardous constituents to the environment under reasonably foreseeable conditions.

[60 FR 25542, May 11, 1995, as amended at 64 FR 36489, July 6, 1999; 70 FR 45522, Aug. 5, 2005]

§273.34 Labeling/marking.

A large quantity handler of universal waste must label or mark the universal waste to identify the type of universal waste as specified below:

(a) Universal waste batteries (*i.e.*, each battery), or a container or tank in which the batteries are contained, must be labeled or marked clearly with any one of the following phrases: "Universal Waste—Battery(ies)," or "Waste Battery(ies)," or "Used Battery(ies);"

(b) A container (or multiple container package unit), tank, transport vehicle or vessel in which recalled universal waste pesticides as described in 40 CFR 273.3(a)(1) are contained must be labeled or marked clearly with:

(1) The label that was on or accompanied the product as sold or distributed; and

(2) The words "Universal Waste—Pesticide(s)" or "Waste—Pesticide(s);"

(c) A container, tank, or transport vehicle or vessel in which unused pesticide products as described in 40 CFR 273.3(a)(2) are contained must be labeled or marked clearly with:

(1)(i) The label that was on the product when purchased, if still legible;

(ii) If using the labels described in paragraph (c)(1)(i) of this section is not feasible, the appropriate label as required under the Department of Transportation regulation 49 CFR part 172;

(iii) If using the labels described in paragraphs (c)(1)(i) and (1)(ii) of this section is not feasible, another label prescribed or designated by the pesticide collection program; and

(2) The words "Universal Waste—Pesticide(s)" or "Waste—Pesticide(s)."

(d) (1) Mercury-containing equipment (*i.e.*, each device), or a container in which the equipment is contained, must be labeled or marked clearly with any of the following phrases: "Universal Waste—Mercury Containing Equipment," "Waste Mercury-Containing Equipment," or "Used Mercury-Containing Equipment."

(2) A universal waste mercury-containing thermostat or container containing only universal waste mercury-containing thermostats may be labeled or marked clearly with any of the following phrases: "Universal Waste—Mercury Thermostat(s)," "Waste Mercury Thermostat(s)," or "Used Mercury Thermostat(s)."

(e) Each lamp or a container or package in which such lamps are contained must be labeled or marked clearly with any one of the following phrases: "Universal Waste—Lamp(s)," or "Waste Lamp(s)," or "Used Lamp(s)".

[60 FR 25542, May 11, 1995, as amended at 64 FR 36489, July 6, 1999; 70 FR 45522, Aug. 5, 2005; 71 FR 40280, July 14, 2006]

§273.35 Accumulation time limits.

(a) A large quantity handler of universal waste may accumulate universal waste for no longer than one year from the date the universal waste is generated, or received from another handler, unless the requirements of paragraph (b) of this section are met.

(b) A large quantity handler of universal waste may accumulate universal waste for longer than one year from the date the universal waste is generated, or received from another handler, if such activity is solely for the purpose of accumulation of such quantities of universal waste as necessary to facilitate proper recovery, treatment, or disposal. However, the handler bears the burden of proving that such activity was solely for the purpose of accumulation of such quantities of universal waste as necessary to facilitate proper recovery, treatment, or disposal.

(c) A large quantity handler of universal waste must be able to demonstrate the length of time that the universal waste has been accumulated from the date it becomes a waste or is received. The handler may make this demonstration by:

(1) Placing the universal waste in a container and marking or labeling the container with the earliest date that any universal waste in the container became a waste or was received;

(2) Marking or labeling the individual item of universal waste (*e.g.*, each battery or thermostat) with the date it became a waste or was received;

(3) Maintaining an inventory system on-site that identifies the date the universal waste being accumulated became a waste or was received;

(4) Maintaining an inventory system on-site that identifies the earliest date that any universal waste in a group of universal waste items or a group of containers of universal waste became a waste or was received;

(5) Placing the universal waste in a specific accumulation area and identifying the earliest date that any universal waste in the area became a waste or was received; or

(6) Any other method which clearly demonstrates the length of time that the universal waste has been accumulated from the date it becomes a waste or is received.

§273.36 Employee training. 📖 6.4.5

A large quantity handler of universal waste must ensure that all employees are thoroughly familiar with proper waste handling and emergency procedures, relative to their responsibilities during normal facility operations and emergencies.

§273.37 Response to releases.

(a) A large quantity handler of universal waste must immediately contain all releases of universal wastes and other residues from universal wastes.

(b) A large quantity handler of universal waste must determine whether any material resulting from the release is hazardous waste, and if so, must manage the hazardous waste in compliance with all applicable requirements of 40 CFR parts 260 through 272. The handler is considered the generator of the material resulting from the release, and is subject to 40 CFR part 262.

§273.38 Off-site shipments. 📖 6.6.7

(a) A large quantity handler of universal waste is prohibited from sending or taking universal waste to a place other than another universal waste handler, a destination facility, or a foreign destination.

(b) If a large quantity handler of universal waste self-transports universal waste off-site, the handler becomes a universal waste transporter for those self-transportation activities and must comply with the transporter requirements of subpart D of this part while transporting the universal waste.

(c) If a universal waste being offered for off-site transportation meets the definition of hazardous materials under 49 CFR 171 through 180, a large quantity handler of universal waste must package, label, mark and placard the shipment, and prepare the proper shipping papers in accordance with the applicable Department of Transportation regulations under 49 CFR parts 172 through 180;

(d) Prior to sending a shipment of universal waste to another universal waste handler, the originating handler must ensure that the receiving handler agrees to receive the shipment.

(e) If a large quantity handler of universal waste sends a shipment of universal waste to another handler or to a destination facility and the shipment is rejected by the receiving handler or destination facility, the originating handler must either:

(1) Receive the waste back when notified that the shipment has been rejected, or

(2) Agree with the receiving handler on a destination facility to which the shipment will be sent.

(f) A large quantity handler of universal waste may reject a shipment containing universal waste, or a portion of a shipment containing universal waste that he has received from another handler. If a handler rejects a shipment or a portion of a shipment, he must contact the originating handler to notify him of the rejection and to discuss reshipment of the load. The handler must:

(1) Send the shipment back to the originating handler, or

(2) If agreed to by both the originating and receiving handler, send the shipment to a destination facility.

(g) If a large quantity handler of universal waste receives a shipment containing hazardous waste that is not a universal waste, the handler must immediately notify the appropriate regional EPA office of the illegal shipment, and provide the name, address, and phone number of the originating shipper. The EPA regional office will provide instructions for managing the hazardous waste.

(h) If a large quantity handler of universal waste receives a shipment of non-hazardous, non-universal waste, the handler may manage the waste in any way that is in compliance with applicable federal, state or local solid waste regulations.

§273.39 Tracking universal waste shipments.

(a) *Receipt of shipments.* A large quantity handler of universal waste must keep a record of each shipment of universal waste received at the facility. The record may take the form of a log, invoice, manifest, bill of lading, or other shipping document. The record for each shipment of universal waste received must include the following information:

(1) The name and address of the originating universal waste handler or foreign shipper from whom the universal waste was sent;

(2) The quantity of each type of universal waste received (*e.g.*, batteries, pesticides, thermostats);

(3) The date of receipt of the shipment of universal waste.

(b) *Shipments off-site.* A large quantity handler of universal waste must keep a record of each shipment of universal waste sent from the handler to other facilities. The record may take the form of a log, invoice, manifest, bill of lading or other shipping document. The record for each shipment of universal waste sent must include the following information:

(1) The name and address of the universal waste handler, destination facility, or foreign destination to whom the universal waste was sent;

(2) The quantity of each type of universal waste sent (*e.g.*, batteries, pesticides, thermostats);

(3) The date the shipment of universal waste left the facility.

(c) *Record retention.* (1) A large quantity handler of universal waste must retain the records described in paragraph (a) of this section for at least three years from the date of receipt of a shipment of universal waste.

(2) A large quantity handler of universal waste must retain the records described in paragraph (b) of this section for at least three years from the date a shipment of universal waste left the facility.

§273.40 Exports.

A large quantity handler of universal waste who sends universal waste to a foreign destination other than to those OECD countries specified in 40 CFR 262.58(a)(1) (in which case the handler is subject to the requirements of 40 CFR part 262, subpart H) must:

(a) Comply with the requirements applicable to a primary exporter in 40 CFR 262.53, 262.56(a)(1) through (4), (6), and (b) and 262.57;

(b) Export such universal waste only upon consent of the receiving country and in conformance with the EPA Acknowledgement of Consent as defined in subpart E of part 262 of this chapter; and

(c) Provide a copy of the EPA Acknowledgement of Consent for the shipment to the transporter transporting the shipment for export.

[60 FR 25542, May 11, 1995, as amended at 61 FR 16316, Apr. 12, 1996]

Subpart D—Standards for Universal Waste Transporters

8.4.1

§273.50 Applicability.

This subpart applies to universal waste transporters (as defined in §273.9).

[64 FR 36490, July 6, 1999]

§273.51 Prohibitions.

A universal waste transporter is:

(a) Prohibited from disposing of universal waste; and

(b) Prohibited from diluting or treating universal waste, except by responding to releases as provided in 40 CFR 273.54.

§273.52 Waste management.

(a) A universal waste transporter must comply with all applicable U.S. Department of Transportation regulations in 49 CFR part 171 through 180 for transport of any universal waste that meets the definition of hazardous material in 49 CFR 171.8. For purposes of the Department of Transportation regulations, a material is considered a hazardous waste if it is subject to the Hazardous Waste Manifest Requirements of the U.S. Environmental Protection Agency specified in 40 CFR part 262. Because universal waste does not require a hazardous waste manifest, it is not considered hazardous waste under the Department of Transportation regulations.

(b) Some universal waste materials are regulated by the Department of Transportation as hazardous materials because they meet the criteria for one or more hazard classes specified in 49 CFR 173.2. As universal waste shipments do not require a manifest under 40 CFR 262, they may not be described by the DOT proper shipping name "hazardous waste, (l) or (s), n.o.s.", nor may the hazardous material's proper shipping name be modified by adding the word "waste".

§273.53 Storage time limits.

(a) A universal waste transporter may only store the universal waste at a universal waste transfer facility for ten days or less.

(b) If a universal waste transporter stores universal waste for more than ten days, the transporter becomes a universal waste handler and must comply with the applicable requirements of subparts B or C of this part while storing the universal waste.

§273.54 Response to releases.

(a) A universal waste transporter must immediately contain all releases of universal wastes and other residues from universal wastes.

(b) A universal waste transporter must determine whether any material resulting from the release is hazardous waste, and if so, it is subject to all applicable requirements of 40 CFR parts 260 through 272. If the waste is determined to be a hazardous waste, the transporter is subject to 40 CFR part 262.

§273.55 Off-site shipments.

(a) A universal waste transporter is prohibited from transporting the universal waste to a place other than a universal waste handler, a destination facility, or a foreign destination.

(b) If the universal waste being shipped off-site meets the Department of Transportation's definition of hazardous materials under 49 CFR 171.8, the shipment must be properly described on a shipping paper in accordance with the applicable Department of Transportation regulations under 49 CFR part 172.

§273.56 Exports.

A universal waste transporter transporting a shipment of universal waste to a foreign destination other than to those OECD countries specified in 40 CFR 262.58(a)(1) (in which case the transporter is subject to the requirements of 40 CFR part 262, subpart H) may not accept a shipment if the transporter knows the shipment does not conform to the EPA Acknowledgment of Consent. In addition the transporter must ensure that:

(a) A copy of the EPA Acknowledgment of Consent accompanies the shipment; and

(b) The shipment is delivered to the facility designated by the person initiating the shipment.

[60 FR 25542, May 11, 1995, as amended at 61 FR 16316]

Subpart E—Standards for Destination Facilities

📖 8.4.2

§273.60 Applicability.

(a) The owner or operator of a destination facility (as defined in §273.9) is subject to all applicable requirements of parts 264, 265, 266, 268, 270, and 124 of this chapter, and the notification requirement under section 3010 of RCRA. 📖 13.13.3

(b) The owner or operator of a destination facility that recycles a particular universal waste without storing that universal waste before it is recycled must comply with 40 CFR 261.6(c)(2).

[60 FR 25542, May 11, 1995, as amended at 64 FR 36490, July 6, 1999]

§273.61 Off-site shipments.

(a) The owner or operator of a destination facility is prohibited from sending or taking universal waste to a place other than a universal waste handler, another destination facility or foreign destination.

(b) The owner or operator of a destination facility may reject a shipment containing universal waste, or a portion of a shipment containing universal waste. If the owner or operator of the destination facility rejects a shipment or a portion of a shipment, he must contact the shipper to notify him of the rejection and to discuss reshipment of the load. The owner or operator of the destination facility must:

(1) Send the shipment back to the original shipper, or

(2) If agreed to by both the shipper and the owner or operator of the destination facility, send the shipment to another destination facility.

(c) If the a owner or operator of a destination facility receives a shipment containing hazardous waste that is not a universal waste, the owner or operator of the destination facility must immediately notify the appropriate regional EPA office of the illegal shipment, and provide the name, address, and phone number of the shipper. The EPA regional office will provide instructions for managing the hazardous waste.

(d) If the owner or operator of a destination facility receives a shipment of non-hazardous, non-universal waste, the owner or operator may manage the waste in any way that is in compliance with applicable federal or state solid waste regulations.

§273.62 Tracking universal waste shipments.

(a) The owner or operator of a destination facility must keep a record of each shipment of universal waste received at the facility. The record may take the form of a log, invoice, manifest, bill of lading, or other shipping document. The record for each shipment of universal waste received must include the following information:

(1) The name and address of the universal waste handler, destination facility, or foreign shipper from whom the universal waste was sent;

(2) The quantity of each type of universal waste received (*e.g.*, batteries, pesticides, thermostats);

(3) The date of receipt of the shipment of universal waste.

(b) The owner or operator of a destination facility must retain the records described in paragraph (a) of this section for at least three years from the date of receipt of a shipment of universal waste.

Subpart F—Import Requirements

§273.70 Imports.

Persons managing universal waste that is imported from a foreign country into the United States are subject to the applicable requirements of this part, immediately after the waste enters the United States, as indicated in paragraphs (a) through (c) of this section:

(a) A universal waste transporter is subject to the universal waste transporter requirements of subpart D of this part.

(b) A universal waste handler is subject to the small or large quantity handler of universal waste requirements of subparts B or C, as applicable.

(c) An owner or operator of a destination facility is subject to the destination facility requirements of subpart E of this part.

(d) Persons managing universal waste that is imported from an OECD country as specified in 40 CFR 262.58(a)(1) are subject to paragraphs (a) through (c) of this section, in addition to the requirements of 40 CFR part 262, subpart H.

[60 FR 25542, May 11, 1995, as amended at 61 FR 16316]

Subpart G—Petitions to Include Other Wastes Under 40 CFR Part 273

§273.80 General.

(a) Any person seeking to add a hazardous waste or a category of hazardous waste to this part may petition for a regulatory amendment under this subpart and 40 CFR 260.20 and 260.23.

(b) To be successful, the petitioner must demonstrate to the satisfaction of the Administrator that regulation under the universal waste regulations of 40 CFR part 273 is: appropriate for the waste or category of waste; will improve management practices for the waste or category of waste; and will improve implementation of the hazardous waste program. The petition must include the information required by 40 CFR 260.20(b). The petition should also address as many of the factors listed in 40 CFR 273.81 as are appropriate for the waste or waste category addressed in the petition.

(c) The Administrator will evaluate petitions using the factors listed in 40 CFR 273.81. The Administrator will grant or deny a petition using the factors listed in 40 CFR 273.81. The decision will be based on the weight of evidence showing that regulation under 40 CFR part 273 is appropriate for the waste or category of waste, will improve management practices for the waste or category of waste, and will improve implementation of the hazardous waste program.

§273.81 Factors for petitions to include other wastes under 40 CFR part 273.

(a) The waste or category of waste, as generated by a wide variety of generators, is listed in subpart D of part 261 of this chapter, or (if not listed) a proportion of the waste stream exhibits one or more characteristics of hazardous waste identified in subpart C of part 261 of this chapter. (When a characteristic waste is added to the universal waste regulations of this part 273 by using a generic name to identify the waste category (*e.g.*, batteries), the definition of universal waste in §260.10 of this chapter and §273.9 will be amended to include only the hazardous waste portion of the waste category (*e.g.*, hazardous waste batteries).) Thus, only the portion of the waste stream that does exhibit one or more characteristics (*i.e.*, is hazardous waste) is subject to the universal waste regulations of this part 273;

(b) The waste or category of waste is not exclusive to a specific industry or group of industries, is commonly generated by a wide variety of types of establishments (including, for example, households, retail and commercial businesses, office complexes, conditionally exempt small quantity generators, small businesses, government organizations, as well as large industrial facilities);

(c) The waste or category of waste is generated by a large number of generators (*e.g.*, more than 1,000 nationally) and is frequently generated in relatively small quantities by each generator;

(d) Systems to be used for collecting the waste or category of waste (including packaging, marking, and labeling practices) would ensure close stewardship of the waste;

(e) The risk posed by the waste or category of waste during accumulation and transport is relatively low compared to other hazardous wastes, and specific management standards proposed or referenced by the petitioner (*e.g.*, waste management requirements appropriate to be added to 40 CFR 273.13, 273.33, and 273.52; and/or applicable Department of Transportation requirements) would be protective of human health and the environment during accumulation and transport;

(f) Regulation of the waste or category of waste under 40 CFR part 273 will increase the likelihood that the waste will be diverted from non-hazardous waste management systems (*e.g.*, the municipal waste stream, non-hazardous industrial or commercial waste stream, municipal sewer or stormwater systems) to recycling, treatment, or disposal in compliance with Subtitle C of RCRA.

(g) Regulation of the waste or category of waste under 40 CFR part 273 will improve implementation of and compliance with the hazardous waste regulatory program; and/or

(h) Such other factors as may be appropriate.

[60 FR 25542, May 11, 1995, as amended at 64 FR 36490, July 6, 1999]

PART 279—STANDARDS FOR THE MANAGEMENT OF USED OIL

Authority: Sections 1006, 2002(a), 3001 through 3007, 3010, 3014, and 7004 of the Solid Waste Disposal Act, as amended (42 U.S.C. 6905, 6912(a), 6921 through 6927, 6930, 6934, and 6974); and sections 101(37) and 114(c) of CERCLA (42 U.S.C. 9601(37) and 9614(c)).

Source: 57 FR 41612, Sept. 10, 1992, unless otherwise noted.

Subpart A—Definitions

§279.1 Definitions.

Terms that are defined in §§260.10, 261.1, and 280.12 of this chapter have the same meanings when used in this part.

Aboveground tank means a tank used to store or process used oil that is not an underground storage tank as defined in §280.12 of this chapter.

Container means any portable device in which a material is stored, transported, treated, disposed of, or otherwise handled.

Do-it-yourselfer used oil collection center means any site or facility that accepts/aggregates and stores used oil collected only from household do-it-yourselfers.

Existing tank means a tank that is used for the storage or processing of used oil and that is in operation, or for which installation has commenced on or prior to the effective date of the authorized used oil program for the State in which the tank is located. Installation will be considered to have commenced if the owner or operator has obtained all federal, state, and local approvals or permits necessary to begin installation of the tank and if either (1) A continuous on-site installation program has begun, or (2) The owner or operator has entered into contractual obligations—which cannot be canceled or modified without substantial loss—for installation of the tank to be completed within a reasonable time.

Household "do-it-yourselfer" used oil means oil that is derived from households, such as used oil generated by individuals who generate used oil through the maintenance of their personal vehicles.

Household "do-it-yourselfer" used oil generator means an individual who generates household "do-it-yourselfer" used oil.

New tank means a tank that will be used to store or process used oil and for which installation has commenced after the effective date of the authorized used oil program for the State in which the tank is located.

Petroleum refining facility means an establishment primarily engaged in producing gasoline, kerosene, distillate fuel oils, residual fuel oils, and lubricants, through fractionation, straight distillation of crude oil, redistillation of unfinished petroleum derivatives, cracking or other processes (*i.e.*, facilities classified as SIC 2911).

Processing means chemical or physical operations designed to produce from used oil, or to make used oil more amenable for production of, fuel oils, lubricants, or other used oil-derived product. Processing includes, but is not limited to: blending used oil with virgin petroleum products, blending used oils to meet the fuel specification, filtration, simple distillation, chemical or physical separation and re-refining. 📖 12.2.2

Re-refining distillation bottoms means the heavy fraction produced by vacuum distillation of filtered and dehydrated used oil. The composition of still bottoms varies with column operation and feedstock.

Tank means any stationary device, designed to contain an accumulation of used oil which is constructed primarily of non-earthen materials, (*e.g.*, wood, concrete, steel, plastic) which provides structural support.

Used oil means any oil that has been refined from crude oil, or any synthetic oil, that has been used and as a result of such use is contaminated by physical or chemical impurities. 📖 12.1.1, 12.1.6.4

Used oil aggregation point means any site or facility that accepts, aggregates, and/or stores used oil collected only from other used oil generation sites owned or operated by the owner or operator of the aggregation point, from which used oil is transported to the aggregation point in shipments of no more than 55 gallons. Used oil aggregation points may also accept used oil from household do-it-yourselfers. 📖 12.2.1.2

Used oil burner means a facility where used oil not meeting the specification requirements in §279.11 is burned for energy recovery in devices identified in §279.61(a). 📖 12.3

Used oil collection center means any site or facility that is registered/licensed/permitted/recognized by a state/county/municipal government to manage used oil and accepts/aggregates and stores used oil collected from used oil generators regulated under subpart C of this part who bring used oil to the collection center in shipments of no more than 55 gallons under the provisions of §279.24. Used oil collection centers may also accept used oil from household do-it-yourselfers. 📖 12.2.1.2

Used oil fuel marketer means any person who conducts either of the following activities: 📖 12.3.5

(1) Directs a shipment of off-specification used oil from their facility to a used oil burner; or

(2) First claims that used oil that is to be burned for energy recovery meets the used oil fuel specifications set forth in §279.11 of this part.

Used oil generator means any person, by site, whose act or process produces used oil or whose act first causes used oil to become subject to regulation. 📖 12.2

Used oil processor/re-refiner means a facility that processes used oil. 📖 12.2.2

Used oil transfer facility means any transportation related facility including loading docks, parking areas, storage areas and other areas where shipments of used oil are held for more than 24 hours and not longer than 35 days during the normal course of transportation or prior to an activity performed pursuant to §279.20(b)(2). Transfer facilities that store used oil for more than 35 days are subject to regulation under subpart F of this part.

Used oil transporter means any person who transports used oil, any person who collects used oil from more than one generator and transports the collected oil, and owners and operators of used oil transfer facilities. Used oil transporters may consolidate or aggregate loads of used oil for purposes of transportation but, with the following exception, may not process used oil. Transporters may conduct incidental processing operations that occur in the normal course of used oil transportation (*e.g.*, settling and water separation), but that are not designed to produce (or make more amenable for production of) used oil derived products or used oil fuel. 📖 12.2.1.2

[57 FR 41612, Sept. 10, 1992, as amended at 58 FR 26425, May 3, 1993; 59 FR 10559, Mar. 4, 1994; 71 FR 40280, July 14, 2006]

Subpart B—Applicability

§279.10 Applicability.

📖 12.1

This section identifies those materials which are subject to regulation as used oil under this part. This section also identifies some materials that are not subject to regulation as used oil under this part, and indicates whether these materials may be subject to regulation as hazardous waste under parts 260 through 266, 268, 270, and 124 of this chapter.

(a) *Used oil.* EPA presumes that used oil is to be recycled unless a used oil handler disposes of used oil, or sends used oil for disposal. Except as provided in §279.11, the regulations of this part apply to used oil, and to materials identified in this section as being subject to regulation as used oil, whether or not the used oil or material exhibits any characteristics of hazardous waste identified in subpart C of part 261 of this chapter. **12.1.2**

(b) *Mixtures of used oil and hazardous waste*—(1) *Listed hazardous waste.* (i) Mixtures of used oil and hazardous waste that is listed in subpart D of part 261 of this chapter are subject to regulation as hazardous waste under parts 260 through 266, 268, 270, and 124 of this chapter, rather than as used oil under this part. **12.1.3.2**

(ii) *Rebuttable presumption for used oil.* Used oil containing more than 1,000 ppm total halogens is presumed to be a hazardous waste because it has been mixed with halogenated hazardous waste listed in subpart D of part 261 of this chapter. Persons may rebut this presumption by demonstrating that the used oil does not contain hazardous waste (for example, by showing that the used oil does not contain significant concentrations of halogenated hazardous constituents listed in appendix VIII of part 261 of this chapter). **12.1.4**

(A) The rebuttable presumption does not apply to metalworking oils/fluids containing chlorinated paraffins, if they are processed, through a tolling arrangement as described in §279.24(c), to reclaim metalworking oils/fluids. The presumption does apply to metalworking oils/fluids if such oils/fluids are recycled in any other manner, or disposed. **12.1.4.2**

(B) The rebuttable presumption does not apply to used oils contaminated with chlorofluorocarbons (CFCs) removed from refrigeration units where the CFCs are destined for reclamation. The rebuttable presumption does apply to used oils contaminated with CFCs that have been mixed with used oil from sources other than refrigeration units. **12.1.4.2**

(2) *Characteristic hazardous waste.* Mixtures of used oil and hazardous waste that solely exhibit one or more of the hazardous waste characteristics identified in subpart C of part 261 of this chapter and mixtures of used oil and hazardous waste that is listed in subpart D solely because it exhibits one or more of the characteristics of hazardous waste identified in subpart C are subject to: **7.1.2.2, 12.1.3.1–2**

(i) Except as provided in paragraph (b)(2)(iii) of this section, regulation as hazardous waste under parts 260 through 266, 268, 270, and 124 of this chapter rather than as used oil under this part, if the resultant mixture exhibits any characteristics of hazardous waste identified in subpart C of part 261 of this chapter; or

(ii) Except as specified in §279.10(b)(2)(iii) regulation as used oil under this part, if the resultant mixture does not exhibit any characteristics of hazardous waste identified under subpart C of part 261 of this chapter. **13.13.2**

(iii) Regulation as used oil under this part, if the mixture is of used oil and a waste which is hazardous solely because it exhibits the characteristic of ignitability (*e.g.*, ignitable-only mineral spirits), provided that the resultant mixture does not exhibit the characteristic of ignitability under §261.21 of this chapter.

(3) *Conditionally exempt small quantity generator hazardous waste.* Mixtures of used oil and conditionally exempt small quantity generator hazardous waste regulated under §261.5 of this chapter are subject to regulation as used oil under this part. **12.1.3**

(c) *Materials containing or otherwise contaminated with used oil.* (1) Except as provided in paragraph (c)(2) of this section, materials containing or otherwise contaminated with used oil from which the used oil has been properly drained or removed to the extent possible such that no visible signs of free-flowing oil remain in or on the material: **12.1.6**

(i) Are not used oil and thus not subject to this part, and

(ii) If applicable are subject to the hazardous waste regulations of parts 124, 260 through 266, 268, and 270 of this chapter.

(2) Materials containing or otherwise contaminated with used oil that are burned for energy recovery are subject to regulation as used oil under this part. **12.3.4**

(3) Used oil drained or removed from materials containing or otherwise contaminated with used oil is subject to regulation as used oil under this part.

(d) *Mixtures of used oil with products.* (1) Except as provided in paragraph (d)(2) of this section, mixtures of used oil and fuels or other fuel products are subject to regulation as used oil under this part.

(2) Mixtures of used oil and diesel fuel mixed on-site by the generator of the used oil for use in the generator's own vehicles are not subject to this part once the used oil and diesel fuel have been mixed. Prior to mixing, the used oil is subject to the requirements of subpart C of this part. 📖 12.1.6.1

(e) *Materials derived from used oil.* (1) Materials that are reclaimed from used oil that are used beneficially and are not burned for energy recovery or used in a manner constituting disposal (*e.g.*, re-refined lubricants) are: 📖 12.1.6.3

(i) Not used oil and thus are not subject to this part, and

(ii) Not solid wastes and are thus not subject to the hazardous waste regulations of parts 260 through 266, 268, 270, and 124 of this chapter as provided in §261.3(c)(2)(i) of this chapter.

(2) Materials produced from used oil that are burned for energy recovery (*e.g.*, used oil fuels) are subject to regulation as used oil under this part. 📖 12.1.6.3

(3) Except as provided in paragraph (e)(4) of this section, materials derived from used oil that are disposed of or used in a manner constituting disposal are:

(i) Not used oil and thus are not subject to this Part, and

(ii) Are solid wastes and thus are subject to the hazardous waste regulations of parts 260 through 266, 268, 270, and 124 of this chapter if the materials are listed or identified as hazardous wastes.

(4) Used oil re-refining distillation bottoms that are used as feedstock to manufacture asphalt products are not subject to this part. 📖 12.1.1.2

(f) *Wastewater.* Wastewater, the discharge of which is subject to regulation under either section 402 or section 307(b) of the Clean Water Act (including wastewaters at facilities which have eliminated the discharge of wastewater), contaminated with *de minimis* quantities of used oil are not subject to the requirements of this part. For purposes of this paragraph, "*de minimis*" quantities of used oils are defined as small spills, leaks, or drippings from pumps, machinery, pipes, and other similar equipment during normal operations or small amounts of oil lost to the wastewater treatment system during washing or draining operations. This exception will not apply if the used oil is discarded as a result of abnormal manufacturing operations resulting in substantial leaks, spills, or other releases, or to used oil recovered from wastewaters. 📖 12.1.6.4

(g) *Used oil introduced into crude oil pipelines or a petroleum refining facility.* (1) Used oil mixed with crude oil or natural gas liquids (*e.g.*, in a production separator or crude oil stock tank) for insertion into a crude oil pipeline is exempt from the requirements of this part. The used oil is subject to the requirements of this part prior to the mixing of used oil with crude oil or natural gas liquids.

(2) Mixtures of used oil and crude oil or natural gas liquids containing less than 1% used oil that are being stored or transported to a crude oil pipeline or petroleum refining facility for insertion into the refining process at a point prior to crude distillation or catalytic cracking are exempt from the requirements of this part.

(3) Used oil that is inserted into the petroleum refining facility process before crude distillation or catalytic cracking without prior mixing with crude oil is exempt from the requirements of this part provided that the used oil constitutes less than 1% of the crude oil feed to any petroleum refining facility process unit at any given time. Prior to insertion into the petroleum refining facility process, the used oil is subject to the requirements of this part.

(4) Except as provided in paragraph (g)(5) of this section, used oil that is introduced into a petroleum refining facility process after crude distillation or catalytic cracking is exempt from the requirements of this part only if the used oil meets the specification of §279.11. Prior to insertion into the petroleum refining facility process, the used oil is subject to the requirements of this part.

(5) Used oil that is incidentally captured by a hydrocarbon recovery system or wastewater treatment system as part of routine process operations at a petroleum refining facility and inserted into the petroleum refining facility process is exempt from the requirements of this part. This exemption does not extend to used oil which is intentionally introduced into a hydrocarbon recovery system (*e.g.*, by pouring collected used oil into the waste water treatment system).

(6) Tank bottoms from stock tanks containing exempt mixtures of used oil and crude oil or natural gas liquids are exempt from the requirements of this part.

(h) *Used oil on vessels.* Used oil produced on vessels from normal shipboard operations is not subject to this part until it is transported ashore.

(i) *Used oil containing PCBs.* Used oil containing PCBs (as defined at 40 CFR 761.3) at any concentration less than 50 ppm is subject to the requirements of this Part unless, because of dilution, it is regulated under 40 CFR Part 761 as a used oil containing PCBs at 50 ppm or greater. PCB-containing used oil subject to the requirements of this Part may also be subject to the prohibitions and requirements found at 40 CFR Part 761, including § 761.20(d) and (e). Used oil containing PCBs at concentrations of 50 ppm or greater is not subject to the requirements of this Part, but is subject to regulation under 40 CFR Part 761. No person may avoid these provisions by diluting used oil containing PCBs, unless otherwise specifically provided for in this Part or Part 761 of this chapter. 📖 12.1.7

[57 FR 41612, Sept. 10, 1992, as amended at 58 FR 26425, May 3, 1993; 59 FR 10559, Mar. 4, 1994; 61 FR 33693, June 28, 1996; 63 FR 24969, May 6, 1998; 63 FR 37782, July 14, 1998; 68 FR 44665, July 30, 2003; 70 FR 34591, June 14, 2005; 71 FR 40280, July 14, 2006]

§279.11 Used oil specifications. 📖 12.3.1

Used oil burned for energy recovery, and any fuel produced from used oil by processing, blending, or other treatment, is subject to regulation under this part unless it is shown not to exceed any of the allowable levels of the constituents and properties shown in Table 1. Once used oil that is to be burned for energy recovery has been shown not to exceed any allowable level and the person making that showing complies with §§279.72, 279.73, and 279.74(b), the used oil is no longer subject to this part. 📖 12.3.2

Table 1—Used Oil Not Exceeding Any Allowable Level Shown Below Is Not Subject to This Part When Burned for Energy Recovery[1]

Constituent/property	Allowable level
Arsenic	5 ppm maximum
Cadmium	2 ppm maximum
Chromium	10 ppm maximum
Lead	100 ppm maximum
Flash point	100° F minimum
Total halogens	4,000 ppm maximum[2]

Note: Applicable standards for the burning of used oil containing PCBs are imposed by 40 CFR 761.20(e).

[1]The allowable levels do not apply to mixtures of used oil and hazardous waste that continue to be regulated as hazardous waste (see §279.10(b)).

[2]Used oil containing more than 1,000 ppm total halogens is presumed to be a hazardous waste under the rebuttable presumption provided under §279.10(b)(1). Such used oil is subject to subpart H of part 266 of this chapter rather than this part when burned for energy recovery unless the presumption of mixing can be successfully rebutted.

[57 FR 41612, Sept. 10, 1992, as amended at 58 FR 26425, May 3, 1993; 71 FR 40280, July 14, 2006]

§279.12 Prohibitions.

(a) *Surface impoundment prohibition.* Used oil shall not be managed in surface impoundments or waste piles unless the units are subject to regulation under parts 264 or 265 of this chapter.

(b) *Use as a dust suppressant.* The use of used oil as a dust suppressant is prohibited, except when such activity takes place in one of the states listed in §279.82(c).

(c) *Burning in particular units.* Off-specification used oil fuel may be burned for energy recovery in only the following devices: 📖 12.3.3

(1) Industrial furnaces identified in §260.10 of this chapter;

(2) Boilers, as defined in §260.10 of this chapter, that are identified as follows:

(i) Industrial boilers located on the site of a facility engaged in a manufacturing process where substances are transformed into new products, including the component parts of products, by mechanical or chemical processes;

(ii) Utility boilers used to produce electric power, steam, heated or cooled air, or other gases or fluids for sale; or

(iii) Used oil-fired space heaters provided that the burner meets the provisions of §279.23.

(3) Hazardous waste incinerators subject to regulation under subpart O of parts 264 or 265 of this chapter.

[57 FR 41612, Sept. 10, 1992, as amended at 58 FR 26425, May 3, 1993]

Subpart C—Standards for Used Oil Generators 📖 12.2

§279.20 Applicability.

(a) *General.* Except as provided in paragraphs (a)(1) through (a)(4) of this section, this subpart applies to all used oil generators. A used oil generator is any person, by site, whose act or process produces used oil or whose act first causes used oil to become subject to regulation.

(1) *Household "do-it-yourselfer" used oil generators.* Household "do-it-yourselfer" used oil generators are not subject to regulation under this part.

(2) *Vessels.* Vessels at sea or at port are not subject to this subpart. For purposes of this subpart, used oil produced on vessels from normal shipboard operations is considered to be generated at the time it is transported ashore. The owner or operator of the vessel and the person(s) removing or accepting used oil from the vessel are co-generators of the used oil and are both responsible for managing the waste in compliance with this subpart once the used oil is transported ashore. The co-generators may decide among them which party will fulfill the requirements of this subpart.

(3) *Diesel fuel.* Mixtures of used oil and diesel fuel mixed by the generator of the used oil for use in the generator's own vehicles are not subject to this part

once the used oil and diesel fuel have been mixed. Prior to mixing, the used oil fuel is subject to the requirements of this subpart.

(4) *Farmers.* Farmers who generate an average of 25 gallons per month or less of used oil from vehicles or machinery used on the farm in a calendar year are not subject to the requirements of this part.

(b) *Other applicable provisions.* Used oil generators who conduct the following activities are subject to the requirements of other applicable provisions of this part as indicated in paragraphs (b)(1) through (5) of this section:

(1) Generators who transport used oil, except under the self-transport provisions of §279.24 (a) and (b), must also comply with subpart E of this part.

(2)(i) Except as provided in paragraph (b)(2)(ii) of this section, generators who process or re-refine used oil must also comply with subpart F of this part. 12.2.2

(ii) Generators who perform the following activities are not processors provided that the used oil is generated on-site and is not being sent off-site to a burner of on- or off-specification used oil fuel.

(A) Filtering, cleaning, or otherwise reconditioning used oil before returning it for reuse by the generator;

(B) Separating used oil from wastewater generated on-site to make the wastewater acceptable for discharge or reuse pursuant to section 402 or section 307(b) of the Clean Water Act or other applicable Federal or state regulations governing the management or discharge of wastewaters;

(C) Using oil mist collectors to remove small droplets of used oil from in-plant air to make plant air suitable for continued recirculation;

(D) Draining or otherwise removing used oil from materials containing or otherwise contaminated with used oil in order to remove excessive oil to the extent possible pursuant to §279.10(c); or

(E) Filtering, separating or otherwise reconditioning used oil before burning it in a space heater pursuant to §279.23.

(3) Generators who burn off-specification used oil for energy recovery, except under the on-site space heater provisions of §279.23, must also comply with subpart G of this part. 12.3

(4) Generators who direct shipments of off-specification used oil from their facility to a used oil burner or first claim that used oil that is to be burned for energy recovery meets the used oil fuel specifications set forth in §279.11 must also comply with subpart H of this part. 12.3.5

(5) Generators who dispose of used oil, including the use of used oil as a dust suppressant, must also comply with subpart I of this part. 12.2.3

[57 FR 41612, Sept. 10, 1992, as amended at 59 FR 10560, Mar. 4, 1994]

§279.21 Hazardous waste mixing.

(a) Mixtures of used oil and hazardous waste must be managed in accordance with §279.10(b).

(b) The rebuttable presumption for used oil of §279.10 (b)(1)(ii) applies to used oil managed by generators. Under the rebuttable presumption for used oil of §279.10(b)(1)(ii), used oil containing greater than 1,000 ppm total halogens is presumed to be a hazardous waste and thus must be managed as hazardous waste and not as used oil unless the presumption is rebutted. However, the rebuttable presumption does not apply to certain metalworking oils/fluids and certain used oils removed from refrigeration units.

[57 FR 41612, Sept. 10, 1992, as amended at 58 FR 26425, May 3, 1993]

§279.22 Used oil storage. 12.2.1.1

Used oil generators are subject to all applicable Spill Prevention, Control and Countermeasures (40 CFR part 112) in addition to the requirements of this Subpart. Used oil generators are also subject to the Underground Storage Tank (40 CFR part 280) standards for used oil stored in underground tanks whether or not the used oil exhibits any characteristics of hazardous waste, in addition to the requirements of this subpart.

(a) *Storage units.* Used oil generators shall not store used oil in units other than tanks, containers, or units subject to regulation under parts 264 or 265 of this chapter. 12.2.1.1.1

(b) *Condition of units.* Containers and aboveground tanks used to store used oil at generator facilities must be:

(1) In good condition (no severe rusting, apparent structural defects or deterioration); and

(2) Not leaking (no visible leaks).

(c) *Labels.* (1) Containers and aboveground tanks used to store used oil at generator facilities must be labeled or marked clearly with the words "Used Oil."

12.2.1.1.1, 16.1.10

(2) Fill pipes used to transfer used oil into underground storage tanks at generator facilities must be labeled or marked clearly with the words "Used Oil."

12.2.1.1.2, 16.1.10

(d) *Response to releases.* Upon detection of a release of used oil to the environment that is not subject to the requirements of part 280, subpart F of this chapter and which has occurred after the effective date of the recycled used oil management program in effect in the State in which the release is located, a generator must perform the following cleanup steps: 📖 12.2.1.1.1, 14.4.5.2

(1) Stop the release;

(2) Contain the released used oil;

(3) Clean up and manage properly the released used oil and other materials; and

(4) If necessary, repair or replace any leaking used oil storage containers or tanks prior to returning them to service.

[57 FR 41612, Sept. 10, 1992, as amended at 58 FR 26425, May 3, 1993; 63 FR 24969, May 6, 1998]

§279.23 On-site burning in space heaters. 📖 12.3.3.2

Generators may burn used oil in used oil-fired space heaters provided that:

(a) The heater burns only used oil that the owner or operator generates or used oil received from household do-it-yourself used oil generators;

(b) The heater is designed to have a maximum capacity of not more than 0.5 million Btu per hour; and

(c) The combustion gases from the heater are vented to the ambient air.

[57 FR 41612, Sept. 10, 1992, as amended at 58 FR 26425, May 3, 1993]

§279.24 Off-site shipments. 📖 12.2.1.2

Except as provided in paragraphs (a) through (c) of this section, generators must ensure that their used oil is transported only by transporters who have obtained EPA identification numbers.

(a) *Self-transportation of small amounts to approved collection centers.* Generators may transport, without an EPA identification number, used oil that is generated at the generator's site and used oil collected from household do-it-yourselfers to a used oil collection center provided that:

(1) The generator transports the used oil in a vehicle owned by the generator or owned by an employee of the generator;

(2) The generator transports no more than 55 gallons of used oil at any time; and

(3) The generator transports the used oil to a used oil collection center that is registered, licensed, permitted, or recognized by a state/county/municipal government to manage used oil.

(b) *Self-transportation of small amounts to aggregation points owned by the generator.* Generators may transport, without an EPA identification number, used oil that is generated at the generator's site to an aggregation point provided that:

(1) The generator transports the used oil in a vehicle owned by the generator or owned by an employee of the generator;

(2) The generator transports no more than 55 gallons of used oil at any time; and

(3) The generator transports the used oil to an aggregation point that is owned and/or operated by the same generator.

(c) *Tolling arrangements.* Used oil generators may arrange for used oil to be transported by a transporter without an EPA identification number if the used oil is reclaimed under a contractual agreement pursuant to which reclaimed oil is returned by the processor/re-refiner to the generator for use as a lubricant, cutting oil, or coolant. The contract (known as a "tolling arrangement") must indicate:

(1) The type of used oil and the frequency of shipments;

(2) That the vehicle used to transport the used oil to the processing/re-refining facility and to deliver recycled used oil back to the generator is owned and operated by the used oil processor/re-refiner; and

(3) That reclaimed oil will be returned to the generator.

Subpart D—Standards for Used Oil Collection Centers and Aggregation Points

§279.30 Do-it-yourselfer used oil collection centers.

(a) *Applicability.* This section applies to owners or operators of all do-it-yourselfer (DIY) used oil collection centers. A DIY used oil collection center is any site or facility that accepts/aggregates and stores used oil collected only from household do-it-yourselfers.

(b) *DIY used oil collection center requirements.* Owners or operators of all DIY used oil collection centers must comply with the generator standards in subpart C of this part.

§279.31 Used oil collection centers.

(a) *Applicability.* This section applies to owners or operators of used oil collection centers. A used oil collection center is any site or facility that accepts/aggregates and stores used oil collected from used oil generators regulated under subpart C of this part who bring used oil to the collection center in shipments of no more than 55 gallons under the provisions of §279.24(a). Used oil collection centers may also accept used oil from household do-it-yourselfers.

(b) *Used oil collection center requirements.* Owners or operators of all used oil collection centers must:

(1) Comply with the generator standards in subpart C of this part; and

(2) Be registered/licensed/permitted/recognized by a state/county/municipal government to manage used oil.

§279.32 Used oil aggregation points owned by the generator.

(a) *Applicability.* This section applies to owners or operators of all used oil aggregation points. A used oil aggregation point is any site or facility that accepts, aggregates, and/or stores used oil collected only from other used oil generation sites owned or operated by the owner or operator of the aggregation point, from which used oil is transported to the aggregation point in shipments of no more than 55 gallons under the provisions of §279.24(b). Used oil aggregation points may also accept used oil from household do-it-yourselfers.

(b) *Used oil aggregation point requirements.* Owners or operators of all used oil aggregation points must comply with the generator standards in subpart C of this part.

Subpart E—Standards for Used Oil Transporter and Transfer Facilities

§279.40 Applicability.

(a) *General.* Except as provided in paragraphs (a)(1) through (a)(4) of this section, this subpart applies to all used oil transporters. Used oil transporters are persons who transport used oil, persons who collect used oil from more than one generator and transport the collected oil, and owners and operators of used oil transfer facilities.

(1) This subpart does not apply to on-site transportation.

(2) This subpart does not apply to generators who transport shipments of used oil totalling 55 gallons or less from the generator to a used oil collection center as specified in §279.24(a).

(3) This subpart does not apply to generators who transport shipments of used oil totalling 55 gallons or less from the generator to a used oil aggregation point owned or operated by the same generator as specified in §279.24(b).

(4) This subpart does not apply to transportation of used oil from household do-it-yourselfers to a regulated used oil generator, collection center, aggregation point, processor/re-refiner, or burner subject to the requirements of this part. Except as provided in paragraphs (a)(1) through (a)(3) of this section, this subpart does, however, apply to transportation of collected household do-it-yourselfer used oil from regulated used oil generators, collection centers, aggregation points, or other facilities where household do-it-yourselfer used oil is collected.

(b) *Imports and exports.* Transporters who import used oil from abroad or export used oil outside of the United States are subject to the requirements of this subpart from the time the used oil enters and until the time it exits the United States.

(c) *Trucks used to transport hazardous waste.* Unless trucks previously used to transport hazardous waste are emptied as described in §261.7 of this chapter prior to transporting used oil, the used oil is considered to have been mixed with the hazardous waste and must be managed as hazardous waste unless, under the provisions of §279.10(b), the hazardous waste/used oil mixture is determined not to be hazardous waste.

(d) *Other applicable provisions.* Used oil transporters who conduct the following activities are also subject to other applicable provisions of this part as indicated in paragraphs (d)(1) through (5) of this section:

(1) Transporters who generate used oil must also comply with subpart C of this part;

(2) Transporters who process or re-refine used oil, except as provided in §279.41, must also comply with subpart F of this part;

(3) Transporters who burn off-specification used oil for energy recovery must also comply with subpart G of this part;

(4) Transporters who direct shipments of off-specification used oil from their facility to a used oil burner or first claim that used oil that is to be burned for energy recovery meets the used oil fuel specifications set forth in §279.11 must also comply with subpart H of this part; and

(5) Transporters who dispose of used oil, including the use of used oil as a dust suppressant, must also comply with subpart I of this part.

[57 FR 41612, Sept. 10, 1992, as amended at 58 FR 26425, May 3, 1993]

§279.41 Restrictions on transporters who are not also processors or re-refiners.

(a) Used oil transporters may consolidate or aggregate loads of used oil for purposes of transportation. However, except as provided in paragraph (b) of this section, used oil transporters may not process used oil unless they also comply with the requirements for processors/re-refiners in subpart F of this part.

(b) Transporters may conduct incidental processing operations that occur in the normal course of used oil transportation (*e.g.*, settling and water separation), but that are not designed to produce (or make more amenable for production of) used oil derived products unless they also comply with the processor/re-refiner requirements in subpart F of this part.

(c) Transporters of used oil that is removed from oil bearing electrical transformers and turbines and filtered by the transporter or at a transfer facility prior to being returned to its original use are not subject to the processor/re-refiner requirements in subpart F of this part.

[57 FR 41612, Sept. 10, 1992, as amended at 59 FR 10560, Mar. 4, 1994]

§279.42 Notification.

(a) *Identification numbers.* Used oil transporters who have not previously complied with the notification requirements of RCRA section 3010 must comply with these requirements and obtain an EPA identification number.

(b) *Mechanics of notification.* A used oil transporter who has not received an EPA identification number may obtain one by notifying the Regional Administrator of their used oil activity by submitting either:

(1) A completed EPA Form 8700-12 (To obtain ordering information for EPA Form 8700-12 call RCRA/Superfund Hotline at 1-800-424-9346 or 703-920-9810); or

(2) A letter requesting an EPA identification number.

Call RCRA/Superfund Hotline to determine where to send a letter requesting an EPA identification number. The letter should include the following information:

(i) Transporter company name;

(ii) Owner of the transporter company;

(iii) Mailing address for the transporter;

(iv) Name and telephone number for the transporter point of contact;

(v) Type of transport activity (*i.e.*, transport only, transport and transfer facility, transfer facility only);

(vi) Location of all transfer facilities at which used oil is stored;

(vii) Name and telephone number for a contact at each transfer facility.

[57 FR 41612, Sept. 10, 1992, as amended at 58 FR 26425, May 3, 1993; 58 FR 33342, June 17, 1993]

§279.43 Used oil transportation.

(a) *Deliveries.* A used oil transporter must deliver all used oil received to:

(1) Another used oil transporter, provided that the transporter has obtained an EPA identification number;

(2) A used oil processing/re-refining facility who has obtained an EPA identification number;

(3) An off-specification used oil burner facility who has obtained an EPA identification number; or

(4) An on-specification used oil burner facility.

(b) *DOT Requirements.* Used oil transporters must comply with all applicable requirements under the U.S. Department of Transportation regulations in 49 CFR parts 171 through 180. Persons transporting used oil that meets the definition of a hazardous material in 49 CFR 171.8 must comply with all applicable regulations in 49 CFR parts 171 through 180.

(c) *Used oil discharges.* (1) In the event of a discharge of used oil during transportation, the transporter must take appropriate immediate action to protect human health and the environment (*e.g.*, notify local authorities, dike the discharge area).

(2) If a discharge of used oil occurs during transportation and an official (State or local government or a Federal Agency) acting within the scope of official responsibilities determines that immediate removal of the used oil is necessary to protect human health or the environment, that official may authorize the removal of the used oil by transporters who do not have EPA identification numbers.

(3) An air, rail, highway, or water transporter who has discharged used oil must:

(i) Give notice, if required by 49 CFR 171.15, to the National Response Center (800-424-8802 or 202-426-2675); and

(ii) Report in writing as required by 49 CFR 171.16 to the Director, Office of Hazardous Materials Regulations, Materials Transportation Bureau, Department of Transportation, Washington, DC 20590.

(4) A water transporter who has discharged used oil must give notice as required by 33 CFR 153.203.

(5) A transporter must clean up any used oil discharge that occurs during transportation or take such action as may be required or approved by federal, state, or local officials so that the used oil discharge no longer presents a hazard to human health or the environment.

[57 FR 41612, Sept. 10, 1992, as amended at 58 FR 26425, May 3, 1993; 71 FR 40280, July 14, 2006]

§279.44 Rebuttable presumption for used oil.

📖 12.1.4

(a) To ensure that used oil is not a hazardous waste under the rebuttable presumption of §279.10(b)(1)(ii), the used oil transporter must determine whether the total halogen content of used oil being transported or stored at a transfer facility is above or below 1,000 ppm.

(b) The transporter must make this determination by:

(1) Testing the used oil; or

(2) Applying knowledge of the halogen content of the used oil in light of the materials or processes used.

(c) If the used oil contains greater than or equal to 1,000 ppm total halogens, it is presumed to be a hazardous waste because it has been mixed with halogenated hazardous waste listed in subpart D of part 261 of this chapter. The owner or operator may rebut the presumption by demonstrating that the used oil does not contain hazardous waste (for example, by showing that the used oil does not contain significant concentrations of halogenated hazardous constituents listed in appendix VIII of part 261 of this chapter).

(1) The rebuttable presumption does not apply to metalworking oils/fluids containing chlorinated paraffins, if they are processed, through a tolling arrangement as described in §279.24(c), to reclaim metalworking oils/fluids. The presumption does apply to metalworking oils/fluids if such oils/fluids are recycled in any other manner, or disposed.

(2) The rebuttable presumption does not apply to used oils contaminated with chlorofluorocarbons (CFCs) removed from refrigeration units if the CFCs are destined for reclamation. The rebuttable presumption does apply to used oils contaminated with CFCs that have been mixed with used oil from sources other than refrigeration units.

(d) *Record retention.* Records of analyses conducted or information used to comply with paragraphs (a), (b), and (c) of this section must be maintained by the transporter for at least 3 years.

[57 FR 41612, Sept. 10, 1992, as amended at 59 FR 10560, Mar. 4, 1994; 70 FR 34591, June 14, 2005; 71 FR 40280, July 14, 2006]

§279.45 Used oil storage at transfer facilities.

Used oil transporters are subject to all applicable Spill Prevention, Control and Countermeasures (40 CFR part 112) in addition to the requirements of this subpart. Used oil transporters are also subject to the Underground Storage Tank (40 CFR part 280) standards for used oil stored in underground tanks whether or not the used oil exhibits any characteristics of hazardous waste, in addition to the requirements of this subpart.

(a) *Applicability.* This section applies to used oil transfer facilities. Used oil transfer facilities are transportation related facilities including loading docks, parking areas, storage areas, and other areas where shipments of used oil are held for more than 24 hours during the normal course of transportation and not longer than 35 days. Transfer facilities that store used oil for more than 35 days are subject to regulation under subpart F of this part.

(b) *Storage units.* Owners or operators of used oil transfer facilities may not store used oil in units other than tanks, containers, or units subject to regulation under parts 264 or 265 of this chapter.

(c) *Condition of units.* Containers and aboveground tanks used to store used oil at transfer facilities must be:

(1) In good condition (no severe rusting, apparent structural defects or deterioration); and

(2) Not leaking (no visible leaks).

(d) *Secondary containment for containers.* Containers used to store used oil at transfer facilities must be equipped with a secondary containment system.

(1) The secondary containment system must consist of, at a minimum:

(i) Dikes, berms or retaining walls; and

(ii) A floor. The floor must cover the entire area within the dikes, berms, or retaining walls; or

(iii) An equivalent secondary containment system.

(2) The entire containment system, including walls and floors, must be sufficiently impervious to used oil to prevent any used oil released into the containment system from migrating out of the system to the soil, groundwater, or surface water.

(e) *Secondary containment for existing aboveground tanks.* Existing aboveground tanks used to store used oil at transfer facilities must be equipped with a secondary containment system.

(1) The secondary containment system must consist of, at a minimum:

(i) Dikes, berms or retaining walls; and

(ii) A floor. The floor must cover the entire area within the dike, berm, or retaining wall except areas where existing portions of the tank meet the ground; or

(iii) An equivalent secondary containment system.

(2) The entire containment system, including walls and floors, must be sufficiently impervious to used oil to prevent any used oil released into the containment system from migrating out of the system to the soil, groundwater, or surface water.

(f) *Secondary containment for new aboveground tanks.* New aboveground tanks used to store used oil at transfer facilities must be equipped with a secondary containment system.

(1) The secondary containment system must consist of, at a minimum:

(i) Dikes, berms or retaining walls; and

(ii) A floor. The floor must cover the entire area within the dike, berm, or retaining wall; or

(iii) An equivalent secondary containment system.

(2) The entire containment system, including walls and floors, must be sufficiently impervious to used oil to prevent any used oil released into the containment system from migrating out of the system to the soil, groundwater, or surface water.

(g) *Labels.* (1) Containers and aboveground tanks used to store used oil at transfer facilities must be labeled or marked clearly with the words "Used Oil."

(2) Fill pipes used to transfer used oil into underground storage tanks at transfer facilities must be labeled or marked clearly with the words "Used Oil."

(h) *Response to releases.* Upon detection of a release of used oil to the environment that is not subject to the requirements of part 280, subpart F of this chapter and which has occurred after the effective date of the recycled used oil management program in effect in the State in which the release is located, the owner/operator of a transfer facility must perform the following cleanup steps:

(1) Stop the release;

(2) Contain the released used oil;

(3) Clean up and manage properly the released used oil and other materials; and

(4) If necessary, repair or replace any leaking used oil storage containers or tanks prior to returning them to service.

[57 FR 41612, Sept. 10, 1992, as amended at 58 FR 26426, May 3, 1993; 63 FR 24969, May 6, 1998; 71 FR 40280, July 14, 2006]

§279.46 Tracking.

(a) *Acceptance.* Used oil transporters must keep a record of each used oil shipment accepted for transport. Records for each shipment must include:

(1) The name and address of the generator, transporter, or processor/re-refiner who provided the used oil for transport;

(2) The EPA identification number (if applicable) of the generator, transporter, or processor/re-refiner who provided the used oil for transport;

(3) The quantity of used oil accepted;

(4) The date of acceptance; and

(5)(i) Except as provided in paragraph (a)(5)(ii) of this section, the signature, dated upon receipt of the used oil, of a representative of the generator, transporter, or processor/re-refiner who provided the used oil for transport.

(ii) Intermediate rail transporters are not required to sign the record of acceptance.

(b) *Deliveries.* Used oil transporters must keep a record of each shipment of used oil that is delivered to another used oil transporter, or to a used oil burner, processor/re-refiner, or disposal facility. Records of each delivery must include:

(1) The name and address of the receiving facility or transporter;

(2) The EPA identification number of the receiving facility or transporter;

(3) The quantity of used oil delivered;

(4) The date of delivery;

(5)(i) Except as provided in paragraph (b)(5)(ii) of this section, the signature, dated upon receipt of the used oil, of a representative of the receiving facility or transporter.

(ii) Intermediate rail transporters are not required to sign the record of delivery.

(c) *Exports of used oil.* Used oil transporters must maintain the records described in paragraphs (b)(1) through (b)(4) of this section for each shipment of used oil exported to any foreign country.

(d) *Record retention.* The records described in paragraphs (a), (b), and (c) of this section must be maintained for at least three years.

[57 FR 41612, Sept. 10, 1992, as amended at 59 FR 10560, Mar. 4, 1994]

§279.47 Management of residues.

Transporters who generate residues from the storage or transport of used oil must manage the residues as specified in §279.10(e).

Subpart F—Standards for Used Oil Processors and Re-Refiners

§279.50 Applicability.

(a) The requirements of this subpart apply to owners and operators of facilities that process used oil. Processing means chemical or physical operations designed to produce from used oil, or to make used oil more amenable for production of, fuel oils, lubricants, or other used oil-derived products. Processing includes, but is not limited to: blending used oil with virgin petroleum products, blending used oils to meet the fuel specification, filtration, simple distillation, chemical or physical separation and re-refining. The requirements of this subpart do not apply to:

(1) Transporters that conduct incidental processing operations that occur during the normal course of transportation as provided in §279.41; or

(2) Burners that conduct incidental processing operations that occur during the normal course of used oil management prior to burning as provided in §279.61(b).

(b) *Other applicable provisions.* Used oil processors/re-refiners who conduct the following activities are also subject to the requirements of other applicable provisions of this part as indicated in paragraphs (b)(1) through (b)(5) of this section.

(1) Processors/re-refiners who generate used oil must also comply with subpart C of this part;

(2) Processors/re-refiners who transport used oil must also comply with subpart E of this part;

(3) Except as provided in paragraphs (b)(3)(i) and (b)(3)(ii) of this section, processors/re-refiners who burn off-specification used oil for energy recovery must also comply with subpart G of this part. Processor/re-refiners burning used oil for energy recovery under the following conditions are not subject to subpart G of this part:

(i) The used oil is burned in an on-site space heater that meets the requirements of §279.23; or

(ii) The used oil is burned for purposes of processing used oil, which is considered burning incidentally to used oil processing;

(4) Processors/re-refiners who direct shipments of off-specification used oil from their facility to a used oil burner or first claim that used oil that is to be burned for energy recovery meets the used oil fuel specifications set forth in §279.11 must also comply with subpart H of this part; and 📖 12.3.5

(5) Processors/re-refiners who dispose of used oil, including the use of used oil as a dust suppressant, also must comply with subpart I of this part.

§279.51 Notification.

(a) *Identification numbers.* Used oil processors and re-refiners who have not previously complied with the notification requirements of RCRA section 3010 must comply with these requirements and obtain an EPA identification number.

(b) *Mechanics of notification.* A used oil processor or re-refiner who has not received an EPA identification number may obtain one by notifying the Regional Administrator of their used oil activity by submitting either:

(1) A completed EPA Form 8700-12 (To obtain EPA Form 8700-12 call RCRA/Superfund Hotline at 1-800-424-9346 or 703-920-9810); or

(2) A letter requesting an EPA identification number. Call RCRA/Superfund Hotline to determine where to send a letter requesting an EPA identification number. The letter should include the following information:

(i) Processor or re-refiner company name;

(ii) Owner of the processor or re-refiner company;

(iii) Mailing address for the processor or re-refiner;

(iv) Name and telephone number for the processor or re-refiner point of contact;

(v) Type of used oil activity (*i.e.*, process only, process and re-refine);

(vi) Location of the processor or re-refiner facility.

[57 FR 41612, Sept. 10, 1992, as amended at 58 FR 33342, June 17, 1993; 71 FR 40280, July 14, 2006]

§279.52 General facility standards.

(a) *Preparedness and prevention.* Owners and operators of used oil processing and re-refining facilities must comply with the following requirements:

(1) *Maintenance and operation of facility.* Facilities must be maintained and operated to minimize the possibility of a fire, explosion, or any unplanned sudden or non-sudden release of used oil to air, soil, or surface water which could threaten human health or the environment.

(2) *Required equipment.* All facilities must be equipped with the following, unless none of the hazards posed by used oil handled at the facility could require a particular kind of equipment specified in paragraphs (a)(2)(i) through (iv) of this section:

(i) An internal communications or alarm system capable of providing immediate emergency instruction (voice or signal) to facility personnel;

(ii) A device, such as a telephone (immediately available at the scene of operations) or a hand-held two-way radio, capable of summoning emergency assistance from local police departments, fire departments, or State or local emergency response teams;

(iii) Portable fire extinguishers, fire control equipment (including special extinguishing equipment, such as that using foam, inert gas, or dry chemicals), spill control equipment and decontamination equipment; and

(iv) Water at adequate volume and pressure to supply water hose streams, or foam producing equipment, or automatic sprinklers, or water spray systems.

(3) *Testing and maintenance of equipment.* All facility communications or alarm systems, fire protection equipment, spill control equipment, and decontamination equipment, where required, must be tested and maintained as necessary to assure its proper operation in time of emergency.

(4) *Access to communications or alarm system.* (i) Whenever used oil is being poured, mixed, spread, or otherwise handled, all personnel involved in the

PART 279—Subpart F

operation must have immediate access to an internal alarm or emergency communication device, either directly or through visual or voice contact with another employee, unless such a device is not required in paragraph (a)(2) of this section.

(ii) If there is ever just one employee on the premises while the facility is operating, the employee must have immediate access to a device, such as a telephone (immediately available at the scene of operation) or a hand-held two-way radio, capable of summoning external emergency assistance, unless such a device is not required in paragraph (a)(2) of this section.

(5) *Required aisle space.* The owner or operator must maintain aisle space to allow the unobstructed movement of personnel, fire protection equipment, spill control equipment, and decontamination equipment to any area of facility operation in an emergency, unless aisle space is not needed for any of these purposes.

(6) *Arrangements with local authorities.* (i) The owner or operator must attempt to make the following arrangements, as appropriate for the type of used oil handled at the facility and the potential need for the services of these organizations:

(A) Arrangements to familiarize police, fire departments, and emergency response teams with the layout of the facility, properties of used oil handled at the facility and associated hazards, places where facility personnel would normally be working, entrances to roads inside the facility, and possible evacuation routes;

(B) Where more than one police and fire department might respond to an emergency, agreements designating primary emergency authority to a specific police and a specific fire department, and agreements with any others to provide support to the primary emergency authority;

(C) Agreements with State emergency response teams, emergency response contractors, and equipment suppliers; and

(D) Arrangements to familiarize local hospitals with the properties of used oil handled at the facility and the types of injuries or illnesses which could result from fires, explosions, or releases at the facility.

(ii) Where State or local authorities decline to enter into such arrangements, the owner or operator must document the refusal in the operating record.

(b) *Contingency plan and emergency procedures.* Owners and operators of used oil processing and re-refining facilities must comply with the following requirements:

(1) *Purpose and implementation of contingency plan.* (i) Each owner or operator must have a contingency plan for the facility. The contingency plan must be designed to minimize hazards to human health or the environment from fires, explosions, or any unplanned sudden or non-sudden release of used oil to air, soil, or surface water.

(ii) The provisions of the plan must be carried out immediately whenever there is a fire, explosion, or release of used oil which could threaten human health or the environment.

(2) *Content of contingency plan.* (i) The contingency plan must describe the actions facility personnel must take to comply with paragraphs (b) (1) and (6) of this section in response to fires, explosions, or any unplanned sudden or non-sudden release of used oil to air, soil, or surface water at the facility.

(ii) If the owner or operator has already prepared a Spill Prevention, Control, and Countermeasures (SPCC) Plan in accordance with part 112 of this chapter, or part 1510 of chapter V of this title, or some other emergency or contingency plan, the owner or operator need only amend that plan to incorporate used oil management provisions that are sufficient to comply with the requirements of this part.

(iii) The plan must describe arrangements agreed to by local police departments, fire departments, hospitals, contractors, and State and local emergency response teams to coordinate emergency services, pursuant to paragraph (a)(6) of this section.

(iv) The plan must list names, addresses, and phone numbers (office and home) of all persons qualified to act as emergency coordinator (see paragraph (b)(5) of this section), and this list must be kept up to date. Where more than one person is listed, one must be named as primary emergency coordinator and others must be listed in the order in which they will assume responsibility as alternates.

(v) The plan must include a list of all emergency equipment at the facility (such as fire extinguishing systems, spill control equipment, communications and alarm systems (internal and external), and decontamination equipment), where this equipment is required. This list must be kept up to date. In addition, the plan must include the location and a physical description of each item on the list, and a brief outline of its capabilities.

(vi) The plan must include an evacuation plan for facility personnel where there is a possibility that evacuation could be necessary. This plan must describe signal(s) to be used to begin evacuation, evacuation routes, and alternate evacuation routes (in cases where the primary routes could be blocked by releases of used oil or fires).

(3) *Copies of contingency plan.* A copy of the contingency plan and all revisions to the plan must be:

(i) Maintained at the facility; and

(ii) Submitted to all local police departments, fire departments, hospitals, and State and local emergency response teams that may be called upon to provide emergency services.

(4) *Amendment of contingency plan.* The contingency plan must be reviewed, and immediately amended, if necessary, whenever:

(i) Applicable regulations are revised;

(ii) The plan fails in an emergency;

(iii) The facility changes—in its design, construction, operation, maintenance, or other circumstances—in a way that materially increases the potential for fires, explosions, or releases of used oil, or changes the response necessary in an emergency;

(iv) The list of emergency coordinators changes; or

(v) The list of emergency equipment changes.

(5) *Emergency coordinator.* At all times, there must be at least one employee either on the facility premises or on call (*i.e.*, available to respond to an emergency by reaching the facility within a short period of time) with the responsibility for coordinating all emergency response measures. This emergency coordinator must be thoroughly familiar with all aspects of the facility's contingency plan, all operations and activities at the facility, the location and characteristic of used oil handled, the location of all records within the facility, and facility layout. In addition, this person must have the authority to commit the resources needed to carry out the contingency plan.

Guidance: The emergency coordinator's responsibilities are more fully spelled out in paragraph (b)(6) of this section. Applicable responsibilities for the emergency coordinator vary, depending on factors such as type and variety of used oil handled by the facility, and type and complexity of the facility.

(6) *Emergency procedures.* (i) Whenever there is an imminent or actual emergency situation, the emergency coordinator (or the designee when the emergency coordinator is on call) must immediately:

(A) Activate internal facility alarms or communication systems, where applicable, to notify all facility personnel; and

(B) Notify appropriate State or local agencies with designated response roles if their help is needed.

(ii) Whenever there is a release, fire, or explosion, the emergency coordinator must immediately identify the character, exact source, amount, and areal extent of any released materials. He may do this by observation or review of facility records or manifests and, if necessary, by chemical analyses.

(iii) Concurrently, the emergency coordinator must assess possible hazards to human health or the environment that may result from the release, fire, or explosion. This assessment must consider both direct and indirect effects of the release, fire, or explosion (*e.g.*, the effects of any toxic, irritating, or asphyxiating gases that are generated, or the effects of any hazardous surface water run-offs from water or chemical agents used to control fire and heat-induced explosions).

(iv) If the emergency coordinator determines that the facility has had a release, fire, or explosion which could threaten human health, or the environment, outside the facility, he must report his findings as follows:

(A) If his assessment indicated that evacuation of local areas may be advisable, he must immediately notify appropriate local authorities. He must be available to help appropriate officials decide whether local areas should be evacuated; and

(B) He must immediately notify either the government official designated as the on-scene coordinator for the geographical area (in the applicable regional contingency plan under part 1510 of this title), or the National Response Center (using their 24-hour toll free number 800/424-8802). The report must include:

(*1*) Name and telephone number of reporter;

(*2*) Name and address of facility;

(*3*) Time and type of incident (*e.g.*, release, fire);

(*4*) Name and quantity of material(s) involved, to the extent known;

(*5*) The extent of injuries, if any; and

(*6*) The possible hazards to human health, or the environment, outside the facility.

(v) During an emergency, the emergency coordinator must take all reasonable measures necessary to ensure that fires, explosions, and releases do not occur, recur, or spread to other used oil or hazardous waste at the facility. These measures must include, where applicable, stopping processes and operation, collecting and containing released used oil, and removing or isolating containers.

(vi) If the facility stops operation in response to a fire, explosion, or release, the emergency coordinator must monitor for leaks, pressure buildup, gas generation, or ruptures in valves, pipes, or other equipment, wherever this is appropriate.

(vii) Immediately after an emergency, the emergency coordinator must provide for recycling, storing, or disposing of recovered used oil, contaminated soil or surface water, or any other material that results from a release, fire, or explosion at the facility.

(viii) The emergency coordinator must ensure that, in the affected area(s) of the facility:

(A) No waste or used oil that may be incompatible with the released material is recycled, treated, stored, or disposed of until cleanup procedures are completed; and

(B) All emergency equipment listed in the contingency plan is cleaned and fit for its intended use before operations are resumed.

(C) The owner or operator must notify the Regional Administrator, and appropriate State and local authorities that the facility is in compliance with paragraphs (b)(6)(viii)(A) and (B) of this section before operations are resumed in the affected area(s) of the facility.

(ix) The owner or operator must note in the operating record the time, date and details of any incident that requires implementing the contingency plan. Within 15 days after the incident, he must submit a written report on the incident to the Regional Administrator. The report must include:

(A) Name, address, and telephone number of the owner or operator;

(B) Name, address, and telephone number of the facility;

(C) Date, time, and type of incident (*e.g.*, fire, explosion);

(D) Name and quantity of material(s) involved;

(E) The extent of injuries, if any;

(F) An assessment of actual or potential hazards to human health or the environment, where this is applicable;

(G) Estimated quantity and disposition of recovered material that resulted from the incident.

[57 FR 41612, Sept. 10, 1992, as amended at 58 FR 26426, May 3, 1993; 71 FR 40280, July 14, 2006]

§279.53 Rebuttable presumption for used oil. 12.1.4

(a) To ensure that used oil managed at a processing/re-refining facility is not hazardous waste under the rebuttable presumption of §279.10(b)(1)(ii), the owner or operator of a used oil processing/re-refining facility must determine whether the total halogen content of used oil managed at the facility is above or below 1,000 ppm.

(b) The owner or operator must make this determination by:

(1) Testing the used oil; or

(2) Applying knowledge of the halogen content of the used oil in light of the materials or processes used.

(c) If the used oil contains greater than or equal to 1,000 ppm total halogens, it is presumed to be a hazardous waste because it has been mixed with halogenated hazardous waste listed in subpart D of part 261 of this chapter. The owner or operator may rebut the presumption by demonstrating that the used oil does not contain hazardous waste (for example, by showing that the used oil does not contain significant concentrations of halogenated hazardous constituents listed in appendix VIII of part 261 of this chapter).

(1) The rebuttable presumption does not apply to metalworking oils/fluids containing chlorinated paraffins, if they are processed, through a tolling agreement, to reclaim metalworking oils/fluids. The presumption does apply to metalworking oils/fluids if such oils/fluids are recycled in any other manner, or disposed.

(2) The rebuttable presumption does not apply to used oils contaminated with chlorofluorocarbons (CFCs) removed from refrigeration units where the CFCs are destined for reclamation. The rebuttable presumption does apply to used oils contaminated with CFCs that have been mixed with used oil from sources other than refrigeration units.

[57 FR 41612, Sept. 10, 1992, as amended at 59 FR 10560, Mar. 4, 1994; 70 FR 34591, June 14, 2005]

§279.54 Used oil management.

Used oil processor/re-refiners are subject to all applicable Spill Prevention, Control and Countermeasures (40 CFR part 112) in addition to the requirements of this subpart. Used oil processors/re-refiners are also subject to the Underground Storage Tank (40 CFR part 280) standards for used oil stored in underground tanks whether or not the used oil exhibits any characteristics of hazardous waste, in addition to the requirements of this subpart.

(a) *Management units.* Used oil processors/re-refiners may not store used oil in units other than tanks, containers, or units subject to regulation under part 264 or 265 of this chapter.

(b) *Condition of units.* Containers and aboveground tanks used to store or process used oil at processing and re-refining facilities must be:

(1) In good condition (no severe rusting, apparent structural defects or deterioration); and

(2) Not leaking (no visible leaks).

(c) *Secondary containment for containers.* Containers used to store or process used oil at processing and re-refining facilities must be equipped with a secondary containment system.

(1) The secondary containment system must consist of, at a minimum:

(i) Dikes, berms or retaining walls; and

(ii) A floor. The floor must cover the entire area within the dike, berm, or retaining wall; or

(iii) An equivalent secondary containment system.

(2) The entire containment system, including walls and floor, must be sufficiently impervious to used oil to prevent any used oil released into the containment system from migrating out of the system to the soil, groundwater, or surface water.

(d) *Secondary containment for existing aboveground tanks.* Existing aboveground tanks used to store or process used oil at processing and re-refining facilities must be equipped with a secondary containment system.

(1) The secondary containment system must consist of, at a minimum:

(i) Dikes, berms or retaining walls; and

(ii) A floor. The floor must cover the entire area within the dike, berm, or retaining wall except areas where existing portions of the tank meet the ground; or

(iii) An equivalent secondary containment system.

(2) The entire containment system, including walls and floor, must be sufficiently impervious to used oil to prevent any used oil released into the containment system from migrating out of the system to the soil, groundwater, or surface water.

(e) *Secondary containment for new aboveground tanks.* New aboveground tanks used to store or process used oil at processing and re-refining facilities must be equipped with a secondary containment system.

(1) The secondary containment system must consist of, at a minimum:

(i) Dikes, berms or retaining walls; and

(ii) A floor. The floor must cover the entire area within the dike, berm, or retaining wall; or

(iii) An equivalent secondary containment system.

(2) The entire containment system, including walls and floor, must be sufficiently impervious to used oil to prevent any used oil released into the containment system from migrating out of the system to the soil, groundwater, or surface water.

(f) *Labels.* (1) Containers and aboveground tanks used to store or process used oil at processing and re-refining facilities must be labeled or marked clearly with the words "Used Oil."

(2) Fill pipes used to transfer used oil into underground storage tanks at processing and re-refining facilities must be labeled or marked clearly with the words "Used Oil."

(g) *Response to releases.* Upon detection of a release of used oil to the environment that is not subject to the requirements of part 280, subpart F of this chapter and which has occurred after the effective date of the recycled used oil management program in effect in the State in which the release is located, an owner/operator must perform the following cleanup steps:

(1) Stop the release;

(2) Contain the released used oil;

(3) Clean up and manage properly the released used oil and other materials; and

(4) If necessary, repair or replace any leaking used oil storage containers or tanks prior to returning them to service.

(h) *Closure*—(1) *Aboveground tanks.* Owners and operators who store or process used oil in aboveground tanks must comply with the following requirements:

(i) At closure of a tank system, the owner or operator must remove or decontaminate used oil residues in tanks, contaminated containment system components, contaminated soils, and structures and equipment contaminated with used oil, and manage them as hazardous waste, unless the materials are not hazardous waste under this chapter.

(ii) If the owner or operator demonstrates that not all contaminated soils can be practicably removed or decontaminated as required in paragraph (h)(1)(i) of this section, then the owner or operator must close the tank system and perform post-closure care in accordance with the closure and post-closure care requirements that apply to hazardous waste landfills (§265.310 of this chapter).

(2) *Containers.* Owners and operators who store used oil in containers must comply with the following requirements:

(i) At closure, containers holding used oils or residues of used oil must be removed from the site;

(ii) The owner or operator must remove or decontaminate used oil residues, contaminated containment system components, contaminated soils, and structures and equipment contaminated with used oil, and manage them as hazardous waste, unless the materials are not hazardous waste under part 261 of this chapter.

[57 FR 41612, Sept. 10, 1992, as amended at 58 FR 26426, May 3, 1993; 63 FR 24969, May 6, 1998]

§279.55 Analysis plan.

Owners or operators of used oil processing and re-refining facilities must develop and follow a written analysis plan describing the procedures that will be used to comply with the analysis requirements of §279.53 and, if applicable, §279.72. The owner or operator must keep the plan at the facility.

(a) *Rebuttable presumption for used oil in §279.53.* At a minimum, the plan must specify the following:

(1) Whether sample analyses or knowledge of the halogen content of the used oil will be used to make this determination.

(2) If sample analyses are used to make this determination:

(i) The sampling method used to obtain representative samples to be analyzed. A representative sample may be obtained using either:

(A) One of the sampling methods in appendix I of part 261 of this chapter; or

(B) A method shown to be equivalent under §§260.20 and 260.21 of this chapter;

(ii) The frequency of sampling to be performed, and whether the analysis will be performed on-site or off-site; and

(iii) The methods used to analyze used oil for the parameters specified in §279.53; and

(3) The type of information that will be used to determine the halogen content of the used oil.

(b) *On-specification used oil fuel in §279.72.* At a minimum, the plan must specify the following if §279.72 is applicable:

(1) Whether sample analyses or other information will be used to make this determination;

(2) If sample analyses are used to make this determination:

(i) The sampling method used to obtain representative samples to be analyzed. A representative sample may be obtained using either:

(A) One of the sampling methods in appendix I of part 261 of this chapter; or

(B) A method shown to be equivalent under §§260.20 and 260.21 of this chapter;

(ii) Whether used oil will be sampled and analyzed prior to or after any processing/re-refining;

(iii) The frequency of sampling to be performed, and whether the analysis will be performed on-site or off-site; and

(iv) The methods used to analyze used oil for the parameters specified in §279.72; and

(3) The type of information that will be used to make the on-specification used oil fuel determination.

[57 FR 41612, Sept. 10, 1992, as amended at 71 FR 40280, July 14, 2006]

§279.56 Tracking.

(a) *Acceptance.* Used oil processors/re-refiners must keep a record of each used oil shipment accepted for processing/re-refining. These records may take the form of a log, invoice, manifest, bill of lading or other shipping documents. Records for each shipment must include the following information:

(1) The name and address of the transporter who delivered the used oil to the processor/re-refiner;

(2) The name and address of the generator or processor/re-refiner from whom the used oil was sent for processing/re-refining;

(3) The EPA identification number of the transporter who delivered the used oil to the processor/re-refiner;

(4) The EPA identification number (if applicable) of the generator or processor/re-refiner from whom the used oil was sent for processing/re-refining;

(5) The quantity of used oil accepted; and

(6) The date of acceptance.

(b) *Delivery.* Used oil processor/re-refiners must keep a record of each shipment of used oil that is shipped to a used oil burner, processor/re-refiner, or disposal facility. These records may take the form of a log, invoice, manifest, bill of lading or other shipping documents. Records for each shipment must include the following information:

(1) The name and address of the transporter who delivers the used oil to the burner, processor/re-refiner or disposal facility;

(2) The name and address of the burner, processor/re-refiner or disposal facility who will receive the used oil;

(3) The EPA identification number of the transporter who delivers the used oil to the burner, processor/re-refiner or disposal facility;

(4) The EPA identification number of the burner, processor/re-refiner, or disposal facility who will receive the used oil;

(5) The quantity of used oil shipped; and

(6) The date of shipment.

(c) *Record retention.* The records described in paragraphs (a) and (b) of this section must be maintained for at least three years.

[57 FR 41612, Sept. 10, 1992, as amended at 71 FR 40280, July 14, 2006]

§279.57 Operating record and reporting.

(a) *Operating record.* (1) The owner or operator must keep a written operating record at the facility.

(2) The following information must be recorded, as it becomes available, and maintained in the operating record until closure of the facility;

(i) Records and results of used oil analyses performed as described in the analysis plan required under §279.55; and

(ii) Summary reports and details of all incidents that require implementation of the contingency plan as specified in §279.52(b).

(b) *Reporting.* A used oil processor/re-refiner must report to the Regional Administrator, in the form of a letter, on a biennial basis (by March 1 of each even numbered year), the following information concerning used oil activities during the previous calendar year;

(1) The EPA identification number, name, and address of the processor/re-refiner;

(2) The calendar year covered by the report; and

(3) The quantities of used oil accepted for processing/re-refining and the manner in which the used oil is processed/re-refined, including the specific processes employed.

[57 FR 41612, Sept. 10, 1992, as amended at 71 FR 40280, July 14, 2006]

§279.58 Off-site shipments of used oil.

Used oil processors/re-refiners who initiate shipments of used oil off-site must ship the used oil using a used oil transporter who has obtained an EPA identification number.

§279.59 Management of residues.

Owners and operators who generate residues from the storage, processing, or re-refining of used oil must manage the residues as specified in §279.10(e).

[57 FR 41612, Sept. 10, 1992, as amended at 71 FR 40280, July 14, 2006]

Subpart G—Standards for Used Oil Burners Who Burn Off-Specification Used Oil for Energy Recovery

§279.60 Applicability. 📖 12.3.3

(a) *General.* The requirements of this subpart apply to used oil burners except as specified in paragraphs (a)(1) and (a)(2) of this section. A used oil burner is a facility where used oil not meeting the specification requirements in §279.11 is burned for energy recovery in devices identified in §279.61(a). Facilities burning used oil for energy recovery under the following conditions are not subject to this Subpart:

(1) The used oil is burned by the generator in an on-site space heater under the provisions of §279.23; or

(2) The used oil is burned by a processor/re-refiner for purposes of processing used oil, which is considered burning incidentally to used oil processing.

(b) *Other applicable provisions.* Used oil burners who conduct the following activities are also subject to the requirements of other applicable provisions of this part as indicated below.

(1) Burners who generate used oil must also comply with subpart C of this part;

(2) Burners who transport used oil must also comply with subpart E of this part;

(3) Except as provided in §279.61(b), burners who process or re-refine used oil must also comply with subpart F of this part;

(4) Burners who direct shipments of off-specification used oil from their facility to a used oil burner or first claim that used oil that is to be burned for energy recovery meets the used oil fuel specifications set forth in §279.11 must also comply with subpart H of this part; and 📖 12.3.5

(5) Burners who dispose of used oil, including the use of used oil as a dust suppressant, must comply with subpart I of this part.

(c) *Specification fuel.* This subpart does not apply to persons burning used oil that meets the used oil fuel specification of §279.11, provided that the burner complies with the requirements of subpart H of this part.

[57 FR 41612, Sept. 10, 1992, as amended at 58 FR 26426, May 3, 1993]

§279.61 Restrictions on burning.

(a) Off-specification used oil fuel may be burned for energy recovery in only the following devices: 📖 12.3.3.1

(1) Industrial furnaces identified in §260.10 of this chapter;

(2) Boilers, as defined in §260.10 of this chapter, that are identified as follows:

(i) Industrial boilers located on the site of a facility engaged in a manufacturing process where substances are transformed into new products, including the component parts of products, by mechanical or chemical processes;

(ii) Utility boilers used to produce electric power, steam, heated or cooled air, or other gases or fluids for sale; or

(iii) Used oil-fired space heaters provided that the burner meets the provisions of §279.23; or

(3) Hazardous waste incinerators subject to regulation under subpart O of parts 264 or 265 of this chapter.

(b)(1) With the following exception, used oil burners may not process used oil unless they also comply with the requirements of subpart F of this part.

(2) Used oil burners may aggregate off-specification used oil with virgin oil or on-specification used oil for purposes of burning, but may not aggregate for purposes of producing on-specification used oil.

§279.62 Notification

(a) *Identification numbers.* Used oil burners which have not previously complied with the notification requirements of RCRA section 3010 must comply with these requirements and obtain an EPA identification number.

(b) *Mechanics of notification.* A used oil burner who has not received an EPA identification number may obtain one by notifying the Regional Administrator of their used oil activity by submitting either:

(1) A completed EPA Form 8700-12 (To obtain EPA Form 8700-12 call RCRA/Superfund Hotline at 1-800-424-9346 or 703-920-9810); or

(2) A letter requesting an EPA identification number. Call the RCRA/Superfund Hotline to determine where to send a letter requesting an EPA identification number. The letter should include the following information:

(i) Burner company name;

(ii) Owner of the burner company;

(iii) Mailing address for the burner;

(iv) Name and telephone number for the burner point of contact;

(v) Type of used oil activity; and

(vi) Location of the burner facility.

[57 FR 41612, Sept. 10, 1992, as amended at 58 FR 33342, June 17, 1993]

§279.63 Rebuttable presumption for used oil. 12.1.4

(a) To ensure that used oil managed at a used oil burner facility is not hazardous waste under the rebuttable presumption of §279.10(b)(1)(ii), a used oil burner must determine whether the total halogen content of used oil managed at the facility is above or below 1,000 ppm.

(b) The used oil burner must determine if the used oil contains above or below 1,000 ppm total halogens by:

(1) Testing the used oil;

(2) Applying knowledge of the halogen content of the used oil in light of the materials or processes used; or

(3) If the used oil has been received from a processor/re-refiner subject to regulation under subpart F of this part, using information provided by the processor/re-refiner.

(c) If the used oil contains greater than or equal to 1,000 ppm total halogens, it is presumed to be a hazardous waste because it has been mixed with halogenated hazardous waste listed in subpart D of part 261 of this chapter. The owner or operator may rebut the presumption by demonstrating that the used oil does not contain hazardous waste (for example, by showing that the used oil does not contain significant concentrations of halogenated hazardous constituents listed in appendix VIII of part 261 of this chapter).

(1) The rebuttable presumption does not apply to metalworking oils/fluids containing chlorinated paraffins, if they are processed, through a tolling arrangement as described in §279.24(c), to reclaim metalworking oils/fluids. The presumption does apply to metalworking oils/fluids if such oils/fluids are recycled in any other manner, or disposed.

(2) The rebuttable presumption does not apply to used oils contaminated with chlorofluorocarbons (CFCs) removed from refrigeration units where the CFCs are destined for reclamation. The rebuttable presumption does apply to used oils contaminated with CFCs that have been mixed with used oil from sources other than refrigeration units.

(d) *Record retention.* Records of analyses conducted or information used to comply with paragraphs (a), (b), and (c) of this section must be maintained by the burner for at least 3 years.

[57 FR 41612, Sept. 10, 1992, as amended at 59 FR 10560, Mar. 4, 1994; 70 FR 34591, June 14, 2005; 71 FR 40280, July 14, 2006]

§279.64 Used oil storage.

Used oil burners are subject to all applicable Spill Prevention, Control and Countermeasures (40 CFR part 112) in addition to the requirements of this subpart. Used oil burners are also subject to the Underground Storage Tank (40 CFR part 280) standards for used oil stored in underground tanks whether or not the used oil exhibits any characteristics of hazardous waste, in addition to the requirements of this subpart.

(a) *Storage units.* Used oil burners may not store used oil in units other than tanks, containers, or units subject to regulation under parts 264 or 265 of this chapter.

(b) *Condition of units.* Containers and aboveground tanks used to store oil at burner facilities must be:

(1) In good condition (no severe rusting, apparent structural defects or deterioration); and

(2) Not leaking (no visible leaks).

(c) *Secondary containment for containers.* Containers used to store used oil at burner facilities must be equipped with a secondary containment system.

(1) The secondary containment system must consist of, at a minimum:

(i) Dikes, berms or retaining walls; and

(ii) A floor. The floor must cover the entire area within the dike, berm, or retaining wall.

(2) The entire containment system, including walls and floor, must be sufficiently impervious to used oil to prevent any used oil released into the containment system from migrating out of the system to the soil, groundwater, or surface water.

(d) *Secondary containment for existing aboveground tanks.* Existing aboveground tanks used to store used oil at burner facilities must be equipped with a secondary containment system.

(1) The secondary containment system must consist of, at a minimum:

(i) Dikes, berms or retaining walls; and

(ii) A floor. The floor must cover the entire area within the dike, berm, or retaining wall except areas where existing portions of the tank meet the ground; or

(iii) An equivalent secondary containment system.

(2) The entire containment system, including walls and floor, must be sufficiently impervious to used oil to prevent any used oil released into the containment system from migrating out of the system to the soil, groundwater, or surface water.

(e) *Secondary containment for new aboveground tanks.* New aboveground tanks used to store used oil at burner facilities must be equipped with a secondary containment system.

(1) The secondary containment system must consist of, at a minimum:

(i) Dikes, berms or retaining walls; and

(ii) A floor. The floor must cover the entire area within the dike, berm, or retaining wall; or

(iii) An equivalent secondary containment system.

(2) The entire containment system, including walls and floor, must be sufficiently impervious to used oil to prevent any used oil released into the containment system from migrating out of the system to the soil, groundwater, or surface water.

(f) *Labels.* (1) Containers and aboveground tanks used to store used oil at burner facilities must be labeled or marked clearly with the words "Used Oil."

(2) Fill pipes used to transfer used oil into underground storage tanks at burner facilities must be labeled or marked clearly with the words "Used Oil."

(g) *Response to releases.* Upon the detection of a release of used oil to the environment that is not subject to the requirements of part 280, subpart F of this chapter and which has occurred after the effective date of the recycled used oil management program in effect in the State in which the release is located, a burner must perform the following cleanup steps:

(1) Stop the release;

(2) Contain the released used oil;

(3) Clean up and manage properly the released used oil and other materials; and

(4) If necessary, repair or replace any leaking used oil storage containers or tanks prior to returning them to service.

[57 FR 41612, Sept. 10, 1992, as amended at 58 FR 26426, May 3, 1993; 63 FR 24969, May 6, 1998; 71 FR 40280, July 14, 2006]

§279.65 Tracking.

(a) *Acceptance.* Used oil burners must keep a record of each used oil shipment accepted for burning. These records may take the form of a log, invoice, manifest, bill of lading, or other shipping documents. Records for each shipment must include the following information:

(1) The name and address of the transporter who delivered the used oil to the burner;

(2) The name and address of the generator or processor/re-refiner from whom the used oil was sent to the burner;

(3) The EPA identification number of the transporter who delivered the used oil to the burner;

(4) The EPA identification number (if applicable) of the generator or processor/re-refiner from whom the used oil was sent to the burner;

(5) The quantity of used oil accepted; and

(6) The date of acceptance.

(b) *Record retention.* The records described in paragraph (a) of this section must be maintained for at least three years.

§279.66 Notices.

(a) *Certification.* Before a burner accepts the first shipment of off-specification used oil fuel from a generator, transporter, or processor/re-refiner, the burner must provide to the generator, transporter, or processor/re-refiner a one-time written and signed notice certifying that:

(1) The burner has notified EPA stating the location and general description of his used oil management activities; and

(2) The burner will burn the used oil only in an industrial furnace or boiler identified in §279.61(a).

(b) *Certification retention.* The certification described in paragraph (a) of this section must be maintained for three years from the date the burner last receives shipment of off-specification used oil from that generator, transporter, or processor/re-refiner.

§279.67 Management of residues.

Burners who generate residues from the storage or burning of used oil must manage the residues as specified in §279.10(e).

Subpart H—Standards for Used Oil Fuel Marketers

§279.70 Applicability. 12.3.5

(a) Any person who conducts either of the following activities is subject to the requirements of this subpart:

(1) Directs a shipment of off-specification used oil from their facility to a used oil burner; or

(2) First claims that used oil that is to be burned for energy recovery meets the used oil fuel specifications set forth in §279.11.

(b) The following persons are not marketers subject to this subpart:

(1) Used oil generators, and transporters who transport used oil received only from generators, unless the generator or transporter directs a shipment of off-specification used oil from their facility to a used oil burner. However, processors/re-refiners who burn some used oil fuel for purposes of processing are considered to be burning incidentally to processing. Thus, generators and transporters who direct shipments of off-specification used oil to processor/re-refiners who incidentally burn used oil are not marketers subject to this Subpart;

(2) Persons who direct shipments of on-specification used oil and who are not the first person to claim the oil meets the used oil fuel specifications of §279.11.

(c) Any person subject to the requirements of this Subpart must also comply with one of the following:

(1) Subpart C of this part—Standards for Used Oil Generators;

(2) Subpart E of this part—Standards for Used Oil Transporters and Transfer Facilities;

(3) Subpart F of this part—Standards for Used Oil Processors and Re-refiners; or

(4) Subpart G of this part—Standards for Used Oil Burners who Burn Off-Specification Used Oil for Energy Recovery.

[57 FR 41612, Sept. 10, 1992, as amended at 58 FR 26426, May 3, 1993; 71 FR 40280, July 14, 2006]

§279.71 Prohibitions.

A used oil fuel marketer may initiate a shipment of off-specification used oil only to a used oil burner who:

(a) Has an EPA identification number; and

(b) Burns the used oil in an industrial furnace or boiler identified in §279.61(a).

§279.72 On-specification used oil fuel. 12.3.5

(a) *Analysis of used oil fuel.* A generator, transporter, processor/re-refiner, or burner may determine that used oil that is to be burned for energy recovery meets the fuel specifications of §279.11 by performing analyses or obtaining copies of analyses or other information documenting that the used oil fuel meets the specifications.

(b) *Record retention.* A generator, transporter, processor/re-refiner, or burner who first claims that used oil that is to be burned for energy recovery meets the specifications for used oil fuel under §279.11, must keep copies of analyses of the used oil (or other information used to make the determination) for three years.

[57 FR 41612, Sept. 10, 1992, as amended at 58 FR 26426, May 3, 1993]

§279.73 Notification.

(a) *Identification numbers.* A used oil fuel marketer subject to the requirements of this subpart who has not previously complied with the notification requirements of RCRA section 3010 must comply with these requirements and obtain an EPA identification number.

(b) A marketer who has not received an EPA identification number may obtain one by notifying the Regional Administrator of their used oil activity by submitting either:

(1) A completed EPA Form 8700-12; or

(2) A letter requesting an EPA identification number. The letter should include the following information:

(i) Marketer company name;

(ii) Owner of the marketer;

(iii) Mailing address for the marketer;

(iv) Name and telephone number for the marketer point of contact; and

(v) Type of used oil activity (*i.e.*, generator directing shipments of off-specification used oil to a burner).

[57 FR 41612, Sept. 10, 1992, as amended at 58 FR 33342, June 17, 1993]

§279.74 Tracking.

(a) *Off-specification used oil delivery.* Any used oil marketer who directs a shipment of off-specification used oil to a burner must keep a record of each shipment of used oil to a used oil burner. These records may take the form of a log, invoice, manifest, bill of lading or other shipping documents. Records for each shipment must include the following information:

(1) The name and address of the transporter who delivers the used oil to the burner;

(2) The name and address of the burner who will receive the used oil;

(3) The EPA identification number of the transporter who delivers the used oil to the burner;

(4) The EPA identification number of the burner;

(5) The quantity of used oil shipped; and

(6) The date of shipment.

(b) *On-specification used oil delivery.* A generator, transporter, processor/rerefiner, or burner who first claims that used oil that is to be burned for energy recovery meets the fuel specifications under § 279.11 must keep a record of each shipment of used oil to the facility to which it delivers the used oil. Records for each shipment must include the following information:

(1) The name and address of the facility receiving the shipment;

(2) The quantity of used oil fuel delivered;

(3) The date of shipment or delivery; and

(4) A cross-reference to the record of used oil analysis or other information used to make the determination that the oil meets the specification as required under § 279.72(a).

(c) *Record retention.* The records described in paragraphs (a) and (b) of this section must be maintained for at least three years.

[57 FR 41612, Sept. 10, 1992, as amended at 58 FR 26426, May 3, 1993; 63 FR 24969, May 6, 1998; 63 FR 37782, July 14, 1998; 68 FR 44665, July 30, 2003]

§279.75 Notices.

(a) *Certification.* Before a used oil generator, transporter, or processor/re-refiner directs the first shipment of off-specification used oil fuel to a burner, he must obtain a one-time written and signed notice from the burner certifying that:

(1) The burner has notified EPA stating the location and general description of used oil management activities; and

(2) The burner will burn the off-specification used oil only in an industrial furnace or boiler identified in §279.61(a).

(b) *Certification retention.* The certification described in paragraph (a) of this section must be maintained for three years from the date the last shipment of off-specification used oil is shipped to the burner.

Subpart I—Standards for Use as a Dust Suppressant and Disposal of Used Oil

§279.80 Applicability.

The requirements of this subpart apply to all used oils that cannot be recycled and are therefore being disposed.

§279.81 Disposal. 12.2.3

(a) *Disposal of hazardous used oils.* Used oils that are identified as a hazardous waste and cannot be recycled in accordance with this part must be managed in accordance with the hazardous waste management requirements of parts 260 through 266, 268, 270 and 124 of this chapter.

(b) *Disposal of nonhazardous used oils.* Used oils that are not hazardous wastes and cannot be recycled under this part must be disposed in accordance with the requirements of parts 257 and 258 of this chapter.

§279.82 Use as a dust suppressant. 12.2.3

(a) The use of used oil as a dust suppressant is prohibited, except when such activity takes place in one of the states listed in paragraph (c) of this section.

(b) A State may petition (*e.g.*, as part of its authorization petition submitted to EPA under §271.5 of this chapter or by a separate submission) EPA to allow the use of used oil (that is not mixed with hazardous waste and does not exhibit a characteristic other than ignitability) as a dust suppressant. The State must show that it has a program in place to prevent the use of used oil/hazardous waste mixtures or used oil exhibiting a characteristic other than ignitability as a dust suppressant. In addition, such programs must minimize the impacts of use as a dust suppressant on the environment.

(c) *List of States.* [Reserved]

PART 280—TECHNICAL STANDARDS AND CORRECTIVE ACTION REQUIREMENTS FOR OWNERS AND OPERATORS OF UNDERGROUND STORAGE TANKS (UST)

Appendix III to Part 280—Statement for Shipping Tickets and Invoices

Authority: 42 U.S.C. 6912, 6991, 6991a, 6991b, 6991c, 6991d, 6991e, 6991f, 6991g, 6991h.

Source: 53 FR 37194, Sept. 23, 1988, unless otherwise noted.

Subpart A—Program Scope and Interim Prohibition

§280.10 Applicability.

(a) The requirements of this part apply to all owners and operators of an UST system as defined in §280.12 except as otherwise provided in paragraphs (b), (c), and (d) of this section. Any UST system listed in paragraph (c) of this section must meet the requirements of §280.11. 📖 12.2.1.1.2

(b) The following UST systems are excluded from the requirements of this part:

(1) Any UST system holding hazardous wastes listed or identified under Subtitle C of the Solid Waste Disposal Act, or a mixture of such hazardous waste and other regulated substances. 📖 10.1.2.3

(2) Any wastewater treatment tank system that is part of a wastewater treatment facility regulated under section 402 or 307(b) of the Clean Water Act. 📖 7.2

(3) Equipment or machinery that contains regulated substances for operational purposes such as hydraulic lift tanks and electrical equipment tanks.

(4) Any UST system whose capacity is 110 gallons or less.

(5) Any UST system that contains a *de minimis* concentration of regulated substances.

(6) Any emergency spill or overflow containment UST system that is expeditiously emptied after use.

(c) *Deferrals.* Subparts B, C, D, E, and G do not apply to any of the following types of UST systems:

(1) Wastewater treatment tank systems;

(2) Any UST systems containing radioactive material that are regulated under the Atomic Energy Act of 1954 (42 U.S.C. 2011 and following);

(3) Any UST system that is part of an emergency generator system at nuclear power generation facilities regulated by the Nuclear Regulatory Commission under 10 CFR part 50, appendix A;

(4) Airport hydrant fuel distribution systems; and

(5) UST systems with field-constructed tanks.

(d) *Deferrals.* Subpart D does not apply to any UST system that stores fuel solely for use by emergency power generators.

§280.11 Interim prohibition for deferred UST systems.

(a) No person may install an UST system listed in §280.10(c) for the purpose of storing regulated substances unless the UST system (whether of single- or double-wall construction):

(1) Will prevent releases due to corrosion or structural failure for the operational life of the UST system;

(2) Is cathodically protected against corrosion, constructed of noncorrodible material, steel clad with a noncorrodible material, or designed in a manner to prevent the release or threatened release of any stored substance; and

(3) Is constructed or lined with material that is compatible with the stored substance.

(b) Notwithstanding paragraph (a) of this section, an UST system without corrosion protection may be installed at a site that is determined by a corrosion expert not to be corrosive enough to cause it to have a release due to corrosion during its operating life. Owners and operators must maintain records that demonstrate compliance with the requirements of this paragraph for the remaining life of the tank.

Note: The National Association of Corrosion Engineers Standard RP-02-85, "Control of External Corrosion on Metallic Buried, Partially Buried, or Submerged Liquid Storage Systems," may be used as guidance for complying with paragraph (b) of this section.

§280.12 Definitions.

Aboveground release means any release to the surface of the land or to surface water. This includes, but is not limited to, releases from the above-ground portion of an UST system and aboveground releases associated with overfills and transfer operations as the regulated substance moves to or from an UST system.

Ancillary equipment means any devices including, but not limited to, such devices as piping, fittings, flanges, valves, and pumps used to distribute, meter, or control the flow of regulated substances to and from an UST.

Belowground release means any release to the subsurface of the land and to ground water. This includes, but is not limited to, releases from the belowground portions of an underground storage tank system and belowground releases associated with overfills and transfer operations as the regulated substance moves to or from an underground storage tank.

Beneath the surface of the ground means beneath the ground surface or otherwise covered with earthen materials.

Cathodic protection is a technique to prevent corrosion of a metal surface by making that surface the cathode of an electrochemical cell. For example, a tank system can be cathodically protected through the application of either galvanic anodes or impressed current.

Cathodic protection tester means a person who can demonstrate an understanding of the principles and measurements of all common types of cathodic protection systems as applied to buried or submerged metal piping and tank systems. At a minimum, such persons must have education and experience in soil resistivity, stray current, structure-to-soil potential, and component electrical isolation measurements of buried metal piping and tank systems.

CERCLA means the Comprehensive Environmental Response, Compensation, and Liability Act of 1980, as amended.

Compatible means the ability of two or more substances to maintain their respective physical and chemical properties upon contact with one another for the design life of the tank system under conditions likely to be encountered in the UST.

Connected piping means all underground piping including valves, elbows, joints, flanges, and flexible connectors attached to a tank system through which regulated substances flow. For the purpose of determining how much piping is connected to any individual UST system, the piping that joins two UST systems should be allocated equally between them.

Consumptive use with respect to heating oil means consumed on the premises.

Corrosion expert means a person who, by reason of thorough knowledge of the physical sciences and the principles of engineering and mathematics acquired by a professional education and related practical experience, is qualified to engage in the practice of corrosion control on buried or submerged metal piping systems and metal tanks. Such a person must be accredited or certified as being qualified by the National Association of Corrosion Engineers or be a registered professional engineer who has certification or licensing that includes education and experience in corrosion control of buried or submerged metal piping systems and metal tanks.

Dielectric material means a material that does not conduct direct electrical current. Dielectric coatings are used to electrically isolate UST systems from the surrounding soils. Dielectric bushings are used to electrically isolate portions of the UST system (e.g., tank from piping).

Electrical equipment means underground equipment that contains dielectric fluid that is necessary for the operation of equipment such as transformers and buried electrical cable.

Excavation zone means the volume containing the tank system and backfill material bounded by the ground surface, walls, and floor of the pit and trenches into which the UST system is placed at the time of installation.

Existing tank system means a tank system used to contain an accumulation of regulated substances or for which installation has commenced on or before December 22, 1988. Installation is considered to have commenced if:

(a) The owner or operator has obtained all federal, state, and local approvals or permits necessary to begin physical construction of the site or installation of the tank system; and if,

(b)(1) Either a continuous on-site physical construction or installation program has begun; or,

(2) The owner or operator has entered into contractual obligations—which cannot be cancelled or modified without substantial loss—for physical construction at the site or installation of the tank system to be completed within a reasonable time.

Farm tank is a tank located on a tract of land devoted to the production of crops or raising animals, including fish, and associated residences and improvements. A farm tank must be located on the farm property. "Farm" includes fish hatcheries, rangeland and nurseries with growing operations.

Flow-through process tank is a tank that forms an integral part of a production process through which there is a steady, variable, recurring, or intermittent flow of materials during the operation of the process. Flow-through process tanks do not include tanks used for the storage of materials prior to their introduction into the production process or for the storage of finished products or by-products from the production process.

Free product refers to a regulated substance that is present as a non-aqueous phase liquid (e.g., liquid not dissolved in water.) 📖 **14.4.7.1**

Gathering lines means any pipeline, equipment, facility, or building used in the transportation of oil or gas during oil or gas production or gathering operations.

Hazardous substance UST system means an underground storage tank system that contains a hazardous substance defined in section 101(14) of the Comprehensive Environmental Response, Compensation and Liability Act of 1980 (but not including any substance regulated as a hazardous waste under subtitle C) or any mixture of such substances and petroleum, and which is not a petroleum UST system. 📖 **10.1.2.3**

Heating oil means petroleum that is No. 1, No. 2, No. 4—light, No. 4—heavy, No. 5—light, No. 5—heavy, and No. 6 technical grades of fuel oil; other residual fuel oils (including Navy Special Fuel Oil and Bunker C); and other fuels when used as substitutes for one of these fuel oils. Heating oil is typically used in the operation of heating equipment, boilers, or furnaces.

Hydraulic lift tank means a tank holding hydraulic fluid for a closed-loop mechanical system that uses compressed air or hydraulic fluid to operate lifts, elevators, and other similar devices.

Implementing agency means EPA, or, in the case of a state with a program approved under section 9004 (or pursuant to a memorandum of agreement with EPA), the designated state or local agency responsible for carrying out an approved UST program.

Liquid trap means sumps, well cellars, and other traps used in association with oil and gas production, gathering, and extraction operations (including gas production plants), for the purpose of collecting oil, water, and other liquids. These liquid traps may temporarily collect liquids for subsequent disposition or reinjection into a production or pipeline stream, or may collect and separate liquids from a gas stream.

Maintenance means the normal operational upkeep to prevent an underground storage tank system from releasing product.

Motor fuel means petroleum or a petroleum-based substance that is motor gasoline, aviation gasoline, No. 1 or No. 2 diesel fuel, or any grade of gasohol, and is typically used in the operation of a motor engine.

New tank system means a tank system that will be used to contain an accumulation of regulated substances and for which installation has commenced after December 22, 1988. (See also "Existing Tank System.")

Noncommercial purposes with respect to motor fuel means not for resale.

On the premises where stored with respect to heating oil means UST systems located on the same property where the stored heating oil is used.

Operational life refers to the period beginning when installation of the tank system has commenced until the time the tank system is properly closed under Subpart G.

Operator means any person in control of, or having responsibility for, the daily operation of the UST system.

Overfill release is a release that occurs when a tank is filled beyond its capacity, resulting in a discharge of the regulated substance to the environment.

Owner means:

(a) In the case of an UST system in use on November 8, 1984, or brought into use after that date, any person who owns an UST system used for storage, use, or dispensing of regulated substances; and

(b) In the case of any UST system in use before November 8, 1984, but no longer in use on that date, any person who owned such UST immediately before the discontinuation of its use.

Person means an individual, trust, firm, joint stock company, Federal agency, corporation, state, municipality, commission, political subdivision of a state, or any interstate body. "Person" also includes a consortium, a joint venture, a commercial entity, and the United States Government.

Petroleum UST system means an underground storage tank system that contains petroleum or a mixture of petroleum with *de minimis* quantities of other regulated substances. Such systems include those containing motor fuels, jet fuels, distillate fuel oils, residual fuel oils, lubricants, petroleum solvents, and used oils. 📖 10.1.2.3

Pipe or Piping means a hollow cylinder or tubular conduit that is constructed of non-earthen materials.

Pipeline facilities (including gathering lines) are new and existing pipe rights-of-way and any associated equipment, facilities, or buildings.

Regulated substance means:

(a) Any substance defined in section 101(14) of the Comprehensive Environmental Response, Compensation and Liability Act (CERCLA) of 1980 (but not including any substance regulated as a hazardous waste under subtitle C), and

(b) Petroleum, including crude oil or any fraction thereof that is liquid at standard conditions of temperature and pressure (60 degrees Fahrenheit and 14.7 pounds per square inch absolute).

The term "regulated substance" includes but is not limited to petroleum and petroleum-based substances comprised of a complex blend of hydrocarbons derived from crude oil though processes of separation, conversion, upgrading, and finishing, such as motor fuels, jet fuels, distillate fuel oils, residual fuel oils, lubricants, petroleum solvents, and used oils. 📖 12.2.1.1.2

Release means any spilling, leaking, emitting, discharging, escaping, leaching or disposing from an UST into ground water, surface water or subsurface soils.

Release detection means determining whether a release of a regulated substance has occurred from the UST system into the environment or into the interstitial space between the UST system and its secondary barrier or secondary containment around it.

Repair means to restore a tank or UST system component that has caused a release of product from the UST system.

Residential tank is a tank located on property used primarily for dwelling purposes.

SARA means the Superfund Amendments and Reauthorization Act of 1986.

Septic tank is a water-tight covered receptacle designed to receive or process, through liquid separation or biological digestion, the sewage discharged from a building sewer. The effluent from such receptacle is distributed for disposal through the soil and settled solids and scum from the tank are pumped out periodically and hauled to a treatment facility.

Storm-water or wastewater collection system means piping, pumps, conduits, and any other equipment necessary to collect and transport the flow of surface water run-off resulting from precipitation, or domestic, commercial, or industrial wastewater to and from retention areas or any areas where treatment is designated to occur. The collection of storm water and wastewater does not include treatment except where incidental to conveyance.

Surface impoundment is a natural topographic depression, man-made excavation, or diked area formed primarily of earthen materials (although it may be lined with man-made materials) that is not an injection well.

Tank is a stationary device designed to contain an accumulation of regulated substances and constructed of non-earthen materials (e.g., concrete, steel, plastic) that provide structural support.

Underground area means an underground room, such as a basement, cellar, shaft or vault, providing enough space for physical inspection of the exterior of the tank situated on or above the surface of the floor.

Underground release means any belowground release.

Underground storage tank or *UST* means any one or combination of tanks (including underground pipes connected thereto) that is used to contain an accumulation of regulated substances, and the volume of which (including the volume of underground pipes connected thereto) is 10 percent or more beneath the surface of the ground. This term does not include any:

(a) Farm or residential tank of 1,100 gallons or less capacity used for storing motor fuel for noncommercial purposes;

(b) Tank used for storing heating oil for consumptive use on the premises where stored;

(c) Septic tank;

(d) Pipeline facility (including gathering lines) regulated under:

(1) The Natural Gas Pipeline Safety Act of 1968 (49 U.S.C. App. 1671, *et seq.*), or

(2) The Hazardous Liquid Pipeline Safety Act of 1979 (49 U.S.C. App. 2001, *et seq.*), or

(3) Which is an intrastate pipeline facility regulated under state laws comparable to the provisions of the law referred to in paragraph (d)(1) or (d)(2) of this definition;

(e) Surface impoundment, pit, pond, or lagoon;

(f) Storm-water or wastewater collection system;

(g) Flow-through process tank;

(h) Liquid trap or associated gathering lines directly related to oil or gas production and gathering operations; or

(i) Storage tank situated in an underground area (such as a basement, cellar, mineworking, drift, shaft, or tunnel) if the storage tank is situated upon or above the surface of the floor.

The term "underground storage tank" or "UST" does not include any pipes connected to any tank which is described in paragraphs (a) through (i) of this definition.

Upgrade means the addition or retrofit of some systems such as cathodic protection, lining, or spill and overfill controls to improve the ability of an underground storage tank system to prevent the release of product.

UST system or *Tank system* means an underground storage tank, connected underground piping, underground ancillary equipment, and containment system, if any.

Wastewater treatment tank means a tank that is designed to receive and treat an influent wastewater through physical, chemical, or biological methods.

Subpart B—UST Systems: Design, Construction, Installation and Notification

§280.20 Performance standards for new UST systems.

In order to prevent releases due to structural failure, corrosion, or spills and overfills for as long as the UST system is used to store regulated substances, all owners and operators of new UST systems must meet the following requirements.

(a) *Tanks.* Each tank must be properly designed and constructed, and any portion underground that routinely contains product must be protected from corrosion, in accordance with a code of practice developed by a nationally recognized association or independent testing laboratory as specified below:

(1) The tank is constructed of fiberglass-reinforced plastic; or

Note: The following industry codes may be used to comply with paragraph (a)(1) of this section: Underwriters Laboratories Standard 1316, "Standard for Glass- Fiber-Reinforced Plastic Underground Storage Tanks for Petroleum Products"; Underwriter's Laboratories of Canada CAN4-S615-M83, "Standard for Reinforced Plastic Underground Tanks for Petroleum Products"; or American Society of Testing and Materials Standard D4021-86, "Standard Specification for Glass-Fiber-Reinforced Polyester Underground Petroleum Storage Tanks."

(2) The tank is constructed of steel and cathodically protected in the following manner:

(i) The tank is coated with a suitable dielectric material;

(ii) Field-installed cathodic protection systems are designed by a corrosion expert;

(iii) Impressed current systems are designed to allow determination of current operating status as required in §280.31(c); and

(iv) Cathodic protection systems are operated and maintained in accordance with §280.31 or according to guidelines established by the implementing agency; or

Note: The following codes and standards may be used to comply with paragraph (a)(2) of this section:

(A) Steel Tank Institute "Specification for STI-P3 System of External Corrosion Protection of Underground Steel Storage Tanks";

(B) Underwriters Laboratories Standard 1746, "Corrosion Protection Systems for Underground Storage Tanks";

(C) Underwriters Laboratories of Canada CAN4-S603-M85, "Standard for Steel Underground Tanks for Flammable and Combustible Liquids," and CAN4-G03.1-M85, "Standard for Galvanic Corrosion Protection Systems for Underground Tanks for Flammable and Combustible Liquids," and CAN4-S631-M84, "Isolating Bushings for Steel Underground Tanks Protected with Coatings and Galvanic Systems"; or

(D) National Association of Corrosion Engineers Standard RP-02-85, "Control of External Corrosion on Metallic Buried, Partially Buried, or Submerged Liquid Storage Systems," and Underwriters Laboratories Standard 58, "Standard for Steel Underground Tanks for Flammable and Combustible Liquids."

(3) The tank is constructed of a steel-fiberglass-reinforced-plastic composite; or

Note: The following industry codes may be used to comply with paragraph (a)(3) of this section: Underwriters Laboratories Standard 1746, "Corrosion Protection Systems for Underground Storage Tanks," or the Association for Composite Tanks ACT-100, "Specification for the Fabrication of FRP Clad Underground Storage Tanks."

(4) The tank is constructed of metal without additional corrosion protection measures provided that:

(i) The tank is installed at a site that is determined by a corrosion expert not to be corrosive enough to cause it to have a release due to corrosion during its operating life; and

(ii) Owners and operators maintain records that demonstrate compliance with the requirements of paragraphs (a)(4)(i) for the remaining life of the tank; or

(5) The tank construction and corrosion protection are determined by the implementing agency to be designed to prevent the release or threatened release of any stored regulated substance in a manner that is no less protective of human health and the environment than paragraphs (a) (1) through (4) of this section.

(b) *Piping.* The piping that routinely contains regulated substances and is in contact with the ground must be properly designed, constructed, and protected from corrosion in accordance with a code of practice developed by a nationally recognized association or independent testing laboratory as specified below:

(1) The piping is constructed of fiberglass-reinforced plastic; or

Note: The following codes and standards may be used to comply with paragraph (b)(1) of this section:

(A) Underwriters Laboratories Subject 971, "UL Listed Non-Metal Pipe";

(B) Underwriters Laboratories Standard 567, "Pipe Connectors for Flammable and Combustible and LP Gas";

(C) Underwriters Laboratories of Canada Guide ULC-107, "Glass Fiber Reinforced Plastic Pipe and Fittings for Flammable Liquids"; and

(D) Underwriters Laboratories of Canada Standard CAN 4-S633-M81, "Flexible Underground Hose Connectors."

(2) The piping is constructed of steel and cathodically protected in the following manner:

(i) The piping is coated with a suitable dielectric material;

(ii) Field-installed cathodic protection systems are designed by a corrosion expert;

(iii) Impressed current systems are designed to allow determination of current operating status as required in §280.31(c); and

(iv) Cathodic protection systems are operated and maintained in accordance with §280.31 or guidelines established by the implementing agency; or

Note: The following codes and standards may be used to comply with paragraph (b)(2) of this section:

(A) National Fire Protection Association Standard 30, "Flammable and Combustible Liquids Code";

(B) American Petroleum Institute Publication 1615, "Installation of Underground Petroleum Storage Systems";

(C) American Petroleum Institute Publication 1632, "Cathodic Protection of Underground Petroleum Storage Tanks and Piping Systems"; and

(D) National Association of Corrosion Engineers Standard RP-01-69, "Control of External Corrosion on Submerged Metallic Piping Systems."

(3) The piping is constructed of metal without additional corrosion protection measures provided that:

(i) The piping is installed at a site that is determined by a corrosion expert to not be corrosive enough to cause it to have a release due to corrosion during its operating life; and

(ii) Owners and operators maintain records that demonstrate compliance with the requirements of paragraph (b)(3)(i) of this section for the remaining life of the piping; or

Note: National Fire Protection Association Standard 30, "Flammable and Combustible Liquids Code"; and National Association of Corrosion Engineers Standard RP-01-69, "Control of External Corrosion on Submerged Metallic Piping Systems," may be used to comply with paragraph (b)(3) of this section.

(4) The piping construction and corrosion protection are determined by the implementing agency to be designed to prevent the release or threatened release of any stored regulated substance in a manner that is no less protective of human health and the environment than the requirements in paragraphs (b) (1) through (3) of this section.

(c) *Spill and overfill prevention equipment.* (1) Except as provided in paragraph (c)(2) of this section, to prevent spilling and overfilling associated with product transfer to the UST system, owners and operators must use the following spill and overfill prevention equipment:

(i) Spill prevention equipment that will prevent release of product to the environment when the transfer hose is detached from the fill pipe (for example, a spill catchment basin); and

(ii) Overfill prevention equipment that will:

(A) Automatically shut off flow into the tank when the tank is no more than 95 percent full; or

(B) Alert the transfer operator when the tank is no more than 90 percent full by restricting the flow into the tank or triggering a high-level alarm; or

(C) Restrict flow 30 minutes prior to overfilling, alert the operator with a high level alarm one minute before overfilling, or automatically shut off flow into the tank so that none of the fittings located on top of the tank are exposed to product due to overfilling.

(2) Owners and operators are not required to use the spill and overfill prevention equipment specified in paragraph (c)(1) of this section if:

(i) Alternative equipment is used that is determined by the implementing agency to be no less protective of human health and the environment than the equipment specified in paragraph (c)(1) (i) or (ii) of this section; or

(ii) The UST system is filled by transfers of no more than 25 gallons at one time.

(d) *Installation.* All tanks and piping must be properly installed in accordance with a code of practice developed by a nationally recognized association or independent testing laboratory and in accordance with the manufacturer's instructions.

Note: Tank and piping system installation practices and procedures described in the following codes may be used to comply with the requirements of paragraph (d) of this section:

(i) American Petroleum Institute Publication 1615, "Installation of Underground Petroleum Storage System"; or

(ii) Petroleum Equipment Institute Publication RP100, "Recommended Practices for Installation of Underground Liquid Storage Systems"; or

(iii) American National Standards Institute Standard B31.3, "Petroleum Refinery Piping," and American National Standards Institute Standard B31.4 "Liquid Petroleum Transportation Piping System."

(e) *Certification of installation.* All owners and operators must ensure that one or more of the following methods of certification, testing, or inspection is used to demonstrate compliance with paragraph (d) of this section by providing a certification of compliance on the UST notification form in accordance with §280.22.

(1) The installer has been certified by the tank and piping manufacturers; or

(2) The installer has been certified or licensed by the implementing agency; or

(3) The installation has been inspected and certified by a registered professional engineer with education and experience in UST system installation; or

(4) The installation has been inspected and approved by the implementing agency; or

(5) All work listed in the manufacturer's installation checklists has been completed; or

(6) The owner and operator have complied with another method for ensuring compliance with paragraph (d) of this section that is determined by the implementing agency to be no less protective of human health and the environment.

[53 FR 37194, Sept. 23, 1988, as amended at 56 FR 38344, Aug. 13, 1991]

§280.21 Upgrading of existing UST systems.

(a) *Alternatives allowed.* Not later than December 22, 1998, all existing UST systems must comply with one of the following requirements:

(1) New UST system performance standards under §280.20;

(2) The upgrading requirements in paragraphs (b) through (d) of this section; or

(3) Closure requirements under subpart G of this part, including applicable requirements for corrective action under subpart F.

(b) *Tank upgrading requirements.* Steel tanks must be upgraded to meet one of the following requirements in accordance with a code of practice developed by a nationally recognized association or independent testing laboratory:

(1) *Interior lining.* A tank may be upgraded by internal lining if:

(i) The lining is installed in accordance with the requirements of §280.33, and

(ii) Within 10 years after lining, and every 5 years thereafter, the lined tank is internally inspected and found to be structurally sound with the lining still performing in accordance with original design specifications.

(2) *Cathodic protection.* A tank may be upgraded by cathodic protection if the cathodic protection system meets the requirements of §280.20(a)(2) (ii), (iii), and (iv) and the integrity of the tank is ensured using one of the following methods:

(i) The tank is internally inspected and assessed to ensure that the tank is structurally sound and free of corrosion holes prior to installing the cathodic protection system; or

(ii) The tank has been installed for less than 10 years and is monitored monthly for releases in accordance with §280.43 (d) through (h); or

(iii) The tank has been installed for less than 10 years and is assessed for corrosion holes by conducting two (2) tightness tests that meet the requirements of §280.43(c). The first tightness test must be conducted prior to installing the cathodic protection system. The second tightness test must be conducted between three (3) and six (6) months following the first operation of the cathodic protection system; or

(iv) The tank is assessed for corrosion holes by a method that is determined by the implementing agency to prevent releases in a manner that is no less protective of human health and the environment than paragraphs (b)(2) (i) through (iii) of this section.

(3) *Internal lining combined with cathodic protection.* A tank may be upgraded by both internal lining and cathodic protection if:

(i) The lining is installed in accordance with the requirements of §280.33; and

(ii) The cathodic protection system meets the requirements of §280.20(a)(2) (ii), (iii), and (iv).

Note: The following codes and standards may be used to comply with this section:

(A) American Petroleum Institute Publication 1631, "Recommended Practice for the Interior Lining of Existing Steel Underground Storage Tanks";

(B) National Leak Prevention Association Standard 631, "Spill Prevention, Minimum 10 Year Life Extension of Existing Steel Underground Tanks by Lining Without the Addition of Cathodic Protection";

(C) National Association of Corrosion Engineers Standard RP-02-85, "Control of External Corrosion on Metallic Buried, Partially Buried, or Submerged Liquid Storage Systems"; and

(D) American Petroleum Institute Publication 1632, "Cathodic Protection of Underground Petroleum Storage Tanks and Piping Systems."

(c) *Piping upgrading requirements.* Metal piping that routinely contains regulated substances and is in contact with the ground must be cathodically protected in accordance with a code of practice developed by a nationally recognized association or independent testing laboratory and must meet the requirements of §280.20(b)(2) (ii), (iii), and (iv).

Note: The codes and standards listed in the note following §280.20(b)(2) may be used to comply with this requirement.

(d) *Spill and overfill prevention equipment.* To prevent spilling and overfilling associated with product transfer to the UST system, all existing UST systems must comply with new UST system spill and overfill prevention equipment requirements specified in §280.20(c).

§280.22 Notification requirements.

(a) Any owner who brings an underground storage tank system into use after May 8, 1986, must within 30 days of bringing such tank into use, submit, in the form prescribed in appendix I of this part, a notice of existence of such tank system to the state or local agency or department designated in appendix II of this part to receive such notice.

Note: Owners and operators of UST systems that were in the ground on or after May 8, 1986, unless taken out of operation on or before January 1, 1974, were required to notify the designated state or local agency in accordance with the Hazardous and Solid Waste Amendments of 1984,

Pub. L. 98-616, on a form published by EPA on November 8, 1985 (50 FR 46602) unless notice was given pursuant to section 103(c) of CERCLA. Owners and operators who have not complied with the notification requirements may use portions I through VI of the notification form contained in appendix I of this part.

(b) In states where state law, regulations, or procedures require owners to use forms that differ from those set forth in appendix I of this part to fulfill the requirements of this section, the state forms may be submitted in lieu of the forms set forth in Appendix I of this part. If a state requires that its form be used in lieu of the form presented in this regulation, such form must meet the requirements of section 9002.

(c) Owners required to submit notices under paragraph (a) of this section must provide notices to the appropriate agencies or departments identified in appendix II of this part for each tank they own. Owners may provide notice for several tanks using one notification form, but owners who own tanks located at more than one place of operation must file a separate notification form for each separate place of operation.

(d) Notices required to be submitted under paragraph (a) of this section must provide all of the information in sections I through VI of the prescribed form (or appropriate state form) for each tank for which notice must be given. Notices for tanks installed after December 22, 1988 must also provide all of the information in section VII of the prescribed form (or appropriate state form) for each tank for which notice must be given.

(e) All owners and operators of new UST systems must certify in the notification form compliance with the following requirements:

(1) Installation of tanks and piping under §280.20(e);

(2) Cathodic protection of steel tanks and piping under §280.20 (a) and (b);

(3) Financial responsibility under subpart H of this part; and

(4) Release detection under §§280.41 and 280.42.

(f) All owners and operators of new UST systems must ensure that the installer certifies in the notification form that the methods used to install the tanks and piping complies with the requirements in §280.20(d).

(g) Beginning October 24, 1988, any person who sells a tank intended to be used as an underground storage tank must notify the purchaser of such tank of the owner's notification obligations under paragraph (a) of this section. The form provided in appendix III of this part may be used to comply with this requirement.

Subpart C—General Operating Requirements

§280.30 Spill and overfill control.

(a) Owners and operators must ensure that releases due to spilling or overfilling do not occur. The owner and operator must ensure that the volume available in the tank is greater than the volume of product to be transferred to the tank before the transfer is made and that the transfer operation is monitored constantly to prevent overfilling and spilling.

Note: The transfer procedures described in National Fire Protection Association Publication 385 may be used to comply with paragraph (a) of this section. Further guidance on spill and overfill prevention appears in American Petroleum Institute Publication 1621, "Recommended Practice for Bulk Liquid Stock Control at Retail Outlets," and National Fire Protection Association Standard 30, "Flammable and Combustible Liquids Code."

(b) The owner and operator must report, investigate, and clean up any spills and overfills in accordance with §280.53.

§280.31 Operation and maintenance of corrosion protection.

All owners and operators of steel UST systems with corrosion protection must comply with the following requirements to ensure that releases due to corrosion are prevented for as long as the UST system is used to store regulated substances:

(a) All corrosion protection systems must be operated and maintained to continuously provide corrosion protection to the metal components of that portion of the tank and piping that routinely contain regulated substances and are in contact with the ground.

(b) All UST systems equipped with cathodic protection systems must be inspected for proper operation by a qualified cathodic protection tester in accordance with the following requirements:

(1) *Frequency.* All cathodic protection systems must be tested within 6 months of installation and at least every 3 years thereafter or according to another reasonable time frame established by the implementing agency; and

(2) *Inspection criteria.* The criteria that are used to determine that cathodic protection is adequate as required by this section must be in accordance with a code of practice developed by a nationally recognized association.

Note: National Association of Corrosion Engineers Standard RP-02-85, "Control of External Corrosion on Metallic Buried, Partially Buried, or Submerged Liquid Storage Systems," may be used to comply with paragraph (b)(2) of this section.

(c) UST systems with impressed current cathodic protection systems must also be inspected every 60 days to ensure the equipment is running properly.

(d) For UST systems using cathodic protection, records of the operation of the cathodic protection must be maintained (in accordance with §280.34) to demonstrate compliance with the performance standards in this section. These records must provide the following:

(1) The results of the last three inspections required in paragraph (c) of this section; and

(2) The results of testing from the last two inspections required in paragraph (b) of this section.

§280.32 Compatibility.

Owners and operators must use an UST system made of or lined with materials that are compatible with the substance stored in the UST system.

Note: Owners and operators storing alcohol blends may use the following codes to comply with the requirements of this section:

(a) American Petroleum Institute Publication 1626, "Storing and Handling Ethanol and Gasoline-Ethanol Blends at Distribution Terminals and Service Stations"; and

(b) American Petroleum Institute Publication 1627, "Storage and Handling of Gasoline-Methanol/Cosolvent Blends at Distribution Terminals and Service Stations."

§280.33 Repairs allowed.

Owners and operators of UST systems must ensure that repairs will prevent releases due to structural failure or corrosion as long as the UST system is used to store regulated substances. The repairs must meet the following requirements:

(a) Repairs to UST systems must be properly conducted in accordance with a code of practice developed by a nationally recognized association or an independent testing laboratory.

Note: The following codes and standards may be used to comply with paragraph (a) of this section: National Fire Protection Association Standard 30, "Flammable and Combustible Liquids Code"; American Petroleum Institute Publication 2200, "Repairing Crude Oil, Liquified Petroleum Gas, and Product Pipelines"; American Petroleum Institute Publication 1631, "Recommended Practice for the Interior Lining of Existing Steel Underground Storage Tanks"; and National Leak Prevention Association Standard 631, "Spill Prevention, Minimum 10 Year Life Extension of Existing Steel Underground Tanks by Lining Without the Addition of Cathodic Protection."

(b) Repairs to fiberglass-reinforced plastic tanks may be made by the manufacturer's authorized representatives or in accordance with a code of practice developed by a nationally recognized association or an independent testing laboratory.

(c) Metal pipe sections and fittings that have released product as a result of corrosion or other damage must be replaced. Fiberglass pipes and fittings may be repaired in accordance with the manufacturer's specifications.

(d) Repaired tanks and piping must be tightness tested in accordance with §280.43(c) and §280.44(b) within 30 days following the date of the completion of the repair except as provided in paragraphs (d) (1) through (3), of this section:

(1) The repaired tank is internally inspected in accordance with a code of practice developed by a nationally recognized association or an independent testing laboratory; or

(2) The repaired portion of the UST system is monitored monthly for releases in accordance with a method specified in §280.43 (d) through (h); or

(3) Another test method is used that is determined by the implementing agency to be no less protective of human health and the environment than those listed above.

(e) Within 6 months following the repair of any cathodically protected UST system, the cathodic protection system must be tested in accordance with §280.31 (b) and (c) to ensure that it is operating properly.

(f) UST system owners and operators must maintain records of each repair for the remaining operating life of the UST system that demonstrate compliance with the requirements of this section.

§280.34 Reporting and recordkeeping.

Owners and operators of UST systems must cooperate fully with inspections, monitoring and testing conducted by the implementing agency, as well as requests for document submission, testing, and monitoring by the owner or operator pursuant to section 9005 of Subtitle I of the Resource Conservation and Recovery Act, as amended.

(a) *Reporting*. Owners and operators must submit the following information to the implementing agency:

(1) Notification for all UST systems (§280.22), which includes certification of installation for new UST systems (§280.20(e)),

(2) Reports of all releases including suspected releases (§280.50), spills and overfills (§280.53), and confirmed releases (§280.61);

(3) Corrective actions planned or taken including initial abatement measures (§280.62), initial site characterization (§280.63), free product removal (§280.64), investigation of soil and ground-water cleanup (§280.65), and corrective action plan (§280.66); and

(4) A notification before permanent closure or change-in-service (§280.71).

(b) *Recordkeeping.* Owners and operators must maintain the following information:

(1) A corrosion expert's analysis of site corrosion potential if corrosion protection equipment is not used (§280.20(a)(4); §280.20(b)(3)).

(2) Documentation of operation of corrosion protection equipment (§280.31);

(3) Documentation of UST system repairs (§280.33(f));

(4) Recent compliance with release detection requirements (§280.45); and

(5) Results of the site investigation conducted at permanent closure (§280.74).

(c) *Availability and Maintenance of Records.* Owners and operators must keep the records required either:

(1) At the UST site and immediately available for inspection by the implementing agency; or

(2) At a readily available alternative site and be provided for inspection to the implementing agency upon request.

(3) In the case of permanent closure records required under §280.74, owners and operators are also provided with the additional alternative of mailing closure records to the implementing agency if they cannot be kept at the site or an alternative site as indicated above.

Subpart D—Release Detection

§280.40 General requirements for all UST systems.

(a) Owners and operators of new and existing UST systems must provide a method, or combination of methods, of release detection that:

(1) Can detect a release from any portion of the tank and the connected underground piping that routinely contains product;

(2) Is installed, calibrated, operated, and maintained in accordance with the manufacturer's instructions, including routine maintenance and service checks for operability or running condition; and

(3) Meets the performance requirements in §280.43 or 280.44, with any performance claims and their manner of determination described in writing by the equipment manufacturer or installer. In addition, methods used after the date shown in the following table corresponding with the specified method except for methods permanently installed prior to that date, must be capable of detecting the leak rate or quantity specified for that method in the corresponding section of the rule (also shown in the table) with a probability of detection (Pd) of 0.95 and a probability of false alarm (Pfa) of 0.05.

Method	Section	Date after which Pd/Pfa must be demonstrated
Manual Tank Gauging	280.43(b)	December 22, 1990
Tank Tightness Testing	280.43(c)	December 22, 1990
Automatic Tank Gauging	280.43(d)	December 22, 1990
Automatic Line Leak Detectors	280.44(a)	September 22, 1991
Line Tightness Testing	280.44(b)	December 22, 1990

(b) When a release detection method operated in accordance with the performance standards in §280.43 and §280.44 indicates a release may have occurred, owners and operators must notify the implementing agency in accordance with subpart E.

(c) Owners and operators of all UST systems must comply with the release detection requirements of this subpart by December 22 of the year listed in the following table:

Schedule for Phase-In of Release Detection

Year system was installed	Year when release detection is required (by December 22 of the year indicated)				
	1989	1990	1991	1992	1993
Before 1965 or date unknown	RD	P			
1965-69		P/RD			
1970-74		P	RD		
1975-79		P		RD	
1980-88		P			RD
New tanks (after December 22) immediately upon installation.					

P = Must begin release detection for all pressurized piping as defined in §280.41(b)(1).

RD = Must begin release detection for tanks and suction piping in accordance with §280.41(a), §280.41(b)(2), and §280.42.

(d) Any existing UST system that cannot apply a method of release detection that complies with the requirements of this subpart must complete the closure procedures in subpart G by the date on which release detection is required for that UST system under paragraph (c) of this section.

[53 FR 37194, Sept. 23, 1988, as amended at 55 FR 17753, Apr. 27, 1990; 55 FR 23738, June 12, 1990; 56 FR 26, Jan. 2, 1991]

§280.41 Requirements for petroleum UST systems.

Owners and operators of petroleum UST systems must provide release detection for tanks and piping as follows:

(a) *Tanks.* Tanks must be monitored at least every 30 days for releases using one of the methods listed in §280.43 (d) through (h) except that:

(1) UST systems that meet the performance standards in §280.20 or §280.21, and the monthly inventory control requirements in §280.43 (a) or (b), may use tank tightness testing (conducted in accordance with §280.43(c)) at least every 5 years until December 22, 1998, or until 10 years after the tank is installed or upgraded under §280.21(b), whichever is later;

(2) UST systems that do not meet the performance standards in §280.20 or §280.21 may use monthly inventory controls (conducted in accordance with §280.43(a) or (b)) and annual tank tightness testing (conducted in accordance with §280.43(c)) until December 22, 1998 when the tank must be upgraded under §280.21 or permanently closed under §280.71; and

(3) Tanks with capacity of 550 gallons or less may use weekly tank gauging (conducted in accordance with §280.43(b)).

(b) *Piping.* Underground piping that routinely contains regulated substances must be monitored for releases in a manner that meets one of the following requirements:

(1) *Pressurized piping.* Underground piping that conveys regulated substances under pressure must:

(i) Be equipped with an automatic line leak detector conducted in accordance with §280.44(a); and

(ii) Have an annual line tightness test conducted in accordance with §280.44(b) or have monthly monitoring conducted in accordance with §280.44(c).

(2) *Suction piping.* Underground piping that conveys regulated substances under suction must either have a line tightness test conducted at least every 3 years and in accordance with §280.44(b), or use a monthly monitoring method conduct in accordance with §280.44(c). No release detection is required for suction piping that is designed and constructed to meet the following standards:

(i) The below-grade piping operates at less than atmospheric pressure;

(ii) The below-grade piping is sloped so that the contents of the pipe will drain back into the storage tank if the suction is released;

(iii) Only one check valve is included in each suction line;

(iv) The check valve is located directly below and as close as practical to the suction pump; and

(v) A method is provided that allows compliance with paragraphs (b)(2) (ii)-(iv) of this section to be readily determined.

§280.42 Requirements for hazardous substance UST systems. Owners and operators of hazardous substance UST systems must provide release detection that meets the following requirements:

(a) Release detection at existing UST systems must meet the requirements for petroleum UST systems in §280.41. By December 22, 1998, all existing hazardous substance UST systems must meet the release detection requirements for new systems in paragraph (b) of this section.

(b) Release detection at new hazardous substance UST systems must meet the following requirements:

(1) Secondary containment systems must be designed, constructed and installed to:

(i) Contain regulated substances released from the tank system until they are detected and removed;

(ii) Prevent the release of regulated substances to the environment at any time during the operational life of the UST system; and

(iii) Be checked for evidence of a release at least every 30 days.

Note: The provisions of 40 CFR 265.193, Containment and Detection of Releases, may be used to comply with these requirements.

(2) Double-walled tanks must be designed, constructed, and installed to:

(i) Contain a release from any portion of the inner tank within the outer wall; and

(ii) Detect the failure of the inner wall.

(3) External liners (including vaults) must be designed, constructed, and installed to:

(i) Contain 100 percent of the capacity of the largest tank within its boundary;

(ii) Prevent the interference of precipitation or groundwater intrusion with the ability to contain or detect a release of regulated substances; and

(iii) Surround the tank completely (i.e., it is capable of preventing lateral as well as vertical migration of regulated substances).

(4) Underground piping must be equipped with secondary containment that satisfies the requirements of paragraph (b)(1) of this section (e.g., trench liners, jacketing of double-walled pipe). In addition, underground piping that conveys regulated substances under pressure must be equipped with an automatic line leak detector in accordance with §280.44(a).

(5) Other methods of release detection may be used if owners and operators:

(i) Demonstrate to the implementing agency that an alternate method can detect a release of the stored substance as effectively as any of the methods allowed in §§280.43(b) through (h) can detect a release of petroleum;

(ii) Provide information to the implementing agency on effective corrective action technologies, health risks, and chemical and physical properties of the stored substance, and the characteristics of the UST site; and,

(iii) Obtain approval from the implementing agency to use the alternate release detection method before the installation and operation of the new UST system.

§280.43 Methods of release detection for tanks.

Each method of release detection for tanks used to meet the requirements of §280.41 must be conducted in accordance with the following:

(a) *Inventory control.* Product inventory control (or another test of equivalent performance) must be conducted monthly to detect a release of at least 1.0 percent of flow-through plus 130 gallons on a monthly basis in the following manner:

(1) Inventory volume measurements for regulated substance inputs, withdrawals, and the amount still remaining in the tank are recorded each operating day;

(2) The equipment used is capable of measuring the level of product over the full range of the tank's height to the nearest one-eighth of an inch;

(3) The regulated substance inputs are reconciled with delivery receipts by measurement of the tank inventory volume before and after delivery;

(4) Deliveries are made through a drop tube that extends to within one foot of the tank bottom;

(5) Product dispensing is metered and recorded within the local standards for meter calibration or an accuracy of 6 cubic inches for every 5 gallons of product withdrawn; and

(6) The measurement of any water level in the bottom of the tank is made to the nearest one-eighth of an inch at least once a month.

Note: Practices described in the American Petroleum Institute Publication 1621, "Recommended Practice for Bulk Liquid Stock Control at Retail Outlets," may be used, where applicable, as guidance in meeting the requirements of this paragraph.

(b) *Manual tank gauging.* Manual tank gauging must meet the following requirements:

(1) Tank liquid level measurements are taken at the beginning and ending of a period of at least 36 hours during which no liquid is added to or removed from the tank;

(2) Level measurements are based on an average of two consecutive stick readings at both the beginning and ending of the period;

(3) The equipment used is capable of measuring the level of product over the full range of the tank's height to the nearest one-eighth of an inch;

(4) A leak is suspected and subject to the requirements of subpart E if the variation between beginning and ending measurements exceeds the weekly or monthly standards in the following table:

Nominal tank capacity	Weekly standard (one test)	Monthly standard (average of four tests)
550 gallons or less	10 gallons	5 gallons
551-1,000 gallons	13 gallons	7 gallons
1,001-2,000 gallons	26 gallons	13 gallons

(5) Only tanks of 550 gallons or less nominal capacity may use this as the sole method of release detection. Tanks of 551 to 2,000 gallons may use the method in place of manual inventory control in §280.43(a). Tanks of greater than 2,000 gallons nominal capacity may not use this method to meet the requirements of this subpart.

(c) *Tank tightness testing.* Tank tightness testing (or another test of equivalent performance) must be capable of detecting a 0.1 gallon per hour leak rate from any portion of the tank that routinely contains product while accounting for the effects of thermal expansion or contraction of the product, vapor pockets, tank deformation, evaporation or condensation, and the location of the water table.

(d) *Automatic tank gauging.* Equipment for automatic tank gauging that tests for the loss of product and conducts inventory control must meet the following requirements:

(1) The automatic product level monitor test can detect a 0.2 gallon per hour leak rate from any portion of the tank that routinely contains product; and

(2) Inventory control (or another test of equivalent performance) is conducted in accordance with the requirements of §280.43(a).

(e) *Vapor monitoring.* Testing or monitoring for vapors within the soil gas of the excavation zone must meet the following requirements:

(1) The materials used as backfill are sufficiently porous (e.g., gravel, sand, crushed rock) to readily allow diffusion of vapors from releases into the excavation area;

(2) The stored regulated substance, or a tracer compound placed in the tank system, is sufficiently volatile (e.g., gasoline) to result in a vapor level that is detectable by the monitoring devices located in the excavation zone in the event of a release from the tank;

(3) The measurement of vapors by the monitoring device is not rendered inoperative by the ground water, rainfall, or soil moisture or other known interferences so that a release could go undetected for more than 30 days;

(4) The level of background contamination in the excavation zone will not interfere with the method used to detect releases from the tank;

(5) The vapor monitors are designed and operated to detect any significant increase in concentration above background of the regulated substance stored in the tank system, a component or components of that substance, or a tracer compound placed in the tank system;

(6) In the UST excavation zone, the site is assessed to ensure compliance with the requirements in paragraphs (e) (1) through (4) of this section and to establish the number and positioning of monitoring wells that will detect releases within the excavation zone from any portion of the tank that routinely contains product; and

(7) Monitoring wells are clearly marked and secured to avoid unauthorized access and tampering.

(f) *Ground-water monitoring.* Testing or monitoring for liquids on the ground water must meet the following requirements:

(1) The regulated substance stored is immiscible in water and has a specific gravity of less than one;

(2) Ground water is never more than 20 feet from the ground surface and the hydraulic conductivity of the soil(s) between the UST system and the monitoring wells or devices is not less than 0.01 cm/sec (e.g., the soil should consist of gravels, coarse to medium sands, coarse silts or other permeable materials);

(3) The slotted portion of the monitoring well casing must be designed to prevent migration of natural soils or filter pack into the well and to allow entry of regulated substance on the water table into the well under both high and low ground-water conditions;

(4) Monitoring wells shall be sealed from the ground surface to the top of the filter pack;

(5) Monitoring wells or devices intercept the excavation zone or are as close to it as is technically feasible;

(6) The continuous monitoring devices or manual methods used can detect the presence of at least one-eighth of an inch of free product on top of the ground water in the monitoring wells;

(7) Within and immediately below the UST system excavation zone, the site is assessed to ensure compliance with the requirements in paragraphs (f) (1) through (5) of this section and to establish the number and positioning of monitoring wells or devices that will detect releases from any portion of the tank that routinely contains product; and

(8) Monitoring wells are clearly marked and secured to avoid unauthorized access and tampering.

(g) *Interstitial monitoring.* Interstitial monitoring between the UST system and a secondary barrier immediately around or beneath it may be used, but only if the system is designed, constructed and installed to detect a leak from any portion of the tank that routinely contains product and also meets one of the following requirements:

(1) For double-walled UST systems, the sampling or testing method can detect a release through the inner wall in any portion of the tank that routinely contains product;

Note: The provisions outlined in the Steel Tank Institute's "Standard for Dual Wall Underground Storage Tanks" may be used as guidance for aspects of the design and construction of underground steel double-walled tanks.

(2) For UST systems with a secondary barrier within the excavation zone, the sampling or testing method used can detect a release between the UST system and the secondary barrier;

(i) The secondary barrier around or beneath the UST system consists of artificially constructed material that is sufficiently thick and impermeable (at least 10^{-6} cm/sec for the regulated substance stored) to direct a release to the monitoring point and permit its detection;

(ii) The barrier is compatible with the regulated substance stored so that a release from the UST system will not cause a deterioration of the barrier allowing a release to pass through undetected;

(iii) For cathodically protected tanks, the secondary barrier must be installed so that it does not interfere with the proper operation of the cathodic protection system;

(iv) The ground water, soil moisture, or rainfall will not render the testing or sampling method used inoperative so that a release could go undetected for more than 30 days;

(v) The site is assessed to ensure that the secondary barrier is always above the ground water and not in a 25-year flood plain, unless the barrier and monitoring designs are for use under such conditions; and,

(vi) Monitoring wells are clearly marked and secured to avoid unauthorized access and tampering.

(3) For tanks with an internally fitted liner, an automated device can detect a release between the inner wall of the tank and the liner, and the liner is compatible with the substance stored.

(h) *Other methods.* Any other type of release detection method, or combination of methods, can be used if:

(1) It can detect a 0.2 gallon per hour leak rate or a release of 150 gallons within a month with a probability of detection of 0.95 and a probability of false alarm of 0.05; or

(2) The implementing agency may approve another method if the owner and operator can demonstrate that the method can detect a release as effectively as any of the methods allowed in paragraphs (c) through (h) of this section. In comparing methods, the implementing agency shall consider the size of release that the method can detect and the frequency and reliability with which it can be detected. If the method is approved, the owner and operator must comply with any conditions imposed by the implementing agency on its use to ensure the protection of human health and the environment.

§280.44 Methods of release detection for piping.

Each method of release detection for piping used to meet the requirements of §280.41 must be conducted in accordance with the following:

(a) *Automatic line leak detectors.* Methods which alert the operator to the presence of a leak by restricting or shutting off the flow of regulated substances through piping or triggering an audible or visual alarm may be used only if they detect leaks of 3 gallons per hour at 10 pounds per square inch line pressure within 1 hour. An annual test of the operation of the leak detector must be conducted in accordance with the manufacturer's requirements.

(b) *Line tightness testing.* A periodic test of piping may be conducted only if it can detect a 0.1 gallon per hour leak rate at one and one-half times the operating pressure.

(c) *Applicable tank methods.* Any of the methods in §280.43 (e) through (h) may be used if they are designed to detect a release from any portion of the underground piping that routinely contains regulated substances.

§280.45 Release detection recordkeeping.

All UST system owners and operators must maintain records in accordance with §280.34 demonstrating compliance with all applicable requirements of this subpart. These records must include the following:

(a) All written performance claims pertaining to any release detection system used, and the manner in which these claims have been justified or tested by the equipment manufacturer or installer, must be maintained for 5 years, or for another reasonable period of time determined by the implementing agency, from the date of installation;

(b) The results of any sampling, testing, or monitoring must be maintained for at least 1 year, or for another reasonable period of time determined by the implementing agency, except that the results of tank tightness testing conducted in accordance with §280.43(c) must be retained until the next test is conducted; and

(c) Written documentation of all calibration, maintenance, and repair of release detection equipment permanently located on-site must be maintained for at least one year after the servicing work is completed, or for another reasonable time period determined by the implementing agency. Any schedules of required calibration and maintenance provided by the release detection equipment manufacturer must be retained for 5 years from the date of installation.

Subpart E—Release Reporting, Investigation, and Confirmation

§280.50 Reporting of suspected releases.

Owners and operators of UST systems must report to the implementing agency within 24 hours, or another reasonable time period specified by the implementing agency, and follow the procedures in §280.52 for any of the following conditions:

(a) The discovery by owners and operators or others of released regulated substances at the UST site or in the surrounding area (such as the presence of free product or vapors in soils, basements, sewer and utility lines, and nearby surface water).

(b) Unusual operating conditions observed by owners and operators (such as the erratic behavior of product dispensing equipment, the sudden loss of product from the UST system, or an unexplained presence of water in the tank), unless system equipment is found to be defective but not leaking, and is immediately repaired or replaced; and,

(c) Monitoring results from a release detection method required under §280.41 and §280.42 that indicate a release may have occurred unless:

(1) The monitoring device is found to be defective, and is immediately repaired, recalibrated or replaced, and additional monitoring does not confirm the initial result; or

(2) In the case of inventory control, a second month of data does not confirm the initial result.

§280.51 Investigation due to off-site impacts.

When required by the implementing agency, owners and operators of UST systems must follow the procedures in §280.52 to determine if the UST system is the source of off-site impacts. These impacts include the discovery of regulated substances (such as the presence of free product or vapors in soils, basements, sewer and utility lines, and nearby surface and drinking waters) that has been observed by the implementing agency or brought to its attention by another party.

§280.52 Release investigation and confirmation steps.

Unless corrective action is initiated in accordance with subpart F, owners and operators must immediately investigate and confirm all suspected releases of regulated substances requiring reporting under §280.50 within 7 days, or another reasonable time period specified by the implementing agency, using either the following steps or another procedure approved by the implementing agency:

(a) *System test.* Owners and operators must conduct tests (according to the requirements for tightness testing in §280.43(c) and §280.44(b)) that determine whether a leak exists in that portion of the tank that routinely contains product, or the attached delivery piping, or both.

(1) Owners and operators must repair, replace or upgrade the UST system, and begin corrective action in accordance with subpart F if the test results for the system, tank, or delivery piping indicate that a leak exists.

(2) Further investigation is not required if the test results for the system, tank, and delivery piping do not indicate that a leak exists and if environmental contamination is not the basis for suspecting a release.

(3) Owners and operators must conduct a site check as described in paragraph (b) of this section if the test results for the system, tank, and delivery piping do not indicate that a leak exists but environmental contamination is the basis for suspecting a release.

(b) *Site check.* Owners and operators must measure for the presence of a release where contamination is most likely to be present at the UST site. In selecting sample types, sample locations, and measurement methods, owners and operators must consider the nature of the stored substance, the type of initial alarm or cause for suspicion, the type of backfill, the depth of ground water, and other factors appropriate for identifying the presence and source of the release.

(1) If the test results for the excavation zone or the UST site indicate that a release has occurred, owners and operators must begin corrective action in accordance with subpart F;

(2) If the test results for the excavation zone or the UST site do not indicate that a release has occurred, further investigation is not required.

§280.53 Reporting and cleanup of spills and overfills.

(a) Owners and operators of UST systems must contain and immediately clean up a spill or overfill and report to the implementing agency within 24 hours, or another reasonable time period specified by the implementing agency, and begin corrective action in accordance with subpart F in the following cases:

(1) Spill or overfill of petroleum that results in a release to the environment that exceeds 25 gallons or another reasonable amount specified by the implementing agency, or that causes a sheen on nearby surface water; and

(2) Spill or overfill of a hazardous substance that results in a release to the environment that equals or exceeds its reportable quantity under CERCLA (40 CFR part 302).

(b) Owners and operators of UST systems must contain and immediately clean up a spill or overfill of petroleum that is less than 25 gallons or another reasonable amount specified by the implementing agency, and a spill or overfill of a hazardous substance that is less than the reportable quantity. If cleanup cannot be accomplished within 24 hours, or another reasonable time period established by the implementing agency, owners and operators must immediately notify the implementing agency.

Note: Pursuant to §§302.6 and 355.40, a release of a hazardous substance equal to or in excess of its reportable quantity must also be reported immediately (rather than within 24 hours) to the National Response Center under sections 102 and 103 of the Comprehensive Environmental Response, Compensation, and Liability Act of 1980 and to appropriate state and local authorities under Title III of the Superfund Amendments and Reauthorization Act of 1986.

Subpart F—Release Response and Corrective Action for UST Systems Containing Petroleum or Hazardous Substances

📖 2.6.4

§280.60 General.

Owners and operators of petroleum or hazardous substance UST systems must, in response to a confirmed release from the UST system, comply with the requirements of this subpart except for USTs excluded under §280.10(b) and UST systems subject to RCRA Subtitle C corrective action requirements under section 3004(u) of the Resource Conservation and Recovery Act, as amended.

§280.61 Initial response.

Upon confirmation of a release in accordance with §280.52 or after a release from the UST system is identified in any other manner, owners and operators must perform the following initial response actions within 24 hours of a release or within another reasonable period of time determined by the implementing agency:

(a) Report the release to the implementing agency (e.g., by telephone or electronic mail);

(b) Take immediate action to prevent any further release of the regulated substance into the environment; and

(c) Identify and mitigate fire, explosion, and vapor hazards.

§280.62 Initial abatement measures and site check.

(a) Unless directed to do otherwise by the implementing agency, owners and operators must perform the following abatement measures:

(1) Remove as much of the regulated substance from the UST system as is necessary to prevent further release to the environment;

(2) Visually inspect any aboveground releases or exposed belowground releases and prevent further migration of the released substance into surrounding soils and ground water;

(3) Continue to monitor and mitigate any additional fire and safety hazards posed by vapors or free product that have migrated from the UST excavation zone and entered into subsurface structures (such as sewers or basements);

(4) Remedy hazards posed by contaminated soils that are excavated or exposed as a result of release confirmation, site investigation, abatement, or corrective action activities. If these remedies include treatment or disposal of soils, the owner and operator must comply with applicable State and local requirements;

(5) Measure for the presence of a release where contamination is most likely to be present at the UST site, unless the presence and source of the release have been confirmed in accordance with the site check required by §280.52(b) or the closure site assessment of §280.72(a). In selecting sample types, sample locations, and measurement methods, the owner and operator must consider the nature of the stored substance, the type of backfill, depth to ground water and other factors as appropriate for identifying the presence and source of the release; and

(6) Investigate to determine the possible presence of free product, and begin free product removal as soon as practicable and in accordance with §280.64.

(b) Within 20 days after release confirmation, or within another reasonable period of time determined by the implementing agency, owners and operators must submit a report to the implementing agency summarizing the initial abatement steps taken under paragraph (a) of this section and any resulting information or data.

§280.63 Initial site characterization.

(a) Unless directed to do otherwise by the implementing agency, owners and operators must assemble information about the site and the nature of the release, including information gained while confirming the release or completing the initial abatement measures in §§280.60 and 280.61. This information must include, but is not necessarily limited to the following:

(1) Data on the nature and estimated quantity of release;

(2) Data from available sources and/or site investigations concerning the following factors: surrounding populations, water quality, use and approximate locations of wells potentially affected by the release, subsurface soil conditions, locations of subsurface sewers, climatological conditions, and land use;

(3) Results of the site check required under §280.62(a)(5); and

(4) Results of the free product investigations required under §280.62(a)(6), to be used by owners and operators to determine whether free product must be recovered under §280.64.

(b) Within 45 days of release confirmation or another reasonable period of time determined by the implementing agency, owners and operators must submit the information collected in compliance with paragraph (a) of this section to the implementing agency in a manner that demonstrates its applicability and technical adequacy, or in a format and according to the schedule required by the implementing agency.

§280.64 Free product removal. 14.4.7.1

At sites where investigations under §280.62(a)(6) indicate the presence of free product, owners and operators must remove free product to the maximum extent practicable as determined by the implementing agency while continuing, as necessary, any actions initiated under §§280.61 through 280.63, or preparing for actions required under §§280.65 through 280.66. In meeting the requirements of this section, owners and operators must:

(a) Conduct free product removal in a manner that minimizes the spread of contamination into previously uncontaminated zones by using recovery and disposal techniques appropriate to the hydrogeologic conditions at the site, and that properly treats, discharges or disposes of recovery byproducts in compliance with applicable local, State and Federal regulations;

(b) Use abatement of free product migration as a minimum objective for the design of the free product removal system;

(c) Handle any flammable products in a safe and competent manner to prevent fires or explosions; and

(d) Unless directed to do otherwise by the implementing agency, prepare and submit to the implementing agency, within 45 days after confirming a release, a free product removal report that provides at least the following information:

(1) The name of the person(s) responsible for implementing the free product removal measures;

(2) The estimated quantity, type, and thickness of free product observed or measured in wells, boreholes, and excavations;

(3) The type of free product recovery system used;

(4) Whether any discharge will take place on-site or off-site during the recovery operation and where this discharge will be located;

(5) The type of treatment applied to, and the effluent quality expected from, any discharge;

(6) The steps that have been or are being taken to obtain necessary permits for any discharge; and

(7) The disposition of the recovered free product.

§280.65 Investigations for soil and ground-water cleanup.

(a) In order to determine the full extent and location of soils contaminated by the release and the presence and concentrations of dissolved product contamination in the ground water, owners and operators must conduct investigations of the release, the release site, and the surrounding area possibly affected by the release if any of the following conditions exist:

(1) There is evidence that ground-water wells have been affected by the release (e.g., as found during release confirmation or previous corrective action measures);

(2) Free product is found to need recovery in compliance with §280.64;

(3) There is evidence that contaminated soils may be in contact with ground water (e.g., as found during conduct of the initial response measures or investigations required under §§280.60 through 280.64); and

(4) The implementing agency requests an investigation, based on the potential effects of contaminated soil or ground water on nearby surface water and ground-water resources.

(b) Owners and operators must submit the information collected under paragraph (a) of this section as soon as practicable or in accordance with a schedule established by the implementing agency.

§280.66 Corrective action plan.

(a) At any point after reviewing the information submitted in compliance with §§280.61 through 280.63, the implementing agency may require owners and operators to submit additional information or to develop and submit a corrective action plan for responding to contaminated soils and ground water. If a plan is required, owners and operators must submit the plan according to a schedule and format established by the implementing agency. Alternatively, owners and operators may, after fulfilling the requirements of §§280.61 through 280.63, choose to submit a corrective action plan for responding to contaminated soil and ground water. In either case, owners and operators are responsible for submitting a plan that provides for adequate protection of human health and the environment as determined by the implementing agency, and must modify their plan as necessary to meet this standard.

(b) The implementing agency will approve the corrective action plan only after ensuring that implementation of the plan will adequately protect human health, safety, and the environment. In making this determination, the implementing agency should consider the following factors as appropriate:

(1) The physical and chemical characteristics of the regulated substance, including its toxicity, persistence, and potential for migration;

(2) The hydrogeologic characteristics of the facility and the surrounding area;

(3) The proximity, quality, and current and future uses of nearby surface water and ground water;

(4) The potential effects of residual contamination on nearby surface water and ground water;

(5) An exposure assessment; and

(6) Any information assembled in compliance with this subpart.

(c) Upon approval of the corrective action plan or as directed by the implementing agency, owners and operators must implement the plan, including modifications to the plan made by the implementing agency. They must monitor, evaluate, and report the results of implementing the plan in accordance with a schedule and in a format established by the implementing agency.

(d) Owners and operators may, in the interest of minimizing environmental contamination and promoting more effective cleanup, begin cleanup of soil and ground water before the corrective action plan is approved provided that they:

(1) Notify the implementing agency of their intention to begin cleanup;

(2) Comply with any conditions imposed by the implementing agency, including halting cleanup or mitigating adverse consequences from cleanup activities; and

(3) Incorporate these self-initiated cleanup measures in the corrective action plan that is submitted to the implementing agency for approval.

§280.67 Public participation.

(a) For each confirmed release that requires a corrective action plan, the implementing agency must provide notice to the public by means designed to reach those members of the public directly affected by the release and the planned corrective action. This notice may include, but is not limited to, public notice in local newspapers, block advertisements, public service announcements, publication in a state register, letters to individual households, or personal contacts by field staff.

(b) The implementing agency must ensure that site release information and decisions concerning the corrective action plan are made available to the public for inspection upon request.

(c) Before approving a corrective action plan, the implementing agency may hold a public meeting to consider comments on the proposed corrective action plan if there is sufficient public interest, or for any other reason.

(d) The implementing agency must give public notice that complies with paragraph (a) of this section if implementation of an approved corrective action plan does not achieve the established cleanup levels in the plan and termination of that plan is under consideration by the implementing agency.

Subpart G—Out-of-Service UST Systems and Closure

§280.70 Temporary closure.

(a) When an UST system is temporarily closed, owners and operators must continue operation and maintenance of corrosion protection in accordance with §280.31, and any release detection in accordance with subpart D. Subparts E and F must be complied with if a release is suspected or confirmed. However, release detection is not required as long as the UST system is empty. The UST system is empty when all materials have been removed using commonly employed practices so that no more than 2.5 centimeters (one inch) of residue, or 0.3 percent by weight of the total capacity of the UST system, remain in the system.

(b) When an UST system is temporarily closed for 3 months or more, owners and operators must also comply with the following requirements:

(1) Leave vent lines open and functioning; and

(2) Cap and secure all other lines, pumps, manways, and ancillary equipment.

(c) When an UST system is temporarily closed for more than 12 months, owners and operators must permanently close the UST system if it does not meet either performance standards in §280.20 for new UST systems or the upgrading requirements in §280.21, except that the spill and overfill equipment requirements do not have to be met. Owners and operators must permanently close the substandard UST systems at the end of this 12-month period in accordance with §§280.71–280.74, unless the implementing agency provides an extension of the 12-month temporary closure period. Owners and operators must complete a site assessment in accordance with §280.72 before such an extension can be applied for.

§280.71 Permanent closure and changes-in-service.

(a) At least 30 days before beginning either permanent closure or a change-in-service under paragraphs (b) and (c) of this section, or within another reasonable time period determined by the implementing agency, owners and operators must notify the implementing agency of their intent to permanently close or make the change-in-service, unless such action is in response to corrective action. The required assessment of the excavation zone under §280.72 must be performed after notifying the implementing agency but before completion of the permanent closure or a change-in-service.

(b) To permanently close a tank, owners and operators must empty and clean it by removing all liquids and accumulated sludges. All tanks taken out of service permanently must also be either removed from the ground or filled with an inert solid material.

(c) Continued use of an UST system to store a non-regulated substance is considered a change-in-service. Before a change-in-service, owners and operators must empty and clean the tank by removing all liquid and accumulated sludge and conduct a site assessment in accordance with §280.72.

Note: The following cleaning and closure procedures may be used to comply with this section:

(A) American Petroleum Institute Recommended Practice 1604, "Removal and Disposal of Used Underground Petroleum Storage Tanks";

(B) American Petroleum Institute Publication 2015, "Cleaning Petroleum Storage Tanks";

(C) American Petroleum Institute Recommended Practice 1631, "Interior Lining of Underground Storage Tanks," may be used as guidance for compliance with this section; and

(D) The National Institute for Occupational Safety and Health "Criteria for a Recommended Standard * * * Working in Confined Space" may be used as guidance for conducting safe closure procedures at some hazardous substance tanks.

§280.72 Assessing the site at closure or change-in-service.

(a) Before permanent closure or a change-in-service is completed, owners and operators must measure for the presence of a release where contamination is most likely to be present at the UST site. In selecting sample types, sample locations, and measurement methods, owners and operators must consider the method of closure, the nature of the stored substance, the type of backfill, the depth to ground water, and other factors appropriate for identifying the presence of a release. The requirements of this section are satisfied if one of the external release detection methods allowed in §280.43 (e) and (f) is operating in accordance with the requirements in §280.43 at the time of closure, and indicates no release has occurred.

(b) If contaminated soils, contaminated ground water, or free product as a liquid or vapor is discovered under paragraph (a) of this section, or by any other manner, owners and operators must begin corrective action in accordance with subpart F.

§280.73 Applicability to previously closed UST systems.

When directed by the implementing agency, the owner and operator of an UST system permanently closed before December 22, 1988 must assess the excavation zone and close the UST system in accordance with this subpart if releases from the UST may, in the judgment of the implementing agency, pose a current or potential threat to human health and the environment.

§280.74 Closure records.

Owners and operators must maintain records in accordance with §280.34 that are capable of demonstrating compliance with closure requirements under this subpart. The results of the excavation zone assessment required in §280.72 must be maintained for at least 3 years after completion of permanent closure or change-in-service in one of the following ways:

(a) By the owners and operators who took the UST system out of service;

(b) By the current owners and operators of the UST system site; or

(c) By mailing these records to the implementing agency if they cannot be maintained at the closed facility.

Subpart H—Financial Responsibility

Source: 53 FR 43370, Oct. 26, 1988, unless otherwise noted.

§280.90 Applicability.

(a) This subpart applies to owners and operators of all petroleum underground storage tank (UST) systems except as otherwise provided in this section.

(b) Owners and operators of petroleum UST systems are subject to these requirements if they are in operation on or after the date for compliance established in §280.91.

(c) State and Federal government entities whose debts and liabilities are the debts and liabilities of a state or the United States are exempt from the requirements of this subpart.

(d) The requirements of this subpart do not apply to owners and operators of any UST system described in §280.10 (b) or (c).

(e) If the owner and operator of a petroleum underground storage tank are separate persons, only one person is required to demonstrate financial responsibility; however, both parties are liable in event of noncompliance. Regardless of which party complies, the date set for compliance at a particular facility is determined by the characteristics of the owner as set forth in §280.91.

§280.91 Compliance dates.

Owners of petroleum underground storage tanks are required to comply with the requirements of this subpart by the following dates:

(a) All petroleum marketing firms owning 1,000 or more USTs and all other UST owners that report a tangible net worth of $20 million or more to the U.S. Securities and Exchange Commission (SEC), Dun and Bradstreet, the Energy Information Administration, or the Rural Electrification Administration; January 24, 1989, except that compliance with §280.94(b) is required by: July 24, 1989.

(b) All petroleum marketing firms owning 100-999 USTs; October 26, 1989.

(c) All petroleum marketing firms owning 13-99 USTs at more than one facility; April 26, 1991.

(d) All petroleum UST owners not described in paragraphs (a), (b), or (c) of this section, excluding local government entities; December 31, 1993.

(e) All local government entities (including Indian tribes) not included in paragraph (f) of this section; February 18, 1994.

(f) Indian tribes that own USTs on Indian lands which meet the applicable technical requirements of this part; December 31, 1998. [53 FR 43370, Oct. 26, 1988, as amended at 54 FR 5452, Feb. 3, 1989; 55 FR 18567, May 2, 1990; 55 FR 46025, Oct. 31, 1990; 56 FR 66373, Dec. 23, 1991; 59 FR 9607, Feb. 28, 1994]

§280.92 Definition of terms.

When used in this subpart, the following terms shall have the meanings given below:

Accidental release means any sudden or nonsudden release of petroleum from an underground storage tank that results in a need for corrective action and/or compensation for bodily injury or property damage neither expected nor intended by the tank owner or operator.

Bodily injury shall have the meaning given to this term by applicable state law; however, this term shall not include those liabilities which, consistent with standard insurance industry practices, are excluded from coverage in liability insurance policies for bodily injury.

Chief Financial Officer, in the case of local government owners and operators, means the individual with the overall authority and responsibility for the collection, disbursement, and use of funds by the local government.

Controlling interest means direct ownership of at least 50 percent of the voting stock of another entity.

Director of the Implementing Agency means the EPA Regional Administrator, or, in the case of a state with a program approved under section 9004, the Director of the designated state or local agency responsible for carrying out an approved UST program.

Financial reporting year means the latest consecutive twelve-month period for which any of the following reports used to support a financial test is prepared:

(1) a 10-K report submitted to the SEC;

(2) an annual report of tangible net worth submitted to Dun and Bradstreet; or

(3) annual reports submitted to the Energy Information Administration or the Rural Electrification Administration.

"Financial reporting year" may thus comprise a fiscal or a calendar year period.

Legal defense cost is any expense that an owner or operator or provider of financial assurance incurs in defending against claims or actions brought,

(1) By EPA or a state to require corrective action or to recover the costs of corrective action;

(2) By or on behalf of a third party for bodily injury or property damage caused by an accidental release; or

(3) By any person to enforce the terms of a financial assurance mechanism.

Local government shall have the meaning given this term by applicable state law and includes Indian tribes. The term is generally intended to include: (1) Counties, municipalities, townships, separately chartered and operated special districts (including local government public transit systems and redevelopment authorities), and independent school districts authorized as governmental bodies by state charter or constitution; and (2) Special districts and independent school districts established by counties, municipalities, townships, and other general purpose governments to provide essential services.

Occurrence means an accident, including continuous or repeated exposure to conditions, which results in a release from an underground storage tank.

Note: This definition is intended to assist in the understanding of these regulations and is not intended either to limit the meaning of "occurrence" in a way that conflicts with standard insurance usage or to prevent the use of other standard insurance terms in place of "occurrence."

Owner or operator, when the owner or operator are separate parties, refers to the party that is obtaining or has obtained financial assurances.

Petroleum marketing facilities include all facilities at which petroleum is produced or refined and all facilities from which petroleum is sold or transferred to other petroleum marketers or to the public.

Petroleum marketing firms are all firms owning petroleum marketing facilities. Firms owning other types of facilities with USTs as well as petroleum marketing facilities are considered to be petroleum marketing firms.

Property damage shall have the meaning given this term by applicable state law. This term shall not include those liabilities which, consistent with standard insurance industry practices, are excluded from coverage in liability insurance policies for property damage. However, such exclusions for property damage shall not include corrective action associated with releases from tanks which are covered by the policy.

Provider of financial assurance means an entity that provides financial assurance to an owner or operator of an underground storage tank through one of the mechanisms listed in §§280.95-280.103, including a guarantor, insurer, risk retention group, surety, issuer of a letter of credit, issuer of a state-required mechanism, or a state.

Substantial business relationship means the extent of a business relationship necessary under applicable state law to make a guarantee contract issued incident to that relationship valid and enforceable. A guarantee contract is issued "incident to that relationship" if it arises from and depends on existing economic transactions between the guarantor and the owner or operator.

Substantial governmental relationship means the extent of a governmental relationship necessary under applicable state law to make an added guarantee contract issued incident to that relationship valid and enforceable. A guarantee contract is issued "incident to that relationship" if it arises from a clear commonality of interest in the event of an UST release such as coterminous boundaries, overlapping constituencies, common ground-water aquifer, or other relationship other than monetary compensation that provides a motivation for the guarantor to provide a guarantee.

Tangible net worth means the tangible assets that remain after deducting liabilities; such assets do not include intangibles such as goodwill and rights to patents or royalties. For purposes of this definition, "assets" means all existing and all probable future economic benefits obtained or controlled by a particular entity as a result of past transactions.

Termination under §280.97(b)(1) and §280.97(b)(2) means only those changes that could result in a gap in coverage as where the insured has not obtained substitute coverage or has obtained substitute coverage with a different retroactive date than the retroactive date of the original policy.

[53 FR 43370, Oct. 26, 1988, as amended at 54 FR 47081, Nov. 9, 1989; 58 FR 9050, Feb. 18, 1993]

§280.93 Amount and scope of required financial responsibility.

(a) Owners or operators of petroleum underground storage tanks must demonstrate financial responsibility for taking corrective action and for compensating third parties for bodily injury and property damage caused by accidental releases arising from the operation of petroleum underground storage tanks in at least the following per-occurrence amounts:

(1) For owners or operators of petroleum underground storage tanks that are located at petroleum marketing facilities, or that handle an average of more than 10,000 gallons of petroleum per month based on annual throughput for the previous calendar year; $1 million.

(2) For all other owners or operators of petroleum underground storage tanks; $500,000.

(b) Owners or operators of petroleum underground storage tanks must demonstrate financial responsibility for taking corrective action and for compensating third parties for bodily injury and property damage caused by accidental releases arising from the operation of petroleum underground storage tanks in at least the following annual aggregate amounts:

(1) For owners or operators of 1 to 100 petroleum underground storage tanks, $1 million; and

(2) For owners or operators of 101 or more petroleum underground storage tanks, $2 million.

(c) For the purposes of paragraphs (b) and (f) of this section, only, "a petroleum underground storage tank" means a single containment unit and does not mean combinations of single containment units.

(d) Except as provided in paragraph (e) of this section, if the owner or operator uses separate mechanisms or separate combinations of mechanisms to demonstrate financial responsibility for:

(1) Taking corrective action;

(2) Compensating third parties for bodily injury and property damage caused by sudden accidental releases; or

(3) Compensating third parties for bodily injury and property damage caused by nonsudden accidental releases, the amount of assurance provided by each mechanism or combination of mechanisms must be in the full amount specified in paragraphs (a) and (b) of this section.

(e) If an owner or operator uses separate mechanisms or separate combinations of mechanisms to demonstrate financial responsibility for different petroleum underground storage tanks, the annual aggregate required shall be based on the number of tanks covered by each such separate mechanism or combination of mechanisms.

(f) Owners or operators shall review the amount of aggregate assurance provided whenever additional petroleum underground storage tanks are acquired or installed. If the number of petroleum underground storage tanks for which assurance must be provided exceeds 100, the owner or operator shall demonstrate financial responsibility in the amount of at least $2 million of annual aggregate assurance by the anniversary of the date on which the mechanism demonstrating financial responsibility became effective. If assurance is being demonstrated by a combination of mechanisms, the owner or operator shall demonstrate financial responsibility in the amount of at least $2 million of annual aggregate assurance by the first-occurring effective date anniversary of any one of the mechanisms combined (other than a financial test or guarantee) to provide assurance.

(g) The amounts of assurance required under this section exclude legal defense costs.

(h) The required per-occurrence and annual aggregate coverage amounts do not in any way limit the liability of the owner or operator.

§280.94 Allowable mechanisms and combinations of mechanisms.

(a) Subject to the limitations of paragraphs (b) and (c) of this section,

(1) An owner or operator, including a local government owner or operator, may use any one or combination of the mechanisms listed in §§280.95 through 280.103 to demonstrate financial responsibility under this subpart for one or more underground storage tanks, and

(2) A local government owner or operator may use any one or combination of the mechanisms listed in §§280.104 through 280.107 to demonstrate financial responsibility under this subpart for one or more underground storage tanks.

(b) An owner or operator may use a guarantee under §280.96 or surety bond under §280.98 to establish financial responsibility only if the Attorney(s) General of the state(s) in which the underground storage tanks are located has (have) submitted a written statement to the implementing agency that a guarantee or surety bond executed as described in this section is a legally valid and enforceable obligation in that state.

(c) An owner or operator may use self-insurance in combination with a guarantee only if, for the purpose of meeting the requirements of the financial test under this rule, the financial statements of the owner or operator are not consolidated with the financial statements of the guarantor.

[53 FR 43370, Oct. 26, 1988, as amended at 58 FR 9051, Feb. 18, 1993]

§280.95 Financial test of self-insurance.

(a) An owner or operator, and/or guarantor, may satisfy the requirements of §280.93 by passing a financial test as specified in this section. To pass the financial test of self-insurance, the owner or operator, and/or guarantor must meet the criteria of paragraph (b) or (c) of this section based on year-end financial statements for the latest completed fiscal year.

(b)(1) The owner or operator, and/or guarantor, must have a tangible net worth of at least ten times:

(i) The total of the applicable aggregate amount required by §280.93, based on the number of underground storage tanks for which a financial test is used to demonstrate financial responsibility to EPA under this section or to a state implementing agency under a state program approved by EPA under 40 CFR part 281;

(ii) The sum of the corrective action cost estimates, the current closure and post-closure care cost estimates, and amount of liability coverage for which a financial test is used to demonstrate financial responsibility to EPA under 40 CFR 264.101, 264.143, 264.145, 265.143, 165.145, 264.147, and 265.147 or to a state implementing agency under a state program authorized by EPA under 40 CFR part 271; and

(iii) The sum of current plugging and abandonment cost estimates for which a financial test is used to demonstrate financial responsibility to EPA under 40 CFR 144.63 or to a state implementing agency under a state program authorized by EPA under 40 CFR part 145.

(2) The owner or operator, and/or guarantor, must have a tangible net worth of at least $10 million.

(3) The owner or operator, and/or guarantor, must have a letter signed by the chief financial officer worded as specified in paragraph (d) of this section.

(4) The owner or operator, and/or guarantor, must either:

(i) File financial statements annually with the U.S. Securities and Exchange Commission, the Energy Information Administration, or the Rural Electrification Administration; or

(ii) Report annually the firm's tangible net worth to Dun and Bradstreet, and Dun and Bradstreet must have assigned the firm a financial strength rating of 4A or 5A.

(5) The firm's year-end financial statements, if independently audited, cannot include an adverse auditor's opinion, a disclaimer of opinion, or a "going concern" qualification.

(c)(1) The owner or operator, and/or guarantor must meet the financial test requirements of 40 CFR 264.147(f)(1), substituting the appropriate amounts specified in §280.93 (b)(1) and (b)(2) for the "amount of liability coverage" each time specified in that section.

(2) The fiscal year-end financial statements of the owner or operator, and/or guarantor, must be examined by an independent certified public accountant and be accompanied by the accountant's report of the examination.

(3) The firm's year-end financial statements cannot include an adverse auditor's opinion, a disclaimer of opinion, or a "going concern" qualification.

(4) The owner or operator, and/or guarantor, must have a letter signed by the chief financial officer, worded as specified in paragraph (d) of this section.

(5) If the financial statements of the owner or operator, and/or guarantor, are not submitted annually to the U.S. Securities and Exchange Commission, the Energy Information Administration or the Rural Electrification Administration, the owner or operator, and/or guarantor, must obtain a special report by an independent certified public accountant stating that:

(i) He has compared the data that the letter form the chief financial officer specifies as having been derived from the latest year-end financial statements of the owner or operator, and/or guarantor, with the amounts in such financial statements; and

(ii) In connection with that comparison, no matters came to his attention which caused him to believe that the specified data should be adjusted.

(d) To demonstrate that it meets the financial test under paragraph (b) or (c) of this section, the chief financial officer of the owner or operator, or guarantor, must sign, within 120 days of the close of each financial reporting year, as defined by the twelve-month period for which financial statements used to support the financial test are prepared, a letter worded exactly as follows, except that the instructions in brackets are to be replaced by the relevant information and the brackets deleted:

Letter from Chief Financial Officer

I am the chief financial officer of [insert: name and address of the owner or operator, or guarantor]. This letter is in support of the use of [insert: "the financial test of self-insurance," and/or "guarantee"] to demonstrate financial responsibility for [insert: "taking corrective action" and/or "compensating third parties for bodily injury and property damage"] caused by [insert: "sudden accidental releases" and/or "nonsudden accidental releases"] in the amount of at least [insert: dollar amount] per occurrence and [insert: dollar amount] annual aggregate arising from operating (an) underground storage tank(s).

Underground storage tanks at the following facilities are assured by this financial test or a financial test under an authorized State program by this [insert: "owner or operator," and/or "guarantor"]: [List for each facility: the name and address of the facility where tanks assured by this financial test are located, and whether tanks are assured by this financial test or a financial test under a State program approved under 40 CFR part 281. If separate mechanisms or combinations of mechanisms are being used to assure any of the tanks at this facility, list each tank assured by this financial test or a financial test under a State program authorized under 40 CFR part 281 by the tank identification number provided in the notification submitted pursuant to 40 CFR 280.22 or the corresponding State requirements.]

A [insert: "financial test," and/or "guarantee"] is also used by this [insert: "owner or operator," or "guarantor"] to demonstrate evidence of financial responsibility in the following amounts under other EPA regulations or state programs authorized by EPA under 40 CFR parts 271 and 145:

EPA Regulations	*Amount*
Closure (§§264.143 and 265.143)	$ ________
Post-Closure Care (§§264.145 and 265.145)	$ ________
Liability Coverage (§§264.147 and 265.147)	$ ________
Corrective Action (§§264.101(b))	$ ________
Plugging and Abandonment (§144.63)	$ ________
Closure	$ ________
Post-Closure Care	$ ________
Liability Coverage	$ ________
Corrective Action	$ ________
Plugging and Abandonment	$ ________
Total	$ ________

This [insert: "owner or operator," or "guarantor"] has not received an adverse opinion, a disclaimer of opinion, or a "going concern" qualification from an independent auditor on his financial statements for the latest completed fiscal year.

[Fill in the information for Alternative I if the criteria of paragraph (b) of §280.95 are being used to demonstrate compliance with the financial test requirements. Fill in the information for Alternative II if the criteria of paragraph (c) of §280.95 are being used to demonstrate compliance with the financial test requirements.]

Alternative I

1. Amount of annual UST aggregate coverage being assured by a financial test, and/or guarantee $ ________
2. Amount of corrective action, closure and post-closure care costs, liability coverage, and plugging and abandonment costs covered by a financial test, and/or guarantee $ ________
3. Sum of lines 1 and 2 $ ________
4. Total tangible assets $ ________
5. Total liabilities [if any of the amount reported on line 3 is included in total liabilities, you may deduct that amount from this line and add that amount to line 6] $ ________
6. Tangible net worth [subtract line 5 from line 4] $ ________

	Yes	No
7. Is line 6 at least $10 million?	___	___
8. Is line 6 at least 10 times line 3?	___	___
9. Have financial statements for the latest fiscal year been filed with the Securities and Exchange Commission?	___	___
10. Have financial statements for the latest fiscal year been filed with the Energy Information Administration?	___	___

11. Have financial statements for the latest fiscal year been filed with the Rural Electrification Administration? .... ___ ___
12. Has financial information been provided to Dun and Bradstreet, and has Dun and Bradstreet provided a financial strength rating of 4A or 5A? [Answer "Yes" only if both criteria have been met.] .... ___ ___

Alternative II

1. Amount of annual UST aggregate coverage being assured by a test, and/or guarantee .... $ ________
2. Amount of corrective action, closure and post-closure care costs, liability coverage, and plugging and abandonment costs covered by a financial test, and/or guarantee.......................... $ ________
3. Sum of lines 1 and 2 .... $ ________
4. Total tangible assets .... $ ________
5. Total liabilities [if any of the amount reported on line 3 is included in total liabilities, you may deduct that amount from this line and add that amount to line 6] .... $ ________
6. Tangible net worth [subtract line 5 from line 4].. $ ________
7. Total assets in the U.S. [required only if less than 90 percent of assets are located in the U.S.] ..... $ ________

Yes No

8. Is line 6 at least $10 million?.................. ___ ___
9. Is line 6 at least 6 times line 3? .... ___ ___
10. Are at least 90 percent of assets located in the U.S.? [If "No," complete line 11.] .... ___ ___
11. Is line 7 at least 6 times line 3? [Fill in either lines 12-15 or lines 16-18:] .... ___ ___
12. Current assets .... $ ________
13. Current liabilities .... $ ________
14. Net working capital [subtract line 13 from line 12] $ ________

Yes No

15. Is line 14 at least 6 times line 3? .... ___ ___
16. Current bond rating of most recent bond issue .. ___ ___
17. Name of rating service .... ___ ___
18. Date of maturity of bond .... ___ ___
19. Have financial statements for the latest fiscal year been filed with the SEC, the Energy Information Administration, or the Rural Electrification Administration?...................... ___ ___

    [If "No," please attach a report from an independent certified public accountant certifying that there are no material differences between the data as reported in lines 4-18 above and the financial statements for the latest fiscal year.]

[For both Alternative I and Alternative II complete the certification with this statement.]

I hereby certify that the wording of this letter is identical to the wording specified in 40 CFR part 280.95(d) as such regulations were constituted on the date shown immediately below.

[Signature]

[Name]

[Title]

[Date]

(e) If an owner or operator using the test to provide financial assurance finds that he or she no longer meets the requirements of the financial test based on the year-end financial statements, the owner or operator must obtain alternative coverage within 150 days of the end of the year for which financial statements have been prepared.

(f) The Director of the implementing agency may require reports of financial condition at any time from the owner or operator, and/or guarantor. If the Director finds, on the basis of such reports or other information, that the owner or operator, and/or guarantor, no longer meets the financial test requirements of §280.95(b) or (c) and (d), the owner or operator must obtain alternate coverage within 30 days after notification of such a finding.

(g) If the owner or operator fails to obtain alternate assurance within 150 days of finding that he or she no longer meets the requirements of the financial test based on the year-end financial statements, or within 30 days of notification by the Director of the implementing agency that he or she no longer meets the requirements of the financial test, the owner or operator must notify the Director of such failure within 10 days.

§280.96 Guarantee.

(a) An owner or operator may satisfy the requirements of §280.93 by obtaining a guarantee that conforms to the requirements of this section. The guarantor must be:

(1) A firm that (i) possesses a controlling interest in the owner or operator; (ii) possesses a controlling interest in a firm described under paragraph (a)(1)(i) of this section; or, (iii) is controlled through stock ownership by a common parent firm that possesses a controlling interest in the owner or operator; or,

(2) A firm engaged in a substantial business relationship with the owner or operator and issuing the guarantee as an act incident to that business relationship.

(b) Within 120 days of the close of each financial reporting year the guarantor must demonstrate that it meets the financial test criteria of §280.95 based on year-end financial statements for the latest completed financial reporting year by completing the letter from the chief financial officer described in §280.95(d) and must deliver the letter to the owner or operator. If the guarantor fails to meet the requirements of the financial test at the end of any financial reporting year, within 120 days of the end of that financial reporting year the guarantor shall send by certified mail, before cancellation or nonrenewal of the guarantee, notice to the owner or operator. If the Director of the implementing agency notifies the guarantor that he no longer meets the requirements of the financial test of §280.95 (b) or (c) and (d), the guarantor must notify the owner or operator within 10 days of receiving such notification from the Director. In both cases, the guarantee will terminate no less than 120 days after the date the owner or operator receives the notification, as evidenced by the return receipt. The owner or operator must obtain alternative coverage as specified in §280.110(c).

(c) The guarantee must be worded as follows, except that instructions in brackets are to be replaced with the relevant information and the brackets deleted:

Guarantee

Guarantee made this [date] by [name of guaranteeing entity], a business entity organized under the laws of the state of [name of state], herein referred to as guarantor, to [the state implementing agency] and to any and all third parties, and obligees, on behalf of [owner or operator] of [business address].

Recitals.

(1) Guarantor meets or exceeds the financial test criteria of 40 CFR 280.95 (b) or (c) and (d) and agrees to comply with the requirements for guarantors as specified in 40 CFR 280.96(b).

(2) [Owner or operator] owns or operates the following underground storage tank(s) covered by this guarantee: [List the number of tanks at each facility and the name(s) and address(es) of the facility(ies) where the tanks are located. If more than one instrument is used to assure different tanks at any one facility, for each tank covered by this instrument, list the tank identification number provided in the notification submitted pursuant to 40 CFR 280.22 or the corresponding state requirement, and the name and address of the facility.] This guarantee satisfies 40 CFR part 280, subpart H requirements for assuring funding for [insert: "taking corrective action" and/or "compensating third parties for bodily injury and property damage caused by" either "sudden accidental releases" or "nonsudden accidental releases" or "accidental releases"; if coverage is different for different tanks or locations, indicate the type of coverage applicable to each tank or location] arising from operating the above-identified underground storage tank(s) in the amount of [insert dollar amount] per occurrence and [insert dollar amount] annual aggregate.

(3) [Insert appropriate phrase: "On behalf of our subsidiary" (if guarantor is corporate parent of the owner or operator); "On behalf of our affiliate" (if guarantor is a related firm of the owner or operator); or "Incident to our business relationship with" (if guarantor is providing the guarantee as an incident to a substantial business relationship with owner or operator)] [owner or operator], guarantor guarantees to [implementing agency] and to any and all third parties that:

In the event that [owner or operator] fails to provide alternative coverage within 60 days after receipt of a notice of cancellation of this guarantee and the [Director of the implementing agency] has determined or suspects that a release has occurred at an underground storage tank covered by this guarantee, the guarantor, upon instructions from the [Director], shall fund a standby trust fund in accordance with the provisions of 40 CFR 280.108, in an amount not to exceed the coverage limits specified above.

In the event that the [Director] determines that [owner or operator] has failed to perform corrective action for releases arising out of the operation of the above-identified tank(s) in accordance with 40 CFR part 280, subpart F, the guarantor upon written instructions from the [Director] shall fund a standby trust in accordance with the provisions of 40 CFR 280.108, in an amount not to exceed the coverage limits specified above.

If [owner or operator] fails to satisfy a judgment or award based on a determination of liability for bodily injury or property damage to third parties caused by ["sudden" and/or "nonsudden"] accidental releases arising from the operation of the above-identified tank(s), or fails to pay an amount agreed to in settlement of a claim arising from or alleged to arise from such injury or damage, the guarantor, upon written instructions from the [Director], shall fund a standby trust in accordance with the provisions of 40 CFR 280.108 to satisfy such judgment(s), award(s), or settlement agreement(s) up to the limits of coverage specified above.

(4) Guarantor agrees that if, at the end of any fiscal year before cancellation of this guarantee, the guarantor fails to meet the financial test criteria of 40 CFR 280.95 (b) or (c) and (d), guarantor shall send within 120 days of such failure, by certified mail, notice to [owner or operator]. The guarantee will terminate 120 days from the date of receipt of the notice by [owner or operator], as evidenced by the return receipt.

(5) Guarantor agrees to notify [owner or operator] by certified mail of a voluntary or involuntary proceeding under Title 11 (Bankruptcy), U.S. Code naming guarantor as debtor, within 10 days after commencement of the proceeding.

(6) Guarantor agrees to remain bound under this guarantee notwithstanding any modification or alteration of any obligation of [owner or operator] pursuant to 40 CFR part 280.

(7) Guarantor agrees to remain bound under this guarantee for so long as [owner or operator] must comply with the applicable financial responsibility requirements of 40 CFR part 280, subpart H for the above-identified tank(s), except that guarantor may cancel this guarantee by sending notice by certified mail to [owner or operator], such cancellation to become effective no earlier than 120 days after receipt of such notice by [owner or operator], as evidenced by the return receipt.

(8) The guarantor's obligation does not apply to any of the following:

(a) Any obligation of [insert owner or operator] under a workers' compensation, disability benefits, or unemployment compensation law or other similar law;

(b) Bodily injury to an employee of [insert owner or operator] arising from, and in the course of, employment by [insert owner or operator];

(c) Bodily injury or property damage arising from the ownership, maintenance, use, or entrustment to others of any aircraft, motor vehicle, or watercraft;

(d) Property damage to any property owned, rented, loaded to, in the care, custody, or control of, or occupied by [insert owner or operator] that is not the direct result of a release from a petroleum underground storage tank;

(e) Bodily damage or property damage for which [insert owner or operator] is obligated to pay damages by reason of the assumption of liability in a contract or agreement other than a contract or agreement entered into to meet the requirements of 40 CFR 280.93.

(9) Guarantor expressly waives notice of acceptance of this guarantee by [the implementing agency], by any or all third parties, or by [owner or operator].

I hereby certify that the wording of this guarantee is identical to the wording specified in 40 CFR 280.96(c) as such regulations were constituted on the effective date shown immediately below.

Effective date: ____________________

[Name of guarantor]

[Authorized signature for guarantor]

[Name of person signing]

[Title of person signing]

Signature of witness or notary: ____________________

(d) An owner or operator who uses a guarantee to satisfy the requirements of §280.93 must establish a standby trust fund when the guarantee is obtained. Under the terms of the guarantee, all amounts paid by the guarantor under the guarantee will be deposited directly into the standby trust fund in accordance with instructions from the Director of the implementing agency under §280.108. This standby trust fund must meet the requirements specified in §280.103.

§280.97 Insurance and risk retention group coverage.

(a) An owner or operator may satisfy the requirements of §290.93 by obtaining liability insurance that conforms to the requirements of this section from a qualified insurer or risk retention group. Such insurance may be in the form of a separate insurance policy or an endorsement to an existing insurance policy.

(b) Each insurance policy must be amended by an endorsement worded as specified in paragraph (b)(1) of this section, or evidenced by a certificate of insurance worded as specified in paragraph (b)(2) of this section, except that instructions in brackets must be replaced with the relevant information and the brackets deleted:

(1) Endorsement

Name: [name of each covered location]________________

____

Address: [address of each covered location]________________

____

Policy Number: ________________

Period of Coverage: [current policy period] ________________

____

Name of [Insurer or Risk Retention Group]:________________

____

Address of [Insurer or Risk Retention Group]: ________________

____

Name of Insured:________________

Address of Insured: ________________

____

Endorsement:

1. This endorsement certifies that the policy to which the endorsement is attached provides liability insurance covering the following underground storage tanks:

[List the number of tanks at each facility and the name(s) and address(es) of the facility(ies) where the tanks are located. If more than one instrument is used to assure different tanks at any one facility, for each tank covered by this instrument, list the tank identification number provided in the notification submitted pursuant to 40 CFR 280.22, or the corresponding state requirement, and the name and address of the facility.]

for [insert: "taking corrective action" and/or "compensating third parties for bodily injury and property damage caused by" either "sudden accidental releases" or "nonsudden accidental releases" or "accidental releases"; in accordance with and subject to the limits of liability, exclusions, conditions, and other terms of the policy; if coverage is different for different tanks or locations, indicate the type of coverage applicable to each tank or location] arising from operating the underground storage tank(s) identified above.

The limits of liability are [insert the dollar amount of the "each occurrence" and "annual aggregate" limits of the Insurer's or Group's liability; if the amount of coverage is different for different types of coverage or for different underground storage tanks or locations, indicate the amount of coverage for each type of coverage and/or for each underground storage tank or location], exclusive of legal defense costs, which are subject to a separate limit under the policy. This coverage is provided under [policy number]. The effective date of said policy is [date].

2. The insurance afforded with respect to such occurrences is subject to all of the terms and conditions of the policy; provided, however, that any provisions inconsistent with subsections (a) through (e) of this Paragraph 2 are hereby amended to conform with subsections (a) through (e);

a. Bankruptcy or insolvency of the insured shall not relieve the ["Insurer" or "Group"] of its obligations under the policy to which this endorsement is attached.

b. The ["Insurer" or "Group"] is liable for the payment of amounts within any deductible applicable to the policy to the provider of corrective action or a damaged third-party, with a right of reimbursement by the insured for any such payment made by the ["Insurer" or "Group"]. This provision does not apply with respect to that amount of any deductible for which coverage is demonstrated under another mechanism or combination of mechanisms as specified in 40 CFR 280.95-280.102.

c. Whenever requested by [a Director of an implementing agency], the ["Insurer" or "Group"] agrees to furnish to [the Director] a signed duplicate original of the policy and all endorsements.

d. Cancellation or any other termination of the insurance by the ["Insurer" or "Group"], except for non-payment of premium or misrepresentation by the insured, will be effective only upon written notice and only after the expiration of 60 days after a copy of such written notice is received by the insured. Cancellation for non-payment of premium or misrepresentation by the insured will be effective only upon written notice and only after expiration of a minimum of 10 days after a copy of such written notice is received by the insured.

[Insert for claims-made policies:

e. The insurance covers claims otherwise covered by the policy that are reported to the ["Insurer" or "Group"] within six months of the effective date of cancellation or non-renewal of the policy except where the new or renewed policy has the same retroactive date or a retroactive date earlier than that of the prior policy, and which arise out of any covered occurrence that commenced after the policy retroactive date, if applicable, and prior to such policy renewal or termination date. Claims reported during such extended reporting period are subject to the terms, conditions, limits, including limits of liability, and exclusions of the policy.]

I hereby certify that the wording of this instrument is identical to the wording in 40 CFR 280.97(b)(1) and that the ["Insurer" or "Group"] is ["licensed to transact the business of insurance or eligible to provide insurance as an excess or surplus lines insurer in one or more states"].

[Signature of authorized representative of Insurer or Risk Retention Group]

[Name of person signing]

[Title of person signing], Authorized Representative of [name of Insurer or Risk Retention Group]

[Address of Representative]

(2) Certificate of Insurance

Name: [name of each covered location] ____________________

Address: [address of each covered location] ____________________

Policy Number: ____________________

Endorsement (if applicable): ____________________

Period of Coverage: [current policy period] ____________________

Name of [Insurer or Risk Retention Group]: ____________________

Address of [Insurer or Risk Retention Group]: ____________________

Name of Insured: ____________________

Address of Insured: ____________________

Certification:

1. [Name of Insurer or Risk Retention Group], [the "Insurer" or "Group"], as identified above, hereby certifies that it has issued liability insurance covering the following underground storage tank(s):

[List the number of tanks at each facility and the name(s) and address(es) of the facility(ies) where the tanks are located. If more than one instrument is used to assure different tanks at any one facility, for each tank covered by this instrument, list the tank identification number provided in the notification submitted pursuant to 40 CFR 280.22, or the corresponding state requirement, and the name and address of the facility.]

for [insert: "taking corrective action" and/or "compensating third parties for bodily injury and property damage caused by" either "sudden accidental releases" or "nonsudden accidental releases" or "accidental releases"; in accordance with and subject to the limits of liability, exclusions, conditions, and other terms of the policy; if coverage is different for different tanks or locations, indicate the type of coverage applicable to each tank or location] arising from operating the underground storage tank(s) identified above.

The limits of liability are [insert the dollar amount of the "each occurrence" and "annual aggregate" limits of the Insurer's or Group's liability; if the amount of coverage is different for different types of coverage or for different underground storage tanks or locations, indicate the amount of coverage for each type of coverage and/or for each underground storage tank or location], exclusive of legal defense costs, which are subject to a separate limit under the policy. This coverage is provided under [policy number]. The effective date of said policy is [date].

2. The ["Insurer" or "Group"] further certifies the following with respect to the insurance described in Paragraph 1:

a. Bankruptcy or insolvency of the insured shall not relieve the ["Insurer" or "Group"] of its obligations under the policy to which this certificate applies.

b. The ["Insurer" or "Group"] is liable for the payment of amounts within any deductible applicable to the policy to the provider of corrective action or a damaged third-party, with a right of reimbursement by the insured for any such payment made by the ["Insurer" or "Group"]. This provision does not apply with respect to that amount of any deductible for which coverage is demonstrated under another mechanism or combination of mechanisms as specified in 40 CFR 280.95-280.102.

c. Whenever requested by [a Director of an implementing agency], the ["Insurer" or "Group"] agrees to furnish to [the Director] a signed duplicate original of the policy and all endorsements.

d. Cancellation or any other termination of the insurance by the ["Insurer" or "Group"], except for non-payment of premium or misrepresentation by the insured, will be effective only upon written notice and only after the expiration of 60 days after a copy of such written notice is received by the insured. Cancellation for non-payment of premium or misrepresentation by the insured will be effective only upon written notice and only after expiration of a minimum of 10 days after a copy of such written notice is received by the insured. [Insert for claims-made policies:

e. The insurance covers claims otherwise covered by the policy that are reported to the ["Insurer" or "Group"] within six months of the effective date of cancellation or non-renewal of the policy except where the new or renewed policy has the same retroactive date or a retroactive date earlier than that of the prior policy, and which arise out of any covered occurrence that commenced after the policy retroactive date, if applicable, and prior to such policy renewal or termination date. Claims reported during such extended reporting period are subject to the terms, conditions, limits, including limits of liability, and exclusions of the policy.]

I hereby certify that the wording of this instrument is identical to the wording in 40 CFR 280.97(b)(2) and that the ["Insurer" or "Group"] is ["licensed to transact the business of insurance, or eligible to provide insurance as an excess or surplus lines insurer, in one or more states"].

[Signature of authorized representative of Insurer]

[Type name]

[Title], Authorized Representative of [name of Insurer or Risk Retention Group]

[Address of Representative]

(c) Each insurance policy must be issued by an insurer or a risk retention group that, at a minimum, is licensed to transact the business of insurance or eligible to provide insurance as an excess or surplus lines insurer in one or more states.

[53 FR 43370, Oct. 26, 1988, as amended at 54 FR 47081, Nov. 9, 1989]

§280.98 Surety bond.

(a) An owner or operator may satisfy the requirements of §280.93 by obtaining a surety bond that conforms to the requirements of this section. The surety company issuing the bond must be among those listed as acceptable sureties on federal bonds in the latest Circular 570 of the U.S. Department of the Treasury.

(b) The surety bond must be worded as follows, except that instructions in brackets must be replaced with the relevant information and the brackets deleted:

Performance Bond

Date bond executed: ____________________

Period of coverage: ____________________

Principal: [legal name and business address of owner or operator]

Type of organization: [insert "individual," "joint venture," "partnership," or "corporation"] ____________________

State of incorporation (if applicable): ____________________

Surety(ies): [name(s) and business address(es)] ______________

____

Scope of Coverage: [List the number of tanks at each facility and the name(s) and address(es) of the facility(ies) where the tanks are located. If more than one instrument is used to assure different tanks at any one facility, for each tank covered by this instrument, list the tank identification number provided in the notification submitted pursuant to 40 CFR 280.22, or the corresponding state requirement, and the name and address of the facility. List the coverage guaranteed by the bond: "taking corrective action" and/or "compensating third parties for bodily injury and property damage caused by" either "sudden accidental releases" or "nonsudden accidental releases" or "accidental releases" "arising from operating the underground storage tank"].

Penal sums of bond:

Per occurrence $ ______________

Annual aggregate $ ______________

Surety's bond number:______________

Know All Persons by These Presents, that we, the Principal and Surety(ies), hereto are firmly bound to [the implementing agency], in the above penal sums for the payment of which we bind ourselves, our heirs, executors, administrators, successors, and assigns jointly and severally; provided that, where the Surety(ies) are corporations acting as co-sureties, we, the Sureties, bind ourselves in such sums jointly and severally only for the purpose of allowing a joint action or actions against any or all of us, and for all other purposes each Surety binds itself, jointly and severally with the Principal, for the payment of such sums only as is set forth opposite the name of such Surety, but if no limit of liability is indicated, the limit of liability shall be the full amount of the penal sums.

Whereas said Principal is required under Subtitle I of the Resource Conservation and Recovery Act (RCRA), as amended, to provide financial assurance for [insert: "taking corrective action" and/or "compensating third parties for bodily injury and property damage caused by" either "sudden accidental releases" or "nonsudden accidental releases" or "accidental releases"; if coverage is different for different tanks or locations, indicate the type of coverage applicable to each tank or location] arising from operating the underground storage tanks identified above, and

Whereas said Principal shall establish a standby trust fund as is required when a surety bond is used to provide such financial assurance;

Now, therefore, the conditions of the obligation are such that if the Principal shall faithfully ["take corrective action, in accordance with 40 CFR part 280, subpart F and the Director of the state implementing agency's instructions for," and/or "compensate injured third parties for bodily injury and property damage caused by" either "sudden" or "nonsudden" or "sudden and nonsudden"] accidental releases arising from operating the tank(s) identified above, or if the Principal shall provide alternate financial assurance, as specified in 40 CFR part 280, subpart H, within 120 days after the date the notice of cancellation is received by the Principal from the Surety(ies), then this obligation shall be null and void; otherwise it is to remain in full force and effect.

Such obligation does not apply to any of the following:

(a) Any obligation of [insert owner or operator] under a workers' compensation, disability benefits, or unemployment compensation law or other similar law;

(b) Bodily injury to an employee of [insert owner or operator] arising from, and in the course of, employment by [insert owner or operator];

(c) Bodily injury or property damage arising from the ownership, maintenance, use, or entrustment to others of any aircraft, motor vehicle, or watercraft;

(d) Property damage to any property owned, rented, loaned to, in the care, custody, or control of, or occupied by [insert owner or operator] that is not the direct result of a release from a petroleum underground storage tank;

(e) Bodily injury or property damage for which [insert owner or operator] is obligated to pay damages by reason of the assumption of liability in a contract or agreement other than a contract or agreement entered into to meet the requirements of 40 CFR 280.93.

The Surety(ies) shall become liable on this bond obligation only when the Principal has failed to fulfill the conditions described above.

Upon notification by [the Director of the implementing agency] that the Principal has failed to ["take corrective action, in accordance with 40 CFR part 280, subpart F and the Director's instructions," and/ or "compensate injured third parties"] as guaranteed by this bond, the Surety(ies) shall either perform ["corrective action in accordance with 40 CFR part 280 and the Director's instructions," and/or "third-party liability compensation"] or place funds in an amount up to the annual aggregate penal sum into the standby trust fund as directed by [the Regional Administrator or the Director] under 40 CFR 280.108.

Upon notification by [the Director] that the Principal has failed to provide alternate financial assurance within 60 days after the date the notice of cancellation is received by the Principal from the Surety(ies) and that [the Director] has determined or suspects that a release has occurred, the Surety(ies) shall place funds in an amount not exceeding the annual aggregate penal sum into the standby trust fund as directed by [the Director] under 40 CFR 280.108.

The Surety(ies) hereby waive(s) notification of amendments to applicable laws, statutes, rules, and regulations and agrees that no such amendment shall in any way alleviate its (their) obligation on this bond.

The liability of the Surety(ies) shall not be discharged by any payment or succession of payments hereunder, unless and until such payment or payments shall amount in the annual aggregate to the penal sum shown on the face of the bond, but in no event shall the obligation of the Surety(ies) hereunder exceed the amount of said annual aggregate penal sum.

The Surety(ies) may cancel the bond by sending notice of cancellation by certified mail to the Principal, provided, however, that cancellation shall not occur during the 120 days beginning on the date of receipt of the notice of cancellation by the Principal, as evidenced by the return receipt.

The Principal may terminate this bond by sending written notice to the Surety(ies).

In Witness Thereof, the Principal and Surety(ies) have executed this Bond and have affixed their seals on the date set forth above.

The persons whose signatures appear below hereby certify that they are authorized to execute this surety bond on behalf of the Principal and Surety(ies) and that the wording of this surety bond is identical to the wording specified in 40 CFR 280.98(b) as such regulations were constituted on the date this bond was executed.

Principal

[Signature(s)]

[Names(s)]

[Title(s)]

[Corporate seal]

Corporate Surety(ies)

[Name and address]

[State of Incorporation: ______________

[Liability limit: $ ______________

[Signature(s)]

[Names(s) and title(s)]

[Corporate seal]

[For every co-surety, provide signature(s), corporate seal, and other information in the same manner as for Surety above.]

Bond premium: $______________________

(c) Under the terms of the bond, the surety will become liable on the bond obligation when the owner or operator fails to perform as guaranteed by the bond. In all cases, the surety's liability is limited to the per-occurrence and annual aggregate penal sums.

(d) The owner or operator who uses a surety bond to satisfy the requirements of §280.93 must establish a standby trust fund when the surety bond is acquired. Under the terms of the bond, all amounts paid by the surety under the bond will be deposited directly into the standby trust fund in accordance with instructions from the Director under §280.108. This standby trust fund must meet the requirements specified in §280.103.

§280.99 Letter of credit.

(a) An owner or operator may satisfy the requirements of §280.93 by obtaining an irrevocable standby letter of credit that conforms to the requirements of this section. The issuing institution must be an entity that has the authority to issue letters of credit in each state where used and whose letter-of-credit operations are regulated and examined by a federal or state agency.

(b) The letter of credit must be worded as follows, except that instructions in brackets are to be replaced with the relevant information and the brackets deleted:

Irrevocable Standby Letter of Credit

[Name and address of issuing institution]

[Name and address of Director(s) of state implementing agency(ies)]

Dear Sir or Madam: We hereby establish our Irrevocable Standby Letter of Credit No. ______ in your favor, at the request and for the account of [owner or operator name] of [address] up to the aggregate amount of [in words] U.S. dollars ($[insert dollar amount]), available upon presentation [insert, if more than one Director of a state implementing agency is a beneficiary, "by any one of you"] of

(1) your sight draft, bearing reference to this letter of credit, No.________, and

(2) your signed statement reading as follows: "I certify that the amount of the draft is payable pursuant to regulations issued under authority of Subtitle I of the Resource Conservation and Recovery Act of 1976, as amended."

This letter of credit may be drawn on to cover [insert: "taking corrective action" and/or "compensating third parties for bodily injury and property damage caused by" either "sudden accidental releases" or "nonsudden accidental releases" or "accidental releases"] arising from operating the underground storage tank(s) identified below in the amount of [in words] $[insert dollar amount] per occurrence and [in words] $[insert dollar amount] annual aggregate:

[List the number of tanks at each facility and the name(s) and address(es) of the facility(ies) where the tanks are located. If more than one instrument is used to assure different tanks at any one facility, for each tank covered by this instrument, list the tank identification number provided in the notification submitted pursuant to 40 CFR 280.22, or the corresponding state requirement, and the name and address of the facility.]

The letter of credit may not be drawn on to cover any of the following:

(a) Any obligation of [insert owner or operator] under a workers' compensation, disability benefits, or unemployment compensation law or other similar law;

(b) Bodily injury to an employee of [insert owner or operator] arising from, and in the course of, employment by [insert owner or operator];

(c) Bodily injury or property damage arising from the ownership, maintenance, use, or entrustment to others of any aircraft, motor vehicle, or watercraft;

(d) Property damage to any property owned, rented, loaned to, in the care, custody, or control of, or occupied by [insert owner or operator] that is not the direct result of a release from a petroleum underground storage tank;

(e) Bodily injury or property damage for which [insert owner or operator] is obligated to pay damages by reason of the assumption of liability in a contract or agreement other than a contract or agreement entered into to meet the requirements of 40 CFR 280.93.

This letter of credit is effective as of [date] and shall expire on [date], but such expiration date shall be automatically extended for a period of [at least the length of the original term] on [expiration date] and on each successive expiration date, unless, at least 120 days before the current expiration date, we notify [owner or operator] by certified mail that we have decided not to extend this letter of credit beyond the current expiration date. In the event that [owner or operator] is so notified, any unused portion of the credit shall be available upon presentation of your sight draft for 120 days after the date of receipt by [owner or operator], as shown on the signed return receipt.

Whenever this letter of credit is drawn on under and in compliance with the terms of this credit, we shall duly honor such draft upon presentation to us, and we shall deposit the amount of the draft directly into the standby trust fund of [owner or operator] in accordance with your instructions.

We certify that the wording of this letter of credit is identical to the wording specified in 40 CFR 280.99(b) as such regulations were constituted on the date shown immediately below.

[Signature(s) and title(s) of official(s) of issuing institution]

[Date]

This credit is subject to [insert "the most recent edition of the Uniform Customs and Practice for Documentary Credits, published and copyrighted by the International Chamber of Commerce," or "the Uniform Commercial Code"].

(c) An owner or operator who uses a letter of credit to satisfy the requirements of §280.93 must also establish a standby trust fund when the letter of credit is acquired. Under the terms of the letter of credit, all amounts paid pursuant to a draft by the Director of the implementing agency will be deposited by the issuing institution directly into the standby trust fund in accordance with instructions from the Director under §280.108. This standby trust fund must meet the requirements specified in §280.103.

(d) The letter of credit must be irrevocable with a term specified by the issuing institution. The letter of credit must provide that credit be automatically renewed for the same term as the original term, unless, at least 120 days before the current expiration date, the issuing institution notifies the owner or operator by certified mail of its decision not to renew the letter of credit. Under the terms of the letter of credit, the 120 days will begin on the date when the owner or operator receives the notice, as evidenced by the return receipt.

[53 FR 37194, Sept. 23, 1988, as amended at 59 FR 29960, June 10, 1994]

§280.100 Use of state-required mechanism.

(a) For underground storage tanks located in a state that does not have an approved program, and where the state requires owners or operators of underground storage tanks to demonstrate financial responsibility for taking corrective action and/or for compensating third parties for bodily injury and property damage, an owner or operator may use a state-required financial mechanism to meet the requirements of §280.93 if the Regional Administrator determines that the state mechanism is at least equivalent to the financial mechanisms specified in this subpart.

(b) The Regional Administrator will evaluate the equivalency of a state-required mechanism principally in terms of: certainty of the availability of funds for taking corrective action and/or for compensating third parties; the amount of funds that will be made available; and the types of costs covered. The Regional Administrator may also consider other factors as is necessary.

(c) The state, an owner or operator, or any other interested party may submit to the Regional Administrator a written petition requesting that one or more of the state-required mechanisms be considered acceptable for meeting the requirements of §280.93. The submission must include copies of the appropriate state statutory and regulatory requirements and must show the amount of funds for corrective action and/or for compensating third parties assured by the mechanism(s). The Regional Administrator may require the petitioner to submit additional information as is deemed necessary to make this determination.

(d) Any petition under this section may be submitted on behalf of all of the state's underground storage tank owners and operators.

(e) The Regional Administrator will notify the petitioner of his determination regarding the mechanism's acceptability in lieu of financial mechanisms specified in this subpart. Pending this determination, the owners and operators using such mechanisms will be deemed to be in compliance with the requirements of §280.93 for underground storage tanks located in the state for the amounts and types of costs covered by such mechanisms.

[53 FR 43370, Oct. 26, 1988; 53 FR 51274, Dec. 21, 1988]

§280.101 State fund or other state assurance.

(a) An owner or operator may satisfy the requirements of §280.93 for underground storage tanks located in a state, where EPA is administering the requirements of this subpart, which assures that monies will be available from a state fund or state assurance program to cover costs up to the limits specified in §280.93 or otherwise assures that such costs will be paid if the Regional Administrator determines that the state's assurance is at least equivalent to the financial mechanisms specified in this subpart.

(b) The Regional Administrator will evaluate the equivalency of a state fund or other state assurance principally in terms of: Certainty of the availability of funds for taking corrective action and/or for compensating third parties; the amount of funds that will be made available; and the types of costs covered. The Regional Administrator may also consider other factors as is necessary.

(c) The state must submit to the Regional Administrator a description of the state fund or other state assurance to be supplied as financial assurance, along with a list of the classes of underground storage tanks to which the funds may be applied. The Regional Administrator may require the state to submit additional information as is deemed necessary to make a determination regarding the acceptability of the state fund or other state assurance. Pending the determination by the Regional Administrator, the owner or operator of a covered class of USTs will be deemed to be in compliance with the requirements of §280.93 for the amounts and types of costs covered by the state fund or other state assurance.

(d) The Regional Administrator will notify the state of his determination regarding the acceptability of the state's fund or other assurance in lieu of financial mechanisms specified in this subpart. Within 60 days after the Regional Administrator notifies a state that a state fund or other state assurance is acceptable, the state must provide to each owner or operator for which it is assuming financial responsibility a letter or certificate describing the nature of the state's assumption of responsibility. The letter or certificate from the state must include, or have attached to it, the following information: the facility's name and address and the amount of funds for corrective action and/or for compensating third parties that is assured by the state. The owner or operator must maintain this letter or certificate on file as proof of financial responsibility in accordance with §280.107(b)(5).

Publisher's Note: The section referenced above, §280.107(b)(5), is not in the RCRA regulations.

§280.102 Trust fund.

(a) An owner or operator may satisfy the requirements of §280.93 by establishing a trust fund that conforms to the requirements of this section. The trustee must be an entity that has the authority to act as a trustee and whose trust operations are regulated and examined by a federal agency or an agency of the state in which the fund is established.

(b) The wording of the trust agreement must be identical to the wording specified in §280.103(b)(1), and must be accompanied by a formal certification of acknowledgement as specified in §280.103(b)(2).

(c) The trust fund, when established, must be funded for the full required amount of coverage, or funded for part of the required amount of coverage and used in combination with other mechanism(s) that provide the remaining required coverage.

(d) If the value of the trust fund is greater than the required amount of coverage, the owner or operator may submit a written request to the Director of the implementing agency for release of the excess.

(e) If other financial assurance as specified in this subpart is substituted for all or part of the trust fund, the owner or operator may submit a written request to the Director of the implementing agency for release of the excess.

(f) Within 60 days after receiving a request from the owner or operator for release of funds as specified in paragraph (d) or (e) of this section, the Director of the implementing agency will instruct the trustee to release to the owner or operator such funds as the Director specifies in writing.

§280.103 Standby trust fund.

(a) An owner or operator using any one of the mechanisms authorized by §§280.96, 280.98, or 280.99 must establish a standby trust fund when the mechanism is acquired. The trustee of the standby trust fund must be an entity that has the authority to act as a trustee and whose trust operations are regulated and examined by a Federal agency or an agency of the state in which the fund is established.

(b)(1) The standby trust agreement, or trust agreement, must be worded as follows, except that instructions in brackets are to be replaced with the relevant information and the brackets deleted:

Trust Agreement

Trust agreement, the "Agreement," entered into as of [date] by and between [name of the owner or operator], a [name of state] [insert "corporation," "partnership," "association," or "proprietorship"], the "Grantor," and [name of corporate trustee], [insert "Incorporated in the state of ______" or "a national bank"], the "Trustee."

Whereas, the United States Environmental Protection Agency, "EPA," an agency of the United States Government, has established certain regulations applicable to the Grantor, requiring that an owner or operator of an underground storage tank shall provide assurance that funds will be available when needed for corrective action and third-party compensation for bodily injury and property damage caused by sudden and nonsudden accidental releases arising from the operation of the underground storage tank. The attached Schedule A lists the number of tanks at each facility and the name(s) and address(es) of the facility(ies) where the tanks are located that are covered by the standpoint trust agreement.

[Whereas, the Grantor has elected to establish [insert either "a guarantee," "surety bond," or "letter of credit"] to provide all or part of such financial assurance for the underground storage tanks identified herein and is required to establish a standby trust fund able to accept payments from the instrument (This paragraph is only applicable to the standby trust agreement.)];

Whereas, the Grantor, acting through its duly authorized officers, has selected the Trustee to be the trustee under this agreement, and the Trustee is willing to act as trustee;

Now, therefore, the Grantor and the Trustee agree as follows:

Section 1. Definitions

As used in this Agreement:

(a) The term "Grantor" means the owner or operator who enters into this Agreement and any successors or assigns of the Grantor.

(b) The term "Trustee" means the Trustee who enters into this Agreement and any successor Trustee.

Section 2. Identification of the Financial Assurance Mechanism

This Agreement pertains to the [identify the financial assurance mechanism, either a guarantee, surety bond, or letter of credit, from which the standby trust fund is established to receive payments (This paragraph is only applicable to the standby trust agreement.)].

Section 3. Establishment of Fund

The Grantor and the Trustee hereby establish a trust fund, the "Fund," for the benefit of [implementing agency]. The Grantor and the Trustee intend that no third party have access to the Fund except as herein provided. [The Fund is established initially as a standby to receive payments and shall not consist of any property.] Payments made by the provider of financial assurance pursuant to [the Director of the implementing agency's] instruction are transferred to the Trustee and are referred to as the Fund, together with all earnings and profits thereon, less any payments or distributions made by the Trustee pursuant to this Agreement. The Fund shall be held by the Trustee, IN TRUST, as hereinafter provided. The Trustee shall not be responsible nor shall it undertake any responsibility for the amount or adequacy of, nor any duty to collect from the Grantor as provider of financial assurance, any payments necessary to discharge any liability of the Grantor established by [the state implementing agency]

Section 4. Payment for ["Corrective Action" and/or Third-Party Liability Claims"]

The Trustee shall make payments from the Fund as [the Director of the implementing agency] shall direct, in writing, to provide for the payment of the costs of [insert: "taking corrective action" and/ or compensating third parties for bodily injury and property damage caused by" either "sudden accidental releases" or "nonsudden accidental releases" or "accidental releases"] arising from operating the tanks covered by the financial assurance mechanism identified in this Agreement.

The Fund may not be drawn upon to cover any of the following:

(a) Any obligation of [insert owner or operator] under a workers' compensation, disability benefits, or unemployment compensation law or other similar law;

(b) Bodily injury to an employee of [insert owner or operator] arising from, and in the course of employment by [insert owner or operator];

(c) Bodily injury or property damage arising from the ownership, maintenance, use, or entrustment to others of any aircraft, motor vehicle, or watercraft;

(d) Property damage to any property owned, rented, loaned to, in the care, custody, or control of, or occupied by [insert owner or operator] that is not the direct result of a release from a petroleum underground storage tank;

(e) Bodily injury or property damage for which [insert owner or operator] is obligated to pay damages by reason of the assumption of liability in a contract or agreement other than a contract or agreement entered into to meet the requirements of 40 CFR 280.93.

The Trustee shall reimburse the Grantor, or other persons as specified by [the Director], from the Fund for corrective action expenditures and/or third-party liability claims in such amounts as [the Director] shall direct in writing. In addition, the Trustee shall refund to the Grantor such amounts as [the Director] specifies in writing. Upon refund, such funds shall no longer constitute part of the Fund as defined herein.

Section 5. Payments Comprising the Fund

Payments made to the Trustee for the Fund shall consist of cash and securities acceptable to the Trustee.

Section 6. Trustee Management

The Trustee shall invest and reinvest the principal and income of the Fund and keep the Fund invested as a single fund, without distinction between principal and income, in accordance with general investment policies and guidelines which the Grantor may communicate in writing to the Trustee from time to time, subject, however, to the provisions of this Section. In investing, reinvesting, exchanging, selling, and managing the Fund, the Trustee shall discharge his duties with respect to the trust fund solely in the interest of the beneficiaries and with the care, skill, prudence, and diligence under the circumstances then prevailing which persons of prudence, acting in a like capacity and familiar with such matters, would use in the conduct of an enterprise of a like character and with like aims; except that:

(i) Securities or other obligations of the Grantor, or any other owner or operator of the tanks, or any of their affiliates as defined in the Investment Company Act of 1940, as amended, 15 U.S.C. 80a-2(a), shall not be acquired or held, unless they are securities or other obligations of the federal or a state government;

(ii) The Trustee is authorized to invest the Fund in time or demand deposits of the Trustee, to the extent insured by an agency of the federal or state government; and

(iii) The Trustee is authorized to hold cash awaiting investment or distribution uninvested for a reasonable time and without liability for the payment of interest thereon.

Section 7. Commingling and Investment

The Trustee is expressly authorized in its discretion:

(a) To transfer from time to time any or all of the assets of the Fund to any common, commingled, or collective trust fund created by the Trustee in which the Fund is eligible to participate, subject to all of the provisions thereof, to be commingled with the assets of other trusts participating therein; and

(b) To purchase shares in any investment company registered under the Investment Company Act of 1940, 15 U.S.C. 80a-1 et seq., including one which may be created, managed, underwritten, or to which investment advice is rendered or the shares of which are sold by the Trustee. The Trustee may vote such shares in its discretion.

Section 8. Express Powers of Trustee

Without in any way limiting the powers and discretions conferred upon the Trustee by the other provisions of this Agreement or by law, the Trustee is expressly authorized and empowered:

(a) To sell, exchange, convey, transfer, or otherwise dispose of any property held by it, by public or private sale. No person dealing with the Trustee shall be bound to see to the application of the purchase money or to inquire into the validity or expediency of any such sale or other disposition;

(b) To make, execute, acknowledge, and deliver any and all documents of transfer and conveyance and any and all other instruments that may be necessary or appropriate to carry out the powers herein granted;

(c) To register any securities held in the Fund in its own name or in the name of a nominee and to hold any security in bearer form or in book entry, or to combine certificates representing such securities with certificates of the same issue held by the Trustee in other fiduciary capacities, or to deposit or arrange for the deposit of such securities in a qualified central depository even though, when so deposited, such securities may be merged and held in bulk in the name of the nominee of such depository with other securities deposited therein by another person, or to deposit or arrange for the deposit of any securities issued by the United States Government, or any agency or instrumentality thereof, with a Federal Reserve bank, but the books and records of the Trustee shall at all times show that all such securities are part of the Fund;

(d) To deposit any cash in the Fund in interest-bearing accounts maintained or savings certificates issued by the Trustee, in its separate corporate capacity, or in any other banking institution affiliated with the Trustee, to the extent insured by an agency of the federal or state government; and

(e) To compromise or otherwise adjust all claims in favor of or against the Fund.

Section 9. Taxes and Expenses

All taxes of any kind that may be assessed or levied against or in respect of the Fund and all brokerage commissions incurred by the Fund shall be paid from the Fund. All other expenses incurred by the Trustee in connection with the administration of this Trust, including fees for legal services rendered to the Trustee, the compensation of the Trustee to the extent not paid directly by the Grantor, and all other proper charges and disbursements of the Trustee shall be paid from the Fund.

Section 10. Advice of Counsel

The Trustee may from time to time consult with counsel, who may be counsel to the Grantor, with respect to any questions arising as to the construction of this Agreement or any action to be taken hereunder. The Trustee shall be fully protected, to the extent permitted by law, in acting upon the advice of counsel.

Section 11. Trustee Compensation

The Trustee shall be entitled to reasonable compensation for its services as agreed upon in writing from time to time with the Grantor.

Section 12. Successor Trustee

The Trustee may resign or the Grantor may replace the Trustee, but such resignation or replacement shall not be effective until the Grantor has appointed a successor trustee and this successor accepts the appointment. The successor trustee shall have the same powers and duties as those conferred upon the Trustee hereunder. Upon the successor trustee's acceptance of the appointment, the Trustee shall assign, transfer, and pay over to the successor trustee the funds and properties then constituting the Fund. If for any reason the Grantor cannot or does not act in the event of the resignation of the Trustee, the Trustee may apply to a court of competent jurisdiction for the appointment of a successor trustee or for instructions. The successor trustee shall specify the date on which it assumes administration of the trust in writing sent to the Grantor and the present Trustee by certified mail 10 days before such change becomes effective. Any expenses incurred by the Trustee as a result of any of the acts contemplated by this Section shall be paid as provided in Section 9.

Section 13. Instructions to the Trustee

All orders, requests, and instructions by the Grantor to the Trustee shall be in writing, signed by such persons as are designated in the attached Schedule B or such other designees as the Grantor may designate by amendment to Schedule B. The Trustee shall be fully protected in acting without inquiry in accordance with the Grantor's orders, requests, and instructions. All orders, requests, and instructions by [the Director of the implementing agency] to the Trustee shall be in writing, signed by [the Director], and the Trustee shall act and shall be fully protected in acting in accordance with such orders, requests, and instructions. The Trustee shall have the right to assume, in the absence of written notice to the contrary, that no event constituting a change or a termination of the authority of any person to act on behalf of the Grantor or [the director] hereunder has occurred. The Trustee shall have no duty to act in the absence of such orders, requests, and instructions from the Grantor and/or [the Director], except as provided for herein.

Section 14. Amendment of Agreement

This Agreement may be amended by an instrument in writing executed by the Grantor and the Trustee, or by the Trustee and [the Director of the implementing agency] if the Grantor ceases to exist.

Section 15. Irrevocability and Termination

Subject to the right of the parties to amend this Agreement as provided in Section 14, this Trust shall be irrevocable and shall continue until terminated at the written direction of the Grantor and the Trustee, or by the Trustee and [the Director of the implementing agency], if the Grantor ceases to exist. Upon termination of the Trust, all remaining trust property, less final trust administration expenses, shall be delivered to the Grantor.

Section 16. Immunity and Indemnification

The Trustee shall not incur personal liability of any nature in connection with any act or omission, made in good faith, in the administration of this Trust, or in carrying out any directions by the Grantor or [the Director of the implementing agency] issued in accordance with this Agreement. The Trustee shall be indemnified and saved harmless by the Grantor, from and against any personal liability to which the Trustee may be subjected by reason of any act or conduct in its official capacity, including all expenses reasonably incurred in its defense in the event the Grantor fails to provide such defense.

Section 17. Choice of Law

This Agreement shall be administered, construed, and enforced according to the laws of the state of [insert name of state], or the Comptroller of the Currency in the case of National Association banks.

Section 18. Interpretation

As used in this Agreement, words in the singular include the plural and words in the plural include the singular. The descriptive headings for each section of this Agreement shall not affect the interpretation or the legal efficacy of this Agreement.

In Witness whereof the parties have caused this Agreement to be executed by their respective officers duly authorized and their corporate seals (if applicable) to be hereunto affixed and attested as of the date first above written. The parties below certify that the wording of this Agreement is identical to the wording specified in 40 CFR 280.103(b)(1) as such regulations were constituted on the date written above.

[Signature of Grantor]

[Name of the Grantor]

[Title]

Attest:

[Signature of Trustee]

[Name of the Trustee]

[Title]

[Seal]

[Signature of Witness]

[Name of the Witness]

[Title]

[Seal]

(2) The standby trust agreement, or trust agreement must be accompanied by a formal certification of acknowledgement similar to the following. State requirements may differ on the proper content of this acknowledgment.

State of ____________________

County of ____________________

On this [date], before me personally came [owner or operator] to me known, who, being by me duly sworn, did depose and say that she/he resides at [address], that she/he is [title] of [corporation], the corporation described in and which executed the above instrument; that she/he knows the seal of said corporation; that the seal affixed to such instrument is such corporate seal; that it was so affixed by order of the Board of Directors of said corporation; and that she/he signed her/ his name thereto by like order.

[Signature of Notary Public]

[Name of Notary Public]

(c) The Director of the implementing agency will instruct the trustee to refund the balance of the standby trust fund to the provider of financial assurance if the Director determines that no additional corrective action costs or third-party liability claims will occur as a result of a release covered by the financial assurance mechanism for which the standby trust fund was established.

(d) An owner or operator may establish one trust fund as the depository mechanism for all funds assured in compliance with this rule.

[53 FR 43370, Oct. 26, 1988; 53 FR 51274, Dec. 21, 1988]

§280.104 Local government bond rating test.

(a) A general purpose local government owner or operator and/or local government serving as a guarantor may satisfy the requirements of §280.93 by having a currently outstanding issue or issues of general obligation bonds of $1 million or more, excluding refunded obligations, with a Moody's rating of Aaa, Aa, A, or Baa, or a Standard & Poor's rating of AAA, AA, A, or BBB. Where a local government has multiple outstanding issues, or where a local government's bonds are rated by both Moody's and Standard and Poor's, the lowest rating must be used to determine eligibility. Bonds that are backed by credit enhancement other than municipal bond insurance may not be considered in determining the amount of applicable bonds outstanding.

(b) A local government owner or operator or local government serving as a guarantor that is not a general-purpose local government and does not have the legal authority to issue general obligation bonds may satisfy the requirements of §280.93 by having a currently outstanding issue or issues of revenue bonds of $1 million or more, excluding refunded issues and by also having a Moody's rating of Aaa, A, A, or Baa, or a Standard & Poor's rating of AAA, AA, A, or BBB as the lowest rating for any rated revenue bond issued by the local government. Where bonds are rated by both Moody's and Standard & Poor's, the lower rating for each bond must be used to determine eligibility. Bonds that are backed by credit enhancement may not be considered in determining the amount of applicable bonds outstanding.

(c) The local government owner or operator and/or guarantor must maintain a copy of its bond rating published within the last 12 months by Moody's or Standard & Poor's.

(d) To demonstrate that it meets the local government bond rating test, the chief financial officer of a general purpose local government owner or operator and/or guarantor must sign a letter worded exactly as follows, except that the instructions in brackets are to be replaced by the relevant information and the brackets deleted:

Letter from Chief Financial Officer

I am the chief financial officer of [insert: name and address of local government owner or operator, or guarantor]. This letter is in support of the use of the bond rating test to demonstrate financial responsibility for [insert: "taking corrective action" and/or "compensating third parties for bodily injury and property damage"] caused by [insert: "sudden accidental releases" and/or "nonsudden accidental releases"] in the amount of at least [insert: dollar amount] per occurrence and [insert: dollar amount] annual aggregate arising from operating (an) underground storage tank(s).

Underground storage tanks at the following facilities are assured by this bond rating test: [List for each facility: the name and address of the facility where tanks are assured by the bond rating test].

The details of the issue date, maturity, outstanding amount, bond rating, and bond rating agency of all outstanding bond issues that are being used by [name of local government owner or operator, or guarantor] to demonstrate financial responsibility are as follows: [complete table]

Issue date	Maturity date	Outstanding amount	Bond rating	Rating agency
				[Moody's or Standard & Poor's]

The total outstanding obligation of [insert amount], excluding refunded bond issues, exceeds the minimum amount of $1 million. All outstanding general obligation bonds issued by this government that have been rated by Moody's or Standard & Poor's are rated as at least investment grade (Moody's Baa or Standard & Poor's BBB) based on the most recent ratings published within the last 12 months. Neither rating service has provided notification within the last 12 months of downgrading of bond ratings below investment grade or of withdrawal of bond rating other than for repayment of outstanding bond issues.

I hereby certify that the wording of this letter is identical to the wording specified in 40 CFR Part 280.104(d) as such regulations were constituted on the date shown immediately below.

[Date] ______________________

[Signature] ______________________

[Name] ______________________

[Title] ______________________

(e) To demonstrate that it meets the local government bond rating test, the chief financial officer of local government owner or operator and/or guarantor other than a general purpose government must sign a letter worded exactly as follows, except that the instructions in brackets are to be replaced by the relevant information and the brackets deleted:

Letter from Chief Financial Officer

I am the chief financial officer of [insert: name and address of local government owner or operator, or guarantor]. This letter is in support of the use of the bond rating test to demonstrate financial responsibility for [insert: "taking corrective action" and/or "compensating third parties for bodily injury and property damage"] caused by [insert : "sudden accidental releases" and/or "nonsudden accidental releases"] in the amount of at least [insert: dollar amount] per occurrence and [insert: dollar amount] annual aggregate arising from operating (an) underground storage tank(s). This local government is not organized to provide general governmental services and does not have the legal authority under state law or constitutional provisions to issue general obligation debt.

Underground storage tanks at the following facilities are assured by this bond rating test: [List for each facility: the name and address of the facility where tanks are assured by the bond rating test].

The details of the issue date, maturity, outstanding amount, bond rating, and bond rating agency of all outstanding revenue bond issues that are being used by [name of local government owner or operator, or guarantor] to demonstrate financial responsibility are as follows: [complete table]

Issue date	Maturity date	Outstanding amount	Bond rating	Rating agency
				[Moody's or Standard & Poor's]

The total outstanding obligation of [insert amount], excluding refunded bond issues, exceeds the minimum amount of $1 million. All outstanding revenue bonds issued by this government that have been rated by Moody's or Standard & Poor's are rated as at least investment grade (Moody's Baa or Standard & Poor's BBB) based on the most recent ratings published within the last 12 months. The revenue bonds listed are not backed by third-party credit enhancement or are insured by a municipal bond insurance company. Neither rating service has provided notification within the last 12 months of downgrading of bond ratings below investment grade or of withdrawal of bond rating other than for repayment of outstanding bond issues.

I hereby certify that the wording of this letter is identical to the wording specified in 40 CFR part 280.104(e) as such regulations were constituted on the date shown immediately below.

[Date] __________

[Signature] __________

[Name] __________

[Title] __________

(f) The Director of the implementing agency may require reports of financial condition at any time from the local government owner or operator, and/or local government guarantor. If the Director finds, on the basis of such reports or other information, that the local government owner or operator, and/or guarantor, no longer meets the local government bond rating test requirements of §280.104, the local government owner or operator must obtain alternative coverage within 30 days after notification of such a finding.

(g) If a local government owner or operator using the bond rating test to provide financial assurance finds that it no longer meets the bond rating test requirements, the local government owner or operator must obtain alternative coverage within 150 days of the change in status.

[58 FR 9053, Feb. 18, 1993]

§280.105 Local government financial test.

(a) A local government owner or operator may satisfy the requirements of §280.93 by passing the financial test specified in this section. To be eligible to use the financial test, the local government owner or operator must have the ability and authority to assess and levy taxes or to freely establish fees and charges. To pass the local government financial test, the owner or operator must meet the criteria of paragraphs (b)(2) and (b)(3) of this section based on year- end financial statements for the latest completed fiscal year.

(b)(1) The local government owner or operator must have the following information available, as shown in the year-end financial statements for the latest completed fiscal year:

(i) *Total revenues*: Consists of the sum of general fund operating and non-operating revenues including net local taxes, licenses and permits, fines and forfeitures, revenues from use of money and property, charges for services, investment earnings, sales (property, publications, etc.), intergovernmental revenues (restricted and unrestricted), and total revenues from all other governmental funds including enterprise, debt service, capital projects, and special revenues, but excluding revenues to funds held in a trust or agency capacity. For purposes of this test, the calculation of total revenues shall exclude all transfers between funds under the direct control of the local government using the financial test (interfund transfers), liquidation of investments, and issuance of debt.

(ii) *Total expenditures*: Consists of the sum of general fund operating and non-operating expenditures including public safety, public utilities, transportation, public works, environmental protection, cultural and recreational, community development, revenue sharing, employee benefits and compensation, office management, planning and zoning, capital projects, interest payments on debt, payments for retirement of debt principal, and total expenditures from all other governmental funds including enterprise, debt service, capital projects, and special revenues. For purposes of this test, the calculation of total expenditures shall exclude all transfers between funds under the direct control of the local government using the financial test (interfund transfers).

(iii) *Local revenues*: Consists of total revenues (as defined in paragraph (b)(1)(i) of this section) minus the sum of all transfers from other governmental entities, including all monies received from Federal, state, or local government sources.

(iv) *Debt service*: Consists of the sum of all interest and principal payments on all long-term credit obligations and all interest-bearing short-term credit obligations. Includes interest and principal payments on general obligation bonds, revenue bonds, notes, mortgages, judgments, and interest bearing warrants. Excludes payments on non-interest-bearing short-term obligations, interfund obligations, amounts owed in a trust or agency capacity, and advances and contingent loans from other governments.

(v) *Total funds*: Consists of the sum of cash and investment securities from all funds, including general, enterprise, debt service, capital projects, and special revenue funds, but excluding employee retirement funds, at the end of the local government's financial reporting year. Includes Federal securities, Federal agency securities, state and local government securities, and other securities such as bonds, notes and mortgages. For purposes of this test, the calculation of total funds shall exclude agency funds, private trust funds, accounts receivable, value of real property, and other non-security assets.

(vi) *Population* consists of the number of people in the area served by the local government.

(2) The local government's year-end financial statements, if independently audited, cannot include an adverse auditor's opinion or a disclaimer of opinion. The local government cannot have outstanding issues of general obligation or revenue bonds that are rated as less than investment grade.

(3) The local government owner or operator must have a letter signed by the chief financial officer worded as specified in paragraph (c) of this section.

(c) To demonstrate that it meets the financial test under paragraph (b) of this section, the chief financial officer of the local government owner or operator, must sign, within 120 days of the close of each financial reporting year, as defined by the twelve-month period for which financial statements used to support the financial test are prepared, a letter worded exactly as follows, except that the instructions in brackets are to be replaced by the relevant information and the brackets deleted:

Letter from Chief Financial Officer

I am the chief financial officer of [insert: name and address of the owner or operator]. This letter is in support of the use of the local government financial test to demonstrate financial responsibility for [insert: "taking corrective action" and/or "compensating third parties for bodily injury and property damage"] caused by [insert: "sudden accidental releases" and/or "nonsudden accidental releases"] in the amount of at least [insert: dollar amount] per occurrence and [insert: dollar amount] annual aggregate arising from operating [an] underground storage tank[s].

Underground storage tanks at the following facilities are assured by this financial test [List for each facility: the name and address of the facility where tanks assured by this financial test are located. If separate mechanisms or combinations of mechanisms are being used to assure any of the tanks at this facility, list each tank assured by this financial test by the tank identification number provided in the notification submitted pursuant to 40 CFR Part 280.22 or the corresponding state requirements.]

This owner or operator has not received an adverse opinion, or a disclaimer of opinion from an independent auditor on its financial statements for the latest completed fiscal year. Any outstanding issues of general obligation or revenue bonds, if rated, have a Moody's rating of Aaa, Aa, A, or Baa or a Standard and Poor's rating of AAA, AA, A, or BBB; if rated by both firms, the bonds have a Moody's rating of Aaa, Aa, A, or Baa and a Standard and Poor's rating of AAA, AA, A, or BBB.

Worksheet for Municipal Financial Test

Part I: Basic Information

1. Total Revenues
   a. Revenues (dollars) ____________
   Value of revenues excludes liquidation of investments and issuance of debt. Value includes all general fund operating and non-operating revenues, as well as all revenues from all other governmental funds including enterprise, debt service, capital projects, and special revenues, but excluding revenues to funds held in a trust or agency capacity.
   b. Subtract interfund transfers (dollars) ____________
   c. Total Revenues (dollars) ____________
2. Total Expenditures
   a. Expenditures (dollars) ____________
   Value consists of the sum of general fund operating and non- operating expenditures including interest payments on debt, payments for retirement of debt principal, and total expenditures from all other governmental funds including enterprise, debt service, capital projects, and special revenues.
   b. Subtract interfund transfers (dollars) ____________
   c. Total Expenditures (dollars) ____________
3. Local Revenues
   a. Total Revenues (from 1c) (dollars) ____________
   b. Subtract total intergovernmental transfers (dollars) ____________
   c. Local Revenues (dollars) ____________
4. Debt Service
   a. Interest and fiscal charges (dollars) ____________
   b. Add debt retirement (dollars) ____________
   c. Total Debt Service (dollars) ____________
5. Total Funds (Dollars) ____________
   (Sum of amounts held as cash and investment securities from all funds, excluding amounts held for employee retirement funds, agency funds, and trust funds)
6. Population (Persons) ____________

Part II: Application of Test

7. Total Revenues to Population
   a. Total Revenues (from 1c) ____________
   b. Population (from 6) ____________
   c. Divide 7a by 7b ____________
   d. Subtract 417 ____________
   e. Divide by 5,212 ____________
   f. Multiply by 4.095 ____________
8. Total Expenses to Population
   a. Total Expenses (from 2c) ____________
   b. Population (from 6) ____________
   c. Divide 8a by 8b ____________
   d. Subtract 524 ____________

e. Divide by 5,401 ________
f. Multiply by 4.095 ________
9. Local Revenues to Total Revenues
a. Local Revenues (from 3c) ________
b. Total Revenues (from 1c) ________
c. Divide 9a by 9b ________
d. Subtract .695 ________
e. Divide by .205 ________
f. Multiply by 2.840 ________
10. Debt Service to Population
a. Debt Service (from 4d) ________
b. Population (from 6) ________
c. Divide 10a by 10b ________
d. Subtract 51 ________
e. Divide by 1,038 ________
f. Multiply by -1.866 ________
11. Debt Service to Total Revenues
a. Debt Service (from 4d) ________
b. Total Revenues (from 1c) ________
c. Divide 11a by 11b ________
d. Subtract .068 ________
e. Divide by .259 ________
f. Multiply by -3.533 ________
12. Total Revenues to Total Expenses
a. Total Revenues (from 1c) ________
b. Total Expenses (from 2c) ________
c. Divide 12a by 12b ________
d. Subtract .910 ________
e. Divide by .899 ________
f. Multiply by 3.458 ________
13. Funds Balance to Total Revenues
a. Total Funds (from 5) ________
b. Total Revenues (from 1c) ________
c. Divide 13a by 13b ________
d. Subtract .891 ________
e. Divide by 9.156 ________
f. Multiply by 3.270 ________
14. Funds Balance to Total Expenses
a. Total Funds (from 5) ________
b. Total Expenses (from 2c) ________
c. Divide 14a by 14b ________
d. Subtract .866 ________
e. Divide by 6.409 ________
f. Multiply by 3.270 ________
15. Total Funds to Population ________
a. Total Funds (from 5) ________
b. Population (from 6) ________
c. Divide 15a by 15b ________
d. Subtract 270 ________
e. Divide by 4,548 ________
f. Multiply by 1.866 ________
16. Add 7f + 8f + 9f + 10f + 11f + 12f + 13f + 14f + 15f + 4.937 ________

I hereby certify that the financial index shown on line 16 of the worksheet is greater than zero and that the wording of this letter is identical to the wording specified in 40 CFR part 280.105(c) as such regulations were constituted on the date shown immediately below.
[Date]
[Signature]
[Name]
[Title]

(d) If a local government owner or operator using the test to provide financial assurance finds that it no longer meets the requirements of the financial test based on the year-end financial statements, the owner or operator must obtain alternative coverage within 150 days of the end of the year for which financial statements have been prepared.

(e) The Director of the implementing agency may require reports of financial condition at any time from the local government owner or operator. If the Director finds, on the basis of such reports or other information, that the local government owner or operator no longer meets the financial test requirements of §280.105 (b) and (c), the owner or operator must obtain alternate coverage within 30 days after notification of such a finding.

(f) If the local government owner or operator fails to obtain alternate assurance within 150 days of finding that it no longer meets the requirements of the financial test based on the year-end financial statements or within 30 days of notification by the Director of the implementing agency that it no longer meets the requirements of the financial test, the owner or operator must notify the Director of such failure within 10 days.

[58 FR 9054, Feb. 18, 1993]

§280.106 Local government guarantee.

(a) A local government owner or operator may satisfy the requirements of §280.93 by obtaining a guarantee that conforms to the requirements of this section. The guarantor must be either the state in which the local government owner or operator is located or a local government having a "substantial governmental relationship" with the owner and operator and issuing the guarantee as an act incident to that relationship. A local government acting as the guarantor must:

(1) demonstrate that it meets the bond rating test requirement of §280.104 and deliver a copy of the chief financial officer's letter as contained in §280.104(c) to the local government owner or operator; or

(2) demonstrate that it meets the worksheet test requirements of §280.105 and deliver a copy of the chief financial officer's letter as contained in §280.105(c) to the local government owner or operator; or

(3) demonstrate that it meets the local government fund requirements of §280.107(a), §280.107(b), or §280.107(c) and deliver a copy of the chief financial officer's letter as contained in §280.107 to the local government owner or operator.

(b) If the local government guarantor is unable to demonstrate financial assurance under any of §§280.104, 280.105, 280.107(a), 280.107(b), or 280.107(c), at the end of the financial reporting year, the guarantor shall send by certified mail, before cancellation or non-renewal of the guarantee, notice to the owner or operator. The guarantee will terminate no less than 120 days after the date the owner or operator receives the notification, as evidenced by the return receipt. The owner or operator must obtain alternative coverage as specified in §280.114(c).

(c) The guarantee agreement must be worded as specified in paragraph (d) or (e) of this section, depending on which of the following alternative guarantee arrangements is selected:

(1) If, in the default or incapacity of the owner or operator, the guarantor guarantees to fund a standby trust as directed by the Director of the implementing agency, the guarantee shall be worded as specified in paragraph (d) of this section.

(2) If, in the default or incapacity of the owner or operator, the guarantor guarantees to make payments as directed by the Director of the implementing agency for taking corrective action or compensating third parties for bodily injury and property damage, the guarantee shall be worded as specified in paragraph (e) of this section.

(d) If the guarantor is a state, the local government guarantee with standby trust must be worded exactly as follows, except that instructions in brackets are to be replaced with relevant information and the brackets deleted:

Local Government Guarantee With Standby Trust Made by a State

Guarantee made this [date] by [name of state], herein referred to as guarantor, to [the state implementing agency] and to any and all third parties, and obliges, on behalf of [local government owner or operator].

Recitals

(1) Guarantor is a state.

(2) [Local government owner or operator] owns or operates the following underground storage tank(s) covered by this guarantee: [List the number of tanks at each facility and the name(s) and address(es) of the facility(ies) where the tanks are located. If more than one instrument is used to assure different tanks at any one facility, for each tank covered by this instrument, list the tank identification number provided in the notification submitted pursuant to 40 CFR part 280 or the corresponding state requirement, and the name and address of the facility.] This guarantee satisfies 40 CFR part 280, subpart H requirements for assuring funding for [insert: "taking corrective action" and/or "compensating third parties for bodily injury and property damage caused by" either "sudden accidental releases" or "nonsudden accidental releases" or "accidental releases"; if coverage is different for different tanks or locations, indicate the type of coverage applicable to each tank or location] arising from operating the above-identified underground storage tank(s) in the amount of [insert dollar amount] per occurrence and [insert dollar amount] annual aggregate.

(3) Guarantor guarantees to [implementing agency] and to any and all third parties that:

In the event that [local government owner or operator] fails to provide alternative coverage within 60 days after receipt of a notice of cancellation of this guarantee and the [Director of the implementing agency] has determined or suspects that a release has occurred at an underground storage tank covered by this guarantee, the guarantor, upon instructions from the [Director] shall fund a standby trust fund in accordance with the provisions of 40 CFR part 280.112, in an amount not to exceed the coverage limits specified above.

In the event that the [Director] determines that [local government owner or operator] has failed to perform corrective action for releases arising out of the operation of the above-identified tank(s) in accordance with 40 CFR part 280, subpart F, the guarantor upon written instructions from the [Director] shall fund a standby trust fund in accordance with the provisions of 40 CFR part 280.112, in an amount not to exceed the coverage limits specified above.

If [owner or operator] fails to satisfy a judgment or award based on a determination of liability for bodily injury or property damage to third parties caused by ["sudden" and/or "nonsudden"] accidental releases arising from the operation of the above-identified tank(s), or fails to pay an amount agreed to in settlement of a claim arising from or alleged to arise from such injury or damage, the guarantor, upon written instructions from the [Director], shall fund a standby trust in accordance with the provisions of 40 CFR part 280.112 to satisfy such judgment(s), award(s), or settlement agreement(s) up to the limits of coverage specified above.

(4) Guarantor agrees to notify [owner or operator] by certified mail of a voluntary or involuntary proceeding under Title 11 (Bankruptcy), U.S. Code naming guarantor as debtor, within 10 days after commencement of the proceeding.

(5) Guarantor agrees to remain bound under this guarantee notwithstanding any modification or alteration of any obligation of [owner or operator] pursuant to 40 CFR part 280.

(6) Guarantor agrees to remain bound under this guarantee for so long as [local government owner or operator] must comply with the applicable financial responsibility requirements of 40 CFR part 280, subpart H for the above identified tank(s), except that guarantor may cancel this guarantee by sending notice by certified mail to [owner or operator], such cancellation to become effective no earlier than 120 days after receipt of such notice by [owner or operator], as evidenced by the return receipt.

(7) The guarantor's obligation does not apply to any of the following:

(a) Any obligation of [local government owner or operator] under a workers' compensation, disability benefits, or unemployment compensation law or other similar law;

(b) Bodily injury to an employee of [insert: local government owner or operator] arising from, and in the course of, employment by [insert: local government owner or operator];

(c) Bodily injury or property damage arising from the ownership, maintenance, use, or entrustment to others of any aircraft, motor vehicle, or watercraft;

(d) Property damage to any property owned, rented, loaded to, in the care, custody, or control of, or occupied by [insert: local government owner or operator] that is not the direct result of a release from a petroleum underground storage tank;

(e) Bodily damage or property damage for which [insert owner or operator] is obligated to pay damages by reason of the assumption of liability in a contract or agreement other than a contract or agreement entered into to meet the requirements of 40 CFR part 280.93.

(8) Guarantor expressly waives notice of acceptance of this guarantee by [the implementing agency], by any or all third parties, or by [local government owner or operator], I hereby certify that the wording of this guarantee is identical to the wording specified in 40 CFR part 280.106(d) as such regulations were constituted on the effective date shown immediately below.

Effective date:____________________

[Name of guarantor]
[Authorized signature for guarantor]
[Name of person signing]
[Title of person signing]
Signature of witness or notary:

If the guarantor is a local government, the local government guarantee with standby trust must be worded exactly as follows, except that instructions in brackets are to be replaced with relevant information and the brackets deleted:

Local Government Guarantee With Standby Trust Made by a Local Government

Guarantee made this [date] by [name of guaranteeing entity], a local government organized under the laws of [name of state], herein referred to as guarantor, to [the state implementing agency] and to any and all third parties, and obliges, on behalf of [local government owner or operator].

Recitals

(1) Guarantor meets or exceeds [select one: the local government bond rating test requirements of 40 CFR part 280.104, the local government financial test requirements of 40 CFR part 280.105, or the local government fund under 40 CFR part 280.107(a), 280.107(b), or 280.107(c)].

(2) [Local government owner or operator] owns or operates the following underground storage tank(s) covered by this guarantee: [List the number of tanks at each facility and the name(s) and address(es) of the facility(ies) where the tanks are located. If more than one instrument is used to assure different tanks at any one facility, for each tank covered by this instrument, list the tank identification number provided in the notification submitted pursuant to 40 CFR part 280 or the corresponding state requirement, and the name and address of the facility.] This guarantee satisfies 40 CFR part 280, subpart H requirements for assuring funding for [insert: "taking corrective action" and/or "compensating third parties for bodily injury and property damage caused by" either "sudden accidental releases" or "nonsudden accidental releases" or "accidental releases"; if coverage is different for different tanks or locations, indicate the type of coverage applicable to each tank or location] arising from operating the above-identified underground storage tank(s) in the amount of [insert dollar amount] per occurrence and [insert: dollar amount] annual aggregate.

(3) Incident to our substantial governmental relationship with [local government owner or operator], guarantor guarantees to [implementing agency] and to any and all third parties that:

In the event that [local government owner or operator] fails to provide alternative coverage within 60 days after receipt of a notice of cancellation of this guarantee and the [Director of the implementing agency] has determined or suspects that a release has occurred at an underground storage tank covered by this guarantee, the guarantor, upon instructions from the [Director] shall fund a standby trust fund in accordance with the provisions of 40 CFR part 280.112, in an amount not to exceed the coverage limits specified above.

In the event that the [Director] determines that [local government owner or operator] has failed to perform corrective action for releases arising out of the operation of the above-identified tank(s) in accordance with 40 CFR part 280, subpart F, the guarantor upon written instructions from the [Director] shall fund a standby trust fund in accordance with the provisions of 40 CFR part 280.112, in an amount not to exceed the coverage limits specified above.

If [owner or operator] fails to satisfy a judgment or award based on a determination of liability for bodily injury or property damage to third parties caused by ["sudden" and/or "nonsudden"] accidental releases arising from the operation of the above-identified tank(s), or fails to pay an amount agreed to in settlement of a claim arising from or alleged to arise from such injury or damage, the guarantor, upon written instructions from the [Director], shall fund a standby trust in accordance with the provisions of 40 CFR part 280.112 to satisfy such judgment(s), award(s), or settlement agreement(s) up to the limits of coverage specified above.

(4) Guarantor agrees that, if at the end of any fiscal year before cancellation of this guarantee, the guarantor fails to meet or exceed the requirements of the financial responsibility mechanism specified in paragraph (1), guarantor shall send within 120 days of such failure, by certified mail, notice to [local government owner or operator], as evidenced by the return receipt.

(5) Guarantor agrees to notify [owner or operator] by certified mail of a voluntary or involuntary proceeding under Title 11 (Bankruptcy), U.S. Code naming guarantor as debtor, within 10 days after commencement of the proceeding.

(6) Guarantor agrees to remain bound under this guarantee notwithstanding any modification or alteration of any obligation of [owner or operator] pursuant to 40 CFR part 280.

(7) Guarantor agrees to remain bound under this guarantee for so long as [local government owner or operator] must comply with the applicable financial responsibility requirements of 40 CFR part 280, subpart H for the above identified tank(s), except that guarantor may cancel this guarantee by sending notice by certified mail to [owner or operator], such cancellation to become effective no earlier than 120 days after receipt of such notice by [owner or operator], as evidenced by the return receipt.

(8) The guarantor's obligation does not apply to any of the following:

(a) Any obligation of [local government owner or operator] under a workers' compensation, disability benefits, or unemployment compensation law or other similar law;

(b) Bodily injury to an employee of [insert: local government owner or operator] arising from, and in the course of, employment by [insert: local government owner or operator];

(c) Bodily injury or property damage arising from the ownership, maintenance, use, or entrustment to others of any aircraft, motor vehicle, or watercraft;

(d) Property damage to any property owned, rented, loaned to, in the care, custody, or control of, or occupied by [insert: local government owner or operator] that is not the direct result of a release from a petroleum underground storage tank;

(e) Bodily damage or property damage for which [insert: owner or operator] is obligated to pay damages by reason of the assumption of liability in a contract or agreement other than a contract or agreement entered into to meet the requirements of 40 CFR part 280.93. (9) Guarantor expressly waives notice of acceptance of this guarantee by [the implementing agency], by any or all third parties, or by [local government owner or operator].

I hereby certify that the wording of this guarantee is identical to the wording specified in 40 CFR part 280.106(d) as such regulations were constituted on the effective date shown immediately below.

Effective date: ____________________

[Name of guarantor]
[Authorized signature for guarantor]
[Name of person signing]
[Title of person signing]

Signature of witness or notary: ____________________

(e) If the guarantor is a state, the local government guarantee without standby trust must be worded exactly as follows, except that instructions in brackets are to be replaced with relevant information and the brackets deleted:

Local Government Guarantee Without Standby Trust Made by a State

Guarantee made this [date] by [name of state], herein referred to as guarantor, to [the state implementing agency] and to any and all third parties, and obliges, on behalf of [local government owner or operator].

Recitals

(1) Guarantor is a state.

(2) [Local government owner or operator] owns or operates the following underground storage tank(s) covered by this guarantee: [List the number of tanks at each facility and the name(s) and address(es) of the facility(ies) where the tanks are located. If more than one instrument is used to assure different tanks at any one facility, for each tank covered by this instrument, list the tank identification number provided in the notification submitted pursuant to 40 CFR part 280 or the corresponding state requirement, and the name and address of the facility.] This guarantee satisfies 40 CFR part 280, subpart H requirements for assuring funding for [insert: "taking corrective action" and/or "compensating third parties for bodily injury and property damage caused by" either "sudden accidental releases" or "nonsudden accidental releases" or "accidental releases"; if coverage is different for different tanks or locations, indicate the type of coverage applicable to each tank or location] arising from operating the above-identified underground storage tank(s) in the amount of [insert: dollar amount] per occurrence and [insert: dollar amount] annual aggregate.

(3) Guarantor guarantees to [implementing agency] and to any and all third parties and obliges that:

In the event that [local government owner or operator] fails to provide alternative coverage within 60 days after receipt of a notice of cancellation of this guarantee and the [Director of the implementing agency] has determined or suspects that a release has occurred at an underground storage tank covered by this guarantee, the guarantor, upon written instructions from the [Director] shall make funds available to pay for corrective actions and compensate third parties for bodily injury and property damage in an amount not to exceed the coverage limits specified above.

In the event that the [Director] determines that [local government owner or operator] has failed to perform corrective action for releases arising out of the operation of the above-identified tank(s) in accordance with 40 CFR part 280, subpart F, the guarantor upon written instructions from the [Director] shall make funds available to pay for corrective actions in an amount not to exceed the coverage limits specified above.

If [owner or operator] fails to satisfy a judgment or award based on a determination of liability for bodily injury or property damage to third parties caused by ["sudden" and/or "nonsudden"] accidental releases arising from the operation of the above-identified tank(s), or fails to pay an amount agreed to in settlement of a claim arising from or alleged to arise from such injury or damage, the guarantor, upon written instructions from the [Director], shall make funds available to compensate third parties for bodily injury and property damage in an amount not to exceed the coverage limits specified above.

(4) Guarantor agrees to notify [owner or operator] by certified mail of a voluntary or involuntary proceeding under Title 11 (Bankruptcy), U.S. Code naming guarantor as debtor, within 10 days after commencement of the proceeding.

(5) Guarantor agrees to remain bound under this guarantee notwithstanding any modification or alteration of any obligation of [owner or operator] pursuant to 40 CFR part 280.

(6) Guarantor agrees to remain bound under this guarantee for so long as [local government owner or operator] must comply with the applicable financial responsibility requirements of 40 CFR part 280, subpart H for the above identified tank(s), except that guarantor may cancel this guarantee by sending notice by certified mail to [owner or operator], such cancellation to become effective no earlier than 120 days after receipt of such notice by [owner or operator], as evidenced by the return receipt. If notified of a probable release, the guarantor agrees to remain bound to the terms of this guarantee for all charges arising from the release, up to the coverage limits specified above, notwithstanding the cancellation of the guarantee with respect to future releases.

(7) The guarantor's obligation does not apply to any of the following:

(a) Any obligation of [local government owner or operator] under a workers' compensation disability benefits, or unemployment compensation law or other similar law;

(b) Bodily injury to an employee of [insert local government owner or operator] arising from, and in the course of, employment by [insert: local government owner or operator];

(c) Bodily injury or property damage arising from the ownership, maintenance, use, or entrustment to others of any aircraft, motor vehicle, or watercraft;

(d) Property damage to any property owned, rented, loaded to, in the care, custody, or control of, or occupied by [insert: local government owner or operator] that is not the direct result of a release from a petroleum underground storage tank;

(e) Bodily damage or property damage for which [insert: owner or operator] is obligated to pay damages by reason of the assumption of liability in a contract or agreement other than a contract or agreement entered into to meet the requirements of 40 CFR part 280.93.

(8) Guarantor expressly waives notice of acceptance of this guarantee by [the implementing agency], by any or all third parties, or by [local government owner or operator].

I hereby certify that the wording of this guarantee is identical to the wording specified in 40 CFR part 280.106(e) as such regulations were constituted on the effective date shown immediately below.

Effective date: ____________________

[Name of guarantor]
[Authorized signature for guarantor]
[Name of person signing]
[Title of person signing]

Signature of witness or notary: ____________________

If the guarantor is a local government, the local government guarantee without standby trust must be worded exactly as follows, except that instructions in brackets are to be replaced with relevant information and the brackets deleted:

Local Government Guarantee Without Standby Trust Made by a Local Government

Guarantee made this [date] by [name of guaranteeing entity], a local government organized under the laws of [name of state], herein referred to as guarantor, to [the state implementing agency] and to any and all third parties, and obliges, on behalf of [local government owner or operator].

Recitals

(1) Guarantor meets or exceeds [select one: the local government bond rating test requirements of 40 CFR part 280.104, the local government financial test requirements of 40 part CFR 280.105, the local government fund under 40 CFR part 280.107(a), 280.107(b), or 280.107(c).

(2) [Local government owner or operator] owns or operates the following underground storage tank(s) covered by this guarantee: [List the number of tanks at each facility and the name(s) and address(es) of the facility(ies) where the tanks are located. If more than one instrument is used to assure different tanks at any one facility, for each tank covered by this instrument, list the tank identification number provided in the notification submitted pursuant to 40 CFR part 280 or the corresponding state requirement, and the name and address of the facility.] This guarantee satisfies 40 CFR part 280, subpart H requirements for assuring funding for [insert: "taking corrective action" and/or "compensating third parties for bodily injury and property damage caused by" either "sudden accidental releases" or "nonsudden accidental releases" or "accidental releases"; if coverage is different for different tanks or locations, indicate the type of coverage applicable to each tank or location] arising from operating the above-identified underground storage tank(s) in the amount of [insert: dollar amount] per occurrence and [insert: dollar amount] annual aggregate.

(3) Incident to our substantial governmental relationship with [local government owner or operator], guarantor guarantees to [implementing agency] and to any and all third parties and obliges that:

In the event that [local government owner or operator] fails to provide alternative coverage within 60 days after receipt of a notice of cancellation of this guarantee and the [Director of the implementing agency] has determined or suspects that a release has occurred at an underground storage tank covered by this guarantee, the guarantor, upon written instructions from the [Director] shall make funds available to pay for corrective actions and compensate third parties for bodily injury and property damage in an amount not to exceed the coverage limits specified above.

In the event that the [Director] determines that [local government owner or operator] has failed to perform corrective action for releases arising out of the operation of the above-identified tank(s) in accordance with 40 CFR part 280, subpart F, the guarantor upon written instructions from the [Director] shall make funds available to pay for corrective actions in an amount not to exceed the coverage limits specified above.

If [owner or operator] fails to satisfy a judgment or award based on a determination of liability for bodily injury or property damage to third parties caused by ["sudden" and/or "nonsudden"] accidental releases arising from the operation of the above-identified tank(s), or fails to pay an amount agreed to in settlement of a claim arising from or alleged to arise from such injury or damage, the guarantor, upon written instructions from the [Director], shall make funds available to compensate third parties for bodily injury and property damage in an amount not to exceed the coverage limits specified above.

(4) Guarantor agrees that if at the end of any fiscal year before cancellation of this guarantee, the guarantor fails to meet or exceed the requirements of the financial responsibility mechanism specified in paragraph (1), guarantor shall send within 120 days of such failure, by certified mail, notice to [local government owner or operator], as evidenced by the return receipt.

(5) Guarantor agrees to notify [owner or operator] by certified mail of a voluntary or involuntary proceeding under Title 11 (Bankruptcy), U.S. Code naming guarantor as debtor, within 10 days after commencement of the proceeding.

(6) Guarantor agrees to remain bound under this guarantee notwithstanding any modification or alteration of any obligation of [owner or operator] pursuant to 40 CFR part 280.

(7) Guarantor agrees to remain bound under this guarantee for so long as [local government owner or operator] must comply with the applicable financial responsibility requirements of 40 CFR part 280, subpart H for the above identified tank(s), except that guarantor may cancel this guarantee by sending notice by certified mail to [owner or operator], such cancellation to become effective no earlier than 120 days after receipt of such notice by [owner or operator], as evidenced by the return receipt. If notified of a probable release, the guarantor agrees to remain bound to the terms of this guarantee for all charges arising from the release, up to the coverage limits specified above, notwithstanding the cancellation of the guarantee with respect to future releases.

(8) The guarantor's obligation does not apply to any of the following:

(a) Any obligation of [local government owner or operator] under a workers' compensation disability benefits, or unemployment compensation law or other similar law;

(b) Bodily injury to an employee of [insert: local government owner or operator] arising from, and in the course of, employment by [insert: local government owner or operator];

(c) Bodily injury or property damage arising from the ownership, maintenance, use, or entrustment to others of any aircraft, motor vehicle, or watercraft;

(d) Property damage to any property owned, rented, loaded to, in the care, custody, or control of, or occupied by [insert: local government owner or operator] that is not the direct result of a release from a petroleum underground storage tank;

(e) Bodily damage or property damage for which [insert: owner or operator] is obligated to pay damages by reason of the assumption of liability in a contract or agreement other than a contract or agreement entered into to meet the requirements of 40 CFR part 280.93.

(9) Guarantor expressly waives notice of acceptance of this guarantee by [the implementing agency], by any or all third parties, or by [local government owner or operator], I hereby certify that the wording of this guarantee is identical to the wording specified in 40 CFR part 280.106(e) as such regulations were constituted on the effective date shown immediately below.

Effective date:________________

[Name of guarantor]
[Authorized signature for guarantor]
[Name of person signing]
[Title of person signing]

Signature of witness or notary: ________________

[58 FR 9056, Feb. 18, 1993]

§280.107 Local government fund.

A local government owner or operator may satisfy the requirements of §280.93 by establishing a dedicated fund account that conforms to the requirements of this section. Except as specified in paragraph (b), a dedicated fund may not be commingled with other funds or otherwise used in normal operations. A dedicated fund will be considered eligible if it meets one of the following requirements:

(a) The fund is dedicated by state constitutional provision, or local government statute, charter, ordinance, or order to pay for taking corrective action and for compensating third parties for bodily injury and property damage caused by accidental releases arising from the operation of petroleum underground storage tanks and is funded for the full amount of coverage required under §280.93, or funded for part of the required amount of coverage and used in combination with other mechanism(s) that provide the remaining coverage; or

(b) The fund is dedicated by state constitutional provision, or local government statute, charter, ordinance, or order as a contingency fund for general emergencies, including taking corrective action and compensating third parties for bodily injury and property damage caused by accidental releases arising from the operation of petroleum underground storage tanks, and is funded for five times the full amount of coverage required under §280.93, or funded for part of the required amount of coverage and used in combination with other mechanism(s) that provide the remaining coverage. If the fund is funded for less than five times the amount of coverage required under §280.93, the amount of financial responsibility demonstrated by the fund may not exceed one-fifth the amount in the fund; or

(c) The fund is dedicated by state constitutional provision, or local government statute, charter, ordinance or order to pay for taking corrective action and for compensating third parties for bodily injury and property damage caused by accidental releases arising from the operation of petroleum underground storage tanks. A payment is made to the fund once every year for seven years until the fund is fully-funded. This seven year period is hereafter referred to as the "pay-in-period." The amount of each payment must be determined by this formula:

$$\frac{TF - CF}{Y}$$

Where TF is the total required financial assurance for the owner or operator, CF is the current amount in the fund, and Y is the number of years remaining in the pay-in-period, and;

(1) The local government owner or operator has available bonding authority, approved through voter referendum (if such approval is necessary prior to the issuance of bonds), for an amount equal to the difference between the required amount of coverage and the amount held in the dedicated fund. This bonding authority shall be available for taking corrective action and for compensating third parties for bodily injury and property damage caused by accidental releases arising from the operation of petroleum underground storage tanks, or

(2) The local government owner or operator has a letter signed by the appropriate state attorney general stating that the use of the bonding authority will not increase the local government's debt beyond the legal debt ceilings established by the relevant state laws. The letter must also state that prior voter approval is not necessary before use of the bonding authority.

(d) To demonstrate that it meets the requirements of the local government fund, the chief financial officer of the local government owner or operator and/or guarantor must sign a letter worded exactly as follows, except that the instructions in brackets are to be replaced by the relevant information and the brackets deleted:

Letter from Chief Financial Officer

I am the chief financial officer of [insert: name and address of local government owner or operator, or guarantor]. This letter is in support of the use of the local government fund mechanism to demonstrate financial responsibility for [insert: "taking corrective action" and/ or "compensating third parties for bodily injury and property damage"] caused by [insert: "sudden accidental releases" and/or "nonsudden accidental releases"] in the amount of at least [insert: dollar amount] per occurrence and [insert: dollar amount] annual aggregate arising from operating (an) underground storage tank(s).

Underground storage tanks at the following facilities are assured by this local government fund mechanism: [List for each facility: the name and address of the facility where tanks are assured by the local government fund].

[Insert: "The local government fund is funded for the full amount of coverage required under §280.93, or funded for part of the required amount of coverage and used in combination with other mechanism(s) that provide the remaining coverage." or "The local government fund is funded for ten times the full amount of coverage required under §280.93, or funded for part of the required amount of coverage and used in combination with other mechanisms(s) that provide the remaining coverage," or "A payment is made to the fund once every year for seven years until the fund is fully-funded and [name of local government owner or operator] has available bonding authority, approved through voter referendum, of an amount equal to the difference between the required amount of coverage and the amount held in the dedicated fund" or "A payment is made to the fund once every year for seven years until the fund is fully-funded and I have attached a letter signed by the State Attorney General stating that (1) the use of the bonding authority will not increase the local government's debt beyond the legal debt ceilings established by the relevant state laws and (2) that prior voter approval is not necessary before use of the bonding authority"].

The details of the local government fund are as follows:

Amount in Fund (market value of fund at close of last fiscal year): __________

[If fund balance is incrementally funded as specified in §280.107(c), insert:

Amount added to fund in the most recently completed fiscal year: __________

Number of years remaining in the pay-in period:__________]

A copy of the state constitutional provision, or local government statute, charter, ordinance or order dedicating the fund is attached.

I hereby certify that the wording of this letter is identical to the wording specified in 40 CFR 280.107(d) as such regulations were constituted on the date shown immediately below.

[Date]
[Signature]
[Name]
[Title]

[58 FR 9059, Feb. 18, 1993]

§280.108 Substitution of financial assurance mechanisms by owner or operator.

(a) An owner or operator may substitute any alternate financial assurance mechanisms as specified in this subpart, provided that at all times he maintains an effective financial assurance mechanism or combination of mechanisms that satisfies the requirements of §280.93.

(b) After obtaining alternate financial assurance as specified in this subpart, an owner or operator may cancel a financial assurance mechanism by providing notice to the provider of financial assurance.

[53 FR 43370, Oct. 26, 1988. Redesignated at 58 FR 9051, Feb. 18, 1993]

§280.109 Cancellation or nonrenewal by a provider of financial assurance.

(a) Except as otherwise provided, a provider of financial assurance may cancel or fail to renew an assurance mechanism by sending a notice of termination by certified mail to the owner or operator.

(1) Termination of a local government guarantee, a guarantee, a surety bond, or a letter of credit may not occur until 120 days after the date on which the owner or operator receives the notice of termination, as evidenced by the return receipt.

(2) Termination of insurance or risk retention coverage, except for non-payment or misrepresentation by the insured, or state-funded assurance may not occur until 60 days after the date on which the owner or operator receives the notice of termination, as evidenced by the return receipt. Termination for non-payment of premium or misrepresentation by the insured may not occur until a minimum of 10 days after the date on which the owner or operator receives the notice of termination, as evidenced by the return receipt.

(b) If a provider of financial responsibility cancels or fails to renew for reasons other than incapacity of the provider as specified in §280.114, the owner or operator must obtain alternate coverage as specified in this section within 60 days after receipt of the notice of termination. If the owner or operator fails to obtain alternate coverage within 60 days after receipt of the notice of termination, the owner or operator must notify the Director of the implementing agency of such failure and submit:

(1) The name and address of the provider of financial assurance;

(2) The effective date of termination; and

(3) The evidence of the financial assistance mechanism subject to the termination maintained in accordance with §280.107(b).

[58 FR 9051, Feb. 18, 1993]

§280.110 Reporting by owner or operator.

(a) An owner or operator must submit the appropriate forms listed in §280.111(b) documenting current evidence of financial responsibility to the Director of the implementing agency:

(1) Within 30 days after the owner or operator identifies a release from an underground storage tank required to be reported under §280.53 or §280.61;

(2) If the owner or operator fails to obtain alternate coverage as required by this subpart, within 30 days after the owner or operator receives notice of:

(i) Commencement of a voluntary or involuntary proceeding under Title 11 (Bankruptcy), U.S. Code, naming a provider of financial assurance as a debtor,

(ii) Suspension or revocation of the authority of a provider of financial assurance to issue a financial assurance mechanism,

(iii) Failure of a guarantor to meet the requirements of the financial test,

(iv) Other incapacity of a provider of financial assurance; or

(3) As required by §280.95(g) and §280.109(b).

(b) An owner or operator must certify compliance with the financial responsibility requirements of this part as specified in the new tank notification form when notifying the appropriate state or local agency of the installation of a new underground storage tank under §280.22.

(c) The Director of the Implementing Agency may require an owner or operator to submit evidence of financial assurance as described in §280.111(b) or other information relevant to compliance with this subpart at any time.

[58 FR 9051, Feb. 18, 1993]

§280.111 Recordkeeping.

(a) Owners or operators must maintain evidence of all financial assurance mechanisms used to demonstrate financial responsibility under this subpart for an underground storage tank until released from the requirements of this subpart under §208.113. An owner or operator must maintain such evidence at the underground storage tank site or the owner's or operator's place of work. Records maintained off-site must be made available upon request of the implementing agency.

(b) An owner or operator must maintain the following types of evidence of financial responsibility:

(1) An owner or operator using an assurance mechanism specified in §§280.95 through 280.100 or §280.102 or §§280.104 through 280.107 must maintain a copy of the instrument worded as specified.

(2) An owner or operator using a financial test or guarantee, or a local government financial test or a local government guarantee supported by the local government financial test must maintain a copy of the chief financial officer's letter based on year-end financial statements for the most recent completed financial reporting year. Such evidence must be on file no later than 120 days after the close of the financial reporting year.

(3) An owner or operator using a guarantee, surety bond, or letter of credit must maintain a copy of the signed standby trust fund agreement and copies of any amendments to the agreement.

(4) A local government owner or operator using a local government guarantee under §280.106(d) must maintain a copy of the signed standby trust fund agreement and copies of any amendments to the agreement.

(5) A local government owner or operator using the local government bond rating test under §280.104 must maintain a copy of its bond rating published within the last twelve months by Moody's or Standard & Poor's.

(6) A local government owner or operator using the local government guarantee under §280.106, where the guarantor's demonstration of financial responsibility relies on the bond rating test under §280.104 must maintain a copy of the guarantor's bond rating published within the last twelve months by Moody's or Standard & Poor's.

(7) An owner or operator using an insurance policy or risk retention group coverage must maintain a copy of the signed insurance policy or risk retention group coverage policy, with the endorsement or certificate of insurance and any amendments to the agreements.

(8) An owner or operator covered by a state fund or other state assurance must maintain on file a copy of any evidence of coverage supplied by or required by the state under §280.101(d).

(9) An owner or operator using a local government fund under §280.107 must maintain the following documents:

(i) A copy of the state constitutional provision or local government statute, charter, ordinance, or order dedicating the fund, and

(ii) Year-end financial statements for the most recent completed financial reporting year showing the amount in the fund. If the fund is established under §280.107(a)(3) using incremental funding backed by bonding authority, the financial statements must show the previous year's balance, the amount of funding during the year, and the closing balance in the fund.

Publisher's Note: The section referenced above, §280.107(a)(3), is not in the RCRA regulations.

(iii) If the fund is established under §280.107(a)(3) using incremental funding backed by bonding authority, the owner or operator must also maintain documentation of the required bonding authority, including either the results of a voter referendum (under §280.107(a)(3)(i)), or attestation by the State Attorney General as specified under §280.107(a)(3)(ii).

Publisher's Note: The section referenced above, §280.107(a)(3), is not in the RCRA regulations.

(10) A local government owner or operator using the local government guarantee supported by the local government fund must maintain a copy of the guarantor's year-end financial statements for the most recent completed financial reporting year showing the amount of the fund.

(11)(i) An owner or operator using an assurance mechanism specified in §§280.95 through 280.107 must maintain an updated copy of a certification of financial responsibility worded as follows, except that instructions in brackets are to be replaced with the relevant information and the brackets deleted:

Certification of Financial Responsibility

[Owner or operator] hereby certifies that it is in compliance with the requirements of subpart H of 40 CFR part 280.

The financial assurance mechanism(s) used to demonstrate financial responsibility under subpart H of 40 CFR part 280 is (are) as follows:

[For each mechanism, list the type of mechanism, name of issuer, mechanism number (if applicable), amount of coverage, effective period of coverage and whether the mechanism covers "taking corrective action" and/or "compensating third parties for bodily injury and property damage caused by" either "sudden accidental releases" or "nonsudden accidental releases" or "accidental releases."]

[Signature of owner or operator]

[Name of owner or operator]

[Title]

[Date]

[Signature of witness or notary]

[Name of witness or notary]

[Date]

(ii) The owner or operator must update this certification whenever the financial assurance mechanism(s) used to demonstrate financial responsibility change(s).

[58 FR 9051, Feb. 18, 1993]

§280.112 Drawing on financial assurance mechanisms.

(a) Except as specified in paragraph (d) of this section, the Director of the implementing agency shall require the guarantor, surety, or institution issuing a letter of credit to place the amount of funds stipulated by the Director, up to the limit of funds provided by the financial assurance mechanism, into the standby trust if:

(1)(i) The owner or operator fails to establish alternate financial assurance within 60 days after receiving notice of cancellation of the guarantee, surety bond, letter of credit, or, as applicable, other financial assurance mechanism; and

(ii) The Director determines or suspects that a release from an underground storage tank covered by the mechanism has occurred and so notifies the owner or operator or the owner or operator has notified the Director pursuant to subparts E or F of a release from an underground storage tank covered by the mechanism; or

(2) The conditions of paragraph (b)(1) or (b)(2) (i) or (ii) of this section are satisfied.

(b) The Director of the implementing agency may draw on a standby trust fund when:

(1) The Director makes a final determination that a release has occurred and immediate or long-term corrective action for the release is needed, and the owner or operator, after appropriate notice and opportunity to comply, has not conducted corrective action as required under 40 CFR part 280, subpart F; or

(2) The Director has received either:

(i) Certification from the owner or operator and the third-party liability claimant(s) and from attorneys representing the owner or operator and the third-party liability claimant(s) that a third-party liability claim should be paid. The certification must be worded as follows, except that instructions in brackets are to be replaced with the relevant information and the brackets deleted:

Certification of Valid Claim

The undersigned, as principals and as legal representatives of [insert: owner or operator] and [insert: name and address of third-party claimant], hereby certify that the claim of bodily injury [and/or] property damage caused by an accidental release arising from operating [owner's or operator's] underground storage tank should be paid in the amount of $[____________].

[Signatures]

Owner or Operator
Attorney for Owner or Operator
(Notary) Date

[Signatures]

Claimant(s) Attorney(s) for Claimant(s)
(Notary)
Date

or (ii) A valid final court order establishing a judgment against the owner or operator for bodily injury or property damage caused by an accidental release from an underground storage tank covered by financial assurance under this subpart and the Director determines that the owner or operator has not satisfied the judgment.

(c) If the Director of the implementing agency determines that the amount of corrective action costs and third-party liability claims eligible for payment under paragraph (b) of this section may exceed the balance of the standby trust fund and the obligation of the provider of financial assurance, the first priority for payment shall be corrective action costs necessary to protect human health and the environment. The Director shall pay third-party liability claims in the order in which the Director receives certifications under paragraph (b)(2)(i) of this section, and valid court orders under paragraph (b)(2)(ii) of this section.

(d) A governmental entity acting as guarantor under §280.106(e), the local government guarantee without standby trust, shall make payments as directed by the Director under the circumstances described in §280.112 (a), (b), and (c).

[58 FR 9052, Feb. 18, 1993]

§280.113 Release from the requirements.

An owner or operator is no longer required to maintain financial responsibility under this subpart for an underground storage tank after the tank has been properly closed or, if corrective action is required, after corrective action has been completed and the tank has been properly closed as required by 40 CFR part 280, subpart G.

[53 FR 43370, Oct. 26, 1988. Redesignated at 58 FR 9051, Feb. 18, 1993]

§280.114 Bankruptcy or other incapacity of owner or operator or provider of financial assurance.

(a) Within 10 days after commencement of a voluntary or involuntary proceeding under Title 11 (Bankruptcy), U.S. Code, naming an owner or operator as debtor, the owner or operator must notify the Director of the implementing agency by certified mail of such commencement and submit the appropriate forms listed in §280.111(b) documenting current financial responsibility.

(b) Within 10 days after commencement of a voluntary or involuntary proceeding under Title 11 (Bankruptcy), U.S. Code, naming a guarantor providing financial assurance as debtor, such guarantor must notify the owner or operator by certified mail of such commencement as required under the terms of the guarantee specified in §280.96.

(c) Within 10 days after commencement of a voluntary or involuntary proceeding under Title 11 (Bankruptcy), U.S. Code, naming a local government owner or operator as debtor, the local government owner or operator must notify the Director of the implementing agency by certified mail of such commencement and submit the appropriate forms listed in §280.111(b) documenting current financial responsibility.

(d) Within 10 days after commencement of a voluntary or involuntary proceeding under Title 11 (Bankruptcy), U.S. Code, naming a guarantor providing a local government financial assurance as debtor, such guarantor must notify the local government owner or operator by certified mail of such commencement as required under the terms of the guarantee specified in §280.106.

(e) An owner or operator who obtains financial assurance by a mechanism other than the financial test of self-insurance will be deemed to be without the required financial assurance in the event of a bankruptcy or incapacity of its provider of financial assurance, or a suspension or revocation of the authority of the provider of financial assurance to issue a guarantee, insurance policy, risk retention group coverage policy, surety bond, letter of credit, or state-required mechanism. The owner or operator must obtain alternate financial assurance as specified in this subpart within 30 days after receiving notice of such an event. If the owner or operator does not obtain alternate coverage within 30 days after such notification, he must notify the Director of the implementing agency.

(f) Within 30 days after receipt of notification that a state fund or other state assurance has become incapable of paying for assured corrective action or third-party compensation costs, the owner or operator must obtain alternate financial assurance.

[58 FR 9053, Feb. 18, 1993]

§280.115 Replenishment of guarantees, letters of credit, or surety bonds.

(a) If at any time after a standby trust is funded upon the instruction of the Director of the implementing agency with funds drawn from a guarantee, local government guarantee with standby trust, letter of credit, or surety bond, and the amount in the standby trust is reduced below the full amount of coverage required, the owner or operator shall by the anniversary date of the financial mechanism from which the funds were drawn:

(1) Replenish the value of financial assurance to equal the full amount of coverage required, or

(2) Acquire another financial assurance mechanism for the amount by which funds in the standby trust have been reduced.

(b) For purposes of this section, the full amount of coverage required is the amount of coverage to be provided by §280.93 of this subpart. If a combination of mechanisms was used to provide the assurance funds which were drawn upon, replenishment shall occur by the earliest anniversary date among the mechanisms.

[58 FR 9053, Feb. 18, 1993]

§280.116 Suspension of enforcement. [Reserved]

Subpart I—Lender Liability

Source: 60 FR 46711, Sept. 7, 1995, unless otherwise noted.

§280.200 Definitions.

(a) *UST technical standards*, as used in this subpart, refers to the UST preventative and operating requirements under 40 CFR part 280, subparts B, C, D, G, and §280.50 of subpart E.

(b) *Petroleum production, refining, and marketing.*

(1) *Petroleum production* means the production of crude oil or other forms of petroleum (as defined in §280.12) as well as the production of petroleum products from purchased materials.

(2) *Petroleum refining* means the cracking, distillation, separation, conversion, upgrading, and finishing of refined petroleum or petroleum products.

(3) *Petroleum marketing* means the distribution, transfer, or sale of petroleum or petroleum products for wholesale or retail purposes.

(c) *Indicia of ownership* means evidence of a secured interest, evidence of an interest in a security interest, or evidence of an interest in real or personal property securing a loan or other obligation, including any legal or equitable title or deed to real or personal property acquired through or incident to foreclosure. Evidence of such interests include, but are not limited to, mortgages, deeds of trust, liens, surety bonds and guarantees of obligations, title held pursuant to a lease financing transaction in which the lessor does not select initially the leased property (hereinafter "lease financing transaction"), and legal or equitable title obtained pursuant to foreclosure. Evidence of such interests also includes assignments, pledges, or other rights to or other forms of encumbrance against property that are held primarily to protect a security interest. A person is not required to hold title or a security interest in order to maintain indicia of ownership.

(d) *A holder* is a person who, upon the effective date of this regulation or in the future, maintains indicia of ownership (as defined in §280.200(c)) primarily to protect a security interest (as defined in §280.200(f)(1)) in a petroleum UST or UST system or facility or property on which a petroleum UST or UST system is located. A holder includes the initial holder (such as a loan originator); any subsequent holder (such as a successor-in-interest or subsequent purchaser of the security interest on the secondary market); a guarantor of an obligation, surety, or any other person who holds ownership indicia primarily to protect a security interest; or a receiver or other person who acts on behalf or for the benefit of a holder.

(e) *A borrower, debtor, or obligor* is a person whose UST or UST system or facility or property on which the UST or UST system is located is encumbered by a security interest. These terms may be used interchangeably.

(f) *Primarily to protect a security interest* means that the holder's indicia of ownership are held primarily for the purpose of securing payment or performance of an obligation.

(1) *Security interest* means an interest in a petroleum UST or UST system or in the facility or property on which a petroleum UST or UST system is located, created or established for the purpose of securing a loan or other obligation. Security interests include but are not limited to mortgages, deeds of trusts, liens, and title pursuant to lease financing transactions. Security interests may also arise from transactions such as sale and leasebacks, conditional sales, installment sales, trust receipt transactions, certain assignments, factoring agreements, accounts receivable financing arrangements, and consignments, if the transaction creates or establishes an interest in an UST or UST system or in the facility or property on which the UST or UST system is located, for the purpose of securing a loan or other obligation.

(2) *Primarily to protect a security interest*, as used in this subpart, does not include indicia of ownership held primarily for investment purposes, nor ownership indicia held primarily for purposes other than as protection for a security interest. A holder may have other, secondary reasons for maintaining indicia of ownership, but the primary reason why any ownership indicia are held must be as protection for a security interest.

(g) *Operation* means, for purposes of this subpart, the use, storage, filling, or dispensing of petroleum contained in an UST or UST system.

§280.210 Participation in management.

The term "participating in the management of an UST or UST system" means that, subsequent to the effective date of this subpart, December 6, 1995, the holder is engaging in decisionmaking control of, or activities related to, operation of the UST or UST system, as defined herein.

(a) Actions that are participation in management.

(1) Participation in the management of an UST or UST system means, for purposes of this subpart, actual participation by the holder in the management or control of decisionmaking related to the operation of an UST or UST system. Participation in management does not include the mere capacity or ability to influence or the unexercised right to control UST or UST system operations. A holder is participating in the management of the UST or UST system only if the holder either:

(i) Exercises decisionmaking control over the operational (as opposed to financial or administrative) aspects of the UST or UST system, such that the holder has undertaken responsibility for all or substantially all of the management of the UST or UST system; or

(ii) Exercises control at a level comparable to that of a manager of the borrower's enterprise, such that the holder has assumed or manifested responsibility for the overall management of the enterprise encompassing the day-to-day decisionmaking of the enterprise with respect to all, or substantially all, of the operational (as opposed to financial or administrative) aspects of the enterprise.

(2) Operational aspects of the enterprise relate to the use, storage, filling, or dispensing of petroleum contained in an UST or UST system, and include functions such as that of a facility or plant manager, operations manager, chief operating officer, or chief executive officer. Financial or administrative aspects include functions such as that of a credit manager, accounts payable/receivable manager, personnel manager, controller, chief financial officer, or similar functions. Operational aspects of the enterprise do not include the financial or administrative aspects of the enterprise, or actions associated with environmental compliance, or actions undertaken voluntarily to protect the environment in accordance with applicable requirements in 40 CFR part 280 or applicable state requirements in those states that have been delegated authority by EPA to administer the UST program pursuant to 42 USC 6991c and 40 CFR part 281.

(b) Actions that are not participation in management pre-foreclosure.

(1) Actions at the inception of the loan or other transaction. No act or omission prior to the time that indicia of ownership are held primarily to protect a security interest constitutes evidence of participation in management within the meaning of this subpart. A prospective holder who undertakes or requires an environmental investigation (which could include a site assessment, inspection, and/or audit) of the UST or UST system or facility or property on which the UST or UST system is located (in which indicia of ownership are to be held), or requires a prospective borrower to clean up contamination from the UST or UST system or to comply or come into compliance (whether prior or subsequent to the time that indicia of ownership are held primarily to protect a security interest) with any applicable law or regulation, is not by such action considered to be participating in the management of the UST or UST system or facility or property on which the UST or UST system is located.

(2) Loan policing and work out. Actions that are consistent with holding ownership indicia primarily to protect a security interest do not constitute participation in management for purposes of this subpart. The authority for the holder to take such actions may, but need not, be contained in contractual or other documents specifying requirements for financial, environmental, and other warranties, covenants, conditions, representations or promises from the borrower. Loan policing and work out activities cover and include all such activities up to foreclosure, exclusive of any activities that constitute participation in management.

(i) Policing the security interest or loan.

(A) A holder who engages in policing activities prior to foreclosure will remain within the exemption provided that the holder does not together with other actions participate in the management of the UST or UST system as provided in §280.210(a). Such policing actions include, but are not limited to, requiring the borrower to clean up contamination from the UST or UST system during the term of the security interest; requiring the borrower to comply or come into compliance with applicable federal, state, and local environmental and other laws, rules, and regulations during the term of the security interest; securing or exercising authority to monitor or inspect the UST or UST system or facility or property on which the UST or UST system is located (including on-site inspections) in which indicia of ownership are maintained, or the borrower's business or financial condition during the term of the security interest; or taking other actions to adequately police the loan or security interest (such as requiring a borrower to comply with any warranties, covenants, conditions, representations, or promises from the borrower).

(B) Policing activities also include undertaking by the holder of UST environmental compliance actions and voluntary environmental actions taken in compliance with 40 CFR part 280, provided that the holder does not otherwise participate in the management or daily operation of the UST or UST system as provided in §280.210(a) and §280.230. Such allowable actions include, but are not limited to, release detection and release reporting, release response and corrective action, temporary or permanent closure of an UST or UST system, UST upgrading or replacement, and maintenance of corrosion protection. A holder who undertakes these actions must do so in compliance with the applicable requirements in 40 CFR part 280 or applicable state requirements in those states that have been delegated authority by EPA to administer the UST program pursuant to 42 U.S.C. 6991c and 40 CFR part 281. A holder may directly oversee these environmental compliance actions and voluntary environmental actions, and directly hire contractors to perform the work, and is not by such action considered to be participating in the management of the UST or UST system.

(ii) Loan work out. A holder who engages in work out activities prior to foreclosure will remain within the exemption provided that the holder does not together with other actions participate in the management of the UST or UST system as provided in §280.210(a). For purposes of this rule, "work out" refers to those actions by which a holder, at any time prior to foreclosure, seeks to prevent, cure, or mitigate a default by the borrower or obligor; or to preserve, or prevent the diminution of, the value of the security. Work out activities include, but are not limited to, restructuring or renegotiating the terms of the security interest; requiring payment of additional rent or interest; exercising forbearance; requiring or exercising rights pursuant to an assignment of accounts or other amounts owing to an obligor; requiring or exercising rights pursuant to an escrow agreement pertaining to amounts owing to an obligor; providing specific or general financial or other advice, suggestions, counseling, or guidance; and exercising any right or remedy the holder is entitled to by law or under any warranties, covenants, conditions, representations, or promises from the borrower.

(c) Foreclosure on an UST or UST system or facility or property on which an UST or UST system is located, and participation in management activities post-foreclosure.

(1) Foreclosure. (i) Indicia of ownership that are held primarily to protect a security interest include legal or equitable title or deed to real or personal property acquired through or incident to foreclosure. For purposes of this subpart, the term "foreclosure" means that legal, marketable or equitable title or deed has been issued, approved, and recorded, and that the holder has obtained access to the UST, UST system, UST facility, and property on which the UST or UST system is located, provided that the holder acted diligently to acquire marketable title or deed and to gain access to the UST, UST system, UST facility, and property on which the UST or UST system is located. The indicia of ownership held after foreclosure continue to be maintained primarily as protection for a security interest provided that the holder undertakes to sell, release an UST or UST system or facility or property on which the UST or UST system is located, held pursuant to a lease financing transaction (whether by a new lease financing transaction or substitution of the lessee), or otherwise divest itself of the UST or UST system or facility or property on which the UST or UST system is located, in a reasonably expeditious manner, using whatever commercially reasonable means are relevant or appropriate with respect to the UST or UST system or facility or property on which the UST or UST system is located, taking all facts and circumstances into consideration, and provided that the holder does not participate in management (as defined in §280.210(a)) prior to or after foreclosure.

(ii) For purposes of establishing that a holder is seeking to sell, re-lease pursuant to a lease financing transaction (whether by a new lease financing transaction or substitution of the lessee), or divest in a reasonably expeditious manner an UST or UST system or facility or property on which the UST or UST system is located, the holder may use whatever commercially reasonable means as are relevant or appropriate with respect to the UST or UST system or facility or property on which the UST or UST system is located, or may employ the means specified in §280.210(c)(2). A holder that outbids, rejects, or fails to act upon a written *bona fide*, firm offer of fair consideration for the UST or UST system or facility or property on which the UST or UST system is located, as provided in §280.210(c)(2), is not considered to hold indicia of ownership primarily to protect a security interest.

(2) Holding foreclosed property for disposition and liquidation. A holder, who does not participate in management prior to or after foreclosure, may sell, re-lease, pursuant to a lease financing transaction (whether by a new lease financing transaction or substitution of the lessee), an UST or UST system or facility or property on which the UST or UST system is located, liquidate, wind up operations, and take measures, prior to sale or other disposition, to preserve, protect, or prepare the secured UST or UST system or facility or property on which the UST or UST system is located. A holder may also arrange for an existing or new operator to continue or initiate operation of the UST or UST system. The holder may conduct these activities without voiding the security interest exemption, subject to the requirements of this subpart.

(i) A holder establishes that the ownership indicia maintained after foreclosure continue to be held primarily to protect a security interest by, within 12 months following foreclosure, listing the UST or UST system or the facility or property on which the

UST or UST system is located, with a broker, dealer, or agent who deals with the type of property in question, or by advertising the UST or UST system or facility or property on which the UST or UST system is located, as being for sale or disposition on at least a monthly basis in either a real estate publication or a trade or other publication suitable for the UST or UST system or facility or property on which the UST or UST system is located, or a newspaper of general circulation (defined as one with a circulation over 10,000, or one suitable under any applicable federal, state, or local rules of court for publication required by court order or rules of civil procedure) covering the location of the UST or UST system or facility or property on which the UST or UST system is located. For purposes of this provision, the 12-month period begins to run from December 6, 1995 or from the date that the marketable title or deed has been issued, approved and recorded, and the holder has obtained access to the UST, UST system, UST facility and property on which the UST or UST system is located, whichever is later, provided that the holder acted diligently to acquire marketable title or deed and to obtain access to the UST, UST system, UST facility and property on which the UST or UST system is located. If the holder fails to act diligently to acquire marketable title or deed or to gain access to the UST or UST system, the 12-month period begins to run from December 6, 1995 or from the date on which the holder first acquires either title to or possession of the secured UST or UST system, or facility or property on which the UST or UST system is located, whichever is later.

(ii) A holder that outbids, rejects, or fails to act upon an offer of fair consideration for the UST or UST system or the facility or property on which the UST or UST system is located, establishes by such outbidding, rejection, or failure to act, that the ownership indicia in the secured UST or UST system or facility or property on which the UST or UST system is located are not held primarily to protect the security interest, unless the holder is required, in order to avoid liability under federal or state law, to make a higher bid, to obtain a higher offer, or to seek or obtain an offer in a different manner.

(A) Fair consideration, in the case of a holder maintaining indicia of ownership primarily to protect a senior security interest in the UST or UST system or facility or property on which the UST or UST system is located, is the value of the security interest as defined in this section. The value of the security interest includes all debt and costs incurred by the security interest holder, and is calculated as an amount equal to or in excess of the sum of the outstanding principal (or comparable amount in the case of a lease that constitutes a security interest) owed to the holder immediately preceding the acquisition of full title (or possession in the case of a lease financing transaction) pursuant to foreclosure, plus any unpaid interest, rent, or penalties (whether arising before or after foreclosure). The value of the security interest also includes all reasonable and necessary costs, fees, or other charges incurred by the holder incident to work out, foreclosure, retention, preserving, protecting, and preparing, prior to sale, the UST or UST system or facility or property on which the UST or UST system is located, re-lease, pursuant to a lease financing transaction (whether by a new lease financing transaction or substitution of the lessee), of an UST or UST system or facility or property on which the UST or UST system is located, or other disposition. The value of the security interest also includes environmental investigation costs (which could include a site assessment, inspection, and/or audit of the UST or UST system or facility or property on which the UST or UST system is located), and corrective action costs incurred under §§280.51 through 280.67 or any other costs incurred as a result of reasonable efforts to comply with any other applicable federal, state or local law or regulation; less any amounts received by the holder in connection with any partial disposition of the property and any amounts paid by the borrower (if not already applied to the borrower's obligations) subsequent to the acquisition of full title (or possession in the case of a lease financing transaction) pursuant to foreclosure. In the case of a holder maintaining indicia of ownership primarily to protect a junior security interest, fair consideration is the value of all outstanding higher priority security interests plus the value of the security interest held by the junior holder, each calculated as set forth in this paragraph.

(B) Outbids, rejects, or fails to act upon an offer of fair consideration means that the holder outbids, rejects, or fails to act upon within 90 days of receipt, a written, *bona fide*, firm offer of fair consideration for the UST or UST system or facility or property on which the UST or UST system is located received at any time after six months following foreclosure, as defined in §280.210(c). A "written, *bona fide*, firm offer" means a legally enforceable, commercially reasonable, cash offer solely for the foreclosed UST or UST system or facility or property on which the UST or UST system is located, including all material terms of the transaction, from a ready, willing, and able purchaser who demonstrates to the holder's satisfaction the ability to perform. For purposes of this provision, the six-month period begins to run from December 6, 1995 or from the date that marketable title or deed has been issued, approved and recorded to the holder, and the holder has obtained access to the UST, UST system, UST facility and property on which the UST or UST system is located, whichever is later, provided that the holder was acting diligently to acquire marketable title or deed and to obtain access to the UST or UST system, UST facility and property on which the UST or UST system is located. If the holder fails to act diligently to acquire marketable title or deed or to gain access to the UST or UST system, the six-month period begins to run from December 6, 1995 or from the date on which the holder first acquires either title to or possession of the secured UST or UST system, or facility or property on which the UST or UST system is located, whichever is later.

(3) Actions that are not participation in management post-foreclosure. A holder is not considered to be participating in the management of an UST or UST system or facility or property on which the UST or UST system is located when undertaking actions under 40 CFR part 280, provided that the holder does not otherwise participate in the management or daily operation of the UST or UST system as provided in §280.210(a) and §280.230. Such allowable actions include, but are not limited to, release detection and release reporting, release response and corrective action, temporary or permanent closure of an UST or UST system, UST upgrading or replacement, and maintenance of corrosion protection. A holder who undertakes these actions must do so in compliance with the applicable requirements in 40 CFR part 280 or applicable state requirements in those states that have been delegated authority by EPA to administer the UST program pursuant to 42 U.S.C. 6991c and 40 CFR part 281. A holder may directly oversee these environmental compliance actions and voluntary environmental actions, and directly hire contractors to perform the work, and is not by such action considered to be participating in the management of the UST or UST system.

§280.220 Ownership of an underground storage tank or underground storage tank system or facility or property on which an underground storage tank or underground storage tank system is located.

Ownership of an UST or UST system or facility or property on which an UST or UST system is located. A holder is not an "owner" of a petroleum UST or UST system or facility or property on which a petroleum UST or UST system is located for purposes of compliance with the UST technical standards as defined in §280.200(a), the UST corrective action requirements under §§280.51 through 280.67, and the UST financial responsibility requirements under §§280.90 through 280.111, provided the person:

(a) Does not participate in the management of the UST or UST system as defined in §280.210; and

(b) Does not engage in petroleum production, refining, and marketing as defined in §280.200(b).

§280.230 Operating an underground storage tank or underground storage tank system.

(a) Operating an UST or UST system prior to foreclosure. A holder, prior to foreclosure, as defined in §280.210(c), is not an "operator" of a petroleum UST or UST system for purposes of compliance with the UST technical standards as defined in §280.200(a), the UST corrective action requirements under §§280.51 through 280.67, and the UST financial responsibility requirements under §§280.90 through 280.111, provided that, after December 6, 1995, the holder is not in control of or does not have responsibility for the daily operation of the UST or UST system.

(b) Operating an UST or UST system after foreclosure. The following provisions apply to a holder who, through foreclosure, as defined in §280.210(c), acquires a petroleum UST or UST system or facility or property on which a petroleum UST or UST system is located.

(1) A holder is not an "operator" of a petroleum UST or UST system for purposes of compliance with 40 CFR part 280 if there is an operator, other than the holder, who is in control of or has responsibility for the daily operation of the UST or UST system, and who can be held responsible for compliance with applicable requirements of 40 CFR part 280 or applicable state requirements in those states that have been delegated authority by EPA to administer the UST program pursuant to 42 U.S.C. 6991c and 40 CFR part 281.

(2) If another operator does not exist, as provided for under paragraph (b)(1) of this section, a holder is not an "operator" of the UST or UST system, for purposes of compliance with the UST technical standards as defined in §280.200(a), the UST corrective action requirements under §§280.51 through 280.67, and the UST financial responsibility requirements under §§280.90 through 280.111, provided that the holder:

(i) Empties all of its known USTs and UST systems within 60 calendar days after foreclosure or within 60 calendar days after December 6, 1995, whichever is later, or another reasonable time period specified by the implementing agency, so that no more than 2.5 centimeters (one inch) of residue, or 0.3 percent by weight of the total capacity of the UST system, remains in the system; leaves vent lines open and functioning; and caps and secures all other lines, pumps, manways, and ancillary equipment; and

(ii) Empties those USTs and UST systems that are discovered after foreclosure within 60 calendar days after discovery or within 60 calendar days after December 6, 1995, whichever is later, or another reasonable time period specified by the implementing agency, so that no more than 2.5 centimeters (one inch) of residue, or 0.3 percent by weight of the total capacity of the UST system, remains in the system; leaves vent lines open and functioning; and caps and secures all other lines, pumps, manways, and ancillary equipment.

(3) If another operator does not exist, as provided for under paragraph (b)(1) of this section, in addition to satisfying the conditions under paragraph (b)(2) of this section, the holder must either:

(i) Permanently close the UST or UST system in accordance with §§280.71 through 280.74, except §280.72(b); or

(ii) Temporarily close the UST or UST system in accordance with the following applicable provisions of §280.70:

(A) Continue operation and maintenance of corrosion protection in accordance with §280.31;

(B) Report suspected releases to the implementing agency; and

(C) Conduct a site assessment in accordance with §280.72(a) if the UST system is temporarily closed for more than 12 months and the UST system does not meet either the performance standards in §280.20 for new UST systems or the upgrading requirements in §280.21, except that the spill and overfill equipment requirements do not have to be met. The holder must report any suspected releases to the implementing agency. For purposes of this provision, the 12-month period begins to run from December 6, 1995 or from the date on which the UST system is emptied and secured under paragraph (b)(2) of this section, whichever is later.

(4) The UST system can remain in temporary closure until a subsequent purchaser has acquired marketable title to the UST or UST system or facility or property on which the UST or UST system is located. Once a subsequent purchaser acquires marketable title to the UST or UST system or facility or property on which the UST or UST system is located, the purchaser must decide whether to operate or close the UST or UST system in accordance with applicable requirements in 40 CFR part 280 or applicable state requirements in those states that have been delegated authority by EPA to administer the UST program pursuant to 42 U.S.C. 6991c and 40 CFR part 281.

Appendix I to Part 280—Notification for Underground Storage Tanks (Form)

EPA

United States
Environmental Protection Agency
Washington, DC 20460

Form Approved.
OMB No.2050-0068

Notification for Underground Storage Tanks

State Agency Name and Address:

STATE USE ONLY

ID NUMBER:

DATE RECEIVED:

DATE ENTERED INTO COMPUTER:

DATA ENTRY CLERK INITIALS:

OWNER WAS CONTACTED TO CLARIFY RESPONSES, COMMENTS:

TYPE OF NOTIFICATION

☐ A. NEW FACILITY ☐ B. AMENDED ☐ C. CLOSURE

_____ Number of tanks at facility

_____ Number of continuation sheets attached

INSTRUCTIONS AND GENERAL INFORMATION

Please type or print in ink. Also, be sure you have signatures in ink for sections VIII and XI. Complete a notification form for each location containing underground storage tanks. If more than 5 tanks are owned at this location, you may photocopy pages 3 through 5 and use them for additional tanks.

The primary purpose of this notification program is to locate and evaluate underground storage tank systems (USTs) that store or have stored petroleum or hazardous substances. The information you provide will be based on reasonably available records, or in the absence of such records, your knowledge or recollection.

Federal law requires UST owners to use this notification form for all USTs storing regulated substances that are brought into use after May 8, 1986, or USTs in the ground as of May 8, 1986 that have stored regulated substances at any time since January 1, 1974. The information requested is required by Section 9002 of the Resource Conservation and Recovery Act (RCRA), as amended.

Who Must Notify? Section 9002 of RCRA, as amended, requires owners of USTs that store regulated substances (unless exempted) to notify designated State or local agencies of the existence of their USTs. "Owner" is defined as:

- In the case of an UST in use on November 8, 1984, or brought into use after that date, any person who owns an UST used for storage, use, or dispensing of regulated substances; or
- In the case of an UST in use before November 8, 1984, but no longer in use on that date, any person who owned the UST immediately before its discontinuation.

Also, if the State so requires, any facility that has made any changes to facility information or UST system status, must submit a notification form (only amended information needs to be included).

What USTs Are Included? An UST system is defined as any one or combination of tanks that (1) is used to contain an accumulation of regulated substances, and (2) whose volume (including connected underground piping) is 10% or more beneath the ground. Regulated USTs store petroleum or hazardous substances (see the following "What Substances Are Covered").

What Tanks Are Excluded From Notification?

- Tanks removed from the ground before May 8, 1986;
- Farm or residential tanks of 1,100 gallons or less capacity storing motor fuel for noncommercial purposes;
- Tanks storing heating oil for use on the premises where stored;
- Septic tanks;
- Pipeline facilities (including gathering lines) regulated under the Natural Gas Pipeline Safety Act of 1968, or the Hazardous Liquid Pipeline Safety Act of 1979, or which is an intrastate pipeline facility regulated under State laws;
- Surface impoundments, pits, ponds, or lagoons;
- Storm water or waste water collection systems;
- Flow-through process tanks;
- Liquid traps or associated gathering lines directly related to oil or gas production and gathering operations;
- Tanks on or above the floor of underground areas, such as basements or tunnels;
- Tanks with a capacity of 110 gallons or less.

What Substances Are Covered? The notification requirements apply to USTs containing petroleum or certain hazardous substances. Petroleum includes gasoline, used oil, diesel fuel, crude oil or any fraction thereof which is liquid at standard conditions of temperature and pressure (60 degrees Fahrenheit and 14.7 pounds per square inch absolute). Hazardous substances are those found in Section 101 (14) of the Comprehensive Environmental Response, Compensation and Liability Act of 1980 (CERCLA), with the exception of those substances regulated as hazardous waste under Subtitle C of RCRA.

Where To Notify? Send completed forms to:

When To Notify? 1. Owners of USTs in use or that have been taken out of operation after January 1, 1974, but still in the ground, must notify by May 8, 1986. 2. Owners who bring USTs into use after May 8, 1986, must notify within 30 days of bringing the UST into use. 3. If the State requires notification of any amendments to facility, send information to State agency immediately.

Penalties: Any owner who knowingly fails to notify or submits false information shall be subject to a civil penalty not to exceed $11,000 for each tank for which notification is not given or for which false information is given.

I. OWNERSHIP OF UST(s)

Owner Name (Corporation, Individual, Public Agency, or Other Entity)

Street Address

County

City	State	Zip Code

Phone Number (Include Area Code)

II. LOCATION OF UST(s)

If required by State, give the geographic location of USTs by degrees, minutes, and seconds. Example: Latitude 42 ° 36' 12" N, Longitude 85 ° 24' 17" W

Latitude ______________ **Longitude** ______________

Facility Name or Company Site Identifier, as applicable

Q If address is the same as in Section I, check the box and proceed to section III.
If address is different, enter address below:

Street Address

County

City	State	Zip Code

EPA

United States
Environmental Protection Agency
Washington, DC 20460

Form Approved.
OMB No.2050-0068

Notification for Underground Storage Tanks

III. TYPE OF OWNER

☐ Federal Government
☐ State Government ☐ Commercial
☐ Local Government ☐ Private

IV. INDIAN COUNTRY

USTs are located on land within an Indian Reservation or on trust lands outside reservation boundaries. ☐

USTs are owned by a Native American nation or tribe. ☐

Tribe or Nation where USTs are located:

V. TYPE OF FACILITY

☐ Gas Station	☐ Railroad	☐ Trucking/Transport
☐ Petroleum Distributor	☐ Federal - Non-Military	☐ Utilities
☐ Air Taxi (Airline)	☐ Federal - Military	☐ Residential
☐ Aircraft Owner	☐ Industrial	☐ Farm
☐ Auto Dealership	☐ Contractor	☐ Other (Explain) ______________

VI. CONTACT PERSON IN CHARGE OF TANKS

Name:	Job Title:	Address:	Phone Number (Include Area Code):

VII. FINANCIAL RESPONSIBILITY

☐ I have met the financial responsibility requirements (in accordance with 40 CFR Subpart H) by using the following mechanisms:

Check All that Apply

☐ Self Insurance	☐ Guarantee	☐ State Funds
☐ Commercial Insurance	☐ Surety Bond	☐ Trust Fund
☐ Risk Retention Group	☐ Letter of Credit	☐ Other Method (describe here)
☐ Local Government Financial Test	☐ Bond Rating Test	______________

VIII. CERTIFICATION (Read and sign after completing ALL SECTIONS of this notification form)

I certify under penalty of law that I have personally examined and am familiar with the information submitted in Sections I through XI of this notification form and all attached documents, and that based on my inquiry of those individuals immediately responsible for obtaining the information, I believe that the submitted information is true, accurate, and complete.

Name and official title of owner or owner's authorized representative (Print)	Signature	Date Signed

Paperwork Reduction Act Notice

EPA estimates public reporting burden for this form to average 30 minutes per response including time for reviewing instructions, gathering and maintaining the data needed and completing and reviewing the form. Send comments regarding this burden estimate to Director, OP, Regulatory Information Division (2137), U.S. Environmental Protection Agency, 401 M Street, Washington D.C. 20460, marked "Attention Desk Officer for EPA." This form amends the previous notification form as printed in 40 CFR Part 280, Appendix I. Previous editions of this notification form may be used while supplies last.

EPA Form 7530-1 (Rev. 9-98) Electronic and paper versions acceptable.
Previous editions may be used while supplies last.

Page 2 of 5

United States
Environmental Protection Agency
Washington, DC 20460

Form Approved.
OMB No.2050-0068

Notification for Underground Storage Tanks

IX. DESCRIPTION OF UNDERGROUND STORAGE TANKS (Complete for all tanks and piping at this location.)

Tank Identification Number	Tank No. ____	Tank No. ____	Tank No. ____	Tank No. ____	Tank No. ____
1. Status of Tank (check only one) Currently In Use	☐	☐	☐	☐	☐
Temporarily Closed	☐	☐	☐	☐	☐
Permanently Closed	☐	☐	☐	☐	☐
2. Date of Installation (month/year)					
3. Estimated Total Capacity (gallons)					
4. Material of Construction (check all that apply)					
Asphalt Coated or Bare Steel	☐	☐	☐	☐	☐
Cathodically Protected Steel	☐	☐	☐	☐	☐
Coated and Cathodically Protected Steel	☐	☐	☐	☐	☐
Composite (Steel Clad with Fiberglass)	☐	☐	☐	☐	☐
Fiberglass Reinforced Plastic	☐	☐	☐	☐	☐
Lined Interior	☐	☐	☐	☐	☐
Excavation Liner	☐	☐	☐	☐	☐
Double Walled	☐	☐	☐	☐	☐
Polyethylene Tank Jacket	☐	☐	☐	☐	☐
Concrete	☐	☐	☐	☐	☐
Unknown	☐	☐	☐	☐	☐
If Other, please specify here	________	________	________	________	________
Check box if tank has ever been repaired	☐	☐	☐	☐	☐
5. Piping Material (check all that apply) Bare Steel	☐	☐	☐	☐	☐
Galvanized Steel	☐	☐	☐	☐	☐
Fiberglass Reinforced Plastic	☐	☐	☐	☐	☐
Copper	☐	☐	☐	☐	☐
Cathodically Protected	☐	☐	☐	☐	☐
Double Walled	☐	☐	☐	☐	☐
Secondary Containment	☐	☐	☐	☐	☐
Unknown	☐	☐	☐	☐	☐
Other, please specify	________	________	________	________	________
6. Piping Type (Check all that apply) "Safe" Suction (no valve at tank)	☐	☐	☐	☐	☐
"U.S." Suction (valve at tank)	☐	☐	☐	☐	☐
Pressure	☐	☐	☐	☐	☐
Gravity Feed	☐	☐	☐	☐	☐
Check box if piping has ever been repaired	☐	☐	☐	☐	☐

EPA Form 7530-1 (Rev. 9-98) Electronic and paper versions acceptable.
Previous editions may be used while supplies last.

Page 3 of 5

EPA

United States
Environmental Protection Agency
Washington, DC 20460

Form Approved.
OMB No.2050-0068

Notification for Underground Storage Tanks

Tank Identification Number	Tank No. ____	Tank No. ____	Tank No. ____	Tank No. ____	Tank No. ____
7. Substance Currently Stored (or last stored in the case of closed tanks) (Check all that apply) Gasoline	☐	☐	☐	☐	☐
Diesel	☐	☐	☐	☐	☐
Gasohol	☐	☐	☐	☐	☐
Kerosene	☐	☐	☐	☐	☐
Heating Oil	☐	☐	☐	☐	☐
Used Oil	☐	☐	☐	☐	☐
If Other, please specify here	____	____	____	____	____
Hazardous Substance	☐	☐	☐	☐	☐
CERCLA name and/or	____	____	____	____	____
CAS number	____	____	____	____	____
Mixture of Substances	☐	☐	☐	☐	☐
Please specify here	____	____	____	____	____

8. **Release Detection** (check all that apply)	TANK	PIPE	TANK	PIPE	TANK	PIPE	TANK	PIPE	TANK	PIPE
Manual tank gauging	☐		☐		☐		☐		☐	
Tank tightness testing	☐		☐		☐		☐		☐	
Inventory Control	☐		☐		☐		☐		☐	
Automatic tank gauging	☐	☐	☐	☐	☐	☐	☐	☐	☐	☐
Vapor monitoring	☐	☐	☐	☐	☐	☐	☐	☐	☐	☐
Groundwater monitoring	☐	☐	☐	☐	☐	☐	☐	☐	☐	☐
Interstitial monitoring	☐	☐	☐	☐	☐	☐	☐	☐	☐	☐
Automatic line leak detectors		☐		☐		☐		☐		☐
Line tightness testing		☐		☐		☐		☐		☐
No release detection required (such as some types of suction piping, emergency generator tanks or field constructed tanks)	☐	☐	☐	☐	☐	☐	☐	☐	☐	☐
Other method allowed by implementing agency (such as SIR)	☐		☐		☐		☐		☐	
Please specify other method here	____		____		____		____		____	

9. Spill and Overfill Protection					
Overfill device installed	☐	☐	☐	☐	☐
Spill device installed	☐	☐	☐	☐	☐

EPA Form 7530-1 (Rev. 9-98) Electronic and paper versions acceptable.
Previous editions may be used while supplies last.

EPA

United States
Environmental Protection Agency
Washington, DC 20460

Form Approved.
OMB No.2050-0068

Notification for Underground Storage Tanks

Tank Identification Number	Tank No. ____	Tank No. ____	Tank No. ____	Tank No. ____	Tank No. ____
X. CLOSURE OR CHANGE IN SERVICE					
1. **Closure or Change in Service**					
Estimated date the UST was last used for storing regulated substances (month/day/year)	____	____	____	____	____
Check box if this is a change in service	☐	☐	☐	☐	☐
2. **Tank Closure**					
Estimated date tank closed (month/day/year)	____	____	____	____	____
(check all that apply below)					
Tank was removed from ground	☐	☐	☐	☐	☐
Tank was closed in ground	☐	☐	☐	☐	☐
Tank filled with inert material	☐	☐	☐	☐	☐
Describe the inert fill material here	____	____	____	____	____
3. **Site Assessment**					
Check box if the site assessment was completed	☐	☐	☐	☐	☐
Check box if evidence of a leak was detected	☐	☐	☐	☐	☐
XI. CERTIFICATION OF INSTALLATION (COMPLETE FOR UST SYSTEMS INSTALLED AFTER DECEMBER 22, 1988)					
Installer Of Tank And Piping Must Check All That Apply:					
Installer certified by tank and piping manufacturers	☐	☐	☐	☐	☐
Installer certified or licensed by the implementing agency	☐	☐	☐	☐	☐
Installation inspected by a registered engineer	☐	☐	☐	☐	☐
Installation inspected and approved by implementing agency	☐	☐	☐	☐	☐
Manufacturer's installation checklists have been completed	☐	☐	☐	☐	☐
Another method allowed by State agency If so, please specify here	☐ ____	☐ ____	☐ ____	☐ ____	☐ ____

Signature of UST Installer Certifying Proper Installation of UST System

Name	Signature	Date
Position	Company	

EPA Form 7530-1 (Rev. 9-98) Electronic and paper versions acceptable.
Previous editions may be used while supplies last

Page 5 of 5

PART 280—Appendices

Appendix II to Part 280—List of Agencies Designated To Receive Notifications

Alabama (EPA Form), Alabama Department of Environmental Management, Ground Water Section/Water Division, 1751 Congressman W.L. Dickinson Drive, Montgomery, Alabama 36130, 205/271-7823

Alaska (EPA Form), Department of Environmental Conservation, Box 0, Juneau, Alaska 99811-1800, 970/465-2653

American Samoa (EPA Form), Executive Secretary, Environmental Quality Commission, Office of the Governor, American Samoan Government, Pago Pago, American Samoa 96799; Attention: UST Notification

Arizona (EPA Form), Attention: UST Coordinator, Arizona Department of Environmental Quality, Environmental Health Services, 2005 N. Central, Phoenix, Arizona 85004

Arkansas (EPA Form), Arkansas Department of Pollution Control and Ecology, P.O. Box 9583, Little Rock, Arkansas 72219, 501/562-7444

California (State Form), Executive Director, State Water Resources Control Board, P.O. Box 100, Sacramento, California 95801, 916/445-1533

Co1orado (EPA Form), Section Chief, Colorado Department of Health, Waste Management Division, Underground Tank Program, 4210 East 11th Avenue, Denver, Colorado 80220, 303/320-8333

Connecticut (State Form), Hazardous Materials Management Unit, Department of Environmental Protection, State Office Building, 165 Capitol Avenue, Hartford, Connecticut 06106

Delaware (State Form), Division of Air and Waste Management, Department of Natural Resources and Environmental Control, P.O. Box 1401, 89 Kings Highway, Dover, Delaware 19903, 302/726-5409

District of Columbia (EPA Form), Attention: UST Notification Form, Department of Consumer and Regulatory Affairs, Pesticides and Hazardous Waste Management Branch, Room 114, 5010 Overlook Avenue SW., Washington, DC 20032

Florida (State Form), Florida Department of Environmental Regulation, Solid Waste Section, Twin Towers Office Building, 2600 Blair Stone Road, Tallahassee, Florida 32399, 904/487-4398

Georgia (EPA Form), Georgia Department of Natural Resources, Environmental Protection Division, Underground Storage Tank Program, 3420 Norman Berry Drive, 7th Floor, Hapeville, Georgia 30354, 404/656- 7404

Guam (State Form), Administrator, Guam Environmental Protection Agency, P.O. Box 2999, Agana, Guam 96910, Overseas Operator (Commercial call 646-8863)

Hawaii (EPA Form), Administrator, Hazardous Waste Program, 645 Halekauwila Street, Honolulu, Hawaii 96813, 808/548-2270

Idaho (EPA Form), Underground Storage Tank Coordinator, Water Quality Bureau, Division of Environmental Quality, Idaho Department of Health and Welfare, 450 W. State Street, Boise, Idaho 83720, 208/334-4251

Illinois (EPA Form), Underground Storage Tank Coordinator, Division of Fire Prevention, Office of State Fire Marshal, 3150 Executive Park Drive, Springfield, Illinois 62703-4599

Indiana (EPA Form), Underground Storage Tank Program, Office of Environmental Response, Indiana Department of Environmental Management, 105 South Meridian Street, Indianapolis, Indiana 46225

Iowa (State Form), UST Coordinator, Iowa Department of Natural Resources, Henry A. Wallace Building, 900 East Grand, Des Moines, Iowa 50219, 512/281-8135

Kansas (EPA Form), Kansas Department of Health and Environment, Forbes Field, Building 740, Topeka, Kansas 66620, 913/296-1594

Kentucky (State Form), Department of Environmental Protection, Hazardous Waste Branch, Fort Boone Plaza, Building #2, 18 Reilly Road, Frankfort, Kentucky 40601, 501/564-6716

Louisiana (State Form), Secretary, Louisiana Department of Environmental Quality, P.O. Box 44066, Baton Rouge, Louisiana 70804, 501/342-1265

Maine (State Form), Attention: Underground Tanks Program, Bureau of Oil and Hazardous Material Control, Department of Environmental Protection, State House—Station 17, Augusta, Maine 04333

Maryland (EPA Form), Science and Health Advisory Group, Office of Environmental Programs, 201 West Preston Street, Baltimore, Maryland 21201

Massachusetts (EPA Form), UST Registry, Department of Public Safety, 1010 Commonwealth Avenue, Boston, Massachusetts 02215, 617/566-4500

Michigan (EPA Form), Michigan Department of State Police, Fire Marshal Division, General Office Building, 7150 Harris Drive, Lansing, Michigan 48913

Minnesota (State Form), Underground Storage Tank Program, Division of Solid and Hazardous Wastes, Minnesota Pollution Control Agency, 520 West Lafayette Road, St. Paul, Minnesota 55155

Mississippi (State Form), Department of Natural Resources, Bureau of Pollution Control, Underground Storage Tank Section, P.O. Box 10385, Jackson, Mississippi 39209, 601/961-5171

Missouri (EPA Form), UST Coordinator, Missouri Department of Natural Resources, P.O. Box 176, Jefferson City, Missouri 65102, 314/751-7428

Montana (EPA Form), Solid and Hazardous Waste Bureau, Department of Health and Environmental Science, Cogswell Bldg., Room B-201, Helena, Montana 59620

Nebraska (EPA Form), Nebraska State Fire Marshal, P.O. Box 94677, Lincoln, Nebraska 68509-4677, 402/471-9465

Nevada (EPA Form), Attention: UST Coordinator, Division of Environmental Protection, Department of Conservation and Natural Resources, Capitol Complex 201 S. Fall Street, Carson City, Nevada 89710, 800/992-0900, Ext. 4670, 702/885-4670

New Hampshire (EPA Form), NH Dept. of Environmental Services, Water Supply and Pollution Control Division, Hazen Drive, P.O. Box 95, Concord, New Hampshire 03301, Attention: UST Registration

New Jersey (State Form), Underground Storage Tank Coordinator, Department of Environmental Protection, Division of Water Resources (CN-029), Trenton, New Jersey 08625, 609/292-0424

New Mexico (EPA Form), New Mexico Environmental Improvement Division, Groundwater/Hazardous Waste Bureau, P.O. Box 968, Santa Fe, New Mexico 37504, 505/827-2933

New York (EPA Form), Bulk Storage Section, Division of Water, Department of Environmental Conservation, 50 Wolf Road, Room 326, Albany, New York 12233-0001, 518/457-4351

North Carolina (EPA Form), Division of Environmental Management, Ground-Water Operations Branch, Department of

Natural Resources and Community Development, P.O. Box 27687, Raleigh, North Carolina 27611, 919/733-3221

North Dakota (State Form), Division of Hazardous Management and Special Studies, North Dakota Department of Health, Box 5520, Bismarck, North Dakota 58502-5520

Northern Mariana Islands (EPA Form), Chief, Division of Environmental Quality, P.O. Box 1304, Commonwealth of Northern Mariana Islands, Saipan, CM 96950, Cable Address: Gov. NMI Saipan, Overseas Operator: 6984

Ohio (State Form), State Fire Marshal's Office, Department of Commerce, 8895 E. Main Street, Reynoldsburg, Ohio 43068, State Hotline: 800/282- 1927

Oklahoma (EPA Form), Underground Storage Tank Program, Oklahoma Corporation Comm., Jim Thorpe Building, Oklahoma City, Oklahoma 73105

Oregon (State Form), Underground Storage Tank Program, Hazardous and Solid Waste Division, Department of Environmental Quality, 811 S.W. Sixth Avenue, Portland, Oregon 98204, 503/229-5788

Pennsylvania (EPA Form), PA Department of Environmental Resources, Bureau of Water Quality Management, Ground Water Unit, 9th Floor Fulton Building, P.O. Box 2063, Harrisburg, Pennsylvania 17120

Puerto Rico (EPA Form), Director, Water Quality Control Area, Environmental Quality Board, Commonwealth of Puerto Rico, Santurce, Puerto Rico, 809/725-0717

Rhode Island (EPA Form), UST Registration, Department of Environmental Management, 83 Park Street, Providence, Rhode Island 02903, 401/277-2234

South Carolina (State Form), Ground-Water Protection Division, South Carolina Department of Health and Environmental Control, 2600 Bull Street, Columbia, South Carolina 29201, 803/758-5213

South Dakota (EPA Form), Office of Water Quality, Department of Water and Natural Resources, Joe Foss Building, Pierre, South Dakota 57501

Tennessee (EPA Form), Tennessee Department of Health and Environment, Division of Superfund Underground Storage Tank Section, 150 Ninth Avenue, North, Nashville, Tennessee 37219-5404, 615/741-0690

Texas (EPA Form), Underground Storage Tank Program, Texas Water Commission, P.O. Box 13087, Austin, Texas 78711

Utah (EPA Form), Division of Environmental Health, P.O. Box 45500, Salt Lake City, Utah 84145-0500

Vermont (State Form), Underground Storage Tank Program, Vermont AEC/Waste Management Division, State Office Building, Montpelier, Vermont 05602, 802/828-3395

Virginia (EPA Form), Virginia Water Control Board, P.O. Box 11143, Richmond, Virginia 23230-1143, 804/257-6685

Virgin Islands (EPA Form), 205(J) Coordinator, Division of Natural Resources Management, 14 F Building 111, Watergut Homes, Christianstead, St. Croix, Virgin Islands 00820

Washington (State Form), Underground Storage Tank Notification, Solid and Hazardous Waste Program, Department of Ecology, M/S PV-11, Olympia, Washington 98504-8711, 206/459-6316

West Virginia (EPA Form), Attention: UST Notification, Solid and Hazardous Waste, Ground Water Branch, West Virginia Department of Natural Resources, 1201 Greenbriar Street, Charleston, West Virginia 25311

Wisconsin (State Form), Bureau of Petroleum Inspection, P.O. Box 7969, Madison, Wisconsin 53707, 608/266-7605

Wyoming (EPA Form), Water Quality Division, Department of Environmental Quality, Herschler Building, 4th Floor West, 122 West 25th Street, Cheyenne, Wyoming 82002, 307/777-7781.

Appendix III to Part 280—Statement for Shipping Tickets and Invoices

Note—A Federal law (the Resource Conservation and Recovery Act (RCRA), as amended (Pub. L. 98-616)) requires owners of certain underground storage tanks to notify designated State or local agencies by May 8, 1986, of the existence of their tanks. Notifications for tanks brought into use after May 8, 1986, must be made within 30 days. Consult EPA's regulations, issued on November 8, 1985 (40 CFR part 280) to determine if you are affected by this law.

PART 148—HAZARDOUS WASTE INJECTION RESTRICTIONS

Authority: Section 3004, Resource Conservation and Recovery Act, 42 U.S.C. 6901 *et seq.*

Source: 53 FR 28154, July 26, 1988, unless otherwise noted.

Subpart A—General

§148.1 Purpose, scope and applicability.

13.1

(a) This part identifies wastes that are restricted from disposal into Class I wells and defines those circumstances under which a waste, otherwise prohibited from injection, may be injected.

(b) The requirements of this part apply to owners or operators of Class I hazardous waste injection wells used to inject hazardous waste.

(c) Wastes otherwise prohibited from injection may continue to be injected:

(1) If an extension from the effective date of a prohibition has been granted pursuant to §148.4 with respect to such wastes; or

(2) If an exemption from a prohibition has been granted in response to a petition filed under §148.20 to allow injection of restricted wastes with respect to those wastes and wells covered by the exemption; or

(3) If the waste is generated by a conditionally exempt small quantity generator, as defined in §261.5.

(d) Wastes that are hazardous only because they exhibit a hazardous characteristic, and which are otherwise prohibited under this part, or part 268 of this chapter, are not prohibited if the wastes: 13.4.1

(1) Are disposed into a nonhazardous or hazardous injection well as defined under 40 CFR §146.6(a); and

(2) Do not exhibit any prohibited characteristic of hazardous waste identified in 40 CFR part 261, subpart C at the point of injection.

[53 FR 28154, July 26, 1988, as amended at 55 FR 22683, June 1, 1990; 57 FR 8088, Mar. 6, 1992; 57 FR 31763, July 20, 1992; 60 FR 33932, June 29, 1995; 61 FR 15596, Apr. 8, 1996; 61 FR 33682, June 28, 1996]

§148.2 Definitions.

Injection interval means that part of the injection zone in which the well is screened, or in which the waste is otherwise directly emplaced.

Transmissive fault or *fracture* is a fault or fracture that has sufficient permeability and vertical extent to allow fluids to move between formations.

§148.3 Dilution prohibited as a substitute for treatment.

The prohibition of §268.3 shall apply to owners or operators of Class I hazardous waste injection wells. 13.11

§148.4 Procedures for case-by-case extensions to an effective date.

The owner or operator of a Class I hazardous waste injection well may submit an application to the Administrator for an extension of the effective date of any applicable prohibition established under subpart B of this part according to the procedures of §268.5.

§148.5 Waste analysis.

Generators of hazardous wastes that are disposed of into Class I injection wells must comply with the applicable requirements of §268.7 (a) and (b). Owners or operators of Class I hazardous waste injection wells must comply with the applicable requirements of §268.7(c).

Subpart B—Prohibitions on Injection

13.1

§148.10 Waste specific prohibitions—solvent wastes.

(a) Effective August 8, 1988, the spent solvent wastes specified in §261.31 as EPA Hazardous Waste Nos. F001, F002, F003, F004, and F005 are prohibited from underground injection unless the solvent waste is a solvent-water mixture or solvent-containing sludge containing less than 1 percent total F001-F005 solvent constituents listed in Table A of this section.

(b) Effective August 8, 1990, all spent F001-F005 solvent wastes containing less than 1 percent total F001-F005 solvent constituents listed in Table A of this section are prohibited from injection.

(c) Effective August 8, 1990, all spent F002 and F005 wastes containing solvent constituents listed in Table B of this section are prohibited from underground injection at off-site injection facilities.

(d) Effective November 8, 1990, the wastes specified in paragraph (c) of this section are prohibited from underground injection at on-site injection facilities.

(e) The requirements of paragraphs (a) and (b) of this section do not apply:

(1) If the wastes meet or are treated to meet the applicable standards specified in subpart D of part 268; or

(2) If an exemption from a prohibition has been granted in response to a petition under subpart C of this part; or

(3) During the period of extension of the applicable effective date, if an extension has been granted under §148.4 of this part.

Table A

Acetone	Methylene chloride (from the pharmaceutical industry)
n-Butyl alcohol	Methyl ethyl ketone
Carbon disulfide	Methyl isobutyl ketone
Carbon tetrachloride	Nitrobenzene
Chlorobenzene	Pyridine
Cresols and cresylic acid	Tetrachloroethylene
Cyclohexanone	Toluene
1,2-dichlorobenzene	1,1,1-Trichloroethane
Ethyl acetate	1,2,2-Trichloro-1,2,2-trifluoroethane
Ethyl benzene	Trichloroethylene
Ethyl ether	Trichlorofluoromethane
Isobutanol	Xylene
Methanol	
Methylene chloride	

Table B

Benzene	2-Nitropropane
2-Ethoxyethanol	1,1,2-Trichloroethane

[53 FR 28154, July 26, 1988, as amended at 54 FR 25422, June 14, 1989; 56 FR 3876, Jan. 31, 1991; 57 FR 8088, Mar. 6, 1992]

§148.11 Waste specific prohibitions—dioxin-containing wastes.

(a) Effective August 8, 1988, the dioxin-containing wastes specified in §261.31 as EPA Hazardous Waste Nos. F020, F021, F022, F023, F026, F027, and F028, and prohibited from underground injection.

(b) The requirements of paragraph (a) of this section do not apply:

(1) If the wastes meet or are treated to meet the applicable standards specified in subpart D of part 268; or

(2) If an exemption from a prohibition has been granted in response to a petition under subpart C of this part; or

(3) During the period of extension of the applicable effective date, if an extension has been granted under §148.4 of this part.

[53 FR 28154, July 26, 1988, as amended at 54 FR 25422, June 14, 1989]

§148.12 Waste specific prohibitions—California list wastes.

(a) Effective August 8, 1988, the hazardous wastes listed in 40 CFR 268.32 containing polychlorinated biphenyls at concentrations greater than or equal to 50 ppm or halogenated organic compounds at concentrations greater than or equal to 10,000 mg/kg are prohibited from underground injection.

(b) Effective August 8, 1990, the following hazardous wastes are prohibited from underground injection:

(1) Liquid hazardous wastes, including free liquids associated with any solid or sludge, containing free cyanides at concentrations greater than or equal to 1,000 mg/l;

(2) Liquid hazardous wastes, including free liquids associated with any solid or sludge, containing the following metals (or elements) or compounds of these metals (or elements) at concentrations greater than or equal to those specified below:

(i) Arsenic and/or compounds (as As) 500 mg/l;

(ii) Cadmium and/or compounds (as Cd) 100 mg/l;

(iii) Chromium (VI) and/or compounds (as Cr VI) 500 mg/l;

(iv) Lead and/or compounds (as Pb) 500 mg/l;

(v) Mercury and/or compounds (as Hg) 20 mg/l;

(vi) Nickel and/or compounds (as Ni) 134 mg/l;

(vii) Selenium and/or compounds (as Se) 100 mg/l; and

(viii) Thallium and/or compounds (as Tl) 130 mg/l;

(3) Liquid hazardous waste having a pH less than or equal to two (2.0); and

(4) Hazardous wastes containing halogenated organic compounds in total concentration less than 10,000 mg/kg but greater than or equal to 1,000 mg/kg.

(c) The requirements of paragraphs (a) and (b) of this section do not apply:

(1) If the wastes meet or are treated to meet the applicable standards specified in subpart D of part 268; or

(2) If an exemption from a prohibition has been granted in response to a petition under subpart C of this part; or

(3) During the period of extension of the applicable effective date, if an extension is granted under §148.4 of this part.

[53 FR 30918, Aug. 16, 1988, as amended at 53 FR 41602, Oct. 24, 1988]

§148.14 Waste specific prohibitions—first third wastes.

(a) Effective June 7, 1989, the wastes specified in 40 CFR 261.31 as EPA Hazardous Waste numbers F006 (nonwastewaters) and the wastes specified in 40 CFR 261.32 as EPA Hazardous Waste numbers K001, K015 (wastewaters), K016 (at concentrations greater than or equal to 1%), K018, K019, K020, K021 (nonwastewaters generated by the process described in the waste listing description and disposed after August 17, 1988, and not generated in the course of treating wastewater forms of these wastes), K022 (nonwastewaters), K024, K030, K036 (nonwastewaters generated by the process described in the waste listing description and disposed after August 17, 1988, and not generated in the course of treating wastewater forms of these wastes), K037, K044, K045, nonexplosive K046 (nonwastewaters), K047, K048, K060 (nonwastewaters generated by the process described in the waste listing description and disposed after August 17, 1988, and not generated in the course of treating wastewater forms of these wastes), K061 (nonwastewaters), noncalcium sulfate K069 (nonwastewaters generated by the process described in the waste listing description and disposed after August 17, 1988, and not generated in the course of treating wastewater forms of these wastes), K086 solvent washes, K087, K099, K101 (all wastewaters and less than 1% total arsenic nonwastewaters), K102 (all wastewaters and less than 1% total arsenic nonwastewaters), and K103 are prohibited from underground injection.

(b) Effective June 8, 1989, the waste specified in 40 CFR 261.32 as EPA Hazardous Waste number K036 (wastewaters); and the wastes specified in 40 CFR 261.33 as P030, P039, P041, P063, P071, P089, P094, P097, U221, and U223 are prohibited from underground injection.

(c) Effective July 8, 1989, the wastes specified in 40 CFR 261.31 as EPA Hazardous Waste numbers F008 and F009 are prohibited from underground injection.

(d) Effective August 8, 1990, the wastes specified in 40 CFR 261.31 as EPA Hazardous Waste Number F006 (wastewaters) and F019; the wastes specified in 40 CFR 261.32 as EPA Hazardous Waste Numbers K004, K008, K015 (nonwastewaters), K017, K021 (wastewaters), K022 (wastewaters), K031, K035, K046 (reactive nonwastewaters and all wastewaters), K060 (wastewaters), K061 (wastewaters), K069 (calcium sulfate nonwastewaters and all wastewaters), K073, K083, K084, K085, K086 (all but solvent washes), K101 (high arsenic nonwastewaters), K102 (high arsenic nonwastewaters), and K106; and the wastes specified in 40 CFR part 261.33 as EPA Hazardous Waste Numbers P001, P004, P005, P010, P011, P012, P015, P016, P018, P020, P036, P037, P048, P050, P058, P059, P068, P069, P070, P081, P082, P084, P087, P092, P102, P105, P108, P110, P115, P120, P122, P123, U007, U009, U010, U012, U016, U018, U019, U022, U029, U031, U036, U037, U041, U043, U044, U046, U050, U051, U053, U061, U063, U064, U066, U067, U074, U077, U078, U086, U089, U103, U105, U108, U115, U122, U124, U129, U130, U133, U134, U137, U151, U154, U155, U157, U158, U159, U171, U177, U180, U185, U188, U192, U200, U209, U210, U211, U219, U220, U226, U227, U228, U237, U238, U248, and U249 are prohibited from underground injection at off-site injection facilities.

(e) Effective August 8, 1990, the wastes specified in 40 CFR 261.32 as EPA Hazardous Waste numbers K049, K050, K051, K052, K062, K071, and K104 are prohibited from underground injection.

(f) Effective November 8, 1990, the wastes specified in paragraph (d) of this section are prohibited from underground injection at on-site injection facilities.

(g) Effective June 7, 1991, the wastes specified in 40 CFR 261.32 as EPA Hazardous Waste numbers K016 (at concentrations less than 1%) are prohibited from underground injection.

(h) Effective June 8, 1991, the waste specified in 40 CFR 261.31 as EPA Hazardous Waste number F007; and the wastes specified in 40 CFR 261.32 as K011 (nonwastewaters) and K013 (nonwastewaters) are prohibited from underground injection.

(i) Effective May 8, 1992, the wastes specified in 40 CFR 261.32 and 261.33 as EPA Hazardous Waste Numbers

K011 (wastewaters), K013 (wastewaters), and K014 are prohibited from underground injection.

(j) The requirements of paragraphs (a) through (i) of this section do not apply:

(1) If the wastes meet or are treated to meet the applicable standards specified in subpart D of part 268; or

(2) If an exemption from a prohibition has been granted in response to a petition under subpart C of this part; or

(3) During the period of extension of the applicable effective date, if an extension has been granted under §148.4 of this part.

[54 FR 25423, June 14, 1989, as amended at 54 FR 26647, June 23, 1989; 54 FR 35328, Aug. 25, 1989; 55 FR 22683, June 1, 1990]

§148.15 Waste specific prohibitions—second third wastes.

(a) Effective June 7, 1989, the wastes specified in 40 CFR 261.32 as EPA Hazardous Waste numbers K025 (nonwastewaters generated by the process described in the waste listing description and disposed after August 17, 1988, and not generated in the course of treating wastewater forms of these wastes) are prohibited from underground injection.

(b) Effective June 8, 1989, the wastes specified in 40 CFR 261.31 as EPA Hazardous Waste numbers F010, F024; the wastes specified in 40 CFR 261.32 as K009 (nonwastewaters), K010, K027, K028, K029 (nonwastewaters), K038, K039, K040, K043, K095 (nonwastewaters), K096 (nonwastewaters), K113, K114, K115, K116; and wastes specified in 40 CFR 261.33 as P029, P040, P043, P044, P062, P074, P085, P098, P104, P106, P111, U028, U058, U107, and U235 are prohibited from underground injection.

(c) Effective July 8, 1989, and continuing until December 8, 1989, the wastes specified in 40 CFR 261.31 as EPA Hazardous Waste numbers F011 and F012 are prohibited from underground injection pursuant to the treatment standards specified in §§268.41 and 268.43 applicable to F007, F008, and F009 wastewaters and nonwastewaters. Effective December 8, 1989, F011 (nonwastewaters) and F012 (nonwastewaters) are prohibited pursuant to the treatment standards specified in §§268.41 and 268.43 applicable to F011 and F012 wastewaters and nonwastewaters.

(d) Effective August 8, 1990, the wastes specified in 40 CFR 261.32 as EPA Hazardous Waste Number K025 (wastewaters), K029 (wastewaters), K041, K042, K095 (wastewaters), K096 (wastewaters), K097, K098, and K105; and the wastes specified in 40 CFR part 261.33 as P002, P003, P007, P008, P014, P026, P027, P049, P054, P057, P060, P066, P067, P072, P107, P112, P113, P114, U002, U003, U005, U008, U011, U014, U015, U020, U021, U023, U025, U026, U032, U035, U047, U049, U057, U059, U060, U062, U070, U073, U080, U083, U092, U093, U094, U095, U097, U098, U099, U101, U106, U109, U110, U111, U114, U116, U119, U127, U128, U131, U135, U138, U140, U142, U143, U144, U146, U147, U149, U150, U161, U162, U163, U164, U165, U168, U169, U170, U172, U173, U174, U176, U178, U179, U189, U193, U196, U203, U205, U206, U208, U213, U214, U215, U216, U217, U218, U239, and U244 are prohibited from underground injection at off-site injection facilities.

(e) Effective June 8, 1991, the waste specified in 40 CFR 261.32 as EPA Hazardous Waste number K009 (wastewaters) is prohibited from underground injection.

(f) Effective November 8, 1990, the wastes specified in paragraph (d) of this section are prohibited from underground injection at on-site injection facilities.

(g) The requirements of paragraphs (a) through (f) of this section do not apply:

(1) If the wastes meet or are treated to meet the applicable standards specified in subpart D of part 268; or

(2) If an exemption from a prohibition has been granted in response to a petition under subpart C of this part; or

(3) During the period of extension of the applicable effective date, if an extension has been granted under §148.4 of this part.

[54 FR 25423, June 14, 1989, as amended at 54 FR 26647, June 23, 1989; 55 FR 22683, June 1, 1990]

§148.16 Waste specific prohibitions—third third wastes.

(a) Effective June 7, 1989, the wastes specified in 40 CFR 261.32 as EPA Hazardous Waste numbers K100 (nonwastewaters generated by the process described in the waste listing description and disposed after August 17, 1988, and not generated in the course of treating wastewater forms of these wastes) are prohibited from underground injection.

(b) Effective June 8, 1989, the wastes specified in 40 CFR 261.32 as EPA Hazardous Waste numbers K005 (nonwastewaters), K007 (nonwastewaters), K023, K093, K094; and the wastes specified in 40 CFR 261.33 as P013, P021, P099, P109, P121, U069, U087, U088, U102, and U190 are prohibited from underground injection.

(c) Effective August 8, 1990, the wastes identified in 40 CFR 261.31 as EPA Hazardous Waste Number F039 (nonwastewaters); the wastes specified in 40 CFR 261.32 as EPA Hazardous Waste Numbers K002, K003, K005 (wastewaters), K006, K007 (wastewaters), K026, K032, K033, K034, and K100 (wastewaters); the wastes specified in 40 CFR 261.33 as P006, P009, P017, P022, P023, P024, P028, P031, P033, P034, P038, P042, P045, P046, P047, P051, P056, P064, P065, P073, P075, P076, P077, P078, P088, P093, P095, P096, P101, P103, P116, P118, P119, U001, U004, U006, U017, U024, U027, U030, U033, U034, U038, U039, U042, U045, U048, U052, U055, U056, U068, U071, U072, U075, U076, U079, U081, U082, U084, U085, U090, U091, U096, U112, U113, U117, U118, U120, U121, U123, U125, U126, U132, U136, U141, U145, U148, U152, U153, U156, U160, U166, U167, U181, U182, U183, U184, U186, U187, U191, U194, U197, U201, U202, U204, U207, U222, U225, U234, U236, U240, U243, U246, and U247; and the wastes identified in 40 CFR 261.21, 261.23 or 261.24 as hazardous based on a characteristic alone, designated as D001, D004, D005, D006, D008, D009 (wastewaters), D010, D011, D012, D013, D014, D015, D016, D017, and newly listed waste F025 are prohibited from underground injection at off-site injection facilities.

(d) Effective August 8, 1990, mixed radioactive/hazardous waste in 40 CFR 268.10, 268.11, and 268.12, that are mixed radioactive and hazardous wastes, are prohibited from underground injection.

(e) Effective November 8, 1990, the wastes specified in paragraph (c) of this section are prohibited from underground injection at on-site injection facilities. These effective dates do not apply to the wastes listed in 40 CFR 148.12(b) which are prohibited from underground injection on August 8, 1990.

(f) Effective May 8, 1992, the waste identified in 40 CFR 261.31 as EPA Hazardous Waste Number F039 (wastewaters); the wastes identified in 40 CFR 261.22, 261.23 or 261.24 as hazardous based on a characteristic alone, designated as D002 (wastewaters and nonwastewaters), D003 (wastewaters and nonwastewaters), D007 (wastewaters and nonwastewaters), and D009 (nonwastewaters) are prohibited from underground injection. These effective dates do not apply to the wastes listed in 40 CFR 148.12(b) which are prohibited from underground injection on August 8, 1990.

(g) The requirements of paragraphs (a) through (f) of this section do not apply:

(1) If the wastes meet or are treated to meet the applicable standards specified in subpart D of part 268; or

(2) If an exemption from a prohibition has been granted in response to a petition under subpart C of this part; or

(3) During the period of extension of the applicable effective date, if an extension has been granted under §148.4 of this part.

[54 FR 25423, June 14, 1989, as amended at 54 FR 26647, June 23, 1989; 55 FR 22683, June 1, 1990; 55 FR 33694, Aug. 17, 1990; 56 FR 3876, Jan. 31, 1991]

§148.17 Waste specific prohibitions; newly listed wastes.

(a) Effective November 9, 1992, the wastes specified in 40 CFR part 261 as EPA hazardous waste numbers F037, F038, K107, K108, K109, K110, K111, K112, K117, K118, K123, K124, K125, K126, K131, K136, U328, U353, and U359 are prohibited from underground injection.

(b) Effective December 19, 1994 the wastes specified in 40 CFR 261.32 as EPA Hazardous waste numbers K141, K142, K143, K144, K145, K147, K148, K149, K150, and K151, are prohibited from underground injection.

(c) [Reserved]

(d) Effective June 30, 1995, the wastes specified in 40 CFR part 261 as EPA Hazardous waste numbers K117, K118, K131, and K132 are prohibited from underground injection.

(e) The requirements of paragraphs (a) and (b) of this section do not apply:

(1) If the wastes meet or are treated to meet the applicable standards specified in subpart D of part 268; or

(2) If an exemption from a prohibition has been granted in response to a petition under subpart C of this part; or

(3) During the period of extension of the applicable effective date, if an extension has been granted under §148.4 of this part.

[57 FR 37263, Aug. 18, 1992, as amended at 59 FR 48041, Sept. 19, 1994; 61 FR 15662, Apr. 8, 1996]

§148.18 Waste specific prohibitions—newly listed and identified wastes.

(a) Effective August 24, 1998, all newly identified D004-D011 wastes and characteristic mineral processing wastes, except those identified in paragraph (b) of this section, are prohibited from underground injection.

(b) Effective May 26, 2000, characteristic hazardous wastes from titanium dioxide mineral processing, and radioactive wastes mixed with newly identified D004-D011 or mixed with newly identified characteristic mineral processing wastes, are prohibited from underground injection.

(c) Effective August 11, 1997, the wastes specified in 40 CFR part 261 as EPA Hazardous waste numbers

F032, F034, F035 are prohibited from underground injection.

(d) Effective May 12, 1999, the wastes specified in 40 CFR part 261 as EPA Hazardous waste numbers F032, F034, F035 that are mixed with radioactive wastes are prohibited from underground injection.

(e) On July 8, 1996, the wastes specified in 40 CFR 261.32 as EPA Hazardous waste numbers K156-K161, P127, P128, P185, P188-P192, P194, P196-P199, P201-P205, U271, U277-U280, U364-U367, U372, U373, U375-U379, U381-387, U389-U396, U400-U404, U407, and U409-U411 are prohibited from underground injection.

(f) On January 8, 1997, the wastes specified in 40 CFR 261.32 as EPA Hazardous waste number K088 is prohibited from underground injection.

(g) On April 8, 1998, the wastes specified in 40 CFR part 261 as EPA Hazardous waste numbers D018-043, and Mixed TC/Radioactive wastes, are prohibited from underground injection.

(h) [Reserved]

(i) Effective February 8, 1999, the wastes specified in 40 CFR 261.32 as EPA Hazardous Waste Numbers K169, K170, K171, and K172 are prohibited from underground injection.

(j) Effective May 8, 2001, the wastes specified in 40 CFR 261.32 as EPA Hazardous Waste Numbers K174 and K175 are prohibited from underground injection.

(k) Effective May 20, 2002, the wastes specified in 40 CFR 261.32 as EPA Hazardous Waste Numbers K176, K177, and K178 are prohibited from underground injection.

(l) Effective August 23, 2005, the waste specified in 40 CFR 261.32 as EPA Hazardous Waste Number K181 is prohibited from underground injection.

(m) The requirements of paragraphs (a) through (l) of this section do not apply:

(1) If the wastes meet or are treated to meet the applicable standards specified in subpart D of 40 CFR part 268; or

(2) If an exemption from a prohibition has been granted in response to a petition under subpart C of this part; or

(3) During the period of extension of the applicable effective date, if an extension has been granted under §148.4.

[61 FR 15662, Apr. 8, 1996, as amended at 62 FR 26018, May 12, 1997; 63 FR 24624, May 4, 1998; 63 FR 28636, May 26, 1998; 63 FR 35149, June 29, 1998; 63 FR 42184, Aug. 6, 1998; 65 FR 14474, Mar. 17, 2000; 65 FR 36366, June 8, 2000, 65 FR 67126, Nov. 8, 2000; 66 FR 58297, Nov. 20, 2001; 70 FR 9174, Feb. 24, 2005]

Subpart C—Petition Standards and Procedures

§148.20 Petitions to allow injection of a waste prohibited under subpart B.

(a) Any person seeking an exemption from a prohibition under subpart B of this part for the injection of a restricted hazardous waste into an injection well or wells shall submit a petition to the Director demonstrating that, to a reasonable degree of certainty, there will be no migration of hazardous constituents from the injection zone for as long as the waste remains hazardous. This demonstration requires a showing that:

(1) The hydrogeological and geochemical conditions at the sites and the physiochemical nature of the waste stream(s) are such that reliable predictions can be made that:

(i) Fluid movement conditions are such that the injected fluids will not migrate within 10,000 years:

(A) Vertically upward out of the injection zone; or

(B) Laterally within the injection zone to a point of discharge or interface with an Underground Source of Drinking Water (USDW) as defined in 40 CFR part 146; or

(ii) Before the injected fluids migrate out of the injection zone or to a point of discharge or interface with USDW, the fluid will no longer be hazardous because of attenuation, transformation, or immobilization of hazardous constituents within the injection zone by hydrolysis, chemical interactions or other means; and

(2) For each well the petition has:

(i) Demonstrated that the injection well's area of review complies with the substantive requirements of §146.63;

(ii) Located, identified, and ascertained the condition of all wells within the injection well's area of review (as specified in §146.63) that penetrate the injection zone or the confining zone by use of a protocol acceptable to the Director that meets the substantive requirements of §146.64;

(iii) Submitted a corrective action plan that meets the substantive requirements of §146.64, the implementation of which shall become a condition of petition approval; and

(iv) Submitted the results of pressure and radioactive tracer tests performed within one year prior to submission of the petition demonstrating the mechanical integrity of the well's long string casing, injection tube, annular seal, and bottom hole cement. In cases where the petition has not been approved or denied within one year after the initial demonstration of mechanical integrity, the Director may require the owner or operator to perform the tests again and submit the results of the new tests.

Note: The requirements of §148.20(a)(2) need not be incorporated in a permit at the time of petition approval.

(b) A demonstration under §148.20(a)(1)(i) shall identify the strata within the injection zone which will confine fluid movement above the injection interval and include a showing that this strata is free of known transmissive faults of fractures and that there is a confining zone above the injection zone.

(c) A demonstration under §148.20(a)(1)(ii) shall identify the strata within the injection zone where waste transformation will be accomplished and include a showing that this strata is free of known transmissive faults or fractures and that there is a confining zone above the injection zone.

(d) A demonstration may include a showing that:

(1) Treatment methods, the implementation of which shall become a condition of petition approval, will be utilized that reduce the toxicity or mobility of the wastes; or

(2) A monitoring plan, the implementation of which shall become a condition of petition approval, will be utilized to enhance confidence in one or more aspects of the demonstration.

(e) Any person who has been granted an exemption pursuant to this section may submit a petition for reissuance of the exemption to include an additional restricted waste or wastes or to modify any conditions placed on the exemption by the Director. The Director shall reissue the petition if the petitioner complies with the requirements of paragraphs (a), (b) and (c) of this section.

(f) Any person who has been granted an exemption pursuant to this section may submit a petition to modify an exemption to include an additional (hazardous) waste or wastes. The Director may grant the modification if he determines, to a reasonable degree of certainty, that the additional waste or wastes will behave hydraulically and chemically in a manner similar to previously included wastes and that it will not interfere with the containment capability of the injection zone.

§148.21 Information to be submitted in support of petitions.

(a) Information submitted in support of §148.20 must meet the following criteria:

(1) All waste analysis and any new testing performed by the petitioner shall be accurate and reproducible and performed in accordance with quality assurance standards;

(2) Estimation techniques shall be appropriate, and EPA-certified test protocols shall be used where available and appropriate;

(3) Predictive models shall have been verified and validated, shall be appropriate for the specific site, waste streams, and injection conditions of the operation, and shall be calibrated for existing sites where sufficient data are available;

(4) An approved quality assurance and quality control plan shall address all aspects of the demonstration;

(5) Reasonably conservative values shall be used whenever values taken from the literature or estimated on the basis of known information are used instead of site-specific measurements; and

(6) An analysis shall be performed to identify and assess aspects of the demonstration that contribute significantly to uncertainty. The petitioner shall conduct a sensitivity analysis to determine the effect that significant uncertainty may contribute to the demonstration. The demonstration shall then be based on conservative assumptions identified in the analysis.

(b) Any petitioner under §148.20(a)(1)(i) shall provide sufficient site-specific information to support the demonstration, such as:

(1) Thickness, porosity, permeability and extent of the various strata in the injection zone;

(2) Thickness, porosity, permeability, extent, and continuity of the confining zone;

(3) Hydraulic gradient in the injection zone;

(4) Hydrostatic pressure in the injection zone; and

(5) Geochemical conditions of the site.

(c) In addition to the information in §148.21(b), any petitioner under §148.20(a)(1)(ii) shall provide sufficient waste-specific information to ensure reasonably reliant predictions about the waste transformation. The petitioner shall provide the information necessary to support the demonstration, such as:

(1) Description of the chemical processes or other means that will lead to waste transformation; and

(2) Results of laboratory experiments verifying the waste transformation.

§148.22 Requirements for petition submission, review and approval or denial.

(a) Any petition submitted to the Director pursuant to §148.20(a) shall include the following components:

(1) An identification of the specific waste or wastes and the specific injection well or wells for which the demonstration will be made;

(2) A waste analysis to describe fully the chemical and physical characteristics of the subject wastes;

(3) Such additional information as is required by the Director to support the petition under §§148.20 and 148.21; and

(4) This statement signed by the petitioner or an authorized representative:

> I certify under penalty of law that I have personally examined and am familiar with the information submitted in this petition and all attached documents, and that, based on my inquiry of those individuals immediately responsible for obtaining the information, I believe that submitted information is true, accurate, and complete. I am aware that there are significant penalties for submitting false information, including the possibility of fine and imprisonment.

(b) The Director shall provide public notice and an opportunity for public comment in accordance with the procedures in §124.10 of the intent to approve or deny a petition. The final decision on a petition will be published in the *Federal Register.*

(c) If an exemption is granted it will apply only to the underground injection of the specific restricted waste or wastes identified in the petition into a Class I hazardous waste injection well or wells specifically identified in the petition (unless the exemption is modified or reissued pursuant to §148.20(e) or (f).

(d) Upon request by any petitioner who obtains an exemption for a well under this subpart, the Director shall initiate and reasonably expedite the necessary procedures to issue or reissue a permit or permits for the hazardous waste well or wells covered by the exemption for a term not to exceed ten years.

§148.23 Review of exemptions granted pursuant to a petition.

(a) When considering whether to reissue a permit for the operation of a Class I hazardous waste injection well, the Director shall review any petition filed pursuant to §148.20 and require a new demonstration if information shows that the basis for granting the exemption may no longer be valid.

(b) Whenever the Director determines that the basis for approval of a petition may no longer be valid, the Director shall require a new demonstration in accordance with §148.20.

§148.24 Termination of approved petition.

(a) The Director may terminate an exemption granted under §148.20 for the following causes:

(1) Noncompliance by the petitioner with any condition of the exemption;

(2) The petitioner's failure in the petition or during the review and approval to disclose fully all relevant facts, or the petitioner's misrepresentation of any relevant facts at any time; or

(3) A determination that new information shows that the basis for approval of the petition is no longer valid.

(b) The Director shall terminate an exemption granted under §148.20 for the following causes:

(1) The petitioner's willful withholding during the review and approval of the petition of facts directly and materially relevant to the Director's decision on the petition;

(2) A determination that there has been migration from the injection zone or the well that is not in accordance with the terms of the exemption, except that the Director may at his discretion decide not to terminate where:

(i) The migration resulted from a mechanical failure of the well that can be corrected promptly through a repair to the injection well itself or from an undetected well or conduit that can be plugged promptly; and

(ii) The requirements of §146.67(i) are satisfied.

(c) The Director shall follow the procedures in §124.5 in terminating any exemption under this section.

C

C

C

D

E

F

G

H

I

N

O

P

Q

R

R

S

S

S

S

T

V

W